W9-DDR-368

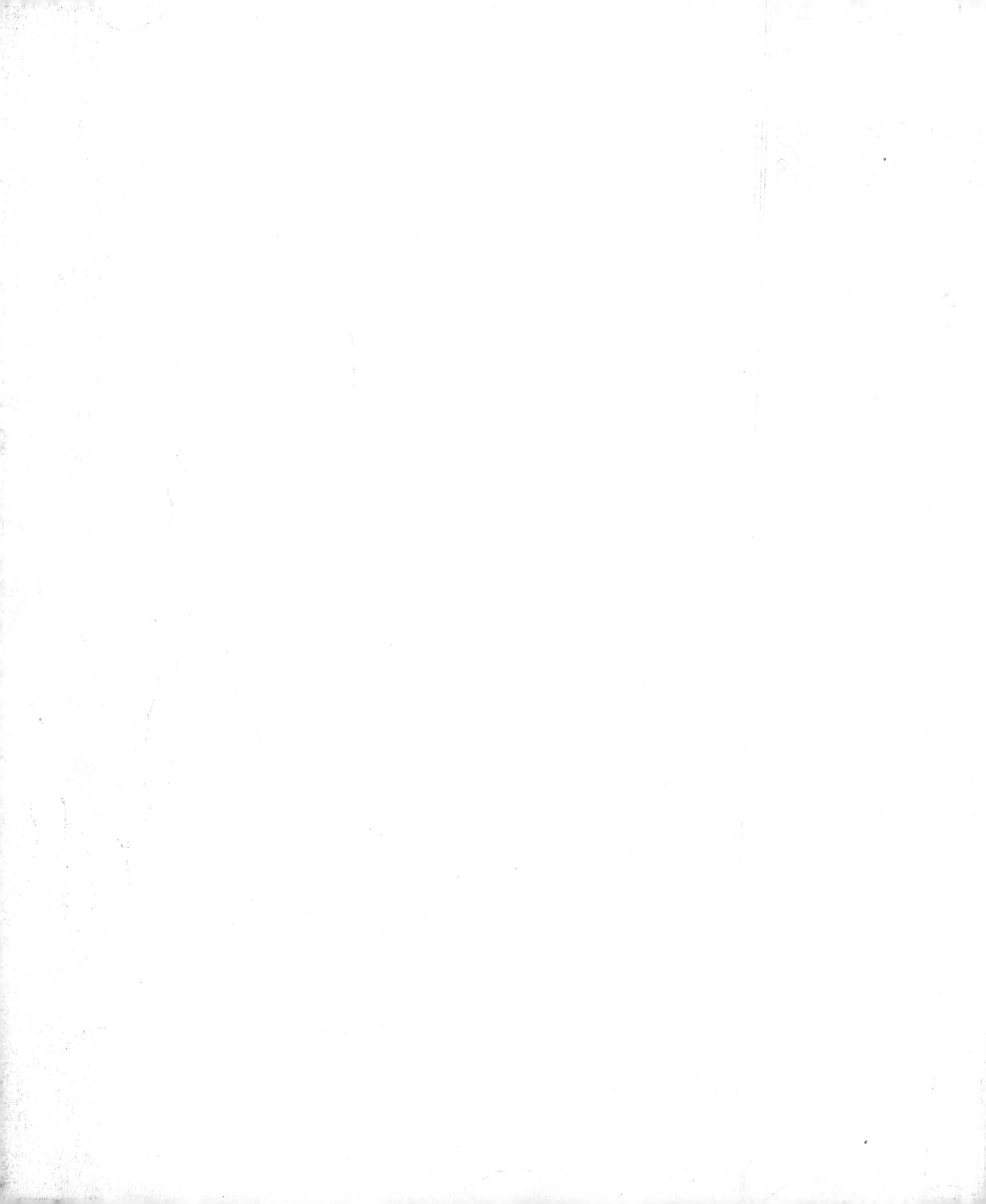

INDIANA

Miller & Levine Biology

Kenneth R. Miller, Ph.D.
Professor of Biology, Brown University
Providence, Rhode Island

Joseph S. Levine, Ph.D.
Science Writer and Producer
Concord, Massachusetts

PEARSON

Boston, Massachusetts • Chandler, Arizona • Glenview, Illinois • Upper Saddle River, New Jersey

INDIANA

Print Components

Indiana Student Edition
Indiana Teacher's Edition
Indiana Progress Monitoring Assessments Teacher's Edition
Indiana Standardized Test Preparation Workbook
Study Workbook A
Study Workbook A, Teacher's Edition
Study Workbook B: Reading Foundations
Study Workbook B: Reading Foundations, Teacher's Edition
Laboratory Manual A
Laboratory Manual A, Teacher's Edition
Laboratory Manual B: Skill Foundations
Laboratory Manual B: Skill Foundations, Teacher's Edition
Probeware Lab Manual
Assessment Resources
Transparencies

Technology Components

Indiana Biology.com
Indiana ExamView® CD-ROM
Indiana Classroom Resources DVD-ROM with Indiana Standards Review Teacher's Presentation
Untamed Science® Video Series: BioAdventures DVD
Virtual BioLab DVD-ROM with Lab Manual

English Language Learners

Teacher's ELL Handbook
Multilingual Glossary

Spanish Components

Spanish Student Edition (with online Spanish audio)
Spanish Teacher's Guide
Spanish Study Workbook

Photographs Every effort has been made to secure permission and provide appropriate credit for photographic material. The publisher deeply regrets any omission and pledges to correct errors called to its attention in subsequent editions. Unless otherwise acknowledged, all photographs are the property of Pearson Education, Inc.

Front Matter Acknowledgments: IN T1: ©Ralph A Clevenger/Corbis. **IN T3:** Stew Milne. **IN T4:** (L) Courtesy Grant Wiggins; (R) Jen-Yi Wu. **IN T6:** Jeremy Edwards/iStockphoto. **IN T7:** (T) ©Pete Oxford/Minden Pictures; (B) Piotr Naskrecki, Minden Pictures. **IN T8:** ©Ed Rescheke/Peter Arnold, Inc. **IN T9:** Andrew Syred/Photo Researchers, Inc. **IN T10:** (T) Colin Keates/DK Images; (B) Colin Keates©Dorling Kindersley, Courtesy of the Natural History Museum, London. **IN T11:** (TR) Southhampton General Hospital/Science Photo Library/Photo Researchers, Inc.; (B Bkgrnd) ©Neil Lucas/npl/Minden Pictures; (BL) ©Georgette Douwma/GettyImages; (ML) ©Peter Chadwick/DK Images. **IN T12:** (T) ©Ben Twist/istockphoto.com; (B) ©Nature Picture Library/Alamy. **IN T13:** (L) ©Ingo Arndt, MINDEN PICTURES; (R) ©Nigel J. Dennis; Gallo Images/CORBIS. **IN T14:** Ilene MacDonald/Al. **IN T17:** Willy Seto/iStockphoto. **IN T19:** Denali55/Dreamstime LLC. **IN T20:** (T) ©DAVID M. DENNIS/Animals Animals—Earth Scenes. (B) WIL MEINDERTS/FOTO NATURA/Minden Pictures. **IN T22:** Danny Kerr. **IN T23:** ©Peter Chadwick/DK Images. **IN T24:** (T) ©Stephen Dalton/Minden Pictures; (B) ©Richard Cummins/SuperStock. **IN T25:** ©Mark Bolton/Corbis. **IN T26–T27:** (L) ©Jean-Paul Ferrero/Auscape/Minden Pictures; (R) ©Hallmark Institute/Photolibrary Group. **IN T28:** Jen-Yi Wu. **IN T30–T31:** ©Norbert Wu/Minden Pictures. **IN T49:** (Inset, L) blickwinkel/Hartl/Alamy Images; (L) Henryk Sadura/Shutterstock; (Inset, R) Scott Smith/Animals Animals Earth Scenes; (R) Steve Geer/iStockphoto. **IN T50:** (Inset, R) FLPA/S & D & K Maslowski/Minden Pictures; (Inset, L) Robert J. Erwin/Photo Researchers, Inc.; (L) Tamama/Alamy; (R) The Nature Conservancy. **IN T51:** (L, R) Indiana Department of Natural Resources/Outdoor Indiana Magazine; (Inset, L) Ruth Cole/Animals Animals/Earth Scenes; (Inset, R) David M. Dennis/Animals Animals/Earth Scenes. **IN T52:** (R, L) Indiana Department of Natural Resources/Outdoor Indiana Magazine; (Inset, R) Zigmund Leszczynski/Animals Animals/Earth Scenes; (Inset, L) Robert Winslow/Animals Animals/Earth Scenes. **IN T53:** James Pauls/iStockphoto. **IN T54:** Creatas/SuperStock. **IN T58:** Alexey Stiop/Dreamstime LLC. **IN T60:** Superstock RF/SuperStock; **IN T63:** Steve Byland/Shutterstock.

Additional acknowledgments begin on page C–0, which constitutes an extension of this copyright page.

Student Edition ISBN-13: 978-0-13-253462-8
Student Edition ISBN-10: 0-13-253462-2
Teacher's Edition ISBN-13: 978-0-13-253463-5
Teacher's Edition ISBN-10: 0-13-253463-0
1 2 3 4 5 6 7 8 9 10 V063 14 13 12 11 10

About the Authors

Kenneth R. Miller grew up in Rahway, New Jersey, attended the local public schools, and graduated from Rahway High School in 1966. Miller attended Brown University on a scholarship and graduated with honors. He was awarded a National Defense Education Act fellowship for graduate study, and earned his Ph.D. in Biology at the University of Colorado. Miller is professor of Biology at Brown University in Providence, Rhode Island, where he teaches courses in general biology and cell biology.

Miller's research specialty is the structure of biological membranes. He has published more than 70 research papers in journals such as *Cell, Nature*, and *Scientific American*. He has also written the popular trade books *Finding Darwin's God* and *Only a Theory*. He is a fellow of the American Association for the Advancement of Science.

Miller lives with his wife, Jody, on a small farm in Rehoboth, Massachusetts. He is the father of two daughters, one a wildlife biologist and the other a high-school history teacher. He swims competitively in the masters' swimming program and umpires high school and collegiate softball.

Joseph S. Levine was born in Mount Vernon, New York, where he attended public schools. He earned a B.S. in Biology at Tufts University, a master's degree from the Boston University Marine Program, and a Ph.D. at Harvard University. His research has been published in scientific journals ranging from *Science* to *Scientific American*, and in several academic books. He has taught introductory biology, ecology, marine biology, neurobiology, and coral reef biology at Boston College and in the Boston University Marine Program. He has also co-taught a field biology course for high-school teachers entitled "Rainforests and Reefs" at the Organization for Tropical Studies in Costa Rica.

After receiving a Macy Fellowship in Science Broadcast Journalism at WGBH-TV, Levine dedicated himself to improving public understanding of science. His popular scientific writing has appeared in five trade books and in magazines such as *Smithsonian*, *GEO*, and *Natural History*. He has produced science features for National Public Radio and has designed exhibit programs for state aquarium projects in Texas, New Jersey, and Florida. Since 1987, Levine has served as scientific advisor at WGBH, where he worked on NOVA programs including *Judgment Day*, and on projects including the OMNI-MAX films *Cocos: Island of Sharks* and *Coral Reef Adventure*. He also served as science editor for the PBS series *The Secret of Life* and *The Evolution Project*.

Levine and his family live in Concord, Massachusetts, a short distance from Thoreau's Walden Pond.

Consultants/Reviewers

Grant Wiggins, Ed.D. is a co-author of Understanding by Design® (UbD), a philosophy of instructional design. UbD is a disciplined way of thinking about curriculum design, assessment, and instruction that moves teaching from covering the content to ensuring understanding.

Big idea Big Ideas are one of the core components of UbD in *Miller & Levine Biology.* These Big Ideas, such as Science as a Way of Knowing and the Cellular Basis of Life, establish a conceptual framework for the program. In the Student Edition, look for opportunities throughout each chapter to link back to the Big Ideas. And, since Understanding by Design is by nature a teaching tool, see the Teacher's Edition for additional applications of this philosophy.

Jim Cummins is Professor and Canada Research Chair in the Curriculum, Teaching and Learning department at the Ontario Institute for Studies in Education at the University of Toronto. His research focuses on literacy development in multilingual schools and the role of technology in promoting language and literacy development.

Program materials for *Miller & Levine Biology* incorporate research-based essential principles using Dr. Cummins's Into/Through/Beyond structure. You will find ample support for ELL instruction in the Teacher's Edition, Teacher's ELL Handbook, the Multilingual Glossary, as well as the Spanish components offered with this program.

Content Reviewers

Lily Chen
Associate Professor
Department of Biology
San Francisco State University
San Francisco, CA

Elizabeth Coolidge-Stolz, MD
Medical/Life Science Writer/Editor
North Reading, MA

Elizabeth A. De Stasio, Ph.D.
Raymond H. Herzog
Professor of Science
Associate Professor of Biology
Lawrence University
Appleton, WI

Jennifer C. Drew, Ph.D.
Lecturer/Scientist
University of Florida
Kennedy Space Center, FL

Donna H. Duckworth, Ph.D.
Professor Emeritus
College of Medicine
University of Florida
Gainesville, FL

Alan Gishlick, Ph.D.
Assistant Professor
Gustavus Adolphus College
St. Peter, MN

Deborah L. Gumucio, Ph.D.
Professor
Department of Cell and Developmental Biology
University of Michigan
Ann Arbor, MI

Janet Lanza, Ph.D.
Professor of Biology
University of Arkansas at Little Rock
Little Rock, AR

Charles F. Lytle, Ph.D.
Professor of Zoology
North Carolina State University
Raleigh, NC

Martha Newsome, DDS
Adjunct Instructor of Biology
Cy-Fair College, Fairbanks Center
Houston, TX

Jan A. Pechenik, Ph.D.
Professor of Biology
Tufts University
Medford, MA

Imara Y. Perera, Ph.D.
Research Assistant, Professor
Department of Plant Biology
North Carolina State University
Raleigh, NC

Daniel M. Raben, Ph.D.
Professor
Department of Biological Chemistry
Johns Hopkins University
Baltimore, MD

Megan Rokop, Ph.D.
Educational Outreach Program Director
Broad Institute of MIT and Harvard
Cambridge, MA

Gerald P. Sanders
Former Biology Instructor
Grossmont College
Julian, CA

Ronald Sass, Ph.D.
Professor Emeritus
Rice University
Houston, TX

Linda Silveria, Ph.D.
Professor
University of Redlands
Redlands, CA

Richard K. Stucky, Ph.D.
Curator of Paleontology and Evolution
Denver Museum of Nature and Science
Denver, CO

Robert Thornton, Ph.D.
Senior Lecturer Emeritus
Department of Plant Biology
College of Biological Sciences
University of California at Davis
Davis, CA

Edward J. Zalisko, Ph.D.
Professor of Biology
Blackburn College
Carlinville, IL

ESL Lecturer

Nancy Vincent Montgomery, Ed.D.
Southern Methodist University
Dallas, TX

High-School Reviewers

Christine Bill
Sayreville War Memorial High School
Parlin, NJ

Jean T. (Caye) Boone
Central Gwinnett High School
Lawrenceville, GA

Samuel J. Clifford, Ph.D.
Biology Teacher
Round Rock High School
Round Rock, TX

Jennifer Collins, M.A.
South County Secondary School
Lorton, VA

Roy Connor, M.S.
Science Department Head
Muncie Central High School
Muncie, IN

Norm Dahm, Jr.
Belleville East High School
Belleville, IL

Cora Nadine Dickson
Science Department Chair
Jersey Village High School
Cypress Fairbanks ISD
Houston, TX

Dennis M. Dudley
Science Department Chair/Teacher
Shaler Area High School
Pittsburgh, PA

Mary K. Dulko
Sharon High School
Sharon, MA

Erica Everett, M.A.T., M.Ed.
Science Department Chair
Manchester-Essex Regional High School
Manchester, MA

Heather M. Gannon
Elisabeth Ann Johnson High School
Mt. Morris, MI

Virginia Glasscock
Science Teacher
California High School
Whittier, CA

Ruth Gleicher
Biology Teacher
Niles West High School
Skokie, IL

Lance Goodlock
Biology Teacher/Science Department Chairperson
Sturgis High School
Sturgis, MI

W. Tony Heiting, Ph.D.
State Science Supervisor (retired)
Iowa Department of Education
Panora, IA

Patricia Anne Johnson, M.S.
Biology Teacher
Ridgewood High School
Ridgewood, NJ

Judith Decherd Jones, M.A.T.
NBCT AYA Science
East Chapel Hill High School
Chapel Hill, NC

Shellie Jones
Science Teacher
California High School
Whittier, CA

Michelle Lauria, M.A.T.
Biology Teacher
Hopkinton High School
Hopkinton, MA

Kimberly Lewis
Science Department Chair
Wellston High School
Wellston, OH

Consultants *(continued)*

Lenora Lewis
Teacher
Creekview High School
Canton, GA

JoAnn Lindell-Overton, M.Ed.
Supervisor of Secondary Science
Chesapeake Public Schools
Chesapeake, VA

Lender Luse
H.W. Byers High School
Holly Springs, MS

Molly J. Markey, Ph.D.
Science Teacher
Newton Country Day School of the Sacred Heart
Newton, MA

Rebecca McLelland-Crawley
Biological Sciences Teacher
Piscataway, NJ

Mark L. Mettert, M.S. Ed.
Science Department Chair
New Haven High School
New Haven, IN

Jane Parker
Lewisville High School North
Lewisville, TX

Ian Pearce
Educator
Austin, TX

Jim Peters
Science Resource Teacher
Carroll County Public Schools
Westminster, MD

Michelle Phillips, M.A.T.
Secondary Science: Education Science Teacher
Jordan High School
Durham, NC

Randy E. Phillips
Science Teacher/Department Chair
Green Bay East High School
Green Bay, WI

Nancy Richey
Educator
Longmont, CO

Linda Roberson
Department Chairman
Jenks Freshman Academy
Jenks, OK

Sharon D. Spencer
Assistant Principal
Bronx Center for Science and Math
Bronx, NY

Stephen David Wright, M.S.
Biology Teacher
Montgomery County Public Schools
Columbia, MD

Alan W. Zimroth, M.S.
Science Teacher/Department Chairperson
Hialeah-Miami Lakes High School
Hialeah, FL

Indianapolis, Indiana

Contents

Ecosystems of Indiana . . . IN 21
Indiana Academic Standards for Biology I . . . IN 25

UNIT 1 The Nature of Life 1–60

1 The Science of Biology . . . 2

Big idea What role does science play in the study of life?

1.1 What Is Science? . . . 4
1.2 Science in Context . . . 10
1.3 Studying Life . . . 17
IN Standardized Test Practice for Indiana . . . 31

2 The Chemistry of Life . . . 32

Big idea What are the basic chemical principles that affect living things?

2.1 The Nature of Matter . . . 34
2.2 Properties of Water . . . 40
2.3 Carbon Compounds . . . 45
2.4 Chemical Reactions and Enzymes . . . 50
IN Standardized Test Practice for Indiana . . . 59

Unit 1 Project . . . 60

UNIT 2 Ecology 61–186

3 The Biosphere . . . 62

Big idea How do living and nonliving parts of the Earth interact and affect the survival of organisms?

3.1 What Is Ecology? . . . 64
3.2 Energy, Producers, and Consumers . . . 69
3.3 Energy Flow in Ecosystems . . . 73
3.4 Cycles of Matter . . . 79
IN Standardized Test Practice for Indiana . . . 93

4 Ecosystems and Communities . . . 94

Big idea How do abiotic and biotic factors shape ecosystems?

4.1 Climate . . . 96
4.2 Niches and Community Interactions . . . 99
4.3 Succession . . . 106
4.4 Biomes . . . 110
4.5 Aquatic Ecosystems . . . 117
IN Standardized Test Practice for Indiana . . . 127

BIOLOGY.com • Go Digital. See what awaits you at Biology.com.

5 Populations 128

Big idea What factors contribute to changes in populations?

5.1 How Populations Grow 130
5.2 Limits to Growth 137
5.3 Human Population Growth 142
IN Standardized Test Practice for Indiana 151

6 Humans in the Biosphere 152

Big idea How have human activities shaped local and global ecology?

6.1 A Changing Landscape 154
6.2 Using Resources Wisely 158
6.3 Biodiversity 166
6.4 Meeting Ecological Challenges 173
IN Standardized Test Practice for Indiana 185

Unit 2 Project 186

UNIT 3 Cells 187–304

7 Cell Structure and Function 188

Big idea How are cell structures adapted to their functions?

7.1 Life Is Cellular 190
7.2 Cell Structure 196
7.3 Cell Transport 208
7.4 Homeostasis and Cells 214
IN Standardized Test Practice for Indiana 223

8 Photosynthesis 224

Big idea How do plants and other organisms capture energy from the sun?

8.1 Energy and Life 226
8.2 Photosynthesis: An Overview 230
8.3 The Process of Photosynthesis 235
IN Standardized Test Practice for Indiana 247

9 Cellular Respiration and Fermentation 248

Big idea How do organisms obtain energy?

9.1 Cellular Respiration: An Overview 250
9.2 The Process of Cellular Respiration 254
9.3 Fermentation 262
IN Standardized Test Practice for Indiana 271

10 Cell Growth and Division 272

Big idea How does a cell produce a new cell?

10.1 Cell Growth, Division, and Reproduction 274
10.2 The Process of Cell Division 279
10.3 Regulating the Cell Cycle 286
10.4 Cell Differentiation 292
IN Standardized Test Practice for Indiana 303

Unit 3 Project 304

UNIT 4 Genetics 305–446

11 Introduction to Genetics 306

Big idea How does cellular information pass from one generation to another?

11.1 The Work of Gregor Mendel 308
11.2 Applying Mendel's Principles 313
11.3 Other Patterns of Inheritance 319
11.4 Meiosis 323
IN Standardized Test Practice for Indiana 335

12 DNA 336

Big idea What is the structure of DNA, and how does it function in genetic inheritance?

12.1 Identifying the Substance of Genes 338
12.2 The Structure of DNA 344
12.3 DNA Replication 350
IN Standardized Test Practice for Indiana 359

13 RNA and Protein Synthesis 360

Big idea How does information flow from the cell nucleus to direct the synthesis of proteins in the cytoplasm?

13.1 RNA 362
13.2 Ribosomes and Protein Synthesis 366
13.3 Mutations 372
13.4 Gene Regulation and Expression 377
IN Standardized Test Practice for Indiana 389

14 Human Heredity 390

Big idea How can we use genetics to study human inheritance?

14.1 Human Chromosomes 392
14.2 Human Genetic Disorders 398
14.3 Studying the Human Genome 403
IN Standardized Test Practice for Indiana 415

15 Genetic Engineering . . . 416
Big idea How and why do scientists manipulate DNA in living cells?
15.1 Selective Breeding . . . 418
15.2 Recombinant DNA . . . 421
15.3 Applications of Genetic Engineering . . . 428
15.4 Ethics and Impacts of Biotechnology . . . 436
IN Standardized Test Practice for Indiana . . . 445

Unit 4 Project . . . 446

UNIT 5 Evolution 447–570

16 Darwin's Theory of Evolution . . . 448
Big idea What is natural selection?
16.1 Darwin's Voyage of Discovery . . . 450
16.2 Ideas That Shaped Darwin's Thinking . . . 454
16.3 Darwin Presents His Case . . . 460
16.4 Evidence of Evolution . . . 465
IN Standardized Test Practice for Indiana . . . 479

17 Evolution of Populations . . . 480
Big idea How can populations evolve to form new species?
17.1 Genes and Variation . . . 482
17.2 Evolution as Genetic Change in Populations . . . 487
17.3 The Process of Speciation . . . 494
17.4 Molecular Evolution . . . 498
IN Standardized Test Practice for Indiana . . . 507

18 Classification . . . 508
Big idea What is the goal of biologists who classify living things?
18.1 Finding Order in Diversity . . . 510
18.2 Modern Evolutionary Classification . . . 516
18.3 Building the Tree of Life . . . 523
IN Standardized Test Practice for Indiana . . . 535

19 History of Life . . . 536
Big idea How do fossils help biologists understand the history of life on Earth?
19.1 The Fossil Record . . . 538
19.2 Patterns and Processes of Evolution . . . 546
19.3 Earth's Early History . . . 553
IN Standardized Test Practice for Indiana . . . 569

Unit 5 Project . . . 570

INDIANA

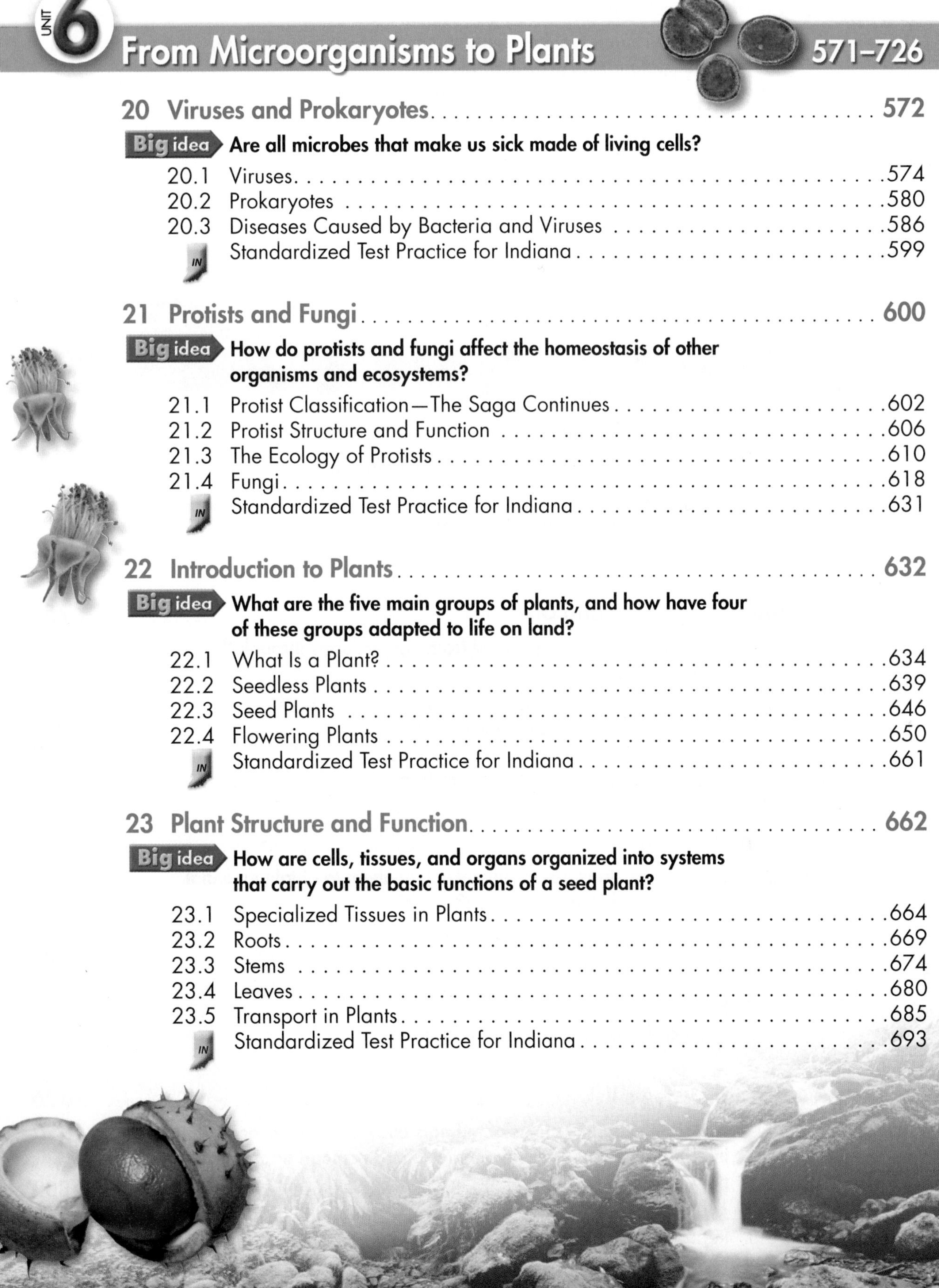

UNIT 6 From Microorganisms to Plants 571–726

20 Viruses and Prokaryotes 572

Big idea Are all microbes that make us sick made of living cells?

20.1 Viruses 574
20.2 Prokaryotes 580
20.3 Diseases Caused by Bacteria and Viruses 586
IN Standardized Test Practice for Indiana 599

21 Protists and Fungi 600

Big idea How do protists and fungi affect the homeostasis of other organisms and ecosystems?

21.1 Protist Classification—The Saga Continues 602
21.2 Protist Structure and Function 606
21.3 The Ecology of Protists 610
21.4 Fungi 618
IN Standardized Test Practice for Indiana 631

22 Introduction to Plants 632

Big idea What are the five main groups of plants, and how have four of these groups adapted to life on land?

22.1 What Is a Plant? 634
22.2 Seedless Plants 639
22.3 Seed Plants 646
22.4 Flowering Plants 650
IN Standardized Test Practice for Indiana 661

23 Plant Structure and Function 662

Big idea How are cells, tissues, and organs organized into systems that carry out the basic functions of a seed plant?

23.1 Specialized Tissues in Plants 664
23.2 Roots 669
23.3 Stems 674
23.4 Leaves 680
23.5 Transport in Plants 685
IN Standardized Test Practice for Indiana 693

Contents

24 Plant Reproduction and Response 694

Big idea How do changes in the environment affect the reproduction, development, and growth of plants?

24.1 Reproduction in Flowering Plants 696
24.2 Fruits and Seeds 704
24.3 Plant Hormones 708
24.4 Plants and Humans 715
IN Standardized Test Practice for Indiana 725

Unit 6 Project 726

UNIT 7 Animals 727–858

25 Introduction to Animals 728

Big idea What characteristics and traits define animals?

25.1 What Is an Animal? 730
25.2 Animal Body Plans and Evolution 737
IN Standardized Test Practice for Indiana 749

26 Animal Evolution and Diversity 750

Big idea How have animals descended from earlier forms through the process of evolution?

26.1 Invertebrate Evolution and Diversity 752
26.2 Chordate Evolution and Diversity 757
26.3 Primate Evolution 765
IN Standardized Test Practice for Indiana 779

27 Animal Systems I 780

Big idea How do the structures of animals allow them to obtain essential materials and eliminate wastes?

27.1 Feeding and Digestion 782
27.2 Respiration 787
27.3 Circulation 791
27.4 Excretion 794
IN Standardized Test Practice for Indiana 805

28 Animal Systems II 806

Big idea How do the body systems of animals allow them to collect information about their environments and respond appropriately?

28.1 Response 808
28.2 Movement and Support 814
28.3 Reproduction 819
28.4 Homeostasis 827
IN Standardized Test Practice for Indiana 837

29 Animal Behavior 838

Big idea How do animals interact with one another and their environments?

29.1 Elements of Behavior 840
29.2 Animals in Their Environments 847
Standardized Test Practice for Indiana 857

Unit 7 Project 858

UNIT 8 The Human Body 859–1034

30 Digestive and Excretory Systems 860

Big idea How are the materials that go into your body and the materials that come from your body related to homeostasis?

30.1 Organization of the Human Body 862
30.2 Food and Nutrition 868
30.3 The Digestive System 875
30.4 The Excretory System 882
Standardized Test Practice for Indiana 893

31 Nervous System 894

Big idea How does the structure of the nervous system allow it to control functions in every part of the body?

31.1 The Neuron 896
31.2 The Central Nervous System 901
31.3 The Peripheral Nervous System 906
31.4 The Senses 909
Standardized Test Practice for Indiana 919

BIOLOGY.com • Go Digital. See what awaits you at Biology.com.

32 Skeletal, Muscular, and Integumentary Systems 920

Big idea **What systems form the structure of the human body?**

32.1 The Skeletal System 922
32.2 The Muscular System 928
32.3 Skin—The Integumentary System 935
IN Standardized Test Practice for Indiana 945

33 Circulatory and Respiratory Systems 946

Big idea **How do the structures of the circulatory and respiratory systems allow for their close functional relationship?**

33.1 The Circulatory System 948
33.2 Blood and the Lymphatic System 954
33.3 The Respiratory System 963
IN Standardized Test Practice for Indiana 975

34 Endocrine and Reproductive Systems 976

Big idea **How does the body use chemical signals to maintain homeostasis?**

34.1 The Endocrine System 978
34.2 Glands of the Endocrine System 982
34.3 The Reproductive System 988
34.4 Fertilization and Development 995
IN Standardized Test Practice for Indiana 1007

35 Immune System and Disease 1008

Big idea **How does the body fight against invading organisms that may disrupt homeostasis?**

35.1 Infectious Disease 1010
35.2 Defenses Against Infection 1014
35.3 Fighting Infectious Disease 1020
35.4 Immune System Disorders 1024
IN Standardized Test Practice for Indiana 1033

Unit 8 Project 1034

Indiana has approximately 63,000 farms with roughly 15,400,000 acres of farmland.

Diversity of Life: A Visual Guide DOL•1–DOL•64

Bacteria .... DOL•6

Archaea .... DOL•8

Protists .... DOL•10

Fungi .... DOL•16

Plants .... DOL•20

Animals .... DOL•30

Appendix A: Science Skills
- Data Tables and Graphs A–1
- Reading Diagrams A–3
- Basic Process Skills A–4
- Organizing Information A–6

Appendix B: Lab Skills
- Conducting an Experiment ... A–8
- The Metric System A–10
- Safety Symbols A–11
- Science Safety Rules A–12
- Use of the Microscope A–14

Appendix C: Technology & Design ... A–16

Appendix D: Math Skills A–18

Appendix E: Periodic Table A–24

English/Spanish Glossary G–1

Index I–1

Credits C–0

Contents

Labs and Activities

Quick Lab

Replicating Procedures 13
Model an Ionic Compound 36
Acidic and Basic Foods 43
How Do Abiotic Factors Affect Different Plant Species? 67
How Do Different Types of Consumers Interact? 72
Successful Succession? 108
How Does Competition Affect Growth? 138
Reduce, Reuse, Recycle 155
What Is a Cell? 193
Making a Model of a Cell 203
What Waste Material Is Produced During Photosynthesis? 234
How Does Exercise Affect Disposal of Wastes From Cellular Respiration? 264
Modeling the Relationship Between Surface Area and Volume 275
Mitosis in Action 283
Classroom Variation 311
How Are Dimples Inherited? 315
Modeling DNA Replication 352
How Does a Cell Interpret Codons? 367
Modeling Mutations 374
How Is Colorblindness Transmitted? 395
Modeling Restriction Enzymes 405
Inserting Genetic Markers 425
Survey Biotechnology Opinions 438
Darwin's Voyage 451
Variation in Peppers 457
Classifying Fruits 513
Constructing a Cladogram 520
Modeling Half-Life 541
How Do Viruses Differ in Structure? 575
What Are Protists? 603
How Does a Paramecium Eat? 612
What Is the Structure of Bread Mold? 620
Are All Plants the Same? 635
What Forms Do Fruits Take? 651
What Parts of Plants Do We Eat? 665
Examining Stomata 683
What Is the Role of Leaves in Transpiration? 686
What Is the Structure of a Flower? 698
How Hydra Feed 732
Binocular Vision 766
Breathing in Clams and Crayfishes 788
Water and Nitrogen Excretion 797
Does a Planarian Have a Head? 810
What Are Some Adaptations of Vertebrae? 816
What Kind of Learning Is Practice? 844
Maintaining Temperature 866
Modeling Bile Action 878
How Do You Respond to an External Stimulus? . . . 908
Observe Calcium Loss 924
What Do Tendons Do? 932
What Factors Affect Heart Rate? 951
What's in the Air? 964
Tracing Human Gamete Formation 990
Embryonic Development 1000
How Do Diseases Spread? 1021

Design Your Own Lab

Temperature and Enzymes 54
Acid Rain and Seeds 180
Regeneration in Planaria 298
Dichotomous Keys 530
Mushroom Farming 626
Identifying Growth Zones in Roots 688
Termite Tracks 852
Tidal Volume and Lung Capacity 970

Forensics Lab

Using DNA to Identify Human Remains 410
Using DNA to Solve Crimes 440
Using Index Fossils 564
Investigating Hominoid Fossils 774
Diagnosing Endocrine Disorders 1002
Detecting Lyme Disease 1028

Real-World Lab

The Effect of Fertilizer on Algae 88
Abiotic Factors and Plant Selection 122
Comparing Fermentation Rates of Sugars 266
Controlling Bacterial Growth 594
Exploring Plant Diversity 656
Plant Hormones and Leaves 720
Comparing Bird and Mammal Bones 832
Digestion of Dairy Products 888
Testing Sensory Receptors for Touch 914

Skills Lab

Using a Microscope to Estimate Size 26
The Growth Cycle of Yeast 146
Detecting Diffusion 218
Plant Pigments and Photosynthesis 242
Modeling Meiosis 330
Extracting DNA 354
From DNA to Protein Synthesis 384
Amino Acid Sequences: Indicators of Evolution . . . 474
Competing for Resources 502
Comparing Invertebrate Body Plans 744
Anatomy of a Squid 800
Comparing Limbs 940

The state flower of Indiana: the peony

Analyzing Data

What's in a Diet? 20
Comparing Fatty Acids 48
The 10 Percent Rule 77
Predator-Prey Dynamics 102
Which Biome? 115
Multiplying Rabbits 135
American Air Pollution Trends 164
Saving the Golden Lion Tamarin 172
Mitochondria Distribution in the Mouse 216
Rates of Photosynthesis 240
You Are What You Eat 251
The Rise and Fall of Cyclins 288
Cellular Differentiation of *C. elegans* 294
Human Blood Types 320
Calculating Haploid and Diploid Numbers 327
Base Percentages 345
The Discovery of RNA Interference 381
The Geography of Malaria 400
Genetically Modified Crops in the United States 429
Molecular Homology in *Hoxc8* 470
Allele Frequency 491
Fishes in Two Lakes 500
Comparing the Domains 524
Extinctions Through Time 548
Comparing Atmospheres 556
MRSA on the Rise 591
Mycorrhizae and Tree Height 624
Keeping Ferns in Check 644
Reading a Tree's History 678
Temperature and Seed Germination 706
Auxins and Plant Growth 710
Differences in Differentiation 740
Feather Evolution 763
Protein Digestion 784
Comparing Ectotherms and Endotherms 828
Caring for Young 850
The Composition of Urine 883
Sound Intensity 910
The Rising Rate of Melanoma 938
Blood Transfusions 956
Immune System "Memory" 1017
Food Allergies 1025

Features

Visual Analogies

Unlocking Enzymes 53
Earth's Recycling Center. 74
The Matter Mill 79
Interlocking Nutrients. 86
The Greenhouse Effect 97
Ecological Footprints 173

The Cell as a Living Factory 196
ATP as a Charged Battery 227
Carrying Electrons. 232
Growing Pains 276
The Main Functions of DNA 342
Master Plans and Blueprints 363
Finch Beak Tools 472
Geologic Time as a Clock 543
How a Lytic Virus Is Like an Outlaw. 576
How Cells Move Like Boats 607
Transpirational Pull 685
Specialized Teeth 785
Excretion in Aquatic Animals 796
A Chain Reaction 899
The Skeleton. 923
A City's Transportation System 948

Technology & Biology

A Nature-Inspired Adhesive 39
Global Ecology From Space. 87
Fluorescence Microscopy 291
Artificial Life? 435
Bar-Coding Life. 529
Low-Tech Weapons Against a High-Tech Parasite. . 617
Bioartificial Kidneys. 799
Studying the Brain and Addiction 905
Testing for Heart Disease 962

Biology & History

Understanding Photosynthesis. 229
Discovering the Role of DNA 349
Origins of Evolutionary Thought 459
The Evolution of Agriculture 719
Human-Fossil Seekers 773
Emerging Diseases 1023

Careers & Biology

Marine Biologist, Park Ranger, Wildlife Photographer 105
Laboratory Technician, Microscopist, Pathologist. . 195
Forensic Scientist, Plant Breeder, Population Geneticist 322
Fossil Preparator, Museum Guide, Paleontologist . . 559
Farmer, Plant Pathologist, Botanical Illustrator 655
Zoo Curator, Beekeeper, Invertebrate Biologist . . . 736

Biology & Society

Who Should Fund Product Safety Studies? 16
What Can Be Done About Invasive Mussels? 136
Should Creatine Supplements Be Regulated? 261
Are Laws Protecting Genetic Privacy Necessary? . 402
Should Antibiotic Use Be Restricted? 493
Should More Vaccinations Be Required? 593
Head for the Hills? 831
Should Marine Mammals Be Kept in Captivity?. . . 846
Who Should Solve America's Obesity Problem? . . 874
Should Student Athletes Be Tested for Steroids?. . . 934

Overview of Indiana Teacher's Edition

Program Highlights . . . . IN T20

Understanding by Design. . . . . IN T22

Deepening Understanding Through Inquiry. . . . . IN T24

Differentiated Instruction . . . . IN T26

Support for English Language Learners . . . . IN T28

Assessment Overview. . . . . IN T29

Biology.com. . . . . IN T30

Indiana Course Overview . . . . IN T32

Indiana Lesson-by-Lesson Correlation and Pacing Guide . . . . IN T38

Quick Lab Materials List . . . . IN T47

Indiana Ecosystems . . . . IN T49 (IN 21)

Indiana Science Framework for Biology. . . . . IN T53 (IN 25)

The round barns of Indiana are part of the historical landscape of Indiana.

IN Miller & Levine Biology: A Comprehensive Approach

The *Miller & Levine Biology* program for Indiana offers a variety of unique product options to support a range of teaching styles. Communicate your love of science to your students in a way that will engage them and that offers support for all levels and all types of learners. Choose the product that suits your teaching style and the needs of your class.

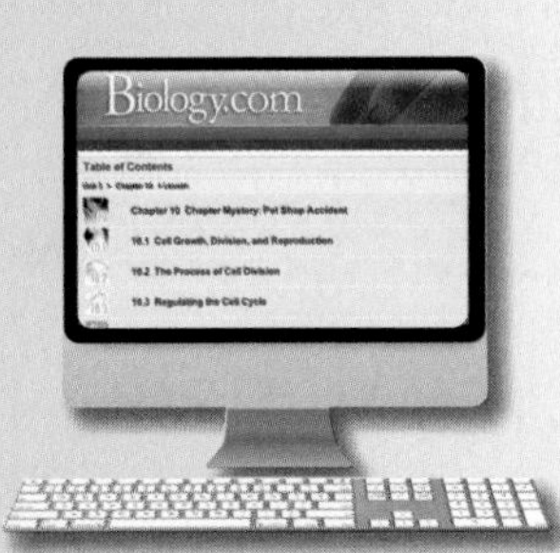

A Comprehensive Approach to Teaching Biology

Miller & Levine Biology

The most complete, accurate, comprehensible, and student-friendly biology program available. Customized for Indiana.

Foundation Edition: *Miller & Levine Biology*

A new program offering accessible content with embedded learning strategies and instructional support to address the needs of struggling students.

Core Edition: *Miller & Levine Biology*

A concise textbook covering the core topics of ecology, cells, genetics, and evolution.

Biology.com and Biology.com Plus

The next generation of digital instruction offering complete online student and teacher editions, plus video, animations, simulations, assessments, and much more!

What customers are saying about *Miller & Levine Biology*

"The Jackson Public School District adopted the Miller & Levine 'Dragonfly' textbook in 2002. The text is easy to comprehend by all learners in the classroom. The authors provide excellent analogies and teaching strategies that will support teachers in providing differentiated instruction for learning styles. With the hands-on support of the authors and a student/teacher friendly textbook, our passing rate on the State Biology Exam has increased from 78.7% in 2002 to 91.8% in 2007."

Sheila Smith, Science Specialist
Jackson Public Schools, Jackson, MS

A Program Backed by Research

In developing *Miller & Levine Biology,* the use of research has been a guiding, central principle. Research on *Biology* indicated key elements of a textbook program that ensure students' success: support for inquiry and assessment in science, while expanding its support for reading and differentiated instruction.

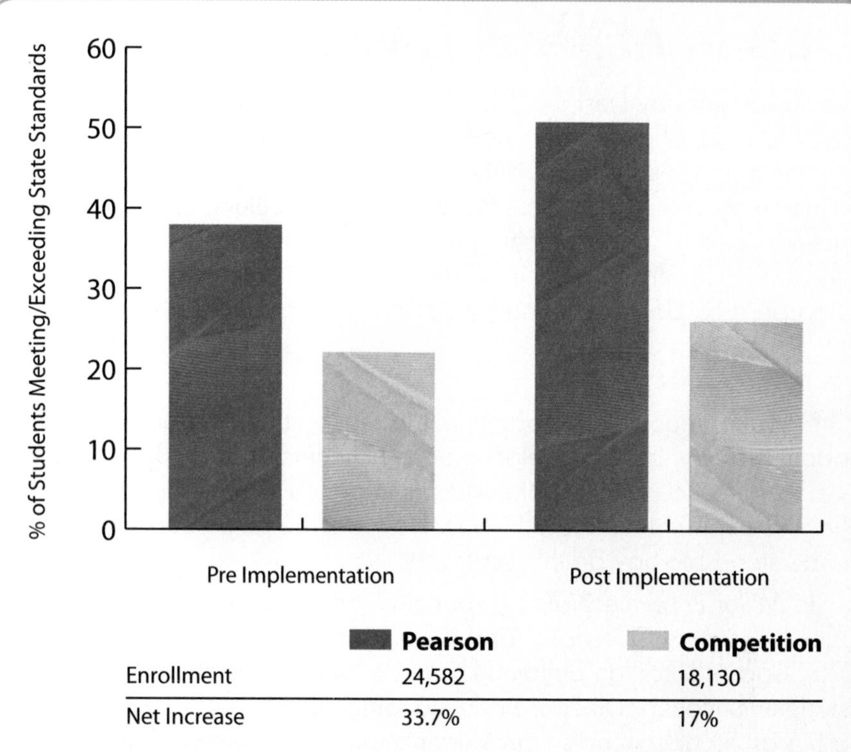

Prentice Hall Biology National Effect-Size Study Highlights Source: Guido G. Gatti, Gatti Evaluation, Inc. See PHSchool.com/research for full project report.

1 Exploratory Needs Assessment

(Quantitative and Qualitative)

Key research events include

- Teacher interviews
- Classroom observations
- Mail surveys
- Reviews of educational research

2 Formative Prototype Development and Field Testing

(Quantitative and Qualitative)

Key research events include

- Field testing of prototypes
- Classroom observations
- Teacher reviews
- Supervisor reviews
- Educator advisory panel

3 Summative Validation Research

(Experimental and Quasi-Experimental Study Designs & Qualitative Research)

Key research events include

- Pre-publication learner verification research
- Post-publication efficacy studies
- Classroom observations
- Effect-size studies

UBD in *Miller & Levine Biology*

Understanding by Design® (UbD), developed by Grant Wiggins and Jay McTighe, offers a framework for creating understanding, not by accident or happenstance, but deliberately by design. UbD is a disciplined way of thinking about the design of curriculum, instruction, and assessment that moves teaching from covering the content to ensuring understanding. In the Teacher's Edition of *Miller & Levine Biology,* we've incorporated Understanding by Design principles into every lesson.

1 Plan for Understanding

The goal of teaching biology is not to teach students a bunch of facts about biology, but to develop a deeper understanding. Biology is the story of life—a narrative of concepts informed by investigations that help us explain the natural world. How do you help your students understand biology on this scale?

In *Miller & Levine Biology,* your students are introduced to Big Ideas, Essential Questions, and Key Questions in the Student Edition. The Teacher's Edition builds on these, providing questions to help students uncover a deeper understanding. These questions lay out a hierarchy of concepts your students need to understand and take away from their study of biology.

*"The big-idea questions signal that education is not just about learning 'the answer' but about **learning how to learn.**"*
—Grant Wiggins, Ed.D.
Educational Consultant
Authentic Education
Concept Development

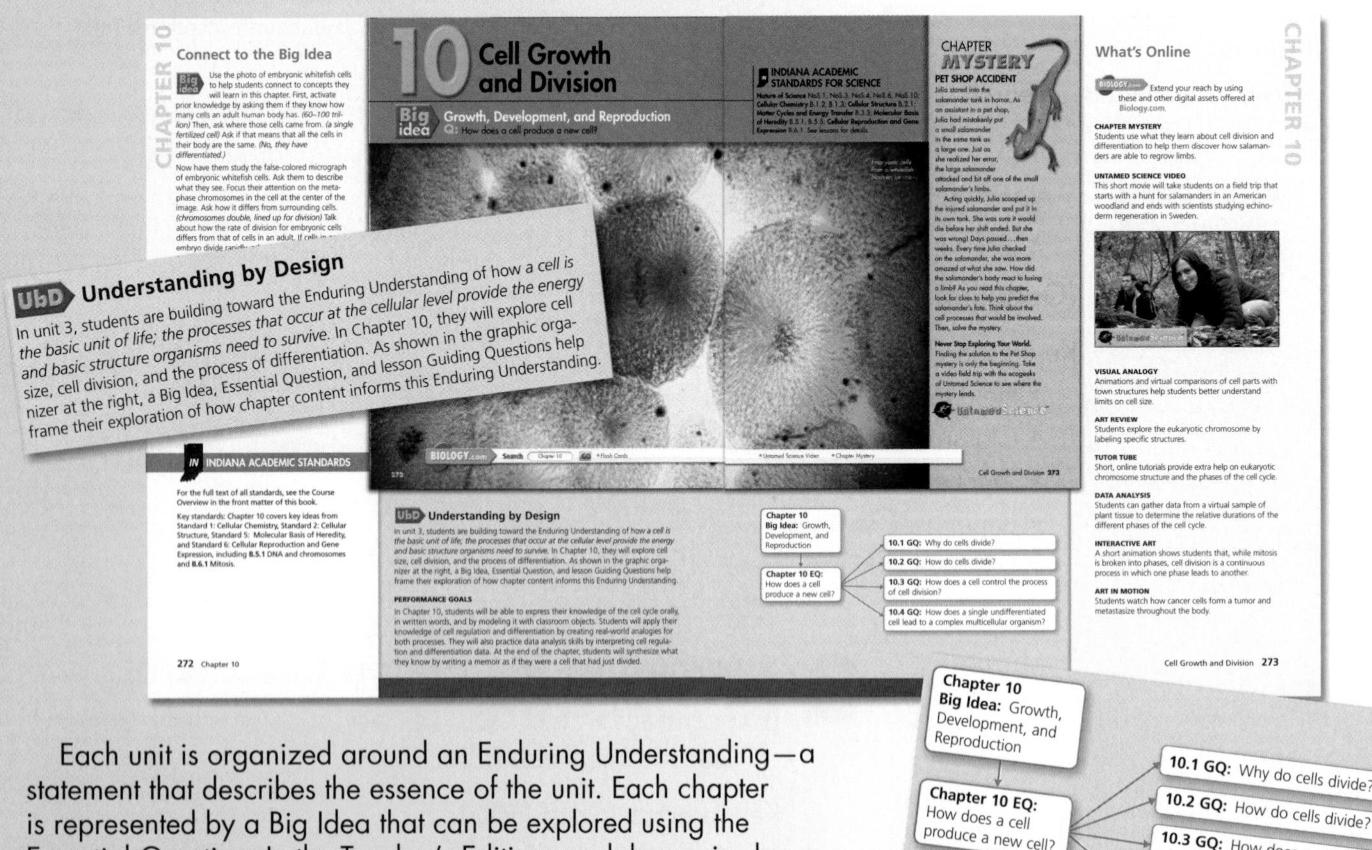

Each unit is organized around an Enduring Understanding—a statement that describes the essence of the unit. Each chapter is represented by a Big Idea that can be explored using the Essential Question. In the Teacher's Edition, each lesson is also accompanied by a Guiding Question that is tied to the Essential Question. If students can answer these questions, you know they have grasped important concepts of biology.

Chapter 10
Big Idea: Growth, Development, and Reproduction

Chapter 10 EQ: How does a cell produce a new cell?

- **10.1 GQ:** Why do cells divide?
- **10.2 GQ:** How do cells divide?
- **10.3 GQ:** How does a cell control the process of cell division?
- **10.4 GQ:** How does a single undifferentiated cell lead to a complex multicellular organism?

Enduring Understandings

Unit 1 The Nature of Life: The process of science helps biologists investigate how nature works at all levels, from the molecules in cells to the biosphere.

Unit 2 Ecology: The existence of life on Earth depends on interactions among organisms and between organisms and their environment.

Unit 3 Cells: A cell is the basic unit of life; the processes that occur at the cellular level provide the energy and basic structure organisms need to survive.

Unit 4 Genetics: DNA is the universal code for life; it enables an organism to transmit hereditary information and, along with the environment, determines an organism's characteristics.

Unit 5 Evolution: The diversity of life is the result of ongoing evolutionary change. Species alive today have evolved from ancient common ancestors.

Unit 6 From Microorganisms to Plants: From microorganisms to plants, organisms vary widely in the way they carry out basic life processes.

Unit 7 Animals: Animals have evolved diverse ways to carry out basic life processes and maintain homeostasis.

Unit 8 The Human Body: The human body is a complex system. The coordinated functions of its many structures support life processes and maintain homeostasis.

2 Set Assessment Goals

A critical aspect of any UbD lesson plan is thinking backwards from the desired goal of enduring understandings to what you will accept as evidence of those understandings. The following features of the Teacher's Edition will help you identify desired accomplishments and plan appropriate assessment goals.

- Performance Goals, Chapter Opener—highlights activities by which students can demonstrate a transfer of a simple knowledge of facts to a broader understanding of biological concepts.
- Evidence of Understanding, Lesson Opener—alternative assessments that help you determine if your students can make meaning from what they read in a lesson.
- Performance Tasks, Chapter Study Guide—suggestions for both a Summative and a Transfer Task to ensure students grasp chapter content.

UbD Teach for Understanding

ENDURING UNDERSTANDING A cell is the basic unit of life; the processes that occur at the cellular level provide the energy and basic structure organisms need to survive.

GUIDING QUESTION Why do cells divide?

EVIDENCE OF UNDERSTANDING *After completing the lesson, give students this assessment to ensure they understand how a small size helps cells survive and function efficiently.* Have students use classroom objects to model how DNA overload or material exchange limits the size of cells. For example, they might limit the number of pencils available to the class. As the class size gets bigger, fewer people can be writing compared to the number who do not have a pencil.

3 Teach the Concepts

In addition to being goal-focused, a UbD lesson plan should include interim assessment tasks to assess students' progress through a lesson. The Teacher's Edition includes **Check for Understanding** boxes that can be used at a specific point in a lesson. These include a variety of informal assessment strategies—for example, follow-up probes, visual representations, question boxes, one-minute responses, and hand signals. Also included are suggestions for adjusting your instruction to address students' misunderstandings or misconceptions mid-lesson.

UbD Check for Understanding

ONE-MINUTE RESPONSE

Write the following prompt on the board, and give students about a minute to write a quick response summarizing their understanding.

Explain why an organized chromosome structure is an important adaptation for eukaryotic organisms. *(Essays should mention that having an organized structure helps cells use and pass on large amounts of DNA in multiple strands exactly and efficiently.)*

ADJUST INSTRUCTION

If student responses are incorrect or incomplete, review the advantages of chromosome structure by comparing it to a spool of thread. Point out that it is easier to sort two spools of thread than two long, tangled threads. Have them use the analogy to help them explain how chromosome structure helps cells divide.

INDIANA

Deepen Understanding Through Inquiry

Miller & Levine Biology for Indiana encourages students to think like scientists, and to enhance their understanding by participating in inquiry-based discovery. The **Chapter Mystery** sets the tone. Students are invited to follow clues throughout the chapter and, by chapter's end, solve a biological mystery.

Miller & Levine Biology offers a range of lab options, providing you with the flexibility to address all types of learners and accommodate your class time and equipment requirements.

Quick Labs

Quick Labs provide students the opportunity to discover science with a variety of investigations through both guided and open-ended inquiry. These labs deepen student understanding of Key Concepts and Big Ideas. Quick Labs are correlated to the Indiana Academic Standards for Biology I.

Chapter Investigations and Pre-Lab

Each chapter ends with a chapter investigation, introduced in the Student Edition by a Pre-Lab. The full lab is provided, in leveled forms, in Lab Manuals A and B. The chapter investigations offer students Skills Labs, Forensics Labs, Real-World Labs, and Design Your Own Labs—and connect back to the Big Idea of the chapter. Chapter Labs are correlated to the Indiana Academic Standards for Biology I.

CHAPTER MYSTERY

MOVING THE MOAI

Easter Island is a tiny speck of land in the vast Pacific Ocean off the coast of Chile with a harsh tropical climate. The original islanders, who called themselves Rapa Nui, came from Polynesia. They carve[d] hundreds of huge stone statues ca[lled] *moai* (moh eye). Starting around 1200 A.D., the Rapa Nui somehow moved these mysterious statues, ea[ch] of which weighed between 10 and 14 tons, from quarries to locations around the island. Nearly all theorie[s] about this process suggest that strong, large logs were necessary to move

MYSTERY CLUE

Easter Island's first colonists brought with them banana trees, taro root, and chickens—and possibly some small mammalian "stowaways." What impact might these new organisms have had on the island's ecosystems?

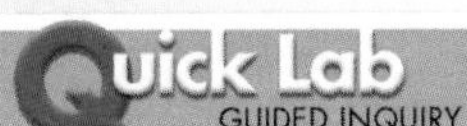

Quick Lab GUIDED INQUIRY

How Does Compe[tition] Affect Growth?

1. Label two paper cu[ps] ... and 15. Make several ... holes in the bottom o[f] ... cup. Fill each cup two ... full with potting soil. ... 3 bean seeds in cup 3, ... plant 15 bean seeds in ...

2. Water both cups ... the soil is moist but n[ot] ... Put them in a locatio[n] ... receives bright indire[ct] ... Water the cups equall[y] ... needed.

3. Count the seedlin[gs] ... other day for two wee[ks]

Analyze and Conclud[e]

1. Observe What di[f] ... did you observe betw[een] ... two cups?

Quick Lab OPEN-ENDED INQUIRY

IN NoS.6, B.2.1

Making a Model of a Cell

1. Your class is going to make a model of a plant cell using the whole classroom. Work with a partner or in a small group to decide what cell part or organelle you would like to model. (Use **Figure 7–14** on pages 206–207 as a starting point. It gives you an idea of the relative sizes of various cell parts and their possible positions.)

2. Using materials of your choice, make a three-dimensional model of the cell part or organelle you chose. Make the model as complete and as accurate as you can.

3. Label an index card with the name of your cell part or organelle, and list its main features and functions. Attach the card to your model.

4. Attach your model to an appropriate place in the room. If possible, attach your model to another related cell part or organelle.

Analyze and Conclude

1. Calculate Assume that a typical plant cell is 50 micrometers wide (50×10^{-6} m). Calculate the scale of your classroom cell model. (*Hint:* Divide the width of the classroom by the width of a cell, making sure to use the same units.) MATH

2. Compare and Contrast How is your model cell part or organelle similar to the real cell part or organelle? How is it different?

3. Evaluate Based on your work with this model, describe how you could make a better model. What new information would your improved model demonstrate?

Design Your Own Lab OPEN-ENDED INQUIRY

IN NoS.1 Develop explanations; NoS.4 Evaluate the work of peers.

Pre-Lab: Regeneration in Planaria

Problem How potent are the stem cells in planaria?

Materials fresh water or spring water, planarians, petri dishes, glass-marking pencil, forceps, scalpel, dissecting microscope, glass microscope slide, lens paper, pipette, small paintbrush, clear ruler

Lab Manual Chapter 10 Lab

Skills Focus Form a Hypothesis, Design an Experiment, Draw Conclusions

Connect to the Big idea All cells come from existing cells. When most cells in a multicellular organism divide, they produce cells just like themselves. However, some cells can differentiate to form different types of cells. These cells enable an organism to repair tissue after an injury or in some cases to regenerate body parts. In this lab, you will investigate the ability of planarians to regenerate body parts.

[...] **Questions**

[...] Contrast What is the difference [...]ent stem cells and multipotent stem [...]

[...] What type of stem cell enables [...]duce cells, such as skin and blood [...]stantly replaced by the body?

[...] What type of stem cell enables a [...]enerate its tail?

[...]ntrast In what way is regeneration of a body part similar to asexual reproduction? In what way is it different?

Pre-Lab Questions

Preview the procedure in the lab manual.

1. Apply Concepts What would you expect to observe if the stem cells in planarians are totipotent? What would you expect to observe if the stem cells are multipotent?
2. Control Variables What will you use as a control in your experiment? Explain why you need this control.
3. Infer Two planarians are cut at different locations. Regeneration occurs in one planarian, but not in the other. Based on these results, what might you infer about stem cells in planarians?

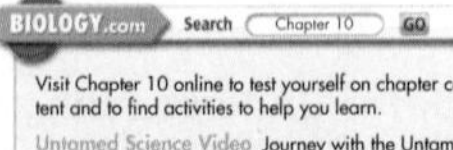

BIOLOGY.com Search Chapter 10 GO

Visit Chapter 10 online to test yourself on chapter content and to find activities to help you learn.

Untamed Science Video Journey with the Untamed Science crew to a research facility in Sweden to learn why scientists are studying regeneration in brittle stars.

Visual Analogy Compare a growing cell to a growing city to understand limits on cell size.

Data Analysis Learn how to time the cell cycle by counting cells in mitosis.

Art Review Test your knowledge of the structure of a eukaryotic chromosome.

Tutor Tube Sort out chromosome structure vocabulary with this simple tutorial video.

InterActive Art See the phases of mitosis in action.

Art in Motion See what happens when cancerous cells invade normal tissue.

298 Chapter 10 • Pre-Lab

Connect to the Big idea All cells come from existing cells. When most cells in a multicellular organism divide, they produce cells just like themselves. However, some cells can differentiate to form different types of cells. These cells enable an organism to repair tissue after an injury or in some cases to regenerate body parts. In this lab, you will investigate the ability of planarians to regenerate body parts.

Inquiry Resources

Lab Manuals

Lab Manual A and Lab Manual B provide the procedures and worksheets for the 35 chapter investigations introduced in Pre-Lab of the Student Edition. The labs in Lab Manual A are intended for on-level students, whereas those in Lab Manual B are written for students who need additional support. Lab Manual A also offers 15 additional labs. Lab Manual B also offers a large selection of Data Analysis activities.

Untamed Science Videos

A perfect blend of energy and scientific knowledge, the Untamed Science team brings core concepts from the textbook into the wild! One video per chapter explores and extends concepts from the Chapter Mystery.

Virtual BioLab

Virtual BioLab provides students with a realistic lab environment, supporting discovery-based learning and offering a method to perform classic experiments quickly and easily.

INDIANA

Differentiated Instruction in *Miller & Levine Biology*

Students develop and learn in different ways at different paces. Accessible content presented in a variety of formats acknowledges these unique differences by providing options for learning. The *Miller & Levine Biology* program presents standards-based instruction in ways that allow all students to participate and achieve. Our effective support helps you close the achievement gap.

Teaching Support Helps You Modify Instruction

Miller & Levine Biology offers teachers many different ways to modify content for particular learner groups.

- Each chapter begins with a **Chapter Planner** that maps out the differentiated instruction activities and program resources available for the chapter.
- Most on-level activities available in the **Teacher's Edition wrap-around** are accompanied by strategies for modifying the activity for less proficient readers, English language learners, special needs students, struggling students, and advanced students.
- Each **Lesson Assessment** is accompanied by a remediation suggestion for students who need extra help.
- **Chapter Tests A and B** in the Assessment Resources Book allow you to assess students with a level of rigor appropriate for different ability levels.
- **Biology.com** allows teachers to customize digital lessons to support differentiated instruction.
- The **Classroom Resources CD-ROM** provides pages of study Workbooks A and B, Lab Manuals A and B, and the Assessment Resources Book that can easily be edited for different learner levels.

Cell Division and Reproduction

How do asexual and sexual reproduction compare?

Reproduction, the formation of new individuals, is one of the most important characteristics of living things. For an organism composed of just one cell, cell division can serve as a perfectly good form of reproduction. You don't have to meet someone else, conduct a courtship, or deal with rivals. All you have to do is to divide, and *presto*—there are two of you!

Bacterium

Hydra

Kalanchoe

FIGURE 10–3 Asexual Reproduction Cell division leads to reproduction in single-celled organisms and some multicellular organisms. Apply Concepts ***What do the offspring of each of these organisms have in common?***

Asexual Reproduction For many single-celled organisms, such as the bacterium in **Figure 10–3,** cell division is the only form of reproduction. The process can be relatively simple, efficient, and effective, enabling populations to increase in number very quickly. In most cases, the two cells produced by cell division are genetically identical to the cell that produced them. This kind of reproduction is called **asexual reproduction. The production of genetically identical offspring from a single parent is known as asexual reproduction.**

Asexual reproduction also occurs in many multicellular organisms. The small bud growing off the hydra will eventually break off and become an independent organism, an example of asexual reproduction in an animal. Each of the small shoots or plantlets on the tip of the kalanchoe leaf may also grow into a new plant.

Sexual Reproduction Unlike asexual reproduction, where cells separate to form a new individual, **sexual reproduction** involves the fusion of two separate parent cells. In sexual reproduction, offspring are produced by the fusion of special reproductive cells formed by each of two parents. **Offspring produced by sexual reproduction inherit some of their genetic information from each parent.** Most animals and plants reproduce sexually, and so do some single-celled organisms. You will learn more about the form of cell division that produces reproductive cells in Chapter 11.

BUILD Vocabulary

PREFIXES The prefix *a-* in *asexual* means "without." **Asexual reproduction** is reproduction without the fusion of reproductive cells.

In Your Notebook *Use a Venn diagram to compare asexual and sexual reproduction.*

Cell Growth and Division **277**

Quick Facts

CELL SIZE

While surface area to volume ratios limit the sizes of cells, not all cells are the same size. In fact, there are a surprising variety of cell sizes that exist in nature. For example, some tiny *Mycoplasma* bacteria measure a scant 0.3 micrometers in diameter. To put that in perspective, it can take hundreds of these bacteria, set end to end, to equal the width of a single human hair, about 50–200 micrometers. On the other extreme, giraffes have nerve cells that stretch for meters along the length of their necks.

LESSON 10.1

Lead a Discussion

Talk about how cell division relates to the process of asexual reproduction. To reinforce students' knowledge, have them apply what they have learned to their everyday lives.

Ask Why do bacterial infections spread so quickly through a school? *(Bacteria can reproduce asexually. So, they can quickly reproduce in the right environment, such as a crowded school.)*

DIFFERENTIATED INSTRUCTION

LPR Less Proficient Readers List the Key Concepts on the board in simplified language. For example, write:

- Offspring of asexual reproduction have the same genetic information.
- Offspring of sexual reproduction have genetic information from both parents.

Suggest that students preview these Key Concepts and keep them in mind as they read the text.

ELL Focus on ELL: Access Content

BEGINNING SPEAKERS Show students how cells combine and divide during asexual and sexual reproduction by drawing these simple diagrams on the board:

Asexual Reproduction **Sexual Reproduction**

Parent Cells

Offspring

Color code the drawings of the parent cells and the label "Parent Cells," as well as the offspring cells and their label. Point to the diagrams as you explain why asexual reproduction results in genetically identical offspring while sexual reproduction produces offspring with a combination of genetic information from both parents.

Answers

FIGURE 10–3 The offspring share the same genetic material as their parent.

IN YOUR NOTEBOOK Venn diagrams should show the following characteristics: For both sexual and asexual reproduction: produces new organisms; For asexual reproduction only: quick, produces genetically identical offspring, one parent; For sexual reproduction only: offspring produced by the fusion of two cells, two parents

Cell Growth and Division **277**

DIFFERENTIATED INSTRUCTION

LPR Less Proficient Readers List the Key Concepts on the board in simplified language. For example, write:

- Offspring of asexual reproduction have the same genetic information.
- Offspring of sexual reproduction have genetic information from both parents.

Sugges
and kee

DIFFERENTIATED INSTRUCTION

L1 Special Needs Use clay models to help students understand that a smaller surface area to volume ratio does not mean the cube is getting smaller. Both surface area and cube volume increase as the length of the side increases.

L1 Struggling Students Some students may have a difficult time understanding the information presented in the table. Point out that the cube directly above each column shows the "cell" that the calculations refer to. Then, explain that the first row shows how to find the surface area for each cubic "cell." Use a clay or plastic model of a cube to expla
width *(l*
one face

DIFFERENTIATED INSTRUCTION

L3 Advanced Students Have students identify and discuss another technological advance that has raised ethical issues. Ask them to talk about why the technology was developed and how its use created an ethical debate.

Student Support Ensures Success

In *Miller & Levine Biology,* differentiated instruction is built directly into student materials—including the Student Edition, Study Workbooks A and B, and **Biology.com.**

Student Edition

- **Key Questions** identify key ideas and focus on the main concepts.
- A captivating **visual learning strand** engages students and helps foster understanding of complex topics.
- **Build Vocabulary** features provide additional language support by focusing on language form and function, as well as academic vocabulary.
- **Quick Labs** and **Analyzing Data** features provide hands-on, inquiry-based exploration of chapter concepts.
- The **Online Student Edition** offers visual and auditory support of biology content.

Study Workbooks A and B

Two versions of the Study Workbook offer leveled activities and strategies to enhance student understanding.

Key features of Study Workbook A include:

- Guiding Questions for the Big Idea.
- Chapter Mystery activity worksheets that reinforce 21st Century Skills.
- Graphic organizers and concept maps that help build student understanding.

Key features of Study Workbook B include:

- Concept maps that organize chapter content.
- Lesson-level vocabulary support to help students master key vocabulary terms.
- Test-taking tips to help students prepare for standardized tests.

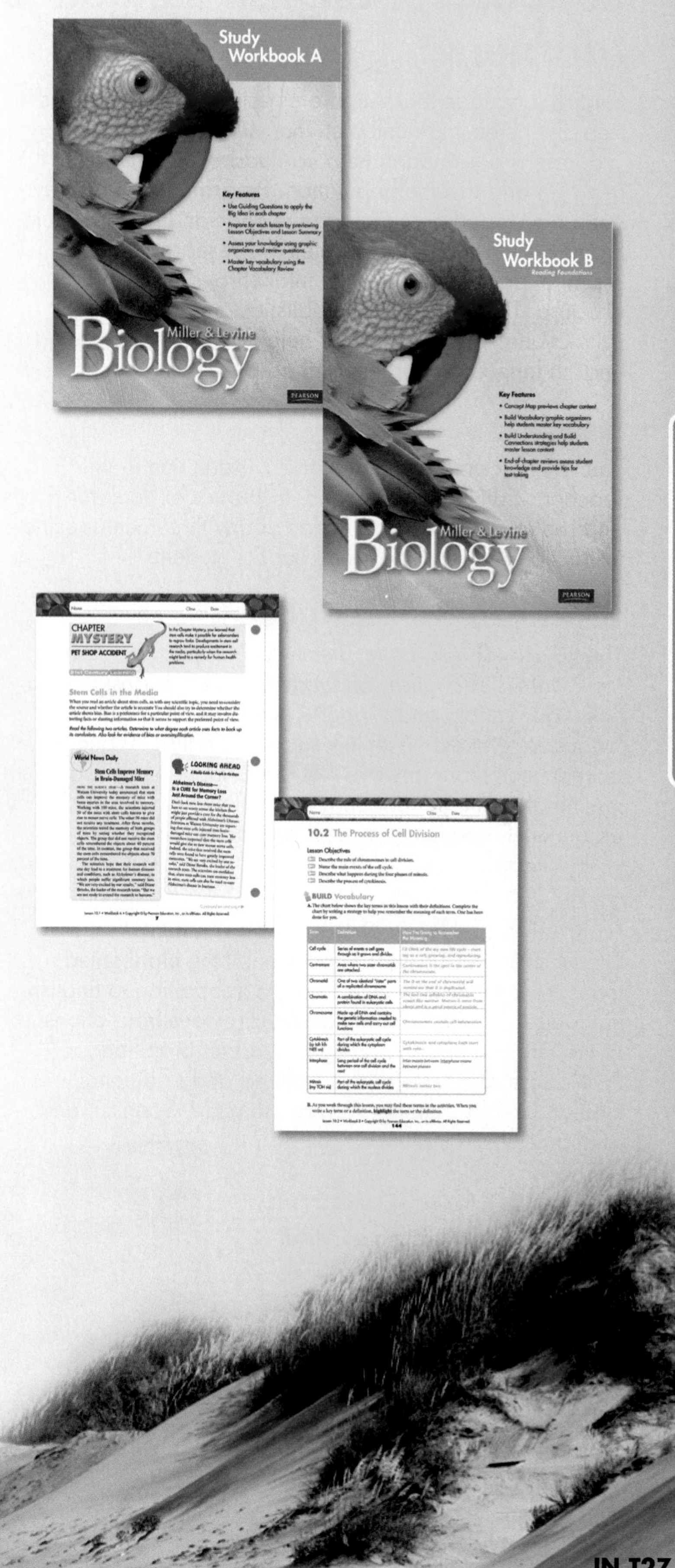

Biology.com

Many of the digital assets on **Biology.com** offer support for differentiated instruction, for example:

- **Vocabulary Flash Cards** provide students with extra opportunities to review and practice chapter vocabulary terms.
- **Visual Analogy** features provide interactive digital support for the Student Edition visual analogies.
- Drag-and-drop labeling activities make **Art Review** features an accessible way to review key Student Edition visuals.
- **Data Analysis** activities challenge students to apply chapter concepts to a real-world problem.

Support for English Language Learners

English language learners are entering U.S. classrooms in steadily increasing numbers. The *Miller & Levine Biology* program is designed to help you address the needs of this growing and diverse population. Program materials have been developed according to the Pearson ELL Curriculum Framework, which incorporates five research-based essential principles within an Into/Through/Beyond structure. This framework establishes an effective instructional scaffold that will help you reach all your English language learners and prepare them for success.

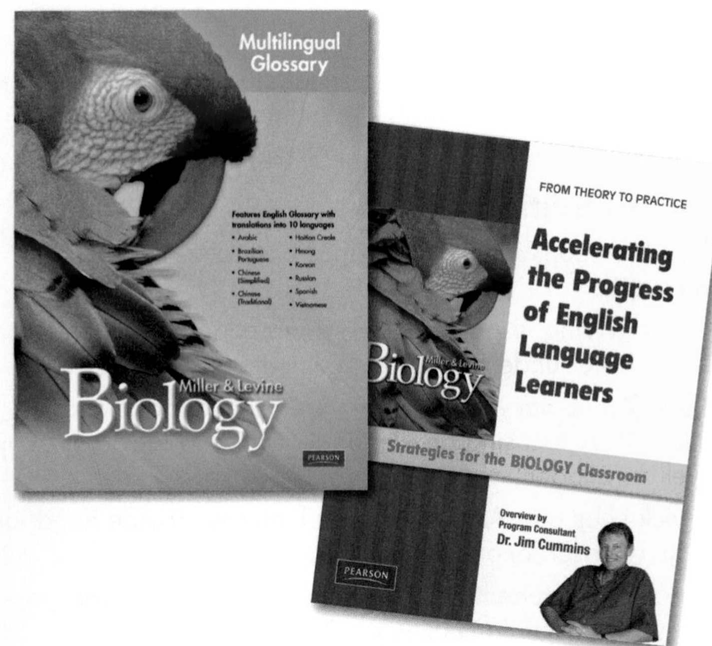

Teacher's Edition

You will find ample support for ELL instruction in this Teacher's Edition wrap-around. In particular, look for Focus on ELL strategies, which provide you with content-specific instructions for working with your ELL students.

Teacher's ELL Handbook

The ELL Handbook, *From Theory to Practice: Accelerating the Progress of English Language Learners*, is designed to help you scaffold and support instruction for your English language learners. With this support, English language learners can learn in ways that are comprehensible and meaningful. The handbook will enable you to promote the academic success and achievement of all your students.

Multilingual Glossary

The Multilingual Glossary contains all the highlighted terms from *Miller & Levine Biology.* In addition to English-language definitions, the glossary provides translations of the terms in these languages: Arabic, Brazilian Portuguese, Chinese (both simplified and traditional), Haitian Creole, Hmong, Korean, Russian, Spanish, and Vietnamese.

Spanish Components

Both the Student Edition of *Miller & Levine Biology* and Study Workbook A are offered in Spanish-language editions, including a Spanish-language Answer Key for the teacher. The Spanish Student Edition with audio is available for your students at **Biology.com**, as are Flash Cards with Spanish translations.

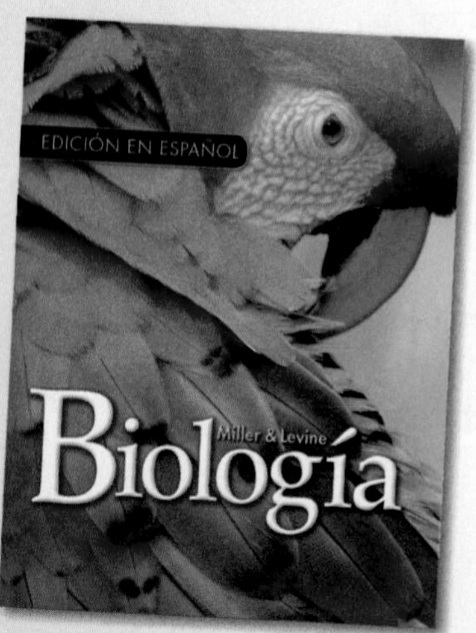

"The knowledge base that research has generated about ELL students' academic trajectories shows clearly that ELL students must be understanding instruction and learning English across the curriculum if they are to catch up in time to meet graduation requirements. Teaching biology affords opportunities for extending ELL students' academic language proficiency. The Pearson ELL Curriculum Framework incorporates the essential elements that teachers need to implement."

—Jim Cummins, Ph.D.
University of Toronto

Assessment to Inform Instruction

A variety of assessment opportunities in the *Miller & Levine Biology* program helps you monitor student progress, evaluate content mastery, and ensure student success on high-stakes tests.

Lesson and Chapter Assessment

Caption questions, Lesson Assessments, Chapter Assessments, and online Self-Assessments enable students to gauge their understanding of the content to prepare for end-of-year tests. Standardized Test Practice in each chapter is correlated to Biology I Indiana Academic Standards.

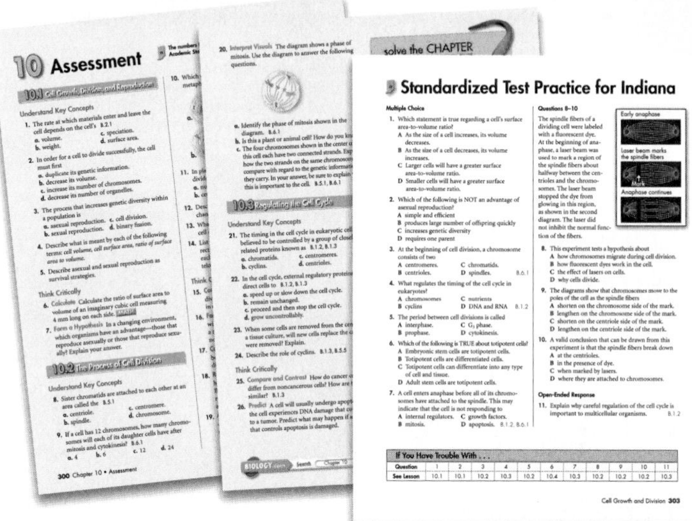

Online Assessment and Remediation

Biology.com provides diagnostic and Benchmark tests with automatic scoring, class reports, and remediation for students.

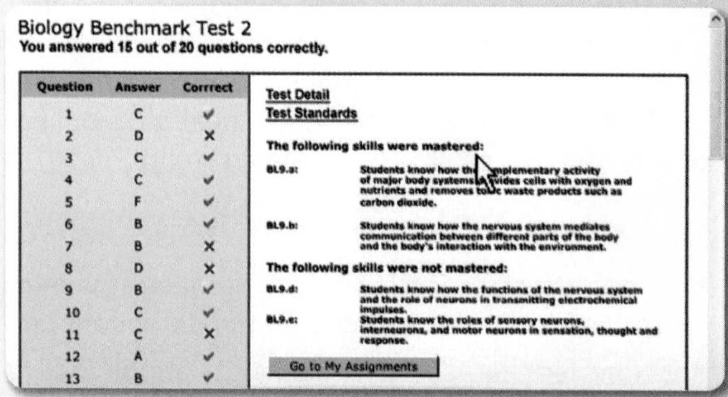

Class Standards Report for Washington Middle/High School — Biology

Key: ✓ Mastered ☒ Not Mastered ☐ Not Attempted

	BL9.a: Students know how the complementary acitivty of major...	BL9.b: Students know how the nervous system communication...	BL9.c: Students know how feedback loops in the nervous and...	BL9.d: Students know the functions of the nervous system...	BL9.e: Studer roles c neuror
# of students who have mastered standards	12	29	25	24	
Total Students	30	30	30	30	
Andrew Lauer	☒	✓	✓	✓	
Belinda Cortez	☒	✓	✓	✓	
Christopher Hale	☒	☒	☒	☒	
Dora diConti	✓	✓	✓	✓	
Edward Robertson	☒	✓	✓	✓	
Emily Whitham	☒	✓	✓	✓	
Felicity Withers	☒	✓	✓	✓	
George Slate	☒	☒	✓	☒	
Kevin Jackson	✓	✓	✓	✓	
Marcus Cooper	☒	✓	✓	✓	
Mark Jacobs	☒	✓	✓	✓	
Susan Kim	☒	✓	✓	✓	

Assessment Resources

The Assessment Resources book includes two levels of chapter and unit assessments as well as visual quizzes for alternative testing. Indiana Progress Monitoring Assessments offers diagnostic and benchmark tests that monitor mastery of Biology I Indiana Academic Standards for Science. Finally, the Indiana Standardized Test Preparation Workbook provides students with practice for the Biology I End-of-Course Assessment.

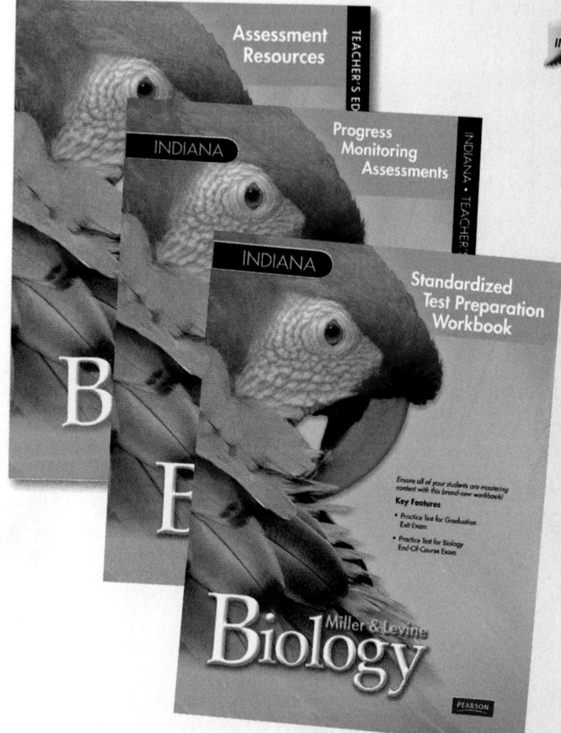

ExamView® Assessment Suite CD-ROM

Create and print custom tests in minutes that correlate to your state standards. This test bank includes over 4000 test questions and is compatible with Quick-Take software.

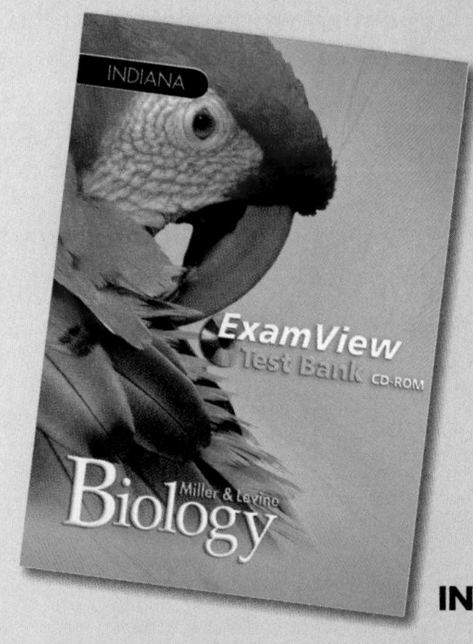

Assessment

INDIANA

IN Biology.com: Changing the World of Biology Education

Biology.com is the next generation of digital instruction offering complete online student and teacher editions, a comprehensive teacher center, digital lessons, interactive animations, simulations, and assessments in one place. Featuring the latest in digital instructional technology, **Biology.com** integrates the key concepts from the text and brings them alive online. **Search and assign content correlated to Indiana standards.**

Enhanced Classroom Instruction

- A sophisticated classroom management system allows you to organize your class reports and track student progress easily.
- Online Teacher Center contains assignable activities, homework, quizzes, and tests with automatic grading capabilities.

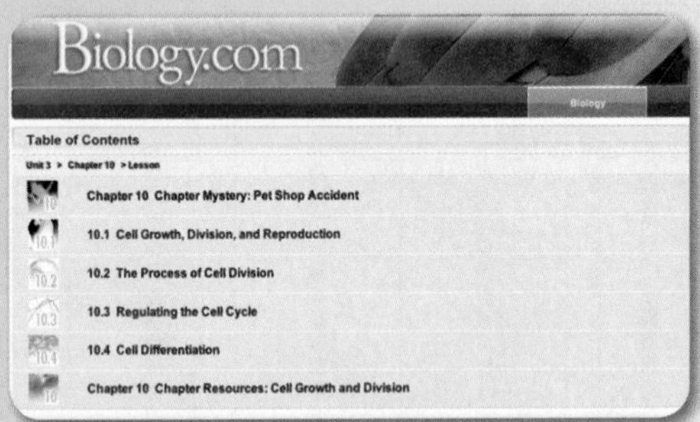

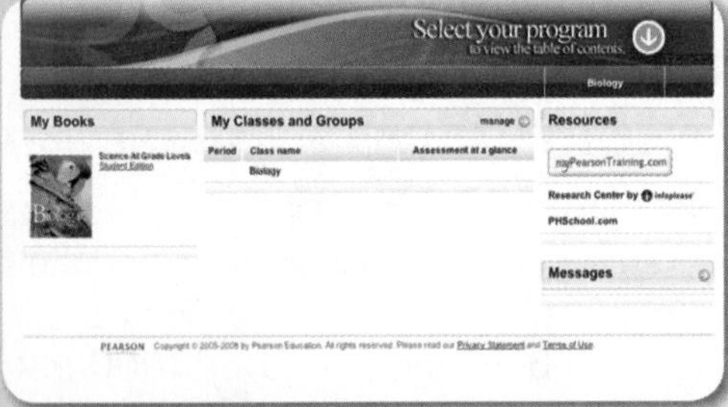

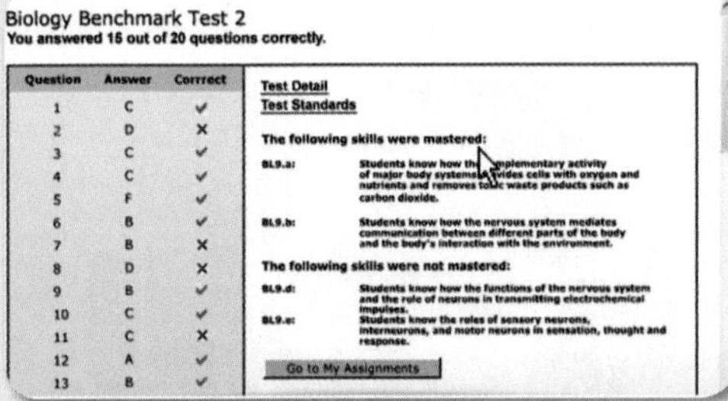

- Customize worksheets from the Study Workbooks, Lab Manuals, and Assessment Resources Book to meet your students' needs.
- The Indiana online Teacher's Edition allows you flexible, easy access to teacher support and instruction.
- Access training at point of use to support your instructional needs and maximize your use of **Biology.com.** Go to **mypearsontraining.com.**

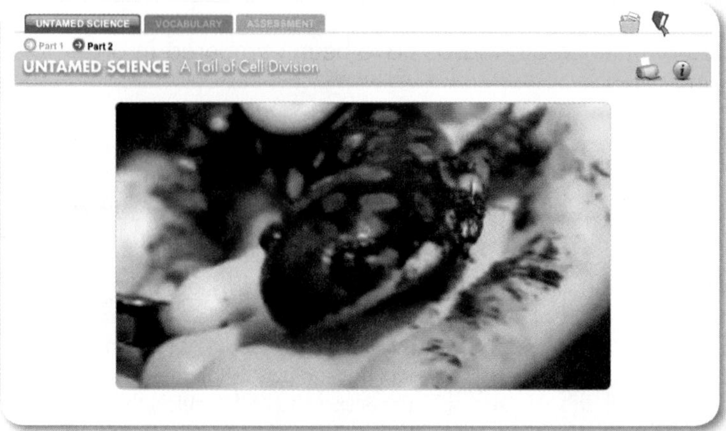

Online Student Explorations

Students can solve the Chapter Mystery online at their own pace. They can visually explore chapter concepts by watching the Untamed Science video.

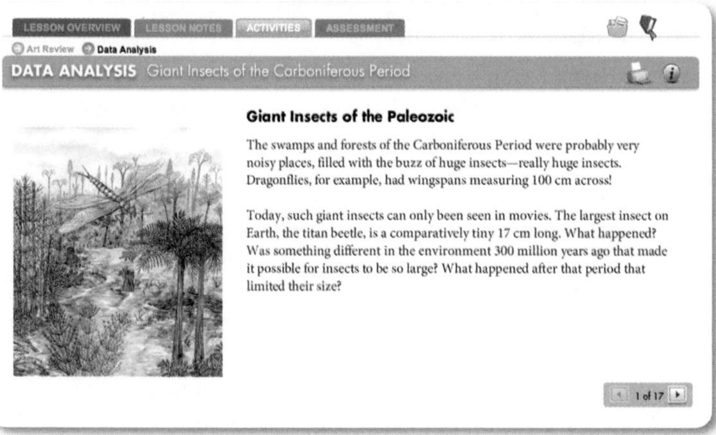

Digital Inquiry Activities

Develop student inquiry skills and deepen understanding of Key Concepts with Data Analysis activities.

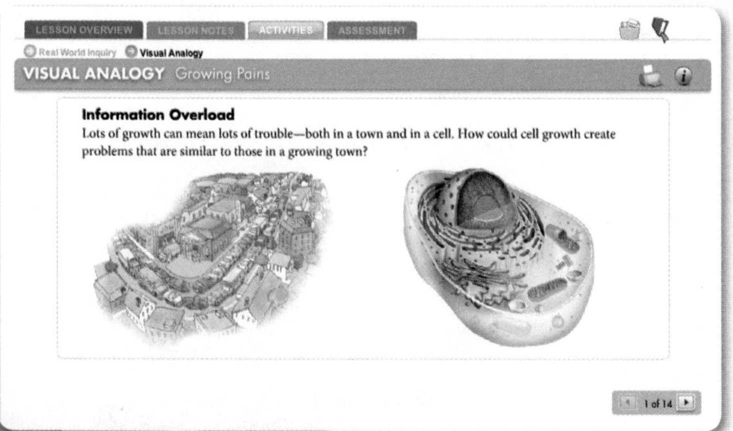

Interactive Visuals

Support all your students and reinforce concepts with a variety of interactive visuals including InterActive Art activities, animated Visual Analogies, vocabulary Flash Cards, Art in Motion animations, and Tutor Tube videos.

Additional Online Support

- An integrated online Student Edition allows your students to reference key concepts from the text easily.
- Graphic organizers, digital notes, and highlighting features help students organize their work.
- Students can assess their understanding anytime with online self-checks and quizzes.

Course Overview

The overview lists Indiana's Academic Standards for Biology I. Use this chart to see the coverage of Indiana's Biology curriculum in *Miller & Levine Biology*. The Nature of Science Standards have been numbered in order to refer to them on the pages of the Student Edition.

Indiana's Academic Standards for Biology I

THE NATURE OF SCIENCE

Students should understand that scientific knowledge is gained from observation of natural phenomena and experimentation, by designing and conducting investigations guided by theory, and by evaluating and communicating the results of those investigations according to accepted procedures. Thus, scientific knowledge is scientists' best explanations for the data from many investigations. Further, ideas about objects in the microscopic world that we cannot directly sense are often understood in terms of concepts developed to understand objects in the macroscopic world that we can see and touch. In the science classroom student work should align with this process of science and should be guided by the following principles. These should be woven throughout the daily work that students are doing when learning the content presented in the standard indicators.

Academic Standard	Where You Will Find It
NoS.1 Develop explanations based on reproducible data and observations gathered during laboratory investigations.	• Appendix B • Lab Manual A: CL 1, 2, 6, 7, 8, 10, 15, 17, 20, 23, 24, 31; AL 9
NoS.2 Recognize that their explanations must be based both on their data and other known information from investigations of others.	• Lessons 1.1, 4.4 • Analyzing Data: p. 115 • Lab Manual A: CL 1, 2, 16, 26, 29, 31; AL 11
NoS.3 Clearly communicate their ideas and results of investigations verbally and in written form using tables, graphs, diagrams, and photographs.	• Lessons 1.1, 1.2, 1.3, 4.4 • Quick Lab: p. 13 • All Analyzing Data Features • Appendix A • Lab Manual A: CL 2, 4, 6; AL 6, 11; Appendix B • Chapter Assessment: All Use Science Graphics; All Write About Science; All Analyzing Data
NoS.4 Regularly evaluate the work of their peers and in turn have their work evaluated by their peers.	• Lesson 1.2 • Lab Manual A: CL 10, 16, 22; AL 11
NoS.5 Apply standard techniques in laboratory investigations to measure physical quantities in appropriate units and convert known quantities to other units as necessary.	• Lesson 1.3 • Lab Manual A: CL 1, 2, 5, 6, 23, 26, 28, 33; AL 3; Appendix D • Biology.com: DA 1
NoS.6 Use analogies and models (mathematical and physical) to simplify and represent systems that are difficult to understand or directly experience due to their size, time scale, or complexity, and recognize the limitations of analogies and models.	• Lessons 2.1, 2.2, 2.3, 3.1, 4.1, 5.1, 9.1, 17.2, 18.2, 18.3, 20.1 • Quick Lab: pp. 36, 203, 395, 405, 520, 575 • Analyzing Data: p. 491 • Lab Manual A: CL 6, 7, 11, 13, 14, 17, 18, 19; AL1, 2, 3, 7, 14, 15 • Biology.com: all Visual Analogies
NoS.7 Focus on the development of explanatory models based on their observations during laboratory investigations.	• Appendix B • Lab Manual A: CL 13, 14, 32; AL 7, 8, 14, 15
NoS.8 Explain that the body of scientific knowledge is organized into major theories, which are derived from and supported by the results of many experiments, and allow us to make testable predictions.	• Lessons 1.2, 1.3 • Lab Manual A: AL 8 • Workbook B: pp. 4–5
NoS.9 Recognize that new scientific discoveries often lead to a re-evaluation of previously accepted scientific knowledge and of commonly held ideas.	• Lessons 1.1, 7.1, 16.2, 18.1, 18.2, 18.3 • Features: B&H all • Biology.com: AI 1; AM 1; AR 1
NoS.10 Describe how scientific discoveries lead to the development of new technologies, and conversely how technological advances can lead to scientific discoveries through new experimental methods and equipment.	• Lessons 1.2, 7.1, 14.3, 15.2, 15.3 • Features: CM 1, 15, 17; T&B all • Analyzing Data: p. 429
NoS.11 Explain how scientific knowledge can be used to guide decisions on environmental and social issues.	• Lessons 1.2, 6.2, 6.3, 6.4, 15.3, 15.4, 35.3 • Features: B&S all; CM 35; T&B p. 962 • Quick Lab: p. 1021 • Analyzing Data: pp. 164, 172, 429

STANDARD 1: CELLULAR CHEMISTRY

Core Standard Describe the basic molecular structure and function of the four major categories of organic compounds (carbohydrates, lipids, proteins and nucleic acids) essential to cellular function.

Core Standard Describe how work done in cells is performed by a variety of organic molecules, especially proteins, whose functions depend on the sequence of their monomers and the consequent shape of the molecule.

Academic Standard	Where You Will Find It
B.1.1 Describe the structure of the major categories of organic compounds which make up living organisms in terms of their building blocks and the small number of chemical elements (carbon, hydrogen, nitrogen, oxygen, phosphorous, and sulfur) from which they are composed.	• Lessons 2.3, 2.4, 30.2 • Analyzing Data: p. 48 • Lab Manual A: AL 1
B.1.2 Understand that the shape of a molecule determines its role in the many different types of cellular processes including metabolism, homeostasis, growth and development, and heredity, and understand that the majority of these processes involve proteins that act as enzymes.	• Lessons 2.3, 2.4, 8.1, 9.2, 10.3, 12.3, 13.1, 13.2, 13.4, 14.2, 24.3, 30.2, 33.2, 34.1, 35.2 • Features: CM 2 • Quick Lab: p. 352 • Analyzing Data: pp. 288, 381, 956 • Unit 3 Project • Lab Manual A: CL 2; AL 2 • Biology.com: TT 13; VA 2
B.1.3 Explain and give examples of how the function and differentiation of cells is influenced by their external environment, including temperature, acidity and the concentration of certain molecules, and that changes in these conditions may affect how a cell functions.	• Lessons 2.4, 7.4, 10.3, 10.4, 11.3, 13.4 • Features: CM 2 • Analyzing Data: p. 288 • Unit 3 Project • Lab Manual A: AL 3, 6 • Biology.com: AM 2; DA 2

STANDARD 2: CELLULAR STRUCTURE

Core Standard Describe features that are common to all cells and contrast those with distinctive features that allow cells to carry out specific functions.

Academic Standard	Where You Will Find It
B.2.1 Describe features common to all cells that are essential for growth and survival, and explain their functions.	• Lessons 7.2, 7.3, 7.4, 10.1 • Quick Lab: p. 203 • Unit 3 Project • Biology.com: AI 10; AM 7; AR 7, 10; DA 7; VA 7; TT 7
B.2.2 Describe the structure of a cell membrane and explain how it regulates the transport of materials into and out of the cell and prevents harmful materials from entering the cell.	• Lessons 7.2, 7.3 • Unit 3 Project • Lab Manual A: CL 7; AL 4 • Biology.com: AI 7; AM 7; AR 7
B.2.3 Explain that most cells contain mitochondria, the key sites of cellular respiration, where stored chemical energy is converted into useable energy for the cell and some cells, including many plant cells, contain chloroplasts, the key sites of photosynthesis, where the energy of light is captured for use in chemical work.	• Lessons 7.2, 8.2, 8.3, 9.2 • Unit 3 Project • Biology.com: AI 8; AM 8, 9; AR 9; TT 8, 9; VA 7, 8
B.2.4 Explain that all cells contain ribosomes, the key sites for protein synthesis, where genetic material is decoded in order to form unique proteins.	• Lessons 7.2, 13.2 • Unit 3 Project • Biology.com: AI 13; TT 13

Key to Textbook and Ancillary Features:
AL: Additional Lab, B&H: Biology & History, B&S: Biology & Society, C&B: Careers & Biology, CL: Chapter Lab, CM: Chapter Mystery, DOL: Diversity of Life, HO: Hands-On Activities, LS: Lab Skills, T&B: Technology & Biology, TCS: Twenty-first Century Skills

Key to Biology.com Activities
AM: Art in Motion, AR: Art Review, DA: Data Analysis, IA: InterActive Art, TT: Tutor Tube, VA: Visual Analogy

Course Overview *(continued)*

INDIANA

STANDARD 2: CELLULAR STRUCTURE *(continued)*	
B.2.5 Explain that cells use proteins to form structures, including cilia, flagella, which allow them to carry out specific functions, including movement, adhesion, and absorption.	• Lessons 7.2, 7.3, 7.4, 21.2 • Unit 3 Project • Biology.com: AI 21; VA 7, 21
B.2.6 Investigate a variety of different cell types and relate the proportion of different organelles within these cells to their functions.	• Lessons 7.2, 7.4, 23.1, 23.4 • Unit 3 Project • Biology.com: AI 7; AR 7, 23; AM 7; DA 23; TT 7; VA 7
STANDARD 3: MATTER CYCLES AND ENERGY TRANSFER ***Core Standard*** Describe how the sun's energy is captured and used to construct sugar molecules which can be used as a form of energy or serve as building blocks of organic molecules. ***Core Standard*** Diagram how matter and energy cycle through an ecosystem.	
Academic Standard	**Where You Will Find It**
B.3.1 Describe how some organisms capture the sun's energy through the process of photosynthesis by converting carbon dioxide and water into high energy compounds and releasing oxygen.	• Lessons 3.2, 8.1, 8.2, 8.3, 9.1 • Features: CM 8 • Quick Lab: p. 234 • Analyzing Data: p. 240 • Lab Manual A: AL 5 • Biology.com: AI 8, 9; AR 8; AM 9; DA 8; TT 3; VA 3, 8
B.3.2 Describe how most organisms can combine and recombine the elements contained in sugar molecules into a variety of biologically essential compounds by utilizing the energy from cellular respiration.	• Lessons 8.1, 9.1, 9.2 • Lab Manual A: AL 5 • Biology.com: VA 8
B.3.3 Recognize and describe that metabolism consists of all of the biochemical reactions that occur inside cells, including the production, modification, transport, and exchange of materials that are required for the maintenance of life.	• Lessons 1.3, 7.4, 8.1, 10.4 • Biology.com: AI 7; AR 7; AM 7; DA 7, 10; TT 7; VA 7
B.3.4 Describe how matter cycles through an ecosystem by way of food chains and food webs and how organisms convert that matter into a variety of organic molecules to be used in part in their own cellular structures.	• Lessons 3.2, 3.3, 3.4 • Biology.com: AI 3; AR 3; TT 3; VA 3
B.3.5 Describe how energy from the sun flows through an ecosystem by way of food chains and food webs and only a small portion of that energy is used by individual organisms while the majority of energy is lost as heat.	• Lessons 3.2, 3.3, 3.4, 8.1 • Analyzing Data: p. 77 • Biology.com: AI 3; AR 3; TT 3; VA 37
STANDARD 4: INTERDEPENDENCE ***Core Standard*** Describe the relationship between living and nonliving components of ecosystems and describe how that relationship is in flux due to natural changes and human actions.	
Academic Standard	**Where You Will Find It**
B.4.1 Explain that the amount of life an environment can support is limited by the available energy, water, oxygen, and minerals, and by the ability of ecosystems to recycle the remains of dead organisms.	• Lessons 3.1, 3.4, 4.2, 4.5, 5.1, 5.2 • Features: CM 4 • Quick Lab: p. 67 • Analyzing Data: p. 102 • Lab Manual A: CL 3, 4, 5 • Biology.com: AI 5; AR 5
B.4.2 Describe how human activities and natural phenomena can change the flow and of matter and energy in an ecosystem and how those changes impact other species.	• Lessons 3.4, 4.3, 5.2, 6.1, 6.2, 6.3, 6.4, 24.4 • Features: CM 3, 6 • Quick Lab: p. 155 • Analyzing Data: p. 172 • Unit 2 Project • Lab Manual A: CL 3, 6 • Biology.com: AM 5,6; DA 6, 24; VA 6

B.4.3 Describe the consequences of introducing non-native species into an ecosystem and identify the impact it may have on that ecosystem.	• Lessons 5.1, 5.2, 6.3 • Features: B&S p. 136; CM 5, 6 • Biology.com: AR 6
B.4.4 Describe how climate, the pattern of matter and energy flow, the birth and death of new organisms, and the interaction between those organisms contribute to the long term stability of an ecosystem.	• Lessons 3.1, 3.3, 3.4, 4.1, 4.2, 4.3, 5.1, 5.2, 6.3, 20.2, 21.3, 21.4 • Features: CM 3, 4, 5, 6 • Quick Lab: pp. 102, 138 • Lab Manual A: CL 5, 6 • Biology.com: AR 5; AM 4; DA 4, 5

STANDARD 5: MOLECULAR BASIS OF HEREDITY

Core Standard Describe the basic structure of DNA and how this structure enables DNA to function as the hereditary molecule that directs the production of RNA and proteins.

Core Standard Understand that proteins largely determine the traits of an organism.

Academic Standard	Where You Will Find It
B.5.1 Describe the relationship between chromosomes and DNA along with their basic structure and function.	• Lessons 2.3, 10.2, 12.1, 12.2, 14.1 • Unit 4 Project • Biology.com: AI 10, 12, 14; AR 10; DA 12
B.5.2 Describe how hereditary information passed from parents to offspring is encoded in regions of DNA molecules called genes.	• Lessons 1.3, 11.1, 12.1, 14.2, 17.1 • Unit 4 Project • Lab Manual A: AL 7 • Biology.com: AI 11, 13; AR 11; DA 11, 14; TT 11, 14
B.5.3 Describe the process by which DNA directs the production of protein within a cell.	• Lessons 13.1, 13.2, 13.3 • Quick Lab: p. 367 • Unit 4 Project • Lab Manual A: CL 13 • Biology.com: AI 13; AM 13; DA 13; TT 13; VA 13
B.5.4 Explain how the unique shape and activity of each protein is determined by the sequence of its amino acids.	• Lessons 2.3, 2.4, 13.3, 14.2 • Biology.com: AI 13; TT 13
B.5.5 Understand that proteins are responsible for the observable traits of an organism and for most of the functions within an organism.	• Lessons 2.3, 2.4, 10.3, 11.1, 13.2, 13.3, 13.4, 14.2, 30.3, 35.2 • Analyzing Data: pp. 288, 1017 • Lab Manual A: CL 30
B.5.6 Recognize that traits can be structural, physiological or behavioral and can include readily observable characteristics at the organismal level or less recognizable features at the molecular and cellular level.	• Lessons 11.1, 11.3, 14.1, 14.2, 17.1, 29.1 • Features: CM 14 • Quick Lab: p. 311 • Lab Manual A: AL 7

STANDARD 6: CELLULAR REPRODUCTION AND GENE EXPRESSION

Core Standard Explain the processes, both mitosis and meiosis, by which new cells are formed from existing cells and how in multicellular organisms, groups of cells cooperate to perform essential functions within an organism.

Core Standard Explain the cellular processes that occur to generate natural genetic variations between parents and offspring.

Academic Standard	Where You Will Find It
B.6.1 Describe the process of mitosis and explain that this process ordinarily results in daughter cells with a genetic make-up identical to the parent cells.	• Lesson 10.2 • Quick Lab: p. 283 • Biology.com: AI 10; AR 10; DA 10; TT 10
B.6.2 Understand that most cells of a multicellular organism contain the same genes, but develop from a single cell (e.g., a fertilized egg) in different ways due to differential gene expression.	• Lessons 1.3, 13.4 • Unit 4 Project • Biology.com: DA 13
B.6.3 Explain that in multicellular organisms the zygote produced during fertilization undergoes a series of cell divisions that lead to clusters of cells that go on to specialize and become the organism's tissues and organs.	• Lessons 1.3, 7.4, 10.4, 25.2, 34.4 • Quick Lab: p. 1000 • Analyzing Data: p. 740 • Biology.com: AM 11, 24

INDIANA

STANDARD 6: CELLULAR REPRODUCTION AND GENE EXPRESSION *(continued)*	
B.6.4 Describe and model the process of meiosis and explain the relationship between the genetic make-up of the parent cell and the daughter cells (gametes).	• Lessons 11.4, 28.3, 34.3 • Quick Lab: p. 990 • Lab Manual A: CL 11; AL 7 • Biology.com: TT 11
B.6.5 Explain how, in sexual reproduction, crossing over, independent assortment, and random fertilization, result in offspring that are genetically different from the parents.	• Lessons 11.4, 17.1, 17.4, 19.3 • Lab Manual A: AL 7 • Biology.com: TT 11

STANDARD 7: GENETICS

Core Standard Explain how the genetic information from parents determines the unique characteristics of their offspring.

Academic Standard	Where You Will Find It
B.7.1 Distinguish between dominant and recessive alleles and determine the phenotype that would result from the different possible combinations of alleles in an offspring.	• Lessons 11.1, 11.2 • Features: CM 11, 14 • Quick Lab: p. 311, 315 • Lab Manual A: AL 7 • Biology.com: AI 11; AR 11
B.7.2 Describe dominant, recessive, codominant, sex-linked, incompletely dominant, multiply allelic, and polygenic traits and illustrate their inheritance patterns over multiple generations.	• Lessons 11.1, 11.2, 11.3, 14.1 • Quick Labs: pp. 311, 315, 395 • Lab Manual A: AL 7 • Biology.com: AI 11; AR 11
B.7.3 Determine the likelihood of the appearance of a specific trait in an offspring given the genetic make-up of the parents.	• Lessons 11.1, 11.2, 11.3, 14.1 • Quick Labs: pp. 311, 315 • Analyzing Data: p. 320 • Lab Manual A: CL 14; AL 7 • Biology.com: AI 11
B.7.4 Explain the process by which a cell copies its DNA and identify factors that can damage DNA and cause changes in its nucleotide sequence.	• Lessons 12.3, 13.3 • Features: CM 12 • Quick Lab: pp. 352, 374 • Biology.com: AI 12, 13; AR 12, 13; VA 13
B.7.5 Explain and demonstrate how inserting, substituting or deleting segments of a DNA molecule can alter a gene, which is then passed to every cell that develops from it and that the results may be beneficial, harmful or have little or no effect on the organism.	• Lessons 13.3, 14.2, 15.1, 17.1, 17.4 • Features: CM 13 • Quick Lab: p. 374 • Analyzing Data: p. 400 • Lab Manual A: AL 8 • Biology.com: AR 13; AM 14

STANDARD 8: EVOLUTION

Core Standard Describe how biochemical, fossil, anatomical, developmental, and genetic findings are used to determine relationships among organisms, producing modern classification systems.

Core Standard Describe how modern evolutionary theory provides an explanation of the history of life on earth and the similarities between organisms that exist today.

Academic Standard	Where You Will Find It
B.8.1 Explain how anatomical and molecular similarities among organisms suggests that life on earth began as simple, one-celled organisms about 4 billion years ago and multicellular organisms evolved later.	• Lessons 13.2, 19.3, 21.1, 22.1, 22.3, 22.4, 26.1, 26.2, 26.3 • Unit 5 Project • Biology.com: AI 26; AR 16, 19; AM 25; DA 18, 25
B.8.2 Explain how organisms are classified and named based on their evolutionary relationships into taxonomic categories.	• Lessons 18.1, 18.2, 18.3, 20.2, 21.1, 21.4, 22.1, 22.2, 22.3, 22.4, 25.1, 25.2, 26.1, 26.2, 26.3 • Features: CM 18, 25; T&B p. 529 • Quick Labs: pp. 513, 520, 603 • Analyzing Data: pp. 524, 763 • Unit 6 Project • Lab Manual A: CL 16, 22, 26; AL 9 • Biology.com: AI 26; AR 16; AM 25; DA 18, 25

B.8.3 Use anatomical and molecular evidence to establish evolutionary relationships between organisms.	• Lessons 16.4, 17.4, 18.2, 18.3 • Quick Labs: p. 520 • Analyzing Data: pp. 470, 500, 763 • Unit 6 Project • Lab Manual A: CL 16, 25, 26 • Biology.com: AI 18; AR 16
B.8.4 Understand that molecular evidence supports the anatomical evidence for these evolutionary relationships and provides additional information about the order in which different lines of descent branched.	• Lessons 16.4, 17.4, 18.2, 18.3, 20.2, 21.1 • Features: CM 18 • Analyzing Data: pp. 470, 500 • Unit 5 Project • Lab Manual A: CL 16 • Biology.com: AI 18; DA 18
B.8.5 Describe how due to genetic variations, environmental forces, and reproductive pressures, organisms with beneficial traits are more likely to survive, reproduce, and pass on their genetic information.	• Lessons 16.3, 16.4, 17.1, 17.2, 17.3, 19.2, 29.1, 29.2 • Features: CM 16, 17, 29 • Analyzing Data: p. 850 • Unit 5 Project • Lab Manual A: CL 17; AL 8 • Biology.com: AM 19; DA 19; TT 17; VA 16
B.8.6 Explain how genetic variation within a population (a species) can be attributed to mutations as well as a random assortment of existing genes.	• Lessons 17.1, 17.4, 19.3 • Lab Manual A: AL 7 • Biology.com: AM 17
B.8.7 Describe the modern scientific theory of the origins of life on earth, and evaluate the evidence that supports it.	• Lesson 19.3 • Biology.com: AR 19

Lesson-by-Lesson Correlation and Pacing Guide

This chart helps you plan your instruction time. The specific Academic Standards covered in each lesson are provided. Objectives in **purple** type indicate places that particular objective is covered in depth. The Nature of Science Standards have been numbered for easy reference. The Fast Track column indicates those lessons, features, labs, and projects required to provide in-depth coverage of Indiana's Academic Standards for Biology I. Lessons, features, labs, and projects providing supplementary information are indicated under Enrichments. Chapter pacing helps you plan how much time to spend teaching and assessing each chapter. By following the pacing guide, you will be able to cover chapter concepts while still keeping 20 days open for chapter labs, assessment, and standardized testing.

Chapters/Lessons	Academic Standards for Biology I	Fast Track	Enrichments
Chapter 1 The Science of Biology			4 periods, 2 blocks
1.1 What Is Science?	NoS.2, NoS.3, NoS.9	●	
1.2 Science in Context	NoS.3, NoS.4, NoS.8, NoS.10, NoS.11	●	
Biology & Society			●
1.3 Studying Life	NoS.3, **NoS.5**, **NoS.8**, B.3.3, B.5.2, B.6.2, B.6.3	●	
Skills Lab	**NoS.1**, NoS.2, NoS.5	●	
Chapter 2 The Chemistry of Life			5 periods, 2.5 blocks
2.1 The Nature of Matter	NoS.6		●
Technology & BIOLOGY	NoS.10		●
2.2 Properties of Water	NoS.6		●
2.3 Carbon Compounds	NoS.3, NoS.6, **B.1.1**, **B.1.2**, B.5.1, B.5.4, B.5.5	●	
2.4 Chemical Reactions and Enzymes	NoS.6, **B.1.1**, **B.1.2**, **B.1.3**, **B.5.4**, B.5.5	●	
Design Your Own Lab	**NoS.1**, NoS.2, NoS.3, NoS.5, B.1.2	●	
Unit 1 Project			●
Chapter 3 The Biosphere			4.5 periods, 2.25 blocks
3.1 What Is Ecology?	**NoS.6**, B.4.1, B.4.4	●	
3.2 Energy, Producers, and Consumers	**B.3.1**, **B.3.4**, **B.3.5**	●	
3.3 Energy Flow in Ecosystems	NoS.3, NoS.6, **B.3.4**, **B.3.5**, B.4.4	●	
3.4 Cycles of Matter	NoS.6, **B.3.4**, B.3.5, **B.4.1**, **B.4.2**, B.4.4	●	
Technology & BIOLOGY			●
Real-World Lab	B.4.1, B.4.2		●

INDIANA

Chapters/Lessons	Academic Standards for Biology I	Fast Track	Enrichments
Chapter 4 Ecosystems and Communities		**5.5 periods, 2.75 blocks**	
4.1 Climate	NoS.6, B.4.4		●
4.2 Niches and Community Interactions	NoS.3, B.4.1, **B.4.4**	●	
Careers & BIOLOGY			●
4.3 Succession	B.4.2, **B.4.4**	●	
4.4 Biomes	NoS.2, NoS.3		●
4.5 Aquatic Ecosystems	**B.4.1**	●	
Real-World Lab	NoS.3, B.4.1		●
Chapter 5 Populations		**3.5 periods, 1.75 blocks**	
5.1 How Populations Grow	NoS.3, **NoS.6**, B.4.1, **B.4.3**, B.4.4	●	
Biology & Society	B.4.3		●
5.2 Limits to Growth	**B.4.1**, B.4.2, **B.4.3**, **B.4.4**	●	
5.3 Human Population Growth			●
Skills Lab	NoS.5, B.4.1, B.4.4		●
Chapter 6 Humans in the Biosphere		**4.5 periods, 2.25 blocks**	
6.1 A Changing Landscape	**B.4.2**	●	
6.2 Using Resources Wisely	NoS.3, NoS.11, **B.4.2**	●	
6.3 Biodiversity	NoS.3, NoS.11, **B.4.2**, **B.4.3**, B.4.4	●	
6.4 Meeting Ecological Challenges	NoS.6, NoS.11, **B.4.2**	●	
Design Your Own Lab	**NoS.1**, NoS.3, NoS.5, NoS.6, B.4.2, B.4.4	●	
Unit 2 Project	B.4.2		●
Chapter 7 Cell Structure and Function		**5.5 periods, 2.75 blocks**	
7.1 Life Is Cellular	NoS.9, **NoS.10**	●	
Careers & BIOLOGY			●
7.2 Cell Structure	NoS.6, **B.2.1**, **B.2.2**, **B.2.3**, **B.2.4**, **B.2.5**, B.2.6	●	
7.3 Cell Transport	**B.1.2**, **B.2.2**, B.2.5	●	
7.4 Homeostasis and Cells	NoS.3, **B.1.3**, **B.2.1**, B.2.5, B.3.3, B.6.3, **B.2.6**	●	
Skills Lab	**NoS.1**, NoS.6, B.2.2	●	

Lesson-by-Lesson Correlation and Pacing Guide *(continued)*

INDIANA

Chapters/Lessons	Academic Standards for Biology I	Fast Track	Enrichments
Chapter 8 Photosynthesis			4 periods, 2 blocks
8.1 Energy and Life	NoS.6, B.1.2, B.3.1, **B.3.2**, B.3.3, B.3.5	●	
Biology & HISTORY			●
8.2 Photosynthesis: An Overview	NoS.6, **B.2.3**, **B.3.1**	●	
8.3 The Process of Photosynthesis	NoS.3, **B.2.3**, **B.3.1**	●	
Skills Lab	**NoS.1**	●	
Chapter 9 Cellular Respiration and Fermentation			4.5 periods, 2.25 blocks
9.1 Cellular Respiration: An Overview	NoS.3, NoS.6, **B.3.1**, **B.3.2**	●	
9.2 The Process of Cellular Respiration	B.1.2, **B.2.3**, **B.3.2**	●	
Biology & Society			●
9.3 Fermentation			●
Real-World Lab			●
Chapter 10 Cell Growth and Division			6 periods, 3 blocks
10.1 Cell Growth, Division, and Reproduction	NoS.6, B.2.1		●
10.2 The Process of Cell Division	**B.5.1**, **B.6.1**	●	
10.3 Regulating the Cell Cycle	NoS.3, **B.1.2**, **B.1.3**, B.3.3, **B.5.5**	●	
Technology & BIOLOGY	NoS.10		●
10.4 Cell Differentiation	NoS.3, **B.1.3**, B.3.3, B.6.3	●	
Design Your Own Lab	**NoS.1**, NoS.4	●	
Unit 3 Project	B.1.2, B.1.3, B.2.1 through B.2.6		
Chapter 11 Introduction to Genetics			5.5 periods, 2.75 blocks
11.1 The Work of Gregor Mendel	B.5.2, B.5.5, **B.5.6**, **B.7.1**, **B.7.2**, **B.7.3**	●	
11.2 Applying Mendel's Principles	B.7.1, **B.7.2**, **B.7.3**	●	
11.3 Other Patterns of Inheritance	NoS.3, B.1.3, **B.5.6**, **B.7.2**, B.7.3	●	
Careers & BIOLOGY			●
11.4 Meiosis	NoS.3, **B.6.4**, **B.6.5**	●	
Skills Lab	NoS.6, B.6.4		●

Chapters/Lessons	Academic Standards for Biology I	Fast Track	Enrichments
Chapter 12 DNA			4 periods, 2 blocks
12.1 Identifying the Substance of Genes	NoS.6, B.5.1, B.5.2	●	
12.2 The Structure of DNA	NoS.3, B.5.1	●	
Biology & HISTORY			●
12.3 DNA Replication	B.1.2, B.7.4	●	
Skills Lab			●
Chapter 13 RNA and Protein Synthesis			6 periods, 3 blocks
13.1 RNA	NoS.6, B.1.2, B.5.3	●	
13.2 Ribosomes and Protein Synthesis	B.1.2, B.2.4, B.5.3, B.5.5, B.8.1	●	
13.3 Mutations	B.5.3, B.5.4, B.5.5, B.7.4, B.7.5	●	
13.4 Gene Regulation and Expression	NoS.3, B.1.2, B.1.3, B.5.5, B.6.2	●	
Skills Lab	NoS.6, NoS.7, B.5.3	●	
Chapter 14 Human Heredity			3.5 periods, 1.75 blocks
14.1 Human Chromosomes	NoS.6, B.5.1, B.5.6, B.7.2, B.7.3	●	
14.2 Human Genetic Disorders	NoS.3, B.1.2, B.5.2, B.5.4, B.5.5, B.5.6, B.7.5	●	
Biology & Society			●
14.3 Studying the Human Genome	NoS.6, NoS.10	●	
Forensics Lab	NoS.6, NoS.7, B.7.3	●	
Chapter 15 Genetic Engineering			5 periods, 2.5 blocks
15.1 Selective Breeding	B.7.5		●
15.2 Recombinant DNA	NoS.10		●
15.3 Applications of Genetic Engineering	NoS.3, NoS.10, NoS.11	●	
Technology & BIOLOGY	NoS.10		●
15.4 Ethics and Impacts of Biotechnology	NoS.11	●	
Forensics Lab	NoS.1	●	
Unit 4 Project	B.5.1, B.5.2, B.5.3, and B.6.2		●

INDIANA

Lesson-by-Lesson Correlation and Pacing Guide *(continued)*

Chapters/Lessons	Academic Standards for Biology I	Fast Track	Enrichments
Chapter 16 Darwin's Theory of Evolution			5 periods, 2.5 blocks
16.1 Darwin's Voyage of Discovery			●
16.2 Ideas that Shaped Darwin's Thinking	NoS.9	●	
Biology & HISTORY	NoS.9	●	
16.3 Darwin Presents His Case	B.8.5	●	
16.4 Evidence of Evolution	NoS.3, NoS.6, B.8.3, B.8.4, B.8.5	●	
Skills Lab	NoS.2, NoS.4, B.8.2, B.8.3, B.8.4		●
Chapter 17 Evolution of Populations			5 periods, 2.5 blocks
17.1 Genes and Variation	B.5.2, B.5.6, B.6.5, B.7.5, B.8.5, B.8.6	●	
17.2 Evolution as Genetic Change in Populations	NoS.3, NoS.6, B.8.5	●	
Biology & Society			●
17.3 The Process of Speciation	B.8.5	●	
17.4 Molecular Evolution	NoS.3, B.6.5, B.7.5, B.8.3, B.8.4, B.8.6	●	
Skills Lab	NoS.1, NoS.6, B.8.5	●	
Chapter 18 Classification			4 periods, 2 blocks
18.1 Finding Order in Diversity	NoS.9, B.8.2	●	
18.2 Modern Evolutionary Classification	NoS.9, NoS.6, B.8.2, B.8.3, B.8.4	●	
18.3 Building the Tree of Life	NoS.3, NoS.6, NoS.9, B.8.2, B.8.3, B.8.4	●	
Technology & BIOLOGY	NoS.10, B.8.2		●
Design Your Own Lab	NoS.6		●
Chapter 19 History of Life			4 periods, 2 blocks
19.1 The Fossil Record	NoS.6		●
19.2 Patterns and Processes of Evolution	NoS.3, B.8.5		●
19.3 Earth's Early History	NoS.3, B.6.5, B.8.1, B.8.6, B.8.7	●	
Careers & BIOLOGY			●
Forensics Lab	NoS.6		●
Unit 5 Project	B.8.1, B.8.4 and B.8.5		●

Chapters/Lessons	Academic Standards for Biology I	Fast Track	Enrichments
Chapter 20 Viruses and Prokaryotes			**3.5 periods, 1.75 blocks**
20.1 Viruses	NoS.6		●
20.2 Prokaryotes	B.4.4, B.8.2, B.8.4		●
20.3 Diseases Caused by Bacteria and Viruses	NoS.3		●
Biology & Society	NoS.11		●
Real-World Lab	**NoS.1**	●	
Chapter 21 "Protists" and Fungi			**4 periods, 2 blocks**
21.1 Protist Classification—The Saga Continues	B.8.1, **B.8.2**, B.8.4	●	
21.2 Protist Structure and Function	NoS.6, **B.2.5**	●	
21.3 The Ecology of Protists	B.4.4		●
Technology & BIOLOGY			●
21.4 Fungi	NoS.3, **B.4.4**, B.8.2	●	
Design Your Own Lab			●
Chapter 22 Introduction to Plants			**5 periods, 2.5 blocks**
22.1 What Is a Plant?	B.8.1, B.8.2		●
22.2 Seedless Plants	NoS.3, B.8.2		●
22.3 Seed Plants	B.8.1, B.8.2		●
22.4 Flowering Plants	B.8.1, B.8.2		●
Careers & BIOLOGY			●
Real-World Lab	NoS.4, B.8.2		●
Chapter 23 Plant Structure and Function			**5 periods, 2.5 blocks**
23.1 Specialized Tissues in Plants	**B.2.6**	●	
23.2 Roots			●
23.3 Stems	NoS.3		●
23.4 Leaves	**B.2.6**	●	
23.5 Transport in Plants	NoS.6		●
Design Your Own Lab	**NoS.1**, NoS.5	●	

Lesson-by-Lesson Correlation and Pacing Guide *(continued)*

INDIANA

Chapters/Lessons	Academic Standards for Biology I	Fast Track	Enrichments
Chapter 24 Plant Reproduction and Response			5 periods, 2.5 blocks
24.1 Reproduction in Flowering Plants			●
24.2 Fruits and Seeds	NoS.3		●
24.3 Plant Hormones	NoS.3, B.1.2		●
24.4 Plants and Humans	**B.4.2**	●	
Biology & HISTORY			●
Real-World Lab	**NoS.1**	●	
Unit 6 Project	B.8.2 and B.8.3		●
Chapter 25 Introduction to Animals			3.5 periods, 1.75 blocks
25.1 What Is an Animal?	B.8.2		●
Careers & BIOLOGY			●
25.2 Animal Body Plans and Evolution	NoS.3, **B.6.3**, B.8.2	●	
Skills Lab	B.8.3		●
Chapter 26 Animal Evolution and Diversity			3.5 periods, 1.75 blocks
26.1 Invertebrate Evolution and Diversity	NoS.6, **B.8.1,** B.8.2	●	
26.2 Chordate Evolution and Diversity	NoS.3, NoS.6, **B.8.1,** B.8.2	●	
26.3 Primate Evolution	NoS.6, **B.8.1,** B.8.2	●	
Biology & HISTORY			●
Forensics Lab	NoS.2, NoS.5, B.8.2, B.8.3		●
Chapter 27 Animal Systems I			4.5 periods, 2.25 blocks
27.1 Feeding and Digestion	NoS.3, NoS.6		●
27.2 Respiration			●
27.3 Circulation			●
27.4 Excretion	NoS.6		●
Technology & Biology	NoS.10		●
Skills Lab			●

Chapters/Lessons	Academic Standards for Biology I	Fast Track	Enrichments
Chapter 28 Animal Systems II			5 periods, 2.5 blocks
28.1 Response			●
28.2 Movement and Support			●
28.3 Reproduction	B.6.4		●
28.4 Homeostasis	NoS.3		●
Biology & Society			●
Real-World Lab	NoS.5		●
Chapter 29 Animal Behavior			2.5 periods, 1.25 blocks
29.1 Elements of Behavior	**B.5.6**, B.8.5	●	
Biology & Society			●
29.2 Animals in Their Environments	NoS.3, B.8.5		●
Design Your Own Lab	NoS.2		●
Unit 7 Project			●
Chapter 30 Digestive and Excretory Systems			6 periods, 3 blocks
30.1 Organization of the Human Body			●
30.2 Food and Nutrition	B.1.1, B.1.2		●
Biology & Society			●
30.3 The Digestive System	**B.5.5**	●	
30.4 The Excretory System	NoS.3		●
Real-World Lab	B.5.5		●
Chapter 31 Nervous System			5.5 periods, 2.75 blocks
31.1 The Neuron	NoS.6		●
31.2 The Central Nervous System			●
Technology & Biology	NoS.10		●
31.3 The Peripheral Nervous System			●
31.4 The Senses	NoS.3		●
Real-World Lab	**NoS.1, NoS.2**	●	

Lesson-by-Lesson Correlation and Pacing Guide *(continued)*

INDIANA

Chapters/Lessons	Academic Standards for Biology I	Fast Track	Enrichments
Chapter 32 Skeletal, Muscular, and Integumentary Systems			**4.5 periods, 2.25 blocks**
32.1 The Skeletal System	NoS.6		●
32.2 The Muscular System			●
Biology & Society			●
32.3 Skin—The Integumentary System	NoS.3		●
Skills Lab	**NoS.7**	●	
Chapter 33 Circulatory and Respiratory Systems			**5 periods, 2.5 blocks**
33.1 The Circulatory System	NoS.6		●
33.2 Blood and the Lymphatic System	NoS.3, B.1.2		●
Technology & Biology	NoS.10, NoS.11		●
33.3 The Respiratory System			●
Design Your Own Lab	NoS.5		●
Chapter 34 Endocrine and Reproductive Systems			**5.5 periods, 2.75 blocks**
34.1 The Endocrine System	**B.1.2**	●	
34.2 Glands of the Endocrine System			●
34.3 The Reproductive System	**B.6.4**	●	
34.4 Fertilization and Development	**B.6.3**	●	
Forensics Lab			●
Chapter 35 Immune System and Disease			**4.5 periods, 2.25 blocks**
35.1 Infectious Disease			●
35.2 Defenses Against Infection	NoS.3, B.1.2, B.5.5		●
35.3 Fighting Infectious Disease	NoS.11		●
Biology & HISTORY			●
35.4 Immune System Disorders	NoS.3		●
Forensics Lab			●
Unit 8 Project			●
A Visual Guide to the Diversity of Life			●

Quick Lab Materials List

Live organisms and lab supplies are available from Science Kit. Order at www.sciencekit.com or call 800-828-7777.

Item	*Quantity	Quick Lab
Aphids	40	3.2
Apron, lab	1 per student	for all appropriate labs
Artichoke	1	23.1
Balance	1	27.4
Beaker, 250 mL	3	30.1
Beans		
red	1	14.1
white	3	14.1
Beetles, ladybird	4	3.2
Bell peppers, assorted colors	1	16.2
Blocks	10	1.2
Box or bin (optional)	1	6.1
Bread, moldy	1 piece	21.4
Bromthymol blue solution	2–5 drops	9.3
Calculator	1	11.2
Carmine dye	a few granules	21.3
Celery, raw with leaves	3 stalks	23.5
Chicken		
bone	2	32.1
neck	1	28.2
wing, raw and bleached	1	32.2
Clam, live	1	27.2
Container		
plastic	1	23.5
small	2	27.2
Cotton swab	1	23.5
Coverslips	1 box per class	4.3, 21.1, 21.3, 24.1
Craft materials	See investigation.	7.2, 20.1
Crayfish, live	1	27.2
Culture, live		
Chlorella	1 drop	21.3
Daphnia	1	25.1
Hydra	1	25.1
Paramecium	1 drop	21.3
Protist, mixed	See investigation.	21.1

Item	*Quantity	Quick Lab
Cups		
paper, large	1	19.1
	2	5.2
	4	3.1
plastic, large and clear	1	8.2
	2	14.1
Cutting board	1	18.1, 23.5
Dissecting probe	1	28.2
Dropper pipette	1	2.2, 4.3, 21.1, 24.1, 25.1, 27.2, 34.4
	2	21.3
Elodea plant, freshly cut	1	8.2
Flower	1	24.1
Fluorescent substance (dilute Fluorescein, or Glo Germ™ oil)	1 pkg. per class	35.3
Food coloring	1 drop	27.2
	several drops	23.5
Foods, solid, variety	See investigation.	2.2
Forceps	1	24.1, 32.2
Frog, early-stage embryos	several	34.4
Fruit, different kinds	5	18.1
	See investigation.	22.4
Fruit juices, variety	See investigation.	2.2
Gloves, plastic	1 pair per student	for all appropriate labs
Goggles	1 pair per student	for all appropriate labs
Graduated cylinder		
10-mL	1	9.3, 30.3
25-mL	1	27.4
Hand lens	1	22.1, 22.4
Index card	1	7.2
Jar		
wide-mouth	2	3.2
with lid	1	4.3
	2	32.1
Knife	1	16.2, 18.1
Leaves, different kinds	See investigation.	23.4
Map, world	1	16.1
Marker, black	1	5.2, 14.1
Methyl cellulose	1 drop	21.1

Materials

*Quantities per group

Quick Lab Materials List *(cont.)*

Live organisms and lab supplies are available from Science Kit. Order at www.sciencekit.com or call 800-828-7777.

INDIANA

Item	*Quantity	Quick Lab
Microscope		
compound	1	4.3, 7.1, 10.2, 21.1, 21.3, 21.4, 23.4, 24.1, 25.1, 33.3
dissecting	1	34.4
Mirror (optional)	1	11.1
Nail polish, clear	1	23.4
Olive oil	2 drops	30.3
Onion, raw	1	23.1
Paper, construction		
assorted colors	3 sheets	14.3
black, white	1 sheet of each	28.1
blue, green, orange,	1 sheet of each	12.3
red, white, yellow	1 sheet	
graph	1 sheet	26.3, 29.1, 33.3
grid, 1-cm	4 sheets	10.1
	1 sheet	19.1
notebook	1 sheet	26.3
scrap		31.3
Paper towels, white	1 roll per lab	2.2, 32.2
Pencil, glass-marking	1	9.3, 27.4
Petri dish	1	28.1
	3–5	22.4
Petroleum jelly	1 jar per lab	23.5, 33.3
pH paper	1 pkg. per class	2.2, 4.3
Planarian	1	28.1
Plant material, dried	1 handful	4.3
Plants, different types	3	22.1
Popcorn kernels	1 bag	2.1
Potato	1	23.1
Rubber bands	2	3.2
Ruler, metric	1	20.1, 22.1, 23.5, 29.1
Sand	2 cups	3.1
Scalpel	1	2.2, 22.4, 23.5, 24.1, 32.2
Scissors	1	10.1, 12.3, 14.3, 17.2, 19.1, 20.1, 29.1, 32.2
Screen	1	1.2
Screening, flexible	2 pieces	3.2
Seedlings, bean (potted)	2	3.2

Item	*Quantity	Quick Lab
Seeds		
bean	18	5.2
rice, presoaked	10	3.1
rye or wheat, presoaked	10	3.1
Slides		
microscope	1	21.1, 21.3, 21.4, 23.4, 24.1
	3–4	4.3
	5	33.3
depression	1 box per class	25.1, 34.4
Slides, prepared		
bacteria	1	7.1
frog embryos	1	34.4
leaf, stem, or cross section	1	7.1
onion root tips	1	10.2
nerve cells	1	7.1
paramecia	1	7.1
Soap, liquid	5–10 mL per class	30.3
Sodium bicarbonate solution (5 g/L)	250 mL	8.2
Soil, potting	1 large bag per class	3.1, 5.2
Straw, large, clear plastic	1	9.3
Tape, transparent	1	10.1, 12.3, 14.3, 17.2, 20.1, 21.4, 23.4
Test tube, large	1	8.2
	2	9.3, 27.4, 30.3
Test-tube rack	1	27.4
Test-tube stopper, large	2	27.4
Thermometer	1	30.1
Toothpicks	1 box per class	21.3
Trash bag, large	1	6.1
Ultraviolet lamp	1	35.3
Urea	2 grams	27.4
Uric acid	2 grams	27.4
Vinegar	250 mL	32.1
Watch or clock (with a second hand)	1	9.3, 28.1, 29.1, 33.1
Water		
pond (boiled) or sterile spring	500 mL	4.3
spring	100 mL	28.1

*Quantities per group

Ecosystems of Indiana

Much of Indiana's landscape was shaped by ice sheets that scoured the bedrock and deposited rock debris and soils over long distances. Today, a network of surface and underground rivers continue to carve their way through Indiana's rolling plains and rugged hills. These features, combined with the rainfall and temperatures of the changing seasons, differences in elevation, soil characteristics, and flooding regime support rich terrestrial and aquatic ecosystems for a wide variety of plants and animals.

This book will help you understand the components of Indiana's ecosystems, and the interactions that occur within them, some of which are described here. Why do you study biology? Because it's all around you!

Lake Trout

Lakes

Lake Michigan is the largest of Indiana's many lakes. And, unlike smaller lakes, it not only experiences currents created by wind, but also by Earth's rotation. Lake Michigan even experiences a small tidal effect. Birds such as the common loon and the Caspian tern prey on lake trout, steelhead trout, and chinook salmon. In turn, these fish prey on smaller fish, which ultimately feed on phytoplankton, as do the lake's mussels. Careful management is helping fight the effects of overfishing and invasive, nonnative species, such as the sea lamprey, which have caused significant declines in some fish populations. Lake trout are the largest fish in Lake Michigan and can reach more than 22.5 kilograms (50 pounds). Their preference for cold temperatures, between 13°C–7°C, means that they will move into waters that are 30 to 60 meters deep during the summer and winter. These deep-water hunters will swim for miles to catch their prey, typically other fish, but they will also eat crustaceans and insects if they must.

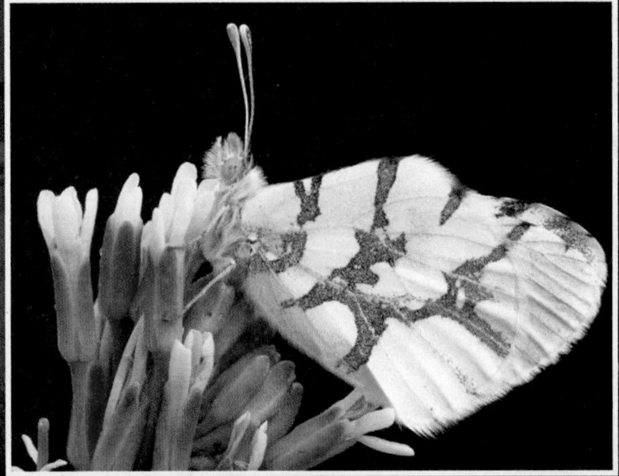

Olympia Marblewing

Beaches and Dunes

On the shores of Lake Michigan, winds and waves reshape the beaches by moving the sands from place to place. Behind the beaches are a series of sand dunes that reflect the changing shoreline. Only a few plants, such as American beach grass, grow on the young, windswept dunes closest to shore. On the older, stable dunes farther from the beach, you may find the threatened Pitcher's thistle and prairie grasses such as little bluestem. Farther from shore, forests of shrubs and trees such as oaks and pines have become established. Therefore, it isn't surprising that many kinds of animals live here. Although you may hear the trilling of birds like the spotted sandpiper, most other animals, including lizards such as the six-lined racer, are much quieter. You may even see a rare Olympia marblewing butterfly laying its eggs on a single flower bud or leaves of a violet. These eggs will change color from white, to red, and finally grey. And then, the caterpillars are ready to hatch.

Ecosystems of Indiana *(continued)*

Hellbender

Streams and Rivers

Many waterways weave their way through Indiana. Parts of the Ohio, Wabash, and White Rivers in south-west Indiana are not only home to the red-shouldered hawk and the Baltimore oriole, but also to more than 100 fish species. This is partly because large rivers have a great variety of environments that vary in depth, rate of flow, and vegetation. Alongside fish such as silvery minnows, gizzard shad, and channel catfish, you can also find gars and sturgeon. These rivers are also known for hosting more than 55 species of freshwater mussels, some of which may live for up to 50 years. Where the water is particularly clean and rocky, you may even find the increasingly rare hellbender. Despite having lungs, these salamanders are completely aquatic and exchange gases entirely through their skin. They can grow up to 0.75 meters long, preying on crayfish, small fish, and even each other. They secrete a noxious chemical through their skin and may even bite if provoked, so it's best to leave them alone.

Swamp Rabbit

Swamps and Marshes

Swamps and marshes are types of wetlands. Wetlands are ecosystems in which the plants are adapted to flooded soils for significant portions of the year. The difference between swamps and marshes is that swamps are dominated by trees, while marshes are dominated by grasses. At the Twin Swamps Nature Preserve, you can find one of the few remaining swamps of bald cypress and swamp cottonwood trees in Indiana. The surface of the water can be clogged with spider lillies and some of the world's smallest flowering plants, duckweed and water meal. Reptiles and amphibians such as the siren salamander do very well here, as do many birds including herons, warblers, ducks, and woodpeckers. One of the more interesting mammals that live in Indiana's swamps is the swamp rabbit. These rabbits can reach speeds of 72 kilometers per hour as they run in a zig-zag pattern to escape from a predator. They are also excellent swimmers and can sit in shallow water with only their noses above the surface as they wait for danger to pass.

American Kestrel

Prairies

Prairies are grasslands that are maintained by grazing pressure and natural fires, which prevent trees from easily invading the area. Indiana had large areas of wet, dry, short-grass, and tall-grass prairies. Remnants of tall-grass prairies in northwestern Indiana can still hide a person riding a horse. Most prairie lands have been developed for human use, but today many programs are reviving this diverse ecosystem. Indiana's prairies can include more than 500 species of grasses and herbaceous plants. These plants can, in turn, support amphibians and mammals that prey on the more than 3000 species of insects, such as moths, butterflies, bees, and leaf hoppers, found here. Sparrows, wrens, and sandpipers also thrive in prairies, as do predators such as the American kestrel. These kestrels prey on insects, birds, and small mammals. And although the American kestrel can catch insects and bats on the wing, it is also an expert in hover hunting. In prairies, without a place to perch, it will hover over its prey and then dive to strike at lightning speeds.

Cave Crayfish

Caves

More than 2200 caves have been mapped in Indiana. Most of these caves are found southeastward from Greencastle towards the Ohio River. Different animals use these caves differently. The Indiana bat, skunks, and raccoons only spend some of their lives in caves and are called *trogloxenes*. Other animals, such as crickets, earthworms, and some species of fish, which may have moved into a cave but could just as easily live outside, are called *troglophiles*. Those animals that can only survive in caves, such as cave fish, cave salamanders, and cave crayfish, are called *troglobites*. Many troglobites have lost their eyes and have white or colorless bodies. These traits were likely lost because they weren't critical to the animal's survival. A trait common to many of these organisms is a very slow metabolism enables them to survive with little food. Troglobites depend on bacteria that decay organic materials which wash into caves or excretions of animals such as bats. Some troglobites can live for up to 70 years.

Ecosystems of Indiana *(continued)*

Gray Fox

Primary Forests

Primary forests are those that do not show signs of disturbance, such as logging or fires. In Indiana, the primary forests are composed of deciduous hardwood trees such as tuliptrees, sugar maples, beeches, and oaks. These trees can be more than 250 years old, over 20 meters tall, and have trunks that are 1.2 meters thick. Young trees may be half as tall as they grow in the shade of their parents. Closer to the forest floor, dogwood, redbud, and ironwood make up the understory. Squirrels, bats, and many kinds of birds live in the trees, while other animals use the forest floor. Fallen trees or logs are good sites at which to see some of these animals. Insects such as termites, ants, and beetles are quick to break down a log. For salamanders and shrews, these logs serve as an all-you-can-eat buffet. This behavior attracts even larger predators such as the gray fox. And although the gray fox prefers rabbits, small rodents, and birds, it can also live on persimmons, nuts, grasses, and corn.

Eastern Box Turtle

Secondary Forests

A secondary forest is one that shows signs of disturbances, such as fires and logging. Most of Indiana's forests have experienced some form of disturbance, and yet these forests are thriving in protected areas. The two main forest types are maple-beech and oak-hickory forests. Songbirds, bats, and squirrels live and play in the tree tops while shrews, rats, and cottontail rabbits live on the forest floor, ever watchful for coyotes and foxes who would make a meal of them. Rough green snakes, two-lined skinks, small mouthed salamanders, and the Eastern box turtle are also common here. These turtles can live in many different kinds of habitats but do well in forests with moist conditions and a lot of underbrush in which to hide. They maintain a home range of no more than 200 meters and eat nearly anything that they can fit in their mouth. They prefer to eat insects, fruits, and mushrooms, including some that are poisonous to humans. Despite these seemingly strange food habits, they can live to be 50 years old.

Indiana's Academic Standards for Science—Biology I

Indiana's Academic Standards for Science describe the science knowledge and process skills that you are expected to learn before graduating high school.

Why are Indiana's Academic Standards important?

The goal of Indiana's Academic Standards is to ensure that all students learn essential skills in the areas of writing, reading, math, and science.

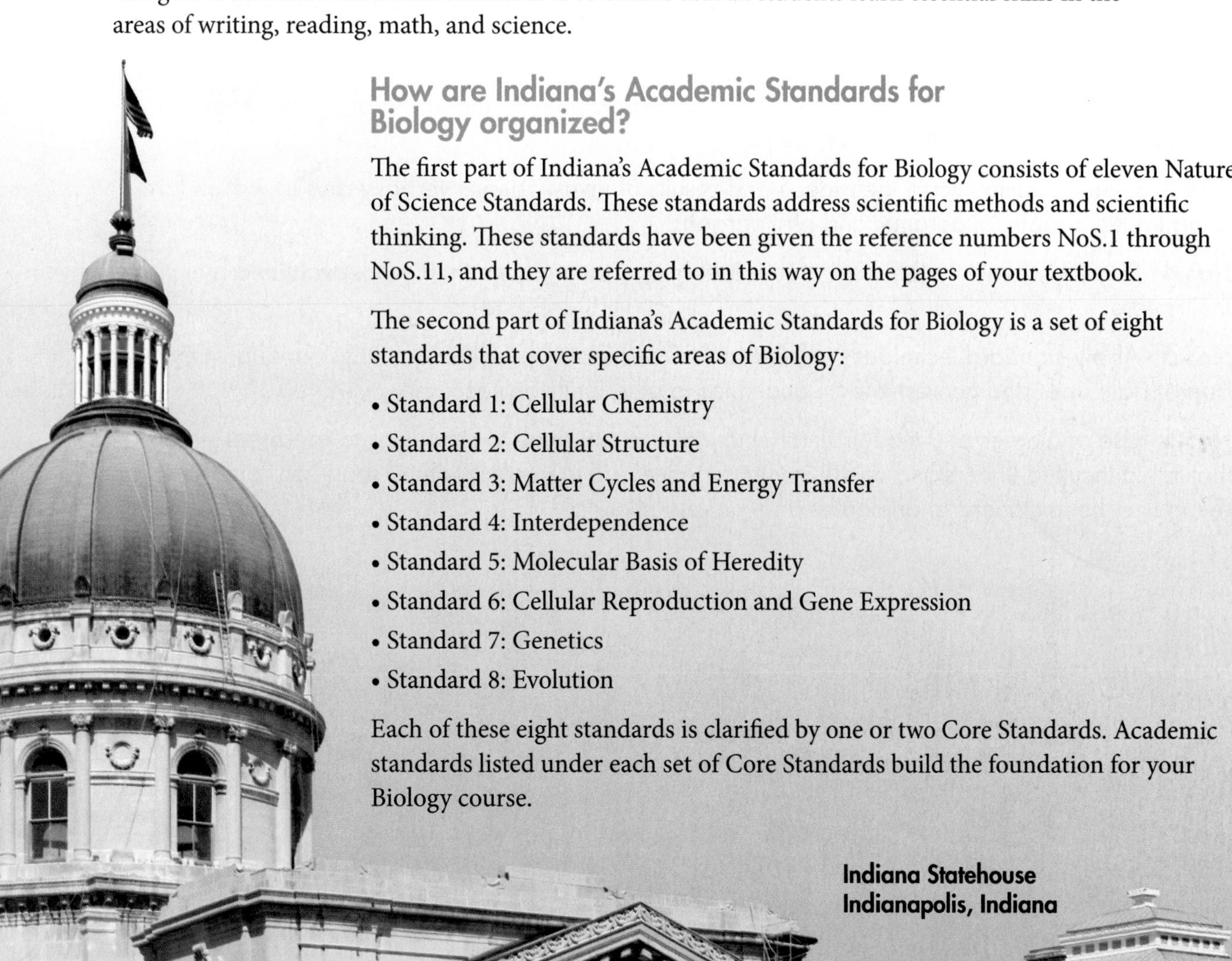

How are Indiana's Academic Standards for Biology organized?

The first part of Indiana's Academic Standards for Biology consists of eleven Nature of Science Standards. These standards address scientific methods and scientific thinking. These standards have been given the reference numbers NoS.1 through NoS.11, and they are referred to in this way on the pages of your textbook.

The second part of Indiana's Academic Standards for Biology is a set of eight standards that cover specific areas of Biology:

- Standard 1: Cellular Chemistry
- Standard 2: Cellular Structure
- Standard 3: Matter Cycles and Energy Transfer
- Standard 4: Interdependence
- Standard 5: Molecular Basis of Heredity
- Standard 6: Cellular Reproduction and Gene Expression
- Standard 7: Genetics
- Standard 8: Evolution

Each of these eight standards is clarified by one or two Core Standards. Academic standards listed under each set of Core Standards build the foundation for your Biology course.

Indiana Statehouse
Indianapolis, Indiana

INDIANA

THE NATURE OF SCIENCE

Students should understand that scientific knowledge is gained from observation of natural phenomena and experimentation, by designing and conducting investigations guided by theory, and by evaluating and communicating the results of those investigations according to accepted procedures. Thus, scientific knowledge is scientists' best explanations for the data from many investigations. Further, ideas about objects in the microscopic world that we cannot directly sense are often understood in terms of concepts developed to understand objects in the macroscopic world that we can see and touch. In the science classroom student work should align with this process of science and should be guided by the following principles. These should be woven throughout the daily work that students are doing when learning the content presented in the standard indicators.

NoS.1 Develop explanations based on reproducible data and observations gathered during laboratory investigations.

NoS.2 Recognize that their explanations must be based both on their data and other known information from investigations of others.

NoS.3 Clearly communicate their ideas and results of investigations verbally and in written form using tables, graphs, diagrams, and photographs.

NoS.4 Regularly evaluate the work of their peers and in turn have their work evaluated by their peers.

NoS.5 Apply standard techniques in laboratory investigations to measure physical quantities in appropriate units and convert known quantities to other units as necessary.

NoS.6 Use analogies and models (mathematical and physical) to simplify and represent systems that are difficult to understand or directly experience due to their size, time scale, or complexity, and recognize the limitations of analogies and models.

Indiana has close to a hundred covered bridges.

THE NATURE OF SCIENCE *(continued)*

NoS.7 Focus on the development of explanatory models based on their observations during laboratory investigations.

NoS.8 Explain that the body of scientific knowledge is organized into major theories, which are derived from and supported by the results of many experiments, and allow us to make testable predictions

NoS.9 Recognize that new scientific discoveries often lead to a re-evaluation of previously accepted scientific knowledge and of commonly held ideas.

NoS.10 Describe how scientific discoveries lead to the development of new technologies, and conversely how technological advances can lead to scientific discoveries through new experimental methods and equipment.

NoS.11 Explain how scientific knowledge can be used to guide decisions on environmental and social issues.

What It Means to You

Scientific investigations require a wide range of skills, including asking questions that can be tested, formulating hypotheses, predicting results, designing experiments, making accurate measurements, collecting data, analyzing data, drawing valid conclusions, and communicating results. The process of science requires constant modification of hypotheses and theories to reflect the most recent discoveries. The development of new tools for investigation, such as new kinds of microscopes, have allowed great advances in the fields of biology and medicine. Furthermore, new developments in science can affect society. For example, the discovery of pollutants that harm the environment or cause cancer can be managed through public policy.

Where You Will Learn It

You will learn about scientific inquiry in Chapters 1, 2, 3, 4, 5, 7, 9, 14, 15, 16, 17, 18, and 20. Additionally, you will practice inquiry skills as you complete the many labs and activities throughout this book.

SAMPLE QUESTIONS

1 In a controlled experiment, the factor that can change is called the

A. hypothesis.
B. control.
C. inference.
D. variable.

2 A scientist finds a new kind of insect. She is interested in finding out how it obtains energy. Which of the following questions might she ask to help her investigate this problem?

A. How does the insect reproduce?
B. How long does the insect live?
C. What types of food does the insect eat?
D. Does the insect have any predators?

INDIANA

STANDARD 1: CELLULAR CHEMISTRY

Core Standard
Describe the basic molecular structure and function of the four major categories of organic compounds (carbohydrates, lipids, proteins and nucleic acids) essential to cellular function.

Core Standard
Describe how work done in cells is performed by a variety of organic molecules, especially proteins, whose functions depend on the sequence of their monomers and the consequent shape of the molecule.

B.1.1 Describe the structure of the major categories of organic compounds which make up living organisms in terms of their building blocks and the small number of chemical elements (carbon, hydrogen, nitrogen, oxygen, phosphorous, and sulfur) from which they are composed.

B.1.2 Understand that the shape of a molecule determines its role in the many different types of cellular processes including metabolism, homeostasis, growth and development, and heredity, and understand that the majority of these processes involve proteins that act as enzymes.

B.1.3 Explain and give examples of how the function and differentiation of cells is influenced by their external environment, including temperature, acidity and the concentration of certain molecules, and that changes in these conditions may affect how a cell functions.

What It Means to You

You will learn about the building blocks of living things. There are three main groups of large carbon compounds, or organic macromolecules: lipids, proteins, and nucleic acids. The structure and shape of a macromolecule determines its function in a cell. The function of a cell is determined by its genetic code as well as by the environment in and around the cell.

Where You Will Learn It

You will learn about cellular chemistry in Chapters 2, 7, 8, 9, 10, 11, 12, 13, 14, 24, 30, 33, 34, and 35.

SAMPLE QUESTIONS

1. Which type of molecule is the main source of energy for living things?
   A. enzymes
   B. proteins
   C. nucleic acids
   D. carbohydrates

2. Which of the following best describes the structure of proteins?
   A. simple chains of identical amino acids
   B. complex, folded chains of identical amino acids
   C. simple chains of different amino acids
   D. complex, folded chains of different amino acids

3. Infer During which part of the cell cycle does cyclin production begin? How quickly is cyclin destroyed?

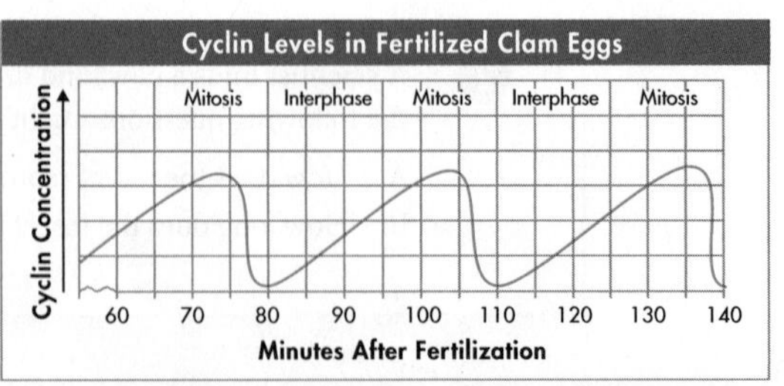

STANDARD 2: CELLULAR STRUCTURE

Core Standard

Describe features that are common to all cells and contrast those with distinctive features that allow cells to carry out specific functions.

B.2.1 Describe features common to all cells that are essential for growth and survival, and explain their functions.

B.2.2 Describe the structure of a cell membrane and explain how it regulates the transport of materials into and out of the cell and prevents harmful materials from entering the cell.

B.2.3 Explain that most cells contain mitochondria, the key sites of cellular respiration, where stored chemical energy is converted into useable energy for the cell and some cells, including many plant cells, contain chloroplasts, the key sites of photosynthesis, where the energy of light is captured for use in chemical work.

B.2.4 Explain that all cells contain ribosomes, the key sites for protein synthesis, where genetic material is decoded in order to form unique proteins.

B.2.5 Explain that cells use proteins to form structures, including cilia, flagella, which allow them to carry out specific functions, including movement, adhesion, and absorption.

B.2.6 Investigate a variety of different cell types and relate the proportion of different organelles within these cells to their functions.

What It Means to You

You will learn about the composition of cells. Cells are the basic units of structure and function in living things. There are organisms composed of only one cell and organisms that have millions of cells. All cells have an external membrane that regulates material flowing into and out of the cell. Cells have other important structures, too. Some have chloroplasts that convert sunlight to chemical energy. Some have mitochondria that release energy stored in chemicals. Most cells have ribosomes that help make the proteins that form all of the parts of a cell. The type and number of organelles in a cell relate to its function.

Where You Will Learn It

You will learn about cellular structure in Chapters 7, 8, 9, 10, 13, 21, and 23.

SAMPLE QUESTION

In osmosis, a substance that moves across a cell membrane tends to move

A. away from the area of equilibrium.
B. away from the area where it is less concentrated.
C. away from the area where it is more concentrated.
D. toward the area where it is more concentrated.

Indiana's Academic Standards

INDIANA

STANDARD 3: MATTER CYCLES AND ENERGY TRANSFER

Core Standard
Describe how the sun's energy is captured and used to construct sugar molecules which can be used as a form of energy or serve as building blocks of organic molecules.

Core Standard
Diagram how matter and energy cycle through an ecosystem.

B.3.1 Describe how some organisms capture the sun's energy through the process of photosynthesis by converting carbon dioxide and water into high energy compounds and releasing oxygen.

B.3.2 Describe how most organisms can combine and recombine the elements contained in sugar molecules into a variety of biologically essential compounds by utilizing the energy from cellular respiration.

B.3.3 Recognize and describe that metabolism consists of all of the biochemical reactions that occur inside cells, including the production, modification, transport, and exchange of materials that are required for the maintenance of life.

Fall Creek Gorge, Indiana

STANDARD 3: MATTER CYCLES AND ENERGY TRANSFER *(continued)*

B.3.4 Describe how matter cycles through an ecosystem by way of food chains and food webs and how organisms convert that matter into a variety of organic molecules to be used in part in their own cellular structures.

B.3.5 Describe how energy from the sun flows through an ecosystem by way of food chains and food webs and only a small portion of that energy is used by individual organisms while the majority of energy is lost as heat.

What It Means to You

You will learn how matter and energy move between organisms and their environment in ecosystems. The original source of energy for most systems is the sun. Producers, such as plants and algae, convert light energy into chemical energy in the process of photosynthesis. Producers and organisms that eat producers release this stored chemical energy through cellular respiration. As organisms feed on one another, matter and energy move up the food chain and through food webs.

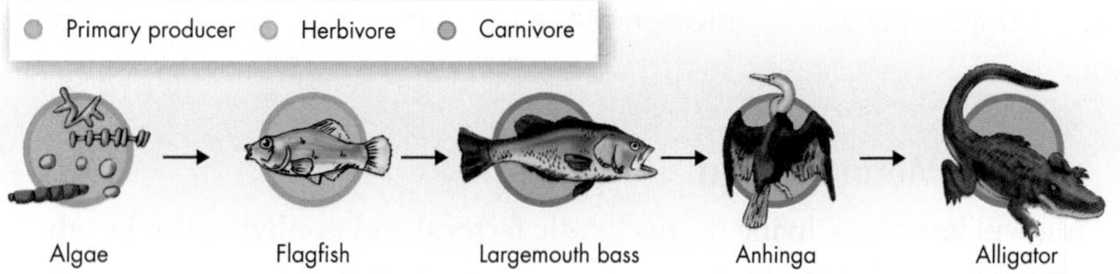

Matter is released back into the environment when organisms die and decay.

Where You Will Learn It

You will learn about matter cycles and the flow of energy in Chapters 1, 3, 7, 8, 9 and 10.

SAMPLE QUESTIONS

1 Photosynthesis is a major process involved in which of the following cycles?

A. nitrogen cycle B. carbon cycle C. water cycle D. phosphorus cycle

2 Which of the following best compares the processes of photosynthesis and cellular respiration?

A. Photosynthesis and respiration are the opposite of each other.
B. Photosynthesis and respiration both add oxygen to the atmosphere.
C. Photosynthesis and respiration both take carbon dioxide from the atmosphere.
D. Photosynthesis and respiration both capture and store energy.

3 Which of the following organisms is a decomposer?

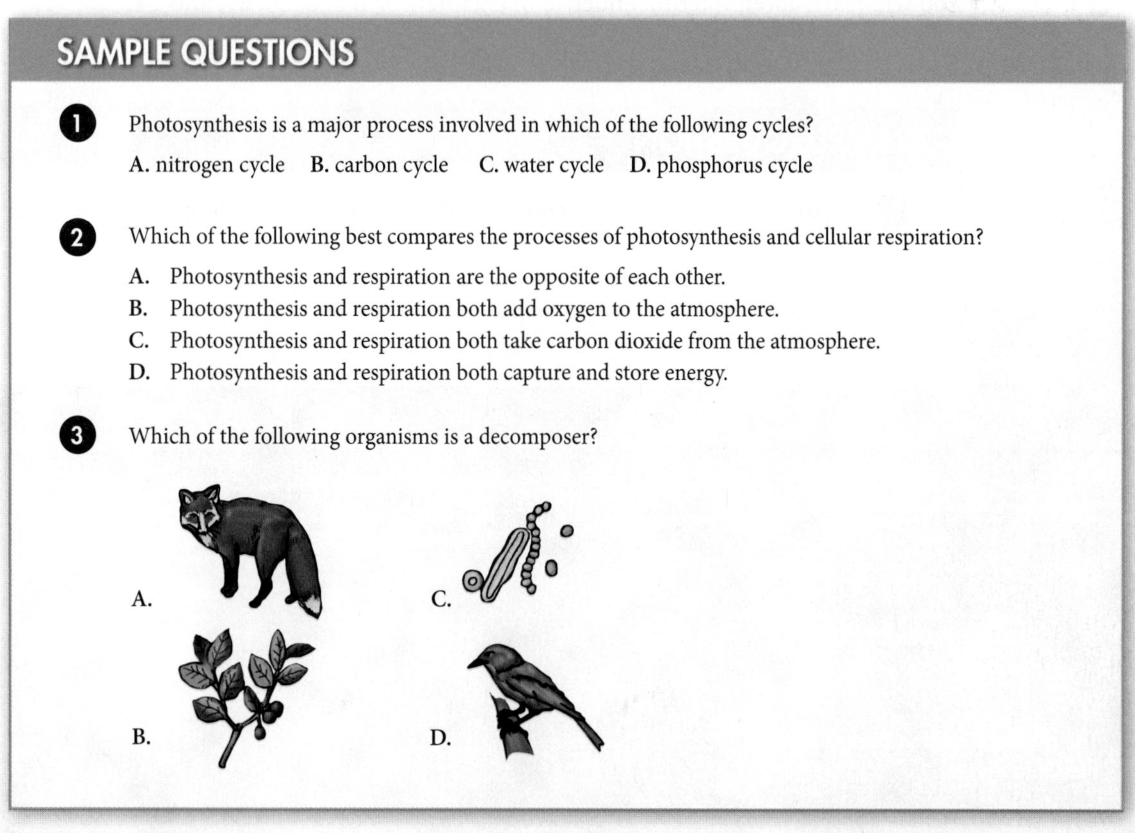

STANDARD 4: INTERDEPENDENCE

Core Standard
Describe the relationship between living and nonliving components of ecosystems and describe how that relationship is in flux due to natural changes and human actions.

B.4.1 Explain that the amount of life an environment can support is limited by the available energy, water, oxygen, and minerals, and by the ability of ecosystems to recycle the remains of dead organisms.

B.4.2 Describe how human activities and natural phenomena can change the flow and of matter and energy in an ecosystem and how those changes impact other species.

B.4.3 Describe the consequences of introducing non-native species into an ecosystem and identify the impact it may have on that ecosystem.

B.4.4 Describe how climate, the pattern of matter and energy flow, the birth and death of new organisms, and the interaction between those organisms contribute to the long term stability of an ecosystem.

What It Means to You

You will learn how living things (biotic factors) and nonliving things (abiotic factors) interact in ecosystems. All living things depend on one another and their environment to survive. You will explore how living things are affected by changes in their environment. Furthermore, you will examine ways that humans change the environment and study the impact of these changes on ecosystems.

Where You Will Learn It

You will learn about interdependence in Chapters 3, 4, 5, 6, 20, 21, and 24.

SAMPLE QUESTION

1. A construction company cuts down a forest to build a new mall. Which of the following is the most likely effect of this action?

   A. an increase in biodiversity
   B. a decrease in food sources for native species
   C. an increase in habitats for native species
   D. a decrease in erosion

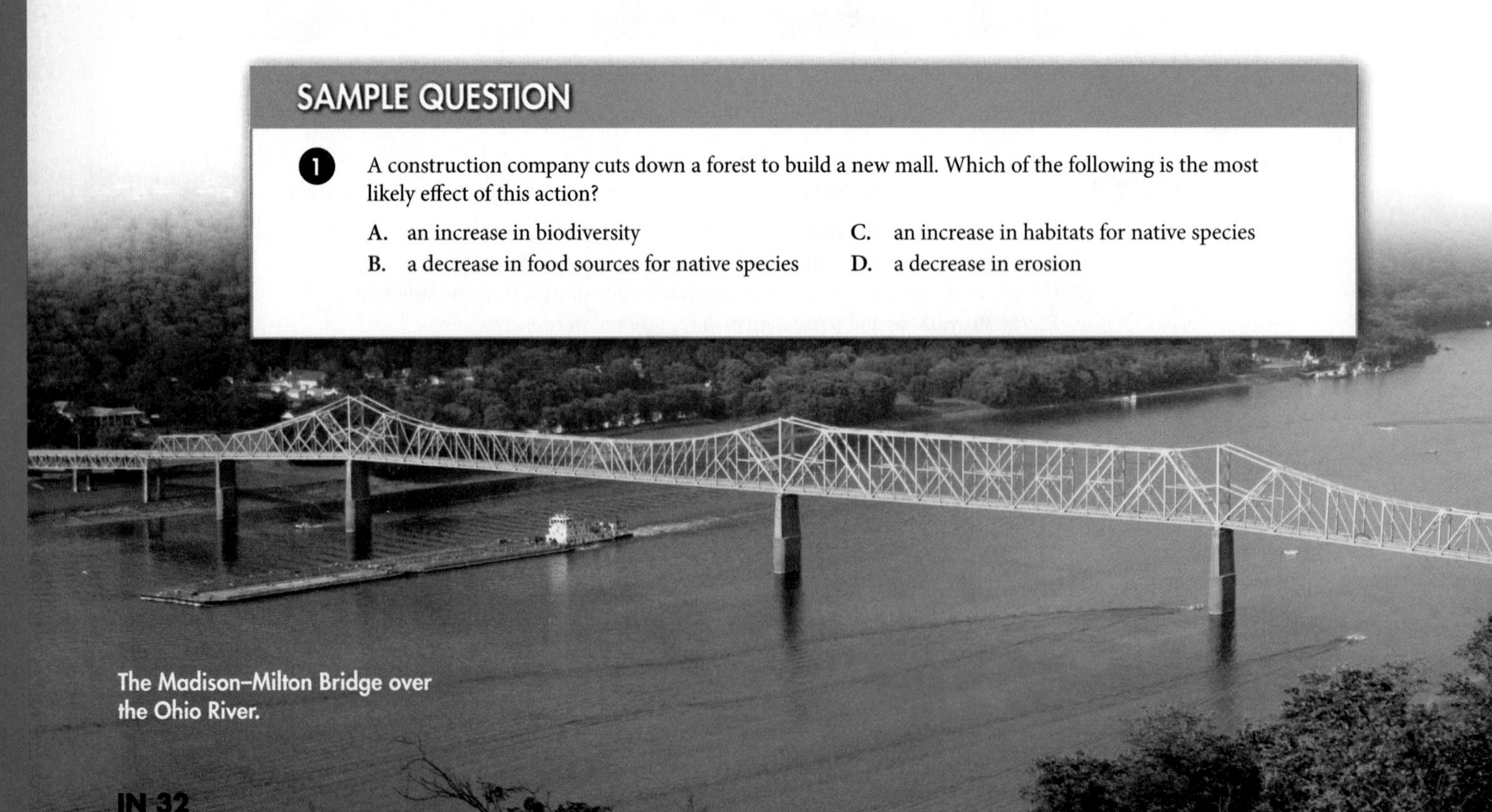

The Madison–Milton Bridge over the Ohio River.

STANDARD 5: MOLECULAR BASIS OF HEREDITY

Core Standard
Describe the basic structure of DNA and how this structure enables DNA to function as the hereditary molecule that directs the production of RNA and proteins.

Core Standard
Understand that proteins largely determine the traits of an organism.

B.5.1 Describe the relationship between chromosomes and DNA along with their basic structure and function.

B.5.2 Describe how hereditary information passed from parents to offspring is encoded in regions of DNA molecules called genes.

B.5.3 Describe the process by which DNA directs the production of protein within a cell.

B.5.4 Explain how the unique shape and activity of each protein is determined by the sequence of its amino acids.

B.5.5 Understand that proteins are responsible for the observable traits of an organism and for most of the functions within an organism.

B.5.6 Recognize that traits can be structural, physiological or behavioral and can include readily observable characteristics at the organismal level or less recognizable features at the molecular and cellular level.

What It Means to You

You will learn how molecules control traits. Genes are sections of DNA, a nucleic acid that carries the genetic code of the cell. DNA is made up of long, double strands of nucleotides. The order of the nucleotides on the strands of DNA determines the order in which amino acids will be put together to make proteins. The order of the amino acids determines the shape of the protein. The shape of a protein determines its function.

Where You Will Learn It

You will learn about the molecular basis of heredity in Chapters 1, 2, 10, 11, 12, 13, 14, 17, 29, 30, and 35.

SAMPLE QUESTIONS

1 In DNA, each codon specifies a particular

A. amino acid.
B. purine.
C. pyrimidine.
D. nucleotide.

2 From which DNA template was this strand of mRNA transcribed?

A. TACTTG B. ATGAAC C. AUGAAC D. UACUUG

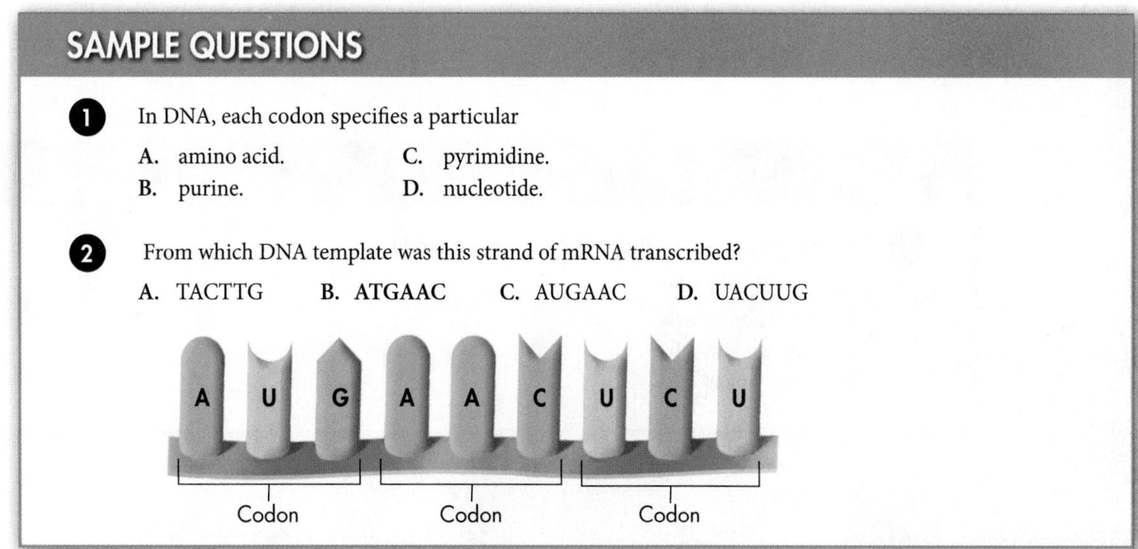

Indiana's Academic Standards

STANDARD 6: CELLULAR REPRODUCTION AND GENE EXPRESSION

Core Standard
Explain the processes, both mitosis and meiosis, by which new cells are formed from existing cells and how in multicellular organisms, groups of cells cooperate to perform essential functions within an organism.

Core Standard
Explain the cellular processes that occur to generate natural genetic variations between parents and offspring.

B.6.1 Describe the process of mitosis and explain that this process ordinarily results in daughter cells with a genetic make-up identical to the parent cells.

B.6.2 Understand that most cells of a multicellular organism contain the same genes, but develop from a single cell (e.g., a fertilized egg) in different ways due to differential gene expression.

B.6.3 Explain that in multicellular organisms the zygote produced during fertilization undergoes a series of cell divisions that lead to clusters of cells that go on to specialize and become the organism's tissues and organs.

B.6.4 Describe and model the process of meiosis and explain the relationship between the genetic make-up of the parent cell and the daughter cells (gametes).

B.6.5 Explain how, in sexual reproduction, crossing over, independent assortment, and random fertilization, result in offspring that are genetically different from the parents.

What It Means to You

You will learn about how cells and organisms reproduce. Many single-celled organisms and the cells of multicellular organisms reproduce asexually by the process of mitosis. In mitosis, a cell divides to produce two cells that have identical genetic information. Asexual reproduction does not increase genetic diversity. In sexual reproduction, the genes of two parents combine to form a new individual. The cells that combine are called gametes. Through the process of meiosis, gametes have half the number of chromosomes that other body cells have. When they combine, the new individual has a complete set of genes, different from the set either parent has.

Where You Will Learn It

You will learn about cellular reproduction and gene expression in Chapters 1, 7, 10, 11, 13, 17, 19, 25, 28, and 34.

SAMPLE QUESTION

Meiosis begins with a single diploid cell and produces

A. two diploid cells.
B. two haploid cells.
C. four diploid cells.
D. four haploid cells.

STANDARD 7: GENETICS

Core Standard
Explain how the genetic information from parents determines the unique characteristics of their offspring.

B.7.1 Distinguish between dominant and recessive alleles and determine the phenotype that would result from the different possible combinations of alleles in an offspring.

B.7.2 Describe dominant, recessive, codominant, sex-linked, incompletely dominant, multiply allelic, and polygenic traits and illustrate their inheritance patterns over multiple generations.

B.7.3 Determine the likelihood of the appearance of a specific trait in an offspring given the genetic make-up of the parents.

B.7.4 Explain the process by which a cell copies its DNA and identify factors that can damage DNA and cause changes in its nucleotide sequence.

B.7.5 Explain and demonstrate how inserting, substituting or deleting segments of a DNA molecule can alter a gene, which is then passed to every cell that develops from it and that the results may be beneficial, harmful or have little or no effect on the organism.

What It Means to You

DNA is the molecule that passes inherited traits from parents to offspring. DNA contains the genes that determine the characteristics of each organism. You will learn how the laws of heredity can be used to predict the chance that an offspring will inherit certain traits. You will also learn about the sources of genetic variation and how mutations can lead to new traits.

Where You Will Learn It

You will learn about genetics in Chapters 11, 12, 13, 14, 15, and 17.

SAMPLE QUESTION

For the flowers of a particular plant, yellow *(Y)* is the dominant allele and white *(y)* is the recessive allele. A yellow-flowered plant *(YY)* is crossed with a white-flowered plant *(yy)*. Which statement best predicts the phenotypes and genotypes of their offspring?

A. 100% yellow-flowered *(Yy)*
B. 100% white-flowered *(yy)*
C. 50% yellow-flowered *(Yy)* and 50% white-flowered *(yy)*
D. 75% yellow-flowered *(Yy)* and 25% white-flowered *(yy)*

Indiana's state bird is the cardinal; the more brightly colored male is shown here.

INDIANA

STANDARD 8: EVOLUTION

Core Standard
Describe how biochemical, fossil, anatomical, developmental, and genetic findings are used to determine relationships among organisms, producing modern classification systems.

Core Standard
Describe how modern evolutionary theory provides an explanation of the history of life on earth and the similarities between organisms that exist today.

B.8.1 Explain how anatomical and molecular similarities among organisms suggests that life on earth began as simple, one-celled organisms about 4 billion years ago and multicellular organisms evolved later.

B.8.2 Explain how organisms are classified and named based on their evolutionary relationships into taxonomic categories.

B.8.3 Use anatomical and molecular evidence to establish evolutionary relationships between organisms.

B.8.4 Understand that molecular evidence supports the anatomical evidence for these evolutionary relationships and provides additional information about the order in which different lines of descent branched.

B.8.5 Describe how due to genetic variations, environmental forces, and reproductive pressures, organisms with beneficial traits are more likely to survive, reproduce, and pass on their genetic information.

B.8.6 Explain how genetic variation within a population (a species) can be attributed to mutations as well as a random assortment of existing genes.

B.8.7 Describe the modern scientific theory of the origins and history of life on earth, and evaluate the evidence that supports it.

What It Means to You

Evolution is the process by which modern organisms have descended from ancient organisms. You will learn how the theory of evolution explains the great diversity of life on Earth and the ways that living things have changed over time.

Where You Will Learn It

You will learn about evolution in Chapters 13, 16, 17, 18, 19, 20, 21, 22, 25, 26, and 29.

SAMPLE QUESTION

1 Which of the following provides evidence that living things have been evolving for millions of years?

A. fossil record
B. natural variation within a species
C. mutations
D. analogous structures

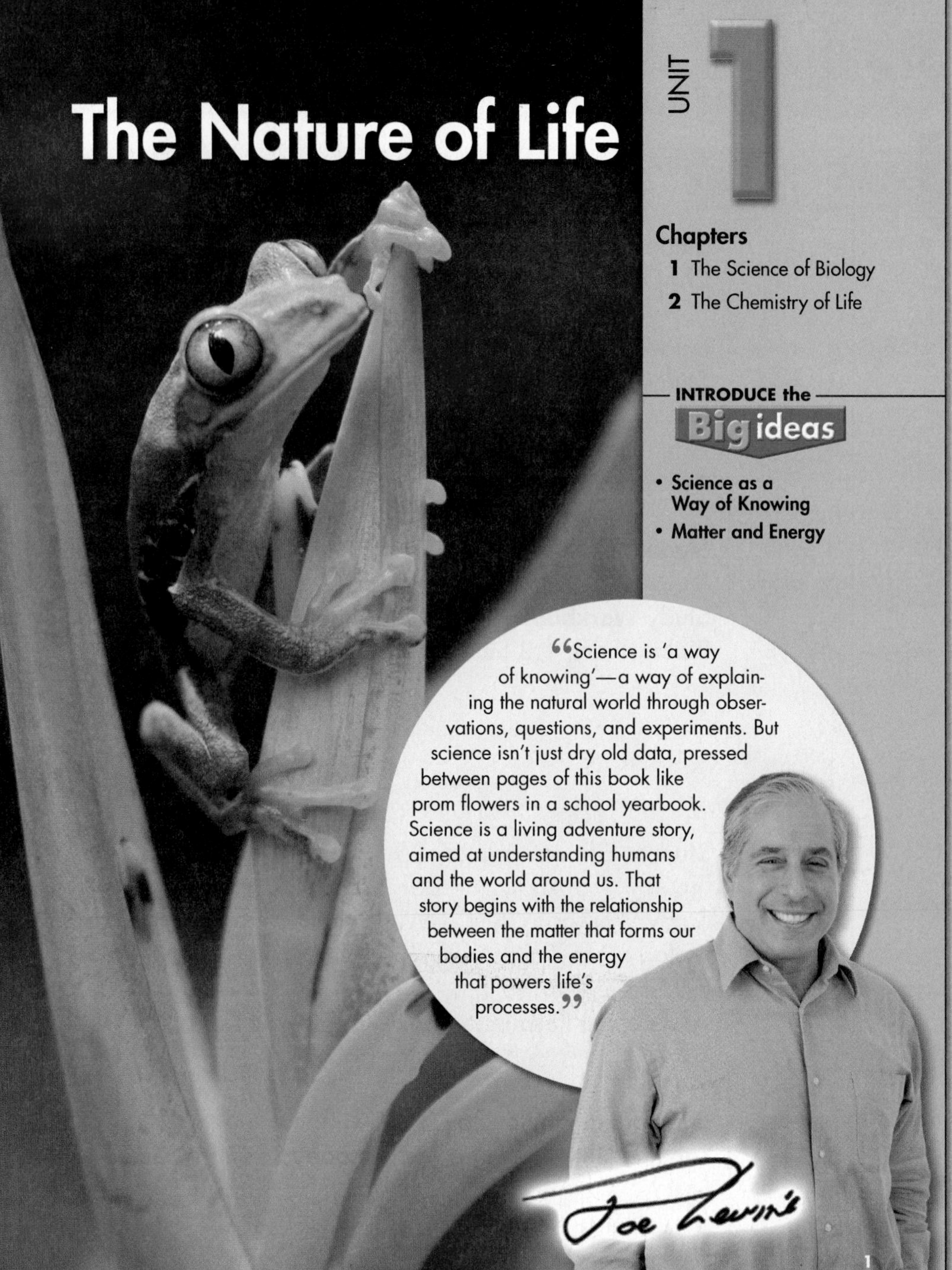

The Nature of Life
UNIT 1
Chapters
1 The Science of Biology
2 The Chemistry of Life
INTRODUCE the Big ideas
• Science as a Way of Knowing
• Matter and Energy
"Science is 'a way of knowing'—a way of explaining the natural world through observations, questions, and experiments. But science isn't just dry old data, pressed between pages of this book like prom flowers in a school yearbook. Science is a living adventure story, aimed at understanding humans and the world around us. That story begins with the relationship between the matter that forms our bodies and the energy that powers life's processes."
1

Dear Colleague,

Trying to cover all of biology in a single textbook is a terrifying, exhilarating, humbling, and sometimes overwhelming experience. But, if we had to pick a single word to describe our experience in writing this book, both of us would say "amazing."

Why? Because the more we learn about biology, the more we are astonished at how much science has progressed since our student days, and how much more we have yet to learn about the natural world. We wrote this book because we want to share with you and your students our amazement at scientific progress, our awe at the wonder of nature, and our delight with the way science works.

It's easy for students to get overwhelmed by the amount of information presented in an intro bio course. From molecules to the biosphere, there's an awful lot of stuff to learn. All this "stuff" can give students the impression that biology "is done"—that everything has been figured out. Scientists, a student once told us, are ashamed to admit that there's anything they don't know.

That student was dead wrong, and we wrote this book to help you correct that kind of misunderstanding. Scientists aren't interested in just memorizing what is known, but in using scientific methodology to explore what is not known. Beginning with Chapter 1, we've tried to present the "stuff" your students are required to know in a context that helps them share in the excitement that scientists feel as we investigate unsolved problems and unexplored territory in the living world.

If you find this book useful, we'll be happy. As teachers, you are the most important part of the scientific community. You are the nurturers of new talent, the caretakers of youthful curiosity. You can help invigorate the scientific enterprise with hope, energy, and vigor. We hope you'll share your thoughts, suggestions, and criticisms of this textbook with us, because we know we'll learn from them. And, most especially, we thank you for the honor of sharing your classroom with us.

CHAPTER PLANNER 1

The Science of Biology

Chapter Contents	IN	Time	Core Resources
Chapter Preview			**Student Edition,** pp. 2–3 **Chapter Mystery,** p. 3
1.1 What Is Science? What Science Is and Is Not • Scientific Methodology: The Heart of Science	NoS.2, NoS.3, NoS.9	1 period 1/2 block	**Student Edition,** pp. 4–9 **Study Workbook A** 1.1 Worksheets L2 **Biology.com** *Art in Motion:* Experimental Design • *Art Review:* Revising Hypotheses **Assessment Resources Book** Visual Quiz L2
1.2 Science in Context Exploration and Discovery: Where Ideas Come From • Communicating Results: Reviewing and Sharing Ideas • Scientific Theories • Science and Society • *Biology & Society: Who Should Fund Product Safety Studies?*	NoS.3, NoS.4, NoS.8, NoS.10, NoS.11	1 period 1/2 block	**Student Edition,** pp. 10–16 **Inquiry** 1.2 Quick Lab, p. 13 L2 **Study Workbook A** 1.2 Worksheets L2 **Biology.com** 1.2 Self-Test • 1.2 Lesson Assessment
1.3 Studying Life Characteristics of Living Things • Big Ideas in Biology • Fields of Biology • Performing Biological Investigations	NoS.3, NoS.5, NoS.8, B.3.3, B.5.2, B.6.2, B.6.3	1 period 1/2 block	**Student Edition,** pp. 17–25 **Inquiry** 1.3 Analyzing Data, p. 20 L2 **Study Workbook A** 1.3 Worksheets L2 **Biology.com** *Data Analysis:* Adventures in Measurement **Assessment Resources Book** Visual Quiz L2
Chapter Pre-Lab	NoS.1, NoS.2, NoS.5	1 period 1/2 block	**Student Edition,** p. 26 L2 **Lab Manual A** *Using a Microscope to Estimate Size* L2

Differentiated Instruction Tools

Study Workbook B includes worksheets with lesson-level differentiated instruction support and explanations of differentiated instruction teaching strategies.

Lab Manual B includes skills labs, simplified chapter labs, and hands-on activities.

ELL Handbook explains ways to make *Biology* more accessible to ELL students.

Spanish Study Workbook is a Spanish translation of Study Workbook A.

Multilingual Glossary is the glossary translated into ten languages.

Differentiated Instruction Key

- L1 Special Needs or Struggling Students
- ELL English Language Learners
- LPR Less Proficient Readers
- L2 On-Level Students
- L3 Advanced Students

Additional Resources

Biology.com Untamed Science Video • Vocabulary Flash Cards

Study Workbook B 1.1 Worksheets L1 ELL LPR
Spanish Study Workbook 1.1 Worksheets ELL
Biology.com *InterActive Art:* Redi and Pasteur's Experiment • 1.1 Lesson Overview • 1.1 Lesson Notes • 1.1 Self-Test • 1.1 Lesson Assessment

Study Workbook B 1.2 Worksheets L1 ELL LPR
Spanish Study Workbook 1.2 Worksheets ELL
Biology.com 1.2 Lesson Overview • 1.2 Lesson Notes

Study Workbook B 1.3 Worksheets L1 ELL LPR
Spanish Study Workbook 1.3 Worksheets ELL
Biology.com 1.3 Lesson Overview • 1.3 Lesson Notes • 1.3 Self-Test • 1.3 Lesson Assessment

Lab Manual B *Using a Microscope to Estimate Size* • Data Analysis: *Picturing Data, What's in a Diet* • Hand-On Activity: *Asking Questions Scientifically* L1 ELL LPR

Chapter Review

Student Edition Study Guide, p. 27 L2
Study Workbook A Chapter 1 Vocabulary Review L2 • Chapter 1 Chapter Mystery/21st Century Skills Activity L2 L3
Transparencies, pp. 1–12 L1 ELL LPR L2
Biology.com Untamed Science Video • Editable Worksheets of Study Workbooks A and B and Lab Manuals A and B • Chapter 1 Flash Cards and Crossword Puzzle

Untamed Science DVD • Classroom Resources CD (includes lesson presentations and editable worksheets)

Chapter Assessment

Student Edition Assessment, pp. 28–31 L2
Study Workbook B Chapter 1 Chapter Review L1 ELL LPR • Chapter 1 Taking a Standardized Test L1 ELL LPR
Assessment Resources Book Chapter 1 Test A L2 • Chapter 1 Test B L1 ELL LPR
Biology.com Chapter 1 Assessment • Editable Worksheets of Chapter 1 Visual Quizzes and Chapter 1 Tests A and B

Exam*View Assessment Suite* • Classroom Resources CD (includes lesson presentations and editable worksheets)

Time: 1 period, 1/2 block

Pressed for Time?

Preview the Chapter Introduce the vocabulary for Lessons 1.1 and 1.3, and preview Figures 1–3 and 1–13.

Cover the Chapter Quickly Have students read *Scientific Methodology: The Heart of Science* in Lesson 1.1, *Scientific Theories* in Lesson 1.2, and all of Lesson 1.3. Discuss Figure 1–13.

Assess Assign students questions 2 and 3 in the 1.1 Assessment, question 3 in the 1.2 Assessment, the 1.3 Assessment, and the Chapter 1 Standardized Test Prep, except question 1.

CHAPTER 1

Connect to the Big Idea

Use the photograph of the paleontologists to start a class discussion of the methods scientists use to gather data. Ask students how these scientists are learning about this species of dinosaur. *(Sample answer: They are observing the dinosaur's skeleton.)* Challenge students to describe other methods scientists use to learn about the natural world. *(Students may identify methods such as experimentation or describe the use of technology to gather information.)* Then, ask students to identify some of the topics that scientists study. Guide students to anticipate the answer to the question, **What role does science play in the study of life?**

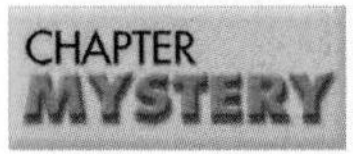

Have students read over the Chapter Mystery and discuss the use of human growth hormone (HGH) in individuals who are short but otherwise healthy. Then, ask students to explain how the Chapter Mystery illustrates the connection between science and society. Help them relate the discussion to the Chapter 1 Big Idea of Science as a Way of Knowing.

BIOLOGY.com Have students preview the chapter vocabulary using the **Flash Cards.**

IN INDIANA ACADEMIC STANDARDS

For the full text of all standards, see the Course Overview in the front matter of this book.

Key standards: Chapter 1 covers key ideas from The Nature of Science, including **NoS.2** Explanations based on data, **NoS.4** Evaluate the work of peers, **NoS.5** Standard laboratory techniques, **NoS.8** Scientific knowledge is organized into theories, **NoS.9** Scientific discoveries affect prior ideas, and **NoS.10** Scientific discoveries and new technologies.

1 The Science of Biology

Big idea Science as a Way of Knowing

Q: What role does science play in the study of life?

BIOLOGY.com Search Chapter 1 GO • Flash Cards

2

UbD Understanding by Design

Chapter 1 describes science, explains the relationship between science and society, and introduces the study of life. The graphic organizer at the right shows how these concepts are framed by the chapter Big Idea, Essential Question, and Guiding Questions. The idea and questions help students begin to explore the Unit 1 Enduring Understanding of how *the process of science helps biologists investigate how nature works at all levels, from the molecules in cells to the biosphere.*

PERFORMANCE GOALS

In Chapter 1, students explore the process of science and the study of biology by reviewing detailed figures. They also preview the Big Ideas that run through biology and this textbook. They synthesize chapter concepts by writing a letter to Aristotle explaining how science has changed over time and an editorial encouraging all students to take a science course.

INDIANA ACADEMIC STANDARDS FOR SCIENCE

Nature of Science NoS.1, NoS.2, NoS.3, NoS.4, NoS.5, NoS.8, NoS.9, NoS.10, NoS.11; **Matter Cycles and Energy Transfers** B.3.3; **Molecular Basis of Heredity** B.5.2; **Cellular Reproduction and Gene Expression** B.6.2, B.6.3. See lessons for details.

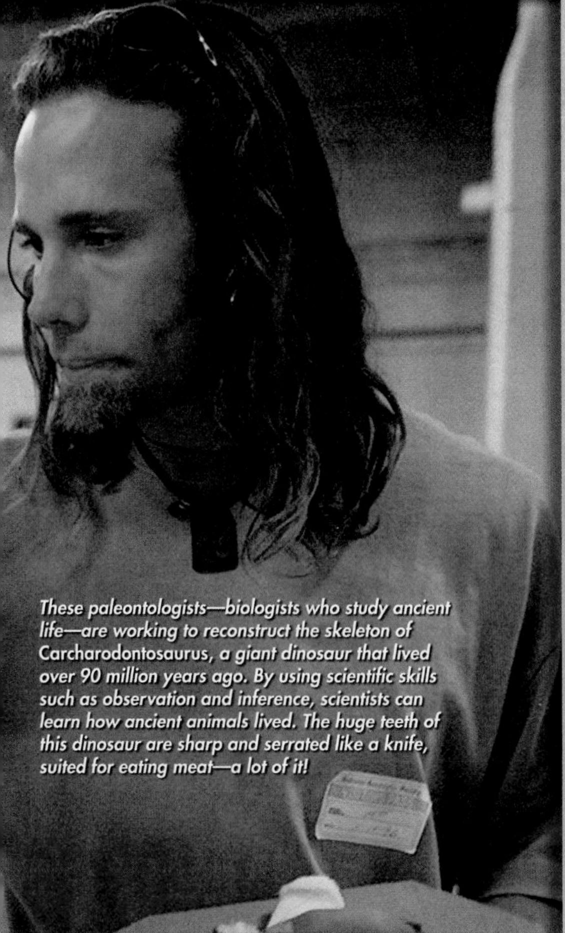

These paleontologists—biologists who study ancient life—are working to reconstruct the skeleton of Carcharodontosaurus, a giant dinosaur that lived over 90 million years ago. By using scientific skills such as observation and inference, scientists can learn how ancient animals lived. The huge teeth of this dinosaur are sharp and serrated like a knife, suited for eating meat—a lot of it!

• Untamed Science Video • Chapter Mystery

CHAPTER MYSTERY

HEIGHT BY PRESCRIPTION

A doctor injects a chemical into the body of an eight-year-old boy named David. This healthy boy shows no signs of disease. The "condition" for which he is being treated is quite common—David is short for his age. The medication he is taking is human growth hormone, or HGH.

HGH, together with genes and diet, controls growth during childhood. People who produce little or no HGH are abnormally short and may have other related health problems. But David has normal HGH levels. He is short simply because his parents are both healthy, short people.

But if David isn't sick, why does his doctor prescribe HGH? Where does medicinal HGH come from? Is it safe? What does this case say about science and society? As you read this chapter, look for clues about the nature of science, the role of technology in our modern world, and the relationship between science and society. Then, solve the mystery.

Never Stop Exploring Your World. Finding the solution to the growth hormone mystery is only the beginning. Take a video field trip with the ecogeeks of Untamed Science to see where this mystery leads.

What's Online

BIOLOGY.com Extend your reach by using these and other digital assets offered at **Biology.com.**

CHAPTER MYSTERY
How are science and society related? Students can use clues about the nature of science, the role of technology in science, and the relationship between science and society to solve a mystery about the non-medical use of human growth hormone.

UNTAMED SCIENCE VIDEO
Follow the Untamed Science crew in the video **What Do Biologists Look Like?** as they find the answers to the question "What is biology?" and dispel misconceptions about biologists.

ART IN MOTION
This activity enables students to change variables in an experiment to see how the results are affected.

INTERACTIVE ART
Students explore historical experiments originally performed by Redi and Pasteur in this interactive activity.

ART REVIEW
This drag-and-drop activity allows students to examine the steps in an experiment, including revision of the original hypothesis.

DATA ANALYSIS
Students review strategies for obtaining measurements when objects cannot be easily or directly measured.

Chapter 1
Big Idea: Science as a Way of Knowing

Chapter 1 EQ: What role does science play in the study of life?

- **1.1 GQ:** How do we find explanations for events in the natural world?
- **1.2 GQ:** How do the scientific community and society influence the process of science?
- **1.3 GQ:** What is biology?

LESSON 1.1

Getting Started

Objectives

1.1.1 State the goals of science.

1.1.2 Describe the steps used in scientific methodology.

Student Resources

Study Workbooks A and B, 1.1 Worksheets

Spanish Study Workbook, 1.1 Worksheets

Lab Manual B, 1.1 Data Analysis Worksheet, 1.1 Hands-On Activity Worksheet

Lesson Overview • Lesson Notes • Activities: Art in Motion, InterActive Art, Art Review • Assessment: Self-Test, Lesson Assessment

For corresponding lesson in the **Foundation Edition**, see pages 4–8.

Activate Prior Knowledge

Write the title of Lesson 1.1, **What Is Science?,** on the board. Ask students to write a one-sentence response to the question. Have several students share their responses with the class, and use students' responses to spark a class discussion of what is—and what is not—science.

1.1 What Is Science?

NoS.2 Explanations based on data; NoS.9 Scientific discoveries affect prior ideas. Also covered: NoS.3.

Key Questions

What are the goals of science?

What procedures are at the core of scientific methodology?

Vocabulary

science • observation • inference • hypothesis • controlled experiment • independent variable • dependent variable • control group • data

Taking Notes

Flowchart As you read, create a flowchart showing the steps scientists use to answer questions about the natural world.

THINK ABOUT IT One day long ago, someone looked around and wondered: Where did plants and animals come from? How did I come to be? Since then, humans have tried to answer those questions in different ways. Some ways of explaining the world have stayed the same over time. Science, however, is always changing.

What Science Is and Is Not

What are the goals of science?

This book contains lots of facts and ideas about living things. Many of those facts are important, and you will be tested on them! But you shouldn't think that biology, or any science, is just a collection of never-changing facts. For one thing, you can be sure that some "facts" presented in this book will change soon—if they haven't changed already. What's more, science is not a collection of unchanging beliefs about the world. Scientific ideas are open to testing, discussion, and revision. So, some ideas presented in this book will also change.

These statements may puzzle you. If "facts" and ideas in science change, why should you bother learning them? And if science is neither a list of facts nor a collection of unchanging beliefs, what is it?

FIGURE 1–1 Studying the Natural World How do whales communicate? How far do they travel? How are they affected by environmental changes? These are questions whale researchers can use science to answer.

INDIANA ACADEMIC STANDARDS

For the full text of all standards, see the Course Overview in the front matter of this book.

NoS.2 Recognize that their explanations must be based both on their data and other known information from investigations of others.

NoS.9 Recognize that new scientific discoveries often lead to a re-evaluation of previously accepted scientific knowledge and of commonly held ideas.

UbD Teach for Understanding

ENDURING UNDERSTANDING The process of science helps biologists investigate how nature works at all levels, from the molecules in cells to the biosphere.

GUIDING QUESTION How do we find explanations for events in the natural world?

EVIDENCE OF UNDERSTANDING *After completing the lesson, give students the following assessment to show their understanding of the role of science in studying life.* Have students work in small groups to make a list of three questions about living things that could be investigated scientifically. Then, have each group choose one of its questions and explain how it could be investigated using scientific methodology.

Science as a Way of Knowing **Science** is an organized way of gathering and analyzing evidence about the natural world. It is a way of observing, a way of thinking, and "a way of knowing" about the world. In other words, science is a *process,* not a "thing." The word *science* also refers to the body of knowledge that scientific studies have gathered over the years.

Several features make science different from other human endeavors. First, science deals only with the natural world. Scientific endeavors never concern, in any way, supernatural phenomena of any kind. Second, scientists collect and organize information in an orderly way, looking for patterns and connections among events. Third, scientists propose explanations that are based on evidence, not belief. Then they test those explanations with more evidence.

The Goals of Science The scientific way of knowing includes the view that the physical universe is a system composed of parts and processes that interact. From a scientific perspective, all objects in the universe, and all interactions among those objects, are governed by universal natural laws. The same natural laws apply whether the objects or events are large or small.

Aristotle and other Greek philosophers were among the first to try to view the universe in this way. They aimed to explain the world around them in terms of events and processes they could observe. Modern scientists continue that tradition. **One goal of science is to provide natural explanations for events in the natural world. Science also aims to use those explanations to understand patterns in nature and to make useful predictions about natural events.**

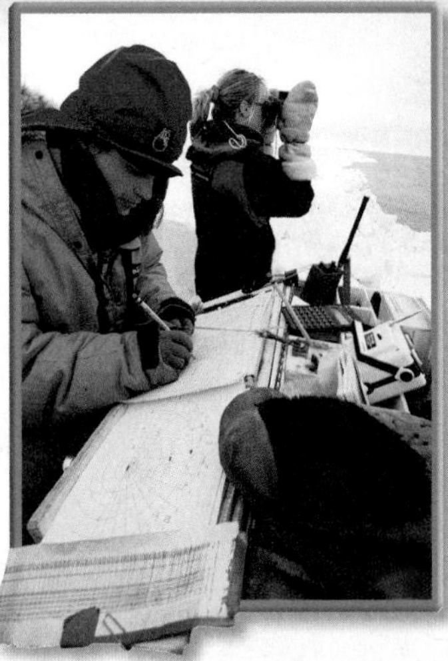

FIGURE 1–2 Science in Action These marine scientists are recording information as they study whales in Alaska.

Science, Change, and Uncertainty Over the centuries, scientists have gathered an enormous amount of information about the natural world. Scientific knowledge helps us cure diseases, place satellites in orbit, and send instantaneous electronic communications. Yet, despite all we know, much of nature remains a mystery. It is a mystery because science never stands still; almost every major scientific discovery raises more questions than it answers. Often, research yields surprises that point future studies in new and unexpected directions. This constant change doesn't mean science has failed. On the contrary, it shows that science continues to advance.

That's why learning about science means more than just understanding what we know. It also means understanding what we don't know. You may be surprised to hear this, but science rarely "proves" anything in absolute terms. Scientists aim for the best understanding of the natural world that current methods can reveal. Uncertainty is part of the scientific process and part of what makes science exciting! Happily, as you'll learn in later chapters, science has allowed us to build enough understanding to make useful predictions about the natural world.

BUILD Vocabulary

WORD ORIGINS The word **science** derives from the Latin word *scientia,* which means "knowledge." Science represents knowledge that has been gathered over time.

In Your Notebook *Explain in your own words why there is uncertainty in science.*

How Science Works

THE SCIENCE OF BIOLOGY IN ANCIENT GREECE

Although the word *biology* was not used until the early nineteenth century, the scientific study of life has a history of thousands of years. Alcmaeon, a Greek physician born about 535 B.C., is thought to be one of the first persons to have studied human anatomy. He discovered the optic nerve and speculated that the brain was the center of intellectual activity. The Greek philosopher Aristotle, born in 384 B.C., was a meticulous observer of living things, classifying over 500 animal species in a strict hierarchy. He even proposed a theory of progressive change among animals—an early suggestion of evolution.

Teach

Lead a Discussion

Ask students the following questions to promote their understanding of what *science* is about.

Ask How do you "know" about something? *(Sample answer: You learn about something, or you see it for yourself.)*

Ask Where does knowledge come from? *(Sample answer: From people who study particular topics.)*

Ask What does it mean to say that science is a process? *(Sample answer: The word* process *indicates that science is something people do, rather than just a group of facts.)*

Ask Do you think the phrase "a way of knowing" accurately describes science as a method of learning? Why or why not? *(Sample answer: Yes, the phrase identifies science as a method or tool used to learn about the natural world.)*

DIFFERENTIATED INSTRUCTION

L1 Struggling Students Write the following sentence on the board:

- Science is an organized way of learning about the natural world.

Explain that this sentence summarizes the main idea presented on the page. Ask each student to give one detail about this main idea they learned by reading the page.

ELL Focus on ELL: Extend Language

BEGINNING AND INTERMEDIATE SPEAKERS Have students write the term *science* in a **Vocabulary Word Map.** Then, have them write words or phrases that describe attributes of science or topics related to science in the lower boxes. Encourage beginning speakers to use one of the boxes to make an illustration to represent the process of science. After students have completed their vocabulary word maps, have them form small groups to discuss how their maps are similar and how they are different. Circulate among the groups, and have students share some of their responses with you.

Study Wkbks A/B, Appendix S32, Vocabulary Word Map. **Transparencies,** GO17.

Answers

IN YOUR NOTEBOOK Sample answer: There is uncertainty in science because science rarely proves anything in absolute terms.

Teach continued

Use Visuals

Have students use **Figure 1–3** to learn about scientific methodology. Point out to students that this figure continues through page 8. Have students make an outline that includes the following main topics: observing and asking questions, inferring and hypothesizing, designing controlled experiments, collecting and analyzing data, and drawing conclusions. As students read the detailed descriptions of these processes, have them add details to their outlines.

DIFFERENTIATED INSTRUCTION

L1 Struggling Students For students who are overwhelmed by the amount of information in **Figure 1–3,** have pairs of students go over each panel one by one. First, have individual students read the head, study the diagrams, and read through the captions below each set of panels. Then, suggest they discuss the panel with their partners. When they have discussed each panel, ask them to use their own words to tell the story presented by the entire series of panels.

Address Misconceptions

The Scientific Method A common misconception among students is that the "scientific method" is a set of five or six simple steps performed by all scientists, always in the same order. The text on this page can be used to address this misconception. Point out the sentences that refer to the dynamic nature of scientific investigations—how there is not any single, rigid set of steps called the scientific method. Tell students scientific methodology describes a general style of investigation and it applies across all the branches of science.

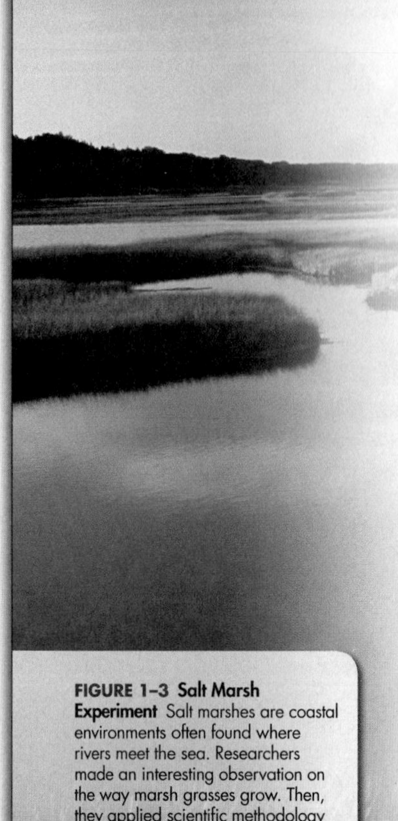

FIGURE 1–3 Salt Marsh Experiment Salt marshes are coastal environments often found where rivers meet the sea. Researchers made an interesting observation on the way marsh grasses grow. Then, they applied scientific methodology to answer questions that arose from their observation.

Scientific Methodology: The Heart of Science

What procedures are at the core of scientific methodology?

You might think that science is a mysterious process, used only by certain people under special circumstances. But that's not true, because you use scientific thinking all the time. Suppose your family's car won't start. What do you do? You use what you know about cars to come up with ideas to test. At first, you might think the battery is dead. So you test that idea by turning the key in the ignition. If the starter motor works but the engine doesn't start, you reject the dead-battery idea. You might guess next that the car is out of gas. A glance at the fuel gauge tests that idea. Again and again, you apply scientific thinking until the problem is solved—or until you run out of ideas and call a mechanic!

Scientists approach research in pretty much the same way. There isn't any single, cut-and-dried "scientific method." There is, however, a general style of investigation that we can call scientific methodology. **Scientific methodology involves observing and asking questions, making inferences and forming hypotheses, conducting controlled experiments, collecting and analyzing data, and drawing conclusions. Figure 1–3** shows how one research team used scientific methodology in its study of New England salt marshes.

Observing and Asking Questions Scientific investigations begin with **observation,** the act of noticing and describing events or processes in a careful, orderly way. Of course, scientific observation involves more than just looking at things. A good scientist can, as the philosopher Arthur Schopenhauer put it, "Think something that nobody has thought yet, while looking at something that everybody sees." That kind of observation leads to questions that no one has asked before.

OBSERVING AND ASKING QUESTIONS

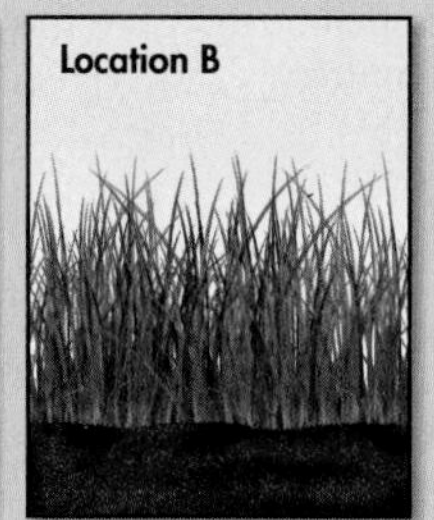

Researchers observed that marsh grass grows taller in some places than others. This observation led to a question: *Why do marsh grasses grow to different heights in different places?*

INFERRING AND HYPOTHESIZING

The researchers inferred that something limits grass growth in some places. It could be any environmental factor—temperature, sunlight, water, or nutrients. Based on their knowledge of salt marshes, they proposed a hypothesis: *Marsh grass growth is limited by available nitrogen.*

BIOLOGY.com Search Lesson 1.1 GO • Art in Motion • InterActive Art

How Science Works

AN EMPHASIS ON EXPERIMENTATION

Galileo Galilei (1564–1642) is generally considered to have established modern scientific methodology, as demonstrated in his investigations. Some stories about Galileo cannot be verified, but his approach to the study of nature is beyond question. His emphasis on experimentation as the way to prove the validity of ideas was part of the broader movement of free thought and skepticism that was characteristic of the European Renaissance. Galileo's scientific legacy includes the challenge to Aristotle's view that the natural state of a body is at rest—a view that had been accepted for 2000 years; and the discovery of Jupiter's moons, which supported the Copernican model of the solar system.

Inferring and Forming a Hypothesis After posing questions, scientists use further observations to make inferences. An **inference** is a logical interpretation based on what scientists already know. Inference, combined with a creative imagination, can lead to a hypothesis. A **hypothesis** is a scientific explanation for a set of observations that can be tested in ways that support or reject it.

Designing Controlled Experiments Testing a scientific hypothesis often involves designing an experiment that keeps track of various factors that can change, or variables. Examples of variables include temperature, light, time, and availability of nutrients. Whenever possible, a hypothesis should be tested by an experiment in which only one variable is changed. All other variables should be kept unchanged, or controlled. This type of experiment is called a **controlled experiment.**

▶ ***Controlling Variables*** Why is it important to control variables? The reason is that if several variables are changed in the experiment, researchers can't easily tell which variable is responsible for any results they observe. The variable that is deliberately changed is called the **independent variable** (also called the manipulated variable). The variable that is observed and that changes in response to the independent variable is called the **dependent variable** (also called the responding variable).

▶ ***Control and Experimental Groups*** Typically, an experiment is divided into control and experimental groups. A **control group** is exposed to the same conditions as the experimental group except for one independent variable. Scientists always try to reproduce or replicate their observations. Therefore, they set up several sets of control and experimental groups, rather than just a single pair.

In Your Notebook *What is the difference between an observation and an inference? List three examples of each.*

DESIGNING CONTROLLED EXPERIMENTS

The researchers selected similar plots of marsh grass. All plots had similar plant density, soil type, input of freshwater, and height above average tide level. The plots were divided into control and experimental groups.

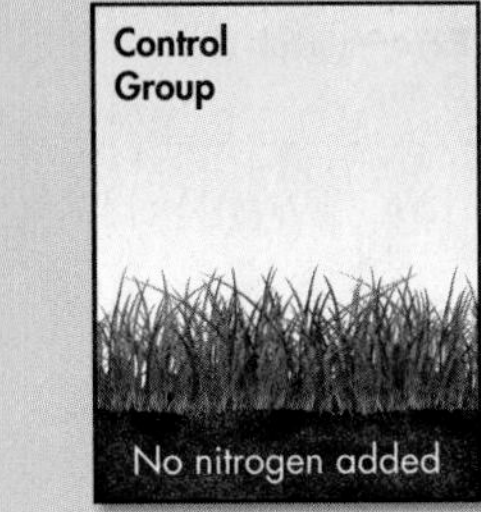

The researchers added nitrogen fertilizer (the independent variable) to the experimental plots. They then observed the growth of marsh grass (the dependent variable) in both experimental and control plots.

Build Science Skills

Divide the class into small groups, and have each group consider this question: Does the amount of sleep a student gets affect how well that student does in school? Ask each group to design an experiment that would address the question. Have each group write a short summary of the procedure it would follow. Then, have groups share their experimental designs with the class.

DIFFERENTIATED INSTRUCTION

L1 Struggling Students Help students understand the meaning of the terms *independent variable* and *dependent variable* in the context of a controlled experiment. Describe a simple experimental scenario to students, for example, giving several plants differing amounts of water to see how their growth is affected. Help students identify the independent variable and dependent variable in the experiment. Continue describing scenarios until they can reliably identify the independent and dependent variables. Then, have them apply this knowledge to the activity described above.

L3 Advanced Students Ask students to use reliable resources to find out about studies of the amount of sleep teens receive and how their school performance is affected. Tell students to learn about the scientific methodology used in the studies. Have them share what they learn with the class.

BIOLOGY.com Have students access **Art in Motion: Experimental Design** to manipulate the variables in the experiment in **Figure 3–1.** Students can also use the **InterActive Art: Redi and Pasteur's Experiments** to explore the idea of spontaneous generation through experimentation.

UbD Check for Understanding

HAND SIGNALS

Present students with the following questions, and ask them to show a thumbs-up sign if they can definitely answer the question, a thumbs-down sign if they cannot, or a waving-hand sign if they are not sure.

- Why is science sometimes referred to as a "way of knowing"?
- What are the goals of science?
- How is a controlled experiment designed?

ADJUST INSTRUCTION

If students are confused by a question, write it on the board and have small groups write a short response. Then, have volunteers from each group post their responses on the board.

Answers

IN YOUR NOTEBOOK Students should explain that an observation, which is something noticed using the senses, is different from an inference, which is a logical interpretation of an observation. Students should list three examples of each.

LESSON 1.1

Teach continued

Build Study Skills

Have students make a **Two-Column Table.** Have them label the left side of the table Qualitative Data and the right side Quantitative Data. Ask students to write definitions for *qualitative data* and *quantitative data* in the appropriate columns. Then, have them list examples of each from their everyday life. After students have completed their tables, ask them to write a paragraph summarizing the information and explaining why both types of data are useful in science.

Study Wkbks A/B, Appendix S31, Two-Column Table. **Transparencies,** GO16.

DIFFERENTIATED INSTRUCTION

L1 Special Needs Have students work with a partner or in small group to complete their **Two-Column Table.** Then, instead of writing a summary paragraph, have them explain to you why scientists collect data when they do experiments.

ELL English Language Learners Define the words *quality* and *quantity*. Point out that they form the roots of the words *qualitative* and *quantitative.* Have pairs of students use the definitions of *quality* and *quantity* to help them write definitions of *qualitative data* and *quantitative data.* Ask pairs to share their definitions with the class.

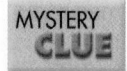

MYSTERY CLUE Students should describe hypothetical experiments that include control groups and clearly identified independent and dependent variables. They should also mention the ethical problems involved in testing medical products in children or testing in humans in general—for example, issues of safety, consent, and long-term health effects. Students can go online to **Biology.com** to gather their evidence.

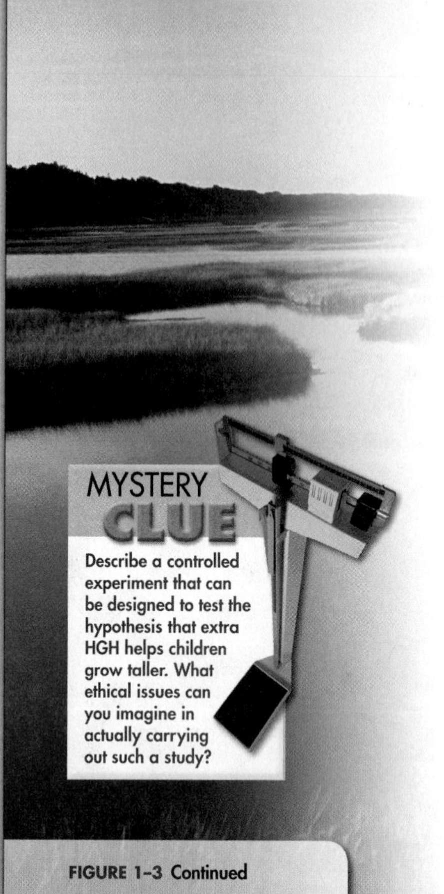

MYSTERY CLUE

Describe a controlled experiment that can be designed to test the hypothesis that extra HGH helps children grow taller. What ethical issues can you imagine in actually carrying out such a study?

Collecting and Analyzing Data Scientists make detailed records of experimental observations, gathering information called **data.** There are two main types of data. Quantitative data are numbers obtained by counting or measuring. In the marsh grass experiment, quantitative data could include the number of plants per plot, the length, width, and weight of each blade of grass, and so on. Qualitative data are descriptive and involve characteristics that cannot usually be counted. Qualitative data in the marsh grass experiment might include notes about foreign objects in the sample plots or information on whether the grass was growing upright or sideways.

▶ ***Research Tools*** Scientists choose appropriate tools for collecting and analyzing data. The tools may range from simple devices such as metersticks and calculators to sophisticated equipment such as machines that measure nitrogen content in plants and soil. Charts and graphs are also tools that help scientists organize their data. In the past, data were recorded by hand, often in notebooks or personal journals. Today, researchers typically enter data into computers, which make organizing and analyzing data easier. Many kinds of data are now gathered directly by computer-controlled equipment.

▶ ***Sources of Error*** Researchers must be careful to avoid errors in data collection and analysis. Tools used to measure the size and weight of marsh grasses, for example, have limited accuracy. Data analysis and sample size must be chosen carefully. In medical studies, for example, both experimental and control groups should be quite large. Why? Because there is always variation among individuals in control and experimental groups. The larger the sample size, the more reliably researchers can analyze that variation and evaluate the differences between experimental and control groups.

FIGURE 1–3 Continued

COLLECTING AND ANALYZING DATA

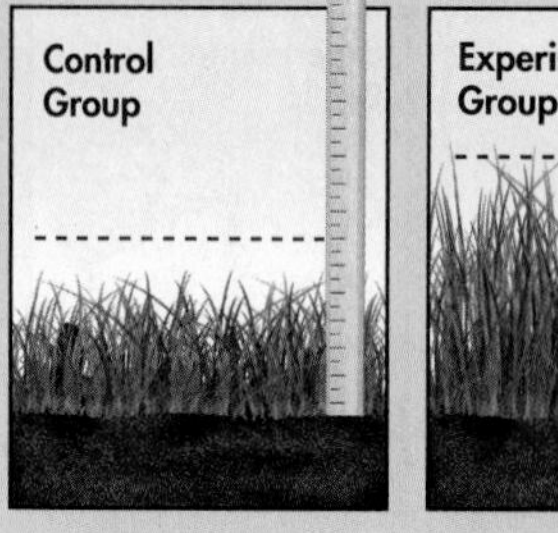

The researchers sampled all the plots throughout the growing season. They measured growth rates and plant sizes, and analyzed the chemical composition of living leaves.

DRAWING CONCLUSIONS

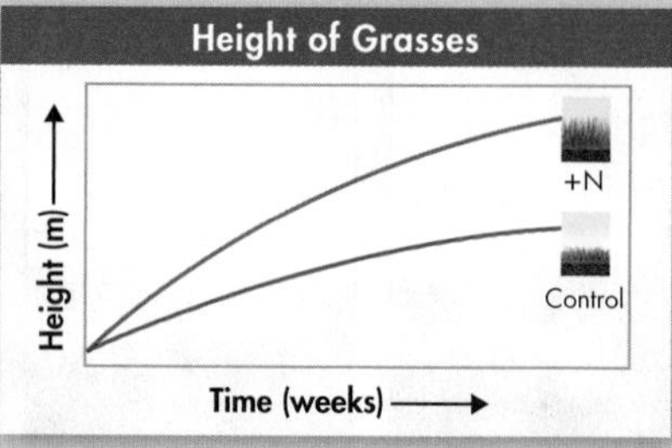

Data from all plots were compared and evaluated by statistical tests. Data analysis confirmed that marsh grasses in experimental plots with additional nitrogen did, in fact, grow taller and larger than controls. The hypothesis and its predictions were supported.

8 Chapter 1 • Lesson 1

How Science Works

THE USE OF STATISTICS IN SCIENCE

Data analysis in science often relies on the use of statistics. Although some statistical calculations are very sophisticated, calculations as basic as finding the mean, median, and mode of a set of values are ways to analyze data using statistics. Statistical tools such as range and standard deviation can be used to assess the variability of data. Statistics can also be used to calculate the percent error of experimental data. Percent error is calculated by obtaining the absolute value of the difference between the accepted value and the experimental value, dividing by the accepted value, and multiplying by 100.

$$\%\ \text{error} = \frac{|\text{experimental value} - \text{accepted value}|}{\text{accepted value}} \times 100$$

Drawing Conclusions Scientists use experimental data as evidence to support, refute, or revise the hypothesis being tested, and to draw a valid conclusion. Hypotheses are often not fully supported or refuted by one set of experiments. Rather, new data may indicate that the researchers have the right general idea but are wrong about a few particulars. In that case, the original hypothesis is reevaluated and revised; new predictions are made, and new experiments are designed. Those new experiments might suggest changes in the experimental treatment or better control of more variables. As shown in **Figure 1–4,** many circuits around this loop are often necessary before a final hypothesis is supported and conclusions can be drawn.

When Experiments Are Not Possible It is not always possible to test a hypothesis with an experiment. In some of these cases, researchers devise hypotheses that can be tested by observations. Animal behavior researchers, for example, might want to learn how animal groups interact in the wild. Investigating this kind of natural behavior requires field observations that disturb the animals as little as possible. When researchers analyze data from these observations, they may devise hypotheses that can be tested in different ways.

Sometimes, ethics prevents certain types of experiments—especially on human subjects. Medical researchers who suspect that a chemical causes cancer, for example, would not intentionally expose people to it! Instead, they search for volunteers who have already been exposed to the chemical. For controls, they study people who have not been exposed to the chemical. The researchers still try to control as many variables as possible. For example, they might exclude volunteers who have serious health problems or known genetic conditions. Medical researchers always try to study large groups of subjects so that individual genetic differences do not produce misleading results.

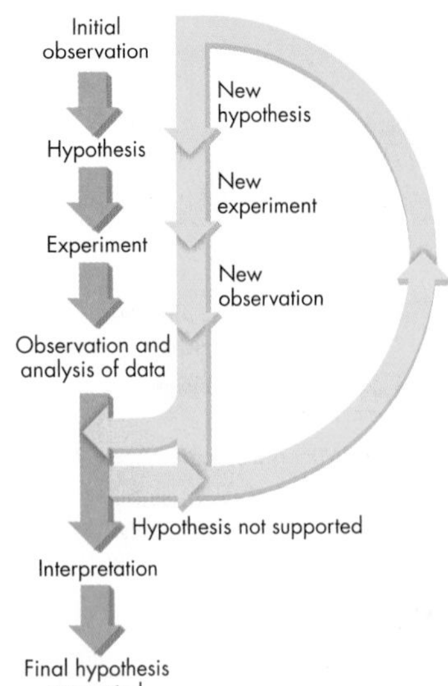

FIGURE 1–4 Revising Hypotheses During the course of an investigation, hypotheses may have to be revised and experiments redone several times.

1.1 Assessment

IN NoS.2, NoS.3, NoS.9

Review Key Concepts

1. a. Review What is science?
   b. Explain What kinds of understandings does science contribute about the natural world?
   c. Form an Opinion Do you think that scientists will ever run out of things to study? Explain your reasoning.
2. a. Review What does scientific methodology involve?
   b. Explain Why are hypotheses so important to controlled experiments?

WRITE ABOUT SCIENCE

Creative Writing

3. A few hundred years ago, observations seemed to indicate that some living things could just suddenly appear: maggots showed up on meat; mice were found on grain; and beetles turned up on cow dung. Those observations led to the incorrect idea of spontaneous generation—the notion that life could arise from nonliving matter. Write a paragraph for a history magazine evaluating the spontaneous generation hypothesis. Why did it seem logical at the time? What evidence was overlooked or ignored?

BIOLOGY.com Search 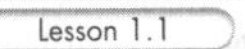 Lesson 1.1  GO • Self-Test • Lesson Assessment • Art Review

BIOLOGY.com Have students find out more about the revision of hypotheses in **Art Review: Revising Hypotheses.**

Assess and Remediate

EVALUATE UNDERSTANDING

Have each student write a sentence that uses two of the lesson vocabulary terms and clearly shows the relationship between the two terms. Call on students to share their sentences with the class. Then, have students complete the 1.1 Assessment.

REMEDIATION SUGGESTION

L1 **Struggling Students** If students have trouble with **Question 2b,** remind them that all experiments begin with a statement to be tested. Ask students what this statement is called. *(hypothesis)*

BIOLOGY.com Students can check their understanding of lesson concepts with the **Self-Test** assessment. They can then take an online version of the **Lesson Assessment**.

Assessment Answers

1a. Science is an organized way of gathering and analyzing evidence gathered about the natural world.

1b. Science provides explanations for events in the natural world, an understanding of patterns in nature, and predictions about natural events.

1c. Sample answer: I don't think that scientists will ever run out of things to study because every discovery raises new questions. Also, as technology improves, there will be new ways to investigate things.

2a. Scientific methodology involves observing and asking questions, inferring and hypothesizing, designing controlled experiments, collecting and analyzing data, and drawing conclusions.

2b. Hypotheses are so important to controlled experiments because they are testable explanations for a set of observations.

WRITE ABOUT SCIENCE

3. Students' paragraphs should explain that the idea of spontaneous generation seemed valid in light of people's everyday observations. However, this idea was not tested using scientific methodology. Evidence that was overlooked or ignored might include the fact that adult flies were present in an area before the maggots "appeared" in that same area.

Getting Started

Objectives

1.2.1 Explain how scientific attitudes generate new ideas.

1.2.2 Describe the importance of peer review.

1.2.3 Explain what a scientific theory is.

1.2.4 Explain the relationship between science and society.

Student Resources

Study Workbooks A and B, 1.2 Worksheets

Spanish Study Workbook, 1.2 Worksheets

Lesson Overview • Lesson Notes • Assessment: Self-Test, Lesson Assessment

For corresponding lesson in the **Foundation Edition**, see pages 9–12.

Build Background

Before class, write a message on the board using a random arrangement of letters rather than recognizable words. When students ask you about the message, point out that they are demonstrating curiosity, one of the scientific habits of mind.

IN INDIANA ACADEMIC STANDARDS

For the full text of all standards, see the Course Overview in the front matter of this book.

NoS.4 Regularly evaluate the work of their peers and in turn have their work evaluated by their peers.

NoS.8 Explain that the body of scientific knowledge is organized into major theories, which are derived from and supported by the results of many experiments, and allow us to make testable predictions.

NoS.10 Describe how scientific discoveries lead to the development of new technologies, and conversely how technological advances can lead to scientific discoveries through new experimental methods and equipment.

1.2 Science in Context

IN NoS.3 Communicate ideas; NoS.4 Evaluate the work of peers; NoS.8 Scientific knowledge is organized into theories; NoS.10 Scientific discoveries and new technologies; NoS.11 Scientific knowledge: environmental and social issues.

Key Questions

What scientific attitudes help generate new ideas?

Why is peer review important?

What is a scientific theory?

What is the relationship between science and society?

Vocabulary

theory • bias

Taking Notes

Preview Visuals Before you read, study **Figure 1–10.** As you read, use the figure to describe the role science plays in society.

THINK ABOUT IT Scientific methodology is the heart of science. But that vital "heart" is only part of the full "body" of science. Science and scientists operate in the context of the scientific community and society at large.

Exploration and Discovery: Where Ideas Come From

What scientific attitudes help generate new ideas?

Scientific methodology is closely linked to exploration and discovery, as shown in **Figure 1–5.** Recall that scientific methodology starts with observations and questions. But where do those observations and questions come from in the first place? They may be inspired by scientific attitudes, practical problems, and new technology.

Scientific Attitudes Good scientists share scientific attitudes, or habits of mind, that lead them to exploration and discovery. **Curiosity, skepticism, open-mindedness, and creativity help scientists generate new ideas.**

▶ ***Curiosity*** A curious researcher, for example, may look at a salt marsh and immediately ask, "What's that plant? Why is it growing here?" Often, results from previous studies also spark curiosity and lead to new questions.

▶ ***Skepticism*** Good scientists are skeptics, which means that they question existing ideas and hypotheses, and they refuse to accept explanations without evidence. Scientists who disagree with hypotheses design experiments to test them. Supporters of hypotheses also undertake rigorous testing of their ideas to confirm them and to address any valid questions raised.

▶ ***Open-Mindedness*** Scientists must remain open-minded, meaning that they are willing to accept different ideas that may not agree with their hypothesis.

▶ ***Creativity*** Researchers also need to think creatively to design experiments that yield accurate data.

FIGURE 1–5 The Process of Science As the arrows indicate, the different aspects of science are interconnected—making the process of science dynamic, flexible, and unpredictable.

Adapted from *Understanding Science*, UC Berkeley, Museum of Paleontology

 BIOLOGY.com Search Lesson 1.2 GO • Lesson Overview • Lesson Notes

UbD Teach for Understanding

ENDURING UNDERSTANDING The process of science helps biologists investigate how nature works at all levels, from the molecules in cells to the biosphere.

GUIDING QUESTION How do the scientific community and society influence the process of science?

EVIDENCE OF UNDERSTANDING *After completing the lesson, give students the following assessment to show their understanding of scientific attitudes.* Have students work with a small group to write and perform a skit that demonstrates how a scientist would employ each of the scientific habits of mind discussed (curiosity, skepticism, open-mindedness, and creativity) when exploring a scientific problem. Have each group perform its skit for the class.

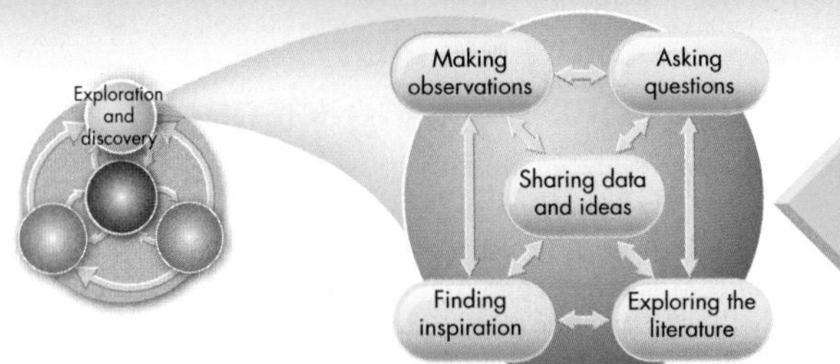

Adapted from *Understanding Science*, UC Berkeley, Museum of Paleontology

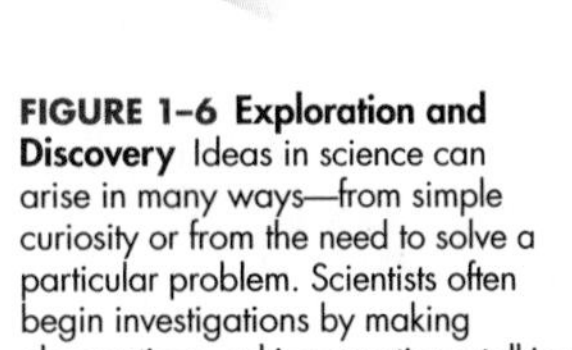

FIGURE 1–6 Exploration and Discovery Ideas in science can arise in many ways—from simple curiosity or from the need to solve a particular problem. Scientists often begin investigations by making observations, asking questions, talking with colleagues, and reading about previous experiments.

Practical Problems Sometimes, ideas for scientific investigations arise from practical problems. Salt marshes, for example, play vital roles in the lives of many ecologically and commercially important organisms, as you will learn in the next unit. Yet they are under intense pressure from industrial and housing development. Should marshes be protected from development? If new houses or farms are located near salt marshes, can they be designed to protect the marshes? These practical questions and issues inspire scientific questions, hypotheses, and experiments.

The Role of Technology Technology, science, and society are closely linked. Discoveries in one field of science may lead to new technologies. Those technologies, in turn, enable scientists in other fields to ask new questions or to gather data in new ways. For example, the development of new portable, remote data-collecting equipment enables field researchers to monitor environmental conditions around the clock, in several locations at once. This capability allows researchers to pose and test new hypotheses. Technological advances can also have big impacts on daily life. In the field of genetics and biotechnology, for instance, it is now possible to mass-produce complex substances—such as vitamins, antibiotics, and hormones—that before were only available naturally.

MYSTERY CLUE

How does the ability to produce artificial HGH impact human life?

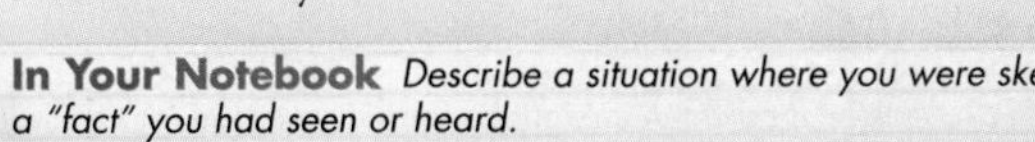

In Your Notebook *Describe a situation where you were skeptical of a "fact" you had seen or heard.*

FIGURE 1–7 Ideas From Practical Problems People living on a strip of land like this one in Murrells Inlet, South Carolina, may face flooding and other problems.
Pose Questions ***What are some scientific questions that can arise from a situation like this one?***

Teach

LESSON 1.2

Connect to Social Studies

Have students work in groups to identify a practical problem in their community, such as pollution, to which scientific investigation could be applied. Have students prepare a report describing the problem, how scientific attitudes could be used to learn more about it, and at least one way technology could be applied to solving it. Have each group share its report with the class.

DIFFERENTIATED INSTRUCTION

L3 Advanced Students Have students research actual examples of how science has been applied to a practical problem in their community or state. Have each student prepare a poster or slideshow with presentation software to share the findings.

ELL Focus on ELL: Access Content

INTERMEDIATE AND ADVANCED SPEAKERS Have students create a **Two-Column Table** as they work through the lesson. Have them write down any new concepts they learn in the first column. In the second column, have them label each concept with a "+" if they understand it fully, or a "?" if they are confused about it. At the end of the lesson, suggest students work in pairs to discuss any concepts labeled with a question mark.

Study Wkbks A/B, Appendix S31, Two-Column Table. **Transparencies,** GO16.

MYSTERY CLUE Guide students to understand that the ability to produce artificial HGH increases its availability and the number of individuals who can receive treatment. It enables people to grow taller than they would naturally. Students can go online to **Biology.com** to gather their evidence.

How Science Works

APPLYING SCIENCE TO PRACTICAL PROBLEMS

The Environmental Protection Agency (EPA) and the Food and Drug Administration (FDA) are examples of government agencies that apply science to practical problems. The EPA helps develop and enforce regulations that protect the environment. The results of scientific studies, carried out either in EPA laboratories or by other researchers, are used when regulations are developed. The FDA applies science to help maintain public health. This agency is responsible for the safety of cosmetics, medical devices, and several other categories of products. Both the EPA and FDA also provide scientifically accurate information to the public for individuals to use as they make decisions about the environment and various products.

Answers

FIGURE 1–7 Sample answer: Can vegetation be used to control flooding on the inlet?

IN YOUR NOTEBOOK Students' notebook entries should identify questionable facts they have encountered, such as unrealistic product claims.

Teach continued

Use Visuals

Have students use **Figure 1–8** to learn more about the role of communication in science.

Ask Why is the term "new ideas" found in the center of the diagram in **Figure 1–8?** *(Each of the four processes in the corners of the diagram can lead to new ideas in science.)*

Ask When a scientific paper is published, does that mean research about that topic is complete? Why or why not? *(Sample answer: Publication of a paper does not mean that research about a topic is complete; it may open doors for many new studies about the same topic.)*

DIFFERENTIATED INSTRUCTION

L1 Struggling Students Use the following sentence prompts to help students understand the information in **Figure 1–8.**

- Peer review can lead to new ideas by . . .
- Replication of results can lead to new ideas by . . .
- Discussion with colleagues can lead to new ideas by . . .
- Publication can lead to new ideas by . . .

Have students complete the sentences verbally or in written form. Discuss the completed sentences with students to be sure they understand how each process contributes to the formation of new ideas in science.

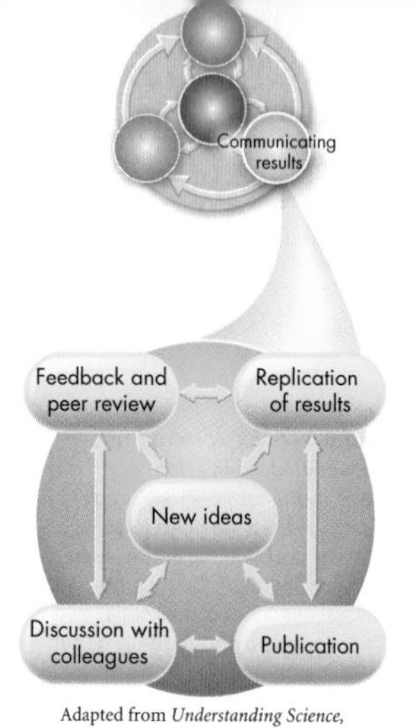
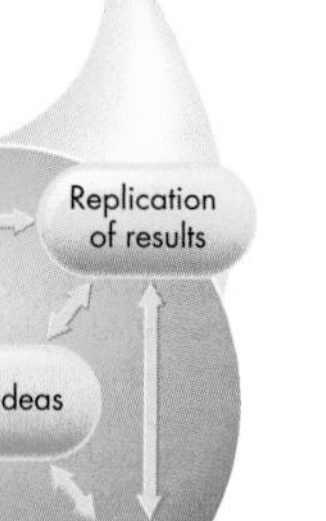

Adapted from *Understanding Science*, UC Berkeley, Museum of Paleontology

FIGURE 1–8 Communicating Results Communication is an important part of science. Scientists review and evaluate one another's work to ensure accuracy. Results from one study may lead to new ideas and further studies.

Communicating Results: Reviewing and Sharing Ideas

Why is peer review important?

Data collection and analysis can be a long process. Scientists may focus intensely on a single study for months or even years. Then, the exciting time comes when researchers communicate their experiments and observations to the scientific community. Communication and sharing of ideas are vital to modern science.

Peer Review Scientists share their findings with the scientific community by publishing articles that have undergone peer review. In peer review, scientific papers are reviewed by anonymous, independent experts. **Publishing peer-reviewed articles in scientific journals allows researchers to share ideas and to test and evaluate each other's work.** Scientific articles are like high-powered versions of your high school lab reports. They contain details about experimental conditions, controls, data, analysis, and conclusions. Reviewers read them looking for oversights, unfair influences, fraud, or mistakes in techniques or reasoning. They provide expert assessment of the work to ensure that the highest standards of quality are met. Peer review does not guarantee that a piece of work is correct, but it does certify that the work meets standards set by the scientific community.

Sharing Knowledge and New Ideas Once research has been published, it enters the dynamic marketplace of scientific ideas, as shown in **Figure 1–8.** How do new findings fit into existing scientific understanding? Perhaps they spark new questions. For example, the finding that growth of salt marsh grasses is limited by available nitrogen suggests other hypotheses: Is the growth of other plants in the same habitat also limited by nitrogen? What about the growth of different plants in similar environments, such as the mangrove swamp shown in **Figure 1–9?** Each of these logical and important questions leads to new hypotheses that must be independently confirmed by controlled experiments.

In Your Notebook *Predict what might happen if an article is published without undergoing peer review.*

FIGURE 1–9 Mangrove Swamp In tropical areas, mangrove swamps serve as the ecological equivalents of temperate salt marshes. The results of the salt marsh experiment suggest that nitrogen might be a limiting nutrient for mangroves and other plants in these similar habitats. **Design an Experiment** ***How would you test this hypothesis?***

Answers

FIGURE 1–9 Sample answer: I would set up a controlled experiment in which extra nitrogen was supplied to a group of mangrove seedlings. I would then compare the growth of these seedlings over time to the growth of mangrove seedlings grown using the same concentration of nitrogen as in the salt marsh.

IN YOUR NOTEBOOK An article published without undergoing peer review might contain oversights or mistakes in techniques or reasoning. The research could also be fraudulent or biased.

Check for Understanding

ONE-MINUTE RESPONSE

Give students about a minute to write a quick response to the following:

- Why is peer review an important part of communicating scientific results?

ADJUST INSTRUCTION

If students do not understand the importance of peer review, discuss the consequences of inaccurate or fraudulent scientific papers being published. Then, have them write a sentence that summarizes the impact this would have on the advancement of science.

Quick Lab
GUIDED INQUIRY

NoS.3

Replicating Procedures

❶ Working with a partner behind a screen, assemble ten blocks into an unusual structure. Write directions that others can use to replicate that structure without seeing it.

❷ Exchange directions with another team. Replicate the team's structure by following its directions.

❸ Compare each replicated structure to the original. Identify which parts of the directions were clear and accurate, and which were unclear or misleading.

Analyze and Conclude

1. Evaluate How could you have written better directions?

2. Infer Why is it important that scientists write procedures that can be replicated?

Scientific Theories

What is a scientific theory?

Evidence from many scientific studies may support several related hypotheses in a way that inspires researchers to propose a scientific **theory** that ties those hypotheses together. As you read this book, you will often come across terms that will be new to you because they are used only in science. But the word *theory* is used both in science and in everyday life. It is important to understand that the meaning you give the word *theory* in daily life is very different from its meaning in science. When you say, "I have a theory," you may mean, "I have a hunch." When a friend says, "That's just a theory" she may mean, "People aren't too certain about that idea." In those same situations, a scientist would probably use the word *hypothesis.* But when scientists talk about gravitational theory or evolutionary theory, they mean something very different from *hunch* or *hypothesis.*

In science, the word *theory* applies to a well-tested explanation that unifies a broad range of observations and hypotheses and that enables scientists to make accurate predictions about new situations. Charles Darwin's early observations and hypotheses about change over time in nature, for example, grew and expanded for years before he collected them into a theory of evolution by natural selection. Today, evolutionary theory is the central organizing principle of all biological and biomedical science. It makes such a wide range of predictions about organisms—from bacteria to whales to humans—that it is mentioned throughout this book.

A useful theory that has been thoroughly tested and supported by many lines of evidence may become the **dominant** view among the majority of scientists, but no theory is considered absolute truth. Science is always changing; as new evidence is uncovered, a theory may be revised or replaced by a more useful explanation.

BUILD Vocabulary

ACADEMIC WORDS A scientific **theory** describes a well-tested explanation for a range of phenomena. Scientific theories are different from scientific laws and it is important to understand that theories do not *become* laws. Laws, such as ideal gas laws in chemistry or Newton's laws of motion, are concise, specific descriptions of how some aspect of the natural world is expected to behave in a certain situation. In contrast, scientific theories, such as cell theory or the theory of evolution, are more dynamic and complex. Scientific theories encompass a greater number of ideas and hypotheses than laws, and are constantly fine-tuned through the process of science.

Lead a Discussion

Have students discuss the difference between the everyday use of the word *theory* and the scientific use of the word *theory*.

Ask How does the everyday use of the word *theory* influence how people think about scientific theories? *(Sample answer: Many people perceive scientific theories to be simply ideas or hunches, based on the everyday use of the word* theory.*)*

Ask In your own words, how would you explain to a friend that a scientific theory is more than a hunch or an idea? *(Sample answer: When the word* theory *is used in science, it refers to an idea that has been thoroughly tested and is supported by a great deal of evidence.)*

DIFFERENTIATED INSTRUCTION

LPR Less Proficient Readers Have students fill out a **Main Ideas and Details Chart** to help them organize the information about scientific theories. Write the following main ideas on the board:

- The scientific use of the word *theory* is different from its everyday use.
- In science, a theory is a well-tested explanation.
- Theories can be revised or replaced.

Have students write these main ideas on their chart. Then, ask them to add at least two details for each main idea in the chart. Call on volunteers to share some of their details with the class.

Study Wkbks A/B, Appendix S28, Main Ideas and Details Chart. **Transparencies,** GO13.

Quick Lab

PURPOSE Students will explain why the replication of scientific procedures depends on clear, detailed instructions.

MATERIALS screen, blocks

PLANNING Set up the classroom so that students can work on their structures out of sight. Possible "screens" include cardboard boxes and posterboards.

ANALYZE AND CONCLUDE

1. Answers will vary. Students should identify additional details or more precise language that would have improved the directions provided to their partners.
2. Scientists would not be able to verify findings if they could not replicate an experiment. Results of scientific studies must be replicable to be accepted. Replication would not be possible without carefully written directions.

Teach continued

Connect to the Real World

Use several of the topics relating to social issues raised in the first paragraph to start a discussion of the role science plays in personal/public health and environmental issues.

Ask How does science influence society? *(Sample answer: Scientific data helps provide answers to questions that affect everyday lives.)*

Help students understand that scientists do not work in a vacuum. Instead, their research is strongly influenced by society.

Ask How does society influence science? *(Sample answer: Society can limit the application of scientific ideas, especially if new scientific ideas conflict with prevailing cultural beliefs.)*

DIFFERENTIATED INSTRUCTION

L3 Advanced Students Have students research a historical example of how scientific advancement was impeded by the society in which a scientist lived. For example, students might research Galileo, Copernicus, Wegener, or Darwin to find out how the acceptance of ideas was influenced by prevailing social beliefs and attitudes. Ask students to discuss their research and describe how—or if—this same situation applies today.

Science and Society

What is the relationship between science and society?

Make a list of health-related things that you need to understand to protect your life and the lives of others close to you. Your list may include drugs and alcohol, smoking and lung disease, AIDS, cancer, and heart disease. Other topics focus on social issues and the environment. How much of the information in your genes should be kept private? Should communities produce electricity using fossil fuels, nuclear power, solar power, wind power, or hydroelectric dams? How should chemical wastes be disposed of?

All these questions require scientific information to answer, and many have inspired important research. But none of these questions can be answered by science alone. These questions involve the society in which we live, our economy, and our laws and moral principles. **Using science involves understanding its context in society and its limitations. Figure 1–10** shows the role science plays in society.

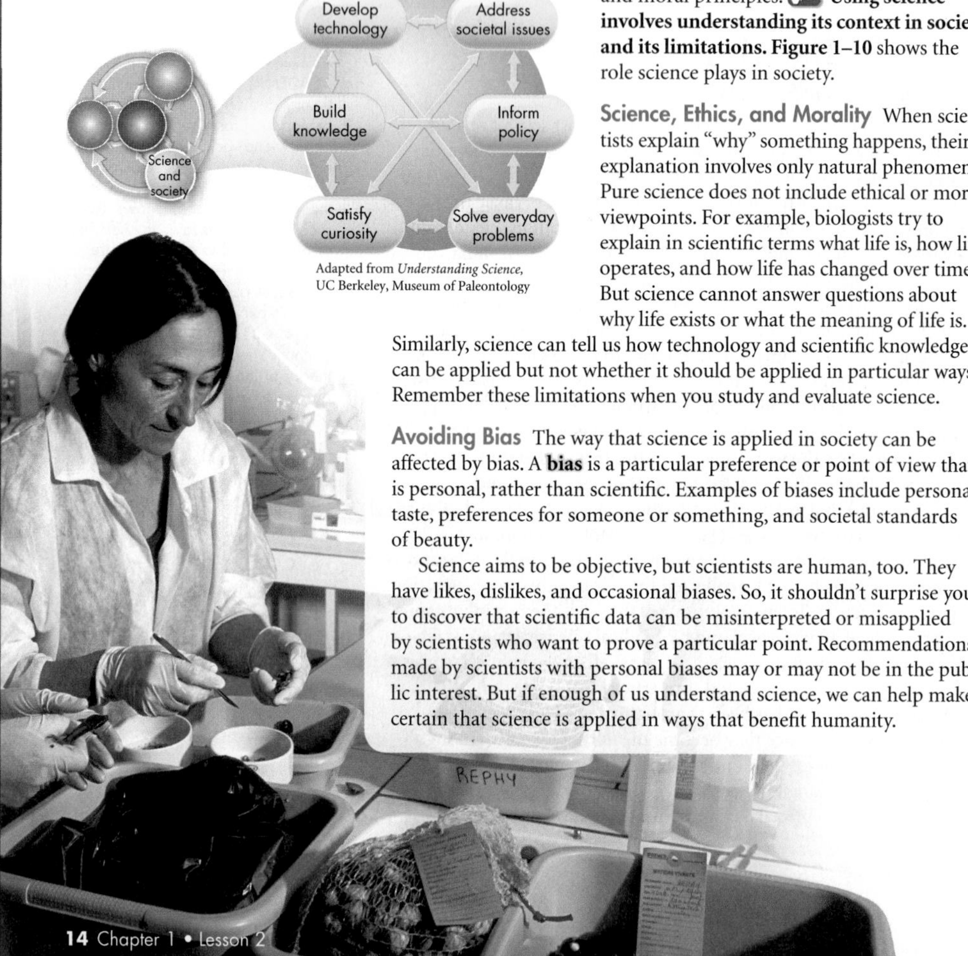

FIGURE 1–10 Science and Society Science both influences society and is influenced by society. The researcher below tests shellfish for toxins that can poison humans. **Form an Opinion** ***Should shellfish be routinely screened for toxins?***

Adapted from *Understanding Science*, UC Berkeley, Museum of Paleontology

Science, Ethics, and Morality When scientists explain "why" something happens, their explanation involves only natural phenomena. Pure science does not include ethical or moral viewpoints. For example, biologists try to explain in scientific terms what life is, how life operates, and how life has changed over time. But science cannot answer questions about why life exists or what the meaning of life is. Similarly, science can tell us how technology and scientific knowledge can be applied but not whether it should be applied in particular ways. Remember these limitations when you study and evaluate science.

Avoiding Bias The way that science is applied in society can be affected by bias. A **bias** is a particular preference or point of view that is personal, rather than scientific. Examples of biases include personal taste, preferences for someone or something, and societal standards of beauty.

Science aims to be objective, but scientists are human, too. They have likes, dislikes, and occasional biases. So, it shouldn't surprise you to discover that scientific data can be misinterpreted or misapplied by scientists who want to prove a particular point. Recommendations made by scientists with personal biases may or may not be in the public interest. But if enough of us understand science, we can help make certain that science is applied in ways that benefit humanity.

UbD Check for Understanding

ORAL QUESTIONING

Use the following prompts to gauge students' understanding of lesson concepts.

- How are science and society related?
- Give an example of an ethical or moral question that science cannot address.
- What might happen if a scientist were biased?

ADJUST INSTRUCTION

A class discussion of students' responses can be used to address concepts about which students have questions.

Answers

FIGURE 1–10 Sample answer: Yes, I think shellfish should be routinely screened for toxins because shellfish are an important source of food for many people. Without routine screening to check for toxins, many people could get sick or even die.

Understanding and Using Science Science will keep changing as long as humans keep wondering about nature. We invite you to join us in that wonder and exploration as you read this book. Think of this text, not as an encyclopedia, but as a "user's guide" to the study of life. Don't just memorize today's scientific facts and ideas. And please don't *believe* them! Instead, try to *understand* how scientists developed those ideas. Try to see the thinking behind experiments we describe. Try to pose the kinds of questions scientists ask.

If you learn to think as scientists think, you will understand the process of science and be comfortable in a world that will keep changing throughout your life. Understanding science will help you make complex decisions that also involve cultural customs, values, and ethical standards.

Furthermore, understanding biology will help you realize that we humans can predict the consequences of our actions and take an active role in directing our future and that of our planet. In our society, scientists make recommendations about big public policy decisions, but they don't make the decisions. Who makes the decisions? Citizens of our democracy do. In a few years, you will be able to exercise the rights of a voting citizen, influencing public policy by the ballots you cast and the messages you send public officials. That's why it is important that you understand how science works and appreciate both the power and the limitations of science.

FIGURE 1–11 Using Science in Everyday Life These student volunteers are planting mangrove saplings as part of a mangrove restoration project.

1.2 Assessment

IN NoS.4, NoS.8, NoS.11

Review Key Concepts 

1. a. Review List the attitudes that lead scientists to explore and discover.
   b. Explain What does it mean to describe a scientist as skeptical? Why is skepticism an important quality in a scientist?
2. a. Review What is peer review?
   b. Apply Concepts An advertisement claims that studies of a new sports drink show it boosts energy. You discover that none of the study results have been peer-reviewed. What would you tell consumers who are considering buying this product?
3. a. Review What is a scientific theory?
   b. Compare and Contrast How does use of the word *theory* differ in science and in daily life?
4. a. Review How is the use of science related to its context in society?
   b. Explain Describe some of the limitations of science.
   c. Apply Concepts A study shows that a new pesticide is safe for use on food crops. The researcher who conducted the study works for the pesticide company. What potential biases may have affected the study?

Apply the Big idea

Science as a Way of Knowing

5. Explain in your own words why science is considered a "way of knowing."

BIOLOGY.com Search Lesson 1.2 GO • Self-Test • Lesson Assessment

Lead a Discussion

Discuss why science is important for all individuals. Ask students why it is important to understand how scientific ideas are developed. *(Sample answer: It helps you assess the validity of the ideas.)* Discuss why knowing the limitations of science is also important. *(Sample answer: It is important to know what questions science cannot answer.)*

DIFFERENTIATED INSTRUCTION

L1 Special Needs Have students make a collage entitled How People Use Science. Help them find pictures that show how science impacts their own life.

Assess and Remediate

EVALUATE UNDERSTANDING

Have each student choose a main topic from the lesson and prepare a brief summary of it. Call on students to share their summaries with the class. Then, have them complete the 1.2 Assessment.

REMEDIATION SUGGESTION

L1 Struggling Students If students are struggling with **Question 1b,** have them review their answer to the In Your Notebook question on page 11.

BIOLOGY.com Students can check their understanding of lesson concepts with the **Self-Test** assessment. They can then take an online version of the **Lesson Assessment.**

Assessment Answers

1a. curiosity, skepticism, open-mindedness, creativity

1b. He or she questions existing ideas and hypotheses. Skepticism is important because scientists should refuse to accept explanations without evidence.

2a. the process by which scientific papers are reviewed by anonymous, independent experts

2b. There is no guarantee that the studies meet scientific standards.

3a. a well-tested explanation that unifies observations and hypotheses and enables scientists to make accurate predictions

3b. In science, *theory* means a well-tested explanation. In everyday usage, *theory* means an idea or a hunch.

4a. Sample answer: Science must take societal issues into account. Many questions cannot be answered by science alone and need input from society.

4b. Sample answer: Science does not include ethical or moral viewpoints. It may also be influenced by bias.

4c. Sample answer: The scientist might be biased by ties to the pesticide company.

5. Big idea Science is considered a way of knowing because it is not just a list of facts. It is a way of applying scientific methodology and attitudes to observations of the world.

Teach

Lead a Discussion

After students have read the feature, discuss their opinions about the funding of product safety studies.

Ask What is an advantage of having independent organizations fund product safety studies? *(Sample answer: Independent organizations are less likely to be biased about a product's safety.)*

Ask What is an advantage of having private industry fund product safety studies? *(Sample answer: Companies would do a better job testing their products than an independent agency, because their company's reputation is at stake.)*

Ask How does knowledge of scientific attitudes and methodology affect the way you evaluate product safety information? *(Sample answer: Scientific attitudes, especially open-mindedness and skepticism, are vital when evaluating information about product safety. Knowledge of scientific methodology allows me to evaluate the studies performed on products.)*

Biology & Society

Who Should Fund Product Safety Studies?

Biology plays a major role in the research, development, and production of food, medicine, and other consumer items. Companies that make these items profit by selling reliable and useful products in the marketplace. For example, the plastics industry provides countless products for everyday use.

But sometimes questions arise concerning product safety. Bisphenol-A (BPA), for instance, is a chemical found in hard plastics. Those plastics are used to make baby bottles, reusable water bottles, and the linings of many food and soft drink cans. Is BPA safe? This type of question can be posed as a scientific hypothesis to be tested. But who does the testing? Who funds the studies and analyzes the results?

Ideally, independent scientists test products for safety and usefulness. That way, the people who gather and analyze data can remain objective—they have nothing to gain by exaggerating the positive effects of products and nothing to lose by stating any risks. However, scientists are often hired by private companies to develop or test their products.

Often, test results are clear: A product is safe or it isn't. Based on these results, the Food and Drug Administration (FDA) or another government agency makes recommendations to protect and promote public health. Sometimes, though, results are tough to interpret.

More than 100 studies have been done on BPA—some funded by the government, some funded by the plastics industry. Most of the independent studies found that low doses of BPA could have negative health effects on laboratory animals. A few studies, mostly funded by the plastics industry, concluded that BPA is safe. In this case, the FDA ultimately declared BPA to be safe. When the issue of BPA safety hit the mass media, government investigations began. So, who should sponsor product safety studies?

The Viewpoints

Independent Organizations Should Fund Safety Studies

Scientists performing safety studies should have no affiliation with private industries, because conflict of interest seems unavoidable. A company, such as a BPA manufacturer, would naturally benefit if its product is declared to be safe. Rather, safety tests should be funded by independent organizations such as universities and government agencies, which should be as independent as possible. This way, recommendations for public health can remain free of biases.

Private Industries Should Fund Safety Studies

There are an awful lot of products out there! Who would pay scientists to test all those products? There are simply too many potentially useful and valuable products being developed by private industry for the government to keep track of and test adequately with public funds. It is in a company's best interest to produce safe products, so it would be inclined to maintain high standards and perform rigorous tests.

Research and Decide

1. Analyze the Viewpoints To make an informed decision, research the current status of the controversy over BPA by using the Internet and other resources. Compare this situation with the history of safety studies on cigarette smoke and the chemical Teflon.

2. Form an Opinion Should private industries be able to pay scientists to perform their product safety studies? How would you deal with the issue of potential bias in interpreting results?

Answers

RESEARCH AND DECIDE

1. Answers will vary. Students' responses should indicate that they have used reliable resources to learn about and compare studies related to BPA, cigarette smoke, and Teflon.
2. Answers will vary. Students' responses should offer well-reasoned support for their opinion and a specific plan for dealing with bias when interpreting results.

Quick Facts

WHAT IS THE U.S. CONSUMER PRODUCT SAFETY COMMISSION?

The U.S. Consumer Product Safety Commission is an agency of the U.S. government that deals with the safety of many products that people use every day. It is an independent agency within the government. Its responsibilities include helping develop voluntary standards that can be followed by manufacturers, collecting information about injuries and other harm caused by consumer products, researching potentially hazardous products, and issuing recalls for products that are hazardous. Individuals who have been harmed by a consumer product can contact the U.S. Consumer Product Safety Commission to report the incident. The agency's Web site offers updated information about product recalls and safety issues.

1.3 Studying Life

NoS.5 Standard laboratory techniques; NoS.8 Scientific knowledge is organized into scientific theories. Also covered: NoS.3, B.3.3, B.5.2, B.6.2, B.6.3.

THINK ABOUT IT Think about important and exciting news stories you've seen or heard. Bird flu spreads around the world, killing thousands of birds and threatening a human epidemic. Users of certain illegal drugs experience permanent damage to their brains and other parts of their nervous systems. Reports surface about efforts to clone human cells to grow new organs to replace those lost to disease or injury. These and many other stories involve biology—the science that employs scientific methodology to study living things. (The Greek word *bios* means "life," and *-logy* means "study of.")

Key Questions

What characteristics do all living things share?

What are the central themes of biology?

How do different fields of biology differ in their approach to studying life?

How is the metric system important in science?

Vocabulary

biology • DNA • stimulus • sexual reproduction • asexual reproduction • homeostasis • metabolism • biosphere

Taking Notes

Concept Map As you read, draw a concept map showing the big ideas in biology.

Characteristics of Living Things

What characteristics do all living things share?

Biology is the study of life. But what is life? What distinguishes living things from nonliving matter? Surprisingly, it isn't as simple as you might think to describe what makes something alive. No single characteristic is enough to describe a living thing. Also, some nonliving things share one or more traits with organisms. For example, a firefly and fire both give off light, and each moves in its own way. Mechanical toys, automobiles, and clouds (which are not alive) move around, while mushrooms and trees (which are alive) stay in one spot. To make matters more complicated, some things, such as viruses, exist at the border between organisms and nonliving things.

Despite these difficulties, we can list characteristics that most living things have in common. **Living things are made up of basic units called cells, are based on a universal genetic code, obtain and use materials and energy, grow and develop, reproduce, respond to their environment, maintain a stable internal environment, and change over time.**

FIGURE 1–12 Is It Alive? The fish are clearly alive, but what about the colorful structure above them? Is it alive? As a matter of fact, it is. The antlerlike structure is actually a marine animal called elkhorn coral. Corals show all the characteristics common to living things.

BIOLOGY.com Search Lesson 1.3 GO • Lesson Overview • Lesson Notes

Getting Started

Objectives

1.3.1 List the characteristics of living things.

1.3.2 Identify the central themes of biology.

1.3.3 Explain how life can be studied at different levels.

1.3.4 Discuss the importance of a universal system of measurement.

Student Resources

Study Workbooks A and B, 1.3 Worksheets

Spanish Study Workbook, 1.3 Worksheets

Lab Manual B, 1.3 Data Analysis Worksheet

BIOLOGY.com Lesson Overview • Lesson Notes • Activities: Data Analysis • Assessment: Self-Test, Lesson Assessment

For corresponding lesson in the **Foundation Edition**, see pages 13–19.

Activate Prior Knowledge

Ask students to identify ways in which all living things are alike. Make a list of their responses on the board. Then, as students read the lesson, have them revise or add to the list.

UbD Teach for Understanding

ENDURING UNDERSTANDING The process of science helps biologists investigate how nature works at all levels, from the molecules in cells to the biosphere.

GUIDING QUESTION What is biology?

EVIDENCE OF UNDERSTANDING *After completing the lesson, give students the following assessment to show their understanding of the study of life.* Have students work with a partner to identify a problem or question related to life science. Then, ask students to compare and contrast how scientists from two different fields of biology would approach this problem. Have each pair write a paragraph summarizing their discussion.

IN INDIANA ACADEMIC STANDARDS

For the full text of all standards, see the Course Overview in the front matter of this book.

NoS.5 Apply standard techniques in laboratory investigations to measure physical quantities in appropriate units and convert known quantities to other units as necessary.

NoS.8 Explain that the body of scientific knowledge is organized into major theories, which are derived from and supported by the results of many experiments, and allow us to make testable predictions.

LESSON 1.3

Teach

VISUAL SUMMARY

Have small groups examine **Figure 1–13** and discuss characteristics of living things. After students have discussed the information in the figure, have them examine two objects: a clock with a working second hand; and an active, live animal such as a fish or an insect. Ask students to compare and contrast the two objects, noting similarities and differences. Then, have each group summarize why one object is living and the other is nonliving.

DIFFERENTIATED INSTRUCTION

L1 Struggling Students Have students use a **Cluster Diagram** to help them organize ideas about the characteristics of living things. In the middle circle of the diagram, have them write the term *Living Things*. Then, have them add information about each of the characteristics shown in **Figure 1–13** to their diagram. Suggest that students use their completed cluster diagram to help them when they complete the activity described above.

Study Wkbks A/B, Appendix S19, Cluster Diagram. **Transparencies,** GO2.

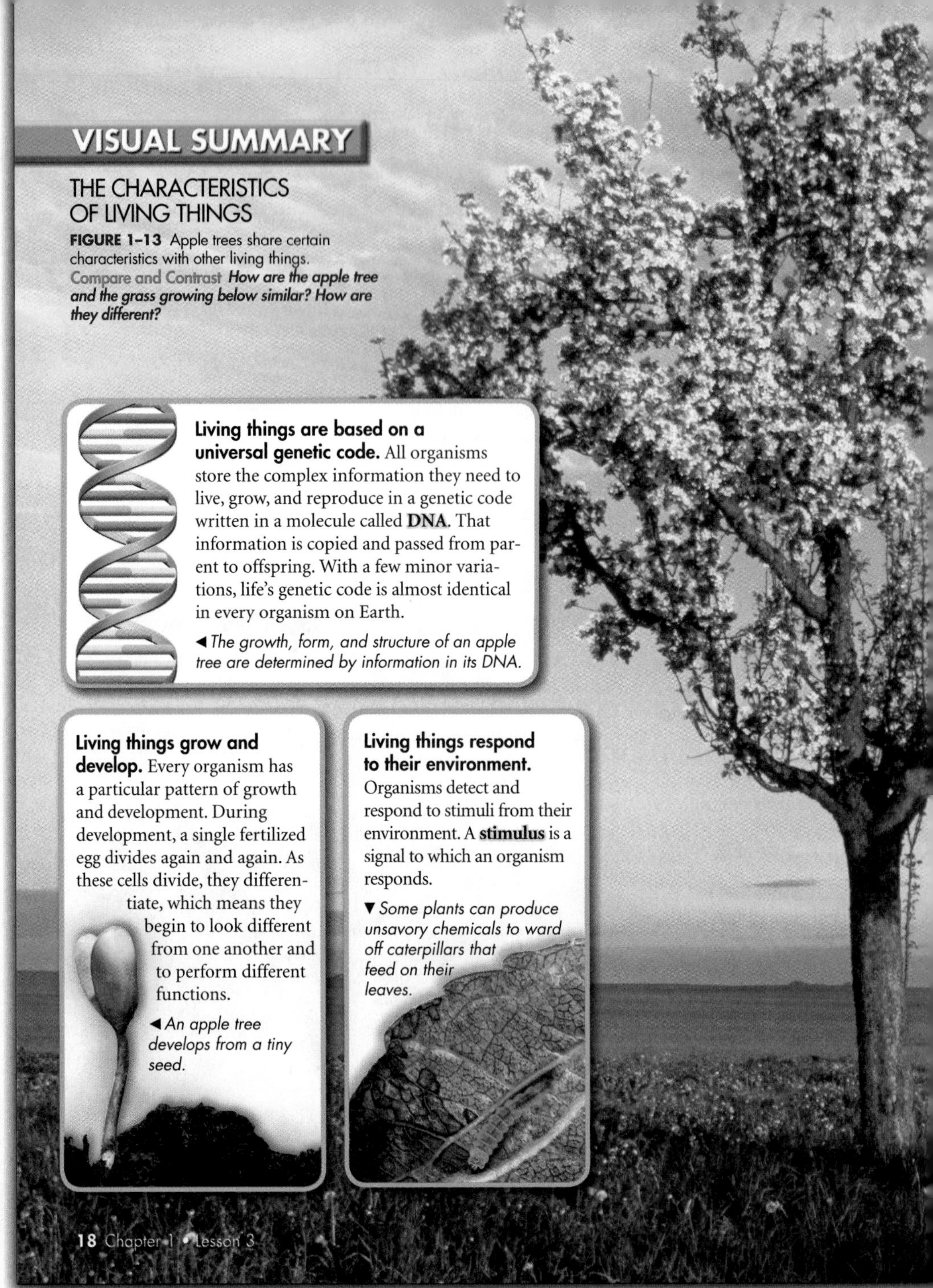

VISUAL SUMMARY

THE CHARACTERISTICS OF LIVING THINGS

FIGURE 1–13 Apple trees share certain characteristics with other living things. Compare and Contrast *How are the apple tree and the grass growing below similar? How are they different?*

Living things are based on a universal genetic code. All organisms store the complex information they need to live, grow, and reproduce in a genetic code written in a molecule called **DNA**. That information is copied and passed from parent to offspring. With a few minor variations, life's genetic code is almost identical in every organism on Earth.

◀ *The growth, form, and structure of an apple tree are determined by information in its DNA.*

Living things grow and develop. Every organism has a particular pattern of growth and development. During development, a single fertilized egg divides again and again. As these cells divide, they differentiate, which means they begin to look different from one another and to perform different functions.

◀ *An apple tree develops from a tiny seed.*

Living things respond to their environment. Organisms detect and respond to stimuli from their environment. A **stimulus** is a signal to which an organism responds.

▼ *Some plants can produce unsavory chemicals to ward off caterpillars that feed on their leaves.*

Answers

FIGURE 1–13 Sample answer: The apple tree and the grass are similar in that both contain DNA, are made of cells, reproduce, grow and develop, use materials and energy, respond to their environment, and maintain a stable environment; they differ in that an apple tree contains many more cells than an individual grass plant.

How Science Works

A CONSTANT "INTERNAL MILIEU"

In 1851, French physiologist Claude Bernard discovered that nerves in an animal's body control the dilation and constriction of blood vessels. He observed that on hot days the blood vessels of the skin become dilated, whereas on cold days those same blood vessels become constricted. Bernard explained that these changes functioned to regulate body temperature. He concluded that, even when the external environment changes, an animal has a way of maintaining a constant "internal milieu." His concept of the maintenance of an internal balance within an organism is incorporated in the modern concept of homeostasis, which literally means "same condition."

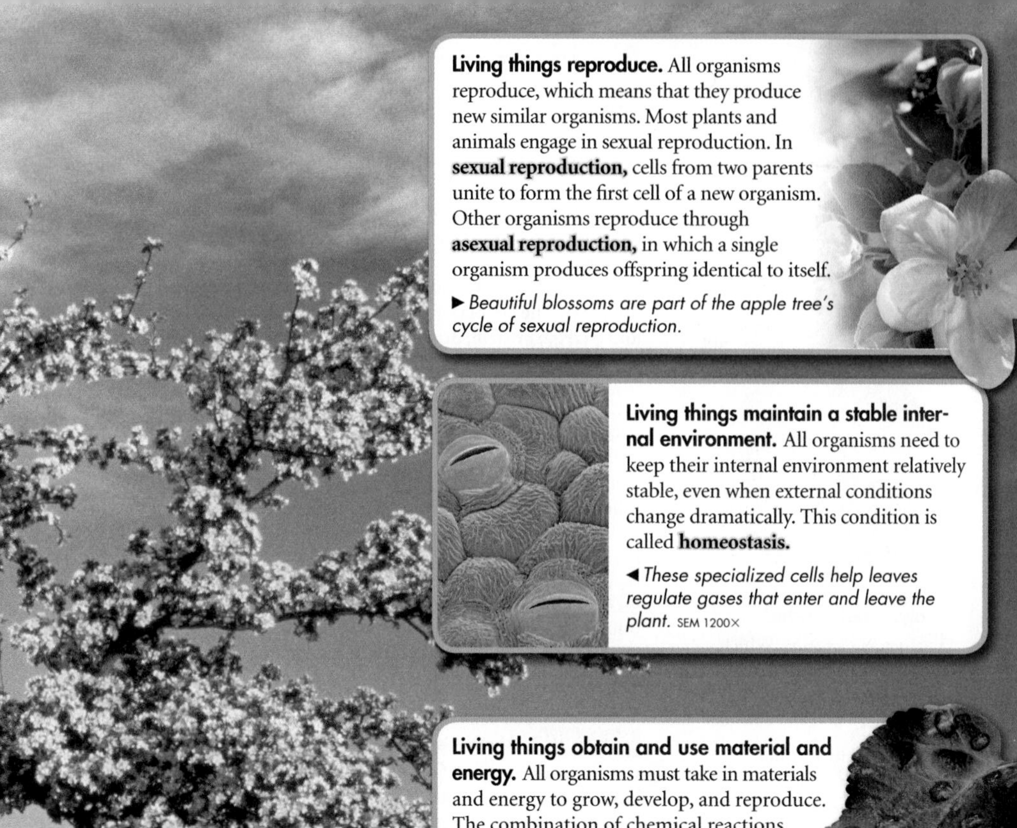

Living things reproduce. All organisms reproduce, which means that they produce new similar organisms. Most plants and animals engage in sexual reproduction. In **sexual reproduction,** cells from two parents unite to form the first cell of a new organism. Other organisms reproduce through **asexual reproduction,** in which a single organism produces offspring identical to itself.

▶ *Beautiful blossoms are part of the apple tree's cycle of sexual reproduction.*

Living things maintain a stable internal environment. All organisms need to keep their internal environment relatively stable, even when external conditions change dramatically. This condition is called **homeostasis.**

◀ *These specialized cells help leaves regulate gases that enter and leave the plant.* SEM 1200×

Living things obtain and use material and energy. All organisms must take in materials and energy to grow, develop, and reproduce. The combination of chemical reactions through which an organism builds up or breaks down materials is called **metabolism.**

▶ *Various metabolic reactions occur in leaves.*

Living things are made up of cells. Organisms are composed of one or more cells—the smallest units considered fully alive. Cells can grow, respond to their surroundings, and reproduce. Despite their small size, cells are complex and highly organized.

▲ *A single branch of an apple tree contains millions of cells.* LM 800×

Taken as a group, living things evolve. Over generations, groups of organisms evolve, or change over time. Evolutionary change links all forms of life to a common origin more than 3.5 billion years ago. Evidence of this shared history is found in all aspects of living and fossil organisms, from physical features to structures of proteins to sequences of information in DNA.

▶ *Signs of one of the first land plants, Cooksonia, are preserved in rock over 400 million years old.*

Expand Vocabulary

Point out that the paragraphs describing the characteristics of living things in **Figure 1–13** contain the majority of this lesson's vocabulary terms. Have students work with a partner to make a flash card for each vocabulary term found on these two pages. Then, have students use the flash cards to review the definitions of the terms with their partner.

DIFFERENTIATED INSTRUCTION

ELL **English Language Learners** Pair students learning English with native English speakers for the activity described above. Encourage these pairs to focus on proper pronunciation of the terms in addition to their definitions. Circulate among pairs, and ask English language learners to share words and definitions with you.

L3 **Advanced Students** Those students who can easily learn the definitions of the vocabulary terms on these pages should be encouraged to use the index of this book to find out what chapters will further explore each of the vocabulary terms. For example, if a student looks up the term *DNA* in the index, he or she will note that DNA will be further discussed in chapters relating to the chemistry of life, genetics, biotechnology, and classification. Ask students to anticipate some of the topics related to each vocabulary term that they will learn about as they read the book.

ELL Focus on ELL: Build Background

ALL SPEAKERS Have students use the information in **Figure 1–13** to develop a class bulletin board on the characteristics of living things. Suggest that beginning and intermediate speakers draw or find visuals that represent each of the eight characteristics. Have these students work with advanced and advanced high speakers to write captions for each visual. The caption should explain how the visual showcases a particular characteristic of life. Ask advanced high students to write short summaries of each characteristic to help organize the bulletin board.

UbD Check for Understanding

USE VOCABULARY

Have students make a crossword puzzle that includes each of the lesson vocabulary terms included in **Figure 1–13.** The clues for each term should be scientifically accurate and based on the definitions given in the text.

ADJUST INSTRUCTION

Collect the crossword puzzles and redistribute them at random. Ask students to complete the crossword puzzle they have been given. Then, have students return the crossword puzzle to the student who made it and talk about any clues they had difficulty matching a term with.

Teach continued

Build Study Skills

Explain that the ten Big Ideas, or central themes, in the study of biology are the overarching ideas found throughout this book. Point out to students that an understanding of these Big Ideas will allow them to relate the specific information in each chapter to a larger, more general concept. Divide the class into ten groups, and assign each group one of the Big Ideas. Have groups prepare a short, creative, memorable presentation to share the information with the rest of the class. Each presentation should include a reference to one or more of the later chapters in the book that are related to the group's Big Idea. Point out that each chapter's Big Idea is listed on the first page of the chapter. Have groups make their presentations to the class.

DIFFERENTIATED INSTRUCTION

LPR Less Proficient Readers Students who struggle to read the text associated with each Big Idea should be encouraged to work in pairs to understand the description of each Big Idea. Suggest that pairs work through the Big Ideas one by one, taking the time to discuss each one before moving on to the next.

What's in a Diet?

The circle graph shows the diet of the siamang gibbon, a type of ape found in the rainforests of Southeast Asia.

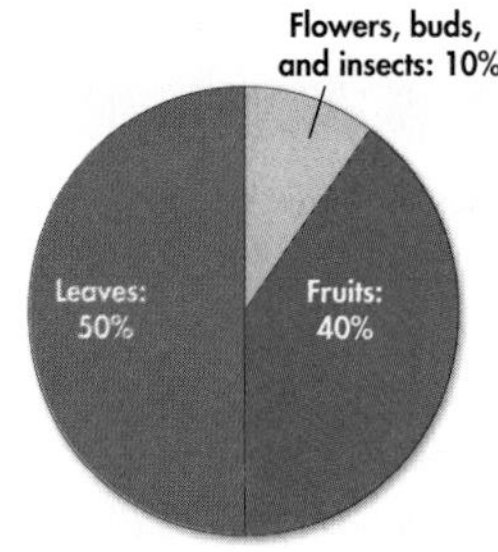

Analyze and Conclude

1. Interpret Graphs Which plant parts do siamangs rely on most as a source of their matter and energy?

2. Predict How would siamangs be affected if the rainforests they live in were cut down?

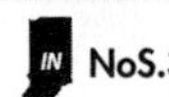
NoS.3

Big Ideas in Biology

What are the central themes of biology?

The units of this book seem to cover different subjects. But we'll let you in on a secret: That's not how biology works. All biological sciences are tied together by themes and methods of study that cut across disciplines. These "big ideas" overlap and interlock, and crop up again and again throughout the book. You'll also notice that several of these big ideas overlap with the characteristics of life or the nature of science.

The study of biology revolves around several interlocking big ideas: The cellular basis of life; information and heredity; matter and energy; growth, development, and reproduction; homeostasis; evolution; structure and function; unity and diversity of life; interdependence in nature; and science as a way of knowing.

Big idea Cellular Basis of Life Living things are made of cells. Many living things consist of only a single cell; they are called unicellular organisms. Plants and animals are multicellular. Cells in multicellular organisms display many different sizes, shapes, and functions. The human body contains 200 or more different cell types.

Big idea Information and Heredity Living things are based on a universal genetic code. The information coded in DNA forms an unbroken chain that stretches back roughly 3.5 billion years. Yet, the DNA inside your cells right now can influence your future—your risk of getting cancer, the amount of cholesterol in your blood, and the color of your children's hair.

Big idea Matter and Energy Living things obtain and use material and energy. Life requires matter that serves as nutrients to build body structures, and energy that fuels life's processes. Some organisms, such as plants, obtain energy from sunlight and take up nutrients from air, water, and soil. Other organisms, including most animals, eat plants or other animals to obtain both nutrients and energy. The need for matter and energy link all living things on Earth in a web of interdependent relationships.

Big idea Growth, Development, and Reproduction All living things reproduce. Newly produced individuals are virtually always smaller than adults, so they grow and develop as they mature. During growth and development, generalized cells typically become more and more different and specialized for particular functions. Specialized cells build tissues, such as brains, muscles, and digestive organs, that serve various functions.

Big idea Homeostasis Living things maintain a relatively stable internal environment, a process known as homeostasis. For most organisms, any breakdown of homeostasis may have serious or even fatal consequences.

In Your Notebook *Describe what happens at the cellular level as a baby grows and develops.*

PURPOSE Students interpret a graph to learn about the diet of the siamang gibbon.

PLANNING Explain to students that a circle graph shows the relative proportions of the parts that make up a whole, in this case, the entire diet of the siamang gibbon.

ANSWERS

1. leaves

2. Sample answer: Siamang gibbons are dependent on the trees in the rainforest, because most of their diet is made up of plant material. Therefore, these animals would not be able to get the food they need if the rainforest were cut down.

Answers

IN YOUR NOTEBOOK Sample answer: As a baby grows and develops, generalized cells become more different and specialized for particular functions.

Big idea **Evolution** Taken as a group, living things evolve. Evolutionary change links all forms of life to a common origin more than 3.5 billion years ago. Evidence of this shared history is found in all aspects of living and fossil organisms, from physical features to structures of proteins to sequences of information in DNA. Evolutionary theory is the central organizing principle of all biological and biomedical sciences.

MYSTERY
CLUE
What human values or biases are involved in the case of giving HGH to healthy children? What role does science play in this case?

Big idea **Structure and Function** Each major group of organisms has evolved its own particular body part "tool kit,"—a collection of structures that have evolved in ways that make particular functions possible. From capturing food to digesting it, and from reproducing to breathing, organisms use structures that have evolved into different forms as species have adapted to life in different environments. The structures of wings, for example, enable birds and insects to fly. The structures of legs enable horses to gallop and kangaroos to hop.

Big idea **Unity and Diversity of Life** Although life takes an almost unbelievable variety of forms, all living things are fundamentally similar at the molecular level. All organisms are composed of a common set of carbon-based molecules, store information in a common genetic code, and use proteins to build their structures and carry out their functions. One great contribution of evolutionary theory is that it explains both this unity of life and its diversity.

Big idea **Interdependence in Nature** All forms of life on Earth are connected into a **biosphere,** which literally means "living planet." Within the biosphere, organisms are linked to one another and to the land, water, and air around them. Relationships between organisms and their environments depend on the cycling of matter and the flow of energy. Human life and the economies of human societies also require matter and energy, so human life depends directly on nature.

Big idea **Science as a Way of Knowing** Science is not a list of facts, but "a way of knowing." The job of science is to use observations, questions, and experiments to explain the natural world in terms of natural forces and events. Successful scientific research reveals rules and patterns that can explain and predict at least some events in nature. Science enables us to take actions that affect events in the world around us. To make certain that scientific knowledge is used for the benefit of society, all of us must understand the nature of science—its strengths, its limitations, and its interactions with our culture.

FIGURE 1–14 Different But Similar The colorful keel-billed toucan is clearly different from the plant on which it perches. Yet, the two organisms are fundamentally similar at the molecular level. Unity and diversity of life is an important theme in biology.

UbD Check for Understanding

INDEX CARD SUMMARIES/QUESTIONS

Give each student an index card. Ask them to identify and describe one of the Big Ideas in biology that they understand on the front of the card. Then, have them identify one Big Idea they do not understand and write it on the back of the card in the form of a question.

ADJUST INSTRUCTION

Note the Big Ideas that are causing confusion for most students. Select those Big Ideas as the topic of a review discussion in which a volunteer reads aloud information about the Big Idea and students are encouraged to ask questions they have about that Big Idea.

Build Reading Skills

Suggest students use an outline to organize the information in **Big Ideas in Biology.** Model this for students by writing Cellular Basis of Life on the board. Under this, write the most important details from the paragraph in the text, such as "Living things are made of cells," and "Some organisms consist of a single cell; others are made up of many cells." Have students outline the remaining nine big ideas using the same format.

DIFFERENTIATED INSTRUCTION

L1 Struggling Students Provide students with a prepared outline that includes the ten Big Ideas with several blank write-on lines below each one. Tell them to write important details about each Big Idea on the lines. Encourage students to rephrase information in their own words rather than copying information directly from the text.

L3 Advanced Students After students have completed their outlines, suggest they consider a topic of personal interest in biology, for example, biotechnology or insects. Then, have them write a paragraph identifying how at least two of the Big Ideas are related to their topic of interest. Have students share their paragraphs with the class.

MYSTERY CLUE Talk about how values and biases are part of the decision to give healthy children HGH. Students' responses should reflect an understanding of the term *bias*. When talking about the role of science in this decision, guide students to understand that, while the role of pure science is to determine what can be done, considering what *should* be done is an important step. Students can go online to **Biology.com** to gather their evidence.

Teach continued

Connect to the Real World

Use the information on these two pages to encourage students' exploration of careers in biology or science in general. Challenge them to think beyond the stereotype of scientists in white coats working in a laboratory setting. Invite a school guidance counselor to speak to the class about careers in science. Encourage students to prepare questions for the guidance counselor about science careers and the required educational preparation for those careers.

DIFFERENTIATED INSTRUCTION

L1 Special Needs Help special needs students learn about biology careers in various fields, including ecology, plant biology, paleontology, wildlife biology, and molecular biology. Make a matching activity in which students match these careers with their descriptions. Write the name of each career on a separate index card. Then, write a description of each career on another set of index cards. Have students match the careers and their descriptions. Finally, ask them to brainstorm a list of other careers in science.

ELL English Language Learners Suggest students read the information on the different fields of biology one by one. Discuss each field with them before moving on to the next. Ask them what aspects of these fields they are most curious about. Then, have them generate one or two written questions they would like to ask a guidance counselor about careers in these fields. Encourage students to practice asking their questions aloud before the guidance counselor's visit.

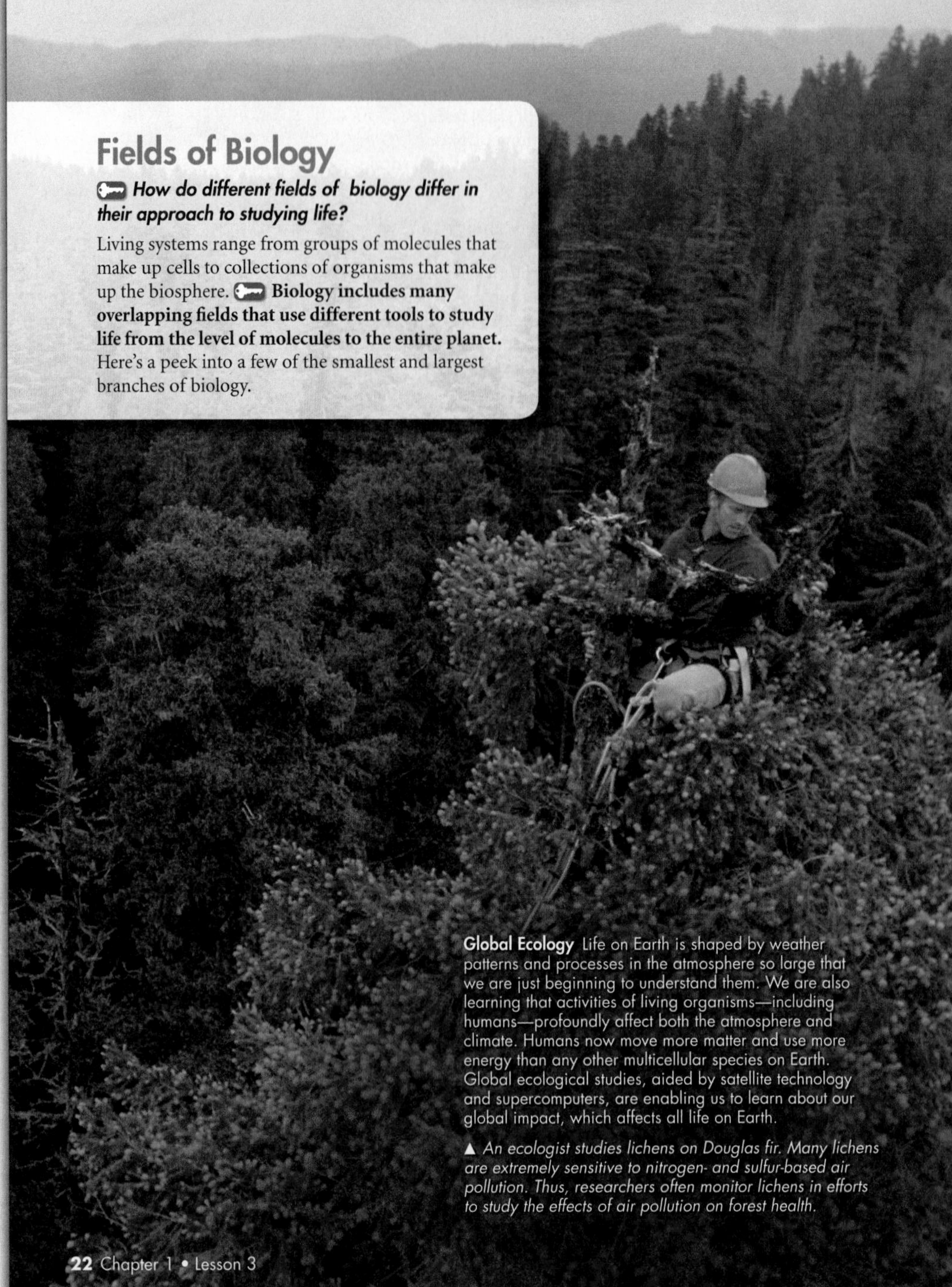

Fields of Biology

How do different fields of biology differ in their approach to studying life?

Living systems range from groups of molecules that make up cells to collections of organisms that make up the biosphere. **Biology includes many overlapping fields that use different tools to study life from the level of molecules to the entire planet.** Here's a peek into a few of the smallest and largest branches of biology.

Global Ecology Life on Earth is shaped by weather patterns and processes in the atmosphere so large that we are just beginning to understand them. We are also learning that activities of living organisms—including humans—profoundly affect both the atmosphere and climate. Humans now move more matter and use more energy than any other multicellular species on Earth. Global ecological studies, aided by satellite technology and supercomputers, are enabling us to learn about our global impact, which affects all life on Earth.

▲ *An ecologist studies lichens on Douglas fir. Many lichens are extremely sensitive to nitrogen- and sulfur-based air pollution. Thus, researchers often monitor lichens in efforts to study the effects of air pollution on forest health.*

Quick Facts

BRANCHES OF BIOLOGY

The branches of biology are numerous. Zoologists, botanists, paleontologists, and ethologists are just a few of the great variety of biologists. Other biologists include biochemists, geneticists, cytologists, ecologists, and microbiologists. Biochemists study the chemistry of living things. Geneticists study heredity and variation among organisms. Cytologists, or cell biologists, study the structure and function of cells. Ecologists study the interactions of organisms in ecosystems. Microbiologists study the structure and function of microorganisms. The list goes on, and those mentioned are just the biologists who pursue knowledge in what is sometimes called theoretical science. There are also many biologists who work in applied or practical science, including physicians, medical researchers, wildlife managers, foresters, and agricultural researchers, to name just a few.

Biotechnology This field, created by the molecular revolution, is based on our ability to "edit" and rewrite the genetic code—in a sense, redesigning the living world to order. We may soon learn to correct or replace damaged genes that cause inherited diseases. Other research seeks to genetically engineer bacteria to clean up toxic wastes. Biotechnology also raises enormous ethical, legal, and social questions. Dare we tamper with the fundamental biological information that makes us human?

► *A plant biologist analyzes genetically modified rice plants.*

Building the Tree of Life Biologists have discovered and identified roughly 1.8 million different kinds of living organisms. That may seem like an incredible number, but researchers estimate that somewhere between 2 and 100 million more forms of life are waiting to be discovered around the globe—from caves deep beneath the surface, to tropical rainforests, to coral reefs and the depths of the sea. Identifying and cataloguing all these life forms is enough work by itself, but biologists aim to do much more. They want to combine the latest genetic information with computer technology to organize all living things into a single universal "Tree of All Life"—and put the results on the Web in a form that anyone can access.

► *A paleontologist studies signs of ancient life—fossilized dinosaur dung!*

Ecology and Evolution of Infectious Diseases HIV, bird flu, and drug-resistant bacteria seem to have appeared out of nowhere, but the science behind their stories shows that relationships between hosts and pathogens are dynamic and constantly changing. Organisms that cause human disease have their own ecology, which involves our bodies, medicines we take, and our interactions with each other and the environment. Over time, disease-causing organisms engage in an "evolutionary arms race" with humans that creates constant challenges to public health around the world. Understanding these interactions is crucial to safeguarding our future.

► *A wildlife biologist studies a group of wild gelada baboons. Pathogens in wild animal populations may evolve in ways that enable them to infect humans.*

Genomics and Molecular Biology These fields focus on studies of DNA and other molecules inside cells. The "molecular revolution" of the 1980s created the field of genomics, which is now looking at the entire sets of DNA code contained in a wide range of organisms. Ever-more-powerful computer analyses enable researchers to compare vast databases of genetic information in a fascinating search for keys to the mysteries of growth, development, aging, cancer, and the history of life on Earth.

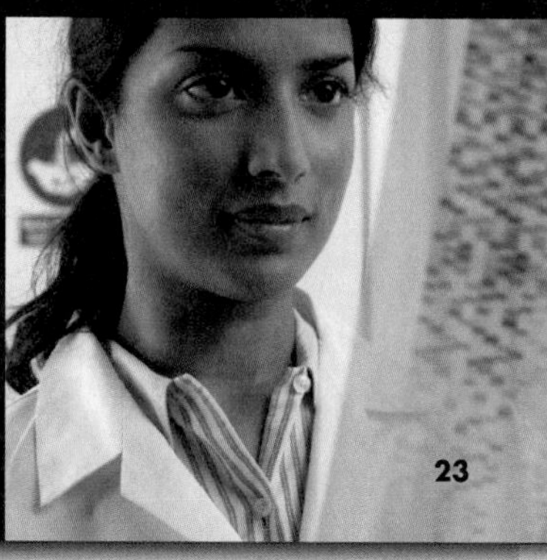

► *A molecular biologist analyzes a DNA sequence.*

23

LESSON 1.3

Lead a Discussion

Point out that some fields of biology described on these pages, such as genomics and molecular biology, did not exist until relatively recently. The development of new technology was instrumental in their creation. Other fields of biology described here, such as paleontology, have existed for many years, although they have been changed dramatically by new technology, as well.

Ask What are some ways that scientists in the fields of biology described on these pages use technology? *(Sample answers: Molecular biologists use computers to analyze DNA sequences. Global ecologists use satellites to gather data.)*

Then, have students consider how the fields of biology described here are interconnected.

Ask How could a wildlife biologist use information generated by a molecular biologist? *(Sample answer: A wildlife biologist could use information generated by a molecular biologist to find out if two similar-appearing species are genetically related.)*

DIFFERENTIATED INSTRUCTION

LPR **Less Proficient Readers** Use the photos on these pages to launch a discussion of fields of biology. Call on students to describe what they see in each picture. After students describe what they see, have them read the italicized sentence related to the photo. Then, ask them to use the picture, discussion, and sentence to write a sentence in their own words about each field of biology.

Check for Understanding

QUESTION BOARD

Establish a section of a bulletin board or white board in the classroom to be used by students to post anonymous questions about careers in biology or identify fields of biology about which they would like to learn more.

ADJUST INSTRUCTION

Read over students' questions to identify common questions or topics of interest. Select several of these as topics for class discussion. Carefully examine the questions to determine if students have any misconceptions about the fields of biology described in the text. If so, address those by helping students review the correct information in the text.

Teach continued

Build Math Skills

Tell students that using the metric system often involves conversions between metric units. For example, a measurement made in centimeters might need to be expressed in meters. To reinforce students' ability to convert between units, write the following problems on the board:

- 1 kilometer = ? meters *(1000)*
- 0.45 liter = ? milliliters *(450)*
- 5000 milligrams= ? grams *(5)*
- 130 meters = ? kilometers *(0.13)*
- 2500 milliliters = ? liters *(2.5)*
- 0.017 grams = ? milligrams *(17)*

Challenge students to calculate the answers to these conversion problems.

DIFFERENTIATED INSTRUCTION

L1 Special Needs Have students fold a piece of paper in half horizontally and then vertically to form four equal-sized squares. In each of the four squares, have them write one of the following terms: length, mass, volume, and temperature. Then, have them write the name of the metric unit used for each quantity in the appropriate box. Students can add pictures of tools used to measure each quantity or other visual reminders that help them remember this information.

ELL English Language Learners Students who have recently moved to the U.S. may be more familiar with the metric system than students who have received most of their education in the U.S. Encourage these students to be the class "experts" on the metric system, by teaching a short lesson about it or by helping other students with the conversion problems listed above.

BIOLOGY.com Have students access **Data Analysis: Adventures in Measurement** to explore strategies used by scientists when direct measurement is difficult.

Answers

FIGURE 1–15 The polar bear's mass would be expressed in kilograms.

Performing Biological Investigations

How is the metric system important in science?

During your study of biology, you will have the opportunity to perform scientific investigations. Biologists, like other scientists, rely on a common system of measurement and practice safety procedures when conducting studies. As you study and experiment, you will become familiar with scientific measurement and safety procedures.

Scientific Measurement Because researchers need to replicate one another's experiments, and because many experiments involve gathering quantitative data, scientists need a common system of measurement. **Most scientists use the metric system when collecting data and performing experiments.** The metric system is a decimal system of measurement whose units are based on certain physical standards and are scaled on multiples of 10. A revised version of the original metric system is called the International System of Units, or SI. The abbreviation *SI* comes from the French *Le Système International d'Unités.*

Because the metric system is based on multiples of 10, it is easy to use. Notice in **Figure 1–15** how the basic unit of length, the meter, can be multiplied or divided to measure objects and distances much larger or smaller than a meter. The same process can be used when measuring volume and mass. You can learn more about the metric system in Appendix B.

BUILD Vocabulary

PREFIXES The SI prefix *milli-* means "thousandth." Therefore, 1 millimeter is one-thousandth of a meter, and 1 milligram is one-thousandth of a gram.

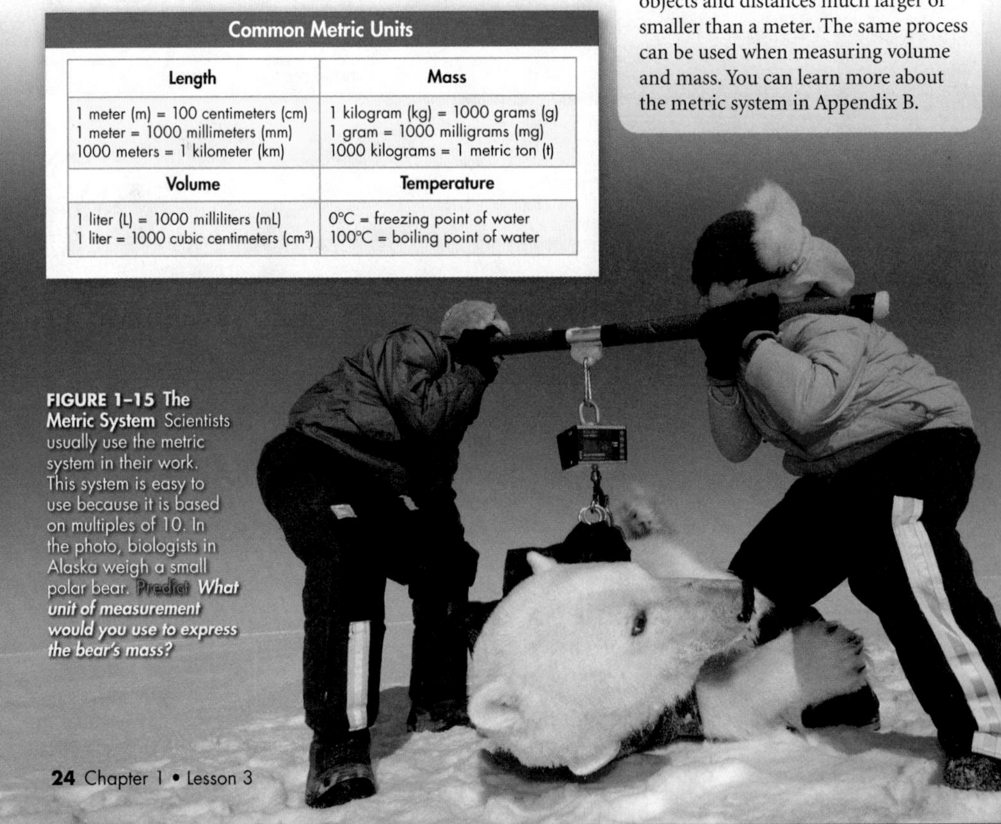

Common Metric Units

Length	Mass
1 meter (m) = 100 centimeters (cm) 1 meter = 1000 millimeters (mm) 1000 meters = 1 kilometer (km)	1 kilogram (kg) = 1000 grams (g) 1 gram = 1000 milligrams (mg) 1000 kilograms = 1 metric ton (t)
Volume	**Temperature**
1 liter (L) = 1000 milliliters (mL) 1 liter = 1000 cubic centimeters (cm^3)	0°C = freezing point of water 100°C = boiling point of water

FIGURE 1–15 The Metric System Scientists usually use the metric system in their work. This system is easy to use because it is based on multiples of 10. In the photo, biologists in Alaska weigh a small polar bear. Predict ***What unit of measurement would you use to express the bear's mass?***

24 Chapter 1 • Lesson 3

Quick Facts

THE INTERNATIONAL SYSTEM OF UNITS

The International Bureau of Weights and Measures, located near Paris, France, oversees the SI system of measurement. The Bureau recognizes seven official base units—meter (length), kilogram (mass), second (time), ampere (electric current), kelvin (temperature), candela (luminous intensity), and mole (amount of substance). Derived units are those that involve more than one base unit. For example, force is expressed in newtons, a unit derived using meters, kilograms, and seconds. Like all aspects of science, the base units and derived units recognized by the International Bureau of Weights and Measures are subject to additions and modifications as new technology and fields of scientific inquiry emerge.

Safety Scientists working in a laboratory or in the field are trained to use safe procedures when carrying out investigations. Laboratory work may involve flames or heating elements, electricity, chemicals, hot liquids, sharp instruments, and breakable glassware. Laboratory work and fieldwork may involve contact with living or dead organisms—not just potentially poisonous plants and venomous animals but also disease-carrying mosquitoes and water contaminated with dangerous microorganisms.

Whenever you work in your biology laboratory, you must follow safe practices as well. Careful preparation is the key to staying safe during scientific activities. Before performing any activity in this course, study the safety rules in Appendix B. Before you start each activity, read all the steps and make sure that you understand the entire procedure, including any safety precautions.

The single most important safety rule is to always follow your teacher's instructions and directions in this textbook. Any time you are in doubt about any part of an activity, ask your teacher for an explanation. And because you may come in contact with organisms you cannot see, it is essential that you wash your hands thoroughly after every scientific activity. Remember that you are responsible for your own safety and that of your teacher and classmates. If you are handling live animals, you are responsible for their safety too.

FIGURE 1–16 Science Safety Wearing appropriate protective gear is important while working in a laboratory.

1.3 Assessment

IN NoS.5, B.3.3, B.5.2, B.6.3

Review Key Concepts 

1. a. Review List the characteristics that define life.
   b. Applying Concepts Suppose you feel hungry, so you reach for a plum you see in a fruit bowl. Explain how both external and internal stimuli are involved in your action.
2. a. Review What are the themes in biology that come up again and again?
   b. Predict Suppose you discover a new organism. What would you expect to see if you studied it under a microscope?
3. a. Review At what levels do biologists study life?
   b. Classify A researcher studies why frogs are disappearing in the wild. What field of biology does the research fall into?
4. a. Review Why do scientists use a common system of measurement?
   b. Relate Cause and Effect Suppose two scientists are trying to perform an experiment that involves dangerous chemicals. How might their safety be affected by not using a common measurement?

PRACTICE PROBLEM

5. In an experiment, you need 250 grams of potting soil for each of 10 plant samples. How many kilograms of soil in total do you need? MATH

BIOLOGY.com Search Lesson 1.3 GO • Data Analysis • Self-Test • Lesson Assessment

Build Science Skills

Have students locate Appendix B, which lists safety rules and symbols used in this book. Have groups write five game-show-style questions about this information. Then, have each group quiz the class with its questions.

DIFFERENTIATED INSTRUCTION

LPR **Less Proficient Readers** Help students locate the sentence on this page describing the most important safety rule.

Ask Why is this the single most important safety rule? *(Sample answer: Following instructions can help me avoid safety hazards.)*

Assess and Remediate

EVALUATE UNDERSTANDING

Call on students to identify and describe one of the big ideas in biology. Continue until all ten Big Ideas identified in this lesson have been described. Then, have students complete the 1.3 Assessment.

REMEDIATION SUGGESTION

ELL **English Language Learners** If students have difficulty answering **Question 1b,** explain that the word *stimuli* is the plural of *stimulus*.

BIOLOGY.com Students can check their understanding of lesson concepts with the **Self-Test** assessment. They can then take an online version of the **Lesson Assessment.**

Assessment Answers

1a. Living things are made up of one or more basic units called cells, are based on a universal genetic code, obtain and use material and energy, grow and develop, reproduce, respond to their environment, maintain a stable internal environment, and, as a group, change over time.

1b. A stimulus is a signal to which an organism responds. In this case, hunger is an internal stimulus, and the sight of the plum is an external stimulus.

2a. the cellular basis of life; information and heredity; matter and energy; growth, development, and reproduction; homeostasis; evolution; structure and function; unity and diversity of life; interdependence in nature; and science as a way of knowing

2b. Like all organisms, this newly discovered organism would consist of cells.

3a. Biologists study life from the level of molecules to the entire planet.

3b. Acceptable answers include ecology and wildlife biology.

4a. Scientists use a common system of measurement because they need to be able to replicate each other's work, and many experiments involve quantitative data.

4b. Sample answer: If these scientists did not use a common system of measurement, they could inadvertently mix the wrong quantities of chemicals, which could potentially be dangerous.

PRACTICE PROBLEM

5. 2.5 kg

CHAPTER LAB

Pre-Lab

Introduce students to the concepts they will explore in the chapter lab by assigning the Pre-Lab questions.

Lab

Tell students they will perform the chapter lab *Using a Microscope to Estimate Size* described in **Lab Manual A.**

 **Struggling Students** A simpler version of the chapter lab is provided in **Lab Manual B.**

SAFETY

Students should use caution when handling the microscope slides.

 Look online for **Editable Lab Worksheets.**

 For corresponding pre-lab in the **Foundation Edition**, see page 20.

GUIDED INQUIRY

IN NoS.1 Develop explanations; NoS.2 Explanations based on data; NoS.5 Standard laboratory techniques.

Pre-Lab: Using a Microscope to Estimate Size

Problem How can you use a microscope to estimate the size of an object?

Materials compound microscope, transparent 15-cm plastic ruler, prepared slide of plant root or stem, prepared slide of bacteria

Lab Manual Chapter 1 Lab

Skills Focus Observe, Measure, Calculate, Predict

Connect to the Big idea Science provides a way of knowing the world. The use of technology to gather data is a central part of modern science. In biology, the compound microscope is a vital tool. With a microscope, you can observe objects that are too tiny to see with the unaided eye. These objects include cells, which are the basis for all life.

In this lab, you will explore another important use of the microscope. You will use the microscope to estimate the size of cells.

Background Questions

a. Explain How did the invention of the microscope help scientists know the natural world?

b. Explain How can a microscope help a scientist use scientific methodology?

c. Infer List one important fact about life that scientists would not know without microscopes. *Hint:* Review the characteristics of living things.

Pre-Lab Questions

Preview the procedure in the lab manual.

1. Review Which lens provides more magnification—a low-power lens or a high-power lens? Which lens provides the larger field of view?
2. Use Analogies A photographer may take wide views and close-ups of the same scene. How are these views similar to the low-power and high-power lenses on a microscope? What is an advantage of each view?
3. Calculate Eight cells fit across a field of view of 160 μm. What is the width of each cell? MATH
4. Predict Which cell do you think will be larger, the plant cell or the bacterial cell? Give a reason for your answer.

BIOLOGY.com Search Chapter 1 GO

Visit Chapter 1 online to test yourself on chapter content and to find activities to help you learn.

Untamed Science Video Be prepared for some surprise answers as the Untamed Science crew hit the streets to ask people basic questions about science and biology.

Art in Motion Learn about the steps scientists use to solve problems. Change the variables, and watch what happens!

Art Review Review your understanding of the various steps of experimental processes.

InterActive Art Design your own experiment to test Redi's and Pasteur's spontaneous generation experiments.

Data Analysis Investigate the different strategies scientists use for measurement.

IN INDIANA ACADEMIC STANDARDS

For the full text of all standards, see the Course Overview in the front matter of this book.

Pre-Lab Answers

BACKGROUND QUESTIONS

a. Sample answer: Microscopes allowed scientists to gather information about parts of the natural world that they could not previously observe.

b. Most students will say that microscopes help scientists observe and collect data. Some may know that microscopes can be used to conduct experiments.

c. Sample answer: Living things are made up of units called cells.

PRE-LAB QUESTIONS

1. The high-power lens provides more magnification. The low-power lens provides the larger field of view.
2. A wide view and low power can show the relationship between objects in space. A close-up and high-power can reveal more details about an object's structure.
3. 20 μm
4. Accept any answer for which a student provides a reason. For example, some students may predict that plant cells are smaller because a plant has more than one cell.

1 Study Guide

Big idea Science as a Way of Knowing

By applying scientific methodology, biologists can find answers to questions that arise in the study of life.

1.1 What Is Science?

One goal of science is to provide natural explanations for events in the natural world. Science also aims to use those explanations to understand patterns in nature and to make useful predictions about natural events.

Scientific methodology involves observing and asking questions, making inferences and forming hypotheses, conducting controlled experiments, collecting and analyzing data, and drawing conclusions.

science (5)
observation (6)
inference (7)
hypothesis (7)
controlled experiment (7)
independent variable (7)
dependent variable (7)
control group (7)
data (8)

1.2 Science in Context

Curiosity, skepticism, open-mindedness, and creativity help scientists generate new ideas.

Publishing peer-reviewed articles in scientific journals allows researchers to share ideas and to test and evaluate each other's work.

In science, the word *theory* applies to a well-tested explanation that unifies a broad range of observations and hypotheses and that enables scientists to make accurate predictions about new situations.

Using science involves understanding its context in society and its limitations.

theory (13)
bias (14)

1.3 Studying Life

Living things are made up of units called cells, are based on a universal genetic code, obtain and use materials and energy, grow and develop, reproduce, respond to their environment, maintain a stable internal environment, and change over time.

The study of biology revolves around several interlocking big ideas: the cellular basis of life; information and heredity; matter and energy; growth, development, and reproduction; homeostasis; evolution; structure and function; unity and diversity of life; interdependence in nature; and science as a way of knowing.

Biology includes many overlapping fields that use different tools to study life from the level of molecules to the entire planet.

Most scientists use the metric system when collecting data and performing experiments.

biology (17)
DNA (18)
stimulus (18)
sexual reproduction (19)
asexual reproduction (19)
homeostasis (19)
metabolism (19)
biosphere (21)

Think Visually Using the information in this chapter, complete the following concept map:

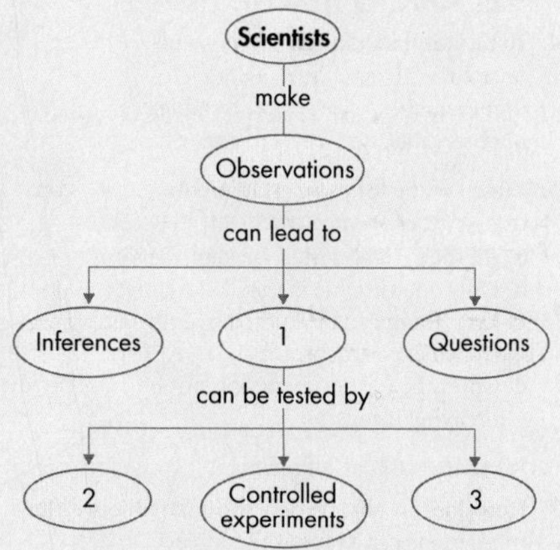

 Search  Chapter 1 GO • Crossword • Chapter Assessment

UbD Performance Tasks

SUMMATIVE TASK Have students recall from the first lesson of this chapter how Aristotle aimed to explain the world around him in terms of events and processes he could observe. Ask them to write a letter to Aristotle describing how science has changed and how it has stayed the same since his time. Challenge students to consider scientific methodology, available technology, and current fields of biology when writing their letters. Remind them to use the proper format for a friendly letter.

TRANSFER TASK Have students write an editorial for the school newspaper that encourages all students to take a science class, regardless of their anticipated career. In their editorial, students should explain how an informed public can make better decisions about issues involving science, and why a knowledge of science has become increasingly important in the society in which we live. Encourage students to submit their editorials to be considered for publication.

Study Online

REVIEW AND ASSESSMENT RESOURCES

Editable Worksheets Pages of Study Workbooks A and B, Lab Manuals A and B, and the Assessment Resources Book are available online. These documents can be easily edited using a word-processing program.

Lesson Overview Have students reread the Lesson Overviews to help them study chapter concepts.

Vocabulary Review The *Flash Cards* and *Crossword* provide an interactive way to review chapter vocabulary.

Chapter Assessment Have students take an online version of the Chapter 1 Assessment.

Standardized Test Prep Students can take an online version of the Standardized Test Prep. You will receive their scores along with ideas for remediation.

Diagnostic and Benchmark Tests Use these tests to monitor your students' progress and supply remediation.

Answers

THINK VISUALLY

1. Hypotheses

2. Observations

3. Field studies

ASSESSMENT

Lesson 1.1

UNDERSTAND KEY CONCEPTS

1. c **2.** a **3.** b

4. c **5.** b

6. The goals of science are to investigate and understand the natural world, to explain events in the natural world, and to use those explanations to make useful predictions.

7. An observation is made using senses to gather information; an inference is a logical interpretation based on prior knowledge and experience.

8. A hypothesis helps scientists understand the natural world by suggesting a testable explanation for a set of observations, which provides the starting point for discovering new information.

9. It makes sense for scientists to test just one variable at a time so that they can tell which variable is responsible for the results they observe.

10. In a controlled experiment, the experimental group is set up to test the effects of different variables (one variable at a time). The control group is exposed to the same conditions as the experimental group except for one independent variable.

11. When drawing a conclusion, scientists use data to support, refute, or revise their hypothesis. If the data indicate the researchers are generally correct but have a few of the details wrong, they may revise their hypothesis and retest it.

12. A graph can make patterns and trends in data easier to recognize and understand.

THINK CRITICALLY

13. Answers will vary. Students' suggested experiments should include one independent variable and a control group. For example, find two young animals of the same species whose weight is approximately the same. Feed each animal a different food, and weigh the animals at intervals to find out which animal grows more quickly.

14. If other key variables are not controlled, there is no way of knowing which variable caused the observed results.

Lesson 1.2

UNDERSTAND KEY CONCEPTS

15. c **16.** d **17.** b

18. Scientific theories are useful because they unify a broad range of observations and enable scientists to make accurate predictions about many new situations.

19. While theories are supported by large amounts of evidence, they aren't considered absolute truths because science is always changing—there is always the possibility that new evidence will require that a theory be modified or even discarded.

THINK CRITICALLY

20. Science is a process, or way of learning about the world, rather than a collection of unchanging facts.

21. Sample answer: Curiosity leads you to ask questions about the new skill; skepticism keeps you from accepting explanations without evidence; open-mindedness enables you to accept different ideas about how the skill could be learned; and creativity helps you explore different ways the skill could be learned.

22. Sample answer: I would look to see whether the researchers who wrote it showed any bias in their conclusions or made any mistakes in their techniques or reasoning. I would make sure their data supported their conclusions.

1 Assessment

The numbers following the questions refer to Indiana's Academic Standards for Biology I.

1.1 What Is Science?

Understand Key Concepts

1. Which of the following statements about the image shown below is NOT an observation?
a. The insect has three legs on the left side.
b. The insect has a pattern on its back.
c. The insect's pattern shows that it is poisonous.
d. The insect is green, white, and black.

2. The statement "The worm is 2 centimeters long" is a(n)
a. observation. **c.** inference.
b. theory. **d.** hypothesis.

3. An inference is
a. the same as an observation.
b. a logical interpretation of an observation.
c. a statement involving numbers.
d. a way to avoid bias.

4. To be useful in science, a hypothesis must be
a. measurable. **c.** testable.
b. observable. **d.** correct.

5. Which of the following statements about a controlled experiment is true?
a. All the variables must be kept the same.
b. Only one variable is tested at a time.
c. Everything can be studied by setting up a controlled experiment.
d. Controlled experiments cannot be performed on living things.

6. What are the goals of science?

7. How does an observation about an object differ from an inference about that object?

8. How does a hypothesis help scientists understand the natural world?

9. Why does it make sense for scientists to test just one variable at a time in an experiment?

10. Distinguish between an experimental group and a control group.

11. What steps are involved in drawing a conclusion?

12. How can a graph of data be more informative than a table of the same data? NoS.3

Think Critically

13. Design an Experiment Suggest an experiment that would show whether one food is better than another at speeding an animal's growth.

14. Control Variables Explain why you cannot draw a conclusion about the effect of one variable in an investigation when the other key variables are not controlled.

1.2 Science in Context

Understand Key Concepts

15. A skeptical attitude in science
a. prevents scientists from accepting new ideas.
b. encourages scientists to readily accept new ideas.
c. means a new idea will only be accepted if it is backed by evidence.
d. is unimportant.

16. The purpose of peer review in science is to ensure that NoS.4
a. all scientific research is funded.
b. the results of experiments are correct.
c. all scientific results are published.
d. published results meet standards set by the scientific community.

17. A scientific theory is
a. the same as a hypothesis.
b. a well-tested explanation that unifies a broad range of observations.
c. the same as the conclusion of an experiment.
d. the first step in a controlled experiment.

18. Why are scientific theories useful? NoS.8

19. Why aren't theories considered absolute truths? NoS.9

Think Critically

20. **Evaluate** Why is it misleading to describe science as a collection of facts?
21. **Propose a Solution** How would having a scientific attitude help you in everyday activities, for example, in trying to learn a new skill?
22. **Conduct Peer Review** If you were one of the anonymous reviewers of a paper submitted for publication, what criteria would you use to determine whether or not the paper should be published? NoS.4

1.3 Studying Life

Understand Key Concepts

23. The process in which two cells from different parents unite to produce the first cell of a new organism is called
    a. homeostasis.
    b. development.
    c. asexual reproduction.
    d. sexual reproduction.
24. The process by which organisms keep their internal conditions relatively stable is called
    a. metabolism.
    b. a genome.
    c. evolution.
    d. homeostasis.
25. How are unicellular and multicellular organisms alike? How are they different?
26. Give an example of changes that take place as cells in a multicellular organism differentiate. B.6.2, B.6.3
27. List three examples of stimuli that a bird responds to.

Think Critically

28. **Measure** Use a ruler to find the precise length and width of this book in millimeters. NoS.5
29. **Interpret Visuals** Each of the following safety symbols might appear in a laboratory activity in this book. Describe what each symbol stands for. (*Hint:* Refer to Appendix B.)

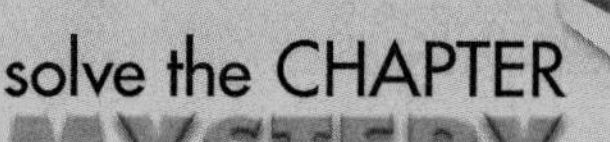

HEIGHT BY PRESCRIPTION

Although scientific studies have not proved that HGH treatment significantly increases adult height, they do suggest that extra HGH may help some short kids grow taller sooner. Parents who learn about this possibility may want treatment for their children. David's doctor prescribed HGH to avoid criticism for not presenting it as an option.

This situation is new. Many years ago, HGH was available only from cadavers, and it was prescribed only for people with severe medical problems. Then, genetic engineering made it possible to mass-produce safe, artificial HGH for medical use—safe medicine for sick people.

However, many people who are shorter than average often face prejudice in our society. This led drug companies to begin marketing HGH to parents of healthy, short kids. The message: "Help your child grow taller!"

As David's case illustrates, science has the powerful potential to change lives, but new scientific knowledge and advances may raise more questions than they answer. Just because science makes something *possible*, does that mean it's *right* to do it? This question is difficult to answer. When considering how science should be applied, we must consider both its limitations and its context in society.

1. **Relate Cause and Effect** Search the Internet for the latest data on HGH treatment of healthy children. What effect does early HGH treatment have on adult height?
2. **Predict** HGH was among the first products of the biotechnology revolution. Many more are in the pipeline. As products become available that could change other inherited traits, what challenges await society?
3. **Connect to the Big idea** Why would it be important for scientists to communicate clearly the results of HGH studies? How might parents benefit by understanding the science behind the results? IN NoS.3

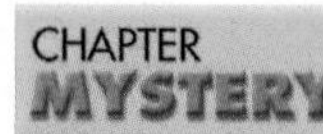

After students have read through the Chapter Mystery, discuss the moral and ethical dilemma presented by the availability of HGH treatment to healthy children.

Ask Do you feel that short but otherwise healthy children should be treated with HGH? Why or why not? *(Answers will vary but should be well supported.)*

Ask Should the government regulate treatments, such as HGH treatment, that are given to essentially healthy individuals? Why or why not? *(Answers will vary but should be well supported.)*

CHAPTER MYSTERY ANSWERS

1. Students' responses may vary depending upon the resources used for research. Students should try to find results from the latest studies possible. Remind students to pay attention to who conducted the studies—whether they were conducted by HGH manufacturers or independent organizations.
2. Sample answer: As more bioengineered products that can change inherited traits become available, society will be challenged to figure out whether the new products are safe and whether they should be used when there is not a true medical need.
3. Big idea Scientists should communicate clearly the results of HGH studies so doctors and other medical professionals can understand the risks and benefits of treatment. Parents with an understanding of the science behind the results can evaluate the reliability of the results and make better-informed decisions about medical treatment.

Have students follow the Untamed Science crew in **What Do Biologists Look Like?** to learn more about biologists and what they study.

Lesson 1.3

UNDERSTAND KEY CONCEPTS

23. d **24.** d

25. Unicellular and multicellular organisms are alike in that they grow and develop, have genetic information stored in DNA, respond to the environment, reproduce, maintain a stable internal environment, obtain and use material and energy, and evolve when considered as a group. In unicellular organisms, all of life's processes occur within a single cell; in multicellular organisms, cells differentiate and have many different sizes, shapes, and functions.

26. Sample answer: During growth and development, generalized cells become more and more different and specialized for particular functions. For example, specialized cells build tissues in the human body such as brain, muscle, and digestive tissues.

27. Answers may vary. Sample answer: the sounds of other birds, the sight of food, a cry from its offspring

THINK CRITICALLY

28. Check that students have reported their answers in centimeters. Students' measurements should be close to the following: 220 mm × 283 mm.

29. (1) This symbol warns that the lab includes glassware that could be hazardous if broken. (2) This symbol is used to indicate the possibility of electric shock. (3) This symbol means that the lab involves the use of sharp objects that could cause injury. (4) This symbol is a reminder to use heat-resistant gloves when handling hot materials.

ASSESSMENT

Connecting Concepts

USE SCIENCE GRAPHICS

30. Graph 1 shows the number of organisms in the population increasing over time. Graph 2 shows an increase in the number of individuals in the population followed by a decrease, which results in no net change in the size of the population. Graph 3 shows several rapid increases in the number of individuals, each followed by a decrease in the number of individuals, resulting in no net change in the size of the population. Graph 4 shows a population that does not change in size over the time period represented in the graph.

31. Numerical values indicating time elapsed on the *x*-axis and number of organisms on the *y*-axis are needed.

32. Sample answer: The shape of Graph 1 could represent a chemical reaction in which a product accumulates, or it could represent the height of a plant over time.

WRITE ABOUT SCIENCE

33. Answers will vary. Students' responses should describe how to use scientific methodology to determine what type of food a cat prefers. Students should include the following steps: observing and asking questions, inferring and hypothesizing, designing a controlled experiment, collecting and analyzing data, and drawing conclusions.

34. Big idea Students' responses should include a testable hypothesis and a description of a controlled experiment in which the independent variable and the variables to be controlled are identified.

Connecting Concepts

Use Science Graphics NoS.3

The following graphs show the size of four different populations over a period of time. Use the graphs to answer questions 30–32.

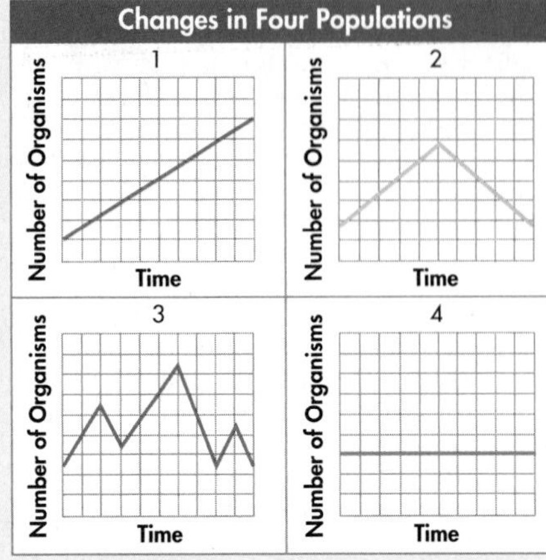

30. Analyze Data Write a sentence summarizing what each graph shows.

31. Interpret Graphs Before any of the graphs could be used to make direct comparisons among the populations, what additional information would be necessary?

32. Compare and Contrast Graphs of completely different events can have the same appearance. Select one of the graphs and explain how the shape of the graph could apply to a different set of events.

Write About Science NoS.3

33. Explanation Suppose you have a pet cat and want to determine which type of cat food it prefers. Write an explanation of how you could use scientific methodology to determine the answer. (*Hint*: Before you start writing, list the steps you might take, and then arrange them in order beginning with the first step.)

34. Assess the Big idea Many people add fertilizer to their house and garden plants. Make a hypothesis about whether you think fertilizers really help plants grow. Next, design an experiment to test your hypothesis. Include in your plan what variable you will test and what variables you will control.

Analyzing Data

IN NoS.3

A researcher studied two groups of fruit flies: Population A was kept in a 0.5 L container; Population B was kept in a 1 L container.

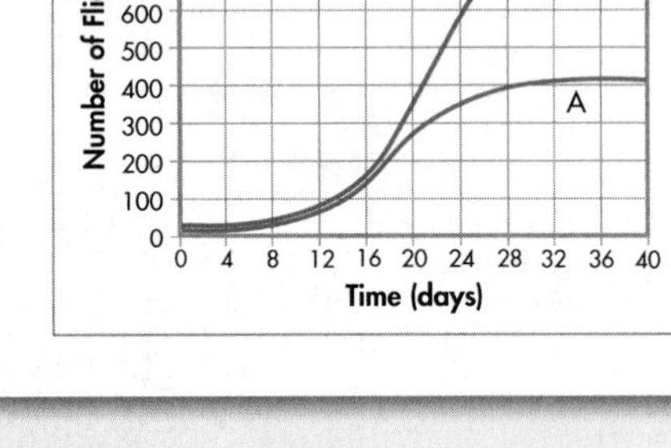

35. Interpret Graphs The independent variable in the controlled experiment was the
- **a.** number of flies.
- **b.** number of groups studied.
- **c.** number of days.
- **d.** size of the containers.

36. Infer Which of the following is a logical inference based on the content of the graph?
- **a.** The flies in Group B were healthier than those in Group A.
- **b.** A fly population with more available space will grow larger than a population with less space.
- **c.** If Group B was observed for 40 more days, the size of the population would double.
- **d.** In 40 more days, the size of both populations would decrease at the same rate.

Analyzing Data

PURPOSE Students will interpret a graph and make inferences about data.

PLANNING Review with students the structure of a line graph and how it can be used to show trends and patterns in data.

ANSWERS

35. d

36. b

Standardized Test Practice for Indiana

Multiple Choice

1. To ensure that a scientific work is free of bias and meets standards set by the scientific community, a research group's work is peer reviewed by
   A anonymous scientific experts.
   B the general public.
   C the researchers' friends.
   D lawmakers. NoS.4

2. Which of the following characteristics is NOT shared by both a horse and the grass it eats?
   A uses energy
   B response to stimulus
   C movement from place to place
   D stable internal environment

3. Which of the following statements about a scientific theory is NOT true?
   A It has the same meaning in science as it does in daily life.
   B It enables scientists to make accurate predictions about new situations.
   C Scientific theories tie many hypotheses together.
   D It is based on a large body of evidence. NoS.8

4. A bird-watcher sees an unusual bird at a feeder. He takes careful notes on the bird's color, shape, and other physical features and then goes to a reference book to see if he can identify the species. What aspect of scientific thinking is most apparent in this situation?
   A observation
   B inference
   C hypothesis formation
   D controlled experimentation

5. Unlike sexual reproduction, asexual reproduction involves
   A two cells.
   B two parents.
   C one parent.
   D one nonliving thing.

6. One meter is equal to
   A 1000 millimeters.
   B 1 millimeter.
   C 10 kilometers.
   D 1 milliliter. NoS.5

Questions 7–8

Once a month, a pet owner recorded the mass of her puppy in a table. When the puppy was 3 months old, she started to feed it a "special puppy food" she saw advertised on TV.

Change in a Puppy's Mass Over Time

Age (months)	Mass at Start of Month (kg)	Change in Mass per Month (kg)
2	5	—
3	8	+3
4	13	+5

7. According to the table, which statement is true?
   A The puppy's mass increased at the same rate for each month shown.
   B The puppy's mass was less than 5 kg at the start of the new diet.
   C The puppy gained 5 kg between age 3 and 4 months.
   D The puppy had gained 13 kg as a result of the new diet.

8. All of the following statements about the pet owner's study are true EXCEPT
   A The owner used the metric system.
   B The owner recorded data.
   C The owner could graph the data.
   D The owner conducted a controlled experiment.

Open-Ended Response

9. Explain how a controlled experiment works.

If You Have Trouble With . . .									
Question	1	2	3	4	5	6	7	8	9
See Lesson	1.2	1.3	1.2	1.1	1.3	1.3	1.1	1.1	1.1

Answers

1. A
2. C
3. A
4. A
5. C
6. A
7. C
8. D
9. Sample answer: In a controlled experiment, a scientific hypothesis is tested by keeping all variables unchanged except for one. The variable that is deliberately changed is called the independent variable, and it should be the only factor that is different between the control group and the experimental group.

Test-Taking Tip

READ ALL THE ANSWER CHOICES

Tell students to be sure to read all of the answer choices on multiple-choice tests, even if the first choice seems to be correct. Remind them that a more-complete or better answer choice may be present among the remaining choices. By reading all of the answer choices, they are more likely to choose the best one.

CHAPTER PLANNER 2 The Chemistry of Life

Chapter Contents	IN	Time	Core Resources
Chapter Preview			**Student Edition,** pp. 32–33 **Chapter Mystery,** p. 33
2.1 The Nature of Matter Atoms • Elements and Isotopes • Chemical Compounds • Chemical Bonds • *Technology & Biology: A Nature-Inspired Adhesive*	NoS.6	1 period 1/2 block	**Student Edition,** pp. 34–39 Inquiry 2.1 Quick Lab, p. 36 L2 **Study Workbook A** 2.1 Worksheets L2 **Biology.com** *Art Review:* Ionic and Covalent Bonding • 2.1 Self-Test • 2.1 Lesson Assessment
2.2 Properties of Water The Water Molecule • Solutions and Suspensions • Acids, Bases, and pH	NoS.6	1 period 1/2 block	**Student Edition,** pp. 40–44 Inquiry 2.2 Quick Lab, p. 43 L2 **Study Workbook A** 2.2 Worksheets L2 **Biology.com** *Art in Motion:* A Salt Solution • *Data Analysis:* Acid Rain • 2.2 Self-Test • 2.2 Lesson Assessment
2.3 Carbon Compounds The Chemistry of Carbon • Macromolecules	NoS.3, NoS.6, B.1.1, B.1.2, B.5.1, B.5.4	1 period 1/2 block	**Student Edition,** pp. 45–49 Inquiry 2.3 Analyzing Data, p. 48 L2 **Study Workbook A** 2.3 Worksheets L2 **Assessment Resources Book** Visual Quiz L2
2.4 Chemical Reactions and Enzymes Chemical Reactions • Energy in Reactions • Enzymes	NoS.6, B.1.1, B.1.2, B.1.3, B.5.4, B.5.5	1 period 1/2 block	**Student Edition,** pp. 50–53 **Study Workbook A** 2.4 Worksheets L2 **Biology.com** *Visual Analogy:* Lock and Key **Assessment Resources Book** Visual Quiz L2
Chapter Pre-Lab	NoS.1, NoS.2, NoS.3, NoS.5, B.1.2	1 period 1/2 block	**Student Edition,** p. 54 L2 **Lab Manual A** *Temperature Affects Enzymes* L2 • *Making Models of Macromolecules* L2 • *Enzymes in Detergents* L2

Differentiated Instruction Tools

Study Workbook B includes worksheets with lesson-level differentiated instruction support and explanations of differentiated instruction teaching strategies.

Lab Manual B includes skills labs, simplified chapter labs, and hands-on activities.

ELL Handbook explains ways to make *Biology* more accessible to ELL students.

Spanish Study Workbook is a Spanish translation of Study Workbook A.

Multilingual Glossary is the glossary translated into ten languages.

Differentiated Instruction Key

- L1 Special Needs or Struggling Students
- ELL English Language Learners
- LPR Less Proficient Readers
- L2 On-Level Students
- L3 Advanced Students

Additional Resources

Biology.com Untamed Science Video • Vocabulary Flash Cards

Study Workbook B 2.1 Worksheets L1 ELL LPR
Spanish Study Workbook 2.1 Worksheets ELL
Biology.com 2.1 Lesson Overview • 2.1 Lesson Notes

Study Workbook B 2.2 Worksheets L1 ELL LPR
Spanish Study Workbook 2.2 Worksheets ELL
Biology.com 2.2 Lesson Overview • 2.2 Lesson Notes

Study Workbook B 2.3 Worksheets L1 ELL LPR
Spanish Study Workbook 2.3 Worksheets ELL
Biology.com 2.3 Lesson Overview • 2.3 Lesson Notes • 2.3 Self-Test • 2.3 Lesson Assessment

Study Workbook B 2.4 Worksheets L1 ELL LPR
Spanish Study Workbook 2.4 Worksheets ELL
Biology.com 2.4 Lesson Overview • 2.4 Lesson Notes • 2.4 Self-Test • 2.4 Lesson Assessment

Lab Manual B *Temperature Affects Enzymes* • Hands-On Activity: *Model an Ionic Compound* • Data Analysis: *Comparing Fatty Acids* L1 ELL LPR

Chapter Review

Student Edition Study Guide, p. 55 L2 • Unit Project, p. 60 L2
Study Workbook A Chapter 2 Vocabulary Review L2 • Chapter 2 Chapter Mystery/21st Century Skills Activity L2 L3
Transparencies, pp. 13–25 L1 ELL LPR L2
Biology.com Untamed Science Video • You're the Director • Editable Worksheets of Study Workbooks A and B and Lab Manuals A and B • Chapter 2 Flash Cards and Match It

Untamed Science DVD • Classroom Resources CD (includes lesson presentations and editable worksheets)

Chapter Assessment

Student Edition Assessment, pp. 56–59 L2
Study Workbook B Chapter 2 Chapter Review L1 ELL LPR • Chapter 2 Taking a Standardized Test L1 ELL LPR
Assessment Resources Book Chapter 2 Test A L2 • Chapter 2 Test B L1 ELL LPR • Unit 1 Test A L2 • Unit 1 Test B L1 ELL LPR
Biology.com Chapter 2 Assessment • Editable Worksheets of Chapter 2 Visual Quizzes, Chapter 2 Tests A and B, and Unit 1 Tests A and B

Exam*View Assessment Suite* • Classroom Resources CD (includes lesson presentations and editable worksheets)

Time: 1 period, 1/2 block

Pressed for Time?

Preview the Chapter Introduce students to the Key Questions and vocabulary for Lessons 2.3 and 2.4.

Cover the Chapter Quickly Have students read *The Water Molecule* in Lesson 2.2 and all of Lesson 2.3, focusing on Figure 2–13. Have them read all of Lesson 2.4 and go over Figure 2–22.

Assess Assign question 1 in the 2.2 Assessment, the 2.3 Assessment, the 2.4 Assessment, and questions 12, 13, 18–24, and 25–37 in the Chapter 2 Assessment.

Connect to the Big Idea

Have students look at the photograph of the polar bear in its icy habitat. Ask them what the bear's habitat consists of. *(mostly ice and water)* Tell them that water is essential not only to polar bears but to all living things as it allows them to carry out basic life processes. This is because water has certain chemical properties that make it unique. Then, have students anticipate the answer to the question, **What are the basic chemical principles that affect living things?**

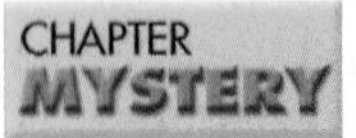

Have students read over the Chapter Mystery. Connect the Chapter Mystery to the Big Idea of Matter and Energy by explaining that most organisms—including ice fish—need oxygen for many body processes. For example, oxygen is needed to break down food molecules for energy. Ask students to predict how liquid blood could carry oxygen gas without hemoglobin to bind with the oxygen. As a hint, tell students that, in carbonated liquids, the bubbles they see are made up of carbon dioxide gas that has come out of the liquid.

BIOLOGY.com Have students preview the chapter vocabulary terms using the **Flash Cards.**

IN INDIANA ACADEMIC STANDARDS

For the full text of all standards, see the Course Overview in the front matter of this book.

Key standards: Chapter 2 covers key ideas from Standard 1: Cellular Chemistry, including **B.1.1** Organic compounds, **B.1.2** Molecules and cellular processes, and **B.1.3** Cell function and differentiation.

2 The Chemistry of Life

Big idea **Matter and Energy**

Q: What are the basic chemical principles that affect living things?

BIOLOGY.com Search Chapter 2 GO • Flash Cards

32

Understanding by Design

Chapter 2 introduces the molecular basis of life, and thereby advances students' comprehension of the Enduring Understanding: *The process of science helps biologists investigate how nature works at all levels, from the molecules in cells to the biosphere.* The Big Idea, Essential Question, and Guiding Questions, listed in the graphic organizer at the right, provide a framework for how students can explore the chemical principles that underlie life processes—from atoms to enzymes.

PERFORMANCE GOALS

In Chapter 2, students will use diagrams, lab activities, and analogies to learn about the chemistry of life. In the Chapter Mystery, they will apply basic chemical principles to understand how certain fish can survive without oxygen-carrying red blood cells. At the end of the chapter, students will demonstrate their understanding of the molecular basis of life by creating a storybook on the topic for a lower grade.

INDIANA ACADEMIC STANDARDS FOR SCIENCE

Nature of Science NoS.1, NoS.2, NoS.3, NoS.5, NoS.6, NoS.10; **Cellular Chemistry** B.1.1, B.1.2, B.1.3; **Molecular Basis of Heredity** B.5.1, B.5.4, B.5.5. See lessons for details.

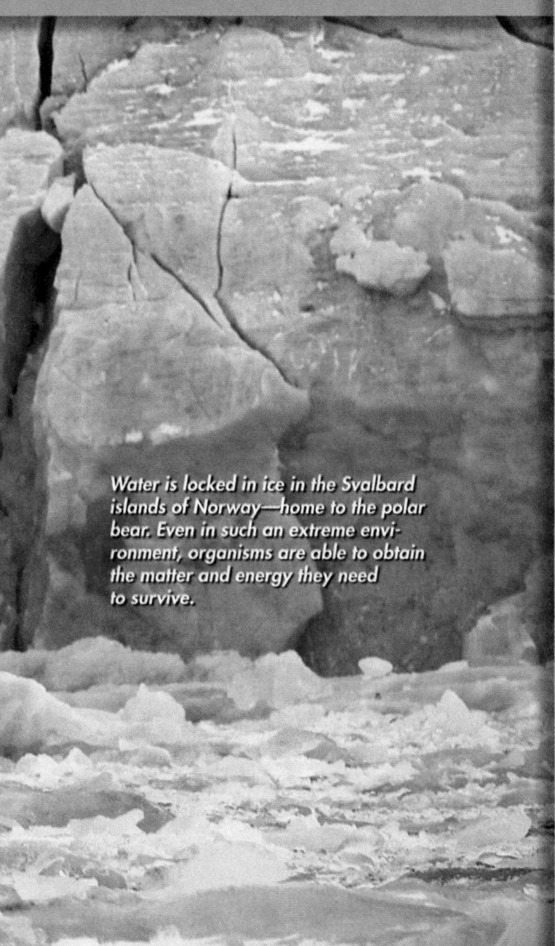

Water is locked in ice in the Svalbard islands of Norway—home to the polar bear. Even in such an extreme environment, organisms are able to obtain the matter and energy they need to survive.

CHAPTER MYSTERY

THE GHOSTLY FISH

Most fish, just like you and other vertebrates, have red blood. Red blood cells carry oxygen, a gas essential for life. The cells' red color comes from an oxygen-binding protein called hemoglobin.

But a very small number of fish don't have such cells. Their blood is clear—almost transparent. Because they live in cold antarctic waters and have a ghostly appearance, they are nicknamed "ice fish." How do these animals manage to survive without red blood cells?

As you read this chapter, look for clues to help you explain the ice fish's unusual feature. Think about the chemistry that might be involved. Then, solve the mystery.

Never Stop Exploring Your World. Finding the solution to the fishy mystery is only the beginning. Take a video field trip with the ecogeeks of Untamed Science to see where this mystery leads.

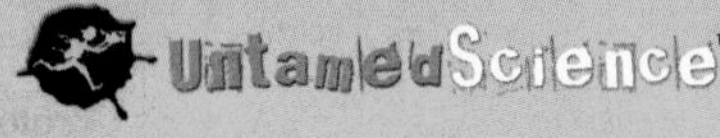

• Untamed Science Video • Chapter Mystery

What's Online

Extend your reach by using these and other digital assets offered at Biology.com.

CHAPTER MYSTERY
In The Ghostly Fish, students can investigate the chemistry involved in an organism that lacks red blood cells.

UNTAMED SCIENCE VIDEO
Follow the Untamed Science crew as they explore the unique chemistry of water.

ART REVIEW
This drag-and-drop activity lets students explore ionic and covalent bonds.

ART IN MOTION
This animation shows the process of salt crystals dissolving in water.

DATA ANALYSIS
Students can analyze data about the ecological impact of acid rain.

VISUAL ANALOGY
Using this animation, students can further explore the lock-and-key analogy for an enzyme and its substrates.

Chapter 2
Big Idea: Matter and Energy

Chapter 2 EQ: What are the basic chemical principles that affect living things?

- **2.1 GQ:** What is the matter in organisms made of?
- **2.2 GQ:** Why are the properties of water important to organisms?
- **2.3 GQ:** How do organisms use different types of carbon compounds?
- **2.4 GQ:** How do chemicals combine and break apart inside living things?

LESSON 2.1

Getting Started

Objectives

2.1.1 Identify the three subatomic particles found in atoms.

2.1.2 Explain how all of the isotopes of an element are similar and how they are different.

2.1.3 Explain how compounds are different from their component elements.

2.1.4 Describe the two main types of chemical bonds.

Student Resources

Study Workbooks A and B, 2.1 Worksheets

Spanish Study Workbook, 2.1 Worksheets

Lab Manual A, 2.1 Quick Lab Worksheet

Lab Manual B, 2.1 Hands-On Activity Worksheet

Lesson Overview • Lesson Notes • Activity: Art Review • Assessment: Self-Test, Lesson Assessment

For corresponding lesson in the **Foundation Edition**, see pages 28–32.

IN INDIANA ACADEMIC STANDARDS

For the full text of all standards, see the Course Overview in the front matter of this book.

NoS.6 Use analogies and models (mathematical and physical) to simplify and represent systems that are difficult to understand or directly experience due to their size, time scale, or complexity, and recognize the limitations of analogies and models.

2.1 The Nature of Matter

IN NoS.6 Use analogies and models.

Key Questions

What three subatomic particles make up atoms?

How are all of the isotopes of an element similar?

In what ways do compounds differ from their component elements?

What are the main types of chemical bonds?

Vocabulary

atom • nucleus • electron • element • isotope • compound • ionic bond • ion • covalent bond • molecule • van der Waals forces

Taking Notes

Outline Before you read, make an outline of the major headings in the lesson. As you read, fill in main ideas and supporting details under each head.

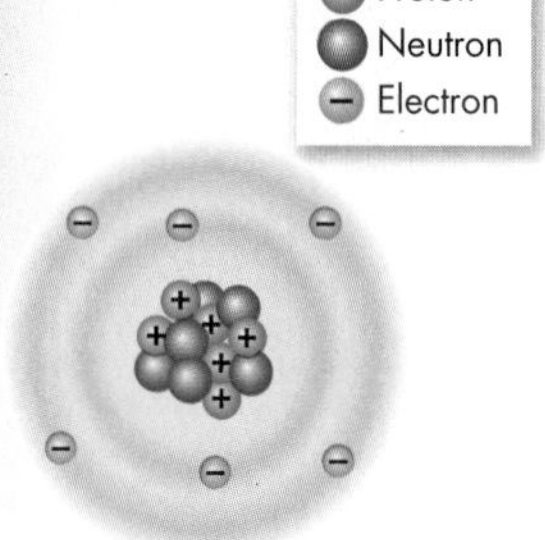

FIGURE 2–1 A Carbon Atom

THINK ABOUT IT What are you made of? Just as buildings are made from bricks, steel, glass, and wood, living things are made from chemical compounds. But it doesn't stop there. When you breathe, eat, or drink, your body uses the substances in air, food, and water to carry out chemical reactions that keep you alive. If the first task of an architect is to understand building materials, then what would be the first job of a biologist? Clearly, it is to understand the chemistry of life.

Atoms

What three subatomic particles make up atoms?

The study of chemistry begins with the basic unit of matter, the **atom.** The concept of the atom came first from the Greek philosopher Democritus, nearly 2500 years ago. Democritus asked a simple question: If you take an object like a stick of chalk and break it in half, are both halves still chalk? The answer, of course, is yes. But what happens if you break it in half again and again and again? Can you continue to divide without limit, or does there come a point at which you cannot divide the fragment of chalk without changing it into something else? Democritus thought that there had to be a limit. He called the smallest fragment the atom, from the Greek word *atomos,* which means "unable to be cut."

Atoms are incredibly small. Placed side by side, 100 million atoms would make a row only about 1 centimeter long—about the width of your little finger! Despite its extremely small size, an atom contains subatomic particles that are even smaller. **Figure 2–1** shows the subatomic particles in a carbon atom. **The subatomic particles that make up atoms are protons, neutrons, and electrons.**

Protons and Neutrons Protons and neutrons have about the same mass. However, protons are positively charged particles (+) and neutrons carry no charge at all. Strong forces bind protons and neutrons together to form the **nucleus,** at the center of the atom.

Electrons The **electron** is a negatively charged particle (–) with only 1/1840 the mass of a proton. Electrons are in constant motion in the space surrounding the nucleus. They are attracted to the positively charged nucleus but remain outside the nucleus because of the energy of their motion. Because atoms have equal numbers of electrons and protons, their positive and negative charges balance out, and atoms themselves are electrically neutral.

UbD Teach for Understanding

ENDURING UNDERSTANDING The process of science helps biologists investigate how nature works at all levels, from the molecules in cells to the biosphere.

GUIDING QUESTION What is the matter in organisms made of?

EVIDENCE OF UNDERSTANDING *After completing the lesson, give students the following assessment to show they understand the chemical basis of the matter that makes up living things.* Divide the class into groups, and ask each group to write a poem in which they answer the Key Questions of the lesson and use each of the lesson vocabulary terms. Give groups a chance to perform their poems for the class.

Elements and Isotopes

How are all of the isotopes of an element similar?

A chemical **element** is a pure substance that consists entirely of one type of atom. More than 100 elements are known, but only about two dozen are commonly found in living organisms. Elements are represented by one- or two-letter symbols. C, for example, stands for carbon, H for hydrogen, Na for sodium, and Hg for mercury. The number of protons in the nucleus of an element is called its atomic number. Carbon's atomic number is 6, meaning that each atom of carbon has six protons and, consequently, six electrons. See Appendix E, The Periodic Table, which shows the elements.

FIGURE 2–2 Droplets of Mercury Mercury, a silvery-white metallic element, is liquid at room temperature and forms droplets. It is extremely poisonous.

Isotopes Atoms of an element may have different numbers of neutrons. For example, although all atoms of carbon have six protons, some have six neutrons, some seven, and a few have eight. Atoms of the same element that differ in the number of neutrons they contain are known as **isotopes.** The total number of protons and neutrons in the nucleus of an atom is called its mass number. Isotopes are identified by their mass numbers. **Figure 2–3** shows the subatomic composition of carbon-12, carbon-13, and carbon-14 atoms. The weighted average of the masses of an element's isotopes is called its atomic mass. "Weighted" means that the abundance of each isotope in nature is considered when the average is calculated. **Because they have the same number of electrons, all isotopes of an element have the same chemical properties.**

Isotopes of Carbon

Isotope	Number of Protons	Number of Electrons	Number of Neutrons
Carbon–12 (nonradioactive)	6	6	6
Carbon–13 (nonradioactive)	6	6	7
Carbon–14 (radioactive)	6	6	8

FIGURE 2–3 Carbon Isotopes Isotopes of carbon all have 6 protons but different numbers of neutrons—6, 7, or 8. They are identified by the total number of protons and neutrons in the nucleus: carbon–12, carbon–13, and carbon–14. **Classify** ***Which isotope of carbon is radioactive?***

Radioactive Isotopes Some isotopes are radioactive, meaning that their nuclei are unstable and break down at a constant rate over time. The radiation these isotopes give off can be dangerous, but radioactive isotopes have a number of important scientific and practical uses.

Geologists can determine the ages of rocks and fossils by analyzing the isotopes found in them. Radiation from certain isotopes can be used to detect and treat cancer and to kill bacteria that cause food to spoil. Radioactive isotopes can also be used as labels or "tracers" to follow the movements of substances within organisms.

In Your Notebook *Draw a diagram of a helium atom, which has an atomic number of 2.*

How Science Works

THE SAME YET DIFFERENT

In the early nineteenth century, British chemist John Dalton proposed several highly significant postulates about matter. One of Dalton's postulates was that all atoms of a given element are identical. About a century later, scientists working on radioactive decay discovered that many atoms seemed to refute Dalton's postulate. For example, another British chemist and physicist, Francis Aston, found that neon atoms can have a mass number of either 20 or 22. He suggested that atoms with both mass numbers should be considered neon, given that they both have the same number of protons and differ only in their number of neutrons. He called them *isotopes*, based on a term coined earlier by the British chemist Frederick Soddy. Soddy had conceived of the idea of isotopes (from the Greek words for "same" and "place") to describe different atoms that could occupy the same place in the periodic table.

Teach

Use Models

Have students model isotopes using beads of two different colors to represent protons and neutrons. Tell them to place six beads of one color and six beads of the other color together in a pile on their desk. Explain that each pile of beads represents the nucleus of a carbon-12 atom. Then, tell students to select more beads as needed to model the nuclei of carbon-13 and carbon-14 isotopes.

Ask How many protons does each isotope have? *(six)* How many electrons? *(six)*

Add a proton bead to a student's model of carbon-14.

Ask Do the beads still model the nucleus of a carbon isotope? *(No; carbon isotopes have six protons.)*

DIFFERENTIATED INSTRUCTION

L1 Struggling Students Have students use a different element to make sure they understand the general relationship between atoms and isotopes. Tell students that an atom of helium has two protons and two neutrons in its nucleus.

Ask How many protons and neutrons are in the nucleus of the isotope helium-5? *(two protons and three neutrons)*

Ask How many electrons do helium and helium-5 have? *(two)*

ELL Focus on ELL: Extend Language

BEGINNING AND INTERMEDIATE SPEAKERS Have students complete an **ELL Frayer Model** for each vocabulary term as it is introduced in the lesson. They should define each term in their own words. For example, they might define the term *atom* as "the tiniest particle that makes up matter." Their drawing of an atom might be based on **Figure 2–1,** and they might list a carbon atom as an example. If possible, have students translate each term into their own language, or have them write a definition of the term in their native language.

Study Wkbks A/B, Appendix S26, ELL Frayer Model. **Transparencies,** GO10.

Answers

FIGURE 2–3 carbon-14

IN YOUR NOTEBOOK Students' diagrams should resemble **Figure 2–1** but show an atom with two protons, two neutrons, and two electrons.

LESSON 2.1

Teach continued

Build Science Skills

Demonstrate how different chemical compounds that contain the same elements may vary in their properties. Place tap water in a beaker labeled H_2O and a dilute solution of hydrogen peroxide in a beaker labeled H_2O_2. As students observe, pour a few drops of each liquid onto two pieces of the same colored fabric. Students will see that the water only wets the fabric, while the hydrogen peroxide bleaches it. Challenge students to infer why the two compounds behave so differently, even though they contain the same elements. *(The elements are combined in different proportions in the two compounds, which gives each compound different chemical properties.)*

DIFFERENTIATED INSTRUCTION

L1 Struggling Students To further help students discern compounds and elements, have them make a **Vocabulary Word Map** for the term *compound*. Their word maps for *compound* might include such attributes as *combination of two or more elements, elements in definite proportions, unique physical and chemical properties,* and *atoms held together by chemical bonds.* Then, have them make another word map for *element.* Have pairs of students discuss the difference between the two terms.

Study Wkbks A/B, Appendix S32, Vocabulary Word Map. **Transparencies,** GO17.

Address Misconceptions

Atomic Models The use of atomic models, like the Bohr models in **Figure 2–4,** can lead to student misconceptions. For example, students may think that electrons travel in fixed orbits around the nucleus of an atom, similar to the way planets revolve around the sun. Rather, electrons travel about in an electron cloud—a "fuzzy" area around the nucleus where electrons are only *likely* to be found. Help them appreciate that models are just representations, not reality. Use the analogy of a model car to make this point by discussing as a class how a model car differs from a real car. Then, explain some of the ways that simple atomic models differ from real atoms.

Chemical Compounds

In what ways do compounds differ from their component elements?

In nature, most elements are found combined with other elements in compounds. A chemical **compound** is a substance formed by the chemical combination of two or more elements in definite proportions. Scientists show the composition of compounds by a kind of shorthand known as a chemical formula. Water, which contains two atoms of hydrogen for each atom of oxygen, has the chemical formula H_2O. The formula for table salt, NaCl, indicates that the elements that make up table salt—sodium and chlorine—combine in a 1 : 1 ratio.

The physical and chemical properties of a compound are usually very different from those of the elements from which it is formed. For example, hydrogen and oxygen, which are gases at room temperature, can combine explosively and form liquid water. Sodium is a silver-colored metal that is soft enough to cut with a knife. It reacts explosively with water. Chlorine is very reactive, too. It is a poisonous, yellow-greenish gas that was used in battles during World War I. Sodium chloride, table salt, is a white solid that dissolves easily in water. As you know, sodium chloride is not poisonous. In fact, it is essential for the survival of most living things.

BUILD Vocabulary

RELATED WORD FORMS The verb *react* means to act in response to something. The adjective *reactive* describes the tendency to respond or react.

Chemical Bonds

What are the main types of chemical bonds?

The atoms in compounds are held together by various types of chemical bonds. Much of chemistry is devoted to understanding how and when chemical bonds form. Bond formation involves the electrons that surround each atomic nucleus. The electrons that are available to form bonds are called valence electrons. **The main types of chemical bonds are ionic bonds and covalent bonds.**

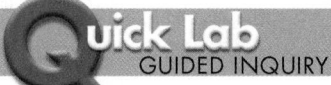

Quick Lab GUIDED INQUIRY — IN NoS.6

Model an Ionic Compound

1. You will be assigned to represent either a sodium atom or a chlorine atom.
2. Obtain the appropriate number of popcorn kernels to represent your electrons.
3. Find a partner with whom you can form the ionic compound sodium chloride—table salt.
4. In table salt, the closely packed sodium and chloride ions form an orderly structure called a crystal. With all your classmates, work as a class to model a sodium chloride crystal.

Analyze and Conclude

1. **Relate Cause and Effect** Describe the exchange of popcorn kernels (electrons) that took place as you formed the ionic bond. What electrical charges resulted from the exchange?
2. **Use Models** How were the "ions" arranged in the model of the crystal? Why did you and your classmates choose this arrangement?

PURPOSE Students will model the attraction between oppositely charged ions in an ionic compound.

MATERIALS bags of popcorn kernels, paper

SAFETY Tell students not to eat any of the popcorn kernels and to wash their hands after they finish the lab.

PLANNING Review how bonds hold together the atoms in compounds. Have students create labels for themselves—either Na or Cl—that they then hold up during the activity.

ANALYZE AND CONCLUDE

1. Students representing Na lose one kernel and become positive. Students representing Cl gain one kernel and become negative.
2. Sample answer: We huddled close together to represent Na^+ ions surrounding Cl^- ions, and Cl^- ions surrounding Na^+ ions. Describe how the ions are closely packed to form a crystal lattice.

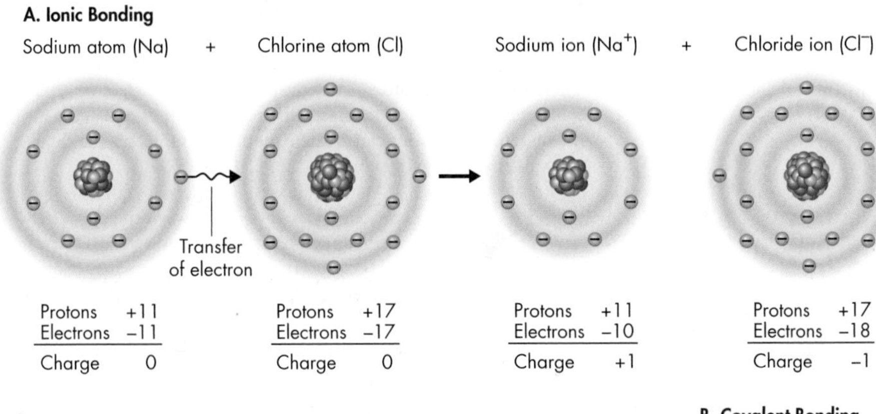

Ionic Bonds An **ionic bond** is formed when one or more electrons are transferred from one atom to another. Recall that atoms are electrically neutral because they have equal numbers of protons and electrons. An atom that loses electrons becomes positively charged. An atom that gains electrons has a negative charge. These positively and negatively charged atoms are known as **ions.**

Figure 2–4A shows how ionic bonds form between sodium and chlorine in table salt. A sodium atom easily loses its one valence electron and becomes a sodium ion (Na^+). A chlorine atom easily gains an electron and becomes a chloride ion (Cl^-). In a salt crystal, there are trillions of sodium and chloride ions. These oppositely charged ions have a strong attraction, forming an ionic bond.

Covalent Bonds Sometimes electrons are shared by atoms instead of being transferred. What does it mean to share electrons? It means that the moving electrons actually travel about the nuclei of both atoms, forming a **covalent bond.** When the atoms share two electrons, the bond is called a single covalent bond. Sometimes the atoms share four electrons and form a double bond. In a few cases, atoms can share six electrons, forming a triple bond. The structure that results when atoms are joined together by covalent bonds is called a molecule. The **molecule** is the smallest unit of most compounds. The diagram of a water molecule in **Figure 2–4B** shows that each hydrogen atom is joined to water's lone oxygen atom by a single covalent bond. When atoms of the same element join together, they also form a molecule. Oxygen molecules in the air you breathe consist of two oxygen atoms joined by covalent bonds.

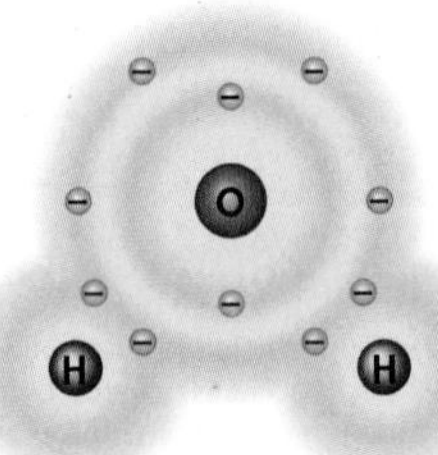

FIGURE 2–4 Ionic Bonding and Covalent Bonding A. The compound sodium chloride forms when sodium loses its valence electron to chlorine. **B.** In a water molecule, each hydrogen atom shares two electrons with the oxygen atom.

In Your Notebook *In your own words, describe the differences between ionic and covalent bonds.*

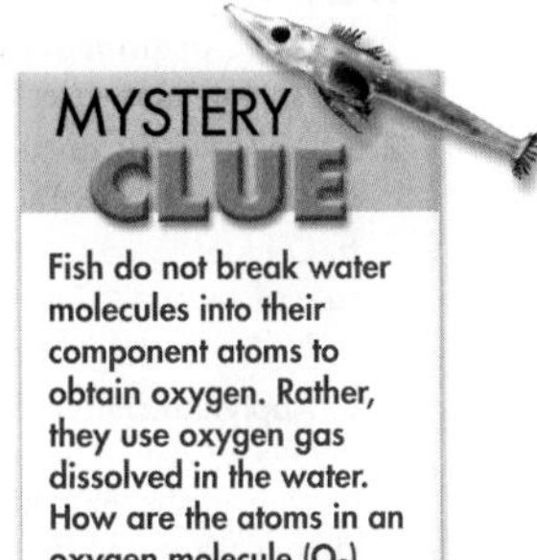

Fish do not break water molecules into their component atoms to obtain oxygen. Rather, they use oxygen gas dissolved in the water. How are the atoms in an oxygen molecule (O_2) joined together?

Build Study Skills

Use familiar phenomena as analogies to help students understand and distinguish between ionic and covalent bonds. After students have read about the two types of bonds, explain that ionic bonding can be summed up as "opposites attract." Electrons are transferred from one atom to the other, forming positive and negative ions that attract and bind with one another like the north and south poles of two magnets. You may want to use magnets to demonstrate this type of attraction. Then, explain that covalent bonding involves the sharing of electrons. When electrons are shared between atoms, the atoms bind together like two people sharing the same umbrella. Challenge students to think of other analogies for covalent bonds in which two people or objects are held together by sharing something between them.

DIFFERENTIATED INSTRUCTION

LPR **Less Proficient Readers** Have students work together in pairs to make a **Venn Diagram** for ionic and covalent bonds. Similarities might include that they hold atoms together. Differences might include that ionic bonds involve the transfer of electrons, whereas covalent bonds involve the sharing of electrons.

Study Wkbks A/B, Appendix S33, Venn Diagram. **Transparencies,** GO18.

L3 **Advanced Students** Challenge creative students to develop three-dimensional or computer-generated models of ionic and covalent bonds. Their models should show how the two types of bonds form and how they differ. Ask students to present their models to the class.

MYSTERY CLUE Students should respond that the atoms in an oxygen molecule are joined together by covalent bonds. Ask them to predict what factors might affect how much oxygen will dissolve in water. Students can go online to Biology.com to gather their evidence.

BIOLOGY.com Students can use drag-and-drop labels to further explore ionic and covalent bonding in **Art Review: Ionic and Covalent Bonding.**

UbD Check for Understanding

VISUAL REPRESENTATION

Ask small groups of students to create a **Concept Map** that relates the following concepts: atom, proton, neutron, electron, element, isotope, compound, ionic bond, ion, covalent bond, and molecule.

Study Wkbks A/B, Appendix S21, Concept Map. **Transparencies,** GO4.

ADJUST INSTRUCTION

If students' concept maps are incorrect or show that they are confused, have students work in small groups. Ask group members to compare concept maps. If they disagree about how any of the concepts are related, have them refer to the text.

Answers

IN YOUR NOTEBOOK Ionic bonds are formed when electrons are transferred from one atom to another. Covalent bonds are formed when atoms share electrons, which hold the atoms together in a molecule.

LESSON 2.1

Teach continued

ZOOMING IN

Ask students if they ever wondered how a lizard—or a fly—could walk up a wall. Explain to them how van der Waals forces make this feat possible. Check that students understand how the three different images in **Figure 2–5** are related.

Ask How could weak intermolecular forces between the gecko's feet and the wall prevent gravity from pulling the gecko off the wall? *(There are so many fibers that the total van der Waals forces are strong enough to counter the force of gravity.)*

Assess and Remediate

EVALUATE UNDERSTANDING

Write the chemical formula for water (H_2O) on the board. Then, ask students to draw and label a model of a water molecule that shows how the atoms in a water molecule "stick" together. *(Students should make and label a drawing similar to **Figure 2–4B.**)* Then, have them complete the 2.1 Assessment.

REMEDIATION SUGGESTION

L1 **Struggling Students** If students have trouble with **Question 5,** have them reread the first paragraph of the lesson.

BIOLOGY.com Students can check their understanding of lesson concepts with the **Self-Test** assessment. They can then take an online version of the **Lesson Assessment.**

Van der Waals Forces Because of their structures, atoms of different elements do not all have the same ability to attract electrons. Some atoms have a stronger attraction for electrons than do other atoms. Therefore, when the atoms in a covalent bond share electrons, the sharing is not always equal. Even when the sharing is equal, the rapid movement of electrons can create regions on a molecule that have a tiny positive or negative charge.

When molecules are close together, a slight attraction can develop between the oppositely charged regions of nearby molecules. Chemists call such intermolecular forces of attraction **van der Waals forces,** after the scientist who discovered them. Although van der Waals forces are not as strong as ionic bonds or covalent bonds, they can hold molecules together, especially when the molecules are large.

ZOOMING IN

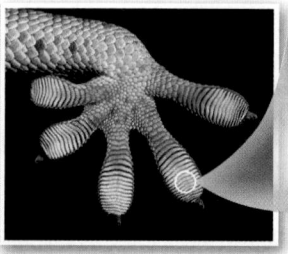

VAN DER WAALS FORCES AT WORK

FIGURE 2–5 The underside of each foot on this Tokay gecko is covered by millions of tiny hairlike projections. The projections themselves are made of even finer fibers, creating more surface area for "sticking" to surfaces at the molecular level. This allows geckos to scurry up walls and across ceilings.

2.1 Assessment

IN NoS.6

Review Key Concepts

1. a. Review Describe the structure of an atom.
b. Infer An atom of calcium contains 20 protons. How many electrons does it have?

2. a. Review Why do all isotopes of an element have the same chemical properties?
b. Compare and Contrast Compare the structure of carbon–12 and carbon–14.

3. a. Review What is a compound?
b. Apply Concepts Water (H_2O) and hydrogen peroxide (H_2O_2) both consists of hydrogen and oxygen atoms. Explain why they have different chemical and physical properties.

4. a. Review What are two types of bonds that hold the atoms within a compound together?
b. Classify A potassium atom easily loses its one valence electron. What type of bond will it form with a chlorine atom?

Apply the Big idea

Matter and Energy

5. Why do you think it is important that biologists have a good understanding of chemistry?

BIOLOGY.com Search Lesson 2.1 GO • Self-Test • Lesson Assessment

Assessment Answers

1a. An atom is an extremely small particle with a nucleus in the center. The nucleus is formed of smaller particles called protons, which are positively charged, and neutrons, which have no charge. Smaller particles called electrons, which are negatively charged, are in constant motion in the space surrounding the nucleus.

1b. 20 electrons

2a. because they all have the same number of protons and electrons

2b. Carbon-12 and carbon-14 each have six protons and six electrons. However, carbon-12 has six neutrons, whereas carbon-14 has eight neutrons.

3a. a substance formed by the chemical combination of two or more elements in definite proportions

3b. The two compounds have different properties because they contain hydrogen and oxygen in different proportions.

4a. ionic bonds and covalent bonds

4b. an ionic bond

5. Big idea Sample answer: Like all matter, living things are made up of elements and chemical compounds. In addition, the survival of living things depends on chemical reactions that take place within and outside their bodies. Therefore, to understand living things, biologists need to have a good understanding of chemistry.

Technology & BIOLOGY

IN NoS.10 Scientific discoveries and new technologies.

A Nature-Inspired Adhesive

People who keep geckos as pets have always marveled at the way these little lizards can climb up vertical surfaces, even smooth glass walls, and then hang on by a single toe despite the pull of gravity. How do they do it? No, they do not have some sort of glue on their feet and they don't have suction cups. Incredibly, they use van der Waals forces.

A gecko foot is covered by as many as half a million tiny hairlike projections. Each projection is further divided into hundreds of tiny, flat-surfaced fibers. This design allows the gecko's foot to come in contact with an extremely large area of the wall at the molecular level. Van der Waals forces form between molecules on the surface of the gecko's foot and molecules on the surface of the wall. This allows the gecko to actually balance the pull of gravity.

If it works for the gecko, why not for us? That's the thinking of researchers at the Massachusetts Institute of Technology, who have now used the same principle to produce a bandage. This new bandage is held to tissue by van der Waals forces alone. Special materials make it possible for the new bandage to work even on moist surfaces, which means that it may be used to reseal internal tissues after surgery. By learning a trick or two from the gecko, scientists may have found a way to help heal wounds, and even save lives in the process.

WRITING **Suppose you are a doctor reviewing this new bandage for its potential applications. In what ways might you use such a bandage? Present your ideas as a list.**

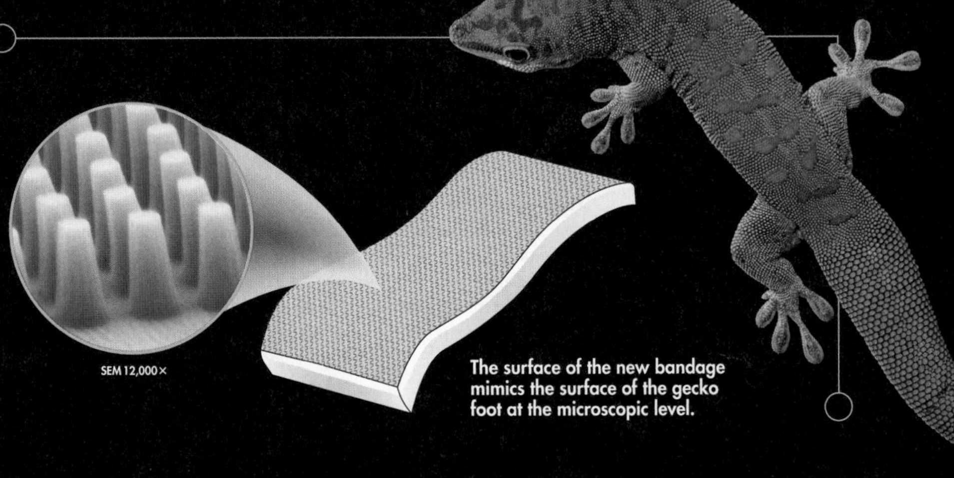

The surface of the new bandage mimics the surface of the gecko foot at the microscopic level.

Teach

Connect to the Real World

After students read the feature, have them discuss their own experiences with adhesive bandages.

Ask What are some situations in which adhesive bandages don't stay on very well? *(when they are placed on hands or other surfaces that often get wet; when they are placed on knees and other places that bend often)*

Ask Why don't bandages stay on well in these situations? *(The adhesive stops sticking after it gets wet or is loosened repeatedly by a joint bending.)*

Ask Why might the new bandages described in the text work better in these situations? *(They stay in place with van der Waals forces even without adhesives.)*

Ask What do doctors typically use to hold together tissues after surgery? *(stitches or staples)*

Ask Why might bandages be a better alternative? *(They might cause less pain and bleeding; they might hold tissues together more smoothly and with fewer gaps than stitches or staples.)*

DIFFERENTIATED INSTRUCTION

L1 **Special Needs** Students may have difficulty relating the nanostructures in the images to the surface of the bandage and the gecko's feet. Let them manipulate a material that has similar projections but on a larger, more comprehensible scale. Bring a small piece of velvet fabric to class. Pass the fabric around, and have students feel the tiny fibers extending from its surface and examine them with a hand lens. Explain how the fibers on the fabric are similar to the nanostructures on the bandage and the gecko's feet.

Quick Facts

NANOSTRUCTURE BANDAGES

The bandage described in the feature is covered with nanostructures—like those on a gecko's foot—that dramatically increase the amount of surface area in contact with the body and, thus, the strength of van der Waals forces holding it in place. The developers of the bandage have tested it in living tissues and found that it is twice as strong as bandages without nanostructures. In addition to its superior adhesion, even on wet tissues, the bandage is waterproof. It is also biodegradable, so it does not have to be removed after surgery. It is biocompatible, as well, which means that it does not cause allergic reactions or other tissue responses. Because it is elastic, the bandage can conform to the irregular shapes of organs and other body structures. It can also be used as a patch to deliver healing medications directly to tissues.

Answers

WRITING Sample answer: to hold together internal tissues after surgeries; to hold together external tissues that are exposed to water or that bend frequently

IN INDIANA ACADEMIC STANDARDS

For the full text of all standards, see the Course Overview in the front matter of this book.

LESSON 2.2

Getting Started

Objectives

2.2.1 Discuss the unique properties of water.

2.2.2 Differentiate between solutions and suspensions.

2.2.3 Explain what acidic solutions and basic solutions are.

Student Resources

Study Workbooks A and B, 2.2 Worksheets

Spanish Study Workbook, 2.2 Worksheets

BIOLOGY.com Lesson Overview • Lesson Notes • Activities: Art in Motion, Data Analysis • Assessment: Self-Test, Lesson Assessment

For corresponding lesson in the **Foundation Edition**, see pages 33–36.

Build Background

Play a guessing game with the class to build background about water and its importance to living things. Tell students the following statements. After each, give volunteers a chance to guess what "it" is.

- We take it for granted, but there would be no life on Earth without it.
- It makes up about 60 percent of the human body.
- It is nicknamed the "universal solvent."

IN INDIANA ACADEMIC STANDARDS

For the full text of all standards, see the Course Overview in the front matter of this book.

NoS.6 Use analogies and models (mathematical and physical) to simplify and represent systems that are difficult to understand or directly experience due to their size, time scale, or complexity, and recognize the limitations of analogies and models.

2.2 Properties of Water

IN NoS.6 Use analogies and models.

Key Questions

How does the structure of water contribute to its unique properties?

How does water's polarity influence its properties as a solvent?

Why is it important for cells to buffer solutions against rapid changes in pH?

Vocabulary

hydrogen bond • cohesion • adhesion • mixture • solution • solute • solvent • suspension • pH scale • acid • base • buffer

Taking Notes

Venn Diagram As you read, draw a Venn diagram showing the differences between solutions and suspensions and the properties that they share.

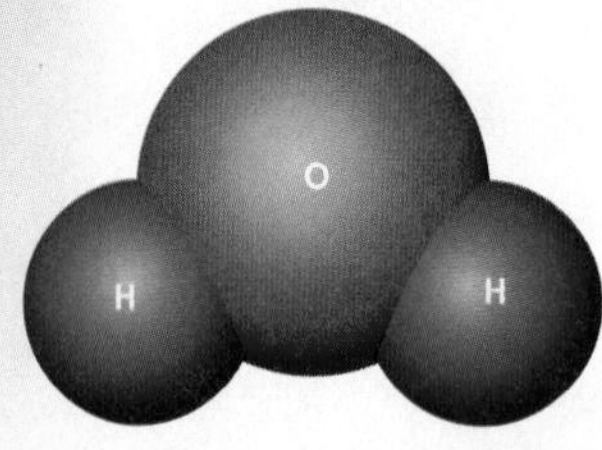

FIGURE 2–6 A Water Molecule A water molecule is polar because there is an uneven distribution of electrons between the oxygen and hydrogen atoms. The negative pole is near the oxygen atom and the positive pole is between the hydrogen atoms.

THINK ABOUT IT Looking back at our beautiful planet, an astronaut in space said that if other beings have seen the Earth, they must surely call it "the blue planet." He referred, of course, to the oceans of water that cover nearly three fourths of Earth's surface. The very presence of liquid water tells a scientist that life may also be present on such a planet. Why should this be so? Why should life itself be connected so strongly to something so ordinary that we often take it for granted? The answers to those questions suggest that there is something very special about water and the role it plays in living things.

The Water Molecule

How does the structure of water contribute to its unique properties?

Water is one of the few compounds found in a liquid state over most of the Earth's surface. Like other molecules, water (H_2O) is neutral. The positive charges on its 10 protons balance out the negative charges on its 10 electrons. However, there is more to the story.

Polarity With 8 protons, water's oxygen nucleus attracts electrons more strongly than the single protons of water's two hydrogen nuclei. As a result, water's shared electrons are more likely to be found near the oxygen nucleus. Because the oxygen nucleus is at one end of the molecule, as shown in **Figure 2–6**, water has a partial negative charge on one end, and a partial positive charge on the other.

A molecule in which the charges are unevenly distributed is said to be "polar," because the molecule is a bit like a magnet with two poles. The partial charges on a polar molecule are written in parentheses, (–) or (+), to show that they are weaker than the charges on ions such as Na^+ and Cl^-.

Hydrogen Bonding Because of their partial positive and negative charges, polar molecules such as water can attract each other. The attraction between a hydrogen atom with a partial positive charge and another atom with a partial negative charge is known as a **hydrogen bond.** The most common partially negative atoms involved in hydrogen bonding are oxygen, nitrogen, and fluorine.

UbD Teach for Understanding

ENDURING UNDERSTANDING The process of science helps biologists investigate how nature works at all levels, from the molecules in cells to the biosphere.

GUIDING QUESTION Why are the properties of water important to organisms?

EVIDENCE OF UNDERSTANDING *After completing the lesson, give students the following assessment to show they understand the properties of water that are important to organisms.* Have pairs of students create three labeled diagrams to illustrate: (1) why water molecules are polar, (2) how they form hydrogen bonds, and (3) how they dissolve other polar or ionic substances.

Hydrogen bonds are not as strong as covalent or ionic bonds, but they give one of life's most important molecules many of its unique characteristics. **Because water is a polar molecule, it is able to form multiple hydrogen bonds, which account for many of water's special properties.** These include the fact that water expands slightly upon freezing, making ice less dense than liquid water. Hydrogen bonding also explains water's ability to dissolve so many other substances, a property essential in living cells.

▶***Cohesion*** **Cohesion** is an attraction between molecules of the same substance. Because a single water molecule may be involved in as many as four hydrogen bonds at the same time, water is extremely cohesive. Cohesion causes water molecules to be drawn together, which is why drops of water form beads on a smooth surface. Cohesion also produces surface tension, explaining why some insects and spiders can walk on a pond's surface, as shown in **Figure 2–7.**

▶***Adhesion*** On the other hand, **adhesion** is an attraction between molecules of different substances. Have you ever been told to read the volume in a graduated cylinder at eye level? As shown in **Figure 2–8,** the surface of the water in the graduated cylinder dips slightly in the center because the adhesion between water molecules and glass molecules is stronger than the cohesion between water molecules. Adhesion between water and glass also causes water to rise in a narrow tube against the force of gravity. This effect is called capillary action. Capillary action is one of the forces that draws water out of the roots of a plant and up into its stems and leaves. Cohesion holds the column of water together as it rises.

▶***Heat Capacity*** Another result of the multiple hydrogen bonds between water molecules is that it takes a large amount of heat energy to cause those molecules to move faster, which raises the temperature of the water. Therefore, water's heat capacity, the amount of heat energy required to increase its temperature, is relatively high. This allows large bodies of water, such as oceans and lakes, to absorb large amounts of heat with only small changes in temperature. The organisms living within are thus protected from drastic changes in temperature. At the cellular level, water absorbs the heat produced by cell processes, regulating the temperature of the cell.

In Your Notebook *Draw a diagram of a meniscus. Label where cohesion and adhesion occur.*

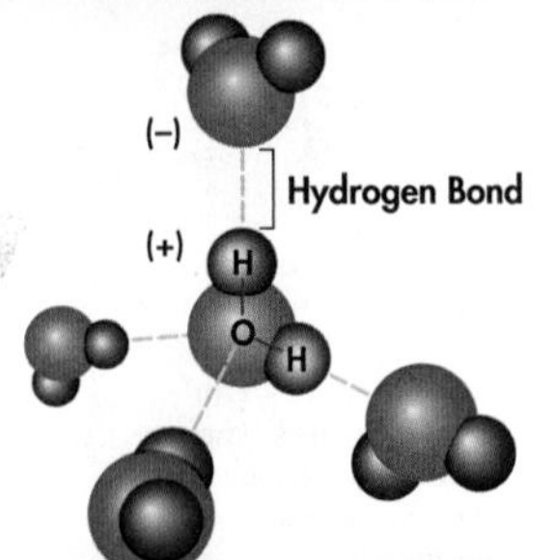

FIGURE 2–7 Hydrogen Bonding and Cohesion Each molecule of water can form multiple hydrogen bonds with other water molecules. The strong attraction between water molecules produces a force sometimes called "surface tension," which can support very lightweight objects, such as this raft spider. Apply Concepts *Why are water molecules attracted to one another?*

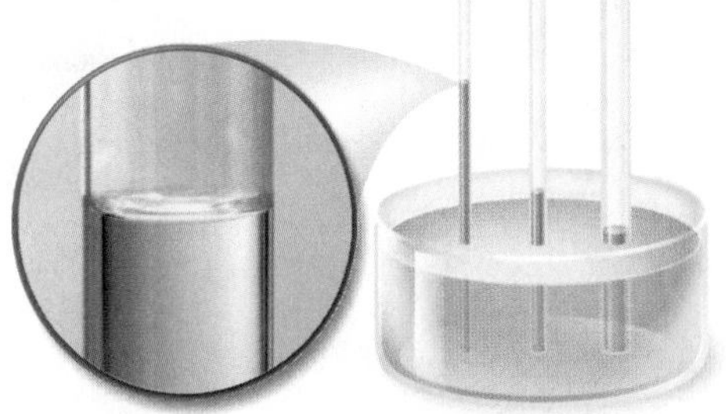

FIGURE 2–8 Adhesion Adhesion between water and glass molecules is responsible for causing the water in these columns to rise. The surface of the water in the glass column dips slightly in the center, forming a curve called a meniscus.

Teach

Build Study Skills

Tell students that visualization is a good way to remember material they are studying. Suggest they form mental images of the major concepts introduced on this page. For example, to remember *cohesion,* they might envision water forming beads on a waxed car. Have the class brainstorm ideas for mental images to help them remember *adhesion* and *high heat capacity*.

DIFFERENTIATED INSTRUCTION

LPR **Less Proficient Readers** Draw a **Cause and Effect Diagram** on the board with one Cause box, and three Effect boxes. Ask students to redraw this diagram on a sheet of paper. Then, have them fill it in to help them relate hydrogen bonding with water's properties of cohesion, adhesion, and high heat capacity. Suggest they use simple sketches to represent hydrogen bonding and each of its effects.

Study Wkbks A/B, Appendix S18, Cause and Effect Diagram. **Transparencies,** GO1.

ELL Focus on ELL: Access Content

ALL SPEAKERS Pair beginning and intermediate speakers with advanced or advanced high speakers. Have partners use the lesson figures to preview the properties of water that are described in the lesson. Tell students to write one or two questions that are raised by each figure. For example, for **Figure 2–6,** they might write, What is a polar molecule? As students read the lesson, they should try to find answers to their questions. At the end of the lesson, as you review lesson content, ask partners to share their questions and answers with the class.

Quick Facts

WATER AND LIFE ON EARTH

In addition to the properties described in the text, water has other unique properties that are important to life on Earth. One property is its high boiling point. Because of this property, water remains in a liquid state over most of Earth's surface. This is crucial for life, because virtually all organisms need liquid water to survive. Unlike most other compounds, water is less dense as a solid than it is as a liquid. This causes ice to float on water in temperate zone lakes in the winter. The floating ice insulates the water beneath it and prevents it from freezing. This, in turn, allows aquatic organisms that live in the water to survive during cold weather.

Answers

FIGURE 2–7 The hydrogen atoms have a slight negative charge, and the oxygen atoms have a slight positive charge.

IN YOUR NOTEBOOK Diagrams should resemble **Figure 2–8,** with the meniscus curving downward. Arrows should point to where water meets glass (adhesion), and to the water (cohesion).

Teach continued

Build Science Skills

Point out that solutes like table salt (NaCl) seem to disappear when they dissolve in water. You may wish to demonstrate this by dissolving salt in a beaker of water. Call on a volunteer to explain why the salt seems to disappear. *(Its ions break apart and move throughout the water, so they no longer form visible, solid crystals.)* Have students predict what happens to the mass and volume of water when salt is dissolved in it. *(Both increase.)*

Ask Besides tasting the water, how could you show that the salt is still there even though you can no longer see it? *(You could measure the mass or volume of the water before and after salt is added.)*

DIFFERENTIATED INSTRUCTION

L1 Struggling Students To better understand the concept of solution, have students focus on the Na^+ and Cl^- ions in the beaker at right in **Figure 2–9.** Suggest students draw a simple diagram showing a solution in which all the salt has dissolved. *(Each Na^+ and Cl^- ion is surrounded by water molecules. The ions are evenly distributed throughout the solution.)*

Students should conclude that the cold temperature of antarctic waters would increase the amount of dissolved oxygen available for ice fish. Explain that oxygen dissolves in water when oxygen molecules are surrounded by water molecules. Challenge students to infer why more oxygen molecules dissolve in water at lower temperatures. *(At lower temperatures, oxygen molecules have less energy on average and are less likely to escape the effects of intermolecular attractions in the solution.)* Students can go online to **Biology.com** to gather their evidence.

BIOLOGY.com Have students further explore solutions using **Art in Motion: A Salt Solution.**

MYSTERY CLUE

The solubility of gases increases as temperatures decrease. Think about when a can of warm soda is opened—the carbon dioxide dissolved in it fizzes out more rapidly because the gas is less soluble at warm temperatures. How might the temperature of antarctic waters affect the amount of dissolved oxygen available for ice fish?

Solutions and Suspensions

How does water's polarity influence its properties as a solvent?

Water is not always pure; it is often found as part of a mixture. A **mixture** is a material composed of two or more elements or compounds that are physically mixed together but not chemically combined. Salt and pepper stirred together constitute a mixture. So do sugar and sand. Earth's atmosphere is a mixture of nitrogen, oxygen, carbon dioxide, and other gases. Living things are in part composed of mixtures involving water. Two types of mixtures that can be made with water are solutions and suspensions.

Solutions If a crystal of table salt is placed in a glass of warm water, sodium and chloride ions on the surface of the crystal are attracted to the polar water molecules. Ions break away from the crystal and are surrounded by water molecules, as illustrated in **Figure 2–9.** The ions gradually become dispersed in the water, forming a type of mixture called a solution. All the components of a **solution** are evenly distributed throughout the solution. In a saltwater solution, table salt is the **solute**—the substance that is dissolved. Water is the **solvent**—the substance in which the solute dissolves. **Water's polarity gives it the ability to dissolve both ionic compounds and other polar molecules.**

Water easily dissolves salts, sugars, minerals, gases, and even other solvents such as alcohol. Without exaggeration, water is the greatest solvent on Earth. But even water has limits. When a given amount of water has dissolved all of the solute it can, the solution is said to be saturated.

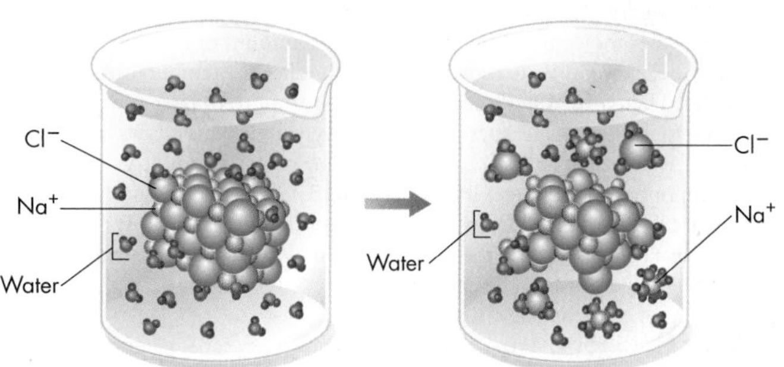

FIGURE 2–9 A Salt Solution When an ionic compound such as sodium chloride is placed in water, water molecules surround and separate the positive and negative ions. Interpret Visuals ***What happens to the sodium ions and chloride ions in the solution?***

Suspensions Some materials do not dissolve when placed in water, but separate into pieces so small that they do not settle out. The movement of water molecules keeps the small particles suspended. Such mixtures of water and nondissolved material are known as **suspensions.** Some of the most important biological fluids are both solutions and suspensions. The blood that circulates through your body is mostly water. The water in the blood contains many dissolved compounds. However, blood also contains cells and other undissolved particles that remain in suspension as the blood moves through the body.

 BIOLOGY.com Search Lesson 2.2 GO • Art in Motion • Data Analysis

UbD Check for Understanding

USE VOCABULARY

Divide the class into small groups, and ask students in each group to work together to create an acrostic poem based on the vocabulary term *polar.* (An acrostic poem is a poem in which the first letter of each line spells out another message.) Their poems should state facts about water that are due to its polarity, such as "P: Possible to dissolve many substances easily."

ADJUST INSTRUCTION

If students' acrostics reveal they are confused by the polar nature of water, have them write two quick summary sentences. These sentences should explain how water's polarity affects its ability to form hydrogen bonds and dissolve other polar molecules. Have pairs share their summaries and then work together to write a new acrostic poem.

Answers

FIGURE 2–9 The ions are surrounded by water molecules, separating the sodium and chloride in solution. Eventually, the ions become evenly distributed throughout the solution.

Acids, Bases, and pH

Why is it important for cells to buffer solutions against rapid changes in pH?

Water molecules sometimes split apart to form ions. This reaction can be summarized by a chemical equation in which double arrows are used to show that the reaction can occur in either direction.

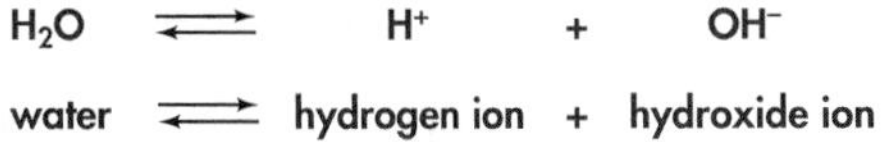

How often does this happen? In pure water, about 1 water molecule in 550 million splits to form ions in this way. Because the number of positive hydrogen ions produced is equal to the number of negative hydroxide ions produced, pure water is neutral.

The pH Scale Chemists devised a measurement system called the **pH scale** to indicate the concentration of H^+ ions in solution. As **Figure 2–10** shows, the pH scale ranges from 0 to 14. At a pH of 7, the concentration of H^+ ions and OH^- ions is equal. Pure water has a pH of 7. Solutions with a pH below 7 are called acidic because they have more H^+ ions than OH^- ions. The lower the pH, the greater the acidity. Solutions with a pH above 7 are called basic because they have more OH^- ions than H^+ ions. The higher the pH, the more basic the solution. Each step on the pH scale represents a factor of 10. For example, a liter of a solution with a pH of 4 has 10 times as many H^+ ions as a liter of a solution with a pH of 5.

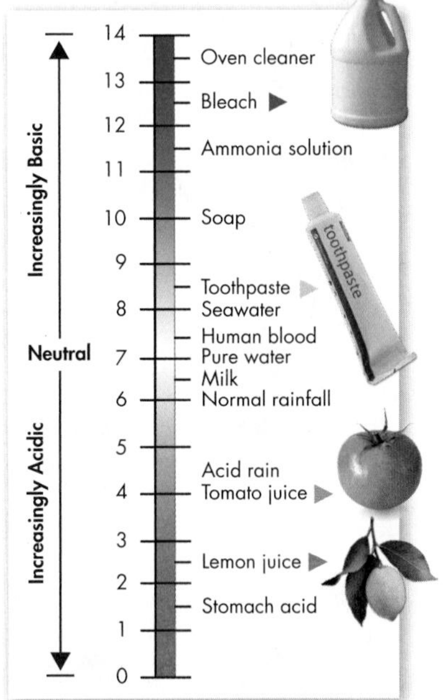

FIGURE 2–10 The pH Scale The concentration of H^+ ions determines whether solutions are acidic or basic. The most acidic material on this pH scale is stomach acid. The most basic material on this scale is oven cleaner.

In Your Notebook *Order these items in order of increasing acidity: soap, lemon juice, milk, acid rain.*

Quick Lab
GUIDED INQUIRY

Acidic and Basic Foods

❶ Predict whether the food samples provided are acidic or basic.

❷ Tear off a 2-inch piece of pH paper for each sample you will test. Place these pieces on a paper towel.

❸ Construct a data table in which you will record the name and pH of each food sample.

❹ Use a scalpel to cut a piece off each solid. **CAUTION:** *Be careful not to cut yourself. Do not eat the food.* Touch the cut surface of each sample to a square of pH paper. Use a dropper pipette to place a drop of any liquid sample on a square of pH paper. Record the pH of each sample in your data table.

Analyze and Conclude

1. **Analyze Data** Were most of the samples acidic or basic?
2. **Evaluate** Was your prediction correct?

Use Visuals

Use **Figure 2–10** to familiarize students with acids, bases, and pH. Point out that pH is a measure of hydrogen ion concentration. Then, explain that acids have a higher hydrogen ion concentration and bases a lower hydrogen ion concentration than pure water. Have students find the value for pure water on the pH scale. *(7)* After explaining that the pH of pure water is the point of neutrality on the scale, have students find the pH of stomach acid and bleach.

Ask How does the hydrogen ion concentration of stomach acid and bleach compare with that of pure water? *(H^+ ion concentration is higher for stomach acid and lower for bleach.)*

DIFFERENTIATED INSTRUCTION

L1 Struggling Students It may seem counterintuitive to students that pH, which measures hydrogen ion concentration, decreases as the hydrogen ion concentration increases. To reinforce the fact that hydrogen ion concentration and pH have an inverse relationship, have students create a simple, **Two-Column Table** to help them remember the relationship between pH and hydrogen ion concentration. Students should make a column for *pH* and another for *Hydrogen ion concentration*. Then, ask them to fill in "high" and "low" accordingly in the table, to show that low pH = high H^+ concentration, and high pH = low H^+ concentration.

Study Wkbks A/B, Appendix S31, Two-Column Table. **Transparencies,** GO16.

Have students access **Data Analysis: Acid Rain** to use data to learn more about the ecological impact of acid rain.

Address Misconceptions

Corrosive Properties of Bases Most students know that strong acids are harsh solutions that may "eat away" other substances, but many do not realize that bases can be corrosive too. Show the class a bottle of drain cleaner. Point out that it contains sodium hydroxide, a base. Sodium hydroxide will "eat away" at the clog, eliminating it.

Answers

IN YOUR NOTEBOOK soap, milk, acid rain, lemon juice

Quick Lab

PURPOSE Students will make and test predictions about which foods are acidic and which are basic.

MATERIALS solid foods and fruit juices, pH paper, paper towel, scalpel, dropper pipette

SAFETY Warn students to handle scalpels with care. Remind them not to eat any of the foods tested in the lab.

PLANNING Prepare small samples of a variety of solid foods and fruit juices. Most foods are at least slightly acidic, but there are a few exceptions, including egg white and tofu. You may want to include one of these foods. If you use egg white, cook it first to kill any bacteria. Items can be placed in small, paper sample cups available from restaurant or party supply stores.

ANALYZE AND CONCLUDE

1. Answers will vary depending on the food and juice samples tested.
2. Students' predictions were correct if they agree with the pH test results.

LESSON 2.2

Teach continued

Connect to Health Science

Explain that normal blood pH is between 7.35–7.45. A lower or higher blood pH can be a sign of ill health. Have students discuss why regulating blood pH is vital to maintaining homeostasis.

DIFFERENTIATED INSTRUCTION

L3 **Advanced Students** Explain that the acidity of blood is reduced by the actions of the kidneys and lungs. The kidneys filter out and excrete excess H^+ ions from the blood, while the lungs exhale more CO_2 when blood acid levels are high. Ask students how blood pH might be affected by a disease that reduced lung function. *(The blood might be more acidic.)*

Assess and Remediate

EVALUATE UNDERSTANDING

Have students write a paragraph that explains how the concentration of hydrogen ions determines the acid-base properties of a solution. Then, have them complete the 2.2 Assessment.

REMEDIATION SUGGESTION

L1 **Special Needs** If students have difficulty answering **Question 1c,** remind them that a polar molecule is like a magnet: it has a positive end and a negative end. Then, have them study **Figure 2–7.**

BIOLOGY.com Students can check their understanding of lesson concepts with the **Self-Test** assessment. They can then take an online version of the **Lesson Assessment.**

FIGURE 2–11 Buffers Buffers help prevent drastic changes in pH. Adding acid to an unbuffered solution causes the pH of the unbuffered solution to drop. If the solution contains a buffer, however, adding the acid will cause only a slight change in pH.

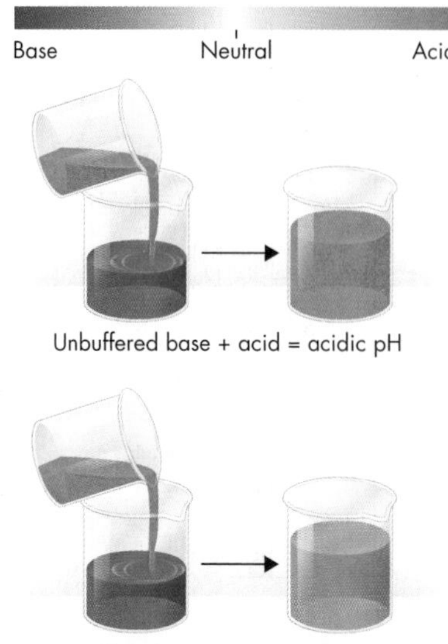

Acids Where do all those extra H^+ ions in a low-pH solution come from? They come from acids. An **acid** is any compound that forms H^+ ions in solution. Acidic solutions contain higher concentrations of H^+ ions than pure water and have pH values below 7. Strong acids tend to have pH values that range from 1 to 3. The hydrochloric acid (HCl) produced by the stomach to help digest food is a strong acid.

Bases A **base** is a compound that produces hydroxide (OH^-) ions in solution. Basic, or alkaline, solutions contain lower concentrations of H^+ ions than pure water and have pH values above 7. Strong bases, such as the lye (commonly NaOH) used in soapmaking, tend to have pH values ranging from 11 to 14.

Buffers The pH of the fluids within most cells in the human body must generally be kept between 6.5 and 7.5. If the pH is lower or higher, it will affect the chemical reactions that take place within the cells. Thus, controlling pH is important for maintaining homeostasis. One of the ways that organisms control pH is through dissolved compounds called buffers. **Buffers** are weak acids or bases that can react with strong acids or bases to prevent sharp, sudden changes in pH. Blood, for example, has a normal pH of 7.4. Sudden changes in blood pH are usually prevented by a number of chemical buffers, such as bicarbonate and phosphate ions. **Buffers dissolved in life's fluids play an important role in maintaining homeostasis in organisms.**

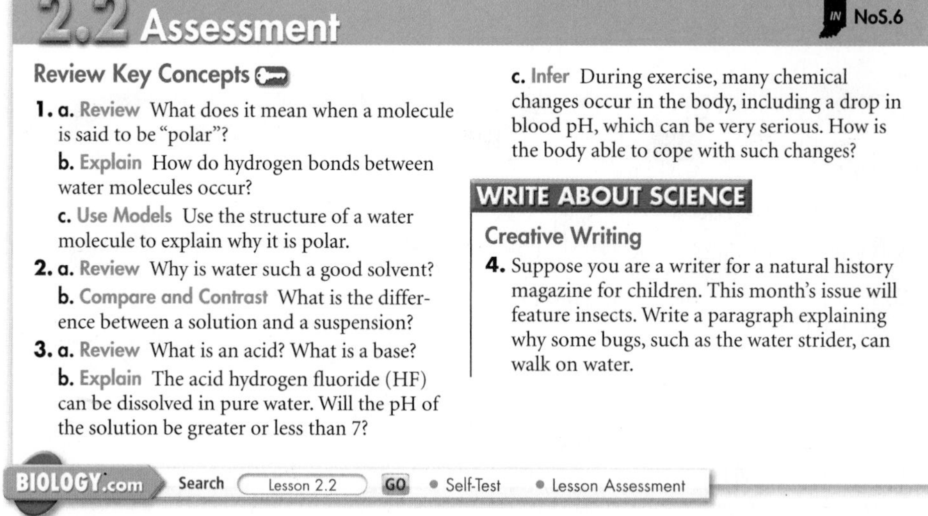

2.2 Assessment

IN NoS.6

Review Key Concepts

1. a. **Review** What does it mean when a molecule is said to be "polar"?
   b. **Explain** How do hydrogen bonds between water molecules occur?
   c. **Use Models** Use the structure of a water molecule to explain why it is polar.
2. a. **Review** Why is water such a good solvent?
   b. **Compare and Contrast** What is the difference between a solution and a suspension?
3. a. **Review** What is an acid? What is a base?
   b. **Explain** The acid hydrogen fluoride (HF) can be dissolved in pure water. Will the pH of the solution be greater or less than 7?
   c. **Infer** During exercise, many chemical changes occur in the body, including a drop in blood pH, which can be very serious. How is the body able to cope with such changes?

WRITE ABOUT SCIENCE

Creative Writing

4. Suppose you are a writer for a natural history magazine for children. This month's issue will feature insects. Write a paragraph explaining why some bugs, such as the water strider, can walk on water.

BIOLOGY.com Search Lesson 2.2 GO • Self-Test • Lesson Assessment

Assessment Answers

1a. A molecule is polar when there is an uneven distribution of electrons between its atoms. This causes the molecule to have an area with a slight negative charge and an area with a slight positive charge.

1b. A hydrogen bond occurs when the slight positive charge on a hydrogen atom in one water molecule is attracted to the slight negative charge on the oxygen atom in another water molecule.

1c. With eight protons in its nucleus, the oxygen atom in a water molecule has a much stronger attraction for electrons than do the hydrogen atoms in the molecule. The oxygen atom is on one end of the molecule, and the hydrogen atoms are on the other end. Therefore, the oxygen end of the molecule is slightly negative while the hydrogen end is slightly positive—resulting in a polar molecule.

2a. Water is such a good solvent because of its polarity. It can dissolve both ionic compounds and other polar molecules.

2b. A solution is a mixture of two or more substances in which the molecules of the substances are evenly distributed. A suspension is a mixture of water and nondissolved materials.

3a. An acid is a compound that forms hydrogen ions in solution. A base forms hydroxide ions in solution.

3b. The pH of the solution will be less than 7.

3c. A drop in blood pH is countered by chemical buffers such as bicarbonate and phosphate ions.

WRITE ABOUT SCIENCE

4. Each molecule of water can form multiple hydrogen bonds with other water molecules. The strong attraction between water molecules produces "surface tension," which can support very lightweight objects, such as the water strider.

2.3 Carbon Compounds

B.1.1 Organic compounds; B.1.2 Molecules and cellular processes. Also covered: NoS.3, NoS.6, B.5.1, B.5.4, B.5.5.

THINK ABOUT IT In the early 1800s, many chemists called the compounds created by organisms "organic," believing they were fundamentally different from compounds in nonliving things. Today we understand that the principles governing the chemistry of living and nonliving things are the same, but the term "organic chemistry" is still around. Today, organic chemistry means the study of compounds that contain bonds between carbon atoms, while inorganic chemistry is the study of all other compounds.

The Chemistry of Carbon

What elements does carbon bond with to make up life's molecules?

Why is carbon so interesting that a whole branch of chemistry should be set aside just to study carbon compounds? There are two reasons for this. First, carbon atoms have four valence electrons, allowing them to form strong covalent bonds with many other elements. **Carbon can bond with many elements, including hydrogen, oxygen, phosphorus, sulfur, and nitrogen to form the molecules of life.** Living organisms are made up of molecules that consist of carbon and these other elements.

Even more important, one carbon atom can bond to another, which gives carbon the ability to form chains that are almost unlimited in length. These carbon-carbon bonds can be single, double, or triple covalent bonds. Chains of carbon atoms can even close up on themselves to form rings, as shown in **Figure 2–12.** Carbon has the ability to form millions of different large and complex structures. No other element even comes close to matching carbon's versatility.

Key Questions

What elements does carbon bond with to make up life's molecules?

What are the functions of each of the four groups of macromolecules?

Vocabulary

monomer • polymer • carbohydrate • monosaccharide • lipid • nucleic acid • nucleotide • protein • amino acid

Taking Notes

Compare/Contrast Table As you read, make a table that compares and contrasts the four groups of organic compounds.

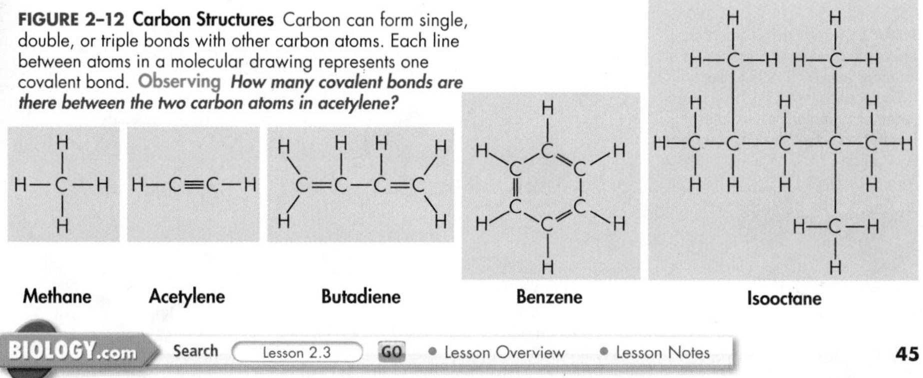

FIGURE 2–12 Carbon Structures Carbon can form single, double, or triple bonds with other carbon atoms. Each line between atoms in a molecular drawing represents one covalent bond. **Observing** ***How many covalent bonds are there between the two carbon atoms in acetylene?***

BIOLOGY.com Search Lesson 2.3 GO • Lesson Overview • Lesson Notes

UbD Teach for Understanding

ENDURING UNDERSTANDING The process of science helps biologists investigate how nature works at all levels, from the molecules in cells to the biosphere.

GUIDING QUESTION How do organisms use different types of carbon compounds?

EVIDENCE OF UNDERSTANDING *After completing the lesson, give students the following assessment to show they understand the functions of the different types of carbon compounds in organisms.* Ask each student to create a four-page brochure, with each page devoted to one of the four major types of carbon compounds in living things. For each type of compound, students should diagram its general structure and describe its functions in organisms.

Getting Started

Objectives

2.3.1 Describe the unique qualities of carbon.

2.3.2 Describe the structures and functions of each of the four groups of macromolecules.

Student Resources

Study Workbooks A and B, 2.3 Worksheets

Spanish Study Workbook, 2.3 Worksheets

Lab Manual B, 2.3 Data Analysis Worksheet

Lesson Overview • Lesson Notes • Assessment: Self-Test, Lesson Assessment

For corresponding lesson in the **Foundation Edition**, see pages 37–41.

Activate Prior Knowledge

Ask students to name compounds they know that contain carbon. As they make suggestions, create a class list on the board. Use their list to start a discussion on the wide variety of carbon compounds that exist in nature.

Answers

FIGURE 2–12 three

IN INDIANA ACADEMIC STANDARDS

For the full text of all standards, see the Course Overview in the front matter of this book.

B.1.1 Describe the structure of the major categories of organic compounds which make up living organisms in terms of their building blocks and the small number of chemical elements (carbon, hydrogen, nitrogen, oxygen, phosphorous, and sulfur) from which they are composed.

B.1.2 Understand that the shape of a molecule determines its role in the many different types of cellular processes including metabolism, homeostasis, growth and development, and heredity, and understand that the majority of these processes involve proteins that act as enzymes.

Teach

Connect to Chemistry

After students read about polymerization, tell them that polymerization commonly occurs in one of two ways: addition polymerization or condensation polymerization. Explain that in addition polymerization, monomers join together without any change in their molecules. In condensation polymerization, a small molecule—often a water molecule—is released each time monomers join together. Next, write the chemical formulas for glucose ($C_6H_{12}O_6$) and sucrose ($C_{12}H_{22}O_{11}$) on the board. Remind students that glucose is a monosaccharide and sucrose is a disaccharide.

Ask Is carbohydrate polymerization an example of addition or condensation polymerization? *(condensation polymerization)*

You may wish to draw a sketch of the reaction on the board, as shown below:

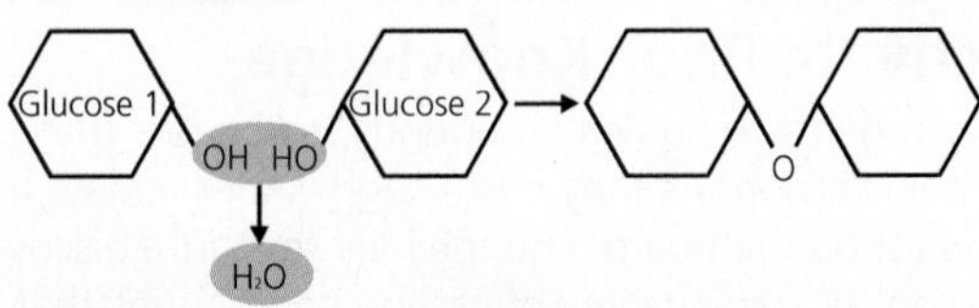

Ask Condensation reactions are sometimes known as *dehydration reactions.* Why? *(A water molecule is lost.* Dehydration *means loss of water.)* Next, show students the opposite of a dehydration reaction, called a *hydrolysis reaction:*

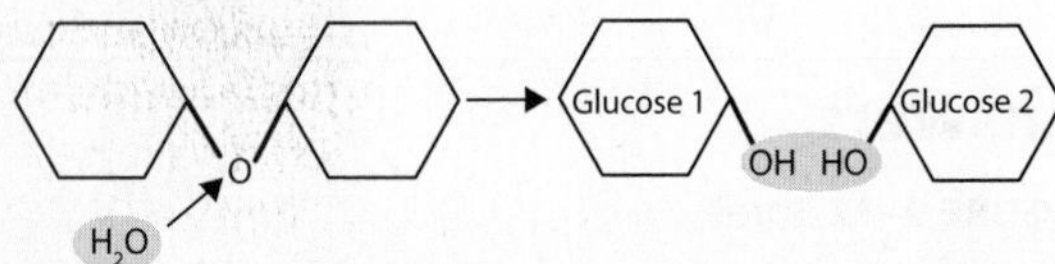

Explain to your students that dehydration and hydrolysis reactions are extremely common in biochemical processes.

DIFFERENTIATED INSTRUCTION

LPR Less Proficient Readers Have students read the **Build Vocabulary** feature on this page. Tell them that a saccharide is a sugar and the prefix *di-* means "two." Then, ask them to predict the meanings of the terms *monosaccharide, disaccharide,* and *polysaccharide. (one sugar, two sugars, and many sugars, respectively)*

Answers

FIGURE 2–13 Links are small units that are joined together to form a chain. In a similar way, monomers are small compounds that are joined together to form large compounds called polymers.

BUILD Vocabulary

WORD ORIGINS Monomer comes from the Greek words *monos,* meaning "single," and *meros,* meaning "part." *Monomer* means "single part." The prefix *poly-* comes from the Greek word *polus,* meaning "many," so **polymer** means "many parts."

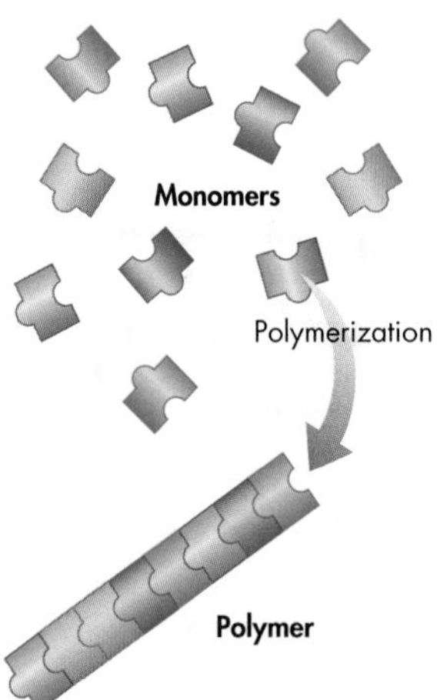

FIGURE 2–13 Polymerization When monomers join together, they form polymers. Using Analogies ***How are monomers similar to links in a chain?***

Macromolecules

What are the functions of each of the four groups of macromolecules?

Many of the organic compounds in living cells are so large that they are known as macromolecules, which means "giant molecules." Macromolecules are made from thousands or even hundreds of thousands of smaller molecules.

Most macromolecules are formed by a process known as polymerization (pah lih mur ih ZAY shun), in which large compounds are built by joining smaller ones together. The smaller units, or **monomers,** join together to form **polymers.** The monomers in a polymer may be identical, like the links on a metal watch band; or the monomers may be different, like the beads in a multicolored necklace. **Figure 2–13** illustrates the process of polymerization.

Biochemists sort the macromolecules found in living things into groups based on their chemical composition. The four major groups of macromolecules found in living things are carbohydrates, lipids, nucleic acids, and proteins. As you read about these molecules, compare their structures and functions.

Carbohydrates Carbohydrates are compounds made up of carbon, hydrogen, and oxygen atoms, usually in a ratio of 1 : 2 : 1. **Living things use carbohydrates as their main source of energy. Plants, some animals, and other organisms also use carbohydrates for structural purposes.** The breakdown of sugars, such as glucose, supplies immediate energy for cell activities. Many organisms store extra sugar as complex carbohydrates known as starches. As shown in **Figure 2–14,** the monomers in starch polymers are sugar molecules.

▶ ***Simple Sugars*** Single sugar molecules are also known as **monosaccharides** (mahn oh SAK uh rydz). Besides glucose, monosaccharides include galactose, which is a component of milk, and fructose, which is found in many fruits. Ordinary table sugar, sucrose, consists of glucose and fructose. Sucrose is a disaccharide, a compound made by joining two simple sugars together.

FIGURE 2–14 Carbohydrates Starches form when sugars join together in a long chain. Each time two glucose molecules are joined together, a molecule of water (H_2O) is released when the covalent bond is formed.

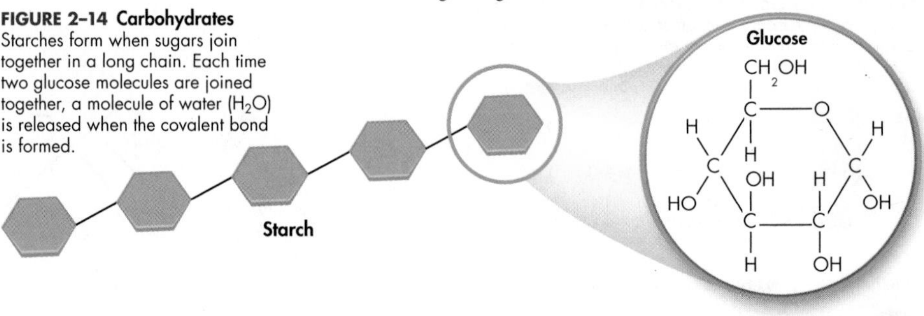

Biology In-Depth

MORE FUNCTIONS OF CARBOHYDRATES

In recent years, researchers have found that carbohydrates have more functions in living things than just providing energy and helping to give organisms structure. They have discovered that carbohydrates also play important roles in the interactions of cells within organisms. Simple sugar molecules attached to larger protein molecules appear to act like ID tags on the larger molecules. For example, these "glycoproteins" may allow sperm to recognize egg cells during fertilization and fetuses to avoid detection and attack by the maternal immune system during gestation. The sugar molecules may also help white blood cells identify infected tissues. Errors in the formation of sugar ID molecules have been implicated in some autoimmune disorders.

▶ *Complex Carbohydrates* The large macromolecules formed from monosaccharides are known as polysaccharides. Many animals store excess sugar in a polysaccharide called glycogen, which is sometimes called "animal starch." When the level of glucose in your blood runs low, glycogen is broken down into glucose, which is then released into the blood. The glycogen stored in your muscles supplies the energy for muscle contraction and, thus, for movement.

Plants use a slightly different polysaccharide, called starch, to store excess sugar. Plants also make another important polysaccharide called cellulose. Tough, flexible cellulose fibers give plants much of their strength and rigidity. Cellulose is the major component of both wood and paper, so you are actually looking at cellulose as you read these words!

Lipids Lipids are a large and varied group of biological molecules that are generally not soluble in water. **Lipids** are made mostly from carbon and hydrogen atoms. The common categories of lipids are fats, oils, and waxes. **Lipids can be used to store energy. Some lipids are important parts of biological membranes and waterproof coverings.** Steroids synthesized by the body are lipids as well. Many steroids, such as hormones, serve as chemical messengers.

Many lipids are formed when a glycerol molecule combines with compounds called fatty acids, as shown in **Figure 2–15.** If each carbon atom in a lipid's fatty acid chains is joined to another carbon atom by a single bond, the lipid is said to be saturated. The term *saturated* is used because the fatty acids contain the maximum possible number of hydrogen atoms.

If there is at least one carbon-carbon double bond in a fatty acid, the fatty acid is said to be unsaturated. Lipids whose fatty acids contain more than one double bond are said to be polyunsaturated. If the terms *saturated* and *polyunsaturated* seem familiar, you have probably seen them on food package labels. Lipids that contain unsaturated fatty acids, such as olive oil, tend to be liquid at room temperature. Other cooking oils, such as corn oil, sesame oil, canola oil, and peanut oil, contain polyunsaturated lipids.

In Your Notebook *Compare and contrast saturated and unsaturated fats.*

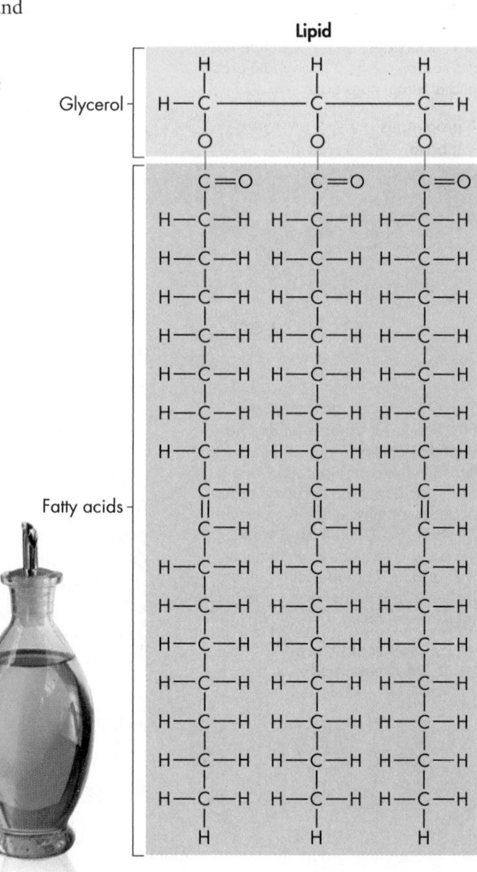

FIGURE 2–15 Lipids Lipid molecules are made up of glycerol and fatty acids. Liquid lipids, such as olive oil, contain mainly unsaturated fatty acids.

Build Reading Skills

Ask students if they ever heard the expression, "A picture is worth 1000 words." Tell them that looking at the photographs, diagrams, and graphs in their textbook when they read can help them understand the material. When they read about carbohydrates, have them examine **Figure 2–14,** and when they read about lipids, have them look at **Figure 2–15.** The figures will help students understand the structures of the two types of macromolecules. For example, **Figure 2–15** will show them the composition of lipids and help them understand how saturated and unsaturated lipids differ. Suggest they check their comprehension by asking themselves: What makes the lipid in **Figure 2–15** unsaturated?

DIFFERENTIATED INSTRUCTION

L1 Special Needs Use **Cloze Prompts** to help students focus on the most important information about lipids. Have them write the following prompts on a sheet of paper and try to fill in the missing words as they read:

- Lipids are made mostly from carbon and ______. (hydrogen atoms)
- Lipids can be used to store ______. (energy)
- Lipids are part of biological ______. (membranes and waterproof coverings)
- Lipids contain glycerol and ______. (fatty acids)
- Lipids that are liquid at room temperature contain ______ fatty acids. (unsaturated)

Study Wkbks A/B, Appendix S2, Cloze Prompts.

L3 Advanced Students Have students learn about the roles of saturated and unsaturated lipids in nutrition and health. Then, ask them, to share what they learn in a presentation to the class. In their presentation, they should include recommendations for food choices that have healthy amounts and types of lipids.

UbD Check for Understanding

QUESTION BOX

Ask students to write a question they have about carbohydrates or lipids on a scrap of paper. Then, pass an empty shoe box around the room, and have students place their questions in the box. This will give students who are uncomfortable asking questions aloud in class a chance to have their questions answered.

ADJUST INSTRUCTION

Review students' questions, and select the most important or fundamental questions that students have raised. Read the questions aloud in class, and call on volunteers to answer them.

Answers

IN YOUR NOTEBOOK Both types of fats are lipids that form when a glycerol molecule combines with fatty acid compounds. In saturated fats, each carbon atom in the fatty acid chains is joined to another carbon atom by a single bond. In unsaturated fats, at least one carbon atom in the fatty acid chains is joined to another carbon atom by a double bond. At room temperature, saturated fats tend to be solids and unsaturated fats tend to be liquids.

Teach continued

Use Models

Challenge individual students to use materials of their choice to create a three-dimensional model of a nucleic acid or a protein. For example, a student might use interlocking brick construction toys in different colors and shapes to represent nitrogenous bases, phosphate groups, and 5-carbon sugars, and join the bricks together in the correct arrangement to model a nucleic acid. Other materials students might use include modeling clay, toothpicks, and beads. Tell students to make a key for their model showing what each part represents. Have students display their models in the classroom as you work through the lesson.

DIFFERENTIATED INSTRUCTION

L1 Struggling Students Have students work in small groups to create models of a nucleic acid and a protein. Suggest they talk about the structure of each molecule and write down a quick plan for how they will model it before they begin construction.

ELL Focus on ELL: Build Background

ALL SPEAKERS Show students visuals of carbohydrates, lipids, nucleic acids, and proteins. Then, have them apply the **Think-Pair-Share** strategy. Give students time to think about what they learned from the visuals. Then, pair beginning and intermediate speakers with advanced and advanced high speakers. Have partners discuss the visuals to help them make a list of descriptive terms and examples that are associated with each type of macromolecule. Ask partners to share their lists with the class.

Study Wkbks A/B, Appendix S14, Think-Pair-Share.

IN NoS.3, B.1.1

Comparing Fatty Acids

The table compares four different fatty acids. Although they all have the same number of carbon atoms, their properties vary.

1. Interpret Data Which of the four fatty acids is saturated? Which are unsaturated?

2. Observe How does melting point change as the number of carbon-carbon double bonds increases?

Effect of Carbon Bonds on Melting Point

Fatty Acid	Number of Carbons	Number of Double Bonds	Melting Point (°C)
Stearic acid	18	0	69.6
Oleic acid	18	1	14
Linoleic acid	18	2	−5
Linolenic acid	18	3	−11

3. Infer If room temperature is 25°C, which fatty acid is a solid at room temperature? Which is liquid at room temperature?

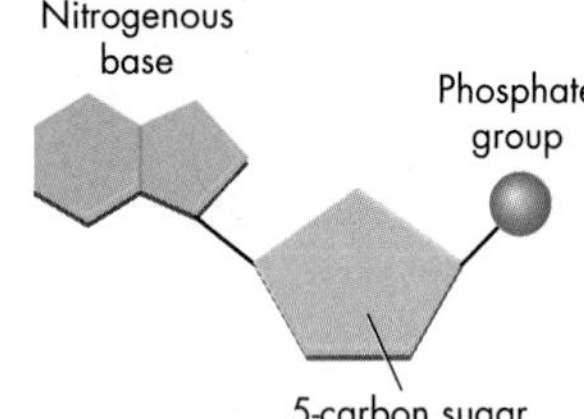

FIGURE 2–16 Nucleic Acids The monomers that make up a nucleic acid are nucleotides. Each nucleotide has a 5-carbon sugar, a phosphate group, and a nitrogenous base.

Nucleic Acids **Nucleic acids** are macromolecules containing hydrogen, oxygen, nitrogen, carbon, and phosphorus. Nucleic acids are polymers assembled from individual monomers known as nucleotides. **Nucleotides** consist of three parts: a 5-carbon sugar, a phosphate group ($-PO_4$), and a nitrogenous base, as shown in **Figure 2–16.** Some nucleotides, including the compound known as adenosine triphosphate (ATP), play important roles in capturing and transferring chemical energy. Individual nucleotides can be joined by covalent bonds to form a polynucleotide, or nucleic acid.

Nucleic acids store and transmit hereditary, or genetic, information. There are two kinds of nucleic acids: ribonucleic acid (RNA) and deoxyribonucleic acid (DNA). As their names indicate, RNA contains the sugar ribose and DNA contains the sugar deoxyribose.

Protein **Proteins** are macromolecules that contain nitrogen as well as carbon, hydrogen, and oxygen. Proteins are polymers of molecules called amino acids, shown in **Figure 2–17. Amino acids** are compounds with an amino group ($-NH_2$) on one end and a carboxyl group ($-COOH$) on the other end. Covalent bonds called peptide bonds link amino acids together to form a polypeptide. A protein is a functional molecule built from one or more polypeptides. **Some proteins control the rate of reactions and regulate cell processes. Others form important cellular structures, while still others transport substances into or out of cells or help to fight disease.**

FIGURE 2–17 Amino Acids and Peptide Bonding Peptide bonds form between the amino group of one amino acid and the carboxyl group of another amino acid. A molecule of water (H_2O) is released when the bond is formed. Note that it is the variable R-group section of the molecule that distinguishes one amino acid from another.

General Structure of Amino Acids

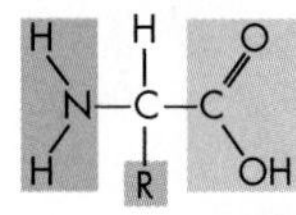

Formation of Peptide Bond

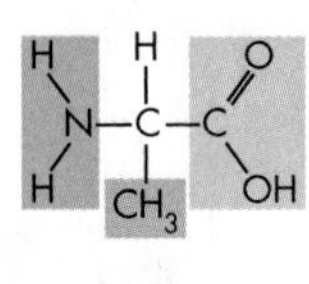

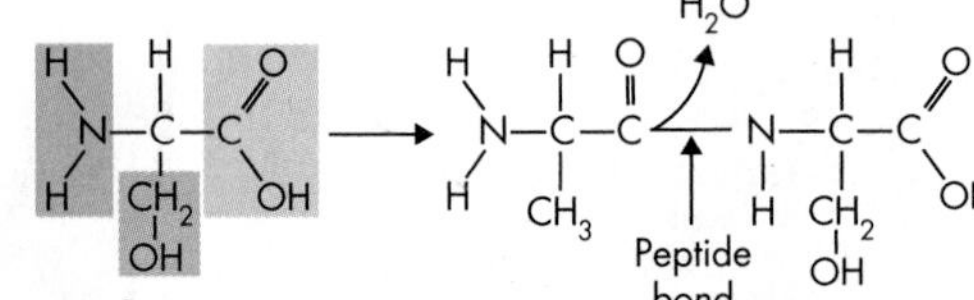

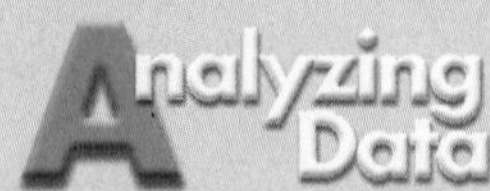

PURPOSE Students will interpret data to infer properties of fatty acids.

PLANNING Before students begin the activity, check that they know how saturated, unsaturated, and polyunsaturated fatty acids are classified and what *melting point* means.

ANSWERS

1. Stearic acid is saturated. The other three fatty acids in the table are unsaturated.
2. Melting point decreases as the number of double bonds increases.
3. Stearic acid is a solid at room temperature. The other three fatty acids are liquids at room temperature.

▶ ***Structure and Function*** More than 20 different amino acids are found in nature. All amino acids are identical in the regions where they may be joined together by covalent bonds. This uniformity allows any amino acid to be joined to any other amino acid—by bonding an amino group to a carboxyl group. Proteins are among the most diverse macromolecules. The reason is that amino acids differ from each other in a side chain called the R-group, which have a range of different properties. Some R-groups are acidic and some are basic. Some are polar, some are nonpolar, and some even contain large ring structures.

▶ ***Levels of Organization*** Amino acids are assembled into polypeptide chains according to instructions coded in DNA. To help understand these large molecules, scientists describe proteins as having four levels of structure. A protein's primary structure is the sequence of its amino acids. Secondary structure is the folding or coiling of the polypeptide chain. Tertiary structure is the complete, three-dimensional arrangement of a polypeptide chain. Proteins with more than one chain are said to have a fourth level of structure, describing the way in which the different polypeptides are arranged with respect to each other. **Figure 2–18** shows these four levels of structure in hemoglobin, a protein found in red blood cells that helps to transport oxygen in the bloodstream. The shape of a protein is maintained by a variety of forces, including ionic and covalent bonds, as well as van der Waals forces and hydrogen bonds. In the next lesson, you will learn why a protein's shape is so important.

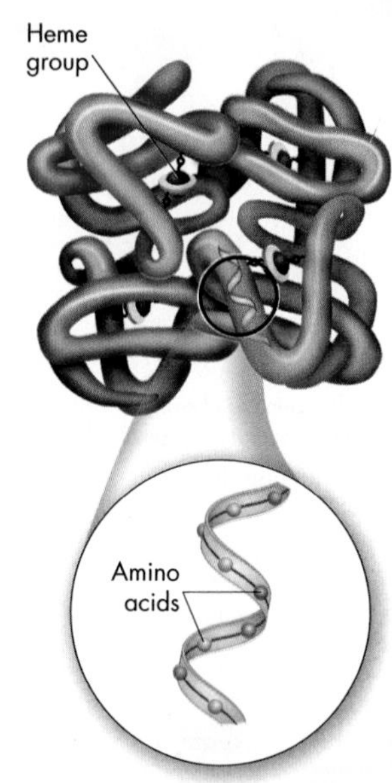

FIGURE 2–18 Protein Structure
The protein hemoglobin consists of four subunits. The iron-containing heme group in the center of each subunit gives hemoglobin its red color. An oxygen molecule binds tightly to each heme molecule. Interpret Visuals ***How many levels of organization does hemoglobin have?***

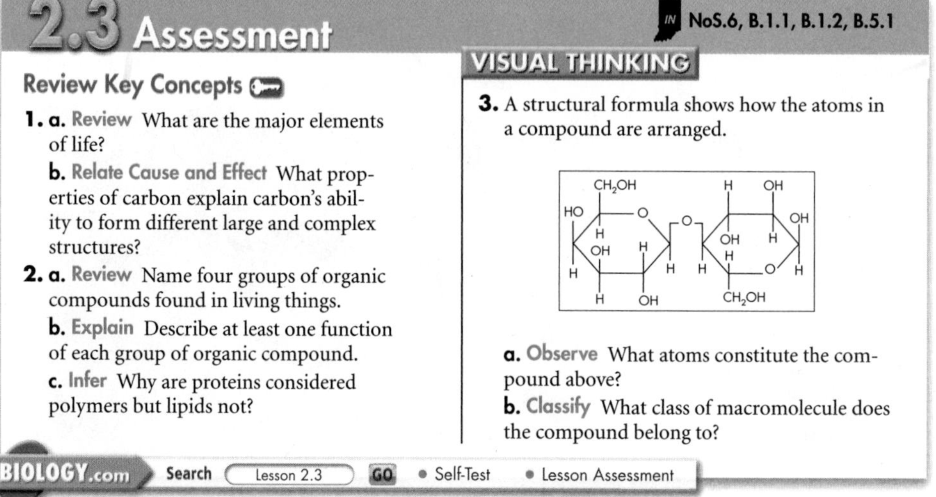

2.3 Assessment

NoS.6, B.1.1, B.1.2, B.5.1

Review Key Concepts

1. a. Review What are the major elements of life?

b. Relate Cause and Effect What properties of carbon explain carbon's ability to form different large and complex structures?

2. a. Review Name four groups of organic compounds found in living things.

b. Explain Describe at least one function of each group of organic compound.

c. Infer Why are proteins considered polymers but lipids not?

VISUAL THINKING

3. A structural formula shows how the atoms in a compound are arranged.

a. Observe What atoms constitute the compound above?

b. Classify What class of macromolecule does the compound belong to?

BIOLOGY.com Search Lesson 2.3 GO • Self-Test • Lesson Assessment

Assess and Remediate

EVALUATE UNDERSTANDING

Ask a volunteer to explain what macromolecules are. Ask another student to go to the board and list the four main groups of macromolecules found in organisms. Call on one student after another to describe the structure or identify a function of one of the groups of macromolecules. Then, have students complete the 2.3 Assessment.

REMEDIATION SUGGESTION

LPR **Less Proficient Readers** If students have trouble with **Question 2c,** have them reread the definition of *polymer*. Then, have them look closely at the structure of lipids in **Figure 2–15** and the structure of proteins in **Figure 2–18.**

BIOLOGY.com Students can check their understanding of lesson concepts with the **Self-Test** assessment. They can then take an online version of the **Lesson Assessment.**

Answers

FIGURE 2–18 four

Assessment Answers

1a. carbon, hydrogen, oxygen, phosphorus, sulfur, and nitrogen

1b. Carbon atoms can bond to the atoms of many other elements. Carbon atoms can also readily bond to one another to form short chains, long chains, or rings, and these bonds can be single, double, or triple covalent bonds. This means that carbon atoms can be combined to make millions of different types of structures.

2a. carbohydrates, lipids, nucleic acids, and proteins

2b. Sample answer: Carbohydrates provide energy, lipids store energy, nucleic acids store and transmit hereditary information, and proteins control the rate of reactions and regulate cell processes.

2c. Proteins are considered polymers because they are made of chains of amino acids. Lipids are not considered polymers because they are not made of chains of smaller units; they are made of a glycerol molecule combined with fatty acids.

VISUAL THINKING

3a. carbon, hydrogen, and oxygen

3b. carbohydrates

LESSON 2.4

Getting Started

Objectives

2.4.1 Explain how chemical reactions affect chemical bonds.

2.4.2 Describe how energy changes affect how easily a chemical reaction will occur.

2.4.3 Explain why enzymes are important to living things.

Student Resources

Study Workbooks A and B, 2.4 Worksheets

Spanish Study Workbook, 2.4 Worksheets

 Lesson Overview • Lesson Notes • Activity: Visual Analogy • Assessment: Self-Test, Lesson Assessment

 For corresponding lesson in the **Foundation Edition**, see pages 42–45.

Activate Prior Knowledge

Ask students if they have ever put together a jigsaw puzzle. Call on a volunteer to draw a simple sketch that shows how two adjacent puzzle pieces might look. Ask students how they can tell that the two puzzle pieces fit together. *(They have complementary shapes.)* Tell them that certain proteins called enzymes fit together with other molecules in a similar way.

2.4 Chemical Reactions and Enzymes

 B.1.1 Organic compounds; B.1.2 Molecules and cellular processes; B.1.3 Cell function and differentiation; B.5.4 Sequence of amino acids: protein shape and activity. Also covered: NoS.6, B.5.5.

Key Questions

What happens to chemical bonds during chemical reactions?

How do energy changes affect whether a chemical reaction will occur?

What role do enzymes play in living things and what affects their function?

Vocabulary

chemical reaction • reactant • product • activation energy • catalyst • enzyme • substrate

Taking Notes

Concept Map As you read, make a concept map that shows the relationship among the vocabulary terms in this lesson.

THINK ABOUT IT Living things, as you have seen, are made up of chemical compounds—some simple and some complex. But chemistry isn't just what life is made of—chemistry is also what life does. Everything that happens in an organism—its growth, its interaction with the environment, its reproduction, and even its movement—is based on chemical reactions.

Chemical Reactions

What happens to chemical bonds during chemical reactions?

A **chemical reaction** is a process that changes, or transforms, one set of chemicals into another. An important scientific principle is that mass and energy are conserved during chemical transformations. This is also true for chemical reactions that occur in living organisms. Some chemical reactions occur slowly, such as the combination of iron and oxygen to form an iron oxide called rust. Other reactions occur quickly. The elements or compounds that enter into a chemical reaction are known as **reactants.** The elements or compounds produced by a chemical reaction are known as **products.** **Chemical reactions involve changes in the chemical bonds that join atoms in compounds.** An important chemical reaction in your bloodstream that enables carbon dioxide to be removed from the body is shown in **Figure 2–19.**

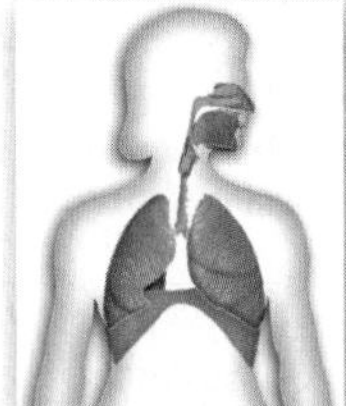

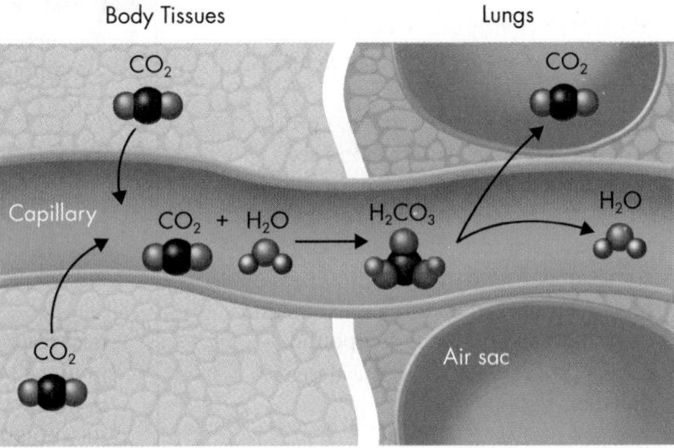

FIGURE 2–19 Carbon Dioxide in the Bloodstream As it enters the blood, carbon dioxide reacts with water to produce carbonic acid (H_2CO_3), which is highly soluble. This reaction enables the blood to carry carbon dioxide to the lungs. In the lungs, the reaction is reversed and produces carbon dioxide gas, which you exhale.

IN INDIANA ACADEMIC STANDARDS

For the full text of all standards, see the Course Overview in the front matter of this book.

B.1.2 Understand that the shape of a molecule determines its role in the many different types of cellular processes including metabolism, homeostasis, growth and development, and heredity, and understand that the majority of these processes involve proteins that act as enzymes.

B.1.3 Explain and give examples of how the function and differentiation of cells is influenced by their external environment, including temperature, acidity and the concentration of certain molecules, and that changes in these conditions may affect how a cell functions.

UbD Teach for Understanding

ENDURING UNDERSTANDING The process of science helps biologists investigate how nature works at all levels, from the molecules in cells to the biosphere.

GUIDING QUESTION How do chemicals combine and break apart inside living things?

EVIDENCE OF UNDERSTANDING *After completing the lesson, give students the following assessment to show they understand how enzymes work.* Ask small groups of students to use various small items (such as different shapes of dry pasta and modeling clay) to create a three-dimensional model of an enzyme-catalyzed reaction. Their model should include symbols for the substrates, enzyme, and products. It should represent each step of the reaction and show how the enzyme is unchanged and ready to catalyze another reaction after it releases the products.

Energy in Reactions

How do energy changes affect whether a chemical reaction will occur?

Energy is released or absorbed whenever chemical bonds are formed or broken. This means that chemical reactions also involve changes in energy.

Energy Changes Some chemical reactions release energy, and other reactions absorb it. Energy changes are one of the most important factors in determining whether a chemical reaction will occur. **Chemical reactions that release energy often occur on their own, or spontaneously. Chemical reactions that absorb energy will not occur without a source of energy.** An example of an energy-releasing reaction is the burning of hydrogen gas, in which hydrogen reacts with oxygen to produce water vapor.

$$2H_2 + O_2 \longrightarrow 2H_2O$$

The energy is released in the form of heat, and sometimes—when hydrogen gas explodes—light and sound.

The reverse reaction, in which water is changed into hydrogen and oxygen gas, absorbs so much energy that it generally doesn't occur by itself. In fact, the only practical way to reverse the reaction is to pass an electrical current through water to decompose water into hydrogen gas and oxygen gas. Thus, in one direction the reaction produces energy, and in the other direction the reaction requires energy.

Energy Sources In order to stay alive, organisms need to carry out reactions that require energy. Because matter and energy are conserved in chemical reactions, every organism must have a source of energy to carry out chemical reactions. Plants get that energy by trapping and storing the energy from sunlight in energy-rich compounds. Animals get their energy when they consume plants or other animals. Humans release the energy needed to grow tall, to breathe, to think, and even to dream through the chemical reactions that occur when we metabolize, or break down, digested food.

Activation Energy Chemical reactions that release energy do not always occur spontaneously. That's a good thing because if they did, the pages of this book might burst into flames. The cellulose in paper burns in the presence of oxygen and releases heat and light. However, paper burns only if you light it with a match, which supplies enough energy to get the reaction started. Chemists call the energy that is needed to get a reaction started the **activation energy.** As **Figure 2–20** shows, activation energy is involved in chemical reactions regardless of whether the overall chemical reaction releases energy or absorbs energy.

FIGURE 2–20 Activation Energy The peak of each graph represents the energy needed for the reaction to go forward. The difference between this required energy and the energy of the reactants is the activation energy. **Interpret Graphs** ***How do the energy of the reactants and products differ between an energy-absorbing reaction and an energy-releasing reaction?***

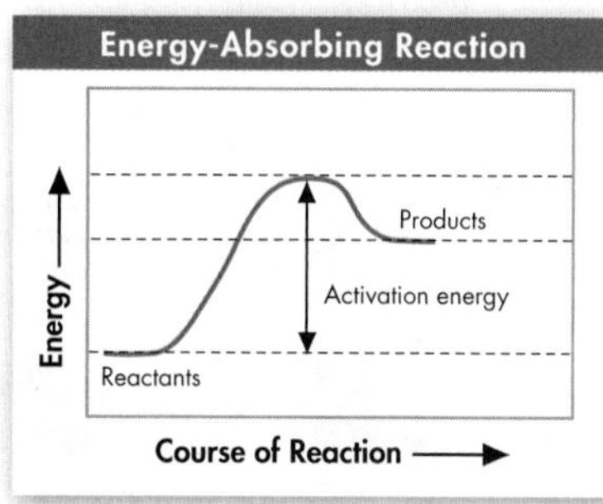

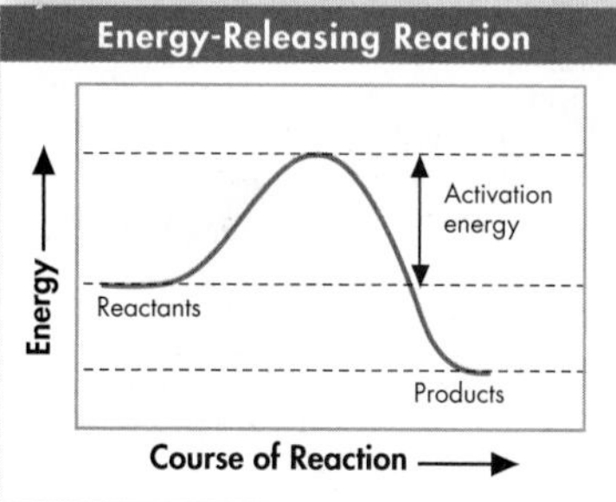

Teach

Use Visuals

Use **Figure 2–20** to help students understand energy changes in reactions. Have each student copy the two graphs in the figure, including all the arrows and labels. When they finish copying the graphs, have them point out the arrows that represent activation energy in the graphs. Then, have students draw similar arrows to represent the difference in energy between the reactants and products in the two reactions. Call on volunteers to describe, in their own words, the difference between the two graphs.

Ask What happens during a chemical reaction when products contain more energy than the reactants? *(Energy is absorbed.)*

Ask What happens during a chemical reaction when products contain less energy than the reactants? *(Energy is released.)*

Ask Which graph could represent a reaction in which food is broken down for energy? *(the energy-releasing reaction)*

DIFFERENTIATED INSTRUCTION

ELL English Language Learners Remind students that reactants are the chemicals at the beginning of a reaction and products are the chemicals at the end of a reaction. One mnemonic device to help the students remember which is which, would be: "Reactants *react* to *produce* products."

Address Misconceptions

Spontaneous Chemical Reactions Students may tend to equate "spontaneous" with "fast." Explain to students that spontaneous reactions do not necessarily occur quickly. A spontaneous reaction proceeds on its own without an added source of energy, but it could take quite a long time. For example, diamonds spontaneously decay into graphite, but this process takes millions of years!

Biology In-Depth

CHEMICAL REACTIONS OF METABOLISM

Metabolism is the sum of all the chemical reactions that take place in living cells. The reactions include both exothermic (energy-releasing) and endothermic (energy-absorbing) reactions. Exothermic reactions make up catabolism—reactions that break down molecules and release energy. An example of catabolism is the breakdown of ATP to form ADP and a phosphate group. This reaction releases about 13 kilocalories of energy per mole and provides most of the energy used by cells. Endothermic reactions make up anabolism—reactions that synthesize macromolecules and absorb energy. An example of anabolism is the synthesis of ATP from ADP and a phosphate group.

Answers

FIGURE 2–20 Energy-absorbing reaction—the energy of the reactants is less than the energy of the products; Energy-releasing reaction—the energy of the reactants is greater than the energy of the products.

Teach continued

Use Visuals

Discuss the importance of enzymes and the way enzymes work. Ask students how the reaction represented by **Figure 2–21** is different with the enzyme than without it. *(The activation energy is lower with the enzyme.)* Explain how lowering the activation energy speeds up the reaction by allowing many more molecules to react. Have students look at **Figure 2–22,** and point out the cyclic nature of the diagram.

Ask Why is a cycle diagram appropriate to show how an enzyme works? *(The enzyme can be used over and over again, which allows the process to keep repeating.)*

DIFFERENTIATED INSTRUCTION

L1 Struggling Students Have students make a simplified **Cycle Diagram** of **Figure 2–22** to show the sequence of steps in an enzyme-catalyzed reaction. For each step in the diagram, they should write a sentence describing in their own words what happens in that step.

Study Wkbks A/B, Appendix S23, Cycle Diagram. **Transparencies,** GO6.

VISUAL ANALOGY

Discuss **Figure 2–23,** the lock-and-key analogy, with the class. Have students identify what the lock, key, and keyhole represent in the analogy. *(lock—enzyme; key—substrates; keyhole—active site)* Tell students that the analogy is a simplified representation of what happens when substrates bind to the active site of an enzyme. For example, rather than being rigid like a keyhole, the active site may actually change shape when substrates bind to it.

BIOLOGY.com With the **Visual Analogy: Lock and Key,** students can interact with an animation to learn more about enzymes and substrates.

Answers

FIGURE 2–22 The carbonic anhydrase is free to catalyze another reaction.

FIGURE 2–21 Effect of Enzymes Notice how the addition of an enzyme lowers the activation energy in this reaction. The enzyme speeds up the reaction.

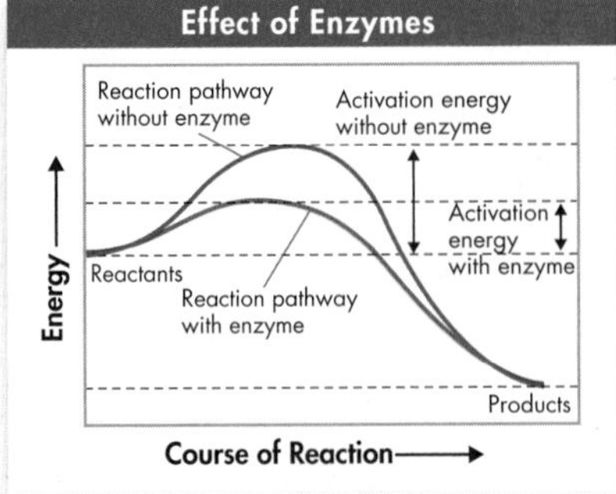

FIGURE 2–22 An Enzyme-Catalyzed Reaction The enzyme carbonic anhydrase converts the substrates carbon dioxide and water into carbonic acid (H_2CO_3). Predicting *What happens to the carbonic anhydrase after the products are released?*

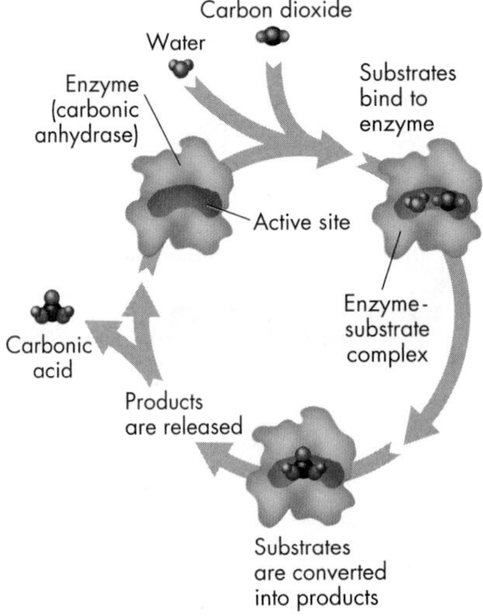

Enzymes

What role do enzymes play in living things and what affects their function?

Some chemical reactions that make life possible are too slow or have activation energies that are too high to make them practical for living tissue. These chemical reactions are made possible by a process that would make any chemist proud—cells make catalysts. A **catalyst** is a substance that speeds up the rate of a chemical reaction. Catalysts work by lowering a reaction's activation energy.

Nature's Catalysts **Enzymes** are proteins that act as biological catalysts. **Enzymes speed up chemical reactions that take place in cells.** Like other catalysts, enzymes act by lowering the activation energies, as illustrated by the graph in **Figure 2–21.** Lowering the activation energy has a dramatic effect on how quickly the reaction is completed. How big an effect does it have? Consider the reaction in which carbon dioxide combines with water to produce carbonic acid.

$$CO_2 + H_2O \longrightarrow H_2CO_3$$

Left to itself, this reaction is so slow that carbon dioxide might build up in the body faster than the bloodstream could remove it. Your bloodstream contains an enzyme called carbonic anhydrase that speeds up the reaction by a factor of 10 million. With carbonic anhydrase on the job, the reaction takes place immediately and carbon dioxide is removed from the blood quickly.

Enzymes are very specific, generally catalyzing only one chemical reaction. For this reason, part of an enzyme's name is usually derived from the reaction it catalyzes. Carbonic anhydrase gets its name because it also catalyzes the reverse reaction that removes water from carbonic acid.

The Enzyme-Substrate Complex How do enzymes do their jobs? For a chemical reaction to take place, the reactants must collide with enough energy so that existing bonds will be broken and new bonds will be formed. If the reactants do not have enough energy, they will be unchanged after the collision.

Enzymes provide a site where reactants can be brought together to react. Such a site reduces the energy needed for reaction. The reactants of enzyme-catalyzed reactions are known as **substrates. Figure 2–22** provides an example of an enzyme-catalyzed reaction.

UbD Check for Understanding

ONE-MINUTE RESPONSE

Ask students to write a one-minute response to the question: What role do enzymes play in living things?

ADJUST INSTRUCTION

Collect and review students' responses. Their responses should show an understanding that enzymes lower the activation energy of chemical reactions and, thereby, greatly speed up chemical processes in cells. Share with the class a few responses that correctly explain the role of enzymes. Clear up any misunderstandings revealed by incorrect responses.

The substrates bind to a site on the enzyme called the active site. The active site and the substrates have complementary shapes. The fit is so precise that the active site and substrates are often compared to a lock and key, as shown in **Figure 2–23.**

Regulation of Enzyme Activity Enzymes play essential roles in controlling chemical pathways, making materials that cells need, releasing energy, and transferring information. Because they are catalysts for reactions, enzymes can be affected by any variable that influences a chemical reaction. **Temperature, pH, and regulatory molecules can affect the activity of enzymes.**

Many enzymes are affected by changes in temperature. Not surprisingly, those enzymes produced by human cells generally work best at temperatures close to 37°C, the normal temperature of the human body. Enzymes work best at certain ionic conditions and pH values. For example, the stomach enzyme pepsin, which begins protein digestion, works best under acidic conditions. In addition, the activities of most enzymes are regulated by molecules that carry chemical signals within cells, switching enzymes "on" or "off" as needed.

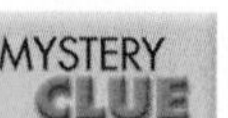

MYSTERY CLUE

The chemical reactions of living things, including those that require oxygen, occur more slowly at low temperatures. How would frigid antarctic waters affect the ice fish's need for oxygen?

VISUAL ANALOGY

UNLOCKING ENZYMES

FIGURE 2–23 This space-filling model shows how a substrate binds to an active site on an enzyme. The fit between an enzyme and its substrates is so specific it is often compared to a lock and key.

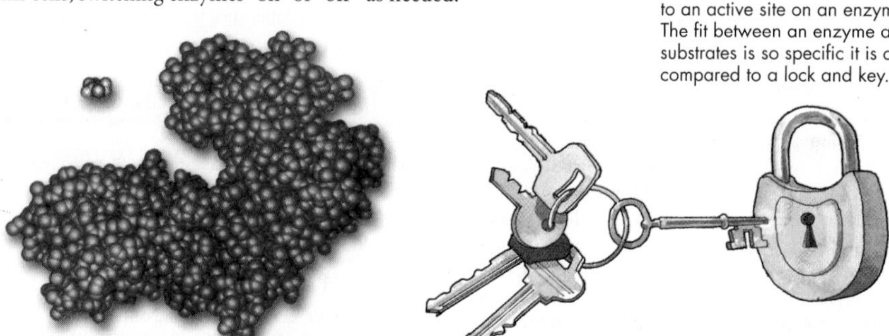

2.4 Assessment

NoS.6, B.1.2, B.1.3

Review Key Concepts

1. a. **Review** What happens to chemical bonds during chemical reactions?
   b. **Apply Concepts** Why is the melting of ice not a chemical reaction?
2. a. **Review** What is activation energy?
   b. **Compare and Contrast** Describe the difference between a reaction that occurs spontaneously and one that does not.
3. a. **Review** What are enzymes?
   b. **Explain** Explain how enzymes work, including the role of the enzyme-substrate complex.
   c. **Use Analogies** A change in pH can change the shape of a protein. How might a change in pH affect the function of an enzyme such as carbonic anhydrase? (*Hint:* Think about the analogy of the lock and key.)

VISUAL THINKING

4. Make a model that demonstrates the fit between an enzyme and its substrate. Show your model to a friend or family member and explain how enzymes work using your model.

BIOLOGY.com Search Lesson 2.4 GO • Self-Test • Lesson Assessment • Visual Analogy

MYSTERY CLUE Frigid water would reduce the fish's need for oxygen, because the fish's chemical reactions would occur more slowly at lower temperatures. Students can go online to Biology.com to gather their evidence.

Assess and Remediate

EVALUATE UNDERSTANDING

Ask students to write a paragraph explaining how chemicals combine and break apart inside living things. Then, have them complete the 2.4 Assessment.

REMEDIATION SUGGESTION

L1 Special Needs If students have trouble with **Question 3c,** have them reexamine **Figure 2–23.** Explain that a change in the shape of an enzyme can be compared to changing the shape of the lock's keyhole. When an enzyme changes shape, it may not fit with its substrate any more.

BIOLOGY.com Students can check their understanding of lesson concepts with the **Self-Test** assessment. They can then take an online version of the **Lesson Assessment.**

Assessment Answers

1a. The bonds change—often they are formed or broken.

1b. because new chemicals are not formed

2a. the energy that is needed to get a reaction started

2b. A reaction that occurs spontaneously releases energy. A reaction that does not occur spontaneously absorbs energy.

3a. proteins that act as biological catalysts

3b. Enzymes provide a site where reactants, called substrates, can be brought together to react. The substrates bind to a site on the enzyme called the active site, forming an enzyme-substrate complex. This reduces the activation energy needed for the reaction.

3c. If a change in pH changes the shape of an enzyme, it might result in the enzyme and substrates no longer fitting together properly. As a result, the enzyme would no longer be able to speed up the chemical reaction.

VISUAL THINKING

4. Students' models should show that the substrates and the active site of the enzyme fit together because they have complementary shapes like a lock and key or like two adjacent pieces of a jigsaw puzzle.

CHAPTER LAB

Pre-Lab

Introduce students to the concepts they will explore in the chapter lab by assigning the Pre-Lab questions.

Lab

Tell students they will perform the chapter lab *Temperature and Enzymes* described in **Lab Manual A.**

L1 Struggling Students A simpler version of the chapter lab is provided in **Lab Manual B.**

SAFETY

Remind students to wear goggles, gloves, and aprons during the lab, because hydrogen peroxide irritates skin and bleaches clothing. Tell them that the puréed liver is raw and may contain bacteria, so it is very important for them to wash their hands after they finish the lab.

Look online for **Editable Lab Worksheets.**

For corresponding pre-lab in the **Foundation Edition**, see page 46.

IN INDIANA ACADEMIC STANDARDS

For the full text of all standards, see the Course Overview in the front matter of this book.

Design Your Own Lab

GUIDED INQUIRY

B.1.2 Molecules and cellular processes. Also covered: NoS.1, NoS.2, NoS.3, NoS.5.

Pre-Lab: Temperature and Enzymes

Problem How does temperature affect the rate of an enzyme-catalyzed reaction?

Materials raw liver, forceps, petri dish, dropper pipette, 1% hydrogen peroxide solution, 25-mL graduated cylinder, 50-mL beakers, puréed liver, filter paper disks, paper towels, timer or clock with a second hand, water baths, thermometers, beaker tongs

Lab Manual Chapter 2 Lab

Skills Focus Form a Hypothesis, Design an Experiment, Measure, Interpret Graphs

Connect to the Big idea Many chemical reactions in living organisms could not take place without enzymes. Enzymes catalyze the reactions that release energy from nutrients. They also catalyze the synthesis of the complex molecules that organisms need to grow and stay healthy. One factor that affects the action of enzymes is temperature. Think about why people store some foods in a refrigerator. The cold temperature limits the ability of enzymes to break down, or spoil, those foods.

Do high temperatures have the opposite effect on enzymes? Do they become more and more active as the temperature rises? In this lab, you will investigate the effect of temperature on an enzyme-catalyzed reaction.

Background Questions

a. **Review** Why do many reactions that occur in cells require enzymes? How do enzymes speed up chemical reactions?

b. **Review** Name three variables that can affect enzyme activity.

c. **Use Analogies** Use eggs and a frying pan on a stove as an analogy for reactants and an enzyme. Use the control knob on the stove burner as an analogy for how a variable can affect the action of an enzyme.

Pre-Lab Questions

Preview the procedure in the lab manual.

1. **Relate Cause and Effect** How will you know that a chemical reaction is taking place in Part A? How will you know in Part B?
2. **Control Variables** In Part B of the lab, which variable will you manipulate? Which variable is the dependent variable?
3. **Relate Cause and Effect** How is the time required for the filter-paper disk to float related to the activity of the enzyme?

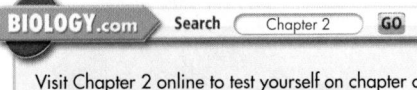

Visit Chapter 2 online to test yourself on chapter content and to find activities to help you learn.

Untamed Science Watch the Untamed Science crew find answers to the mystery of why water is such a special compound.

Art Review Learn about ionic and covalent bonding.

Art in Motion View an animation that shows the process of a salt crystal dissolving in water.

Data Analysis Analyze data that explains the physiological effects of low pH, and the ecological impact of acid rain.

Visual Analogy Compare enzymes and substrates to a lock and key.

Pre-Lab Answers

BACKGROUND QUESTIONS

a. Reactions in cells are often too slow or require an activation energy that is not practical for living tissue. Enzymes lower the activation energy of reactions.

b. pH, temperature, and regulatory molecules

c. Sample answer: The frying pan is like an enzyme. It provides a location where the eggs can be cooked. The control knob allows the user to control the temperature of the frying pan, which affects how fast the eggs cook.

PRE-LAB QUESTIONS

1. I will observe bubbles of oxygen on the surface of the liver. The filter paper disk will rise to the top of the liquid.
2. temperature; reaction time
3. Oxygen produced in the reaction causes the disk to float. The rate of the reaction that produces the oxygen depends on the activity of the enzyme. The more active the enzyme, the faster the oxygen is produced, and the quicker the disk will rise.

2 Study Guide

Big idea Matter and Energy

Chemical bonds join together the molecules and compounds of life. Water and carbon compounds play essential roles in organisms, which carry out chemical reactions in their daily life processes.

2.1 The Nature of Matter

The subatomic particles that make up atoms are protons, neutrons, and electrons.

All isotopes of an element have the same chemical properties, because they have the same number of electrons.

The physical and chemical properties of a compound are usually very different from those of the elements from which it is formed.

The main types of chemical bonds are ionic bonds and covalent bonds.

atom (34)
nucleus (34)
electron (34)
element (35)
isotope (35)
compound (36)
ionic bond (37)
ion (37)
covalent bond (37)
molecule (37)
van der Waals forces (38)

2.2 Properties of Water

Water is a polar molecule. Therefore, it is able to form multiple hydrogen bonds, which account for many of its special properties.

Water's polarity gives it the ability to dissolve both ionic compounds and other polar molecules.

Buffers play an important role in maintaining homeostasis in organisms.

hydrogen bond (41)
cohesion (41)
adhesion (41)
mixture (42)
solution (42)
solute (42)
solvent (42)
suspension (42)
pH scale (43)
acid (44)
base (44)
buffer (44)

2.3 Carbon Compounds

Carbon can bond with many elements, including hydrogen, oxygen, phosphorus, sulfur, and nitrogen to form the molecules of life.

Living things use carbohydrates as their main source of energy. Plants, some animals, and other organisms also use carbohydrates for structural purposes.

Lipids can be used to store energy. Some lipids are important parts of biological membranes and waterproof coverings.

Nucleic acids store and transmit hereditary, or genetic, information.

Some proteins control the rate of reactions and regulate cell processes. Some proteins build tissues such as bone and muscle. Others transport materials or help to fight disease.

monomer (46)
polymer (46)
carbohydrate (46)
monosaccharide (46)
lipid (47)
nucleic acid (48)
nucleotide (48)
protein (48)
amino acid (48)

2.4 Chemical Reactions and Enzymes

Chemical reactions always involve changes in the chemical bonds that join atoms in compounds.

Chemical reactions that release energy often occur spontaneously. Chemical reactions that absorb energy will not occur without a source of energy.

Enzymes speed up chemical reactions that take place in cells.

Temperature, pH, and regulatory molecules can affect the activity of enzymes.

chemical reaction (50)
reactant (50)
product (50)
activation energy (51)
catalyst (52)
enzyme (52)
substrate (52)

Think Visually Create a table in which you compare the structures and functions of the following macromolecules: carbohydrates, lipids, proteins, and nucleic acids.

UbD Performance Tasks

SUMMATIVE TASK Have students work in pairs to create a simple storybook for younger children on the chemistry of living things. In addition to introducing basic concepts such as atoms, molecules, and chemical reactions, students should describe the structure and functions of the four groups of carbon compounds in living things.

TRANSFER TASK Introduce inherited defects in enzymes that are needed for metabolism, or the chemical reactions inside cells. Explain that inherited defects of metabolism can cause serious health problems. Have students work in small groups to identify a particular metabolism defect, such as phenylketonuria (PKU), and create a presentation about it. In their presentation, students should identify the enzyme that is defective, its normal role in metabolism, and how a defect in the enzyme affects metabolism and health.

Study Online

REVIEW AND ASSESSMENT RESOURCES

Editable Worksheets Pages of Study Workbooks A and B, Lab Manuals A and B, and the Assessment Resources Book are available online. These documents can be easily edited using a word-processing program.

Lesson Overview Have students reread the Lesson Overviews to help them study Chapter 2 concepts.

Vocabulary Review The *Flash Cards* and *Match It* provide an interactive way to review chapter vocabulary.

Chapter Assessment Have students take an online version of the Chapter 2 Assessment.

Standardized Test Prep Students can take an online version of the Standardized Test Prep. You will receive their scores along with ideas for remediation.

Diagnostic and Benchmark Tests Use these tests to monitor your students' progress and supply remediation.

Answers

THINK VISUALLY

Student tables should show that

- carbohydrates consist of simple sugars called monosaccharides or chains of sugars called polysaccharides; they provide energy or structure.
- lipids consist of glycerol and fatty acids; they store energy or are part of membranes and waterproof coverings.
- nucleic acids consist of chains of nucleotides; they store and transmit genetic information.
- proteins consist of chains of amino acids; they control the rate of reactions, regulate cell processes, form cell structures, transport substances into or out of cells, or help fight disease.

Lesson 2.1

UNDERSTAND KEY CONCEPTS

1. c **2.** d **3.** b

4. Elements are composed of atoms. Compounds are composed of atoms of two or more elements combined in definite proportions.

5. A radioactive isotope is an isotope with an unstable nucleus that breaks down at a constant rate over time. Scientific uses of radioactive isotopes include determining the age of rocks, treating cancer, killing bacteria in food, and tracing the movements of substances within organisms.

6. Atoms in a compound are held together by chemical bonds.

7. Two electrons are shared in a single covalent bond, four in a double bond, and six in a triple bond.

THINK CRITICALLY

8. The diagram should show that hydrogen and chlorine form a covalent bond. Students can use the chlorine atom in **Figure 2–4** as a starting point and pair one of the seven electrons in its outer level with hydrogen's single electron.

9. 0.1 nm; If 100 million atoms lined up are 1 cm in length, then the diameter of one atom equals 1 cm divided by 100,000,000. This yields 1×10^{-8} cm, or 1×10^{-10} m, which equals 0.1 nm.

Lesson 2.2

UNDERSTAND KEY CONCEPTS

10. b **11.** b **12.** c

13. Cohesion is an attraction between molecules of the same substance. An example is water molecules drawing together, forming beads on a smooth surface. Adhesion is an attraction between molecules of different substances. An example is capillary action.

14. A solution is a mixture in which one substance is dissolved in another. The solute is the substance that is dissolved. The solvent is the substance in which the solute is dissolved.

15. An acid is a compound that forms hydrogen ions in solution. Acidic solutions have pH values less than 7. A base is a compound that forms hydroxide ions in solution. Basic solutions have pH values greater than 7.

2 Assessment

The numbers following the questions refer to Indiana's Academic Standards for Biology I.

2.1 The Nature of Matter

Understand Key Concepts

1. The positively charged particle in an atom is called the
a. neutron. **b.** ion. **c.** proton. **d.** electron.

2. Two or more different atoms are combined in definite proportions in any
a. symbol. **b.** isotope. **c.** element. **d.** compound.

3. A covalent bond is formed by the
a. transfer of electrons.
b. sharing of electrons.
c. gaining of electrons.
d. losing of electrons.

4. Explain the relationship among atoms, elements, and compounds.

5. What is a radioactive isotope? Describe two scientific uses of radioactive isotopes.

6. Describe how the atoms in a compound are held together.

7. Distinguish among single, double, and triple covalent bonds.

Think Critically

8. Use Models Make a diagram like the one in **Figure 2–4** to show how chlorine and hydrogen form from the compound hydrogen chloride, HCl. NoS.6

9. Calculate A nanometer (nm) is one billionth of a meter (1 nm = 10^{-9} m). If 100 million atoms make a row 1 cm in length, what is the diameter of one atom in nanometers? MATH

2.2 Properties of Water

Understand Key Concepts

10. When you shake sugar and sand together in a test tube, you cause them to form a
a. compound. **b.** mixture. **c.** solution. **d.** suspension.

11. A compound that produces hydrogen ions in solution is a(n)
a. salt. **b.** acid. **c.** base. **d.** polymer.

12. Compared to most other substances, a great deal of heat is needed to raise the temperature of water by a given amount. This is because water
a. is an acid.
b. readily forms solutions.
c. has a high heat capacity.
b. acts as a buffer.

13. Explain the properties of cohesion and adhesion. Give an example of each property.

14. What is the relationship among solutions, solutes, and solvents?

15. How are acids and bases different? How do their pH values differ?

Think Critically

16. Propose a Solution Silica is a hard, glassy material that does not dissolve in water. Suppose sodium chloride is accidentally mixed with silica. Describe a way to remove the sodium chloride.

17. Predict As part of the digestive process, the human stomach produces hydrochloric acid, HCl. Sometimes excess acid causes discomfort. In such a case, a person might take an antacid such as magnesium hydroxide, $Mg(OH)_2$. Explain how this substance can reduce the amount of acid in the stomach.

2.3 Carbon Compounds

Understand Key Concepts

18. What does the following formula represent? B.1.1

a. a sugar **b.** a starch **c.** an amino acid **d.** a fatty acid

19. Proteins are polymers formed from B.1.1
a. lipids. **b.** carbohydrates. **c.** amino acids. **d.** nucleic acids.

THINK CRITICALLY

16. The mixture could be separated by adding water. The sodium chloride would dissolve in the water, but the silica would not. The salt could then be retrieved by filtering the silica out of the mixture and evaporating the water.

17. Students should infer that magnesium hydroxide is a base. The base reacts with the acid in the stomach and forms a less acidic product.

Lesson 2.3

UNDERSTAND KEY CONCEPTS

18. c **19.** c

20. Polymers are large macromolecules made up of smaller molecules called monomers. For example, monomers called monosaccharides join together to form polymers called polysaccharides.

21. Proteins control the rate of chemical reactions, regulate cell processes, form important cellular structures, transport substances into or out of cells, and help fight disease.

56 Chapter 2 • Assessment

20. Explain the relationship between monomers and polymers, using polysaccharides as an example. B.1.1

21. Identify three major roles of proteins. B.1.1, B.5.5

22. Describe the parts of a nucleotide. B.1.1

Think Critically

23. **Design an Experiment** Suggest one or two simple experiments to determine whether a solid white substance is a lipid or a carbohydrate. What evidence would you need to support each hypothesis?

24. **Infer** Explain what the name "carbohydrate" might indicate about the chemical composition of sugars. B.1.1

2.4 Chemical Reactions and Enzymes

Understand Key Concepts

25. An enzyme speeds up a reaction by B.1.3
   a. lowering the activation energy.
   b. raising the activation energy.
   c. releasing energy.
   d. absorbing energy.

26. In a chemical reaction, a reactant binds to an enzyme at a region known as the B.1.2
   a. catalyst.
   b. product.
   c. substrate.
   d. active site.

27. Describe the two types of energy changes that can occur in a chemical reaction.

28. What relationship exists between an enzyme and a catalyst? B.1.2

29. Describe some factors that may influence enzyme activity. B.1.3

Think Critically

30. **Infer** Why is it important that energy-releasing reactions take place in living organisms?

31. **Predict** Changing the temperature or pH can change an enzyme's shape. Describe how changing the temperature or pH might affect the function of an enzyme. B.1.3, B.5.4

32. **Use Analogies** Explain why a lock and key are used to describe the way an enzyme works. Describe any ways in which the analogy is not perfect. B.1.3, B.5.4

solve the CHAPTER MYSTERY

THE GHOSTLY FISH

The oxygen-binding abilities of hemoglobin enable the blood of most fish to carry nearly 50 times the oxygen it would without the protein. The ghostly white appearance of the antarctic ice fish results from its clear blood—blood without hemoglobin. Ice fish, however, are able to survive without hemoglobin because of the properties of water at low temperatures.

Oxygen from the air dissolves in seawater, providing the oxygen that fish need to survive. Fish absorb dissolved oxygen directly through their gills, where it passes into their bloodstream. The solubility of oxygen is much greater at low temperatures. Therefore, the icy cold antarctic waters are particularly rich in oxygen.

The large, well-developed gills and scaleless skin of ice fishes allow them to absorb oxygen efficiently from the water. Compared to red-blooded fishes, ice fishes have a higher blood volume, thinner blood, and larger hearts. So, their blood can carry more dissolved oxygen and the large hearts can pump the thinner blood through the body faster. These and other physical features, combined with the chemistry of oxygen in water at low temperatures, enable ice fish to survive where many other organisms cannot.

1. **Relate Cause and Effect** Ice fish produce antifreeze proteins to keep their blood from freezing; their body temperature stays below 0°C. How does low body temperature affect the blood's ability to carry dissolved oxygen?

2. **Infer** People living at high altitudes generally have more hemoglobin in their blood than people living at sea level. Why do you think this is so?

3. **Predict** If the antarctic oceans were to warm up, how might this affect ice fish?

4. **Connect to the**  The chemical reactions in all living things slow down at low temperatures. Since some of the most important reactions in our body require oxygen, how would low temperatures affect the ice fish's need for oxygen? IN B.1.2, B.1.3

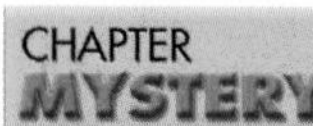

After students have read through the Chapter Mystery, call on volunteers to summarize facts about antarctic waters and ice fish that help explain how the fish can survive without hemoglobin in their blood.

Ask How does the low temperature of the water help ice fish survive? *(The cold temperature allows the water to dissolve more oxygen. The cold temperature also slows the fishes' metabolism so they need less oxygen.)*

Ask What physical adaptations in ice fish help them survive? *(Large gills and scaleless skin allow the fish to absorb more oxygen into their blood. High blood volume, thin blood, and a large heart allow the blood to be pumped around the body faster.)*

CHAPTER MYSTERY ANSWERS

1. Low body temperature would increase the blood's ability to carry dissolved oxygen.
2. At high altitudes, less oxygen is available in the atmosphere than at low altitudes. Therefore, people (and other organisms) need more hemoglobin to ensure that enough oxygen is obtained to supply the tissues of the body.
3. Sample answer: There would be less dissolved oxygen available for the ice fish, and at the same time, their need for oxygen would increase because warmer water temperatures would speed the fish's metabolism. The fish might migrate to colder waters farther south to avoid the temperature change. If, however, colder waters could not be found, the fish would not thrive and might even go extinct. Or, if the change is gradual, the fish may evolve methods to transport oxygen and survive in warmer water.
4. 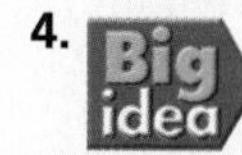 Low temperatures would reduce the ice fish's need for oxygen.

Have students take a video field trip with the Untamed Science crew to learn more about the unique properties of water in **Not a Drop to Drink.**

22. a 5-carbon sugar, a phosphate group, and a nitrogenous base

THINK CRITICALLY

23. Sample answer: Students might suggest trying to dissolve the solid in water, because lipids are generally not water soluble. They also might suggest warming the solid to see if it would soften, because solid lipids tend to soften when heated.
24. "Carbo" indicates that carbon is present; "hydrate" suggests oxygen and hydrogen are present.

Lesson 2.4

UNDERSTAND KEY CONCEPTS

25. a 26. d

27. A chemical reaction can either release or absorb energy.
28. An enzyme is a biological catalyst.
29. Factors that may influence enzyme activity include pH, temperature, and regulatory molecules that switch enzymes "on" or "off" as needed.

THINK CRITICALLY

30. To carry out all life processes, living things need the energy released in chemical reactions.

31. If changing the temperature or pH changed the enzyme's shape, the enzyme might lose its ability to bind with substrates, and an enzyme-substrate complex would not form. As a result, the enzyme would not be able to speed up the reaction it normally catalyzed.

32. The fit of an enzyme and its substrates at the enzyme's active site is so precise that the substrates are like a key and the enzyme is like a lock. Similar to a key in a lock, only substrates of a certain shape can fit into the active site of the enzyme. The analogy isn't perfect because inserting a key into a lock is a physical process, whereas the binding of substrates at the active site of an enzyme is a chemical process. Also, the way substrates fit enzymes is not a rigid process.

Connecting Concepts

USE SCIENCE GRAPHICS

33. 35°C

34. The total product was doubled when the temperature of the reaction increased from 25°C to 35°C. It decreased to almost zero when the temperature was increased to 45°C. Enzymes work best at certain temperatures. The enzyme involved in this reaction works best at about 35°C. A much higher temperature inhibits the enzyme's function.

35. about 1.5 mg

WRITE ABOUT SCIENCE

36. Students' paragraphs may vary. However, they should include a description of the composition and functions in living things of carbohydrates, lipids, nucleic acids, and proteins.

37. Big idea Carbon atoms have four valence electrons, allowing them to form strong covalent bonds with many other elements, including hydrogen, oxygen, phosphorus, sulfur, and nitrogen. Carbon atoms can also bond to each other, which gives carbon the ability to form chains that are almost unlimited in length. Therefore, carbon has the ability to form millions of different large and complex molecules that are the basis of life.

Connecting Concepts

Use Science Graphics NoS.3

The following graph shows the total amount of product from a chemical reaction performed at three different temperatures. The same enzyme was involved in each case. Use the graph to answer questions 33–35.

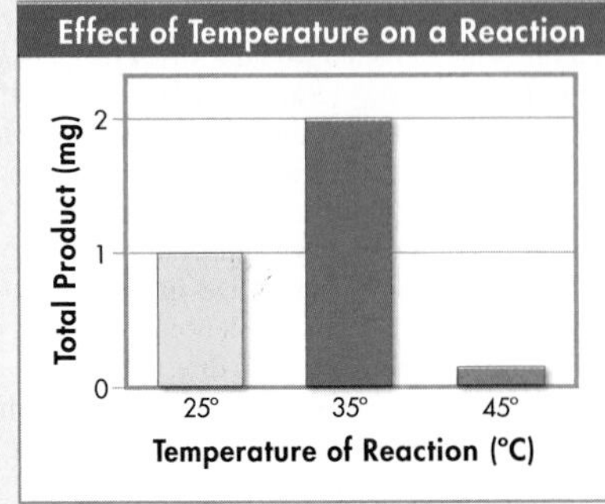

33. Interpret Graphs At which temperature was the greatest amount of product formed?

34. Draw Conclusions Describe the results of each reaction. How can you explain these results? B.1.3

35. Predict A student performs the same chemical reaction at 30°C. Approximately how much product can she expect to obtain? B.1.3

Write About Science NoS.3

36. Explanation Write a paragraph that includes the following: **(a)** a description of the four major classes of organic compounds found in living things, and **(b)** a description of how these organic compounds are used by the human body. B.1.1, B.1.2

37. Assess the Big idea What properties of carbon allow it to play such a major role in the chemistry of living things?

NoS.3

A student measured the pH of water from a small pond at several intervals throughout the day. Use the graph to answer questions 38 and 39.

pH of a Local Pond

pH: 6.0, 6.5, 7.0, 7.5, 8.0, 8.5

Time of Day: 6:00 A.M., 9:00 A.M., Noon, 3:00 P.M., 6:00 P.M., 9:00 P.M., Midnight, 3:00 A.M.

38. Interpret Graphs At what time of day is the pond most acidic?
a. between noon and 6:00 P.M.
b. at noon
c. between midnight and 6:00 A.M.
d. at 6:00 P.M.

39. Form a Hypothesis Which of the following is the most reasonable hypothesis based on the results obtained? B.1.3
a. Pond water maintains constant pH throughout the day.
b. pH rises with increasing daylight and falls with decreasing daylight.
c. Living things cannot survive in this pond because enzymes will be destroyed.
d. pH is higher at night than during the day.

PURPOSE Students will interpret data in a graph and form a hypothesis to explain the data.

PLANNING Remind students that acids have a pH less than 7 and bases have a pH greater than 7.

ANSWERS

38. c

39. b

Standardized Test Practice for Indiana

Multiple Choice

1. The elements or compounds that enter into a chemical reaction are called
   A products.
   B catalysts.
   C active sites.
   D reactants.

2. Chemical bonds that involve the total transfer of electrons from one atom or group of atoms to another are called
   A covalent bonds.
   B ionic bonds.
   C hydrogen bonds.
   D van der Waals bonds.

3. Which of the following is NOT an organic molecule found in living organisms?
   A protein
   B nucleic acid
   C sodium chloride
   D lipid
   B.1.1

4. Which combination of particle and charge is correct?
   A proton: positively charged
   B electron: positively charged
   C neutron: negatively charged
   D electron: no charge

5. In which of the following ways do isotopes of the same element differ?
   A in number of neutrons only
   B in number of protons only
   C in numbers of neutrons and protons
   D in number of neutrons and in mass

6. Which of the following molecules is made up of glycerol and fatty acids?
   A sugars
   B starches
   C lipids
   D nucleic acids
   B.1.1

7. Nucleotides consist of a phosphate group, a nitrogenous base, and a
   A fatty acid.
   B lipid.
   C 5-carbon sugar.
   D 6-carbon sugar.
   B.1.1

Questions 8–9

The enzyme catalase speeds up the chemical reaction that changes hydrogen peroxide into oxygen and water. The amount of oxygen given off is an indication of the rate of the reaction.

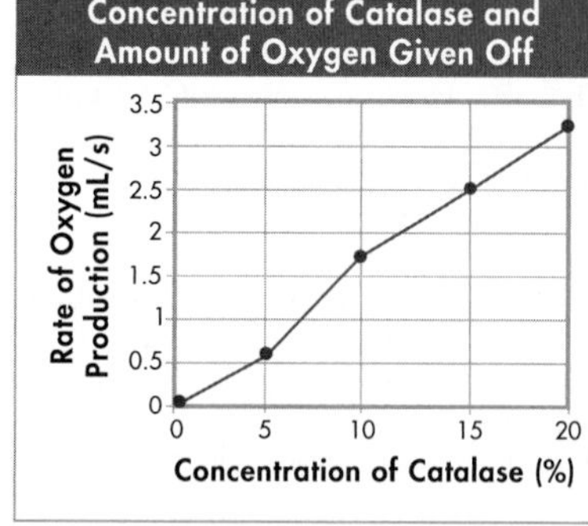

8. Based on the graph, what can you conclude about the relationship between enzyme concentration and reaction rate?
   A Reaction rate decreases with increasing enzyme concentration.
   B Reaction rate increases with decreasing enzyme concentration.
   C Reaction rate increases with increasing enzyme concentration.
   D The variables are indirectly proportional.
   B.1.2, B.1.3

9. Which concentration of catalase will produce the fastest reaction rate?
   A 5%
   B 10%
   C 15%
   D 20%

Open-Ended Response

10. List some of the properties of water that make it such a unique substance.

If You Have Trouble With . . .

Question	1	2	3	4	5	6	7	8	9	10
See Lesson	2.4	2.1	2.3	2.1	2.1	2.3	2.3	2.4	2.4	2.2

Answers

1. D
2. B
3. C
4. A
5. D
6. C
7. C
8. C
9. D
10. Sample answer: Properties of water that make it such a unique substance include the polarity of its molecules, which allows them to form hydrogen bonds with each other. Because of these properties, water exhibits cohesion, adhesion, high heat capacity, and the ability to dissolve many substances.

Test-Taking Tip

USE TIME WISELY

Advise students to skip to the next question if they get stuck on a difficult one. Suggest they respond to the questions they can answer easily first, and then go back to questions they have trouble answering. For these difficult ones, make sure they take the time to reread the entire question before attempting to answer it.

Plan Ahead

After students have read what their task will be in the Unit 1 Project, suggest they review how to design a controlled experiment and what independent and dependent variables are. Also, make sure students understand acids, bases, and pH. If students haven't already tested pH during a previous activity, consider demonstrating how pH paper is used. You may want to direct students to selected experiments in a lab manual to help familiarize them with experimental procedures.

Monitor the Project

Suggest students begin by writing a hypothesis for the first of their three experiments. Briefly check that each student's hypothesis can be tested with a controlled experiment. Then, as they design their experiments, ask individual students questions that will help them identify variables, write a procedure, and think of ways to collect and record data to test the hypothesis.

Ask What are the independent and dependent variables in your experiment?

Ask How will data be collected in this experiment to show whether the medication actually neutralizes stomach acid?

Project Assessment

Make sure students use the rubric and reflection questions to assess their work. Then, use the rubric to assign a final score. Note that it is important to value the creativity of students' work as well as the content when you score their projects. If desired, talk with students about any differences between their self-assessment scores and your assigned score.

Unit Project

Design the Experiment

Did you ever wonder how a medication goes from the lab to your local drug store shelf? A lot of research and experimentation by scientists goes into testing a new medication to make sure it is safe and effective. Imagine you are a scientist working for a pharmaceutical company. Your current project is to test a new medication for heartburn. Heartburn is a painful condition in which acid inside the stomach backs up into the esophagus—the connection between your throat and stomach. This new medication helps neutralize stomach acid to prevent irritation.

Your Task Design *three* possible experiments to test the safety and effectiveness of the new heartburn medication. Before you begin, think about how you will know if the medication actually neutralizes stomach acid. Once you've written your procedures, you will propose the experiments to your company's Executive Board for Research and Development.

For each experiment,

- identify clear independent and dependent variables.
- identify a control.
- form a hypothesis—predict the results you'd expect to find if the medication worked.
- write a specific procedure that tests your hypothesis.

Reflection Questions

1. **Score your experimental designs using the rubric below. What score did you give yourself?**
2. **What did you do well in this project?**
3. **What about your designs needs improvement?**
4. **Are there any ethical dilemmas related to your experiments? Explain.**

Assessment Rubric

Score	Scientific Content	Quality of Experiments
4	Correctly and extensively applies knowledge and understanding of unit concepts (i.e., pH scale) to experimental designs and predictions.	Experimental designs are clever and effectively test the hypotheses. Experimental conditions are carefully controlled and variables are correctly identified.
3	Applies relevant knowledge and understanding of unit concepts (i.e., pH scale) to experimental designs and predictions.	Experimental designs are logical and test the hypotheses. Experimental conditions are controlled and variables are correctly identified.
2	Applies relevant knowledge and understanding of unit concepts (i.e., pH scale) incompletely to experimental designs and predictions.	Experimental designs need some revisions—some parts are unclear or do not fully test the hypotheses. Variables and controls need corrections.
1	Does not correctly apply knowledge and understanding of unit concepts (i.e., pH scale) to experimental designs and predictions.	Experimental designs are unclear and do not test the hypotheses. Variables and controls listed are incorrect or absent.

21st Century Skills

To be successful in the 21st century, students need skills and learning experiences that extend beyond subject area mastery. The Unit 1 Project helps students build the following 21st Century Skills: *Critical Thinking and Systems Thinking; Problem Identification, Formulation, and Solution; Self-Direction;* and *Accountability and Adaptability.*

FOCUS ON COMMUNICATION Extend this Unit Project by having small groups of students design and create a magazine advertisement for a hypothetical heartburn medication. Suggest that the advertisement not only extol the virtues of the medication but also teach the consumer about heartburn medications by briefly describing an experiment that supports the medication's effectiveness. Have groups present their ads to the class.

For more practice building 21st Century Skills, see The Chapter Mystery pages in **Study Workbook A.**

Ecology

UNIT 2

Chapters

3 The Biosphere
4 Ecosystems and Communities
5 Populations
6 Humans in the Biosphere

INTRODUCE the **Big ideas**

- Matter and Energy
- Interdependence in Nature

"Earth is a living planet on which all forms of life are linked to one another, and to land, water, and air. Through those links, energy flows and matter cycles in patterns that support life, including human society. We know enough about these patterns to realize that they are changing, due to human activity, in ways that we don't understand. Our challenge is to study our impact on the biosphere and plan for a healthy future."

Joe Levine

61

Dear Colleague,

Ever since I began helping my dad in the garden as a kid, I've loved plants. So, when my indoor jungle was first invaded by aphids, spider mites, and mealybugs a few years ago, I had a problem. It was too cold to take plants outside to hose them off. But, I wasn't comfortable using insecticides indoors, with my son and our dog running around. On a hunch, I searched the Web for "beneficial insects" and found several sites selling species that prey on plant-eating pests. The best sources supplied information on preferred foods and environmental requirements of each predatory species, so I could select the right ones for my conditions. Soon, my own little Integrated Pest Management system included ladybugs, lacewings, predatory mites, and a beetle named Cryptolaemus*. Those "good bugs" cost a little more than pesticides. But, I could rest easy, knowing that I could keep herbivore populations under control without exposing my son to potentially harmful chemicals.*

This wasn't rocket science. All forms of life on Earth are involved in interactions with one another and with their environment. Natural populations of insects and plants, predators and prey, parasites and hosts, grow and reproduce. They pass through cycles of increase and decrease, rarely going extinct, yet never taking over the planet, either.

Unfortunately, many Americans don't think about food chains or nutrient cycles except during food shortages, droughts, or floods. This level of ecological illiteracy is dangerous, because our species is Earth's most powerful force for change. Human activity now affects not only fish populations in the open ocean, but also vital life-support systems such as the ozone layer and the global greenhouse. I hope this unit helps inspire you to teach your students that human society is part of the biosphere; that biological diversity is a treasure; that clean air, water, and soil are invaluable resources; and that all life is connected. If your students learn these lessons, they and their descendants will enjoy a happier and healthier future.

Joe Levine

The Biosphere

Chapter Contents	IN	Time	Core Resources
Chapter Preview			**Student Edition,** pp. 62–63 **Chapter Mystery,** p. 63
3.1 What Is Ecology? Studying Our Living Planet • Biotic and Abiotic Factors • Ecological Methods	NoS.6, B.4.1, B.4.4	1/2 period 1/4 block	**Student Edition,** pp. 64–68 Inquiry 3.1 Quick Lab, p. 67 L2 **Study Workbook A** 3.1 Worksheets L2 Biology.com *Art in Motion:* Levels of Organization • *Data Analysis:* Counting on Nature • 3.1 Self-Test • 3.1 Lesson Assessment
3.2 Energy, Producers, and Consumers Primary Producers • Consumers	B.3.1, B.3.4, B.3.5	1 period 1/2 block	**Student Edition,** pp. 69–72 Inquiry 3.2 Quick Lab, p. 72 L2 **Study Workbook A** 3.2 Worksheets L2 Biology.com *Art Review:* Producers and Consumers • *Tutor Tube:* Producers and Consumers • 3.2 Self-Test • 3.2 Lesson Assessment
3.3 Energy Flow in Ecosystems Food Chains and Food Webs • Trophic Levels and Ecological Pyramids	NoS.3, NoS.6, B.3.4, B.3.5, B.4.4	1 period 1/2 block	**Student Edition,** pp. 73–78 Inquiry 3.3 Analyzing Data, p. 77 L2 **Study Workbook A** 3.3 Worksheets L2 Biology.com *Visual Analogy:* Earth's Recycling Center **Assessment Resources Book** Visual Quiz L2
3.4 Cycles of Matter Recycling in the Biosphere • The Water Cycle • Nutrient Cycles • Nutrient Limitation • *Technology & Biology: Global Ecology From Space*	NoS.6, B.3.4, B.3.5, B.4.1, B.4.2, B.4.4	1 period 1/2 block	**Student Edition,** pp. 79–87 **Study Workbook A** 3.4 Worksheets L2 Biology.com *InterActive Art:* The Water Cycle • *Visual Analogy:* Interlocking Nutrient Cycles **Assessment Resources Book** Visual Quiz L2
Chapter Pre-Lab	B.4.1, B.4.2	1 period 1/2 block	**Student Edition,** p. 88 L2 **Lab Manual A** *The Effect of Fertilizer on Algae* L2

Differentiated Instruction Tools

Study Workbook B includes worksheets with lesson-level differentiated instruction support and explanations of differentiated instruction teaching strategies.

Lab Manual B includes skills labs, simplified chapter labs, and hands-on activities.

ELL Handbook explains ways to make *Biology* more accessible to ELL students.

Spanish Study Workbook is a Spanish translation of Study Workbook A.

Multilingual Glossary is the glossary translated into ten languages.

Differentiated Instruction Key

- L1 Special Needs or Struggling Students
- ELL English Language Learners
- LPR Less Proficient Readers
- L2 On-Level Students
- L3 Advanced Students

Additional Resources

Biology.com Untamed Science Video • Vocabulary Flash Cards

Study Workbook B 3.1 Worksheets L1 ELL LPR
Spanish Study Workbook 3.1 Worksheets ELL
Biology.com 3.1 Lesson Overview • 3.1 Lesson Notes

Study Workbook B 3.2 Worksheets L1 ELL LPR
Spanish Study Workbook 3.2 Worksheets ELL
Biology.com 3.2 Lesson Overview • 3.2 Lesson Notes

Study Workbook B 3.3 Worksheets L1 ELL LPR
Spanish Study Workbook 3.3 Worksheets ELL
Biology.com 3.3 Lesson Overview • 3.3 Lesson Notes • 3.3 Self-Test • 3.3 Lesson Assessment

Study Workbook B 3.4 Worksheets L1 ELL LPR
Spanish Study Workbook 3.4 Worksheets ELL
Biology.com 3.4 Lesson Overview • 3.4 Lesson Notes • 3.4 Self-Test • 3.4 Lesson Assessment

Lab Manual B *The Effect of Fertilizer on Algae* • Hands-On Activity: *Abiotic Factors: Sand versus Soil* • Data Analysis: *The 10 Percent Rule* L1 ELL LPR

Chapter Review

Student Edition Study Guide, p. 89 L2
Study Workbook A Chapter 3 Vocabulary Review L2 • Chapter 3 Chapter Mystery/21st Century Skills Activity L2 L3
Transparencies, pp. 26–43 L1 ELL LPR L2
Biology.com Untamed Science Video • Editable Worksheets of Study Workbooks A and B and Lab Manuals A and B • Chapter 3 Flash Cards and Match It

Untamed Science DVD • Classroom Resources CD (includes lesson presentations and editable worksheets)

Chapter Assessment

Student Edition Assessment, pp. 90–93 L2
Study Workbook B Chapter 3 Chapter Review L1 ELL LPR • Chapter 3 Taking a Standardized Test L1 ELL LPR
Assessment Resources Book Chapter 3 Test A L2 • Chapter 3 Test B L1 ELL LPR
Biology.com Chapter 3 Assessment • Editable Worksheets of Chapter 3 Visual Quizzes and Chapter 3 Tests A and B

Exam*View* *Assessment Suite* • Classroom Resources CD (includes lesson presentations and editable worksheets)

Time: 1 period, 1/2 block

Pressed for Time?

Preview the Chapter Preview Figures 3–1 and 3–6, and introduce the vocabulary for Lesson 3.2.

Cover the Chapter Quickly Go over Figure 3–1 and have students read *Biotic and Abiotic Factors* in Lesson 3.1. Have students read all of Lesson 3.2, focusing on Figure 3–6. Briefly discuss Figure 3–9, assign students to read *Trophic Levels and Ecological Pyramids* in Lesson 3.3, and go over Figure 3–11. Have students read *Recycling in the Biosphere* in Lesson 3.4.

Assess Assign questions 1 and 2 in the 3.1 Assessment, the 3.2 Assessment, questions 1b, 2, and 3 in the 3.3 Assessment, question 1 in the 3.4 Assessment, and the Chapter 3 Standardized Test Prep except question 5.

Connect to the Big Idea

Big idea The Great White Egret shown in this picture is just one of the many living things found in the Florida Everglades. Ask students to identify some of the other living and nonliving parts of the Great White Egret's environment. *(Sample answers: living: fish, plants; nonliving: water, air)* Have students predict what might happen to the Great White Egret if one of these living or nonliving parts of its environment suddenly vanished. *(Sample answer: The Great White Egret might not find the resources it needs to survive.)* Ask them to anticipate the answer to the question, **How do Earth's living and nonliving parts interact and affect the survival of organisms?**

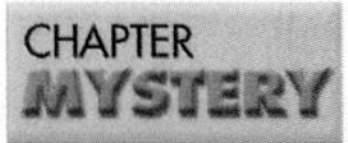

Have students read over the Chapter Mystery. Tell them that the focus of the Chapter Mystery is the interactions that occur among the living and nonliving parts of an ecosystem. Ask students to describe any predictions they might have about the Chapter Mystery's solution. After they have completed the chapter, have them compare their predictions to the Chapter Mystery's solution.

BIOLOGY.com Have students preview the chapter vocabulary terms using the **Flash Cards.**

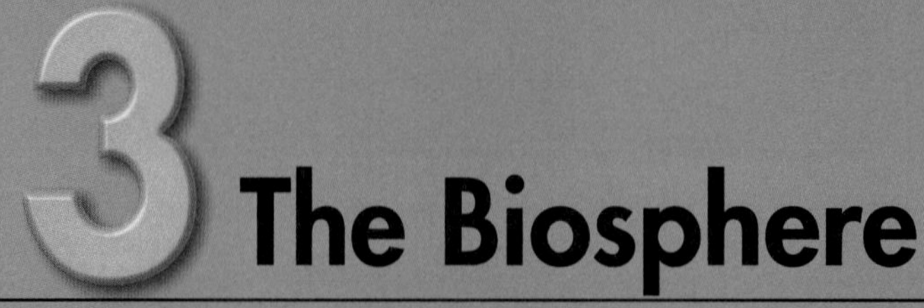

3 The Biosphere

Big ideas **Matter and Energy, Interdependence in Nature**

Q: How do Earth's living and nonliving parts interact and affect the survival of organisms?

Great White Egret among some plants in the Florida Everglades

BIOLOGY.com Search Chapter 3 GO • Flash Cards

62

IN INDIANA ACADEMIC STANDARDS

For the full text of all standards, see the Course Overview in the front matter of this book.

Key standards: Chapter 3 covers key ideas from Standard 3: Matter Cycles and Energy Transfer and Standard 4: Interdependence, including **B.3.4** Matter in food chains and food webs, **B.3.5** Energy in food chains and food webs, **B.4.1** Limiting factors, and **B.4.2** Effects of human activities and natural phenomena.

UbD Understanding by Design

Chapter 3 describes the biosphere and how its living and nonliving parts interact. The graphic organizer at the right shows how these topics connect to the Big Idea, Essential Question, and Guiding Questions. This framework helps students reach the Enduring Understanding of how *the existence of life on Earth depends on interactions among organisms and between organisms and their environment.*

PERFORMANCE GOALS

Students will demonstrate mastery of chapter content through their responses to lesson assessments and their performance of data analysis activities and labs. They will synthesize chapter content while planning a museum display on the movement of matter and energy in ecosystems and while writing a short story written from the point of view of a producer.

INDIANA ACADEMIC STANDARDS FOR SCIENCE

Nature of Science NoS.3, NoS.6; **Matter Cycles and Energy Transfer** B.3.1, B.3.4, B.3.5; **Interdependence** B.4.1, B.4.2, B.4.4. See lessons for details.

CHAPTER
MYSTERY

CHANGES IN THE BAY

Marine life in Rhode Island's Narragansett Bay is changing. One clue to those changes comes from fishing boat captains who boast about catching bluefish in November—a month after those fish used to head south for winter. Catches of winter flounder, however, are not as plentiful as they once were. These changes in fish populations coincide with the disappearance of the annual spring increase in plant and animal growth. Researchers working in the bay, meanwhile, report puzzling changes in the activities of bacteria living in mud on the bay floor. What's going on? Farms, towns, and cities surround the bay, but direct human influence on the bay has not changed much lately. So why are there so many changes to the bay's plant and animal populations? Could these changes be related to mud-dwelling bacteria? As you read the chapter, look for clues to help you understand the interactions of plants, animals, and bacteria in Narragansett Bay. Then, solve the mystery.

Never Stop Exploring Your World. Finding out about Narragansett Bay is only the beginning. Take a video field trip with the ecogeeks of Untamed Science to see where this mystery leads.

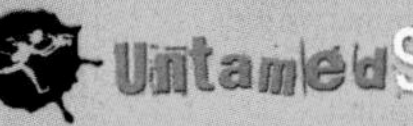

- Untamed Science Video
- Chapter Mystery

Chapter 3
Big Idea: Matter and Energy, Interdependence in Nature

Chapter 3 EQ: How do living and nonliving parts of the Earth interact and affect the survival of organisms?

- **3.1 GQ:** How do we study life?
- **3.2 GQ:** How do different organisms get the energy they need to survive?
- **3.3 GQ:** How does energy move through an ecosystem?
- **3.4 GQ:** Why is the cycling of matter important to life on Earth?

What's Online

BIOLOGY.com Extend your reach by using these and other digital assets offered at Biology.com.

CHAPTER MYSTERY
Students investigate changes in Narragansett Bay to learn more about the interactions of the living and nonliving parts of the ecosystem.

UNTAMED SCIENCE VIDEO
What a tangled web nature weaves! Follow the ecogeeks of Untamed Science as they unravel the relationships in a food web.

ART IN MOTION
Students can zoom in or out to see the levels of organization of living things on Earth.

DATA ANALYSIS
Students simulate a classic ecological data collection method to learn how data are used to monitor a site.

TUTOR TUBE
This online tutorial clarifies producers and consumers and the flow of matter and energy between them.

ART REVIEW
Students can drag and drop labels to reinforce the roles of producers and consumers.

VISUAL ANALOGY
Students compare the reuse of building materials to the recycling of nutrients.

INTERACTIVE ART
This animation lets students interact with the water cycle.

VISUAL ANALOGY
Students can trace the movement of nutrients through the environment.

LESSON 3.1

Getting Started

Objectives

3.1.1 Describe the study of ecology.

3.1.2 Explain how biotic and abiotic factors influence an ecosystem.

3.1.3 Describe the methods used to study ecology.

Student Resources

Study Workbooks A and B, 3.1 Worksheets

Spanish Study Workbook, 3.1 Worksheets

Lab Manual B, 3.1 Hands-On Activity Worksheet

 Lesson Overview • Lesson Notes
- Activities: Art in Motion, Data Analysis
- Assessment: Self-Test, Lesson Assessment

 For corresponding lesson in the **Foundation Edition**, see pages 56–59.

Build Background

Have students identify living and nonliving things in the classroom and record their responses in two bulleted lists on the board. Explain that the classroom is similar to an ecosystem in that it has interacting living and nonliving parts.

3.1 What Is Ecology?

IN NoS.6 Use analogies and models. Also covered: B.4.1, B.4.4.

Key Questions

What is ecology?

What are biotic and abiotic factors?

What methods are used in ecological studies?

Vocabulary

biosphere • species • population • community • ecology • ecosystem • biome • biotic factor • abiotic factor

Taking Notes

Venn Diagram Make a Venn diagram that shows how the environment consists of biotic factors, abiotic factors, and some components that are truly a mixture of both. Use examples from the lesson.

THINK ABOUT IT Lewis Thomas, a twentieth-century science writer, was sufficiently inspired by astronauts' photographs of Earth to write: "Viewed from the distance of the moon, the astonishing thing about the earth ... is that it is alive." Sounds good. But what does it mean? Was Thomas reacting to how green Earth is? Was he talking about how you can see moving clouds from space? How is Earth, in a scientific sense, a "living planet"? And how do we study it?

Studying Our Living Planet

What is ecology?

When biologists want to talk about life on a global scale, they use the term *biosphere*. The **biosphere** consists of all life on Earth and all parts of the Earth in which life exists, including land, water, and the atmosphere. The biosphere contains every organism, from bacteria living underground to giant trees in rain forests, whales in polar seas, mold spores drifting through the air—and, of course, humans. The biosphere extends from about 8 kilometers above Earth's surface to as far as 11 kilometers below the surface of the ocean.

Individual Organism
A **species** is a group of similar organisms that can breed and produce fertile offspring.

A **population** is a group of individuals that belong to the same species and live in the same area.

An assemblage of different populations that live together in a defined area is called a **community.**

IN INDIANA ACADEMIC STANDARDS

For the full text of all standards, see the Course Overview in the front matter of this book.

NoS.6 Use analogies and models (mathematical and physical) to simplify and represent systems that are difficult to understand or directly experience due to their size, time scale, or complexity, and recognize the limitations of analogies and models.

UbD Teach for Understanding

ENDURING UNDERSTANDING The existence of life on Earth depends on interactions among organisms and between organisms and their environment.

GUIDING QUESTION How do we study life?

EVIDENCE OF UNDERSTANDING *After completing the lesson, give students the following assessment to show they understand how ecologists study life and the environment.* Have students work in small groups to identify a question related to ecology. Then, have students identify the method (observation, experimentation, or modeling) that could be used to investigate their question. Have each group write and perform a lecture in which they assume the role of scientists who explain how they would investigate the question they've chosen.

The Science of Ecology Organisms in the biosphere interact with each other and with their surroundings, or environment. The study of these interactions is called **ecology. Ecology is the scientific study of interactions among organisms and between organisms and their physical environment.** The root of the word *ecology* is the Greek word *oikos*, which means "house." So, ecology is the study of nature's "houses" and the organisms that live in those houses.

Interactions within the biosphere produce a web of interdependence between organisms and the environments in which they live. Organisms respond to their environments and can also change their environments, producing an ever-changing, or dynamic, biosphere.

BUILD Vocabulary

PREFIXES The prefix *inter-* means "between or among." *Interdependence* is a noun that means "dependence between or among individuals or things." The physical environment and organisms are considered interdependent because changes in one cause changes in the other.

Ecology and Economics The Greek word *oikos* is also the root of the word *economics*. Economics is concerned with human "houses" and human interactions based on money or trade. Interactions among nature's "houses" are based on energy and nutrients. As their common root implies, human economics and ecology are linked. Humans live within the biosphere and depend on ecological processes to provide such essentials as food and drinkable water that can be bought and sold or traded.

Levels of Organization Ecologists ask many questions about organisms and their environments. Some ecologists focus on the ecology of individual organisms. Others try to understand how interactions among organisms (including humans) influence our global environment. Ecological studies may focus on levels of organization that include those shown in **Figure 3–1.**

In Your Notebook *Draw a circle and label it "Me." Then, draw five concentric circles and label each of them with the appropriate level of organization. Describe your population, community, etc.*

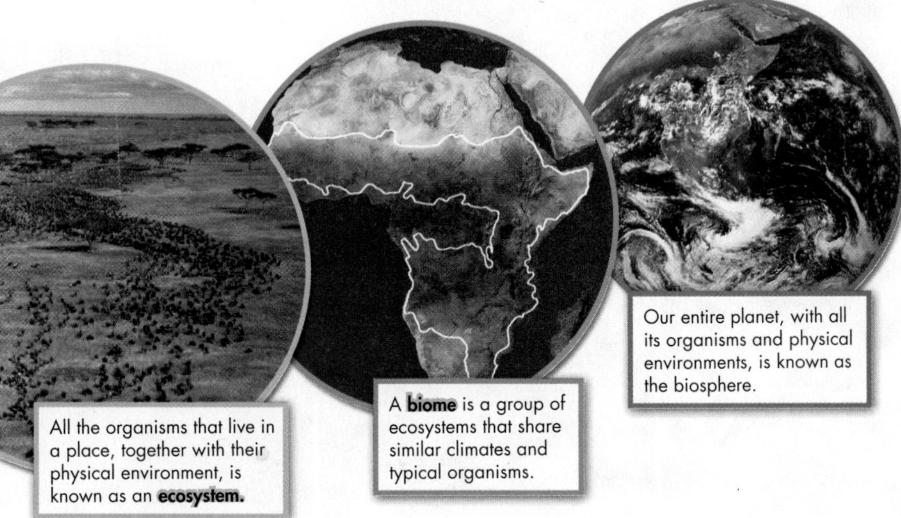

All the organisms that live in a place, together with their physical environment, is known as an **ecosystem.**
A **biome** is a group of ecosystems that share similar climates and typical organisms.
Our entire planet, with all its organisms and physical environments, is known as the biosphere.

FIGURE 3–1 Levels of Organization The kinds of questions that ecologists may ask about the living environment can vary, depending on the level at which the ecologist works. **Interpret Visuals** ***What is the difference between a population and a community?***

How Science Works

SUSTAINABLE DEVELOPMENT

The student text points out the relationship between the terms *ecology* and *economics*. The concept of sustainable development clearly demonstrates the link between these two areas of study. Sustainable development is typically described as development that meets the needs of the current generation while also considering the needs of future generations. Ideals of sustainable development include goals related to ecology, such as the preservation of ecosystems and natural resources, and goals related to economics, such as improved quality of life for individuals in developing areas. The Millennium Development Goals, established by the United Nations, embrace the ideas of sustainable development by including goals such as ending poverty and hunger and sustaining the environment.

Teach

Use Visuals

Use **Figure 3–1** to help students understand how ecologists divide the biosphere into levels. The kinds of questions that ecologists may ask about the living environment can vary depending on the level at which they work. Be sure to discuss all the levels of organization shown in the figure.

Ask What is an example of a question an ecologist studying ecosystems may ask? *(Sample answer: What is the relationship between rainfall and amphibian diversity in an ecosystem?)*

Ask Which levels of organization include nonliving things? *(ecosystem, biome, biosphere)*

DIFFERENTIATED INSTRUCTION

ELL English Language Learners As students read about the root of the word *ecology* (*oikos* means "house"), explain that the suffix *-logy* means "study of." Have students identify other words that contain this suffix. Ask them to predict the meanings of the words they identify.

LPR Less Proficient Readers Have students examine the photographs that make up **Figure 3–1.** For each photo, have a volunteer describe the image using his or her own words. Then, read the label aloud to students. As you move from one photo to the next, point out the relationships between the photos. For example, tell students that the individual organism in the first photo is a member of a population, shown in the second photo.

BIOLOGY.com Students can review online how living things are organized in **Art in Motion: Levels of Organization.**

Answers

FIGURE 3–1 A population is made up of individuals of one species living in the same area. A community includes a variety of species in a particular location.

IN YOUR NOTEBOOK Students' diagrams should include a series of concentric circles with the following labels, starting in the middle circle: Me, Population, Community, Ecosystem, Biome, and Biosphere. Each circle should contain a description along with the appropriate label.

Teach continued

Expand Vocabulary

Point out the word part *bio-* in the term *biotic*. Explain that *bio-* means "life." Explain that the biotic factors in an environment include all of its living parts, such as plants, animals, and bacteria. Then, tell students that the prefix *a-* means "not." Explain that the abiotic factors are the nonliving parts of the environment, such as water, air, and rocks.

DIFFERENTIATED INSTRUCTION

L1 Struggling Students Ask students to define the terms *biotic* and *abiotic* in their own words. Then, have students examine **Figure 3–2.** Ask them to identify and describe the biotic factors shown in the left panel of the figure. Then, have them identify and describe the abiotic factors shown in the right panel. Then, direct their attention to the middle panel, and have them talk about how the environment is made up of both biotic and abiotic factors.

ELL Focus on ELL: Extend Language

BEGINNING AND INTERMEDIATE SPEAKERS Have students write the word *biotic* on one index card and the word *abiotic* on another index card. Show pictures from magazines or this textbook that depict either a living thing or something nonliving. Have students hold up the appropriate index card to describe each picture. Avoid using pictures that include both living and nonliving things. Then, ask students to identify other abiotic and biotic factors that are found in ecosystems. Encourage them to use complete spoken sentences for this activity. For example, "Soil is an abiotic factor."

Biotic and Abiotic Factors

What are biotic and abiotic factors?

Ecologists use the word *environment* to refer to all conditions, or factors, surrounding an organism. Environmental conditions include biotic factors and abiotic factors, as shown in **Figure 3–2.**

Biotic Factors **The biological influences on organisms are called biotic factors.** A **biotic factor** is any living part of the environment with which an organism might interact, including animals, plants, mushrooms, and bacteria. Biotic factors relating to a bullfrog, for example, might include algae it eats as a tadpole, insects it eats as an adult, herons that eat bullfrogs, and other species that compete with bullfrogs for food or space.

Abiotic Factors **Physical components of an ecosystem are called abiotic factors.** An **abiotic factor** is any nonliving part of the environment, such as sunlight, heat, precipitation, humidity, wind or water currents, soil type, and so on. For example, a bullfrog could be affected by abiotic factors such as water availability, temperature, and humidity.

FIGURE 3–2 Biotic and Abiotic Factors Like all ecosystems, this pond is affected by a combination of biotic and abiotic factors. Some environmental factors, such as the "muck" around the edges of the pond, are a mix of biotic and abiotic components. Biotic and abiotic factors are dynamic, meaning that they constantly affect each other. Classify *What biotic factors are visible in this ecosystem?*

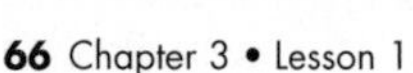

UbD Check for Understanding

ORAL QUESTIONING

Use the following prompts to gauge students' understanding of lesson concepts.

- What levels of organization are used to study parts of the biosphere?
- What are some examples of biotic and abiotic factors found in ecosystems?

ADJUST INSTRUCTION

If students do not understand the levels of organization used in ecology, mention levels of organization with which they are more familiar, for example: student, class, grade level, student body. Ask students to explain how these levels of organization are similar to and different from ecological levels of organization. For students who cannot identify biotic or abiotic factors, have them define the prefixes *bio-* and *a-*.

Answers

FIGURE 3–2 Sample answer: Biotic factors include birds, fish, a frog, trees, grasses, and aquatic plants.

Biotic and Abiotic Factors Together The difference between biotic and abiotic factors may seem to be clear and simple. But if you think carefully, you will realize that many physical factors can be strongly influenced by the activities of organisms. Bullfrogs hang out, for example, in soft "muck" along the shores of ponds. You might think that this muck is strictly part of the physical environment, because it contains nonliving particles of sand and mud. But typical pond muck also contains leaf mold and other decomposing plant material produced by trees and other plants around the pond. That material is decomposing because it serves as "food" for bacteria and fungi that live in the muck.

Taking a slightly wider view, the "abiotic" conditions around that mucky shoreline are strongly influenced by living organisms. A leafy canopy of trees and shrubs often shade the pond's shoreline from direct sun and protect it from strong winds. In this way, organisms living around the pond strongly affect the amount of sunlight the shoreline receives and the range of temperatures it experiences. A forest around a pond also affects the humidity of air close to the ground. The roots of trees and other plants determine how much soil is held in place and how much washes into the pond. Even certain chemical conditions in the soil around the pond are affected by living organisms. If most trees nearby are pines, their decomposing needles make the soil acidic. If the trees nearby are oaks, the soil will be more alkaline. This kind of dynamic mix of biotic and abiotic factors shapes every environment.

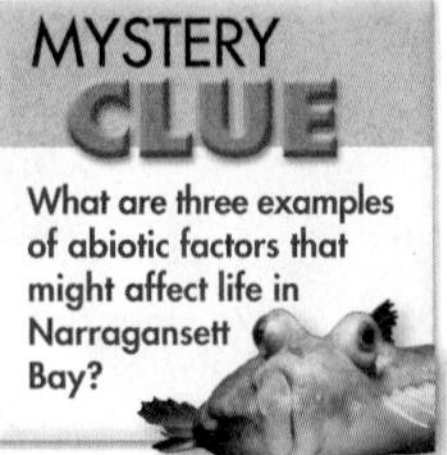

MYSTERY
CLUE
What are three examples of abiotic factors that might affect life in Narragansett Bay?

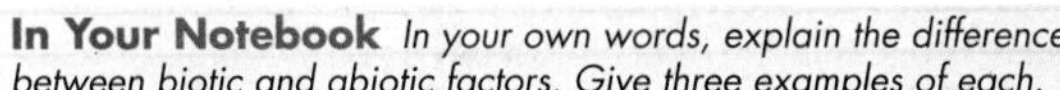
In Your Notebook *In your own words, explain the difference between biotic and abiotic factors. Give three examples of each.*

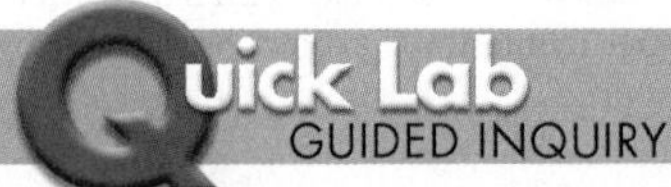
Quick Lab GUIDED INQUIRY

IN B.4.1

How Do Abiotic Factors Affect Different Plant Species?

1. Gather four paper cups. Use a pencil to punch three holes in the bottom of each cup. Fill two cups with equal amounts of sand and two cups with the same amount of potting soil. **CAUTION:** *Wash your hands well with soap and warm water after handling soil or plants.*
2. Plant five rice seeds in one sand-filled cup and five rice seeds in one soil-filled cup. Plant five rye seeds in each of the other two cups. Label each cup with the type of seeds and soil it contains.
3. Place all the cups in a warm, sunny location. Each day for two weeks, water the cups equally and record your observations of any plant growth.

Analyze and Conclude

1. **Analyze Data** In which medium did the rice grow better—sand or soil? Which was the better medium for the growth of rye?
2. **Infer** Soil retains more water than sand does, providing a moister environment. What can you infer from your observations about the kind of environment that favors the growth of rice? What kind of environment favors the growth of rye?
3. **Draw Conclusions** Which would compete more successfully in a dry environment—rice or rye? Which would be more successful in a moist environment?

Connect to Language Arts

Provide students with this more complete version of the Lewis Thomas quote from the Think About It paragraph at the beginning of the lesson: "Viewed from the distance of the moon, the astonishing thing about the earth, catching the breath, is that it is alive. . . . Aloft, floating free beneath the moist, gleaming membrane of the bright blue sky, is the rising earth, the only exuberant thing in this part of the cosmos."

Ask What abiotic factors does Thomas mention in this quote? *(breath, moisture, sky)*

Ask How does this quote show the interdependence of abiotic and biotic factors? *(Sample answer: Although Lewis Thomas mentions only abiotic elements, he describes the Earth as living. Living systems contain abiotic and biotic components.)*

DIFFERENTIATED INSTRUCTION

L1 Special Needs The Lewis Thomas quote uses visual imagery to describe some of Earth's abiotic factors. Ask students to supply other sensory descriptions of abiotic factors, such as the sound of wind or the smell of salt water at the seashore. Further, have students list biotic factors associated with the abiotic factors they have described.

Students should identify three abiotic factors in Narragansett Bay, such as water temperature, levels of nutrients, and water currents. Students can go online to **Biology.com** to gather their evidence.

Students simulate ecological data collection in **Data Analysis: Counting on Nature.**

Quick Lab

PURPOSE Students will be able to describe how abiotic factors affect growth in different plant species.

MATERIALS presoaked rye and rice seeds, sand, potting soil, four paper cups, water

SAFETY Make sure students wear the proper protective equipment and wash their hands after handling plants and soil.

PLANNING Soak the rice and rye seeds in water overnight. Provide trays or shallow containers in which students can place the cups. If rye is not available, wheat seeds can be used instead.

ANALYZE AND CONCLUDE

1. Both rice and rye grew better in soil.
2. Rice requires a moister environment than rye does, but both types of plants benefit from having ample water.
3. Rye would compete more effectively in a dry environment; rice would be more successful in a moist environment.

Answers

IN YOUR NOTEBOOK Students should describe biotic factors as living and abiotic factors as nonliving. Biotic factors include plants, animals, bacteria, and fungi. Abiotic factors include sunlight, air temperature, and precipitation.

Assess and Remediate

EVALUATE UNDERSTANDING

Have students work in groups of four. Ask one group member to name an individual organism. Then, have a second group member identify a population in which that organism belongs. The next student should then describe a community in which the population belongs. Finally, the fourth group member should describe an ecosystem in which the community is found. Then, have students complete the 3.1 Assessment.

REMEDIATION SUGGESTION

ELL **English Language Learners** If your students have trouble with **Question 1b,** have them review the Build Vocabulary feature on the word *interdependence.* Then, have them use the word in a sentence to reinforce its meaning.

BIOLOGY.com Students can check their understanding of lesson concepts with the **Self-Test** assessment. They can then take an online version of the **Lesson Assessment.**

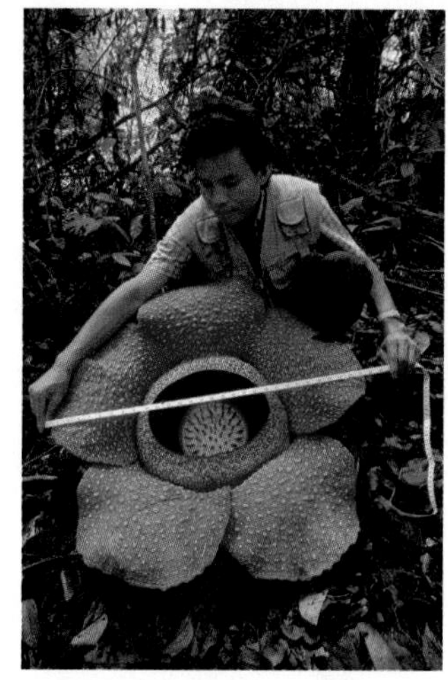

FIGURE 3–3 Ecology Field Work The three fundamental approaches to ecological research involve observing, experimenting, and modeling. This ecologist is measuring a giant *Rafflesia* flower in Borneo.

Ecological Methods

What methods are used in ecological studies?

Some ecologists, like the one in **Figure 3–3,** use measuring tools to assess changes in plant and wildlife communities. Others use DNA studies to identify bacteria in marsh mud. Still others use data gathered by satellites to track ocean surface temperatures. **Regardless of their tools, modern ecologists use three methods in their work: observation, experimentation, and modeling. Each of these approaches relies on scientific methodology to guide inquiry.**

Observation Observation is often the first step in asking ecological questions. Some observations are simple: Which species live here? How many individuals of each species are there? Other observations are more complex: How does an animal protect its young from predators? These types of questions may form the first step in designing experiments and models.

Experimentation Experiments can be used to test hypotheses. An ecologist may, for example, set up an artificial environment in a laboratory or greenhouse to see how growing plants react to different conditions of temperature, lighting, or carbon dioxide concentration. Other experiments carefully alter conditions in selected parts of natural ecosystems.

Modeling Many ecological events, such as effects of global warming on ecosystems, occur over such long periods of time or over such large distances that they are difficult to study directly. Ecologists make models to help them understand these phenomena. Many ecological models consist of mathematical formulas based on data collected through observation and experimentation. Further observations by ecologists can be used to test predictions based on those models.

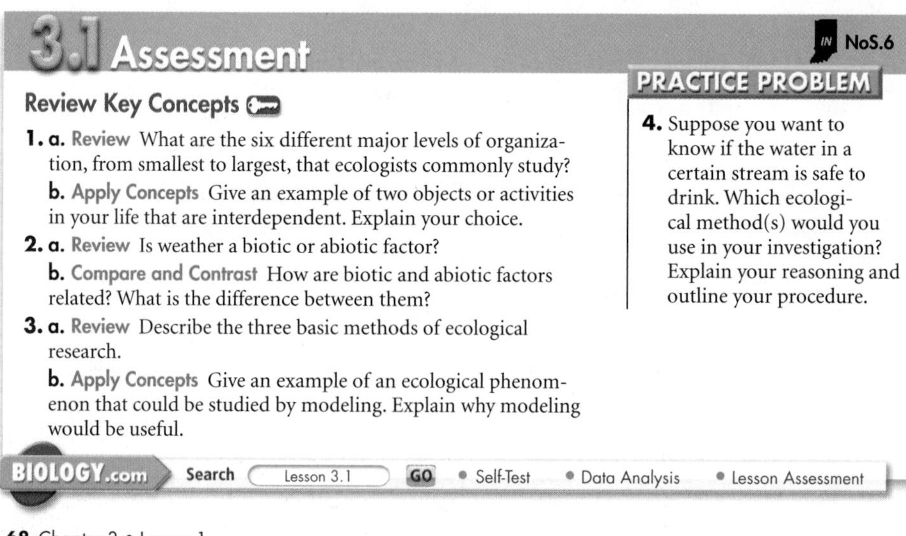

3.1 Assessment

IN NoS.6

Review Key Concepts

1. a. Review What are the six different major levels of organization, from smallest to largest, that ecologists commonly study?

b. Apply Concepts Give an example of two objects or activities in your life that are interdependent. Explain your choice.

2. a. Review Is weather a biotic or abiotic factor?

b. Compare and Contrast How are biotic and abiotic factors related? What is the difference between them?

3. a. Review Describe the three basic methods of ecological research.

b. Apply Concepts Give an example of an ecological phenomenon that could be studied by modeling. Explain why modeling would be useful.

PRACTICE PROBLEM

4. Suppose you want to know if the water in a certain stream is safe to drink. Which ecological method(s) would you use in your investigation? Explain your reasoning and outline your procedure.

BIOLOGY.com Search Lesson 3.1 GO • Self-Test • Data Analysis • Lesson Assessment

Assessment Answers

1a. individual organism, population, community, ecosystem, biome, biosphere

1b. Sample answer: My dance class and my health are interdependent; I need a healthy body to dance and dancing helps me maintain a healthy body.

2a. abiotic

2b. Biotic and abiotic factors are related in that both are parts of ecosystems. Biotic factors are living; abiotic factors are nonliving.

3a. The three methods of ecological research are observing, which is using observations to answer questions about ecology; experimenting, which involves testing a hypothesis in a lab or natural setting; and modeling, which is the use of models, such as mathematical formulas, to answer questions about ecology.

3b. Sample answer: Global warming is an ecological problem that could be studied by modeling more easily than by observation or experimentation, because it occurs over a large area and a long period of time.

PRACTICE PROBLEM

4. Answers will vary. Most students will choose experimenting, which would involve testing a hypothesis about whether the water is safe to drink. Some students might choose modeling, which would involve using a model to investigate whether pollutants or organisms could enter the water.

3.2 Energy, Producers, and Consumers

B.3.1 Photosynthesis; B.3.4 Matter in food chains and food webs; B.3.5 Energy in food chains and food webs.

THINK ABOUT IT At the core of every organism's interaction with the environment is its need for energy to power life's processes. Ants use energy to carry objects many times their size. Birds use energy to migrate thousands of miles. You need energy to get out of bed in the morning! Where does energy in living systems come from? How is it transferred from one organism to another?

Primary Producers

What are primary producers?

Living systems operate by expending energy. Organisms need energy for growth, reproduction, and their own metabolic processes. In short, if there is no energy, there are no life functions! Yet, no organism can create energy—organisms can only use energy from other sources. You probably know that you get your energy from the plants and animals you eat. But where does the energy in your food come from? For most life on Earth, sunlight is the ultimate energy source. Over the last few decades, however, researchers have discovered that there are other energy sources for life. For some organisms, chemical energy stored in inorganic chemical compounds serves as the ultimate energy source for life processes.

Only algae, certain bacteria, and plants like the one in **Figure 3–4** can capture energy from sunlight or chemicals and convert it into forms that living cells can use. These organisms are called **autotrophs.** Autotrophs use solar or chemical energy to produce "food" by assembling inorganic compounds into complex organic molecules. But autotrophs do more than feed themselves. Autotrophs store energy in forms that make it available to other organisms that eat them. That's why autotrophs are also called **primary producers.** **Primary producers are the first producers of energy-rich compounds that are later used by other organisms.** Primary producers are, therefore, essential to the flow of energy through the biosphere.

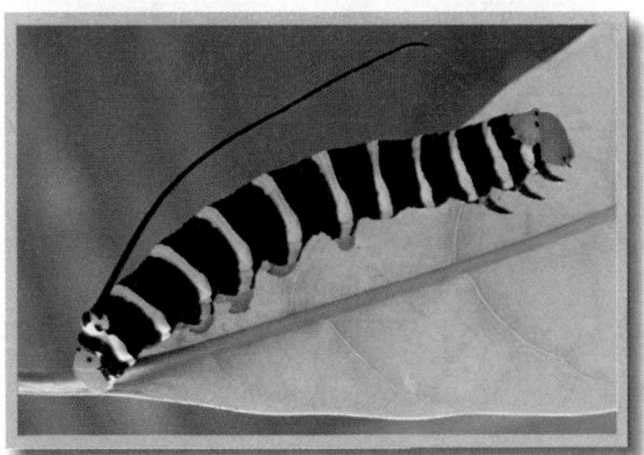

FIGURE 3–4 Primary Producers Plants obtain energy from sunlight and turn it into nutrients that can, in turn, be eaten and used for energy by animals such as this caterpillar.

Key Questions

What are primary producers?

How do consumers obtain energy and nutrients?

Vocabulary

autotroph • primary producer • photosynthesis • chemosynthesis • heterotroph • consumer • carnivore • herbivore • scavenger • omnivore • decomposer • detritivore

Taking Notes

Concept Map As you read, use the highlighted vocabulary words to create a concept map that organizes the information in this lesson.

BUILD Vocabulary

PREFIXES The prefix *auto-* means "by itself." The Greek word *trophikos* means "to feed." An **autotroph** can, therefore, be described as a "self feeder," meaning that it does not need to eat other organisms for food.

Teach for Understanding

ENDURING UNDERSTANDING The existence of life on Earth depends on interactions among organisms and between organisms and their environment.

GUIDING QUESTION How do different organisms get the energy they need to survive?

EVIDENCE OF UNDERSTANDING *After completing the lesson, give students the following assessment to show they understand the ways different organisms get the energy they need to survive.* Have students write a poem that uses all of the vocabulary terms in the lesson. Explain that the poem should convey the meaning of each word as well as use it correctly.

Getting Started

Objectives

3.2.1 Define primary producers.

3.2.2 Describe how consumers obtain energy and nutrients.

Student Resources

Study Workbooks A and B, 3.2 Worksheets

Spanish Study Workbook, 3.2 Worksheets

 Lesson Overview • Lesson Notes
• Activities: Tutor Tube, Art Review
• Assessment: Self-Test, Lesson Assessment

For corresponding lesson in the **Foundation Edition**, see pages 60–62.

Build Background

Make a **T-Chart** on the board, and record students' responses to the following questions: From what do you get energy? For what do you use energy? Students' responses should indicate that they get energy from a variety of foods, and that they use energy for all of their activities and life processes. Tell students that all living things must obtain energy and that all living things use energy.

Study Wkbks A/B, Appendix S30, T-Chart. **Transparencies,** GO15.

 Students can review producers and consumers in **Tutor Tube.**

IN INDIANA ACADEMIC STANDARDS

For the full text of all standards, see the Course Overview in the front matter of this book.

B.3.4 Describe how matter cycles through an ecosystem by way of food chains and food webs and how organisms convert that matter into a variety of organic molecules to be used in part in their own cellular structures.

B.3.5 Describe how energy from the sun flows through an ecosystem by way of food chains and food webs and only a small portion of that energy is used by individual organisms while the majority of energy is lost as heat.

Teach

Connect to Chemistry

Point out the word equation summarizing the processes of photosynthesis in **Figure 3–5.** Explain that photosynthesis is often written using a chemical formula. Write it on the board:

$6CO_2 + 6H_2O \rightarrow C_6H_{12}O_6 + 6O_2$

Show students the correspondence between the word equation on this page and the chemical formula you wrote on the board.

Use this chemical summary of photosynthesis to start a discussion on how the process of photosynthesis affects the atmosphere. Point out that photosynthetic organisms remove carbon dioxide from the atmosphere and add oxygen to it. Tell students they will study the process of photosynthesis in more detail later in this book.

DIFFERENTIATED INSTRUCTION

L1 Struggling Students For students who have difficulty understanding the connection between photosynthesis and chemosynthesis, suggest they focus on **Figure 3–5.** Point out that both processes use energy to produce carbohydrates—energy-rich compounds that organisms can use to power life processes.

Address Misconceptions

Energy in Biological Systems Students may think that energy is formed, or created, by the processes of photosynthesis or chemosynthesis. Students may also believe organisms "use up," or destroy, energy when carrying out life processes. Remind students that photosynthesis and chemosynthesis produce energy-rich compounds, but they *do not* produce energy. Explain that energy cannot be created or destroyed, but it can change form.

Ask Where does the energy for photosynthesis and chemosynthesis come from? *(The energy for photosynthesis comes from the energy in sunlight; the energy for chemosynthesis comes from the energy in the chemical bonds of inorganic molecules.)*

Answers

FIGURE 3–5 Sample answer: Photosynthesis and chemosynthesis are similar in that both use energy to produce carbohydrates.

IN YOUR NOTEBOOK Sample answer: Photosynthetic producers use light energy to produce carbohydrates; chemosynthetic producers use chemical energy to produce carbohydrates. Photosynthetic and chemosynthetic producers are both autotrophs.

Energy From the Sun The best-known and most common primary producers harness solar energy through the process of photosynthesis. **Photosynthesis** captures light energy and uses it to power chemical reactions that convert carbon dioxide and water into oxygen and energy-rich carbohydrates such as sugars and starches. This process, shown in **Figure 3–5** (below left), adds oxygen to the atmosphere and removes carbon dioxide. Without photosynthetic producers, the air would not contain enough oxygen for you to breathe! Plants are the main photosynthetic producers on land. Algae fill that role in freshwater ecosystems and in the sunlit upper layers of the ocean. Photosynthetic bacteria, most commonly cyanobacteria, are important primary producers in ecosystems such as tidal flats and salt marshes.

Life Without Light About 30 years ago, biologists discovered thriving ecosystems around volcanic vents in total darkness on the deep ocean floor. There was no light for photosynthesis, so who or what were the primary producers? Research revealed that these deep-sea ecosystems depended on primary producers that harness chemical energy from inorganic molecules such as hydrogen sulfide. These organisms carry out a process called **chemosynthesis** (kee moh SIN thuh sis) in which chemical energy is used to produce carbohydrates as shown in **Figure 3–5** (below right). Chemosynthetic organisms are not only found in the deepest, darkest ocean, however. Several types of chemosynthetic producers have since been discovered in more parts of the biosphere than anyone expected. Some chemosynthetic bacteria live in harsh environments, such as deep-sea volcanic vents or hot springs. Others live in tidal marshes along the coast.

In Your Notebook *In your own words, explain the differences and similarities between photosynthetic and chemosynthetic producers.*

FIGURE 3–5 Photosynthesis and Chemosynthesis Plants use the energy from sunlight to carry out the process of photosynthesis. Other autotrophs, such as sulfur bacteria, use the energy stored in chemical bonds in a process called chemosynthesis. In both cases, energy-rich carbohydrates are produced. **Compare and Contrast** ***How are photosynthesis and chemosynthesis similar?***

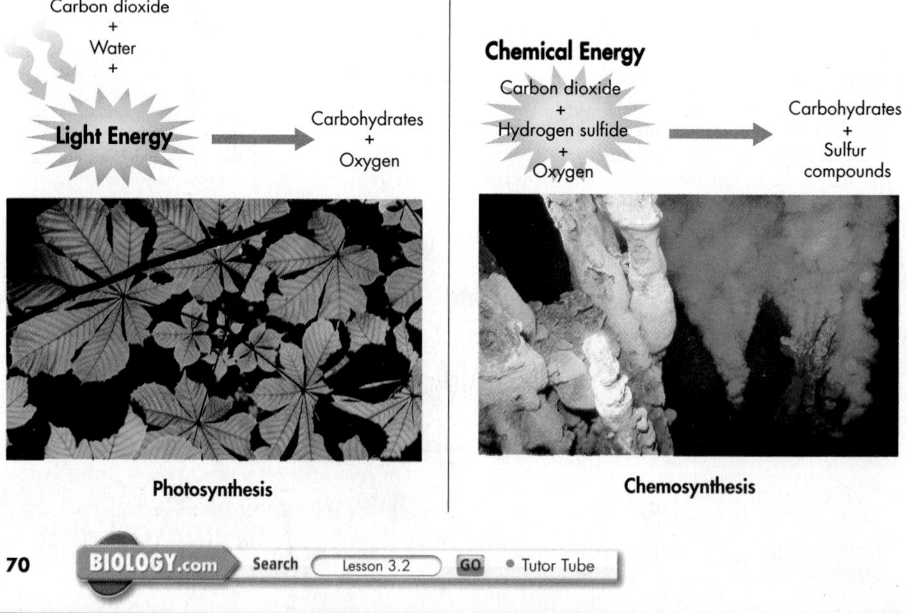

BIOLOGY.com Search Lesson 3.2 GO • Tutor Tube

Quick Facts

POWERING LIFE

Energy from the sun is a vital support of life on Earth. However, much more solar energy reaches Earth each day than is needed to support Earth's producers. Most of the "extra" energy is absorbed or reflected by Earth's surface and atmosphere. In fact, only about 0.06 percent of the solar energy that reaches Earth's producers is converted to chemical energy through the process of photosynthesis. However, even that tiny fraction results in about 170 billion tons of organic matter every year.

Consumers

How do consumers obtain energy and nutrients?

Animals, fungi, and many bacteria cannot directly harness energy from the environment as primary producers do. These organisms, known as **heterotrophs** (HET uh roh trohfs) must acquire energy from other organisms—by ingesting them in one way or another. Heterotrophs are also called **consumers. Organisms that rely on other organisms for energy and nutrients are called consumers.**

Types of Consumers Consumers are classified by the ways in which they acquire energy and nutrients, as shown in **Figure 3–6.** As you will see, the definition of *food* can vary quite a lot among consumers.

FIGURE 3–6 Consumers Consumers rely on other organisms for energy and nutrients. The Amazon rain forest shelters examples of each type of consumer as shown here.

Carnivores kill and eat other animals. Carnivores include snakes, dogs, cats, and this giant river otter. Catching and killing prey can be difficult and requires energy, but meat is generally rich in nutrients and energy and is easy to digest.
Herbivores like this military macaw obtain energy and nutrients by eating plant leaves, roots, seeds, or fruits. Common herbivores include cows, caterpillars, and deer.
Omnivores are animals whose diets naturally include a variety of different foods that usually include both plants and animals. Humans, bears, pigs, and this white-nosed coati are omnivores.
Scavengers are animals that consume the carcasses of other animals that have been killed by predators or have died of other causes. This king vulture is a scavenger.
Decomposers, such as bacteria and fungi (like this mushroom), "feed" by chemically breaking down organic matter. The decay caused by decomposers is part of the process that produces detritus—small pieces of dead and decaying plant and animal remains.
Detritivores (dee TRYT uh vawrz) like this giant earthworm feed on detritus particles, often chewing or grinding them into even smaller pieces. Many types of mites, snails, shrimp, and crabs are detritivores. Detritivores commonly digest decomposers that live on, and in, detritus particles.

BIOLOGY.com Search Lesson 3.2 GO • Art Review

Use Visuals

Have students examine **Figure 3–6.** Divide the class into six groups, and assign one type of consumer shown in the figure to each group. Tell students their group will have about 5 minutes to prepare several questions about their assigned consumer category. Collect the questions, read them to the class, and have volunteers answer any question they did not write. Then, discuss as a class any questions that students have difficulty answering.

DIFFERENTIATED INSTRUCTION

LPR Less Proficient Readers Have students complete a **Frayer Model** for each of the six types of consumers shown in **Figure 3–6.** For each type of consumer, have students write the name of it in the center box, a definition of it in the top left section, a drawing of it in the top right section, an example of it in the bottom left section, and a nonexample in the bottom right section.

Study Wkbks A/B, Appendix S26, Frayer Model. **Transparencies,** GO9.

ELL Focus on ELL: Build Background

BEGINNING AND INTERMEDIATE SPEAKERS Suggest students complete a **Gallery Walk** to build their knowledge of producers and consumers. Post eight sheets of chart paper around the classroom and label each with one of the following: photosynthetic autotroph, chemosynthetic autotroph, carnivore, scavenger, decomposer, herbivore, omnivore, and detritivore. Divide the class equally among the posters, and give a different-colored pen to each group. Have each group write down everything they know about the posted category of organisms. Encourage beginning speakers to draw example organisms. Then, have groups rotate through the posters evaluating previous groups' work and adding any additional information they know.

Study Wkbks A/B, Appendix S6, Gallery Walk.

UbD Check for Understanding

HAND SIGNALS

Present students with the following questions and ask them to show a thumbs-up sign if they understand, a thumbs-down sign if they are confused, or a waving-hand sign if they partially understand.

- How do producers make energy-rich compounds?
- How do consumers get the energy they need for life processes?
- What are some different categories of consumers?

ADJUST INSTRUCTION

Use students' responses to gauge understanding of the topics covered in this lesson. If responses indicate that students are struggling with one or more of these topics, model for students how to make an outline of the lesson. Have each student make an outline, and then have students work in pairs to discuss the topics in their outlines.

BIOLOGY.com Students can drag and drop labels over photographs of an ecosystem in **Art Review: Producers and Consumers.**

LESSON 3.2

Teach continued

PURPOSE Students will identify producers and consumers.

MATERIALS 2 potted bean seedlings, 2 wide-mouth jars, aphids, flexible screening, 2 rubber bands, ladybird beetles, water

SAFETY Students should wash their hands after handling the organisms.

PLANNING Plant bean seedlings two weeks before this lab is performed. Order aphids and ladybird beetles to arrive shortly before the lab is scheduled.

ANALYZE AND CONCLUDE

1. In the jar with no beetles, the aphids harmed the seedling. Less damage to the plant was observed in the jar with beetles. This difference can be explained by the fact that the beetles ate some of the aphids, reducing the number of aphids feeding on the plant.
2. seedling, producer; aphid, consumer (herbivore); beetle, consumer (carnivore)

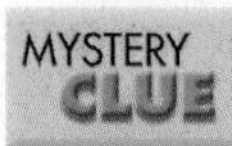

Have students review the role of detritivores and decomposers explained in **Figure 3–6** and link this information to the bacterial community in Narragansett Bay. Students can go online to **Biology.com** to gather their evidence.

Assess and Remediate

EVALUATE UNDERSTANDING

Write each lesson vocabulary term on a separate slip of paper, and place the slips in a container. Have volunteers draw two slips of paper, and use these two words to form a scientifically accurate sentence. Continue until all words have been drawn. Then, have students complete the 3.2 Assessment.

REMEDIATION SUGGESTION

L1 Struggling Students Have students list examples of decomposers and detritivores if they have difficulty answering **Question 2b.**

BIOLOGY.com Students can check their understanding of lesson concepts with the **Self-Test** assessment. They can then take an online version of the **Lesson Assessment.**

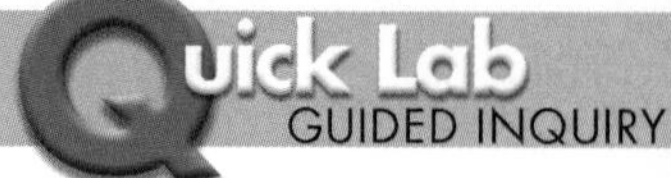

Quick Lab GUIDED INQUIRY

How Do Different Types of Consumers Interact?

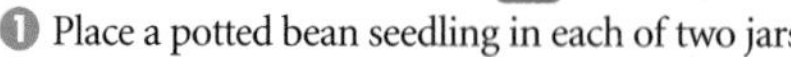

1. Place a potted bean seedling in each of two jars.
2. Add 20 aphids to one jar and cover the jar with screening to prevent the aphids from escaping. Use a rubber band to attach the screening to the jar.
3. Add 20 aphids and 4 ladybird beetles to the second jar. Cover the second jar as you did the first one.
4. Place both jars in a sunny location. Observe the jars each day for one week and record your observations each day. Water the seedlings as needed.

Analyze and Conclude

1. **Observe** What happened to the aphids and the seedling in the jar without the ladybird beetles? What happened in the jar with the ladybird beetles? How can you explain this difference?
2. **Classify** Identify each organism in the jars as a producer or a consumer. If the organism is a consumer, what kind of consumer is it?

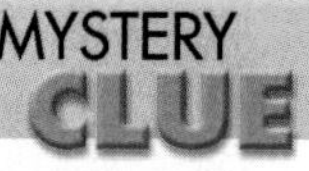

MYSTERY CLUE

Bacteria are important members of the living community in Narragansett Bay. How do you think the bacterial communities on the floor of the bay might be linked to its producers and consumers?

Beyond Consumer Categories Categorizing consumers is important, but these simple categories often don't express the real complexity of nature. Take herbivores, for instance. Seeds and fruits are usually rich in energy and nutrients, and they are often easy to digest. Leaves are generally poor in nutrients and are usually very difficult to digest. For that reason, herbivores that eat different plant parts often differ greatly in the ways they obtain and digest their food. In fact, only a handful of birds eat leaves, because the kind of digestive system needed to handle leaves efficiently is heavy and difficult to fly around with!

Moreover, organisms in nature often do not stay inside the tidy categories ecologists place them in. For example, some animals often described as carnivores, such as hyenas, will scavenge if they get a chance. Many aquatic animals eat a mixture of algae, bits of animal carcasses, and detritus particles—including the feces of other animals! So, these categories make a nice place to start talking about ecosystems, but it is important to expand on this topic by discussing the way that energy and nutrients move through ecosystems.

3.2 Assessment

IN B.3.1

Review Key Concepts

1. a. **Review** What are the two primary sources of energy that power living systems?
   b. **Pose Questions** Propose a question that a scientist might ask about the variety of organisms found around deep-sea vents.
2. a. **Review** Explain how consumers obtain energy.
   b. **Compare and Contrast** How are detritivores different from decomposers? Provide an example of each.

BUILD VOCABULARY

3. The word *autotroph* comes from the Greek words *autos,* meaning "self," and *trophe,* meaning "food or nourishment." Knowing this, what do you think the Greek word *heteros,* as in *heterotroph,* means?

BIOLOGY.com Search Lesson 3.2 GO • Self-Test • Lesson Assessment

Assessment Answers

1a. solar energy and chemical energy

1b. Sample answer: How do organisms that live so deep in the ocean get the energy they need to live?

2a. Consumers get energy by ingesting other organisms or the remains of organisms.

2b. Detritivores are different from decomposers because detritivores feed by eating detritus particles, while decomposers feed by chemically breaking down organic matter on which they live. Decomposers actually produce detritus. In turn, detritivores often consume decomposers that live among detritus.

BUILD VOCABULARY

3. The Greek word *heteros* means "other," or "different."

3.3 Energy Flow in Ecosystems

IN B.3.4 Matter in food chains and food webs; B.3.5 Energy in food chains and food webs. Also covered: NoS.3, NoS.6, B.4.4.

THINK ABOUT IT What happens to energy stored in body tissues when one organism eats another? That energy moves from the "eaten" to the "eater." You've learned that the flow of energy through an ecosystem always begins with either photosynthetic or chemosynthetic primary producers. Where it goes from there depends literally on who eats whom!

Key Questions

How does energy flow through ecosystems?

What do the three types of ecological pyramids illustrate?

Vocabulary

food chain • phytoplankton • food web • zooplankton • trophic level • ecological pyramid • biomass

Taking Notes

Preview Visuals Before you read, look at **Figure 3–7** and **Figure 3–9.** Note how they are similar and how they are different. Based on the figures, write definitions for *food chain* and *food web*.

Food Chains and Food Webs

How does energy flow through ecosystems?

In every ecosystem, primary producers and consumers are linked through feeding relationships. Despite the great variety of feeding relationships in different ecosystems, energy always flows in similar ways.  **Energy flows through an ecosystem in a one-way stream, from primary producers to various consumers.**

Food Chains You can think of energy as passing through an ecosystem along a food chain. A **food chain** is a series of steps in which organisms transfer energy by eating and being eaten. Food chains can vary in length. For example, in a prairie ecosystem, a primary producer, such as grass, is eaten by an herbivore, such as a grazing antelope. A carnivore, such as a coyote, in turn feeds upon the antelope. In this two-step chain, the carnivore is just two steps removed from the primary producer.

In some aquatic food chains, primary producers are a mixture of floating algae called **phytoplankton** and attached algae. As shown in **Figure 3–7,** these primary producers may be eaten by small fishes, such as flagfish. Larger fishes, like the largemouth bass, eat the small fishes. The bass are preyed upon by large wading birds, such as the anhinga, which may ultimately be eaten by an alligator. There are four steps in this food chain. The top carnivore is therefore four steps removed from the primary producer.

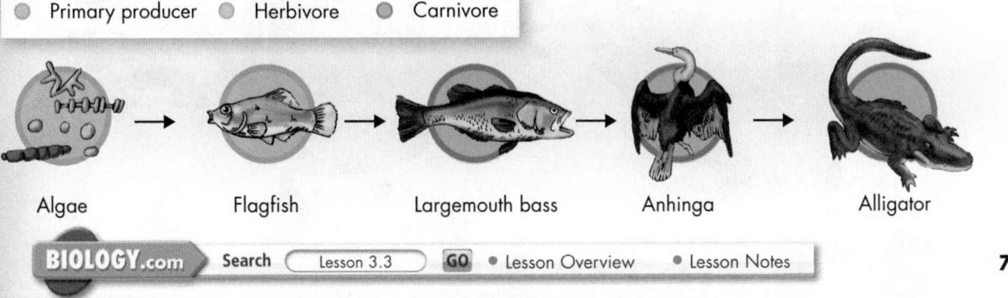

FIGURE 3–7 Food Chains Food chains show the one-way flow of energy in an ecosystem. Apply Concepts *What is the ultimate source of energy for this food chain?*

BIOLOGY.com Search Lesson 3.3 GO • Lesson Overview • Lesson Notes

Getting Started

Objectives

3.3.1 Trace the flow of energy through living systems.

3.3.2 Identify the three types of ecological pyramids.

Student Resources

Study Workbooks A and B, 3.3 Worksheets

Spanish Study Workbook, 3.3 Worksheets

Lab Manual B, 3.3 Data Analysis Worksheet

BIOLOGY.com Lesson Overview • Lesson Notes • Activity: Visual Analogy • Assessment: Self-Test, Lesson Assessment

For corresponding lesson in the **Foundation Edition**, see pages 63–67.

Answers

FIGURE 3–7 sunlight

LESSON 3.3

UbD Teach for Understanding

ENDURING UNDERSTANDING The existence of life on Earth depends on interactions among organisms and between organisms and their environment.

GUIDING QUESTION How does energy move through an ecosystem?

EVIDENCE OF UNDERSTANDING *After completing the lesson, give students the following assessment to show they understand food chains and how energy moves through ecosystems.* Have students write a creative story about the organisms that live and interact in a fictitious ecosystem. Explain that another student should be able to construct a food web for this ecosystem from the details that they include in their stories. Then, have partners exchange stories and draw each other's food webs.

IN INDIANA ACADEMIC STANDARDS

For the full text of all standards, see the Course Overview in the front matter of this book.

B.3.4 Describe how matter cycles through an ecosystem by way of food chains and food webs and how organisms convert that matter into a variety of organic molecules to be used in part in their own cellular structures.

B.3.5 Describe how energy from the sun flows through an ecosystem by way of food chains and food webs and only a small portion of that energy is used by individual organisms while the majority of energy is lost as heat.

LESSON 3.3

Teach

Use Models

Explain that food chains and food webs are types of models. Remind students that modeling is one of three methods used in ecological studies.

Ask Why might scientists study feeding relationships using a model, such as a food chain or food web? *(Sample answer: Feeding relationships may be difficult to observe, and it may be unethical to experiment with them.)*

Ask What type of predictions could be made using a food chain or food web? *(Sample answer: A food web could be used to predict what would happen if a certain population in an ecosystem increased or decreased in size.)*

DIFFERENTIATED INSTRUCTION

L1 Special Needs Show students a picture of a spider web. Have them compare the spider web to a food web.

Ask In what way is a spider's web similar to a food web? *(Sample answer: There are many different connections in both kinds of web.)*

VISUAL ANALOGY

Discuss with students the Visual Analogy shown in **Figure 3–8.**

Ask What do the individual blocks in this analogy represent? *(nutrients)*

Ask What would happen if decomposers were absent from an ecosystem? *(Nutrients would not be released from dead and decaying matter, so there might not be enough nutrients to support the primary producers in an ecosystem.)*

BIOLOGY.com Students compare the breakdown and reuse of building materials to the recycling of nutrients by decomposers in **Visual Analogy: Earth's Recycling Center.**

Answers

FIGURE 3–8 Decomposers break down dead organic matter and release nutrients back into the environment. They recycle nutrients like a city recycling center recycles paper or plastic.

IN YOUR NOTEBOOK A food chain is a portion of a food web. It shows how energy moves from one organism to the next as they feed on one another. A food web is a more complex and complete representation of the feeding relationships in an entire ecosystem.

Food Webs In most ecosystems, feeding relationships are much more complicated than the relationships described in a single, simple chain. One reason for this is that many animals eat more than one kind of food. For example, on Africa's Serengeti Plain, herbivores, such as zebras, gazelles, and buffaloes, often graze upon several different species of grasses. Several predators such as lions, hyenas, and leopards, in turn, often prey upon those herbivores! Ecologists call this network of feeding interactions a **food web.**

▶ ***Food Chains Within Food Webs*** The Everglades are a complex marshland ecosystem in southern Florida. Here, aquatic and terrestrial organisms interact in many overlapping feeding relationships that have been simplified and represented in **Figure 3–9.** Starting with a primary producer (algae or plants), see how many different routes you can take to reach the alligator, vulture, or anhinga. One path, from the algae to the alligator, is the same food chain you saw in **Figure 3–7.** In fact, each path you trace through the food web is a food chain. You can think of a food web, therefore, as linking together all of the food chains in an ecosystem. Realize, however, that this is a highly simplified representation of this food web, in which many species have been left out. Now, you can begin to appreciate how complicated food webs are!

▶ ***Decomposers and Detritivores in Food Webs*** Decomposers and detritivores are as important in most food webs as other consumers are. Look again at the Everglades web. Although white-tailed deer, moorhens, raccoons, grass shrimp, crayfish, and flagfish feed at least partly on primary producers, most producers die without being eaten. In the detritus pathway, decomposers convert that dead material to detritus, which is eaten by detritivores, such as crayfish, grass shrimp, and worms. At the same time, the decomposition process releases nutrients that can be used by primary producers. Thus, decomposers recycle nutrients in food webs as seen in **Figure 3–8.** Without decomposers, nutrients would remain locked within dead organisms.

BUILD Vocabulary

ACADEMIC WORDS The verb **convert** means "to change from one form to another." Decomposers convert, or change, dead plant matter into a form called detritus that is eaten by detritivores.

In Your Notebook *Explain how food chains and food webs are related.*

VISUAL ANALOGY

FIGURE 3–8 Earth's Recycling Center Decomposers break down dead and decaying matter and release nutrients that can be reused by primary producers. Use Analogies ***How are decomposers like a city's recycling center?***

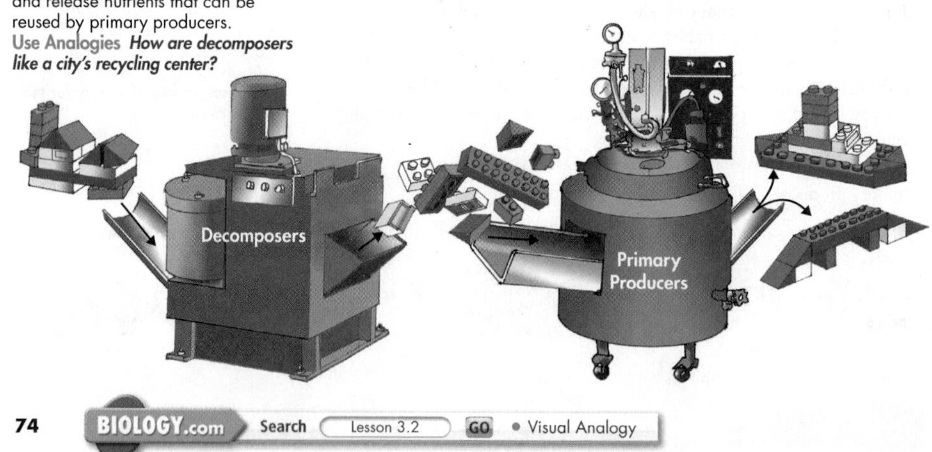

Biology In-Depth

COMPOSTING

Composting is a process that uses decomposers, and sometimes detritivores, to decompose organic wastes. Household composting is usually performed using food and yard wastes. Decomposers break down these organic materials, much as they would in a natural setting. The resulting material, called compost, is full of nutrients and is used to enrich soil. Home composting can range from passive (just throw everything into a pile) to highly controlled. Controlled composting may involve the manipulation of conditions such as temperature, moisture, and oxygen levels to maximize decomposer activity.

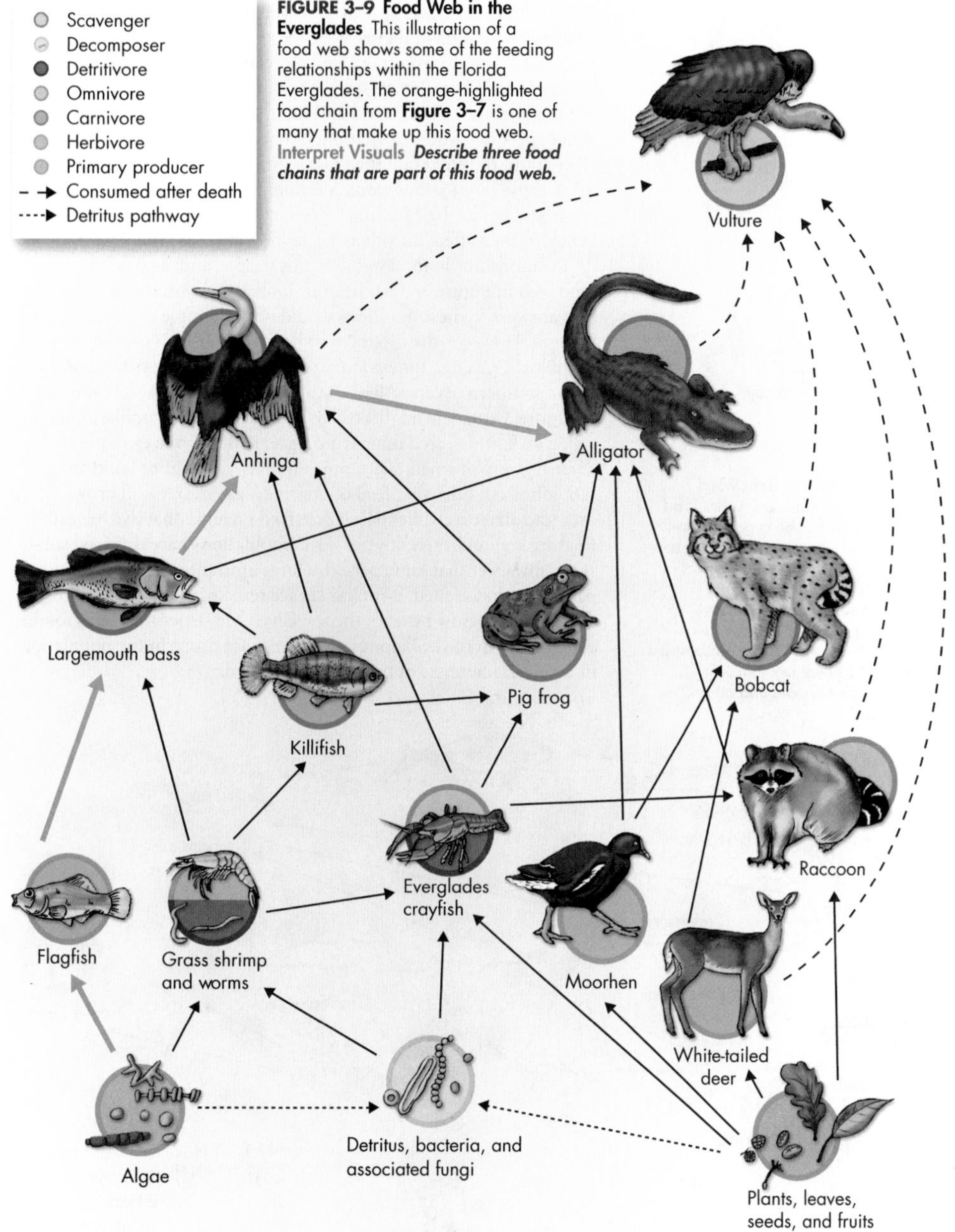

FIGURE 3–9 Food Web in the Everglades This illustration of a food web shows some of the feeding relationships within the Florida Everglades. The orange-highlighted food chain from **Figure 3–7** is one of many that make up this food web. Interpret Visuals ***Describe three food chains that are part of this food web.***

Use Visuals

Students can use **Figure 3–9** to examine feeding relationships in an ecosystem and to review the categories of organisms that make up a food web.

Ask What primary producers are shown in this food web? *(plants, leaves, seeds, fruit, algae)*

Ask What can you infer about vultures from this food web? *(Sample answer: They eat animals that are already dead.)*

DIFFERENTIATED INSTRUCTION

L1 Struggling Students Have students use **Figure 3–9** to examine the structure of a food web and to compare food webs and food chains.

Ask What do the orange arrows in the diagram show? *(the food chain from **Figure 3–7**)*

Ask How does the food chain compare to the food web? *(Sample answer: The food chain is a much simpler diagram; the food web is a more complete representation of the energy flow in an ecosystem.)*

ELL Focus on ELL: Access Content

ALL SPEAKERS Have students work in groups to make a food chain or a food web, using pictures from magazines. Integrate beginning speakers with intermediate, advanced, and advanced high speakers. Have beginning speakers use single written or spoken words to describe the components of their food chain or food web. Intermediate speakers should describe their food chain or food web using simple sentences. Challenge advanced and advanced high speakers to compare and contrast a food chain and food web.

UbD Check for Understanding

FOLLOW-UP PROBES

Ask Why is a food web a more accurate representation of the feeding relationships in an ecosystem than a food chain? *(An organism is rarely food for or feeds on just one other organism; a food web shows the many different feeding relationships that exist between organisms in an ecosystem.)*

ADJUST INSTRUCTION

If responses indicate that students do not understand why a food web is a more accurate representation of feeding relationships than a food chain, have them discuss the foods they eat on a typical day. Point out that they consume foods from many different sources. Explain that most living things feed on more than one type of food, and many living things are themselves food for many other types of organisms.

Answers

FIGURE 3–9 Students should identify three food chains in the food web. Sample answer: Plants are eaten by raccoons; raccoons are eaten by alligators.

LESSON 3.3

Teach continued

Build Science Skills

Have students explore how food webs can be used to make predictions. Explain that food webs, like most models used in science, can be used to predict the impact that a change in one factor will have on other factors. Refer students to **Figure 3–10,** and have them use it to make predictions.

Ask How might an increase in the herring population affect the emperor penguin population? Explain. *(Emperor penguins eat herring. An increase in the emperor penguin's food source would likely lead to an increase in their population.)*

Ask Suppose the killer whale population is significantly reduced by disease. How might this affect the leopard seal population? *(A decrease in the killer whale population might lead to an increase in the leopard seal population, because killer whales are the leopard seal's only predator.)*

DIFFERENTIATED INSTRUCTION

L3 **Advanced Students** Have students work in small groups to research another food web that has been changed by human action or natural disturbance. Have each group share its findings with the class by presenting a short report. Ask each group to include a food web diagram as a part of its report.

Lead students to conclude that zooplankton grazing on the algae will likely reduce or eliminate the late-winter algae bloom. Students can go online to **Biology.com** to gather their evidence.

Answers

FIGURE 3–10 Krill are the only herbivores in this food web; without krill, the animals the killer whale eats would not survive.

Researchers discovered that zooplankton in Narragansett Bay now graze on floating algae more actively through the winter than they ever did before. What effect do you think this might have on the annual late-winter "bloom" of algae that occurs in the water?

Food Webs and Disturbance Food webs are complex, so it is often difficult to predict exactly how they will respond to environmental change. Look again at **Figure 3–9,** and think about the questions an ecologist might ask about the feeding relationships in it following a disturbance. What if an oil spill, for example, caused a serious decline in the number of the bacteria and fungi that break down detritus? What effect do you think that might have on populations of crayfish? How about the effects on the grass shrimp and the worms? Do you think those populations would decline? If they did decline, how might pig frogs change their feeding behavior? How might the change in frog behavior then affect the other species on which the frog feeds?

Relationships in food webs are not simple, and, as you know, the food web in **Figure 3–9** has been simplified! So, you might expect that answers to these questions would not be simple either, and you'd be right. However, disturbances *do* happen, and their effects can be dramatic. Consider, for example, one of the most important food webs in the southern oceans. All of the animals in this food web, shown in **Figure 3–10,** depend directly or indirectly on shrimplike animals called krill, which feed on marine algae. Krill are one example of a diverse group of small, swimming animals, called **zooplankton** (zoh oh PLANK tun), that feed on marine algae. Adult krill browse on algae offshore, while their larvae feed on algae that live beneath floating sea ice. In recent years, krill populations have dropped substantially. Over that same period, a large amount of sea ice around Antarctica has melted. With less sea ice remaining, there are fewer of the algae that grow beneath the ice. Given the structure of this food web, a drop in the krill population can cause drops in the populations of all other members of the food web shown.

FIGURE 3–10 Antarctic Food Web All of the animals in this food web depend on one organism: krill. Disturbances to the krill's food source, marine algae, have the potential to cause changes in all of the populations connected to the algae through this food web. **Interpret Visuals** ***What do ecologists mean when they say that killer whales indirectly depend on krill for survival?***

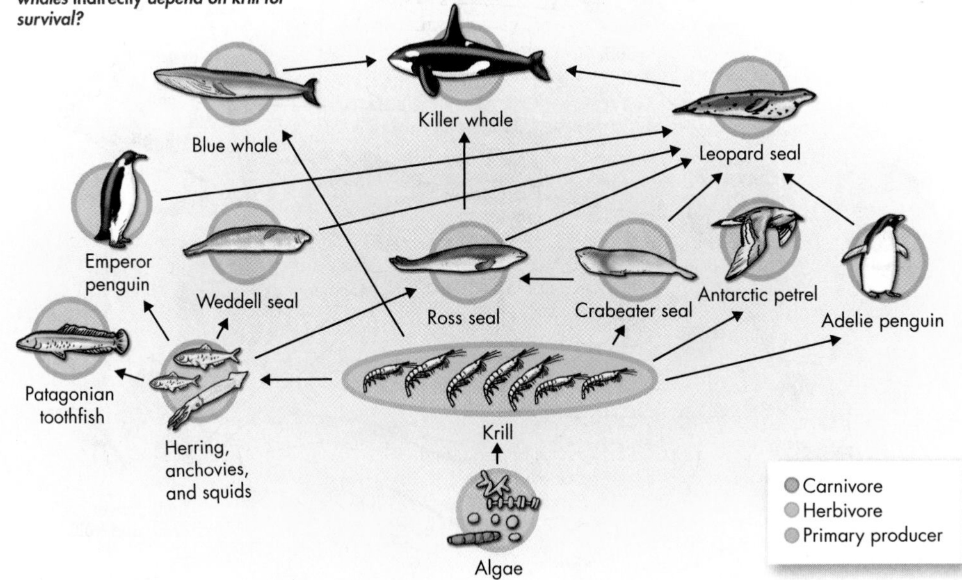

How Science Works

USING ISOTOPES TO STUDY FOOD WEBS

Stable isotopes are naturally occurring, nonradioactive forms of atoms. For example, stable isotopes of carbon and nitrogen include carbon 12 (^{12}C), carbon 13 (^{13}C), nitrogen 14 (^{14}N), and nitrogen 15 (^{15}N). In any given tissue sample, there is a certain amount of all of these isotopes. Finding the ratio of carbon isotopes to each other, as well as the ratio of nitrogen isotopes, helps scientists investigate the donor organism's relative trophic level within an ecosystem. This technique is based on the finding that organisms tend to selectively metabolize the lighter isotopes of carbon and nitrogen (^{12}C and ^{14}N). So, organisms in higher trophic levels often accumulate more of the heavier isotopes (^{13}C and ^{15}N) relative to the lighter ones. In fact, an organism's ^{15}N ratio tends to be about 0.3 percent higher than that of the organisms it eats.

Trophic Levels and Ecological Pyramids

What do the three types of ecological pyramids illustrate?

Each step in a food chain or food web is called a **trophic level.** Primary producers always make up the first trophic level. Various consumers occupy every other level. One way to illustrate the trophic levels in an ecosystem is with an ecological pyramid. **Ecological pyramids** show the relative amount of energy or matter contained within each trophic level in a given food chain or food web. There are three different types of ecological pyramids: pyramids of energy, pyramids of biomass, and pyramids of numbers.

In Your Notebook *Make a two-column chart to compare the three types of ecological pyramids.*

Pyramids of Energy Theoretically, there is no limit to the number of trophic levels in a food web or the number of organisms that live on each level. But there is one catch. Only a small portion of the energy that passes through any given trophic level is ultimately stored in the bodies of organisms at the next level. This is because organisms expend much of the energy they acquire on life processes, such as respiration, movement, growth, and reproduction. Most of the remaining energy is released into the environment as heat—a byproduct of these activities. **Pyramids of energy show the relative amount of energy available at each trophic level of a food chain or food web.**

The efficiency of energy transfer from one trophic level to another varies. On average, about 10 percent of the energy available within one trophic level is transferred to the next trophic level, as shown in **Figure 3–11.** For instance, one tenth of the solar energy captured and stored in the leaves of grasses ends up stored in the tissues of cows and other grazers. One tenth of *that* energy—10 percent of 10 percent, or 1 percent of the original amount—gets stored in the tissues of humans who eat cows. Thus, the more levels that exist between a producer and a given consumer, the smaller the percentage of the original energy from producers that is available to that consumer.

Analyzing Data

The 10 Percent Rule

As shown in **Figure 3–11,** an energy pyramid is a diagram that illustrates the transfer of energy through a food chain or food web. In general, only 10 percent of the energy available in one level is stored in the level above. Look at **Figure 3–11** and answer the questions below.

1. Calculate If there are 1000 units of energy available at the producer level of the energy pyramid, approximately how many units of energy are available to the third-level consumer? MATH

2. Interpret Diagrams What is the original source of the energy that flows through most ecosystems? Why must there be a continuous supply of energy into the ecosystem?

3. Infer Why are there usually fewer organisms in the top levels of an energy pyramid?

IN NoS.3, B.3.5

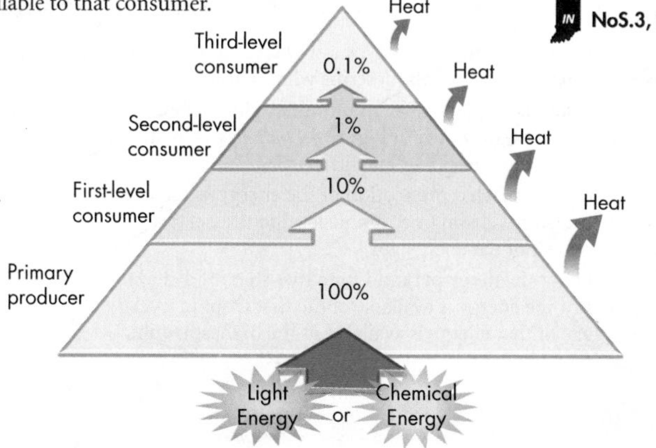

FIGURE 3–11 Pyramid of Energy Pyramids of energy show the relative amount of energy available at each trophic level. An ecosystem requires a constant supply of energy from photosynthetic or chemosynthetic producers. **Apply Concepts** ***Explain how the amount of energy available at each trophic level often limits the number of organisms that each level can support.***

Build Math Skills

Have students examine **Figure 3–11.** Point out that the percentages shown at each level of the pyramid of energy are percentages of the *original* energy entering the food chain. Explain that, at each transfer, about 10 percent of the energy from one trophic level is available to move to the organisms at the next trophic level.

Ask If this food chain included fourth-level consumers, what percentage of the original energy would be available to those organisms? *(0.01%)*

DIFFERENTIATED INSTRUCTION

L1 Struggling Students For students who have difficulty with the percentages in **Figure 3–11,** model the relative loss of energy using example numbers and organisms. Tell students to suppose that a particular plant produces 200 Calories worth of food. Ninety percent of this is either used to power the plant's life processes or lost as heat. Therefore, only 10 percent of the 200 Calories will be available to a mouse (first-level consumer) that eats the plant. On the board, show how to calculate 10 percent of 200 Calories. Write:

200 Calories (0.01) = 20 Calories

Then, explain that of this 20 Calories, only 10 percent will be available to an owl (second-level consumer) that eats the mouse. Write:

20 Calories (0.01) = 2 Calories

Using this example, make sure students understand the overarching concept: only a small part of the energy an organism takes in during its lifetime can be passed to the next organism in the food chain.

PURPOSE Students will calculate the relative amount of energy available at each level of a food chain or web.

PLANNING Remind students that energy is transferred between organisms when one organism eats another. Explain that the amount of energy decreases at each level not because it is "destroyed" but because it is changed to a form (heat) that is lost to the environment and, therefore, unavailable to organisms in higher trophic levels.

ANSWERS

1. 1 unit

2. Solar energy is the original source of energy in most ecosystems. There must be a continuous supply of energy because energy, unlike matter, flows one way through ecosystems. Energy that is converted to heat is lost to the environment, so more energy must enter the ecosystem to replace it.

3. There are usually fewer organisms at the top pyramid levels because there is much less energy available.

Answers

FIGURE 3–11 A trophic level cannot contain more organisms than there is energy to support.

IN YOUR NOTEBOOK Students' charts should list the three types of pyramids in the left column and facts about each type in the right column.

Teach continued

Lead a Discussion

Make sure students can differentiate between a biomass pyramid and a pyramid of numbers.

Ask Which pyramid shows the amount of organic matter at each trophic level? *(biomass pyramid)*

DIFFERENTIATED INSTRUCTION

L3 Advanced Students Have students write a paragraph comparing and contrasting food webs and ecological pyramids. Their paragraph should identify two similarities and two differences.

Assess and Remediate

EVALUATE UNDERSTANDING

On the board, write the question: How does energy move through an ecosystem? Have each student write a short response. Call on volunteers to share their responses with the class. Then, have students complete the 3.3 Assessment.

REMEDIATION SUGGESTION

L1 Struggling Students If students have difficulty answering **Question 3,** suggest they use a finger to trace over the arrows that connect organisms to help them find and follow a food chain within the food web.

BIOLOGY.com Students can check their understanding of lesson concepts with the **Self-Test** assessment. They can then take an online version of the **Lesson Assessment.**

FIGURE 3–12 Pyramids of Biomass and Numbers In most cases, pyramids of biomass and numbers follow the same general pattern. In the field modeled here, there are more individual primary producers than first-level consumers. Likewise, the primary producers collectively have more mass. The same patterns hold for the second and third-level consumers. With each step to a higher trophic level, biomass and numbers decrease.

Pyramids of Biomass and Numbers The total amount of living tissue within a given trophic level is called its **biomass.** Biomass is usually measured in grams of organic matter per unit area. The amount of biomass a given trophic level can support is determined, in part, by the amount of energy available. **A pyramid of biomass illustrates the relative amount of living organic matter available at each trophic level in an ecosystem.**

Ecologists interested in the number of organisms at each trophic level uses a pyramid of numbers. **A pyramid of numbers shows the relative number of individual organisms at each trophic level in an ecosystem.** In most ecosystems, the shape of the pyramid of numbers is similar to the shape of the pyramid of biomass for the same ecosystem. In this shape, the numbers of individuals on each level decrease from the level below it. To understand this point more clearly, imagine that an ecologist marked off several square meters in a field, and then weighed and counted every organism in that area. The result might look something like the pyramid in **Figure 3–12.**

In some cases, however, consumers are much less massive than organisms they feed upon. Thousands of insects may graze on a single tree, for example, and countless mosquitos can feed off a few deer. Both the tree and deer have a lot of biomass, but they each represent only one organism. In such cases, the pyramid of numbers may be turned upside down, but the pyramid of biomass usually has the normal orientation.

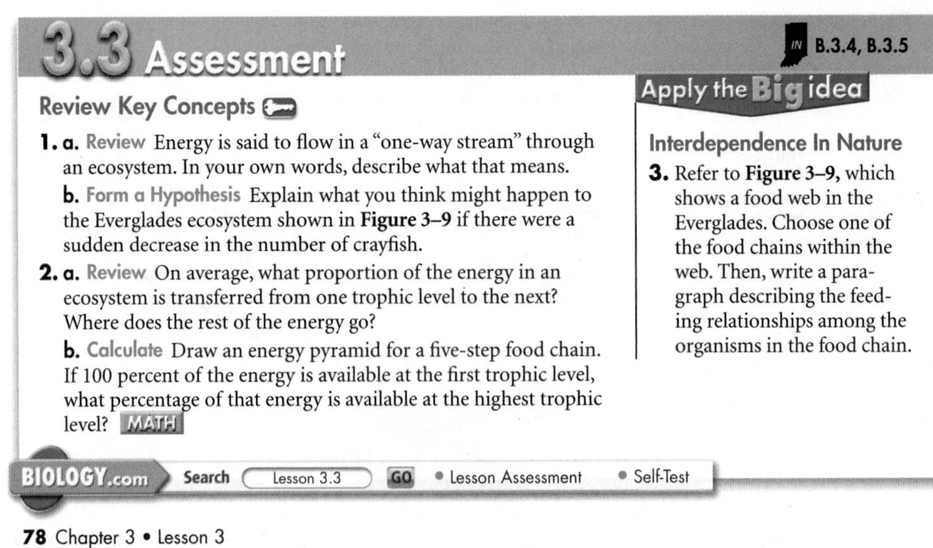

3.3 Assessment

IN B.3.4, B.3.5

Review Key Concepts

1. a. Review Energy is said to flow in a "one-way stream" through an ecosystem. In your own words, describe what that means.
b. Form a Hypothesis Explain what you think might happen to the Everglades ecosystem shown in **Figure 3–9** if there were a sudden decrease in the number of crayfish.

2. a. Review On average, what proportion of the energy in an ecosystem is transferred from one trophic level to the next? Where does the rest of the energy go?
b. Calculate Draw an energy pyramid for a five-step food chain. If 100 percent of the energy is available at the first trophic level, what percentage of that energy is available at the highest trophic level? MATH

Apply the Big idea

Interdependence In Nature

3. Refer to **Figure 3–9,** which shows a food web in the Everglades. Choose one of the food chains within the web. Then, write a paragraph describing the feeding relationships among the organisms in the food chain.

BIOLOGY.com Search Lesson 3.3 GO • Lesson Assessment • Self-Test

Assessment Answers

1a. Sample answer: Energy is not recycled. Energy enters an ecosystem and flows through a food chain, but it is not reused—it is lost as heat.

1b. Sample answer: A decrease in the population of crayfish would likely result in less food available to raccoons, pig frogs, and anhingas. These populations might decrease. Populations on which the crayfish feed, such as plants, detritus, and grass shrimp, may increase.

2a. About 10 percent of the energy at any trophic level is passed to the next trophic level. The remainder of the energy is used for life processes or released into the environment as heat.

2b. Students' pyramids should show 100% of the energy available at the first level, 10% at the second level, 1% at the third level, 0.1% at the fourth level, and 0.01% at the fifth level.

3. Big idea Students may choose and describe any of the food chains in **Figure 3–9.** Check that the food chains contain a primary producer and at least one consumer.

3.4 Cycles of Matter

B.3.4 Matter in food chains and food webs; B.4.1 Limiting factors; B.4.2 Effects of human activities and natural phenomena. Also covered: NoS.6, B.3.5, B.4.4.

THINK ABOUT IT Living organisms are composed mostly of four elements: oxygen, carbon, hydrogen, and nitrogen. These four elements (and a few others, such as sulfur and phosphorus) are the basis of life's most important compounds: water, carbohydrates, lipids, nucleic acids, and proteins. In short, a handful of elements combine to form the building blocks of all known organisms. And yet, organisms cannot manufacture these elements and do not "use them up." So, where do essential elements come from? How does their availability affect ecosystems?

Recycling in the Biosphere

How does matter move through the biosphere?

Matter moves through the biosphere differently than the way in which energy moves. Solar and chemical energy are captured by primary producers and then pass in a one-way fashion from one trophic level to the next—dissipating in the environment as heat along the way. But while energy in the form of sunlight is constantly entering the biosphere, Earth doesn't receive a significant, steady supply of new matter from space. **Unlike the one-way flow of energy, matter is recycled within and between ecosystems.** Elements pass from one organism to another and among parts of the biosphere through closed loops called **biogeochemical cycles,** which are powered by the flow of energy as shown in **Figure 3–13.** As that word suggests, cycles of matter involve *bio*logical processes, *geo*logical processes, and *chem*ical processes. Human activity can also play an important role. As matter moves through these cycles, it is transformed. It is never created or destroyed—just changed.

Key Questions

How does matter move through the biosphere?

How does water cycle through the biosphere?

What is the importance of the main nutrient cycles?

How does nutrient availability relate to the primary productivity of an ecosystem?

Vocabulary

biogeochemical cycle • nutrient • nitrogen fixation • denitrification • limiting nutrient

Taking Notes

Outline Make an outline using the green and blue headings in this lesson. Fill in details as you read to help you organize the information.

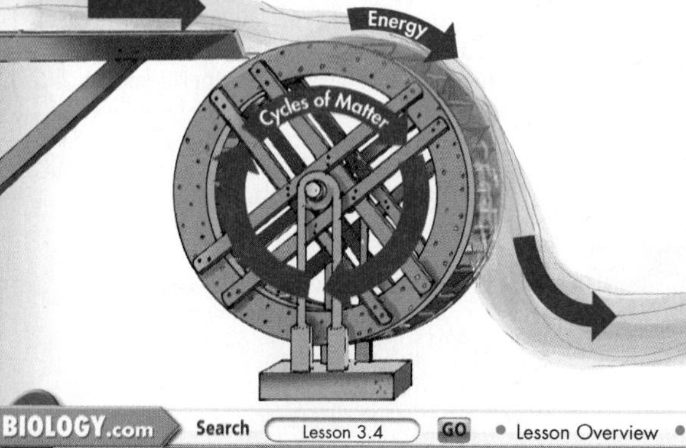

VISUAL ANALOGY

THE MATTER MILL

FIGURE 3–13 Nutrients are recycled through biogeochemical cycles. These cycles are powered by the one-way flow of energy through the biosphere. Use Analogies ***How is the water flowing over the water wheel similar to the flow of energy in the biosphere?***

BIOLOGY.com Search Lesson 3.4 GO • Lesson Overview • Lesson Notes

Getting Started

Objectives

3.4.1 Describe how matter cycles among the living and nonliving parts of an ecosystem.

3.4.2 Describe how water cycles through the biosphere.

3.4.3 Explain why nutrients are important in living systems.

3.4.4 Describe how the availability of nutrients affects the productivity of ecosystems.

For corresponding lesson in the **Foundation Edition**, see pages 68–73.

Student Resources

Study Workbooks A and B, 3.4 Worksheets

Spanish Study Workbook, 3.4 Worksheets

Lesson Overview • Lesson Notes
- Activities: InterActive Art, Visual Analogy
- Assessment: Self-Test, Lesson Assessment

VISUAL ANALOGY

Have students examine **Figure 3–13** and explain how the flow of energy and cycles of matter are different.

Answers

FIGURE 3–13 Sample answer: Like the water over the wheel, energy has a one-way flow through the biosphere; it isn't recycled the way that matter is.

UbD Teach for Understanding

ENDURING UNDERSTANDING The existence of life on Earth depends on interactions among organisms and between organisms and their environment.

GUIDING QUESTION Why is the cycling of matter important to life on Earth?

EVIDENCE OF UNDERSTANDING *After completing the lesson, give students the following assessment to show they understand how matter is cycled through the biosphere.* Have each student make a poster that details one of the cycles discussed in this lesson. Tell them to be as creative as they can, but specify that all of the different processes associated with the cycle should be accurately depicted. Have students share their posters with one another.

IN INDIANA ACADEMIC STANDARDS

For the full text of all standards, see the Course Overview in the front matter of this book.

B.4.1 Explain that the amount of life an environment can support is limited by the available energy, water, oxygen, and minerals, and by the ability of ecosystems to recycle the remains of dead organisms.

B.4.2 Describe how human activities and natural phenomena can change the flow of matter and energy in an ecosystem and how those changes impact other species.

Teach

Lead a Discussion

As a class, discuss the different types of processes that cycle matter through the biosphere. Take a minute to talk about why human activity is discussed separately from biological processes.

Ask Why would the breakdown of rock by ocean waves be considered a geological process, but the breakdown of rock by tree roots be considered a biological process? *(because the latter involves a living organism)*

Ask Why might human activities be considered a separate category from other biological processes involving living organisms? *(because human activities have such a large impact on the ecosystem beyond the simple acts of eating, respiring, and eliminating wastes)*

As students work through the lesson, suggest they take note of how humans influence different biogeochemical cycles.

DIFFERENTIATED INSTRUCTION

ELL English Language Learners Before students read through the lesson and begin discussing the content, prepare a handout that lists the Key Questions and their answers. Be sure the answers are presented in simple sentences. Have students review the handout and underline any unfamiliar words. Then, have them use the Glossary or a dictionary to find the meaning of unfamiliar words. After students complete the lesson, have them work with a partner to review the handout by asking and answering the questions.

LPR Less Proficient Readers Suggest students use the visuals as a reference while you discuss the different ways matter cycles through the biosphere. Talk about why each photo is a good representation of the type of process it is showing.

There are many ways in which the processes involved in biogeochemical cycles can be classified. Here, we will use the following guidelines:

▶ ***Biological Processes*** Biological processes consist of any and all activities performed by living organisms. These processes include eating, breathing, "burning" food, and eliminating waste products.

▶ ***Geological Processes*** Geological processes include volcanic eruptions, the formation and breakdown of rock, and major movements of matter within and below the surface of the earth.

▶ ***Chemical and Physical Processes*** Chemical and physical processes include the formation of clouds and precipitation, the flow of running water, and the action of lightning.

▶ ***Human Activity*** Human activities that affect cycles of matter on a global scale include the mining and burning of fossil fuels, the clearing of land for building and farming, the burning of forests, and the manufacture and use of fertilizers.

These processes, shown in **Figure 3–14,** pass the same atoms and molecules around again and again. Imagine, for a moment, that you are a carbon atom in a molecule of carbon dioxide that has just been shot out of a volcano. The leaf of a blueberry bush in a nearby mountain range absorbs you during photosynthesis. You become part of a carbohydrate molecule in a blueberry. A caribou eats the fruit, and within a few hours, you pass out of the animal's body. You are soon swallowed by a dung beetle, which gets eaten by a hungry shrew. You are combined into the body tissues of the shrew, which is then eaten by an owl. You are released back into the atmosphere when the owl exhales carbon dioxide, dissolve in a drop of rainwater, and flow through a river into the ocean.

This could just be part of the never-ending cycle of a carbon atom through the biosphere. Carbon atoms in your body may once have been part of a rock on the ocean floor, the tail of a dinosaur, or even part of a historical figure such as Julius Caesar!

FIGURE 3–14 Biogeochemical Processes Cycles of matter involve biological, geological, chemical, and human factors.

Quick Facts

PRECIPITATION AND EVAPORATION

Huge quantities of water cycle between Earth's surface and atmosphere. Hydrologists estimate that about 577,000 cubic kilometers of water evaporate from Earth's surface (ocean and land surfaces combined) and enter the atmosphere each year. Considering all forms of precipitation, about 80 percent falls on oceans and about 20 percent on land. However, this same proportion does not hold true for water that evaporates from Earth's surface: approximately 505,000 cubic kilometers (88 percent) of the water in the atmosphere comes from oceans and only about 72,000 cubic kilometers (12 percent) from land. The reason for the difference in proportions is simple: about a third of the precipitation that falls on land runs off into streams and rivers and is carried to oceans annually.

The Water Cycle

How does water cycle through the biosphere?

Every time you see rain or snow, or watch a river flow, you are witnessing part of the water cycle. **Water continuously moves between the oceans, the atmosphere, and land—sometimes outside living organisms and sometimes inside them.** As **Figure 3–15** shows, water molecules typically enter the atmosphere as water vapor, a gas, when they evaporate from the ocean or other bodies of water. Water can also enter the atmosphere by evaporating from the leaves of plants in the process of transpiration (tran spuh RAY shun).

Water vapor may be transported by winds over great distances. If the air carrying it cools, water vapor condenses into tiny droplets that form clouds. When the droplets become large enough, they fall to Earth's surface as precipitation in the form of rain, snow, sleet, or hail. On land, some precipitation flows along the surface in what scientists call runoff, until it enters a river or stream that carries it to an ocean or lake. Precipitation can also be absorbed into the soil and is then called groundwater. Groundwater can enter plants through their roots, or flow into rivers, streams, lakes, or oceans. Some groundwater penetrates deeply enough into the ground to become part of underground reservoirs. Water that re-enters the atmosphere through transpiration or evaporation begins the cycle anew.

In Your Notebook *Define each of the following terms and describe how they relate to the water cycle:* evaporation, transpiration, precipitation, *and* runoff.

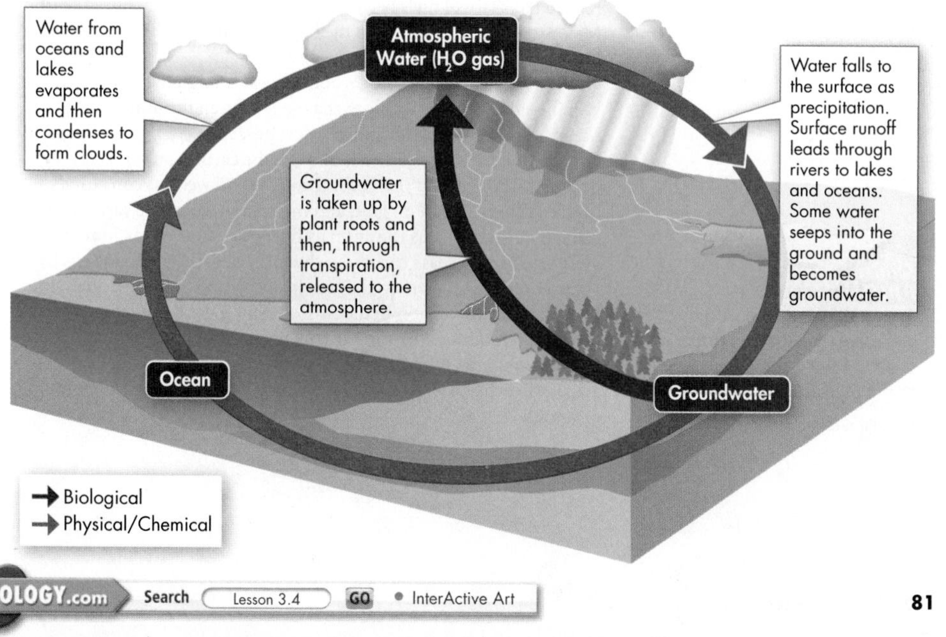

FIGURE 3–15 The Water Cycle This diagram shows the main processes involved in the water cycle. Scientists estimate that it can take a single water molecule as long as 4000 years to complete one cycle. **Interpret Visuals** ***What are the two primary ways in which water that falls to Earth as precipitation passes through the water cycle?***

Use Visuals

Have students use **Figure 3–15** to visualize the paths that water molecules can take in the water cycle.

Ask How are transpiration and evaporation similar? *(Transpiration and evaporation are processes by which water enters the atmosphere.)*

Ask How are transpiration and evaporation different? *(Transpiration is a biological process; evaporation is a physical/chemical process.)*

Ask Do water molecules always follow the same steps though the water cycle? *(No, there is not a single series of steps in the water cycle.)*

DIFFERENTIATED INSTRUCTION

L3 Advanced Students Have students write a paragraph describing how humans and other land animals are involved in the water cycle. In particular, have students consider the role of respiration, a process by which water vapor is released into the air.

BIOLOGY.com Students can see an animation of the water cycle in **InterActive Art: The Water Cycle.**

UbD Check for Understanding

INDEX CARD SUMMARIES

Give each student an index card. Ask students to write one concept about the water cycle that they understand on the front of the card. Have them identify something about the water cycle that they do not understand, and write it on the back of the card in the form of a question.

ADJUST INSTRUCTION

Read over students' cards to identify concepts about the water cycle that are causing confusion for one or more students. Write these topics on the board. Have students use their texts to find facts, lesson vocabulary terms, Key Questions, or other information relevant to each topic. Ask volunteers to share what they have learned with the class, and record their input on the board.

Answers

FIGURE 3–15 Water that falls as precipitation moves to rivers, lakes, and oceans as surface runoff or seeps into the ground and becomes groundwater.

IN YOUR NOTEBOOK Evaporation is the process by which water changes from a liquid to a vapor. Water that evaporates enters the atmosphere. Transpiration is the evaporation of water from plant leaves. Precipitation occurs when water in the atmosphere condenses and falls to Earth's surface. Runoff is precipitation that flows along Earth's surface.

Teach continued

Build Reading Skills

Explain that the information about the carbon cycle on this page is also contained in **Figure 3–17** on the next page. As students read the lesson, have them refer to the figure as each process in the carbon cycle is described.

DIFFERENTIATED INSTRUCTION

ELL English Language Learners Have students practice pronouncing terms associated with the carbon cycle by having them provide an answer to the following question aloud:

Ask What are some compounds and materials that carbon is a part of? *(Sample answers: carbon dioxide, calcium carbonate, fossil fuels, carbonate rocks, carbohydrates, lipids, proteins, nucleic acids)*

Address Misconceptions

Conservation of Matter Students might not understand that matter—like energy—is conserved in the biosphere. Explain that atoms cannot be created or destroyed. They are instead combined and recombined with other atoms to form different compounds. To help, refer students to the last two paragraphs on page 80, which describe how a carbon molecule may cycle through the biosphere.

FIGURE 3–16 Oxygen in the Biosphere The oxygen contained in the carbon dioxide exhaled by this bighorn sheep may be taken up by producers and re-released as oxygen gas. Together, respiration and photosynthesis contribute to oxygen's cycling through the biosphere.

Nutrient Cycles

What is the importance of the main nutrient cycles?

The chemical substances that an organism needs to sustain life are called **nutrients.** **Every organism needs nutrients to build tissues and carry out life functions. Like water, nutrients pass through organisms and the environment through biogeochemical cycles. The three pathways, or cycles that move carbon, nitrogen, and phosphorus through the biosphere are especially critical for life.**

Another element, oxygen, participates in parts of the carbon, nitrogen, and phosphorus cycles by combining with these elements and cycling with them through parts of their journeys. Oxygen gas in the atmosphere is released by one of the most important of all biological activities: photosynthesis. Oxygen is used in respiration by all multicellular forms of life, and many single-celled organisms as well.

The Carbon Cycle Carbon is a major component of all organic compounds, including carbohydrates, lipids, proteins, and nucleic acids. In fact, carbon is such a key ingredient of living tissue and ecosystems that life on Earth is often described as "carbon-based life." Carbon in the form of calcium carbonate ($CaCO_3$) is an important component of many different kinds of animal skeletons and is also found in several kinds of rocks. Carbon and oxygen form carbon dioxide gas (CO_2), which is an important component of the atmosphere and is dissolved in oceans.

Some carbon-containing compounds that were once part of ancient forests have been buried and transformed by geological processes into coal. The bodies of marine organisms containing carbon have been transformed into oil or natural gas. Coal, oil, and natural gas are often referred to as fossil fuels because they are essentially "fossilized" carbon. Major reservoirs of carbon in the biosphere include the atmosphere, oceans, rocks, fossil fuels, and forests.

Figure 3–17 shows how carbon moves through the biosphere. Carbon dioxide is continuously exchanged between the atmosphere and oceans through chemical and physical processes. Plants take in carbon dioxide during photosynthesis and use the carbon to build carbohydrates. Carbohydrates then pass through food webs to consumers. Many animals—both on land and in the sea—combine carbon with calcium and oxygen as the animals build skeletons of calcium carbonate. Organisms release carbon in the form of carbon dioxide gas by respiration. Also, when organisms die, decomposers break down the bodies, releasing carbon to the environment. Geologic forces can turn accumulated carbon into carbon-containing rocks or fossil fuels. Carbon dioxide is released into the atmosphere by volcanic activity or by human activities, such as the burning of fossil fuels and the clearing and burning of forests.

BUILD Vocabulary

ACADEMIC WORDS The verb **accumulate** means "to collect or gather." Carbon accumulates, or collects, in soil and in the oceans where it cycles among organisms or is turned into fossil fuels.

Quick Facts

THE CARBON POOL

According to Climate Change 2007, a report by the Intergovernmental Panel on Climate Change (IPCC), the biosphere's total carbon pool—the total mass of carbon atoms—is estimated to be approximately 44,750 metric gigatons. (1 metric gigaton equals 10^9 metric tons.) Of that total, about 85 percent is contained in Earth's oceans and marine biota. About 8 percent of the carbon pool is contained in fossil fuels. About 5 percent is contained in vegetation, soil, and detritus. Only about 1 percent of the carbon pool is in the atmosphere and less than 1 percent is contained in surface sediments.

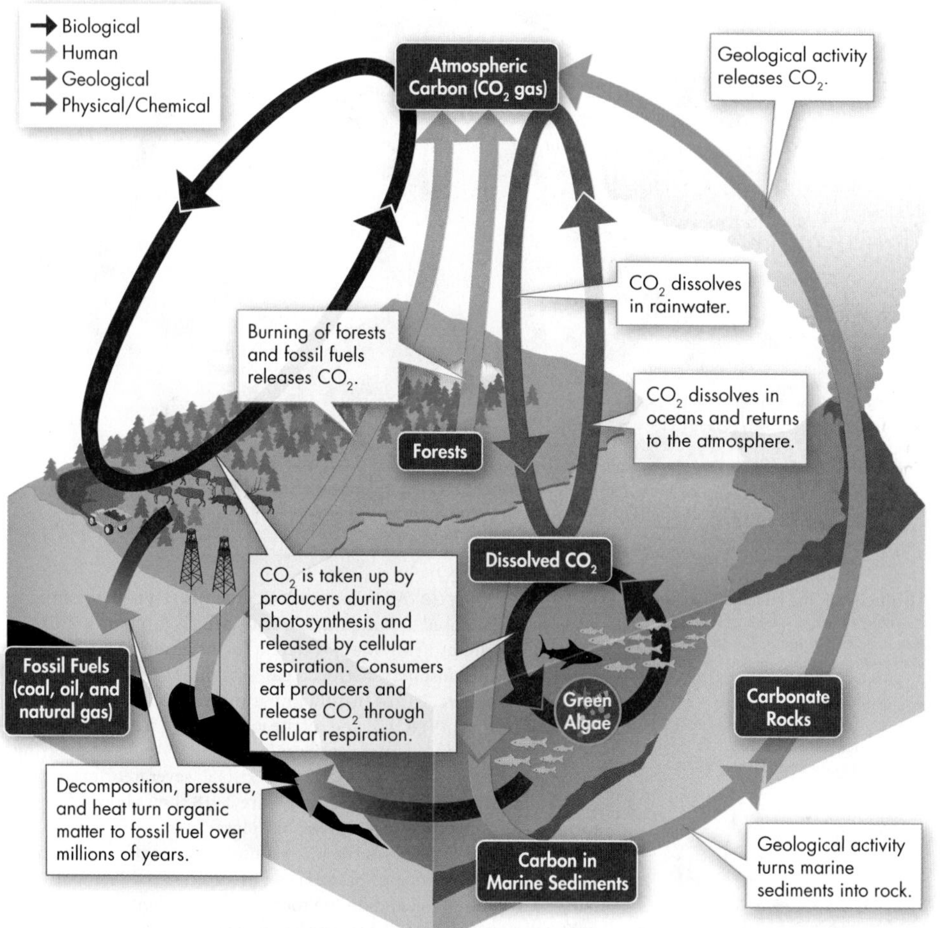
Biological
Human
Geological
Physical/Chemical
Atmospheric Carbon (CO_2 gas)
Geological activity releases CO_2.
CO_2 dissolves in rainwater.
Burning of forests and fossil fuels releases CO_2.
CO_2 dissolves in oceans and returns to the atmosphere.
Forests
Dissolved CO_2
CO_2 is taken up by producers during photosynthesis and released by cellular respiration. Consumers eat producers and release CO_2 through cellular respiration.
Fossil Fuels (coal, oil, and natural gas)
Green Algae
Carbonate Rocks
Decomposition, pressure, and heat turn organic matter to fossil fuel over millions of years.
Carbon in Marine Sediments
Geological activity turns marine sediments into rock.

FIGURE 3–17 The Carbon Cycle Carbon is found in several large reservoirs in the biosphere. In the atmosphere, it is found as carbon dioxide gas (CO_2); in the oceans, as dissolved carbon dioxide; on land, in organisms, rocks, and soil; and underground, as coal, petroleum, and calcium carbonate. **Interpret Visuals** ***What is one of the processes that takes carbon dioxide out of the atmosphere?***

Scientists know a great deal about the biological, geological, chemical, and human processes that are involved in the carbon cycle, but important questions remain. How much carbon moves through each pathway? How do ecosystems respond to changes in atmospheric carbon dioxide concentration? How much carbon dioxide can the ocean absorb? Later in this unit, you will learn why answers to these questions are so important.

In Your Notebook *Describe one biological, one geological, one chemical, and one human activity that is involved in the carbon cycle.*

Use Visuals

Have students use **Figure 3–17** to distinguish the biological, human, geological, and physical/chemical processes that are involved in the carbon cycle. Point out that each set of processes is designated by arrows of a specific color in the figure. (The same colors are used in **Figures 3–14, 3–15, 3–18,** and **3–19.**)

Ask Why does the process of fossil fuel formation start as a biological process and end as geological one? *(because geological forces turn biological, or organic matter, into carbon-containing rocks or fossil fuels)*

Ask How are human activities affecting carbon reservoirs? *(Human activities are taking carbon from fossil fuels and forests and adding it to the atmosphere.)*

DIFFERENTIATED INSTRUCTION

L1 Struggling Students Some students might be overwhelmed by the complexity of the carbon cycle. Divide the class into four groups, and assign each group one of the four sets of processes in the diagram (biological, human, geological, or physical/chemical). Have students in each group work together to become "experts" on their assigned portion of the carbon cycle. Then, have each group give a brief presentation to share its expertise with the rest of the class.

UbD Check for Understanding

ONE-MINUTE RESPONSE

Give students about a minute to write a short paragraph explaining why the carbon cycle is important for sustaining life on Earth. *(Paragraphs should mention that carbon is a major component of organisms and is important in the process of photosynthesis.)*

ADJUST INSTRUCTION

If students' responses reveal confusion about the importance of the carbon cycle, suggest they work in pairs to review the information on the carbon cycle. Then, have pairs write a new, more comprehensive explanation of why the carbon cycle is important for life.

Answers

FIGURE 3–17 Sample answer: Photosynthesis is a process that takes carbon dioxide out of the atmosphere.

IN YOUR NOTEBOOK Sample answer: Photosynthesis is a biological activity that removes carbon dioxide from the atmosphere; volcanic activity is a geologic process that releases carbon dioxide into the atmosphere; dissolving is a physical/chemical process that removes carbon dioxide from the atmosphere; and burning of fossil fuels is a human activity that releases carbon dioxide into the atmosphere.

Teach continued

Lead a Discussion

Have students use the information in **Figure 3–18** to review the nitrogen cycle.

Ask How do humans affect the nitrogen cycle? *(Humans take nitrogen gas from the atmosphere to create fertilizers. When these fertilizers are applied to crops, excess can wash into rivers, streams, and oceans, resulting in increased nitrogen levels.)*

Ask What biological process converts nitrogen gas to ammonia? *(nitrogen fixation)*

DIFFERENTIATED INSTRUCTION

L1 Special Needs Ask the following questions to help students focus on the importance of cycling of matter to life on Earth.

Ask Why do living things need nitrogen? *(Nitrogen is used to make proteins, which are a part of living things' bodies.)*

Ask What would happen if the processes in the nitrogen cycle stopped? *(The nitrogen that living things need would not be available, and living things would die as a result.)*

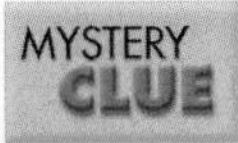

Since human activity hasn't changed much, something else must be adding nitrogen to the bay. Using **Figure 3–18,** lead students to conclude that the bacteria that fix nitrogen have increased, leading to an increase in nitrogen in the bay. Students can go online to Biology.com to gather their evidence.

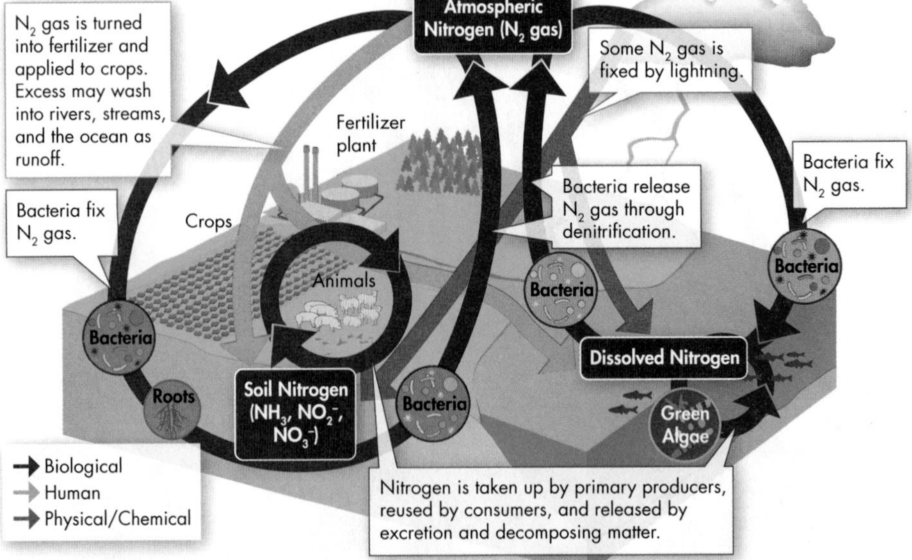

FIGURE 3–18 The Nitrogen Cycle The atmosphere is the largest reservoir of nitrogen in the biosphere. Nitrogen also cycles through the soil and through the tissues of living organisms. **Interpret Visuals** ***Through which two processes does nitrogen gas get converted into usable forms for organisms?***

MYSTERY CLUE

Recently, researchers discovered that levels of dissolved nitrogen in the bay have increased. Given that human activity hasn't changed much, which organisms in the bay do you think might be responsible?

The Nitrogen Cycle All organisms require nitrogen to make amino acids, which are used to build nucleic acids, which combine to form DNA, RNA, and proteins. Many different forms of nitrogen occur naturally in the biosphere. Nitrogen gas (N_2) makes up 78 percent of Earth's atmosphere. Nitrogen-containing substances such as ammonia (NH_3), nitrate ions (NO_3^-), and nitrite ions (NO_2^-) are found in soil, in the wastes produced by many organisms, and in dead and decaying organic matter. Dissolved nitrogen also exists in several forms in the ocean and other large water bodies. **Figure 3–18** shows how different forms of nitrogen cycle through the biosphere.

Although nitrogen gas is the most abundant form of nitrogen on Earth, only certain types of bacteria can use this form directly. These bacteria live in the soil and on the roots of certain plants, such as peanuts and peas, called legumes. The bacteria convert nitrogen gas into ammonia, in a process known as **nitrogen fixation.** Other soil bacteria convert that fixed nitrogen into nitrates and nitrites. Once these forms of nitrogen are available, primary producers can use them to make proteins and nucleic acids. Consumers eat the producers and reuse nitrogen to make their own nitrogen-containing compounds. Decomposers release nitrogen from waste and dead organisms as ammonia, nitrates, and nitrites that producers may take up again. Other soil bacteria obtain energy by converting nitrates into nitrogen gas, which is released into the atmosphere in a process called **denitrification.** A relatively small amount of nitrogen gas is converted to usable forms by lightning in a process called atmospheric nitrogen fixation. Humans add nitrogen to the biosphere through the manufacture and use of fertilizers. Excess fertilizer is often carried into surface water or groundwater by precipitation.

Quick Facts

THE SCARCITY OF USABLE NITROGEN

Nitrogen is abundant in the atmosphere; in fact, it makes up 78 percent of Earth's atmosphere. However, usable forms of nitrogen are scarce in ecosystems. The reason for this is the structure of N_2 gas. It is held together by triple covalent bonds that lightning and certain bacteria can break. Bacteria that fix nitrogen use nitrogenase, an enzyme, to break the covalent bonds in N_2 molecules and produce a form of nitrogen that living things can use. Nitrogenase can function only when it is isolated from oxygen. On land, nitrogen-fixing bacteria are found in the oxygen-excluding environments of root nodules or insulating slime on plant roots. In aquatic ecosystems, cyanobacteria, the primary nitrogen-fixers, have specialized cells called heterocysts that exclude oxygen.

Answers

FIGURE 3–18 Bacteria convert nitrogen gas to ammonia through the process of nitrogen fixation. This ammonia is converted to nitrates and nitrites. Lightning also fixes nitrogen gas.

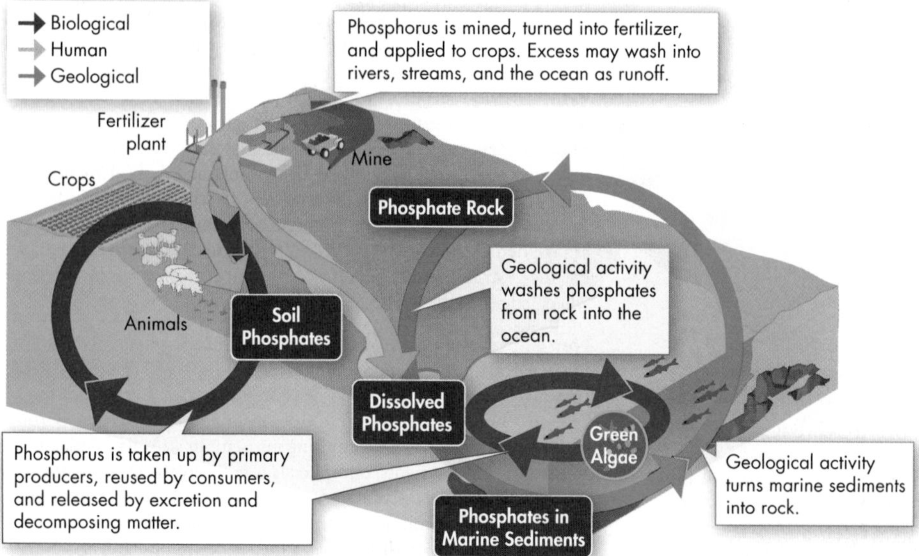
Biological
Human
Geological
Phosphorus is mined, turned into fertilizer, and applied to crops. Excess may wash into rivers, streams, and the ocean as runoff.
Fertilizer plant
Crops
Mine
Phosphate Rock
Geological activity washes phosphates from rock into the ocean.
Animals
Soil Phosphates
Dissolved Phosphates
Green Algae
Phosphorus is taken up by primary producers, reused by consumers, and released by excretion and decomposing matter.
Geological activity turns marine sediments into rock.
Phosphates in Marine Sediments

FIGURE 3–19 The Phosphorus Cycle Phosphorus in the biosphere cycles among the land, ocean sediments, and living organisms. Unlike other nutrients, phosphorus is not found in significant quantities in the atmosphere.

The Phosphorus Cycle Phosphorus is essential to living organisms because it forms a part of vital molecules such as DNA and RNA. Although phosphorus is of great biological importance, it is not abundant in the biosphere. Unlike carbon, oxygen, and nitrogen, phosphorus does not enter the atmosphere in significant amounts. Instead, phosphorus in the form of inorganic phosphate remains mostly on land, in the form of phosphate rock and soil minerals, and in the ocean, as dissolved phosphate and phosphate sediments, as seen in **Figure 3–19.**

As rocks and sediments gradually wear down, phosphate is released. Some phosphate stays on land and cycles between organisms and soil. Plants bind phosphate into organic compounds when they absorb it from soil or water. Organic phosphate moves through the food web, from producers to consumers, and to the rest of the ecosystem. Other phosphate washes into rivers and streams, where it dissolves. This phosphate may eventually makes its way to the ocean, where marine organisms process and incorporate it into biological compounds.

Nutrient Limitation

How does nutrient availability relate to the primary productivity of an ecosystem?

Ecologists are often interested in an ecosystem's primary productivity—the rate at which primary producers create organic material. **If ample sunlight and water are available, the primary productivity of an ecosystem may be limited by the availability of nutrients.** If even a single essential nutrient is in short supply, primary productivity will be limited. The nutrient whose supply limits productivity is called the **limiting nutrient.**

Connect to the Real World

Tell students that at one time, phosphates were an important component of most laundry detergents used in the United States.

Ask If wastewater containing phosphates from laundry detergent made its way into waterways, such as streams, rivers, and lakes, how would that affect the phosphorus cycle? *(It would result in an increase in phosphates in water ecosystems.)*

Ask What is one other way human activity affects the phosphorus cycle? *(The application of fertilizers that contain phosphorus can increase phosphates in aquatic ecosystems.)*

DIFFERENTIATED INSTRUCTION

LPR Less Proficient Readers Have students use the arrows and embedded labels in **Figure 3–19** to help them answer the following questions about the effects of phosphate-laden laundry detergents.

Ask If phosphates were still part of laundry detergent, what color arrow would be used in the diagram to show the flow of phosphates from laundry detergent into waterways? Why? *(Orange, because orange arrows are used to show how human activity impacts the phosphorus cycle.)*

Ask What would you add to the visual to show how phosphates from laundry detergent entered the phosphorus cycle? *(I would draw an orange arrow coming from human homes and entering the river. I would label this arrow to explain how laundry wastewater carried phosphates into waterways.)*

L3 Advanced Students Have students research the impact that phosphates in laundry detergent had on aquatic ecosystems. Also, have them learn about government and industry actions that eliminated most phosphates from laundry detergents. Ask students to prepare a presentation on this topic. Remind them to relate what they find out to the information about the phosphate cycle in the text.

BIOLOGY.com Students can see how the carbon, nitrogen, and phosphorus cycles are connected in the **Visual Analogy: Interlocking Nutrient Cycles.**

UbD Check for Understanding

USE VOCABULARY

Have students write an acrostic poem based on the term *nutrient*. Help them get started by writing the term *nutrient* on the board vertically. Explain that each letter in the term should be used as the beginning letter of a sentence that involves lesson concepts. For example, the first sentence might be: Nitrogen cycles between living and nonliving things. Have students share their completed acrostics with the class.

ADJUST INSTRUCTION

If responses indicate that students have not mastered lesson concepts, ask them to review each figure in the lesson with a partner. Then, have a discussion about the nutrient cycle diagrams.

LESSON 3.4

Teach continued

VISUAL ANALOGY

Have students examine **Figure 3–20.** Tell them that, like these gears, the nutrient cycles in the biosphere are interdependent. Explain that, in this analogy, the slowest-moving gear represents the limiting nutrient in an ecosystem.

Assess and Remediate

EVALUATE UNDERSTANDING

Call on volunteers to name a matter cycle that occurs in the biosphere. Then, ask additional volunteers to supply details about that cycle. Continue until each cycle has been thoroughly described. Then, have students complete the 3.4 Assessment.

REMEDIATION SUGGESTION

L1 **Struggling Students** If students have difficulty answering **Question 5,** explain that the chemical symbol for oxygen is O. Have them use **Figure 3–17** to determine how oxygen atoms move through the biosphere as part of the carbon cycle.

BIOLOGY.com Students can check their understanding of lesson concepts with the **Self-Test** assessment. They can then take an online version of the **Lesson Assessment.**

Answers

FIGURE 3–20 nitrogen

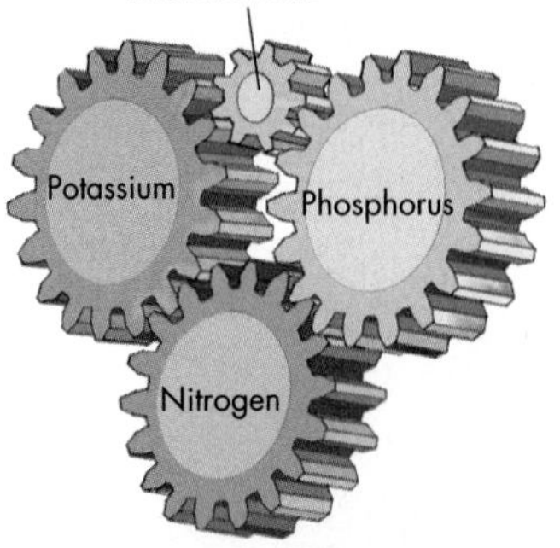

Micronutrients

Potassium

Phosphorus

Nitrogen

VISUAL ANALOGY

INTERLOCKING NUTRIENTS

FIGURE 3–20 The movement of each nutrient through ecosystems depends on the movements of all the others, because all are needed for living systems to function. Use Analogies ***If these gears were modeling nutrient cycling in the ocean, which gear would typically determine how quickly—or slowly—all the other gears turn?***

Nutrient Limitation in Soil In all but the richest soil, the growth of crop plants is typically limited by one or more nutrients that must be taken up by plants through their roots. That's why farmers use fertilizers! Most fertilizers contain large amounts of nitrogen, phosphorus, and potassium, which help plants grow better in poor soil. Micronutrients such as calcium, magnesium, sulfur, iron, and manganese are necessary in relatively small amounts, and these elements are sometimes included in specialty fertilizers. (Carbon is not included in chemical fertilizers because plants acquire carbon dioxide from the atmosphere during photosynthesis.) All nutrient cycles work together like the gears in **Figure 3–20.** If any nutrient is in short supply—if any wheel "sticks"—the whole system slows down or stops altogether.

Nutrient Limitation in Aquatic Ecosystems The open oceans of the world are nutrient-poor compared to many land areas. Seawater typically contains only 0.00005 percent nitrogen, or 1/10,000 of the amount often found in soil. In the ocean and other saltwater environments, nitrogen is often the limiting nutrient. In streams, lakes, and freshwater environments, phosphorus is typically the limiting nutrient.

Sometimes, such as after heavy rains, an aquatic ecosystem receives a large input of a limiting nutrient—for example, runoff from heavily fertilized fields. When this happens, the result can be an algal bloom—a dramatic increase in the amount of algae and other primary producers. Why can runoff from fertilized fields produce algal blooms? More nutrients are available, so producers can grow and reproduce more quickly. If there are not enough consumers to eat the algae, an algal bloom can occur, in which case algae can cover the water's surface and disrupt the functioning of an ecosystem.

3.4 Assessment

IN B.3.4, B.3.5, B.4.1, B.4.2

Review Key Concepts

1. a. Review How does the way that matter flows through an ecosystem differ from the way that energy flows?

b. Apply Concepts What are the four types of processes that cycle matter through the biosphere? Give an example of each.

2. a. Review By what two processes is water cycled from land to the atmosphere?

b. Sequence Describe one way in which water from the ocean may make one complete cycle through the atmosphere and back to the ocean. Include the names of each process involved in your cycle.

3. a. Review Why do living organisms need nutrients?

b. Predict Based on your knowledge of the carbon cycle, what do you think might happen if humans were to continue to clear and burn vast areas of forests for building?

4. a. Review Explain how a nutrient can be a limiting factor in an ecosystem.

b. Apply Concepts Look back at the nitrogen and phosphorus cycles (**Figures 3–18** and **3–19**). How is fertilizer runoff related to algal blooms?

WRITE ABOUT SCIENCE

Explanation

5. Describe how oxygen, although it does not have an independent cycle, moves through the biosphere as part of the carbon cycle. Include a description of the various forms that oxygen takes.

BIOLOGY.com Search Lesson 3.4 GO • Self-Test • Lesson Assessment • Visual Analogy

Assessment Answers

1a. Matter is recycled through ecosystems; no new matter is generated. Energy is continually input into ecosystems, and moves through ecosystems in a one-way path.

1b. Sample answers: biological, such as respiration; geological, such as volcanic eruptions; chemical/physical, such as precipitation; human activity, such as burning fossil fuels

2a. evaporation and transpiration

2b. Sample answer: Water from the ocean evaporates into the atmosphere. It falls to land as precipitation, and then flows into the ocean as surface runoff.

3a. Organisms need nutrients to build tissues and carry out life functions.

3b. If vast amounts of forests are cleared and burned, levels of atmospheric carbon dioxide will likely increase.

4a. Most primary producers need sunlight, water, and nutrients to carry out photosynthesis. If water and sunlight are in ample supply, it is the amount of nutrients that limits the primary productivity.

4b. Fertilizer runoff can supply a large amount of nitrogen and/or phosphorus to an aquatic ecosystem. The algae in the ecosystem may suddenly have a much larger supply of the limiting nutrient in the ecosystem, producing an algal bloom.

WRITE ABOUT SCIENCE

5. Oxygen is a component of carbon dioxide in the atmosphere. During the process of photosynthesis, carbon dioxide is taken up and atmospheric oxygen is released. During cellular respiration, oxygen is combined with carbon and released in the form of carbon dioxide. Oxygen is also found in calcium carbonate, which is a part of animal skeletons and some rocks.

Technology & BIOLOGY

Global Ecology From Space

Can ecologists track plant growth around the world? Can they follow temperature change in oceans from day to day, or the amount of polar ice from year to year? Yes! Satellites can provide these data, essential for understanding global ecology. Satellite sensors can be programmed to scan particular bands of the electromagnetic spectrum to reveal global patterns of temperature, rainfall, or the presence of plants on land or algae in the oceans. The resulting false-color images are both beautiful and filled with vital information.

Changes in Polar Ice Cover Sea ice around the North Pole has been melting more each summer since satellites began gathering data in 1979. The image below shows in white the amount of ice remaining at the end of the summer in 2007. The amount of ice at the same time of year for an average year between 1979 and 2007 is shown in green.

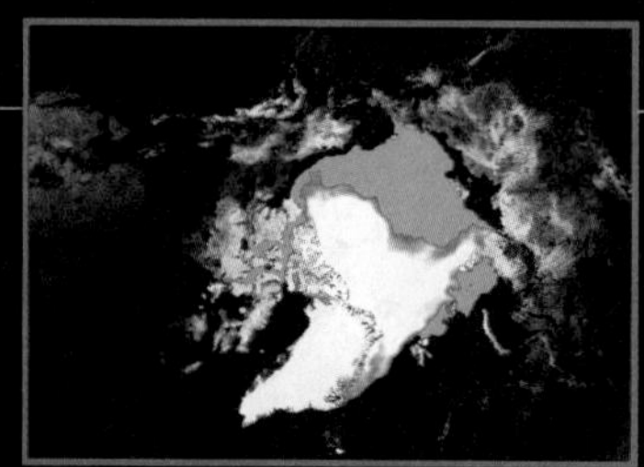

▲
2007 White areas show the average minimum amount of arctic ice cover at the end of the summer, 2007.
1979–2007 Green areas show the average minimum amount of ice cover between 1979 and 2007.

Plant and Algal Growth These data were gathered by NASA's Sea-viewing Wide Field-of-view Sensor (SeaWiFS), which is programmed to monitor the color of reflected light. In the image below, you can see how actively plants on land and algae in the oceans were harnessing solar energy for photosynthesis when these data were taken. A measurement of photosynthesis gives a measure of growth rates and the input of energy and nutrients into the ecosystem.

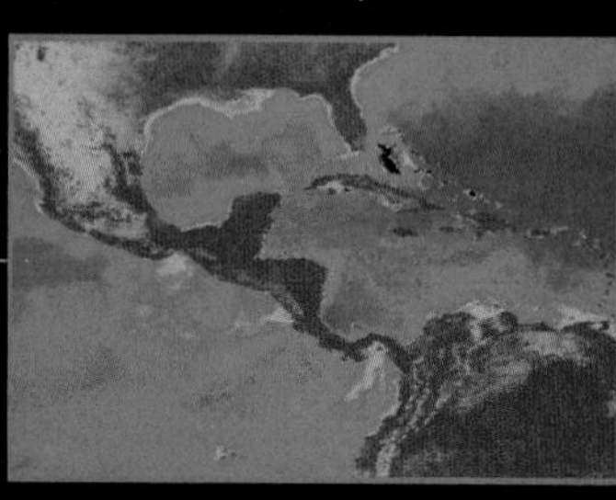

▲
On Land Dark green indicates active plant growth; yellow areas indicate barren deserts or mountains.
In the Sea Dark blue indicates very low active growth of algae. Red indicates the highest active growth.

WRITING Visit the Web site for the Goddard Space Flight Center Scientific Visualization service and select a set of satellite data to examine. Write a brief paragraph explaining what you learned from looking at those data.

Teach

Lead a Discussion

Have students recall the three methods used in ecological studies.

Ask Would you classify the use of satellite images to study ecology as observation, experimentation, or modeling? Explain your response. *(Sample answer: This type of study is observation, because it involves learning about the biosphere by looking at images, rather than experimenting or modeling.)*

Ask How could the satellite images be used to develop models? *(Sample answer: Scientists might develop a model that shows changes in polar ice cover based on satellite observations made over time.)*

Ask How could the satellite images be used to make predictions about future changes on Earth? *(Sample answer: Scientists can use these observations to identify trends, allowing them to predict changes that are likely to occur in the future.)*

DIFFERENTIATED INSTRUCTION

L3 Advanced Students Have students research the use of platform terrestrial transmitter terminals to track migrating animals. Have them explain how this technology uses satellites to monitor the movement of animals, and describe how ecologists can use the data generated with this technology. Ask students to share what they learned with the class.

Answers

WRITING

Students' responses will vary, due to the wide variety of satellite images available. Encourage students to explore several sets of images, and to note images with overlays of graphs that can aid in analysis of the images.

How Science Works

NASA'S EARTH OBSERVING SYSTEM

The National Aeronautics and Space Administration (NASA) program to study Earth is called the Earth Science Enterprise. It includes a series of missions to observe different aspects of Earth and its systems using satellites. Terra, launched in 1999, is considered the "flagship" spacecraft of this program. It collects vast quantities of data about Earth's atmosphere, climate, carbon cycle, water cycle, and weather. Many other missions are a part of the Earth Science Enterprise, including CALIPSO, launched in 2006, which primarily collects data about aerosols and clouds and their relationship to Earth's climate.

CHAPTER LAB

Pre-Lab

Introduce students to the concepts they will explore in the chapter lab by assigning the Pre-Lab questions.

Lab

Tell students they will perform the chapter lab *The Effect of Fertilizer on Algae* described in **Lab Manual A.**

L1 **Struggling Students** A simpler version of the chapter lab is provided in **Lab Manual B.**

SAFETY

Have students be careful when handling cultures and glassware. Protective gloves and goggles should be worn at all times. Make sure students wash hands thoroughly after the lab.

Look online for **Editable Lab Worksheets.**

For corresponding pre-lab in the **Foundation Edition**, see page 74.

IN INDIANA ACADEMIC STANDARDS

For the full text of all standards, see the Course Overview in the front matter of this book.

Real-World Lab

GUIDED INQUIRY

IN B.4.1 Limiting factors. Also covered: B.4.2.

Pre-Lab: The Effect of Fertilizer on Algae

Problem How do excess nutrients affect the growth of algae?

Materials test tubes, test-tube rack, glass-marking pencil, dropper pipettes, algae culture, 25-mL graduated cylinder, spring water, plant food, cotton balls, grow light

Lab Manual Chapter 3 Lab

Skills Predict, Compare and Contrast, Infer

Connect to the Big idea In a healthy ecosystem, nutrients cycle among primary producers, consumers, and decomposers. The growth of primary producers is limited by the availability of nutrients. Humans can intentionally increase the amount of nutrients in an ecosystem. For example, farmers may add fertilizer to the soil in which they grow crops. But the addition of nutrients to an ecosystem is not always planned. For example, runoff from soil that contains fertilizer may flow into coastal waters or freshwater ponds. In this lab, you will observe what happens when algae that live in those waters are provided with excess nutrients.

Background Questions

a. Review What is a limiting nutrient?

b. Explain Why do farmers use fertilizers?

c. Classify What role do algae play in freshwater ecosystems?

Pre-Lab Questions

Preview the procedure in the lab manual.

1. Design an Experiment What is the independent variable in this experiment?
2. Predict After four days, how will you be able to tell which test tube has more algae?
3. Control Variables Why will you grow *Chlorella* in spring water instead of pond water?

BIOLOGY.com Search Chapter 3 GO

Visit Chapter 3 online to test yourself on chapter content and to find activities to help you learn.

Untamed Science Video Help the Untamed Science crew explore food relationships as they turn the ecological pyramid upside down.

Art in Motion View a short animation showing the different levels of organization.

Art Review Review your understanding of which organisms are producers and which are consumers with this drag-and-drop activity.

InterActive Art Build your understanding of the water cycle with this animation.

Data Analysis Collect and analyze some data so you can see how the data is used to monitor a site.

Tutor Tube Get some clarification on producers and consumers and learn how the flow of matter and energy is not what you may think!

Visual Analogies Compare a recycling center to decomposers in this activity. Compare nutrient limitation to a series of cogs in this activity.

Pre-Lab Answers

BACKGROUND QUESTIONS

a. A limiting nutrient is a chemical substance that is necessary for life whose supply determines the primary productivity of an ecosystem.

b. Most fertilizers contain large amounts of nitrogen, phosphorus, and potassium, which are essential nutrients for plants.

c. Algae are the main photosynthetic producers in freshwater ecosystems. They produce energy-rich compounds that are used by other organisms.

PRE-LAB QUESTIONS

1. The independent variable is the presence of fertilizer.
2. Sample answer: In the test tube with more algae, the liquid will have a darker green color and be less transparent to light.
3. Sample answer: Pond water is likely to contain many species of algae. Using spring water ensures that both test tubes have *Chlorella*, and that neither test tube has a different algal species.

3 Study Guide

Big idea Matter and Energy, Interdependence in Nature

The biosphere is composed of an ever-changing mix of living and nonliving components. These components are constantly interacting to form the environments in which organisms struggle to survive and reproduce.

3.1 What Is Ecology?

Ecology is the scientific study of interactions among organisms and between organisms and their physical environment.

The biological influences on organisms are called biotic factors.

Physical components of an ecosystem are called abiotic factors.

Modern ecologists use three methods in their work: observation, experimentation, and modeling. Each of these approaches relies on scientific methodology to guide inquiry.

biosphere (64)
species (64)
population (64)
community (64)
ecology (65)
ecosystem (65)
biome (65)
biotic factor (66)
abiotic factor (66)

3.2 Energy, Producers, and Consumers

Primary producers are the first producers of energy-rich compounds that are later used by other organisms.

Organisms that rely on other organisms for energy and nutrients are called consumers.

autotroph (69)
primary producer (69)
photosynthesis (70)
chemosynthesis (70)
heterotroph (71)
consumer (71)
carnivore (71)
herbivore (71)
scavenger (71)
omnivore (71)
decomposer (71)
detritivore (71)

3.3 Energy Flow in Ecosystems

Energy flows through an ecosystem in a one-way stream, from primary producers to various consumers.

Pyramids of energy show the relative amount of energy available at each trophic level of a food chain or food web. A pyramid of biomass illustrates the relative amount of living organic matter available at each trophic level of an ecosystem. A pyramid of numbers shows the relative number of individual organisms at each trophic level in an ecosystem.

food chain (73)
phytoplankton (73)
food web (74)
zooplankton (76)
trophic level (77)
ecological pyramid (77)
biomass (78)

3.4 Cycles of Matter

Unlike the one-way flow of energy, matter is recycled within and between ecosystems.

Water continuously moves between the oceans, the atmosphere, and land—sometimes outside living organisms and sometimes inside them.

Every organism needs nutrients to build tissues and carry out life functions. Like water, nutrients pass through organisms and the environment through biogeochemical cycles. The carbon, nitrogen, and phosphorus cycles are especially critical for life.

If ample sunlight and water are available, the primary productivity of an ecosystem may be limited by the availability of nutrients.

biogeochemical cycle (79)
nutrient (82)
nitrogen fixation (84)
denitrification (84)
limiting nutrient (85)

Think Visually Using information from this chapter, complete the following flowchart:

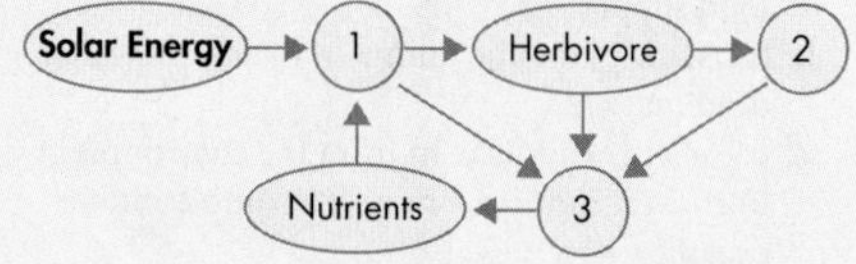

BIOLOGY.com Search Chapter 3 GO • Match It • Chapter Assessment

Study Online

REVIEW AND ASSESSMENT RESOURCES

Editable Worksheets Pages of Study Workbooks A and B, Lab Manuals A and B, and the Assessment Resources Book are available online. These documents can be easily edited using a word-processing program.

Lesson Overview Have students reread the Lesson Overviews to help them study chapter concepts.

Vocabulary Review The *Flash Cards* and *Match It* provide an interactive way to review chapter vocabulary.

Chapter Assessment Have students take an online version of the Chapter 3 Assessment.

Standardized Test Prep Students can take an online version of the Standardized Test Prep. You will receive their scores along with ideas for remediation.

Diagnostic and Benchmark Tests Use these tests to monitor your students' progress and supply remediation.

Answers

THINK VISUALLY

1. Autotroph or Primary Producer
2. Carnivore, Omnivore, or Consumer
3. Decomposer or Detritivore

UbD Performance Tasks

SUMMATIVE TASK Have students imagine they are museum curators who have been asked to design an exhibit about the movement of matter and energy in ecosystems. Explain that the exhibit must consist of three separate displays, each of which can be designed in any way they choose. Have them write a paragraph describing each of the three displays they would design. Then, have them write a paragraph summarizing the display as a whole. Have students consider the scientific terms and concepts each display will introduce as they write their descriptions. Encourage them to include sketches or diagrams with their paragraphs.

TRANSFER TASK Have students write a short story from the point of view of a producer in an ecosystem. The story should be at least one page in length and include the following concepts in a creative and scientifically accurate way.

- What interactions occur between the producer and the other living things in the ecosystem?
- What interactions occur between the producer and the nonliving things in the ecosystem?
- What role does the producer serve in the movement of matter and energy in the ecosystem?

ASSESSMENT

Lesson 3.1

UNDERSTAND KEY CONCEPTS

1. c **2.** b

3. individual organism, population, community, ecosystem, biome, biosphere

4. Ecologists use modeling to study events that occur over such long periods of time or such large areas that they are difficult to study directly.

5. Sample answer: An adult frog eats insects, therefore, frogs influence the insects in their ecosystem.

THINK CRITICALLY

6. Students' hypotheses and experimental designs may vary. Experiments should include controls. For example, students might suggest that a set of seeds be divided into two groups—one exposed to high heat and one not exposed to high heat. All other conditions should be kept the same. Then, the germination rates of the two groups can be compared.

7. Students' questions should indicate they would look for biotic and abiotic factors that might have changed, such as land use around the pond, annual rainfall, and runoff patterns.

Lesson 3.2

UNDERSTAND KEY CONCEPTS

8. c **9.** c **10.** d

11. Chemosynthesis is a process in which chemical energy is used to produce carbohydrates.

THINK CRITICALLY

12. earthworm, detritivore; bear, omnivore; cow, herbivore; snail, detritivore; owl, carnivore; human, omnivore

13. Sample answer: Organic matter may enter the caves from outside via water or animals that come in from outside. There may also be chemosynthetic bacteria in the cave.

3 Assessment

The numbers following the questions refer to Indiana's Academic Standards for Biology I.

3.1 What Is Ecology?

Understand Key Concepts

1. All of life on Earth exists in
a. an ecosystem. **c.** the biosphere.
b. a biome. **d.** ecology.

2. Which term describes a group of different species that live together in a defined area?
a. a population **c.** an ecosystem
b. a community **d.** a biosphere

3. Name the different levels of organization within the biosphere, from smallest to largest.

4. How do ecologists use modeling? NoS.6

5. Give an example of how a biotic factor might influence the organisms in an ecosystem.

Think Critically

6. Design an Experiment Ecologists have discovered that the seeds of many plants that grow in forests cannot germinate unless they have been exposed to fire. Design an experiment to test whether a particular plant has seeds with this requirement. Include your hypothesis statement, a description of control and experimental groups, and an outline of your procedure.

7. Pose Questions You live near a pond that you have observed for years. One year you notice the water is choked with a massive overgrowth of green algae. What are some of the questions you might have about this unusual growth? B.4.4

3.2 Energy, Producers, and Consumers

Understand Key Concepts

8. Primary producers are organisms that
a. rely on other organisms for their energy and food supply.
b. consume plant and animal remains and other dead matter.
c. use energy they take in from the environment to convert inorganic molecules into complex organic molecules.
d. obtain energy by eating only plants.

9. Which of the following organisms is a decomposer?

10. Which of the following describes how ALL consumers get their energy? B.3.5
a. directly from the sun
b. from eating primary producers
c. from inorganic chemicals like hydrogen sulfide
d. from eating organisms that are living or were once living

11. What is chemosynthesis?

Think Critically

12. Classify Classify each of the following as an herbivore, a carnivore, an omnivore, or a detritivore: earthworm, bear, cow, snail, owl, human.

13. Form a Hypothesis People who explore caves where there is running water but no sunlight often find them populated with unique types of fishes and insects. What hypothesis can you make to explain the ultimate source of energy for these organisms?

3.3 Energy Flow in Ecosystems

Understand Key Concepts

14. The series of steps in which a large fish eats a small fish that has eaten algae is a
a. food web. **c.** pyramid of numbers.
b. food chain. **d.** pyramid of biomass.

15. The total amount of living tissue at each trophic level in an ecosystem can be shown in a(n)
a. energy pyramid. **c.** biomass pyramid.
b. pyramid of numbers. **d.** biogeochemical cycle.

Lesson 3.3

UNDERSTAND KEY CONCEPTS

14. b **15.** c

THINK CRITICALLY

16. primary producers

17. Most of the energy organisms consume is used for life processes or released into the environment as heat, which leaves only about 10 percent of the energy available to the next trophic level.

18. Accept all logical food chains that begin with a producer and end with the student.

19. Sample answer: grass, caterpillar, bird, fox; grass, mouse, hawk; grass, mouse, fox; tree, deer, cougar

Think Critically

16. Which group of organisms is always found at the base of a food chain or food web?

17. **Apply Concepts** Why is the transfer of energy in a food chain usually only about 10 percent efficient? B.3.5

18. **Use Models** Describe a food chain of which you are a member. You may draw or use words to describe the chain. B.3.4, B.3.5

19. **Use Models** Create flowcharts that show four different food chains in the food web shown below.

3.4 Cycles of Matter

Understand Key Concepts

20. Nutrients move through an ecosystem in B.3.4
- **a.** biogeochemical cycles.
- **b.** water cycles.
- **c.** energy pyramids.
- **d.** ecological pyramids.

21. Which biogeochemical cycle does NOT include a major path in which the substance cycles through the atmosphere? B.3.4
- **a.** water cycle
- **b.** carbon cycle
- **c.** nitrogen cycle
- **d.** phosphorus cycle

22. List two ways in which water enters the atmosphere in the water cycle.

23. Explain the process of nitrogen fixation.

24. What is meant by "nutrient limitation"? B.4.1

solve the CHAPTER MYSTERY

CHANGES IN THE BAY

According to one hypothesis, rising water temperatures have caused most of the changes reported in Narragansett Bay. The bay's temperature has risen more than 1.5°C (3°F) since 1960. This warmth encourages bluefish to stay in the bay later in the fall. It also allows predatory warm-water shrimp to remain in the bay all winter, feeding on baby flounder. Warmer water also enables zooplankton to graze heavily on marine algae. This eliminates the late-winter algal bloom whose primary production used to provide organic carbon to the entire food web.

Those food web changes, in turn, seem to be driving unexpected shifts in the activities of bacteria that transform nitrogen. When the spring bloom provided organic carbon, bacteria denitrified the water, releasing nitrogen into the atmosphere. Now, the bacterial community has changed and actually fixes nitrogen, bringing more of it into the water. It is still not clear what this change means for the long-term health of the bay and adjacent coastal waters.

1. **Compare and Contrast** Compare the original situation in the bay with the current situation, taking note of changes in both the food web and the nitrogen cycle.

2. **Infer** Narragansett Bay harbors sea jellies that prefer warm water and have previously been present only in summer and early fall. These sea jellies eat fish eggs, fish larvae, and zooplankton. If the bay continues to warm, what do you think might happen to the population of sea jellies in the bay? What might that mean for the organisms the jellies feed on?

3. **Connect to the Big idea** Explain how the Narragansett Bay example demonstrates interconnections among members of a food web and abiotic environmental factors. Can you find similar studies in other aquatic habitats, such as Chesapeake Bay, the Everglades, or the Mississippi River delta? Explain.

IN B.4.2, B.4.4

  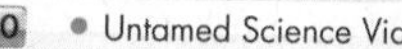

BIOLOGY.com Search Chapter 3 GO • Untamed Science Video • Chapter Mystery

91

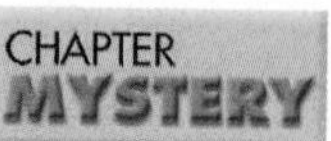

After students have read through the Chapter Mystery, discuss interactions of organisms and the environment.

Ask A change in which abiotic factor triggered the series of changes described in the Chapter Mystery? *(water temperature)*

Ask What is an example of an interaction between two living things in Narragansett Bay that changed as a result of the change in water temperature? *(Sample answer: Warm water shrimp now stay in the bay all winter, feeding on baby flounder.)*

Ask What is an example of an interaction between a living thing and a nonliving thing that has occurred as a result of the increase in water temperature? *(Bacteria in the bay now fix nitrogen, rather than denitrifying the water.)*

CHAPTER MYSTERY ANSWERS

1. Many factors have changed in Narragansett Bay. The water temperature has risen, which has allowed bluefish to stay in the bay later in the year than they used to. It has also permitted shrimp to remain in the bay and feed on baby flounder all year round, which likely decreases the flounder population. The late-winter algae bloom no longer occurs, eliminating a food source for the entire ecosystem. Organisms in the bay used to consume nitrogen that flowed into the bay; now the bacteria in the bay fix nitrogen.

2. Sample answer: If the water temperature rises, sea jellies might arrive in the bay earlier in the year and stay later in the fall. They would feed on fish eggs, fish larvae, and zooplankton and would likely cause the populations of these organisms to decrease in the bay.

3. Big idea The Narragansett Bay example shows how a change in an abiotic factor—water temperature—affects the living things in the ecosystem. In other aquatic habitats, abiotic factors also affect biotic factors. Check that students have found similar studies in other locations.

Lesson 3.4

UNDERSTAND KEY CONCEPTS

20. a **21.** d

22. evaporation and transpiration

23. Bacteria that live in the soil and on roots of plants called legumes convert nitrogen gas into ammonia. Some nitrogen is also fixed by lightning.

24. Nutrient limitation is the concept that, if ample sunlight and water are available, the primary productivity of an ecosystem may be limited by the availability of nutrients.

THINK CRITICALLY

25. The fertilizer was carried into the stream by runoff, which prompted the increased growth of algae. The algae disrupted the ecosystem in a way that caused the fish to die.

26. Students' flowcharts will vary, depending on the organisms included in the food chain. Students' responses should also include a description of decomposers breaking down the dead organic matter when a top-level carnivore dies, which releases the nitrogen in the carnivore's body.

In the short video **Nature's Tangled Web,** the crew of Untamed Science explores feeding relationships and discovers how organisms at the bottom of food chains influence those at the top.

ASSESSMENT

Connecting Concepts

USE SCIENCE GRAPHICS

27. Productivity increases.

28. Students' graphs should show productivity leveling out as rainfall increases between 4000 mm and 6000 mm. Student explanations should state that, beyond 4000 mm, something other than rainfall will begin to limit productivity in the ecosystem.

29. Sample answer: amount of sunlight, availability of nutrients

WRITE ABOUT SCIENCE

30. Answers will vary. Students should name and define the levels of organization including individual organism, population, community, ecosystem, biome, and biosphere. Students might choose any of the levels to study. They should describe how their chosen level can be studied using observation, experimentation, or modeling. The reason for the choice of method should be logical and supported in a way that suggests an understanding of that method.

31. Organic compounds, such as proteins, carbohydrates, nucleic acids, and fats, contain elements such as carbon, oxygen, nitrogen, and phosphorus. Atoms of these elements must be available to organisms, or organic compounds cannot be synthesized. The carbon, nitrogen, and phosphorus cycles move these atoms through ecosystems, making them available to living things.

32. Big idea Sample answer: Carbon is found in the molecules that make up living things. Therefore, it is a part of the biotic factors in an ecosystem, and moves through the ecosystem in food chains and food webs. Carbon is also present as part of soil and air, and therefore, is an abiotic factor in ecosystems as well.

Think Critically

25. Form a Hypothesis Ecologists discovered that trout were dying in a stream that ran through some farmland where nitrogen fertilizer was used on the crops. How might you explain what happened? B.4.2, B.4.4

26. Apply Concepts Using a flowchart, trace the flow of energy in a simple marine food chain. Then, show where nitrogen is cycled through the chain when the top-level carnivore dies and is decomposed. B.3.4, B.3.5, B.4.1

Connecting Concepts

Use Science Graphics NoS.3

The graph below shows the effect of annual rainfall on the rate of primary productivity in an ecosystem. Use the graph to answer questions 27–29.

The Effect of Rainfall on Plant Productivity

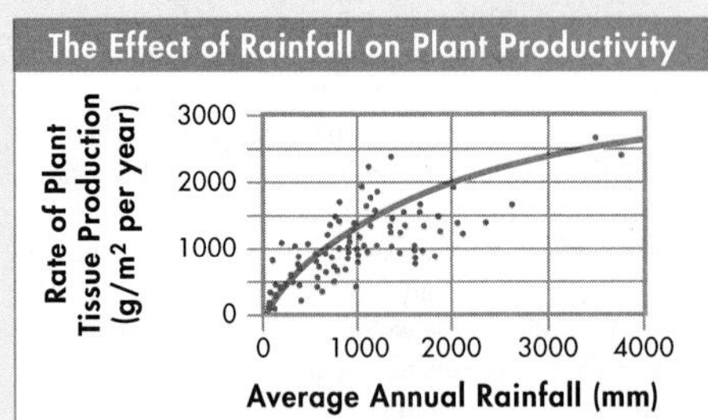

27. Interpret Graphs What happens to productivity as rainfall increases? B.4.1

28. Predict What do you think the graph would look like if the *x*-axis were extended out to 6000 mm? Represent your prediction in a graph and explain your answer.

29. Apply Concepts What factors other than water might affect primary productivity? B.4.1

Write About Science NoS.3

30. Explanation Write a paragraph that (1) names and defines the levels of organization that an ecologist studies; (2) identifies the level that you would choose to study if you were an ecologist; (3) describes the method or methods you would use to study this level; and (4) gives a reason for your choice of method or methods.

31. Description Describe how biogeochemical cycles provide organisms with the raw materials necessary to synthesize complex organic compounds. Refer back to Chapter 2 for help in answering this question. B.3.4

32. Assess the Big idea Explain how an element like carbon can be included in both the biotic and abiotic factors of an ecosystem. B.3.4

Analyzing Data

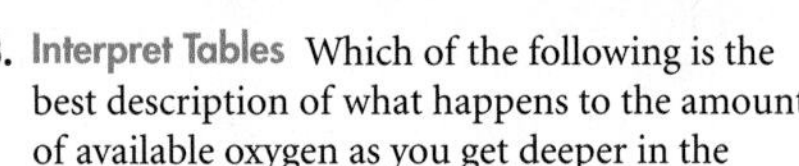

NoS.3

Samples of ocean water are taken at different depths, and the amount of oxygen in the water at each depth is measured. The results are shown in the table.

Concentration of Oxygen

Depth of Sample (m)	Oxygen Concentration (ppm)
0	7.5
50	7.4
100	7.4
150	4.5
200	3.2
250	3.1
300	2.9

33. Interpret Tables Which of the following is the best description of what happens to the amount of available oxygen as you get deeper in the ocean?

a. Available oxygen decreases at a constant rate.
b. Available oxygen increases at a constant rate.
c. Available oxygen remains steady until about 100 m, then drops rapidly.
d. Oxygen is available at all ocean depths.

34. Draw Conclusions Light can penetrate to only a depth of between 50 and 100 m in most ocean water. What effect does this have on the water's oxygen concentration? Explain.

Analyzing Data

PURPOSE Students will analyze data to understand the relationship between the depth of ocean water and its oxygen concentration.

PLANNING Explain that the abbreviation *ppm* means "parts per million," a unit that is used to express concentration.

ANSWERS

33. c

34. The depth to which light can penetrate limits the depths at which photosynthetic organisms can be found. Photosynthetic organisms produce oxygen, so their presence increases oxygen concentrations at the depths where they are found, in this case to about 100 m.

Standardized Test Practice for Indiana

Multiple Choice

1. A group of individuals that belong to a single species and that live together in a defined area is termed a(n)
   A population.
   B ecosystem.
   C community.
   D biome.

2. Which of the following is NOT true about matter in the biosphere?
   A Matter is recycled in the biosphere.
   B Biogeochemical cycles transform and reuse molecules.
   C The total amount of matter decreases over time.
   D Water and nutrients pass between organisms and the environment. B.3.4

3. Which is a source of energy for Earth's living things?
   A wind energy only
   B sunlight only
   C wind energy and sunlight
   D sunlight and chemical energy B.3.5

4. Which of the following is a primary producer?
   A a producer, like algae
   B a carnivore, like a lion
   C an omnivore, like a human
   D a detritivore, like an earthworm

5. Human activities, such as the burning of fossil fuels, move carbon through the carbon cycle. Which other processes also participate in the carbon cycle?
   A biological processes only
   B geochemical processes only
   C chemical processes only
   D a combination of biological, geological, and chemical processes B.4.2

6. What are the physical, or nonliving components of an ecosystem called?
   A abiotic factors
   B temperate conditions
   C biotic factors
   D antibiotic factors

Questions 7–8

The diagrams below represent the amount of biomass and the numbers of organisms in an ecosystem.

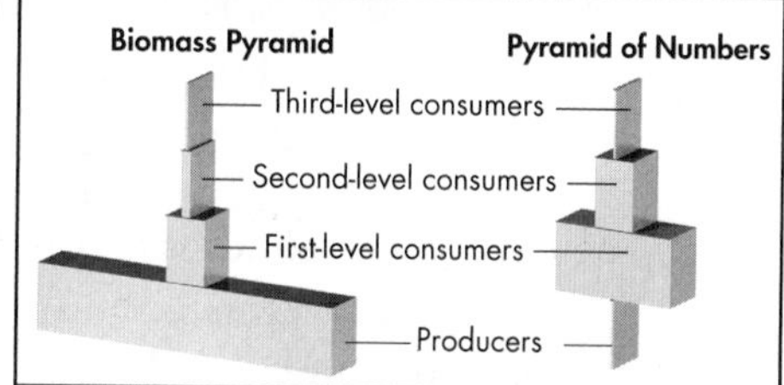

7. What can you conclude about the ecosystem from the pyramid of numbers shown?
   A There are more first-level consumers than producers.
   B There are more third-level consumers than second-level consumers.
   C There are more producers than first-level consumers.
   D There are more second-level consumers than first-level consumers.

8. What can you conclude about the producers in the ecosystem based on the two pyramids shown?
   A The producers in the ecosystem are probably very small organisms.
   B There are no producers in the ecosystem.
   C The producers in the ecosystem are probably large organisms.
   D Decomposers in the ecosystem outnumber the producers in the ecosystem.

Open-Ended Response

9. What ultimately happens to the bulk of matter in any trophic level of a biomass pyramid—that is, the matter that does not get passed to the trophic level above? B.3.4

If You Have Trouble With . . .

Question	1	2	3	4	5	6	7	8	9
See Lesson	3.1	3.4	3.2	3.2	3.4	3.1	3.3	3.3	3.3

Answers

1. A
2. C
3. D
4. A
5. D
6. A
7. A
8. A
9. Decomposers and detritivores consume matter that does not get passed to the next higher trophic level.

Test-Taking Tip

USE TIME WISELY

Tell students to scan the questions to identify those that are about unfamiliar topics and might require pure guesswork on their part. Explain that those questions should be saved for last. After they have competed questions about familiar topics, students should then return to the questions about unfamiliar topics. Explain that using reasoning to eliminate one or more obviously incorrect choices is a technique that can be useful, even if the question is about an unfamiliar topic.

CHAPTER PLANNER 4 Ecosystems and Communities

Chapter Contents	IN	Time	Core Resources
Chapter Preview			**Student Edition,** pp. 94–95 **Chapter Mystery,** p. 95
4.1 Climate Weather and Climate • Factors That Affect Climate	NoS.6, B.4.4	1/2 period 1/4 block	**Student Edition,** pp. 96–98 **Study Workbook A** 4.1 Worksheets L2 Biology.com *Visual Analogy:* The Greenhouse Effect • 4.1 Self-Test • 4.1 Lesson Assessment
4.2 Niches and Community Interactions The Niche • Competition • Predation, Herbivory, and Keystone Species • Symbioses • *Careers & Biology: Marine Biologist, Park Ranger, Wildlife Photographer*	NoS.3, B.4.1, B.4.4	1 period 1/2 block	**Student Edition,** pp. 99–105 Inquiry 4.2 Analyzing Data, p. 102 L2 **Study Workbook A** 4.2 Worksheets L2 Biology.com *Data Analysis:* The Intertidal Zone **Assessment Resources Book** Visual Quizzes L2
4.3 Succession Primary and Secondary Succession • Climax Communities	B.4.2, B.4.4	1 period 1/2 block	**Student Edition,** pp. 106–109 Inquiry 4.3 Quick Lab, p. 108 L2 **Study Workbook A** 4.3 Worksheets L2 Biology.com *Art in Motion:* Primary and Secondary Succession **Assessment Resources Book** Visual Quiz L2
4.4 Biomes The Major Biomes • Other Land Areas	NoS.2, NoS.3	1 period 1/2 block	**Student Edition,** pp. 110–116 Inquiry 4.4 Analyzing Data, p. 115 L2 **Study Workbook A** 4.4 Worksheets L2 Biology.com 4.4 Self-Test • 4.4 Lesson Assessment
4.5 Aquatic Ecosystems Conditions Underwater • Freshwater Ecosystems • Estuaries • Marine Ecosystems	B.4.1	1 period 1/2 block	**Student Edition,** pp. 117–121 **Study Workbook A** 4.5 Worksheets L2 Biology.com *Art Review:* Ocean Zones • 4.5 Self-Test • 4.5 Lesson Assessment
Chapter Pre-Lab	NoS.3, B.4.1	1 period 1/2 block	**Student Edition,** p. 122 L2 **Lab Manual A** *Abiotic Factors and Plant Selection* L2

Additional Resources

Biology.com Untamed Science Video • Vocabulary Flash Cards

Study Workbook B 4.1 Worksheets L1 ELL LPR
Spanish Study Workbook 4.1 Worksheets ELL
Biology.com 4.1 Lesson Overview • 4.1 Lesson Notes

Study Workbook B 4.2 Worksheets L1 ELL LPR
Spanish Study Workbook 4.2 Worksheets ELL
Biology.com 4.2 Lesson Overview • 4.2 Lesson Notes • 4.2 Self-Test • 4.2 Lesson Assessment

Study Workbook B 4.3 Worksheets L1 ELL LPR
Spanish Study Workbook 4.3 Worksheets ELL
Biology.com 4.3 Lesson Overview • 4.3 Lesson Notes • 4.3 Self-Test • 4.3 Lesson Assessment

Study Workbook B 4.4 Worksheets L1 ELL LPR
Spanish Study Workbook 4.4 Worksheets ELL
Biology.com 4.4 Lesson Overview • 4.4 Lesson Notes

Study Workbook B 4.5 Worksheets L1 ELL LPR
Spanish Study Workbook 4.5 Worksheets ELL
Biology.com 4.5 Lesson Overview • 4.5 Lesson Notes

Lab Manual B *Abiotic Factors and Plant Selection* • Hands-On Activity: *Modeling Predator-Prey Interactions* • Data Analyses: *Predator-Prey Dynamics* • *Which Biome?* L1 ELL LPR

Chapter Review

Student Edition Study Guide, p. 123 L2
Study Workbook A Chapter 4 Vocabulary Review L2 • Chapter 4 Chapter Mystery/21st Century Skills Activity L2 L3
Transparencies, pp. 44–54 L1 ELL LPR L2
Biology.com Untamed Science Video • Editable Worksheets of Study Workbooks A and B and Lab Manuals A and B • Chapter 4 Flash Cards and Crossword Puzzle

Untamed Science DVD • Classroom Resources CD (includes lesson presentations and editable worksheets)

Chapter Assessment

Student Edition Assessment, pp. 124–127 L2
Study Workbook B Chapter 4 Chapter Review L1 ELL LPR • Chapter 4 Taking a Standardized Test L1 ELL LPR
Assessment Resources Book Chapter 4 Test A L2 • Chapter 4 Test B L1 ELL LPR
Biology.com Chapter 4 Assessment • Editable Worksheets of Chapter 4 Visual Quizzes and Chapter 4 Tests A and B

Exam*View* *Assessment Suite* • Classroom Resources CD (includes lesson presentations and editable worksheets)

Time: 1 period, 1/2 block

Pressed for Time?

Preview the Chapter Discuss the Key Questions for Lesson 4.2 and introduce the vocabulary for Lessons 4.2 and 4.3.

Cover the Chapter Quickly Have students read all of Lesson 4.2, *Primary and Secondary Succession* in Lesson 4.3, and go over Figures 4–12 and 4–13. For Lesson 4.4, have students read Defining Biomes in *The Major Biomes,* and instruct students to use pp. 112–115 as a reference while doing the Analyzing Data activity. Assign *Conditions Underwater* in Lesson 4.5 and briefly discuss Figure 4–22.

Assess Assign the 4.2 Assessment, questions 1 and 3 in the 4.3 Assessment, questions 1b and 3 in the 4.4 Assessment, question 1 in the 4.5 Assessment, and questions 7–19, 22, and 27 in the Chapter 4 Assessment.

CHAPTER 4

Connect to the Big Idea

Discuss the scene in the photograph to introduce the Big Idea of Interdependence in Nature.

Ask What organisms do you see in the photograph in addition to the cheetah? *(plants)*

Ask What do you think the cheetah eats and what eats the plants? *(zebras or other herbivores)*

Ask What would happen to the cheetah if the plants died because of drought? *(The herbivores it hunts would have nothing to eat and might die or move to another area, so the cheetah would have no food.)*

Lead students to anticipate the answer to the question, **How do abiotic and biotic factors shape ecosystems?**

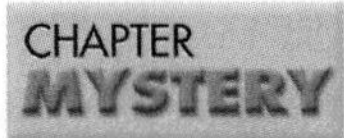

After students have read through the Chapter Mystery, ask them to explain why scientists predicted that reintroducing wolves to Yellowstone National Park would lead to a decline in the number of elk in the park. *(Wolves hunt elk.)* Then, have them predict how fewer elk might affect other organisms in the park. *(Sample answer: Elk eat plants, so with fewer elk, there might be more of some types of plants.)*

BIOLOGY.com Have students preview the chapter vocabulary using the **Flash Cards.**

IN INDIANA ACADEMIC STANDARDS

For the full text of all standards, see the Course Overview in the front matter of this book.

Key standards: Chapter 4 covers key ideas from Standard 4: Interdependence, including **B.4.4** Stability of an ecosystem.

4 Ecosystems and Communities

Big idea Interdependence in Nature

Q: How do abiotic and biotic factors shape ecosystems?

Cheetah looking out across the savanna at the Masai Mara National Reserve in Kenya

BIOLOGY.com Search Chapter 4 GO • Flash Cards

94

UbD Understanding by Design

Chapter 4 continues to explore the unit's Enduring Understanding: *The existence of life on Earth depends on interactions among organisms and between organisms and their environment.* As the graphic organizer at the right shows, the chapter explains how interactions between abiotic factors like climate and biotic factors like organisms shape ecosystems.

PERFORMANCE GOALS

Students will demonstrate their knowledge of ecosystems and communities by analyzing data, interpreting diagrams and graphs, and describing phenomena such as competition and succession. At the end of the chapter, students will create a scrapbook highlighting interactions among organisms and between organisms and their environment in a specific land biome or aquatic ecosystem. They will also create a Web site about a threatened region in a biome and how it can be protected.

INDIANA ACADEMIC STANDARDS FOR SCIENCE

Nature of Science NoS.2, NoS.3, NoS.6; **Interdependence** B.4.1, B.4.2, B.4.4. See lessons for details.

CHAPTER MYSTERY

THE WOLF EFFECT

During the 1920s, hunting and trapping eliminated wolves from Yellowstone National Park. For decades, ecologists hypothesized that the loss of wolves—important predators of elk and other large grazing animals—had changed the park ecosystem. But because there were no before-and-after data, it was impossible to test that hypothesis directly.

Then, in the mid-1990s, wolves were reintroduced to Yellowstone. Researchers watched park ecosystems carefully and sure enough, the number of elk in parts of the park began to fall just as predicted. But, unpredictably, forest and stream communities have changed, too. Could a "wolf effect" be affecting organisms in the park's woods and streams?

As you read this chapter, look for connections among Yellowstone's organisms and their environment. Then, solve the mystery.

Never Stop Exploring Your World. The mystery of the Yellowstone wolves is just the beginning. Take a video field trip with the ecogeeks of Untamed Science to see where this mystery leads.

• Untamed Science Video • Chapter Mystery

What's Online

BIOLOGY.com Extend your reach by using these and other digital assets offered at **Biology.com**.

CHAPTER MYSTERY
Students will explore community interactions in Yellowstone National Park since the reintroduction of wolves in the mid-1990s.

UNTAMED SCIENCE VIDEO
A volcanic eruption can quickly obliterate an existing ecosystem, but it also paves the way for a new one to develop.

VISUAL ANALOGY
Students find out how Earth's atmosphere acts like the glass in a greenhouse.

DATA ANALYSIS
Students analyze tolerance data to explain the zonation patterns of intertidal species.

ART IN MOTION
An animation of primary and secondary succession helps students understand the processes.

ART REVIEW
Students can show an understanding of the ocean's zones with this drag-and-drop activity.

CHAPTER 4

Chapter 4 Big Idea: Interdependence in Nature

Chapter 4 EQ: How do abiotic and biotic factors shape ecosystems?

- **4.1 GQ:** What factors affect global climate?
- **4.2 GQ:** How do organisms interact with one another?
- **4.3 GQ:** How do ecosystems change over time?
- **4.4 GQ:** What are the characteristics of the major biomes?
- **4.5 GQ:** What are the characteristics of aquatic ecosystems?

LESSON 4.1

Getting Started

Objectives

4.1.1 Differentiate between weather and climate.

4.1.2 Identify the factors that influence climate.

Student Resources

Study Workbooks A/B, 4.1 Worksheets

Spanish Study Workbook, 4.1 Worksheets

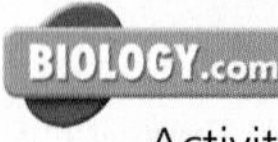

Lesson Overview • Lesson Notes • Activity: Visual Analogy • Assessment: Self-Test, Lesson Assessment

For corresponding lesson in the **Foundation Edition**, see pages 82–84.

Answers

IN YOUR NOTEBOOK Descriptions will vary depending on the climate where students live. They might describe seasonal variations, amounts of precipitation, and high and low temperatures. They may also identify factors such as distance from the equator and presence of bodies of water or mountain ranges.

IN INDIANA ACADEMIC STANDARDS

For the full text of all standards, see the Course Overview in the front matter of this book.

B.4.4 Describe how climate, the pattern of matter and energy flow, the birth and death of new organisms, and the interaction between those organisms contribute to the long term stability of an ecosystem.

4.1 Climate

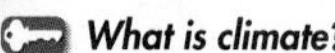
IN B.4.4 Stability of an ecosystem. Also covered: NoS.6.

Key Questions

What is climate?

What factors determine global climate?

Vocabulary

weather
climate
microclimate
greenhouse effect

Taking Notes

Preview Visuals Before you read, look at **Figure 4–2.** What questions do you have about this diagram? Write a prediction that relates this figure to climate.

BUILD Vocabulary

PREFIXES The prefix *hemi-* in *hemisphere* means "half." The Northern Hemisphere encompasses the northern half of Earth.

THINK ABOUT IT When you think about climate, you might think of dramatic headlines: "Hurricane Katrina floods New Orleans!" or "Drought parches the Southeast!" But big storms and seasonal droughts are better described as *weather* rather than *climate.* So, what *is* climate, and how does it differ from weather? How do climate and weather affect organisms and ecosystems?

Weather and Climate

What is climate?

Weather and climate both involve variations in temperature, precipitation, and other environmental factors. **Weather** is the day-to-day condition of Earth's atmosphere. Weather where you live may be clear and sunny one day but rainy and cold the next. **Climate,** on the other hand, refers to average conditions over long periods. **A region's climate is defined by year-after-year patterns of temperature and precipitation.**

It is important to note that climate is rarely uniform even within a region. Environmental conditions can vary over small distances, creating **microclimates.** For example, in the Northern Hemisphere, south-facing sides of trees and buildings receive more sunlight, and are often warmer and drier, than north-facing sides. We may not notice these differences, but they can be very important to many organisms.

Factors That Affect Climate

What factors determine global climate?

A person living in Orlando, Florida, may wear shorts and a T-shirt in December, while someone in Minneapolis, Minnesota, is still wearing a heavy coat in April. It rarely rains in Phoenix, Arizona, but it rains often in Mobile, Alabama. Clearly, these places all have different climates—but why? What causes differences in climate? **Global climate is shaped by many factors, including solar energy trapped in the biosphere, latitude, and the transport of heat by winds and ocean currents.**

In Your Notebook *Describe the climate where you live. What factors influence it?*

UbD Teach for Understanding

ENDURING UNDERSTANDING The existence of life on Earth depends on interactions among organisms and between organisms and their environment.

GUIDING QUESTION What factors affect global climate?

EVIDENCE OF UNDERSTANDING *After completing the lesson, assign students the following assessment to show they understand the factors that affect global climate.* Have groups of three students create three labeled diagrams to explain (1) how greenhouse gases trap heat in the atmosphere, (2) why solar energy varies with latitude, and (3) how heat is transported in the biosphere. Students should brainstorm ideas for their diagrams as a group. Then, each student in the group should draw one of the diagrams.

Solar Energy and the Greenhouse Effect The main force that shapes our climate is solar energy that arrives as sunlight and strikes Earth's surface. Some of that energy is reflected back into space, and some is absorbed and converted into heat. Some of that heat, in turn, radiates back into space, and some is trapped in the biosphere. The balance between heat that stays in the biosphere and heat lost to space determines Earth's average temperature. This balance is largely controlled by concentrations of three gases found in the atmosphere—carbon dioxide, methane, and water vapor.

As shown in **Figure 4–1,** these gases, called greenhouse gases, function like glass in a greenhouse, allowing visible light to enter but trapping heat. This phenomenon is called the **greenhouse effect.** If greenhouse gas concentrations rise, they trap more heat, so Earth warms. If their concentrations fall, more heat escapes, and Earth cools. Without the greenhouse effect, Earth would be about 30° Celsius cooler than it is today. Note that all three of these gases pass in and out of the atmosphere as part of nutrient cycles.

VISUAL ANALOGY

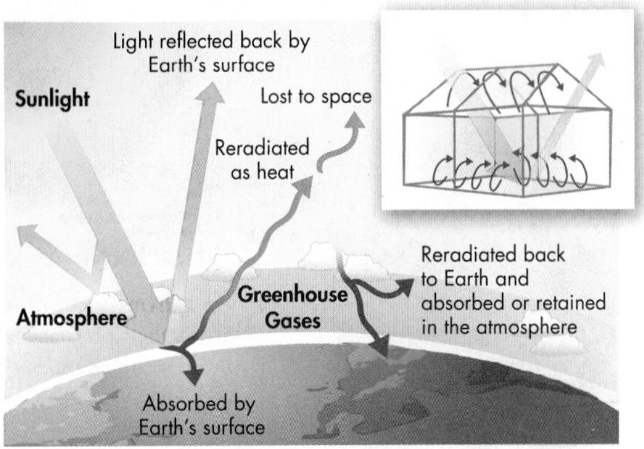

THE GREENHOUSE EFFECT

FIGURE 4–1 Greenhouse gases in the atmosphere allow solar radiation to enter the biosphere but slow down the loss of reradiated heat to space. **Use Analogies** ***What part of a greenhouse is analogous to the greenhouse gases in Earth's atmosphere?***

Latitude and Solar Energy Near the equator, solar energy is intense as the sun is almost directly overhead at noon all year. That's why equatorial regions are generally so warm. As **Figure 4–2** shows, the curvature of Earth causes the same amount of solar energy to spread out over a much larger area near the poles than near the equator. Thus, Earth's polar areas annually receive less intense solar energy, and therefore heat, from the sun. This difference in heat distribution creates three different climate zones: tropical, temperate, and polar.

The tropical zone, or tropics, which includes the equator, is located between 23.5° north and 23.5° south latitudes. This zone receives nearly direct sunlight all year. On either side of the tropical zone are the two temperate zones, between 23.5° and 66.5° north and south latitudes. Beyond the temperate zones are the polar zones, between 66.5° and 90° north and south latitudes. Temperate and polar zones receive very different amounts of solar energy at different times of the year because Earth's axis is tilted. As Earth revolves around the sun, solar radiation strikes different regions at angles that vary from summer to winter. During winter in the temperate and polar zones, the sun is much lower in the sky, days are shorter, and solar energy is less intense.

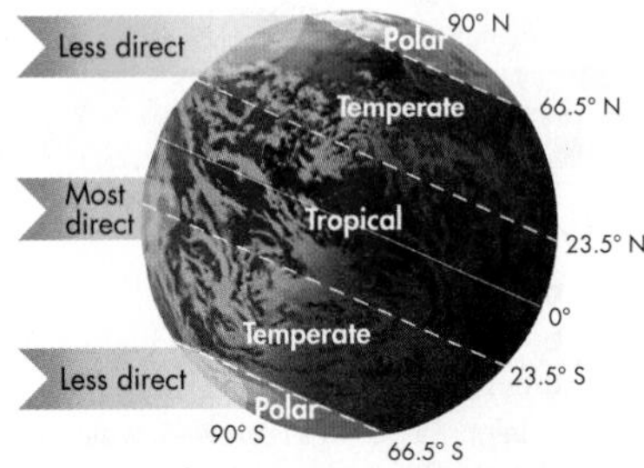

FIGURE 4–2 Climate Zones Earth's climate zones are produced by unequal distribution of the sun's heat on Earth's surface. Polar regions receive less solar energy per unit area, and so less heat, than tropical regions do. The tilt of Earth's axis causes the distribution of sunlight to change over the course of the year.

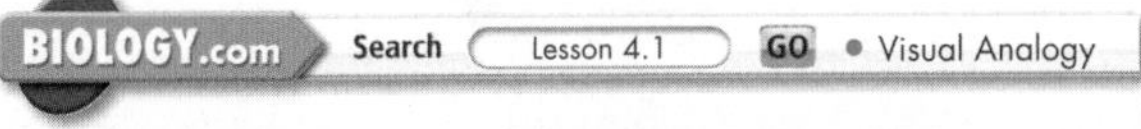

Biology In-Depth

CLIMATE CHANGE AND EARTH'S ORGANISMS

While human actions only enhance the natural greenhouse effect, even a small change in its intensity can cause great disruption in ecosystems worldwide. Not only will global temperatures rise, but an enhanced greenhouse effect can change the precipitation and other weather patterns that are fueled by the temperature differential between equatorial and polar regions. At the current rate of global warming, some of Earth's present climates may disappear and be replaced by different climates over the next century. Many scientists predict these changes to be most pronounced in tropical and subtropical regions. As climates change, so will Earth's organisms. There is already evidence that the ranges of some species, including certain butterflies, are shifting toward the poles. Many other species, which will be unable to move to new areas when climates change, are likely to go extinct.

Teach

Use Models

Have students model the relationship between latitude and solar energy with a globe and flashlight. Ask one student to hold the globe in the same position as the drawing of Earth in **Figure 4–2.** Ask another student to shine the flashlight straight ahead onto northern North America. Ask the class to observe the size of the area that is receiving light. Then, have the student shine the flashlight straight ahead onto the equator. Point out how a smaller area is now receiving the same amount of light.

DIFFERENTIATED INSTRUCTION

L3 Advanced Students Point out that the "beams" of sunlight shown in **Figure 4–2** create different shapes when they hit Earth at different angles—a circle near the equator and an ellipse near the poles. Demonstrate mathematically the difference between the areas of light received at these locations. Use an overhead projector and a piece of paper with a circular cutout to project a circle of light onto a piece of cardboard. Have students trace the shape of the projected circle of light onto the cardboard when it is upright. Then, have them tilt the cardboard 45 degrees back so that the light forms an ellipse. Have students trace this shape. Next, have them measure the lengths of the radius *(r)* of the circle and the semi-major (r_1) and semi-minor (r_2) axes of the ellipse. Finally, have them compare the areas of the two shapes using these formulas:

Area of a circle = πr^2

Area of an ellipse = $\pi(r_1)(r_2)$

VISUAL ANALOGY

Help students understand why only some of the radiation represented by arrows in **Figure 4–1** is reflected by Earth and passes back to space through the atmosphere. Tell them that the arrows represent either visible light or infrared light, which humans perceive as heat. Explain that visible light has shorter wavelengths and can pass through the atmosphere, whereas infrared light has longer wavelengths and can be absorbed by greenhouse gases.

BIOLOGY.com Have students further explore the greenhouse effect with **Visual Analogy: The Greenhouse Effect.**

Answers

FIGURE 4–1 the glass

LESSON 4.1

Assess and Remediate

EVALUATE UNDERSTANDING

Call on students at random to identify factors that influence climate. Call on other students to explain how each factor affects climate. Then, have students complete the 4.1 Assessment.

REMEDIATION SUGGESTION

L1 Struggling Students If students have trouble answering **Question 1c,** give them the background information they need to infer the answer. Explain that air is under less pressure at the top of mountains, so its molecules spread out. When the molecules of a gas spread out, the gas loses heat.

BIOLOGY.com Students can check their understanding of lesson concepts with the **Self-Test** assessment. They can then take an online version of the **Lesson Assessment.**

Answers

FIGURE 4–3 Cold currents in the Northern Hemisphere generally move southward, away from the North Pole and toward the equator.

Equator

Polar easterlies
Westerlies
Northeast trade winds
Southeast trade winds

FIGURE 4–3 Winds and Currents Earth's winds (above left) and ocean currents (above right) interact to help produce climate patterns. The paths of winds and currents are the result of heating and cooling, Earth's rotation, and geographic features. Interpret Visuals *In what direction do cold currents in the Northern Hemisphere generally move?*

Heat Transport in the Biosphere The unequal distribution of heat across the globe creates wind and ocean currents, which transport heat and moisture. Earth has winds because warm air is less dense and rises, and cool air is more dense and sinks. For this reason, air that is heated by a warm area of Earth's surface—such as air near the equator, for example—rises. As this warm air rises, it expands and spreads north and south, losing heat along the way. As it cools, the air sinks. At the same time, in cooler regions, near the poles, chilled air sinks toward Earth's surface, pushing air at the surface outward. This air warms as it travels over the surface. And as the air warms, it rises. These upward and downward movements of air create winds, as shown in **Figure 4–3** (above left). Winds transport heat from regions of rising warmer air to regions of sinking cooler air. Earth's rotation causes winds to blow generally from west to east over the temperate zones and from east to west over the tropics and the poles.

Similar patterns of heating and cooling occur in the oceans. Surface water is pushed by winds. These ocean currents transport enormous amounts of heat. Warm surface currents add moisture and heat to air that passes over them. Cool surface currents cool air that passes over them. In this way, surface currents affect the weather and climate of nearby landmasses. Deep ocean currents are caused by cold water near the poles sinking and flowing along the ocean floor. This water rises in warmer regions through a process called upwelling.

4.1 Assessment

IN B.4.4

Review Key Concepts

1. a. Review What is climate?
   b. Compare and Contrast How are climate and weather different?
   c. Infer Based on **Figure 4–3**, which do you think has a cooler climate: the east or west coast of southern Africa? Why?
2. a. Review What are the main factors that determine climate?
   b. Relate Cause and Effect Explain what would likely happen to global climate if there was a dramatic decrease in greenhouse gases trapped in the atmosphere.

ANALYZING DATA

3. Research average monthly precipitation (in mm) and temperature (in °C) for Quito, Ecuador, a city on the equator. Create a bar graph for the precipitation data. Plot the temperature data in a line graph.

BIOLOGY.com Search Lesson 4.1 GO • Self-Test • Lesson Assessment

Assessment Answers

1a. Climate is the average conditions of a location and is defined by year-after-year temperature and precipitation patterns.

1b. Weather is the day-to-day condition of Earth's atmosphere, whereas climate refers to average conditions over long periods.

1c. The figure shows cold surface currents moving up along the western coast and warm surface currents moving down the eastern coast; this pattern suggests that the west coast of southern Africa has a cooler climate.

2a. Climate is determined by solar energy trapped in the biosphere, latitude, and the transport of heat by winds and ocean currents.

2b. A decrease in greenhouse gases would allow more reradiated heat to escape to space, rather than being absorbed by the atmosphere, so global climate would become cooler.

ANALYZING DATA

3. Graphs should show that average monthly temperatures are very similar from month to month for the entire year, with an average temperature of about 15°C. Precipitation is much more variable. It is low from June through September and high from October through May, ranging from about 25 mm on average for the driest month to about 175 mm on average for the wettest month.

4.2 Niches and Community Interactions

IN B.4.4 Stability of an ecosystem. Also covered: NoS.3, B.4.1.

THINK ABOUT IT If you ask someone where an organism lives, that person might answer "on a coral reef" or "in the desert." These answers are like saying that a person lives "in Miami" or "in Arizona." The answer gives the environment or location. But ecologists need more information to understand fully why an organism lives where it does and how it fits into its surroundings. What else do they need to know?

The Niche

What is a niche?

Organisms occupy different places in part because each species has a range of conditions under which it can grow and reproduce. These conditions help define where and how an organism lives.

Tolerance Every species has its own range of **tolerance,** the ability to survive and reproduce under a range of environmental circumstances, as shown in **Figure 4–4.** When an environmental condition, such as temperature, extends in either direction beyond an organism's optimum range, the organism experiences stress. Why? Because it must expend more energy to maintain homeostasis, and so has less energy left for growth and reproduction. Organisms have an upper and lower limit of tolerance for every environmental factor. Beyond those limits, the organism cannot survive. A species' tolerance for environmental conditions, then, helps determine its "address" or **habitat**—the general place where an organism lives.

Key Questions

What is a niche?

How does competition shape communities?

How do predation and herbivory shape communities?

What are the three primary ways that organisms depend on each other?

Vocabulary

tolerance • habitat • niche • resource • competitive exclusion principle • predation • herbivory • keystone species • symbiosis • mutualism • parasitism • commensalism

Taking Notes

Concept Map Use the highlighted vocabulary words to create a concept map that organizes the information in this lesson.

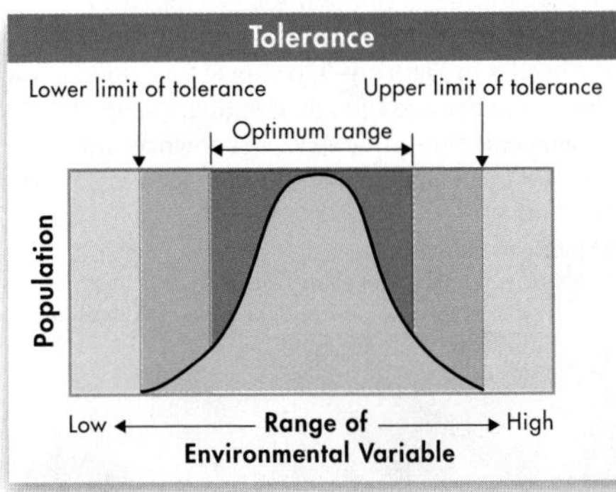

FIGURE 4–4 Tolerance This graph shows the response of a hypothetical organism to different values of a single environmental variable such as sunlight or temperature. At the center of the optimum range, organisms are likely to be most abundant. They become more rare in zones of physiological stress (medium blue), and are absent from zones of intolerance (light blue).

Getting Started

Objectives

4.2.1 Define niche.

4.2.2 Describe the role competition plays in shaping communities.

4.2.3 Describe the role predation and herbivory play in shaping communities.

4.2.4 Identify the three types of symbiotic relationships in nature.

Student Resources

Study Workbooks A/B, 4.2 Worksheets

Spanish Study Workbook, 4.2 Worksheets

Lab Manual B, 4.2 Data Analysis Worksheet, Hands-On Activity Worksheet

BIOLOGY.com Lesson Overview • Lesson Notes • Activity: Data Analysis • Assessment: Self-Test, Lesson Assessment

For corresponding lesson in the **Foundation Edition**, see pages 85–87.

BIOLOGY.com Students explore the tolerance of intertidal species in **Data Analysis: The Intertidal Zone.**

LESSON 4.2

IN INDIANA ACADEMIC STANDARDS

For the full text of all standards, see the Course Overview in the front matter of this book.

B.4.4 Describe how climate, the pattern of matter and energy flow, the birth and death of new organisms, and the interaction between those organisms contribute to the long term stability of an ecosystem.

UbD Teach for Understanding

ENDURING UNDERSTANDING The existence of life on Earth depends on interactions among organisms and between organisms and their environment.

GUIDING QUESTION How do organisms interact with one another?

EVIDENCE OF UNDERSTANDING *After completing the lesson, give students the following assessment to show they understand the types of interactions that can occur between organisms.* Have each student create a crossword puzzle using all of the lesson vocabulary terms. Then, pair students and have partners exchange crossword puzzles and try to solve each other's puzzle.

LESSON 4.2

Teach

Lead a Discussion

Work with students to apply the concepts of habitat and niche to organisms they are familiar with. On the board, write the names of several organisms. Choose a wide range of organisms, such as pine trees, dandelions, raccoons, frogs, and butterflies. Call on students to identify factors that help determine each organism's habitat or describe its niche. Use the exercise to reinforce the differences between habitat and niche and to clarify that niche is a property of organisms, not ecosystems.

DIFFERENTIATED INSTRUCTION

L1 Struggling Students Give students an analogy to help them understand the concept of niche. Tell them that an animal's niche is like the position an athlete plays in a team sport. Ask a student to name a player position for their favorite sport. Then, explain how this position is like a niche. For example, discuss the role a player in a given position fulfills for the team, the physical space the player occupies, and how the player interacts with fellow teammates and competitors.

ELL Focus on ELL: Extend Language

ALL SPEAKERS Ask students to write each of the lesson vocabulary terms on an index card. Then, have them divide each term into parts and read the sentence in which it is highlighted in the text. Tell beginning and intermediate speakers to write a phrase explaining what they think each term means and to make a drawing to illustrate it. Use examples to give them a clearer idea of any terms they do not understand. Instruct advanced and advanced high speakers to write the definition of each term based on its context in the paragraph where it is introduced. Review their definitions and correct any misunderstandings they might have.

Defining the Niche Describing a species' "address" tells only part of its story. Ecologists also study a species' ecological "occupation"—where and how it "makes a living." This idea of occupation is encompassed in the idea of an organism's niche (nich). A **niche** describes not only what an organism does, but also how it interacts with biotic and abiotic factors in the environment. **A niche is the range of physical and biological conditions in which a species lives and the way the species obtains what it needs to survive and reproduce.** Understanding niches is important to understanding how organisms interact to form a community.

▶ ***Resources and the Niche*** The term **resource** can refer to any necessity of life, such as water, nutrients, light, food, or space. For plants, resources can include sunlight, water, and soil nutrients—all of which are essential to survival. For animals, resources can include nesting space, shelter, types of food, and places to feed.

BUILD Vocabulary

ACADEMIC WORDS The noun **aspect** means "part." There are two aspects—or parts—of an organism's niche: physical aspects and biological aspects.

▶ ***Physical Aspects of the Niche*** Part of an organism's niche involves the abiotic factors it requires for survival. Most amphibians, for example, lose and absorb water through their skin, so they must live in moist places. If an area is too hot and dry, or too cold for too long, most amphibians cannot survive.

▶ ***Biological Aspects of the Niche*** Biological aspects of an organism's niche involve the biotic factors it requires for survival. When and how it reproduces, the food it eats, and the way in which it obtains that food are all examples of biological aspects of an organism's niche. Birds on Christmas Island, a small island in the Indian Ocean, for example, all live in the same habitat but they prey on fish of different sizes and feed in different places. Thus, each species occupies a distinct niche.

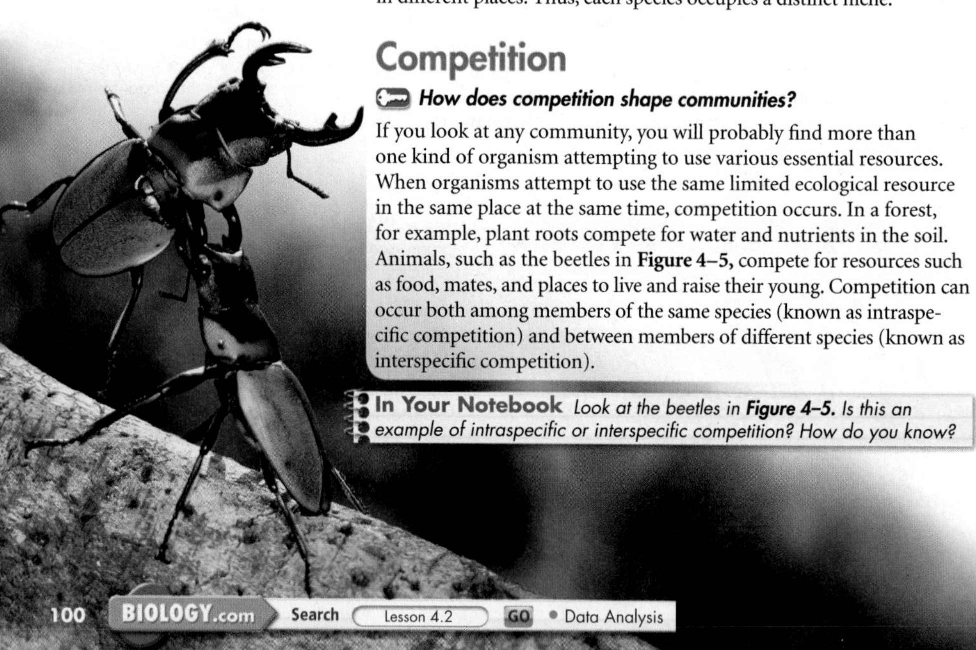

FIGURE 4–5 Competition Animals such as these two male stag beetles compete for limited resources. Infer ***What resource do you think these two males are fighting over?***

Competition

How does competition shape communities?

If you look at any community, you will probably find more than one kind of organism attempting to use various essential resources. When organisms attempt to use the same limited ecological resource in the same place at the same time, competition occurs. In a forest, for example, plant roots compete for water and nutrients in the soil. Animals, such as the beetles in **Figure 4–5,** compete for resources such as food, mates, and places to live and raise their young. Competition can occur both among members of the same species (known as intraspecific competition) and between members of different species (known as interspecific competition).

In Your Notebook *Look at the beetles in **Figure 4–5.** Is this an example of intraspecific or interspecific competition? How do you know?*

How Science Works

COMPETITIVE EXCLUSION PRINCIPLE

The competitive exclusion principle was first introduced by Russian ecologist G.F. Gause in the 1930s. His laboratory experiments with paramecia are described in the text on page 101. When Gause cultured two closely related paramecium species together, one species was less able to resist the toxic wastes that built up in the culture, and that species died out. Subsequent research has shown that Gause's principle applies only when two species have identical niches. If there are slight differences in their niches, two competing species may coexist. This has been demonstrated in many plant and animal species. In some cases, the competing species may prefer different microhabitats. In other cases, each species may do better at different times in a fluctuating environment.

Answers

FIGURE 4–5 Sample answer: I think they are fighting over food, living space, mates, or a place to raise their young.

IN YOUR NOTEBOOK It is probably an example of intraspecific competition, because both beetles appear to belong to the same species.

The Competitive Exclusion Principle Direct competition between different species almost always produces a winner and a loser—and the losing species dies out. One series of experiments demonstrated this using two species of single-celled organisms. When the species were grown in separate cultures under the same conditions, each survived, as shown in **Figure 4–6.** But when both species were grown together in the same culture, one species outcompeted the other. The less competitive species did not survive.

Experiments like this one, along with observations in nature, led to the discovery of an important ecological rule. The **competitive exclusion principle** states that no two species can occupy exactly the same niche in exactly the same habitat at exactly the same time. If two species attempt to occupy the same niche, one species will be better at competing for limited resources and will eventually exclude the other species. As a result, if we look at natural communities, we rarely find species whose niches overlap significantly.

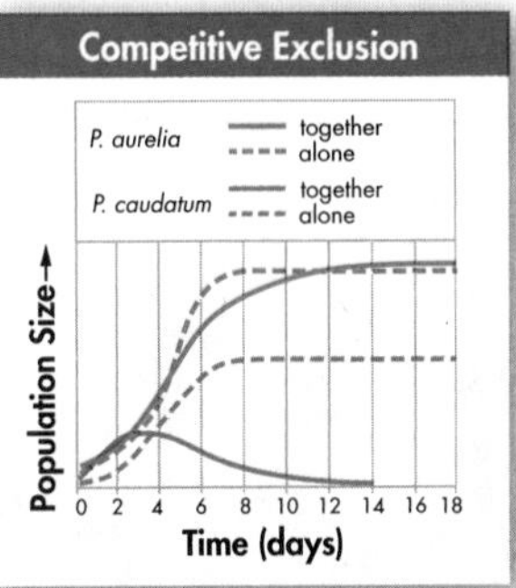

FIGURE 4–6 Competitive Exclusion The two species of paramecia *P. aurelia* and *P. caudatum* have similar requirements. When grown in cultures separately (dashed lines), both populations grow quickly and then level off. When grown together under certain conditions (solid lines), however, *P. aurelia* outcompetes *P. caudatum* and drives it to extinction.

Dividing Resources Instead of competing for similar resources, species usually divide them. For instance, the three species of North American warblers shown in **Figure 4–7** all live in the same trees and feed on insects. But one species feeds on high branches, another feeds on low branches, and another feeds in the middle. The resources utilized by these species are similar yet different. Therefore, each species has its own niche. This division of resources was likely brought about by past competition among the birds. **By causing species to divide resources, competition helps determine the number and kinds of species in a community and the niche each species occupies.**

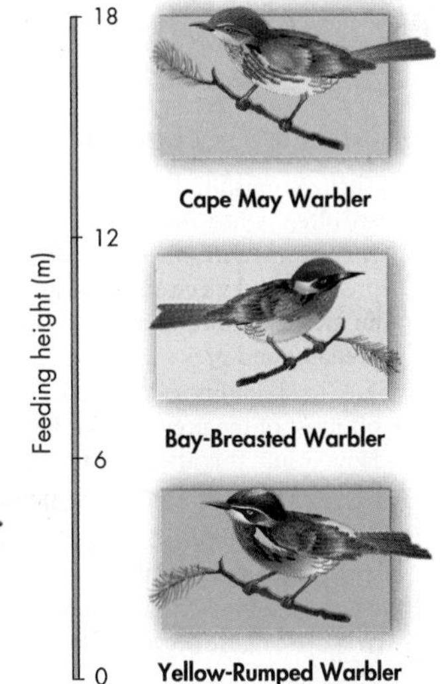

FIGURE 4–7 Resource Sharing Each of these warbler species has a different niche in its spruce tree habitat. By feeding in different areas of the tree, the birds avoid competing directly with one another for food. **Infer** ***What would happen if two of the warbler species tried to occupy the same niche in the same tree at the same time?***

Lead a Discussion

Point out the fighting beetles in **Figure 4–5,** and state that this is only one way in which competition occurs. In fact, competition often occurs without direct physical conflict. Discuss familiar examples, such as the competition for light and nutrients between weeds and tomato plants in a garden. To generate more examples, show students pictures of different ecosystems and ask them to identify resources that are needed by more than one type of organism. *(Examples of resources might include water and space.)* Then, discuss how the organisms pictured compete for these resources.

DIFFERENTIATED INSTRUCTION

LPR **Less Proficient Readers** Help students understand the difference between intraspecific and interspecific competition. Tell them that *intra-* means "within" and *inter-* means "between." Have students look up the meanings of the following pairs of words: intramural and intermural, intrastate and interstate, and intraspecies and interspecies. Have them draw pictures to distinguish between the definitions of each word pair. As a class, write sentences for each word that provide contextual meaning.

L3 **Advanced Students** Tell students that a technical term for competing species dividing similar resources within a habitat is *niche partitioning.* Have them look up the word *partition* and describe in their own words what *niche partitioning* means.

UbD Check for Understanding

ONE-MINUTE RESPONSE

Ask students to write a one-minute response explaining how competition for some, but not all, resources defines the different niches that two competing species occupy. *(The two species must divide or compete for only some of the resources that are available in a habitat. If they competed for all of the same exact resources, then the competitive exclusion principle would predict that one species would eventually die out. Both the resources that they compete for and the resources that they do not have to compete with one another for determine the species' niches.)*

ADJUST INSTRUCTION

Collect and review students' responses. Read aloud a few of the accurate explanations and also any that reveal misunderstandings. Call on volunteers to identify and correct the misunderstandings.

Answers

FIGURE 4–7 One species would be better at competing for food in that niche and would eventually exclude the other species.

Teach continued

Lead a Discussion

If you ask students to name predators and herbivores, they are likely to mention mammals such as wolves and deer. Widen their perspective by discussing examples of the more prevalent yet often less familiar predators and herbivores of the insect world. Tell students that insect herbivores, such as beetles and caterpillars, destroy large numbers of crops worldwide, and insect predators, such as ladybeetles and lacewings, eat many of these crop pests. Ask students to predict how the use of chemical pesticides to kill insect herbivores might affect insect predators. *(Sample answer: The pesticides might kill both types of insects. Then, if insect herbivores increase in numbers again, there might not be enough predators left to control them.)*

DIFFERENTIATED INSTRUCTION

ELL English Language Learners Tell students that the word *prey* is both a noun and a verb. Have students write sentences using each form of the word. Then, explain that, as a noun, it is an uncountable word, which means it cannot be plural or described using numbers. Compare the word *prey* to another uncountable noun, such as *information,* and as a class come up with sentences that demonstrate how these words do not have a plural form.

L3 Advanced Students Encourage students to research defenses that have evolved in organisms as protection against predators and herbivores. Such defenses might include camouflage, quills or thorns, toxins, warning coloration, or mimicry. Have students share their findings with the class in oral reports, posters, or displays.

FIGURE 4–8 Herbivory The ring-tailed lemur is an herbivore—meaning that it obtains its energy and nutrients from plants like the cactus it's eating here.

Predation, Herbivory, and Keystone Species

How do predation and herbivory shape communities?

Virtually all animals, because they are not primary producers, must eat other organisms to obtain energy and nutrients. Yet if a group of animals devours all available food in the area, they will no longer have anything to eat! That's why predator-prey and herbivore-plant interactions are very important in shaping communities.

Predator-Prey Relationships An interaction in which one animal (the predator) captures and feeds on another animal (the prey) is called **predation** (pree DAY shun). **Predators can affect the size of prey populations in a community and determine the places prey can live and feed.** Birds of prey, for example, can play an important role in regulating the population sizes of mice, voles, and other small mammals.

Herbivore-Plant Relationships Interactions between herbivores and plants, like the one shown in **Figure 4–8,** are as important as interactions between predators and prey. An interaction in which one animal (the herbivore) feeds on producers (such as plants) is called **herbivory. Herbivores can affect both the size and distribution of plant populations in a community and determine the places that certain plants can survive and grow.** Herbivores ranging from caterpillars to elk can have major effects on plant survival. For example, very dense populations of white-tailed deer are eliminating their favorite food plants from many places across the United States.

Analyzing Data

IN NoS.3, B.4.1, B.4.4

Predator-Prey Dynamics

The relationships between predator and prey are often tightly intertwined, particularly in an environment in which each prey has a single predator and vice versa. The graph here shows an idealized computer model of changes in predator and prey populations over time.

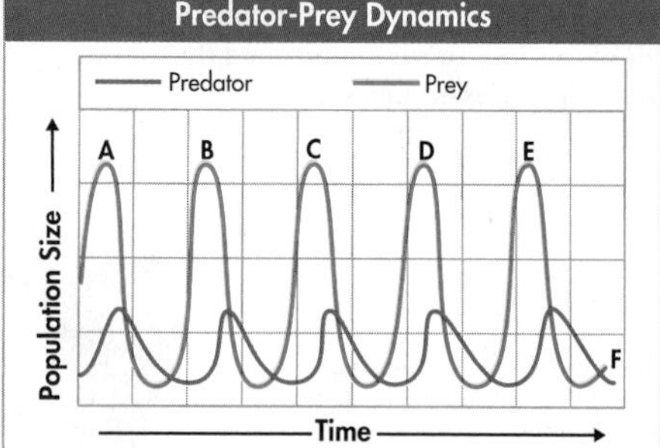

1. **Predict** Suppose a bacterial infection kills off most of the prey at point B on the graph. How would this affect the predator and prey growth curves at point C? At point D?
2. **Predict** Suppose a sudden extended cold spell destroys almost the entire predator population at point F on the graph. How would the next cycle of the prey population appear on the graph?
3. **Relate Cause and Effect** Suppose a viral infection kills all the prey at point D on the graph. What effect would this have on the predator and prey growth curves at point E? What will happen in future years to the predator population? How could ecologists ensure the continued survival of the predators in this ecosystem?

PURPOSE Students will interpret an idealized computer model to infer relationships between predator and prey populations.

PLANNING Before students answer the questions, discuss why there is a time lag between the predator and prey population changes shown in the graph.

ANSWERS

1. If most of the prey were killed off at point B, the predator population would decline between points B and C, allowing the prey population to increase again by point C. Greater numbers of prey would lead to the predator population increasing again, which would be followed by another decline in the prey population. The decline in numbers of prey would lead to another decrease in the predator population, which would allow the prey population to increase yet again at point D.
2. The prey population would increase in the next cycle, reaching a peak that is potentially even higher than the previous peaks.
3. Sample answer: If a viral infection kills all the prey at point D, at point E, the prey population will be zero and the predator population would be decreased, possibly to zero. In future years, if the predators find another food resource, the population may recover. The predator population would not recover in future years without any prey to feed on. To ensure continued survival of the predators in this ecosystem, ecologists could control the viral infection in the prey so that not all of them are killed by the virus, or they could introduce new prey animals to the ecosystem.

Keystone Species Sometimes changes in the population of a single species, often called a **keystone species,** can cause dramatic changes in the structure of a community. In the cold waters off the Pacific coast of North America, for example, sea otters devour large quantities of sea urchins. Urchins, in turn, are herbivores. Their favorite food is kelp, giant algae that grow in undersea "forests."

A century ago, sea otters were nearly eliminated by hunting. Unexpectedly, the kelp forest nearly vanished. What happened? Without otters as predators, the sea urchin population skyrocketed. Armies of urchins devoured kelp down to bare rock. Without kelp to provide habitat, many other animals, including seabirds, disappeared. Clearly, otters were a keystone species in this community. After otters were protected as an endangered species, their population began to recover. As otters returned, the urchin populations dropped, and kelp forests began to thrive again. Recently, however, the otter population has been falling again, and no one knows why.

One of the favorite prey species of the wolves in Yellowstone is elk. How do you think this relationship could affect the ability of certain *plants* to grow in Yellowstone?

In Your Notebook *Not all keystone-species effects are due to predation. Describe the dramatic effects that the dam-building activities of beavers, a keystone species, might have on other types of organisms.*

Symbioses

What are the three primary ways that organisms depend on each other?

Any relationship in which two species live closely together is called **symbiosis** (sim by OH sis), which means "living together." **Biologists recognize three main classes of symbiotic relationships in nature: mutualism, parasitism, and commensalism.**

Mutualism The sea anemone's sting has two functions: to capture prey and to protect the anemone from predators. Even so, certain fish manage to snack on anemone tentacles. The clownfish, however, is immune to anemone stings. When threatened by a predator, clownfish seek shelter by snuggling deep into tentacles that would be deadly to most other fish, as seen in **Figure 4–9.** But if an anemone-eating species tries to attack their living home, the spunky clownfish dart out and fiercely chase away fish many times their size. This kind of relationship between species in which both benefit is known as **mutualism.**

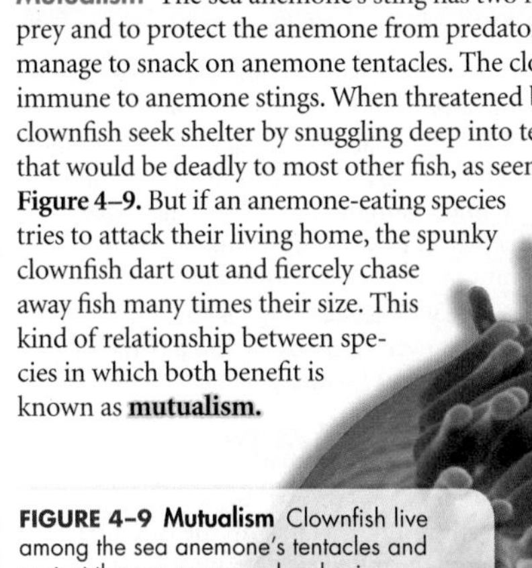

FIGURE 4–9 Mutualism Clownfish live among the sea anemone's tentacles and protect the sea anemone by chasing away would-be attackers. The sea anemone, in turn, protects the clownfish from their predators. **Infer** ***What could happen to the sea anemone if the clownfish died?***

Use Visuals

Use **Figure 4–9, Figure 4–10,** and **Figure 4–11** to introduce the three main classes of symbiotic relationships. For each figure, call on students to identify the two organisms that are involved in the relationship and how they interact. Describe several additional examples of symbiotic relationships, and ask students to identify the class of relationship each example represents. Examples might include flowering plants and their insect pollinators (mutualism); mistletoe and its plant hosts, trees and shrubs (parasitism); and burdock plants and animals with fur that transport their seeds (commensalism). Choose one example of each type of relationship. Then, for each example, discuss with the class how a change in numbers of one species in the relationship might affect numbers of the other species.

DIFFERENTIATED INSTRUCTION

ELL English Language Learners Suggest students fill in a **Compare/Contrast Table** on symbiosis as they read about it in the lesson. Their tables should have a row for each of the three main classes of symbiotic relationships. Columns should address which of the organisms benefit from the relationship and provide examples.

Study Wkbks A/B, Appendix S20, Compare/Contrast Table. **Transparencies,** GO3.

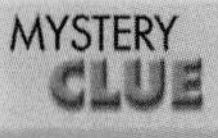

Remind students that elk are herbivores. Have them reread the paragraph with the blue heading, **Herbivore-Plant Relationships,** to help them answer the question. Students are likely to respond that a declining elk population due to wolf predation would give certain plants a better chance of growing, because fewer of them would be eaten by elk. Students can go online to **Biology.com** to gather their evidence.

Quick Facts

THE HUMAN SUPERORGANISM

Humans and the bacteria that live in and on the human body are involved in numerous symbiotic relationships—many of them mutualistic. An example of one mutualistic human-bacterial relationship involves certain bacteria on the skin that process fats produced by the skin and help keep the skin moist. This is just one of an estimated 20 or more different niches of bacteria on the human skin alone. Other mutualistic relationships involve bacteria in the gut, which feast on the products of digestion while helping to break down carbohydrates. Because of the important roles bacteria play in the human animal and the huge numbers of bacteria that inhabit the human body, some microbiologists think that each person should be thought of as a superorganism, composed of one human and trillions of bacteria.

Answers

FIGURE 4–9 The sea anemone might be killed by predators if the clownfish died.

IN YOUR NOTEBOOK Sample answer: Dam building might flood land upstream from the dam and reduce the flow of water downstream from the dam. Land organisms living upstream might die out because their habitats are flooded, and aquatic organisms living downstream might die out because their habitats dry up. Beavers also might destroy most of the trees near the water's edge to build their dams, and this could increase runoff and erosion, which could change the habitat of species that rely on soil.

LESSON 4.2

Assess and Remediate

EVALUATE UNDERSTANDING

On the board, list the six types of community interactions described in the lesson (competition, predation, herbivory, mutualism, parasitism, and commensalism). For each interaction, call on a student to give a definition and another student to give an example. Then, have students complete the 4.2 Assessment.

REMEDIATION SUGGESTION

L1 Struggling Students If students have trouble with **Question 4c,** tell them to think about what happens to prey when they are captured by predators such as lions. Then, suggest they consider what happens to people when they are bitten by parasites such as mosquitoes.

BIOLOGY.com Students can check their understanding of lesson concepts with the **Self-Test** assessment. They can then take an online version of the **Lesson Assessment.**

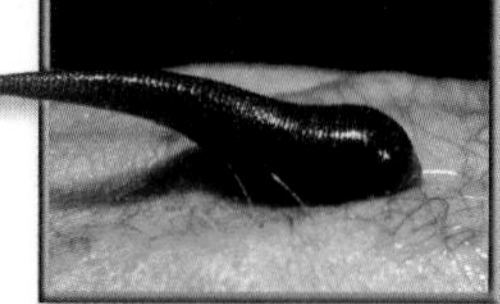

FIGURE 4–10 Parasitism This brown leech is feeding on the blood of its host, a human. In a parasitic relationship, the parasite benefits while the host is harmed.

Parasitism Tapeworms live in the intestines of mammals, where they absorb large amounts of their hosts' food. Fleas, ticks, lice, and leeches live on the bodies of mammals, feeding on their blood and skin, as seen in **Figure 4–10.** These are examples of **parasitism** (PAR uh sit iz um), relationships in which one organism lives inside or on another organism and harms it. The parasite obtains all or part of its nutritional needs from the host organism. Generally, parasites weaken but do not kill their host, which is usually larger than the parasite.

Commensalism Small marine animals called barnacles often attach themselves to a whale's skin, as seen in **Figure 4–11.** The barnacles perform no known service to the whale, nor do they harm it. Yet the barnacles benefit from the constant movement of water—that is full of food particles—past the swimming whale. This is an example of **commensalism** (kuh MEN sul iz um), a relationship in which one organism benefits and the other is neither helped nor harmed.

FIGURE 4–11 Commensalism The barnacles attached to the skin of this grey whale are feeding on food in the water that passes over them as the whale swims. Although the barnacles clearly benefit from their relationship with the whale, they do not appear to affect the whale positively or negatively.

4.2 Assessment

IN B.4.1, B.4.4

Review Key Concepts

1. a. Review What is the difference between a habitat and a niche?

b. Use Analogies How is a niche like a profession? In ecological terms, describe your niche.

2. a. Review What is competition? Why can't two organisms compete if they live in different habitats?

b. Interpret Visuals Look at **Figure 4–7** and describe how the three species of warblers have divided their resources. Does each warbler have its own niche?

3. a. Review What is a keystone species?

b. Infer How might a dramatic decrease in vegetation lead to a decrease in a prey species? (*Hint:* Think of how the vegetation, prey, and predator could be connected in a food chain.)

4. a. Review What is symbiosis? What are the three major types of symbiosis?

b. Explain Bacteria living in a cow's stomach help the cow break down the cellulose in grass, gaining nutrients in the process. Is this an example of commensalism or mutualism? Explain your answer.

c. Apply Concepts What is the difference between a predator and a parasite? Explain your answer.

BUILD VOCABULARY

5. The suffix *-ism* means "the act, practice, or result of." Look up the meaning of *mutual,* and write a definition for *mutualism.*

BIOLOGY.com Search  Lesson 4.2 GO • Self-Test • Lesson Assessment

Assessment Answers

1a. A habitat is the general place where an organism lives. A niche also describes how the organism interacts with its environment.

1b. A profession is the role a person plays in his or her community. Like a profession, a niche is the role an organism plays in its community. Students should describe the physical and biological aspects of their own niche.

2a. Competition is an interaction between organisms in which both organisms attempt to use the same limited ecological resource in the same place at the same time. Two organisms that live in different habitats can't compete because they do not live in the same place.

2b. All three warbler species live in the same trees and feed on insects, but each species has its own niche because it uses resources in a different part of the tree.

3a. A keystone species is a species that causes dramatic changes in the structure of a community if its population changes.

3b. A decrease in vegetation could reduce the number of herbivores. With fewer herbivores, there would be less food for predators, so the predators might decrease in numbers, as well.

4a. Symbiosis is any relationship in which two species live closely together. The three major types of symbiosis are mutualism, parasitism, and commensalism.

4b. This is an example of mutualism, because both the cow and the bacteria benefit from the relationship.

4c. A predator usually kills its prey. A parasite generally only weakens its host.

BUILD VOCABULARY

5. *Mutual* means "shared, or in common," so *mutualism* can be defined as "the act of sharing in common."

Do you enjoy being outdoors? If you do, you might want to consider one of these careers.

MARINE BIOLOGIST

Ocean ecosystems cover over 70 percent of Earth's surface. Marine biologists study the incredible diversity of ocean life. Some marine biologists study organisms found in deep ocean trenches to understand how they survive in extreme conditions. Others work in aquariums, where they might conduct research, educate the public, or rehabilitate rescued marine wildlife.

PARK RANGER

For some people, camping and hiking aren't just recreational activities—they're work. Park rangers work in national, state, and local parks caring for the land and ensuring the safety of visitors. Park rangers perform a variety of tasks, including maintaining campsites and helping with search and rescue. Rangers are also responsible for looking after park wildlife.

WILDLIFE PHOTOGRAPHER

Wildlife photographers capture nature "in action." Their photographs can be used in books, magazines, and on the Internet to educate and entertain the public. Successful wildlife photographers need to be observant and adventurous. They also need to be patient enough to wait for the perfect shot.

CAREER CLOSE-UP

Dudley Edmondson, Wildlife Photographer

Dudley Edmondson began bird-watching at a young age. After high school, he began traveling and photographing the birds he observed. Mr. Edmondson has since been all over the United States taking pictures of everything from the landscapes and grizzly bears of Yellowstone Park to the butterflies that inhabit his own backyard. Through his work, he hopes to inspire people to travel and experience nature for themselves. This, he believes, will encourage a sense of responsibility to protect and preserve the environment.

"What I like most about my work is the unique perspective it gives me on the world. Birds, insects, and plants are totally unaware of things like clocks, deadlines, and technology. When you work with living things, you work on their terms."

WRITING Where have you seen nature photography used or displayed? How do those photos, or Mr. Edmondson's, help the public learn about the natural world?

Teach

Lead a Discussion

After students read the feature, divide the class into three groups, and assign each group one of the careers. Ask students to brainstorm why a person in that career should know about the interactions of organisms in communities. Give groups a chance to share their ideas. Then, use their ideas to start a class discussion of how knowledge of community interactions might benefit anyone with an interest in nature.

DIFFERENTIATED INSTRUCTION

LPR Less Proficient Readers Before students read about the careers described on this page, have them write a question they would like to have answered about each career. Tell them to try to find the answer to their question as they read. If any of their questions remain unanswered, discuss how they could find the answers. Encourage them to follow their plan to locate the information.

L3 Advanced Students Ask interested students to learn more about one of the biology careers described on this page. Then, have them write a short, fictionalized account, based on what they learn, in which they describe a typical workday for a person in that career. Ask students to share their accounts with the class.

Answers

WRITING Sample answer: I have seen nature photography on television shows and in nature magazines and science textbooks. The photos help the public learn about the diversity of life by showing how different organisms look and behave in their natural environment.

Quick Facts

THE BEST OF BOTH FIELDS

Some people have more than one career at the same time or multiple careers in sequence. One example is Ron Austing, who pursued his love of nature by becoming both a park ranger and a wildlife photographer. Although he is now retired from his job as wildlife manager of a 16,000-acre park, Austing is still active as a wildlife photographer. His nature photographs have appeared in numerous publications, including *National Geographic, Audubon, National Wildlife, Sports Illustrated,* and many books. Like Dudley Edmondson, Ron Austing especially enjoys taking photographs of birds.

LESSON 4.3

Getting Started

Objectives

4.3.1 Describe how ecosystems recover from a disturbance.

4.3.2 Compare succession after a natural disturbance with succession after a human-caused disturbance.

Student Resources

Study Workbooks A/B, 4.3 Worksheets

Spanish Study Workbook, 4.3 Worksheets

Lesson Overview • Lesson Notes • Activity: Art in Motion • Assessment: Self-Test, Lesson Assessment

For corresponding lesson in the **Foundation Edition**, see pages 88–90.

Build Background

Describe or show photographs of a local area, familiar to students, that was recently disturbed by a natural event or human actions. Ask students to predict how the area would look in ten years if it were left undisturbed. Tell them they will learn what happens to such disturbed areas in this lesson.

Have students watch animations of succession in **Art in Motion: Primary and Secondary Succession.**

IN INDIANA ACADEMIC STANDARDS

For the full text of all standards, see the Course Overview in the front matter of this book.

B.4.4 Describe how climate, the pattern of matter and energy flow, the birth and death of new organisms, and the interaction between those organisms contribute to the long term stability of an ecosystem.

4.3 Succession

B.4.4 Stability of an ecosystem. Also covered: **B.4.2.**

Key Questions

How do communities change over time?

Do ecosystems return to "normal" following a disturbance?

Vocabulary

ecological succession
primary succession
pioneer species
secondary succession

Taking Notes

Compare/Contrast Table
As you read, create a table comparing primary and secondary succession.

THINK ABOUT IT In 1883, the volcanic island of Krakatau in the Indian Ocean was blown to pieces by an eruption. The tiny island that remained was completely barren. Within two years, grasses were growing. Fourteen years later, there were 49 plant species, along with lizards, birds, bats, and insects. By 1929, a forest containing 300 plant species had grown. Today, the island is blanketed by mature rain forest. How did the island ecosystem recover so quickly?

Primary and Secondary Succession

How do communities change over time?

The story of Krakatau after the eruption is an example of **ecological succession**—a series of more-or-less predictable changes that occur in a community over time. **Ecosystems change over time, especially after disturbances, as some species die out and new species move in.** Over the course of succession, the number of different species present typically increases.

Primary Succession Volcanic explosions like the ones that destroyed Krakatau in 1883 and blew the top off Mount Saint Helens in Washington State in 1980 can create new land or sterilize existing areas. Retreating glaciers can have the same effect, leaving only exposed bare rock behind them. Succession that begins in an area with no remnants of an older community is called **primary succession.** An example of primary succession is shown in **Figure 4–12.**

FIGURE 4–12 Primary Succession Primary succession occurs on newly exposed surfaces. In Glacier Bay, Alaska, a retreating glacier exposed barren rock. Over the course of more than 100 years, a series of changes has led to the hemlock and spruce forest currently found in the area. Changes in this community will continue for centuries.

 BIOLOGY.com Search Lesson 4.3 GO • Lesson Overview • Lesson Notes

UbD Teach for Understanding

ENDURING UNDERSTANDING The existence of life on Earth depends on interactions among organisms and between organisms and their environment.

GUIDING QUESTION How do ecosystems change over time?

EVIDENCE OF UNDERSTANDING *After completing the lesson, assign students the following assessment to show they understand how succession changes ecosystems over time.* Tell students to use the information from the lesson to write a short story about an ecosystem that is disturbed and undergoes either primary or secondary succession. Remind them to write about both biotic and abiotic factors.

The first species to colonize barren areas are called **pioneer species**—named after rugged human pioneers who first settled the wilderness. After pioneers created settlements, different kinds of people with varied skills and living requirements moved into the area. Pioneer species function in similar ways. One ecological pioneer that grows on bare rock is lichen—a mutualistic symbiosis between a fungus and an alga. Over time, lichens convert, or fix, atmospheric nitrogen into useful forms for other organisms, break down rock, and add organic material to form soil. Certain grasses, like those that colonized Krakatau early on, are also pioneer species.

BUILD Vocabulary

WORD ORIGINS The origin of the word *succession* is the Latin word *succedere*, meaning "to come after." **Ecological succession** involves changes that occur one after the other as species move into and out of a community.

Secondary Succession Sometimes, existing communities are not completely destroyed by disturbances. In these situations, where a disturbance affects the community without completely destroying it, **secondary succession** occurs. Secondary succession proceeds faster than primary succession, in part because soil survives the disturbance. As a result, new and surviving vegetation can regrow rapidly. Secondary succession often follows a wildfire, hurricane, or other natural disturbance. We think of these events as disasters, but many species are adapted to them. Although forest fires kill some trees, for example, other trees are spared, and fire can stimulate their seeds to germinate. Secondary succession can also follow human activities like logging and farming. An example of secondary succession is shown in **Figure 4–13.**

Why Succession Occurs Every organism changes the environment it lives in. One model of succession suggests that as one species alters its environment, other species find it easier to compete for resources and survive. As lichens add organic matter and form soil, for example, mosses and other plants can colonize and grow. As organic matter continues to accumulate, other species move in and change the environment further. For example, as trees grow, their branches and leaves produce shade and cooler temperatures nearer the ground. Over time, more and more species can find suitable niches and survive.

In Your Notebook *Summarize what happens in primary and secondary succession.*

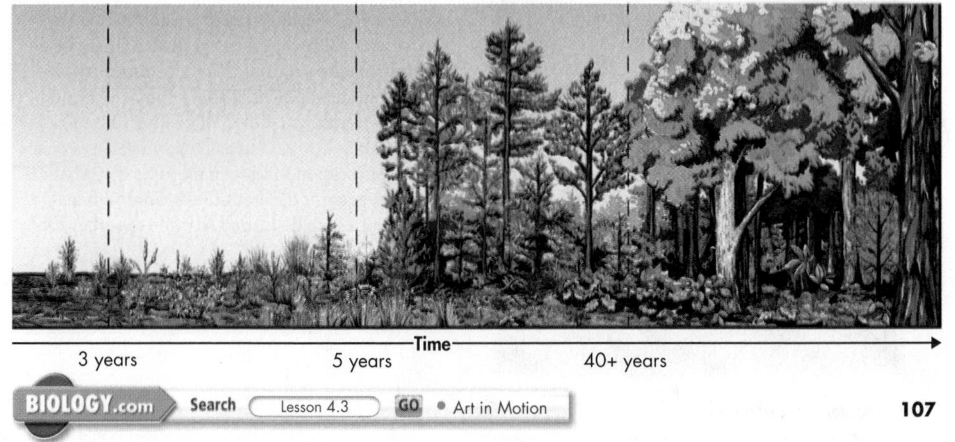

FIGURE 4–13 Secondary Succession Secondary succession occurs in disturbed areas where remnants of previous ecosystems—soil and even plants—remain. This series shows changes taking place in abandoned fields of the Carolinas' Piedmont. Over the last century, these fields have passed through several stages and matured into oak forests. Changes will continue for years to come.

BIOLOGY.com Search Lesson 4.3 GO • Art in Motion

Teach

Use Visuals

Guide students in using **Figures 4–12** and **4–13** to compare and contrast primary and secondary succession.

Ask How are the two areas different when succession first begins? *(The area in **Figure 4–12** is nothing but bare rock and some lichen. The area in **Figure 4–13** already has soil and a few small plants.)*

Ask How long does it take for young trees to grow in each case? *(35 to 80 years for primary succession, and 3 to 5 years for secondary succession)*

DIFFERENTIATED INSTRUCTION

LPR Less Proficient Readers Have students make a **Flowchart** to show the sequence of events that typically occurs during primary succession. Each stage in their flowchart should include a description of that stage and an approximate number of years since the start of succession. Make sure students realize that succession does not always proceed in exactly the same way and that it is a continuous process.

Study Wkbks A/B, Appendix S25, Flowchart. **Transparencies,** GO8.

ELL Focus on ELL: Build Background

ADVANCED AND ADVANCED HIGH SPEAKERS Read a description of the aftermath of the volcanic eruption on Krakatau in 1883. As you read, have students draw a sketch of what you are describing. Encourage them to discuss the description. Then, ask them to fill in column B of a **BKWL Chart** with background from the discussion. Tell them to list anything they can infer about succession after a volcanic explosion in column K and questions they have about it in column W. After students read the lesson, have them complete column L and describe what they have learned.

Study Wkbks A/B, Appendix S27, BKWL Chart. **Transparencies,** GO12.

How Science Works

LEARNING FROM DISASTER

In 1980, when volcanic activity blew up Mount St. Helens in Washington state, all the trees for hundreds of square miles of mature forest around the volcano were scorched, burned to the ground, or toppled like matchsticks. More than 20 square miles were buried to an average depth of 150 feet by the largest debris avalanche in recorded history. The U.S. Congress acted quickly to protect thousands of acres of the destroyed forest from human intervention so scientists could study ecological succession in the unique living laboratory the volcano created. Soon, scientists from more than 70 universities and government agencies had started long-term research projects on Mount St. Helens. Since then, their research has made major contributions to the science of succession. The results of their research are also being applied to help restore other disturbed forests.

Answers

IN YOUR NOTEBOOK Primary succession occurs in areas with no previous community. After pioneer species move in and help form soil, other species gradually colonize. Secondary succession occurs when a community is disturbed but soil remains. Surviving vegetation regrows, and new vegetation moves in.

Teach continued

Lead a Discussion

Help students understand how ideas about succession have changed over the years.

Ask How have ecologists' ideas about climax communities changed? *(Formerly, they thought that the stages of succession were always the same and that stable climax communities were always the end result.)*

Ask What types of information changed their thinking? *(Climax communities resulting from multiple disturbances were more like patchwork quilts than like the original climax community.)*

DIFFERENTIATED INSTRUCTION

L1 Struggling Students Help students understand how climax communities can be unstable. Provide students with visuals of regrowth after a forest fire or lava flow. Then, have them compare these examples with images of the growth of weeds or trees through concrete or asphalt. Ask them to infer why the plants that appear after the forest fire or lava flow are more likely to reach maturity and provide niches for other species than the plants that appear after an area is paved by humans. Compare the periodic maintenance of a road to an area in nature that undergoes frequent disturbances. In both situations the resulting climax community is not stable.

Answers

FIGURE 4–14 Secondary succession occurred, since soil and a few plants remained in the area after the storm.

IN YOUR NOTEBOOK Instability in some climax communities is caused by frequent disturbances.

GUIDED INQUIRY

Successful Succession?

1. Place a handful of dried plant material into a clean jar.
2. Fill the jar with boiled pond water or sterile spring water. Determine the initial pH of the water with pH paper.
3. Cover the jar and place it in an area that receives indirect light.
4. Examine the jar every day for the next few days.
5. When the water in the jar appears cloudy, prepare microscope slides of water from various levels of the jar. Use a pipette to collect the samples.
6. Look at the slides under the low-power objective lens of a microscope and record your observations.

Analyze and Conclude

1. Infer Why did you use boiled or sterile water?
2. Infer Where did the organisms you saw come from?
3. Draw Conclusions Was ecological succession occurring? Give evidence to support your answer.
4. Evaluate and Revise Check your results against those of your classmates. Do they agree? How do you explain any differences?

Climax Communities

Do ecosystems return to "normal" following a disturbance?

Ecologists used to think that succession in a given area always proceeds through the same stages to produce a specific and stable climax community like the mature spruce and hemlock forest that is developing in Glacier Bay. Recent studies, however, have shown that succession doesn't always follow the same path, and that climax communities are not always uniform and stable.

FIGURE 4–14 Recovery From a Natural Disaster These photos show El Yunque Rain Forest in Puerto Rico, immediately following Tropical Storm Jeanne in September 2004, and then again in May, 2007. Apply Concepts ***What kind of succession occurred in this rain forest? How do you know?***

Succession After Natural Disturbances Natural disturbances are common in many communities. Healthy coral reefs and tropical rain forests recover from storms, as shown in **Figure 4–14.** Healthy temperate forests and grasslands recover from wildfires. **Secondary succession in healthy ecosystems following natural disturbances often reproduces the original climax community.** But detailed studies show that some climax communities are not uniform. Often, they look more like patchwork quilts with areas in varying stages of secondary succession following multiple disturbances that took place at different times. Some climax communities are disturbed so often that they can't really be called stable.

In Your Notebook *Describe what causes instability in some climax communities.*

Quick Lab

PURPOSE Students will conclude whether ecological succession has occurred in a closed aquatic community.

MATERIALS dried plant material, jar with lid, boiled pond water or sterile spring water, pH paper, microscope, slides, coverslips, pipette

SAFETY Remind students to handle the slides and pipette carefully and to wash their hands thoroughly after completing the lab.

PLANNING Obtain aquatic plants from a pet or aquarium store and spread them out to dry on baking sheets for a few days. Quart-sized canning jars are a good choice for the lab. You can sterilize them by filling them with boiling water and letting them air dry.

ANALYZE AND CONCLUDE

1. I used boiled water to avoid introducing organisms with the water added to the jar.
2. The organisms came from the dried plant material.
3. Sample answer: Yes, ecological succession was occurring, because the habitat inside the jar was changed by the living things in the jar. Tiny organisms grew in the water, turning it cloudy.
4. Sample answer: We all had organisms growing in the water in our jars, but we observed different numbers and types of organisms. The differences could be due to chance. There may have been different types of organisms in the dried plant material we started with, or we may have sampled different organisms when we prepared the slides.

Succession After Human-Caused Disturbances In North America, land cleared for farming and then abandoned often passes through succession that restores the original climax community. But this is not always the case. **Ecosystems may or may not recover from extensive human-caused disturbances.** Clearing and farming of tropical rain forests, for example, can change the microclimate and soil enough to prevent regrowth of the original community.

Studying Patterns of Succession Ecologists, like the ones seen in **Figure 4–15,** study succession by comparing different cases and looking for similarities and differences. Researchers who swarmed over Mount Saint Helens as soon as it was safe might also have studied Krakatau, for example. In both places, primary succession proceeded through predictable stages. The first plants and animals that arrived had seeds, spores, or adult stages that traveled over long distances. Hardy pioneer species helped stabilize loose volcanic debris, enabling later species to take hold. Historical studies in Krakatau and ongoing studies on Mount Saint Helens confirm that early stages of primary succession are slow, and that chance can play a large role in determining which species colonize at different times.

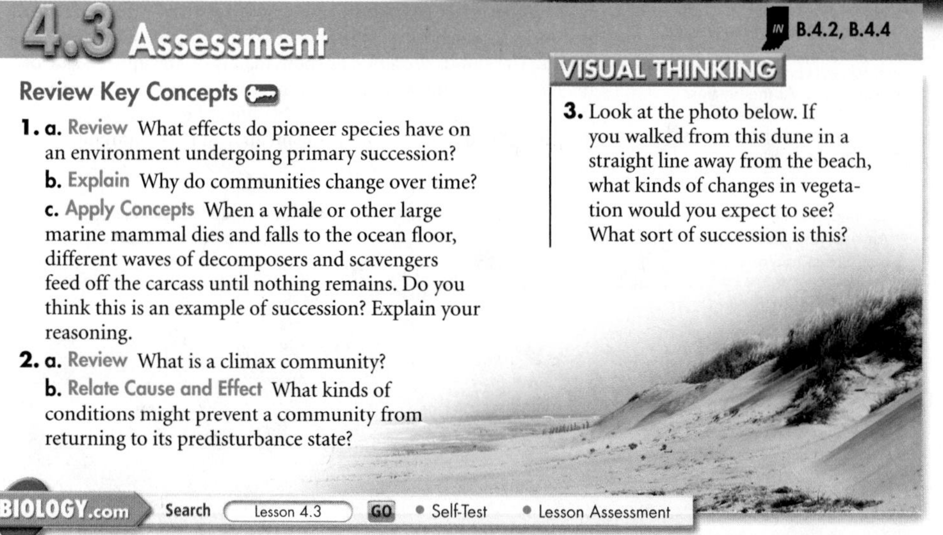

FIGURE 4–15 Studying Succession These Forest Service rangers are surveying some of the plants and animals that have returned to the area around Mount Saint Helens. The volcano erupted in 1980, leaving only barren land for miles.

4.3 Assessment

IN B.4.2, B.4.4

Review Key Concepts

1. a. **Review** What effects do pioneer species have on an environment undergoing primary succession?
   b. **Explain** Why do communities change over time?
   c. **Apply Concepts** When a whale or other large marine mammal dies and falls to the ocean floor, different waves of decomposers and scavengers feed off the carcass until nothing remains. Do you think this is an example of succession? Explain your reasoning.
2. a. **Review** What is a climax community?
   b. **Relate Cause and Effect** What kinds of conditions might prevent a community from returning to its predisturbance state?

VISUAL THINKING

3. Look at the photo below. If you walked from this dune in a straight line away from the beach, what kinds of changes in vegetation would you expect to see? What sort of succession is this?

BIOLOGY.com Search Lesson 4.3 GO • Self-Test • Lesson Assessment

LESSON 4.3

Address Misconceptions

The Nature of Succession Students commonly think that succession always leads to a predetermined climax community. Address this misconception by describing how random factors can influence the outcome of succession. For example, you might discuss such factors as wind direction, rainfall, and the organisms that happen to be actively breeding immediately after a disturbance.

Assess and Remediate

EVALUATE UNDERSTANDING

Ask students to make a series of labeled sketches to show how either primary or secondary succession occurs. Then, have students complete the 4.3 Assessment.

REMEDIATION SUGGESTION

L1 **Struggling Students** If students have trouble with **Question 1c,** have them reread **Why Succession Occurs.** Then, ask them whether a whale carcass changes the environment of the ocean floor and whether the types of organisms that live off of it change over time.

BIOLOGY.com Students can check their understanding of lesson concepts with the **Self-Test** assessment. They can then take an online version of the **Lesson Assessment.**

Assessment Answers

1a. Pioneer species fix atmospheric nitrogen into useful forms for other organisms, break down rock, and add organic material to form soil.

1b. Communities change over time because of natural or human disturbances and because organisms alter their environment and pave the way for other species. For example, when trees grow in an area, they provide shade and cooler temperatures near the ground, allowing shade-loving organisms to move in.

1c. Sample answer: Yes, I think this is an example of succession, because the whale carcass changes over time as each new species creates new niches for other species.

2a. A climax community is the community that is the end result of ecological succession.

2b. A community might not change back to its original state due to repeated disturbances, dramatic changes in the microclimate and soil that prevent regrowth of the original climax community, or chance events that determine which species colonize an area.

VISUAL THINKING

3. Sample answer: You would expect to see increasing numbers and greater diversity of vegetation species and the appearance of slower-growing vegetation such as trees. This is primary succession because the dune starts out without soil or plants.

LESSON 4.4

Getting Started

Objectives

4.4.1 Describe and compare the characteristics of the major land biomes.

4.4.2 Identify the areas that are not classified into a major biome.

Student Resources

Study Workbooks A/B, 4.4 Worksheets

Spanish Study Workbook, 4.4 Worksheets

Lab Manual B, 4.4 Data Analysis Worksheet

BIOLOGY.com
Lesson Overview • Lesson Notes • Assessment: Self-Test, Lesson Assessment

For corresponding lesson in the **Foundation Edition**, see pages 91–95.

Build Background

Ask students who have lived in or visited other parts of the country to describe their climate and vegetation. Try to get descriptions of different biomes, such as southwestern deserts, prairie grasslands, and northwestern coniferous forests. Tell students they will read in this lesson why other parts of the country differ.

IN INDIANA ACADEMIC STANDARDS

For the full text of all standards, see the Course Overview in the front matter of this book.

NoS.3 Clearly communicate their ideas and results of investigations verbally and in written form using tables, graphs, diagrams, and photographs.

4.4 Biomes

NoS.3 Communicate ideas. Also covered: **NoS.2.**

Key Questions

What abiotic and biotic factors characterize biomes?

What areas are not easily classified into a major biome?

Vocabulary

canopy • understory • deciduous • coniferous • humus • taiga • permafrost

Taking Notes

Preview Visuals Before you read, preview **Figure 4–18.** Write down the names of the different biomes. As you read, examine the photographs and list the main characteristics of each biome.

THINK ABOUT IT Why does the character of biological communities vary from one place to another? Why, for example, do temperate rain forests grow in the Pacific Northwest while areas to the east of the Rocky Mountains are much drier? How do similar conditions shape ecosystems elsewhere?

The Major Biomes

What abiotic and biotic factors characterize biomes?

In Lesson 1, you learned that latitude and the heat transported by winds are two factors that affect global climate. But Oregon, Montana, and Vermont have different climates and biological communities, even though those states are at similar latitudes and are all affected by prevailing winds that blow from west to east. Why? The reason is because other factors, among them an area's proximity to an ocean or mountain range, can influence climate.

Regional Climates Oregon, for example, borders the Pacific Ocean. Cold ocean currents that flow from north to south have the effect of making summers in the region cool relative to other places at the same latitude. Similarly, moist air carried by winds traveling west to east is pushed upward when it hits the Rocky Mountains. This air expands and cools, causing the moisture in the air to condense and form clouds. The clouds drop rain or snow, mainly on the upwind side of the mountains—the side that faces the winds, as seen in **Figure 4–16.** West and east Oregon, then, have very different regional climates, and different climates mean different plant and animal communities.

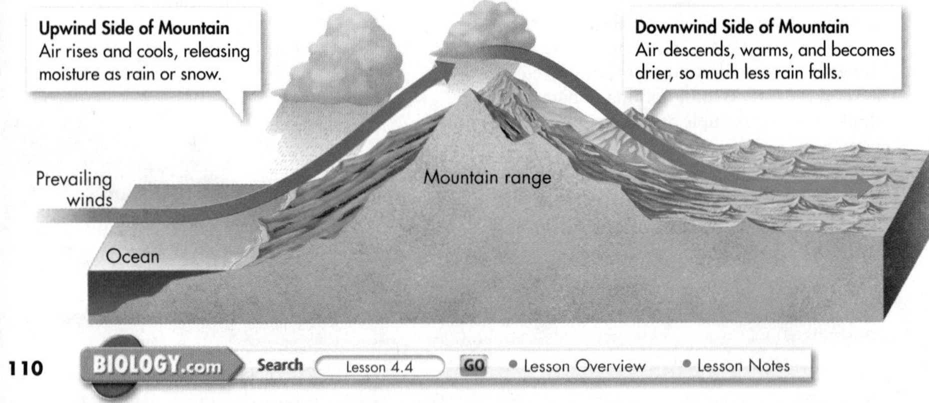
Upwind Side of Mountain
Air rises and cools, releasing moisture as rain or snow.
Downwind Side of Mountain
Air descends, warms, and becomes drier, so much less rain falls.
Prevailing winds
Mountain range
Ocean

FIGURE 4–16 The Effect of Coastal Mountains As moist ocean air rises over the upwind side of coastal mountains, it condenses, cools, and drops precipitation. As the air sinks on the downwind side of the mountain, it expands, warms, and absorbs moisture.

UbD Teach for Understanding

ENDURING UNDERSTANDING The existence of life on Earth depends on interactions among organisms and between organisms and their environment.

GUIDING QUESTION What are the characteristics of the major biomes?

EVIDENCE OF UNDERSTANDING *After completing the lesson, assign students the following assessment to show they understand the characteristics of major biomes.* Randomly assign each student one of the major biomes described in the lesson. Then, ask students to make a travel brochure that portrays the biome, in which they describe some of its abiotic and biotic factors and give at least one example of how the two sets of factors are related. Have them illustrate their brochures with pictures that they find online or draw themselves.

Defining Biomes Ecologists classify Earth's terrestrial ecosystems into at least ten different groups of regional climate communities called biomes. **Biomes are described in terms of abiotic factors like climate and soil type, and biotic factors like plant and animal life.** Major biomes include tropical rain forest, tropical dry forest, tropical grassland/savanna/shrubland, desert, temperate grassland, temperate woodland and shrubland, temperate forest, northwestern coniferous forest, boreal forest/taiga, and tundra. Each biome is associated with seasonal patterns of temperature and precipitation that can be summarized in a graph called a climate diagram, like the one in **Figure 4–17.** Organisms within each biome can be characterized by adaptations that enable them to live and reproduce successfully in the environment. The pages that follow discuss these adaptations and describe each biome's climate.

The distribution of major biomes is shown in **Figure 4–18.** Note that even within a defined biome, there is often considerable variation among plant and animal communities. These variations can be caused by differences in exposure, elevation, or local soil conditions. Local conditions also can change over time because of human activity or because of the community interactions described in this chapter and the next.

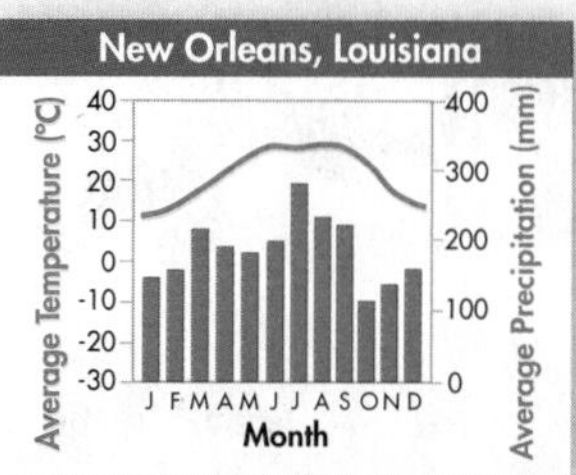

FIGURE 4–17 Climate Diagram A climate diagram shows the average temperature and precipitation at a given location during each month of the year. In this graph, and those to follow, temperature is plotted as a red line, and precipitation is shown as vertical blue bars.

In Your Notebook *On the biome map in **Figure 4–18,** locate the place where you live. Which biome do you live in? Do your climate and environment seem to match the description of the biome on the following pages?*

VISUAL SUMMARY

BIOMES

FIGURE 4–18 This map shows the locations of the world's major biomes. Each biome has a characteristic climate and community of organisms.

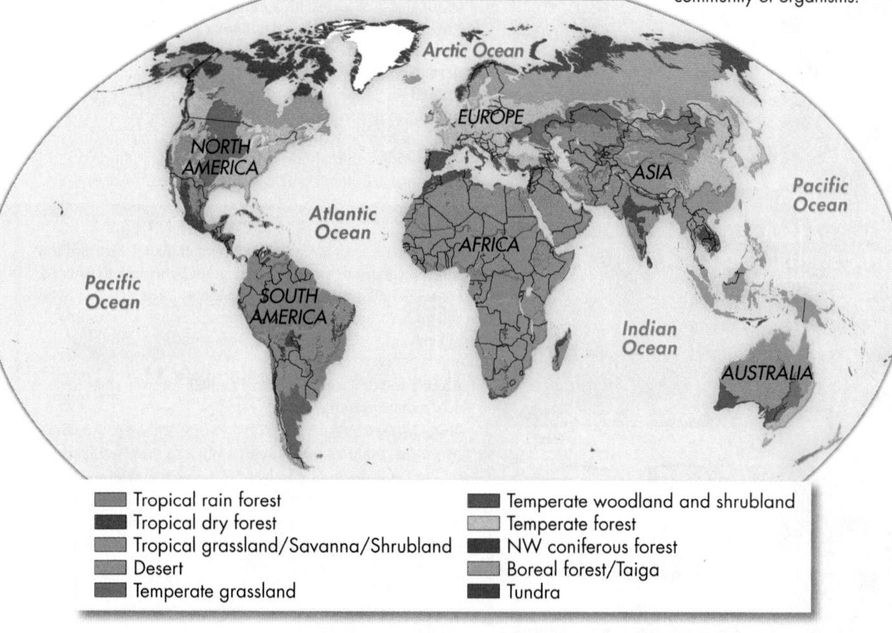

Teach

VISUAL SUMMARY

Use the map in **Figure 4–18** to familiarize students with the distribution of the world's major land biomes. In addition to their own biome, ask students to identify the other biomes found in the continental United States, including Alaska.

Ask Which biomes are not found in the continental United States? *(boreal forest/taiga, tundra, and tropical rain forest)*

Ask Which biome is found only in the United States and Canada? *(northwestern coniferous forest)*

DIFFERENTIATED INSTRUCTION

ELL English Language Learners Write the term *biome* on the board, and tell students the word part *bio-* can be defined as "living things," while the word part *-me* is derived from the Greek word part *-oma* meaning "mass or group." Have them discuss how the meanings of these word parts make sense with the definition of *biome* given in the text. Point out that biomes are comprised of both living and nonliving factors.

Address Misconceptions

Importance of Abiotic Factors Students may have the misconception that biomes are distinguished on the basis of biotic factors alone, because these factors are usually the most visible. Stress that the biotic factors of biomes depend largely on abiotic factors, especially temperature and precipitation. As students learn about the major biomes in the lesson, emphasize how organisms in each biome are adapted to the climatic factors of that biome.

Biology In-Depth

BIOMES AND SOIL TYPES

Each of the major land biomes has a characteristic type of soil, which is determined by several factors, including temperature, precipitation, and type of vegetation. For example, soils of both tropical rain forests and boreal forests have little humus and are nutrient-poor and acidic, but for different reasons. In tropical rain forests, year-round high temperatures cause rapid decomposition, which acidifies the soil and breaks down the humus before it can build up, while heavy rains leach minerals from the soil. In boreal forests, decomposition occurs slowly because of low temperatures, so little humus ever forms, while organic matter from coniferous trees forms an acidic solution that leaches minerals. In temperate forests, in contrast, soil is rich with humus and nutrients but not acidic. Broadleaf deciduous trees annually drop a thick layer of leaves, which decay to form humus without acidifying or leaching the soil.

Answers

IN YOUR NOTEBOOK Answers will depend on where students live. If students live near the edge of a biome, they may not be able to identify their biome from the map alone. In such cases, students should read about nearby biomes on the following pages to see if their climate and environment match one of the descriptions better than the others.

Teach continued

Build Study Skills

Divide the class into ten groups, and assign each group a different biome. Tell group members to use the information in the lesson as a starting point for becoming the "class experts" on their biome. Make sure students realize that the climate diagrams and photographs do not represent the same locations, just the same biomes. For example, there is not likely to be a tiger loose in Chennai, India and there are not herds of buffalo in Dallas, Texas. Let group members divide responsibilities among themselves. For example, different students might be responsible for researching abiotic factors, common plants, and common animals. Ask groups to give a class presentation on their biome, in which they communicate the information they have gathered and answer questions other students may have.

DIFFERENTIATED INSTRUCTION

LPR Less Proficient Readers Suggest that students create a **Compare/Contrast Table** to record important characteristics of each of the major biomes described in the lesson. They should include a row for each biome. Column headings might include: Name of Biome, Temperature, Precipitation, Soil Type, Common Plants, and Common Animals.

Study Wkbks A/B, Appendix S20, Compare/Contrast Table. **Transparencies,** GO3.

ELL Focus on ELL: Access Content

ALL SPEAKERS Pair beginning and intermediate speakers with advanced or advanced high speakers. Have pairs write the following vocabulary terms in the left column of a **T-Chart** and, below each term, a prediction of what it means: *canopy, understory, deciduous, coniferous, humus, taiga, permafrost.* Then, have pairs find the terms where they are first introduced in the lesson, read the context of the terms, and discuss whether their predictions were correct. After students have decided on the correct definitions of the terms, they should write the definitions in the right column of the chart.

Study Wkbks A/B, Appendix S30, T-Chart. **Transparencies,** GO15.

TROPICAL RAIN FOREST

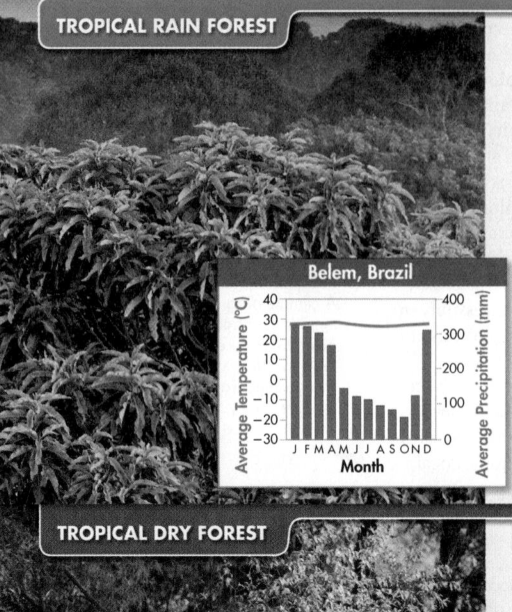

Tropical rain forests are home to more species than all other biomes combined. As the name suggests, rain forests get a lot of rain—at least 2 meters of it a year! Tall trees form a dense, leafy covering called a **canopy** from 50 to 80 meters above the forest floor. In the shade below the canopy, shorter trees and vines form a layer called the **understory.** Organic matter on the forest floor is recycled and reused so quickly that the soil in most tropical rain forests is not very rich in nutrients.

- **Abiotic factors** hot and wet year-round; thin, nutrient-poor soils subject to erosion
- **Biotic factors**
  Plant life: Understory plants compete for sunlight, so most have large leaves that maximize capture of limited light. Tall trees growing in poor shallow soil often have buttress roots for support. Epiphytic plants grow on the branches of tall plants as opposed to soil. This allows epiphytes to take advantage of available sunlight while obtaining nutrients through their host.
  Animal life: Animals are active all year. Many animals use camouflage to hide from predators; some can change color to match their surroundings. Animals that live in the canopy have adaptations for climbing, jumping, and/or flight.

TROPICAL DRY FOREST

Tropical dry forests grow in areas where rainy seasons alternate with dry seasons. In most places, a period of rain is followed by a prolonged period of drought.

- **Abiotic factors** warm year-round; alternating wet and dry seasons; rich soils subject to erosion
- **Biotic factors**
  Plant life: Adaptations to survive the dry season include seasonal loss of leaves. A plant that sheds its leaves during a particular season is called **deciduous**. Some plants also have an extra thick waxy layer on their leaves to reduce water loss, or store water in their tissues.
  Animal life: Many animals reduce their need for water by entering long periods of inactivity called *estivation.* Estivation is similar to hibernation, but typically takes place during a dry season. Other animals, including many birds and primates, move to areas where water is available during the dry season.

TROPICAL GRASSLAND/ SAVANNA/SHRUBLAND

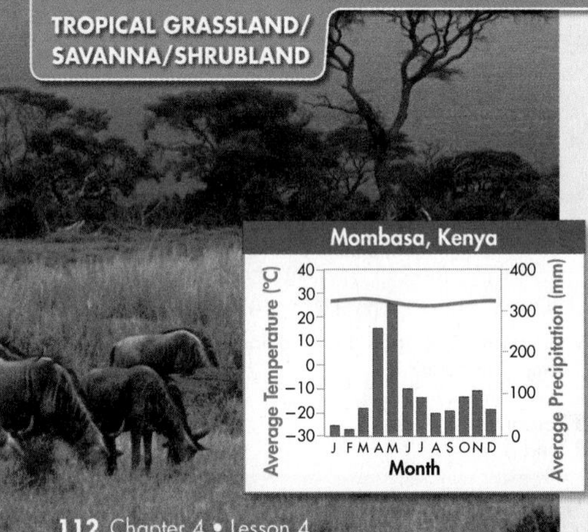

This biome receives more seasonal rainfall than deserts but less than tropical dry forests. Grassy areas are spotted with isolated trees and small groves of trees and shrubs. Compacted soils, fairly frequent fires, and the action of large animals—for example, rhinoceroses and elephants—prevent some areas from turning into dry forest.

- **Abiotic factors** warm; seasonal rainfall; compact soils; frequent fires set by lightning
- **Biotic factors**
  Plant life: Plant adaptations are similar to those in the tropical dry forest, including waxy leaf coverings and seasonal leaf loss. Some grasses have a high silica content that makes them less appetizing to grazing herbivores. Also, unlike most plants, grasses grow from their bases, not their tips, so they can continue to grow after being grazed.
  Animal life: Many animals migrate during the dry season in search of water. Some smaller animals burrow and remain dormant during the dry season.

How Science Works

GPS TECHNOLOGY AND WILDLIFE RESEARCH

The development of GPS (global positioning system) technology has revolutionized how wildlife researchers gather data. The combination of GPS transmitters on collars fitted to individual animals and the network of GPS satellites in Earth's orbit enables researchers to collect data on the precise locations of animals repeatedly throughout each day. For example, the Forest Elephant GPS Telemetry Program uses GPS collars on elephants to track their daily movements in a tropical forest biome in central Africa. GPS tracking of the animals helps scientists better understand the range and migration patterns of this little-known species in an area that is increasingly threatened by human actions, including farming, urban growth, and logging.

DESERT

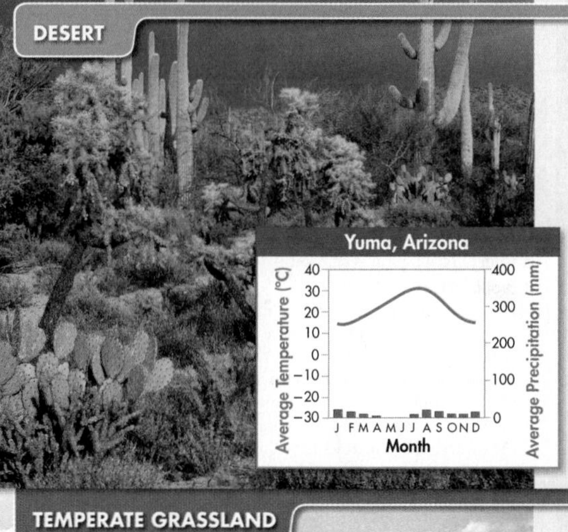

Deserts have less than 25 centimeters of precipitation annually, but otherwise vary greatly, depending on elevation and latitude. Many deserts undergo extreme daily temperature changes, alternating between hot and cold.

- **Abiotic factors** low precipitation; variable temperatures; soils rich in minerals but poor in organic material
- **Biotic factors**
  Plant life: Many plants, including cacti, store water in their tissues, and minimize leaf surface area to cut down on water loss. Cactus spines are actually modified leaves. Many desert plants employ special forms of photosynthesis that enable them to open their leaf pores only at night, allowing them to conserve moisture on hot, dry days.
  Animal life: Many desert animals get the water they need from the food they eat. To avoid the hottest parts of the day, many are nocturnal—active only at night. Large or elongated ears and other extremities are often supplied with many blood vessels close to the surface. These help the animal lose body heat and regulate body temperature.

TEMPERATE GRASSLAND

Plains and prairies, underlain by fertile soils, once covered vast areas of the midwestern and central United States. Periodic fires and heavy grazing by herbivores maintained plant communities dominated by grasses. Today, most have been converted for agriculture because their soil is so rich in nutrients and is ideal for growing crops.

- **Abiotic factors** warm to hot summers; cold winters; moderate seasonal precipitation; fertile soils; occasional fires
- **Biotic factors**
  Plant life: Grassland plants—especially grasses, which grow from their base—are resistant to grazing and fire. Dispersal of seeds by wind is common in this open environment. The root structure and growth habit of native grassland plants helps establish and retain deep, rich, fertile topsoil.
  Animal life: Because temperate grasslands are such open, exposed environments, predation is a constant threat for smaller animals. Camouflage and burrowing are two common protective adaptations.

TEMPERATE WOODLAND AND SHRUBLAND

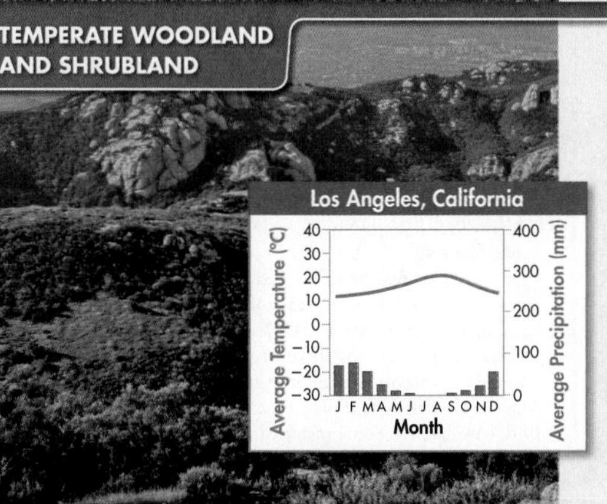

In open woodlands, large areas of grasses and wildflowers such as poppies are interspersed with oak and other trees. Communities that are more shrubland than forest are known as chaparral. Dense low plants that contain flammable oils make fire a constant threat.

- **Abiotic factors** hot dry summers; cool moist winters; thin, nutrient-poor soils; periodic fires
- **Biotic factors**
  Plant life: Plants in this biome have adaptated to drought. Woody chaparral plants have tough waxy leaves that resist water loss. Fire resistance is also important, although the seeds of some plants need fire to germinate.
  Animal life: Animals tend to be browsers—meaning they eat varied diets of grasses, leaves, shrubs, and other vegetation. In exposed shrubland, camouflage is common.

Biology In-Depth

CONVERGENT EVOLUTION AMONG DESERT ORGANISMS

The selective pressures of extreme abiotic factors, such as the very low precipitation in deserts, has led to convergent evolution in organisms that are only distantly related but live in the same biome type. African euphorbias and American cacti are examples. Both types of plants have evolved almost identical adaptations to the aridity of their desert biomes. Both have compact spherical shapes, spines instead of leaves, sunken stomata, and thick outer walls, all of which help reduce water loss. Both also have thick, succulent stems that store water. Another example of convergent evolution in desert animals includes North American horned lizards and Australian thorny devil lizards. Both lizards are very similar morphologically but only distantly related taxonomically.

Connect to Earth Science

Tell students that soil forms when rocks break down through weathering and humus mixes with the weathered rock particles. Explain that weathering can occur when water seeps into cracks and rock expands and contracts through repeated cycles of freezing and thawing. Particles carried by water can also weather rocks. Plant roots and burrowing animals can cause additional weathering. Humus forms when dead plant and animal materials decompose. Too much rain can cause humus to leech from soil, but too little may prevent decomposition. Have students read about temperate grasslands and temperate woodlands/shrublands. Point out that grasslands have thick, humus-rich soils, whereas woodlands/shrublands have thin, humus-poor soils.

Ask What biotic and abiotic factors in the two temperate biomes might help explain these differences in their soils? *(Sample answer: Grasslands are likely to have more weathering and soil formation due to cold winters, moderate precipitation, and abundant plant life; they probably have more humus forming due to their dense grassy vegetation. Woodlands/shrublands are likely to have less weathering and soil formation due to cool, but not cold, winters and lower overall precipitation. They probably have less humus forming due to their scattered woody vegetation.)*

DIFFERENTIATED INSTRUCTION

L1 Special Needs Bring in several different soil mixtures, including a mixture of loam and humus, a mixture of sand and topsoil without humus, and a compacted mixture of clay and topsoil without humus. Let students handle the soils and inspect them with a hand lens to try to identify their components. Explain why the loam-humus mixture is the most fertile and why the other soil mixtures are not as fertile. Pack an equal amount of each soil sample into a funnel, and pour water through the samples to demonstrate how the loam-humus mixture retains water (unlike the sand-soil mixture) without becoming waterlogged (like the clay-soil mixture). Guide students in identifying biomes where the three different types of soil might be found and how soil type is related to the vegetation that grows in each biome.

Teach continued

Use Visuals

Have students find the locations of North American temperate forests and northwestern coniferous forests on the map in **Figure 4–18.** Then, have them compare their climate diagrams on this page.

Ask How are the temperature and precipitation patterns different for the two biomes? *(The summers in the temperate forest are warmer and wetter than those in the northwestern coniferous forest. The winters in the northwestern coniferous forest are warmer and wetter than those in the temperate forest.)* Point out that the two forest biomes are found at some of the same latitudes but have different climates. Explain how the coastal location of northwestern coniferous forests leads to a different pattern of temperature and precipitation than that of temperate forests.

DIFFERENTIATED INSTRUCTION

ELL English Language Learners Pair English language learners with native English speakers. Have one partner read several sentences about each biome. Have the other partner try to identify which biome is being described. Then, have partners switch roles and repeat the exercise.

LPR Less Proficient Readers Some students may be overwhelmed by the detailed descriptions of the major biomes. Suggest they choose one biotic or abiotic factor at a time and read how it varies across biomes. Once they have a sense of the overall variation in each factor, details for the individual biomes should be more meaningful.

TEMPERATE FOREST

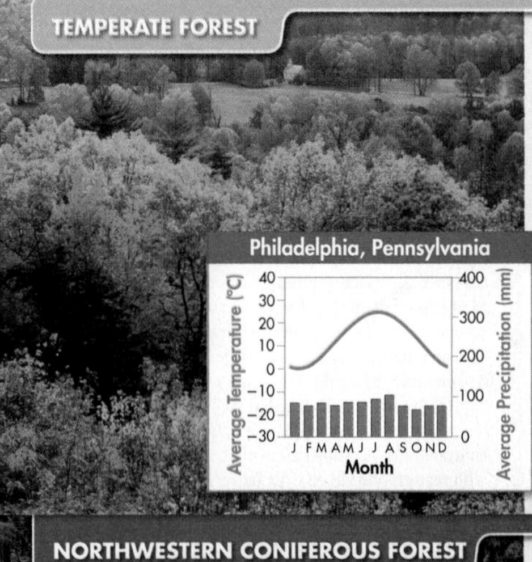

Temperate forests are mostly made up of deciduous and evergreen coniferous (koh NIF ur us) trees. **Coniferous** trees, or conifers, produce seed-bearing cones, and most have leaves shaped like needles, which are coated in a waxy substance that helps reduce water loss. These forests have cold winters. In autumn, deciduous trees shed their leaves. In the spring, small plants burst from the ground and flower. Fertile soils are often rich in **humus,** a material formed from decaying leaves and other organic matter.

- **Abiotic factors** cold to moderate winters; warm summers; year-round precipitation; fertile soils
- **Biotic factors**
  Plant life: Deciduous trees drop their leaves and go into a state of dormancy in winter. Conifers have needlelike leaves that minimize water loss in dry winter air.
  Animal life: Animals must cope with changing weather. Some hibernate; others migrate to warmer climates. Animals that do not hibernate or migrate may be camouflaged to escape predation in the winter when bare trees leave them more exposed.

NORTHWESTERN CONIFEROUS FOREST

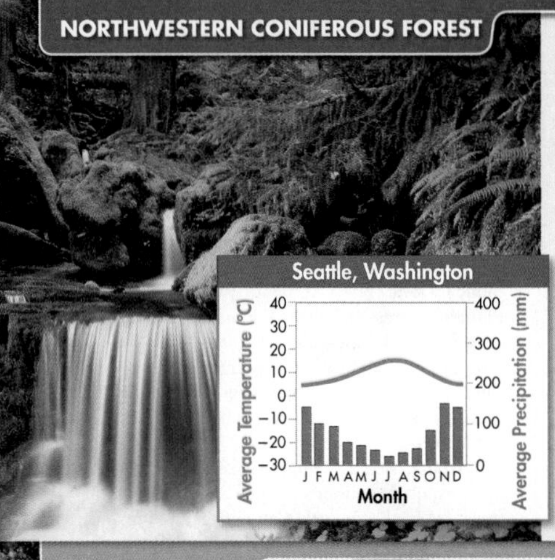

Mild moist air from the Pacific Ocean influenced by the Rocky Mountains provides abundant rainfall to this biome. The forest includes a variety of conifers, from giant redwoods to spruce, fir, and hemlock, along with flowering trees and shrubs such as dogwood and rhododendron. Moss often covers tree trunks and the forest floor. Because of its lush vegetation, the northwestern coniferous forest is sometimes called a "temperate rain forest."

- **Abiotic factors** mild temperatures; abundant precipitation in fall, winter, and spring; cool dry summers; rocky acidic soils
- **Biotic factors**
  Plant life: Because of seasonal temperature variation, there is less diversity in this biome than in tropical rain forests. However, ample water and nutrients support lush, dense plant growth. Adaptations that enable plants to obtain sunlight are common. Trees here are among the world's tallest.
  Animal life: Camouflage helps insects and ground-dwelling mammals avoid predation. Many animals are browsers—they eat a varied diet—an advantage in an environment where vegetation changes seasonally.

BOREAL FOREST

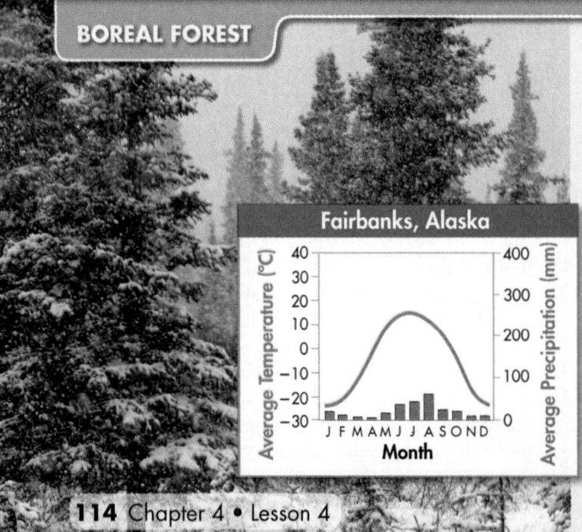

Dense forests of coniferous evergreens along the northern edge of the temperate zone are called boreal forests, or **taiga** (TY guh). Winters are bitterly cold, but summers are mild and long enough to allow the ground to thaw. The word *boreal* comes from the Greek word for "north," reflecting the fact that boreal forests occur mostly in the northern part of the Northern Hemisphere.

- **Abiotic factors** long cold winters; short mild summers; moderate precipitation; high humidity; acidic, nutrient-poor soils
- **Biotic factors**
  Plant life: Conifers are well suited to the boreal-forest environment. Their conical shape sheds snow, and their wax-covered needlelike leaves prevent excess water loss. In addition, the dark green color of most conifers absorbs heat energy.
  Animal life: Staying warm is the major challenge for animals. Most have small extremities and extra insulation in the form of fat or downy feathers. Some migrate to warmer areas in winter.

UbD Check for Understanding

USE VOCABULARY

Ask students to create acrostics based on the words *BIOME FACTS.* Each of the ten letters in the two words should be the first letter of a sentence about a different biome so that all ten biomes are covered. The sentences should include the lesson vocabulary terms. For example, for *B* students might write, *Biotic factors in tropical dry forests include deciduous plants that shed their leaves during the dry season.* For *T* they might write, *Temperate forests often have soils that are rich in humus from decaying leaves.*

ADJUST INSTRUCTION

Display the acrostics in the classroom, and give students a chance to read them. Discuss as a class any statements with which they disagree.

The tundra is characterized by **permafrost,** a layer of permanently frozen subsoil. During the short cool summer, the ground thaws to a depth of a few centimeters and becomes soggy. In winter, the top layer of soil freezes again. This cycle of thawing and freezing, which rips and crushes plant roots, is one reason that tundra plants are small and stunted. Cold temperatures, high winds, a short growing season, and humus-poor soils also limit plant height.

- **Abiotic factors** strong winds; low precipitation; short and soggy summers; long, cold, dark winters; poorly developed soils; permafrost
- **Biotic factors**
  Plant life: By hugging the ground, mosses and other low-growing plants avoid damage from frequent strong winds. Seed dispersal by wind is common. Many plants have adapted to growth in poor soil. Legumes, for example, have nitrogen-fixing bacteria on their roots.
  Animal life: Many animals migrate to avoid long harsh winters. Animals that live in the tundra year-round display adaptations, among them natural antifreeze, small extremities that limit heat loss, and a varied diet.

Analyzing Data

IN NoS.2, NoS.3

Which Biome?

An ecologist collected climate data from two locations. The graph shows the monthly average temperatures in the two locations. The total yearly precipitation in Location A is 273 cm. In Location B, the total yearly precipitation is 11 cm.

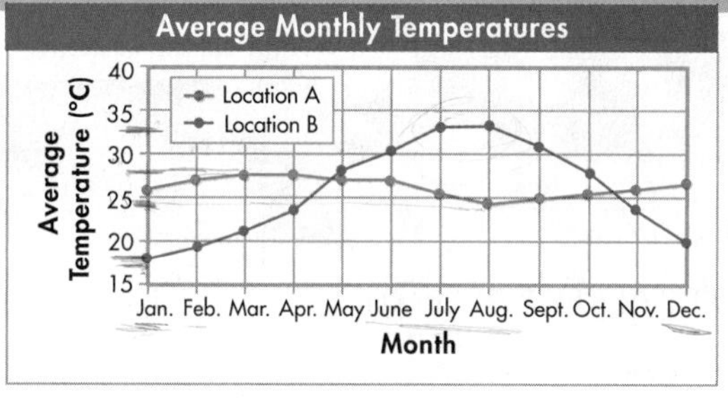

1. **Interpret Graphs** What variable is plotted on the horizontal axis? On the vertical axis?
2. **Interpret Graphs** How would you describe the temperature over the course of the year in Location A? In Location B?
3. **Draw Conclusions** In which biome would you expect to find each location, given the precipitation and temperature data? Explain your answer.
4. **Analyze Data** Look up the average monthly temperature last year in the city you live in. Plot the data. Then look up the monthly rainfall for your city, and plot those data. Based on your results, which biome do you live in? Did the data predict the biome correctly?

LESSON 4.4

Use Models

Freeze some moist soil mixed with peat moss in a metal baking pan and bring the pan of frozen soil to class. Shine a desk lamp on top of the soil so the top couple of centimeters thaw while the bottom of the soil remains frozen. Have students observe as you sprinkle water on top of the soil. The water will not be able to soak in because the bottom is still frozen, so the thawed layer on top will become soggy.

Ask How does this demonstration model the soil in a tundra biome? *(Tundra soil has a layer of permanently frozen subsoil, called permafrost. During the summer, only the top layer of the soil thaws, and it becomes soggy because water cannot seep down through the lower layers.)*

Explain how these features of the soil are related to the types of vegetation that grow in tundra biomes.

DIFFERENTIATED INSTRUCTION

L1 Struggling Students Show students pictures of animals with clearly apparent adaptations to a cold climate, such as thick fur, bulky body shapes, and short extremities. Explain how the adaptations help the animals survive in extreme cold. Ask them to name biomes where the animals in the pictures might be found, based on these adaptations.

Analyzing Data

PURPOSE Students will interpret and generate graphs of temperature and precipitation to identify biomes.

PLANNING Using the tundra climate diagram on this page as an example, show students how they can add up the monthly precipitation totals in millimeters and divide the total by 100 to calculate the average annual precipitation in centimeters. Upon completion, you may wish to reveal that Location A is San Jose, Costa Rica, and Location B is Sharjah, United Arab Emirates.

ANSWERS

1. Time of year by month is plotted on the horizontal axis. Average temperature in degrees Celsius is plotted on the vertical axis.
2. In Location A, the temperature is moderate throughout the year, with little variation. In Location B, the temperature is relatively cool from November through April and hot from May through October, with a peak in July and August.
3. You would expect to find Location A in a rain forest biome, because the total precipitation is close to 3 m, and the average temperature varies little from month to month. You would expect to find Location B in a desert biome, because precipitation is very low, and the temperature varies seasonally from warm to hot.
4. Answers will vary depending on the location where students live. Advise students to format their graphs like the climate diagrams in the lesson for ease of comparison. To improve accuracy, suggest they find average monthly climate data over a several-year period. To predict the biome in which they live, they should compare their completed climate diagram to those on pages 112–115. Then, they can find their biome on the map in **Figure 4–18** to see if the climate data predicted the biome correctly.

Teach continued

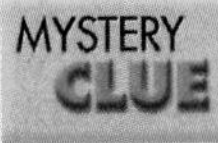

Some students may say moose and elk might prefer to graze in valleys because it would be easier to find food and water. Other students may say the animals might prefer to graze on high mountain slopes, because it would be easier to see and avoid wolves. The growth of certain plants would be curbed more in river valleys or on mountain slopes, depending on where elk prefer to graze. Students can go online to Biology.com to gather their evidence.

Assess and Remediate

EVALUATE UNDERSTANDING

Make overhead transparencies of the climate diagrams for all ten major biomes. Show the transparencies, and call on students to identify each biome from the climate data. Call on other students to name plants and animals found in each biome. Then, have students complete the 4.4 Assessment.

REMEDIATION SUGGESTION

L1 **Struggling Students** If students have trouble with **Question 1c,** suggest they choose two biomes for which they can identify a specific type of plant and animal based on their prior knowledge or the photographs in the text.

BIOLOGY.com Students can check their understanding of lesson concepts with the **Self-Test** assessment. They can then take an online version of the **Lesson Assessment.**

MYSTERY CLUE

Yellowstone has high mountain slopes and valleys with streams. Can you think of any reason why moose and elk might prefer to graze in one of those places rather than the other? How do you think their preference might affect Yellowstone's plant communities?

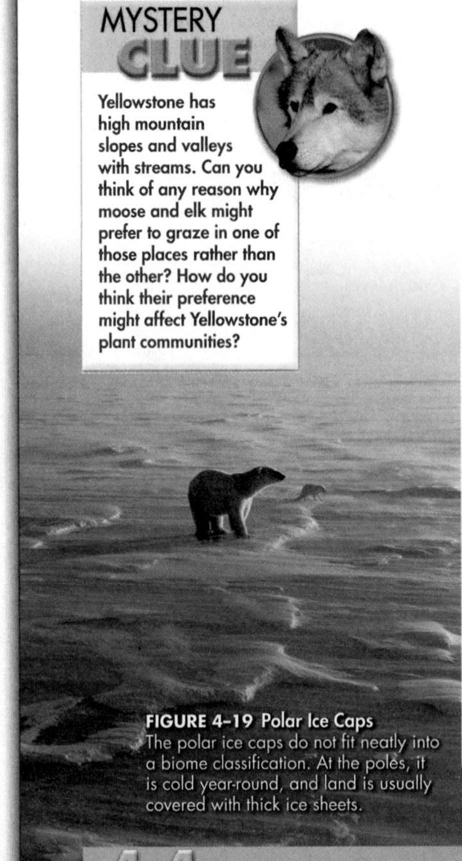

FIGURE 4–19 Polar Ice Caps The polar ice caps do not fit neatly into a biome classification. At the poles, it is cold year-round, and land is usually covered with thick ice sheets.

Other Land Areas

What areas are not easily classified into a major biome?

Some land areas do not fall neatly into one of the major biomes. **Because they are not easily defined in terms of a typical community of plants and animals, mountain ranges and polar ice caps are not usually classified into biomes.**

Mountain Ranges Mountain ranges exist on all continents and in many biomes. On mountains, conditions vary with elevation. From river valley to summit, temperature, precipitation, exposure to wind, and soil types all change, and so do organisms. If you climb the Rocky Mountains in Colorado, for example, you begin in a grassland. You then pass through pine woodland and then a forest of spruce and other conifers. Thickets of aspen and willow trees grow along streambeds in protected valleys. Higher up, soils are thin. Strong winds buffet open fields of wildflowers and stunted vegetation resembling tundra. Glaciers are found at the peaks of many ranges.

Polar Ice Caps Polar regions, like the one in **Figure 4–19,** border the tundra and are cold year-round. Plants are few, though some algae grow on snow and ice. Where rocks and ground are exposed seasonally, mosses and lichens may grow. Marine mammals, insects, and mites are the typical animals. In the north, where polar bears live, the Arctic Ocean is covered with sea ice, although more and more ice is melting each summer. In the south, the continent of Antarctica, inhabited by many species of penguins, is covered by ice nearly 5 kilometers thick in places.

4.4 Assessment

IN NoS.3

Review Key Concepts

1. a. Review List the major biomes, and describe one characteristic of each.
   b. Explain How are biomes classified?
   c. Compare and Contrast Choose two very different biomes. For each biome, select a common plant and animal. Compare how the plants and animals have adaptated to their biomes.
2. a. Review Why aren't mountain ranges or polar ice caps classified as biomes?
   b. Sequence Imagine that you are hiking up a mountain in the temperate forest biome. Describe how the plant life might change as you climb toward the summit.

Apply the Big idea

Interdependence in Nature

3. Choose one of the biomes discussed in this lesson. Then, sketch the biome. Include the biome's characteristic plant and animal life in your sketch. Add labels to identify the organisms, and write a caption describing the content of the sketch.

BIOLOGY.com Search Lesson 4.4 GO • Self-Test • Lesson Assessment

Assessment Answers

1a. The major biomes are tropical rain forest, tropical dry forest, tropical grassland/savanna/shrubland, desert, temperate grassland, temperate woodland and shrubland, temperate forest, northwestern coniferous forest, boreal forest, and tundra. For each biome, students can list any of the facts given for the biomes on pages 112–115.

1b. Biomes are classified in terms of abiotic factors like climate and soil type and biotic factors like typical plant and animal life.

1c. Sample answer: I chose tropical rain forests and deserts. Epiphytes grow in trees of tropical rain forests, which is an adaptation that lets them take advantage of available light. Monkeys live in the canopy of tropical rain forests, and they have adaptations for living in trees, such as hands for climbing. Cacti grow in deserts, and they have tissues that can store water, which is an adaptation to low precipitation. Some snakes that live in deserts are active only at night, which is an adaptation to high daytime temperatures.

2a. Mountain ranges and polar ice caps are not easily defined in terms of a typical community of plants and animals.

2b. Sample answer: I might begin in a grassland, pass through a pine woodland, go through a coniferous forest, and then pass through an open field of wildflowers and stunted vegetation resembling tundra. At the summit, I might find only glaciers and no plant life.

3. Big idea Students can sketch any of the biomes described in the lesson. Their sketch should include labeled drawings of typical plants and animals for that biome. It should also have a caption describing the sketch.

4.5 Aquatic Ecosystems

B.4.1 Limiting factors.

THINK ABOUT IT We call our planet "Earth," yet nearly three-fourths of Earth's surface is covered with water. Despite the vital roles aquatic ecosystems play in the biosphere, many of these ecosystems are only partly understood. What's life like underwater?

Conditions Underwater

What factors affect life in aquatic ecosystems?

Like organisms living on land, underwater organisms are affected by a variety of environmental factors. **Aquatic organisms are affected primarily by the water's depth, temperature, flow, and amount of dissolved nutrients.** Because runoff from land can affect some of these factors, distance from shore also shapes marine communities.

Water Depth Water depth strongly influences aquatic life because sunlight penetrates only a relatively short distance through water, as shown in **Figure 4–20.** The sunlit region near the surface in which photosynthesis can occur is known as the **photic zone.** The photic zone may be as deep as 200 meters in tropical seas, but just a few meters deep or less in rivers and swamps. Photosynthetic algae, called phytoplankton, live in the photic zone. Zooplankton—tiny free-floating animals—eat phytoplankton. This is the first step in many aquatic food webs. Below the photic zone is the dark **aphotic zone,** where photosynthesis cannot occur.

Many aquatic organisms live on, or in, rocks and sediments on the bottoms of lakes, streams, and oceans. These organisms are called the **benthos,** and their habitat is the benthic zone. Where water is shallow enough for the benthos to be within the photic zone, algae and rooted aquatic plants can grow. When the benthic zone is below the photic zone, chemosynthetic autotrophs are the only primary producers.

Key Questions

What factors affect life in aquatic ecosystems?

What are the major categories of freshwater ecosystems?

Why are estuaries so important?

How do ecologists usually classify marine ecosystems?

Vocabulary

photic zone • aphotic zone • benthos • plankton • wetland • estuary

Taking Notes

Compare/Contrast Table As you read, note the similarities and differences between the major freshwater and marine ecosystems in a compare/contrast table.

FIGURE 4–20 The Photic Zone Sunlight penetrates only a limited distance into aquatic ecosystems. Whatever the depth of this photic zone, it is the only area in which photosynthesis can occur. **Infer** ***Why do you think some photic zones are only a few meters deep and others are as much as 200 meters deep?***

BIOLOGY.com Search Lesson 4.5 GO • Lesson Overview • Lesson Notes

Getting Started

Objectives

4.5.1 Discuss the factors that affect aquatic ecosystems.

4.5.2 Identify the major categories of freshwater ecosystems.

4.5.3 Describe the importance of estuaries.

4.5.4 Describe and compare the distinct ocean zones that make up marine ecosystems.

Student Resources

Study Workbooks A/B, 4.5 Worksheets

Spanish Study Workbook, 4.5 Worksheets

BIOLOGY.com Lesson Overview • Lesson Notes • Activity: Art Review • Assessment: Self-Test, Lesson Assessment

For corresponding lesson in the **Foundation Edition**, see pages 96–99.

Answers

FIGURE 4–20 Sample answer: Photic zones vary in depth depending on how clear the water is. The clearer the water, the deeper sunlight can penetrate.

Teach for Understanding

ENDURING UNDERSTANDING The existence of life on Earth depends on interactions among organisms and between organisms and their environment.

GUIDING QUESTION What are the characteristics of aquatic ecosystems?

EVIDENCE OF UNDERSTANDING *After completing the lesson, give students the following assessment to show they understand the characteristics of aquatic ecosystems.* Have students work cooperatively to construct a bulletin board display of the different categories of freshwater and saltwater ecosystems discussed in the lesson. Their display should include pictures they have drawn themselves or found online, as well as labels for the names of the ecosystems, their major characteristics, and types of organisms.

IN INDIANA ACADEMIC STANDARDS

For the full text of all standards, see the Course Overview in the front matter of this book.

B.4.1 Explain that the amount of life an environment can support is limited by the available energy, water, oxygen, and minerals, and by the ability of ecosystems to recycle the remains of dead organisms.

LESSON 4.5

Teach

Connect to the Real World

Assign each of three groups of students one of the categories of freshwater ecosystems. Have members of each group find photographs of the ecosystem (preferably of a local example) and information about the plants and animals found there. Have them share their research with the class in a brief presentation. Then, discuss as a class general characteristics of each category of ecosystem.

DIFFERENTIATED INSTRUCTION

LPR **Less Proficient Readers** Have students use a **Main Ideas and Details Chart** to organize the information about the major categories of freshwater ecosystems as they read about them on this page and the next. They should include notes on both abiotic and biotic factors for each category.

Study Wkbks A/B, Appendix S28, Main Ideas and Details Chart. **Transparencies,** GO13.

ELL Focus on ELL: Access Content

ALL SPEAKERS Pair beginning and intermediate speakers with advanced or advanced high speakers. Assign each pair one of the three paragraphs with blue headings under **Freshwater Ecosystems.** Tell partners to read their paragraph and make drawings to illustrate it. Then, ask each pair to present a brief oral report to the class in which they identify the most important points in their paragraph and share their illustrations.

MYSTERY CLUE Discuss with students the interconnectedness of terrestrial and aquatic organisms along stream banks. Have them reread the paragraph with the blue heading, **Rivers and Streams,** to help them answer the question. Students can go online to **Biology.com** to gather their evidence.

Answers

FIGURE 4–21 Sample answer: Water flows in streams, but it may stay in place in bogs. Bogs have more plants growing in them than streams do.

IN YOUR NOTEBOOK Sample answer: You would expect adaptations that help anchor organisms to rocks or help them to swim against the current.

Temperature and Currents Aquatic habitats, like terrestrial habitats, are warmer near the equator and colder near the poles. Temperature in aquatic habitats also often varies with depth. The deepest parts of lakes and oceans are often colder than surface waters. Currents in lakes and oceans can dramatically affect water temperature because they can carry water that is significantly warmer or cooler than would be typical for any given latitude, depth, or distance from shore.

Nutrient Availability As you learned in Chapter 3, organisms need certain substances to live. These include oxygen, nitrogen, potassium, and phosphorus. The type and availability of these dissolved substances vary within and between bodies of water, greatly affecting the types of organisms that can survive there.

MYSTERY CLUE What is one way in which life in Yellowstone's streams might be affected by the presence or absence of plants along stream banks?

Freshwater Ecosystems

What are the major categories of freshwater ecosystems?

Only 3 percent of Earth's surface water is fresh water, but that small percentage provides terrestrial organisms with drinking water, food, and transportation. Often, a chain of streams, lakes, and rivers begins in the interior of a continent and flows through several biomes to the sea. **Freshwater ecosystems can be divided into three main categories: rivers and streams, lakes and ponds, and freshwater wetlands.** Examples of these ecosystems are shown in **Figure 4–21.**

Rivers and Streams Rivers, streams, creeks, and brooks often originate from underground water sources in mountains or hills. Near a source, water has plenty of dissolved oxygen but little plant life. Downstream, sediments build up and plants establish themselves. Still farther downstream, water may meander slowly through flat areas. Animals in many rivers and streams depend on terrestrial plants and animals that live along their banks for food.

In Your Notebook *What kinds of adaptations would you expect in organisms living in a fast-flowing river or stream?*

FIGURE 4–21 Freshwater Ecosystems and Estuaries Freshwater ecosystems include streams, lakes, and freshwater wetlands (bogs, swamps, and marshes). Salt marshes and mangrove swamps are estuaries—areas where fresh water from rivers meets salt water. **Interpret Visuals** ***Based on these photos, what are two differences between streams and bogs?***

Stream

Lake

Freshwater Wetland: Bog

Quick Facts

SIGNIFICANCE AND LOSS OF WETLANDS

Wetlands can be invaluable ecosystems for surrounding human and natural communities. A single acre of wetland can hold up to 1.5 million gallons of floodwater. In spite of their ecological importance, wetlands were long thought to be synonymous with wastelands. They were filled in or drained for agriculture, development projects, mosquito control, and other purposes. As a result, more than half of the wetlands that once existed in the United States have been destroyed. Although destruction of wetlands has slowed since the 1970s, 60,000 acres of wetlands are still lost each year. Wetlands are almost as biologically diverse and productive as tropical rain forests. For example, as many as half of all North American bird species depend on wetlands for nesting sites or food, and almost a third of plant species live in wetlands. Loss of wetlands, therefore, is a significant cause of species extinctions.

Lakes and Ponds The food webs in lakes and ponds often are based on a combination of plankton and attached algae and plants. **Plankton** is a general term that includes both phytoplankton and zooplankton. Water typically flows in and out of lakes and ponds and circulates between the surface and the benthos during at least some seasons. This circulation distributes heat, oxygen, and nutrients.

Freshwater Wetlands A **wetland** is an ecosystem in which water either covers the soil or is present at or near the surface for at least part of the year. Water may flow through freshwater wetlands or stay in place. Wetlands are often nutrient-rich and highly productive, and they serve as breeding grounds for many organisms. Freshwater wetlands have important environmental functions: They purify water by filtering pollutants and help to prevent flooding by absorbing large amounts of water and slowly releasing it. Three main types of freshwater wetlands are freshwater bogs, freshwater marshes, and freshwater swamps. Saltwater wetlands are called estuaries.

Estuaries

Why are estuaries so important?

An **estuary** (es tyoo er ee) is a special kind of wetland, formed where a river meets the sea. Estuaries contain a mixture of fresh water and salt water, and are affected by the rise and fall of ocean tides. Many are shallow, which means that enough sunlight reaches the benthos to power photosynthesis. Estuaries support an astonishing amount of biomass—although they usually contain fewer species than freshwater or marine ecosystems—which makes them commercially valuable. **Estuaries serve as spawning and nursery grounds for many ecologically and commercially important fish and shellfish species including bluefish, striped bass, shrimp, and crabs.**

Salt marshes are temperate estuaries characterized by salt-tolerant grasses above the low-tide line and seagrasses below water. One of the largest salt marshes in America surrounds the Chesapeake Bay in Maryland (shown below). Mangrove swamps are tropical estuaries characterized by several species of salt-tolerant trees, collectively called mangroves. The largest mangrove area in America is in Florida's Everglades National Park (shown below).

Freshwater Wetland: Marsh

Freshwater Wetland: Swamp

Estuary: Salt Marsh

Estuary: Mangrove Swamp

Lead a Discussion

Discuss with students how the abiotic factors of freshwater wetlands and estuaries relate to the types of organisms that live in the two categories of ecosystems.

Ask How are the abiotic factors of freshwater wetlands and estuaries similar and different? *(Both ecosystems have lots of water. Freshwater wetlands have fresh water while estuaries have a mix of fresh and salt water.)*

Ask Do the same species of aquatic organisms live in both freshwater wetlands and estuaries, and if not, why not? *(No—most species are adapted to certain abiotic factors, such as salt water or fresh water but not both.)*

Give examples to show why most organisms adapted to fresh water cannot tolerate salt water, and vice-versa. For example, explain that saltwater fish have mechanisms for excreting excess salt from their body, whereas freshwater fish have mechanisms for concentrating salt in their body.

DIFFERENTIATED INSTRUCTION

L1 Special Needs Demonstrate the significance of salt tolerance in estuary plants by showing how saltwater affects a salt-intolerant plant. Place the root of a whole carrot with greens attached in a glass of fresh water. Place a second carrot in a glass of salt water. Have students compare the firmness of the leaves and stems and the flexibility of the roots over a period of a few days. Explain that carrots are not salt-tolerant plants, so salt water causes them to lose the fresh water inside their cells and become wilted. Have them infer how a salt-tolerant plant might fare under the same conditions.

L3 Advanced Students Ask students who have taken chemistry classes to learn about the mechanisms by which fish regulate salt balance by either pumping out sodium ions or actively taking up sodium ions, depending on whether they live in salt water or fresh water. Then, have students explain the basic chemistry underlying the mechanisms to the class.

UbD Check for Understanding

INDEX CARD SUMMARIES/QUESTIONS

Give students one index card each. On the front of their card, have them write a summary statement about factors that affect life in freshwater ecosystems. On the back of their card, ask them to write a question they still have about factors that affect life in freshwater ecosystems.

ADJUST INSTRUCTION

Collect the index cards, and share some of the more informative summary statements with the class. Then, read the questions aloud, and call on volunteers to answer them.

LESSON 4.5

Teach continued

Use Visuals

Have students do library or Internet research to identify the organisms depicted in the figure and find others not depicted. Assign each student one of the seven ocean zones, and have them photocopy, print out, or sketch images of organisms from various sources. Be sure they identify each organism, note its zone, and describe some of its salient features. Assemble the images on a bulletin board similar to **Figure 4–22.**

Animals in **Figure 4–22:** *Photic Zone* sea lion, herring, blue whale, great white shark, swordfish, flying fish; *200–1000 m* krill-like shrimp, ocean sunfish, bigeye tuna, cod, giant squid; *1000–4000 m* viperfish, dragonfish, bathypelagic anglerfish, snipe eel; *4000–10,000 m* rattail, gulper eel, tripod fish

DIFFERENTIATED INSTRUCTION

L1 Special Needs Students may not be able to identify many of the organisms in **Figure 4–22.** Show them additional visuals of organisms found in these zones. For comparison, provide them with visuals of nocturnal organisms and organisms that live in dark terrestrial environments. Have students identify some of the similar adaptive features that these organisms have evolved to survive in the dark.

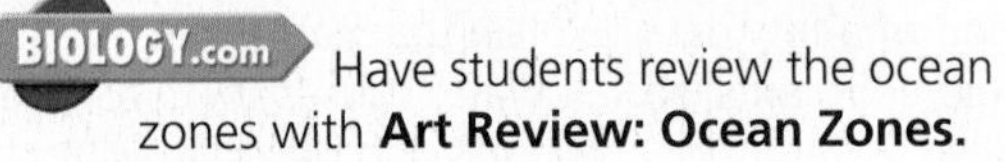

Have students review the ocean zones with **Art Review: Ocean Zones.**

Address Misconceptions

Importance of Marine Phytoplankton A common misconception is that phytoplankton are too small to be important photosynthesizers. Tell students that oceans cover three quarters of Earth's surface, and that each drop of ocean water down to a depth of 100 meters is home to thousands of phytoplankton. Then, tell them that phytoplankton produce 70 percent of Earth's oxygen and are the main consumers of carbon dioxide, a greenhouse gas.

Answers

IN YOUR NOTEBOOK Sample answer: I would expect communities in the open ocean to have lower concentrations of organisms, because there are low nutrient levels in the open ocean. Also, the organisms that live in the aphotic zone would have adaptations that help them survive in deep-water conditions.

Marine Ecosystems

How do ecologists usually classify marine ecosystems?

Just as biomes typically occupy certain latitudes and longitudes, marine ecosystems may typically occupy specific areas within the ocean. **Ecologists typically divide the ocean into zones based on depth and distance from shore.** Starting with the shallowest and closest to land, marine ecosystems include the intertidal zone, the coastal ocean, and the open ocean, as shown in **Figure 4–22.** Within these zones live a number of different communities.

BUILD Vocabulary

MULTIPLE MEANINGS The noun *subject* has many meanings, including "the main theme of a piece of work such as a novel" or "a course of study." The verb *subject,* however, means "to expose" or "to tend toward." Organisms are subjected, or exposed, to extreme conditions in the rocky intertidal zone.

In Your Notebook *How would you expect communities of organisms in the open ocean to differ from those along the coast?*

Intertidal Zone Organisms in the intertidal zone are submerged in seawater at high tide and exposed to air and sunlight at low tide. These organisms, then, are subjected to regular and extreme changes in temperature. They also are often battered by waves and currents. There are many different types of intertidal communities. A typical rocky intertidal community exists in temperate regions where exposed rocks line the shore. There, barnacles and seaweed permanently attach themselves to the rocks.

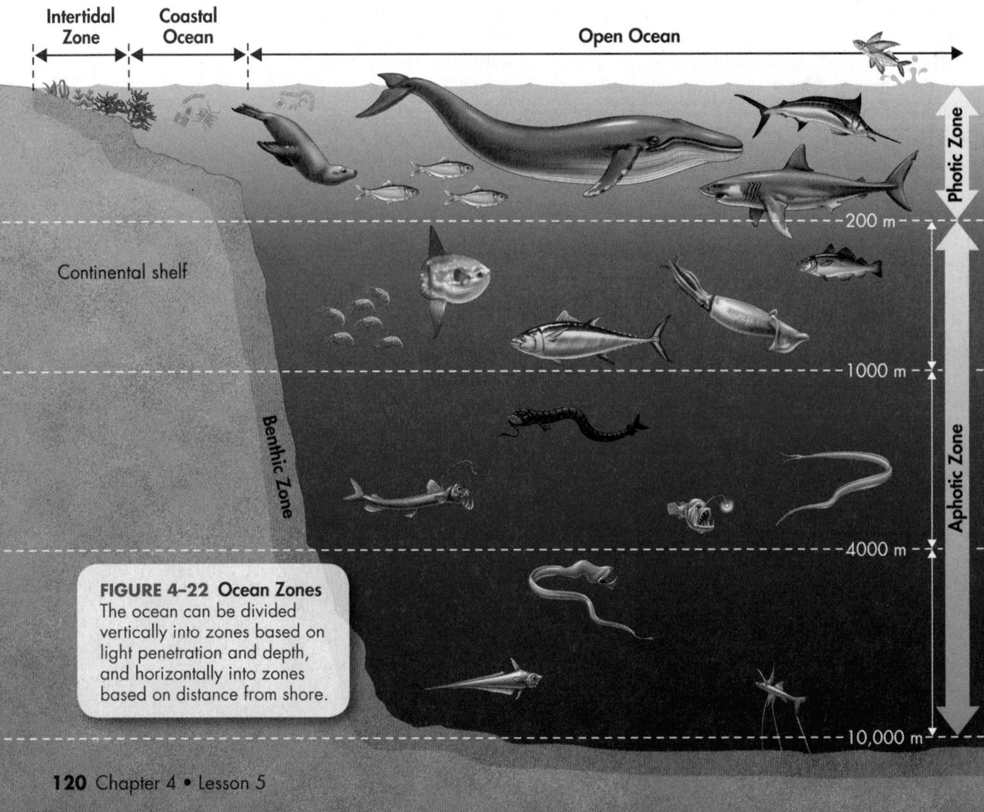

FIGURE 4–22 Ocean Zones The ocean can be divided vertically into zones based on light penetration and depth, and horizontally into zones based on distance from shore.

120 Chapter 4 • Lesson 5

How Science Works

SYLVIA EARLE: OCEAN EXPLORER AND GROUND BREAKER

Also called "Her Deepness" and named a "Hero for the Planet," Dr. Sylvia Earle is a world-famous ocean explorer and marine biologist. For almost four decades, she has also been a trailblazer for women in science. For example, in 1970, when qualified women scientists often experienced difficulty obtaining positions alongside men on research teams, she led an all-female, two-week expedition to the ocean floor. In the 1990s, she was named the first female chief scientist of NOAA. During her exemplary career, Dr. Earle has led more than 60 marine expeditions and spent almost 7000 hours underwater. She has also been instrumental in developing cutting-edge technology for exploring the deep ocean—vehicles and equipment that will likely advance marine research for decades to come. A world record holder in deep sea diving, Dr. Earle is currently National Geographic Society's Explorer-in-Residence and a vocal advocate for the oceans.

Coastal Ocean The coastal ocean extends from the low-tide mark to the outer edge of the continental shelf—the relatively shallow border that surrounds the continents. Water here is brightly lit, and is often supplied with nutrients by freshwater runoff from land. As a result, coastal oceans tend to be highly productive. Kelp forests and coral reefs are two exceptionally important coastal communities.

Open Ocean The open ocean begins at the edge of the continental shelf and extends outward. More than 90 percent of the world's ocean area is considered open ocean. Depth ranges from about 500 meters along continental slopes to more than 10,000 meters in deep ocean trenches. The open ocean can be divided into two main zones according to light penetration: the photic zone and the aphotic zone.

▶ ***The Open Ocean Photic Zone*** The open ocean typically has low nutrient levels and supports only the smallest species of phytoplankton. Still, because of its enormous area, most photosynthesis on Earth occurs in the sunlit top 100 meters of the open ocean.

▶ ***The Open Ocean Aphotic Zone*** The permanently dark aphotic zone includes the deepest parts of the ocean. Food webs here are based either on organisms that fall from the photic zone above, or on chemosynthetic organisms. Deep ocean organisms, like the fish in **Figure 4–23,** are exposed to high pressure, frigid temperatures, and total darkness. Benthic environments in the deep sea were once thought to be nearly devoid of life but are now known to have islands of high productivity. Deep-sea vents, where superheated water boils out of cracks on the ocean floor, support chemosynthetic primary producers.

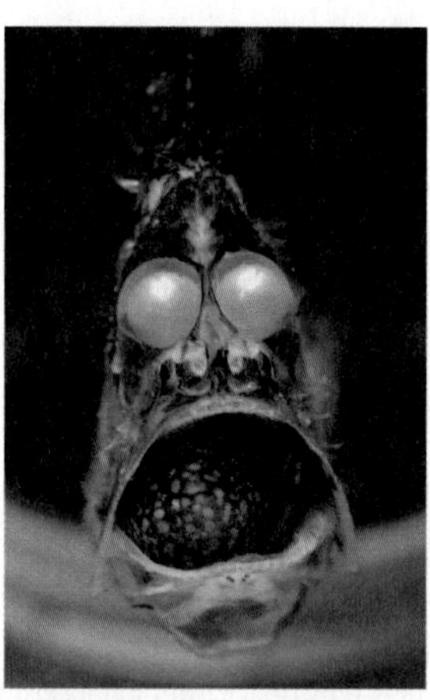

FIGURE 4–23 Creature From the Deep This slender hatchetfish lives in the aphotic zone of the Pacific Ocean off the coast of California. Apply Concepts ***What kinds of adaptations do you think this fish has that enable it to live in the harsh deep-ocean environment?***

4.5 Assessment

B.4.1

Review Key Concepts

1. a. Review What are the primary abiotic factors that affect life underwater?
   b. Compare and Contrast What are some ways in which life in an aphotic zone might differ from life in a photic zone?
2. a. Review What are the major categories of freshwater ecosystems?
   b. Apply Concepts What is a wetland? Why are wetlands important?
3. a. Review Where are estuaries found? Why is it important to protect estuaries?
   b. Predict How might a dam upriver affect an estuary at the river's mouth?
4. a. Review List the three major marine ecological zones. Give two abiotic factors for each zone.
   b. Apply Concepts Using **Figure 4–22** as a guide, draw a cross section of the ocean starting with a beach and ending with an ocean trench. Label the intertidal zone, coastal ocean, and open ocean. Subdivide the open ocean into photic and aphotic zones.

WRITE ABOUT SCIENCE

Explanation

5. Choose three different aquatic ecosystems. For each of these ecosystems, select a plant and an animal, and explain how the organisms have adapted to their environment.

BIOLOGY.com Search Lesson 4.5 GO • Art Review • Self-Test • Lesson Assessment

Assess and Remediate

EVALUATE UNDERSTANDING

Play a quiz game with the class in which you name aquatic ecosystems and teams of students compete to identify their abiotic factors and the organisms that live in them. Then, have students complete the 4.5 Assessment.

REMEDIATION SUGGESTION

L1 Struggling Students If students have difficulty with **Question 5,** model an appropriate answer. For example, describe the waves and currents in the intertidal zone and explain how organisms such as barnacles and seaweed adapt to the moving water by attaching themselves to rocks.

BIOLOGY.com Students can check their understanding of lesson concepts with the **Self-Test** assessment. They can then take an online version of the **Lesson Assessment.**

Answers

FIGURE 4–23 Sample answer: The fish must have adaptations that allow it to endure high pressure, cope with frigid temperatures, and sense its surroundings in total darkness.

Assessment Answers

1a. the water's depth, temperature, flow, and amount of dissolved nutrients

1b. Sample answer: In an aphotic zone, there are no phytoplankton to produce food, because no sunlight penetrates to this depth. Organisms in the aphotic zone must obtain food in some other way than by photosynthesis or by consuming plankton.

2a. rivers and streams, lakes and ponds, and freshwater wetlands

2b. A wetland is an ecosystem in which water either covers the soil or is present at or near the surface for at least part of the year. Wetlands are often highly productive and serve as breeding grounds for many organisms. They also purify water and help prevent flooding.

3a. Estuaries are found where rivers meet the sea. Estuaries serve as spawning and nursery grounds for many fish and shellfish.

3b. Sample answer: It might reduce the amount of freshwater entering an estuary, which would increase the salt concentration of the water.

4a. Sample answer: Intertidal zone: exposure to air and sunlight at low tides and extreme temperature changes; coastal ocean: brightly lit water and nutrients supplied by freshwater runoff; open ocean: low nutrient levels and lack of sunlight below 100 m

4b. Students' drawings should show the intertidal zone, coastal ocean, open ocean, and an ocean trench. Photic and aphotic zones should be labeled.

WRITE ABOUT SCIENCE

5. Students can choose any three freshwater or marine ecosystems. For each, students should explain how a plant and an animal have adapted to its conditions.

CHAPTER LAB

Pre-Lab

Introduce students to the concepts they will explore in the chapter lab by assigning the Pre-Lab questions.

Lab

Tell students they will perform the chapter lab *Abiotic Factors and Plant Selection* described in **Lab Manual A.**

 **Struggling Students** A simpler version of the chapter lab is provided in **Lab Manual B.**

SAFETY

Inform students that soil and sand sometimes contain harmful microorganisms, so they should wash their hands thoroughly after completing the lab.

 Look online for **Editable Lab Worksheets.**

 For corresponding pre-lab in the **Foundation Edition**, see page 100.

OPEN-ENDED INQUIRY

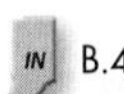 B.4.1 Limiting factors. Also covered: NoS.3.

Pre-Lab: Abiotic Factors and Plant Selection

Problem How can you decide which plants will thrive in a garden?

Materials plant hardiness zone map, plant catalogs, graph paper, tape measure

Lab Manual Chapter 4 Lab

Skills Focus Classify, Analyze Data, Use Models

Connect to the Big idea Why are white birch trees abundant in Minnesota, but not in the Florida Keys? Why do coconut palms grow in the Florida Keys, but not in Minnesota? Simply put, white birch trees could not tolerate the hot summers in the Keys and coconut palms could not tolerate the cold winters in Minnesota. A plant's habitat is determined by its range of tolerance for temperature and other abiotic factors. In other words, abiotic factors limit where a given plant can live.

In this lab, you will plan a garden for a specific location. You will select plants for the garden that can tolerate the abiotic factors in this location.

Background Questions

a. **Review** What is an abiotic factor? List three examples other than temperature.

b. **Review** What kinds of resources do plants need?

c. **Relate Cause and Effect** Give an example of an adaptation that helps a plant survive in a biome with low precipitation.

Pre-Lab Questions

Preview the procedure in the lab manual.

1. **Predict** How will knowing the plant hardiness zone for your area help you plan a garden?
2. **Relate Cause and Effect** What is the relationship between the last frost and the length of the growing season?
3. **Form a Hypothesis** A plant species grows well in one location in a small garden but does not grow as well in another location. Suggest one possible reason for this difference.

 Search Chapter 4 

Visit Chapter 4 online to test yourself on chapter content and to find activities to help you learn.

Untamed Science Video Join the Untamed Science crew as they explore succession after a volcanic eruption on Hawaii.

Visual Analogy Compare Earth's atmosphere to a greenhouse.

Data Analysis Look at data on tolerance of intertidal zone species and use your analysis to explain the zonation patterns of intertidal species.

Art in Motion View a short animation that brings succession to life.

Art Review Review your understanding of ocean zones with this drag-and-drop activity.

IN INDIANA ACADEMIC STANDARDS

For the full text of all standards, see the Course Overview in the front matter of this book.

Pre-Lab Answers

BACKGROUND QUESTIONS

a. Abiotic factors are non-living factors that influence the growth of plants. Possible abiotic factors are sunlight, precipitation, wind, humidity, and soil type.

b. Sample answer: Plants need water, light, nutrients, and space to grow.

c. Possible answers include leaves with limited surface area or leaf pores that open only at night.

PRE-LAB QUESTIONS

1. Sample answer: Knowing the plant hardiness zone will provide information about some abiotic factors. (Some students may know that suppliers of seeds and plants usually provide a range of hardiness zones for each species.)
2. Sample answer: The earlier the last frost occurs, the longer the growing season.
3. Sample answer: One location may have direct sunlight all day and the other may be in the shade for most of the day.

4 Study Guide

Big idea Interdependence in Nature

An organism's tolerance range for temperature, precipitation, and other abiotic factors helps determine where it lives. Biotic factors, such as competition, predation, and herbivory also help to determine an organism's potential habitat and niche.

4.1 Climate

A region's climate is defined by year-after-year patterns of temperature and precipitation.

Global climate is shaped by many factors, including solar energy trapped in the biosphere, latitude, and the transport of heat by winds and ocean currents.

weather (96)
climate (96)
microclimate (96)
greenhouse effect (97)

4.2 Niches and Community Interactions

A niche is the range of physical and biological conditions in which a species lives and the way the species obtains what it needs to survive and reproduce.

By causing species to divide resources, competition helps determine the number and kinds of species in a community and the niche each species occupies.

Predators can affect the size of prey populations in a community and determine the places prey can live and feed.

Herbivores can affect both the size and distribution of plant populations in a community and can determine the places that certain plants can survive and grow.

Biologists recognize three main classes of symbiotic relationships in nature: mutualism, parasitism, and commensalism.

tolerance (99)
habitat (99)
niche (100)
resource (100)
competitive exclusion principle (101)
predation (102)
herbivory (102)
keystone species (103)
symbiosis (103)
mutualism (103)
parasitism (104)
commensalism (104)

4.3 Succession

Ecosystems change over time, especially after disturbances, as some species die out and new species move in.

Secondary succession in healthy ecosystems following natural disturbances often reproduces the original climax community. Ecosystems may or may not recover from human-caused disturbances.

ecological succession (106)
primary succession (106)
pioneer species (107)
secondary succession (107)

4.4 Biomes

Biomes are described in terms of abiotic factors like climate and soil type, and biotic factors like plant and animal life.

Mountain ranges and polar ice caps are not usually classified into biomes because they are not easily defined in terms of a typical community of plants and animals.

canopy (112)
understory (112)
deciduous (112)
coniferous (114)
humus (114)
taiga (114)
permafrost (115)

4.5 Aquatic Ecosystems

Aquatic organisms are affected primarily by the water's depth, temperature, flow, and amount of dissolved nutrients.

Freshwater ecosystems can be divided into three main categories: rivers and streams, lakes and ponds, and freshwater wetlands.

Estuaries serve as spawning and nursery grounds for many ecologically and commercially important fish and shellfish species.

Ecologists typically divide the ocean into zones based on depth and distance from shore.

photic zone (117)
aphotic zone (117)
benthos (117)
plankton (119)
wetland (119)
estuary (119)

Think Visually Create a concept map that includes the following terms: *abiotic factors, biotic factors, community interactions, predation, competition, symbiosis, nutrients, ecosystems, light,* and *oxygen.*

UbD Performance Tasks

SUMMATIVE TASK Have pairs of students select one of the land biomes or aquatic ecosystems described in the chapter and create a scrapbook highlighting its abiotic and biotic factors. Tell students to convey the information about their biome with photographs, maps, graphs, and short passages of text.

TRANSFER TASK Ask groups of students to choose a specific region of a land biome or aquatic ecosystem that is threatened by human actions and create a Web site about the problem and potential solutions. The Web site should include information on why the ecosystem is threatened, why it is important, what is being done to protect it, and what individuals can do to help.

Study Online

REVIEW AND ASSESSMENT RESOURCES

Editable Worksheets Pages of Study Workbooks A and B, Lab Manuals A and B, and the Assessment Resources Book are available online. These documents can be easily edited using a word-processing program.

Lesson Overview Have students reread the Lesson Overviews to help them study chapter concepts.

Vocabulary Review The *Flash Cards* and *Crossword* provide an interactive way to review chapter vocabulary.

Chapter Assessment Have students take an online version of the Chapter 4 Assessment.

Standardized Test Prep Students can take an online version of the Standardized Test Prep. You will receive their scores along with ideas for remediation.

Diagnostic and Benchmark Tests Use these tests to monitor your students' progress and supply remediation.

Answers

THINK VISUALLY

Students' concept maps should show that ecosystems are determined by abiotic factors, including nutrients, light, and oxygen; and by biotic factors, including the community interactions of predation, competition, and symbiosis.

Lesson 4.1

UNDERSTAND KEY CONCEPTS

1. b **2.** d

3. Weather is the day-to-day condition of Earth's atmosphere. Climate refers to average conditions over long periods.

4. solar energy trapped in the biosphere, latitude, and the transport of heat by winds and ocean currents

THINK CRITICALLY

5. The curvature of Earth's surface causes sunlight to strike the surface near the poles at an angle, so solar energy is spread out over a larger area at the poles than at the equator. This difference in the distribution of solar energy at different latitudes explains climate zones. As Earth revolves around the sun, sunlight strikes different regions at angles that vary from summer to winter. This difference in the distribution of solar energy at different times of the year explains seasons.

6. The white paint reflects much of the sunlight so that it does not pass into the greenhouse where it would be trapped as heat.

Lesson 4.2

UNDERSTAND KEY CONCEPTS

7. d **8.** b

9. An organism's habitat is the general location where it lives. Its niche includes not only where it lives but also how it lives, including which abiotic factors it needs, how it reproduces, what it eats, and how it obtains its food.

10. No two species can occupy exactly the same niche at exactly the same time.

THINK CRITICALLY

11. In predation, one organism captures, kills, and eats another organism. In parasitism, one organism lives in or on another organism and uses it for food or other purposes without killing it.

12. Members of the same species have exactly the same niche. Therefore, they are in direct competition for the same resources in their area. Members of two different species are likely to have somewhat different niches, so while they may need some of the same resources, they are likely to use them at different times or in different ways, which means that they do not compete so intensely for them.

13. Sample answer: I reside in a city with a temperate climate. I live in a house with other members of my family and a dog. I interact with many humans, and I take my dog for walks. I eat a variety of plant and animal foods that come from all over the world, and I buy them at local supermarkets and restaurants.

Lesson 4.3

UNDERSTAND KEY CONCEPTS

14. d **15.** d

16. primary succession

17. natural disturbances and human-caused disturbances

THINK CRITICALLY

18. Secondary succession; in 5 years, small trees will probably have started to grow. In 50 years, barring further disturbance, the area is likely to look like it did before the windstorm.

19. Secondary succession usually proceeds faster, because soil and a few plants are already in place when secondary succession starts.

4 Assessment

The numbers following the questions refer to Indiana's Academic Standards for Biology I.

4.1 Climate

Understand Key Concepts

1. An increase in the greenhouse effect causes an increase in
a. carbon dioxide. **c.** oxygen.
b. temperature. **d.** water.

2. A small valley where the average temperature is usually higher than that of the surrounding countryside has its own
a. weather. **c.** rainfall.
b. climate. **d.** microclimate.

3. Distinguish between weather and climate.

4. Describe the three primary abiotic factors that produce Earth's major climate zones.

Think Critically

5. **Apply Concepts** Based on the relative positions of the sun and Earth, explain why Earth has climate zones and seasons.

6. **Infer** A plant grower has a greenhouse where she grows plants in the winter. The greenhouse is exposed to direct sunlight and often gets too hot for the plants. She paints the inside of the glass with a chalky white paint, and the temperature drops to comfortable levels. Explain why this procedure works.

4.2 Niches and Community Interactions

Understand Key Concepts

7. A relationship in which one organism is helped and another organism is neither helped nor hurt is called
a. parasitism. **c.** competition.
b. mutualism. **d.** commensalism.

8. The relationship between a tick and its host is an example of
a. mutualism.
b. parasitism.
c. commensalism.
d. succession.

9. What is the difference between an organism's habitat and its niche?

10. What is the competitive exclusion principle?

Think Critically

11. **Compare and Contrast** How are predation and parasitism similar? How are they different?

12. **Infer** Competition for resources in an area is usually more intense within a single species than between two different species. How would you explain this observation? B.4.1, B.4.4

13. **Apply Concepts** Write a description of your niche in the environment. Include details about your ecosystem, and the biotic and abiotic factors around you. Be sure to describe your feeding habits as well as any interactions you have with members of other species. B.4.4

4.3 Succession

Understand Key Concepts

14. Fires, hurricanes, and other natural disturbances can result in B.4.2
a. commensalism. **c.** parasitism.
b. competition. **d.** succession.

15. The first organisms to repopulate an area affected by a volcanic eruption are called
a. keystone species. **c.** primary producers.
b. climax species. **d.** pioneer species.

16. What type of succession takes place after lava from a volcanic eruption covers an area?

17. Describe two major causes of ecological succession. B.4.2

Think Critically

18. **Predict** A windstorm in a forest blows down the large trees in one part of the forest. Soon, sun-loving plants sprout in the new clearing. What type of succession is this? What do you think this area will look like in 5 years? In 50 years? B.4.2

19. **Relate Cause and Effect** Explain why secondary succession usually proceeds faster than primary succession.

4.4 Biomes

Understand Key Concepts

20. In a tropical rain forest, the dense covering formed by the leafy tops of tall trees is called the
- **a.** canopy.
- **b.** taiga.
- **c.** niche.
- **d.** understory.

21. Permafrost characterizes the biome called
- **a.** taiga.
- **b.** boreal forest.
- **c.** savanna.
- **d.** tundra.

22. What is a biome?

23. Why are plants generally few and far between in a desert? B.4.1

Think Critically

24. **Apply Concepts** Although the amount of precipitation is low, most parts of the tundra are very wet during the summer. How would you explain this apparent contradiction? B.4.4

25. **Infer** Deciduous trees in tropical dry forests lose water through their leaves every day. During summers with adequate rain, the leaves remain on the trees. During the cold dry season, the trees drop their leaves. In an especially dry summer, how might the adaptation of dropping leaves enable a tree to tolerate the drought?

26. **Infer** Consider these two biomes: (1) the temperate grassland and (2) the temperate woodland and shrubland. Coyotes live in both biomes. Describe two adaptations that might enable coyotes to tolerate conditions in both biomes.

4.5 Aquatic Ecosystems

Understand Key Concepts

27. Organisms that live near or on the ocean floor are called
- **a.** parasites.
- **b.** benthos.
- **c.** plankton.
- **d.** mangroves.

28. What is the meaning of the term *plankton*? Name the two types of plankton.

29. What are three types of freshwater wetlands?

30. How are salt marshes and mangrove swamps alike? How are they different?

solve the CHAPTER MYSTERY

THE WOLF EFFECT

Eliminating wolves from Yellowstone National Park contributed to an increase in the number of elk. These elk grazed so heavily, especially along streams, that the seedlings and shoots of aspens and willows, and other trees, could not grow. Fewer trees led to fewer dams being built by beavers and to an increase in runoff and erosion. Aquatic food webs broke down, affecting birds, fish, and other animals. The recent reintroduction of wolves has caused a decrease in the overall elk population and seems to have reduced elk grazing along certain streams. That may be in part because wolves are killing more elk and in part because elk have learned to stay away from places like stream banks and valleys, where wolves can attack them most easily.

In recent years, researchers have shown that streamside vegetation is exhibiting secondary succession and that aspen and willow trees are starting to grow back. There have been numerous other changes as well. Fewer elk mean more food for smaller animals. The increase in small prey, in turn, has brought diverse predators into the community. Carcasses abandoned by the wolves provide food for scavengers. In short, organisms from every trophic level have been affected by the Yellowstone wolves.

1. **Predict** The Yellowstone wolf and elk are linked through a predator-prey relationship. If a disease were to strike the elk population, how would the wolves be affected?

2. **Form an Opinion** Yellowstone is owned by the federal government. The reintroduction of wolves there angered nearby farmers because they feared their animals would be hunted. What level of responsibility do you think national parks should have toward their neighbors?

3. **Connect to the Big idea** Draw a food chain that connects Yellowstone's wolves, aspen and willow trees, and elk. Then write a paragraph that explains why the Yellowstone wolves are a keystone species. IN B.4.1, B.4.4

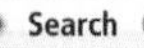

Lesson 4.4

UNDERSTAND KEY CONCEPTS

20. a **21.** d

22. A biome is a group of regional climate communities described in terms of biotic and abiotic factors.

23. The low levels of precipitation in a desert can support only a few plants.

THINK CRITICALLY

24. Because of permafrost, only the top few centimeters of the ground thaw in the summer. What little precipitation that does fall cannot soak into the permanently frozen subsoil, so it makes the ground soggy.

25. By dropping its leaves during an especially dry summer, a tree loses less water and is more likely to tolerate a drought.

26. Sample answer: Coyotes might be able to tolerate conditions in these two different biomes by being adapted to hunt and eat a variety of different prey animals and by being able to withstand hot, dry summers as well as cold winters.

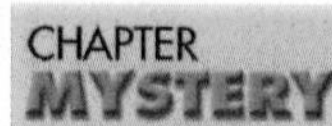

After students have read through the Chapter Mystery, discuss why heavy grazing by elk along streams led to aquatic food webs breaking down. For example, explain that fewer plants would mean that other organisms that eat plants, such as insects, would also have less to eat. Organisms that prey upon these herbivores (like fish) would have less to eat, as well.

Ask Why would it be easier for wolves to attack elk in places such as stream banks and valleys? *(Sample answer: Wolves could hide in reeds and other dense vegetation and sneak up on elk.)*

Ask Why is secondary rather than primary succession occurring in these places? *(The grazing of elk prevented young trees from growing but did not remove the soil or all of the plants.)*

Ask Why would reintroducing wolves increase the number of decomposers? *(There would be more elk carcasses for decomposers to break down for food.)*

CHAPTER MYSTERY ANSWERS

1. If the disease reduced the number of elk, wolves would have less to eat and might decline in number.

2. Sample answer: I think national parks should be allowed to let ecosystems return to their natural state, even if it potentially creates problems for their neighbors, because it is important to preserve natural ecosystems for the sake of the environment and for the large numbers of people who visit the parks. However, the parks should also try to minimize or compensate for the risks. For example, they might plant thickets of brush to help keep wolves inside park boundaries, or they might reimburse neighbors if their domestic animals are killed by wolves.

3. Big idea Students' food chains should show that aspen and willow tree seedlings and shoots are producers, which are consumed by elk, and that elk, in turn, are consumed by wolves. Wolves are a keystone species because reintroducing them had widespread effects on organisms at every trophic level and changed the structure of the Yellowstone community. In addition to reducing the number of elk, it led to regrowth of aspen and willow trees, more food for smaller animals, an increase in the number of predator species, and more food for scavengers.

Students can learn more about succession by watching **Untamed Science: From Lava to Life.**

Lesson 4.5

UNDERSTAND KEY CONCEPTS

27. b

28. Plankton is a combination of phytoplankton (photosynthetic algae) and zooplankton (tiny free-floating animals that eat phytoplankton).

29. rivers and streams, lakes and ponds, and freshwater wetlands

30. Both are estuaries formed where a river meets the sea. Salt marshes are temperate zone estuaries where salt-tolerant grasses and seagrasses grow. Mangrove swamps are tropical zone estuaries where salt-tolerant trees, called mangroves, grow.

THINK CRITICALLY

31. Sample answer: Some animals are able to produce light chemically in order to lure prey. Other animals have very sensitive feelers for detection in the dark. Still others have robust vascular systems that allow them to withstand great pressures and cold temperatures.

32. Sample answer: Filling in a salt marsh to create a coastal resort might bring money into the local economy. However, it would destroy the spawning and nursery grounds for fish and shellfish species, which could harm the local economy. Therefore, I would not support the proposal.

Connecting Concepts

USE SCIENCE GRAPHICS

33. A coral reef is most productive, probably because they are found in coastal ocean zones where the shallow water is brightly lit and often supplied with nutrients from freshwater runoff.

34. because it covers such a huge portion of Earth's surface

35. Answers will vary. Check that students have correctly identified two abiotic factors that affect the productivity of each ecosystem.

36. Sample answer: I think its primary productivity is likely greater, because it gets abundant precipitation for three seasons of the year and is less susceptible to the frequent forest fires that decrease productivity in the savanna.

WRITE ABOUT SCIENCE

37. Answers will vary depending on which biomes students choose. They should identify the biome's abiotic and biotic factors and explain how they are interrelated, using examples.

38. Big idea Abiotic factors determine the types of pioneer species that can live in an area and that are likely to be involved in primary succession following a volcanic eruption.

Think Critically

31. Form a Hypothesis The deep ocean lies within the aphotic zone and is very cold. Suggest some of the unique characteristics that enable animals to live in the deep ocean.

32. Form an Opinion A developer has proposed filling in a salt marsh to create a coastal resort. What positive and negative effects do you think this proposal would have on wildlife and local residents? Would you support the proposal? B.4.2

Connecting Concepts

Use Science Graphics NoS.3

The following table presents primary productivity (measured in grams of organic matter produced per year per square meter) for several ecosystems. Use the table below to answer questions 33–36.

Productivity of Aquatic and Land Ecosystems

Ecosystem	Average Primary Productivity
Aquatic Ecosystems	
Coral reef	2500
Estuary	1800
Open ocean	125
Land Ecosystems	
Tropical rain forest	2200
Tropical savanna	900
Tundra	90

33. Interpret Tables According to the table, which ecosystem is most productive? Use what you know to explain that fact.

34. Infer The open ocean is among the least productive ecosystems, yet it contributes greatly to the overall productivity of the biosphere. How do you explain this paradox?

35. Apply Concepts For each set of ecosystems, aquatic and land, explain how abiotic factors may account for the differences in primary productivity seen. Give two examples. B.4.1

36. Infer Review the description of the Northwest coniferous forest on page 114. Do you think its average primary productivity is greater or less than that of the tropical savanna? Explain your answer.

Write About Science NoS.3

37. Explanation Choose one of the ten major biomes, and write an overview of its characteristics. Explain how abiotic factors and common plants and wildlife are interrelated. Support your explanation with specific examples.

38. Assess the Big idea How do abiotic factors influence what kinds of organisms are involved in the primary succession in an area following a volcanic eruption? B.4.1

Analyzing Data

IN NoS.3

The graph here summarizes the changes in the total volume of ice in all the world's glaciers since 1960. Note that the volume changes on the y-axis are negative, meaning an overall loss of volume.

Global Glacier Volume Change

Cumulative Volume of Change (km^3): 0, −1000, −3000, −5000, −6500

Year: 1960, 1970, 1980, 1990, 2000

39. Interpret Graphs The greatest volume of glacial ice was lost
- **a.** between 1960 and 1970.
- **b.** between 1980 and 1990.
- **c.** between 1995 and 2000.
- **d.** before 1960.

40. Relate Cause and Effect The most reasonable explanation for the loss of glacier mass since 1960 is
- **a.** an increase in the total productivity of the world's oceans.
- **b.** a gradual rise in Earth's average temperature.
- **c.** an increase in the total amount of ice at Earth's poles.
- **d.** an increase in the sun's output of radiant energy.

Analyzing Data

PURPOSE Students will interpret a graph to explain the change in the total volume of ice in the world's glaciers.

PLANNING Discuss with the class how to interpret the slope of a line graph. A line that is horizontal (slope = 0) generally reflects no change. A line that rises from left to right (positive slope) generally reflects an increasing trend. A line that falls from left to right (negative slope) generally reflects a decreasing trend, as is the case here with the decreasing volume of glacial ice.

ANSWERS

39. c

40. b

Standardized Test Practice for Indiana

Multiple Choice

1. The factor that generally has the greatest effect on determining a region's climate is its
   A longitude.
   B abundant plant species.
   C distance from the equator.
   D closeness to a river.

2. All of the following are abiotic factors that affect global climate EXCEPT
   A latitude.
   B longitude.
   C solar energy.
   D ocean currents.

3. The way an organism makes its living, including its interactions with biotic and abiotic factors of its environment, is called the organism's
   A habitat.
   B niche.
   C lifestyle.
   D biome.

4. If a newly introduced species fills a niche that is normally occupied by a native species, the two species compete. One of the species may die out as a result of
   A competitive exclusion.
   B predation.
   C commensalism.
   D mutualism. B.4.3, B.4.4

5. Photosynthetic algae are MOST likely to be found in
   A the open-ocean benthic zone.
   B the aphotic zone.
   C the photic zone.
   D ocean trenches.

6. The water in an estuary is
   A salt water only.
   B poor in nutrients.
   C fresh water only.
   D a mixture of fresh water and salt water.

7. In which biome do organisms have the greatest tolerance to dry conditions?
   A tundra
   B desert
   C tropical savanna
   D boreal forest

Questions 8–9

Month-by-month climate data for the city of Lillehammer, Norway, is shown in the table below.

Climate Data for Lillehammer, Norway

Month	Average Temperature (°C)	Average Precipitation (mm)
Jan.	−8.1	38.1
Feb.	−6.2	27.9
Mar.	−3.9	30.5
Apr.	3.3	35.6
May	8.9	45.7
June	13.9	63.5
July	16.4	81.3
Aug.	14.2	88.9
Sept.	9.5	58.4
Oct.	3.9	63.5
Nov.	−3.8	50.8
Dec.	−6.1	48.3

8. Which type of graph would be BEST suited to showing the precipitation data from the table?
   A bar graph
   B pictograph
   C pie chart
   D scatter plot NoS.3

9. For a given set of data, the range is the difference between highest and lowest points. The average annual temperature range, in °C, for Lillehammer is approximately
   A −8.
   B 8.5.
   C 16.5.
   D 24.5.

Open-Ended Response

10. Why are lichens especially well adapted to play the role of pioneer organisms in an ecological succession?

If You Have Trouble With . . .

Question	1	2	3	4	5	6	7	8	9	10
See Lesson	4.1	4.1	4.2	4.2	4.5	4.5	4.4	4.1	4.1	4.3

Test-Taking Tip

REPHRASE THE QUESTION

Advise students to rewrite difficult test questions in their own words. This will help them better understand what the questions are asking so they can write more appropriate answers. However, caution them to avoid changing the meaning of questions when they rephrase them. Suggest they ask for clarification, if possible, of any questions they still do not understand after rephrasing them.

Answers

1. C
2. B
3. B
4. A
5. C
6. D
7. B
8. A
9. D
10. Lichens are especially well adapted to play the role of pioneer organisms because they can grow on bare rock, fix atmospheric nitrogen into useful forms for other organisms, break down rock, and add organic material to form soil.

Populations

Chapter Contents	IN	Time	Core Resources
Chapter Preview			**Student Edition,** pp. 128–129 **Chapter Mystery,** p. 129
5.1 How Populations Grow Describing Populations • Population Growth • Exponential Growth • Logistic Growth • *Biology & Society: What Can Be Done About Invasive Mussels?*	NoS.3, NoS.6, B.4.1, B.4.3, B.4.4	1 period 1/2 block	**Student Edition,** pp. 130–136 Inquiry 5.1 Analyzing Data, p. 135 L2 **Study Workbook A** 5.1 Worksheets L2 Biology.com *Data Analysis:* Invasion of Zebra Mussels **Assessment Resources Book** Visual Quizzes L2
5.2 Limits to Growth Limiting Factors • Density-Dependent Limiting Factors • Density-Independent Limiting Factors	B.4.1, B.4.2, B.4.3, B.4.4	1 period 1/2 block	**Student Edition,** pp. 137–141 Inquiry 5.2 Quick Lab, p. 138 L2 **Study Workbook A** 5.2 Worksheets L2 Biology.com *InterActive Art:* Moose-Wolf Populations on Isle Royale • 5.2 Self-Test • 5.2 Lesson Assessment
5.3 Human Population Growth Historical Overview • Patterns of Human Population Growth		1/2 period 1/4 block	**Student Edition,** pp. 142–145 **Study Workbook A** 5.3 Worksheets L2 Biology.com *Art in Motion:* Age Structure of World Population **Assessment Resources Book** Visual Quiz L2
Chapter Pre-Lab	NoS.5, B.4.1, B.4.4	1 period 1/2 block	**Student Edition,** p. 146 L2 **Lab Manual A** *The Growth Cycle of Yeast* L2

Differentiated Instruction Tools

Study Workbook B includes worksheets with lesson-level differentiated instruction support and explanations of differentiated instruction teaching strategies.

Lab Manual B includes skills labs, simplified chapter labs, and hands-on activities.

ELL Handbook explains ways to make *Biology* more accessible to ELL students.

Spanish Study Workbook is a Spanish translation of Study Workbook A.

Multilingual Glossary is the glossary translated into ten languages.

Differentiated Instruction Key

- L1 Special Needs or Struggling Students
- ELL English Language Learners
- LPR Less Proficient Readers
- L2 On-Level Students
- L3 Advanced Students

Additional Resources

Biology.com Untamed Science Video • Vocabulary Flash Cards

Study Workbook B 5.1 Worksheets L1 ELL LPR
Spanish Study Workbook 5.1 Worksheets ELL
Biology.com 5.1 Lesson Overview • 5.1 Lesson Notes • 5.1 Self-Test • 5.1 Lesson Assessment

Study Workbook B 5.2 Worksheets L1 ELL LPR
Spanish Study Workbook 5.2 Worksheets ELL
Biology.com *Art Review:* Limiting Factors • 5.2 Lesson Overview • 5.2 Lesson Notes

Study Workbook B 5.3 Worksheets L1 ELL LPR
Spanish Study Workbook 5.3 Worksheets ELL
Biology.com 5.3 Lesson Overview • 5.3 Lesson Notes • 5.3 Self-Test • 5.3 Lesson Assessment

Lab Manual B *The Growth Cycle of Yeast* • Data Analysis: *Multiplying Rabbits* • Hands-On Activity: *How Competition Affects Growth* L1 ELL LPR

Chapter Review

Student Edition Study Guide, p. 147 L2
Study Workbook A Chapter 5 Vocabulary Review L2 • Chapter 5 Chapter Mystery/21st Century Skills Activity L2 L3
Transparencies, pp. 55–63 L1 ELL LPR L2
Biology.com Untamed Science Video • Editable Worksheets of Study Workbooks A and B and Lab Manuals A and B • Chapter 5 Flash Cards and Match It

Untamed Science DVD • Classroom Resources CD (includes lesson presentations and editable worksheets)

Chapter Assessment

Student Edition Assessment, pp. 148–151 L2
Study Workbook B Chapter 5 Chapter Review L1 ELL LPR • Chapter 5 Taking a Standardized Test L1 ELL LPR
Assessment Resources Book Chapter 5 Test A L2 • Chapter 5 Test B L1 ELL LPR
Biology.com Chapter 5 Assessment • Editable Worksheets of Chapter 5 Visual Quizzes and Chapter 5 Tests A and B

Exam*View* *Assessment Suite* • Classroom Resources CD (includes lesson presentations and editable worksheets)

Time: 1 period, 1/2 block

Pressed for Time?

Preview the Chapter Introduce the Key Questions for Lessons 5.1 and 5.2. Preview Figures 5–3 and 5–6.

Cover the Chapter Quickly In Lesson 5.1, have students read *Describing Populations, Population Growth,* and the introductions to *Exponential Growth* and *Logistic Growth* sections. Discuss Figures 5–4 and 5–5. Have students read all of Lesson 5.2, focusing on Figure 5–8.

Assess Assign questions 1, 2, 3b, and 4a in the 5.1 Assessment, the 5.2 Assessment, and questions 1–7, 11–21, and 33–35 in the Chapter 5 Assessment.

Connect to the Big Idea

Big idea Use the photograph of red crabs on Christmas Island to introduce ideas about population size and factors affecting population size. Ask students to identify some of the factors that could cause a change in the number of red crabs on Christmas Island. *(Sample answers: amount of food available, weather, human actions)* Have students predict what would happen to the red crab population as the result of a drought, a hurricane, or the introduction of a predator to the ecosystem. *(Answers will vary, but all responses should be well reasoned.)* Ask them to anticipate the answer to the question, **What factors contribute to changes in populations?**

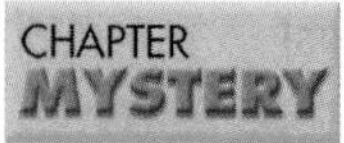

Have students read over the Chapter Mystery. Ask them to brainstorm a list of reasons why the rabbit population in Australia grew so rapidly. After they have completed Chapter 5, have them explain how the solution to the Chapter Mystery is related to the Chapter 5 Essential Question: **What factors contribute to changes in populations?**

BIOLOGY.com Have students preview the chapter vocabulary terms using the **Flash Cards.**

IN INDIANA ACADEMIC STANDARDS

For the full text of all standards, see the Course Overview in the front matter of this book.

Key standards: Chapter 5 covers key ideas from Standard 4: Interdependence, including **B.4.1** Limiting factors, **B.4.3** Non-native species, and **B.4.4** Stability of an ecosystem.

5 Populations

Big idea **Interdependence in Nature**

Q: What factors contribute to changes in populations?

CRABS CROSS HERE

BIOLOGY.com Search Chapter 5 GO • Flash Cards

128

UbD Understanding by Design

Chapter 5 explores ideas about populations and factors affecting population growth, in relation to the Big Idea, Interdependence in Nature. The graphic organizer at the right shows how chapter concepts help students build toward this Big Idea and the Unit 2 Enduring Understanding of how *the existence of life on Earth depends on interactions among organisms and between organisms and their environment.*

PERFORMANCE GOALS

Throughout Chapter 5, students are challenged to answer caption questions and complete In Your Notebook activities to show understanding of populations and the factors that affect them. At the end of the chapter, students must synthesize chapter concepts to help them predict the impact of a change in medical technology on the U.S. population and to help them write a science-fiction story relating the concepts of carrying capacity, limiting factors, and human population growth.

INDIANA ACADEMIC STANDARDS FOR SCIENCE

Nature of Science NoS.3, NoS.5, NoS.6; **Interdependence** B.4.1, B.4.2, B.4.3, B.4.4. See lessons for details.

Millions of red crabs live on Christmas Island in the Indian Ocean. Each year the entire adult crab population migrates from forest to sea to breed, making daily life a bit tricky for human residents!

CHAPTER MYSTERY

A PLAGUE OF RABBITS

In 1859, an Australian farmer released 24 wild European rabbits from England on his ranch. "A few rabbits" he said, "could do little harm and might provide a touch of home, in addition to a spot of hunting."

Seven years later, he and his friends shot 14,253 rabbits. In ten years, more than 2 million rabbits were hunted on that farm alone! But hunters' glee turned into nationwide despair. That "touch of home" was soon covering the countryside like a great gray blanket. The millions of rabbits devoured native plants and pushed native animals to near extinction. They made life miserable for sheep and cattle ranchers.

These cute, fuzzy creatures weren't a problem in England. Why did they turn into a plague in Australia? Could they be stopped? How? As you read this chapter, look for clues on factors that affect population growth. Then, solve the mystery.

Never Stop Exploring Your World. Finding the solution to the rabbit population mystery is only the beginning. Take a video field trip with the ecogeeks of Untamed Science to see where this mystery leads.

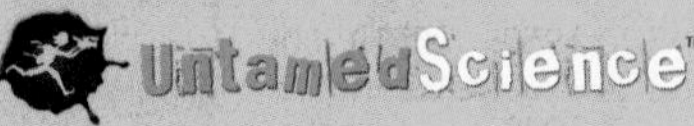

Populations **129**

Chapter 5 Big Idea: Interdependence in Nature

Chapter 5 EQ: What factors contribute to changes in populations?

5.1 GQ: How do populations grow?

5.2 GQ: What factors limit a population's growth?

5.3 GQ: How is the human population growing?

What's Online

BIOLOGY.com Extend your reach by using these and other digital assets offered at Biology.com.

CHAPTER MYSTERY
Students can investigate the explosive growth of the rabbit population in Australia to learn more about population growth, factors that impact population size, and human impact on populations.

UNTAMED SCIENCE VIDEO
In **Census Consensus,** the ecogeeks of Untamed Science investigate how scientists pin down population numbers—including the ones that try to hop away.

DATA ANALYSIS
Students analyze data to make predictions about zebra mussel population growth.

ART REVIEW
Reinforce limiting factors using this drag-and-drop activity.

INTERACTIVE ART
Students manipulate factors to see how predator and prey populations would change over several generations.

ART IN MOTION
This animated time series shows change in the world population age structure.

LESSON 5.1

Getting Started

Objectives

5.1.1 List the characteristics used to describe a population.

5.1.2 Identify factors that affect population growth.

5.1.3 Describe exponential growth.

5.1.4 Describe logistic growth.

Student Resources

Study Workbooks A and B, 5.1 Worksheets

Spanish Study Workbook, 5.1 Worksheets

Lab Manual B, 5.1 Data Analysis Worksheet

Lesson Overview • Lesson Notes • Activity: Data Analysis • Assessment: Self-Test, Lesson Assessment

For corresponding lesson in the **Foundation Edition**, see pages 108–111.

Activate Prior Knowledge

Have students identify populations of living things found in the area where they live. Then, ask them to identify factors that might affect the size of these populations. Write their responses on the board. As students read the lesson, have them revise and add to the lists.

IN INDIANA ACADEMIC STANDARDS

For the full text of all standards, see the Course Overview in the front matter of this book.

NoS.6 Use analogies and models (mathematical and physical) to simplify and represent systems that are difficult to understand or directly experience due to their size, time scale, or complexity, and recognize the limitations of analogies and models.

B.4.3 Describe the consequences of introducing non-native species into an ecosystem and identify the impact it may have on that ecosystem.

5.1 How Populations Grow

NoS.6 Use analogies and models; **B.4.3** Non-native species. Also covered: **NoS.3**, **B.4.1**, **B.4.4**.

Key Questions

How do ecologists study populations?

What factors affect population growth?

What happens during exponential growth?

What is logistic growth?

Vocabulary

population density • age structure • immigration • emigration • exponential growth • logistic growth • carrying capacity

Taking Notes

Concept Map As you read, use the highlighted vocabulary words to create a concept map that organizes the information in this lesson.

THINK ABOUT IT In the 1950s, a fish farmer in Florida tossed a few plants called hydrilla into a canal. Hydrilla was imported from Asia for use in home aquariums because it is hardy and adaptable. The fish farmer assumed that hydrilla was harmless. But the few plants he tossed away reproduced quickly . . . and kept on reproducing. Today, their offspring strangle waterways across Florida and many other states. Tangled stems snag boats in rivers and overtake habitats; native water plants and animals are disappearing. Why did these plants get so out of control? Is there any way to get rid of them?

Meanwhile, people in New England who fish for a living face a different problem. Despite hard work and new equipment, their catch has dropped dramatically. The cod catch in one recent year was 3048 metric tons. Back in 1982, it was 57,200 metric tons—almost 19 times higher! Where did all the fish go? Can anything be done to increase their numbers?

Describing Populations

How do ecologists study populations?

At first glance, the stories of hydrilla and cod may seem unrelated. One is about plants growing out of control, and the other is about fish disappearing. Yet both involve dramatic changes in the size of a population. Recall that a population is a group of organisms of a single species that lives in a given area. **Researchers study populations' geographic range, density and distribution, growth rate, and age structure.**

FIGURE 5–1 Invasive Hydrilla Hydrilla has spread through most of Florida in just a few decades. Efforts to control the waterweed cost millions of dollars a year.

UbD Teach for Understanding

ENDURING UNDERSTANDING The existence of life on Earth depends on interactions among organisms and between organisms and their environment.

GUIDING QUESTION How do populations grow?

EVIDENCE OF UNDERSTANDING *After completing the lesson, give students the following assessment to show their understanding of exponential growth in populations.* Have students work in pairs to model exponential growth in a population of bacteria. First, tell students to draw a single small circle, representing a single bacterium, on a piece of paper. Under the single circle, have them draw two circles, representing the second generation of the population (after the original bacterium divides). Then, have them draw circles to represent the next four generations of bacteria. Finally, have them write a paragraph that explains how this model shows exponential population growth.

Geographic Range The area inhabited by a population is called its geographic range. A population's range can vary enormously in size, depending on the species. A bacterial population in a rotting pumpkin, for example, may have a range smaller than a cubic meter. The population of cod in the western Atlantic, on the other hand, covers a range that stretches from Greenland down to North Carolina. The natural range of one hydrilla population includes parts of southern India and Sri Lanka. The native range of another hydrilla population was in Korea. But humans have carried hydrilla to so many places that its range now includes every continent except Antarctica, and it is found in many places in the United States.

Density and Distribution **Population density** refers to the number of individuals per unit area. Populations of different species often have very different densities, even in the same environment. For example, a population of ducks in a pond may have a low density, while fish in the same pond community may have a higher density. *Distribution* refers to how individuals in a population are spaced out across the range of the population—randomly, uniformly, or mostly concentrated in clumps, as shown in **Figure 5–2.**

Growth Rate A population's growth rate determines whether the size of the population increases, decreases, or stays the same. Hydrilla populations in their native habitats tend to stay more or less the same size over time. These populations have a growth rate of around zero. In other words, they neither increase nor decrease in size. The hydrilla population in Florida, by contrast, has a high growth rate—which means that it increases in size. Populations can also decrease in size, as cod populations have been doing. The cod population has a negative growth rate.

Age Structure To fully understand a plant or animal population, researchers need to know more than just the number of individuals it contains. They also need to know the population's **age structure**—the number of males and females of each age a population contains. Why? Because most plants and animals cannot reproduce until they reach a certain age. Also, among animals, only females can produce offspring.

A. Random

B. Uniform

C. Clumped

FIGURE 5–2 Patterns of Distribution The dots in the inset illustrations represent individual members of a population. **A.** Purple lupines grow randomly in a field of wildflowers. **B.** King penguin populations show uniform spacing between individuals. **C.** Striped catfish form tight clumps.

How Science Works

GEOGRAPHIC RANGE AND CLIMATE CHANGE

Climate is one of the factors that determine the range of a species. A species' range can change, therefore, as a result of climate change. Predicting the effects of climate change on species' ranges is an active area of ecological research. Some ecologists use computer modeling as a tool for this research; a variety of computer modeling systems have been developed for this use. Although current modeling systems have some limitations, scientists can still use these results to assess the vulnerability of species to extinction due to climate change.

Teach

Lead a Discussion

Have students read the descriptions of the four characteristics of populations on this page.

Ask What would happen to a population's density if the population size stayed the same while its geographic range decreased? *(Its density would increase.)*

Ask Which characteristic most directly determines if a population increases or decreases in size over time? *(growth rate)*

DIFFERENTIATED INSTRUCTION

L1 Struggling Students Have students draw a vertical line and a horizontal line on a piece of paper to divide the paper into four equal-sized boxes. Point out the four paragraphs on this page describing characteristics of populations. Have students read each paragraph and then write a short summary and make a drawing that represents each characteristic in a different box.

LPR Less Proficient Readers Have students work in groups of four to complete a modified version of the activity described above. Within each group, assign each student to read and summarize one paragraph. Then, have students discuss their assigned paragraphs with the group. Individual students should then make a drawing to represent each characteristic.

ELL Focus on ELL: Extend Language

BEGINNING AND INTERMEDIATE SPEAKERS Use a **Vocabulary Word Map** to help students organize information about populations. Provide each student with a blank Vocabulary Word Map, and draw a large one on the board. Write the word *populations* in the top box. Have students copy the word into their own map and practice pronouncing it aloud. Then, have them use the information on this page to fill in the four attribute boxes. Beginning speakers can use single words or short phrases to fill in the attribute boxes. Encourage intermediate speakers to use longer phrases or sentences. Have students share their responses orally, and use their responses to fill in the map on the board.

Study Wkbks A/B, Appendix S32, Vocabulary Word Map. **Transparencies,** GO17.

Teach continued

Use Visuals

Use **Figure 5–3** to help students visualize the factors that affect population growth.

Ask What two factors add individuals to the fish population? *(births and immigration)*

Ask What two factors remove individuals from the fish population? *(deaths and emigration)*

Ask If the fish population stays the same size for a one-year period, what can you assume about the number of individuals removed from the population due to death and emigration during that time? *(That number is equal to the number of individuals added to the population by birth or immigration.)*

DIFFERENTIATED INSTRUCTION

ELL English Language Learners Write the term *immigration* on the board. Explain that the word *immigration* is formed using the prefix *im-* meaning "in." The root word *migrate* is based on the Latin word *migrare,* meaning "to move from one location to another." Then, write the word *emigration* on the board. Tell students the word part *e-* means "out." Ask them to relate this to the meaning of the term *emigration*.

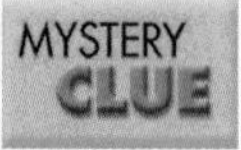

Students should recognize that the rabbit population in Australia exhibited exponential growth. Have pairs of students discuss why the exponential growth of the rabbit population was problematic. Students can go online to **Biology.com** to gather their evidence.

Answers

FIGURE 5–3 Sample answer: I would include an additional arrow to show fish being removed from the population due to fishing.

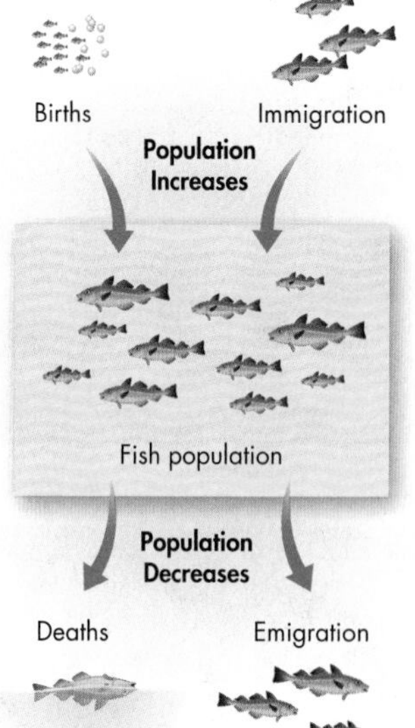

FIGURE 5–3 Natural Factors That Affect the Growth of a Fish Population The numbers of fish that hatch, die, enter, or leave the population affect the growth of the population. Use Models ***How would you expand this model to include the effects of fishing?***

MYSTERY CLUE

What kind of growth does the rabbit population in Australia exhibit? Why does that present a problem?

Population Growth

What factors affect population growth?

What determines whether a population grows, shrinks, or stays the same size? A population will increase or decrease in size depending on how many individuals are added to it or removed from it, as shown in **Figure 5–3. The factors that can affect population size are the birthrate, death rate, and the rate at which individuals enter or leave the population.**

Birthrate and Death Rate Populations can grow if more individuals are born than die in any period of time. In other words, a population can grow when its birthrate is higher than its death rate. If the birthrate equals the death rate, the population may stay the same size. If the death rate is greater than the birthrate, the population is likely to shrink. Note that *birth* means different things in different species. Lions are born much like humans are born. Codfish, however, release eggs that hatch into new individuals.

Immigration and Emigration A population may grow if individuals move into its range from elsewhere, a process called **immigration** (im uh GRAY shun). Suppose, for example, that an oak grove in a forest produces a bumper crop of acorns one year. The squirrel population in that grove may increase as squirrels immigrate in search of food. On the other hand, a population may decrease in size if individuals move out of the population's range, a process called **emigration** (em uh GRAY shun). For example, a local food shortage or overcrowding can cause emigration. Young animals approaching maturity may emigrate from the area where they were born to find mates or establish new territories.

Exponential Growth

What happens during exponential growth?

If you provide a population with all the food and space it needs, protect it from predators and disease, and remove its waste products, the population will grow. Why? The population will increase because members of the population will be able to produce offspring. After a time, those offspring will produce their own offspring. Then, the offspring of *those* offspring will produce offspring. So, over time, the population will grow.

But notice that something interesting will happen: The size of each generation of offspring will be larger than the generation before it. This situation is called exponential (eks poh NEN shul) growth. In **exponential growth,** the larger a population gets, the faster it grows. **Under ideal conditions with unlimited resources, a population will grow exponentially.** Let's examine why this happens under different situations.

UbD Check for Understanding

DEPTH OF UNDERSTANDING

Ask If a population's birthrate is greater than the death rate, what can be determined about the overall change in population size? *(A student with a superficial understanding of the factors that affect population size will automatically assume that the population is growing without taking into consideration the impact of immigration and emigration on population size. A student with a sophisticated understanding would suggest that the overall change in population size cannot be determined without information about immigration and emigration rates.)*

ADJUST INSTRUCTION

If students demonstrate a superficial understanding of the question, use a jar of marbles as a model of a population. Model births and immigration by adding marbles; model deaths and emigration by removing marbles.

Organisms That Reproduce Rapidly We begin a hypothetical experiment with a single bacterium that divides to produce two cells every 20 minutes. We supply it with ideal conditions—and watch. After 20 minutes, the bacterium divides to produce two bacteria. After another 20 minutes, those two bacteria divide to produce four cells. At the end of the first hour, those four bacteria divide to produce eight cells.

Do you see what is happening here? After three 20-minute periods, we have 2 × 2 × 2, or 8 cells. Another way to say this is to use an exponent: 2^3 cells. In another hour (six 20-minute periods), there will be 2^6, or 64 bacteria. In just one more hour, there will be 2^9, or 512. In one day, this bacterial population will grow to an astounding 4,720,000,000,000,000,000,000 individuals. What would happen if this growth continued without slowing down? In a few days, this bacterial population would cover the planet!

If you plot the size of this population on a graph over time, you get a J-shaped curve that rises slowly at first, and then rises faster and faster, as shown in **Figure 5–4.** If nothing interfered with this kind of growth, the population would become larger and larger, faster and faster, until it approached an infinitely large size.

Organisms That Reproduce Slowly Of course, many organisms grow and reproduce much more slowly than bacteria. For example, a female elephant can produce a single offspring only every 2 to 4 years. Newborn elephants take about 10 years to mature. But as you can see in **Figure 5–4,** if exponential growth continued, the result would be impossible. In the unlikely event that all descendants of a single elephant pair survived and reproduced, after 750 years there would be nearly 20 million elephants!

Organisms in New Environments Sometimes, when an organism is moved to a new environment, its population grows exponentially for a time. That's happening with hydrilla in the United States. It also happened when a few European gypsy moths were accidentally released from a laboratory near Boston. Within a few years, these plant-eating pests had spread across the northeastern United States. In peak years, they devoured the leaves of thousands of acres of forest. In some places, they formed a living blanket that covered the ground, sidewalks, and cars.

In Your Notebook *Draw a growth curve for a population of waterweed growing exponentially.*

BUILD Vocabulary

RELATED WORD FORMS An exponent indicates the number of times a number is multiplied by itself. The adjective *exponential* describes something that is expressed using exponents—such as the rate of growth.

Models of Exponential Growth

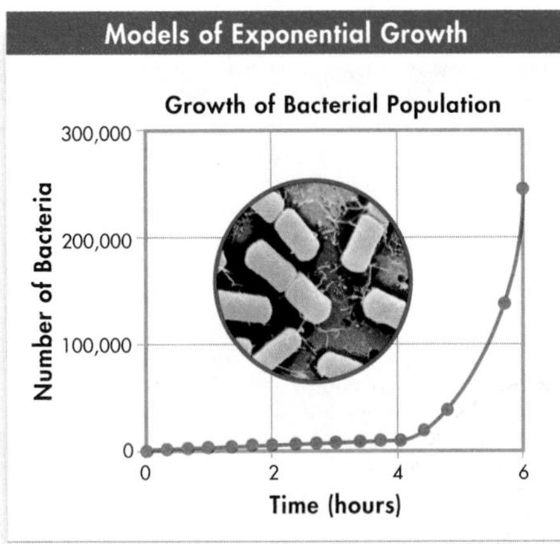

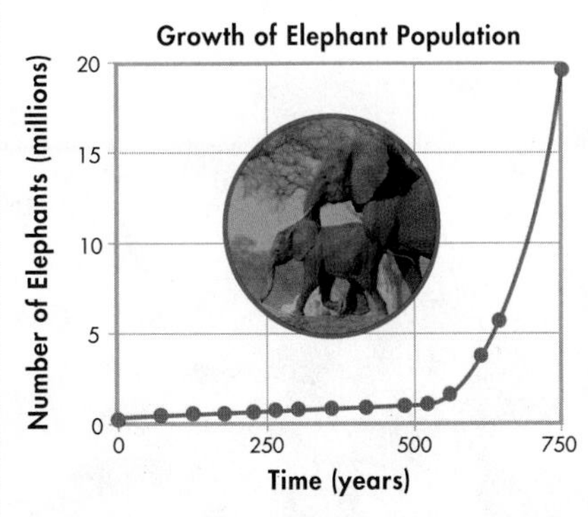

FIGURE 5–4 Exponential Growth In the presence of unlimited resources and in the absence of predation and disease, populations will grow exponentially. Bacteria, which reproduce rapidly, can produce huge populations in a matter of days. It would take elephants, which reproduce slowly, a few hundred years. Both hypothetical graphs show the characteristic J-shape of exponential growth.

BIOLOGY.com Search Lesson 5.1 GO • Data Analysis

Connect to Math

Have students examine the graphs in **Figure 5–4.**

Ask How does the shape of the line representing the growth of the bacterial population compare to the shape of the line representing the growth of the elephant population? *(They are very similar.)*

Ask How do the graphs differ? *(Sample answers: The x-axis of the bacteria graph is marked in 2-hour increments; the x-axis of the elephant graph is marked in 250-year increments. The y-axis of the graph representing the bacterial population is marked in increments of 100,000; the y-axis of the graph representing the elephant population is marked in increments of 5 million.)*

Ask Why are different time increments used in the two graphs? *(Elephants reproduce at a much slower rate than bacteria.)*

DIFFERENTIATED INSTRUCTION

L3 Advanced Students Have students write a paragraph explaining why, in natural settings, exponential growth does not continue indefinitely for any species. Have students share their paragraphs with the class.

Quick Facts

BIOTIC POTENTIAL

The graphs on this page represent how a population would grow in the presence of unlimited resources and the absence of predation and disease. The size a population would reach in these conditions, when all offspring survive and produce young, is called the *biotic potential* of a species. In order for this to happen, there must not be any factors present that limit population growth. In nature, no population ever reaches its biotic potential. The factors that prevent this unlimited growth, called limiting factors, are the focus of Lesson 5.2.

Answers

IN YOUR NOTEBOOK Students should use a J-shaped curve to show the exponential growth of the waterweed population.

Teach continued

VISUAL SUMMARY

Have students examine the graph in **Figure 5–5.**

Ask During which phase does the population grow most rapidly? *(Phase I)*

Ask During which phase does the population size stabilize? *(Phase III)*

Ask What is the carrying capacity of a population? *(the maximum number of individuals of a particular species a particular environment can support)*

DIFFERENTIATED INSTRUCTION

L1 Special Needs Have students examine the graph in **Figure 5–5.** Explain that the shape of the line represents the rate at which the population grows. Tell students a line with a steep, positive slope represents a population growing rapidly. A flat line represents a population that stays a steady size. Have students point to the part of the graph that shows a rapidly growing population. Then, ask them to point to a part of the graph representing a population that stays a steady size.

Address Misconceptions

Population Growth Models Several common misconceptions about population growth are revealed when students are asked to graph population growth. Two common errors in students' graphs are: (1) the omission of Phase II, in which growth slows—students show rapid growth followed by abrupt change to no growth; and (2) the placement of the initial point representing the starting population at the origin, or (0, 0), thus implying the impossible—a population growing from zero. Use the graph in **Figure 5–5** to help address these common misconceptions. Point out Phase II in the graph, and explain that this phase represents a population that is still growing, but more slowly than during Phase I. Also point out the initial point on the graph, and have students note that it is not at the origin. Remind them that all populations must start with at least one individual (in the case of asexually reproducing organisms) or one pair of organisms.

BIOLOGY.com Help students understand exponential growth and logistic growth with **Data Analysis: Invasion of Zebra Mussels.**

Logistic Growth

What is logistic growth?

This ability of populations to grow exponentially presents a puzzle. Obviously, bacteria, elephants, hydrilla, and gypsy moths don't cover the Earth. This means that natural populations don't grow exponentially for long. Sooner or later, something—or several "somethings"—stops exponential growth. What happens?

Phases of Growth One way to begin answering this question is to watch how populations behave in nature. Suppose that a few individuals are introduced into a real-world environment. **Figure 5–5** traces the phases of growth that the population goes through.

▶ ***Phase 1: Exponential Growth*** After a short time, the population begins to grow exponentially. During this phase, resources are unlimited, so individuals grow and reproduce rapidly. Few individuals die, and many offspring are produced, so both the population size and the rate of growth increase more and more rapidly.

▶ ***Phase 2: Growth Slows Down.*** In real-world populations, exponential growth does not continue for long. At some point, the rate of population growth begins to slow down. This does not mean that the population size decreases. The population still grows, but the rate of growth slows down, so the population size increases more slowly.

▶ ***Phase 3: Growth Stops.*** At some point, the rate of population growth drops to zero. This means that the size of the population levels off. Under some conditions, the population will remain at or near this size indefinitely.

VISUAL SUMMARY

LOGISTIC GROWTH

FIGURE 5–5 Real-world populations, such as those of the rhinoceros, show the characteristic S-shaped curve of logistic growth. As resources become limited, population growth slows or stops, leveling off at the carrying capacity.

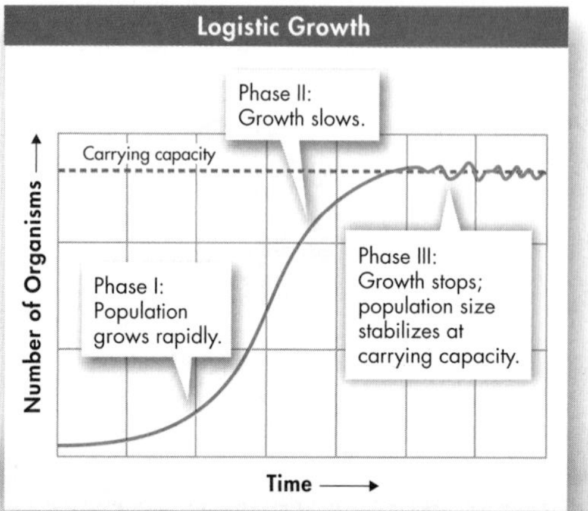

Logistic Growth

Carrying capacity

Phase I: Population grows rapidly.

Phase II: Growth slows.

Phase III: Growth stops; population size stabilizes at carrying capacity.

Number of Organisms →

Time →

Check for Understanding

ONE-MINUTE RESPONSE

Write the following prompt on the board, and give students about a minute to write a quick response summarizing their understanding.

- How are exponential growth and logistic growth related? *(Responses should mention the first phase of logistic growth is exponential growth.)*

ADJUST INSTRUCTION

If responses are incorrect or incomplete, have students examine **Figure 5–5.** Ask them to locate the part of the graph where exponential growth occurs. Lead them to the understanding that exponential growth is one stage of logistic growth.

The Logistic Growth Curve The curve in **Figure 5–5** has an S-shape that represents what is called **logistic growth.** **Logistic growth occurs when a population's growth slows and then stops, following a period of exponential growth.** Many familiar plant and animal populations follow a logistic growth curve.

What kinds of changes in a population's characteristics can produce logistic growth? Remember that a population grows when more organisms are born (or added to it) than die (or leave it). Thus, population growth may slow for several reasons. Growth may slow because the population's birthrate decreases. Growth may also slow if the death rate increases—or if births fall and deaths rise together. Similarly, population growth may slow if the rate of immigration decreases, the rate of emigration increases, or both. There are several reasons why these rates might change in a population, as you will see in the next lesson.

Carrying Capacity When the birthrate and the death rate are the same, and when immigration equals emigration, population growth stops. The population may still rise and fall somewhat, but the ups and downs average out around a certain population size. If you look again at **Figure 5–5,** you will see a broken, horizontal line through the region of the graph where population growth levels off. The point at which that line intersects the y-axis represents what ecologists call the carrying capacity. **Carrying capacity** is the maximum number of individuals of a particular species that a particular environment can support. Once a population reaches the carrying capacity of its environment, a variety of factors act to stabilize it at that size.

Multiplying Rabbits

Suppose that a pair of rabbits produces six offspring: three males and three females. Assume that no offspring die.

1. **Calculate** If each pair of rabbits breeds only once, how many offspring would be produced each year for five generations? MATH
2. **Interpret Graphs** Construct a graph of your data. Plot time on the x-axis and population on the y-axis. What type of growth is the rabbit population going through after 5 years?

IN NoS.3

5.1 Assessment

IN NoS.6, B.4.1

Review Key Concepts

1. a. **Review** List four characteristics that are used to describe a population.
   b. **Infer** On your travels through eastern Canada and the United States, you notice gray squirrels everywhere. What can you infer about the squirrels' geographic range?
2. a. **Review** What natural factors can change a population's size?
   b. **Relate Cause and Effect** More dandelion seedlings develop in a lawn than dandelion plants are removed. What is likely to happen to the lawn's dandelion population?
3. a. **Review** When do populations grow exponentially?
   b. **Apply Concepts** Why does exponential growth show a characteristic J-shaped curve?
4. a. **Review** What is the characteristic shape of a logistic growth curve?
   b. **Explain** Describe when logistic growth occurs.
   c. **Form a Hypothesis** What factors might cause the carrying capacity of a population to change?

PRACTICE PROBLEM

5. Suppose you are studying a population of sunflowers growing in a small field. How would you determine the population density of sunflowers in a square meter of the field and in the entire field? Describe your procedure.

BIOLOGY.com Search Lesson 5.1 GO • Self-Test • Lesson Assessment

Analyzing Data

PURPOSE Students will make a graph to model rabbit population growth.

MATERIALS graph paper

ANSWERS

1. Generation I: 1 pair of rabbits = 6 offspring
   Generation II: 3 pairs of rabbits = 18 offspring
   Generation III: 9 pairs of rabbits = 54 offspring
   Generation IV: 27 pairs of rabbits = 162 offspring
   Generation V: 81 pairs of rabbits = 486 offspring
2. Students' graphs should resemble the graphs showing exponential growth found in the lesson. They should identify that the rabbit population is undergoing exponential growth.

Assess and Remediate

EVALUATE UNDERSTANDING

Have each student write a sentence showing the relationship between two lesson vocabulary terms. Then, have them complete the 5.1 Assessment.

REMEDIATION SUGGESTION

L1 **Struggling Students** If your students struggle with **Question 2a,** help them make a graphic organizer of the factors that impact population growth.

BIOLOGY.com Students can check their understanding of lesson concepts with the **Self-Test** assessment. They can then take an online version of the **Lesson Assessment.**

Assessment Answers

1a. geographic range, density and distribution, growth rate, age structure

1b. Sample answer: Gray squirrels have a very large geographic range.

2a. births, immigration, deaths, emigration

2b. The dandelion population will probably grow. Eventually, dandelions might take over the lawn.

3a. A population grows exponentially when it has all of the resources it needs and disease and predation do not occur.

3b. because with each generation, the number of organisms producing offspring increases, resulting in a rapid increase in population size

4a. A logistic growth curve has an S-shape.

4b. when a population's growth slows following a period of exponential growth and then stops at or near the carrying capacity

4c. Sample answer: Events that destroy a part of an environment, such as a forest fire, would change the carrying capacity of the environment.

PRACTICE PROBLEM

5. Sample answer: First, I would use rope and stakes to set a 1-m^2 plot of field (one meter on each side). I would count the number of sunflowers in the plot. To determine the population density of sunflowers in the entire field, I would estimate the size of the field (in square meters) and multiply that number by the number of sunflowers in 1-m^2.

Teach

Lead a Discussion

Have students read the information about zebra and quagga mussels, then apply what they have learned about populations to this issue. Explain that ships carry water in ballast tanks to maintain buoyancy and stability. The waters are loaded and discharged as the ships travel from port to port. Help students understand how zebra and quagga mussels can be picked up in ballast water by explaining that mussel larvae are tiny and free-swimming. Distinguish this from the adult stage of the mussels' life cycle, in which the mussel typically remains affixed to a hard surface.

Ask Why does the population growth of zebra and quagga mussels in Great Lakes ecosystems differ from the population growth of these mussels in their native ecosystems? *(Sample answer: Factors that limited their growth in their native habitat do not exist in their new habitat.)*

Ask How has the geographic range of zebra mussels changed between the mid-1980s and now? *(It has increased greatly.)*

Answers

RESEARCH AND DECIDE

1. Answers may vary. Students should conclude that the zebra mussel populations are showing exponential growth, and should back up their conclusions with relevant facts from their research.
2. Answers may vary. Students should conclude that the best control is the prevention of further proliferation. According to the USGS, no biological control methods to date have worked, and the release of predators to eat the mussels would be ineffective. To prevent further proliferation of the mussels, people should clean off boats and boat trailers, avoid dumping bait into rivers and lakes (there could be mussel larvae in bait buckets), and decontaminate SCUBA diving gear.

IN INDIANA ACADEMIC STANDARDS

For the full text of all standards, see the Course Overview in the front matter of this book.

Biology & Society

IN B.4.3 Non-native species.

What Can Be Done About Invasive Mussels?

It's hard to imagine that shellfish could cause millions of dollars worth of trouble every year. Meet the zebra mussel and the quagga mussel. Both species were carried to the Great Lakes in the mid-1980s from Eastern Europe in ships' ballast waters (water carried inside boats for balance). As adults, these mussels attach to almost any hard surface, including water pipes and boat hulls. After just a few years, both species colonized the entire Great Lakes region. Since then, they have been spread by recreational boaters who unknowingly carry mussels attached to their boats. By 2008, zebra mussels had been reported in 24 states; quagga mussels are already known in 14 states.

Why have these mussels become such pests? In American waterways, they escape whatever environmental factors keep their numbers in check in their native European habitats. As a result, these introduced species have become invasive species whose exponential growth produces huge populations at high densities—over 10,000 mussels per square meter of water in some places! These mussels grow in layers up to 20 centimeters thick, clogging water pipes that supply power plants and water treatment facilities. They also upset aquatic food webs, filtering so much plankton from the water that some native fishes and shellfish starve. What can be done to control such invasive species?

The Viewpoints

Invasive Species Should Be Destroyed A number of groups contend that zebra mussels should be removed completely. Some engineers are developing robotic submarines that can remove mussels from pipes. Some chemists are testing chemicals for the potential to destroy or disrupt the life cycle of zebra mussels. Other scientists are adding chemicals to paints and plastics to prevent mussels from attaching to new surfaces.

Zebra mussels clog water intake pipes.

Invasive Species Management Should Focus on Control and Prevention Others argue that efforts to physically remove or chemically poison invasive mussels offer only temporary control. The population bounces right back. These removal efforts are also incredibly expensive. In the Great Lakes alone, more than $200 million is spent each year in efforts to get rid of zebra and quagga mussels.

Therefore, many scientists believe that there is no way to remove these mussels and other established invasive species. Instead, these scientists attempt to control the growth of populations and prevent transfer of invasive species to new areas. One regulation, for example, could require boaters to filter and chemically clean all ballast water. Meanwhile, the search continues for some kind of control that naturally limits mussel numbers when they rise.

Research and Decide

1. **Analyze the Viewpoints** Research the current status of invasive mussel populations and the approaches being used to prevent the spread of these and other invasive aquatic species. What trends are zebra mussel populations showing?
2. **Form an Opinion** What kinds of natural population controls do you think would manage these invasive mussels most effectively? Why?

Biology In-Depth

HUMAN IMPACT ON GEOGRAPHIC RANGE OF SPECIES

The explosive population growth of invasive species, such as zebra mussels, is an illustration of the impact of humans on the population growth of other species. In the case of invasive species, human action increases the geographic range of a species, sometimes resulting in a huge increase in population size. Other human actions, such as habitat destruction due to development, can have the opposite effect. By decreasing the geographic range of a species, humans can cause the population size of the species to decrease, reflecting a decrease in carrying capacity.

5.2 Limits to Growth

IN B.4.1 Limiting factors; B.4.3 Non-native species; B.4.4 Stability of an ecosystem. Also covered: B.4.2.

THINK ABOUT IT Now that you've seen *how* populations typically grow in nature, we can explore *why* they grow as they do. If populations tend to grow exponentially, why do they often follow logistic growth? In other words, what determines the carrying capacity of an environment for a particular species? Think again about hydrilla. In its native Asia, populations of hydrilla increase in size until they reach carrying capacity, and then population growth stops. But here in the United States, hydrilla grows out of control. The same is true of gypsy moths and many other introduced plant and animal species. Why does a species that is "well-behaved" in one environment grow out of control in another?

Key Questions

What factors determine carrying capacity?

What limiting factors depend on population density?

What limiting factors do not typically depend on population density?

Vocabulary

limiting factor
density-dependent limiting factor
density-independent limiting factor

Taking Notes

Outline Make an outline using the green and blue headings in this lesson. Fill in details as you read to help you organize the information.

Limiting Factors

What factors determine carrying capacity?

Recall that the productivity of an ecosystem can be controlled by a limiting nutrient. A limiting nutrient is an example of a general ecological concept: a limiting factor. In the context of populations, a **limiting factor** is a factor that controls the growth of a population.

As shown in **Figure 5–6,** there are several kinds of limiting factors. Some—such as competition, predation, parasitism, and disease—depend on population density. Others—including natural disasters and unusual weather—do not depend on population density. **Acting separately or together, limiting factors determine the carrying capacity of an environment for a species.** Limiting factors keep most natural populations somewhere between extinction and overrunning the planet.

Charles Darwin recognized the importance of limiting factors in shaping the history of life on Earth. As you will learn in Unit 5, the limiting factors we describe here produce the pressures of natural selection that stand at the heart of evolutionary theory.

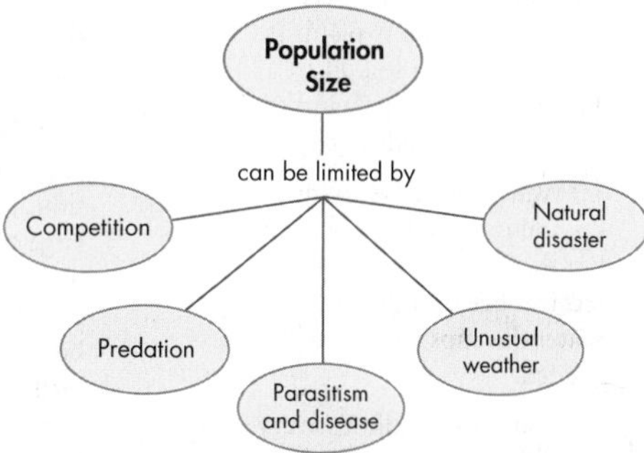

FIGURE 5–6 Limiting Factors Many different factors can limit population growth. Some of these factors depend on population density, while others do not. **Infer** ***How might each of these factors increase the death rate in a population?***

UbD Teach for Understanding

ENDURING UNDERSTANDING The existence of life on Earth depends on interactions among organisms and between organisms and their environment.

GUIDING QUESTION What factors limit a population's growth?

EVIDENCE OF UNDERSTANDING *After completing the lesson, give students the following assessment to show their understanding of the factors that limit population growth.* Have students make a **T-Chart** listing and describing limiting factors. One side of the T-chart should be labeled Density-Dependent Factors, and the other side labeled Density-Independent Factors.

Study Wkbks A/B, Appendix S30, T-Chart. **Transparencies,** GO15.

Getting Started

Objectives

5.2.1 Identify factors that determine carrying capacity.

5.2.2 Identify the limiting factors that depend on population density.

5.2.3 Identify the limiting factors that do not depend on population density.

Student Resources

Study Workbooks A and B, 5.2 Worksheets

Spanish Study Workbook, 5.2 Worksheets

Lab Manual B, 5.2 Hands-On Activity Worksheet

 Lesson Overview • Lesson Notes • Activities: Art Review, InterActive Art • Assessment: Self-Test, Lesson Assessment

 For corresponding lesson in the **Foundation Edition**, see pages 112–116.

 Check understanding of limiting factors with **Art Review: Limiting Factors.**

Answers

FIGURE 5–6 Competition: organisms may not have enough resources to survive; Predation: organisms die when they are eaten; Parasitism and disease: organisms are killed; Natural disaster and unusual weather: organisms are killed or resources are diminished.

IN INDIANA ACADEMIC STANDARDS

For the full text of all standards, see the Course Overview in the front matter of this book.

B.4.1 Explain that the amount of life an environment can support is limited by the available energy, water, oxygen, and minerals, and by the ability of ecosystems to recycle the remains of dead organisms.

B.4.3 Describe the consequences of introducing non-native species into an ecosystem and identify the impact it may have on that ecosystem.

B.4.4 Describe how climate, the pattern of matter and energy flow, the birth and death of new organisms, and the interaction between those organisms contribute to the long term stability of an ecosystem.

LESSON 5.2

Teach

Lead a Discussion

Have students recall from the previous lesson the four factors that affect population growth. *(birthrate, immigration, death rate, emigration)*

Ask How can competition affect the birthrate of a population? *(If competition results in individuals not obtaining enough resources to reproduce, the birthrate of the population may decrease.)*

Ask How can competition affect the death rate of a population? *(If individuals cannot obtain enough resources to survive, the death rate may increase.)*

Ask How can competition affect the rates of immigration and emigration? *(If there is not much competition for the resources in an ecosystem, individuals from other ecosystems may move in, increasing immigration rate. If competition for resources is severe, the rate of emigration may increase as individuals seek other ecosystems in which to live.)*

DIFFERENTIATED INSTRUCTION

L1 Special Needs Help students summarize ways in which competition can affect birthrate, immigration, death rate, and emigration in simple sentences, for example, "Competition can reduce birthrate." Write each sentence on the board. Then, ask students to discuss details related to the main idea summarized in each of the sentences.

FIGURE 5–7 Competition Male wolves may fight one another for territory or access to mates.

Density-Dependent Limiting Factors

What limiting factors depend on population density?

Density-dependent limiting factors operate strongly only when population density—the number of organisms per unit area—reaches a certain level. These factors do not affect small, scattered populations as much. **Density-dependent limiting factors include competition, predation, herbivory, parasitism, disease, and stress from overcrowding.**

Competition When populations become crowded, individuals compete for food, water, space, sunlight, and other essentials. Some individuals obtain enough to survive and reproduce. Others may obtain just enough to live but not enough to enable them to raise offspring. Still others may starve to death or die from lack of shelter. Thus, competition can lower birthrates, increase death rates, or both.

Competition is a density-dependent limiting factor, because the more individuals living in an area, the sooner they use up the available resources. Often, space and food are related to one another. Many grazing animals compete for territories in which to breed and raise offspring. Individuals that do not succeed in establishing a territory find no mates and cannot breed.

Competition can also occur among members of different species that are attempting to use similar or overlapping resources. This type of competition is a major force behind evolutionary change.

Predation and Herbivory The effects of predators on prey and the effects of herbivores on plants are two very important density-dependent population controls. One classic study focuses on the relationship between wolves, moose, and plants on Isle Royale, an island in Lake Superior. The graph in **Figure 5–8** shows that populations of wolves and moose have fluctuated over the years. What drives these changes in population size?

▶ ***Predator-Prey Relationships*** In a predator-prey relationship, populations of predators and prey may cycle up and down over time. Sometimes, the moose population on Isle Royale grows large enough that moose become easy prey for wolves. When wolves have plenty to eat, their population grows. As the wolf population grows, the wolves begin to kill more moose than are born. This causes the moose death rate to rise higher than its birthrate, so the moose population falls. As the moose population drops, wolves begin to starve. Starvation raises the wolves' death rate and lowers their birthrate, so the wolf population also falls. When only a few predators are left, the moose death rate drops, and the cycle repeats.

In Your Notebook *Describe conditions that lead to competition in a population.*

Quick Lab GUIDED INQUIRY

How Does Competition Affect Growth?

1. Label two paper cups 3 and 15. Make several small holes in the bottom of each cup. Fill each cup two-thirds full with potting soil. Plant 3 bean seeds in cup 3, and plant 15 bean seeds in cup 15.
2. Water both cups so that the soil is moist but not wet. Put them in a location that receives bright indirect light. Water the cups equally as needed.
3. Count the seedlings every other day for two weeks.

Analyze and Conclude

1. **Observe** What differences did you observe between the two cups?

IN B.4.4

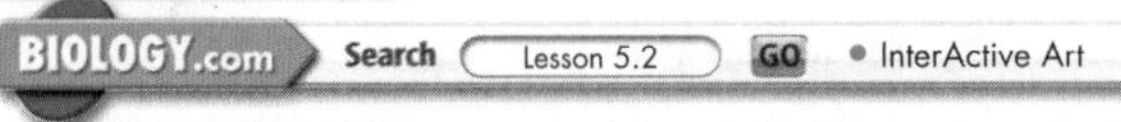

PURPOSE Students will be able to determine that competition affects plant growth.

MATERIALS bean seeds, 2 paper cups, potting soil, waterproof marker

SAFETY Students should wash their hands after planting the seeds.

PLANNING You may want to provide a tray or other waterproof surface on which students can place their cups. Remind them to control variables such as the amount of water and amount of sunlight the cups of seeds receive.

ANALYZE AND CONCLUDE

1. The seedlings in cup 15 will be smaller and less robust than those in cup 3. Some seedlings in cup 15 may die.

Answers

IN YOUR NOTEBOOK When populations become crowded, individuals compete for resources.

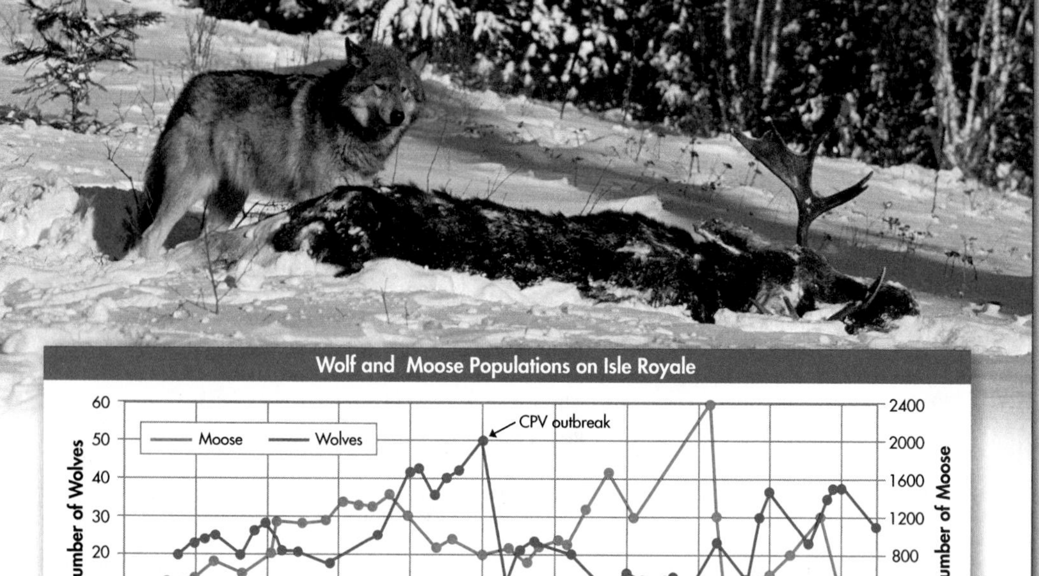

FIGURE 5–8 Moose-Wolf Populations on Isle Royale The relationship between moose and wolves on Isle Royale illustrates how predation can affect population growth. In this case, the moose population was also affected by changes in food supply, and the wolf population was also impacted by a canine parvovirus (CPV) outbreak.

▶ ***Herbivore Effects*** Herbivory can also contribute to changes in population numbers. From a plant's perspective, herbivores are predators. So it isn't surprising that populations of herbivores and plants cycle up and down, just like populations of predators and prey. On parts of Isle Royale, large, dense moose populations can eat so much balsam fir that the population of these favorite food plants drops. When this happens, the moose may suffer from lack of food.

▶ ***Humans as Predators*** In some situations, human activity limits populations. For example, humans are major predators of codfish in New England. Fishing fleets, by catching more and more fish every year, have raised cod death rates so high that birthrates cannot keep up. As a result, the cod population has been dropping. Is there any way to solve the problem? Think of predator-prey interactions. The cod population can recover if we scale back fishing to lower the death rate sufficiently. Biologists are studying birthrates and the age structure of the cod population to determine how many fish can be taken without threatening the survival of the population.

BUILD Vocabulary

ACADEMIC WORDS The verb **fluctuate** means to "rise and fall as if in waves." A population that fluctuates is unstable: Its numbers go up and down irregularly.

How Science Works

RESEARCH ON ISLE ROYALE

Isle Royale, an island in Lake Superior, is a National Park that has been the site of research on the interactions of wolf and moose populations for more than 50 years. It is considered an ideal site for research in the field of population biology because of its isolation. Wolves first moved into the Isle Royale ecosystem in the 1940s via an ice bridge. In the late 1950s, scientists began studying the interactions of the populations of moose and wolves; the study continues today. The long-term nature of the study has allowed scientists to learn not only about direct effects of predator-prey interactions on populations, but also to examine the impact of other factors affecting populations, such as changing pollution levels and environmental legislation.

Use Visuals

Have students examine **Figure 5–8** to help them understand the effects of predator-prey relationships on population size.

Ask What general trends are shown in this graph? *(An increase in the wolf population is usually accompanied by a decrease in the moose population. A decrease in the wolf population is usually accompanied by an increase in the moose population.)*

Ask What factors other than the predator-prey relationship affected the size of these populations during the time period represented in the graph? *(disease, the moose's changing food supply)*

DIFFERENTIATED INSTRUCTION

L1 Struggling Students Make sure students understand that two separate sets of data are plotted on the graph. Point out the left and right vertical axes, which are numbered in different increments. Explain that the left vertical axis and the blue line represent the wolf population; the right vertical axis and the red line represent the moose population.

L3 Advanced Students Have students work in a group to discuss trends they might expect to have occurred in the balsam fir population on Isle Royale over the time period represented in the graph. Ask them to share a brief summary of their discussion with the class.

ELL Focus on ELL: Build Background

ALL SPEAKERS Have students use the **Think-Pair-Share** strategy to help them more fully comprehend density-dependent limiting factors. Pair beginning and intermediate speakers with advanced or advanced high speakers. Have students read the information about density-dependent limiting factors one factor at a time. After they read, suggest they discuss the factor and try to identify an example of it that they may have either seen or read about in the past. For example, for herbivory, some students may have seen an insect eating a plant leaf. Have pairs write down their examples and then share them with the class.

Study Wkbks A/B, Appendix S14, Think-Pair-Share.

BIOLOGY.com Have students explore how predation can affect population growth in **InterActive Art: Moose-Wolf Populations on Isle Royale.**

LESSON 5.2

Teach continued

Build Study Skills

Have students use a **Venn Diagram** to compare and contrast limiting factors. They should use one side to record facts about density-dependent limiting factors and the other side to record facts about density-independent limiting factors. Have them record information applying to both density-dependent and density-independent factors in the middle section.

Study Wkbks A/B, Appendix S33, Venn Diagram. **Transparencies,** GO18.

DIFFERENTIATED INSTRUCTION

L1 Struggling Students Have students make a drawing of a population being affected by a limiting factor. Tell them to make their drawing both creative and scientifically accurate. Instruct students to write a caption for their drawing. Captions should be at least two sentences long and identify the limiting factor depicted in the drawing. It should also categorize the limiting factor as either density-dependent or density-independent, and describe how the limiting factor affects the population shown.

ELL English Language Learners Write the terms *density-independent* and *density-dependent* on the board. Have students locate the definitions of these terms in the text. Then, ask students to write or state a definition for each term in their own words.

Students should identify limiting factors, such as competition, predation, parasitism and disease, overcrowding, severe weather, and natural disasters. Students can go online to Biology.com to gather their evidence.

FIGURE 5–9 Parasitism The ticks feeding on the blood of this hedgehog can transmit bacteria that cause disease.

Parasitism and Disease Parasites and disease-causing organisms feed at the expense of their hosts, weakening them and often causing disease or death. The ticks on the hedgehog in **Figure 5–9,** for example, can carry diseases. Parasitism and disease are density-dependent effects because the denser the host population, the more easily parasites can spread from one host to another.

If you look back at the graph in **Figure 5–8,** you can see a sudden and dramatic drop in the wolf population around 1980. At that time, a viral disease of wolves was accidentally introduced to the island. This virus killed all but 13 wolves on the island—and only three of the survivors were females. The removal of wolves caused moose populations to skyrocket to 2400. The densely packed moose then became infested with winter ticks that caused hair loss and weakness.

Stress From Overcrowding Some species fight amongst themselves if overcrowded. Too much fighting can cause high levels of stress, which can weaken the body's ability to resist disease. In some species, stress from overcrowding can cause females to neglect, kill, or even eat their own offspring. Thus, stress from overcrowding can lower birthrates, raise death rates, or both. It can also increase rates of emigration.

Density-Independent Limiting Factors

What limiting factors do not typically depend on population density?

Density-independent limiting factors affect all populations in similar ways, regardless of population size and density. **Unusual weather such as hurricanes, droughts, or floods, and natural disasters such as wildfires, can act as density-independent limiting factors.** In response to such factors, a population may "crash." After the crash, the population may build up again quickly, or it may stay low for some time.

For some species, storms can nearly extinguish local populations. For example, thrips, aphids, and other insects that feed on leaves can be washed out by a heavy rainstorm. Waves whipped up by hurricanes can devastate shallow coral reefs. Extremes of cold or hot weather also can take their toll, regardless of population density. A severe drought, for example, can kill off great numbers of fish in a river, as shown in **Figure 5–10.**

MYSTERY
CLUE
What factors do you think could limit the size of a rabbit population?

True Density Independence? Sometimes, however, the effects of so-called density-independent factors can actually vary with population density. On Isle Royale, for example, the moose population grew exponentially for a time after the wolf population crashed. Then, a bitterly cold winter with very heavy snowfall covered the plants that moose feed on, making it difficult for the moose to move around to find food.

UbD Check for Understanding

VISUAL REPRESENTATION

Ask students to create a **Concept Map** showing how limiting factors affect populations.

Study Wkbks A/B, Appendix S21, Concept Map. **Transparencies,** GO4.

ADJUST INSTRUCTION

If students' concept maps reveal they are struggling to understand limiting factors, ask them to review their concept maps in small groups. Within each group, have students review and revise their concept maps.

Because this was an island population, emigration was not possible; the moose weakened and many died. So, in this case, the effects of bad weather on the large, dense population were greater than they would have been on a small population. (In a smaller population, the moose would have had more food available because there would have been less competition.) This situation shows that it is sometimes difficult to say that a limiting factor acts *only* in a density-independent way.

Human activities can also place ecological communities under stress in ways that can hamper a population's ability to recover from natural disturbance. You will learn more about that situation in the next chapter.

Controlling Introduced Species In hydrilla's natural environment, density-dependent population limiting factors keep it under control. Perhaps plant-eating insects or fishes devour it. Or perhaps pests or diseases weaken it. Whatever the case, those limiting factors are not found in the United States. The result is runaway population growth!

Efforts at artificial density-independent control measures—such as herbicides and mechanical removal—offer only temporary solutions and are expensive. Researchers have spent decades looking for natural predators and pests of hydrilla. The best means of control so far seems to be an imported fish called grass carp, which view hydrilla as an especially tasty treat. These grass carp are not native to the United States. Only sterilized grass carp can be used to control hydrilla. Can you understand why?

FIGURE 5–10 Effects of a Severe Drought on a Population Dead fish lie rotting on the banks of the once-flowing Paraná de Manaquiri River in Brazil.

5.2 Assessment

IN B.4.1, B.4.4

Review Key Concepts 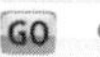

1. a. Review What is a limiting factor?
   b. Apply Concepts How do limiting factors affect the growth of populations?
2. a. Review List three density-dependent limiting factors.
   b. Relate Cause and Effect What is the relationship between competition and population size?
3. a. Review What is a density-independent limiting factor?
   b. Apply Concepts Give three examples of density-independent factors that could severely limit the growth of a population of bats living in a cave.

Apply the Big idea

Interdependence in Nature

4. Study the factors that limit population growth shown in **Figure 5–6.** Classify each factor as biotic or abiotic. (*Hint:* Refer to Lesson 3.1 for information on biotic and abiotic factors.)

BIOLOGY.com Search Lesson 5.2 GO • Self-Test • Lesson Assessment

Build Science Skills

Have students study **Figure 5–10.** Then, ask them to make inferences about the impact of the drought on a variety of populations in this ecosystem. For example, a population of water plants might become overcrowded as a result of a decrease in the water level of the river. Or, plants along the riverbank might dry out and die, limiting nesting places for some birds. Have volunteers discuss their inferences with the class.

DIFFERENTIATED INSTRUCTION

L1 Struggling Students Provide students with a few examples of how the drought pictured in **Figure 5–10** might have affected populations in the ecosystem. Then, have them work in pairs to identify additional examples.

Assess and Remediate

EVALUATE UNDERSTANDING

Name a type of ecosystem, such as forest, pond, or grassland. Have a volunteer identify one population of living things typically found in that ecosystem. Then, ask volunteers to describe as many specific limiting factors affecting the population as possible. As each limiting factor is identified, have students categorize it as density-dependent or density-independent. Then, have students complete the 5.2 Assessment.

REMEDIATION SUGGESTION

L1 Struggling Students Have students work in small groups to brainstorm a list of specific density-independent limiting factors if they are struggling to answer **Question 3b.**

BIOLOGY.com Students can check their understanding of lesson concepts with the **Self-Test** assessment. They can then take an online version of the **Lesson Assessment.**

Assessment Answers

1a. a factor that controls the growth of a population

1b. by determining the carrying capacity of environments for populations

2a. Answers may vary: Factors include competition, predation, herbivory, parasitism, disease, stress from overcrowding.

2b. Competition between individuals increases as population size increases.

3a. a factor that affects populations regardless of their size or density

3b. Sample answer: A drought could limit food supplies outside the cave. A flood could fill the cave with water. A snowstorm could block the entrance to the cave.

4. Big idea Biotic factors include competition, predation, and parasitism and disease. Unusual weather and natural disasters are abiotic factors.

LESSON 5.3

Getting Started

Objectives

5.3.1 Discuss the trend of human population growth.

5.3.2 Explain why population growth rates differ in countries throughout the world.

Student Resources

Study Workbooks A and B, 5.3 Worksheets

Spanish Study Workbook, 5.3 Worksheets

Lesson Overview • Lesson Notes • Activity: Art in Motion • Assessment: Self-Test, Lesson Assessment

For corresponding lesson in the **Foundation Edition**, see pages 117–119.

Build Background

Write the following questions on the board:

- What limiting factors affect the human population?
- How are these limiting factors similar to or different than the limiting factors affecting other populations?

Ask students to write a brief response to each question. Have volunteers share their responses with the class. Use students' responses to help them anticipate the content of this lesson.

Human Population Growth

Key Questions

How has human population size changed over time?

Why do population growth rates differ among countries?

Vocabulary

demography
demographic transition

Taking Notes

Preview Visuals Before you read, preview the graphs in **Figures 5–11, 5–12,** and **5–13.** Make a list of questions about the graphs. Then, as you read, write down the answers to your questions.

THINK ABOUT IT How quickly is the global human population growing? In the United States and other developed countries, the population growth rate is low. But in some developing countries, the population is growing very rapidly. Worldwide, there are more than four human births every second. At this birthrate, the human population is well on its way to reaching 9 billion in your lifetime. What do the present and future of human population growth mean for our species and its interactions with the rest of the biosphere?

Historical Overview

How has human population size changed over time?

The human population, like populations of other organisms, tends to increase. The rate of that increase has changed dramatically over time. For most of human existence, the population grew slowly because life was harsh. Food was hard to find. Predators and diseases were common and life-threatening. These limiting factors kept human death rates very high. Until fairly recently, only half the children in the world survived to adulthood. Because death rates were so high, families had many children, just to make sure that some would survive.

Exponential Human Population Growth As civilization advanced, life became easier, and the human population began to grow more rapidly. That trend continued through the Industrial Revolution in the 1800s. Food supplies became more reliable, and essential goods could be shipped around the globe. Several factors, including improved nutrition, sanitation, medicine, and healthcare, dramatically reduced death rates. Yet, birthrates in most parts of the world remained high. The combination of lower death rates and high birthrates led to exponential growth, as shown in **Figure 5–11.**

BUILD Vocabulary

ACADEMIC WORDS The adverb **dramatically** means "forcefully" or "significantly." When something is described as having changed dramatically, it means it has changed in a striking way.

The Predictions of Malthus As you've learned, this kind of exponential growth cannot continue forever. Two centuries ago, this problem troubled English economist Thomas Malthus. Malthus suggested that only war, famine, and disease could limit human population growth. Can you see what Malthus was suggesting? He thought that human populations would be regulated by competition (war), limited resources (famine), parasitism (disease), and other density-dependent factors. Malthus's work was vitally important to the thinking of Charles Darwin.

UbD Teach for Understanding

ENDURING UNDERSTANDING The existence of life on Earth depends on interactions among organisms and between organisms and their environment.

GUIDING QUESTION How is the human population growing?

EVIDENCE OF UNDERSTANDING *After completing the lesson, give students the following assessment to show their understanding of human population growth.* Have students work in small groups to write a short paragraph explaining why age structure is a key characteristic demographers use when making predictions about human population growth.

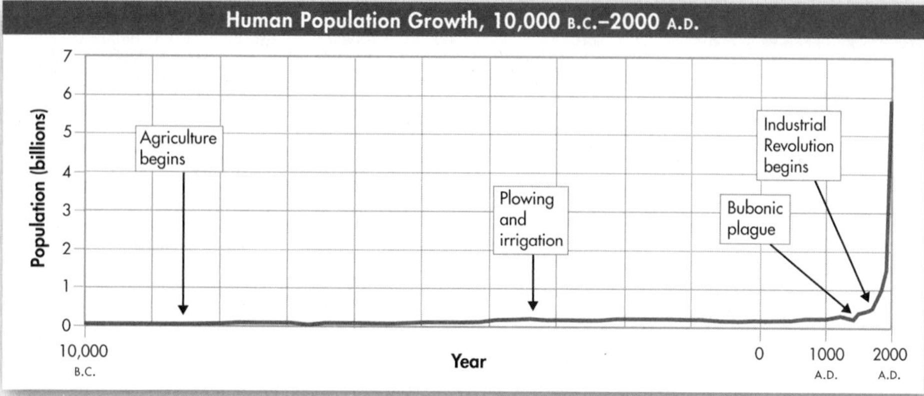

World Population Growth Slows So what is happening to human population growth today? Exponential growth continued up to the second half of the twentieth century. The human population growth rate reached a peak around 1962–1963, and then it began to drop. The size of the global human population is still growing rapidly, but the rate of growth is slowing down.

It took 123 years for the human population to double from 1 billion in 1804 to 2 billion in 1927. Then it took just 33 years for it to grow by another billion people. The time it took for the population to increase each additional billion continued to fall until 1999, when it began, very slowly, to rise. It now takes longer for the global human population to grow by 1 billion than it did 20 years ago. What has been going on?

FIGURE 5–11 Human Population Growth Over Time After a slow start, the human population grew exponentially following advances in civilization. Change can be dramatic; these photos of Katmandu, Nepal, were taken from the same position in 1969 and 1999—just 30 years apart!

Patterns of Human Population Growth

Why do population growth rates differ among countries?

Scientists have identified several social and economic factors that affect human population growth. The scientific study of human populations is called **demography.** Demography examines characteristics of human populations and attempts to explain how those populations will change over time. **Birthrates, death rates, and the age structure of a population help predict why some countries have high growth rates while other countries grow more slowly.**

In Your Notebook *Explain how the size of the global human population can increase while the rate of growth decreases.*

Quick Facts

A GLOBAL POPULATION

International migration plays an increasingly significant role in the population growth of many countries, particularly as fertility declines. According to a United Nations report (*World Population Prospects, The 2006 Revision,* Population Division, Department of Economic and Social Affairs), the net number of international migrants to more developed regions over the period from 2005 to 2050 is projected to be 103 million, which counterbalances the projected number of deaths over births (74 million) for the same period. The countries with the highest net levels of migrants entering the population annually are projected to be: the United States (1.1 million), Canada (200,000), Germany (150,000), Italy (139,000), the United Kingdom (130,000), Spain (123,000), and Australia (100,000). On the contrary, the countries with the highest levels of net emigration are projected to be: China (–329,000), Mexico (–306,000), India (–241,000), the Philippines (–180,000), Pakistan (–167,000), and Indonesia (–164,000).

Teach

Connect to Math

Have students examine the graph of human population growth shown in **Figure 5–11.**

Ask Does this graph have a shape more like exponential growth or logistic growth? *(exponential growth)*

Ask The text states that the human population growth rate has started to slow down. How does this apply to what you have already learned about logistic growth? *(Logistic growth has three phases. During Phase I, growth is exponential; during Phase II, growth slows; and during Phase III, the population size stays fairly steady around a fixed level. Human population growth is showing a slowdown from exponential growth; it may be moving into Phase II of logistic growth.)*

DIFFERENTIATED INSTRUCTION

L1 **Struggling Students** Help students locate and review the information and graphs in Lesson 5.1 showing exponential and logistic growth. Then, have them use these graphs to help them answer the questions above.

ELL Focus on ELL: Access Content

INTERMEDIATE, ADVANCED, AND ADVANCED HIGH SPEAKERS Have students use a **Main Ideas and Details Chart** to organize the information in this lesson. Point out that Key Concepts within the lesson can serve as the main ideas. As they read the text associated with each concept, have them add details. Intermediate speakers can use words or short phrases to record details; encourage advanced students to use complete sentences; require advanced high students to use complete, complex sentences. At the conclusion of the lesson, have students share aloud details from their charts.

Study Wkbks A/B, Appendix S28, Main Ideas and Details Chart. **Transparencies,** GO13.

Answers

IN YOUR NOTEBOOK The growth rate of the human population has not reached zero. The population is still growing, just not as rapidly.

Teach continued

Use Visuals

Students can use **Figure 5–13** to see how age structure is related to population growth.

Ask What overall pattern do you see in the age-structure diagram of Guatemala's population? *(Moving from youngest to oldest, every subgroup of the population is smaller than the one before it.)*

Ask How does this compare to the overall pattern in the age-structure diagram of the U.S. population? *(The age-structure diagram for the U.S. does not exhibit the same pattern. Instead, in the subgroups for individuals up to age 55, there are approximately equal numbers in each subgroup.)*

Ask What does this difference in age structure imply about future growth of each population? *(The number of women in Guatemala who are in the age group likely to bear children will increase every year, meaning population growth will increase every year. In the United States, the number of women in the age group likely to bear children will stay fairly consistent, implying that population growth will stay fairly steady.)*

DIFFERENTIATED INSTRUCTION

L3 Advanced Students Have students make an age-structure diagram for an imaginary country with a population with a negative growth rate. Then, have students research to identify actual countries that have negative growth rates and projected population declines between the present time and 2050. Have students share what they learn with the class.

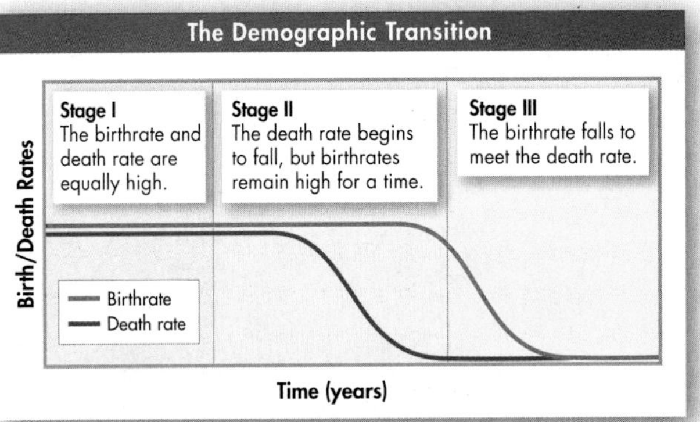

FIGURE 5–12 The Demographic Transition Human birthrates and death rates are high for most of history (Stage I). Advances in nutrition, sanitation, and medicine lead to lower death rates. Birthrates remain high for a time, so births greatly exceed deaths (Stage II), and the population increases exponentially. As levels of education and living standards rise, families have fewer children and the birthrate falls (Stage III), and population growth slows. The demographic transition is complete when the birthrate meets the death rate, and population growth stops.

The Demographic Transition Human societies had equally high birthrates and death rates during most of history. But over the past century, population growth in the United States, Japan, and much of Europe slowed dramatically. Demographers developed a hypothesis to explain this shift. According to this hypothesis, these countries have completed the **demographic transition,** a dramatic change from high birthrates and death rates to low birthrates and death rates. The demographic transition is divided into three stages, as shown in **Figure 5–12.**

To date, the United States, Japan, and Europe have completed the demographic transition. Parts of South America, Africa, and Asia are passing through Stage II. (The United States passed through Stage II between 1790 and 1910.) A large part of ongoing human population growth is happening in only ten countries, with India and China in the lead. Globally, human population is still growing rapidly, but the rate of growth is slowing down. Our J-shaped growth curve may be changing into a logistic growth curve.

Age Structure and Population Growth To understand population growth in different countries, we turn to age-structure diagrams. **Figure 5–13** compares the age structure of the U.S. population with that of Guatemala, a country in Central America. In the United States, there are nearly equal numbers of people in each age group. This age structure predicts a slow but steady growth rate for the near future. In Guatemala, on the other hand, there are many more young children than teenagers, and many more teenagers than adults. This age structure predicts a population that will double in about 30 years.

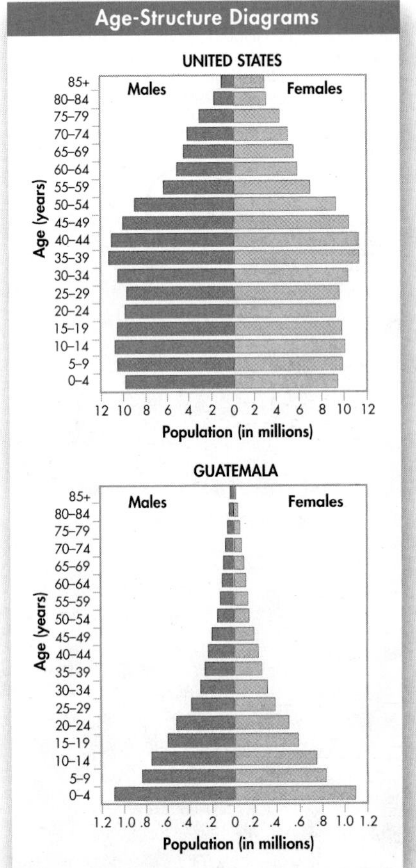

FIGURE 5–13 Comparison of Age Structures These diagrams compare the populations of the United States and Guatemala. Notice the difference in their x-axis scales. **Analyze Data** ***How do the two countries differ in the percentages of 10–14-year-olds in their populations?***

UbD Check for Understanding

FOLLOW-UP PROBES

Ask Why is an age-structure diagram more useful than a total population count in projecting a population's future growth rate? Explain. *(A total population count doesn't distinguish ages and gender, and so can't really be used to predict increases and decreases in the population.)*

ADJUST INSTRUCTION

If responses indicate students do not understand why age structure is an important tool for projecting future population growth, remind them that only females in a certain age range can have children. Explain that an age-structure diagram allows scientists to see how many women will be within that age group both now and in the near future.

Answers

FIGURE 5–13 Guatemala has a higher percentage of 10–14-year-olds in its population than does the United States.

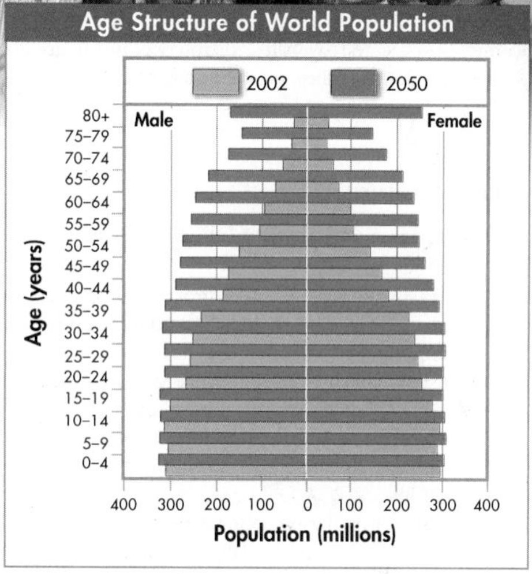

Future Population Growth To predict how the world's human population will grow, demographers consider many factors, including the age structure of each country and the effects of diseases on death rates—especially AIDS in Africa and parts of Asia. Current projections suggest that by 2050 the world population will reach 9 billion people. Will the human population level out to a logistic growth curve and become stable? This may happen if countries that are currently growing rapidly complete the demographic transition.

Current data suggest that global human population will grow more slowly over the next 50 years than it grew over the last 50 years. But because the growth rate will still be higher than zero in 2050, our population will continue to grow. In the next chapter, we will examine the effect of human population growth on the biosphere.

Age Structure of World Population

2002 | 2050

Male | Female

Age (years): 80+, 75–79, 70–74, 65–69, 60–64, 55–59, 50–54, 45–49, 40–44, 35–39, 30–34, 25–29, 20–24, 15–19, 10–14, 5–9, 0–4

Population (millions): 400 300 200 100 0 100 200 300 400

FIGURE 5–14 A Growing Population This graph (from the U.S. Census Bureau, International Database) shows the projected age structure of the world population in 2050. As population numbers climb, cities face various challenges, such as housing. The photo above shows a housing complex in Hong Kong; each apartment building is home to thousands of residents.

5.3 Assessment

Review Key Concepts

1. a. **Review** Describe the general trend of human population growth over time.
   b. **Relate Cause and Effect** What factors contributed to the pattern of growth shown in **Figure 5–11**?
2. a. **Review** Why do populations in different countries grow at different rates?
   b. **Explain** Describe the demographic transition and explain how it could affect a country's population growth rate.
   c. **Form an Opinion** Are age-structure diagrams useful in predicting future population trends?

VISUAL THINKING

3. Describe the changes in human population predicted by **Figure 5–14.** How do you think those changes will affect society?

BIOLOGY.com Search   Lesson 5.3 GO • Self-Test • Lesson Assessment • Art in Motion

LESSON 5.3

BIOLOGY.com Have students watch an animation of the age-structure diagram of world population in **Art in Motion: Age Structure of World Population.**

Assess and Remediate

EVALUATE UNDERSTANDING

Ask volunteers to describe how the human population growth rate has changed over time. Then, have students complete the 5.3 Assessment.

REMEDIATION SUGGESTION

L1 Struggling Students If students have difficulty answering **Question 2b,** suggest they review **Figure 5–12** and discuss it with a partner.

BIOLOGY.com Students can check their understanding of lesson concepts with the **Self-Test** assessment. They can then take an online version of the **Lesson Assessment.**

Assessment Answers

1a. For tens of thousands of years, the human population grew very slowly. Then, about 500 years ago, the population started to grow exponentially and increased dramatically. The growth rate slowed in the second half of the twentieth century; the population is still growing, but at a slower rate.

1b. Harsh living conditions resulted in high death rates that occurred through most of human history. Rapid population growth occurred when advances, such as improved nutrition, healthcare, and sanitation, decreased the death rate.

2a. Different countries have different birthrates, death rates, and age structures.

2b. The demographic transition occurs in three stages. In Stage I, a country has a high birthrate and a high death rate. In Stage II, the death rate drops, but the birthrate remains high. In Stage III, the birthrate drops to meet the death rate. The population growth of a country slows after it has completed the demographic transition.

2c. Sample answer: Yes, age-structure diagrams allow scientists to determine if the number of individuals likely to have children will increase or decrease in the future.

VISUAL THINKING

3. Sample answer: The age structure shown in the diagram would lead me to predict that birthrates will remain fairly constant. There will also be an increase in the percentage of individuals in the oldest age groups. These individuals can contribute a great deal to society, but may also increase the demand for healthcare.

CHAPTER LAB

Pre-Lab

Introduce students to the concepts they will explore in the chapter lab by assigning the Pre-Lab questions.

Lab

Tell students they will perform the chapter lab *The Growth Cycle of Yeast* described in **Lab Manual A.**

 **Struggling Students** A simpler version of the chapter lab is provided in **Lab Manual B.**

SAFETY

Remind students to handle glass items with care and follow your direction about disposal of lab materials. Have them wash their hands with soap and warm water when they complete the lab.

BIOLOGY.com Look online for **Editable Lab Worksheets.**

For corresponding pre-lab in the **Foundation Edition**, see page 120.

IN INDIANA ACADEMIC STANDARDS

For the full text of all standards, see the Course Overview in the front matter of this book.

GUIDED INQUIRY

IN B.4.1 Limiting Factors; B.4.4 Stability of an ecosystem. Also covered: NoS.5.

Pre-Lab: The Growth Cycle of Yeast

Problem What type of population growth occurs in a yeast culture?

Materials yeast culture, stirring rod, dropper pipettes, microscope slides, coverslips, microscope, 10-mL graduated cylinder, test tubes, test-tube rack, graph paper

Lab Manual Chapter 5 Lab

Skills Measure, Calculate, Interpret Graphs

Connect to the Big idea Populations depend on, and are limited by, their environments. A population can grow when its members have the resources they need to survive and reproduce. Factors that can limit those resources include natural disasters, such as forest fires, and competition from other species. Predation and disease are also limiting factors for populations.

In nature, populations often experience cycles of growth and decline. In this lab, you will investigate whether such a cycle occurs in yeast populations.

Background Questions

a. Review What is the carrying capacity of a population?

b. Sequence Briefly describe the three phases of logistic growth.

c. Relate Cause and Effect Describe two different ways that a population might achieve a growth rate of zero.

d. Classify After two weeks of hot and sunny days with very little rain, the blades of grass in a backyard began to wither and die. Were any of the factors that caused the decline of the grass population dependent on density? Explain.

Pre-Lab Questions

Preview the procedure in the lab manual.

1. Infer Why was grape juice used to prepare the yeast cultures instead of plain water?

2. Form a Hypothesis Why will you locate the yeast cells under low power, but switch to high power to count the cells?

3. Calculate Suppose you have to do one dilution of your culture before you are able to count the yeast cells. If you count 21 yeast cells in the diluted sample, how many yeast cells were in the same area of the undiluted sample? MATH

4. Predict What do you think will happen to a yeast population between Day 3 and Day 7? Give reasons for your answer.

 Search 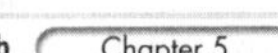 Chapter 5 

Visit Chapter 5 online to test yourself on chapter content and to find activities to help you learn.

Untamed Science Join the Untamed Science crew as they learn the latest techniques for counting populations.

Art in Motion View a short animation that brings age-structure diagrams to life.

Art Review Review your understanding of limiting factors with this drag-and-drop activity.

InterActive Art Manipulate factors such as starting population size, birthrate, and death rate to see how they would impact moose and wolf populations over time.

Data Analysis Analyze logistic growth curves in order to make predictions about zebra mussel growth.

Pre-Lab Answers

BACKGROUND QUESTIONS

a. Carrying capacity is the maximum number of a species that a particular environment can support.

b. Sample answer: In Phase 1 of logistic growth, resources are unlimited and the population grows rapidly. In Phase 2, the rate of growth slows down. In Phase 3, the rate of growth drops to zero and the size of the population levels off.

c. Sample answers: The number of births is equal to the number of deaths, or there were no births or deaths, or as many people moved into the population as moved out.

d. Sample answer: The small amount of rain could be classified as a density-dependent factor because the blades had to compete for this resource. (The heat and sunlight were not density-dependent factors because each blade of grass received about the same amount of heat and light.)

PRE-LAB QUESTIONS

1. Sample answer: The grape juice contains nutrients that the yeast cells need to grow and reproduce.

2. Sample answer: With low power, the field of view is larger, which makes finding the cells easier. With high power, the magnification is greater, which makes counting the cells easier.

3. 21 × 10 or 210 yeast cells

4. Some students may assume that the nutrients are sufficient to sustain rapid growth through Day 7. Others may assume that the nutrients will begin to limit and slow down growth by Day 7.

5 Study Guide

Big idea Interdependence in Nature

The way a population changes depends on many things, including its age structure, the rates at which individuals are added or removed from the population, and factors in the environment that limit its growth.

5.1 How Populations Grow

Researchers study populations' geographic range, density and distribution, growth rate, and age structure.

The factors that can affect population size are the birthrate, the death rate, and the rate at which individuals enter or leave the population.

Under ideal conditions with unlimited resources, a population will grow exponentially.

Logistic growth occurs when a population's growth slows and then stops, following a period of exponential growth.

population density (131)
age structure (131)
immigration (132)
emigration (132)
exponential growth (132)
logistic growth (135)
carrying capacity (135)

5.2 Limits to Growth

Acting separately or together, limiting factors determine the carrying capacity of an environment for a species.

Density-dependent limiting factors operate strongly when population density reaches a certain level. Density-dependent limiting factors include competition, predation, herbivory, parasitism, disease, and stress from overcrowding.

Density-independent limiting factors affect all populations in similar ways, regardless of population size and density. Unusual weather such as hurricanes, droughts, or floods, and natural disasters such as wildfires, can act as density-independent limiting factors.

limiting factor (137)
density-dependent limiting factor (138)
density-independent limiting factor (140)

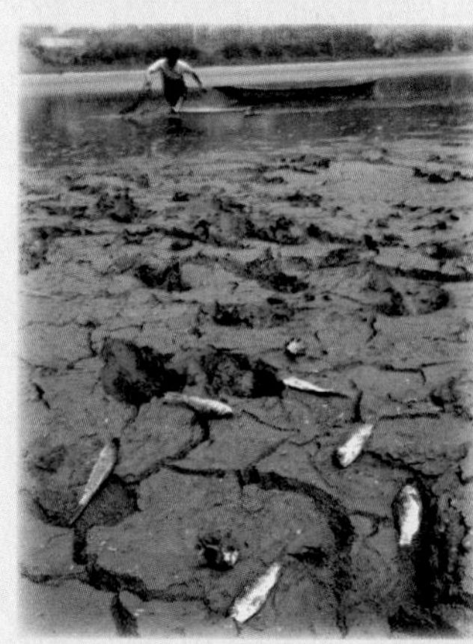

5.3 Human Population Growth

The human population, like populations of other organisms, tends to increase. The rate of that increase has changed dramatically over time.

Birthrates, death rates, and the age structure of a population help predict why some countries have high growth rates while other countries grow more slowly.

demography (143)
demographic transition (144)

Think Visually Create a table in which you describe the phases of logistic growth.

Study Online

REVIEW AND ASSESSMENT RESOURCES

Editable Worksheets Pages of Study Workbooks A and B, Lab Manuals A and B, and the Assessment Resources Book are available online. These documents can be easily edited using a word-processing program.

Lesson Overview Have students reread the Lesson Overviews to help them study chapter concepts.

Vocabulary Review The *Flash Cards* and *Crossword* provide an interactive way to review chapter vocabulary.

Chapter Assessment Have students take an online version of the Chapter 5 Assessment.

Standardized Test Prep Students can take an online version of the Standardized Test Prep. You will receive their scores along with ideas for remediation.

Diagnostic and Benchmark Tests Use these tests to monitor your students' progress and supply remediation.

Answers

THINK VISUALLY

Students' tables should include a description of Phase I, during which the population grows exponentially; Phase II, during which population growth slows; and Phase III, during which population growth stops and the population size remains fairly constant.

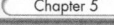

UbD Performance Tasks

SUMMATIVE TASK Have students imagine that an advance in medical technology immediately doubles the average life span of residents of the United States, but does not affect the age of reproduction. Have them use the age-structure diagram of the U.S. in **Figure 5–12** as a starting point for preparing age-structure diagrams for 25 and 50 years in the future reflecting the change in life span. Then, have students write a paragraph describing how—or if—the introduction of the medical technology would change the size, density, growth rate, age structure, birthrate, and death rate of the human population in the U.S.

TRANSFER TASK Have students use what they have learned about characteristics of populations, limiting factors, carrying capacity, and human population growth to write a science fiction story set in the future, at the time when the human population reaches Earth's carrying capacity. Students' stories should be creative, but scientifically accurate. Remind them to include information about limiting factors acting on the human population, a scientifically accurate definition of carrying capacity, and accurate information from the text about human population growth.

Lesson 5.1

UNDERSTAND KEY CONCEPTS

1. c **2.** c **3.** b **4.** b

5. b

6. Immigration is the movement of individuals into a population; emigration is the movement of individuals out of a population.

7. Students' graphs should resemble the graphs shown in **Figure 5–4.**

8. Logistic growth occurs when a population's growth slows following a period of exponential growth and then stops at or near the carrying capacity.

9. Carrying capacity is the maximum number of individuals of a particular species a particular environment can support. Examples will vary.

THINK CRITICALLY

10. The carrying capacity of a city's roads and the carrying capacity of an ecosystem are similar, because they are both limited by the resources available. In the case of a city's roads, the carrying capacity depends on factors such as the number and width of roads and the number of intersections. In an ecosystem, the carrying capacity depends on factors such as the amount of space and food.

Lesson 5.2

UNDERSTAND KEY CONCEPTS

11. a **12.** b

13. Increasing the availability of a limiting nutrient would increase the carrying capacity of the pond.

14. If two species are competing for the same resources, the one that is better at competing for the resource will have a higher birthrate than the other, and may eventually displace the other species. Students may also say that species may adapt by using different resources.

15. A predator-prey relationship can be a mechanism of population control for both species. The population size of predators is limited by the number of prey available to eat. In turn, the number of prey is limited by the predation.

16. Parasites are a limiting factor because they feed on host organisms, weakening the host and often causing disease or death. Parasitism is considered a density-dependent limiting factor because the more crowded a population becomes, the more easily parasites can spread from one individual to another.

5 Assessment

The numbers following the questions refer to Indiana's Academic Standards for Biology I.

5.1 How Populations Grow

Understand Key Concepts

1. The number of individuals of a single species per unit area is known as
a. carrying capacity.
b. logistic growth.
c. population density.
d. population growth rate.

2. The movement of individuals into an area is called
a. demography. **c.** immigration.
b. carrying capacity. **d.** emigration.

3. The area inhabited by a population is known as its
a. growth rate.
b. geographic range.
c. age structure.
d. population density.

4. The graph below represents NoS.6
a. carrying capacity. **c.** logistic growth.
b. exponential growth. **d.** age structure.

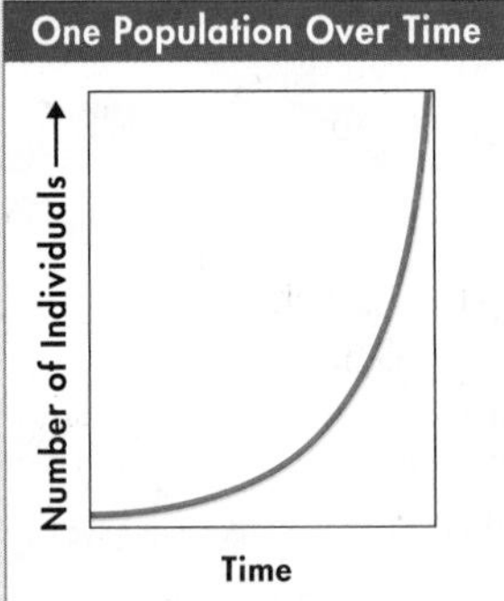

5. The maximum number of organisms of a particular species that can be supported by an environment is called B.4.1
a. logistic growth. **c.** exponential growth.
b. carrying capacity. **d.** population density.

6. What is the difference between immigration and emigration?

7. Sketch the exponential growth curve of a hypothetical population. NoS.6

8. Describe the conditions under which logistic growth occurs.

9. What is carrying capacity? Give an example. B.4.1

Think Critically

10. **Use Analogies** How is the carrying capacity of a city's roads similar to the carrying capacity of an ecosystem? B.4.1

5.2 Limits to Growth

Understand Key Concepts

11. A limiting factor that depends on population size is called a B.4.1
a. density-dependent limiting factor.
b. density-independent limiting factor.
c. predator-prey relationship.
d. parasitic relationship.

12. One example of a density-independent limiting factor is B.4.1
a. predation. **c.** competition.
b. hurricanes. **d.** parasitism.

13. How might increasing the amount of a limiting nutrient in a pond affect the carrying capacity of the pond? B.4.1

14. Describe the long-term effects of competition on populations of two different species competing for the same resources. B.4.1, B.4.4

15. Describe how a predator-prey relationship can control both the predator population and the prey population. B.4.1, B.4.4

16. How do parasites serve as a density-dependent limiting factor? B.4.1, B.4.4

Think Critically

17. **Predict** What would happen to a population of predators if there was a sudden increase in food for the prey? Explain your answer. B.4.1, B.4.4

18. **Apply Concepts** Why would a contagious virus that causes a fatal disease be considered a density-dependent limiting factor? B.4.1

THINK CRITICALLY

17. If a there is a sudden increase in food for a population of prey, the prey population will increase. This means there will be more food for the predators, which will then also increase.

18. A contagious virus spreads more easily in crowded conditions; it is considered a density-dependent factor.

19. In most cases, it will have a greater impact on populations in a small ecosystem. A small population, like those found in small ecosystems, will be more susceptible to serious damage from a density-independent factor such as a storm or a flood.

20. In both parasite-host relationships and predator-prey relationships, the two species involved limit one another's population growth.

21. Sample answer: If the water level drops, the fish population's density increases. This makes the fish population more susceptible to density-dependent limiting factors.

19. **Infer** Would a density-independent limiting factor have more of an effect on population size in a large ecosystem or in a small ecosystem? B.4.1

20. **Compare and Contrast** How is the relationship between parasites and their hosts similar to a predator-prey relationship? B.4.1, B.4.4

21. **Apply Concepts** How would a drop in the water level of a river affect a fish population living in that river? B.4.1

5.3 Human Population Growth

Understand Key Concepts

22. The scientific study of human populations is called
 a. immigration.
 b. emigration.
 c. demographic transition.
 d. demography.

23. The demographic transition is considered complete when
 a. population growth stops.
 b. the birthrate is greater than the death rate.
 c. the death rate begins to fall.
 d. the death rate is greater than the birthrate.

24. How can you account for the fact that the human population has grown more rapidly during the past 500 years than it has at any other time in history?

25. What is the significance of the demographic transition in studies of human population around the world?

26. How does the age structure of a population affect its growth rate?

27. What factors did Thomas Malthus think would eventually limit the human population?

Think Critically

28. **Compare and Contrast** What shape population growth curve would you expect to see in a small town made up mainly of senior citizens? Compare this growth curve to that of a small town made up of newly married couples in their twenties.

29. **Pose Questions** What questions would a demographer need to answer to determine whether a country is approaching the demographic transition?

solve the CHAPTER MYSTERY

A PLAGUE OF RABBITS

Australia had no native rabbit population when the European rabbits arrived, so there were no density-dependent controls to keep their numbers in check. The rabbits' new environment provided many favorable conditions for survival, including fewer predators, parasites, and diseases. The initial small number of rabbits—which can reproduce rapidly—soon multiplied into millions.

High rabbit numbers caused serious environmental and agricultural damage. In an effort to manage the problem, many methods have been tried, including fencing, poisoning, the destruction of burrows, and the use of parasites and disease. In the 1950s, a rabbit virus that causes the fatal rabbit disease myxomatosis was deliberately introduced as a form of biological control. It killed countless rabbits. But the virus and rabbits soon reached an equilibrium that allowed host and parasite to coexist, and the rabbit population rose. Later, a new virus that causes rabbit hemorrhagic disease (RHD) was introduced, and the rabbit population dropped again. In several places, environmental recovery was dramatic: Native animals recovered, and native trees and shrubs thought to be locally extinct began to grow again. But the RHD virus and rabbits appear to have reached a new balance, and the rabbit population is rising again!

1. **Predict** Populations of wildcats and foxes (both also introduced to Australia) have come to depend on rabbits as prey. How do you think wildcats and foxes would be affected by a crash in the rabbit population?

2. **Connect to the Big idea** Why should people be cautious about introducing organisms into new environments?

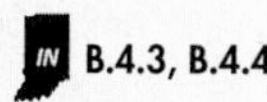
B.4.3, B.4.4

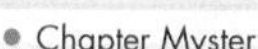

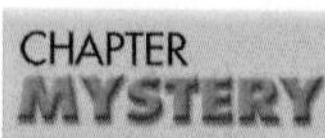
After students have read through the Chapter Mystery, discuss factors influencing the size of the rabbit population in Australia.

Ask Are the diseases that were intentionally introduced into rabbit populations in Australia examples of density-dependent or density-independent factors? *(Disease is a density-dependent factor.)*

Ask In an ecosystem, if the rabbits crowded out a local species competing for the same food supply, how would the carrying capacity for rabbits change? *(The carrying capacity for rabbits would increase as the other species was crowded out of the ecosystem.)*

Ask How does the rapid rate of reproduction in rabbits affect the population growth rate? *(It contributes to rapid population growth.)*

CHAPTER MYSTERY ANSWERS

1. If the rabbit population crashed the size of the populations of wildcats and foxes would probably also crash, due to a decrease in the food supply.

2.  Introduced species can cause severe environmental damage to an ecosystem. Introduced species often grow very rapidly, because the limiting factors from their native ecosystem may not be present in their new ecosystem. Uncontrolled population growth can crowd local species. Also, it can be very difficult (or impossible) to remove a species once it has established itself.

In **Census Consensus,** the Untamed Science crew investigates how scientists pin down population numbers.

Lesson 5.3

UNDERSTAND KEY CONCEPTS

22. d 23. a

24. The human population began growing more rapidly 500 years ago due to conditions that made survival more likely, thereby decreasing the death rate. Reliable food supply, improved sanitation, and better medical care are three factors that caused this change.

25. Studies of populations around the world use the concept of the demographic transition to help make predictions about future growth; they show which human populations have stabilized and which are still increasing.

26. Populations with nearly equal numbers of people in each age group will likely have a slow but steady growth rate for the near future. Populations with many more young people than adults will likely grow at a rapid rate.

27. Malthus suggested war, famine, and disease would limit the human population.

THINK CRITICALLY

28. A town populated mainly with senior citizens would have a population growth curve showing a decreasing population, because the death rate would exceed the birthrate. A town populated by newly married couples would have a population growth curve showing a population increase, because the birthrate would exceed the death rate.

29. He/she would need to learn the birthrate and death rate for the country over the past few decades—indications of whether the rates are generally increasing or decreasing.

Connecting Concepts

USE SCIENCE GRAPHICS

30. 1804, 1999

31. Since reaching the 1-billion-people mark, the growth rate first increased (as shown by the shortening time intervals between each additional billion), then decreased (as shown by the lengthening time intervals between each additional billion).

WRITE ABOUT SCIENCE

32. Answers may vary. Students paragraphs' should include the characteristics of populations (geographic range, density and distribution, growth rate, age structure), and factors that affect population size (immigration, births, emigration, deaths). Students should also describe changes in the human population, and will probably estimate that the human population will be about 9 billion in 2050 (based on information in the text), with a lower growth rate in 2050 than in 2000.

33. Big idea Answers may vary. Students' responses should include a specific sample organism, references to density-dependent and density-independent limiting factors that would change birthrate, death rate, or patterns of immigration and emigration.

Connecting Concepts

Use Science Graphics NoS.3

The following actual and projected data, from the United Nations Department of Economic and Social Affairs, Population Division, show when the global population reached or will reach an additional billion. Use the data table to answer questions 30 and 31.

World Population Milestones

Population (billion)	Year	Time Interval (years)
1	1804	—
2	1927	123
3	1960	33
4	1974	14
5	1987	13
6	1999	12
7	2012	13
8	2027	15
8.9	2050	23

30. Observe When did the world population reach 1 billion people? When did it reach 6 billion?

31. Interpret Tables Describe the trend in population growth since the 1-billion-people mark.

Write About Science NoS.3

32. Explanation Write a paragraph on the human population. Include the characteristics of a population, factors that affect its size, and changes in the size of the population from about 500 years ago to the present. Give a projection of how large the world population might be in the year 2050 and of how the growth rate in 2050 might compare to that in 2000. (*Hint*: Outline your ideas before you begin to write.)

33. Assess the Big idea Choose a specific organism and explain how the population of that organism depends on a number of factors that may cause it to increase, decrease, or remain stable in size.

Analyzing Data

IN NoS.3

The following graph shows the "boom-and-bust" pattern of regular rises and falls in the rabbit population in South Australia. The points at which various population control measures were introduced are indicated. Use the graph to answer questions 34 and 35.

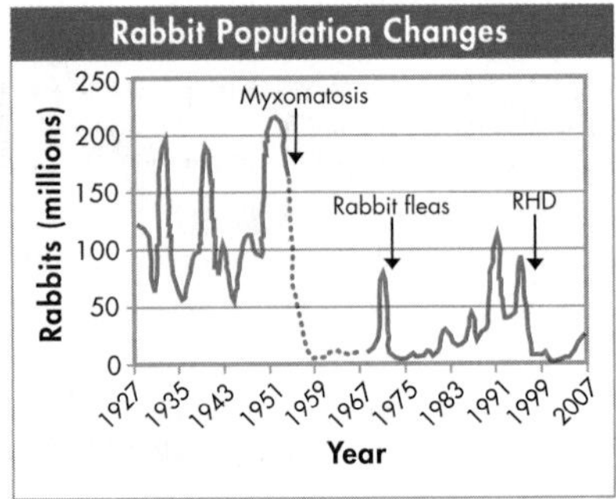

34. Interpret Graphs In which of the following years was the rabbit population density in South Australia most dense?

a. 1936
b. 1952
c. 1975
d. 2000

35. Infer European rabbit fleas were introduced in the late 1960s to help spread the effects of the rabbit disease myxomatosis. Based on the graph, what can you infer about the rabbit population after the fleas were introduced?

a. The rabbit birthrate increased.
b. The rabbit death rate increased.
c. The rabbit death rate decreased.
d. The fleas had no effect on the rabbit population.

PURPOSE Students will analyze data to understand the effects of various population control measures on the rabbit population in Australia.

PLANNING Have students review the Chapter Mystery information throughout the chapter to reinforce their understanding of the rabbit population in Australia.

ANSWERS

34. b

35. b

Standardized Test Practice for Indiana

Multiple Choice

1. The movement of individuals into an area is called
   A immigration.
   B emigration.
   C population growth rate.
   D population density.

2. All other things being equal, the size of a population will decrease if
   A birthrate exceeds the death rate.
   B immigration rate exceeds emigration rate.
   C death rate exceeds birthrate.
   D birthrate equals death rate. NoS.6

3. Which of the following is NOT an example of a density-dependent limiting factor?
   A natural disaster C competition
   B predator D disease B.4.1

4. A population like that of the United States with an age structure of roughly equal numbers in each of the age groups can be predicted to
   A grow rapidly over a 30-year-period and then stabilize.
   B grow little for a generation and then grow rapidly.
   C fall slowly and steadily over many decades.
   D show slow and steady growth for some time into the future.

5. In the presence of unlimited resources and in the absence of disease and predation, what would probably happen to a bacterial population?
   A logistic growth C endangerment
   B exponential growth D extinction B.4.1

6. Which of the following statements best describes human population growth?
   A The growth rate has remained constant over time.
   B Growth continues to increase at the same rate.
   C Growth has been exponential in the last few hundred years.
   D Birthrate equals death rate.

7. Which of the following refers to when a population's birthrate equals its death rate?
   A limiting factor
   B carrying capacity
   C exponential growth
   D population density

Questions 8–9

Use the graph below to answer the following questions.

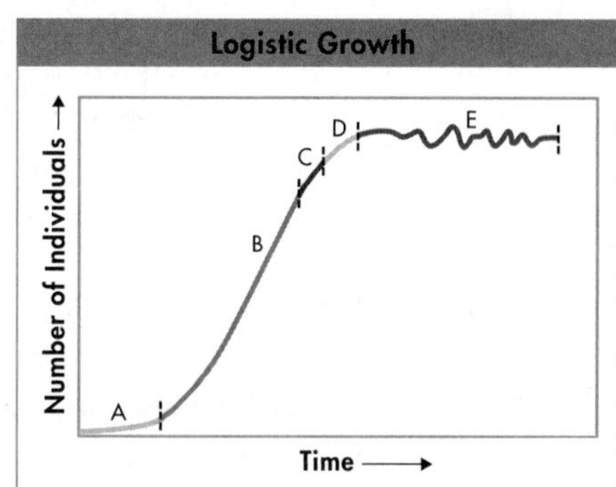

8. Which time interval(s) in the graph shows exponential growth?
   A D and E C C and D
   B A and B D E only NoS.3

9. Which time interval(s) in the graph depicts the effects of limiting factors on the population?
   A A only C C, D, and E
   B A and B D C and D NoS.3

Open-Ended Response

10. When a nonnative species is imported into a new ecosystem, the population sometimes runs wild. Explain why this might be the case. B.4.3

If You Have Trouble With . . .										
Question	1	2	3	4	5	6	7	8	9	10
See Lesson	5.1	5.1	5.2	5.3	5.1	5.3	5.1	5.1	5.2	5.2

Answers

1. A
2. C
3. A
4. D
5. B
6. C
7. B
8. B
9. C
10. Sample answer: The new ecosystem may lack the limiting factors present in the species' native ecosystem, allowing the population to grow exponentially. Introduced organisms may destroy populations of native organisms, and in doing so, may further reduce their competition. It can be very difficult, or impossible, to remove a species once it has been introduced without upsetting the rest of the ecosystem.

Test-Taking Tip

INTERPRET GRAPHS

Tell students to carefully review a graph before they answer any questions that relate to it. Make sure students read the title, axis labels, and any other information on the graph. Suggest they mentally summarize what the graph shows before reading any questions. Once they are sure they fully understand the graph, then suggest they read and answer the questions.

Humans in the Biosphere

Chapter Contents	IN	Time	Core Resources
Chapter Preview			**Student Edition,** pp. 152–153 **Chapter Mystery,** p. 153
6.1 A Changing Landscape The Effect of Human Activity • Sustainable Development	B.4.2	1/2 period 1/4 block	**Student Edition,** pp. 154–157 Inquiry 6.1 Quick Lab, p. 155 L2 **Study Workbook A** 6.1 Worksheets L2 Biology.com 6.1 Self-Test • 6.1 Lesson Assessment
6.2 Using Resources Wisely Soil Resources • Freshwater Resources • Atmospheric Resources	NoS.3, NoS.11, B.4.2	1 period 1/2 block	**Student Edition,** pp. 158–165 Inquiry 6.2 Analyzing Data, p. 164 L2 **Study Workbook A** 6.2 Worksheets L2 Biology.com *Art in Motion:* Biological Magnification • 6.2 Self-Test • 6.2 Lesson Assessment
6.3 Biodiversity The Value of Biodiversity • Threats to Biodiversity • Conserving Biodiversity	NoS.3, NoS.11, B.4.2, B.4.3, B.4.4	1 period 1/2 block	**Student Edition,** pp. 166–172 Inquiry 6.3 Analyzing Data, p. 172 L2 **Study Workbook A** 6.3 Worksheets L2 Biology.com *Data Analysis:* Measuring Biodiversity • *Art Review:* Threats to Biodiversity • 6.3 Self-Test • 6.3 Lesson Assessment
6.4 Meeting Ecological Challenges Ecological Footprints • Ecology in Action	NoS.6, NoS.11, B.4.2	1 period 1/2 block	**Student Edition,** pp. 173–179 **Study Workbook A** 6.4 Worksheets L2 Biology.com *Visual Analogy:* Ecological Footprints **Assessment Resources Book** Visual Quiz L2
Chapter Pre-Lab	NoS.1, NoS.3, NoS.5, NoS.6, B.4.2, B.4.4	1 period 1/2 block	**Student Edition,** p. 180 L2 **Lab Manual A** *Acid Rain and Seeds* L2 • *Oil-Eating Bacteria* L2

Differentiated Instruction Tools

Study Workbook B includes worksheets with lesson-level differentiated instruction support and explanations of differentiated instruction teaching strategies.

Lab Manual B includes skills labs, simplified chapter labs, and hands-on activities.

ELL Handbook explains ways to make *Biology* more accessible to ELL students.

Spanish Study Workbook is a Spanish translation of Study Workbook A.

Multilingual Glossary is the glossary translated into ten languages.

Differentiated Instruction Key

- L1 Special Needs or Struggling Students
- ELL English Language Learners
- LPR Less Proficient Readers
- L2 On-Level Students
- L3 Advanced Students

Additional Resources

Biology.com Untamed Science Video • Vocabulary Flash Cards

Study Workbook B 6.1 Worksheets L1 ELL LPR
Spanish Study Workbook 6.1 Worksheets ELL
Biology.com 6.1 Lesson Overview • 6.1 Lesson Notes

Study Workbook B 6.2 Worksheets L1 ELL LPR
Spanish Study Workbook 6.2 Worksheets ELL
Biology.com 6.2 Lesson Overview • 6.2 Lesson Notes

Study Workbook B 6.3 Worksheets L1 ELL LPR
Spanish Study Workbook 6.3 Worksheets ELL
Biology.com 6.3 Lesson Overview • 6.3 Lesson Notes

Study Workbook B 6.3 Worksheets L1 ELL LPR
Spanish Study Workbook 6.4 Worksheets ELL
Biology.com 6.4 Lesson Overview • 6.4 Lesson Notes • 6.4 Self-Test • 6.4 Lesson Assessment

Lab Manual B *Acid Rain and Seeds* • Data Analysis: *Vehicle Emissions, Saving the Golden Lion Tamarin* • Hands-On Activity: *Overpackaging* L1 ELL LPR

Chapter Review

Student Edition Study Guide, p. 181 L2 •
Unit Project, p. 186 L2
Study Workbook A Chapter 6 Vocabulary Review L2 •
Chapter 6 Chapter Mystery/21st Century Skills Activity L2 L3
Transparencies, pp. 64–77 L1 ELL LPR L2
Biology.com Untamed Science Video • You're the Director • Editable Worksheets of Study Workbooks A and B and Lab Manuals A and B • Chapter 6 Flash Cards and Crossword Puzzle

Untamed Science DVD • Classroom Resources CD (includes lesson presentations and editable worksheets)

Chapter Assessment

Student Edition Assessment, pp. 182–185 L2
Study Workbook B Chapter 6 Chapter Review L1 ELL LPR •
Chapter 6 Taking a Standardized Test L1 ELL LPR
Assessment Resources Book Chapter 6 Test A L2 • Chapter 6 Test B L1 ELL LPR • Unit 2 Test A L2 • Unit 2 Test B L1 ELL LPR
Biology.com Chapter 6 Assessment • Editable Worksheets of Chapter 6 Visual Quiz, Chapter 6 Tests A and B, Unit 2 Tests A and B

Exam*View* *Assessment Suite* • Classroom Resources CD (includes lesson presentations and editable worksheets)

Time: 1 period, 1/2 block

Pressed for Time?

Preview the Chapter Introduce the vocabulary for Lessons 6.2 and 6.3, and have the students preview the major headings in these lessons.

Cover the Chapter Quickly Assign students to read *Sustainable Development* in Lesson 6.1, all of Lesson 6.2, and go over Figure 6–8. Assign students to read *The Value of Biodiversity* and *Threats to Biodiversity* in Lesson 6.3, and briefly discuss Figure 6–20. Assign *Ecological Footprints* in Lesson 6.4.

Assess Assign question 1 in the 6.1 Assessment, the entire 6.2 Assessment, questions 1, 2, and 4 in the 6.3 Assessment, and question 1 in the 6.4 Assessment. Assign the Think Visually activity on p. 181, and questions 7–21, 23, 31, 33, and 34 in the Chapter 6 Assessment.

Connect to the Big Idea

Big idea Have students examine the photograph of Earth from space showing the pattern of lights on the planet. Ask students what a comparison of North and South America tells them about the human activities on the two continents. *(Sample answer: Lights are much more prevalent in North America, which indicates greater development than in South America.)* Ask students what the difference tells them about energy use on the two continents. *(Sample answer: More lights suggest humans are using much more energy in North America than in South America.)* Ask where else the photo suggests humans are using a large amount of energy. *(throughout Europe, in India, in eastern China, and in Japan)* Discuss with students how energy use might affect the ecology of a region. Then, have students anticipate the answer to the question, **How have human activities shaped local and global ecology?**

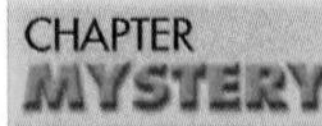

Have students read over the introduction to the Chapter Mystery and predict what happened to the trees on Easter Island. Use their predictions to help them start connecting the Chapter Mystery to the Big Idea of Interdependence in Nature.

BIOLOGY.com Have students preview the chapter vocabulary terms using the **Flash Cards.**

6 Humans in the Biosphere

Big idea Interdependence in Nature

Q: How have human activities shaped local and global ecology?

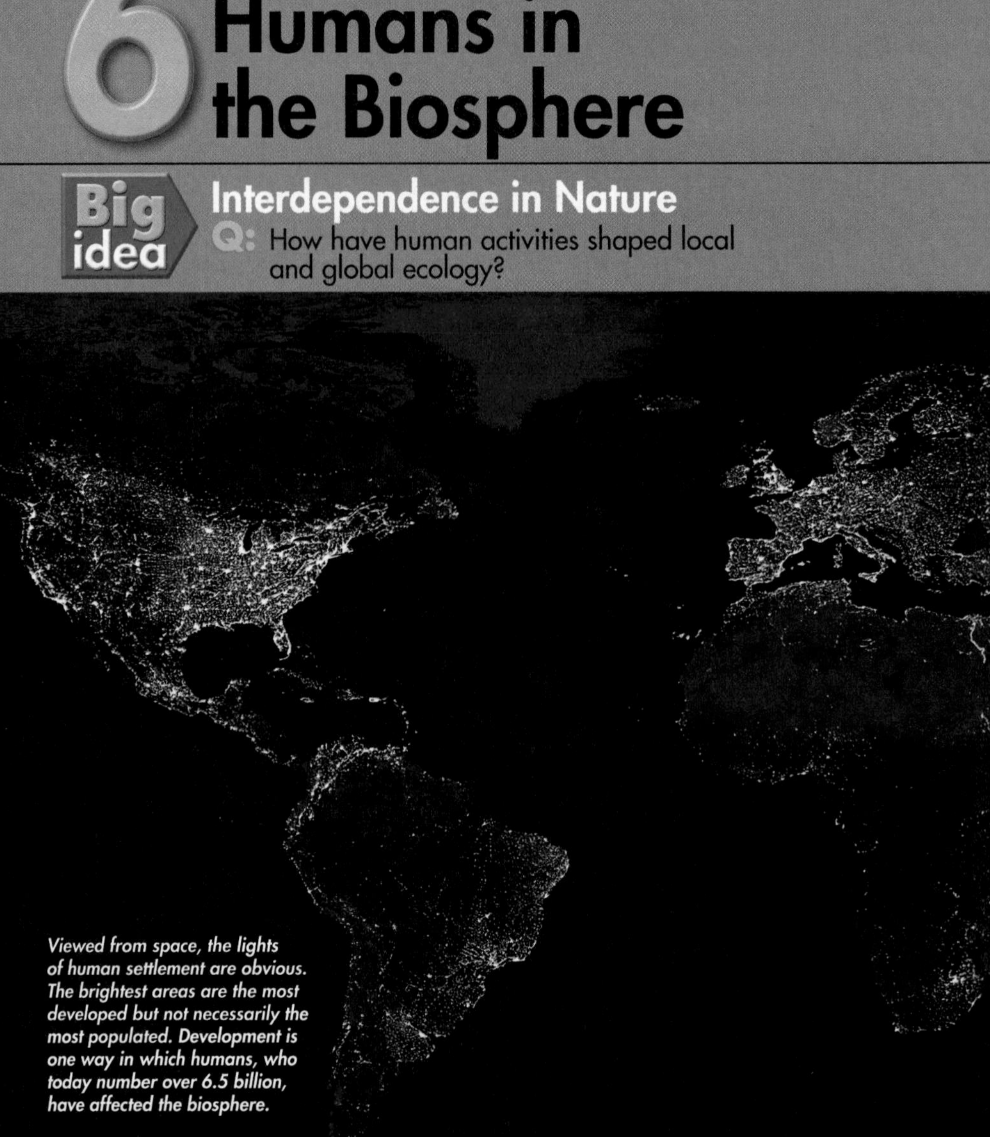

Viewed from space, the lights of human settlement are obvious. The brightest areas are the most developed but not necessarily the most populated. Development is one way in which humans, who today number over 6.5 billion, have affected the biosphere.

BIOLOGY.com Search Chapter 6 GO • Flash Cards

IN INDIANA ACADEMIC STANDARDS

For the full text of all standards, see the Course Overview in the front matter of this book.

Key standards: Chapter 6 covers key ideas from Standard 4: Interdependence, including **B.4.2** Effects of human activities and natural phenomena and **B.4.3** Non-native species.

UbD Understanding by Design

In Chapter 6, students examine the wise use of resources, the importance of biodiversity, and the need to meet ecological challenges. The graphic organizer at the right shows how the Big Idea, Essential Question, and Guiding Questions help frame students' exploration of the Unit 2 Enduring Understanding that *the existence of life on Earth depends on interactions among organisms and between organisms and their environment.*

PERFORMANCE GOALS

In Chapter 6, students will interpret information in maps, graphs, and diagrams. They will also analyze a day's worth of trash to see which items can be reused, recycled, or composted. At the end of the chapter, students will apply their knowledge by writing a magazine article about an environmental activist.

INDIANA ACADEMIC STANDARDS FOR SCIENCE

Nature of Science NoS.1, NoS.3, NoS.5, NoS.6, NoS.11; **Interdependence** B.4.2, B.4.3, B.4.4. See lessons for details.

• Untamed Science Video • Chapter Mystery

CHAPTER MYSTERY

MOVING THE *MOAI*

Easter Island is a tiny speck of land in the vast Pacific Ocean off the coast of Chile with a harsh tropical climate. The original islanders, who called themselves Rapa Nui, came from Polynesia. They carved hundreds of huge stone statues called *moai* (moh eye). Starting around 1200 A.D., the Rapa Nui somehow moved these mysterious statues, each of which weighed between 10 and 14 tons, from quarries to locations around the island. Nearly all theories about this process suggest that strong, large logs were necessary to move the *moai*. Yet by the time Europeans landed on the island in 1722, there was no sign of any trees large enough to provide such logs. What had happened? As you read this chapter, look for clues about the interactions of the Rapa Nui with their island environment. Then, solve the mystery.

Never Stop Exploring Your World. The mystery of the moving *Moais* is just the beginning. Take a video field trip with the ecogeeks of Untamed Science to see where this mystery leads.

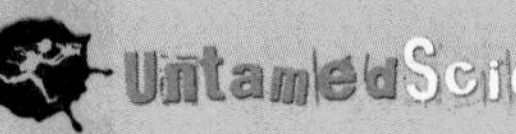

Chapter 6 Big Idea: Interdependence in Nature

Chapter 6 EQ: How have human activities shaped local and global ecology?

6.1 GQ: How does human activity affect the environment?

6.2 GQ: How can we use our natural resources wisely?

6.3 GQ: Why is it important to protect and conserve biodiversity?

6.4 GQ: How can we change our behaviors to help protect our planet?

CHAPTER 6

What's Online

BIOLOGY.com Extend your reach by using these and other digital assets offered at Biology.com.

CHAPTER MYSTERY
Students go online and look into the disappearance of large trees on Easter Island.

UNTAMED SCIENCE VIDEO
The Untamed Science crew go behind the scenes to uncover critical research and conservation programs in progress at the Houston Zoo.

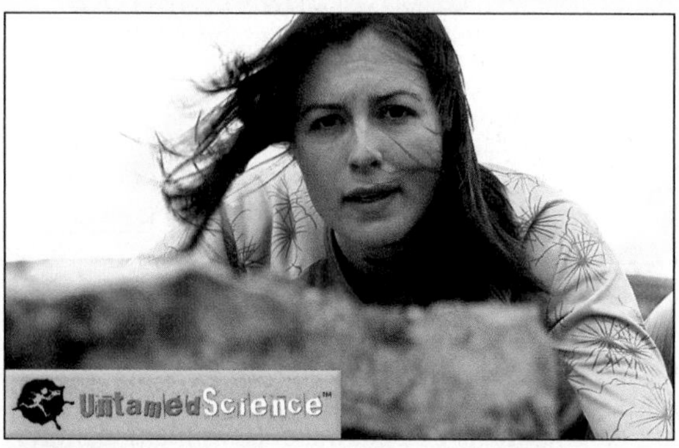

ART IN MOTION
Students watch an animation of biological magnification.

DATA ANALYSIS
Students collect virtual biodiversity data from two sites and use this data to calculate a biodiversity index for the sites.

ART REVIEW
Students review threats to biodiversity in this drag-and-drop activity.

VISUAL ANALOGY
Explore ecological footprints through this visual analogy.

LESSON 6.1

Getting Started

Objectives

6.1.1 Describe human activities that can affect the biosphere.

6.1.2 Describe the relationship between resource use and sustainable development.

Student Resources

Study Workbooks A and B, 6.1 Worksheets

Spanish Study Workbook, 6.1 Worksheets

 Lesson Overview • Lesson Notes • Assessment: Self-Test, Lesson Assessment

 For corresponding lesson in the **Foundation Edition**, see pages 128–131.

Activate Prior Knowledge

Describe a well-known natural area, such as a forest preserve or wetlands, in or near the students' community. Have students imagine that a new housing development will be built there. Have them identify positive and negative impacts of such a project. *(positives: new jobs, new houses; negatives: loss of trees, displaced animals)*

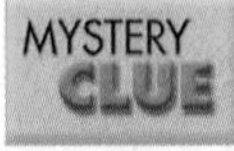 Discuss with students which "mammalian stowaways" likely came to the island on ships. Then, discuss how introducing new organisms to the island ecosystem may have affected the native species. Students can go online to **Biology.com** to gather their evidence.

IN INDIANA ACADEMIC STANDARDS

For the full text of all standards, see the Course Overview in the front matter of this book.

B.4.2 Describe how human activities and natural phenomena can change the flow of matter and energy in an ecosystem and how those changes impact other species.

6.1 A Changing Landscape

IN B.4.2 Effects of human activities and natural phenomena.

Key Questions

How do our daily activities affect the environment?

What is the relationship between resource use and sustainable development?

Vocabulary

monoculture
renewable resource
nonrenewable resource
sustainable development

Taking Notes

Outline As you read, create an outline using the green and blue heads in this lesson. As you read, fill in key words, phrases, and ideas about each heading.

MYSTERY CLUE

Easter Island's first colonists brought with them banana trees, taro root, and chickens—and possibly some small mammalian "stowaways." What impact might these new organisms have had on the island's ecosystems?

THINK ABOUT IT The first humans to settle Hawaii came from Polynesia about 1600 years ago. These island people had customs that protected the natural resources of their new home. For example, they were prohibited from catching certain fish during spawning season and, for every coconut palm tree cut down, they had to plant two palms in its place. But Hawaiians did not treat their islands entirely like nature reserves. They cut trees to plant farms, and they introduced nonnative plants, pigs, chickens, dogs, and rats. This combination drove many native plant and animal species to extinction. Yet for centuries Hawaii's ecosystems provided enough fresh water, fertile soil, fish, and other resources to keep the society self-sufficient. What happened next is a lesson on managing limited resources—a lesson that is as important today as it was over 1000 years ago.

The Effect of Human Activity

How do our daily activities affect the environment?

Beginning in the late 1700s, new waves of settlers arrived in Hawaii. These people did not seem to understand the limits of island ecosystems. They imported dozens more plants and animals that became invasive pests. They cleared vast tracts of forest to grow sugar cane, pineapples, and other crops that required lots of water. And as the island's human population grew, they converted untouched land for other uses, including housing and tourism, as shown in **Figure 6–1.** The effect of these activities on Hawaii's ecosystems and its human inhabitants offers a window onto a globally important question: What happens when a growing human population does not adequately manage natural resources that are both vital and limited?

FIGURE 6–1 The Lesson of Hawaii Kalalau Valley along the Na Pali coast of Kauai looks almost untouched by humans. In contrast, Waikiki Beach on the island of Oahu is surrounded by built-up areas that support tourism.

UbD Teach for Understanding

ENDURING UNDERSTANDING The existence of life on Earth depends on interactions among organisms and between organisms and their environment.

GUIDING QUESTION How does human activity affect the environment?

EVIDENCE OF UNDERSTANDING *After completing this lesson, give students the following assessment to show their understanding of the difference between renewable and nonrenewable resources.* Ask students to each make a list of all the renewable resources and nonrenewable resources they use in a typical day. Have volunteers share their lists with the class.

Living on Island Earth Humans, like all forms of life, rely on Earth's life-support systems. And like all other organisms, we affect our environment when we obtain food, eliminate waste products, and build places to live. The effects of these activities can be most obvious on islands such as Hawaii because of their small size. Living on an island also can make people aware of limited resources and of an area's carrying capacity for humans because anything not available locally must be brought in from far away.

Most of us who live on large continents, however, probably don't think of land, food, and water as limited resources. In the past, environmental problems were local. There was always new land to settle and new sources of food and water. But today human activity has used or altered roughly half of all the land that's not covered with ice and snow. Some people suggest that as the global population reaches 7 billion people, we may be approaching the carrying capacity of the biosphere for humans. **Humans affect regional and global environments through agriculture, development, and industry in ways that have an impact on the quality of Earth's natural resources, including soil, water, and the atmosphere.**

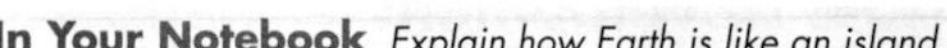
In Your Notebook *Explain how Earth is like an island.*

Agriculture Agriculture is one of the most important inventions in human history. A dependable supply of food that can be stored for later use enabled humans to gather in settlements that grew into towns and cities. Settlements, in turn, encouraged the growth of modern civilization—government, laws, writing, and science. Modern agricultural practices have enabled farmers to double world food production over the last 50 years. **Monoculture,** for example, is the practice of clearing large areas of land to plant a single highly productive crop year after year, like the soybeans in **Figure 6–2.** Monoculture enables efficient sowing, tending, and harvesting of crops using machines. However, providing food for nearly 7 billion people impacts natural resources, including fresh water and fertile soil. Fertilizer production and farm machinery also consume large amounts of fossil fuels.

GUIDED INQUIRY

Reduce, Reuse, Recycle

❶ Collect one day's worth of dry trash.

❷ Sort the trash into items that can be reused, recycled, or discarded because they can't be reused or recycled.

Analyze and Conclude

1. **Analyze Data** Look at the trash you've sorted. Roughly what percentage of the total does each type represent?
2. **Predict** What do you think happens to the trash you produce? Think of at least three ways trash can impact living things.
3. **Evaluate** List three ways you can reduce the amount of trash you produce.

B.4.2

BUILD Vocabulary

PREFIXES The prefix *mono-* in **monoculture** means "one, alone, single." Monoculture is the practice of planting a single productive crop, year after year.

FIGURE 6–2 Monoculture This farmer is using a tractor to plow a large field of soybeans. **Apply Concepts** *How has agriculture helped shape civilization?*

155

LESSON 6.1

Lead a Discussion

Call on a student to define *carrying capacity,* a concept students learned about in Chapter 5. Then, read aloud the sentence in the text that suggests we may be approaching the carrying capacity for humans in the biosphere. Talk about whether students think that number is being reached or not. Encourage them to their express their opinions, though challenge any statements that aren't backed by evidence.

DIFFERENTIATED INSTRUCTION

LPR Less Proficient Readers Before discussing the biosphere's carrying capacity for humans, make sure students understand the three main ways humans affect regional and global environments. Read the bolded Key Concept statement aloud, and then write the three categories on the board: Agriculture, Development, Industry. Call on students to describe how specific examples of each can impact the quality of Earth's natural resources. Make sure students know that the ways these human activities affect environments are not always bad.

Answers

FIGURE 6–2 Agriculture enabled humans to gather in settlements that grew into towns and cities. Settlements, in turn, encouraged the growth of modern civilization.

IN YOUR NOTEBOOK Sample answer: Earth is like an island because the resources here are finite—we can't get water or soil from anywhere else. It's also like an island because humans can't leave to live anywhere else.

PURPOSE Students will analyze the types of dry trash generated during a normal day and evaluate how the amount of trash produced could have been reduced.

MATERIALS gloves; large trash bags, boxes, or bins

SAFETY Make sure students wear gloves when sorting trash. Caution them to be careful when handling glass or metal items.

PLANNING Provide trash bags to students the day before they complete the lab. Encourage them to start collecting their own trash as soon as they start their day. Reinforce that they are collecting *only* their own trash. Discuss the types of dry trash students should collect, including bottles, cans, plastic containers, packaging, and various types of paper.

ANALYZE AND CONCLUDE

1. Answers will vary.
2. Sample answer: Most of the trash goes to a landfill. Some items are recycled. Landfills take space from natural habitats for living things. Chemicals that leak from landfills can contaminate water, and if burned, trash releases greenhouse gases. Animals mistaking trash for food may eat it and become ill.
3. Sample answer: I can recycle more items, reuse some materials instead of throwing them away, and stop buying items that are heavily packaged.

Teach continued

Use Visuals

Have students compare the photo of the wetlands in **Figure 6–3** with the inset photo of the same area as farmland.

Ask Why do you think The Wetlands Initiative would restore this area as wetlands? *(Restoring it as wetlands provides wildlife habitat and a natural filter for the area's water.)*

Ask How is this restoration an example of sustainable development? *(Sample answer: Sustainable development provides for human needs while preserving the ecosystem. Restoring the wetlands provides humans with clean drinking water while preserving the regional ecosystem.)*

DIFFERENTIATED INSTRUCTION

L3 **Advanced Students** Have interested students research The Wetlands Initiative and report what they learn to the class. For example, what is the goal of the project? Who funds the project? What successes have they had? What challenges?

ELL Focus on ELL: Access Content

INTERMEDIATE AND ADVANCED SPEAKERS
Ask students to create a **Compare/Contrast Table** with three columns and three rows. Have them label each row as follows: Agriculture, Development, and Industrial Growth. Then, have them label the second and third columns Positive Effects and Negative Effects. Ask them to fill in the table with a summary statement about the negative and positive effects of each activity. Students can use their charts when participating in discussion and for review.

Study Wkbks A/B, Appendix S20, Compare/Contrast Table. **Transparencies,** GO3.

Development As modern society developed, many people chose to live in cities. In the United States, as urban centers became crowded, people moved to, and built up, suburbs. The growth of cities and suburbs is tied to the high standard of living that Americans enjoy. Yet this development has environmental effects. Dense human communities produce lots of wastes. If these wastes are not disposed of properly, they affect air, water, and soil resources. In addition, development consumes farmland and divides natural habitats into fragments.

Industrial Growth Human society was transformed by the Industrial Revolution of the 1800s. Today, industry and scientific know-how provide us with the conveniences of modern life—from comfortable homes and clothes to electronic devices for work and play. Of course these conveniences require a lot of energy to produce and power. We obtain most of this energy by burning fossil fuels—coal, oil, and natural gas—and that affects the environment. In addition, industries have traditionally discarded wastes from manufacturing and energy production directly into the air, water, and soil.

FIGURE 6–3 Ecosystem Services The Hennepin and Hopper Lakes wetland is managed by The Wetlands Initiative—an organization dedicated to protecting and restoring Illinois's wetlands. The area, originally drained and leveed for farming in 1900, is shown in the inset before its 2003 restoration. Apply Concepts ***What ecological services do wetlands provide?***

Sustainable Development

What is the relationship between resource use and sustainable development?

In the language of economics, *goods* are things that can be bought and sold, that have value in terms of dollars and cents. *Services* are processes or actions that produce goods. Ecosystem goods and services are the goods and services produced by ecosystems that benefit the human economy.

Ecosystem Goods and Services Some ecosystem goods and services—like breathable air and drinkable water—are so basic that we often take them for granted. Healthy ecosystems provide many goods and services naturally and largely free of charge. But, if the environment can't provide these goods and services, society must spend money to produce them. In many places, for example, drinkable water is provided naturally by streams, rivers, and lakes, and filtered by wetlands like the one in **Figure 6–3.** But if water sources or wetlands are polluted or damaged, water quality may fall. In such cases, cities and towns must pay for mechanical or chemical treatment to provide safe drinking water.

In Your Notebook *Describe three ecosystem goods and services you've used today.*

UbD Check for Understanding

ONE-MINUTE RESPONSE

Write the following question on the board, and give students about a minute to write a quick response.

- Clear cutting is the process of removing the majority of trees from a forest for human use. What might a sustainable alternative to clear cutting look like?

ADJUST INSTRUCTION

If student responses show a misunderstanding of sustainable development, remind them that their plan should provide for human needs (wood for building, paper, etc.) while protecting the forest ecosystem. Ask them to think about the question: How can you use trees for wood while still protecting forests? Have students volunteer their ideas.

Answers

FIGURE 6–3 Sample answer: Wetlands filter water and provide a habitat for many kinds of organisms.

IN YOUR NOTEBOOK Sample answer: The air I breathe, the water I drink, and the oil used to make the gasoline burned in our car are three examples.

Renewable and Nonrenewable Resources Ecosystem goods and services are classified as either renewable or nonrenewable, as shown in **Figure 6–4.** A **renewable resource** can be produced or replaced by a healthy ecosystem. A single southern white pine is an example of a renewable resource because a new tree can grow in place of an old tree that dies or is cut down. But some resources are **nonrenewable resources** because natural processes cannot replenish them within a reasonable amount of time. Fossil fuels like coal, oil, and natural gas are nonrenewable resources formed from buried organic materials over millions of years. When existing deposits are depleted, they are essentially gone forever.

Sustainable Resource Use Ecological science can teach us how to use natural resources to meet our needs without causing long-term environmental harm. Using resources in such an environmentally conscious way is called **sustainable development.** **Sustainable development provides for human needs while preserving the ecosystems that produce natural resources.**

What should sustainable development look like? It should cause no long-term harm to the soil, water, and climate on which it depends. It should consume as little energy and material as possible. Sustainable development must be flexible enough to survive environmental stresses like droughts, floods, and heat waves or cold snaps. Finally, sustainable development must take into account human economic systems as well as ecosystem goods and services. It must do more than just enable people to survive. It must help them improve their situation.

FIGURE 6–4 Natural Resources Natural resources are classified as renewable or nonrenewable. Wind and coal are both natural resources that can provide energy. But wind is renewable, while coal—like other fossil fuels—is not.

6.1 Assessment

IN B.4.2

Review Key Concepts

1. a. **Review** List the three primary types of human activities that have affected regional and global environments. For each, give one benefit and one environmental cost.
   b. **Relate Cause and Effect** How might more productive agricultural practices affect a developing nation's population? Its environmental health?
   c. **Apply Concepts** In addition to filtering water, wetlands provide flood control by absorbing excess water. Explain how society would provide these services (for a cost) if the ecosystem could not.
2. a. **Review** What is sustainable development? How can it help minimize the negative impacts of human activities?
   b. **Explain** Explain why energy from the sun is a renewable resource but energy from oil is a nonrenewable resource.

WRITE ABOUT SCIENCE

Description

3. What signs of growth do you see in your community? Write a paragraph telling how this growth might affect local ecosystems.

BIOLOGY.com Search  Lesson 6.1 GO • Self-Test • Lesson Assessment

LESSON 6.1

Assess and Remediate

EVALUATE UNDERSTANDING

Have each student write a brief paragraph that describes, in their own words, how sustainable development can help reduce the negative impacts of agriculture, industry, and development. Then, have students complete the 6.1 Assessment.

REMEDIATION SUGGESTION

L1 **Struggling Students** If students have difficulty answering **Question 2b,** review the difference between renewable and nonrenewable resources. Then, call on students to help make lists of each on the board. Choose a resource from each list, and ask volunteers to explain why they are either renewable or nonrenewable resources.

BIOLOGY.com Students can check their understanding of lesson concepts with the **Self-Test** assessment. They can then take an online version of the **Lesson Assessment.**

Assessment Answers

1a. Sample answer: Agriculture: benefit, food production; cost, impacts on fresh water and fertile soil. Development: benefit, higher standard of living; cost, production of lots of wastes. Industrial growth: benefit, conveniences of modern life; cost, requires lots of energy to produce and power products.

1b. Sample answer: More productive agricultural practices would increase a nation's population since there would be more food available. However, it would likely worsen the nation's environmental health.

2a. Sustainable development means using resources in an environmentally conscious way. It provides for human needs while preserving ecosystems that produce natural resources.

2b. Sample answer: Energy from the sun is renewable because it can be replaced (the sun will keep burning). However, natural processes cannot replenish oil supplies within a reasonable amount of time, so oil is a nonrenewable resource.

2c. Sample answer: If there were no wetlands to provide flood control, societies would have to build more dams and barriers to prevent excess water from flooding cities and agricultural land.

WRITE ABOUT SCIENCE

3. Answers will vary depending on the community. Students might mention the spread of housing developments, the building of malls and other shopping areas, and the construction of highways and then explain how these affect their local ecosystem by necessitating new sources of power and materials.

LESSON 6.2

Getting Started

Objectives

6.2.1 Describe how human activities affect soil and land.

6.2.2 Describe how human activities affect water resources.

6.2.3 Describe how human activities affect air resources.

Student Resources

Study Workbooks A and B, 6.2 Worksheets

Spanish Study Workbook, 6.2 Worksheets

Lab Manual B, 6.2 Data Analysis Worksheet

Lesson Overview • Lesson Notes • Activity: Art in Motion • Assessment: Self-Test, Lesson Assessment

For corresponding lesson in the **Foundation Edition**, see pages 132–137.

Build Background

From a library, obtain a recording of Woody Guthrie's *Dust Bowl Ballads,* and play the song "The Great Dust Storm" for students. Lyrics for this song can be found online. Explain that Guthrie, one of America's great folksingers, lived during the "dust bowl" that occurred in the Great Plains during the 1930s. Describe the huge dust storms that occurred during the dust bowl, and point out the photo of a dust storm in **Figure 6–5.**

IN INDIANA ACADEMIC STANDARDS

For the full text of all standards, see the Course Overview in the front matter of this book.

NoS.11 Explain how scientific knowledge can be used to guide decisions on environmental and social issues.

B.4.2 Describe how human activities and natural phenomena can change the flow of matter and energy in an ecosystem and how those changes impact other species.

6.2 Using Resources Wisely

NoS.11 Scientific knowledge: environmental and social issues; **B.4.2** Effects of human activities and natural phenomena. Also covered: **NoS.3.**

Key Questions

Why is soil important, and how do we protect it?

What are the primary sources of water pollution?

What are the major forms of air pollution?

Vocabulary

desertification
deforestation
pollutant
biological magnification
smog
acid rain

Taking Notes

Concept Map As you read, create a concept map to organize the information in this lesson.

THINK ABOUT IT Our economy is built on the use of natural resources, so leaving those resources untouched is not an option. Humans need to eat, for example, so we can't just stop cultivating land for farming. But the goods and services provided by healthy ecosystems are essential to life. We can't grow anything in soil that has lost its nutrients due to overfarming. If we don't properly manage agriculture, then, we may one day lose the natural resource on which it depends. So how do we find a balance? How do we obtain what we need from local and global environments without destroying those environments?

Soil Resources

Why is soil important, and how do we protect it?

When you think of natural resources, soil may not be something that comes to mind. But many objects you come into contact with daily rely on soil—from the grain in your breakfast cereal, to the wood in your home, to the pages of this textbook. **Healthy soil supports both agriculture and forestry.** The mineral- and nutrient-rich portion of soil is called topsoil. Good topsoil absorbs and retains moisture yet allows water to drain. It is rich in organic matter and nutrients, but low in salts. Good topsoil is produced by long-term interactions between soil and the plants growing in it.

Topsoil can be a renewable resource if it is managed properly, but it can be damaged or lost if it is mismanaged. Healthy soil can take centuries to form but can be lost very quickly. And the loss of fertile soil can have dire consequences. Years of poorly managed farming in addition to severe drought in the 1930s badly eroded the once-fertile soil of the Great Plains. Thousands upon thousands of people lost their jobs and homes. The area essentially turned to desert, or, as it came to be known, a "dust bowl," as seen in **Figure 6–5.** What causes soil erosion, and how can we prevent it?

FIGURE 6–5 The Dust Bowl A ranch in Boise City, Idaho, is about to be hit by a cloud of dry soil on April 15, 1935.

UbD Teach for Understanding

ENDURING UNDERSTANDING The existence of life on Earth depends on interactions among organisms and between organisms and their environment.

GUIDING QUESTION How can we use our natural resources wisely?

EVIDENCE OF UNDERSTANDING *After completing this lesson, give students the following assessment to show their understanding of sustainable resource use.* Have students work in pairs to make a **Flowchart** that shows one example of how the environment may be harmed through human activities. For example, they might make a flowchart showing the process of desertification, deforestation, the formation of a dead zone in a body of water, or the formation of smog. Then, have them make a second flowchart that shows how the negative effects can be lessened by sustainable resource use. Place well-made flowcharts on the classroom wall.

Study Wkbks A/B, Appendix S25, Flowchart. **Transparencies,** GO8.

Soil Erosion The dust bowl of the 1930s was caused, in part, by conversion of prairie land to cropland in ways that left soil vulnerable to erosion. Soil erosion is the removal of soil by water or wind. Soil erosion is often worse when land is plowed and left barren between plantings. When no roots are left to hold soil in place, it is easily washed away. And when soil is badly eroded, organic matter and minerals that make it fertile are often carried away with the soil. In parts of the world with dry climates, a combination of farming, overgrazing, seasonal drought, and climate change can turn farmland into desert. This process is called **desertification,** and it is what happened to the Great Plains in the 1930s. Roughly 40 percent of Earth's land is considered at risk for desertification. **Figure 6–6** shows vulnerable areas in North and South America.

Deforestation, or loss of forests, can also have a negative effect on soil quality. Healthy forests not only provide wood, but also hold soil in place, protect the quality of fresh water supplies, absorb carbon dioxide, and help moderate local climate. Unfortunately, more than half of the world's old-growth forests (forests that had never been cut) have already been lost to deforestation. In some temperate areas, such as the Eastern United States, forests can regrow after cutting. But it takes centuries for succession to produce mature, old-growth forests. In some places, such as in parts of the tropics, forests don't grow back at all after logging. This is why old-growth forests are usually considered nonrenewable resources.

Deforestation can lead to severe erosion, especially on mountainsides. Grazing or plowing after deforestation can permanently change local soils and microclimates in ways that prevent the regrowth of trees. Tropical rain forests, for example, look lush and rich, so you might assume they would grow back after logging. Unfortunately, topsoil in these forests is generally thin, and organic matter decomposes rapidly under high heat and humidity. When tropical rain forests are cleared for timber or for agriculture, their soil is typically useful for just a few years. After that the areas become wastelands, the harsh conditions there preventing regrowth.

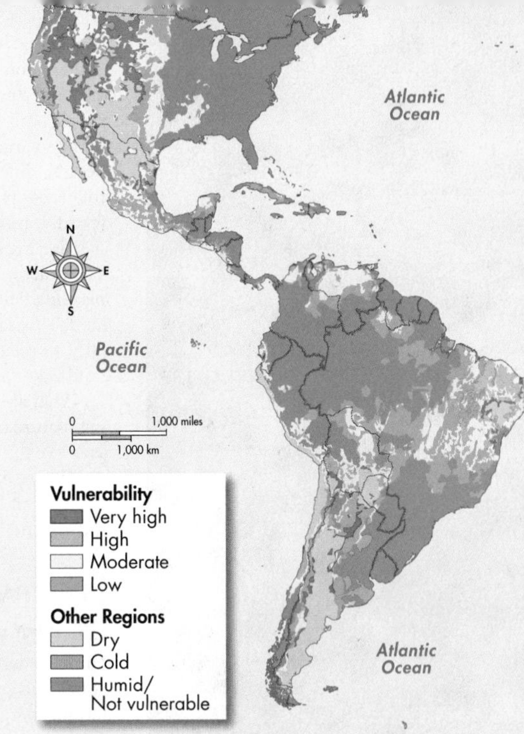

FIGURE 6–6 Desertification Risk The U.S. Department of Agriculture assigns desertification risk categories based on soil type and climate. Interpret Visuals ***Find your approximate location on the map. What category of desertification risk is your area in?***

MYSTERY CLUE

Forests of palm trees with strong, tall trunks and edible seeds once covered most of Easter Island. Why would the islanders have cut down these forests? What effect would deforestation have had?

In Your Notebook *Describe the relationship between agriculture and soil quality.*

Teach

Use Visuals

Have students examine the map in **Figure 6–6.** Call on a student to read aloud the definition of *desertification,* and then discuss why some regions are at risk and some are not.

Ask What factors put a region at risk for desertification? *(a dry climate combined with farming, overgrazing, seasonal drought, or climate change)*

Ask Why isn't the eastern United States at risk for desertification? *(That region of the United States doesn't have a dry climate.)*

DIFFERENTIATED INSTRUCTION

L3 Advanced Students Have interested students research the causes and effects of deforestation in the Amazon region of South America. Ask students to find out whether deforestation in the Amazon has resulted in areas becoming wastelands, as described in their text.

Have students review the introduction to the Chapter Mystery to find one reason why islanders cut down trees. *(for use as logs on which to move the* moai*)* Encourage them to think of other reasons why societies cut down trees. *(to burn wood for cooking and heating, to use wood in building houses)* Students can go online to Biology.com to gather their evidence.

Quick Facts

THE DUST BOWL

The dust bowl of the 1930s was one of the worst environmental disasters in U.S. history. Here are some quick facts about the dust bowl.

- The main causes were drought and poor farming practices as natural grasslands were converted for growing wheat in the early twentieth century.
- States primarily affected by the dust bowl were Texas, Oklahoma, Kansas, Colorado, and New Mexico.
- Visibility during huge dust storms was reduced to less than 1 mile (1.6 km).
- By the mid-1930s, over 1 million acres of farmland had lost all or most of their topsoil.

Answers

FIGURE 6–6 Answers will vary depending on students' location. Areas in the eastern United States are not vulnerable to desertification. Many areas in the West have very high vulnerability.

IN YOUR NOTEBOOK Sample answer: Agriculture depends on healthy soil. Without nutrient-rich topsoil, crops cannot grow, and without crops or other plants, soil is more likely to erode.

Teach continued

Lead a Discussion

Hold up a gallon of bottled water and a glass of tap water. Ask students to compare the sources of the water. *(Sample answer: Most tap water is produced at a local water plant or comes from a well; sources vary, but about one fourth of bottled water comes from municipal water supplies.)* Then, ask what happens to the bottle after the water is consumed. *(Sample answer: It's usually thrown away; sometimes it's recycled.)* Finally, have students assess which water—bottled or tap—uses more of Earth's resources and judge which is a wiser use of those resources.

DIFFERENTIATED INSTRUCTION

LPR **Less Proficient Readers** Display a map of the United States, and show students the extent of the Ogallala aquifer, from South Dakota to northern Texas. Explain that an aquifer is an underground supply of water that can be tapped for wells and used as a source of agricultural irrigation. Ask why this water is not an example of a renewable resource. *(It would take too long to replenish if all the water were pumped out.)*

ELL Focus on ELL: Extend Language

BEGINNER AND INTERMEDIATE SPEAKERS
Have students make a **Word Wall** to help them learn lesson vocabulary terms, as well as any other difficult terms they encounter. On the word wall, students should divide terms into word parts, collaborate on writing a definition, make a pronunciation guide for each term, and, if possible, write translations for each term. Students can also add drawings to help them remember each term's meaning.

Study Wkbks A/B, Appendix S17, Word Wall.

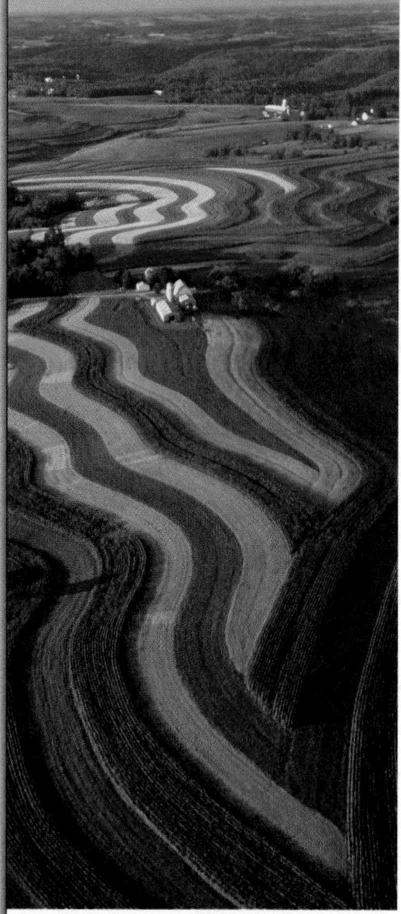

FIGURE 6–7 Contour Plowing Planting crops parallel to the land's natural contours can help reduce soil erosion.

Soil Use and Sustainability **It is possible to minimize soil erosion through careful management of both agriculture and forestry.** Soil is most vulnerable to erosion when it is completely bare. Leaving stems and roots of the previous year's crop in the soil can help hold soil in place between plantings. And because different plants take different nutrients from the soil, crop rotation—planting different crops at different seasons or in different years—can help prevent both erosion and nutrient loss.

Altering the shape of the land is another way to limit erosion. The practice of contour plowing, shown in **Figure 6–7,** involves planting fields of crops across, instead of down, the slope of the land. This can reduce water runoff and therefore erosion. Similarly, terracing—shaping the land to create level "steps"—helps hold water and soil.

What are options for sustainable forestry? Selectively harvesting mature trees can promote the growth of younger trees and preserve the forest ecosystem, including its soil. In the southeastern United States, conditions enable foresters to plant, harvest, and replant tree farms. A well-managed tree farm both protects the soil and makes the trees themselves a renewable resource.

Freshwater Resources

What are the primary sources of water pollution?

Humans depend on fresh water and freshwater ecosystems for goods and services, including drinking water, industry, transportation, energy, and waste disposal. Some of the most productive American farmland relies heavily on irrigation, in which fresh water is brought in from other sources.

While fresh water is usually considered a renewable resource, some sources of fresh water are not renewable. The Ogallala aquifer, for example, spans eight states from South Dakota to Texas. The aquifer took more than a million years to collect and is not replenished by rainfall today. So much water is being pumped out of the Ogallala that it is expected to run dry in 20 to 40 years. In many places, freshwater supplies are limited. Only 3 percent of Earth's water is fresh water—and most of that is locked in ice at the poles. Since we can't infinitely expand our use of a finite resource, we must protect the ecosystems that collect and purify fresh water.

Water Pollution Freshwater sources can be affected by different kinds of pollution. A **pollutant** is a harmful material that can enter the biosphere. Sometimes pollutants enter water supplies from a single source—a factory or an oil spill, for example. This is called point source pollution. Often, however, pollutants enter water supplies from many smaller sources—the grease and oil washed off streets by rain or the chemicals released into the air by factories and automobiles. These pollutants are called nonpoint sources.

160 Chapter 6 • Lesson 2

Biology In-Depth

OGALLALA AQUIFER

The Ogallala aquifer underlies parts of eight states, including South Dakota, Wyoming, Nebraska, Kansas, Colorado, New Mexico, Oklahoma, and Texas. The Ogallala is the main source of water throughout the area for irrigation, as well as home and industrial water needs. Most of the discharge from the aquifer is for agricultural irrigation, and farmers began withdrawing the water in the 1930s. The aquifer is recharged—that is, water is added—mainly by precipitation. Because of the high withdrawal rate and the low rate of recharge, the water level has declined as much as 100 feet in some areas since the 1940s. State and local governments have developed plans to promote water conservation, including more efficient irrigation practices.

Pollutants may enter both surface water and underground water supplies that we access with wells. Once contaminants are present, they can be extremely difficult to get rid of. **The primary sources of water pollution are industrial and agricultural chemicals, residential sewage, and nonpoint sources.**

▶ ***Industrial and Agricultural Chemicals*** One industrial pollutant is a class of organic chemicals called PCBs that were widely used in industry until the 1970s. After several large-scale contamination events, PCBs were banned. However, because PCBs often enter mud and sand beneath bodies of water, they can be difficult, if not impossible, to eliminate. Parts of the Great Lakes and some coastal areas, for example, are still polluted with PCBs. Other harmful industrial pollutants are heavy metals like cadmium, lead, mercury, and zinc.

Large-scale monoculture has increased the use of pesticides and insecticides. These chemicals can enter the water supply in the form of runoff after heavy rains, or they can seep directly into groundwater. Pesticides can be very dangerous pollutants. DDT, which is both cheap and long lasting, effectively controls agricultural pests and disease-carrying mosquitoes. But when DDT gets into a water supply, it has disastrous effects on the organisms that directly and indirectly rely on that water—a function of a phenomenon called biological magnification.

Biological magnification occurs if a pollutant, such as DDT, mercury, or a PCB, is picked up by an organism and is not broken down or eliminated from its body. Instead, the pollutant collects in body tissues. Primary producers pick up a pollutant from the environment. Herbivores that eat those producers concentrate and store the compound. Pollutant concentrations in herbivores may be more than ten times the levels in producers. When carnivores eat the herbivores, the compound is still further concentrated. Thus, pollutant concentration increases at higher trophic levels. In the highest trophic levels, pollutant concentrations may reach 10 million times their original concentration in the environment, as shown in **Figure 6–8.**

These high concentrations can cause serious problems for wildlife and humans. Widespread DDT use in the 1950s threatened fish-eating birds like pelicans, osprey, falcons, and bald eagles. It caused females to lay eggs with thin, fragile shells, reducing hatching rates and causing a drop in bird populations. Since DDT was banned in the 1970s, bird populations have recovered. Still a concern is mercury, which accumulates in the bodies of certain marine fish such as tuna and swordfish.

In Your Notebook *In your own words, explain the process of biological magnification.*

FIGURE 6–8 Biological Magnification In the process of biological magnification, the concentration of a pollutant like DDT—represented by the orange dots—is multiplied as it passes up the food chain from producers to consumers. Calculate ***By what number is the concentration of DDT multiplied at each successive trophic level?*** MATH

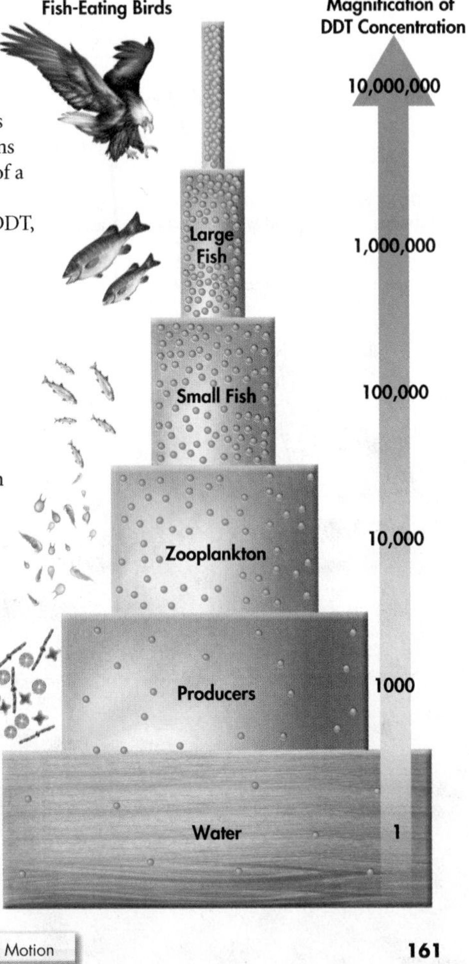

BIOLOGY.com Search Lesson 6.2 GO • Art in Motion

Use Visuals

Begin a discussion of **Figure 6–8** by pointing out that the figure represents a food chain, which students learned about in Chapter 3. Point out that the pyramid shows the concentration of DDT as orange dots in each trophic level. After students have examined the figure, ask them to fill in the blanks of this statement using the words *decreases* or *increases.*

- In a food chain, the concentration of a pollutant _____ *(increases)* as the number of organisms at a trophic level _____ *(decreases).*

DIFFERENTIATED INSTRUCTION

L1 Struggling Students Explain that the figure shows relative numbers, not absolute numbers. In other words, the figure is a model for how the concentration of the pollutant is magnified from one trophic level to the next higher level.

Ask If the level of a pollutant were 2 parts per million at the first trophic level, what would its concentration be at the second trophic level?
(20 parts per million, or 2 × 10)

BIOLOGY.com Students can watch an animation of biological magnification by accessing **Art in Motion: Biological Magnification.**

Address Misconceptions

Pollutants in a Food Chain Some students may believe that pollutants such as DDT undergo no changes as they move through a food chain. Explain that chemicals may affect different kinds of animals differently, and chemicals may change in form as they move through a food chain. Point out that DDT was once widely used in the United States because it was effective in killing insects, mainly by affecting insect nervous systems. In fish-eating birds, though, the chemical affects the formation of eggshells, which was not foreseen by those who spread the chemical.

How Science Works

USES OF DDT

The pesticide DDT (dichloro-diphenyl-trichloroethane) was discovered in the 1940s, and was first used during World War II to control body lice. In the 1950s, DDT was used extensively to combat diseases spread by insects and for insect control in general. In the United States, the use of DDT declined after the publication of *Silent Spring* by Rachel Carson in 1962. The book widely publicized the harmful effects of the pesticide. Since the 1970s, the use of DDT has been banned in many countries, including the United States and Canada. Because of its success in controlling disease-carrying insects, though, DDT has continued to be used in other parts of the world. In 2006, the World Health Organization (WHO) approved its use in Africa to fight malaria-carrying mosquitoes.

Answers

FIGURE 6–8 10

IN YOUR NOTEBOOK Sample answer: Biological magnification is the process by which a pollutant becomes more concentrated in the bodies of organisms at higher trophic levels.

Teach continued

Connect to Earth Science

Make sure students understand the idea behind watershed conservation—that cleaning up pollution in a local area does no good if nothing is done about water pollution elsewhere in the watershed. Show students a map of their state or their region. Have them identify a river that runs through or close to their community. Then, have them try to identify the watershed their river is part of. What body of water does their river run into? What river runs into their river? Suggest various places where the watershed might be polluted, and have students identify communities downstream from that source that would be affected by the pollution.

DIFFERENTIATED INSTRUCTION

L1 Special Needs To help students understand watersheds, use clay to create a tactile model of a branching river system. Explain to students that if a pollutant were added to one river branch, it would eventually find its way into larger and larger rivers until it reached the ocean. Have students trace the path of a pollutant molecule from a site on one river branch through the waterways in their model watershed.

L3 Advanced Students Point out that water conservation is important to the sustainable use of water resources. Ask students to brainstorm ideas about how they can conserve water in their own lives. Have them use their ideas to make a poster or pamphlet that could be used to inform the public about simple ways to conserve water.

▶ ***Residential Sewage*** Have you ever stopped to think what happens after you flush your toilet? Those wastes don't disappear! They become residential sewage. Sewage isn't poisonous, but it does contain lots of nitrogen and phosphorus. Reasonable amounts of these nutrients can be processed by and absorbed into healthy ecosystems. But large amounts of sewage can stimulate blooms of bacteria and algae that rob water of oxygen. Oxygen-poor areas called "dead zones" can appear in both fresh and salt water. Raw sewage also contains microorganisms that can spread disease.

Water Quality and Sustainability One key to sustainable water use is to protect the natural systems involved in the water cycle. For example, as water flows slowly through a wetland, densely growing plants absorb some excess nutrients and filter out certain pollutants. Similarly, forests and other vegetation help purify water that seeps into the ground or runs off into rivers and lakes. Protecting these ecosystems is a critical part of watershed conservation. A watershed includes all the land whose groundwater, streams, and rivers drain into the same place—such as a large lake or river. The idea behind watershed conservation is simple: Cleaning up the pollution in a local area can't do much good if the water running into it is polluted. You must consider the entire watershed to achieve long-lasting results.

Pollution control can have direct and positive effects on the water quality in a watershed. Sewage treatment can lower levels of sewage-associated bacteria and help prevent dead zones in bodies of water receiving the runoff. In some situations, agriculture can use integrated pest management (IPM) instead of pesticides. IPM techniques include biological control—using predators and parasites to regulate for pest insects—the use of less-poisonous sprays, and crop rotation.

Conserving water is, of course, also important. One example of water conservation in agriculture is drip irrigation, shown in **Figure 6–9**, which delivers water drop by drop directly to the roots of plants that need it.

BUILD Vocabulary

RELATED WORD FORMS The verb *purify* is related to the noun *pure*. *To purify* means "to make pure or clean." Wetlands purify water by removing pollutants.

FIGURE 6–9 Drip Irrigation These cabbages are supplied water directly to their roots through drip irrigation. Tiny holes in water hoses (inset) allow farmers to deliver water only where it's needed.

Biology In-Depth

TURNING WASTE INTO ENERGY

Some companies have been developing technology that turns waste matter and industrial pollution into energy resources. For example, with the support of the U.S. Environmental Protection Agency (EPA), a Georgia company has developed a process that converts municipal sewage and other organic wastes into a high-energy liquid fuel. This fuel burns more cleanly than coal. In addition to the production of a new energy source, this process eliminates problems associated with waste disposal, including odor, the release of air pollutants, and the use of land for landfills.

Atmospheric Resources

What are the major forms of air pollution?

The atmosphere is a common resource whose quality has direct effects on health. After all, the atmosphere provides the oxygen we breathe! In addition, ozone, a form of oxygen that is found naturally in the upper atmosphere, absorbs harmful ultraviolet radiation from sunlight before it reaches Earth's surface. It is the ozone layer that protects our skin from damage that can cause cancer.

The atmosphere provides many other services. For example, the atmosphere's greenhouse gases, including carbon dioxide, methane, and water vapor, regulate global temperature. As you've learned, without the greenhouse effect, Earth's average temperature would be about 30° Celsius cooler than it is today.

The atmosphere is never "used up." So, classifying it as a renewable or nonrenewable resource is not as important as understanding how human activities affect the quality of the atmosphere. For most of Earth's history, the quality of the atmosphere has been naturally maintained by biogeochemical cycles. However, if we disrupt those cycles, or if we overload the atmosphere with pollutants, the effects on its quality can last a very long time.

FIGURE 6–10 Smog Despite closing factories and restricting vehicle access to the city, Beijing remained under a blanket of dense smog just days before the 2008 Summer Olympics. Apply Concepts ***What component of smog is beneficial when part of the atmosphere, but harmful when at ground level?***

Air Pollution What happens when the quality of Earth's atmosphere is reduced? For one thing, respiratory illnesses such as asthma are made worse and skin diseases tend to increase. Globally, climate patterns may be affected. What causes poor air quality? Industrial processes and the burning of fossil fuels can release pollutants of several kinds. **Common forms of air pollution include smog, acid rain, greenhouse gases, and particulates.**

▶ ***Smog*** If you live in a large city, you've probably seen **smog,** a gray-brown haze formed by chemical reactions among pollutants released into the air by industrial processes and automobile exhaust. Ozone is one product of these reactions. While ozone high up in the atmosphere helps protect life on Earth from ultraviolet radiation, at ground level, ozone and other pollutants threaten the health of people, especially those with respiratory conditions. Many athletes participating in the 2008 Summer Olympics in Beijing, China, expressed concern over how the intense smog, seen in **Figure 6–10,** would affect their performance and health.

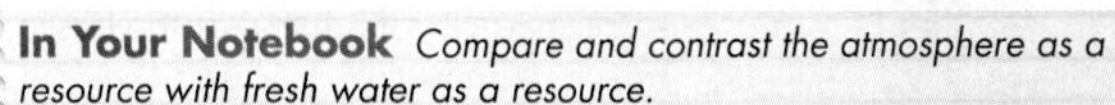

In Your Notebook *Compare and contrast the atmosphere as a resource with fresh water as a resource.*

Build Reading Skills

Explain that making an outline can help students understand the material and put it in a useful form for review. Have each student outline the subsection **Air Pollution.** Begin the outline on the board by writing the title Air Pollution. Tell students the primary heads of the outline should be the four common forms of air pollution described: Smog, Acid Rain, Greenhouse Gases, and Particulates. Under each primary head, they should add details about that form of air pollution. After they have finished their outlines, divide the class into small groups to compare outlines. Ask students to revise their outlines as they talk with other group members about the details they included.

DIFFERENTIATED INSTRUCTION

ELL English Language Learners Point out to English language learners that the term *smog* may remind them of another English word, *fog*. Explain that the two words are related. The origins of *smog* come from a description of this form of pollution in the early twentieth century, when gray-brown haze was described as a "smoky fog." Parts of the two words were put together to make the word *smog*.

UbD Check for Understanding

INDEX CARD SUMMARIES

Give each student an index card, and ask them to write one concept they understand about using resources wisely on the front of the card. Then, have them write something about using resources wisely that they do not understand on the back of the card in the form of a question.

ADJUST INSTRUCTION

Read over students' cards to get a sense of which concepts they are having trouble with. If the question will be answered by reading the rest of the chapter, such as by reading the case studies in Lesson 6.4, use the card to emphasize a concept. If the answer to the question is necessary to move forward, review the topic as a class to allow students to hear the concept discussed in different ways.

Answers

FIGURE 6–10 ozone

IN YOUR NOTEBOOK Sample answer: Both the atmosphere and fresh water are needed for healthy ecosystems, and both can be contaminated with pollutants. Fresh water is usually considered a renewable resource, though some sources of fresh water are not renewable. Fresh water may be possible to treat if it's polluted. The atmosphere is never used up, and so it is neither renewable nor nonrenewable—but to protect the atmosphere, we need to prevent pollutants from being released in the first place.

LESSON 6.2

Teach continued

Use Visuals

Have students examine the effects of acid rain in **Figure 6–11.**

Ask What human activities produce the nitrogen and sulfur compounds that result in acid rain? *(the burning of fossil fuels)*

Point out that fossil fuels are burned in homes, in addition to factories.

Ask What do most Americans use in their homes that ultimately is derived from the burning of fossil fuels? *(They use electricity, which is often produced in coal-fired or oil-fired power plants. Home heating is also usually generated by either oil or natural gas.)*

DIFFERENTIATED INSTRUCTION

L3 **Advanced Students** Have students collect samples of rainwater from various outdoor locations. Provide them with litmus paper for testing the pH of each sample. Have them also test tap water and compare the pH of the samples with the pH of tap water. Explain that all rainwater is slightly acidic (pH 6–7) because of carbon dioxide in the air. A pH of less than 5.5 qualifies as acid rain. Have students report their findings to the class.

Answers

IN YOUR NOTEBOOK Flowcharts may vary, but should include this basic information: (1) Burning fossil fuels releases nitrogen and sulfur compounds. (2) The compounds combine with water vapor in the air and form nitric and sulfuric acids. (3) The acids can drift for many kilometers before falling as acid rain.

IN NoS.3, NoS.11

American Air Pollution Trends

Each year, the U.S. Environmental Protection Agency (EPA) estimates emissions from a variety of sources. Look at the graph in **Figure 6–12.** The combined emissions of six common pollutants are plotted along with trends in energy consumption and automobile travel between 1980 and 2007. The values shown are the total percentage change. For example, in 1995, aggregate emissions had dropped about 30 percent from their level in 1980.

1. Interpret Data Describe the overall trend in emissions since 1980. Is this what you would expect given the trends in energy consumption and automobile travel? Explain your answer.

2. Interpret Data How does this graph differ from one that shows *absolute* values for emissions? Would that graph start at zero as this one does?

3. Infer What do you think has contributed to the trends you see in this graph? Why would the EPA be particularly interested in these data?

FIGURE 6–11 Acid Rain Acid rain results from the chemical transformation of nitrogen and sulfur products that come from human activities. These reactions can cause damage to stone statues and plant life.

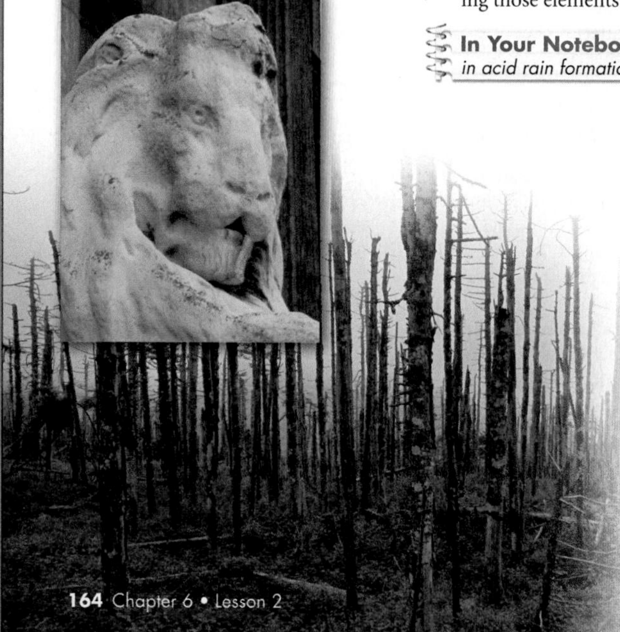

▶ ***Acid Rain*** When we burn fossil fuels in our factories and homes, we release nitrogen and sulfur compounds. When those compounds combine with water vapor in the air, they form nitric and sulfuric acids. These airborne acids can drift for many kilometers before they fall as **acid rain.** Acidic water vapor can also affect ecosystems as fog or snow. In some areas, acid rain kills plants by damaging their leaves and changing the chemistry of soils and surface water. Examples of its effects are shown in **Figure 6–11.** Acid precipitation also can dissolve and release mercury and other toxic elements from soil, freeing those elements to enter other parts of the biosphere.

In Your Notebook *Create a flowchart that shows the steps in acid rain formation.*

▶ ***Greenhouse Gases*** Burning fossil fuels and forests releases stored carbon into the atmosphere as carbon dioxide, a greenhouse gas. Agricultural practices from raising cattle to farming rice release methane, another greenhouse gas. Although some greenhouse gases are necessary, when excess greenhouse gases accumulate in the atmosphere, they contribute to global warming and climate change.

▶ ***Particulates*** Particulates are microscopic particles of ash and dust released by certain industrial processes and certain kinds of diesel engines. Very small particulates can pass through the nose and mouth and enter the lungs, where they can cause serious health problems.

Analyzing Data

PURPOSE Students will interpret data about air pollution trends in the United States and infer what contributed to those trends.

PLANNING Review with students how the burning of fossil fuels contributes to air pollution. Point out that the graph shows percent change, not absolute values. Make sure students understand what an absolute value for each of the three variables (vehicle miles traveled, energy consumption, and aggregate emissions) might be.

ANSWERS

1. Sample answer: The overall trend is a decrease in emissions. This is unexpected, because the trend for vehicle miles traveled has risen sharply during the same period. The trend for energy consumption has also risen, though not as sharply.
2. Sample answer: That graph would not start at zero for emissions. Rather, the label on the vertical axis would be a measure of emissions, such as parts per million, and the graph would start with the absolute value for emissions in 1980.
3. Sample answer: The trend in emissions is likely the result of improvements in technology such as more-efficient vehicle engines and less-polluting gasoline and other fuels. Part of the EPA's job is to develop environmental regulations such as gas mileage mandates. These data show that, at least in part, these regulations have been working.

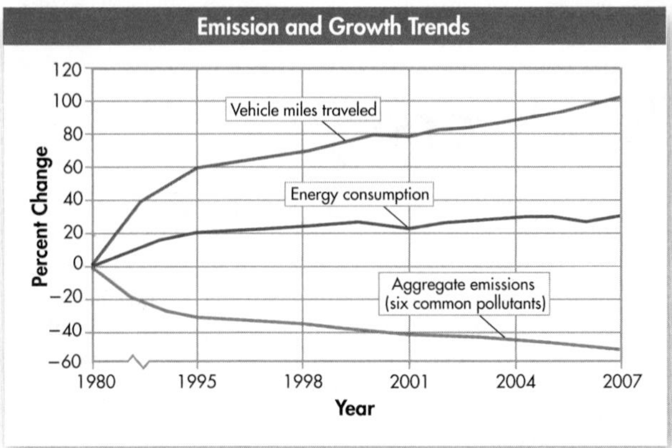

FIGURE 6–12 Air Pollution Trends This graph summarizes EPA findings of the total percentage change from 1980 to 2007 in vehicle miles traveled, energy consumption, and the combined emissions of six common pollutants—carbon monoxide, lead, nitrogen oxides, organic compounds, particulates, and sulfur dioxide. **Calculate** ***In 1980, motorists in the Puget Sound region of Washington State traveled 36.4 million miles. Assuming that these motorists increased their miles traveled at the national rate, approximately how many miles did they travel in 2007?*** MATH

Air Quality and Sustainability Improving air quality is difficult. Air doesn't stay in one place and doesn't "belong" to anyone. Automobile emission standards and clean-air regulations have improved air quality in some regions, however, and seem to be having a net positive effect, as shown in **Figure 6–12.** Efforts like these also have improved the atmosphere globally. At one time, for example, all gasoline was enriched with lead. But as leaded gasoline burned, lead was released in exhaust fumes and ultimately washed onto land and into rivers and streams. U.S. efforts to phase out leaded gasoline started in 1973 and were completed in 1996 when the sale of leaded gasoline was banned. Now that unleaded gasoline is used widely across the United States, lead levels in soils, rivers, and streams around the country have dropped significantly from earlier, higher levels.

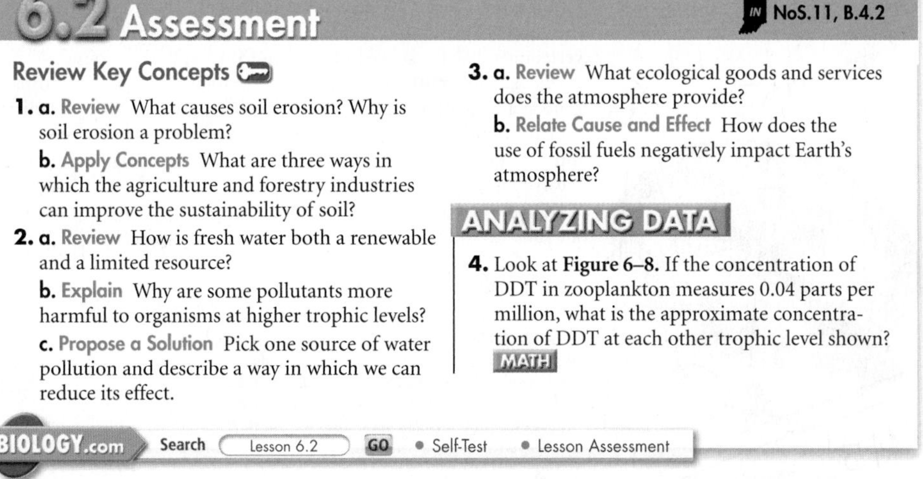

6.2 Assessment

IN NoS.11, B.4.2

Review Key Concepts

1. a. Review What causes soil erosion? Why is soil erosion a problem?

b. Apply Concepts What are three ways in which the agriculture and forestry industries can improve the sustainability of soil?

2. a. Review How is fresh water both a renewable and a limited resource?

b. Explain Why are some pollutants more harmful to organisms at higher trophic levels?

c. Propose a Solution Pick one source of water pollution and describe a way in which we can reduce its effect.

3. a. Review What ecological goods and services does the atmosphere provide?

b. Relate Cause and Effect How does the use of fossil fuels negatively impact Earth's atmosphere?

ANALYZING DATA

4. Look at **Figure 6–8.** If the concentration of DDT in zooplankton measures 0.04 parts per million, what is the approximate concentration of DDT at each other trophic level shown? MATH

BIOLOGY.com Search Lesson 6.2 GO • Self-Test • Lesson Assessment

LESSON 6.2

Assess and Remediate

EVALUATE UNDERSTANDING

Call on students at random to identify specific human activities that result in harm to soil resources, freshwater resources, and atmospheric resources. Then, have students complete the 6.2 Assessment.

REMEDIATION SUGGESTION

L1 Struggling Students If your students have difficulty answering **Question 4,** make sure they first understand by what number the pollutant is multiplied at each successive level. Then, make sure students understand that the concentration of 0.04 ppm is for the second trophic level. Finally, help them find the concentration for the first level by dividing by 10, and for levels above the second level by multiplying by 10 at each successive level.

BIOLOGY.com Students can check their understanding of lesson concepts with the **Self-Test** assessment. They can then take an online version of the **Lesson Assessment.**

Answers

FIGURE 6–12 72.8 million miles

Assessment Answers

1a. Sample answer: Soil erosion is caused when no roots are left to hold soil in place. When soil is badly eroded, organic matter and minerals that make it fertile are often carried away with the soil.

1b. Sample answer: Leaving stems and roots of the previous year's crop in the soil between plantings can help hold soil in place. Crop rotation can help prevent soil erosion. The practice of contour plowing can limit erosion.

2a. Sample answer: The water cycle naturally renews Earth's fresh water. In some places, though, freshwater supplies are limited.

2b. Some pollutants are more harmful to organisms at higher trophic levels because they undergo biological magnification and become more concentrated in the bodies of organisms at these levels.

2c. Sample answer: Agricultural chemicals are one source of water pollutants. We could reduce their effects by using as little fertilizer as possible.

3a. the oxygen we breathe, the ozone layer that absorbs harmful ultraviolet radiation, and the greenhouse gases that regulate global temperature

3b. The burning of fossil fuels releases pollutants of several kinds, including greenhouse gases, particulates, and the pollutants that produce smog and acid rain.

ANALYZING DATA

4. Producers, 0.004 ppm; small fish, 0.4 ppm; larger fish, 4 ppm; fish-eating birds, 40 ppm

LESSON 6.3

Getting Started

Objectives

6.3.1 Define biodiversity and explain its value.

6.3.2 Identify current threats to biodiversity.

6.3.3 Describe how biodiversity can be preserved.

Student Resources

Study Workbooks A and B, 6.3 Worksheets

Spanish Study Workbook, 6.3 Worksheets

Lab Manual B, 6.3 Data Analysis Worksheet

Lesson Overview • Lesson Notes • Activities: Data Analysis, Art Review • Assessment: Self-Test, Lesson Assessment

For corresponding lesson in the **Foundation Edition**, see pages 138–142.

Build Background

Show students photos of ivory products. Explain that the source of ivory is mostly of elephant tusks. Point out that there are laws against killing elephants to take their tusks, and trade in ivory products has been banned by international law, but a market for ivory still exists. Ask students to predict how this demand for ivory affects elephant populations and the biosphere.

Answers

FIGURE 6–13 Sample answer: There is much greater species diversity in a tropical area than in a desert. Ecosystem diversity is also greater in a tropical area.

INDIANA ACADEMIC STANDARDS

For the full text of all standards, see the Course Overview in the front matter of this book.

B.4.2 Describe how human activities and natural phenomena can change the flow of matter and energy in an ecosystem and how those changes impact other species.

B.4.3 Describe the consequences of introducing non-native species into an ecosystem and identify the impact it may have on that ecosystem.

6.3 Biodiversity

B.4.2 Effects of human activities and natural phenomenon; **B.4.3** Non-native species. Also covered: **NoS.3, NoS.11, B.4.4.**

Key Questions

Why is biodiversity important?

What are the most significant threats to biodiversity?

How do we preserve biodiversity?

Vocabulary

biodiversity
ecosystem diversity
species diversity
genetic diversity
habitat fragmentation
ecological hot spot

Taking Notes

Preview Visuals Before you read, look at **Figure 6–20.** Record three questions you have about the map. When you've finished reading, answer the questions.

THINK ABOUT IT Those of us who love nature are awed by the incredible variety of living things that share our planet. From multicolored coral reefs to moss-draped forests, *variety*, is "the spice of life." But variety in the biosphere gives us more than interesting things to look at. Our well-being is closely tied to the well-being of a great number of other organisms, including many that are neither majestic nor beautiful to our eyes.

The Value of Biodiversity

Why is biodiversity important?

Biological diversity, or **biodiversity,** is the total of all the genetically based variation in all organisms in the biosphere. To biologists, biodiversity is precious, worth preserving for its own sake. But what kinds of biodiversity exist, and what value do they offer society?

Types of Biodiversity Biodiversity exists on three levels: ecosystem diversity, species diversity, and genetic diversity. **Ecosystem diversity** refers to the variety of habitats, communities, and ecological processes in the biosphere. The number of different species in the biosphere, or in a particular area, is called **species diversity.** To date, biologists have identified and named more than 1.8 million species, and they estimate that at least 30 million more are yet be discovered. Much of this diversity exists among single-celled organisms. But new species of vertebrates, like the snake in **Figure 6–13,** are still being found.

Genetic diversity can refer to the sum total of all different forms of genetic information carried by a particular species, or by all organisms on Earth. Within each species, genetic diversity refers to the total of all different forms of genes present in that species. In many ways, genetic diversity is the most basic kind of biodiversity. It is also the hardest kind to see and appreciate. Yet, genetic diversity is vitally important to the survival and evolution of species in a changing world.

FIGURE 6–13 A New Species This tiny snake, native to the island of Barbados, is one of many recently discovered species. Photos of the snake were released in 2008. **Infer** *Why are you more likely to discover a new vertebrate species in a tropical area than in a desert?*

UbD Teach for Understanding

ENDURING UNDERSTANDING The existence of life on Earth depends on interactions among organisms and between organisms and their environment.

GUIDING QUESTION Why is it important to protect and conserve biodiversity?

EVIDENCE OF UNDERSTANDING *After completing this lesson, give students the following assessment to show they understand the importance of conserving biodiversity.* Have students work in pairs. Ask each pair to create a cartoon strip of six to eight panels that explains one way to conserve biodiversity. Ask volunteers to pass around their comic strips to other students in the class.

Valuing Biodiversity You can't touch, smell, or eat biodiversity, so many people don't think of it as a natural resource. But biodiversity is one of Earth's greatest natural resources. **Biodiversity's benefits to society include contributions to medicine and agriculture, and the provision of ecosystem goods and services.** When biodiversity is lost, significant value to the biosphere and to humanity may be lost along with it.

▶ ***Biodiversity and Medicine*** Wild species are the original source of many medicines, including painkillers like aspirin and antibiotics like penicillin. The chemicals in wild species are used to treat diseases like depression and cancer. For example, the foxglove, shown in **Figure 6–14,** contains compounds called digitalins that are used to treat heart disease. These plant compounds are assembled according to instructions coded in genes. So the genetic information carried by diverse species is like a "natural library" from which we have a great deal to learn.

▶ ***Biodiversity and Agriculture*** Genetic diversity is also important in agriculture. Most crop plants have wild relatives, like the potatoes in **Figure 6–15.** These wild plants may carry genes we can use—through plant breeding or genetic engineering—to transfer disease or pest resistance, or other useful traits, to crop plants.

▶ ***Biodiversity and Ecosystem Services*** The number and variety of species in an ecosystem can influence that ecosystem's stability, productivity, and value to humans. Sometimes the presence or absence of a single keystone species, like the sea otter in **Figure 6–16,** can completely change the nature of life in an ecosystem. Also, healthy and diverse ecosystems play a vital role in maintaining soil, water, and air quality.

FIGURE 6–14 Medicinal Plants Digoxin, a drug derived from digitalin compounds in the foxglove plant, is used to treat heart disease.

FIGURE 6–15 Potato Diversity The genetic diversity of wild potatoes in South America can be seen in the colorful varieties shown here. The International Potato Center, based in Peru, houses a "library" of more than 4500 tuber varieties.

FIGURE 6–16 Keystone Species The sea otter is a keystone species. When the otter population falls, the population of its favorite prey, sea urchins, goes up. Population increases in sea urchins, in turn, cause a dramatic decrease in the population of sea kelp, the sea urchin's favorite food.

BIOLOGY.com Search Lesson 6.3 GO • Data Analysis

167

Teach

Lead a Discussion

As a class, discuss the value of biodiversity, including the types of biodiversity and biodiversity's benefits to society. Make sure students understand that biodiversity exists on three levels: ecosystem diversity, species diversity, and genetic diversity.

Ask If an ecologist were to describe the number and variety of habitats in a biome, what level of biodiversity would he or she be referring to? *(ecosystem diversity)*

Ask What could happen that would cause farmers to turn to a wild relative of a crop plant? *(Sample answer: A devastating disease could spread through a crop. If a wild relative were resistant to the disease, then farmers could turn to those plants to replace or modify the crop plants.)*

DIFFERENTIATED INSTRUCTION

ELL **English Language Learners** Tell students that the term *biodiversity* is a shortened form of *biological diversity.* Explain that *diversity* means "a variety." Talking about biodiversity, then, is a way of talking about the variety of organisms in an ecosystem or in the biosphere. Point out that they may have heard the term *diversity* used in describing the population of the United States, which includes a diversity of races and ethnic groups.

LPR **Less Proficient Readers** Have students make bulleted lists under the headings **Biodiversity and Medicine, Biodiversity and Agriculture,** and **Biodiversity and Ecosystem Services.** Each list should include details and examples about benefits of biodiversity to society.

BIOLOGY.com Students compare data from two sites and learn to quantify biodiversity in the activity **Data Analysis: Measuring Biodiversity.**

LESSON 6.3

Biology In-Depth

A KEYSTONE SPECIES

When a keystone species is removed from an ecosystem, dramatic changes usually follow. The sea otter is an example of a keystone species in the intertidal zone. This mammal once was native to much of the Pacific Coast of the North America. Hunting sea otters for fur caused their decline in the nineteenth century. Now, sea otter populations have been restored in some areas, such as California and southeastern Alaska. Where sea otters have returned, the population of sea urchins has declined, because otters hunt sea urchins. Kelp forests have grown, because sea urchins eat kelp. And, the population of bald eagles has increased, because bald eagles eat fish that thrive in kelp forests.

Teach continued

Connect to the Real World

After students have read about habitat fragmentation, call on volunteers to name parks or other natural areas in their community. Make a list of these natural areas on the board. Then, have students estimate the size of each area on the list (or look up the areas ahead of time). Add the square areas of all the parks together, and circle the sum.

Ask What difference would it make to the area's biodiversity if there were one natural area equal in size to the sum of all the existing natural areas? *(Sample answer: There would be greater biodiversity in the one big area, with more genetic diversity and likely more species diversity.)*

DIFFERENTIATED INSTRUCTION

L1 Struggling Students To help students understand habitat fragmentation, have them think of a busy highway with forests on either side. What happens to animals when they try to cross the road to the other part of the forest—habitat that was once part of their geographic range? Often, they are injured or killed; this is a consequence of habitat fragmentation.

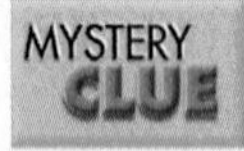

Discuss with students why a lack of biodiversity can make organisms more vulnerable to extinction and less able to survive disturbances caused by human activities. Students can go online to Biology.com to gather their evidence.

BIOLOGY.com Have students use **Art Review: Threats to Biodiversity** to drag and drop labels onto a photo showing a region that has been developed by humans.

MYSTERY CLUE

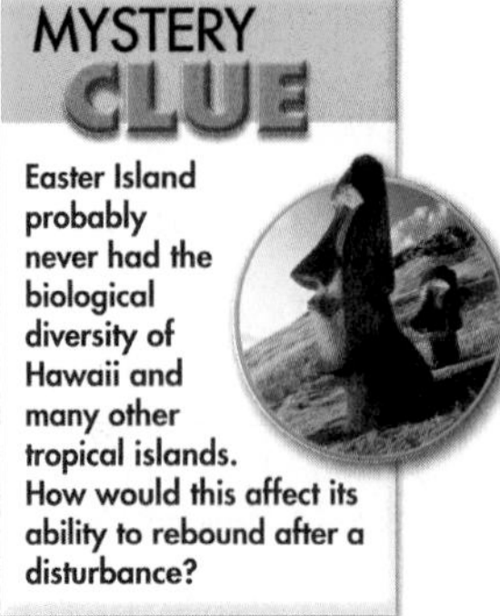

Easter Island probably never had the biological diversity of Hawaii and many other tropical islands. How would this affect its ability to rebound after a disturbance?

Threats to Biodiversity

What are the most significant threats to biodiversity?

Species have been evolving, changing, and dying out since life began. In fact scientists estimate that over 99 percent of the species that have ever lived are now extinct. So extinction is not new. But human activity today is causing the greatest wave of extinctions since dinosaurs disappeared. The current rate of species loss is approaching 1000 times the "typical" rate. And as species disappear, the potential contribution to human knowledge that is carried in their genes is lost.

Species diversity is related to genetic diversity. The more genetically diverse a species is, the greater its chances of surviving disturbances. So, as human activity reduces genetic diversity, species are put at a greater risk for extinction. Species diversity, in turn, is linked to ecosystem diversity. Therefore, as ecosystems are damaged, the organisms that inhabit them become more vulnerable to extinction.

How are humans influencing biodiversity? **Humans reduce biodiversity by altering habitats, hunting, introducing invasive species, releasing pollution into food webs, and contributing to climate change.** Biologists compare loss of biodiversity to destroying a library before its books are ever read.

Altered Habitats When natural habitats are eliminated for agriculture or for urban development, the number of species in those habitats drops, and some species may become extinct. But, habitats don't need to be completely destroyed to put species at risk. Development often splits ecosystems into pieces, a process called **habitat fragmentation,** leaving habitat "islands." You probably think of islands as bits of land surrounded by water, but a biological island can be any patch of habitat surrounded by a different habitat, as shown in **Figure 6–17.** The smaller a habitat island, the fewer the species that can live there and the smaller their populations. Both changes make habitats and species more vulnerable to other disturbance.

BUILD Vocabulary

ACADEMIC WORDS The adjective **vulnerable** means "open to attack or damage." Fragmented habitats are more vulnerable, or more apt to be damaged, than larger undisturbed habitats because they contain fewer species and smaller populations of organisms.

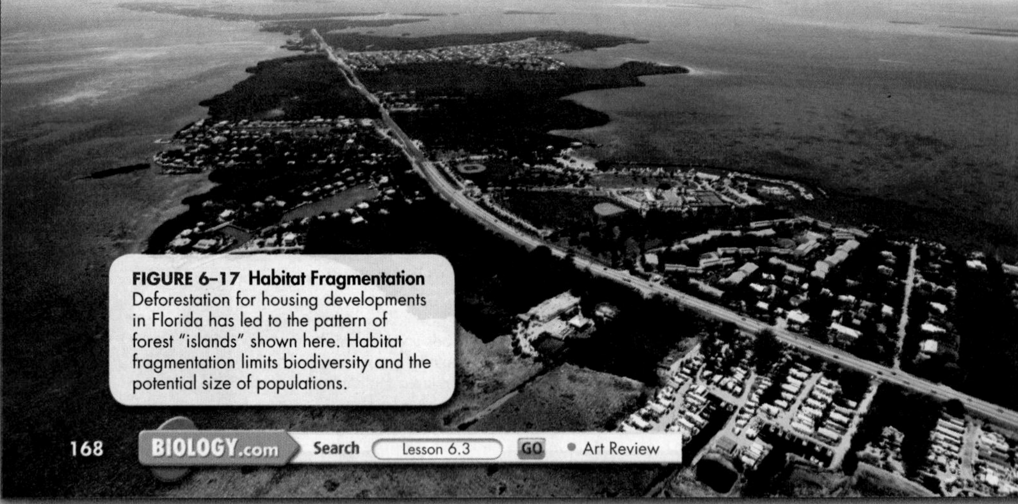

FIGURE 6–17 Habitat Fragmentation Deforestation for housing developments in Florida has led to the pattern of forest "islands" shown here. Habitat fragmentation limits biodiversity and the potential size of populations.

 BIOLOGY.com Search Lesson 6.3 GO • Art Review

Quick Facts

MAMMAL EXTINCTIONS

In 2008, the International Union for Conservation of Nature (IUCN) released the results of a study of mammals and extinction. The study involved more than 1700 scientists in 130 countries. The findings included these:

- Of the 5487 species of mammals they counted in the world, at least 1141, or about 21 percent, face extinction.
- The organization listed 188 mammal species as critically endangered and another 29 mammal species as possibly already extinct.
- In the last 500 years, 76 mammal species have become extinct.
- The loss or degradation of habitat is affecting 40 percent of the world's mammal species.

FIGURE 6–18 Hunted and Sold as Pets *These caged green parrots were captured in the Amazon rainforest and brought to a market in Peru.* Infer ***What impact do you think hunting has on the animals left behind?***

Hunting and the Demand for Wildlife Products Humans can push species to extinction by hunting. In the 1800s, hunting wiped out the Carolina parakeet and the passenger pigeon. Today endangered species in the United States are protected from hunting, but hunting still threatens rare animals in Africa, South America, and Southeast Asia. Some animals, like many birds, are hunted for meat. Others are hunted for their commercially valuable hides or skins or because people believe their body parts have medicinal properties. Still others, like the parrots in **Figure 6–18,** are hunted to be sold as pets. Hunted species are affected even more than other species by habitat fragmentation because fragmentation increases access for hunters and limits available hiding spaces for prey. The Convention on International Trade in Endangered Species (CITES) bans international trade in products from a list of endangered species. Unfortunately, it's difficult to enforce laws in remote wilderness areas.

Introduced Species Recall that organisms introduced to new habitats can become invasive and threaten biodiversity. For example, more than 130 introduced species live in the Great Lakes, where they have been changing aquatic ecosystems and driving native species close to extinction. One European weed, leafy spurge, infests millions of hectares across the Northern Great Plains. On rangelands, leafy spurge displaces grasses and other food plants, and its milky latex can sicken or kill cattle and horses. Each year, ranchers and farmers suffer losses of more than $120 million because of this single pest.

Pollution Many of the pollutants described in the last lesson also threaten biodiversity. DDT, for example, prevents birds from laying healthy eggs. In the United States, brown pelican, peregrine falcon, and other bird populations plummeted with widespread use of the chemical. Acid rain places stress on land and water organisms. Increased carbon dioxide in the atmosphere is dissolving in oceans, making them more acidic, which threatens biodiversity on coral reefs and in other marine ecosystems.

In Your Notebook *Why is acidic water harmful to coral?*

Almost all the coconut shells found by researchers on Easter Island show signs of having been gnawed on by nonnative rats. Coconuts contain the seeds of the coconut palm. What effect do you think the rats had on the coconut palm population?

LESSON 6.3

Build Study Skills

Divide the class into small groups, and have each group discuss the five significant threats to biodiversity. Encourage students to ask group members for help in clarifying any concept they do not understand. Then, ask each group to write ten questions, two for each threat. After groups have finished writing their questions, pair up groups and have group members ask each other their questions.

DIFFERENTIATED INSTRUCTION

L3 **Advanced Students** Ask a small group of students to work together to access the Web site for the Convention on International Trade in Endangered Species (CITES) to find out more about what the agreement is and how it works. Have the students prepare a brief presentation about the agreement.

Have students infer where the nonnative rats came from. *(The ships brought them to the island. The rats were the mammalian "stowaways.")* Then, have students describe how they think the rats likely affected the coconut palm population. Students can go online to Biology.com to gather their evidence.

Quick Facts

CITES

The Convention on International Trade in Endangered Species of Wild Fauna and Flora (CITES) is an agreement between governments to make sure trade in wild animals and plants does not threaten their survival. The agreement came into force in 1975. By 2008, there were 173 countries that had joined in the agreement, including the United States. At that time, about 5000 species of animals and 28,000 species of plants were protected against exploitation in international trade. CITES is a voluntary agreement among countries, and its rules do not take the place of each country's laws, which vary around the world.

Answers

FIGURE 6–18 Sample answer: There are fewer individuals of the species left to reproduce, and therefore hunting decreases the genetic diversity of the species and lessens its chances of surviving ecological disturbances.

IN YOUR NOTEBOOK Sample answer: Corals, most of which have a "skeleton" of calcium carbonate, have evolved to thrive at a certain water pH. Acid rain makes the water more acidic, which can dissolve coral.

LESSON 6.3

Teach continued

Lead a Discussion

Talk about the two strategies for conserving biodiversity (protecting individual species and preserving habitats and ecosystems). Make sure students understand why both are important.

Ask How does a national park such as Yellowstone National Park help in conserving biodiversity? *(It conserves biodiversity by preserving habitats and ecosystems.)*

Ask Why do you think human interests must be taken into account in conservation efforts? *(Sample answer: If human interests are taken into account, populations around the world are more likely to support conservation efforts.)*

DIFFERENTIATED INSTRUCTION

LPR Less Proficient Readers Before leading the discussion above, write the Key Concept statement for the section on the board, with important words deleted.

- To conserve __________, we must protect individual __________, preserve habitats and __________, and make certain that human neighbors of __________ areas benefit from participating in __________ efforts.

Ask students to fill in the blanks, using these words: *biodiversity, conservation, ecosystems, protected, species. (Correct order should be biodiversity, species, ecosystems, protected, conservation.)*

L3 Advanced Students Have interested students find out whether the local zoo or aquarium is a member of the Association of Zoos and Aquariums. Ask students to inquire specifically about whether the zoo or aquarium participates in the Species Survival Plan Program. Have students report to the class on what they learned.

Climate Change Climate change (a topic in the next lesson) is a major threat to biodiversity. Remember that organisms are adapted to their environments and have specific tolerance ranges to temperature and other abiotic conditions. If conditions change beyond an organism's tolerance, the organism must move to a more suitable location or face extinction. Species in fragmented habitats are particularly vulnerable to climate change because if conditions change they may not be able to move easily to a suitable habitat. Estimates vary regarding the effects of climate change on biodiversity. If global temperatures increase 1.5°C–2.5°C over late twentieth-century temperatures, 30 percent of species studied are likely to face increased risk of extinction. If the global temperature increase goes beyond 3.5°C, it is likely that 40–70 percent of species studied will face extinction.

Conserving Biodiversity

How do we preserve biodiversity?

What can we do to protect biodiversity? Should we focus on a particular organism like the scarlet macaw? Or should we try to save an entire ecosystem like the Amazon rain forest? We must do both. At the same time, conservation efforts must take human interests into account. **To conserve biodiversity, we must protect individual species, preserve habitats and ecosystems, and make certain that human neighbors of protected areas benefit from participating in conservation efforts.**

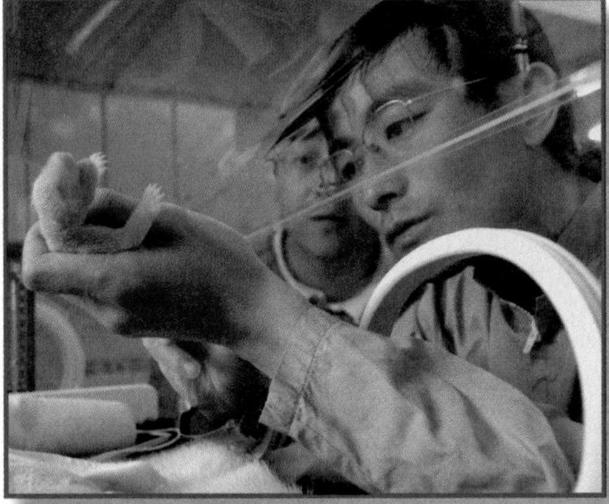

FIGURE 6–19 Saving an Individual Species Efforts to save the giant panda include a comprehensive captive breeding and reintroduction program. Here, a researcher examines an infant panda at China's Wolong Nature Reserve. Apply Concepts ***How does captive breeding affect a population's genetic diversity?***

Protecting Individual Species In the past, most conservation efforts focused on individual species, and some of this work continues today. The Association of Zoos and Aquariums (AZA), for example, oversees species survival plans (SSPs) designed to protect threatened and endangered species. A key part of those plans is a captive breeding program. Members of the AZA carefully select and manage mating pairs of animals to ensure maximum genetic diversity. The ultimate goal of an SSP is to reintroduce individuals to the wild. Research, public education, and breeding programs all contribute to that goal. More than 180 species, including the giant panda shown in **Figure 6–19,** are currently covered by SSPs.

Preserving Habitats and Ecosystems The main thrust of global conservation efforts today is to protect not just individual species but entire ecosystems. The goal is to preserve the natural interactions of many species at once. To that end, governments and conservation groups work to set aside land as parks and reserves. The United States has national parks, forests, and other protected areas. Marine sanctuaries are being created to protect coral reefs and marine mammals.

Quick Facts

COSTA RICA'S BIOLOGICAL RESERVES

The Central American nation of Costa Rica has become a world leader in the effort to protect biodiversity. In exchange for reduction in its international debt, the Costa Rican government established eight biological reserves—extensive regions that include one or more undisturbed areas surrounded by buffer zones that are used by people for economic gain. The buffer zones provide a steady, lasting supply of forest products, water, and hydroelectric power and also support sustainable agriculture and ecotourism. Destructive practices that are incompatible with long-term ecosystem stability are prohibited in these zones. Costa Rica expects its biological reserves system to maintain at least 80 percent of the country's native species. In addition, its thriving ecotourism industry is a significant source of income for the country.

Answers

FIGURE 6–19 Sample answer: Captive breeding increases a population's genetic diversity by mating only the most genetically dissimilar animals. Also, as the program succeeds, there will be more individuals contributing to the gene pool.

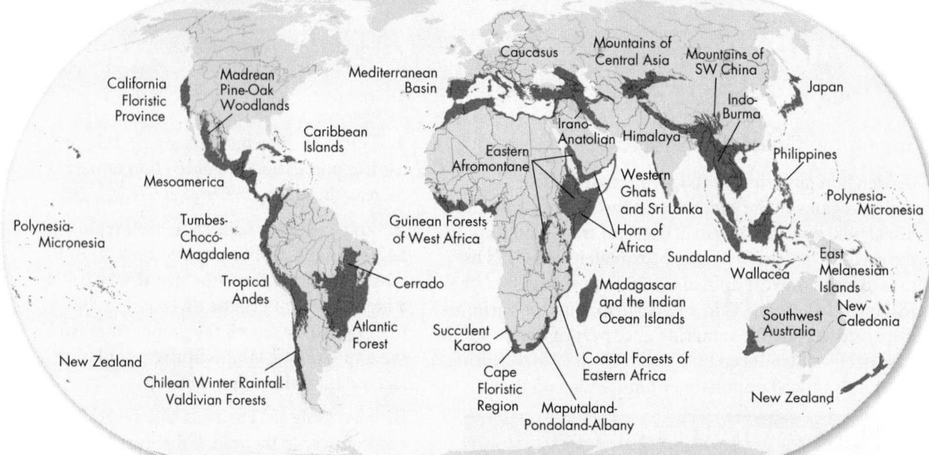

The challenge is protecting areas that are large enough and that contain the right resources to protect biodiversity. To make sure that conservation efforts are concentrated in the most important places, conservation biologists have identified ecological "hot spots," shown in red in **Figure 6–20.** An **ecological hot spot** is a place where significant numbers of species and habitats are in immediate danger of extinction. By identifying these areas, ecologists hope that scientists and governments can better target their efforts to save as many species as possible.

FIGURE 6–20 Ecological Hot Spots Conservation International identifies biodiversity hot spots using two criteria. The area (1) must contain at least 1500 species of native vascular plants, and (2) it must have lost at least 70 percent of its original habitat. The 34 hot spots seen here cover just 2.3 percent of Earth's land surface, but they contain over 50 percent of the world's plant species and 42 percent of its terrestrial vertebrates.

Considering Local Interests Protecting biodiversity often demands that individuals change their habits or the way they earn their living. In these cases it is helpful to offer some reward or incentive to the people or communities involved. The United States government, for example, has offered tax credits to people who've installed solar panels or bought hybrid cars. Similarly, many communities in Africa, Central America, and Southeast Asia have set aside land for national parks and nature reserves, like the park shown in **Figure 6–21,** to attract tourist dollars. In some Australian communities, farmers were paid to plant trees along rivers and streams as part of wildlife corridors connecting forest fragments. Not only did the trees help improve local water quality; they also improved the health of the farmers' cows, which were able to enjoy shade on hot days!

The use of carbon credits is one strategy aimed at encouraging industries to cut fossil fuels use. Companies are allowed to release a certain amount of carbon into the environment. Any unused carbon may be sold back at a set market value or traded to other companies. This strategy encourages industries to pay for lower-emission machinery and to adopt carbon-saving practices. In this way, pollution is capped or cut without adding a financial burden to the industry involved. This helps protect the economy while reducing biodiversity loss due to pollution. These examples show that conservation efforts work best when they are both informed by solid scientific information and benefit the communities affected by them.

FIGURE 6–21 Ecotourism A tourist gets an elephant-size kiss from one of the over 30 rescued elephants at Thailand's Elephant Nature Park.

Check for Understanding

DEPTH OF UNDERSTANDING

To gauge students' relative understanding of biodiversity, ask them to answer the following question.

- To conserve biodiversity, why must both individual species be protected *and* habitats and ecosystems be preserved?

Students with a limited understanding of biodiversity might respond that species need a habitat. Students with a more sophisticated understanding of biodiversity will explain that addressing both issues will help all three levels of biodiversity.

ADJUST INSTRUCTION

Review with students the three levels of biodiversity. Discuss ways in which all three levels can be conserved.

Use Visuals

Have students examine the map in **Figure 6–20** and read the caption. Make sure they understand the purpose of identifying these areas.

Ask What does Conservation International hope will result from identifying these ecological hot spots around the world? *(They hope scientists and countries will direct their efforts at conserving biodiversity in these areas.)*

Ask Which ecological hot spot includes part of the continental United States? *(California Floristic Province)*

Explain that this ecological hot spot includes most of the California coast and some of inland California. Point out that one endangered species in this area is the California condor.

DIFFERENTIATED INSTRUCTION

L1 Struggling Students Have pairs of students work through **Figure 6–20.** Suggest they start by identifying the world's continents. Then, have them describe where hot spots are on the map. Have pairs read aloud the figure caption and then discuss it. Then, suggest they discuss the strategy of preserving habitats and ecosystems that are ecological hot spots.

ELL Focus on ELL: Build Background

ALL SPEAKERS Help students build their understanding of lesson concepts by setting up a **Gallery Walk** on biodiversity. Write the lesson vocabulary terms on separate pieces of chart paper and post them around the room. Have small groups rotate from term to term. At each term, group members should write what they know about it, using a particular color of pen. When the next group rotates to the term, its members should add to the previous group's comments or correct mistakes and misunderstandings, using a different-colored pen. When groups return to the term they addressed first, have members summarize information about that term for the class.

Study Wkbks A/B, Appendix S6, Gallery Walk.

PURPOSE Students will analyze data about the recovery and reintroduction of golden lion tamarins.

PLANNING Review with students how species survival plans are designed to protect threatened and endangered species.

ANSWERS

1. 445%
2. 400
3. They must be the offspring of the 153 GLTs that have been reintroduced from zoos since 1984.
4. Sample answer: Yes. Without the protection of zoos and aquariums, the animals might become extinct.

Assess and Remediate

EVALUATE UNDERSTANDING

Call on students to identify and describe the three types of biodiversity. Then, have students complete the 6.3 Assessment.

REMEDIATION SUGGESTION

L1 **Struggling Students** If students struggle to answer **Question 2b,** review with them the subsection, **Altered Habitats.**

BIOLOGY.com Students can check their understanding of lesson concepts with the **Self-Test** assessment. They can then take an online version of the **Lesson Assessment.**

Analyzing Data

IN NoS.3, NoS.11, B.4.2

Saving the Golden Lion Tamarin

Golden lion tamarins (GLTs) are primates native to the coastal regions of the Amazon rain forest. They have been threatened by habitat destruction and fragmentation. In the early 1970s, there were approximately 200 GLTs in the wild and only 91 animals in 26 zoos. As of 2007, the SSP included 496 GLTs in 145 participating zoos around the world. About 153 tamarins once part of the program have been reintroduced to the wild since 1984, resulting in a reintroduced population of more than 650.

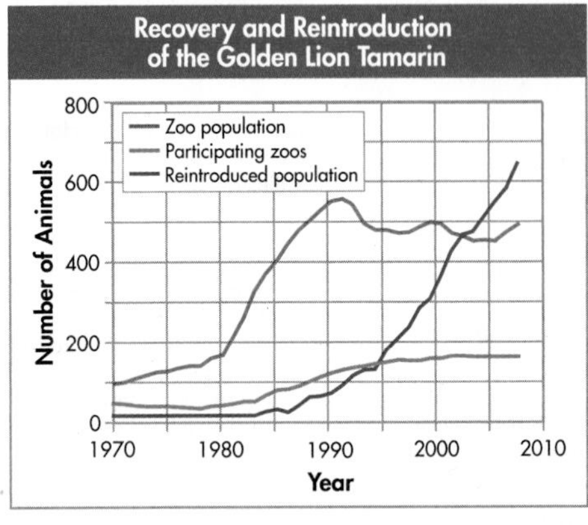

1. **Calculate** By what percentage did the captive population of golden lion tamarins increase between 1970 and 2007? MATH
2. **Analyze Data** Reintroduction typically begins once a captive population has reached a target size—the size at which a high degree of genetic diversity can be maintained. Based on the graph, what is the approximate target captive population size for the golden lion tamarin?
3. **Infer** Only 153 tamarins have been reintroduced to the wild. If there are now 650 tamarins in the reintroduced population, where did the other 497 come from?
4. **Form an Opinion** When populations of wild animals get very small, do you think they should be removed from the wild and brought into captivity? Why or why not?

Adapted from J. D. Ballou and J. Mickelberg, *International Studbook for Golden Lion Tamarins* (Washington, D.C.: National Zoological Park, Smithsonian Institution, 2007). B. Holst et al., *Lion Tamarin Population and Habitat Viability Assessment Workshop 2005, Final Report* (Apple Valley, MN: IUCN/SSC Conservation Breeding Specialist Group, 2006.)

6.3 Assessment

IN NoS.11, B.4.2, B.4.3

Review Key Concepts

1. a. **Review** Describe the different components of global biodiversity.
   b. **Apply Concepts** What benefits does society get from biodiversity?
2. a. **Review** What are the major threats to biodiversity?
   b. **Relate Cause and Effect** Explain the relationship between habitat size and species diversity.
3. a. **Review** What is the goal of a species survival plan?
   b. **Form an Opinion** Do you think that the hot spot strategy is a good one? Explain your answer.

VISUAL THINKING

4. Look back at the biome map on page 111. Compare it to the map in **Figure 6–20.** Are there any similarities among the biomes the hot spots belong to? Using what you know about biomes, are you surprised by what you've found? Explain your answer.

Assessment Answers

1a. Ecosystem diversity refers to the variety of habitats, communities, and ecological processes in the biosphere. Species diversity is the number of different species in the biosphere or in a particular area. Genetic diversity refers to the different forms of genetic information carried by individuals in a species or in the biosphere.

1b. Answers will vary. Students should mention specific benefits in medicine, agriculture, and ecosystem services.

2a. altering habitats, hunting, introducing invasive species, releasing pollution into food webs, and climate change

2b. Sample answer: The smaller the habitat size, the less species diversity there is. The reason is that smaller size limits the number of species that can live in the space.

3a. to reintroduce genetically diverse individuals to the wild

3b. Sample answer: The strategy is a good one because it will conserve a high concentration of endangered species with one directed effort.

VISUAL THINKING

4. Sample answer: The hot spots mostly occur in areas classified as tropical rain forests or temperate woodland and shrubland. The correlation with tropical rain forests is not surprising, because this biome contains the greatest biodiversity. The correlation with temperate woodland and shrubland is somewhat surprising, though these areas also contain great biodiversity.

6.4 Meeting Ecological Challenges

B.4.2 Effects of human activities and natural phenomenon. Also covered: NoS.6, NoS.11.

THINK ABOUT IT Every year, the EPA awards up to ten President's Environmental Youth Awards. Past winners have included an Eagle Scout from Massachusetts who encouraged people who fish to stop using lead weights that contaminate water and poison organisms, students from Washington State who reduced waste at their school and saved more than half a million dollars in the process, and a student from Florida who developed an outreach program to protect local sea turtles. What do these award winners have in common? They came up with ideas that protect the environment while satisfying both present and future needs. This kind of leadership is what will help us chart a new course for the future.

Key Questions

How does the average ecological footprint in America compare to the world's average?

How can ecology guide us toward a sustainable future?

Vocabulary

ecological footprint
ozone layer
aquaculture
global warming

Taking Notes

Compare/Contrast Table As you read, create a table comparing the challenges associated with the ozone layer, fisheries, and global climate. Note the problem observed, the causes identified, and the solutions implemented.

Ecological Footprints

How does the average ecological footprint in America compare to the world's average?

What is our impact on the biosphere today? To answer that question, think about the kind and amount of resources each of us uses. Ecologists refer to the human impact on the biosphere using a concept called the ecological footprint. The **ecological footprint** describes the total area of functioning land and water ecosystems needed both to provide the resources an individual or population uses and to absorb and make harmless the wastes that individual or population generates. Ecological footprints take into account the need to provide resources such as energy, food, water, and shelter, and to absorb such wastes as sewage and greenhouse gases. Ecologists use footprint calculations to estimate the biosphere's carrying capacity for humans. An artist's rendition of an ecological footprint is shown in **Figure 6–22.**

VISUAL ANALOGY

ECOLOGICAL FOOTPRINTS

FIGURE 6–22 The food you eat, the miles you travel, and the electricity you use all contribute to your—and the population's—ecological footprint.

Footprint Limitations Ecologists talk about the ecological footprints of individuals, of countries, and of the world's population. Calculating actual numbers for ecological footprints, however, is complicated. The concept is so new that there is no universally accepted way to calculate footprint size. What's more, footprints give only a "snapshot" of the situation at a particular point in time.

BIOLOGY.com Search Lesson 6.4 GO • Lesson Overview • Lesson Notes • Visual Analogy

Teach for Understanding

ENDURING UNDERSTANDING The existence of life on Earth depends on interactions among organisms and between organisms and their environment.

GUIDING QUESTION How can we change our behaviors to help protect our planet?

EVIDENCE OF UNDERSTANDING *After completing this lesson, give students the following assessment to show their understanding of an ecological challenge.* Ask each student to write a summary of one of the case studies in this lesson. The summary should be two or three paragraphs long, and should describe the problem, identify the cause, and describe changes that could be made to address the problem. Call on volunteers to read their summaries to the class.

Getting Started

Objectives

6.4.1 Explain the concept of ecological footprint.

6.4.2 Identify the role of ecology in a sustainable future.

Student Resources

Study Workbooks A and B, 6.4 Worksheets

Spanish Study Workbook, 6.4 Worksheets

Lab Manual B, 6.4 Hands-On Activity Worksheet

Lesson Overview • Lesson Notes • Activity: Visual Analogy • Assessment: Self-Test, Lesson Assessment

For corresponding lesson in the **Foundation Edition**, see pages 143–149.

VISUAL ANALOGY

Have students read the description of an ecological footprint and examine **Figure 6–22.** Call on students to identify items representing uses of resources in the analogy, such as the boat, airplane, electric plant, and planted fields. Ask students to describe how the natural resources used for each item shown contribute to the community's ecological footprint.

Students can further explore the analogy by watching how the "size" of a footprint changes when factors such as energy use change in the **Visual Analogy: Ecological Footprints.**

IN INDIANA ACADEMIC STANDARDS

For the full text of all standards, see the Course Overview in the front matter of this book.

B.4.2 Describe how human activities and natural phenomena can change the flow of matter and energy in an ecosystem and how those changes impact other species.

Teach continued

Use Visuals

Ask students to examine the map in **Figure 6–23** and read the caption. Make sure they understand the color key and why the continents are shaped as they are.

Ask Why is North America so much larger than South America on this map? *(Areas that have larger relative footprints are shown to be bigger than areas that have smaller footprints.)*

Then, have students compare the ecological footprints of regions and countries with the chapter opener image of Earth from space.

Ask What do you notice about the areas with the largest ecological deficits? *(These areas—United States, Western Europe, South Korea, and Japan—are also the areas with the densest lights as seen from space, which makes sense since those areas are the most developed.)*

DIFFERENTIATED INSTRUCTION

L1 Special Needs Have students start by comparing a specific area on the inset map with its corresponding area on the footprint map. For example, ask them to compare Africa on both maps and describe how the relative size of this area changes from one map to the other. Then, guide them to understand the relationship between the two maps. Explain that the footprint map shows each country in proportion to its ecological footprint, while the inset map shows the countries in their correct sizes. Suggest pairs of students discuss and compare the United States on each map.

Answers

IN YOUR NOTEBOOK Sample answer: waking up to a clock radio, turning on lights, using water to take a shower, flushing the toilet, preparing food for breakfast, wearing manufactured clothing, talking on a rechargeable cell phone, riding in a car to school, listening to music on a battery-powered MP3 player, sitting in a heated classroom

Comparing Footprints Although calculating *absolute* footprints is difficult, ecological footprints can be useful for making *comparisons* among different populations, as shown in **Figure 6–23.** **According to one data set, the average American has an ecological footprint over four times larger than the global average.** The per person use of resources in America is almost twice that in England, more than twice that in Japan, and almost six times that in China. To determine the ecological footprint of an entire country, researchers calculate the footprint for a typical citizen and then multiply that by the size of the population.

In Your Notebook *How have you contributed to your ecological footprint today? Give at least ten examples.*

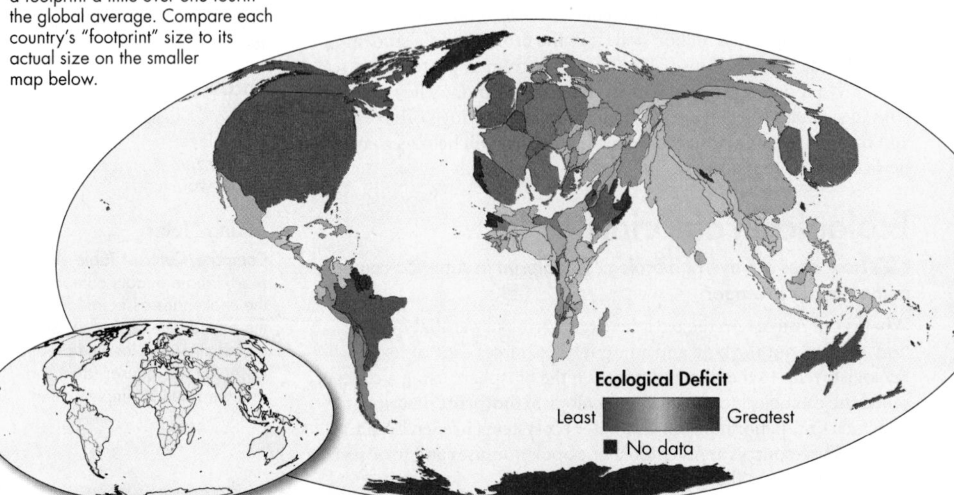

FIGURE 6–23 Relative Footprints This world map shows each country in proportion to its ecological footprint. The United States has an ecological footprint about twice the world's average. By contrast, the African nation of Zambia has a footprint a little over one-fourth the global average. Compare each country's "footprint" size to its actual size on the smaller map below.

Ecology in Action

How can ecology guide us toward a sustainable future?

The future of the biosphere depends on our ecological footprints, global population growth, and technological development. Right now it's more common to hear stories of ecological challenges than successes. Given the size of those challenges, you might be tempted to give up, to feel that things are getting worse, and that there is nothing we can do about it. But ecological research, properly collected, analyzed, and applied, can help us make decisions that will produce profoundly positive effects on the human condition. The basic principles of ecology can guide us toward a sustainable future. **By (1) recognizing a problem in the environment, (2) researching that problem to determine its cause, and then (3) using scientific understanding to change our behavior, we can have a positive impact on the global environment.** The following case studies illustrate the importance of the steps.

How Science Works

ECOLOGICAL FOOTPRINTS

Students may confuse the concept of ecological footprint with the concept of carbon footprint, which they have probably heard about. In general, a carbon footprint is a measure of human activities as they produce greenhouse gases and impact climate change. An ecological footprint is a larger and more complicated concept than a carbon footprint. In fact, an ecological footprint includes a version of the carbon footprint. The important idea to emphasize for students is that ecological and carbon footprints are valid concepts and good ways to compare environmental impacts of countries and cultures at a specific time.

Case Study #1: Atmospheric Ozone

Between 20 and 50 kilometers above Earth's surface, the atmosphere contains a relatively high concentration of ozone called the **ozone layer.** Ozone at ground level is a pollutant, but the natural ozone layer absorbs harmful ultraviolet (UV) radiation from sunlight. Overexposure to UV radiation is the main cause of sunburn. It also can cause cancer, damage eyes, and lower resistance to disease. And intense UV radiation can damage plants and algae. By absorbing UV light, the ozone layer serves as a global sunscreen.

The following is an ecological success story. Over four decades, society has recognized a problem, identified its cause, and cooperated internationally to address a global issue.

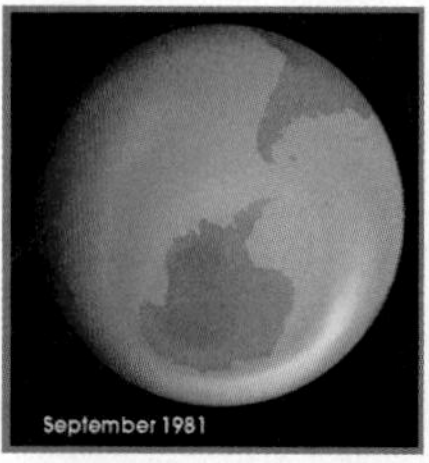

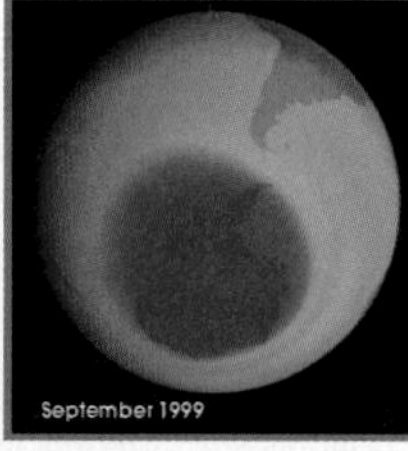

FIGURE 6–24 The Disappearing Ozone

1 Recognizing a Problem: "Hole" in the Ozone Layer Beginning in the 1970s, satellite data revealed that the ozone concentration over Antarctica was dropping during the southern winter. An area of lower ozone concentration is commonly called an ozone hole. It isn't really a "hole" in the atmosphere, of course, but an area where little ozone is present. For several years after the ozone hole was first discovered, it grew larger and lasted longer each year. **Figure 6–24** shows the progression from 1981 to 1999. The darker blue color in the later image indicates that the ozone layer had thinned since 1981.

FIGURE 6–25 CFC-Containing Refrigerators

2 Researching the Cause: CFCs In 1974 a research team led by Mario Molina, F. Sherwood Rowland, and Paul J. Crutzen demonstrated that gases called chlorofluorocarbons (CFCs) could damage the ozone layer. This research earned the team a Nobel Prize in 1995. CFCs were once widely used as propellants in aerosol cans; as coolant in refrigerators, freezers, and air conditioners; and in the production of plastic foams.

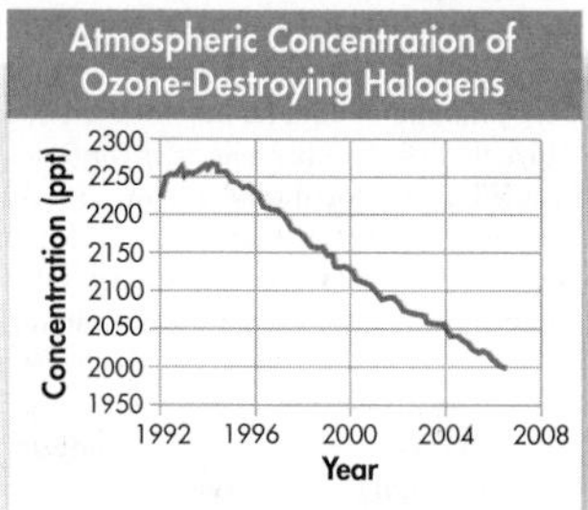

FIGURE 6–26 The Decline of CFCs

3 Changing Behavior: Regulation of CFCs Once the research on CFCs was published and accepted by the scientific community, the rest was up to policymakers—and in this case, their response was tremendous. Following the recommendations of ozone researchers, 191 countries signed a major agreement, the Montreal Protocol, which banned most uses of CFCs. Because CFCs can remain in the atmosphere for a century, their effects on the ozone layer are still visible. But ozone-destroying halogens from CFCs have been steadily decreasing since about 1994, as shown in **Figure 6–26,** evidence that the CFC ban has had positive long-term effects. In fact, current data predict that although the ozone hole will continue to fluctuate in size from year to year, it should disappear for good around the middle of this century.

Connect to Chemistry

Explain that ozone is a form of pure oxygen, though different from the form we need for respiration. A molecule of oxygen has two atoms (O_2), while a molecule of ozone has three atoms (O_3). Further explain that CFCs degrade in the upper atmosphere, releasing fluorine and chlorine. Fluorine and chlorine are part of a group of elements called halogens. The halogens released by the CFCs combine with ozone molecules, destroying them. To emphasize how regulation of CFCs had a positive effect on the problem, focus students' attention on the graph in **Figure 6–26.**

Ask What trend does the graph show between 1996 and 2007? *(The atmospheric concentration of ozone-destroying halogens steadily decreased.)*

Ask What caused this trend? *(regulation of CFCs)*

DIFFERENTIATED INSTRUCTION

L1 Struggling Students To help students better understand what the ozone layer is, show them a labeled diagram of the layers of the atmosphere from an Earth science textbook. Point out that the ozone layer is part of the stratosphere, which is the layer just above the layer of the atmosphere next to Earth's surface.

LPR Less Proficient Readers For struggling readers, take the time to preview the basic structure of how each case study is presented. Point out that step 1 explains how humans recognized there was a problem, step 2 details how scientists pinpoint what was or is causing the problem, and step 3 explains how humans are changing their behavior to help address it. Suggest students create a three-row table for each case study and fill it in with a summary sentence for each step.

UbD Check for Understanding

FOLLOW-UP PROBES

Ask Why is a "hole" in the ozone layer a problem, and what caused the "hole"? *(The "hole" in the ozone layer is a problem because the ozone layer absorbs ultraviolet rays from the sun that can cause cancer and do other damage to life on Earth. The cause of the "hole" was the use of CFCs in aerosol cans, refrigerators, air conditioners, and plastic foams.)*

ADJUST INSTRUCTION

If students have difficulty answering the question, have them reread the introduction to the case study and the paragraph (step 2) about the cause of the problem. Then, review the answer to the question in class discussion.

Teach continued

Use Visuals

Focus students' attention on the information in the graph in **Figure 6–27** to discuss the case study of North Atlantic fisheries. Make sure students understand the meanings of *biomass* and *catch*. Explain that biomass refers to the total mass of cod in the North Atlantic, while catch refers to the total mass of the cod caught by the fishing boats.

Ask What caused the sharp increase in the catch between the late 1970s and the early 1980s? *(Larger boats and high-tech fish-finding equipment made fishing more efficient, and the catch grew larger.)*

Ask How do you know the decline in catch in the late 1980s was due to overfishing and not to something else, like a decline in fishing? *(The biomass line shows that there was a sharp decline in the number of cod in the Atlantic during that time.)*

Discuss the regulation of fisheries and why restoring fish populations has been slow.

DIFFERENTIATED INSTRUCTION

ELL English Language Learners Students may not understand the term *overfishing*. Explain that the prefix *over-* means "excessive" or "too much." Overfishing, then, refers to too much fishing, which in this case resulted in fish being caught faster than they could replace themselves through reproduction. Point out that overfishing caused a once-renewable resource to become a nonrenewable resource.

Case Study #2: North Atlantic Fisheries

From 1950 to 1997, the annual world seafood catch grew from 19 million tons to more than 90 million tons. This growth led many to believe that the fish supply was an endless, renewable resource. However, recent dramatic declines in commercial fish populations have proved otherwise. This problem is one society is still working on.

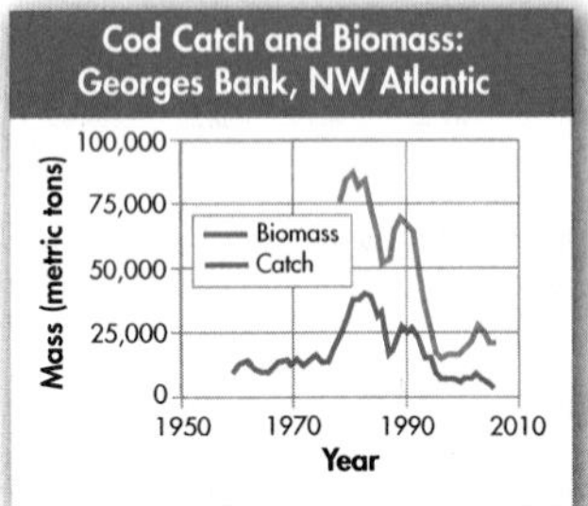

FIGURE 6–27 The Decline of Cod

FIGURE 6–28 Overfishing

FIGURE 6–29 Aquaculture

1 Recognizing a Problem: More Work, Fewer Fish The cod catch has been rising and falling over the last century. Some of that fluctuation has been due to natural variations in ocean ecosystems. But often, low fish catches resulted when boats started taking too many fish. From the 1950s through the 1970s, larger boats and high-tech fish-finding equipment made the fishing effort both more intense and more efficient. Catches rose for a time but then began falling. The difference this time, was that fish catches continued to fall despite the most intense fishing effort in history. As shown in **Figure 6–27**, the total mass of cod caught has decreased significantly since the 1980s because of the sharp decrease of cod biomass in the ocean. You can't catch what isn't there.

2 Researching the Cause: Overfishing Fishery ecologists gathered data including age structure and growth rates. Analysis of these data showed that fish populations were shrinking. By the 1990s, cod and haddock populations had dropped so low that researchers feared these fish might disappear for good. It has become clear that recent declines in fish catches were the result of overfishing, as seen in **Figure 6–28.** Fish were being caught faster than they could be replaced by reproduction. In other words, the death rates of commercial fish populations were exceeding birth rates.

3 Changing Behavior: Regulation of Fisheries The U.S. National Marine Fisheries Service used its best data to create guidelines for commercial fishing. The guidelines specified how many fish of what size could be caught in U.S. waters. In 1996, the Sustainable Fisheries Act closed certain areas to fishing until stocks recover. Other areas are closed seasonally to allow fish to breed and spawn. These regulations are helping some fish populations recover, but not all. **Aquaculture**—the farming of aquatic animals—offers a good alternative to commercial fishing with limited environmental damage if properly managed.

Overall, however, progress in restoring fish populations has been slow. International cooperation on fisheries has not been as good as it was with ozone. Huge fleets from other countries continue to fish the ocean waters outside U.S. territorial waters. Some are reluctant to accept conservation efforts because regulations that protect fish populations for the future cause job and income losses today. Of course, if fish stocks disappear, the result will be even more devastating to the fishing industry than temporary fishing bans. The challenge is to come up with sustainable practices that ensure the long-term health of fisheries with minimal short-term impact on the fishing industry. Exactly how to meet that challenge is still up for debate.

Quick Facts

GEORGES BANK

Georges Bank is located about 120 km off the coast of North America between Cape Cod and Nova Scotia. The Basques established a salted fish trade here around the year 1000. They retained control of the area until 1497 when John Cabot, who was searching for a northern spice route on behalf of King Henry VII of England, discovered it. Georges Bank owes its productivity to its position at the interception of two currents—the cold, nutrient-rich Labrador current and the warmer Gulf stream. Once among the most productive fisheries, the National Marine Fisheries Service reported in 1994 that cod stock on Georges Bank had declined 40 percent in just four years. They concluded that in order to be sustainable, fishing fleets would have to be cut in half.

Case Study #3: Climate Change

Global climate involves cycles of matter across the biosphere and everything modern humans do—from cutting and burning forests to manufacturing, driving cars, and generating electricity. The most reliable current information available on this subject comes from the 2007 report of the Intergovernmental Panel On Climate Change (IPCC). The IPCC is an international organization established in 1988 to provide the best possible scientific information on climate change. IPCC reports contain data and analyses that have been agreed upon and accepted by 2500 climate scientists from around the world and the governments participating in the study.

1 Recognizing a Problem: Global Warming The IPCC report confirms earlier observations that global temperatures are rising. This increase in average temperature is called **global warming.** Remember that winds and ocean currents, which are driven by differences in temperature across the biosphere, shape climate. Given this link between temperature and climate, it isn't surprising that the IPCC report discusses more than warming. The report also discusses climate change—changes in patterns of temperature, rainfall, and other physical environmental factors that can result from global warming. There are many lines of evidence, both physical and biological, that have contributed to our current understanding of the climate change issue.

- **Physical Evidence** Physical evidence of global warming comes from several sources. The graphs in **Figure 6–30,** taken from data in the 2007 IPCC report, show that Earth's temperatures are getting warmer, its sea ice is melting, and its sea levels are rising. Eleven of the twelve years between 1995 and 2006 were among the warmest years since temperature recording began in 1850. Between 1906 and 2005, Earth's average global temperature rose 0.74°C. The largest changes are occurring in and near the Arctic Circle. Average temperatures in Alaska, for example, increased 2.4°C over the last 50 years. Sea level has risen since 1961 at a rate of 1.8 mm each year. This increase is caused by warmer water expanding and by melting glaciers, ice caps, and polar ice sheets. Satellite data confirm that arctic sea ice, glaciers, and snow cover are decreasing.

FIGURE 6–30 A Warming Earth

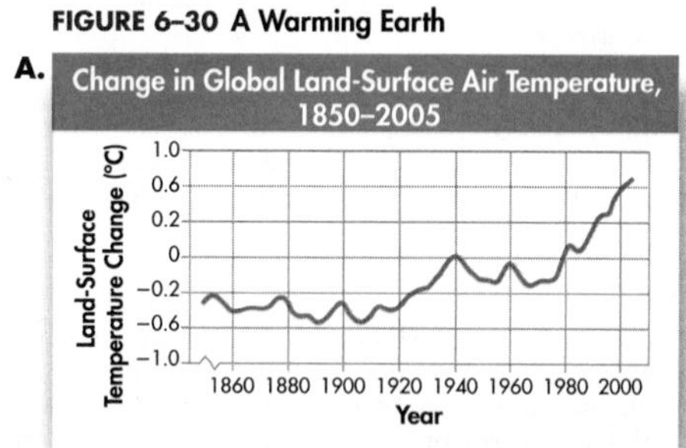

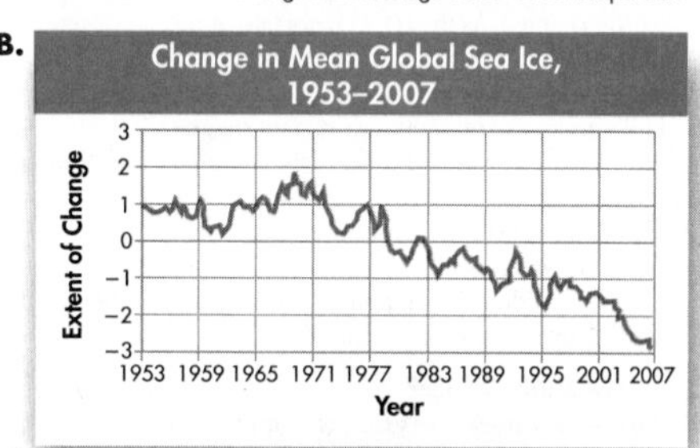

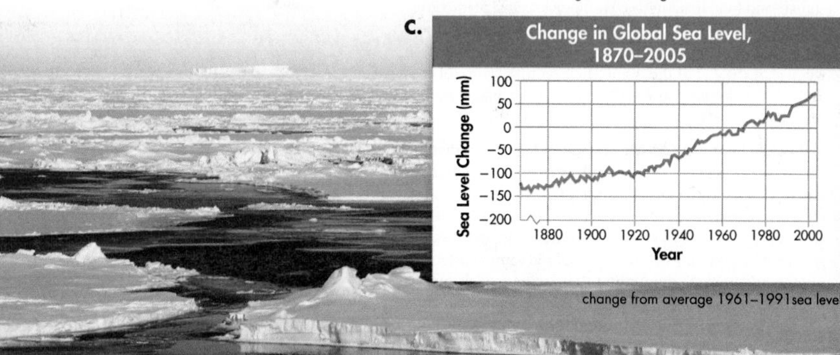

Use Visuals

Have students study the graphs in **Figure 6–30.** Make sure they understand the source of the data. Then, talk about the physical evidence of global warming.

Ask Between 1860 and 1920, did the land-surface air temperature change? *(Sample answer: yes, but the fluctuations weren't large enough to change the approximate average temperature)*

Ask When did the downward trend in mean global sea ice begin? *(in about the late 1960s)*

Ask What has been the trend in global sea level since about 1920? *(The trend since about 1920 is a rising sea level.)*

DIFFERENTIATED INSTRUCTION

ELL English Language Learners Explain to students new to English that *global* is the adjectival form of the word *globe,* which means a "sphere" or rounded ball. Explain that the term *globe* is often used as a synonym for Earth or the world. The adjective *global,* then, means "worldwide."

LPR Less Proficient Readers Students may have difficulty distinguishing between the terms *global warming* and *climate change,* since the two terms are often used interchangeably in common speech. Ask a volunteer to read the definitions of the two terms aloud. Then, point out that the two have a cause-and-effect relationship.

Ask Which is the cause, and which is the effect? *(Global warming is the cause; climate change is the effect.)*

Quick Facts

THE IPCC

The World Meteorological Organization and the United Nations Environment Programme (UNEP) established the Intergovernmental Panel on Climate Change (IPCC) in 1988. The IPCC does not conduct research on its own. Instead, its scientists assess scientific, technical, and economic data related to climate change. The information the organization provides in its reports is based on scientific evidence, and the IPCC makes no policy recommendations to governments.

Teach continued

Lead a Discussion

Talk about how much warming is expected to occur and what the consequences will be.

Ask What are the possible effects for towns and cities along the coasts of the United States? *(Because of the rise in sea level, some towns and cities may be flooded.)*

Ask Why is it possible that global warming will cause the Sahara Desert to become greener? *(Sample answer: Global warming will cause changes in weather patterns throughout the world. If weather patterns change in a certain way, the Sahara could receive more rain than is normal today.)*

Turn students' attention to what might occur in their local region as a result of global warming. Have them predict changes both for humans and for other organisms native to the region.

DIFFERENTIATED INSTRUCTION

L3 **Advanced Students** Have interested students conduct research to answer this question: How can scientists know about the concentration of greenhouse gases over 2000 years ago? Students should find out about ice core analysis. Have them share what they learn with the class.

ELL Focus on ELL: Access Content

BEGINNING AND INTERMEDIATE SPEAKERS

Have pairs of students make a **Cause and Effect Diagram** for **Case Study #3.** Start the diagram for them by identifying climate change as the cause. Suggest they read the paragraphs on the biological and physical evidence associated with climate change to help them identify effects. Accept words or short phrases from beginning speakers. Suggest intermediate speakers write a simple sentence to identify each effect.

Study Wkbks A/B, Appendix S18, Cause and Effect Diagram. **Transparencies,** GO1.

Address Misconceptions

Climate vs. Weather Some students may doubt predictions about climate change because they have witnessed many wrong predictions about the weather. Explain that there is a big difference between weather and climate. Predicting atmospheric conditions in local areas is very difficult, but climate is much more predictable.

Case Study #3: Climate Change (continued)

• **Biological Evidence** Small changes in climate that humans scarcely notice can be important to other organisms. Remember that each organism's range is determined by factors like temperature, humidity, and rainfall. If those conditions change, the organisms can be affected. If temperature rises, for example, organisms would usually move toward cooler places away from the equator and from warm lowlands to cooler, higher altitudes. In addition, plant flowering and animal breeding are often cued by seasonal changes. If warming is occurring, these organisms should respond as though spring begins earlier.

The IPCC report summarizes data from 75 studies covering 1700 species of plants and animals. These data confirm that many species and communities are responding as though they are experiencing rising temperatures. The yellow-bellied marmot in **Figure 6–31,** for example, is coming out of hibernation over a month earlier than it used to.

FIGURE 6–31 Waking Up Too Early

2 Researching the Cause: Models and Questions
What is causing global warming? Earth's climate has changed often during its history. So researchers had to determine whether current warming is part of a natural cycle or whether it is caused by human activity or by astronomical and geological changes. As the IPCC report documents, concentrations of carbon dioxide and several other greenhouse gases have increased significantly over the last 200 years, as shown in **Figure 6–32.** Several kinds of data suggest this increase is due to the burning of fossil fuels, combined with the cutting and burning of forests worldwide. These activities add carbon dioxide to the atmosphere faster than the carbon cycle removes it. Most climate scientists agree that this added carbon dioxide is strengthening the natural greenhouse effect, causing the biosphere to retain more heat.

• **How Much Change?** How much warming is expected? For answers, researchers turn to computer models based on data. The models are complex and involve assumptions about climate and human activities. For these reasons, predictions are open to debate. The IPCC reports the result of six different models, which predict that average global temperatures will rise by the end of the twenty-first century from just under 2°C to as much as 6.4°C higher than they were in the year 2000.

• **Possible Effects of Climate Change** What does climate change mean? Some changes are likely to threaten ecosystems ranging from tundra and northern forests to coral reefs and the Amazon rain forest. The western United States is likely to get drier. The Sahara Desert, on the other hand, may become greener. Sea level may rise enough to flood some coastal ecosystems and human communities. And some models suggest that parts of North America may experience more droughts during the summer growing season.

FIGURE 6–32 Greenhouse Gases

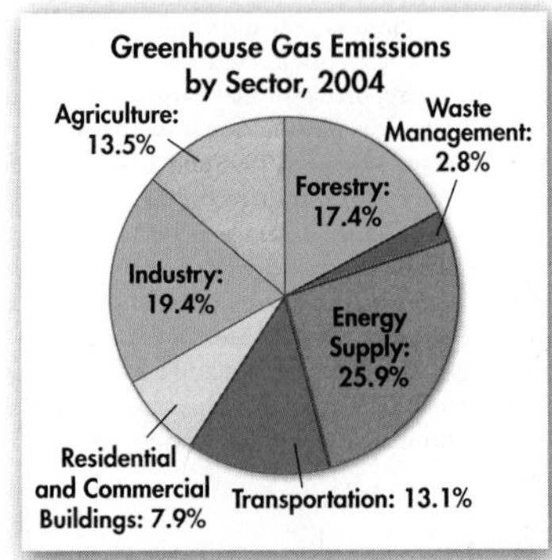

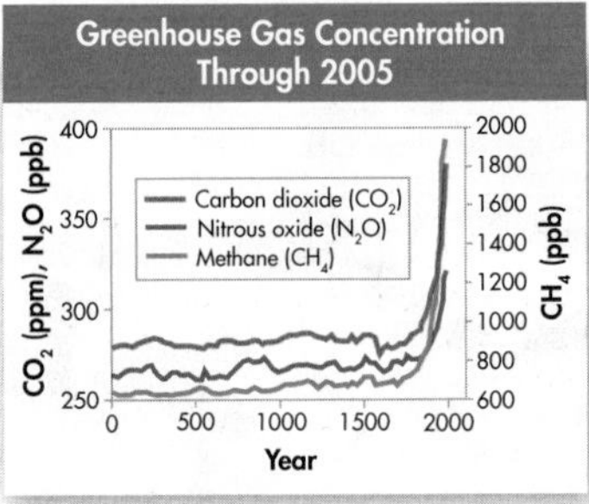

UbD Check for Understanding

HAND SIGNALS

Give students the following questions, and ask them to show a thumbs-up sign if they can answer a question, a thumbs-down sign if they can't, or a waving-hand sign if they're not sure.

- What changes in patterns does climate change involve?
- What is strengthening the atmosphere's natural greenhouse effect?
- What changes in behavior need to occur to minimize further global warming?

ADJUST INSTRUCTION

For any question that received thumbs-down or waving-hand sign, have students write a one-sentence response to the question using the text as a resource.

Case Study #3: Climate Change (continued)

3 Changing Behavior: The Challenges Ahead You have seen how research has led to actions that are preserving the ozone layer and attempting to restore fisheries. In terms of global climate, great challenges lie ahead of us. Scientists have been saying for more than two decades that the world needs to recognize the importance of climate change and take steps to minimize further warming. The changes in behavior needed to cut back on greenhouse gas emissions will be major and will require input from economics and many other fields beyond biology. Some changes will rely on new technology for renewable energy and more efficient energy use. Because changing our use of fossil fuels and other behaviors will be difficult, researchers continue to gather data as they try to make more accurate models. In the meantime, we have begun to see the emergence of electric cars, recycled products, and green buildings.

Nations of the world have begun holding international climate summits, at which they attempt to work out agreements to protect the atmosphere and climate—both of which are truly global issues. As the world, and our own government, tries to work through these challenges, remember that the purpose of ecology is not to predict disaster or to prevent people from enjoying modern life. The world is our island of life. Hopefully, humanity can work toward a day when scientific information and human ingenuity help us reach the common goal of preserving the quality of life on Earth.

FIGURE 6–33 Little Changes, Big Results

6.4 Assessment

IN NoS.11, B.4.2

Review Key Concepts

1. a. Review What are ecological footprints?
   b. Apply Concepts What are the limitations of the ecological footprint model, and how can ecologists best use it?
2. a. Review Why is the ozone layer important to living things?
   b. Explain What are the major types of physical and biological evidence for climate change?
   c. Propose a Solution Suggest one solution for the fisheries problem. Your solution can be at the international, national, regional, or individual level. Explain how it would help, and what challenges you see in implementing it.

Apply the Big idea

Interdependence in Nature

3. Refer to the carbon cycle on page 83. Describe how extensive burning of fossil fuels is affecting other reservoirs of carbon in the biosphere.

BIOLOGY.com Search Lesson 6.4  • Self-Test • Lesson Assessment

Assess and Remediate

EVALUATE UNDERSTANDING

Call on students to explain ecological footprints and describe how they are useful tools for ecologists. Also, call on students to summarize the steps outlined in each of the three case studies in this lesson. Then, have students complete the 6.4 Assessment.

REMEDIATION SUGGESTION

L1 Struggling Students If your students have trouble answering **Question 2b,** have them make bulleted lists of the subsections **Physical Evidence** and **Biological Evidence** in **Case Study #3.**

BIOLOGY.com Students can check their understanding of lesson concepts with the **Self-Test** assessment. They can then take an online version of the **Lesson Assessment.**

Assessment Answers

1a. An ecological footprint describes the total area of functioning land and water ecosystems needed both to provide the resources an individual or population uses and to absorb and make harmless the wastes that an individual or population generates.

1b. The limitations are that there is no universally accepted way to calculate footprint size and footprints give only a "snapshot" of the situation at a particular point in time. Ecologists can best use them to make comparisons among different populations.

2a. It absorbs harmful UV radiation from sunlight.

2b. Physical evidence: Data show that Earth's temperatures are getting warmer, its sea ice is melting, and its sea levels are rising. Biological evidence: Data confirm that many species are responding as though they are experiencing rising temperatures.

2c. Sample answer: A solution would be to place strict, worldwide limits on catching all types of fishes for many years. This would help by giving fish populations time to increase to sustainable levels. The challenge in implementing such limits would be to persuade all countries to go along with the plan. Incentives for fishing companies would likely be needed.

3. Big idea Sample answer: The burning of fossil fuels is adding more carbon dioxide to the atmosphere and depleting it from fossil fuel reservoirs. Since carbon from the atmosphere can dissolve in water, it is also increasing the amount of carbon in bodies of water.

CHAPTER LAB

Pre-Lab

Introduce students to the concepts they will explore in the chapter lab by assigning the Pre-Lab questions.

Lab

Tell students they will perform the chapter lab *Acid Rain and Plants* described in **Lab Manual A.**

 **Struggling Students** A simpler version of the chapter lab is provided in **Lab Manual B.**

SAFETY

Make sure students wear goggles and a lab apron. Caution them to be careful in handling glassware and other breakable materials and to avoid getting the solutions on their skin. Have students wash their hands at the end of the lab.

BIOLOGY.com Look online for **Editable Lab Worksheets.**

For corresponding pre-lab in the **Foundation Edition**, see page 150.

IN INDIANA ACADEMIC STANDARDS

For the full text of all standards, see the Course Overview in the front matter of this book.

Design Your Own Lab

OPEN-ENDED INQUIRY

IN B.4.2 Effects of human activities and natural phenomena. Also covered: **NoS.1, NoS.3, NoS.5, NoS.6, B.4.4.**

Pre-Lab: Acid Rain and Seeds

Problem How does acid rain affect seed germination?

Materials white vinegar, distilled water, large test tubes, test-tube rack, glass-marking pencil, 25-mL graduated cylinder, food coloring, pipette, pH paper, dried beans, paper towels, zip-close plastic bags, stick-on labels, hand lens

Lab Manual Chapter 6 Lab

Skills Focus Design an Experiment, Organize Data, Measure, Graph

Connect to the Big idea Every organism alters its environment in some way. Elephants uproot trees, prairie dogs dig tunnels, and corals build reefs. But no other organism has as much impact on the global environment as humans. One of the ways that humans affect global ecology is by burning fossil fuels. The burning produces carbon dioxide, which can accumulate in the atmosphere and cause climate change. Other products react with water to form nitric and sulfuric acids. Rain that contains these acids can damage many things, including stone statues and growing plants. In this lab, you will investigate the effect of acid rain on seeds.

Background Questions

a. Review What does a pH scale measure?

b. Review Which solution is more acidic, one with a pH of 4.0 or one with a pH of 5.0, and why?

c. Explain Use the water cycle to trace the path from acids in water vapor to plants.

Pre-Lab Questions

Preview the procedure in the lab manual.

1. Design an Experiment What do you think the purpose is of adding food coloring to the vinegar in Part A?
2. Infer How will you know that a seed has germinated?
3. Using Models In this lab, what do the solutions represent?

Visit Chapter 6 online to test yourself on chapter content and to find activities to help you learn.

Untamed Science Video The Untamed Science crew visits a zoo to learn about the important work that goes on behind the scenes.

Art in Motion View a short animation of biological magnification.

Art Review Review your understanding of the various threats to biodiversity with this activity.

Visual Analogy Compare human impact on the biosphere to a footprint in this activity.

Data Analysis Simulate data collection in order to compare two sites, and learn how to calculate a biodiversity index to quantify biodiversity.

Pre-Lab Answers

BACKGROUND QUESTIONS

a. A pH scale measures the concentration of H^+ ions in a solution.

b. The solution with a pH of 4.0 is more acidic because it has a greater concentration of H^+ ions (ten times as many per unit volume).

c. Sample answer: Water vapor in the atmosphere can condense and fall to Earth's surface as rain, which can contain dissolved acids. Some rain is absorbed into the soil where it can enter plants through their roots.

PRE-LAB QUESTIONS

1. Sample answer: As the vinegar is diluted with water, the intensity of the color will decrease. The food coloring provides a visual indicator for the decreased concentration of acid (H^+ ions) in the solutions.
2. Sample answer: The seed coat will crack and a root will be visible.
3. Sample answer: The solutions represent rain with different concentrations of acids.

6 Study Guide

Big idea Interdependence in Nature

Humans affect natural ecological processes through agriculture, urban development, and industry. But ecological science gives us strategies for sustainable development, ways we can protect the environment without slowing human progress.

6.1 A Changing Landscape

Humans affect regional and global environments through agriculture, development, and industry in ways that have an impact on the quality of Earth's natural resources, including soil, water, and the atmosphere.

Sustainable development provides for human needs while preserving the ecosystems that produce natural resources.

monoculture (155)
renewable resource (157)
nonrenewable resource (157)
sustainable development (157)

6.2 Using Resources Wisely

Healthy soil supports both agriculture and forestry.

It is possible to minimize soil erosion through careful management of both agriculture and forestry.

The primary sources of water pollution are industrial and agricultural chemicals, residential sewage, and nonpoint sources.

Common forms of air pollution include smog, acid rain, greenhouse gases, and particulates.

desertification (159)
deforestation (159)
pollutant (160)
biological magnification (161)
smog (163)
acid rain (164)

6.3 Biodiversity

Biodiversity's benefits to society include contributions to medicine and agriculture, and the provision of ecosystem goods and services.

Humans reduce biodiversity by altering habitats, hunting, introducing invasive species, releasing pollution into food webs, and contributing to climate change.

To conserve biodiversity, we must protect individual species, preserve habitats and ecosystems, and make certain that human neighbors of protected areas benefit from participating in conservation efforts.

biodiversity (166)
ecosystem diversity (166)
species diversity (166)
genetic diversity (166)
habitat fragmentation (168)
ecological hot spot (171)

6.4 Meeting Ecological Challenges

According to one data set, the average American has an ecological footprint over four times larger than the global average.

By (1) recognizing a problem in the environment, (2) researching that problem to determine its cause, and then (3) using scientific understanding to change our behavior we can have a positive impact on the global environment.

ecological footprint (173)
ozone layer (175)
aquaculture (176)
global warming (177)

Think Visually

Create a flowchart that shows the steps in the biological magnification of DDT. Your flowchart should show how DDT enters the food web and what effects it has on organisms.

BIOLOGY.com Search Chapter 6 GO • Crossword • Chapter Assessment

UbD Performance Tasks

SUMMATIVE TASK Have students work in small groups to create a pamphlet that could be distributed throughout the community to teach people about the impact humans have on the environment. Tell groups they should include information on sustainable development; using soil, water, and atmospheric resources wisely; the importance of biodiversity; and the challenges humans face in the future. Pamphlets should be a combination of text and illustrations.

TRANSFER TASK Have each student write a magazine article describing a success story of an environmental activist who persuaded a community to change a development plan in order to conserve biodiversity or use resources wisely. Explain to students that, although the situation is hypothetical, their description of humans' impact on the environment should reflect what they have learned in the chapter.

Study Online

REVIEW AND ASSESSMENT RESOURCES

Editable Worksheets Pages of Study Workbooks A and B, Lab Manuals A and B, and the Assessment Resources Book are available online. These documents can be easily edited using a word-processing program.

Lesson Overview Have students reread the Lesson Overviews to help them study chapter concepts.

Vocabulary Review The *Flash Cards* and *Crossword* provide an interactive way to review chapter vocabulary.

Chapter Assessment Have students take an online version of the Chapter 6 Assessment.

Standardized Test Prep Students can take an online version of the Standardized Test Prep. You will receive their scores along with ideas for remediation.

Diagnostic and Benchmark Tests Use these tests to monitor your students' progress and supply remediation.

Answers

THINK VISUALLY

Sample answer: (1) Primary producers in an aquatic food web pick up DDT in the water. (2) Zooplankton consume primary producers, and the concentration of DDT is magnified by 10. (3) Small fish consume zooplankton, and the concentration of DDT is magnified by 10. (4) Large fish consume small fish, and the concentration of DDT is magnified by 10. (5) Fish-eating birds consume large fish, and the concentration of DDT is magnified by 10. (6) The concentration of DDT in the fish-eating birds is high enough to cause females to produce thin, fragile eggshells. (7) The hatching rate falls, and the population of the birds decreases.

ASSESSMENT

Lesson 6.1

UNDERSTAND KEY CONCEPTS

1. d 2. c
3. They cut trees to plant crops and introduced nonnative plants, pigs, chickens, dogs, and rats.
4. Sample answer: breathable air, drinkable water, fertile soil, fossil fuels

THINK CRITICALLY

5. Sample answer: Every possible material should be placed in recycle bins, including cans, bottles, plastics, and paper. Food wastes should be composted. Hazardous wastes should be collected and disposed of in safe ways.
6. Sample answer: Both renewable and nonrenewable resources are made by natural ecosystems. However, renewable resources can be produced or replaced by a healthy ecosystem while nonrenewable resources cannot be within a reasonable amount of time.
7. Sample answer: Because they are large and homogeneous, monocultures are more vulnerable to disease and pests because if a disease attacks one plant, it can quickly spread to all the other plants and destroy the entire monoculture.

Lesson 6.2

UNDERSTAND KEY CONCEPTS

8. c 9. b 10. b 11. a
12. In sustainable forestry, trees are replanted after they are cut, and no more are cut down than are needed or that can be replaced. In deforestation, trees are cut arbitrarily and are not replanted.
13. industrial and agricultural chemicals, residential sewage, and nonpoint sources such as grease and oil washed off streets by rain or the chemicals released into the air by factories and automobiles

THINK CRITICALLY

14. Sample answer: Covering soil with mulch or compost near the bases of plants could reduce soil erosion. A simple experiment to test this hypothesis would be to grow two areas of the same crop, using mulch or compost in one area and not in the other. Results would support the hypothesis if the area of crops with mulch or compost produced more than the area without.

6 Assessment

The numbers following the questions refer to Indiana's Academic Standards for Biology I.

6.1 A Changing Landscape

Understand Key Concepts

1. Which of the following human activities has NOT had an important role in transforming the biosphere to date? B.4.2
   a. agriculture c. development
   b. industry d. aquaculture
2. A resource that cannot easily be replenished by natural processes is called
   a. common. c. nonrenewable.
   b. renewable. d. conserved.
3. Describe how Hawaiian settlers negatively affected the islands after the 1700s. B.4.2, B.4.4
4. Name four services that ecosystems provide for the biosphere.

Think Critically

5. **Propose a Solution** Devise guidelines your biology class can use to dispose of its nonlab trash in a safe, "environmentally friendly" way.
6. **Compare and Contrast** How are renewable and nonrenewable resources alike? How are they different?
7. **Form a Hypothesis** Monoculture fields are usually very large and homogeneous. Do you think this makes them more or less vulnerable to disease and pests? Explain. B.4.2

6.2 Using Resources Wisely

Understand Key Concepts

8. The conversion of a once soil-rich area to an area of little to no vegetation is called
   a. fragmentation. c. desertification.
   b. deforestation. d. acid rain.
9. The loss of fertile soils from an area through the action of water or wind is called
   a. acid rain. c. desertification.
   b. erosion. d. monoculture.
10. The concept of using natural resources at a rate that does not deplete them is called
    a. conservation.
    b. sustainable development.
    c. reforestation.
    d. successful use.
11. Examine the food web below. Which of the following organisms would accumulate the highest levels of a pesticide? B.4.2
    a. hawk c. frog
    b. rabbit d. grasses

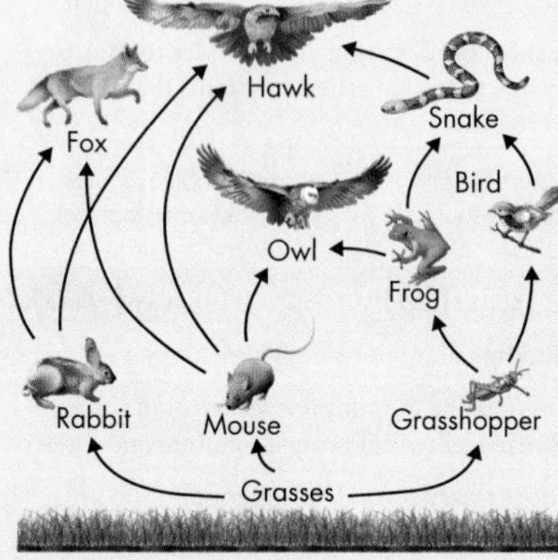

12. What is the difference between sustainable forestry and deforestation?
13. Identify some of the common sources of water pollution. B.4.2

Think Critically

14. **Design an Experiment** Can covering soil with mulch or compost near the bases of plants help reduce soil erosion? Design an experiment to answer this question. NoS.11, B.4.2
15. **Calculate** The concentration of a toxic chemical is magnified ten times at each trophic level. What will the concentration of the toxin be in organisms at the fifth trophic level if primary producers have concentrations of 40 parts per million? MATH
16. **Infer** Why are lakes that have been affected by acid rain often clear and blue? B.4.2

15. 400,000 parts per million
16. Sample answer: The acid rain kills organisms in the affected lakes. Without organisms, their wastes, and the turbulence caused by their activities, the water remains clear and blue.

Lesson 6.3

UNDERSTAND KEY CONCEPTS

17. b
18. a small area of habitat surrounded by a different habitat
19. ecosystem diversity, species diversity, genetic diversity

6.3 Biodiversity

Understand Key Concepts

17. A species that is introduced to an environment where it has not lived before is described as B.4.3
    a. native. c. threatened.
    b. nonnative. d. predatory.
18. What is a habitat fragment?
19. List three different kinds of biodiversity that might be described in a given biome.

Think Critically

20. **Predict** How do you think the loss of biodiversity would adversely affect humans?
21. **Compare and Contrast** Explain the difference between species diversity and ecosystem diversity.

6.4 Meeting Ecological Challenges

Understand Key Concepts

22. The burning of fossil fuels is a direct cause of each the following EXCEPT
    a. acid rain. c. smog.
    b. global warming. d. the ozone hole.
23. The total impact a person has on the biosphere can be represented by his or her
    a. contribution to climate change.
    b. ecological footprint.
    c. consumption of fossil fuel.
    d. production of carbon dioxide.
24. Cite three examples of physical evidence for global warming.
25. What are some of the biological effects of climate change?

Think Critically

26. **Relate Cause and Effect** Why hasn't the ozone layer repaired itself fully since the widespread ban of CFCs in 1987? NoS.11
27. **Apply Concepts** Describe some of the steps taken to counter the effects of overfishing cod in the North Atlantic. Why is overfishing such a complex environmental issue? NoS.11

solve the CHAPTER MYSTERY

MOVING THE *MOAI*

Easter Island's environment was not as biologically diverse, and not as resistant to ecological damage, as the Hawaiian Islands. The Rapa Nui cut palm trees for agriculture, for logs to move *moai*, and for wood to make fishing canoes. They mismanaged cleared fields, so fertile topsoil washed away.

Meanwhile, rats they brought to the island became invasive. Hordes of the rodents destroyed palm seedlings, ate coconuts, and digested palm seeds before they could germinate. Hawaiians also brought rats to their islands, and rats did serious damage to native Hawaiian plants. But in Hawaii's more diverse forests, some plant species were not as hard hit by rats and survived.

The combination of human activity and the effects of an invasive species led to the destruction of virtually all of Easter Island's forests. This combination, along with the effects of a harsh climate, limited the island's carrying capacity for humans from then on.

1. **Relate Cause and Effect** How did the small size of the island (about half the size of Long Island, New York) affect the outcome of deforestation and pest invasion?
2. **Compare and Contrast** Gather information on differences in geography, climate, and biological diversity between Hawaii and Easter Island. How do you think those differences made the islands respond differently to human settlement?
3. **Connect to the Big idea** All human cultures throughout history have interacted with their environments. Do you think that global human society has any lessons to learn from the experiences of the Rapa Nui, the Hawaiians, and other historic cultures? NoS.11

IN B.4.2, B.4.3, B.4.4

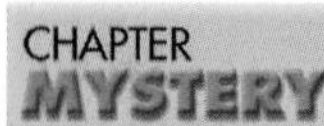

After students have read through the Chapter Mystery, discuss how the actions of the Rapa Nui resulted in the destruction of the forests on Easter Island.

Ask What activities of the Rapa Nui resulted in destruction of Easter Island's forests? *(They cleared trees for agriculture, cut trees to use the logs in moving the moai, and cut trees to make canoes.)*

Ask How did the rats reach Easter Island? *(They came as stowaways on the Rapa Nui's boats.)*

Ask How did an invasive species contribute to the deforestation of the island? *(The rats destroyed coconuts that contained the trees' seeds.)*

CHAPTER MYSTERY ANSWERS

1. Sample answer: Because of the small size of the island, relatively few species lived there, and the populations of those species were relatively small. The lack of species diversity and genetic diversity made the organisms native to the island vulnerable to disturbance.
2. Sample answer: Easter Island is smaller, the climate is harsher, and the biological diversity is more limited than in the Hawaiian Islands. Those differences made the ecosystem on Easter Island much more vulnerable to the disturbances of human activities than were the ecosystems on the Hawaiian Islands.
3. Big idea Sample answer: The experiences of the Rapa Nui, especially, should be a lesson to global human society. The Rapa Nui both intentionally and unintentionally destroyed Easter Island's forests, making life for humans impossible on the island. Global human society should learn from that example to use resources wisely and be aware of changes in the environment that could make human life on Earth difficult in the future.

Have students watch the video **What Do Zoos . . . Do?** in which the Untamed Science crew explores a zoo's role in protecting biodiversity.

THINK CRITICALLY

20. Sample answer: The loss of biodiversity would limit the medicines that could be developed, make crop plants more vulnerable to diseases, and it would make ecosystems less stable, productive, and valuable.
21. Species diversity is the number of different species in the biosphere or in a particular area. Ecosystem diversity refers to the variety of habitats, communities, and ecological processes in the biosphere.

Lesson 6.4

UNDERSTAND KEY CONCEPTS

22. d **23.** b

24. Earth's temperatures are getting warmer, sea ice is melting, and sea levels are rising.
25. Sample answer: Organisms move toward cooler places away from the equator and from warm lowlands to cooler, higher altitudes. Plants flower and animals breed earlier as though spring begins earlier.

THINK CRITICALLY

26. The ozone layer hasn't repaired itself fully yet because CFCs can remain in the atmosphere for a century. CFCs were widely used for many decades before the ban went into place, so their effects are still visible.

27. Sample answer: The steps taken include regulating how many fish could be caught in U.S. waters, closing certain areas to fishing until stocks recover, closing some areas seasonally to allow fishes to breed and spawn, and using aquaculture as an alternative to fishing. Overfishing is a complex issue because fleets from other countries fish outside of U.S. territorial waters, and countries are reluctant to accept conservation efforts that could cause job loss.

Connecting Concepts

USE SCIENCE GRAPHICS

28. Sample answer: The catch would decrease.

29. Sample answer: The fishing of bluefin tuna should be regulated, strictly limiting the catch for at least the next decade.

WRITE ABOUT SCIENCE

30. Sample answer: Wetlands naturally filter toxins and other materials from water, making the water resources safer for humans, as well as healthier for affected ecosystems. In addition, wetlands provide habitats for many species, increasing an area's ecosystem diversity and species diversity.

31. Big idea Sample answer: Species diversity in an area contributes to the overall biodiversity of the area. Biodiversity's benefits to society include contributions to medicine and agriculture and the provision of ecosystem goods and services.

32. Big idea Sample answer: Most coastal waters are in the photic zone. As a result, they receive plenty of solar energy for the producers that support the food chains there. In addition, runoff from rivers and streams may bring nutrients to coastal waters that also increase the productivity of these ecosystems. Finally, estuaries, the intertidal zone, and the coastal ocean provide varied habitats that encourage biodiversity.

Connecting Concepts

Use Science Graphics NoS.3

The graph shows the amount of bluefin tuna caught by the United States in the Atlantic Ocean between 2002 and 2006. Use the graph to answer questions 28 and 29.

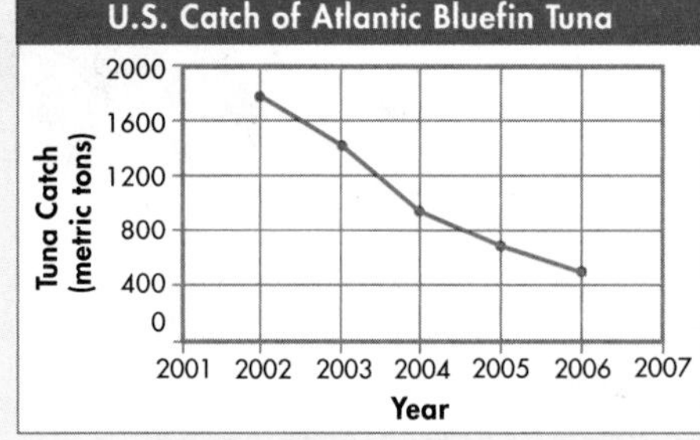

28. Predict What trend would you expect to see in the annual catch from 2006 to 2007?

29. Propose a Solution What recommendations would you make to help the bluefin tuna population recover in the next decade or two? NoS.11

Write About Science NoS.3

30. Explanation Write a paragraph explaining the value of wetlands to human societies. In your paragraph, include the concept of biodiversity as well as the role of wetlands in maintaining water resources for human use.

31. Assess the Big idea Why is it important to maintain species diversity in areas where humans live?

32. Assess the Big idea What environmental factors make high levels of biodiversity possible in most coastal waters? Refer to the discussion of abiotic and biotic factors in Chapter 4 if you need help answering this question.

Analyzing Data

NoS.3

The following graph shows the number of species introduced to new habitats in the United States in the last century. Some of the species were relocated to new habitats within the United States while others were imported from other countries.

Introduced Species
Domestic Foreign
Number of Species
600 500 400 300 200 100 0
1850–1900 1901–1950 1951–1996
Years

33. Interpret Graphs Of domestic species and foreign species, which showed the greatest percentage increase between the 1901–1950 period and the 1951–1996 period?

a. domestic species
b. foreign species
c. Both increased the same amount.
d. There is not enough information to tell.

34. Draw Conclusions Which of the following statements about introduced species is most likely true based on the data shown?

a. Species introduced from foreign countries are always more harmful than species relocated within the country.
b. All introduced species are brought into this country by accident.
c. It is likely that the increase in the number of introduced species is due to increased global travel, trade, and communication.
d. The number of introduced species is likely to fall in the next half-century.

184 Chapter 6 • Assessment

PURPOSE Students will draw conclusions about the effect of introduced species in the United States.

PLANNING Review with students how species introduced to new habitats can become invasive and threaten biodiversity in the habitat.

ANSWERS

33. b

34. c

Standardized Test Practice for Indiana

Multiple Choice

1. Which of the following statements about renewable resources is TRUE?
   A They are found only in tropical climates.
   B They can never be depleted.
   C They are replaceable by natural means.
   D They can never regenerate.

2. Which of the following is a nonrenewable resource?
   A wind
   B fresh water
   C coal
   D topsoil

3. Which of the following is NOT a direct effect of deforestation?
   A decreased productivity of the ecosystem
   B soil erosion
   C biological magnification
   D habitat destruction B.4.2

4. The total variety of organisms in the biosphere is called
   A biodiversity.
   B species diversity.
   C ecosystem diversity.
   D genetic diversity.

5. Ozone is made up of
   A hydrogen.
   B oxygen.
   C nitrogen.
   D chlorine.

6. Ozone depletion in the atmosphere has been caused by
   A monoculture.
   B CFCs.
   C suburban sprawl.
   D soil erosion. B.4.2

7. In a food chain, concentrations of harmful substances increase in higher trophic levels in a process is known as
   A biological magnification.
   B genetic drift.
   C biological succession.
   D pesticide resistance. B.4.2

Questions 8 and 9

Fire ants first arrived in the United States in 1918, probably on a ship traveling from South America to Alabama. The maps below show the geographic location of the U.S. fire ant population in 1953 and 2001.

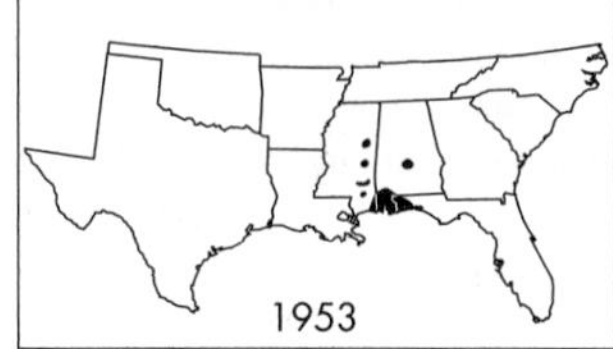

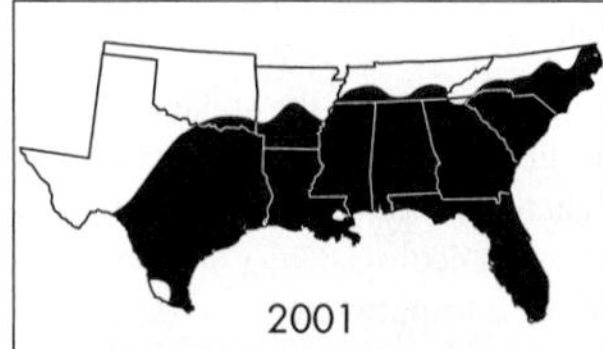

8. Which of the following statements about fire ants in the United States is TRUE?
   A They reproduce slowly.
   B They are a native species of the United States.
   C They are an invasive species.
   D They do not compete with other ant species. B.4.3

9. By 2010, fire ants are MOST likely to
   A have spread to a larger area.
   B have reached their carrying capacity.
   C die out.
   D return to South America. B.4.3

Open-Response

10. Describe how ecologists use the ecological footprint concept.

If You Have Trouble With . . .

Question	1	2	3	4	5	6	7	8	9	10
See Lesson	6.1	6.2	6.2	6.3	6.2	6.4	6.2	6.3	6.3	6.4

Test-Taking Tip

USE TIME WISELY

Advise students that if they are taking a long time to answer a question, they should move on to other questions and come back to the difficult question later. In answering other questions, they may remember the information needed to answer the skipped question.

Answers

1. C
2. C
3. C
4. A
5. B
6. B
7. A
8. C
9. A
10. Sample answer: They can use it to analyze human impact on ecosystems and make comparisons among different populations.

UNIT 2

Plan Ahead

Have students preview the Unit 2 Project a few days before the day of debate. Suggest they review ways in which human activities can affect the environment. Then, divide the class into groups of four. Assign each member of the groups one of the four roles for the debate. Tell students they might search online to find evidence to support the position assigned. Encourage students to talk to classmates with the same role about evidence and arguments that could be persuasive in a debate.

Materials Internet access for research

Monitor the Project

Suggest students make lists of evidence and arguments supporting the position of the role they have taken. Ask individual students how they are preparing for the debate and what evidence they have found that supports their position. On debate day, each group could be given about 10 minutes to debate the issue, or students with the same role could collaborate in a debate that includes the entire class.

Project Assessment

Make sure students use the rubric and reflection questions to assess their work. Then, use the rubric to assign a final score. If desired, talk with students about any differences between their self-assessment scores and your assigned score.

Unit Project

Development Debate

A large company wants to build a new factory on your town's wetlands. Many people in the town are opposed to the idea, claiming it will disturb the local ecosystem and cause problems for residents. Others support the development, arguing that the new factory will bring jobs and money into the town. Representatives have been called in to debate the issue before the town council.

Your Task Take on one of the stakeholder roles listed below. Find evidence to support that point of view and debate the issue in class. The roles are

- Conservation ecologist
- CEO of the company
- Town mayor who supports the development
- Resident of the town who lives next to the wetlands

Be sure to

- justify your arguments with credible information.
- present your arguments in a clear and convincing manner.

Reflection Questions

1. **Score your performance using the rubric below. What score did you give yourself?**
2. **What did you do well in this project?**
3. **What about your performance needs improvement?**
4. **After hearing various sides of the argument, meet with a partner and discuss which side you agree with the most. Justify your opinion.**

Assessment Rubric

Score	Evidence Provided	Quality of Performance
4	Student justifies his/her argument with sophisticated and highly credible information.	Ideas are presented in a highly convincing and clear manner. Student shows a deep understanding of the issues involved.
3	Student justifies his/her argument with logical and credible information.	Ideas are presented in an effective and clear manner. Student shows a solid understanding of the issues involved.
2	Student provides some credible information, but other points are weak or inaccurate.	Some ideas are presented in an unclear manner. Student shows a limited understanding of the issues involved.
1	Student provides mostly illogical and invalid evidence to support his/her argument.	Most ideas are presented in an unclear manner. Student shows a very limited understanding of the issues involved.

21st Century Skills

To be successful in the 21st century, students need skills and learning experiences that extend beyond subject area mastery. The Unit 2 Project helps students build the following 21st Century Skills: *Information and Media Literacy; Communication Skills; Critical Thinking and Systems Thinking; Problem Identification, Formulation, and Solution; Interpersonal and Collaborative Skills; Self-Direction; Accountability and Adaptability;* and *Social Responsibility.*

FOCUS ON CREATIVITY AND INTELLECTUAL CURIOSITY Extend this Unit Project by asking small groups of students to use what they have learned from the debate to write a screenplay about an environmental controversy within a community.

For more practice building 21st Century Skills, see The Chapter Mystery pages in **Study Workbook A.**

IN INDIANA ACADEMIC STANDARDS

B.4.2 Effects of human activities and natural phenomena

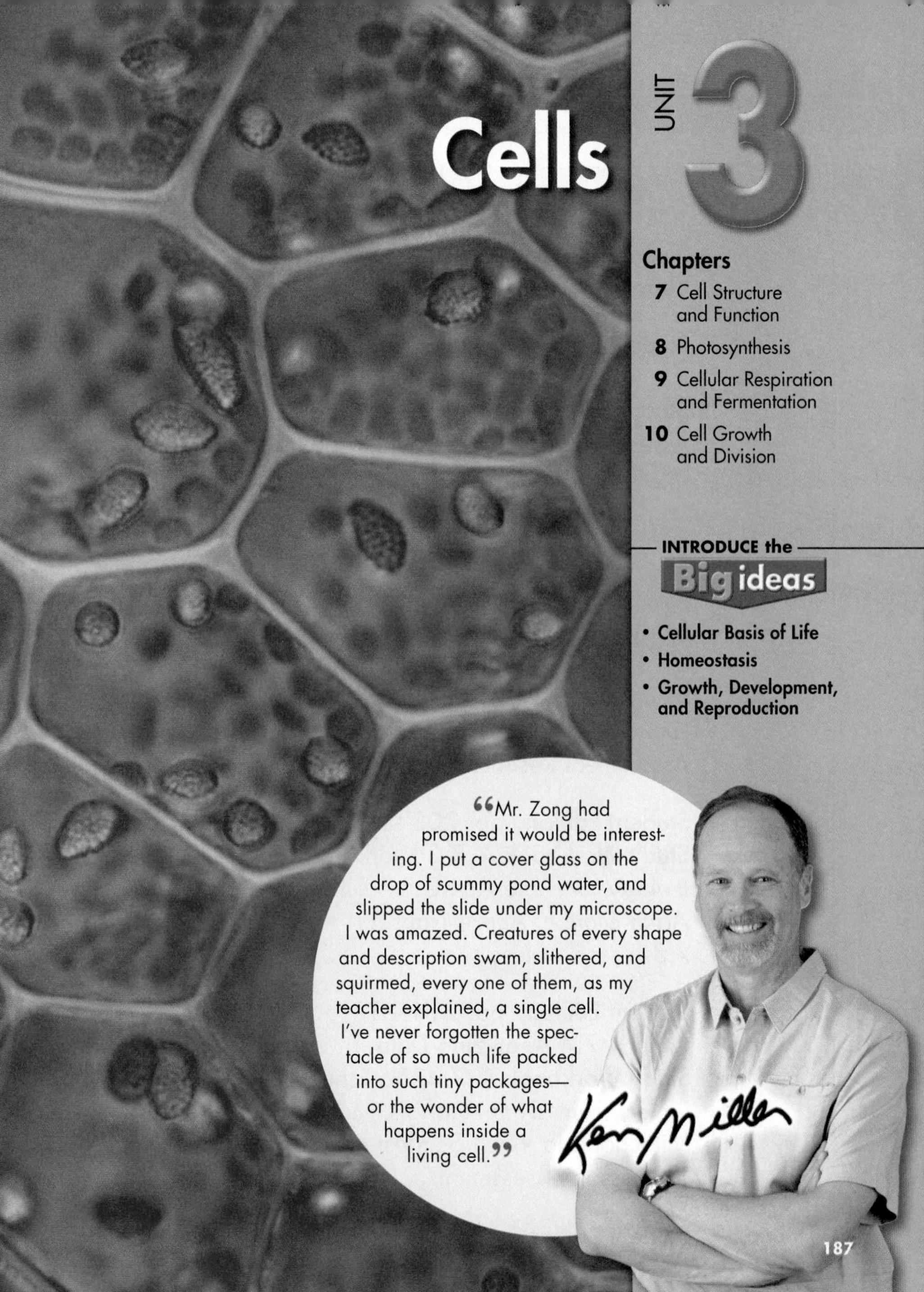

Cells
UNIT 3
Chapters
7 Cell Structure and Function
8 Photosynthesis
9 Cellular Respiration and Fermentation
10 Cell Growth and Division
INTRODUCE the Big ideas
• Cellular Basis of Life
• Homeostasis
• Growth, Development, and Reproduction
“Mr. Zong had promised it would be interesting. I put a cover glass on the drop of scummy pond water, and slipped the slide under my microscope. I was amazed. Creatures of every shape and description swam, slithered, and squirmed, every one of them, as my teacher explained, a single cell. I've never forgotten the spectacle of so much life packed into such tiny packages—or the wonder of what happens inside a living cell.”
187

Dear Colleague,

I can still remember the first time I looked through a microscope and saw a living cell. It was in Paul Zong's ninth-grade biology class in my hometown high school in New Jersey. After carefully instructing us in the proper use of the microscope, our teacher placed a drop of water on every student's slide and told us to have a look. I couldn't believe my eyes. Glistening creatures swam across the field of view. They twisted and turned, I thought, almost as if they were alive. I think I said that out loud, because I can remember Mr. Zong's deep, gentle laugh and a pat on my shoulder. "They are alive, Kenny! They're alive just like you and me."

Later that year, I transformed a corner of the small room I shared with my brother into a miniature laboratory. A tiny desk lamp glowed day and night, providing energy for nearly a dozen test-tube colonies of Euglena. *At the end of the year, those cells would become a science project, the very first research I would ever do on my own. What stuck with me from that first experience was the realization that the cell is life itself. Everything that we associate with life, from growth and reproduction to digestion and movement, happens at the level of the cell.*

I won a ribbon that year for my study of light's effect on the growth of Euglena. *Although I have long since misplaced the ribbon, I hope I never lose the greater gift that came from a year of study in that biology classroom—a sense of amazement that returns every time I sit down at a microscope in my laboratory.*

I hope that you and your students will find some of that amazement written into the pages of this unit. As a cell biologist, I especially hope to give students an appreciation of the roles that cells play in every aspect of life. In these four chapters, we have done our best to explain how cells live and grow, how they transform energy, and how they pass information along from one generation to the next.

Ken Miller

Cell Structure and Function

Chapter Contents	IN	Time	Core Resources
Chapter Preview			**Student Edition,** pp. 188–189 **Chapter Mystery,** p. 189
7.1 Life Is Cellular The Discovery of the Cell • Exploring the Cell • Prokaryotes and Eukaryotes • *Careers & Biology: Laboratory Technician, Microscopist, Pathologist*	NoS.9, NoS.10	1 period 1/2 block	**Student Edition,** pp. 190–195 Inquiry 7.1 Quick Lab, p. 193 L2 **Study Workbook A** 7.1 Worksheets L2 **Assessment Resources Book** Visual Quiz L2
7.2 Cell Structure Cell Organization • Organelles That Store, Clean Up, and Support • Organelles That Build Proteins • Organelles That Capture and Release Energy • Cellular Boundaries	NoS.6, B.2.1, B.2.2, B.2.3, B.2.4, B.2.5, B.2.6	2 periods 1 block	**Student Edition,** pp. 196–207 Inquiry 7.2 Quick Lab, p. 203 L2 **Study Workbook A** 7.2 Worksheets L2 Biology.com *Art Review:* Plant and Animal Cells • *Visual Analogy:* A Cell as a Living Factory • *Tutor Tube:* Plants Have Mitochondria Too **Assessment Resources Book** Visual Quiz L2
7.3 Cell Transport Passive Transport • Active Transport	B.1.2, B.2.2, B.2.5	1 period 1/2 block	**Student Edition,** pp. 208–213 **Study Workbook A** 7.3 Worksheets L2 Biology.com *InterActive Art:* Diffusion and Osmosis • *Art in Motion:* Active Transport • 7.3 Self-Test • 7.3 Lesson Assessment
7.4 Homeostasis and Cells The Cell as an Organism • Multicellular Life	NoS.3, B.1.3, B.2.1, B.2.5, B.2.6, B.3.3, B.6.3	1/2 period 1/4 block	**Student Edition,** pp. 214–217 Inquiry 7.4 Analyzing Data, p. 216 L2 **Study Workbook A** 7.4 Worksheets L2 Biology.com *Data Analysis:* Maximizing Mitochondria • 7.4 Self-Test • 7.4 Lesson Assessment
Chapter Pre-Lab	NoS.1, NoS.6, B.2.2	1 period 1/2 block	**Student Edition,** p. 218 L2 **Lab Manual A** *Detecting Diffusion* L2 • *Osmosis* L2

Differentiated Instruction Tools

Study Workbook B includes worksheets with lesson-level differentiated instruction support and explanations of differentiated instruction teaching strategies.

Lab Manual B includes skills labs, simplified chapter labs, and hands-on activities.

ELL Handbook explains ways to make *Biology* more accessible to ELL students.

Spanish Study Workbook is a Spanish translation of Study Workbook A.

Multilingual Glossary is the glossary translated into ten languages.

Differentiated Instruction Key

- L1 Special Needs or Struggling Students
- ELL English Language Learners
- LPR Less Proficient Readers
- L2 On-Level Students
- L3 Advanced Students

Additional Resources

Biology.com Untamed Science Video • Vocabulary Flash Cards

Study Workbook B 7.1 Worksheets L1 ELL LPR
Spanish Study Workbook 7.1 Worksheets ELL
Biology.com 7.1 Lesson Overview • 7.1 Lesson Notes • 7.1 Self-Test • 7.1 Lesson Assessment

Study Workbook B 7.2 Worksheets L1 ELL LPR
Spanish Study Workbook 7.2 Worksheets ELL
Biology.com 7.2 Lesson Overview • 7.2 Lesson Notes • 7.2 Self-Test • 7.2 Lesson Assessment

Study Workbook B 7.3 Worksheets L1 ELL LPR
Spanish Study Workbook 7.3 Worksheets ELL
Biology.com 7.3 Lesson Overview • 7.3 Lesson Notes

Study Workbook B 7.4 Worksheets L1 ELL LPR
Spanish Study Workbook 7.4 Worksheets ELL
Biology.com 7.4 Lesson Overview • 7.4 Lesson Notes

Lab Manual B *Detecting Diffusion* • Hands-On Activity: *Making a Model of a Cell* • Data Analysis: *Mitochondria Distribution in the Mouse* L1 ELL LPR

Chapter Review

Student Edition Study Guide, p. 219 L2
Study Workbook A Chapter 7 Vocabulary Review L2 • Chapter 7 Chapter Mystery/21st Century Skills Activity L2 L3
Transparencies, pp. 78–98 L1 ELL LPR L2
Biology.com Untamed Science Video • Editable Worksheets of Study Workbooks A and B and Lab Manuals A and B • Chapter 7 Flash Cards and Match It

Untamed Science DVD • Classroom Resources CD (includes lesson presentations and editable worksheets)

Chapter Assessment

Student Edition Assessment, pp. 220–223 L2
Study Workbook B Chapter 7 Chapter Review L1 ELL LPR • Chapter 7 Taking a Standardized Test L1 ELL LPR
Assessment Resources Book Chapter 7 Test A L2 • Chapter 7 Test B L1 ELL LPR
Biology.com Chapter 7 Assessment • Editable Worksheets of Chapter 7 Visual Quizzes and Chapter 7 Tests A and B

Exam*View* *Assessment Suite* • Classroom Resources CD (includes lesson presentations and editable worksheets)

Time: 1 period, 1/2 block

Pressed for Time?

Preview the Chapter Introduce the Key Questions for Lesson 7.2 and preview the Lesson 7.2 vocabulary.

Cover the Chapter Quickly Have students read *The Discovery of the Cell* and *Prokaryotes and Eukaryotes* in Lesson 7.1. Assign all of Lesson 7.2 and go over Figure 7–14. Assign all of Lesson 7.3, focusing on Figures 7–18 and 7–19.

Assess Assign questions 1 and 4 in the 7.1 Assessment, the 7.2 Assessment, the 7.3 Assessment, and questions 1–3 and 6–22 in the Chapter 7 Assessment.

Connect to the Big Idea

Big idea Diatoms are single-celled organisms found in both fresh and salt water. Use the photograph of freshwater diatoms to help students understand that cells make up all living things, whether an organism consists of one cell, like a diatom, or many cells, as in a human or a corn plant. Emphasize that cells are dynamic. They are equipped with intricate parts, each of which has a specific function. Have students predict some of the challenges faced by cells. *(Sample answers: They must take in and give off water and other raw materials, use energy, reproduce, and live in balance with their environment. At this point, accept all reasonable answers.)* Explain that cells face the same challenges whether they are a single diatom in a human body, or in a plant. Tell students that, as they read this chapter, they should be guided by the Chapter 7 Essential Question, **How are cell structures adapted to their functions?**

CHAPTER MYSTERY Have students read over the Chapter Mystery. Ask what they might already know about the importance of water for living things. Have them suggest reasons why the runner suffered ill effects from the intake of water rather than benefiting from it. Use points made during the discussion to help students start connecting the Chapter Mystery to the Big Ideas of the Cellular Basis of Life and Homeostasis.

BIOLOGY.com Have students preview the chapter vocabulary using the **Flash Cards.**

IN INDIANA ACADEMIC STANDARDS

For the full text of all standards, see the Course Overview in the front matter of this book.

Key standards: Chapter 7 covers key ideas from Standard 1: Cellular Chemistry and Standard 2: Cellular Structure, including **B.1.2** Molecules and cellular processes, **B.1.3** Cell function and differentiation, **B.2.1** Features common to all cells, **B.2.2** Cell membrane, and **B.2.3** Mitochondria and chloroplasts.

7 Cell Structure and Function

Big ideas **Cellular Basis of Life, Homeostasis**

Q: How are cell structures adapted to their functions?

BIOLOGY.com Search Chapter 7 GO • Flash Cards

188

UbD Understanding by Design

In Unit 3, students build toward the Enduring Understanding that *a cell is the basic unit of life; the processes that occur at the cellular level provide the energy and basic structure organisms need to survive.* In Chapter 7, students learn about the cell theory and the structure and function of parts in prokaryotic and eukaryotic cells. The graphic organizer to the right summarizes how the Big Ideas relate to the chapter Essential Question and the four lesson-level Guiding Questions.

PERFORMANCE GOALS

Students will build a model cell with detailed parts and explore an analogy that compares a cell to a factory. They will also analyze data about the number of mitochondria in cells of different organs. In a summative task, students will imagine themselves within a cell and write an account of how the cell functions.

INDIANA ACADEMIC STANDARDS FOR SCIENCE

Nature of Science NoS.1, NoS.3, NoS.6, NoS.9, NoS.10; **Cellular Chemistry** B.1.2, B.1.3; **Cellular Structure** B.2.1, B.2.2, B.2.3, B.2.4, B.2.5, B.2.6; **Matter Cycles and Energy Transfer** B.3.3; **Cellular Reproduction and Gene Expression** B.6.3. See lessons for details.

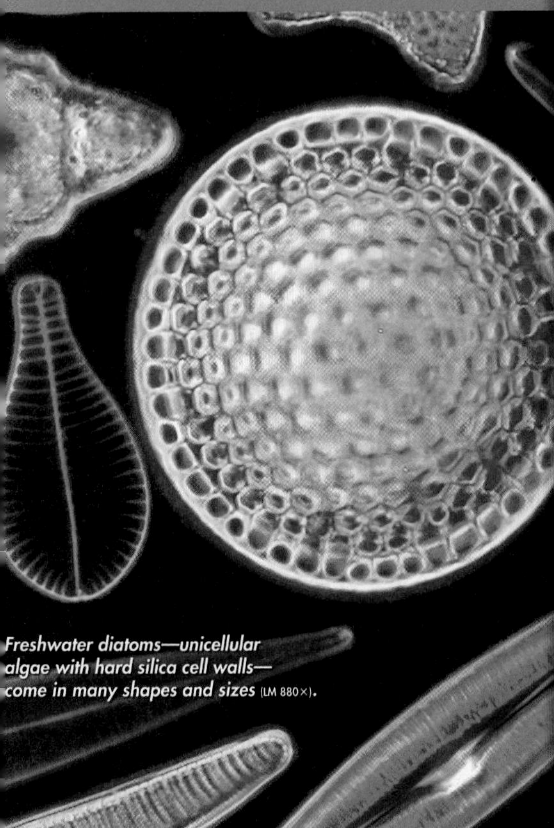

Freshwater diatoms—unicellular algae with hard silica cell walls—come in many shapes and sizes (LM 880×).

• Untamed Science Video • Chapter Mystery

CHAPTER MYSTERY

DEATH BY ... WATER?

Michelle was a healthy 25-year-old running in her first marathon. The hot and humid weather had made all the runners sweat profusely, so Michelle made sure she drank water at every opportunity. Gradually, she began to feel weak and confused. At the end of the marathon, Michelle staggered into a medical tent. Complaining of headache and nausea, she collapsed onto the floor. Volunteers quickly gave Michelle water for dehydration. Soon, her condition worsened and Michelle was rushed to the hospital, where she was gripped by a seizure and went into a coma. Why did treating Michelle with water make her condition worse? As you read this chapter, look for clues to help you predict how water made Michelle sick. Then, solve the mystery.

Never Stop Exploring Your World. Michelle's mysterious illness is just the beginning. Take a video field trip with the ecogeeks of Untamed Science to see where this mystery leads.

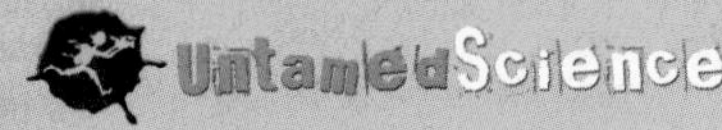

Chapter 7 Big Ideas: Cellular Basis of Life and Homeostasis

Chapter 7 EQ: How are cell structures adapted to their functions?

- **7.1 GQ:** Why is it important to study cells?
- **7.2 GQ:** How do cell structures enable a cell to carry out basic life processes?
- **7.3 GQ:** How does a cell transport materials across the cell membrane?
- **7.4 GQ:** How does a cell maintain homeostasis both within itself and as part of a multicellular organism?

What's Online

BIOLOGY.com Extend your reach by using these and other digital assets offered at **Biology.com.**

CHAPTER MYSTERY
Students use what they learn about cellular homeostasis to figure out why a runner suffered ill effects when she drank large amounts of water during a race.

UNTAMED SCIENCE VIDEO
Deep in the ocean, the Untamed Science crew explores how fishes maintain homeostasis.

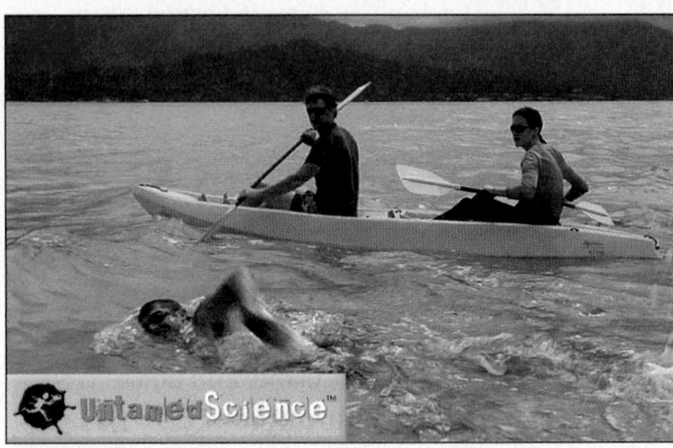

VISUAL ANALOGY
Cell parts are compared with factory parts and their functions in this online activity.

ART REVIEW
Students label structures in typical plant cells and animal cells.

TUTOR TUBE
Students are reminded that plants have mitochondria in addition to chloroplasts.

INTERACTIVE ART
Explore diffusion and osmosis with an animation and an activity.

ART IN MOTION
The different types of active transport are reviewed in this short animation.

DATA ANALYSIS
Students analyze how mitochondrial function is related to human health and longevity.

LESSON 7.1

Getting Started

Objectives

7.1.1 State the cell theory.

7.1.2 Describe how the different types of microscopes work.

7.1.3 Distinguish between prokaryotes and eukaryotes.

Student Resources

Study Workbooks A and B, 7.1 Worksheets

Spanish Study Workbook, 7.1 Worksheets

Lesson Overview • Lesson Notes • Assessment: Self-Test, Lesson Assessment

For corresponding lesson in the **Foundation Edition**, see pages 160–163.

Build Background

To get students thinking about life at the cellular level, show photographs of plants and animals. Ask **What keeps these organisms alive?** *(Sample answers: soil, water, oxygen, food)* Tell students each organism is made up of small units called cells that keep organisms functioning. Explain that, until the invention of the microscope, scientists didn't know that all organisms are made up of cells. Have students suggest ways improved microscopes helped in the study of cells. *(Sample answer: They provided more accurate images of structures and how living things function.)*

IN INDIANA ACADEMIC STANDARDS

For the full text of all standards, see the Course Overview in the front matter of this book.

NoS.10 Describe how scientific discoveries lead to the development of new technologies, and conversely how technological advances can lead to scientific discoveries through new experimental methods and equipment.

7.1 Life Is Cellular

IN **NoS.9** Scientific discoveries affect prior ideas; **NoS.10** Scientific discoveries and new technologies.

Key Questions

What is the cell theory?

How do microscopes work?

How are prokaryotic and eukaryotic cells different?

Vocabulary

cell • cell theory • cell membrane • nucleus • eukaryote • prokaryote

Taking Notes

Outline Before you read, make an outline using the green and blue headings in the text. As you read, fill in notes under each heading.

THINK ABOUT IT What's the smallest part of any living thing that still counts as being "alive"? Is a leaf alive? How about your big toe? How about a drop of blood? Can we just keep dividing living things into smaller and smaller parts, or is there a point at which what's left is no longer alive? As you will see, there is such a limit, the smallest living unit of any organism—the cell.

The Discovery of the Cell

What is the cell theory?

"Seeing is believing," an old saying goes. It would be hard to find a better example of this than the discovery of the cell. Without the instruments to make them visible, cells remained out of sight and, therefore, out of mind for most of human history. All of this changed with a dramatic advance in technology—the invention of the microscope.

Early Microscopes In the late 1500s, eyeglass makers in Europe discovered that using several glass lenses in combination could magnify even the smallest objects to make them easy to see. Before long, they had built the first true microscopes from these lenses, opening the door to the study of biology as we know it today.

In 1665, Englishman Robert Hooke used an early compound microscope to look at a nonliving thin slice of cork, a plant material. Under the microscope, cork seemed to be made of thousands of tiny empty chambers. Hooke called these chambers "cells" because they reminded him of a monastery's tiny rooms, which were called cells. The term *cell* is used in biology to this day. Today we know that living cells are not empty chambers, that in fact they contain a huge array of working parts, each with its own function.

In Holland around the same time, Anton van Leeuwenhoek used a single-lens microscope to observe pond water and other things. To his amazement, the microscope revealed a fantastic world of tiny living organisms that seemed to be everywhere, in the water he and his neighbors drank, and even in his own mouth. Leeuwenhoek's illustrations of the organisms he found in the human mouth—which today we call bacteria—are shown in **Figure 7–1.**

FIGURE 7–1 Early Microscope Images Using a simple microscope, Anton van Leeuwenhoek was the first to observe living microorganisms. These drawings, taken from one of his letters, show bacteria in the human mouth.

UbD Teach for Understanding

ENDURING UNDERSTANDING A cell is the basic unit of life; the processes that occur at the cellular level provide the energy and basic structure organisms need to survive.

GUIDING QUESTION Why is it important to study cells?

EVIDENCE OF UNDERSTANDING *After completing the lesson, give students the following assessment to show they understand why it is important to study cells.* Have students work in small groups to create a poster that advertises the importance of learning about cells. Posters should include the three parts of the cell theory.

The Cell Theory Soon after van Leeuwenhoek, observations by scientists made it clear that **cells** are the basic units of life. In 1838, German botanist Matthias Schleiden concluded that all plants are made of cells. The next year, German biologist Theodor Schwann stated that all animals are made of cells. In 1855, German physician Rudolf Virchow concluded that new cells can be produced only from the division of existing cells, confirming a suggestion made by German Lorenz Oken 50 years earlier. These discoveries, confirmed by many biologists, are summarized in the **cell theory,** a fundamental concept of biology. **The cell theory states:**

- **All living things are made up of cells.**
- **Cells are the basic units of structure and function in living things.**
- **New cells are produced from existing cells.**

Exploring the Cell

How do microscopes work?

A microscope, as you know, produces an enlarged image of something very small. **Most microscopes use lenses to magnify the image of an object by focusing light or electrons.** Following in the footsteps of Hooke, Virchow, and others, modern biologists still use microscopes to explore the cell. But today's researchers use technology more powerful than the pioneers of biology could ever have imagined.

Light Microscopes and Cell Stains The type of microscope you are probably most familiar with is the compound light microscope. A typical light microscope allows light to pass through a specimen and uses two lenses to form an image. The first lens, called the objective lens, is located just above the specimen. This lens enlarges the image of the specimen. Most light microscopes have several objective lenses so that the power of magnification can be varied. The second lens, called the ocular lens, magnifies this image still further. Unfortunately, light itself limits the detail, or resolution, of images in a microscope. Like all forms of radiation, lightwaves are diffracted, or scattered, as they pass through matter. Because of this, light microscopes can produce clear images of objects only to a magnification of about 1000 times.

Another problem with light microscopy is that most living cells are nearly transparent. Using chemical stains or dyes, as in **Figure 7–2,** can usually solve this problem. Some of these stains are so specific that they reveal only certain compounds or structures within the cell. Many of the slides you'll examine in your biology class laboratory will be stained this way.

A powerful variation on these staining techniques uses dyes that give off light of a particular color when viewed under specific wavelengths of light, a property called fluorescence. Fluorescent dyes can be attached to specific molecules and can then be made visible using a special fluorescence microscope. New techniques, in fact, enable scientists to engineer cells that attach fluorescent labels of different colors to specific molecules as they are produced. Fluorescence microscopy makes it possible to see and identify the locations of these molecules and even allows scientists to watch them move around in a living cell.

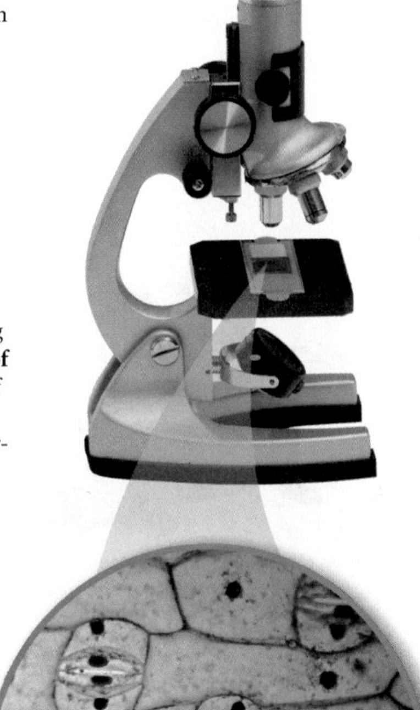

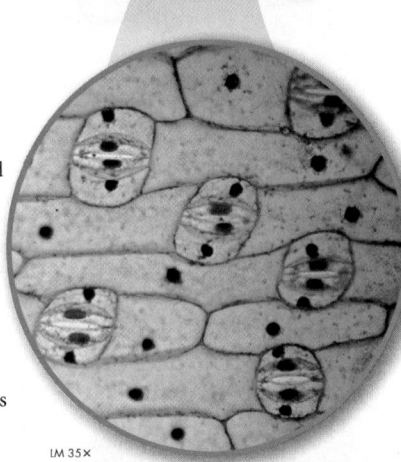

LM 35×

FIGURE 7–2 Light Microscope and Cell Stains This specimen of onion leaf skin has been stained with a compound called toluidine blue. The dye makes the cell boundaries and nuclei clearly visible.

Quick Facts

SCANNING PROBE MICROSCOPY

Like scanning electron microscopes, scanning probe microscopes form images of surfaces. Scanning probe microscopes use a sharply pointed probe to scan samples. This type of microscope includes scanning tunneling microscopes (STM) and atomic force microscopes (AFM). An STM probe does not quite touch a sample. Instead, an electric current between the probe and the surface of the specimen tracks the topography of the surface. This technique is limited to specimens that are good conductors. The limitation was overcome in 1985, when the AFM was introduced. The AFM can image almost any type of surface and has several modes of operation, making it very versatile. In the contact mode, the probe of an AFM gently touches the sample surface in a way similar to the needle used on an LP record. The needle slides over the surface of the sample without causing damage and sends data about the surface to a processor.

Teach

Lead a Discussion

Have students create a time line of dates, people, and events leading to the development of the cell theory. Then, ask the following questions.

Ask What are some ways the discovery of new ideas can take place? *(Sample answer: Some discoveries come about as new technologies are developed.)*

Ask What technology helped in the discovery of cells? *(the microscope)*

Ask What are the three parts of the cell theory? *(All living things are made up of cells; cells are the basic units of structure and function in living things; new cells are produced from existing cells.)*

DIFFERENTIATED INSTRUCTION

LPR Less Proficient Readers Have pairs of students make a **T-Chart** to organize information from the text about using microscopes and stains. Have them label the left side of the chart Technology and the right side Benefits and write Light Microscope and Stain in rows under Technology. They can complete the chart by writing one benefit in the right column opposite each technology. *(Sample answer: Light Microscope, enlarged image; Stain, makes cell parts visible)*

Study Wkbks A/B, Appendix S30, T-Chart. **Transparencies,** GO15.

ELL Focus on ELL: Build Background

BEGINNING AND ADVANCED SPEAKERS To access students' prior knowledge, begin by writing the word *cell* on the board. Explain to students that the word *cell* has many meanings, but in this exercise they should concentrate on the biological meaning. Say the word aloud, and then have ELL students pronounce it. Ask students to say words and phrases they associate with the word *cell.* Write the answers in the form of a **Cluster Diagram** around the word *cell.* If students do not volunteer the three parts of the cell theory, write them on the diagram yourself.

Study Wkbks A/B, Appendix S19, Cluster Diagram. **Transparencies,** GO2.

Teach continued

Use Visuals

Make sure students understand that all three images in **Figure 7–3** are of the same thing—yeast. Use this to reinforce that different kinds of microscopes produce different kinds of images. Collect images from other sources to show additional examples of LMs, TEMs, and SEMs—some black and white and some with added coloring. Have students look at other photos in this chapter and identify the types of microscopes used to create the images from information in the captions.

DIFFERENTIATED INSTRUCTION

LPR Less Proficient Readers Have students reread the text to learn, specifically, the characteristics of different types of microscopes. Then, supply students with a partially completed **Compare/Contrast Table** that identifies the type of microscope (light, transmission electron, or scanning electron), whether it forms surface or interior images, and what its limitations are. Have students fill in the missing information in the table.

Study Wkbks A/B, Appendix S20, Compare/Contrast Table. **Transparencies,** GO3.

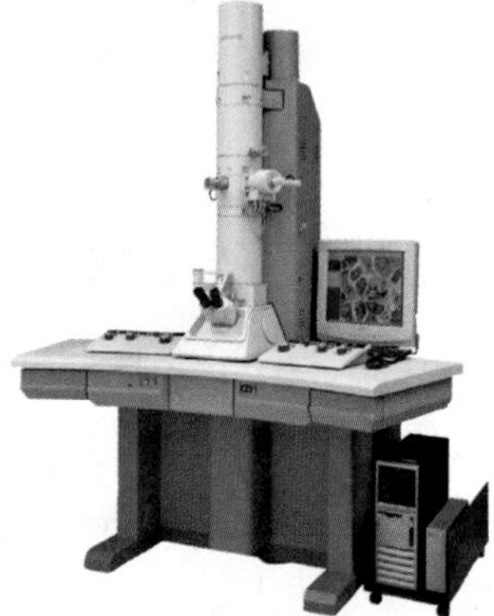

Transmission Electron Microscope

Electron Microscopes Light microscopes can be used to see cells and cell structures as small as 1 millionth of a meter—certainly pretty small! But what if scientists want to study something smaller than that, such as a virus or a DNA molecule? For that, they need electron microscopes. Instead of using light, electron microscopes use beams of electrons that are focused by magnetic fields. Electron microscopes offer much higher resolution than light microscopes. Some types of electron microscopes can be used to study cellular structures that are 1 billionth of a meter in size.

There are two major types of electron microscopes: transmission and scanning. Transmission electron microscopes make it possible to explore cell structures and large protein molecules. But because beams of electrons can only pass through thin samples, cells and tissues must be cut into ultrathin slices before they can be examined. This is the reason that such images often appear flat and two dimensional.

In scanning electron microscopes, a pencil-like beam of electrons is scanned over the surface of a specimen. Because the image is formed at the specimen's surface, samples do not have to be cut into thin slices to be seen. The scanning electron microscope produces stunning three-dimensional images of the specimen's surface.

Electrons are easily scattered by molecules in the air, which means samples must be placed in a vacuum to be studied with an electron microscope. As a result, researchers must chemically preserve their samples. Electron microscopy, then, can only be used to examine nonliving cells and tissues.

Look at **Figure 7–3,** which shows yeast cells as they might look under a light microscope, transmission electron microscope, and scanning electron microscope. You may wonder why the cells appear to be different colors in each micrograph. (A micrograph is a photo of an object seen through a microscope.) The colors in light micrographs come from the cells themselves, or from the stains and dyes used to highlight them. Electron micrographs, however, are actually black and white. Electrons, unlike light, don't come in colors. So scientists often use computer techniques to add "false color" to make certain structures stand out.

In Your Notebook *You are presented with a specimen to examine. What are two questions you would ask to determine the best microscope to use?*

FIGURE 7–3 Micrographs Different types of microscopes can be used to examine cells. Here, yeast cells are shown in a light micrograph (LM 500×), transmission electron micrograph (TEM 4375×), and a scanning electron micrograph (SEM 3750×).
Infer ***If scientists were studying a structure found on the surface of yeast, which kind of microscope would they likely use?***

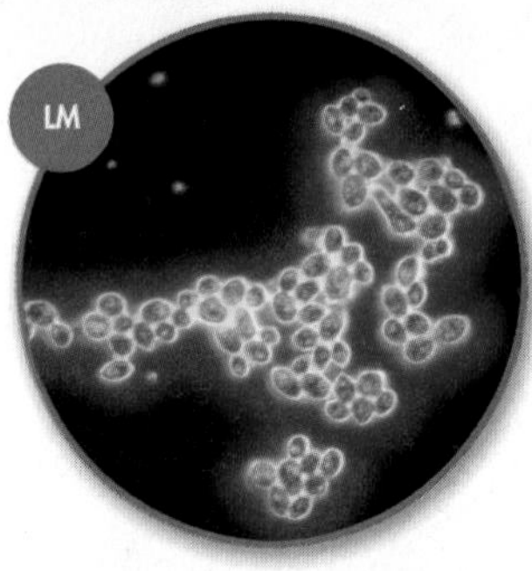

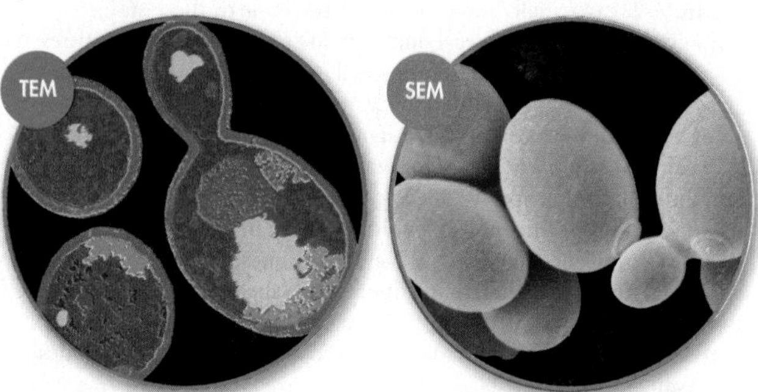

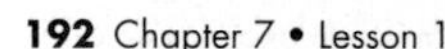

UbD Check for Understanding

HAND SIGNALS

Write the following questions on the board. Ask students to show a thumbs-up sign if they know and understand the topic, a thumbs-down sign if they don't know or are confused about it, or a waving-hand sign if they understand it partially.

- What are the three parts of the cell theory?
- How does a light microscope magnify an image?
- Name one difference between a transmission and a scanning electron microscope.

ADJUST INSTRUCTION

If more than one student has difficulty with a question, have the class work together to rephrase the concept as it is discussed in the text and then write a short response to the question.

Answers

FIGURE 7–3 Scientists would most likely use a scanning electron microscope.

IN YOUR NOTEBOOK Sample answer: Is the specimen alive? What is to be observed—the surface of the specimen or the internal structures of the specimen?

Quick Lab
GUIDED INQUIRY

What Is a Cell?

1. Look through a microscope at a slide of a plant leaf or stem cross section. Sketch one or more cells. Record a description of their shape and internal parts.
2. Repeat step 1 with slides of nerve cells, bacteria, and paramecia.
3. Compare the cells by listing the characteristics they have in common and some of the differences among them.

Analyze and Conclude

1. Classify Classify the cells you observed into two or more groups. Explain what characteristics you used to put each cell in a particular group.

Prokaryotes and Eukaryotes

How are prokaryotic and eukaryotic cells different?

Cells come in an amazing variety of shapes and sizes, some of which are shown in **Figure 7–4.** Although typical cells range from 5 to 50 micrometers in diameter, the smallest *Mycoplasma* bacteria are only 0.2 micrometer across, so small that they are difficult to see under even the best light microscopes. In contrast, the giant amoeba *Chaos chaos* can be 1000 micrometers (1 millimeter) in diameter, large enough to be seen with the unaided eye as a tiny speck in pond water. Despite their differences, all cells, at some point in their lives, contain DNA, the molecule that carries biological information. In addition, all cells are surrounded by a thin flexible barrier called a **cell membrane.** (The cell membrane is sometimes called the *plasma membrane* because many cells in the body are in direct contact with the fluid portion of the blood—the plasma.) There are other similarities as well, as you will learn in the next lesson.

Cells fall into two broad categories, depending on whether they contain a nucleus. The **nucleus** (plural: nuclei) is a large membrane-enclosed structure that contains genetic material in the form of DNA and controls many of the cell's activities. **Eukaryotes** (yoo KAR ee ohts) are cells that enclose their DNA in nuclei. **Prokaryotes** (pro KAR ee ohts) are cells that do not enclose DNA in nuclei.

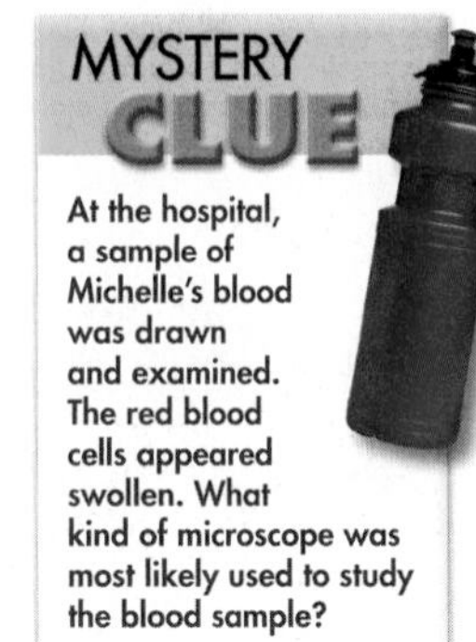

At the hospital, a sample of Michelle's blood was drawn and examined. The red blood cells appeared swollen. What kind of microscope was most likely used to study the blood sample?

FIGURE 7–4 Cell Size Is Relative The human eye can see objects larger than about 0.5 mm. Most of what interests cell biologists, however, is much smaller than that. Microscopes make seeing the cellular and subcellular world possible.

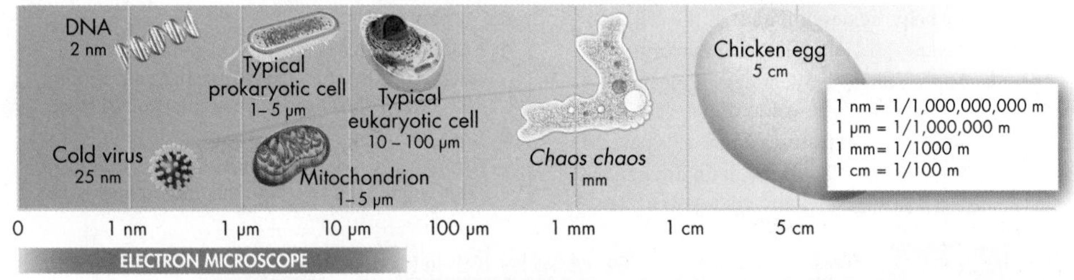

MYSTERY CLUE Students should infer that a light microscope was probably used to study the blood sample, because the focus was on cells rather than smaller objects such as viruses. For a hint of what red blood cells look like under various conditions of hydration, students can turn to **Figure 7–18.** Students also can go online to Biology.com to gather evidence.

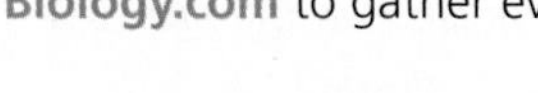

Connect to Math

Draw students' attention to **Figure 7–4** to give them an idea of how small a cell or cell part is compared to a familiar object (the chicken egg). Point out that the items in the illustration are not drawn to scale; e.g., in the illustration, the bacterium, mitochondrion, and eukaryotic cell are all roughly the same size, but in actuality, these items have sizes that are very different from one another.

Then, discuss the abbreviations for units of measurement that appear in the illustration. Explain that *nm* is the abbreviation for nanometer, and *μm* is the abbreviation for micrometer. Explain that *μ* is the Greek letter *mu*.

DIFFERENTIATED INSTRUCTION

L1 Struggling Students Call students' attention to the conversion table on the right side of **Figure 7–4.** Go over this conversion scale, explaining all the conversions, e.g., that one nanometer is equal to one one-billionth of a meter. It may help to reverse the relationship, i.e., to explain that one meter contains one billion nanometers and one million micrometers.

To help students understand the actual relationship in size between some of the items in the illustration, you might draw a typical prokaryotic cell and a typical eukaryotic cell to scale on a large sheet of paper. Use circles to represent the cells. To represent the prokaryotic cell, draw a circle with a diameter of 0.5 cm. For the eukaryotic cell, draw a circle with a diameter of 25 cm.

Quick Lab

PURPOSE Students will compare and contrast the characteristics of various kinds of cells.

MATERIALS compound microscope; slides of plant leaves or stems, nerve cells, bacteria, and paramecia

PLANNING Review how to use a compound microscope. Have students read the entire procedure before beginning. Suggest they label their drawings as they observe the cells.

ANALYZE AND CONCLUDE

1. Accept all classifications that are supported by logical reasons. Sample answer: Plant Cells (leaf and stem cells): green structures, thick cell walls, visible nucleus; Animal Cells (nerve cells): more irregular shape than plant cells, visible nucleus, no green structures; Single-Celled Organisms (bacteria and paramecia): appear more flexible than plant cells, no green structures

Teach continued

Use Visuals

Ask students to compare the model cells of prokaryotes and eukaryotes in **Figure 7–5** and describe how they differ. *(Students should identify differences in size and the absence of a nucleus in the prokaryotic cell.)*

DIFFERENTIATED INSTRUCTION

L1 Struggling Students Alert students that these same images will appear throughout Lesson 7.2 to help them focus on individual cell parts.

Assess and Remediate

EVALUATE UNDERSTANDING

Have students construct **Venn Diagrams** comparing light microscopes and electron microscopes. Then, have them complete the 7.1 Assessment.

Study Wkbks A/B, Appendix S33, Venn Diagram. **Transparencies,** GO18.

REMEDIATION SUGGESTION

L1 Struggling Students If students have trouble with **Question 2,** direct them to reread the first paragraph under **Light Microscopes and Cell Stains** and the first paragraph under **Electron Microscopes.**

BIOLOGY.com Students can check their understanding of lesson concepts with the **Self-Test** assessment. They can then take an online version of the **Lesson Assessment.**

BUILD Vocabulary

WORD ORIGINS The noun prokaryote comes from the Greek word *karyon*, meaning "kernel," or nucleus. The prefix *pro-* means "before." Prokaryotic cells first evolved before nuclei developed.

Prokaryotes As seen in **Figure 7–5,** prokaryotic cells are generally smaller and simpler than eukaryotic cells, although there are many exceptions to this rule. **Prokaryotic cells do not separate their genetic material within a nucleus.** Despite their simplicity, prokaryotes carry out every activity associated with living things. They grow, reproduce, respond to the environment, and, in some cases, glide along surfaces or swim through liquids. The organisms we call bacteria are prokaryotes.

Eukaryotes Eukaryotic cells are generally larger and more complex than prokaryotic cells. Most eukaryotic cells contain dozens of structures and internal membranes, and many are highly specialized. **In eukaryotic cells, the nucleus separates the genetic material from the rest of the cell.** Eukaryotes display great variety: some, like the ones commonly called "protists," live solitary lives as unicellular organisms; others form large, multicellular organisms—plants, animals, and fungi.

FIGURE 7–5 Cell Types In general, eukaryotic cells (including plant and animal cells) are more complex than prokaryotic cells.

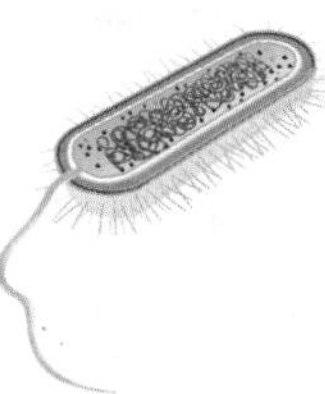

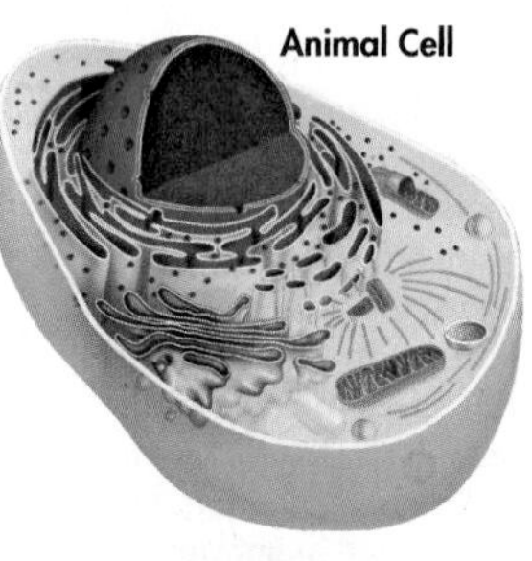

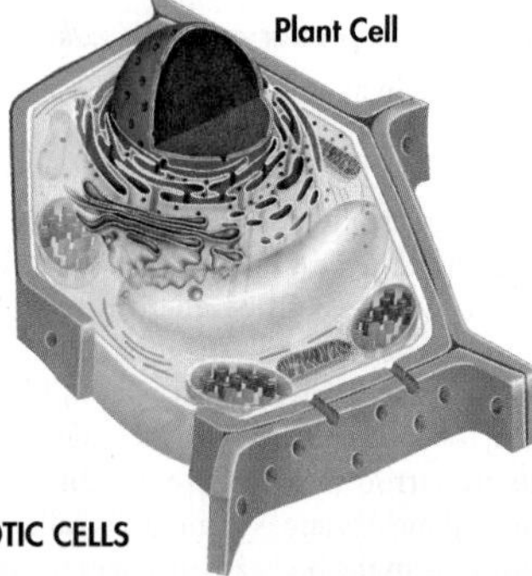

7.1 Assessment

NoS.10

Review Key Concepts

1. a. **Review** What is a cell?
   b. **Explain** What three statements make up the cell theory?
   c. **Infer** How did the invention of the microscope help the development of the cell theory?
2. a. **Review** How do microscopes work?
   b. **Apply Concepts** What does it mean if a micrograph is "false-colored?"
3. a. **Review** What features do all cells have?
   b. **Summarize** What is the main difference between prokaryotes and eukaryotes?

PRACTICE PROBLEMS MATH

A light microscope can magnify images up to 1000 times. To calculate the total magnification of a specimen, multiply the magnification of the eyepiece lens by the magnification of the objective lens used. (For more information on microscopes, see Appendix B.)

4. **Calculate** What is the total magnification of a microscope that has an eyepiece magnification of 10× and an objective lens magnification of 50×.
5. **Calculate** A 10 micrometer cell is viewed through a 10× objective and a 10× eyepiece. How large will the cell appear to the microscope user?

BIOLOGY.com Search Lesson 7.1 GO • Self-Test • Lesson Assessment

Assessment Answers

1a. the basic unit of life

1b. All living things are made up of cells. Cells are the basic units of structure and function in living things. New cells are produced from existing cells.

1c. The microscope enabled people to see cells and study the parts of cells. This ability enabled scientists to learn that all organisms are composed of cells.

2a. Microscopes contain lenses, which focus light or electrons to produce an enlarged image of something that is otherwise too small to see.

2b. False coloring is sometimes added to electron micrographs by computers to make certain structures easier to see.

3a. All cells have DNA at some time in their lives, and all cells are surrounded by a thin, flexible cell membrane.

3b. Prokaryotes do not have DNA enclosed in a nucleus. Eukaryotes have DNA enclosed in a nucleus.

PRACTICE PROBLEMS

4. total magnification: 500×

5. 1000 micrometers (1 mm)

Cells are the basic unit of all known life. If cells interest you, you might want to consider one of the following careers.

LABORATORY TECHNICIAN

Ever wonder what happens to the blood your doctor collects during your annual physical? It goes to a laboratory technician. Laboratory technicians perform routine procedures using microscopes, computers, and other equipment. Many laboratory technicians work in the medical field, evaluating and analyzing test results.

MICROSCOPIST

The images in **Figure 7–3** were captured by a microscopist. Microscopists make it possible to study structures too small to be seen without magnification. There are a variety of microscopy techniques, including staining and fluorescence, that microscopists can use to make images clear and informative for researchers. Some of these images are so striking that they have become a form of scientific art.

PATHOLOGIST

Pathologists are like detectives: They collect cellular information and tissue evidence to diagnose illness. Using a broad knowledge of disease characteristics and the best-available technology, pathologists analyze cells and tissues under a microscope and discuss their diagnoses with other doctors.

CAREER CLOSE-UP

Dr. Tanasa Osborne, Veterinary Pathologist

Dr. Tanasa Osborne studies osteosarcoma, the most common malignant bone tumor in children and adolescents. Her research with the National Institutes of Health and the National Cancer Institute is focused on improving outcomes for patients whose cancer has spread from one organ or system to another. Dr. Osborne is not a medical doctor, however—she is a veterinarian. Animals are often used as models to study human disease. Dr. Osborne's research, therefore, contributes to both animal and human health. Veterinary pathologists investigate many important issues in addition to cancer, including West Nile virus, avian flu, and other emerging infectious diseases that affect humans as well as animals.

"My distinctive background allows me to approach science from a global (or cross-species) and systemic perspective."

WRITING Explain how Dr. Osborne's research is an example of the effect science can have on society.

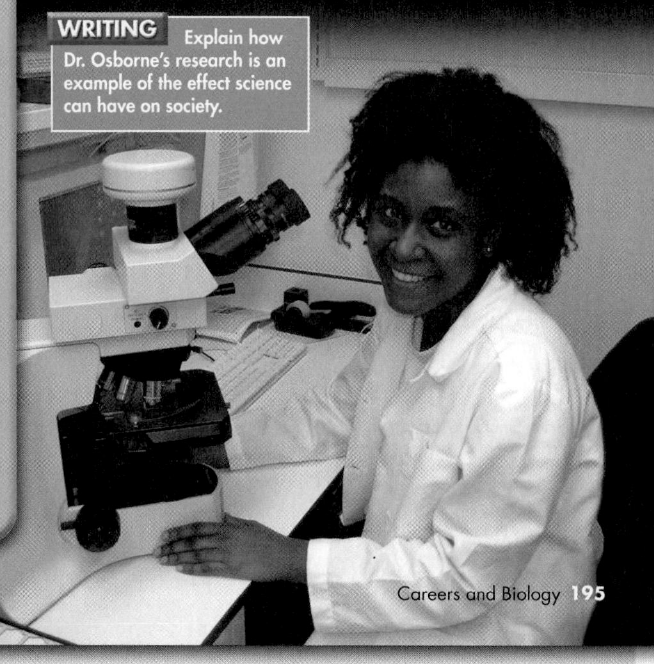

Teach

Connect to Real Life

Ask how many students have ever had blood drawn at a doctor's office. Did they wonder how their blood sample was examined?

Call attention to the careers of microscopist and laboratory technician. Ask students to compare what microscopists and lab technicians do. *(Microscopists concentrate on using microscopes to produce clear images. The work of lab technicians is more general, in that they perform a variety of tasks and use different kinds of equipment.)*

Ask students what pathologists do. *(They examine cells and tissues to diagnose illnesses.)* Point out that the photo shows Dr. Osborne with a light microscope. Ask how pathologists might use a light microscope. *(Sample answers: Dr. Osborne probably uses a light microscope to study cancer cells. Other pathologists might use them to study diseases of cells.)*

DIFFERENTIATED INSTRUCTION

ELL English Language Learners Have students select one of the following terms: *microscopist, pathologist, technician,* or *veterinarian*. Then, ask them to work in pairs to find the meaning of the word. The pairs should collaborate on constructing a **Vocabulary Word Map** to help them remember the definition of the term. Have them write the word in the top box and attributes of the word in the lower boxes. For example, attributes for *microscopist* might include "works with microscopes," "creates clear images," "may use stains," and "may use fluorescence."

Study Wkbks A/B, Appendix S32, Vocabulary Word Map. **Transparencies,** GO17.

Quick Facts

BECOMING A FORENSIC PATHOLOGIST

Forensic pathology is one branch of pathology. A forensic pathologist is a highly trained medical doctor who performs autopsies to determine cause of death, usually in connection with criminal or legal investigations. Forensic pathologists biopsy tissues and analyze blood to determine the time and manner of death, including whether death was natural or caused by injury. Forensic pathologists work for cities, counties, states, the military, and hospitals. While most forensic pathologists autopsy dead persons, some clinical forensic pathologists examine and collect tissue samples from live victims of crime.

Those interested in forensic pathology as a career are encouraged to take all the basic sciences, such as biology, chemistry, and physics. College is followed by four years of medical school, four to five years of training in pathology, and on-the-job training.

Answers

WRITING Answers will vary. Students may mention that Dr. Osborne's research has the potential to help in the treatment of cancer in humans. Therefore, her research can benefit society.

LESSON 7.2

Getting Started

Objectives

7.2.1 Describe the structure and function of the cell nucleus.

7.2.2 Describe the role of vacuoles, lysosomes, and the cytoskeleton.

7.2.3 Identify the role of ribosomes, endoplasmic reticulum, and Golgi apparatus in making proteins.

7.2.4 Describe the function of the chloroplasts and mitochondria in the cell.

7.2.5 Describe the function of the cell membrane.

Student Resources

Study Workbooks A and B, 7.2 Worksheets

Spanish Study Workbook, 7.2 Worksheets

Lab Manual A, 7.2 Quick Lab Worksheet

Lab Manual B, 7.2 Hands-On Activity Worksheet

BIOLOGY.com Lesson Overview • Lesson Notes • Activities: Visual Analogy, Art Review, Tutor Tube • Assessment: Self-Test, Lesson Assessment

For corresponding lesson in the **Foundation Edition**, see pages 164–175.

7.2 Cell Structure

B.2.1 Features common to all cells; **B.2.2** Cell membranes; **B.2.3** Mitochondria and chloroplasts; **B.2.4** Protein synthesis; **B.2.5** Protein structures. Also covered: NoS.6, B.2.6.

Key Questions

What is the role of the cell nucleus?

What are the functions of vacuoles, lysosomes, and the cytoskeleton?

What organelles help make and transport proteins?

What are the functions of chloroplasts and mitochondria?

What is the function of the cell membrane?

Vocabulary

cytoplasm • organelle • vacuole • lysosome • cytoskeleton • centriole • ribosome • endoplasmic reticulum • Golgi apparatus • chloroplast • mitochondrion • cell wall • lipid bilayer • selectively permeable

Taking Notes

Venn Diagram Create a Venn diagram that illustrates the similarities and differences between prokaryotes and eukaryotes.

THINK ABOUT IT At first glance, a factory is a puzzling place. Machines buzz and clatter; people move quickly in different directions. So much activity can be confusing. However, if you take the time to watch carefully, what might at first seem like chaos begins to make sense. The same is true for the living cell.

Cell Organization

What is the role of the cell nucleus?

The eukaryotic cell is a complex and busy place. But if you look closely at eukaryotic cells, patterns begin to emerge. For example, it's easy to divide each cell into two major parts: the nucleus and the cytoplasm. The **cytoplasm** is the portion of the cell outside the nucleus. As you will see, the nucleus and cytoplasm work together in the business of life. Prokaryotic cells have cytoplasm too, even though they do not have a nucleus.

In our discussion of cell structure, we consider each major component of plant and animal eukaryotic cells—some of which are also found in prokaryotic cells—one by one. Because many of these structures act like specialized organs, they are known as **organelles,** literally "little organs." Understanding what each organelle does helps us understand the cell as a whole. A summary of cell structure can be found on pages 206–207.

VISUAL ANALOGY

THE CELL AS A LIVING FACTORY

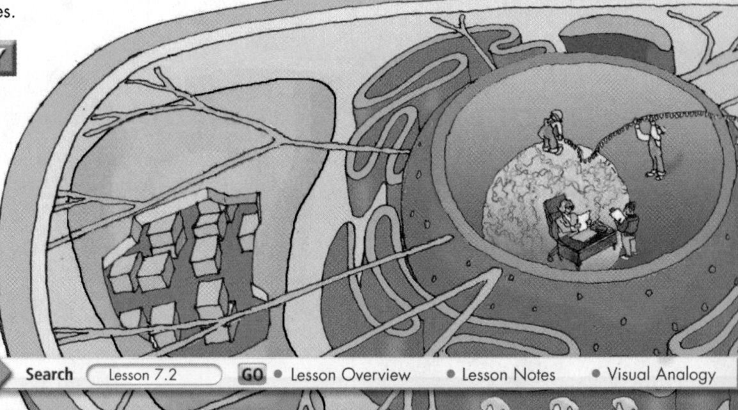

FIGURE 7–6 The specialization and organization of work and workers contribute to the productivity of a factory. In much the same way, the specialized parts in a cell contribute to the cell's overall stability and survival.

BIOLOGY.com Search Lesson 7.2 GO • Lesson Overview • Lesson Notes • Visual Analogy

IN INDIANA ACADEMIC STANDARDS

For the full text of all standards, see the Course Overview in the front matter of this book.

B.2.1 Describe features common to all cells that are essential for growth and survival, and explain their functions.

B.2.2 Describe the structure of a cell membrane and explain how it regulates the transport of materials into and out of the cell and prevents harmful materials from entering the cell.

B.2.3 Explain that most cells contain mitochondria, the key sites of cellular respiration, where stored chemical energy is converted into useable energy for the cell and some cells, including many plant cells, contain chloroplasts, the key sites of photosynthesis, where the energy of light is captured for use in chemical work.

UbD Teach for Understanding

ENDURING UNDERSTANDING A cell is the basic unit of life; the processes that occur at the cellular level provide the energy and basic structure organisms need to survive.

GUIDING QUESTION How do cell structures enable a cell to carry out basic life processes?

EVIDENCE OF UNDERSTANDING *After completing the lesson, give students the following assessment to show they understand how cell structures enable them to carry out life processes.* Provide each student with an unlabeled copy of the cells in **Figure 7–14.** Have them work in pairs to identify each type of cell, label the structures of each cell, and write a function for each cell part.

Comparing the Cell to a Factory In some respects, the eukaryotic cell is much like a living version of a modern factory (**Figure 7–6**). The different organelles of the cell can be compared to the specialized machines and assembly lines of the factory. In addition, cells, like factories, follow instructions and produce products. As we look through the organization of the cell, we'll find plenty of places in which the comparison works so well that it will help us understand how cells work.

The Nucleus In the same way that the main office controls a large factory, the nucleus is the control center of the cell. **The nucleus contains nearly all the cell's DNA and, with it, the coded instructions for making proteins and other important molecules.** Prokaryotic cells lack a nucleus, but they do have DNA that contains the same kinds of instructions.

The nucleus, shown in **Figure 7–7**, is surrounded by a nuclear envelope composed of two membranes. The nuclear envelope is dotted with thousands of nuclear pores, which allow material to move into and out of the nucleus. Like messages, instructions, and blueprints moving in and out of a factory's main office, a steady stream of proteins, RNA, and other molecules move through the nuclear pores to and from the rest of the cell.

Chromosomes, which carry the cell's genetic information, are also found in the nucleus. Most of the time, the threadlike chromosomes are spread throughout the nucleus in the form of chromatin—a complex of DNA bound to proteins. When a cell divides, its chromosomes condense and can be seen under a microscope. You will learn more about chromosomes in later chapters.

Most nuclei also contain a small dense region known as the nucleolus (noo KLEE uh lus). The nucleolus is where the assembly of ribosomes begins.

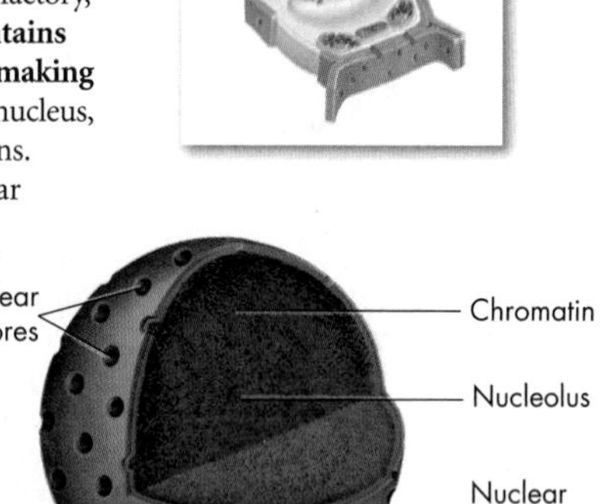

FIGURE 7–7 The Nucleus The nucleus controls most cell processes and contains DNA. The small, dense region in the nucleus is known as the nucleolus.

In Your Notebook *Describe the structure of the nucleus. Include the words* nuclear envelope, nuclear pore, chromatin, chromosomes, *and* nucleolus *in your description.*

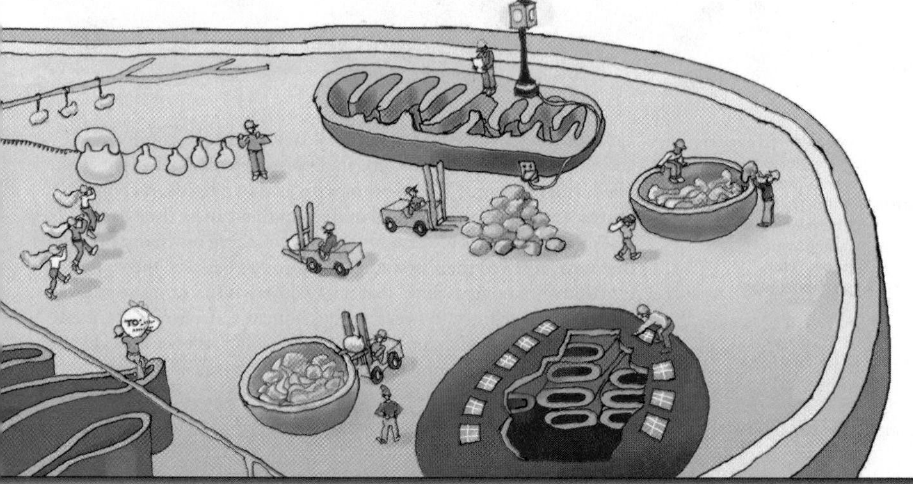

How Science Works

THE NUCLEUS AND THE CELL

During the 1930s and 1940s, the Danish biologist Joachim Hämmerling performed a series of experiments that demonstrated the link between a cell's nucleus and the physical characteristics of the cell. Two species of *Acetabularia* algae were used in the experiments. This marine alga, though 5 cm long, is a single cell. Each cell consists of three areas—a cuplike cap, a stalk, and a holdfast at the bottom, where the cell's nucleus is found. The two species have different-shaped caps. Hämmerling found that when he grafted a nucleate portion of the first species to an enucleate stalk fragment of the second species, the resulting cell regenerated a cap. Initially, the new cap resembled that of the decapitated species, but if the cap was removed or the cell was allowed to age, then eventually the cap took the form of the donor species. This suggested that the nucleus contained information that determined the type of cap formed, and also that this information was somehow stored in the cytoplasm before the cap is actually produced.

Teach

Build Study Skills

Explain to students that at various points in this lesson, they will see small locator drawings such as the one at the top of this page. Students should use these drawings to focus on where cell parts discussed in the lesson are located and in which types of cells they are found.

DIFFERENTIATED INSTRUCTION

L1 Special Needs Use models to help students understand **Figure 7–7.** Cut away a quarter of a tennis ball, and put a smaller, solid ball and loose yarn inside. Explain what the parts of your model represent, and correlate them to the structures in **Figure 7–7.**

VISUAL ANALOGY

Explore the analogy in **Figure 7–6** by asking students if cells were like a factory, what can be inferred about the nature of cells. *(Cells are complex and dynamic, with various parts that work together.)*

BIOLOGY.com Students can extend the analogy of a cell to a factory in **Visual Analogy: The Cell as a Living Factory.**

ELL Focus on ELL: Access Content

INTERMEDIATE AND ADVANCED SPEAKERS Have students work in pairs to use the **Directed Reading-Thinking Activity** to learn the content of this lesson. They should begin by previewing the lesson. In their notebooks, they should write what they know about this topic and a prediction of what they will learn. Periodically throughout the lesson, have students evaluate whether their predictions were accurate. After they read the lesson, they should write what they have learned.

Study Wkbks A/B, Appendix S5, Directed Reading-Thinking Activity.

Answers

IN YOUR NOTEBOOK The nucleus has a double-layered nuclear envelope pierced by nuclear pores. Inside the nucleus are threadlike chromosomes in the form of chromatin. Most nuclei contain a nucleolus, where ribosomes form.

Teach continued

Use Visuals

Call students' attention to **Figure 7–8,** which shows different types of vacuoles. Explain that plant cells generally have large central vacuoles whose sizes change depending on water availability—when there is a lot of water, the central vacuoles are larger, and when there is less water, the vacuoles are smaller.

Ask What happens to vacuoles that causes a plant to wilt? *(The vacuoles lose water.)*

Explain that once the plant is watered, the vacuoles refill and the plant stands upright again.

Focus students' attention on the image of the paramecium. Explain that a paramecium regulates water balance with its contractile vacuole. The contractile vacuole continually fills with excess water from cytoplasm, and then expels it.

You may want to point out to students that the only difference between vacuoles and vesicles is size. Vesicles are smaller.

DIFFERENTIATED INSTRUCTION

L1 Special Needs Tell students that a model often makes something easier to understand. Make a model of a plant's central vacuole (shown in **Figure 7–8**) by placing a small inflated balloon inside a small plastic food container. Ask students to recall what plant cells store in their vacuoles. *(water, salts, proteins, and carbohydrates)*

LPR Less Proficient Readers To help students to focus on the important information in this lesson, ask them to write the Key Questions in their notebooks. Have them find the answers as they read, and write them in their notebooks.

Answers

FIGURE 7–8 The pressure of the liquid in the vacuoles makes the plant rigid, which allows it to hold up stems, leaves, and flowers.

Organelles That Store, Clean Up, and Support

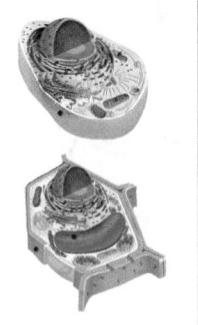

What are the functions of vacuoles, lysosomes, and the cytoskeleton?

Many of the organelles outside the nucleus of a eukaryotic cell have specific functions, or roles. Among them are structures called vacuoles, lysosomes, and cytoskeleton. These organelles represent the cellular factory's storage space, cleanup crew, and support structures.

Vacuoles and Vesicles Every factory needs a place to store things, and so does every cell. Many cells contain large, saclike, membrane-enclosed structures called **vacuoles.** **Vacuoles store materials like water, salts, proteins, and carbohydrates.** In many plant cells, there is a single, large central vacuole filled with liquid. The pressure of the central vacuole in these cells increases their rigidity, making it possible for plants to support heavy structures, such as leaves and flowers. The image on the left in **Figure 7–8** shows a typical plant cell's large central vacuole.

Vacuoles are also found in some unicellular organisms and in some animals. The paramecium on the right in **Figure 7–8** contains an organelle called a contractile vacuole. By contracting rhythmically, this specialized vacuole pumps excess water out of the cell. In addition, nearly all eukaryotic cells contain smaller membrane-enclosed structures called vesicles. Vesicles store and move materials between cell organelles, as well as to and from the cell surface.

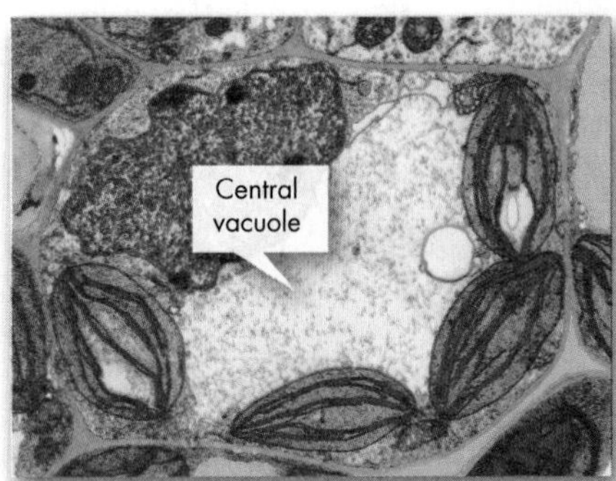

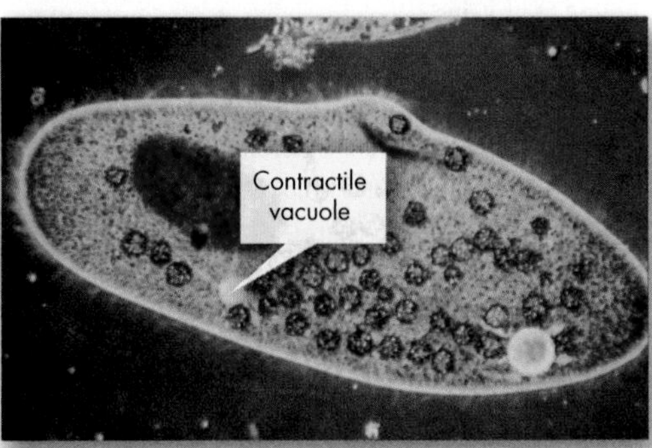

FIGURE 7–8 Vacuoles The central vacuole of plant cells stores salts, proteins, and carbohydrates. A paramecium's contractile vacuole controls the water content of the organism by pumping water out. **Apply Concepts** ***How do vacuoles help support plant structures?***

Lysosomes Even the neatest, cleanest factory needs a cleanup crew, and that's where lysosomes come in. **Lysosomes** are small organelles filled with enzymes. **Lysosomes break down lipids, carbohydrates, and proteins into small molecules that can be used by the rest of the cell. They are also involved in breaking down organelles that have outlived their usefulness.** Lysosomes perform the vital function of removing "junk" that might otherwise accumulate and clutter up the cell. A number of serious human diseases can be traced to lysosomes that fail to function properly. Biologists once thought that lysosomes were only found in animal cells, but it is now clear that lysosomes are also found in a few specialized types of plant cells as well.

198 Chapter 7 • Lesson 2

Biology In-Depth

LYSOSOMES

In functioning cells, lysosomes take in, fuse with, or engulf materials, which are then broken down by hydrolytic enzymes. The resulting products are used by the cell or carried to the cell surface and expelled. The presence of lysosomes in plant cells has been confirmed by detection of hydrolytic enzymes, even when lysosome structures are not obvious. Neimann-Pick disease and Fabry disease are examples of diseases caused by abnormal lysosomal activity in humans. Fabry disease is characterized by inadequate amounts or the absence of an enzyme in lysosomes that normally breaks down the fat, GL-3. As a result, GL-3 accumulates in blood vessel walls in major body organs. In Neimann-Pick disease, the absence of an enzyme causes a buildup of a harmful substance in the bone marrow, liver, and spleen.

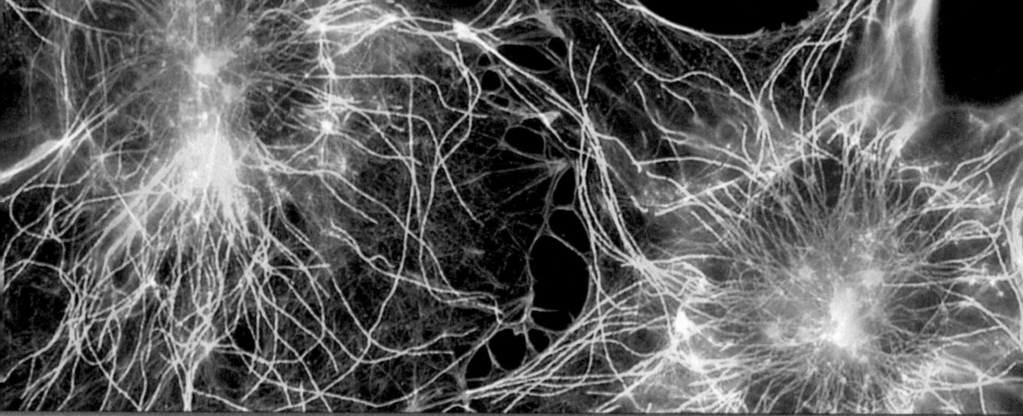

LM 1175×

The Cytoskeleton As you know, a factory building is supported by steel or cement beams and by columns that hold up its walls and roof. Eukaryotic cells are given their shape and internal organization by a network of protein filaments known as the **cytoskeleton.** Certain parts of the cytoskeleton also help transport materials between different parts of the cell, much like the conveyor belts that carry materials from one part of a factory to another. Cytoskeletal components may also be involved in moving the entire cell as in cell flagella and cilia. **The cytoskeleton helps the cell maintain its shape and is also involved in movement.** Fluorescence imaging, as seen in **Figure 7–9,** clearly shows the complexity of a cell's cytoskeletal network. Microfilaments (pale purple) and microtubules (yellow) are two of the principal protein filaments that make up the cytoskeleton.

▶ ***Microfilaments*** Microfilaments are threadlike structures made up of a protein called actin. They form extensive networks in some cells and produce a tough flexible framework that supports the cell. Microfilaments also help cells move. Microfilament assembly and disassembly are responsible for the cytoplasmic movements that allow amoebas and other cells to crawl along surfaces.

▶ ***Microtubules*** Microtubules are hollow structures made up of proteins known as tubulins. In many cells, they play critical roles in maintaining cell shape. Microtubules are also important in cell division, where they form a structure known as the mitotic spindle, which helps to separate chromosomes. In animal cells, organelles called centrioles are also formed from tubulins. **Centrioles** are located near the nucleus and help organize cell division. Centrioles are not found in plant cells.

Microtubules also help build projections from the cell surface—known as cilia (singular: cilium) and flagella (singular: flagellum)—that enable cells to swim rapidly through liquid. The microtubules in cilia and flagella are arranged in a "9 + 2" pattern, as shown in **Figure 7–10.** Small cross-bridges between the microtubules in these organelles use chemical energy to pull on, or slide along, the microtubles, producing controlled movements.

FIGURE 7–9 Cytoskeleton The cytoskeleton supports and gives shape to the cell, and is involved in many forms of cell movement. These connective tissue fibroblast cells have been treated with fluorescent tags that bind to certain elements. Microfilaments are pale purple, microtubules are yellow, and the nuclei are green.

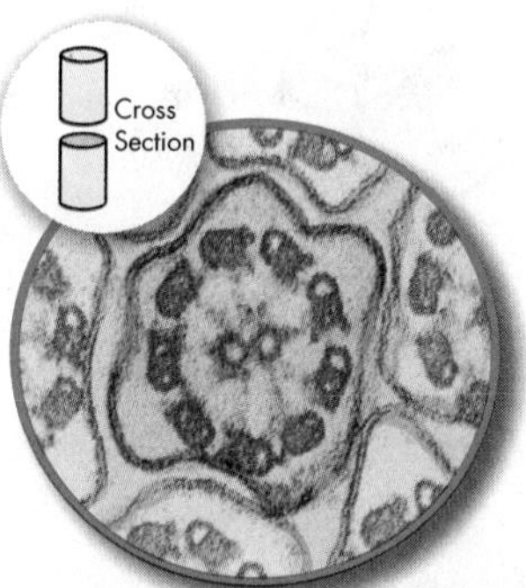

FIGURE 7–10 The "9 + 2" Pattern of Microtubules In this micrograph showing the cross section of a cilium, you can clearly see the 9 + 2 arrangement of the red microtubules. Apply Concepts ***What is the function of cilia?***

Check for Understanding

ONE-MINUTE RESPONSE

Give students one minute to write a summary that identifies the role of the cytoskeleton in the cell. *(The cytoskeleton helps maintain the cell's shape and is also involved in movement.)*

ADJUST INSTRUCTION

If students are unable to describe the role of the cytoskeleton, have them work in pairs to review the text explanation and edit their original responses. Ask volunteers to share their revised summaries with the class.

Lead a Discussion

Ask students if they have ever been inside a circus tent. Have them describe the structure of the tent, including the poles and extensive networks of ropes and guy wires. Ask students to suggest what those structures are used for. Draw students' attention to **Figure 7–9.** Explain that cells have an extensive network of filaments in the cytoplasm called the cytoskeleton.

Ask students to suggest how some of the functions of their own skeleton (shape, support, and movement) might help them understand the function of a cell's cytoskeleton.

DIFFERENTIATED INSTRUCTION

LPR **Less Proficient Readers** Pair struggling readers with more proficient readers to construct a **Concept Map** of the information on this page to show the relationship between the cytoskeleton, microfilaments, and microtubules.

Study Wkbks A/B, Appendix S21, Concept Map. **Transparencies,** GO4.

L3 **Advanced Students** Extend the content of this topic by having students independently research how the cytoskeleton was discovered and how its discovery is connected with developments in microscopy. Ask students to share what they learn with the class.

Answers

FIGURE 7–8 Cilia project from cells and enable them to move through liquids.

Teach continued

Build Study Skills

Prepare students to understand the importance of proteins and the complex process by which they are made in cells by using a **Directed Reading-Thinking Activity.** First, tell students to skim the section titled, **Organelles That Build Proteins,** looking at the headings, the highlighted vocabulary terms, and **Figure 7–11.** Then, have students predict what the text will be about. Finally, have them read the section and verify their predictions with specific sentences from the text. Students should conclude the exercise by writing what they have learned.

Study Wkbks A/B, Appendix S5, Directed Reading-Thinking Activity.

DIFFERENTIATED INSTRUCTION

LPR Less Proficient Readers For students who are overwhelmed by applying the **Directed Reading-Thinking Activity** to all the text on these two pages, have them begin by focusing on ribosomes. Assist them by drawing their attention to the blue heading, **Ribosomes.** Show them that this heading gives them a clue about what the text that follows the heading will explain. After students have skimmed the text about ribosomes and **Figure 7–11,** made their predictions, and written what they have learned, ask them to identify the function of ribosomes. *(Ribosomes produce proteins according to a code derived from DNA.)*

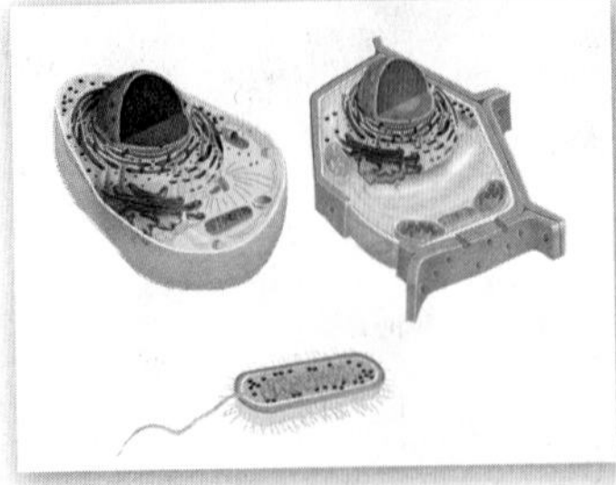

Organelles That Build Proteins

What organelles help make and transport proteins?

Life is a dynamic process, and living things are always working, building new molecules all the time, especially proteins, which catalyze chemical reactions and make up important structures in the cell. Because proteins carry out so many of the essential functions of living things, a big part of the cell is devoted to their production and distribution. Proteins are synthesized on ribosomes, sometimes in association with the rough endoplasmic reticulum in eukaryotes. The process of making proteins is summarized in **Figure 7–11.**

Ribosomes One of the most important jobs carried out in the cellular "factory" is making proteins. **Proteins are assembled on ribosomes. Ribosomes** are small particles of RNA and protein found throughout the cytoplasm in all cells. Ribosomes produce proteins by following coded instructions that come from DNA. Each ribosome, in its own way, is like a small machine in a factory, turning out proteins on orders that come from its DNA "boss." Cells that are especially active in protein synthesis often contain large numbers of ribosomes.

Endoplasmic Reticulum Eukaryotic cells contain an internal membrane system known as the **endoplasmic reticulum** (en doh PLAZ mik rih TIK yuh lum), or ER. The endoplasmic reticulum is where lipid components of the cell membrane are assembled, along with proteins and other materials that are exported from the cell.

The portion of the ER involved in the synthesis of proteins is called rough endoplasmic reticulum, or rough ER. It is given this name because of the ribosomes found on its surface. Newly made proteins leave these ribosomes and are inserted into the rough ER, where they may be chemically modified.

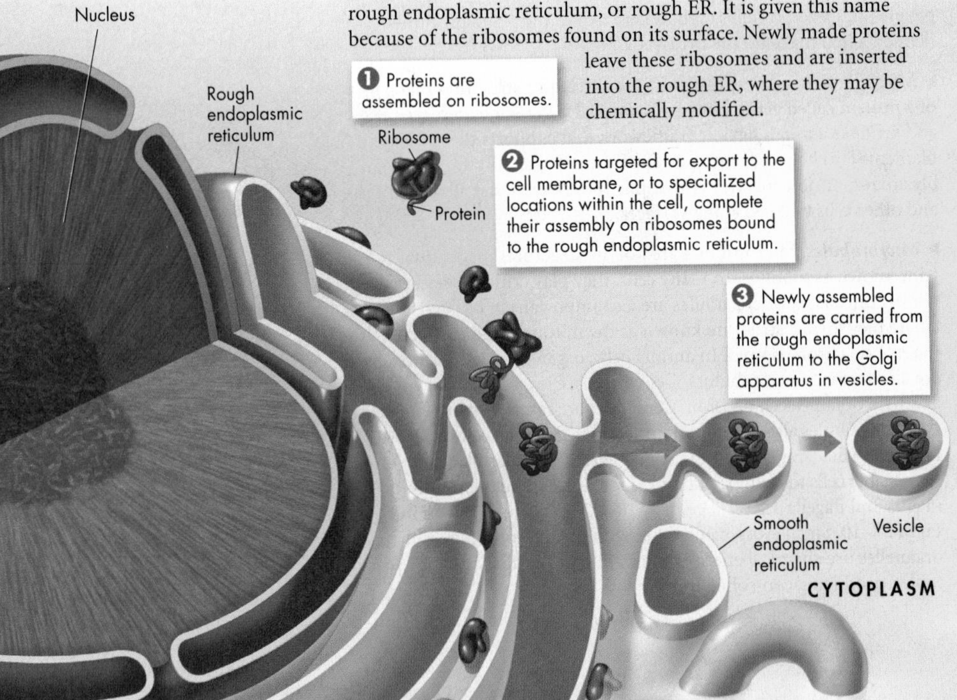
Nucleus
Rough endoplasmic reticulum
1 Proteins are assembled on ribosomes.
Ribosome
Protein
2 Proteins targeted for export to the cell membrane, or to specialized locations within the cell, complete their assembly on ribosomes bound to the rough endoplasmic reticulum.
3 Newly assembled proteins are carried from the rough endoplasmic reticulum to the Golgi apparatus in vesicles.
Smooth endoplasmic reticulum
Vesicle
CYTOPLASM

UbD Check for Understanding

QUESTION BOX

Provide a box into which students can put their questions about ribosomes and the endoplasmic reticulum. Encourage students to write questions about aspects of the text that they do not understand.

ADJUST INSTRUCTION

If most students write essentially the same questions, discuss these topics with the class as a whole. Answer the questions, referring to specific content in the text and **Figure 7–11.** Then, to determine whether students now understand the concepts, ask volunteers to explain the answers to the questions in their own words. Work with students individually or in small groups to address any topics that only a few students do not comprehend.

Proteins made on the rough ER include those that will be released, or secreted, from the cell as well as many membrane proteins and proteins destined for lysosomes and other specialized locations within the cell. Rough ER is abundant in cells that produce large amounts of protein for export. Other cellular proteins are made on "free" ribosomes, which are not attached to membranes.

The other portion of the ER is known as smooth endoplasmic reticulum (smooth ER) because ribosomes are not found on its surface. In many cells, the smooth ER contains collections of enzymes that perform specialized tasks, including the synthesis of membrane lipids and the detoxification of drugs. Liver cells, which play a key role in detoxifying drugs, often contain large amounts of smooth ER.

Golgi Apparatus In eukaryotic cells, proteins produced in the rough ER move next into an organelle called the **Golgi apparatus,** which appears as a stack of flattened membranes. As proteins leave the rough ER, molecular "address tags" get them to the right destinations. As these tags are "read" by the cell, the proteins are bundled into tiny vesicles that bud from the ER and carry them to the Golgi apparatus. **The Golgi apparatus modifies, sorts, and packages proteins and other materials from the endoplasmic reticulum for storage in the cell or release outside the cell.** The Golgi apparatus is somewhat like a customization shop, where the finishing touches are put on proteins before they are ready to leave the "factory." From the Golgi apparatus, proteins are "shipped" to their final destination inside or outside the cell.

In Your Notebook *Make a flowchart that shows how proteins are assembled in a cell.*

VISUAL SUMMARY

MAKING PROTEINS

FIGURE 7–11 Together, ribosomes, the endoplasmic reticulum, and the Golgi apparatus synthesize, modify, package, and ship proteins. **Infer** ***What can you infer about a cell that is packed with more than the typical number of ribosomes?***

4 The Golgi apparatus further modifies proteins before sorting and packaging them in membrane-bound vesicles.
5 Vesicles from the Golgi apparatus are shipped to their final destination in, or out of, the cell.
Cell membrane
Golgi apparatus

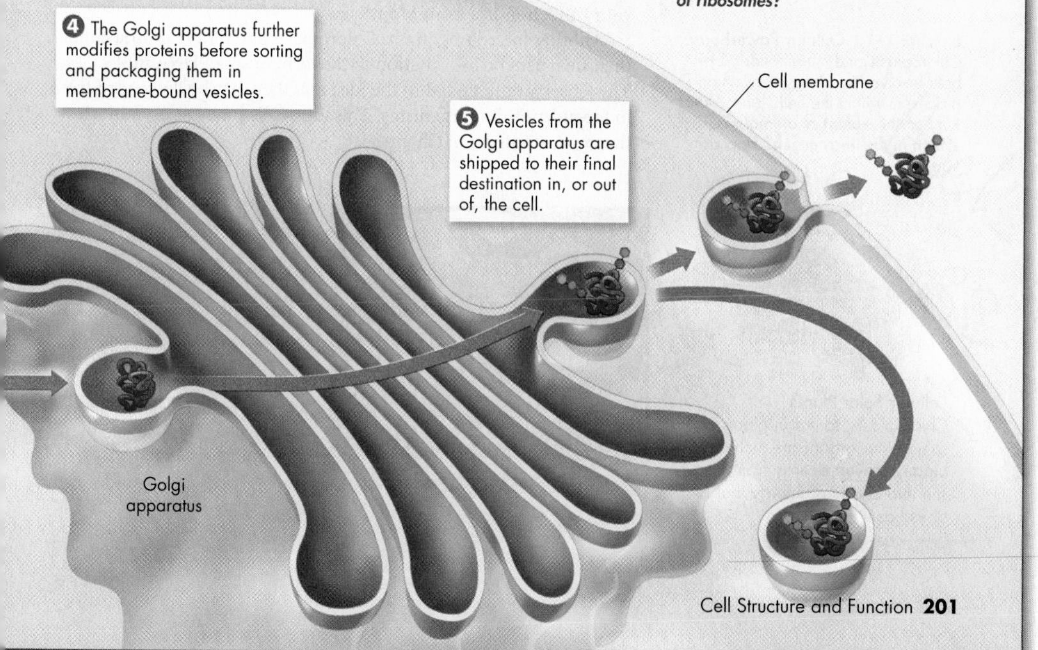

VISUAL SUMMARY

Use **Figure 7–11** to discuss protein production and reinforce the details of the process. Write these questions on the board, and have students share their responses orally.

- Where are proteins assembled? *(on ribosomes)*
- Where is the synthesis of membrane proteins completed? *(in the ER)*
- How are proteins transported to the Golgi apparatus? *(in vesicles)*
- What happens to proteins leaving the Golgi apparatus? *(They are sent out of the cell or back into the cytoplasm to be used.)*

DIFFERENTIATED INSTRUCTION

LPR **Less Proficient Readers** Explain to students that an important part of reading comprehension is taking note of art and using it to understand what is written in the text. Point out that **Figure 7–11** summarizes the process of protein assembly and export in a series of numbered steps. Tell students that they can use these steps to help them understand the section, **Organelles That Build Proteins,** and to complete the In Your Notebook.

Quick Facts

WHAT HAPPENS WITHIN THE GOLGI APPARATUS?

In a cell, the Golgi apparatus is analogous to a person who takes a product that has been only roughly manufactured and, with hundreds of separate orders to fill, finishes off the rough edges, makes requested changes, and turns out products that meet specific individual orders. The Golgi apparatus has two general regions: the *cis* end and the *trans* end. The end closer to the endoplasmic reticulum is referred to as the *cis* end. It receives materials from the ER enclosed in membranous vesicles. The vesicles deliver their newly manufactured proteins by fusing with the membranes of the *cis* end. The materials are then passed through the layers, or *cisternae,* of the Golgi apparatus. They leave from the opposite, or *trans,* end, which is farther away from the ER. In transit, the proteins are modified and finished by enzymes before being distributed. Materials that will leave the cell are packed in vesicles that bud off from the Golgi apparatus and eventually fuse with the cell membrane.

Answers

FIGURE 7–11 Ribosomes are sites of protein production. When a cell has more than the typical number of ribosomes, you might infer that it produces more proteins than other cells.

IN YOUR NOTEBOOK Flowcharts should summarize the steps in **Figure 7–11.**

Teach continued

Lead a Discussion

Make sure students understand how important energy is to living things. Discuss why chloroplasts might be referred to as "solar collectors" and mitochondria as "power plants." Have students discuss why animals must consume food to obtain energy, whereas plants are able to produce their own food, using energy from sunlight.

DIFFERENTIATED INSTRUCTION

L1 Struggling Students Pair struggling students with more proficient students to create a **Flowchart** beginning with "Sunlight" and ending with "Release of energy from food."

Study Wkbks A/B, Appendix S25, Flowchart. **Transparencies,** GO8.

LPR Less Proficient Readers Ask students to preview the first three paragraphs on this page, keeping in mind the following questions:

- Which organelle captures energy from sunlight and converts it to chemical energy in cells? *(chloroplast)*
- Which organelle converts or releases chemical energy from food in cells? *(mitochondrion)*

Address Misconceptions

Mitochondria and Chloroplasts Some students may think that mitochondria are found only in animal cells and chloroplasts are found only in plant cells. Clarify that mitochondria are found in nearly all eukaryotes, including plants. Chloroplasts are found outside of the plant clade, in photosynthetic "protists," such as red and brown algae and euglenas. Try to get students to associate mitochondria and chloroplasts with their function—eukaryotes that undergo cellular respiration have mitochondria, and eukaryotes that undergo photosynthesis have chloroplasts and mitochondria. Therefore, plants, which undergo both processes, have both types of organelles, while animals have only mitochondria.

Answers

FIGURE 7–12 The cell is a plant cell, because it contains chloroplasts.

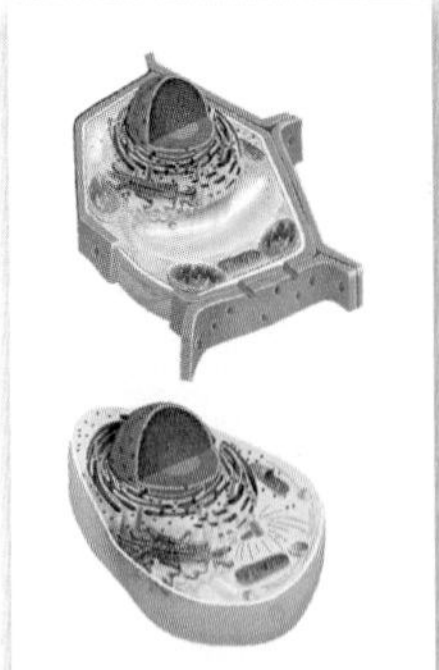

Organelles That Capture and Release Energy

What are the functions of chloroplasts and mitochondria?

All living things require a source of energy. Factories are hooked up to the local power company, but how do cells get energy? Most cells are powered by food molecules that are built using energy from the sun.

Chloroplasts Plants and some other organisms contain chloroplasts (KLAWR uh plasts). **Chloroplasts** are the biological equivalents of solar power plants. **Chloroplasts capture the energy from sunlight and convert it into food that contains chemical energy in a process called photosynthesis.** Two membranes surround chloroplasts. Inside the organelle are large stacks of other membranes, which contain the green pigment chlorophyll.

Mitochondria Nearly all eukaryotic cells, including plants, contain mitochondria (myt oh KAHN dree uh; singular: mitochondrion). **Mitochondria** are the power plants of the cell. **Mitochondria convert the chemical energy stored in food into compounds that are more convenient for the cell to use.** Like chloroplasts, two membranes—an outer membrane and an inner membrane—enclose mitochondria. The inner membrane is folded up inside the organelle, as shown in **Figure 7–12.**

One of the most interesting aspects of mitochondria is the way in which they are inherited. In humans, all or nearly all of our mitochondria come from the cytoplasm of the ovum, or egg cell. This means that when your relatives are discussing which side of the family should take credit for your best characteristics, you can tell them that you got your mitochondria from Mom!

Another interesting point: Chloroplasts and mitochondria contain their own genetic information in the form of small DNA molecules. This observation has led to the idea that they may be descended from independent microorganisms. This idea, called the endosymbiotic theory, is discussed in Chapter 19.

FIGURE 7–12 Cellular Powerhouses Chloroplasts and mitochondria are both involved in energy conversion processes within the cell. **Infer** ***What kind of cell—plant or animal—is shown in the micrograph? How do you know?***

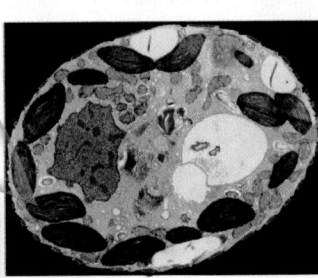

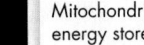

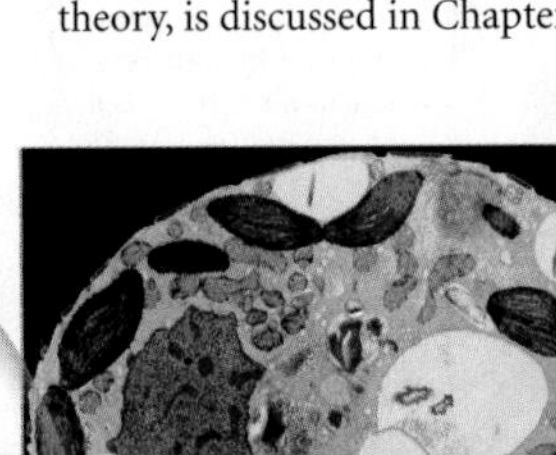

Cellular Solar Plants
Chloroplasts, found in plants and some other organisms such as algae, convert energy from the sun into chemical energy that is stored as food.

TEM 4500×

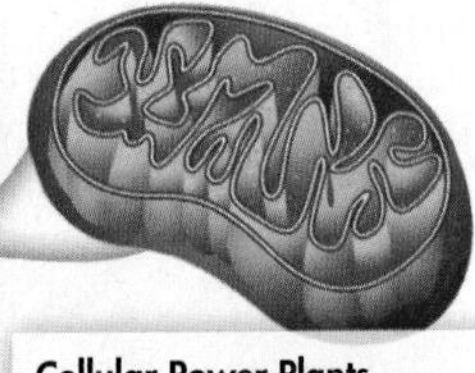

Cellular Power Plants
Mitochondria convert chemical energy stored in food into a form that can be used easily by the cell.

Quick Facts

MITOCHONDRIAL DISEASES

The health of an individual organism depends on the health of its organelles. For example, defects in mitochondria cause some forms of deafness, blindness, and diseases that affect muscles and nerves. Cells are dependent on energy that is normally released by chemical reactions in mitochondria. Many mitochondrial diseases affect muscles, which may have thousands of mitochondria in each cell. If mitochondria lack oxidative-phosphorylation enzymes, toxic substances accumulate, and energy cannot be released from food. The muscle weakness that appears in muscular dystrophy is related to defective mitochondria. Other conditions related to mitochondrial dysfunctions are retinitis pigmentosa, diabetes mellitus, and some forms of deafness. Mitochondrial diseases can result from mutations in nuclear DNA or mitochondrial DNA.

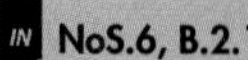

Quick Lab
OPEN-ENDED INQUIRY

NoS.6, B.2.1

Making a Model of a Cell

1. Your class is going to make a model of a plant cell using the whole classroom. Work with a partner or in a small group to decide what cell part or organelle you would like to model. (Use **Figure 7–14** on pages 206–207 as a starting point. It gives you an idea of the relative sizes of various cell parts and their possible positions.)

2. Using materials of your choice, make a three-dimensional model of the cell part or organelle you chose. Make the model as complete and as accurate as you can.

3. Label an index card with the name of your cell part or organelle, and list its main features and functions. Attach the card to your model.

4. Attach your model to an appropriate place in the room. If possible, attach your model to another related cell part or organelle.

Analyze and Conclude

1. **Calculate** Assume that a typical plant cell is 50 micrometers wide (50×10^{-6} m). Calculate the scale of your classroom cell model. (*Hint:* Divide the width of the classroom by the width of a cell, making sure to use the same units.) MATH

2. **Compare and Contrast** How is your model cell part or organelle similar to the real cell part or organelle? How is it different?

3. **Evaluate** Based on your work with this model, describe how you could make a better model. What new information would your improved model demonstrate?

Cellular Boundaries

What is the function of the cell membrane?

A working factory needs walls and a roof to protect it from the environment outside, and also to serve as a barrier that keeps its products safe and secure until they are ready to be shipped out. Cells have similar needs, and they meet them in a similar way. As you have learned, all cells are surrounded by a barrier known as the cell membrane. Many cells, including most prokaryotes, also produce a strong supporting layer around the membrane known as a **cell wall.**

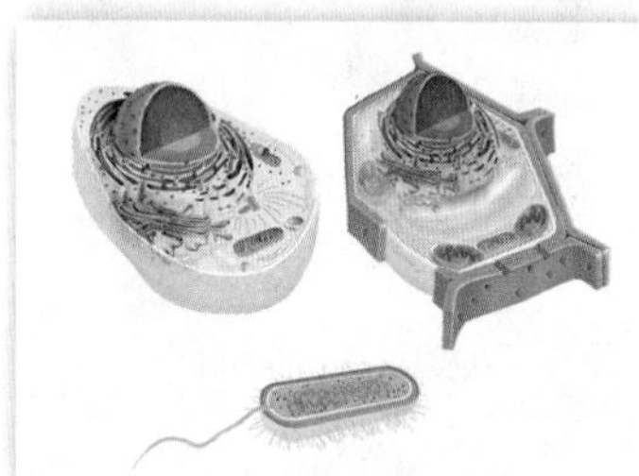

Cell Walls Many organisms have cell walls in addition to cell membranes. The main function of the cell wall is to support, shape, and protect the cell. Most prokaryotes and many eukaryotes have cell walls. Animal cells do not have cell walls. Cell walls lie outside the cell membrane. Most cell walls are porous enough to allow water, oxygen, carbon dioxide, and certain other substances to pass through easily.

Cell walls provide much of the strength needed for plants to stand against the force of gravity. In trees and other large plants, nearly all of the tissue we call wood is made up of cell walls. The cellulose fiber used for paper as well as the lumber used for building comes from these walls. So if you are reading these words off a sheet of paper from a book resting on a wooden desk, you've got cell walls all around you.

BUILD Vocabulary

ACADEMIC WORDS The adjective **porous** means "allowing materials to pass through." A porous cell wall allows substances like water and oxygen to pass through it.

Quick Lab

PURPOSE Students will make models of cell parts and organelles to better understand cell structure.

MATERIALS various craft supplies, index cards

PLANNING Collect a variety of craft items, such as construction paper, yarn, balloons, tape, cardboard tubes, and glue. Allow students to use other items as desired.

ANALYZE AND CONCLUDE

1. Scales will vary depending on the size of the classroom. If a room is 5 m (500,000,000 micrometers) across and a typical cell is 50 micrometers across, the scale would be 1,000,000 : 1.
2. Model organelles and cell parts should be similar in shape and structure to the real objects. The models are different in that they are much larger, are made of different materials, and do not function.
3. Students should suggest ways to make better models than the original ones.

Lead a Discussion

Ask students to consider what happens when a property owner puts up a fence. What purpose does the fence serve? How do people get in and out? Are there different kinds of fences? Use the analogy to explain that a cell's contents are also confined within a barrier. Have students use the reduced cell images on this page and the larger version in **Figure 7–14** to find out which cells have cell walls and where cell walls are located in cells. Then, write this prompt on the board, and have students defend or refute it: All cells have a cell membrane, but not all cells have a cell wall.

DIFFERENTIATED INSTRUCTION

L1 Special Needs If students do not understand the analogy comparing cell membranes/walls to fences, show a photograph or illustration of a fence. Ask students what the function of the fence is. *(A fence keeps some things inside and other things outside.)* Then, refer students to **Figure 7–14.**

Ask Where are the cell membrane and cell wall found? *(on the outside edge of the cell, surrounding the cell contents)*

Ask Do you think the mitochondria, nucleus, and other organelles can cross the cell membrane? *(no)*

L3 Advanced Students Have students find out what chemical compound is most commonly found in cell walls that makes certain plants useful for building materials and paper making. *(cellulose)* Have them describe their findings in writing.

Teach continued

ZOOMING IN

Direct students' attention to **Figure 7–13,** and have them read the caption. Then, focus their attention on the illustration to learn how the lipid bilayer of a cell membrane is constructed. Point out that a lipid molecule has two distinct ends. One end (the hydrophilic end) is electrically attracted to water molecules in much the same way that the north end of a magnet is attracted to the south end of another magnet. When the hydrophilic end pulls toward water molecules, the hydrophobic end of the lipid molecule is repelled. Explain that cells contain water in their cytoplasm and are surrounded by water. Have pairs of students use this information to discuss how the structure of a double-layered membrane is related to its function.

DIFFERENTIATED INSTRUCTION

L1 Special Needs Make sure that students understand the relationship between the different components of **Figure 7–13** and also the perspective shown by the illustration. Clarify that the illustration shows a tiny part of a cell membrane, similar to the membrane that surrounds the cell in the micrograph. Explain that the illustration is a cross section. To model a cross section, you might cut a lemon or orange in half and show how the cut reveals a cross section of the rind. Finally, show how you can tell, by looking at the "whoosh" in the illustration, that the lipid molecule is an enlargement of one tiny part of the cross section of the membrane.

L3 Advanced Students Have students work in pairs to develop an analogy related to the fluid mosaic model. Emphasize that the protein and lipid molecules in the membrane can move.

Answers

FIGURE 7–13 The hydrophobic end of the lipid molecules turns away from water molecules, but the hydrophilic end of lipid molecules is attracted to water molecules both inside and outside the cell. With water on both sides, a two-layer, or bilayer, system of lipid molecules forms, with the phobic portions within the membrane.

Cell Membranes All cells contain cell membranes, which almost always are made up of a double-layered sheet called a lipid bilayer, as shown in **Figure 7–13.** The **lipid bilayer** gives cell membranes a flexible structure that forms a strong barrier between the cell and its surroundings. **The cell membrane regulates what enters and leaves the cell and also protects and supports the cell.**

▶ ***The Properties of Lipids*** The layered structure of cell membranes reflects the chemical properties of the lipids that make them up. You may recall that many lipids have oily fatty acid chains attached to chemical groups that interact strongly with water. In the language of a chemist, the fatty acid portions of this kind of lipid are hydrophobic (hy druh FOH bik), or "water-hating," while the opposite end of the molecule is hydrophilic (hy druh FIL ik), or "water-loving." When these lipids, including the phospholipids that are common in animal cell membranes, are mixed with water, their hydrophobic fatty acid "tails" cluster together while their hydrophilic "heads" are attracted to water. A lipid bilayer is the result. As you can see in **Figure 7–13,** the head groups of lipids in a bilayer are exposed to the outside of the cell, while the fatty acid tails form an oily layer inside the membrane that keeps water out.

ZOOMING IN

THE CELL MEMBRANE

FIGURE 7-13 Every cell has a membrane that regulates the movement of materials. Nearly all cell membranes are made up of a lipid bilayer in which proteins and carbohydrates are embedded. Apply Concepts ***Explain why lipids "self-assemble" into a bilayer when exposed to water.***

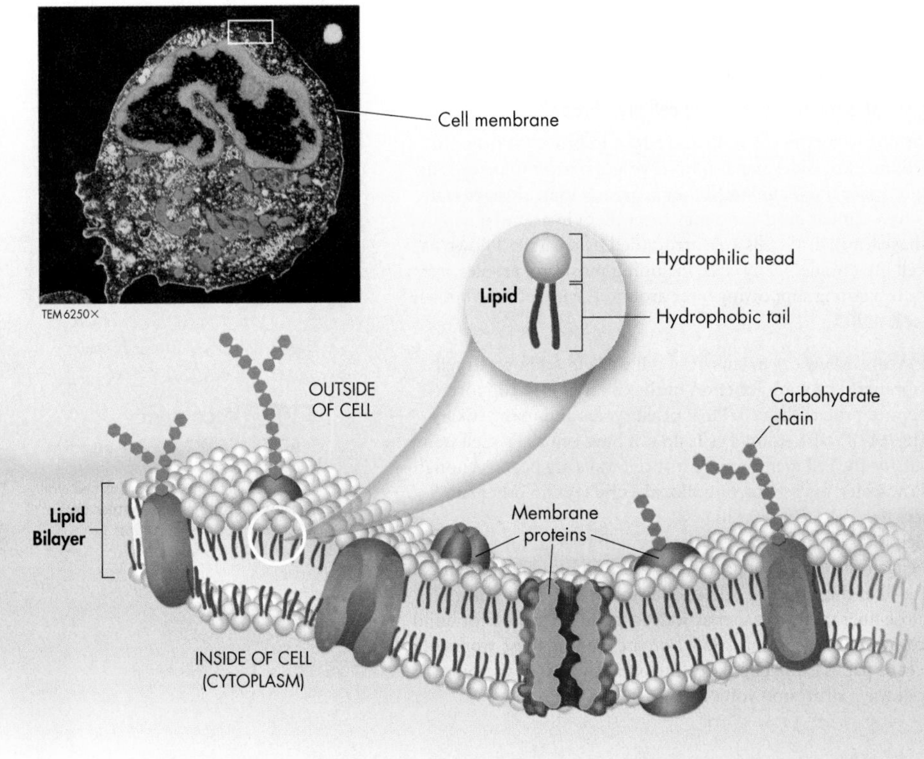

UbD Check for Understanding

ONE-MINUTE RESPONSE

Give students one minute to write a response to:

- How do cell membranes regulate what enters and leaves the cell, and how do they protect the cell? *(Cell membranes are selectively permeable, which means that some materials can enter them, but some are too large or too strongly charged. Keeping out or expelling some materials is a form of protection.)*

ADJUST INSTRUCTION

If responses show that students are confused by the role of the cell membrane, suggest they work in pairs to discuss what might happen to a cell that did not have a selectively permeable membrane. Then, ask pairs to rewrite a response to the question.

▶ ***The Fluid Mosaic Model*** Embedded in the lipid bilayer of most cell membranes are protein molecules. Carbohydrate molecules are attached to many of these proteins. Because the proteins embedded in the lipid bilayer can move around and "float" among the lipids, and because so many different kinds of molecules make up the cell membrane, scientists describe the cell membrane as a "fluid mosaic." A mosaic is a kind of art that involves bits and pieces of different colors or materials. What are all these different molecules doing? As you will see, some of the proteins form channels and pumps that help to move material across the cell membrane. Many of the carbohydrate molecules act like chemical identification cards, allowing individual cells to identify one another. Some proteins attach directly to the cytoskeleton, enabling cells to respond to their environment by using their membranes to help move or change shape.

As you know, some things are allowed to enter and leave a factory, and some are not. The same is true for living cells. Although many substances can cross biological membranes, some are too large or too strongly charged to cross the lipid bilayer. If a substance is able to cross a membrane, the membrane is said to be permeable to it. A membrane is impermeable to substances that cannot pass across it. Most biological membranes are **selectively permeable,** meaning that some substances can pass across them and others cannot. Selectively permeable membranes are also called semipermeable membranes.

7.2 Assessment

IN B.2.1, B.2.2, B.2.3, B.2.4

Review Key Concepts

1. a. Review What are the two major parts of the cell?

b. Use Analogies How is the role of the nucleus in a cell similar to the role of the captain on a sports team?

2. a. Review What is the function of lysosomes?

b. Apply Concepts How do contractile vacuoles help maintain water balance?

3. a. Review What is the difference between rough and smooth ER?

b. Sequence Describe the steps involved in the synthesis, packaging, and export of a protein from a cell.

4. a. Review What is the function of mitochondria?

b. Infer You examine an unknown cell under a microscope and discover that the cell contains chloroplasts. From what type of organism does the cell likely come?

5. a. Review Why is the cell membrane sometimes referred to as a fluid mosaic? What part of the cell membrane acts like a fluid? And what makes it like a mosaic?

b. Explain How do the properties of lipids help explain the structure of a cell membrane?

c. Infer Why do you think it's important that cell membranes are *selectively* permeable?

VISUAL THINKING

6. Using the cells on the next page as a guide, draw your own models of a prokaryotic cell, a plant cell, and an animal cell. Then use each of the vocabulary words from this lesson to label your cells.

BIOLOGY.com Search  Lesson 7.2 GO • Self-Test • Lesson Assessment

LESSON 7.2

Assess and Remediate

EVALUATE UNDERSTANDING

Have volunteers describe how keeping some large molecules out of a cell is an example of selective permeability. Then, have students complete the 7.2 Assessment.

REMEDIATION SUGGESTION

L1 Struggling Students If students have trouble with **Question 5b,** have them review **Figure 7–13** and the text under **Cell Membranes.**

BIOLOGY.com Students can check their understanding of lesson concepts with the **Self-Test** assessment. They can then take the online version of the **Lesson Assessment.**

Assessment Answers

1a. cytoplasm with organelles, nucleus

1b. The nucleus controls cell activities as a captain controls plays and players.

2a. Their enzymes break down nutrients and old organelles.

2b. by pumping out excess water

3a. Rough ER has surface ribosomes; smooth ER does not.

3b. Students should describe the steps in **Figure 7–11.**

4a. converting chemical energy in food into compounds the cell can use

4b. a plant or photosynthetic protist

5a. because, like a real mosaic, it is made of many parts that can float around in the membrane

5b. Hydrophilic lipid heads are attracted to water; hydrophobic fatty acid tails turn away from water. A bilayer forms when lipid heads turn toward water inside and outside the cell.

5c. Selective permeability allows needed substances to enter the cell and wastes to leave, while keeping out molecules that are not needed.

VISUAL THINKING

6. Students' labeled illustrations should reflect characteristics of all three types of cells and include all lesson vocabulary terms.

LESSON 7.2

Teach

VISUAL SUMMARY

Use **Figure 7–14** to review the parts of typical cells. Divide the class into small groups, and have each group submit a question about a cell function to be answered by the class. Answers should incorporate specific vocabulary terms shown in the figure.

DIFFERENTIATED INSTRUCTION

LPR Less Proficient Readers Pair less proficient readers with proficient readers. Have students use **Figure 7–14** to write questions on index cards about cell parts and then use the cards to quiz each other without looking at the table on the opposite page. *(Sample question: What cell part enables a cell to release energy?)* Collect the cards, and use them for a class review.

L3 Advanced Students Have interested students conduct research and draw labeled models of typical fungi and protist cells. Hang their drawings on the wall for other students to see. These models will be helpful when studying protists and fungi in Unit 6.

BIOLOGY.com Students can review plant and animal cell structures by checking **Art Review: Plant and Animal Cells.** To reinforce that plants have mitochondria, have students watch **Tutor Tube.**

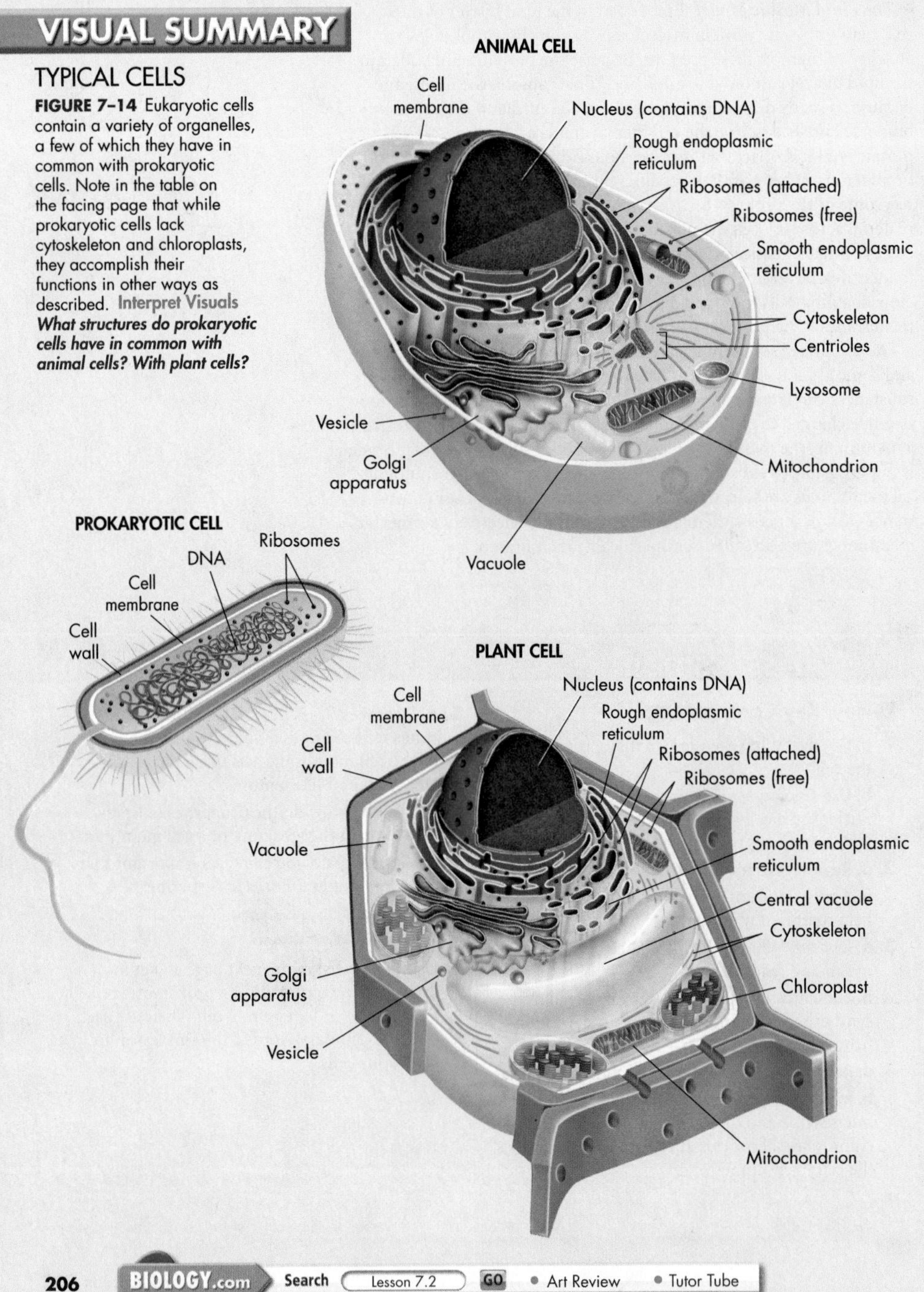

VISUAL SUMMARY

TYPICAL CELLS

FIGURE 7–14 Eukaryotic cells contain a variety of organelles, a few of which they have in common with prokaryotic cells. Note in the table on the facing page that while prokaryotic cells lack cytoskeleton and chloroplasts, they accomplish their functions in other ways as described. **Interpret Visuals** ***What structures do prokaryotic cells have in common with animal cells? With plant cells?***

Biology In-Depth

THE ORIGIN OF EUKARYOTES

The idea that chloroplasts and mitochondria originated in symbiotic relationships with prokaryotic cells is called the endosymbiotic hypothesis. According to this hypothesis, chloroplasts may have originated when cyanobacteria became established in larger prokaryotes, either as parasites or as prey that were not digested. Mitochondria may have been anaerobic heterotrophs that found a safe existence inside larger prokaryotes as oxygen became more abundant in the atmosphere. Over time, host and symbionts became more and more interdependent, and the organisms merged to become a single eukaryotic cell. The endosymbiotic hypothesis is covered in Chapter 19.

Answers

FIGURE 7–14 Prokaryotic cells have a cell membrane, DNA (though not enclosed in a nucleus), and ribosomes in common with animal cells. Prokaryotic cells have a cell membrane, cell wall, DNA (though not in a nucleus), and ribosomes in common with plant cells.

	Structure	Function	Prokaryote	Eukaryote: Animal	Plant
Cellular Control Center	Nucleus	Contains DNA	*Prokaryote DNA is found in cytoplasm.*	✓	✓
Organelles That Store, Clean-Up, and Support	Vacuoles and vesicles	Store materials		✓	✓
	Lysosomes	Break down and recycle macromolecules		✓	✓ (rare)
	Cytoskeleton	Maintains cell shape; moves cell parts; helps cells move	*Prokaryotic cells have protein filaments similar to actin and tubulin.*	✓	✓
	Centrioles	Organize cell division		✓	
Organelles That Build Proteins	Ribosomes	Synthesize proteins	✓	✓	✓
	Endoplasmic reticulum	Assembles proteins and lipids		✓	✓
	Golgi apparatus	Modifies, sorts, and packages proteins and lipids for storage or transport out of the cell		✓	✓
Organelles That Capture and Release Energy	Chloroplasts	Convert solar energy to chemical energy stored in food	*In some prokaryotic cells, photosynthesis occurs in association with internal photosynthetic membranes.*		✓
	Mitochondria	Convert chemical energy in food to usable compounds	*Prokaryotes carry out these reactions in the cytoplasm rather than in specialized organelles.*	✓	✓
Cellular Boundaries	Cell wall	Shapes, supports, and protects the cell	✓		✓
	Cell membrane	Regulates materials entering and leaving cell; protects and supports cell	✓	✓	✓

Check for Understanding

INDEX CARD SUMMARY

Provide students with an index card on which is written two structures from the cells depicted in **Figure 7–14.** Ask students to write a sentence that describes how the structures are related to each other.

ADJUST INSTRUCTION

If students have difficulty relating structures, have pairs use the table in **Figure 7–14** to discuss how their different structures might be related. Then, have students exchange cards and write new sentences that show the relationship between the listed structures.

Build Study Skills

Call students' attention to the table, which summarizes the structures and functions of cells and can help students distinguish between prokaryotes and eukaryotes. Discuss how the table is set up into columns, rows, and cells. Ask what a checkmark in the table means. *(The structure is present in a cell.)* Ask what an empty box indicates. (*The structure is not present in a cell.)* Finally, make sure students know that there are other eukaryotes (fungi and "protists") besides animals and plants, though for simplicity, only those are listed in this table.

DIFFERENTIATED INSTRUCTION

L1 Struggling Students Write cell functions on individual index cards. Then, have students select a card and name the cell part or organelle and the kind of cell it is found in. For example, Traps sunlight: *chloroplast, plant cell.*

ELL Focus on ELL: Access Content

ADVANCED AND ADVANCED HIGH SPEAKERS
Have students use **Figure 7–14** and Lesson 7.2 to complete a **Jigsaw Review.** Form groups of five. Tell students this is their "learning circle." Assign each student a number from 1 to 5 within each group. Then, form "study groups" by having students with the same number (all the 2s, all the 5s, and so on) come together. Assign each study group a cell characteristic from the table. (See the left-most column of the table—**Cellular Control Center,** and so on.) Tell students they will have 10 minutes to use the information in the figure and text to create a presentation on their assigned characteristic. Finally, have students return to their learning circles. Each student in the learning circle should present his or her assigned characteristic to the rest of the group.

Study Wkbks A/B, Appendix S7, Jigsaw Review.

LESSON 7.3

Getting Started

Objectives

7.3.1 Describe passive transport.

7.3.2 Describe active transport.

Student Resources

Study Workbooks A and B, 7.3 Worksheets

Spanish Study Workbook, 7.3 Worksheets

Lesson Overview • Lesson Notes
- Activities: InterActive Art, Art in Motion
- Assessment: Self-Test, Lesson Assessment

For corresponding lesson in the **Foundation Edition**, see pages 176–180.

Activate Prior Knowledge

Have students read the analogy of the cell as a nation in Think About It and discuss ways materials might enter and leave a country. Then, ask students to predict how materials might enter or leave a cell.

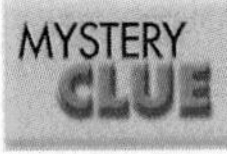

Remind students what they already know about the cell membrane, and suggest they skim the first four pages of this lesson. Ask what characteristic of a cell membrane might have contributed to Michelle's problem. *(its permeability to water)* The difference in salt concentration inside and outside the red blood cells caused excessive water to enter the cells. Students can go online to **Biology.com** to collect evidence.

IN INDIANA ACADEMIC STANDARDS

For the full text of all standards, see the Course Overview in the front matter of this book.

B.1.2 Understand that the shape of a molecule determines its role in the many different types of cellular processes including metabolism, homeostasis, growth and development, and heredity, and understand that the majority of these processes involve proteins that act as enzymes.

B.2.2 Describe the structure of a cell membrane and explain how it regulates the transport of materials into and out of the cell and prevents harmful materials from entering the cell.

7.3 Cell Transport

B.2.1 Features common to all cells; **B.2.2** Cell membrane. Also covered: **B.2.5.**

Key Questions

- *What is passive transport?*
- *What is active transport?*

Vocabulary

diffusion • facilitated diffusion • aquaporin • osmosis • isotonic • hypertonic • hypotonic • osmotic pressure

Taking Notes

Compare/Contrast Table As you read, create a compare/contrast table for passive and active transport.

THINK ABOUT IT In the previous lesson, cell walls and cell membranes were compared to the roof and walls of a factory. When you think about how cells move materials in and out, it can be helpful to think of a cell as a nation. Before you can learn anything about a nation, it's important to understand where it begins and where it ends. The boundaries of a nation are its borders, and nearly every country tries to regulate and control the goods that move across those borders, like the shipping containers seen here entering and leaving the port of Seattle. Each cell has its own border, which separates the cell from its surroundings and also determines what comes in and what goes out. How can a cell separate itself from its environment and still allow material to enter and leave? That's where transport across its border, the cell membrane, comes in.

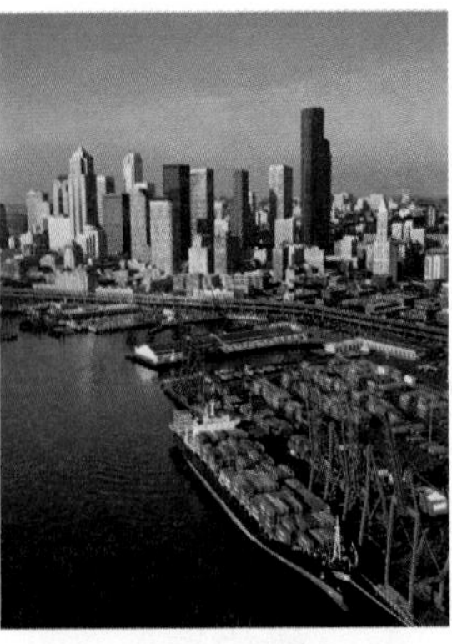

MYSTERY CLUE

As Michelle ran, she perspired, losing salts from her bloodstream. And as she drank more and more water during the race, the concentration of dissolved salts and minerals in her bloodstream decreased. How do you think these phenomena contributed to Michelle's condition?

Passive Transport

What is passive transport?

Every living cell exists in a liquid environment. One of the most important functions of the cell membrane is to keep the cell's internal conditions relatively constant. It does this by regulating the movement of molecules from one side of the membrane to the other.

Diffusion Cellular cytoplasm consists of many different substances dissolved in water. In any solution, solute particles move constantly. They collide with one another and tend to spread out randomly. As a result, the particles tend to move from an area where they are more concentrated to an area where they are less concentrated. When you add sugar to coffee or tea, for example, the sugar molecules move away from their original positions in the sugar crystals and disperse throughout the hot liquid. The process by which particles move from an area of high concentration to an area of lower concentration is known as **diffusion** (dih FYOO zhun). Diffusion is the driving force behind the movement of many substances across the cell membrane.

UbD Teach for Understanding

ENDURING UNDERSTANDING A cell is the basic unit of life; the processes that occur at the cellular level provide the energy and basic structure organisms need to survive.

GUIDING QUESTION How does a cell transport materials across the cell membrane?

EVIDENCE OF UNDERSTANDING *After completing the lesson, give students the following assessment to show they understand how a cell transports materials across the cell membrane.* Have students work in small groups to construct analogies that describe how materials move into and out of cells across cell membranes. The analogies can be illustrated.

What does diffusion have to do with the cell membrane? Suppose a substance is present in unequal concentrations on either side of a cell membrane, as shown in **Figure 7–15.** If the substance can cross the cell membrane, its particles will tend to move toward the area where it is less concentrated until it is evenly distributed. Once the concentration of the substance on both sides of the cell membrane is the same, equilibrium is reached.

Even when equilibrium is reached, particles of a solution continue to move across the membrane in both directions. However, because almost equal numbers of particles move in each direction, there is no further net change in the concentration on either side.

Diffusion depends on random particle movements. Therefore, substances diffuse across membranes without requiring the cell to use additional energy. **The movement of materials across the cell membrane without using cellular energy is called passive transport.**

FIGURE 7–15 Diffusion Diffusion is the process by which molecules of a substance move from an area of higher concentration to an area of lower concentration. It does not require the cell to use energy. **Predict** ***How would the movement of solute particles seen here be different if the initial area of high concentration had been on the inside of the cell instead of the outside?***

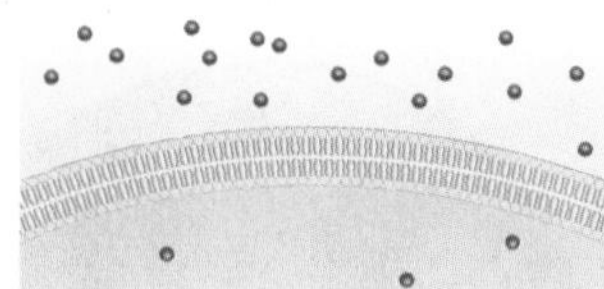

There is a higher concentration of solute on one side of the membrane than on the other.

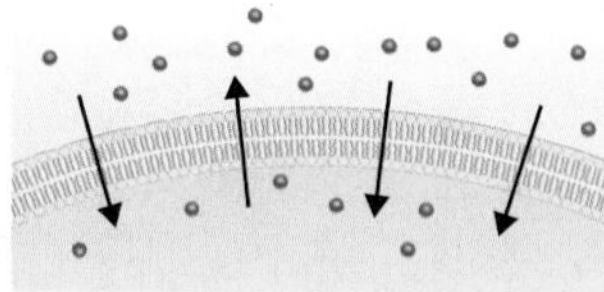

Diffusion causes a net movement of solute particles from the side of the membrane with the higher solute concentration to the side with the lower solute concentration.

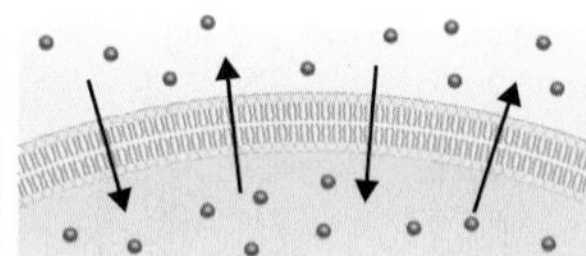

Once equilibrium is reached, solute particles continue to diffuse across the membrane in both directions but at approximately equal rates, so there is no net change in solute concentration.

Facilitated Diffusion Since cell membranes are built around lipid bilayers, the molecules that pass through them most easily are small and uncharged. These properties allow them to dissolve in the membrane's lipid environment. But many ions, like Cl^-, and large molecules, like the sugar glucose, seem to pass through cell membranes much more quickly than they should. It's almost as if they have a shortcut across the membrane.

How does this happen? Proteins in the cell membrane act as carriers, or channels, making it easy for certain molecules to cross. Red blood cells, for example, have protein carriers that allow glucose to pass through them in either direction. Only glucose can pass through these protein carriers. These cell membrane channels facilitate, or help, the diffusion of glucose across the membrane. This process, in which molecules that cannot directly diffuse across the membrane pass through special protein channels, is known as **facilitated diffusion.** Hundreds of different proteins have been found that allow particular substances to cross cell membranes. Although facilitated diffusion is fast and specific, it is still diffusion, so it does not require any additional use of the cell's energy.

In Your Notebook *Explain how you can demonstrate diffusion by spraying air freshener in a large room.*

Teach

Use Visuals

Explain to students that some materials, such as oxygen, diffuse across the cell membrane, without using energy, while others require energy to pass through. Draw attention to **Figure 7–15,** and explain that it illustrates one type of passive transport: diffusion directly through the cell membrane.

Ask How do the first and second drawings differ? *(The first shows a higher concentration of a solute outside than inside a cell. The second shows a greater number of molecules moving in than moving out, as indicated by more arrows pointing in than out.)*

Ask How do you know equilibrium has been reached in the third illustration? *(There are equal numbers of molecules on both sides of the membrane, and the arrows show about the same number of molecules moving in and moving out.)*

Emphasize that equilibrium does not mean that movement stops; rather it continues in both directions, and the same concentration is maintained on both sides of the membrane.

DIFFERENTIATED INSTRUCTION

ELL English Language Learners Explain to English learners that *concentration* has multiple meanings in English. Reassure students who are already familiar with the definition of *concentration* as "directed effort or attention" that this is one correct definition. Then, point out *concentration* has a specific meaning in science. The scientific meaning of *concentration* refers to the relative amount of one substance in another, for example, the concentration of salt in water.

LPR Less Proficient Readers If students have trouble answering the caption question, rephrase it to read: What would be different if the high concentration had been inside the cell to start with?

Biology In-Depth

RATE OF FACILITATED DIFFUSION

In simple diffusion, concentration is the only factor that affects rate. In facilitated diffusion, the rate also depends upon the number of specific carrier protein molecules in the membrane, because the diffusing molecules can move across the membrane only through those proteins. An example is the diffusion of glucose into cells. Such diffusion occurs most of the time as facilitated diffusion. No matter how much the cell "needs" glucose or how great the difference in concentration is between the inside and outside of the cell, the rate at which the glucose can diffuse into the cell has a limit because of the limited number of glucose carrier protein molecules in the lipid bilayer.

Answers

FIGURE 7–15 If the concentration of solute particles had been higher on the inside of the cell, more solute particles would have moved out of the cell than into the cell.

IN YOUR NOTEBOOK Students' answers should reflect an understanding that in diffusion, molecules move randomly from an area where they are more concentrated to areas where they are less concentrated. So, when air freshener is sprayed in a room, the smell will diffuse from its point of origin until it can be detected everywhere.

LESSON 7.3

Teach continued

Use Visuals

Use **Figure 7–17** to introduce osmosis.

Ask What happens to the concentrations on each side of the membrane as water diffuses through? *(The concentrations change until they reach equilibrium.)* Why does the water level rise in the right side of the tube and drop in the left side? (*The net movement of water molecules is to the right side, because initially the concentration of water is lower there. The movement of water molecules across the barrier changes the water level on both sides of the tube.)*

Ask volunteers to explain what the white arrows in part B of the figure represent. *(movement of water molecules through aquaporins)*

DIFFERENTIATED INSTRUCTION

L1 **Struggling Students** Immerse a tea bag in a beaker of hot water. Tell students the bag represents a cell membrane. Ask how they know something is passing through the bag. *(The water turns color.)* Ask if there is anything that cannot pass through the bag. *(tea leaves)* Relate this to **Figure 7–17** (water molecules can move through the barrier, but sugar molecules cannot).

ELL Focus on ELL: Extend Language

ALL SPEAKERS Have students use the **Think-Pair-Share** strategy to discuss the word *osmosis*. Pair beginning speakers with advanced speakers of the same language. Have students read and discuss the information about osmosis. Encourage advanced speakers to explain the concepts in their native language.

Study Wkbks A/B, Appendix S14, Think-Pair-Share.

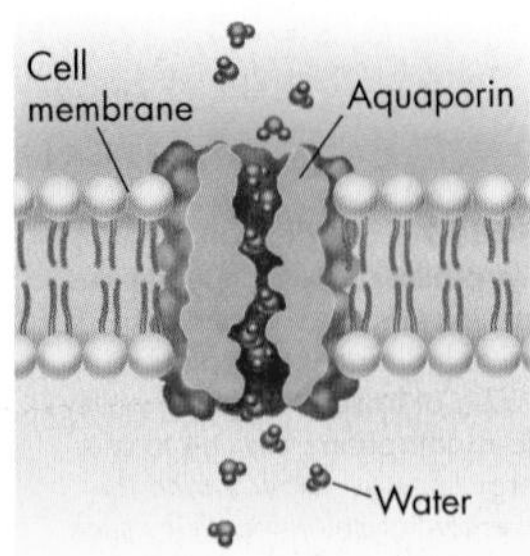

FIGURE 7–16 An Aquaporin

Osmosis: An Example of Facilitated Diffusion Surprising new research has added water to the list of molecules that enter cells by facilitated diffusion. Recall that the inside of a cell's lipid bilayer is hydrophobic, or "water-hating." Because of this, water molecules have a tough time passing through the cell membrane. However, many cells contain water channel proteins, known as **aquaporins** (ak wuh PAWR inz), that allow water to pass right through them, as shown in **Figure 7–16.** The movement of water through cell membranes by facilitated diffusion is an extremely important biological process—the process of osmosis.

Osmosis is the diffusion of water through a selectively permeable membrane. In osmosis, as in other forms of diffusion, molecules move from an area of higher concentration to an area of lower concentration. The only difference is that the molecules that move in the case of osmosis are water molecules, not solute molecules. The process of osmosis is shown in **Figure 7–17.**

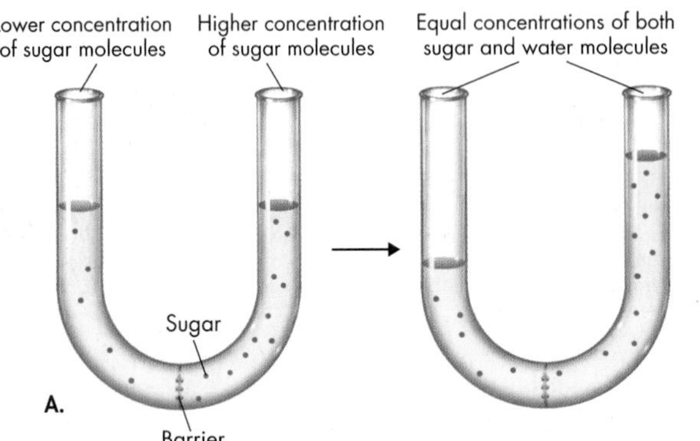

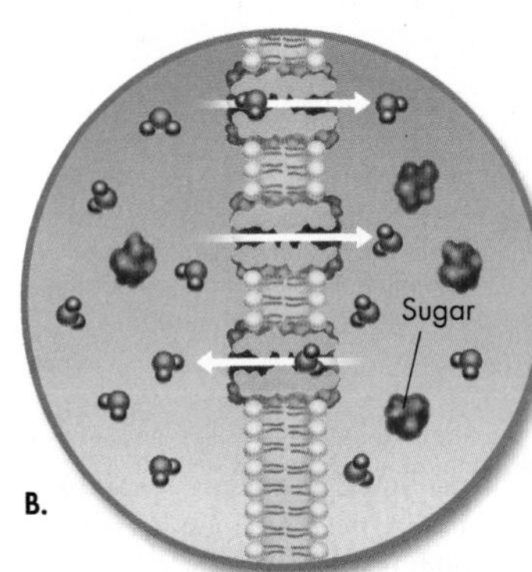

FIGURE 7–17 Osmosis Osmosis is a form of facilitated diffusion. **A.** In a laboratory experiment, water moves through a selectively permeable barrier from an area of lower to higher solute concentration until equilibrium is reached. **B.** In the cell, water passes in through aquaporins embedded in the cell membrane. Although water moves in both directions through aquaporins, there is a net movement of water from an area of lower to higher sugar concentration. Apply Concepts ***Does osmosis require the cell to use energy?***

▶ ***How Osmosis Works*** Look at the experimental setup in **Figure 7–17A.** The barrier is permeable to water but not to sugar. This means that water can cross the barrier in both directions, but sugar cannot. To start, there are more sugar molecules on the right side of the barrier than on the left side. Therefore, the concentration of water is lower on the right, where more of the solution is made of sugar. Although water molecules move in both directions across the membrane, there is a net movement of water toward the concentrated sugar solution.

Water will tend to move across the membrane until equilibrium is reached. At that point, the concentrations of water and sugar will be the same on both sides of the membrane. When this happens, the two solutions will be **isotonic,** which means "same strength." Note that "strength" refers to the amount of solute, not water. When the experiment began, the more concentrated sugar solution (right side of the tube) was **hypertonic,** or "above strength," compared to the left side. So the dilute sugar solution (left side of the tube) was **hypotonic,** or "below strength," compared to the right side. **Figure 7–17B** shows how osmosis works across a cell membrane.

BIOLOGY.com Encourage students to use **Inter-Active Art: Diffusion and Osmosis** to reinforce diffusion of water through a selectively permeable membrane.

Biology In-Depth

AQUAPORINS

Osmosis is easily observed in cells, yet for a long time, it was a mystery as to how water could cross cell membranes so quickly. Water is a polar molecule and is not soluble in lipids. Water would not be expected to cross a membrane made up of a lipid bilayer. In 1990, Peter Agre discovered channels through which water molecules can cross cell membranes. The channels, called aquaporins, are proteins that span the depth of the membrane. Polar water molecules are able to move through channels because of how they relate to charges within the proteins. Aquaporins have been found in prokaryotic and eukaryotic cells. Eleven different types of aquaporins have been found in humans. One type plays an active role in water balance in the kidneys. Some aquaporins in plants appear to close in response to stress. For his discovery, Peter Agre received the Nobel Prize in Chemistry in 2003.

Answers

FIGURE 7–17 Osmosis is a form of diffusion. It does not require energy.

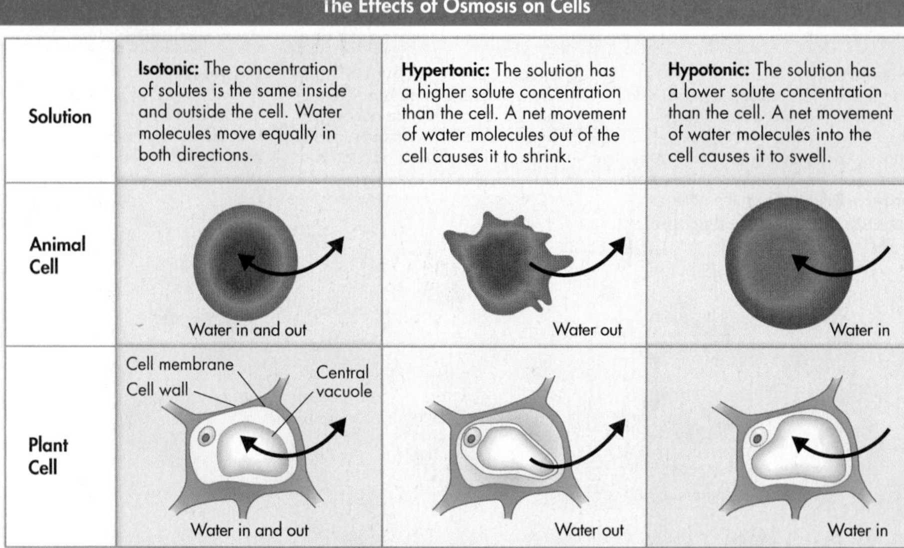

The Effects of Osmosis on Cells

Solution	**Isotonic:** The concentration of solutes is the same inside and outside the cell. Water molecules move equally in both directions.	**Hypertonic:** The solution has a higher solute concentration than the cell. A net movement of water molecules out of the cell causes it to shrink.	**Hypotonic:** The solution has a lower solute concentration than the cell. A net movement of water molecules into the cell causes it to swell.
Animal Cell	Water in and out	Water out	Water in
Plant Cell	Cell membrane, Cell wall, Central vacuole; Water in and out	Water out	Water in

▶ *Osmotic Pressure* Driven by differences in solute concentration, the net movement of water out of or into a cell produces a force known as **osmotic pressure.** As shown in **Figure 7–18,** osmotic pressure can cause an animal cell in a hypertonic solution to shrink, and one in a hypotonic solution to swell. Because cells contain salts, sugars, proteins, and other dissolved molecules, they are almost always hypertonic to fresh water. As a result, water tends to move quickly into a cell surrounded by fresh water, causing it to swell. Eventually, the cell may burst like an overinflated balloon. In plant cells, osmotic pressure can cause changes in the size of the central vacuole, which shrinks or swells as water moves into or out of the cell.

Fortunately cells in large organisms are not in danger of bursting because most of them do not come in contact with fresh water. Instead, the cells are bathed in blood or other isotonic fluids. The concentrations of dissolved materials in these isotonic fluids are roughly equal to those in the cells themselves.

What happens when cells do come in contact with fresh water? Some, like the eggs laid in fresh water by fish and frogs, lack water channels. As a result, water moves into them so slowly that osmotic pressure is not a problem. Others, including bacteria and plant cells, are surrounded by tough walls. The cell walls prevent the cells from expanding, even under tremendous osmotic pressure. Notice how the plant cell in **Figure 7–18** holds its shape in both hypertonic and hypotonic solutions while the animal red blood cell does not. However, increased osmotic pressure makes plant cells extremely vulnerable to cell wall injuries.

In Your Notebook *In your own words, explain why osmosis is really just a special case of facilitated diffusion.*

FIGURE 7–18 Osmotic Pressure Water molecules move equally into and out of cells placed in an isotonic solution. In a hypertonic solution, animal cells, like the red blood cell shown, shrink, and plant cell central vacuoles collapse. In a hypotonic solution, animal cells swell and burst. The central vacuoles of plant cells also swell, pushing the cell contents out against the cell wall. **Predict** ***What would happen to the cells of a saltwater plant if the plant were placed in fresh water?***

Connect to the Real World

Relate the illustrations in the bottom row of **Figure 7–18** to what happens when a lawn care company sprays a fertilizer-water mixture onto grass. Point out that if too much fertilizer and too little water are sprayed on grass, the grass may die and the lawn may turn brown.

Ask Would the grass cells have gained or lost water? *(lost water)*

Ask Which plant cell in **Figure 7–18** shows what would happen to the grass at the cellular level? *(the plant cell in the middle column, which shows water going out)*

Ask Was the fertilizer-water mixture hypotonic or hypertonic compared to the cytoplasm in the grass cells? *(The fertilizer-water mixture was hypertonic compared to the cytoplasm in the grass cells.)*

DIFFERENTIATED INSTRUCTION

L1 Struggling Students Some students may be confused by the two-headed arrow in **Figure 7–18,** which depicts an isotonic condition. Explain that the arrow with two heads means that water is moving both into and out of the cell at the same time. Suggest that it is similar to people streaming out one door at a movie theater as others stream in through another door.

UbD Check for Understanding

ONE-MINUTE RESPONSE

Present students with a drawing of a blood cell, and tell them the cell is in fresh water. Have students draw an arrow showing the direction in which water will move. Finally, ask them to write a sentence defending their choice of direction, using the appropriate term or terms—isotonic, hypotonic, or hypertonic. *(Responses should show the arrow going into the cell. Sample sentence: Fresh water is hypotonic to the inside of the cell, so the water will diffuse into the cell.)*

ADJUST INSTRUCTION

If responses show that students do not understand the effect of solute concentration on the direction of the flow of water in a cell, have them review the table in **Figure 7–18** and adjust their answer accordingly.

Answers

FIGURE 7–18 Fresh water would diffuse into the cytoplasm and the central vacuole of the saltwater plant. The cell would become rigid and push against the cell wall, possibly causing damage to the cells.

IN YOUR NOTEBOOK Sample answer: Osmosis is diffusion of water when there is a concentration difference across a membrane. As with all types of diffusion, no energy is required. Osmosis is a special case of facilitated diffusion, because facilitated diffusion occurs when molecules move across the membrane through specific protein channels, and in osmosis, water moves through aquaporins.

Teach continued

Connect to Physics

Before students read about active transport, help them to understand and compare the role of energy in moving materials. Have small groups set up ramps using a board and books. Ask them to roll a ball down the ramp and describe how easy or difficult it is to do. Then, have them push the ball back up the ramp using a pencil. Ask which process required energy to accomplish. Have students suggest ways to move the ball back up the ramp more easily. Ask what processes they think a cell might have evolved to make the process of moving materials more efficient.

DIFFERENTIATED INSTRUCTION

L1 **Special Needs** *Use an analogy of going into a building through an open door or going in through a revolving door to illustrate active transport.* Ask how an open door is like a carrier protein in facilitated diffusion. *(It is easy to walk through and requires no extra energy.)* Ask how moving through a revolving door is like active transport. *(A person has to use energy to push the door and move through the doorway in a small compartment.)*

VISUAL SUMMARY

Use **Figure 7–19** to explain that energy is needed to get certain substances into or out of a cell, because the cell membrane is selective. For substances that cannot pass through the membrane freely, active transport is used, and it requires energy. Draw students' attention to the annotation about protein pumps. Tell them that the change from ATP to ADP represents the use of energy by a cell.

BIOLOGY.com **Art in Motion: Active Transport** dynamically explores protein pumps, endocytosis, and exocytosis.

Protein Pumps
Energy from ATP is used to pump small molecules and ions across the cell membrane. Active transport proteins change shape during the process, binding substances on one side of the membrane, and releasing them on the other.

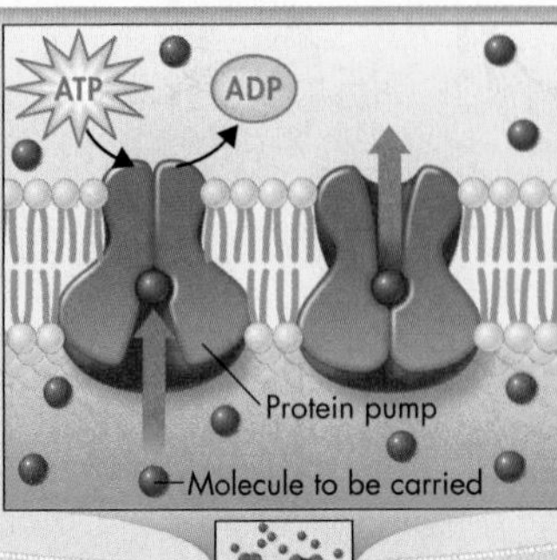

Endocytosis
The membrane forms a pocket around a particle. The pocket then breaks loose from the outer portion of the cell membrane and forms a vesicle within the cytoplasm.

Exocytosis
The membrane of a vesicle surrounds the material then fuses with the cell membrane. The contents are forced out of the cell.

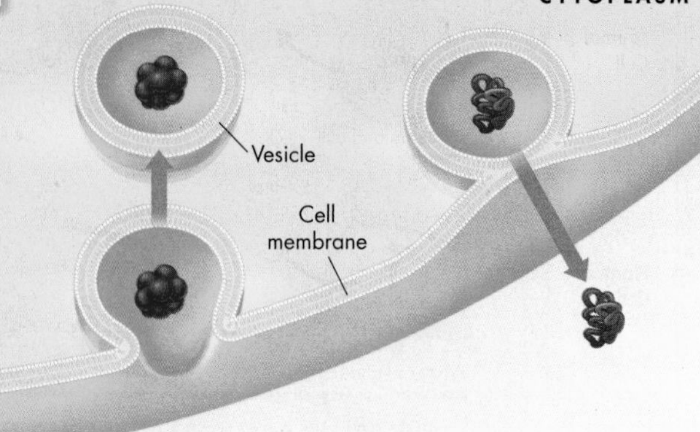

VISUAL SUMMARY

ACTIVE TRANSPORT

FIGURE 7–19 Energy from the cell is required to move particles against a concentration gradient. Compare and Contrast *What are the similarities and differences between facilitated diffusion and active transport by protein pump?*

Active Transport

What is active transport?

As powerful as diffusion is, cells sometimes must move materials against a concentration difference. **The movement of materials against a concentration difference is known as active transport. Active transport requires energy.** The active transport of small molecules or ions across a cell membrane is generally carried out by transport proteins—protein pumps—that are found in the membrane itself. Larger molecules and clumps of material can also be actively transported across the cell membrane by processes known as endocytosis and exocytosis. The transport of these larger materials sometimes involves changes in the shape of the cell membrane. The major types of active transport are shown in **Figure 7–19.**

Molecular Transport Small molecules and ions are carried across membranes by proteins in the membrane that act like pumps. Many cells use protein pumps to move calcium, potassium, and sodium ions across cell membranes. Changes in protein shape seem to play an important role in the pumping process. A considerable portion of the energy used by cells in their daily activities is spent providing the energy to keep this form of active transport working. The use of energy in these systems enables cells to concentrate substances in a particular location, even when the forces of diffusion might tend to move these substances in the opposite direction.

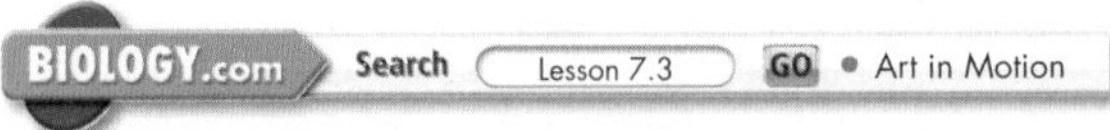

Quick Facts

PROTEIN MOLECULES AND ACTIVE TRANSPORT

One of the most important examples of active transport is the sodium-potassium pump, in which sodium ions are maintained at a lower concentration inside a cell than outside, and potassium ions are maintained at a higher concentration inside the cell than outside. The active transport of these ions by protein molecules is vital to the production of electrochemical impulses along nerve cells. At one time, scientists thought the protein molecules rotated as they transported substances through the cell membrane, picking up molecules on the outside, rotating, and then dumping them into the cell. Now, scientists think the transported molecules are squeezed through the transport proteins, because it has been observed that the proteins change their configuration to accommodate the incoming molecules.

Answers

FIGURE 7–19 Facilitated diffusion and active transport by protein pumps are similar, because they both make use of protein carriers to get materials across the cell membrane. They differ, because facilitated diffusion acts in the direction of the concentration gradient and does not use energy, while active transport requires energy to transport materials against the concentration gradient.

Bulk Transport Larger molecules and even solid clumps of material can be transported by movements of the cell membrane known as bulk transport. Bulk transport can take several forms, depending on the size and shape of the material moved into or out of the cell.

► ***Endocytosis*** Endocytosis (en doh sy TOH sis) is the process of taking material into the cell by means of infoldings, or pockets, of the cell membrane. The pocket that results breaks loose from the outer portion of the cell membrane and forms a vesicle or vacuole within the cytoplasm. Large molecules, clumps of food, even whole cells can be taken up in this way.

Phagocytosis (fag oh sy TOH sis) is a type of endocytosis, in which extensions of cytoplasm surround a particle and package it within a food vacuole. The cell then engulfs it. Amoebas use this method for taking in food, and white blood cells use phagocytosis to "eat" damaged cells, as shown in **Figure 7–20.** Engulfing material in this way requires a considerable amount of energy and is considered a form of active transport.

In a process similar to phagocytosis, many cells take up liquid from the surrounding environment. Tiny pockets form along the cell membrane, fill with liquid, and pinch off to form vacuoles within the cell. This type of endocytosis is known as pinocytosis (py nuh sy TOH sis).

► ***Exocytosis*** Many cells also release large amounts of material, a process known as exocytosis (ek soh sy TOH sis). During exocytosis, the membrane of the vacuole surrounding the material fuses with the cell membrane, forcing the contents out of the cell. The removal of water by means of a contractile vacuole is one example of this kind of active transport.

BUILD Vocabulary

PREFIXES The prefix *endo-* in *endocytosis* comes from a Greek word meaning "inside" or "within." The prefix *exo-* in *exocytosis* means "outside."

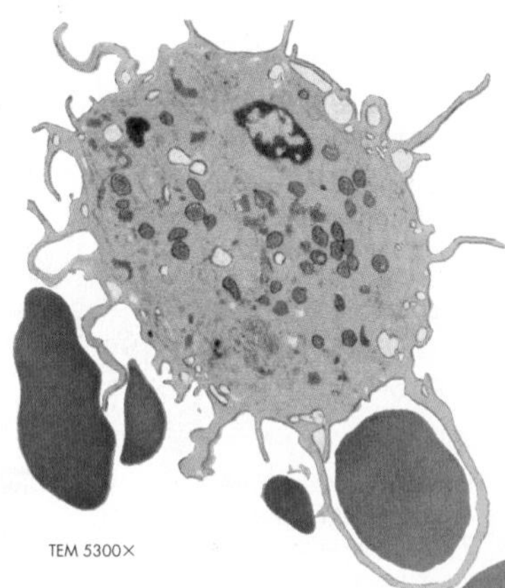

FIGURE 7–20 Endocytosis The white blood cell seen here is engulfing a damaged red blood cell by phagocytosis—a form of endocytosis. Extensions, or "arms," of the white blood cell's cell membrane have completely surrounded the red blood cell.

7.3 Assessment

IN B.1.2, B.2.2, B.2.5

Review Key Concepts

1. a. Review What happens during diffusion?
   b. Explain Describe the process of osmosis.
   c. Compare and Contrast What is the difference between diffusion and facilitated diffusion?
2. a. Review How is active transport different from passive transport?
   b. Explain Describe the two major types of active transport.
   c. Compare and Contrast How is endocytosis different from exocytosis?

BUILD VOCABULARY

3. Based on the meanings of *isotonic, hypertonic,* and *hypotonic,* write definitions for the prefixes *iso-, hyper-,* and *hypo-*. Then come up with another set of words that uses these prefixes (the words do not need to have the same suffixes).
4. The prefix *phago-* means "to eat." The prefix *pino-* means "to drink." Look up the definition of *-cytosis,* and write definitions for *phagocytosis* and *pinocytosis.*

BIOLOGY.com Search  Lesson 7.3 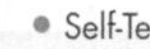 GO • Self-Test • Lesson Assessment

Lead a Discussion

Have students discuss why endocytosis is an example of active transport and not facilitated diffusion. *(Endocytosis requires energy to engulf a particle and form a vesicle around it.)*

DIFFERENTIATED INSTRUCTION

L1 Struggling Students To help students understand endocytosis, use clay to model a macrophage engulfing a bacterium.

Assess and Remediate

EVALUATE UNDERSTANDING

Ask students to write a paragraph distinguishing active transport from diffusion. Then, have them complete the 7.3 Assessment.

REMEDIATION SUGGESTION

L1 Struggling Students If students have trouble answering **Question 2a,** have them use a **Venn Diagram** to compare the two processes.

Study Wkbks A/B, Appendix S33, Venn Diagram. **Transparencies,** GO18.

BIOLOGY.com Students can check their understanding of lesson concepts with the **Self-Test** assessment. They can then take an online version of the **Lesson Assessment.**

Assessment Answers

1a. Particles move from a more to a less concentrated area.

1b. Water diffuses across a selectively permeable membrane from a more to a less concentrated area.

1c. Diffusion occurs when molecules spread out by moving randomly. Facilitated diffusion occurs when protein channels help molecules move across the cell membrane.

2a. Active transport uses energy to move materials across a cell membrane against a concentration gradient. Passive transport moves materials across a cell membrane in the direction of a concentration gradient, without using energy.

2b. In molecular transport, energy is used by protein pumps to carry small molecules across the cell membrane. In bulk transport, vesicles or vacuoles are used to move large molecules across the cell membrane.

2c. In endocytosis, a vesicle forms from an infolding of the cell membrane, surrounds large molecules entering the cell, and breaks off into the cytoplasm. In exocytosis, a vesicle fuses with the cell membrane and forces the material to be expelled out of the cell.

BUILD VOCABULARY

3. Sample answers: *Iso-* means "same"; *hyper-* means "over"; *hypo-* means "under"; isometric, hyperbole, hypodermic

4. The word part *-cytosis* refers to cells. Phagocytosis is the engulfing of foreign particles. Pinocytosis is the ingestion of fluid.

LESSON 7.4

Getting Started

Objectives

7.4.1 Explain how unicellular organisms maintain homeostasis.

7.4.2 Explain how multicellular organisms maintain homeostasis.

Student Resources

Study Workbooks A and B, 7.4 Worksheets

Spanish Study Workbook, 7.4 Worksheets

Lab Manual B, 7.4 Data Analysis Worksheet

Lesson Overview • Lesson Notes • Activity: Data Analysis • Assessment: Self-Test, Lesson Assessment

For corresponding lesson in the **Foundation Edition**, see pages 181–183.

Build Background

Ask students how often during the day they encounter single-celled organisms. Many students may not realize that they come in contact with millions of bacteria every time they brush their teeth, eat a piece of fruit, touch a doorknob, or take a breath of air. Ask students why these organisms are so successful. Ask what these organisms need to stay alive. *(water, energy)* Introduce the term *homeostasis*. Tie the discussion to what students have already learned about cell organelles and their specific functions by asking how a single cell can stay in balance in its environment.

IN INDIANA ACADEMIC STANDARDS

For the full text of all standards, see the Course Overview in the front matter of this book.

B.1.3 Explain and give examples of how the function and differentiation of cells is influenced by their external environment, including temperature, acidity and the concentration of certain molecules, and that changes in these conditions may affect how a cell functions.

B.2.1 Describe features common to all cells that are essential for growth and survival, and explain their functions.

7.4 Homeostasis and Cells

B.1.3 Cell function and differentiation; **B.2.1** Features common to all cells; **B.2.6** Variation in cell structure and function. Also covered: **NoS.3, B.2.5, B.3.3, B.6.3.**

Key Questions

How do individual cells maintain homeostasis?

How do the cells of multicellular organisms work together to maintain homeostasis?

Vocabulary

homeostasis • tissue • organ • organ system • receptor

Taking Notes

Preview Visuals Before you read, look at **Figures 7–22** and **7–23.** Then write two questions you have about the micrographs. As you read, write answers to your questions.

THINK ABOUT IT From its simple beginnings, life has spread to every corner of our planet, penetrating deep into the earth and far beneath the surface of the seas. The diversity of life is so great that you might have to remind yourself that all living things are composed of cells, have the same basic chemical makeup, and even contain the same kinds of organelles. This does not mean that all living things are the same: Differences arise from the ways in which cells are specialized and the ways in which cells associate with one another to form multicellular organisms.

The Cell as an Organism

How do individual cells maintain homeostasis?

Cells are the basic living units of all organisms, but sometimes a single cell is the organism. In fact, in terms of their numbers, unicellular organisms dominate life on Earth. A single-celled organism does everything you would expect a living thing to do. Just like other living things, unicellular organisms must maintain **homeostasis,** relatively constant internal physical and chemical conditions. **To maintain homeostasis, unicellular organisms grow, respond to the environment, transform energy, and reproduce.**

Unicellular organisms include both prokaryotes and eukaryotes. Prokaryotes, especially bacteria, are remarkably adaptable. Bacteria live almost everywhere—in the soil, on leaves, in the ocean, in the air, even within the human body.

Many eukaryotes, like the protozoan in **Figure 7–21,** also spend their lives as single cells. Some types of algae, which contain chloroplasts and are found in oceans, lakes, and streams around the world, are single celled. Yeasts, or unicellular fungi, are also widespread. Yeasts play an important role in breaking down complex nutrients, making them available for other organisms. People use yeasts to make bread and other foods.

Don't make the mistake of thinking that single-celled organisms are always simple. Prokaryote or eukaryote, homeostasis is still an issue for each unicellular organism. That tiny cell in a pond or on the surface of your pencil still needs to find sources of energy or food, to keep concentrations of water and minerals within certain levels, and to respond quickly to changes in its environment. The microscopic world around us is filled with unicellular organisms that are successfully maintaining that homeostatic balance.

FIGURE 7–21 Unicellular Life Single-celled organisms, like this freshwater protozoan, must be able to carry out all of the functions necessary for life (SEM 600×).

UbD Teach for Understanding

ENDURING UNDERSTANDING A cell is the basic unit of life; the processes that occur at the cellular level provide the energy and basic structure organisms need to survive.

GUIDING QUESTION How does a cell maintain homeostasis both within itself and as part of a multicellular organism?

EVIDENCE OF UNDERSTANDING *After completing the lesson, give students the following assessment to show they understand how a cell maintains homeostasis.* Have small groups of students write a script consisting of a series of creative, content-based questions that might be used to interview a cell about maintaining homeostasis. The script should supply answers to the questions.

Multicellular Life

How do the cells of multicellular organisms work together to maintain homeostasis?

Unlike most unicellular organisms, the cells of human beings and other multicellular organisms do not live on their own. They are interdependent; and like the members of a winning baseball team, they work together. In baseball, each player plays a particular position: pitcher, catcher, infielder, outfielder. And to play the game effectively, players and coaches communicate with one another, sending and receiving signals. Cells in a multicellular organism work the same way. **The cells of multicellular organisms become specialized for particular tasks and communicate with one another to maintain homeostasis.**

Cell Specialization The cells of a multicellular organism are specialized, with different cell types playing different roles. Some cells are specialized to move; others, to react to the environment; still others, to produce substances that the organism needs. No matter what its role, each specialized cell, like the ones in **Figures 7–22** and **7–23**, contributes to homeostasis in the organism.

In Your Notebook *Where in the human body do you think you would find cells that are specialized to produce digestive enzymes? Why?*

BUILD Vocabulary

PREFIXES The prefix *homeo-* in **homeostasis** means "the same." Organisms are constantly trying to maintain homeostasis, to keep their internal physical and chemical conditions relatively constant despite changes in their internal and external environments.

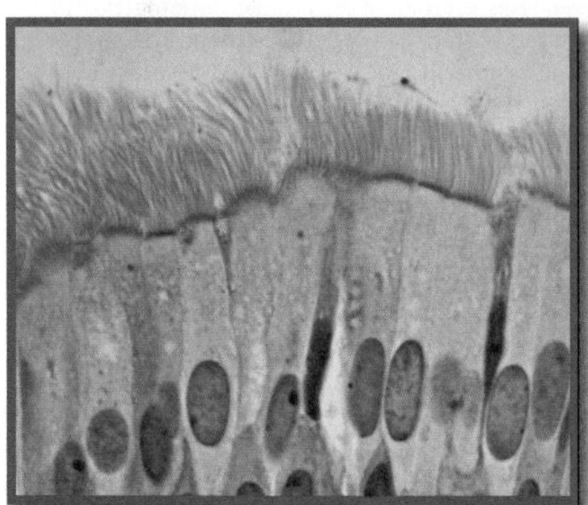

FIGURE 7–22 Specialized Animal Cells: Human Trachea Epithelium (LM 1000×)

▶ ***Specialized Animal Cells*** Even the cleanest, freshest air is dirty, containing particles of dust, smoke, and bacteria. What keeps this bad stuff from getting into your lungs? That's the job of millions of cells that work like street sweepers. These cells line the upper air passages. As you breathe, they work night and day sweeping mucus, debris, and bacteria out of your lungs. These cells are filled with mitochondria, which produce a steady supply of the ATP that powers the cilia on their upper surfaces to keep your lungs clean.

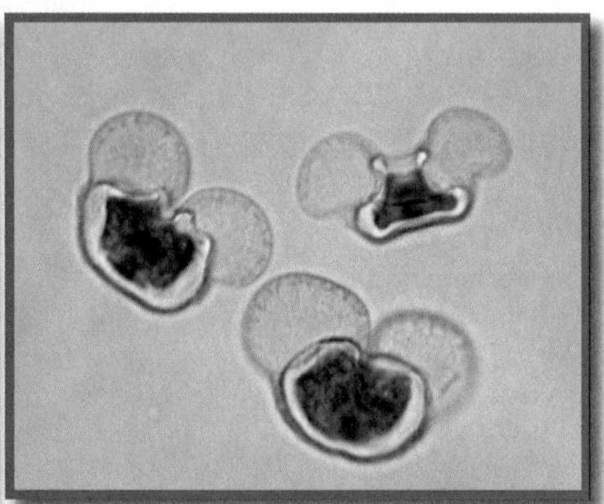

FIGURE 7–23 Specialized Plant Cells: Pine Pollen (LM 430×)

▶ ***Specialized Plant Cells*** How can a pine tree, literally rooted in place, produce offspring with another tree hundreds of meters away? It releases pollen grains, some of the world's most specialized cells. Pollen grains are tiny and light, despite tough walls to protect the cells inside. In addition, pine pollen grains have two tiny wings that enable them to float in the slightest breeze. Pine trees release millions of pollen grains like these to scatter in the wind, land on seed cones, and begin the essential work of starting a new generation.

Teach

Lead a Discussion

Use the analogy of a baseball team to introduce the idea that multicellular organisms are made up of many different kinds of cells, each specialized for different functions. Ask students to suggest specializations a multicellular organism needs to maintain homeostasis. List these suggestions on the board. Then, focus students' attention on **Figures 7–22** and **7–23.** Ask how each kind of cell is specialized for the role it plays. *(A trachea epithelium cell has cilia that clear debris; a pine pollen cell is tiny, lightweight, and floats in air.)*

DIFFERENTIATED INSTRUCTION

L1 Special Needs Some students might have difficulty finding the main idea on the page. Have them read aloud the paragraph under the subheading, **Cell Specialization.** Ask them to state three ways that cells are specialized. *(Some cells move, some react to the environment, and others produce substances the organism needs.)* Extend this by having students look at **Figures 7–22** and **7–23** and identifying what makes these cells specialized.

Quick Facts

THE BASIC TYPES OF TISSUES

A tissue is a group of specialized cells that have a common structure and a common function. In most instances, all the cells in a tissue look alike. Despite the great diversity of animals that have evolved, there are only four basic types of animal tissues: epithelial, connective, muscle, and nervous tissues. Epithelial tissue consists of tightly packed cells, which line the cavities inside the body and cover the outside of the body. A primary function of epithelial tissue is protection against injury, invaders, and fluid loss. Connective tissue connects and supports other tissues. It includes fat, bone, cartilage, blood, and fibrous strands such as tendons and ligaments. Muscle tissue consists of long cells that contract. It is the most abundant tissue in most animals. Nervous tissue includes cells that sense stimuli and transmit signals from one part of the body to another.

Answers

IN YOUR NOTEBOOK Sample answer: in the digestive system, because enzymes are needed to break down food

LESSON 7.4

Teach continued

Use Visuals

Use **Figure 7–24** to introduce students to the way specialized cells are organized in humans. Point out the progression from muscle cell, to smooth muscle tissue, etc. Ask students to brainstorm some other kinds of cells in the body that are organized into organs and systems. *(Sample answer: nerve cells→ nervous tissue→brain→nervous system)*

Remind students that plants are multicellular organisms, as well. Ask if there are specializations in plant cells and, if so, what organs there are in plants. *(roots, stems, leaves, flowers)*

DIFFERENTIATED INSTRUCTION

LPR Less Proficient Readers Have students look at **Figure 7–24.** Then, have them reread the text on this page. Help students connect the text to the different parts of the illustration by showing how each of the highlighted words is represented by a part of the figure.

BIOLOGY.com Students can analyze how the compound resveratrol affects mitochondrial function and its implications for human health and longevity in **Data Analysis: Maximizing Mitochondria.**

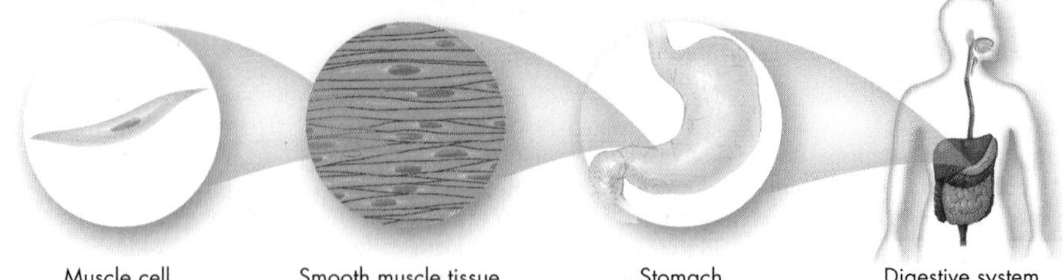

FIGURE 7–24 Levels of Organization From least complex to most complex, the levels of organization in a multicellular organism include cells, tissues, organs, and organ systems.

Levels of Organization The specialized cells of multicellular organisms are organized into tissues, then into organs, and finally into organ systems, as shown in **Figure 7–24.** A **tissue** is a group of similar cells that performs a particular function. Many tasks in the body are too complicated to be carried out by just one type of tissue. In these cases, many groups of tissues work together as an **organ.** For example, each muscle in your body is an individual organ. Within a muscle, however, there is much more than muscle tissue. There are nervous tissues and connective tissues too. Each type of tissue performs an essential task to help the organ function. In most cases, an organ completes a series of specialized tasks. A group of organs that work together to perform a specific function is called an **organ system.** For example, the stomach, pancreas, and intestines work together as the digestive system.

IN NoS.3

Mitochondria Distribution in the Mouse

Scientists studied the composition of several organs in the mouse. They found that some organs and tissues contain more mitochondria than others. They described the amount of mitochondria present as a percentage of total cell volume. The higher the percentage volume made up of mitochondria, the more mitochondria present in the cells of the organ. The data are shown in the graph.

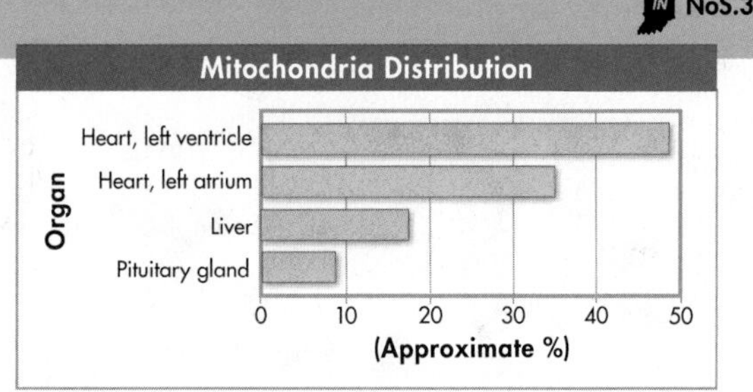

1. **Interpret Graphs** What approximate percentage of cell volume in the mouse liver is composed of mitochondria?
2. **Calculate** Approximately how much more cellular volume is composed of mitochondria in the left ventricle than in the pituitary gland? 
3. **Infer** There are four chambers in the mouse heart, the right and left ventricles, and the right and left atria. Based on the data given, which chamber, the left ventricle or left atrium, do you think pumps blood from the heart to the rest of the body? Explain your answer.

 BIOLOGY.com Search Lesson 7.4 GO • Data Analysis

PURPOSE Students will interpret data to determine the percentage of cell volume taken up by mitochondria in three different mouse organs and suggest the effect that a higher percentage of mitochondria might have on an organ's function.

PLANNING Remind students that bar graphs commonly are used in order to show comparisons.

ANSWERS

1. about 18 percent
2. About 40 percent more cellular volume is composed of mitochondria in the left ventricle. (49% – 9% = 40%)
3. The left ventricle pumps blood from the heart to the rest of the body. It has more mitochondria per cellular volume than the left atrium. Therefore, it probably pumps with more force.

The organization of the body's cells into tissues, organs, and organ systems creates a division of labor among those cells that allows the organism to maintain homeostasis. Specialization and interdependence are two of the remarkable attributes of living things. Appreciating these characteristics is an important step in understanding the nature of living things.

Cellular Communication Cells in a large organism communicate by means of chemical signals that are passed from one cell to another. These cellular signals can speed up or slow down the activities of the cells that receive them and can even cause a cell to change what it is doing in a most dramatic way.

Certain cells, including those in the heart and liver, form connections, or cellular junctions, to neighboring cells. Some of these junctions, like those in **Figure 7–25,** hold cells together firmly. Others allow small molecules carrying chemical messages or signals to pass directly from one cell to the next. To respond to one of these chemical signals, a cell must have a **receptor** to which the signaling molecule can bind. Some receptors are on the cell membrane; receptors for other types of signals are inside the cytoplasm. The chemical signals sent by various types of cells can cause important changes in cellular activity. For example, the electrical signal that causes heart muscle cells to contract begins in a region of the muscle known as the pacemaker. Ions carry that electrical signal from cell to cell through a special connection known as a gap junction, enabling millions of heart muscle cells to contract as one in a single heartbeat. Other junctions hold the cells together, so the force of contraction does not tear the muscle tissue. Both types of junctions are essential for the heart to pump blood effectively.

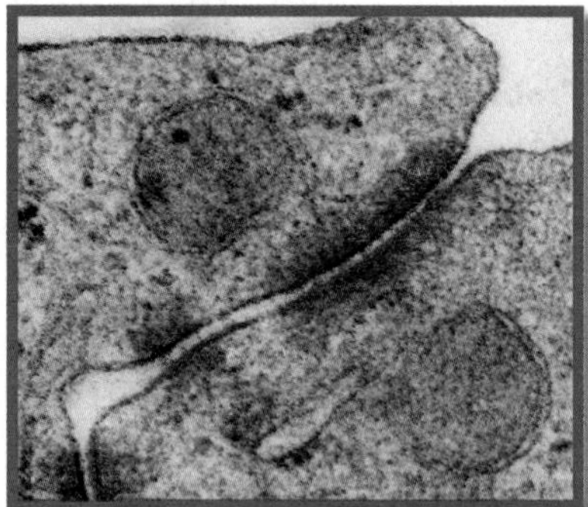

FIGURE 7–25 Cellular Junctions Some junctions, like those seen in dark pink in this micrograph of epithelial cells in the central nervous system (blue and green), hold cells together in tight formations (TEM 21,600×).

7.4 Assessment

IN B.1.3, B.2.1, B.2.6, B.6.3

Review Key Concepts 

1. a. Review What is homeostasis?

b. Explain What do unicellular organisms do to maintain homeostasis?

c. Apply Concepts The contractile vacuole is an organelle found in paramecia, a group of unicellular organisms. Contractile vacuoles pump out fresh water that accumulates in the organisms by osmosis. Explain how this is an example of the way paramecia maintain homeostasis.

2. a. Review What is cellular specialization?

b. Explain How do cellular junctions and receptors help an organism maintain homeostasis?

c. Predict Using what you know about the ways muscles move, predict which organelles would be most common in muscle cells.

WRITE ABOUT SCIENCE

Description

3. Use an area in your life—such as school, sports, or extracurricular activities—to construct an analogy that explains why specialization and communication are necessary for you to function well.

BIOLOGY.com Search (Lesson 7.4) GO • Self-Test • Lesson Assessment

Expand Vocabulary

Explain that in biology, a receptor is a structure that responds to a stimulus. In cellular communication, it is a molecule to which a signaling molecule can bind, producing a change that can affect cell activity. In physiology, it is a structure in the nervous system that detects and responds to an environmental stimulus, such as light.

DIFFERENTIATED INSTRUCTION

LPR Less Proficient Readers Explain how the word *receptor* is related to the word *receive*; a receptor is a receiver. Have students use a dictionary to find meanings and origins of both words.

Assess and Remediate

EVALUATE UNDERSTANDING

Review concepts covered in the lesson by using true/false statements. For example, "Single-celled organisms cannot maintain homeostasis." Have one student tell if the statement is true or false. Have another student justify or revise the answer choice. Then, have students complete the 7.4 Assessment.

REMEDIATION SUGGESTION

L1 Struggling Students If students have trouble with **Question 1c,** have them review in Lesson 7.3 what happens to cells in hypotonic solutions.

BIOLOGY.com Students can check their understanding of lesson concepts with the **Self-Test** assessment. They can then take an online version of the **Lesson Assessment.**

Assessment Answers

1a. Homeostasis is the maintenance of relatively stable internal physical and chemical conditions by an organism.

1b. They maintain homeostasis by growing, responding to changes in their environment, transforming energy, and reproducing.

1c. The contractile vacuole helps maintain water balance in paramecia by expelling excess water that would otherwise accumulate and burst the cell.

2a. Cellular specialization describes how, in multicellular organisms, groups of cells play different, specific roles.

2b. Cellular junctions help organisms maintain homeostasis by connecting cells to their neighbors, thus enabling communication between cells. Receptors allow cells to respond to chemical messages.

2c. Answers may vary. Predictions should note that muscle cells need energy to move and, therefore, probably contain a large number of mitochondria.

WRITE ABOUT SCIENCE

3. Sample answer: The members of a basketball team are like specialized cells, because different members play different roles. For example, the point guard calls the plays and the center shoots the ball. The whole team is like a body system, because team members work together to try to win the game.

CHAPTER LAB

Pre-Lab

Introduce students to the concepts they will explore in the chapter lab by assigning the Pre-Lab questions.

Lab

Tell students they will perform the chapter lab *Detecting Diffusion* described in **Lab Manual A.**

 **Struggling Students** A simpler version of the chapter lab is provided in **Lab Manual B.**

SAFETY

Students should wear goggles, disposable gloves, and aprons. Caution them to handle solutions containing iodine with care. Make sure they wash their hands thoroughly after the lab.

Look online for **Editable Lab Worksheets.**

For corresponding pre-lab in the **Foundation Edition**, see page 184.

IN INDIANA ACADEMIC STANDARDS

For the full text of all standards, see the Course Overview in the front matter of this book.

GUIDED INQUIRY

IN B.2.2 Cell membrane. Also covered: NoS.1, NoS.6.

Pre-Lab: Detecting Diffusion

Problem How can you determine whether solutes are diffusing across a membrane?

Materials dialysis tubing, scissors, metric ruler, 250 mL beakers, twist ties, 10-mL graduated cylinders, 1% starch solution, iodine solution, forceps, 15% glucose solution, glucose test strip

Lab Manual Chapter 7 Lab

Skills Focus Use Models, Infer, Compare and Contrast

Connect to the Big idea The cell membrane forms a thin flexible barrier between a cell and its surroundings. The cell membrane controls what enters the cell and what leaves the cell. Diffusion is the process responsible for much of the movement across a cell membrane. During diffusion, solutes move from an area of high concentration to an area of lower concentration. When water is the molecule that is diffusing, the process is called osmosis. Proteins embedded in the membrane can facilitate the diffusion of many particles, including water. In this lab, you will use dialysis tubing to model the diffusion of small molecules.

Background Questions

a. **Review** What does it mean to say that a membrane is selectively permeable?

b. **Explain** Does the movement of molecules stop when the concentration of a solute is equal on both sides of a membrane? Explain.

c. **Compare and Contrast** What is the main difference between passive transport and active transport?

Pre-Lab Questions

Preview the procedure in the lab manual.

1. **Draw Conclusions** How will you know whether starch has diffused across the membrane in Part A? How will you know whether iodine has diffused across the membrane?
2. **Draw Conclusions** How will you be able to tell whether glucose has diffused across the membrane in Part B?
3. **Use Analogies** How is a window screen similar to a cell membrane?

BIOLOGY.com Search Chapter 7 GO

Visit Chapter 7 online to test yourself on chapter content and to find activities to help you learn.

Untamed Science Video Travel to the ocean's depths with the Untamed Science crew to explore how fish maintain water homeostasis.

Art in Motion View a short animation that explains the different types of active transport.

Art Review Review your understanding of plant and animal cell structures with this activity.

InterActive Art Build your understanding of osmosis and diffusion with these animations.

Visual Analogy Compare the structures of the cell to the parts of a factory.

Data Analysis Analyze data that explains why some cell types have more mitochondria than others.

Tutor Tube Hear suggestions from the tutor for help in remembering cell structures.

Pre-Lab Answers

BACKGROUND QUESTIONS

a. Some substances can pass through the membrane while other substances cannot pass through the membrane.

b. The movement does not stop, but an equal number of molecules move in each direction to maintain equilibrium.

c. The movement of substances through passive transport does not require energy; the movement of substances through active transport requires energy.

PRE-LAB QUESTIONS

1. If the solution outside the tubing turns blue black, then starch diffused out of the tubing. If the solution inside the tubing turns blue black, then iodine diffused into the tubing.
2. A glucose test strip will change color in the presence of glucose.
3. Sample answer: Like a cell membrane, a window screen prevents the passage of some things, such as insects, while allowing other things, such as air, to flow in and out of a house.

7 Study Guide

Big ideas Cellular Basis of Life, Homeostasis

Cells are the basic units of life. Their structures are specifically adapted to their function and the overall goal of maintaining homeostasis. In multicellular organisms, cells may become specialized to carry out a particular function.

7.1 Life Is Cellular

The cell theory states that (1) all living things are made up of cells, (2) cells are the basic units of structure and function in living things, and (3) new cells are produced from existing cells.

Most microscopes use lenses to magnify the image of an object by focusing light or electrons.

Prokaryotic cells do not separate their genetic material within a nucleus. In eukaryotic cells, the nucleus separates the genetic material from the rest of the cell.

cell (191)
cell theory (191)
cell membrane (193)
nucleus (193)
eukaryote (193)
prokaryote (193)

7.2 Cell Structure

The nucleus contains nearly all the cell's DNA and, with it, the coded instructions for making proteins and other important molecules.

Vacuoles store materials like water, salts, proteins, and carbohydrates. Lysosomes break down large molecules into smaller ones that can be used by the cell. They are also involved in breaking down organelles that have outlived their usefulness. The cytoskeleton helps the cell maintain its shape and is also involved in movement.

Proteins are assembled on ribosomes.

Proteins made on the rough ER include those that will be released from the cell as well as many membrane proteins and proteins destined for specialized locations within the cell. The Golgi apparatus then modifies, sorts, and packages proteins and other materials for storage in the cell or release outside the cell.

Chloroplasts capture the energy from sunlight and convert it into food that contains chemical energy in a process called photosynthesis. Mitochondria convert the chemical energy stored in food into compounds that are more convenient for the cell to use.

The cell membrane regulates what enters and leaves the cell and also protects and supports the cell.

cytoplasm (196)
organelle (196)
vacuole (198)
lysosome (198)
cytoskeleton (199)
centriole (199)
ribosome (200)
endoplasmic reticulum (200)
Golgi apparatus (201)
chloroplast (202)
mitochondrion (202)
cell wall (203)
lipid bilayer (204)
selectively permeable (205)

7.3 Cell Transport

Passive transport (including diffusion and osmosis) is the movement of materials across the cell membrane without cellular energy.

The movement of materials against a concentration difference is known as active transport. Active transport requires energy.

diffusion (208)
facilitated diffusion (209)
aquaporin (210)
osmosis (210)
isotonic (210)
hypertonic (210)
hypotonic (210)
osmotic pressure (211)

7.4 Homeostasis and Cells

To maintain homeostasis, unicellular organisms grow, respond to the environment, transform energy, and reproduce.

The cells of multicellular organisms become specialized for particular tasks and communicate with one another to maintain homeostasis.

homeostasis (214)
tissue (216)
organ (216)
organ system (216)
receptor (217)

Think Visually Use the terms *diffusion, facilitated diffusion, osmosis, active transport, endocytosis, phagocytosis, pinocytosis,* and *exocytosis* to create a concept map about the ways substances can move into and out of cells.

Search 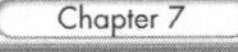   • Match It • Chapter Assessment

UbD Performance Tasks

SUMMATIVE TASK Have students imagine they are small enough to live within a one-celled organism. Have them write a seven-day account describing how the cell obtains, manufactures, and/or uses such things as food, proteins, and sufficient water. Students should describe how they got into the cell and how they will leave. Students need to include all of the parts of the cell they have studied and the processes of active and passive transport.

TRANSFER TASK Have the class plan a series of five newspaper articles that will run in a hypothetical newspaper over a period of five days. Have students decide on five topics that will cover cell structure and function and answer the Essential Question: How are cell structures adapted to their functions? Each group should submit a storyboard showing what the article will say, how it will be illustrated, what its headline will be, and how it will be presented to the class.

Study Online

REVIEW AND ASSESSMENT RESOURCES

Editable Worksheets Pages of Study Workbooks A and B, Lab Manuals A and B, and the Assessment Resources Book are available online. These documents can be easily edited using a word-processing program.

Lesson Overview Have students reread the Lesson Overviews to help them study chapter concepts.

Vocabulary Review The *Flash Cards* and *Match It* provide an interactive way to review chapter vocabulary.

Chapter Assessment Have students take an online version of the Chapter 7 Assessment.

Standardized Test Prep Students can take an online version of the Standardized Test Prep. You will receive their scores along with ideas for remediation.

Diagnostic and Benchmark Tests Use these tests to monitor your students' progress and supply remediation.

Answers

THINK VISUALLY

Answers may vary. Check the accuracy of concept maps. To make certain that students clearly understand the differences among these concepts, suggest they add a caption or small drawing by each term.

ASSESSMENT

Lesson 7.1

UNDERSTAND KEY CONCEPTS

1. d **2.** b **3.** b

4. Tables can have two columns. Left column head should be Scientist, with rows Hooke, Schleiden, Schwann, and Virchow. Right column head should be Contribution, with rows cork "cells," plants made of cells, all animals made of cells, existing cells divide to make new cells.

THINK CRITICALLY

5. a light microscope

6. Alike: both have a cell membrane, DNA, and ribosomes; Different: prokaryotic DNA is not found in a nucleus.

Lesson 7.2

UNDERSTAND KEY CONCEPTS

7. c **8.** b **9.** a

10. Students' drawings should be similar to the nucleus in **Figure 7–7,** with nuclear membrane, nuclear pores, nucleolus, and chromatin labeled and their functions identified.

11. Ribosomes assemble proteins according to coded directions from DNA.

12. The Golgi apparatus modifies, sorts, and packages proteins and other materials from the ER for storage or release through the cell membrane.

THINK CRITICALLY

13. Because enzymes are proteins, ribosomes, the endoplasmic reticulum, and the Golgi apparatus would be involved in producing them.

14. Prokaryotes (Pro) and Eukaryotes (Eu)

cell membrane: Pro and Eu

mitochondria: Eu

ribosome: Pro and Eu

Golgi apparatus: Eu

nucleus: Eu

cytoplasm: Pro and Eu

DNA: Pro and Eu

Lesson 7.3

UNDERSTAND KEY CONCEPTS

15. d **16.** c

7 Assessment

The numbers following the questions refer to Indiana's Academic Standards for Biology I.

7.1 Life Is Cellular

Understand Key Concepts

1. In many cells, the structure that controls the cell's activities is the B.2.1
a. cell membrane. **c.** nucleolus.
b. organelle. **d.** nucleus.

2. Despite differences in size and shape, at some point all cells have DNA and a B.2.1
a. cell wall. **c.** mitochondrion.
b. cell membrane. **d.** nucleus.

3. What distinguishes a eukaryotic cell from a prokaryotic cell is the presence of
a. a cell wall. **c.** DNA.
b. a nucleus. **d.** ribosomes.

4. Create a table that summarizes the contributions made to the cell theory by Robert Hooke, Matthias Schleiden, Theodor Schwann, and Rudolf Virchow. NoS.10

Think Critically

5. Apply Concepts If you wanted to observe a living organism—an amoeba, for example—which type of microscope would you use?

6. Compare and Contrast How are prokaryotic and eukaryotic cells alike? How do they differ?

7.2 Cell Structure

Understand Key Concepts

7. In eukaryotic cells, chromosomes carrying genetic information are found in the B.2.1
a. ribosomes. **c.** nucleus.
b. lysosomes. **d.** cell membrane.

8. The organelles that break down lipids, carbohydrates, and proteins into small molecules that can be used by the cell are called B.2.1
a. vacuoles.
b. lysosomes.
c. ribosomes.
d. microfilaments.

9. Cell membranes consist mainly of B.2.1, B.2.2
a. lipid bilayers. **c.** carbohydrates.
b. protein pumps. **d.** proteins.

10. Draw a cell nucleus. Label and give the function of the following structures: chromatin, nucleolus, and nuclear envelope. B.2.1

11. What is the function of a ribosome? B.2.1, B.2.4

12. Describe the role of the Golgi apparatus. B.2.1, B.2.4

Think Critically

13. Infer The pancreas, an organ present in certain animals, produces enzymes used elsewhere in the animals' digestive systems. Which type of cell structure(s) might produce those enzymes? Explain your answer. B.2.4

14. Classify For each of the following, indicate if the structure is found only in eukaryotes, or if it is found in eukaryotes and prokaryotes: cell membrane, mitochondria, ribosome, Golgi apparatus, nucleus, cytoplasm, and DNA. B.2.1

7.3 Cell Transport

Understand Key Concepts

15. The movement of water molecules across a selectively permeable membrane is known as B.2.2
a. exocytosis. **c.** endocytosis.
b. phagocytosis. **d.** osmosis.

16. A substance that moves by passive transport tends to move
a. away from the area of equilibrium.
b. away from the area where it is less concentrated.
c. away from the area where it is more concentrated.
d. toward the area where it is more concentrated.

17. Describe the process of diffusion, including a detailed explanation of equilibrium.

18. What is the relationship between diffusion and osmosis? By definition, what's the only substance that undergoes osmosis?

19. What is the difference between passive transport and active transport? B.2.2

220 Chapter 7 • Assessment

17. In diffusion, particles move randomly from areas of higher concentration to areas of lower concentration until equilibrium is reached. At equilibrium, the concentration is more or less the same throughout.

18. Osmosis is the diffusion of water through a selectively permeable membrane. Only water can move by osmosis.

19. Passive transport acts to equalize concentrations on both sides of the membrane and does not require energy. Active transport requires energy and moves materials against a concentration gradient.

Think Critically

20. **Predict** The beaker in the diagram below has a selectively permeable membrane separating two solutions. Assume that both water and salt can pass freely through the membrane. When equilibrium is reached, will the fluid levels be the same as they are now? Explain.

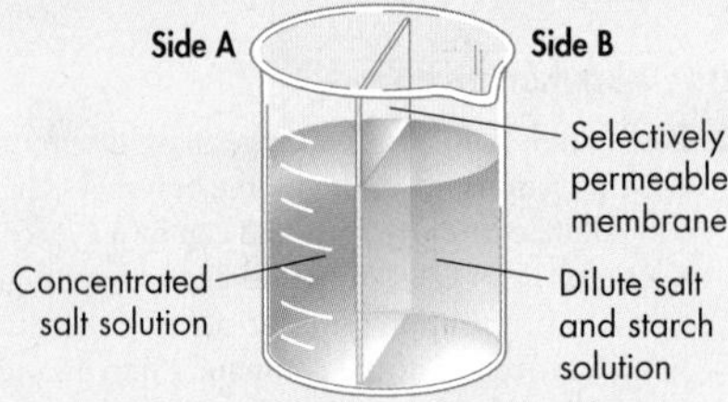

21. **Predict** What would happen to a sample of your red blood cells if they were placed in a hypotonic solution? Explain.
22. **Design Experiments** You are given food coloring and three beakers. The first beaker contains water at room temperature, the second beaker contains ice water, and the third beaker contains hot water. Design a controlled experiment to determine the effects of temperature on the rate of diffusion. Be sure to state your hypothesis.

7.4 Homeostasis and Cells

Understand Key Concepts

23. Which of the following is true of ALL single-celled organisms?
    a. They are all prokaryotes.
    b. They are all bacteria.
    c. They all reproduce.
    d. They all have a nucleus.
24. A tissue is composed of a group of
    a. similar cells.
    b. related organelles.
    c. organ systems.
    d. related organs.
25. Explain the relationship among cell specialization, multicellular organisms, and homeostasis. B.2.6, B.6.3
26. Describe the relationship among cells, tissues, organs, and organ systems.

solve the CHAPTER MYSTERY

DEATH BY ... WATER?

During the race, Michelle drank plenty of water, but she didn't replace the salts she lost due to sweating. As a result, her blood became hypotonic, and osmotic pressure led the cells in her brain (and throughout her body) to swell.

As Michelle's blood became more dilute, cells in her brain sent chemical signals to her kidneys to stop removing sodium chloride and other salts from her bloodstream. However, as she continued to sweat, she continued to lose salt through her skin.

By the end of the race, Michelle had lost a large quantity of salt and minerals and had taken in so much water that homeostasis had broken down, and her cells were damaged by unregulated osmotic pressure.

When Michelle was rushed to the hospital, the doctors discovered that she was suffering from hyponatremia, or water intoxication. Left untreated, this condition can lead to death.

1. **Relate Cause and Effect** When a person sweats, water and essential solutes called electrolytes are lost from body fluid. Michelle drank lots of water but did not replace lost electrolytes. What effect did this have on her cells?
2. **Infer** Had Michelle alternated between drinking water and a sports drink with electrolytes would her condition be the same?
3. **Infer** Do you think that hyponatremia results from osmosis or active transport? Explain your reasoning. B.2.2
4. **Connect to the Big idea** Explain how hyponatremia disrupts homeostasis in the body.

     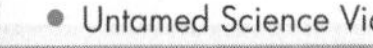
BIOLOGY.com Search Chapter 7 GO • Untamed Science Video • Chapter Mystery

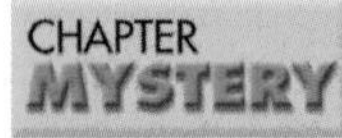
CHAPTER MYSTERY Have students reread the clues and then read the Chapter Mystery solution. Ask students to use **Figure 7–18** to review conditions that can affect the flow of water into and out of cells and the osmotic pressure in the cells. Lack of electrolytes in the water Michelle was drinking upset the homeostasis of her body.

Ask Besides water, what substances did Michelle lose in sweat? *(sodium and other electrolytes)*

Ask How did the loss of those substances affect homeostasis in her body? *(Loss of those substances drastically upset the equilibrium between water in her cells and water in her bloodstream.)*

CHAPTER MYSTERY ANSWERS

1. Drinking water without replacing electrolytes increased water concentration in her bloodstream in comparison to water concentration in the cytoplasm of her cells. Water diffused into her cells.
2. No, taking in electrolytes would have restored equilibrium between the electrolytes in her cells and those in her bloodstream.
3. Hyponatremia results from osmosis, because it happens when cells are in a hypotonic solution and water moves passively into the cells.
4. Big idea Sample answer: Hyponatremia disrupts homeostasis in the body, because the high concentration of water in the bloodstream results in the movement of water into cells. The excessive water interferes with the cells' functioning, and may even destroy the cells.

Students can watch **Untamed Science: Fishing for the Right Balance** to find out how saltwater fishes maintain water homeostasis.

THINK CRITICALLY

20. The diffusing salt particles (the sodium and chloride ions that make up salt) and water molecules will eventually reach equilibrium without a change in the fluid on either side.
21. The blood cells would swell and burst, because the concentration of solute is higher inside the cells than in the solution outside. Therefore, the solution outside the cells would tend to diffuse into the cells.
22. Answers may vary. Students might hypothesize that diffusion will take place most rapidly in the beaker with hot water. Experiments should include the following steps: Drops of food coloring will be placed in the beakers at the same time, and the same number of drops will be placed in each beaker. Diffusion in the three beakers will be observed and compared after a set amount of time; alternatively, the time that it takes each beaker to reach a uniform color will be measured.

Lesson 7.4

UNDERSTAND KEY CONCEPTS

23. c **24.** a

25. In multicellular organisms, each cell has a specialized role to play to maintain homeostasis, so all cells must work together to maintain homeostasis.
26. Groups of similar cells that perform a particular function form tissues. Different types of tissues that perform a specific function work together as an organ. A group of organs that work together for a specific function form an organ system.

THINK CRITICALLY

27. Predictions should say that muscle cells contain more mitochondria. Because muscle cells are responsible for movement, they require more energy than skin cells.

28. If a person needs a pacemaker, his or her heart cells may have lost some of their ability to send chemical messages or to respond to messages.

Connecting Concepts

USE SCIENCE GRAPHICS

29. Prokaryotes: *Escherichia coli, Streptococcus pneumoniae*

Eukaryotes: human erythrocyte, human ovum, *Saccharomyces cerevisiae*

30. In general, prokaryotes are much smaller than eukaryotes.

31. Based upon size, *Chlamydomonas reinhardtii* is likely to be a eukaryote.

WRITE ABOUT SCIENCE

32. Sample answer: Companies that market high-solute drinks should not say that the drinks quench thirst. If you drink something with a high solute concentration, water will move out of the body cells and into the bloodstream. This can actually increase thirst.

33. Active transport is one way in which organisms maintain homeostasis. For example, an amoeba uses phagocytosis to take in food. The amoeba needs the food for energy and growth.

Think Critically

27. Infer Would you expect skin cells to contain more or fewer mitochondria than muscle cells? Explain your answer. B.2.3, B.2.5

28. Infer Pacemakers are devices that help keep heart muscle cells contracting at a steady rate. If a person needs a pacemaker, what does that suggest about his or her heart cells' ability to send and receive chemical messages?

Connecting Concepts

Use Science Graphics NoS.3

Use the data table to answer questions 29–31.

Cell Sizes

Cell	Approximate Diameter
Escherichia coli (bacterium)	0.5–0.8 μm
Human erythrocyte (red blood cell)	6–8 μm
Human ovum (egg cell)	100 μm
Saccharomyces cerevisiae (yeast)	5–10 μm
Streptococcus pneumoniae (bacterium)	0.5–1.3 μm

29. Classify Classify each of the cells listed as prokaryotic or eukaryotic.

30. Compare and Contrast Compare the sizes of the prokaryotic cells and eukaryotic cells.

31. Infer *Chlamydomonas reinhardtii* is a single-celled organism with an approximate diameter of 10 μm. Is it more likely a prokaryotic or eukaryotic organism? Explain your answer.

Write About Science NoS.3

32. Persuasion Different beverages have different concentrations of solutes. Some beverages have low solute concentrations and can be a source of water for body cells. Other beverages have high solute concentrations and can actually dehydrate your body cells. Should companies that market high-solute drinks say that the drinks quench thirst?

33. Assess the Big idea What is the relationship between active transport and homeostasis? Give one example of active transport in an organism, and explain how the organism uses energy to maintain homeostasis. B.2.2

Analyzing Data

IN NoS.3

Most materials entering the cell pass across the cell membrane by diffusion. In general, the larger the molecule, the slower the molecule diffuses across the membrane. The graph shows the sizes of several molecules that can diffuse across a lipid bilayer.

Size of Molecules

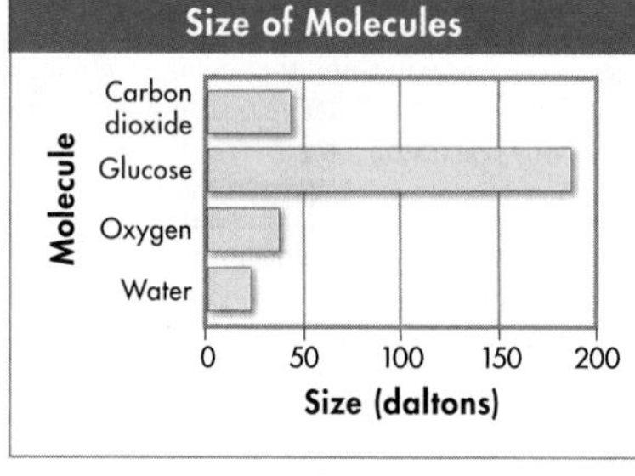

34. Calculate By approximately what percentage is a molecule of carbon dioxide smaller than a molecule of glucose? MATH

a. 25% **b.** 50% **c.** 75% **d.** 100%

35. Formulate Hypotheses Which of the following is a logical hypothesis based on the graph shown?

a. Cells contain more glucose than oxygen.

b. Oxygen molecules diffuse across the cell membrane faster than water molecules.

c. Glucose molecules must cross the cell membrane by active transport.

d. Carbon dioxide crosses the cell membrane faster than glucose.

PURPOSE Students will calculate the relative size of molecules and hypothesize how the size of molecules affects their diffusion.

PLANNING Review how to calculate percent differences. Then, compare specific percent differences with more familiar indicators of difference, e.g., by equating a twofold increase with a 100 percent increase.

ANSWERS

34. c

35. d

Standardized Test Practice for Indiana

Multiple Choice

1. Animal cells have all of the following EXCEPT
   A mitochondria.
   B chloroplasts.
   C a nucleus.
   D a cell membrane. B.2.1, B.2.5

2. The nucleus includes all of the following structures EXCEPT
   A cytoplasm. C DNA.
   B a nuclear envelope. D a nucleolus. B.2.1

3. The human brain is an example of a(n)
   A cell.
   B tissue.
   C organ.
   D organ system.

4. Which cell structures are sometimes found attached to the endoplasmic reticulum?
   A chloroplasts
   B nuclei
   C mitochondria
   D ribosomes B.2.1

5. Which process always involves the movement of materials from inside the cell to outside the cell?
   A phagocytosis
   B exocytosis
   C endocytosis
   D osmosis B.2.2

6. Which of the following is an example of active transport?
   A facilitated diffusion
   B osmosis
   C diffusion
   D endocytosis B.2.2

7. The difference between prokaryotic and eukaryotic cells involves the presence of
   A a nucleus.
   B genetic material in the form of DNA.
   C chloroplasts.
   D a cell membrane. B.2.1, B.2.5

Questions 8–10

In an experiment, plant cells were placed in sucrose solutions of varying concentrations, and the rate at which they absorbed sucrose from the solution was measured. The results are shown in the graph below.

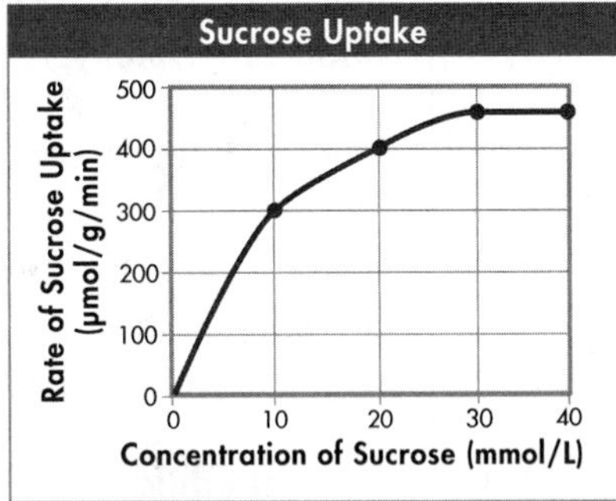

8. In this experiment, sucrose probably entered the cells by means of
   A endocytosis. C osmosis.
   B phagocytosis. D active transport. B.2.2

9. The graph shows that as the concentration of sucrose increased from 10 to 30 mmol/L, the plant cells
   A took in sucrose more slowly.
   B took in sucrose more quickly.
   C failed to take in more sucrose.
   D secreted sucrose more slowly.

10. Based on the graph, the rate of sucrose uptake
    A increased at a constant rate from 0 to 30 mmol/L.
    B decreased at varying rates from 0 to 30 mmol/L.
    C was less at 25 mmol/L than at 5 mmol/L.
    D was constant between 30 and 40 mmol/L.

Open-Ended Response

11. What would you expect to happen if you placed a typical cell in fresh water? B.2.2

If You Have Trouble With . . .

Question	1	2	3	4	5	6	7	8	9	10	11
See Lesson	7.2	7.2	7.4	7.2	7.3	7.3	7.1	7.3	7.3	7.3	7.3

Answers

1. B
2. A
3. C
4. D
5. B
6. D
7. A
8. D
9. A
10. D
11. A typical cell in fresh water will take in water, swell, and may burst.

Test-Taking Tip

INTERPRET GRAPHS

Tell students that when answering a question based on experimental data, they should read the description of the experiment carefully to determine the steps followed. They should also examine the description of the experiment and the labels on the graph axes to determine the independent and dependent variables. Suggest they look for any trends in the data. For example, when studying a graph, they should ask, "If *x* increases, what happens to *y*?"

Photosynthesis

Chapter Contents	IN	Time	Core Resources
Chapter Preview			**Student Edition,** pp. 224–225 **Chapter Mystery,** p. 225
8.1 Energy and Life Chemical Energy and ATP • Heterotrophs and Autotrophs • *Biology & History: Understanding Photosynthesis*	NoS.6, B.1.2, B.3.1, B.3.2, B.3.3, B.3.5	1/2 period 1/4 block	**Student Edition,** pp. 226–229 **Study Workbook A** 8.1 Worksheets L2 **Biology.com** *Visual Analogy:* ATP as a Charged Battery **Assessment Resources Book** Visual Quiz L2
8.2 Photosynthesis: An Overview Chlorophyll and Chloroplasts • High-Energy Electrons • An Overview of Photosynthesis	NoS.6, B.2.3, B.3.1	1 period 1/2 block	**Student Edition,** pp. 230–234 Inquiry 8.2 Quick Lab, p. 234 L2 **Study Workbook A** 8.2 Worksheets L2 **Biology.com** *InterActive Art:* Photosynthesis • *Data Analysis:* Shedding Light on Marine Algae **Assessment Resources Book** Visual Quiz L2
8.3 The Process of Photosynthesis The Light-Dependent Reactions: Generating ATP and NADPH • The Light-Independent Reactions: Producing Sugars • Factors Affecting Photosynthesis	NoS.3, B.2.3, B.3.1	1 1/2 periods 3/4 block	**Student Edition,** pp. 235–241 Inquiry 8.3 Analyzing Data, p. 240 L2 **Study Workbook A** 8.3 Worksheets L2 **Biology.com** *Art in Motion:* Light-Dependent Reactions • *Art Review:* Light-Independent Reactions **Assessment Resources Book** Visual Quiz L2
Chapter Pre-Lab	NoS.1	1 period 1/2 block	**Student Edition,** p. 242 L2 **Lab Manual A** *Plant Pigments and Photosynthesis* L2

Differentiated Instruction Tools

Study Workbook B includes worksheets with lesson-level differentiated instruction support and explanations of differentiated instruction teaching strategies.

Lab Manual B includes skills labs, simplified chapter labs, and hands-on activities.

ELL Handbook explains ways to make *Biology* more accessible to ELL students.

Spanish Study Workbook is a Spanish translation of Study Workbook A.

Multilingual Glossary is the glossary translated into ten languages.

Differentiated Instruction Key

- L1 Special Needs or Struggling Students
- ELL English Language Learners
- LPR Less Proficient Readers
- L2 On-Level Students
- L3 Advanced Students

Additional Resources

Biology.com Untamed Science Video • Vocabulary Flash Cards

Study Workbook B 8.1 Worksheets L1 ELL LPR
Spanish Study Workbook 8.1 Worksheets ELL
Biology.com 8.1 Lesson Overview • 8.1 Lesson Notes • 8.1 Self-Test • 8.1 Lesson Assessment

Study Workbook B 8.2 Worksheets L1 ELL LPR
Spanish Study Workbook 8.2 Worksheets ELL
Biology.com *Visual Analogy:* Carrying Electrons • *Tutor Tube:* Sorting Out Light-Independent and Light-Dependent Reactions • 8.2 Lesson Overview • 8.2 Lesson Notes • 8.2 Self-Test • 8.2 Lesson Assessment

Study Workbook B 8.3 Worksheets L1 ELL LPR
Spanish Study Workbook 8.3 Worksheets ELL
Biology.com 8.3 Lesson Overview • 8.3 Lesson Notes • 8.3 Self-Test • 8.3 Lesson Assessment

Lab Manual B *Plant Pigments and Photosynthesis* • Data Analysis: *Rates of Photosynthesis* L1 ELL LPR

Chapter Review

Student Edition Study Guide, p. 243 L2
Study Workbook A Chapter 8 Vocabulary Review L2 • Chapter 8 Chapter Mystery/21st Century Skills Activity L2 L3
Transparencies, pp. 99–110 L1 ELL LPR L2
Biology.com Untamed Science Video • Editable Worksheets of Study Workbooks A and B and Lab Manuals A and B • Chapter 8 Flash Cards and Crossword Puzzle

Untamed Science DVD • Classroom Resources CD (includes lesson presentations and editable worksheets)

Chapter Assessment

Student Edition Assessment, pp. 244–247 L2
Study Workbook B Chapter 8 Chapter Review L1 ELL LPR • Chapter 8 Taking a Standardized Test L1 ELL LPR
Assessment Resources Book Chapter 8 Test A L2 • Chapter 8 Test B L1 ELL LPR
Biology.com Chapter 8 Assessment • Editable Worksheets of Chapter 8 Visual Quizzes and Chapter 8 Tests A and B

Exam*View* *Assessment Suite* • Classroom Resources CD (includes lesson presentations and editable worksheets)

Time: 1 period, 1/2 block

Pressed for Time?

Preview the Chapter Introduce students to the vocabulary terms for Lesson 8.1 and preview Figure 8–7.

Cover the Chapter Quickly Have students read all of Lesson 8.1 and all of Lesson 8.2, focusing on Figure 8–7.

Assess Assign the 8.1 Assessment, the 8.2 Assessment, and questions 1–17 in the Chapter 8 Assessment.

CHAPTER 8

Connect to the Big Idea

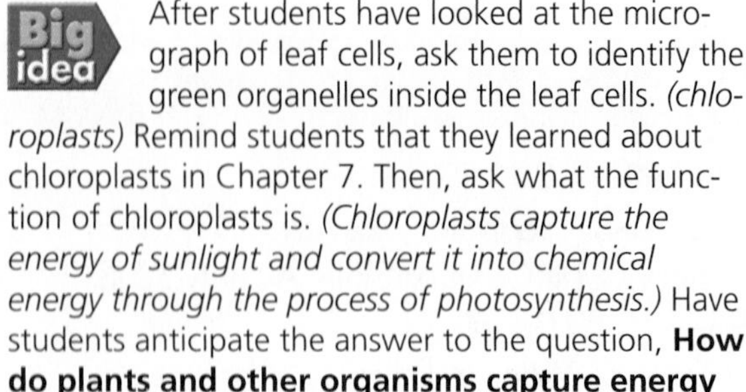

After students have looked at the micrograph of leaf cells, ask them to identify the green organelles inside the leaf cells. *(chloroplasts)* Remind students that they learned about chloroplasts in Chapter 7. Then, ask what the function of chloroplasts is. *(Chloroplasts capture the energy of sunlight and convert it into chemical energy through the process of photosynthesis.)* Have students anticipate the answer to the question, **How do plants and other organisms capture energy from the sun?**

Finally, help students make a connection between energy from the sun, photosynthesis, and the food we eat. If you have studied ecology in Unit 2, remind students of the concepts of food chains, primary producers, and consumers. Then, ask if the energy we get from eating food is the same energy that plants harness from sunlight.

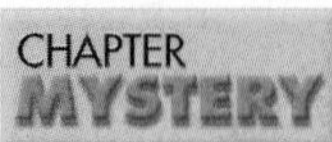

CHAPTER MYSTERY Have students read over the Chapter Mystery and predict how they think the willow tree gained the extra 75 kilograms in Jan van Helmont's investigation. Ask them what process occurring at the cellular level in the plant might be connected to its gain in mass. *(photosynthesis)* Explain that the Chapter Mystery image is a sixteenth-century watering can.

BIOLOGY.com Have students preview the chapter vocabulary using the **Flash Cards.**

IN INDIANA ACADEMIC STANDARDS

For the full text of all standards, see the Course Overview in the front matter of this book.

Key standards: Chapter 8 covers key ideas from Standard 2: Cellular Structure and Standard 3: Matter Cycles and Energy Transfer, including **B.2.3** Mitochondria and chloroplasts, **B.3.1** Photosynthesis, and **B.3.2** Cellular respiration.

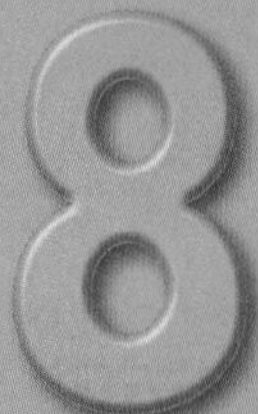

8 Photosynthesis

Big idea Cellular Basis of Life

Q: How do plants and other organisms capture energy from the sun?

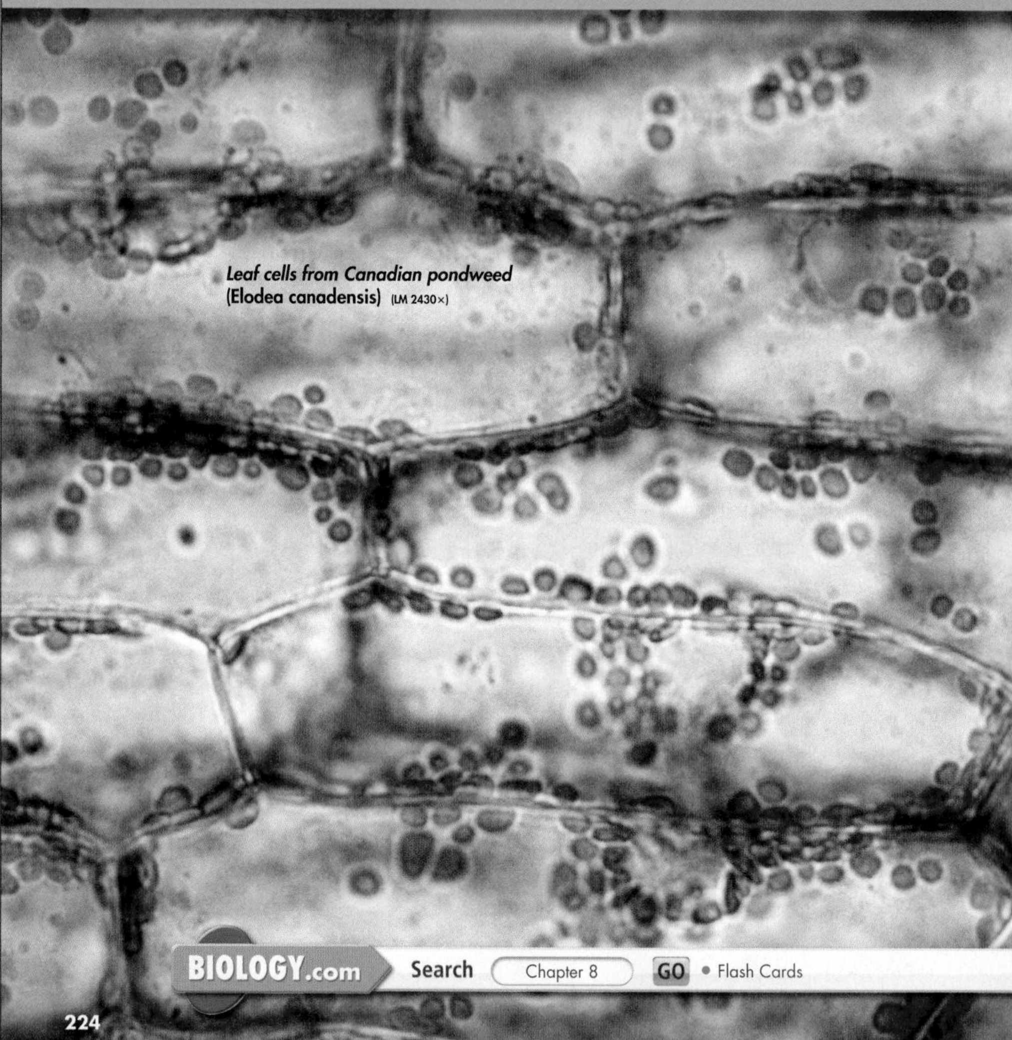

Leaf cells from Canadian pondweed (Elodea canadensis) (LM 2430×)

BIOLOGY.com Search Chapter 8 GO • Flash Cards

UbD Understanding by Design

In Chapter 8, students learn about the process of photosynthesis and further explore the Enduring Understanding of how *a cell is the basic unit of life; the processes that occur at the cellular level provide the energy and basic structure organisms need to survive.* Clearly, the ability of photosynthetic cells to harness the sun's energy gives them a special function in the biosphere. The Big Idea, Essential Question, and Guiding Questions shown in the graphic organizer at the right help frame students' exploration.

PERFORMANCE GOALS

In Chapter 8, students will learn about the organisms and cellular structures involved in photosynthesis as well as the two stages of chemical reactions that make up the process. They explore analogies that help them understand the function of ATP and electron carriers as well as complete an activity in which they observe a byproduct of photosynthesis—oxygen—collecting on the leaves of a water plant.

INDIANA ACADEMIC STANDARDS FOR SCIENCE

Nature of Science NoS.1, NoS.3, NoS.6; **Cellular Chemistry** B.1.2; **Cellular Structure** B.2.3; **Matter Cycles and Energy Transfer** B.3.1, B.3.2, B.3.3, B.3.5. See lessons for details.

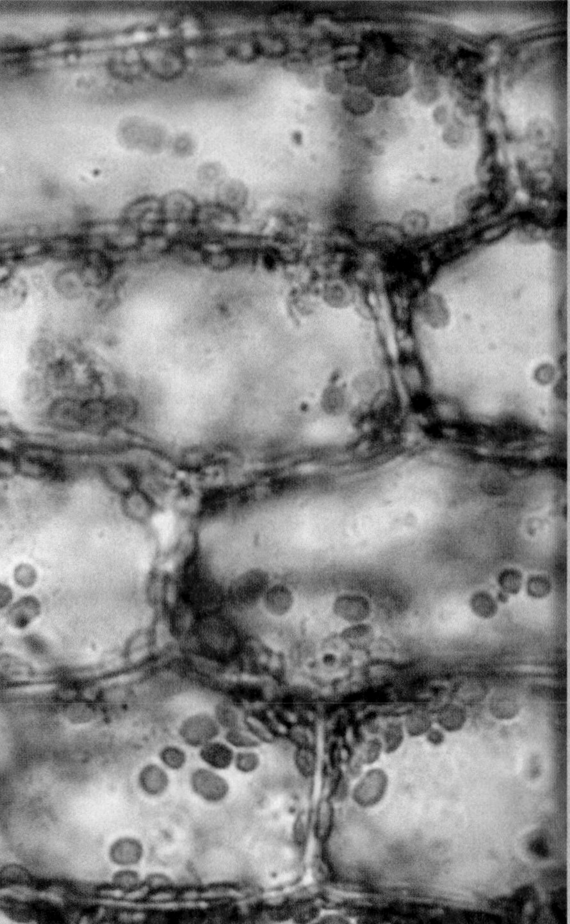

- Untamed Science Video
- Chapter Mystery

CHAPTER **MYSTERY**

OUT OF THIN AIR?

One of the earliest clues as to how photosynthesis works came from a simple study of plant growth. When a tiny seed grows into a massive tree, where does all its extra mass come from? More than 300 years ago, a Flemish physician named Jan van Helmont decided to find out. He planted a young willow tree, with a mass of just 2 kilograms, in a pot with 90 kilograms of dry soil. He watered the plant as needed and allowed it to grow in bright sunlight. Five years later, he carefully removed the tree from the pot and weighed it. It had a mass of about 77 kilograms. Where did the extra 75 kilograms come from? The soil, the water—or, maybe, right out of thin air? As you read this chapter, look for clues to help you discover where the willow tree's extra mass came from. Then, solve the mystery.

Never Stop Exploring Your World. Understanding Jan van Helmont's experiments is just the beginning. Take a video field trip with the ecogeeks of Untamed Science to see where this mystery leads.

Chapter 8 Big Idea: Cellular Basis of Life

Chapter 8 EQ: How do plants and other organisms capture energy from the sun?

- **8.1 GQ:** How do organisms store energy?
- **8.2 GQ:** What cellular structures and molecules are involved in photosynthesis?
- **8.3 GQ:** How do photosynthetic organisms convert the sun's energy into chemical energy?

What's Online

Extend your reach by using these and other digital assets offered at **Biology.com**.

CHAPTER MYSTERY
The Chapter Mystery explores the question: As a tree grows and gains mass, where does the mass come from?

UNTAMED SCIENCE VIDEO
Students go to Panama with researchers looking into how plants respond to increased levels of CO_2.

VISUAL ANALOGIES
Students use analogies to understand how cells can release energy stored in ATP, and how high-energy electrons can be carried from one place to another in a cell.

INTERACTIVE ART
Students interact with the reactants and products of photosynthesis.

TUTOR TUBE
Short, online tutorials help students identify the reactants and products of photosynthesis.

ART IN MOTION
This short animation shows how the light-dependent reactions of photosynthesis proceed.

ART REVIEW
Students drag and drop figure labels to explore the light-independent reactions.

DATA ANALYSIS
Students gather and analyze data about photosynthesis in marine algae.

LESSON 8.1

Getting Started

Objectives

8.1.1 Describe the role of ATP in cellular activities.

8.1.2 Explain where plants get the energy they need to produce food.

Student Resources

Study Workbooks A and B, 8.1 Worksheets

Spanish Study Workbook, 8.1 Worksheets

 Lesson Overview • Lesson Notes • Activity: Visual Analogy • Assessment: Self-Test, Lesson Assessment

 For corresponding lesson in the **Foundation Edition**, see pages 192–194.

Activate Prior Knowledge

Show students a living plant, and ask what they think would happen if the plant were watered but kept away from light for several weeks. *(The plant would probably turn yellow and not grow much.)* Then, ask how plants use light to survive and grow. *(They use the energy from sunlight to carry out photosynthesis.)* Tell students that in this chapter they will learn how plant cells capture and use the energy in sunlight.

IN INDIANA ACADEMIC STANDARDS

For the full text of all standards, see the Course Overview in the front matter of this book.

B.3.2 Describe how most organisms can combine and recombine the elements contained in sugar molecules into a variety of biologically essential compounds by utilizing the energy from cellular respiration.

8.1 Energy and Life

IN B.3.2 Cellular respiration. Also covered: NoS.6, B.1.2, B.3.1, B.3.3, B.3.5.

Key Questions

Why is ATP useful to cells?

What happens during the process of photosynthesis?

Vocabulary

adenosine triphosphate (ATP) • heterotroph • autotroph • photosynthesis

Taking Notes

Compare/Contrast Table As you read, create a table that compares autotrophs and heterotrophs. Think about how they obtain energy, and include a few examples of each.

BUILD Vocabulary

ACADEMIC WORDS The verb **obtain** means "to get" or "to gain." Organisms must obtain energy in order to carry out life functions.

THINK ABOUT IT Homeostasis is hard work. Just to stay alive, organisms and the cells within them have to grow and develop, move materials around, build new molecules, and respond to environmental changes. Plenty of energy is needed to accomplish all this work. What powers so much activity, and where does that power come from?

Chemical Energy and ATP

Why is ATP useful to cells?

Energy is the ability to do work. Nearly every activity in modern society depends upon energy. When a car runs out of fuel—more precisely, out of the chemical energy in gasoline—it comes to a sputtering halt. Without electrical energy, lights, appliances, and computers stop working. Living things depend on energy, too. Sometimes the need for energy is easy to see. It takes plenty of energy to play soccer or other sports. However, there are times when that need is less obvious. Even when you are sleeping, your cells are quietly busy using energy to build new molecules, contract muscles, and carry out active transport. Simply put, without the ability to obtain and use energy, life would cease to exist.

Energy comes in many forms, including light, heat, and electricity. Energy can be stored in chemical compounds, too. For example, when you light a candle, the wax melts, soaks into the wick, and is burned. As the candle burns, chemical bonds between carbon and hydrogen atoms in the wax are broken. New bonds then form between these atoms and oxygen, producing CO_2 and H_2O (carbon dioxide and water). These new bonds are at a lower energy state than the original chemical bonds in the wax. The energy lost is released as heat and light in the glow of the candle's flame.

Living things use chemical fuels as well. One of the most important compounds that cells use to store and release energy is **adenosine triphosphate** (uh DEN uh seen try FAHS fayt), abbreviated **ATP.** As shown in **Figure 8–1,** ATP consists of adenine, a 5-carbon sugar called ribose, and three phosphate groups. As you'll see, those phosphate groups are the key to ATP's ability to store and release energy.

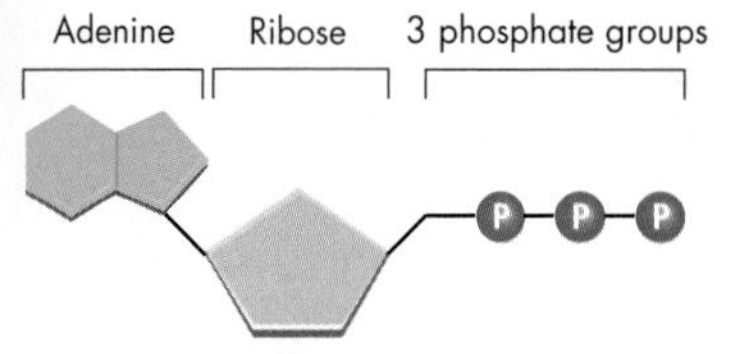

FIGURE 8–1 ATP ATP is the basic energy source used by all types of cells.

UbD Teach for Understanding

ENDURING UNDERSTANDING A cell is the basic unit of life; the processes that occur at the cellular level provide the energy and basic structure organisms need to survive.

GUIDING QUESTION How do organisms store energy?

EVIDENCE OF UNDERSTANDING *After students have finished the lesson, this assessment should show their understanding of how cells use ATP as an energy source for cell activities.* Have students work in pairs to create a newspaper-style comic strip that shows how cells use ATP to get the energy they need to carry out cell activities. Ask students to also include how ATP molecules store and release energy. Tell students the strip should be 3–5 panels long, and they can draw the cartoon figures in any way they want.

Storing Energy Adenosine diphosphate (ADP) is a compound that looks almost like ATP, except that it has two phosphate groups instead of three. This difference is the key to the way in which living things store energy. When a cell has energy available, it can store small amounts of it by adding phosphate groups to ADP molecules, producing ATP. As seen in **Figure 8–2,** ADP is like a rechargeable battery that powers the machinery of the cell.

Releasing Energy Cells can release the energy stored in ATP by the controlled breaking of the chemical bonds between the second and third phosphate groups. Because a cell can add or subtract these phosphate groups, it has an efficient way of storing and releasing energy as needed. **ATP can easily release and store energy by breaking and re-forming the bonds between its phosphate groups. This characteristic of ATP makes it exceptionally useful as a basic energy source for all cells.**

Using Biochemical Energy One way cells use the energy provided by ATP is to carry out active transport. Many cell membranes contain sodium-potassium pumps, membrane proteins that pump sodium ions (Na^+) out of the cell and potassium ions (K^+) into it. ATP provides the energy that keeps this pump working, maintaining a carefully regulated balance of ions on both sides of the cell membrane. In addition, ATP powers movement, providing the energy for motor proteins that contract muscle and power the wavelike movement of cilia and flagella.

Energy from ATP powers other important events in the cell, including the synthesis of proteins and responses to chemical signals at the cell surface. The energy from ATP can even be used to produce light. In fact, the blink of a firefly on a summer night comes from an enzyme that is powered by ATP!

ATP is such a useful source of energy that you might think cells would be packed with ATP to get them through the day—but this is not the case. In fact, most cells have only a small amount of ATP—enough to last for a few seconds of activity. Why? Even though ATP is a great molecule for transferring energy, it is not a good one for storing large amounts of energy over the long term. A single molecule of the sugar glucose, for example, stores more than 90 times the energy required to add a phosphate group to ADP to produce ATP. Therefore, it is more efficient for cells to keep only a small supply of ATP on hand. Instead, cells can regenerate ATP from ADP as needed by using the energy in foods like glucose. As you will see, that's exactly what they do.

In Your Notebook *With respect to energy, how are ATP and glucose similar? How are they different?*

VISUAL ANALOGY

ATP AS A CHARGED BATTERY

FIGURE 8–2 When a phosphate group is added to an ADP molecule, ATP is produced. ADP contains some energy, but not as much as ATP. In this way, ADP is like a partially charged battery that can be fully charged by the addition of a phosphate group. **Use Analogies** ***Explain the difference between the beams of light produced by the flashlight "powered" by ADP and the flashlight "powered" by ATP.***

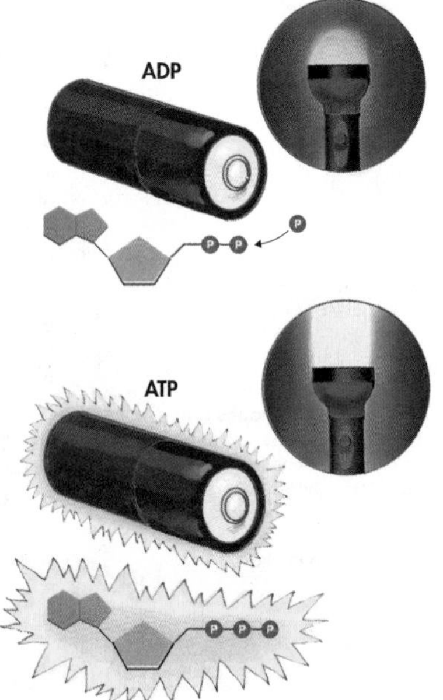

Teach

Use Visuals

Use **Figure 8–1** to discuss where chemical energy is stored in a chemical compound and how ATP can easily store and release energy.

Ask Where is energy stored in the molecule of ATP? *(In the chemical bonds that hold the parts of the molecule together, represented in the figure by thin black lines.)*

Ask How would you change the figure to show a molecule of ADP? *(Take away the third phosphate group and the bond that holds it to the molecule.)*

DIFFERENTIATED INSTRUCTION

L3 Advanced Students Ask students to search the Internet for amazing facts about ATP. For example, have them find out how often an ATP molecule gains and loses a phosphate group, how much ATP is consumed during vigorous exercise, or how much ATP is generated in the body per second—any facts they can find that they think are amazing. Ask them to report the facts to the class.

VISUAL ANALOGY

To help students understand the analogy in **Figure 8–2,** bring to class a battery-powered device, a rechargeable battery, and a charger. Turn on the device, and tell students it is like a cell carrying out cellular activities. Just as the device is using energy from the battery, the cell uses energy from ATP as it releases a phosphate group. And just as the charger can recharge the battery, the process that adds a phosphate group to ADP can "recharge" ATP.

BIOLOGY.com Students can further explore the analogy in **Figure 8–2** by watching **Visual Analogy: ATP as a Charged Battery.**

Biology In-Depth

PHOTOAUTOTROPHS AND CHEMOAUTOTROPHS

In this chapter, students are introduced to autotrophs. In Chapter 20, they will learn about a major distinction among autotrophs. The autotrophs discussed here are called photoautotrophs, or organisms that use light energy to produce food. Autotrophs also include chemoautotrophs, which are organisms that use energy directly from chemical compounds to produce carbon molecules. For example, prokaryotes that live deep in the ocean near hydrothermal vents are chemoautotrophs. They derive energy from chemical compounds in the waters emerging from vents.

Answers

FIGURE 8–2 The beam produced by the ATP-"powered" flashlight is much brighter than the beam produced by the ADP-"powered" flashlight because ATP contains more stored energy than ADP.

IN YOUR NOTEBOOK Similar: both store energy in their chemical bonds; Different: a single molecule of glucose stores 90 times more energy than a molecule of ATP, but ATP is much more useful for transferring energy than is glucose.

LESSON 8.1

Focus on ELL: Extend Language

BEGINNING AND INTERMEDIATE SPEAKERS Have students use a dictionary to find the meaning of the word parts that make up *autotroph* and *heterotroph*. Give each student two note cards. On each card, have them write one of the terms, divide it into word parts, and draw a picture that will remind them of the word's meaning.

Ask students what it means for an organism's growth to be able to make its own food. Students can go online to Biology.com to gather their evidence.

MYSTERY CLUE

Like all plants, the willow tree van Helmont planted was an autotroph. What might its ability to harness the sun's energy and store it in food have to do with the tree's gain in mass?

Heterotrophs and Autotrophs

What happens during the process of photosynthesis?

Cells are not "born" with a supply of ATP—they must somehow produce it. So, where do living things get the energy they use to produce ATP? The simple answer is that it comes from the chemical compounds that we call food. Organisms that obtain food by consuming other living things are known as **heterotrophs.** Some heterotrophs get their food by eating plants such as grasses. Other heterotrophs, such as the cheetah in **Figure 8–3,** obtain food from plants indirectly by feeding on plant-eating animals. Still other heterotrophs—mushrooms, for example—obtain food by absorbing nutrients from decomposing organisms in the environment.

Originally, however, the energy in nearly all food molecules comes from the sun. Plants, algae, and some bacteria are able to use light energy from the sun to produce food. Organisms that make their own food are called **autotrophs.** Ultimately, nearly all life on Earth, including ourselves, depends on the ability of autotrophs to capture the energy of sunlight and store it in the molecules that make up food. The process by which autotrophs use the energy of sunlight to produce high-energy carbohydrates—sugars and starches—that can be used as food is known as **photosynthesis.** *Photosynthesis* comes from the Greek words *photo*, meaning "light," and *synthesis*, meaning "putting together." Therefore, photosynthesis means "using light to put something together." **In the process of photosynthesis, plants convert the energy of sunlight into chemical energy stored in the bonds of carbohydrates.** In the rest of this chapter, you will learn how this process works.

FIGURE 8–3 Autotrophs and Heterotrophs Grass, an autotroph, uses energy from the sun to produce food. African hares get their energy by eating grass. Cheetahs, in turn, get their energy by eating other organisms, like the hare.

Assess and Remediate

EVALUATE UNDERSTANDING

Call on students at random to explain the difference between autotrophs and heterotrophs. Then, have them complete the 8.1 Assessment.

REMEDIATION SUGGESTION

L1 Struggling Students If your students have trouble with **Question 2c,** suggest they read the definition of *decomposer* in the Glossary.

8.1 Assessment

IN B.3.1, B.3.2, B.3.5

Review Key Concepts

1. a. Review What is ATP and what is its role in the cell?
   b. Explain How does the structure of ATP make it an ideal source of energy for the cell?
   c. Use Analogies Explain how ADP and ATP are each like a battery. Which one is "partially charged" and which one is "fully charged?" Why?
2. a. Review What is the ultimate source of energy for plants?
   b. Explain How do heterotrophs obtain energy? How is this different from how autotrophs obtain energy?
   c. Infer Why are decomposers, such as mushrooms, considered heterotrophs and not autotrophs?

Apply the Big idea

Interdependence in Nature

3. Recall that energy flows—and that nutrients cycle—through the biosphere. How does the process of photosynthesis impact both the flow of energy and the cycling of nutrients? You may wish to refer to Chapter 3 to help you answer this question.

BIOLOGY.com Search Lesson 8.1 GO • Lesson Assessment • Self-Test

Assessment Answers

1a. ATP is an abbreviation for the compound adenosine triphosphate. Cells use ATP to store and release energy.

1b. ATP can easily release and store energy by breaking and re-forming the bonds between its phosphate groups.

1c. ADP and ATP are like batteries because they store energy in the chemical bonds they contain. ADP has only two phosphate groups (and fewer bonds), so it's like a partially charged battery. ATP has three phosphate groups, so it is like a fully charged battery and has more bonds available for energy storage.

2a. the sun

2b. Heterotrophs obtain energy by feeding on other living things. Autotrophs, by contrast, make their own food.

2c. Decomposers consume the remains of living things for energy and cannot make their own food.

3. Big idea Sample answer: Photosynthesis provides the base for the one-way flow of energy through the biosphere. Plants convert energy from the sun into sugars, which provide fuel for themselves and for other organisms. Photosynthesis also cycles carbon and oxygen nutrients through the biosphere.

Understanding Photosynthesis Many scientists have contributed to understanding how plants carry out photosynthesis. Early research focused on the overall process. Later, researchers investigated the detailed chemical pathways.

1650
1700
1750
1800
1850
1900
1950
2000
1643
▲ After analyzing his measurements of a willow tree's water intake and mass increase, Jan van Helmont concludes that trees gain most of their mass from water.
1771
Joseph Priestley experiments with a bell jar, a candle, and a plant and concludes that the plant releases oxygen. ▼
1779
Jan Ingenhousz finds that aquatic plants produce oxygen bubbles in the light but not in the dark. He concludes that plants need sunlight to produce oxygen. ▼
1845
Julius Robert Mayer proposes that plants convert light energy into chemical energy.
1948
Melvin Calvin traces the chemical path that carbon follows to form glucose. These reactions are also known as the Calvin cycle.
1992
Rudolph Marcus wins the Nobel Prize in chemistry for describing the process by which electrons are transferred from one molecule to another in the electron transport chain.
2004
▲ So Iwata and Jim Barber identify the precise mechanism by which water molecules are split in the process of photosynthesis. Their research may one day be applied to artificial photosynthesis technologies in order to produce a cheap supply of hydrogen gas that can be used as fuel.
PRIESTLEY

WRITING Use the Internet or library resources to research the experiments conducted by one of these scientists. Then, write a summary describing how the scientist contributed to the modern understanding of photosynthesis.

Teach

Lead a Discussion

Call on volunteers to read aloud the annotations that describe how each of the scientists contributed to an understanding of photosynthesis. Then, ask students to explain how the discovery of one scientist could have provided the basis for the discovery of a later scientist. For example, ask how the discovery by Jan Ingenhousz built on the discovery by Joseph Priestley. *(Priestley concluded that plants give off oxygen. That conclusion could have helped lead Ingenhousz to investigate the conditions under which aquatic plants produce oxygen bubbles.)*

DIFFERENTIATED INSTRUCTION

L3 Advanced Students Ask students to write a paragraph that answers this question: In your opinion, if one of these scientists had not done the relevant experiment and had not made a discovery about photosynthesis, how might our understanding of how photosynthesis works have been affected? *(Answers will vary. A typical answer might suggest that advances in science build on previous advances. In all likelihood, if one of the scientists had not made a discovery, another scientist of the same time would have built upon what was previously known to make a similar advance in knowledge. Although the series of advances may not have taken place exactly as it did, by now we would probably know the details of photosynthesis.)*

How Science Works

PRIESTLEY'S EXPERIMENT "PURIFIES" AIR

Joseph Priestley (1733–1804), a British Unitarian minister, never formally studied science. His interest in science was encouraged when he met Benjamin Franklin in London in the 1760s. For one of his many experiments, Priestley used an apparatus that consisted of enclosed containers of air, sealed at the bottom by a trough of mercury. He discovered that a burning candle in one of the closed containers caused the air to become "impure," eventually putting out the flame. He also found that a mouse placed inside the container of "impure" air died. He expected the same to happen to a sprig of spearmint. Much to his surprise, instead of dying, the plant flourished. Furthermore, he discovered that the plant "purified" the air, since after leaving the plant in the space for several weeks, a candle would burn or a mouse could live in the same enclosed space.

Answers

WRITING Summaries will vary. Students' summaries should provide basic information about how one of the scientists included on the time line contributed to the understanding of photosynthesis. Make sure students cite their sources of information, either by including the publication information for a book or the address of a reliable Web site.

LESSON 8.2

Getting Started

Objectives

8.2.1 Explain the role of light and pigments in photosynthesis.

8.2.2 Explain the role of electron carrier molecules in photosynthesis.

8.2.3 State the overall equation for photosynthesis.

Student Resources

Study Workbooks A and B, 8.2 Worksheets

Spanish Study Workbook, 8.2 Worksheets

 Lesson Overview • Lesson Notes • Activities: Visual Analogy, InterActive Art, Tutor Tube • Assessment: Self-Test, Lesson Assessment

 For corresponding lesson in the **Foundation Edition**, see pages 195–198.

Build Background

As students observe, pass light through a prism. They should observe that the light separates into the colors of the rainbow. Explain that white light is made up of different colors of light, each with a different wavelength, and the separation occurs because each different wavelength of light refracts, or bends, a different amount. Then, have students look at the graph in **Figure 8–4.** Point out that the graph shows photosynthetic pigments absorb some colors well but do not absorb other colors well.

IN INDIANA ACADEMIC STANDARDS

For the full text of all standards, see the Course Overview in the front matter of this book.

B.2.3 Explain that most cells contain mitochondria, the key sites of cellular respiration, where stored chemical energy is converted into useable energy for the cell and some cells, including many plant cells, contain chloroplasts, the key sites of photosynthesis, where the energy of light is captured for use in chemical work.

B.3.1 Describe how some organisms capture the sun's energy through the process of photosynthesis by converting carbon dioxide and water into high energy compounds and releasing oxygen.

8.2 Photosynthesis: An Overview

IN B.2.3 Mitochondria and chloroplasts; B.3.1 Photosynthesis. Also covered: NoS.6.

Key Questions

What role do pigments play in the process of photosynthesis?

What are electron carrier molecules?

What are the reactants and products of photosynthesis?

Vocabulary

pigment • chlorophyll • thylakoid • stroma • NADP$^+$ • light-dependent reactions • light-independent reactions

Taking Notes

Outline Make an outline using the green and blue headings in this lesson. Fill in details as you read to help you organize the information.

THINK ABOUT IT How would you design a system to capture the energy of sunlight and convert it into a useful form? First, you'd have to collect that energy. Maybe you'd spread out lots of flat panels to catch the light. You might then coat the panels with light-absorbing compounds, but what then? How could you take the energy, trapped ever so briefly in these chemical compounds, and get it into a stable, useful, chemical form? Solving such problems may well be the key to making solar power a practical energy alternative. But plants have already solved all these issues on their own terms—and maybe we can learn a trick or two from them.

Chlorophyll and Chloroplasts

What role do pigments play in the process of photosynthesis?

Our lives, and the lives of nearly every living thing on the surface of Earth, are made possible by the sun and the process of photosynthesis. In order for photosynthesis to occur, light energy from the sun must somehow be captured.

Light Energy from the sun travels to Earth in the form of light. Sunlight, which our eyes perceive as "white" light, is actually a mixture of different wavelengths. Many of these wavelengths are visible to our eyes and make up what is known as the visible spectrum. Our eyes see the different wavelengths of the visible spectrum as different colors: shades of red, orange, yellow, green, blue, indigo, and violet.

FIGURE 8–4 Light Absorption

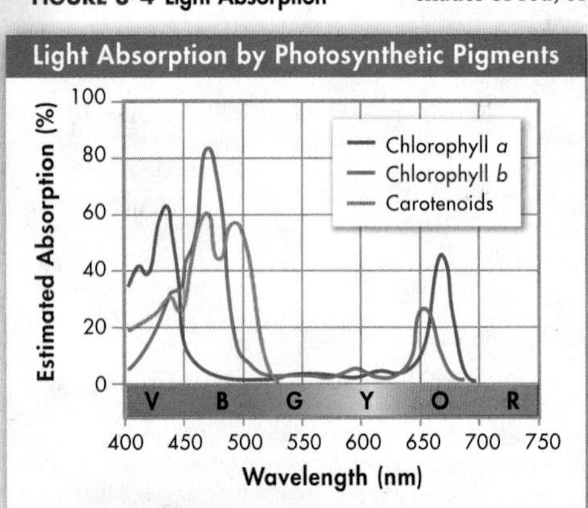

Pigments Plants gather the sun's energy with light-absorbing molecules called **pigments.** **Photosynthetic organisms capture energy from sunlight with pigments.** The plants' principal pigment is **chlorophyll** (KLAWR uh fil). The two types of chlorophyll found in plants, chlorophyll *a* and chlorophyll *b*, absorb light very well in the blue-violet and red regions of the visible spectrum. However, chlorophyll does not absorb light well in the green region of the spectrum, as shown in **Figure 8–4.**

230 BIOLOGY.com Search Lesson 8.2 GO • Lesson Overview • Lesson Notes • Data Analysis

UbD Teach for Understanding

ENDURING UNDERSTANDING A cell is the basic unit of life; the processes that occur at the cellular level provide the energy and basic structure organisms need to survive.

GUIDING QUESTION What cellular structures and molecules are involved in photosynthesis?

EVIDENCE OF UNDERSTANDING *After students have finished the lesson, this assessment should show their understanding of the structures and processes involved in photosynthesis.* Have students work in small groups. Have each group member choose one or more of the following elements of photosynthesis: sunlight, chlorophyll molecule, chloroplast, high-energy electrons, light-dependent reactions, light-independent reactions. Have group members imagine they are their chosen elements and offer a first-person explanation of how they are involved in the process of photosynthesis.

Leaves reflect green light, which is why plants look green. Plants also contain red and orange pigments such as carotene that absorb light in other regions of the spectrum. Most of the time, the intense green color of chlorophyll overwhelms the accessory pigments, so we don't notice them. As temperatures drop late in the year, however, chlorophyll molecules break down first, leaving the reds and oranges of the accessory pigments for all to see. The beautiful colors of fall in some parts of the country are the result of this process.

Chloroplasts Recall from Chapter 7 that in plants and other photosynthetic eukaryotes, photosynthesis takes place inside organelles called chloroplasts. Chloroplasts contain an abundance of saclike photosynthetic membranes called **thylakoids** (THY luh koydz). Thylakoids are interconnected and arranged in stacks known as grana (singular: granum). Pigments such as chlorophyll are located in the thylakoid membranes. The fluid portion of the chloroplast, outside of the thylakoids, is known as the **stroma.** The structure of a typical chloroplast is shown in **Figure 8–5.**

Energy Collection What's so special about chlorophyll that makes it important for photosynthesis? Because light is a form of energy, any compound that absorbs light absorbs energy. Chlorophyll absorbs visible light especially well. In addition, when chlorophyll absorbs light, a large fraction of that light energy is transferred directly to electrons in the chlorophyll molecule itself. By raising the energy levels of these electrons, light energy can produce a steady supply of high-energy electrons, which is what makes photosynthesis work.

In Your Notebook *In your own words, explain why most plants will not grow well if kept under green light.*

ZOOMING IN

THE CHLOROPLAST

FIGURE 8–5 In plants, photosynthesis takes place inside chloroplasts. **Observe** *How are thylakoids arranged in the chloroplast?*

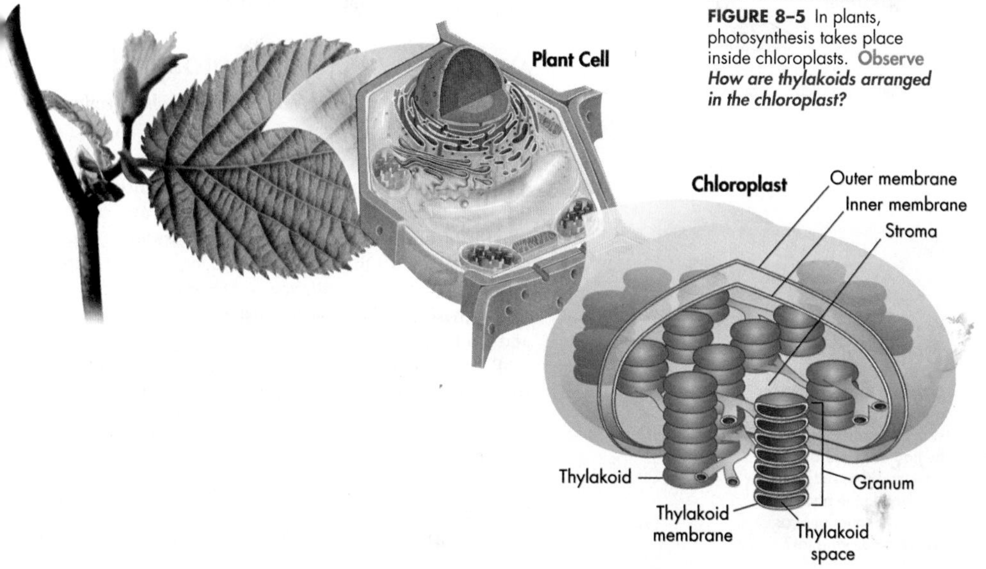

Plant Cell

Chloroplast

Outer membrane

Inner membrane

Stroma

Thylakoid

Granum

Thylakoid membrane

Thylakoid space

LESSON 8.2

Teach

ZOOMING IN

Have students use **Figure 8–5** to discuss the location and structure of the chloroplast. Point out that the figure shows a leaf, a cell within the leaf, and a chloroplast within the cell. Then, make a **Two-Column Table** on the board. Title the left column Structure, and write the names of all the chloroplast structures that are labeled in the figure. Title the right column Description. Call on students to provide descriptions or definitions of each structure.

Study Wkbks A/B, Appendix S31, Two-Column Table. **Transparencies,** GO16.

DIFFERENTIATED INSTRUCTION

L1 Struggling Students Provide students with an unlabeled drawing of a chloroplast, similar to the chloroplast in the figure. Then, have students work in pairs to label the structures on their drawing.

ELL Focus on ELL: Access Content

ADVANCED AND ADVANCED HIGH SPEAKERS To help students understand the relationship between color and light absorption, assign them a **Problem and Solution** activity. Ask students: What change would you see in a plant whose chlorophyll pigments suddenly stop working? Have them refer to **Figure 8–4** and write a three- to four-sentence response. Then, have them present their solutions to the class. Students should infer that the plant's leaves would change color from green to yellow, orange, or red.

Study Wkbks A/B, Appendix S9, Problem and Solution.

Quick Facts

PHOTOSYNTHETIC PIGMENTS

There are three main kinds of photosynthetic pigments in living things.

1. Chlorophylls—green pigments
   - Chlorophyll *a* is found in all plants, algae, and cyanobacteria.
   - Chlorophyll *b* is found in all plants and green algae.
   - Chlorophyll *c* is found in diatoms and brown algae.
   - Chlorophyll *d* is found in red algae.
2. Carotenoids—red, orange, or yellow pigments
   - Carotene is found in most plants and some algae.
   - Carotene gives carrots their color.
   - Fucoxanthin is found in brown algae and diatoms.
3. Phycobilins—blue or red pigments
   - Phycobilins are found only in red algae and cyanobacteria.
   - Some phycobilins are fluorescent.

Answers

FIGURE 8–5 in stacks known as grana

IN YOUR NOTEBOOK Sample answer: Plants need to be able to absorb energy from the sun to photosynthesize and grow. Chlorophyll in plants does not absorb green light well—it reflects it. Because chlorophyll is the principal pigment in plants that captures energy from sunlight, plants under green light will not capture enough energy.

Teach continued

Lead a Discussion

Explain that electron carriers are compounds that can transfer electrons energized by sunlight to a chemical reaction elsewhere in the cell.

Ask In the conversion of NADP+ to NADPH, what happens to the energy absorbed by chlorophyll from sunlight? *(The conversion of NADP+ to NADPH traps the energy of sunlight in chemical form.)*

DIFFERENTIATED INSTRUCTION

LPR Less Proficient Readers Make a **Flowchart** on the board to clarify the role of electron carriers in photosynthesis. Use these steps:

1. Chlorophyll absorbs light.
2. Absorption of light produces high-energy electrons.
3. Each electron carrier NADP+ picks up 2 high-energy electrons and 1 hydrogen ion.
4. Picking up the electrons and the hydrogen ion changes NADP+ into NADPH.
5. NADPH carries the high-energy electrons to chemical reactions elsewhere in the cell.

As you write each step, point out where in the text this step is discussed. Have students copy the flowchart in their notebook.

Study Wkbks A/B, Appendix S25, Flowchart. **Transparencies,** GO8.

VISUAL ANALOGY

Ask students what the oven mitt represents. *(the electron carrier NADP+)* Make sure they understand the mitt picks up more than just the "hot potato," representing 2 high-energy electrons. Ask what else the electron carrier picks up. *(a hydrogen ion)*

BIOLOGY.com Students can further explore the analogy of oven mitts and electron carriers in **Visual Analogy: Carrying Electrons.**

Discuss with students why it would have seemed logical to van Helmont to conclude that water provided the extra mass. *(He watered the plant regularly.)* Then, point to the overall reaction for photosynthesis for the answer to the question. *(CO_2)* Students can go online to **Biology.com** to gather their evidence.

VISUAL ANALOGY

CARRYING ELECTRONS

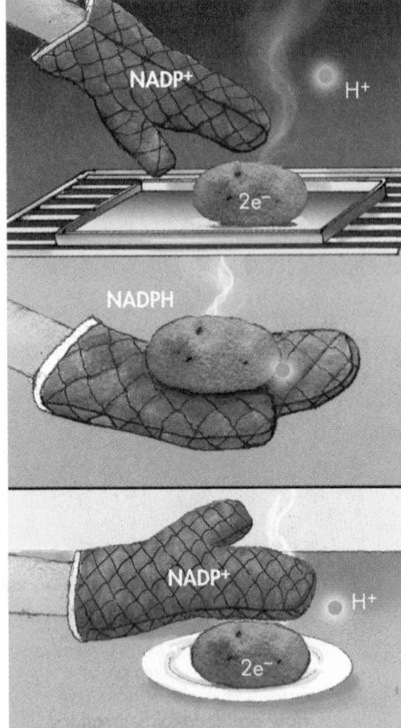

FIGURE 8–6 $NADP^+$ is a carrier molecule that transports pairs of electrons (and an H^+ ion) in photosynthetic organisms, similar to how an oven mitt is used to transport a hot object such as a baked potato.

High-Energy Electrons

What are electron carrier molecules?

In a chemical sense, the high-energy electrons produced by chlorophyll are highly reactive and require a special "carrier." Think of a high-energy electron as being similar to a hot potato straight from the oven. If you wanted to move the potato from one place to another, you wouldn't pick it up in your hands. You would use an oven mitt—a carrier—to transport it, as shown in **Figure 8–6.** Plant cells treat high-energy electrons in the same way. Instead of an oven mitt, however, they use electron carriers to transport high-energy electrons from chlorophyll to other molecules. **An electron carrier is a compound that can accept a pair of high-energy electrons and transfer them, along with most of their energy, to another molecule.**

One of these carrier molecules is a compound known as **$NADP^+$** (nicotinamide adenine dinucleotide phosphate). The name is complicated, but the job that $NADP^+$ has is simple. $NADP^+$ accepts and holds 2 high-energy electrons, along with a hydrogen ion (H^+). This converts the $NADP^+$ into NADPH. The conversion of $NADP^+$ into NADPH is one way in which some of the energy of sunlight can be trapped in chemical form. The NADPH can then carry the high-energy electrons that were produced by light absorption in chlorophyll to chemical reactions elsewhere in the cell. These high-energy electron carriers are used to help build a variety of molecules the cell needs, including carbohydrates like glucose.

An Overview of Photosynthesis

What are the reactants and products of photosynthesis?

Many steps are involved in the process of photosynthesis. However, the overall process of photosynthesis can be summarized in one sentence. **Photosynthesis uses the energy of sunlight to convert water and carbon dioxide (reactants) into high-energy sugars and oxygen (products).** Plants then use the sugars to produce complex carbohydrates such as starches, and to provide energy for the synthesis of other compounds, including proteins and lipids.

Because photosynthesis usually produces 6-carbon sugars ($C_6H_{12}O_6$) as the final product, the overall reaction for photosynthesis can be shown as follows:

In Symbols:

$$6CO_2 + 6H_2O \xrightarrow{\text{light}} C_6H_{12}O_6 + 6O_2$$

In Words:

$$\text{Carbon dioxide} + \text{Water} \xrightarrow{\text{light}} \text{Sugars} + \text{Oxygen}$$

MYSTERY CLUE

Van Helmont concluded that water must have provided the extra mass gained by the tree. Further studies would prove that he had only half of the answer. What reactant involved in the photosynthesis equation was he not accounting for?

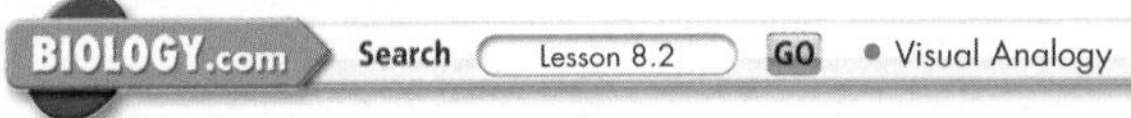

Biology In-Depth

WHY BOTH ATP AND NADPH?

Students may wonder why cells need two different forms of a chemical intermediate—or "go between." Both the phosphate-bond compound ATP and the electron carrier NADPH store a significant amount of chemical energy, and so both are capable of providing the energy needed to make energy-requiring reactions possible. Some reactions, however, specifically require the addition of a pair of electrons, and these include the reactions in the pathways of the Calvin cycle that utilize NADPH. In addition—as students will see when they study cellular respiration—most of the energy-yielding reactions of the Krebs cycle directly yield high-energy electrons. Those high-energy electrons must be passed to an electron carrier in order to produce the ATP needed for other energy-requiring reactions.

Light-Dependent Reactions Although the equation for photosynthesis looks simple, there are many steps to get from the reactants to the final products. In fact, photosynthesis actually involves two sets of reactions. The first set of reactions is known as the **light-dependent reactions** because they require the direct involvement of light and light-absorbing pigments. The light-dependent reactions use energy from sunlight to produce energy-rich compounds such as ATP. These reactions take place within the thylakoids—specifically, in the thylakoid membranes—of the chloroplast. Water is required in these reactions as a source of electrons and hydrogen ions. Oxygen is released as a byproduct.

Light-Independent Reactions Plants absorb carbon dioxide from the atmosphere and complete the process of photosynthesis by producing carbon-containing sugars and other carbohydrates. During the **light-independent reactions,** ATP and NADPH molecules produced in the light-dependent reactions are used to produce high-energy sugars from carbon dioxide. As the name implies, no light is required to power the light-independent reactions. The light-independent reactions take place outside the thylakoids, in the stroma.

The interdependent relationship between the light-dependent and light-independent reactions is shown in **Figure 8–7.** As you can see, the two sets of reactions work together to capture the energy of sunlight and transform it into energy-rich compounds such as carbohydrates.

In Your Notebook *Create a two-column compare/contrast table that shows the similarities and differences between the light-dependent and light-independent reactions of photosynthesis.*

BUILD Vocabulary

ACADEMIC WORDS The noun **byproduct** means "anything produced in the course of making another thing." Oxygen is considered a byproduct of the light-dependent reactions of photosynthesis because it is produced as a result of extracting electrons from water. Also, unlike ATP and NADPH, oxygen is not used in the second stage of the process, the light-independent reactions.

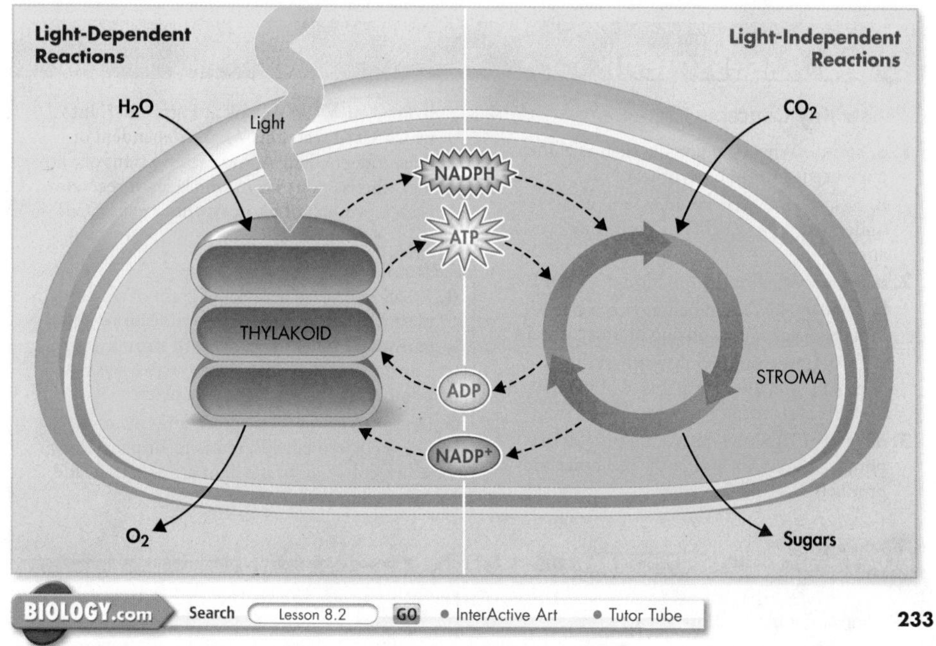

FIGURE 8–7 The Stages of Photosynthesis There are two stages of photosynthesis: light-dependent reactions and light-independent reactions. **Interpret Diagrams** ***What happens to the ATP and NADPH produced in the light-dependent reactions?***

BIOLOGY.com Search Lesson 8.2 GO • InterActive Art • Tutor Tube

Use Visuals

Use **Figure 8–7** to help students differentiate between the light-dependent and light-independent reactions of photosynthesis. Call on a volunteer to explain why the first set of reactions is called the light-dependent reactions. *(These reactions require the direct involvement of light.)* Then, make sure students can identify where each set of reactions takes place and what each stage produces. Also, make sure students recognize how NADPH/NADP+ and ATP/ADP are "recycled" between the light-dependent and light-independent reactions. Finally, point out the two exterior "inputs" *(H_2O and CO_2)* and "outputs" *(O_2 and sugars).*

DIFFERENTIATED INSTRUCTION

L1 Special Needs To make sure students understand the difference between the two stages of photosynthesis, call on volunteers to classify each of the following situations as either light-dependent or light-independent.

- Sleeping *(light-independent)*
- Reading a book *(light-dependent)*
- Watching a race *(light-dependent)*
- Listening to music *(light-independent)*

ELL English Language Learners Explain that the prefix *in-* means "not," and the word *dependent* means "relying on." Then, ask what the word *independent* means. *(not relying on)*

Ask Which stage of photosynthesis relies on light in order to take place? *(the light-dependent reactions)*

BIOLOGY.com By accessing the **InterActive Art: Photosynthesis** activity, students can learn more about the overall photosynthesis reaction. Suggest students watch the **Tutor Tube: Sorting Out Light-Independent and Light-Dependent Reactions** for extra help distinguishing between the two stages of photosynthesis.

UbD Check for Understanding

HAND SIGNALS

Present students with the following questions, and ask them to show a thumbs-up sign if they know the answer and understand the concept, a thumbs-down sign if they do not know or understand, or a waving hand if they partially know or understand.

- What is the principal pigment in plants?
- How do plant cells use electron carriers?
- What are the two sets of reactions that make up photosynthesis?

ADJUST INSTRUCTION

For each question that received a thumbs-down or waving-hand sign, ask students to write a brief answer using the text. Call on volunteers to share their answers.

Answers

FIGURE 8–7 Both ATP and NADPH from the light-dependent reactions are used to produce high-energy sugars in the light-independent reactions.

IN YOUR NOTEBOOK Students' tables may vary. A typical table will have one column for light-dependent reactions and the other for light-independent reactions. Included in the rows might be information about the location of reactions, whether light is needed, what reactants are needed, and what products are produced.

LESSON 8.2

Quick Lab

PURPOSE Students will be able to conclude that oxygen is produced by plants during photosynthesis.

MATERIALS large clear plastic cup, sodium bicarbonate solution, *Elodea* plant, large test tube

SAFETY Warn students to handle glass carefully. Students should wash their hands after the lab.

PLANNING Prepare the sodium bicarbonate solution by mixing 5 g of sodium bicarbonate into each liter of water. Obtain the *Elodea* plants.

ANALYZE AND CONCLUDE

1. bubbles of a gas (up to 30 minutes after setup)
2. oxygen; yes, it would be considered a waste product because the plant released it.
3. the chloroplast

Assess and Remediate

EVALUATE UNDERSTANDING

Have students describe how plants produce sugars. Then, have them complete the 8.2 Assessment.

REMEDIATION SUGGESTION

L1 **Struggling Students** If students have trouble with **Question 1b,** have them refer to **Figure 8–4.**

BIOLOGY.com Students can then check their understanding of lesson concepts with the **Self-Test** assessment. They can then take an online version of the **Lesson Assessment.**

Quick Lab GUIDED INQUIRY

IN B.3.1

What Waste Material Is Produced During Photosynthesis?

1 Fill a large, clear, plastic cup about halfway full with sodium bicarbonate solution. The sodium bicarbonate solution is a source of carbon dioxide.

2 Place a freshly cut *Elodea* plant (with the cut stem at the bottom) in a large test tube. Fill the tube with sodium bicarbonate solution. **CAUTION:** *Handle the test tube carefully.*

3 Hold your finger over the mouth of the test tube. Turn the test tube over, and lower it to the bottom of the cup. Make sure no air is trapped in the test tube.

4 Place the cup in bright light.

5 After no fewer than 20 minutes, look closely at the elodea leaves. Record your observations.

Analyze and Conclude

1. **Observe** What did you observe on the *Elodea* leaves?
2. **Infer** What substance accumulated on the leaves? Should that substance be considered a waste product? Explain.
3. **Apply Concepts** Which plant organelle carries out photosynthesis and produces the gas?

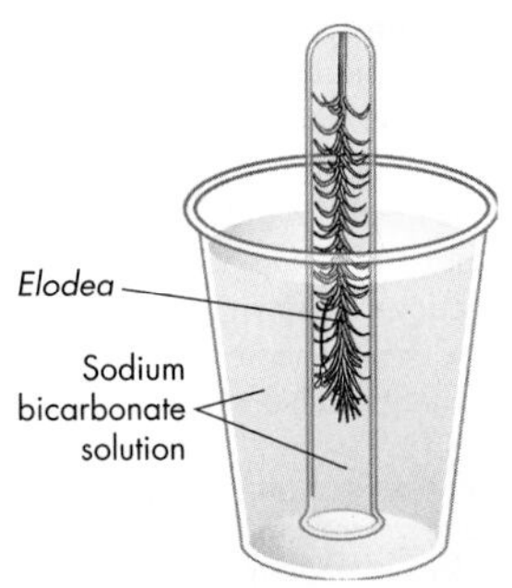

8.2 Assessment

IN B.2.3, B.3.1

Review Key Concepts

1. a. **Review** Why are pigments such as chlorophyll needed for photosynthesis?
   b. **Predict** How well would a plant grow under pure yellow light? Explain your answer.
2. a. **Review** What is the function of NADPH?
   b. **Explain** How is light energy converted into chemical energy during photosynthesis?
   c. **Infer** How would photosynthesis be affected if there were a shortage of $NADP^+$ in the cells of plants?
3. a. **Review** Describe the overall process of photosynthesis, including the reactants and products.
   b. **Interpret Visuals** Look at **Figure 8–7.** Into which set of reactions—light-dependent or light-independent—does each reactant of photosynthesis enter? From which set of reactions is each product of photosynthesis generated?

VISUAL THINKING

4. Create your own labeled diagram of a chloroplast. Using **Figure 8–5** as a guide, draw and label the thylakoids, grana, and stroma. Indicate on your drawing where the two sets of photosynthesis reactions take place.
5. Draw two leaves—one green and one orange. Using colored pencils, markers, or pens, show which colors of visible light are absorbed and reflected by each leaf.

BIOLOGY.com Search  GO • Self-Test • Lesson Assessment

Assessment Answers

1a. They capture energy from sunlight.

1b. It would not grow well because chlorophyll does not absorb much light in the yellow region of the visible spectrum.

2a. NADPH transferes high-energy electrons between molecules.

2b. Light energy absorbed by pigments produces high-energy electrons that are used to convert $NADP^+$ and ADP to the compounds NADPH and ATP, trapping the energy in chemical form.

2c. Because photosynthesis depends on the conversion of $NADP^+$ to NADPH to carry electrons to chemical reactions in other parts of the cell, the process could not occur efficiently if there were a shortage of $NADP^+$ in the cells of plants.

3a. Photosynthesis uses the energy of sunlight to convert water and carbon dioxide (reactants) into high-energy sugars and oxygen (products).

3b. Light-dependent reactions: sunlight and water enter; oxygen is lost as a byproduct; ATP and NADPH are produced. Light-independent reactions: carbon dioxide enters; glucose is made using the energy provided by ATP and NADPH; ADP and $NADP^+$ are cycled back for re-use in the light-dependent reactions.

VISUAL THINKING

4. Diagrams should have labels for the thylakoids, grana, and stroma and should indicate that the light-dependent reactions occur in the thylakoids and the light-independent reactions occur in the stroma.

5. Drawings should show an understanding that the green leaf reflects primarily green light and absorbs violet, blue, orange, and red light (and poorly absorbs yellow light). The orange leaf reflects primarily orange light and absorbs violet, blue, and green light (and poorly absorbs red and yellow).

The Process of Photosynthesis

 B.2.3 Mitochondria and chloroplasts; B.3.1 Photosynthesis. Also covered: NoS.3.

THINK ABOUT IT Why membranes? Why do chloroplasts contain so many membranes? Is there something about biological membranes that makes them absolutely essential for the process of photosynthesis? As you'll see, there is. When most pigments absorb light, they eventually lose most of that energy as heat. In a sense, the "trade secret" of the chloroplast is how it avoids such losses, capturing light energy in the form of high-energy electrons—and membranes are the key. Without them, photosynthesis simply wouldn't work.

Key Questions

What happens during the light-dependent reactions?

What happens during the light-independent reactions?

What factors affect photosynthesis?

Vocabulary

photosystem • electron transport chain • ATP synthase • Calvin cycle

Taking Notes

Flowchart As you read, create a flowchart that clearly shows the steps involved in the light-dependent reactions.

The Light-Dependent Reactions: Generating ATP and NADPH

What happens during the light-dependent reactions?

Recall that the process of photosynthesis involves two primary sets of reactions: the light-dependent and the light-independent reactions. The light-dependent reactions encompass the steps of photosynthesis that directly involve sunlight. These reactions explain why plants need light to grow. **The light-dependent reactions use energy from sunlight to produce oxygen and convert ADP and $NADP^+$ into the energy carriers ATP and NADPH.**

The light-dependent reactions occur in the thylakoids of chloroplasts. Thylakoids are saclike membranes containing most of the machinery needed to carry out these reactions. Thylakoids contain clusters of chlorophyll and proteins known as **photosystems.** The photosystems, which are surrounded by accessory pigments, are essential to the light-dependent reactions. Photosystems absorb sunlight and generate high-energy electrons that are then passed to a series of electron carriers embedded in the thylakoid membrane. Light absorption by the photosystems is just the beginning of this important process.

FIGURE 8–8 The Importance of Light Like most plants, this rice plant needs light to grow. Apply Concepts *Which stage of photosynthesis requires light?*

Getting Started

Objectives

8.3.1 Describe what happens during the light-dependent reactions.

8.3.2 Describe what happens during the light-independent reactions.

8.3.3 Identify factors that affect the rate at which photosynthesis occurs.

Student Resources

Study Workbooks A and B, 8.3 Worksheets

Spanish Study Workbook, 8.3 Worksheets

Lab Manual B, 8.3 Data Analysis Worksheet

 BIOLOGY.com Lesson Overview • Lesson Notes • Activities: Art in Motion, Art Review, Data Analysis • Assessment: Self-Test, Lesson Assessment

For corresponding lesson in the **Foundation Edition**, see pages 199–203.

Answers

FIGURE 8–8 the light-dependent reactions

UbD Teach for Understanding

ENDURING UNDERSTANDING A cell is the basic unit of life; the processes that occur at the cellular level provide the energy and basic structure organisms need to survive.

GUIDING QUESTION How do photosynthetic organisms convert the sun's energy into chemical energy?

EVIDENCE OF UNDERSTANDING *After students have finished the lesson, this assessment should show their understanding of the steps that make up the process of photosynthesis.* Have students work in small groups, and assign each group one of the steps in the process of photosynthesis. (If there are enough groups, you could assign each group the material in one of the subsections marked by the blue heads.) Ask the students in each group to become experts on that step and make a presentation to the class explaining what happens. Groups should be prepared to take questions from classmates.

IN INDIANA ACADEMIC STANDARDS

For the full text of all standards, see the Course Overview in the front matter of this book.

B.2.3 Explain that most cells contain mitochondria, the key sites of cellular respiration, where stored chemical energy is converted into useable energy for the cell and some cells, including many plant cells, contain chloroplasts, the key sites of photosynthesis, where the energy of light is captured for use in chemical work.

B.3.1 Describe how some organisms capture the sun's energy through the process of photosynthesis by converting carbon dioxide and water into high energy compounds and releasing oxygen.

Teach

Build Study Skills

Tell students that a good way to learn difficult material is by making an outline. Have them work in small groups to make an outline of the section, **The Light-Dependent Reactions: Generating ATP and NADPH.** Students should use the blue headings for the second level of their outlines, and under each, add important details from the subsection.

DIFFERENTIATED INSTRUCTION

LPR Less Proficient Readers Have students work in pairs to write five questions about the light-dependent reactions on a piece of paper. Ask them to write the answers on another piece of paper. Then, have each pair trade questions with another pair. Partners should work together to answer the new set of questions. Then, have the two pairs confer on the answers. If a question is not answered correctly, all four students should work together to review the material and form an answer they all agree upon.

ELL Focus on ELL: Build Background

BEGINNING SPEAKERS Have students fill in a **Cluster Diagram** for the topic of photosynthesis. Ask them to think of words that relate to *photosynthesis* and write them in boxes connected to the circle. Then, lead a discussion on the words students recorded and how the words relate to photosynthesis. Make sure words not associated with photosynthesis are not validated as such.

Study Wkbks A/B, Appendix S19, Cluster Diagram. **Transparencies,** GO2.

FIGURE 8–9 Why Green? The green color of most plants is caused by the reflection of green light by the pigment chlorophyll. Pigments capture light energy during the light-dependent reactions of photosynthesis.

Photosystem II The light-dependent reactions, shown in **Figure 8–10,** begin when pigments in photosystem II absorb light. (This first photosystem is called photosystem II simply because it was discovered after photosystem I.) Light energy is absorbed by electrons in the pigments found within photosystem II, increasing the electrons' energy level. These high-energy electrons (e^-) are passed to the electron transport chain. An **electron transport chain** is a series of electron carrier proteins that shuttle high-energy electrons during ATP-generating reactions.

As light continues to shine, more and more high-energy electrons are passed to the electron transport chain. Does this mean that chlorophyll eventually runs out of electrons? No, the thylakoid membrane contains a system that provides new electrons to chlorophyll to replace the ones it has lost. These new electrons come from water molecules (H_2O). Enzymes on the inner surface of the thylakoid break up each water molecule into 2 electrons, 2 H^+ ions, and 1 oxygen atom. The 2 electrons replace the high-energy electrons that have been lost to the electron transport chain. As plants remove electrons from water, oxygen is left behind and is released into the air. This reaction is the source of nearly all of the oxygen in Earth's atmosphere, and it is another way in which photosynthesis makes our lives possible. The hydrogen ions left behind when water is broken apart are released inside the thylakoid.

In Your Notebook *Explain in your own words why photosynthetic organisms need water and sunlight.*

Electron Transport Chain What happens to the electrons as they move down the electron transport chain? Energy from the electrons is used by the proteins in the chain to pump H^+ ions from the stroma into the thylakoid space. At the end of the electron transport chain, the electrons themselves pass to a second photosystem called photosystem I.

Photosystem I Because some energy has been used to pump H^+ ions across the thylakoid membrane, electrons do not contain as much energy as they used to when they reach photosystem I. Pigments in photosystem I use energy from light to reenergize the electrons. At the end of a short second electron transport chain, $NADP^+$ molecules in the stroma pick up the high-energy electrons, along with H^+ ions, at the outer surface of the thylakoid membrane, to become NADPH. This NADPH becomes very important, as you will see, in the light-independent reactions of photosynthesis.

Hydrogen Ion Movement and ATP Formation Recall that in photosystem II, hydrogen ions began to accumulate within the thylakoid space. Some were left behind from the splitting of water at the end of the electron transport chain. Other hydrogen ions were "pumped" in from the stroma. The buildup of hydrogen ions makes the stroma negatively charged relative to the space within the thylakoids. This **gradient,** the difference in both charge and H^+ ion concentration across the membrane, provides the energy to make ATP.

BUILD Vocabulary

ACADEMIC WORDS The noun **gradient** refers to "an area over which something changes." There is a charge gradient across the thylakoid membrane because there is a positive charge on one side and a negative charge on the other.

How Science Works

SAME STAGES, DIFFERENT NAMES

In the early 1900s, British plant physiologist F. F. Blackman concluded that photosynthesis occurs in two stages, a stage that depends on light followed by a stage that can take place in darkness. The terms *light reactions* and *dark reactions* have been commonly used for the two stages since that time. Yet, the term *dark reactions* implies that those reactions can occur only in darkness, which is not the case. It's just that the dark reactions do not depend on sunlight. To avoid ambiguity, the authors of many modern textbooks have labeled the two stages *light-dependent reactions* and *light-independent reactions.* Some authors have gone a step further toward clarity by labeling the light-independent reactions the *Calvin cycle,* the name of the series of reactions that make up the light-independent reactions in most photosynthetic organisms.

Answers

IN YOUR NOTEBOOK Sample answer: Water is needed for the electrons and H^+ ions used in the reactions of photosynthesis. Sunlight is needed to supply the energy that is absorbed by pigments in chloroplasts, which increases the energy of electrons in photosystems.

H^+ ions cannot cross the membrane directly. However, the thylakoid membrane contains a protein called **ATP synthase** that spans the membrane and allows H^+ ions to pass through it. Powered by the gradient, H^+ ions pass through ATP synthase and force it to rotate, almost like a turbine being spun by water in a hydroelectric power plant. As it rotates, ATP synthase binds ADP and a phosphate group together to produce ATP. This process, which is known as chemiosmosis (kem ee ahz MOH sis), enables light-dependent electron transport to produce not only NADPH (at the end of the electron transport chain), but ATP as well.

Summary of Light-Dependent Reactions The light-dependent reactions produce oxygen gas and convert ADP and $NADP^+$ into the energy carriers ATP and NADPH. What good are these compounds? As we will see, they have an important role to play in the cell: They provide the energy needed to build high-energy sugars from low-energy carbon dioxide.

ZOOMING IN

LIGHT-DEPENDENT REACTIONS

FIGURE 8–10 The light-dependent reactions of photosynthesis take place in the thylakoids of the chloroplast. They use energy from sunlight to produce ATP, NADPH, and oxygen. **Interpret Visuals** ***How many molecules of NADPH are produced per water molecule used in photosynthetic electron transport?***

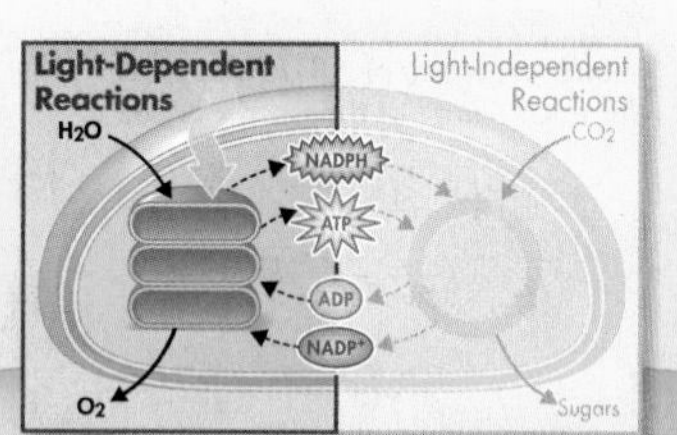

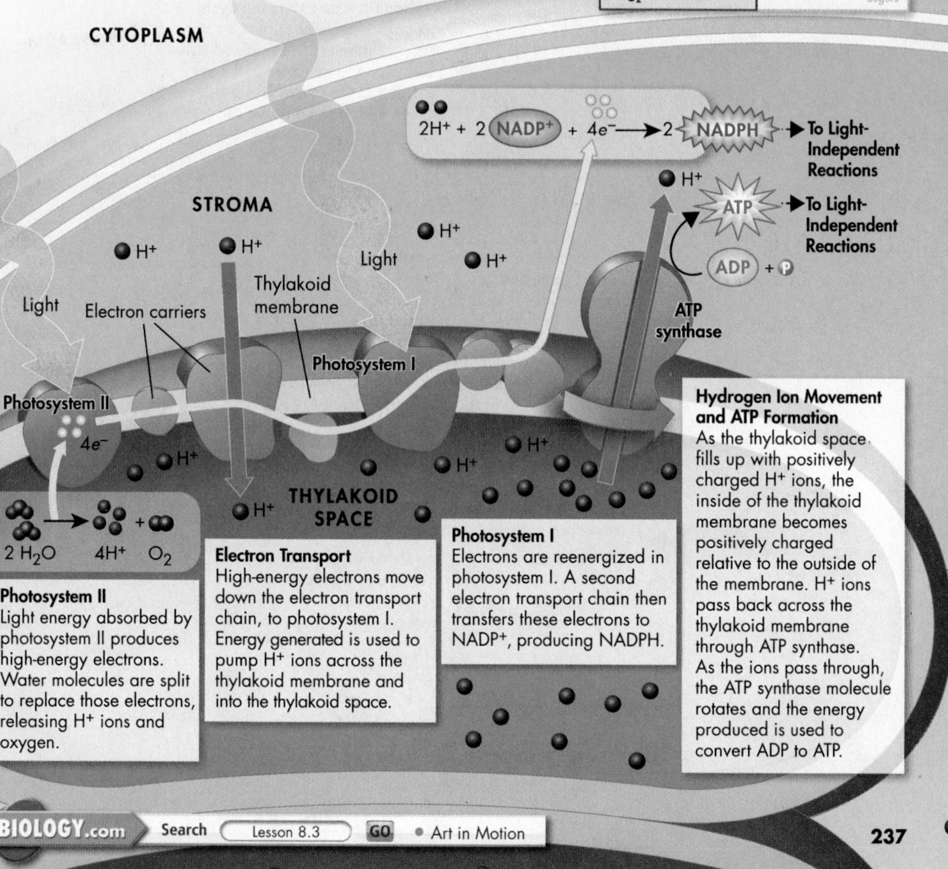

CYTOPLASM
STROMA
$2H^+ + 2NADP^+ + 4e^- \rightarrow 2NADPH$
To Light-Independent Reactions
ATP
To Light-Independent Reactions
ADP + P
H^+
Light
Electron carriers
Thylakoid membrane
Photosystem I
Photosystem II
ATP synthase
$4e^-$
THYLAKOID SPACE
$2H_2O$ → $4H^+$ + O_2
Photosystem II
Light energy absorbed by photosystem II produces high-energy electrons. Water molecules are split to replace those electrons, releasing H^+ ions and oxygen.
Electron Transport
High-energy electrons move down the electron transport chain, to photosystem I. Energy generated is used to pump H^+ ions across the thylakoid membrane and into the thylakoid space.
Photosystem I
Electrons are reenergized in photosystem I. A second electron transport chain then transfers these electrons to $NADP^+$, producing NADPH.
Hydrogen Ion Movement and ATP Formation
As the thylakoid space fills up with positively charged H^+ ions, the inside of the thylakoid membrane becomes positively charged relative to the outside of the membrane. H^+ ions pass back across the thylakoid membrane through ATP synthase. As the ions pass through, the ATP synthase molecule rotates and the energy produced is used to convert ADP to ATP.

Quick Facts

THE H^+ ION IN PHOTOSYNTHESIS

One of the important events in the light-dependent reactions is the removal of electrons and H^+ ions from water molecules. Both the electrons and the H^+ ions play important roles in the production of ATP and NADPH. Another way to identify the H^+ ions would be to simply call them protons. A hydrogen atom consists of 1 proton and 1 electron. An H^+ ion, then, is a hydrogen atom without its electron—that is, an H^+ ion is 1 proton. Therefore, the buildup of hydrogen ions in the thylakoid space is, to put it another way, a buildup of protons.

ZOOMING IN

Have small groups of students work through the steps shown in **Figure 8–10.** Then, review the figure in a full-class discussion. Begin by asking a volunteer to read aloud the first annotation, **Photosystem II.** Call on students at random to explain what is happening in that step. Continue in the same manner with the other annotations. If students have trouble understanding a step, read aloud the passage in the text that explains it.

DIFFERENTIATED INSTRUCTION

L1 Struggling Students Many students may find interpreting **Figure 8–10** difficult. Redraw the figure in simplified form on the board, using a line to represent the thylakoid membrane and four circles to represent the two photosystems and a protein in between and to the right. Ask students to tell you where to draw sunlight hitting the photosystems. Show how electrons move down the chain and hydrogen ions build up in the thylakoid space. Draw an ATP synthase molecule on the line, and then have students tell you how to draw the production of ATP as H^+ ions pass through the ATP synthase.

Ask What happens to the ATP molecules produced as H^+ ions pass through ATP synthase? *(They move to the light-independent reactions.)*

L3 Advanced Students Encourage interested students to work together to use what they've learned about the oxygen produced by photosynthesis to make a poster showing the value in conserving the great forests of the world, including the Amazon rain forest. Suggest they use online or library resources to investigate how the oxygen produced by plants benefits the whole biosphere.

BIOLOGY.com To see how ATP is produced through the rotation of ATP synthase, suggest students watch **Art in Motion: Light-Dependent Reactions.**

Answers

FIGURE 8–10 The figure shows 2 NADPH molecules produced for every 2 water molecules split (or 1 per water molecule).

Teach continued

ZOOMING IN

Use **Figure 8–11** to discuss the main steps of the light-independent reactions. Call on a volunteer to read aloud the annotation, **Carbon Dioxide Enters the Cycle.** Then call on another student to read the annotation **Sugar Production.**

Ask Where do the light-independent reactions occur? *(in the stroma of the chloroplast)*

Ask What products of the light-dependent reactions are used in the light-independent reactions? *(the electron carriers ATP and NADPH)*

Ask What is the main product of the Calvin cycle? *(sugars and other compounds)*

DIFFERENTIATED INSTRUCTION

L1 Struggling Students Some students may have a difficult time understanding the light-independent reactions as presented in **Figure 8–11.** Simplify the information by writing the important concepts on the board:

- The light-independent reactions occur in the stroma of the chloroplast.
- ATP and NADPH molecules produced in the light-dependent reactions enter the stroma.
- Carbon dioxide molecules from the atmosphere combine with other carbon molecules in the stroma to begin the cycle.
- Energy from ATP and NADPH is used to produce high-energy sugars in the Calvin cycle, another name for the light-independent reactions.

ELL English Language Learners Have students look up *stable* in a dictionary to find a definition that best fits the context in which it is used here: ATP and NADPH are not *stable* enough to store energy for more than a few minutes. Point out that *stable* is a good description of the high-energy sugars produced in photosynthesis, but not a good description of the electron carriers ATP and NADPH.

BIOLOGY.com Have students further explore the light-independent reactions by viewing **Art Review: Light-Independent Reactions.**

The Light-Independent Reactions: Producing Sugars

What happens during the light-independent reactions?

The ATP and NADPH formed by the light-dependent reactions contain an abundance of chemical energy, but they are not stable enough to store that energy for more than a few minutes. During the light-independent reactions, commonly referred to as the **Calvin cycle,** plants use the energy that ATP and NADPH contain to build stable high-energy carbohydrate compounds that can be stored for a long time. **During the light-independent reactions, ATP and NADPH from the light-dependent reactions are used to produce high-energy sugars.** The Calvin cycle is named after the American scientist Melvin Calvin, who worked out the details of this remarkable cycle. Follow **Figure 8–11** to see each step in this set of reactions.

ZOOMING IN

LIGHT-INDEPENDENT REACTIONS

FIGURE 8–11 The light-independent reactions of photosynthesis take place in the stroma of the chloroplast. The reactions use ATP and NADPH from the light-dependent reactions to produce high-energy sugars such as glucose. **Interpret Visuals** ***How many molecules of ATP are needed for each "turn" of the Calvin cycle?***

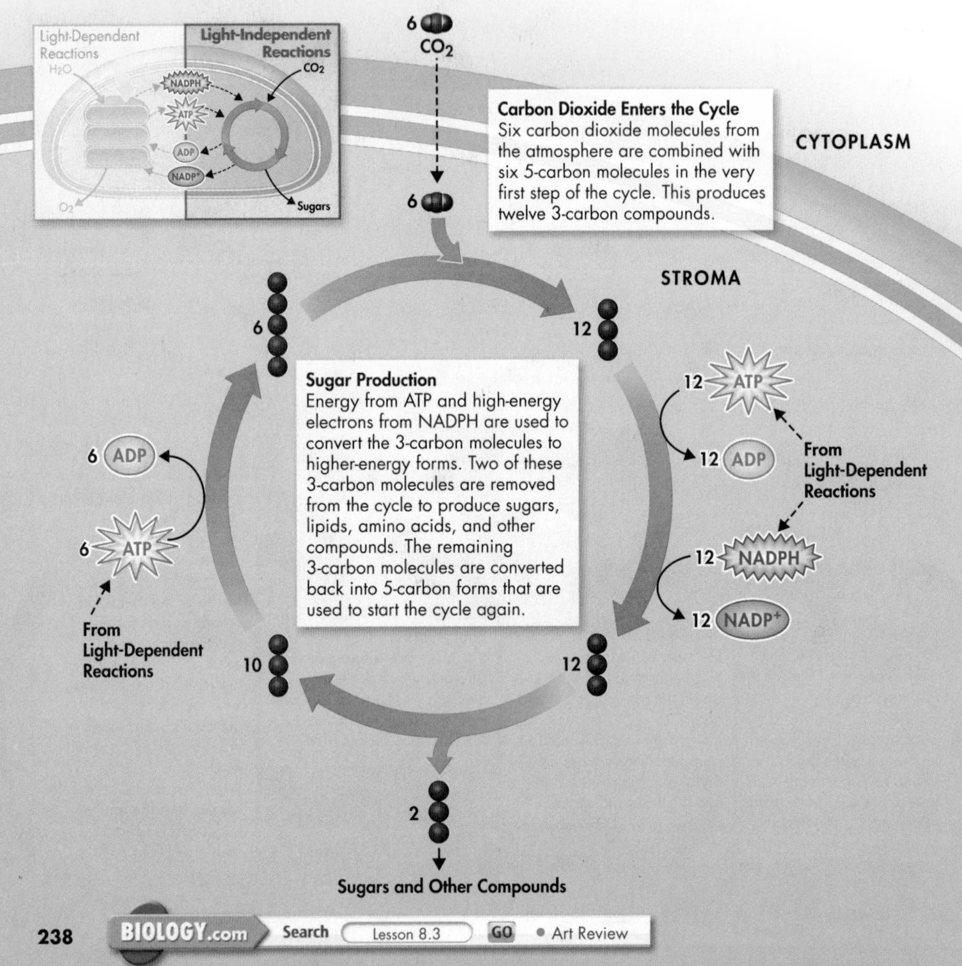

Light-Dependent Reactions
Light-Independent Reactions
H_2O
CO_2
NADPH
ATP
ADP
NADP+
O_2
Sugars
6 CO_2
Carbon Dioxide Enters the Cycle
Six carbon dioxide molecules from the atmosphere are combined with six 5-carbon molecules in the very first step of the cycle. This produces twelve 3-carbon compounds.
CYTOPLASM
STROMA
6
12
12 ATP
12 ADP
From Light-Dependent Reactions
12 NADPH
12 NADP+
Sugar Production
Energy from ATP and high-energy electrons from NADPH are used to convert the 3-carbon molecules to higher-energy forms. Two of these 3-carbon molecules are removed from the cycle to produce sugars, lipids, amino acids, and other compounds. The remaining 3-carbon molecules are converted back into 5-carbon forms that are used to start the cycle again.
6 ADP
6 ATP
From Light-Dependent Reactions
10
12
2
Sugars and Other Compounds

 BIOLOGY.com Search Lesson 8.3 GO • Art Review

Check for Understanding

DEPTH OF UNDERSTANDING

Ask Why is the conversion of ADP and $NADP^+$ to ATP and NADPH essential for cell function?

Students with a superficial understanding of photosynthesis might simply say these compounds carry energy. Students with a more sophisticated understanding will be able to explain that the formation of these compounds is the result of the conversion of energy from sunlight to chemical energy in the light-dependent reactions, which is then used in the light-independent reactions to produce the high-energy sugars that provide energy for cell processes.

ADJUST INSTRUCTION

Have students create a flowchart to show energy flow in photosynthesis.

Answers

FIGURE 8–11 Eighteen ATP molecules are needed for each turn of the Calvin cycle.

Carbon Dioxide Enters the Cycle Carbon dioxide molecules enter the Calvin cycle from the atmosphere. An enzyme in the stroma of the chloroplast combines these carbon dioxide molecules with 5-carbon compounds that are already present in the organelle, producing 3-carbon compounds that continue into the cycle. For every 6 carbon dioxide molecules that enter the cycle, a total of twelve 3-carbon compounds are produced. Other enzymes in the chloroplast then convert these compounds into higher-energy forms in the rest of the cycle. The energy for these conversions comes from ATP and high-energy electrons from NADPH.

Sugar Production At midcycle, two of the twelve 3-carbon molecules are removed from the cycle. This is a very special step because these molecules become the building blocks that the plant cell uses to produce sugars, lipids, amino acids, and other compounds. In other words, this step in the Calvin cycle contributes to all of the products needed for plant metabolism and growth.

The remaining ten 3-carbon molecules are converted back into six 5-carbon molecules. These molecules combine with six new carbon dioxide molecules to begin the next cycle.

Summary of the Calvin Cycle The Calvin cycle uses 6 molecules of carbon dioxide to produce a single 6-carbon sugar molecule. The energy for the reactions that make this possible is supplied by compounds produced in the light-dependent reactions. As photosynthesis proceeds, the Calvin cycle works steadily, removing carbon dioxide from the atmosphere and turning out energy-rich sugars. The plant uses the sugars to meet its energy needs and to build macromolecules needed for growth and development, including lipids, proteins, and complex carbohydrates such as cellulose. When other organisms eat plants, they, too, can use the energy and raw materials stored in these compounds.

The End Results The two sets of photosynthetic reactions work together—the light-dependent reactions trap the energy of sunlight in chemical form, and the light-independent reactions use that chemical energy to produce stable, high-energy sugars from carbon dioxide and water. And, in the process, animals, including ourselves, get plenty of food and an atmosphere filled with oxygen. Not a bad deal at all!

In Your Notebook *What happens to the NADP+, ADP, and sugars produced by the Calvin cycle?*

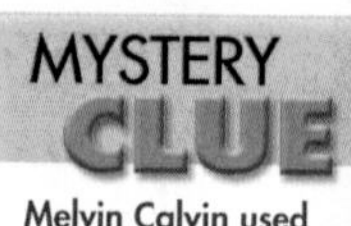

Melvin Calvin used radioactively labeled carbon atoms in carbon dioxide to show what happens to the carbon used in the light-independent reactions. Where does this carbon end up?

Biology In-Depth

THAT PESKY CRAB GRASS

C4 plants (discussed on page 241) have modified pathways that allow them to photosynthesize under harsh conditions. If students live in an area where most houses have their own lawns, they may be familiar with the battle many homeowners fight with a plant commonly called crab grass. Crab grass grows along with ordinary grass, and early in the growing season crab grass may not even be noticeable. In late summer, though, when many lawns dry out and become brown, patches of crab grass remain green and outgrow ordinary grass, creating unsightly patches. Why does crab grass do so well when ordinary grass struggles in late summer? *Digitaria sanguinalis,* as crab grass is properly known, is a C4 plant, whereas most common grasses are C3 plants. The C4 pathway enables crab grass to thrive under conditions where ordinary grasses grow slowly or start to turn brown.

Lead a Discussion

Some students may have difficulty following the events described when carbon dioxide enters the Calvin cycle. Help them understand the number of 3-carbon compounds produced by working through the math on the board.

Ask How many carbon atoms does a molecule of CO_2 contain? *(1)*

Ask When a carbon dioxide molecule combines with a 5-carbon compound, how many 3-carbon compounds are produced? *(two, because $1 + 5 = 6$; $6 \div 3 = 2$)*

Ask If for every carbon dioxide molecule that enters the cycle, two 3-carbon compounds are produced, then how many 3-carbon compounds are produced when six carbon dioxide molecules enter the cycle? *(twelve, because $2 \times 6 = 12$)*

DIFFERENTIATED INSTRUCTION

L1 Struggling Students Some students may have a hard time following the steps of the light-independent reactions. To help these students, read aloud a sentence from the text and then call attention to that step as shown in **Figure 8–11.** Continue this process through the Calvin cycle.

Discuss with students what product of photosynthesis contains carbon atoms. Suggest they look back to the overall equation for photosynthesis. Students can go online at **Biology.com** to gather their evidence.

Address Misconceptions

Increase of Matter From a Gas Some students may have difficulty understanding that photosynthesis uses a gas—carbon dioxide—to produce solid sugars. Address this concept by showing students an orange. Most students know oranges contain sugars. Write the formula for glucose on the board: $C_6H_{12}O_6$. Explain that an orange contains glucose. Then, ask what molecule enters the Calvin Cycle that contains carbon, symbolized by C. *(carbon dioxide)* Explain that the carbon in carbon dioxide contributes the carbon atoms in glucose. Therefore, through photosynthesis, a gas is used to make a solid.

Answers

IN YOUR NOTEBOOK ADP and NADP+ become available to pick up more high-energy electrons from the light-dependent reactions. High-energy sugars are used to meet energy needs or are converted to other materials used for growth and development.

Teach continued

Build Science Skills

Explain that scientists make predictions about natural occurrences based on evidence, experience, and knowledge. Have students work in small groups to predict how and why the rate of photosynthesis in plants would be affected by each of the following situations.

- An area in the Midwest experienced a drought that lasted for months. Lakes and rivers dropped to levels lower than anyone could remember.
- During August in a New England city, the temperature rose every day to 37–38°C (98.6–104°F).
- A series of huge volcanoes erupted, and the volcanic ash accumulated in Earth's atmosphere, reducing the intensity of sunlight for many days.

DIFFERENTIATED INSTRUCTION

LPR Less Proficient Readers Struggling readers may stumble over the phrase "intensity of light." Demonstrate varying intensities by shining a light directly onto a plant and then setting the light on a table a distance from the plant. Ask students which time the light shined more intensely on the plant. *(the closer, direct light)* Then, ask students to describe a condition when the intensity of sunlight is at its maximum. *(sunlight on a summer day when the sun is directly above)*

L3 Advanced Students Have small groups of students do further research on either C4 photosynthesis or Crassulacean Acid Metabolism (CAM). Ask each group to make a poster that includes drawings and labels explaining the process they researched. Have groups present their posters to the class.

BIOLOGY.com In **Data Analysis: Shedding Light on Marine Algae,** students can gather and analyze data derived from the relationship between light frequency and pigments in marine algae.

Answers

IN YOUR NOTEBOOK Enzymes are compounds that speed up chemical reactions, including those involved in photosynthesis.

Analyzing Data

IN NoS.3, B.3.1

Rates of Photosynthesis

The rate at which a plant carries out photosynthesis depends in part on environmental factors such as temperature, amount of water available, and light intensity. The graph shows how the average rates of photosynthesis between sun plants and shade plants changes with light intensity.

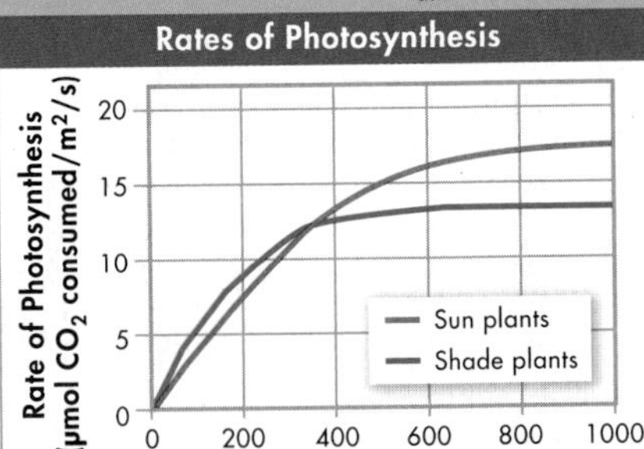

1. Use Tables and Graphs When light intensity is below 200 µmol photons/m²/s, do sun plants or shade plants have a higher rate of photosynthesis?

2. Infer Light intensity in the Sonoran Desert averages about 400 µmol photons/m²/s. According to the graph, what would be the approximate rate of photosynthesis for sun plants that grow in this environment?

3. Form a Hypothesis Suppose you transplant a sun plant to a shaded forest floor that receives about 100 µmol photons/m²/s. Do you think this plant will grow and thrive? Why or why not? How does the graph help you answer this question?

Factors Affecting Photosynthesis

What factors affect photosynthesis?

BUILD Vocabulary

MULTIPLE MEANINGS The noun *intensity* is commonly used to refer to something or someone who is very emotional, focused, or active. In science, however, *intensity* refers to energy. Thus, light intensity is a measure of the amount of energy available in light. More intense light has more energy.

Temperature, Light, and Water Many factors influence the rate of photosynthesis. **Among the most important factors that affect photosynthesis are temperature, light intensity, and the availability of water.** The reactions of photosynthesis are made possible by enzymes that function best between 0°C and 35°C. Temperatures above or below this range may affect those enzymes, slowing down the rate of photosynthesis. At very low temperatures, photosynthesis may stop entirely.

The intensity of light also affects the rate at which photosynthesis occurs. As you might expect, high light intensity increases the rate of photosynthesis. After the light intensity reaches a certain level, however, the plant reaches its maximum rate of photosynthesis.

Because water is one of the raw materials of photosynthesis, a shortage of water can slow or even stop photosynthesis. Water loss can also damage plant tissues. To deal with these dangers, plants (such as desert plants and conifers) that live in dry conditions often have waxy coatings on their leaves that reduce water loss. They may also have biochemical adaptations that make photosynthesis more efficient under dry conditions.

In Your Notebook *Explain in your own words what role enzymes play in chemical reactions such as photosynthesis.*

PURPOSE Students will infer the relationship between photosynthesis and light intensity.

PLANNING Tell students that understanding the units of measure along the axes are not as important as recognizing that the rate increases in units of 5 along the *y*-axis and light intensity increases in units of 200 along the *x*-axis.

ANSWERS

1. shade plants
2. about 13–14 µmol CO_2 consumed/m²/s
3. The sun plant will grow less well on the shady forest floor because its rate of photosynthesis will greatly decrease. The graph shows the rate will decrease from about 13 µmol CO_2 consumed/m²/s at 400 µmol photons/m²/s to only about 4 µmol CO_2 consumed/m²/s at 100 µmol photons/m²/s in a shaded forest.

Photosynthesis Under Extreme Conditions In order to conserve water, most plants under bright, hot conditions (of the sorts often found in the tropics) close the small openings in their leaves that normally admit carbon dioxide. While this keeps the plants from drying out, it causes carbon dioxide within the leaves to fall to very low levels. When this happens to most plants, photosynthesis slows down or even stops. However, some plants have adapted to extremely bright, hot conditions. There are two major groups of these specialized plants: C4 plants and CAM plants. C4 and CAM plants have biochemical adaptations that minimize water loss while still allowing photosynthesis to take place in intense sunlight.

▶ ***C4 Photosynthesis*** C4 plants have a specialized chemical pathway that allows them to capture even very low levels of carbon dioxide and pass it to the Calvin cycle. The name "C4 plant" comes from the fact that the first compound formed in this pathway contains 4 carbon atoms. The C4 pathway enables photosynthesis to keep working under intense light and high temperatures, but it requires extra energy in the form of ATP to function. C4 organisms include important crop plants like corn, sugar cane, and sorghum.

▶ ***CAM Plants*** Other plants adapted to dry climates use a different strategy to obtain carbon dioxide while minimizing water loss. These include members of the family Crassulaceae. Because carbon dioxide becomes incorporated into organic acids during photosynthesis, the process is called Crassulacean Acid Metabolism (CAM). CAM plants admit air into their leaves only at night. In the cool darkness, carbon dioxide is combined with existing molecules to produce organic acids, "trapping" the carbon within the leaves. During the daytime, when leaves are tightly sealed to prevent the loss of water, these compounds release carbon dioxide, enabling carbohydrate production. CAM plants include pineapple trees, many desert cacti, and also the fleshy "ice plants" shown in **Figure 8–12,** which are frequently planted near freeways along the west coast to retard brush fires and prevent erosion.

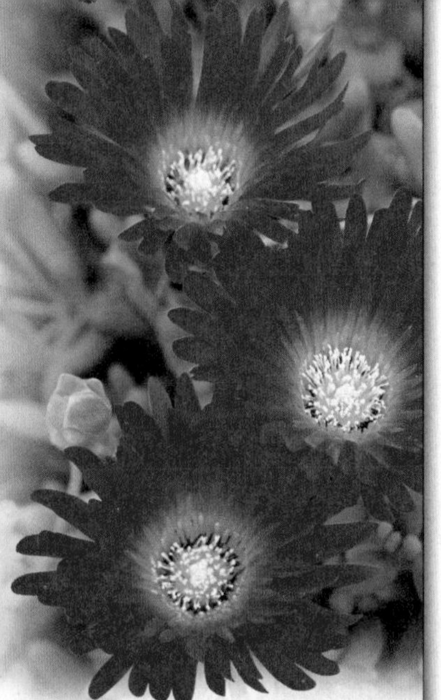

FIGURE 8–12 CAM Plants Plants like this ice plant can survive in dry conditions due to their modified light-independent reactions. Air is allowed into the leaves only at night, minimizing water loss.

8.3 Assessment

IN B.3.1

Review Key Concepts

1. a. Review Summarize what happens during the light-dependent reactions of photosynthesis.
b. Sequence Put the events of the light-dependent reactions in the order in which they occur and describe how each step is dependent on the step that comes before it.

2. a. Review What is the Calvin cycle?
b. Compare and Contrast List at least three differences between the light-dependent and light-independent reactions of photosynthesis.

3. a. Review What are the three primary factors that affect the rate of photosynthesis?
b. Interpret Graphs Look at the graph on page 240. What are the independent and dependent variables being tested?

BUILD VOCABULARY

4. The word *carbohydrate* comes from the prefix *carbo-*, meaning "carbon," and the word *hydrate*. Based on the reactants of the photosynthesis equation, what does *hydrate* mean?

BIOLOGY.com Search Lesson 8.3  GO • Lesson Assessment • Self-Test

Expand Vocabulary

Minimum and *maximum* are concepts commonly used in a scientific context. Have students look up *minimize* in a dictionary and then write a sentence explaining what it means to "minimize water loss."

DIFFERENTIATED INSTRUCTION

ELL English Language Learners Explain that *minimize* is the verb form of the word *minimum,* which means "the least quantity possible." Then, explain that the opposite of *minimum* is *maximum,* or "the greatest quantity possible." The verb form of *maximum* is *maximize.*

Assess and Remediate

EVALUATE UNDERSTANDING

Ask students to write two short summary paragraphs, one on the light-dependent reactions and another on the light-independent reactions. Then, have them complete the 8.3 Assessment.

REMEDIATION SUGGESTION

L1 Struggling Students If students have trouble with **Question 2b,** suggest they look at what is needed to begin each set of reactions and what the products of each set are. Review the difference between the independent variable and the dependent variable in a controlled experiment if students get stuck on **Question 3b.**

BIOLOGY.com Students can check their understanding of lesson concepts with the **Self-Test** assessment. They can then take an online version of the **Lesson Assessment.**

Assessment Answers

1a. The light-dependent reactions use energy from sunlight to produce oxygen and convert ADP and $NADP^+$ into the energy carriers ATP and NADPH.

1b. Sample answer: (1) Light energy is absorbed by electrons in the pigments and water molecules are split into H^+ ions, oxygen, and electrons. (2) High-energy electrons (from the splitting of water) move down the electron transport chain, where energy from the electrons is used to pump H^+ ions into the thylakoid space. (3) At the end of the chain, $NADP^+$ molecules pick up the high-energy electrons along with H^+ ions to become NADPH. (4) H^+ ions in the thylakoid space (pumped across in step 2) pass through ATP synthase in the thylakoid membrane, causing the ATP synthase base to rotate and produce ATP.

2a. The Calvin cycle is another name for the light-independent reactions in which ATP and NADPH from the light-dependent reactions are used to produce high-energy sugars. It is named for Melvin Calvin, who worked on its details.

2b. Sample answer: The light-dependent reactions require light and water, occur in the thylakoids, and produce ATP and NADPH. The light-independent reactions require carbon dioxide, occur in the stroma, and produce high-energy sugars.

3a. temperature, light intensity, availability of water

3b. independent variable: light intensity; dependent variable: rate of photosynthesis

BUILD VOCABULARY

4. (to combine with) water

CHAPTER LAB

Pre-Lab

Introduce students to the concepts they will explore in the chapter lab by assigning the Pre-Lab questions.

Lab

Tell students they will perform the chapter lab *Plant Pigments and Photosynthesis* described in **Lab Manual A.**

 **Struggling Students** A simpler version of the chapter lab is provided in **Lab Manual B.**

SAFETY

Make sure students work in a well-ventilated area. Caution them to avoid breathing the fumes and to use care when handling glassware. Students should wash their hands thoroughly after the lab.

Look online for **Editable Lab Worksheets**.

For corresponding pre-lab in the **Foundation Edition**, see page 204.

IN INDIANA ACADEMIC STANDARDS

For the full text of all standards, see the Course Overview in the front matter of this book.

GUIDED INQUIRY

Pre-Lab: Plant Pigments and Photosynthesis

Problem Do red leaves have the same pigments as green leaves?

Materials paper clips, one-hole rubber stoppers, chromatography paper strips, metric ruler, green and red leaves, coin, sheet of paper, large test tubes, test tube rack, glass-marking pencil, 10-mL graduated cylinder, isopropyl alcohol, colored pencils

Lab Manual Chapter 8 Lab

Skills Focus Predict, Analyze Data, Draw Conclusions

Connect to the Big idea Almost all life on Earth depends, directly or indirectly, on energy from sunlight. Photosynthesis is the process in which light energy is captured and converted to chemical energy. Many reactions are required for this conversion, which takes place in the chloroplasts of plant cells. Some of the reactions depend on light and some do not. Plant pigments play a major role in the light-dependent reactions. In this lab, you will use chromatography to compare the pigments in red leaves with those in green leaves.

Background Questions

a. **Compare and Contrast** What do all plant pigments have in common? How are they different?

b. **Review** Why do most leaves appear green?

c. **Review** What property makes chlorophyll so important for photosynthesis?

Pre-Lab Questions

Preview the procedure in the lab manual.

1. **Design an Experiment** What is the purpose of this lab?
2. **Control Variables** What is the control in this lab?
3. **Design an Experiment** Why must you place a leaf about 2 cm from the bottom of the paper before rubbing the leaf with the coin?
4. **Predict** Will red leaves contain the same amount of chlorophyll as green leaves? Why or why not?

BIOLOGY.com Search 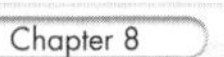 GO

Visit Chapter 8 online to test yourself on chapter content and to find activities to help you learn.

Untamed Science Video Journey to Panama with the Untamed Science crew to discover how CO_2 affects plant growth.

Data Analysis Look at pigment color data in the ocean to find out how marine algae photosynthesize in the blue light available underwater.

Tutor Tube Learn how to sort out the products and reactants in both the light-dependent and light-independent reactions.

Art Review Focus on the thylakoid membrane to review your knowledge of the light-dependent reactions.

InterActive Art Bring the components of photosynthesis together to run an animation.

Art in Motion Watch the steps of the light-dependent reactions in motion at the molecular level.

Visual Analogies Compare ATP production to a charged battery. See how the electron transport chain is like passing a hot potato.

Pre-Lab Answers

BACKGROUND QUESTIONS

a. Sample answer: All the pigments are light-absorbing molecules. They differ in how well they absorb different wavelengths of light.

b. Leaves reflect green light because chlorophyll does not absorb light well in the green region of the spectrum.

c. Sample answer: Much of the energy absorbed by chlorophyll molecules is transferred directly to electrons in the chlorophyll molecule.

PRE-LAB QUESTIONS

1. The purpose is to find out whether red leaves have the same pigments as green leaves.
2. Students may say that the green leaf or the chromatogram made from the green leaf is the control.
3. Sample answer: When the strips are placed in the test tube, the pigment line must be above the surface of the alcohol.
4. Sample answer: Red leaves will have less chlorophyll than green leaves because they are not green.

8 Study Guide

Big idea Cellular Basis of Life

Photosynthesis is the process by which organisms convert light energy into chemical energy that all organisms can use directly, or indirectly, to carry out life functions.

8.1 Energy and Life

ATP can easily release and store energy by breaking and re-forming the bonds between its phosphate groups. This characteristic of ATP makes it exceptionally useful as a basic energy source for all cells.

In the process of photosynthesis, plants convert the energy of sunlight into chemical energy stored in the bonds of carbohydrates.

adenosine triphosphate (ATP) (226)
heterotroph (228)
autotroph (228)
photosynthesis (228)

8.2 Photosynthesis: An Overview

Photosynthetic organisms capture energy from sunlight with pigments.

An electron carrier is a compound that can accept a pair of high-energy electrons and transfer them, along with most of their energy, to another molecule.

Photosynthesis uses the energy of sunlight to convert water and carbon dioxide (reactants) into high-energy sugars and oxygen (products).

pigment (230)
chlorophyll (230)
thylakoid (231)
stroma (231)
NADP$^+$ (232)
light-dependent reactions (233)
light-independent reactions (233)

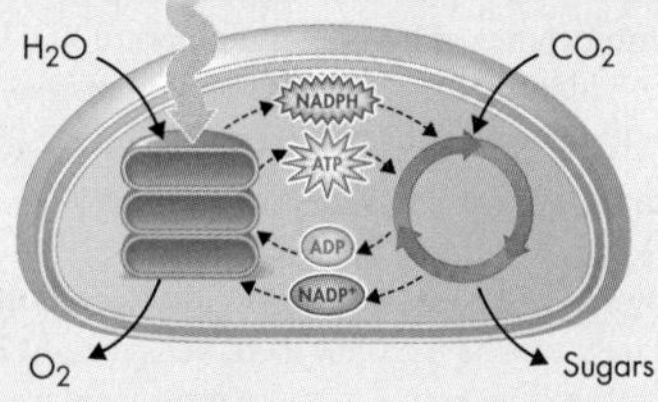

8.3 The Process of Photosynthesis

The light-dependent reactions use energy from sunlight to produce oxygen and convert ADP and NADP$^+$ into the energy carriers ATP and NADPH.

During the light-independent reactions, ATP and NADPH from the light-dependent reactions are used to produce high-energy sugars.

Among the most important factors that affect photosynthesis are temperature, light intensity, and the availability of water.

photosystem (235)
electron transport chain (236)
ATP synthase (237)
Calvin cycle (238)

Think Visually
Using the information in this chapter, complete the following flowchart about photosynthesis.

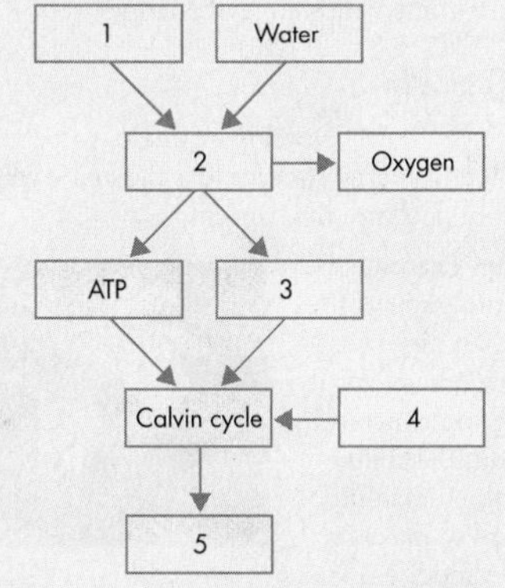

Study Online

REVIEW AND ASSESSMENT RESOURCES

Editable Worksheets Pages of Study Workbooks A and B, Lab Manuals A and B, and the Assessment Resources Book are available online. These documents can be easily edited using a word-processing program.

Lesson Overview Have students reread the Lesson Overviews to help them study chapter concepts.

Vocabulary Review The *Flash Cards* and *Crossword* provide an interactive way to review chapter vocabulary.

Chapter Assessment Have students take an online version of the Chapter 8 Assessment.

Standardized Test Prep Students can take an online version of the Standardized Test Prep. You will receive their scores along with ideas for remediation.

Diagnostic and Benchmark Tests Use these tests to monitor your students' progress and supply remediation.

Answers

THINK VISUALLY

1. light
2. light-dependent reactions
3. NADPH
4. carbon dioxide
5. sugars

UbD Performance Tasks

SUMMATIVE TASK Have students work in small groups to make a model of photosynthesis that includes both the light-dependent and light-independent reactions. Their model could be constructed on a base of cardboard or poster board and use materials such as clay, string or yarn; wooden beads, and colored markers or pencils. Students should also label their model. Ask each group to display its completed model for other students to observe and ask questions about.

TRANSFER TASK In a class discussion, have students review the difference between heterotrophs and autotrophs. Point out that now that they have learned about photosynthesis, they should have a much deeper understanding of how autotrophs make their own food, as well as how autotrophs provide heterotrophs with the food they need to produce the ATP used by their cells for energy. Then, ask each student to create a series of scenes that "runs the movie backward"—beginning with a human activity and ending with sunlight being absorbed by chlorophyll. Give students a choice of how they create their scenes. For example, they could draw a series of cartoons, make a flowchart, or write an essay. Explain that they will learn the details in the next chapter of how cells use food to make ATP, but for this task all they need to include on that subject is that a heterotroph's cells can use food to make ATP.

ASSESSMENT

Lesson 8.1

UNDERSTAND KEY CONCEPTS

1. b **2.** b **3.** b **4.** c

5. Heterotrophs obtain energy by consuming other organisms; autotrophs obtain energy by consuming the food they make.

6. An ATP molecule consists of a nitrogen-containing compound called adenine, a 5-carbon sugar called ribose, and three phosphate groups.

7. A single molecule of glucose stores more than 90 times the energy stored by ATP. ATP, though, transfers energy quickly and is used by the cell as an immediate source of energy.

THINK CRITICALLY

8. Answers should include an understanding that ATP stores only a small amount of energy and, thus, is efficient for only short-term storage. Answers should also acknowledge that energy in ATP is stored as chemical bonds, and energy is released when bonds are broken to form ADP and stored when bonds are added to re-form ATP (energy transfer).

9. The Indian pipe plant appears to have no chlorophyll or any other pigment. Without a pigment, this organism cannot carry out photosynthesis to make its own food. Therefore, it must be a heterotroph, which obtains food by consuming other living things.

Lesson 8.2

UNDERSTAND KEY CONCEPTS

10. d **11.** c

12. carbon dioxide + water $\xrightarrow{\text{light}}$ sugars + oxygen

13. Plant pigments absorb sunlight—the energy source for photosynthesis.

14. A=stroma; B=granum; C=thylakoid; the light-dependent reactions take place within the thylakoids that make up grana (C and/or B); the light-independent reactions take place in the stroma (A).

THINK CRITICALLY

15. The chlorophyll molecules break down first as temperatures drop in the fall, leaving the yellow and red light reflected by the accessory pigments for all to see.

Assessment

The numbers following the questions refer to Indiana's Academic Standards for Biology I.

8.1 Energy and Life

Understand Key Concepts

1. Which of the following are autotrophs?
a. deer **c.** leopards
b. plants **d.** mushrooms

2. The principal chemical compound that living things use to store energy is
a. DNA. **c.** H_2O.
b. ATP. **d.** CO_2.

3. The amount of energy stored in a molecule of ATP compared to the amount stored in a molecule of glucose is
a. greater.
b. less.
c. the same.
d. variable, depending on conditions.

4. When a candle burns, energy is released in the form of
a. carbon dioxide and water.
b. the chemical substance ATP.
c. light and heat.
d. electricity and motion.

5. How do heterotrophs and autotrophs differ in the way they obtain energy? B.3.5

6. Describe the three parts of an ATP molecule.

7. Compare the amounts of energy stored by ATP and glucose. Which compound is used by the cell as an immediate source of energy?

Think Critically

8. **Use Analogies** Develop an analogy to explain ATP and energy transfer to a classmate who does not understand the concept.

9. **Infer** Examine the photograph of the Indian pipe plant shown here. What can you conclude about the ability of the Indian pipe plant to make its own food? Explain your answer. B.3.1

8.2 Photosynthesis: An Overview

Understand Key Concepts

10. In addition to light and chlorophyll, photosynthesis requires B.3.1
a. water and oxygen.
b. water and sugars.
c. oxygen and carbon dioxide.
d. water and carbon dioxide.

11. The leaves of a plant appear green because chlorophyll
a. reflects blue light. **c.** reflects green light.
b. absorbs blue light. **d.** absorbs green light.

12. Write the basic equation for photosynthesis using the names of the starting and final substances of the process. B.3.1

13. What role do plant pigments play in the process of photosynthesis?

14. Identify the chloroplast structures labeled A, B, and C. In which structure(s) do the light-dependent reactions occur? In which structure(s) do the light-independent reactions take place? B.2.3

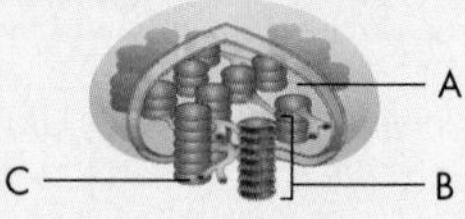

Think Critically

15. **Form a Hypothesis** Although they appear green, some plant leaves contain yellow and red pigments as well as chlorophyll. In the fall, those leaves may become red or yellow. Suggest an explanation for these color changes.

16. **Design an Experiment** Design an experiment that uses pond water and algae to demonstrate the importance of light energy to pond life. Be sure to identify the variables you will control and the variable you will change. B.3.1

17. **Predict** Suppose you water a potted plant and place it by a window in a transparent, airtight jar. Predict how the rate of photosynthesis might be affected over the next few days. What might happen if the plant were left there for several weeks? Explain. B.3.1

16. Sample answer: Start with two samples of the same type of algae, and place equal amounts of the algae samples in the same amount of pond water. Put one sample in a dark place and the other in a location that receives sunlight daily. Temperatures should be kept the same in both places. After two weeks, compare the two samples to determine the growth and health of the two samples of algae.

17. Sample answer: The plant would grow normally for a short period of time, and then the rate of photosynthesis would drop because of a lack of CO_2, which is necessary for carrying out photosynthesis. Eventually, the plant might die, because without the CO_2 necessary to carry out photosynthesis, the plant would not have the energy-storing sugars needed to carry out cell activities.

8.3 The Process of Photosynthesis

Understand Key Concepts

18. The first process in the light-dependent reactions of photosynthesis is
a. light absorption. **c.** oxygen production.
b. electron transport. **d.** ATP formation.

19. Which substance from the light-dependent reactions of photosynthesis is a source of energy for the Calvin cycle?
a. ADP **c.** H_2O
b. NADPH **d.** pyruvic acid

20. The light-independent reactions of photosynthesis are also known as the B.3.1
a. Calvin cycle. **c.** carbon cycle.
b. sugar cycle. **d.** ATP cycle.

21. ATP synthase in the chloroplast membrane makes ATP, utilizing the energy of highly concentrated
a. chlorophyll. **c.** hydrogen ions.
b. electrons. **d.** NADPH.

22. CAM plants are specialized to survive under what conditions that would harm most other kinds of plants?
a. low temperatures **c.** hot, dry conditions
b. excess water **d.** long day lengths

23. Explain the role of $NADP^+$ as an energy carrier in photosynthesis.

24. Describe the role of ATP synthase and explain how it works. B.1.2

25. Summarize the events of the Calvin cycle.

26. Discuss three factors that affect the rate at which photosynthesis occurs. B.1.2, B.3.1

Think Critically

27. Interpret Graphs Study **Figure 8–11** on page 238 and give evidence to support the idea that the Calvin cycle does not depend on light.

28. Apply Concepts How do the events in the Calvin cycle depend on the light-dependent reactions of photosynthesis? B.3.1

29. Form a Hypothesis Many of the sun's rays may be blocked by dust or clouds formed by volcanic eruptions or pollution. What are some possible short-term and long-term effects of this on photosynthesis? On other forms of life? B.3.1

solve the CHAPTER MYSTERY

OUT OF THIN AIR?

Most plants grow out of the soil, of course, and you might hypothesize, as Jan van Helmont did, that soil contributes to plant mass. At the conclusion of his experiment with the willow tree, however, van Helmont discovered that the mass of the soil was essentially unchanged, but that the tree had increased in mass by nearly 75 kilograms. Van Helmont concluded that the mass must have come from water, because water was the only thing he had added throughout the experiment. What he didn't know, however, was that the increased bulk of the tree was built from carbon, as well as from the oxygen and hydrogen in water. We now know that most of that carbon comes from carbon dioxide in the air. Thus, mass accumulates from two sources: carbon dioxide and water. What form does the added mass take? Think about the origin of the word *carbohydrate*, from *carbo-*, meaning "carbon," and *hydrate*, meaning "to combine with water," and you have your answer.

1. **Infer** Although soil does not significantly contribute to plant mass, how might it help plants grow?
2. **Infer** If a scientist were able to measure the exact mass of carbon dioxide and water that entered a plant, and the exact mass of the sugars produced, would the masses be identical? Why or why not? B.3.1
3. **Apply Concepts** What do plants do with all of the carbohydrates they produce by photosynthesis? (*Hint*: Plant cells have mitochondria in addition to chloroplasts. What do mitochondria do?) B.2.3, B.3.2
4. **Connect to the Big idea** Explain how the experiments carried out by van Helmont and Calvin contributed to our understanding of how nutrients cycle in the biosphere.

BIOLOGY.com Search 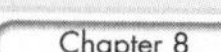  • Untamed Science Video • Chapter Mystery

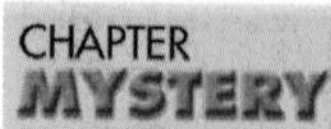

After students have read through the Chapter Mystery, discuss what van Helmont concluded as well as what he could not know about the process of photosynthesis.

Ask How do you think most people of van Helmont's time thought trees gained their mass as they grew? *(They thought that trees somehow gained their mass by taking in the soil.)*

Ask Why couldn't van Helmont know that trees gained much of their mass through taking in carbon dioxide from the atmosphere? *(He didn't have the modern technology that might have detected how plants use carbon dioxide.)*

Ask Van Helmont was right that plants use water to build mass, though he didn't know how. How do plants use water to increase mass? *(Sample answer: Plants use water in the light-dependent reactions of photosynthesis. The water molecules are split, and the electrons and hydrogen ions are picked up by electron carriers and then used in the light-independent reactions to produce high-energy sugars.)*

CHAPTER MYSTERY ANSWERS

1. Soil provides a base into which a plant can anchor itself. The soil holds the water that plants take in and use in photosynthesis. The soil provides nutrients the plant needs.
2. The masses would not be identical. The mass of the water and carbon dioxide would be more than the mass of the sugars because the oxygen atoms in water are expelled from the plant cells in the first stage of photosynthesis.
3. Plants use the carbohydrates as a source of energy to carry out cell activities. The mitochondria in plant cells convert the energy in the carbohydrates into compounds that are more convenient for the cells to use.
4. Big idea Van Helmont's work was the beginning of many experiments that led to the understanding that the sources of a plant's increase in mass are water and carbon dioxide that, through photosynthesis, combine to make sugars. Calvin was able to trace the chemical path carbon follows. Both van Helmont and Calvin contributed to an understanding of photosynthesis, which is involved in the cycling of both oxygen and carbon in the biosphere. Inorganic carbon and hydrogen are combined to form organic sugars. In turn, oxygen is released to the atmosphere.

Students can explore the connection between plant growth, carbon, and photosynthesis deep in the jungles of Panama by watching **Soaking Up the CO_2.**

Lesson 8.3

UNDERSTAND KEY CONCEPTS

18. a **19.** b **20.** a
21. c **22.** c

23. $NADP^+$ molecules pick up high-energy electrons along with H^+ ions in the light-dependent reactions to become NADPH. This NADPH is used in the light-independent reactions to produce high-energy sugars.

24. ATP synthase is a protein that spans the thylakoid membrane and allows H^+ ions to pass through. As H^+ ions from the thylakoid space pass through the ATP synthase and into the stroma, the ATP synthase molecule rotates and the energy produced is used to convert ADP to ATP.

25. The Calvin cycle uses 6 molecules of carbon dioxide to produce a single 6-carbon sugar molecule. The energy for the reactions that make this possible is supplied by ATP and NADPH, which are produced in the light-dependent reactions. The Calvin cycle works steadily, removing carbon dioxide from the atmosphere and turning out energy-rich sugars.

26. Sample answer: Because the enzymes that make photosynthesis possible work best between 0°C and 35°C, temperatures above or below this range may slow down the rate of photosynthesis. High light intensity increases the rate of photosynthesis, though after the light intensity reaches a certain level the plant reaches its maximum rate. A shortage of water can slow or even stop photosynthesis.

THINK CRITICALLY

27. No step in the Calvin cycle depends on the presence of light. Instead, the cycle uses energy stored in ATP and NADPH.

28. The energy used in the Calvin cycle comes from ATP and NADPH produced in the light-dependent reactions.

29. Sample answer: If enough of the sun's rays are blocked, the rate of photosynthesis would slow down. In the short term, plants and other photosynthetic organisms may not grow normally. In the long run, some plants, and organisms that depend on plants, may not survive.

Connecting Concepts

USE SCIENCE GRAPHICS

30. Students' graphs should show Distance From Light (cm) on the *x*-axis and Bubbles Produced per Minute on the *y*-axis. The line should show a curve that descends from left to right.

31. The number of bubbles decreases as the light is placed further away. There would be fewer than 5 bubbles if the light were 50 cm away.

32. The farther the light is from the plant, the fewer the number of bubbles produced. The reason is that a decrease in light intensity results in a decrease in the rate of photosynthesis—and therefore a decrease in oxygen produced.

33. because that is where light intensity is greatest

WRITE ABOUT SCIENCE

34. Stories and illustrations will vary. Students should recognize that both the oxygen atom and the hydrogen atoms enter a chloroplast together as a water molecule, H_2O. The oxygen atom is split from the hydrogen atoms in the light-dependent stage of photosynthesis and leaves the plant as oxygen gas. The hydrogen atoms become involved in the formation of NADPH, the production of ATP, and the production of high-energy sugars in the Calvin cycle.

35. Big idea The chloroplasts are specialized to produce sugars such as glucose, but this process cannot occur without an input of energy. The sun's rays provide that energy, and chlorophyll captures the sun's rays.

Connecting Concepts

Use Science Graphics NoS.3

A water plant placed under bright light gives off bubbles of oxygen. The table below contains the results of an experiment in which the distance from the light to the plant was varied. Use the data table to answer questions 30–33.

Oxygen Production

Distance From Light (cm)	Bubbles Produced per Minute
10	39
20	22
30	8
40	5

30. Graph Use the data in the table to make a line graph. MATH

31. Interpret Graphs Describe the observed trend. How many bubbles would you predict if the light was moved to 50 cm away? Explain.

32. Draw Conclusions What relationship exists between the plant's distance from the light and the number of bubbles produced? What process is occuring? Explain your answer. B.3.1

33. Apply Concepts Based on the results of this experiment, explain why most aquatic primary producers live in the uppermost regions of deep oceans, lakes, and ponds. B.3.1

Write About Science NoS.3

34. Creative Writing Imagine that you are an oxygen atom and two of your friends are hydrogen atoms. Together, you make up a water molecule. Describe the events and changes that happen to you and your friends as you journey through the light-dependent reactions and the Calvin cycle of photosynthesis. Include illustrations with your description. B.3.1

35. Assess the Big idea In eukaryotic plants, chlorophyll is found only in chloroplasts. Explain how the function of chlorophyll is related to its very specific location in the cell. B.2.3

Analyzing Data

IN NoS.3

An experimenter subjected corn plants and bean plants to different concentrations of carbon dioxide and measured the amount of CO_2 taken up by the plants and used in photosynthesis. Data for the two plants are shown in the following graph.

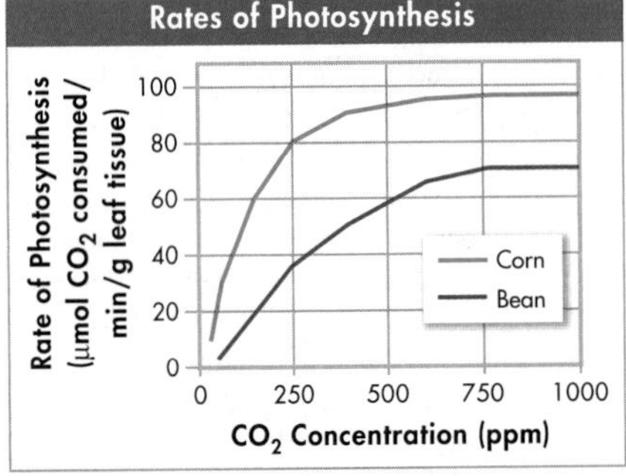

36. Interpret Graphs Bean plants reach their maximum rate of photosynthesis at what concentration of carbon dioxide?

a. about 50 ppm
b. about 200 ppm
c. about 750 ppm
d. 1000 ppm

37. Draw Conclusions From the data it is possible to conclude that

a. beans contain more chlorophyll than corn contains.
b. corn reaches its maximum photosynthetic rate at lower concentrations than beans do.
c. beans reach their maximum photosynthetic rate at lower concentrations than corn does.
d. beans use carbon dioxide more efficiently than corn does.

246 Chapter 8 • Assessment

PURPOSE Students will analyze data to understand how varying concentrations of CO_2 affect rates of photosynthesis and that different plants respond to CO_2 concentration in different ways.

PLANNING Review with students factors that affect photosynthesis. Also remind students that a line graph shows how a variable plotted on the vertical axis changes in response to changes in the variable plotted on the horizontal axis. Tell students that understanding the unit of measure for the rate of photosynthesis is not as important as recognizing that the rate increases in units of 20 along the vertical axis. Finally, you may wish to ask students which of the two plants is a C4 plant and how they know. *(Corn is C4; it has a higher rate of photosynthesis, even at very low CO_2 concentrations.)*

ANSWERS

36. c

37. b

Standardized Test Practice for Indiana

Multiple Choice

1. Autotrophs differ from heterotrophs because they
   A utilize oxygen to burn food.
   B do not require oxygen to live.
   C make carbon dioxide as a product of using food.
   D make their own food from carbon dioxide and water.

2. The principal pigment in plants is
   A chlorophyll.
   B oxygen.
   C ATP.
   D NADPH.

3. Which of the following is NOT produced in the light-dependent reactions of photosynthesis?
   A NADPH
   B sugars
   C hydrogen ions
   D ATP

4. Which of the following correctly summarizes the process of photosynthesis?
   A $H_2O + CO_2 \xrightarrow{\text{light}} \text{sugars} + O_2$
   B $\text{sugars} + O_2 \xrightarrow{\text{light}} H_2O + CO_2$
   C $H_2O + O_2 \xrightarrow{\text{light}} \text{sugars} + CO_2$
   D $\text{sugars} + CO_2 \xrightarrow{\text{light}} H_2O + O_2$ B.3.1

5. The color of light that is LEAST useful to a plant during photosynthesis is
   A red.
   B blue.
   C green.
   D violet.

6. The first step in photosynthesis is the
   A synthesis of water.
   B production of oxygen.
   C breakdown of carbon dioxide.
   D absorption of light energy. B.3.1

7. In a typical plant, all of the following factors are necessary for photosynthesis EXCEPT
   A chlorophyll.
   B light.
   C oxygen.
   D water. B.3.1

Questions 8–10

Several drops of concentrated pigment were extracted from spinach leaves. These drops were placed at the bottom of a strip of highly absorbent paper. After the extract dried, the paper was suspended in a test tube containing alcohol so that only the tip of the paper was in the alcohol. As the alcohol was absorbed and moved up the paper, the various pigments contained in the extract separated as shown in the diagram.

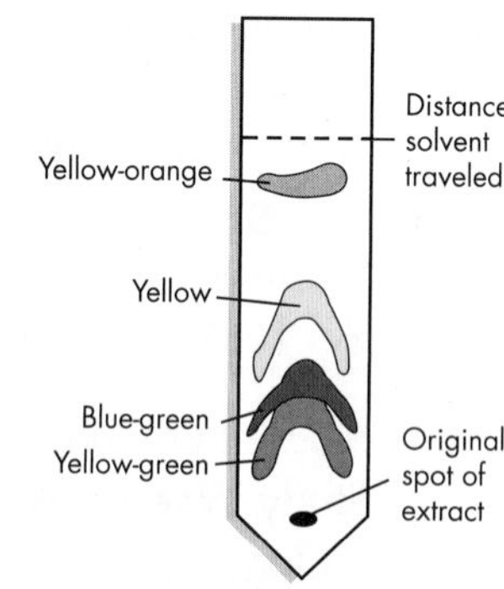

8. Which pigment traveled the shortest distance?
   A yellow-orange
   B yellow
   C blue-green
   D yellow-green

9. A valid conclusion that can be drawn from this information is that spinach leaves
   A use only chlorophyll during photosynthesis.
   B contain several pigments.
   C contain more orange pigment than yellow pigment.
   D are yellow-orange rather than green.

10. In which organelle would MOST of these pigments be found?
    A vacuoles
    B centrioles
    C mitochondria
    D chloroplasts B.2.3

Open-Ended Response

11. Describe how high-energy electrons are ultimately responsible for driving the photosynthetic reactions.

If You Have Trouble With . . .

Question	1	2	3	4	5	6	7	8	9	10	11
See Lesson	8.1	8.2	8.2	8.2	8.2	8.3	8.3	8.2	8.2	8.2	8.3

Test-Taking Tip

INTERPRET VISUALS

When a paragraph and related questions accompany a visual, tell students to first carefully read the paragraph and all the labels on the visual. The accompanying paragraph often will put the visual in some context, as well as provide a description or explanation of the visual itself. Reading the labels carefully lets the reader know what specific structures, events, or measurements are shown on the visual. After reading the paragraph and labels, look for any trends or comparisons that the visual presents. After taking these steps to interpret the visual, read and answer the questions.

Answers

1. D
2. A
3. B
4. A
5. C
6. D
7. C
8. D
9. B
10. D
11. Light is absorbed by electrons in pigments, increasing the electrons' energy level. These high-energy electrons are used in the light-dependent reactions to convert ADP and $NADP^+$ into the molecules ATP and NADPH. In the light-independent reactions, ATP and NADPH are then used to produce high-energy sugars.

CHAPTER PLANNER 9 Cellular Respiration and Fermentation

Chapter Contents	IN	Time	Core Resources
Chapter Preview			**Student Edition,** pp. 248–249 **Chapter Mystery,** p. 249
9.1 Cellular Respiration: An Overview Chemical Energy and Food • Overview of Cellular Respiration • Comparing Photosynthesis and Cellular Respiration	NoS.3, NoS.6, B.3.1, B.3.2	1 period 1/2 block	**Student Edition,** pp. 250–253 Inquiry 9.1 Analyzing Data, p. 251 L2 **Study Workbook A** 9.1 Worksheets L2 **Biology.com** *Art in Motion:* Opposite Processes: Respiration and Photosynthesis • 9.1 Self-Test • 9.1 Lesson Assessment
9.2 The Process of Cellular Respiration Glycolysis • The Krebs Cycle • Electron Transport and ATP Synthesis • The Totals • *Biology & Society: Should Creatine Supplements Be Regulated?*	B.1.2, B.2.3, B.3.2	1 1/2 periods 3/4 block	**Student Edition,** pp. 254–261 **Study Workbook A** 9.2 Worksheets L2 **Biology.com** *InterActive Art:* Cellular Respiration and Fermentation • *Tutor Tube:* Oxygen as the Acceptor of Cellular Respiration Waste **Assessment Resources Book** Visual Quiz L2
9.3 Fermentation Fermentation • Energy and Exercise		1 period 1/2 block	**Student Edition,** pp. 262–265 Inquiry 9.3 Quick Lab, p. 264 L2 **Study Workbook A** 9.3 Worksheets L2 **Biology.com** *Data Analysis:* Lactic Acid and Athletes • 9.3 Self-Test • 9.3 Lesson Assessment
Chapter Pre-Lab		1 period 1/2 block	**Student Edition,** p. 266 L2 **Lab Manual A** *Comparing the Fermentation Rates of Sugars* L2 • *Investigating the Fermentation of Kimchi* L2 • *Photosynthesis and Respiration* L2

Differentiated Instruction Tools

Study Workbook B includes worksheets with lesson-level differentiated instruction support and explanations of differentiated instruction teaching strategies.

Lab Manual B includes skills labs, simplified chapter labs, and hands-on activities.

ELL Handbook explains ways to make *Biology* more accessible to ELL students.

Spanish Study Workbook is a Spanish translation of Study Workbook A.

Multilingual Glossary is the glossary translated into ten languages.

Differentiated Instruction Key

- L1 Special Needs or Struggling Students
- ELL English Language Learners
- LPR Less Proficient Readers
- L2 On-Level Students
- L3 Advanced Students

Additional Resources

Biology.com Untamed Science Video • Vocabulary Flash Cards

Study Workbook B 9.1 Worksheets L1 ELL LPR
Spanish Study Workbook 9.1 Worksheets ELL
Biology.com 9.1 Lesson Overview • 9.1 Lesson Notes

Study Workbook B 9.2 Worksheets L1 ELL LPR
Spanish Study Workbook 9.2 Worksheets ELL
Biology.com *Art Review:* Electron Transport and ATP Synthesis • 9.2 Lesson Overview • 9.2 Lesson Notes • 9.2 Self-Test • 9.2 Lesson Assessment

Study Workbook B 9.3 Worksheets L1 ELL LPR
Spanish Study Workbook 9.3 Worksheets ELL
Biology.com 9.3 Lesson Overview • 9.3 Lesson Notes

Lab Manual B *Comparing Fermentation Rates of Sugars* • Data Analysis: *You Are What You Eat* • Hands-On Activity: *CO_2 and You* L1 ELL LPR

Chapter Review

Student Edition Study Guide, p. 267 L2
Study Workbook A Chapter 9 Vocabulary Review L2 • Chapter 9 Chapter Mystery/21st Century Skills Activity L2 L3
Transparencies, pp. 111–121 L1 ELL LPR L2
Biology.com Untamed Science Video • Editable Worksheets of Study Workbooks A and B and Lab Manuals A and B • Chapter 9 Flash Cards and Match It

Untamed Science DVD • Classroom Resources CD (includes lesson presentations and editable worksheets)

Chapter Assessment

Student Edition Assessment, pp. 268–271 L2
Study Workbook B Chapter 9 Chapter Review L1 ELL LPR • Chapter 9 Taking a Standardized Test L1 ELL LPR
Assessment Resources Book Chapter 9 Test A L2 • Chapter 9 Test B L1 ELL LPR
Biology.com Chapter 9 Assessment • Editable Worksheets of Chapter 9 Visual Quiz and Chapter 9 Tests A and B

Exam*View* *Assessment Suite* • Classroom Resources CD (includes lesson presentations and editable worksheets)

Time: 1 period, 1/2 block

Pressed for Time?

Preview the Chapter Have students read the Key Questions for Lesson 9.1 and preview Figure 9–2.

Cover the Chapter Quickly Have students read all of Lesson 9.1 focusing on Figure 9–2. Assign *The Totals* in Lesson 9.2 and *Fermentation* in Lesson 9.3.

Assess Assign the 9.1 Assessment, question 4 in the 9.2 Assessment, question 1 in the 9.3 Assessment, and the Chapter 9 Standardized Test Prep except questions 2, 3, and 11.

Connect to the Big Idea

Use the micrograph of the mitochondria to help students start thinking about the concepts of cellular respiration and fermentation. First, activate prior knowledge by asking them if they know what mitochondria are and what their function is. *(cellular organelles that convert the chemical energy stored in food into chemical compounds that cells can use)*

Now ask students what links the cereal they had for breakfast with the mitochondria in the micrograph. *(energy)* Point out that food, like this morning's cereal, contains molecules that the mitochondria can use to make energy available to cells. Then, ask why cells need energy. *(to carry out cell activities)* Ask students to anticipate the answer to the question, **How do organisms obtain energy?**

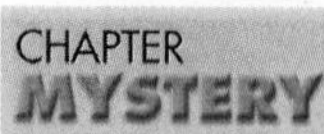
Have students read over the Chapter Mystery and predict how sperm whales can stay active for so long on only one breath. To make their predictions, suggest students think about how cells obtain and release the energy whales need to dive. Use their predictions to help them start connecting the Chapter Mystery to the Big Idea of the Cellular Basis of Life.

BIOLOGY.com Have students preview the chapter vocabulary terms using the **Flash Cards.**

IN INDIANA ACADEMIC STANDARDS

For the full text of all standards, see the Course Overview in the front matter of this book.

Key standards: Chapter 9 covers key ideas from Standard 2: Cellular Structure and Standard 3: Matter Cycles and Energy Transfer, including **B.2.3** Mitochondria and chloroplasts, **B.3.1** Photosynthesis, and **B.3.2** Cellular respiration.

Big idea **Cellular Basis of Life**

Q: How do organisms obtain energy?

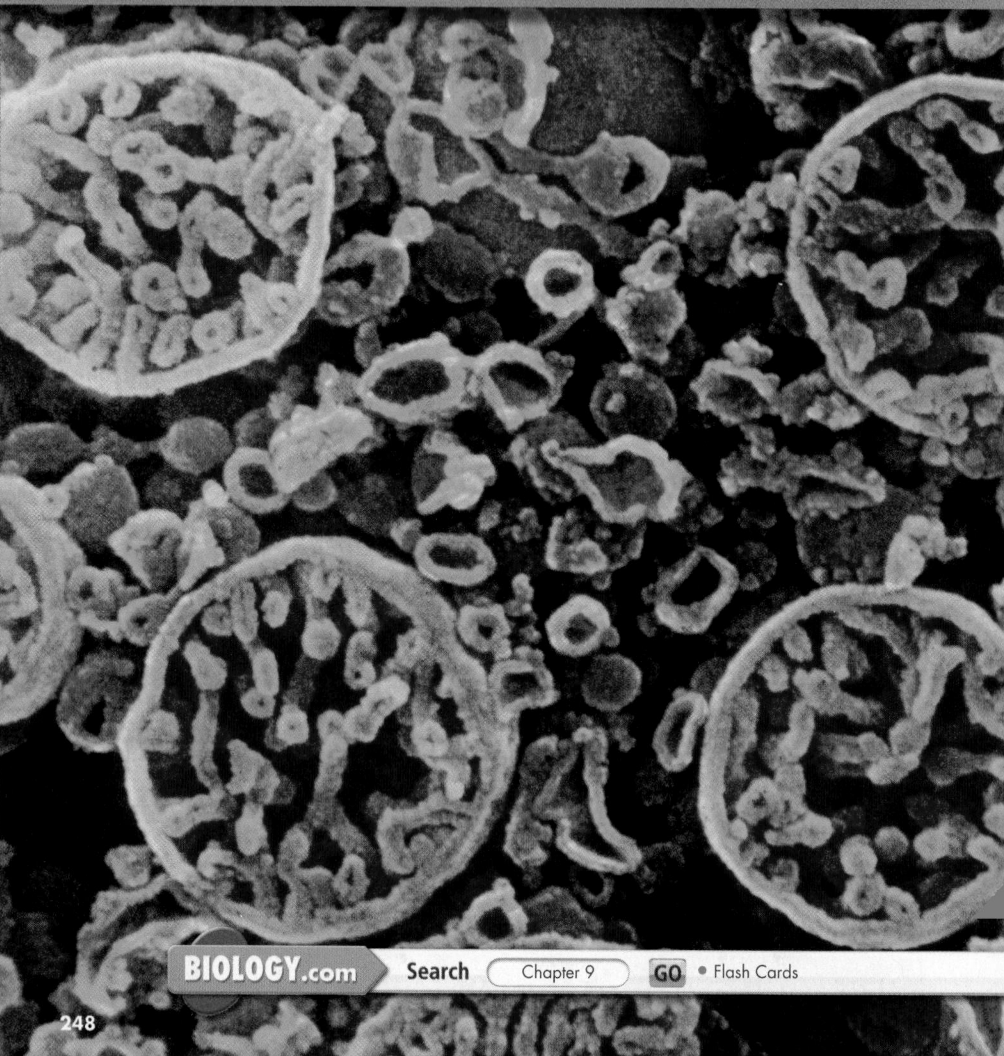

BIOLOGY.com Search Chapter 9 GO • Flash Cards

248

UbD Understanding by Design

A cell is the basic unit of life; the processes that occur at the cellular level provide the energy and basic structure organisms need to survive. Students explore this Enduring Understanding in Chapter 9 by examining the processes of cellular respiration and fermentation. As shown in the graphic organizer at the right, the Big Idea, Essential Question, and lesson-level Guiding Questions help frame their exploration.

PERFORMANCE GOALS

In Chapter 9, students will learn how cellular respiration and fermentation provide organisms with the energy they need to survive. Students will show this understanding by interpreting multiple, detailed figures. They will also practice their data analysis skills by collecting and interpreting data on the byproducts of cellular respiration. At the end of the chapter, students will transfer their knowledge by keeping an exercise journal and relating the entries to cellular respiration and fermentation.

INDIANA ACADEMIC STANDARDS FOR SCIENCE

Nature of Science NoS.3, NoS.6; **Cellular Chemistry** B.1.2; **Cellular Structure** B.2.3; **Matter Cycles and Energy Transfer** B.3.1, B.3.2. See lessons for details.

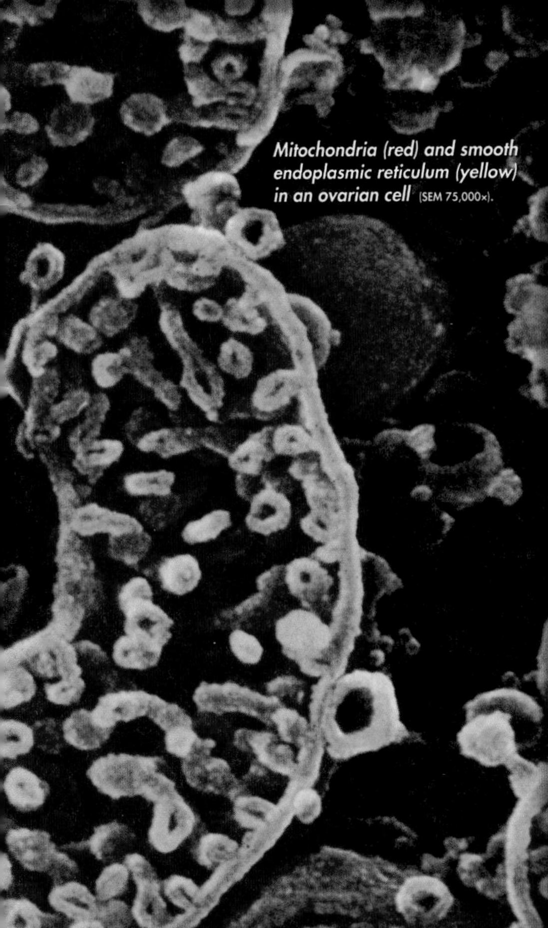

Mitochondria (red) and smooth endoplasmic reticulum (yellow) in an ovarian cell (SEM 75,000×).

• Untamed Science Video • Chapter Mystery

CHAPTER MYSTERY

DIVING WITHOUT A BREATH

Everyone is familiar with the sensation of being "out of breath." Just a few minutes of vigorous exercise can have humans huffing and puffing for air. But what if you couldn't get air? What if you were asked to hold your breath and exercise? Before too long, you'd pass out due to a lack of oxygen. This may seem like a silly thought experiment, but there are animals that exercise without breathing and without passing out all the time—whales. Unlike most animals that live their entire lives in water, whales still rely on oxygen obtained from air when they surface. Amazingly, sperm whales routinely stay underwater for 45 minutes or more when diving. Some scientists suspect that they can stay underwater for 90 minutes! How is that possible? Diving takes a lot of energy. How do whales stay active for so long on only one breath? As you read this chapter, look for clues. Then, solve the mystery.

Never Stop Exploring Your World. Learning about whales and their extraordinary ability to hold their breaths is just the beginning. Take a video field trip with the ecogeeks of Untamed Science to see where this mystery leads.

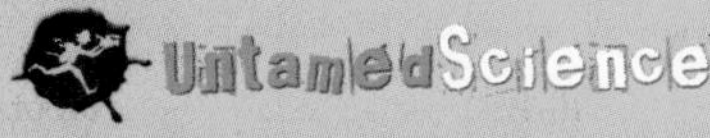

Chapter 9 Big Idea: Cellular Basis of Life

Chapter 9 EQ: How do organisms obtain energy?

9.1 GQ: Why do most organisms undergo the process of cellular respiration?

9.2 GQ: How do cells release energy from food in the presence of oxygen?

9.3 GQ: How do cells release energy from food without oxygen?

What's Online

BIOLOGY.com Extend your reach by using these and other digital assets offered at **Biology.com**.

CHAPTER MYSTERY
Discover how the processes of cellular respiration and fermentation can affect the behavior and function of an entire organism—in this case, how often whales need to breathe.

UNTAMED SCIENCE
Dive below the ocean surface to explore how marine mammals can survive on a single breath for as long as they do.

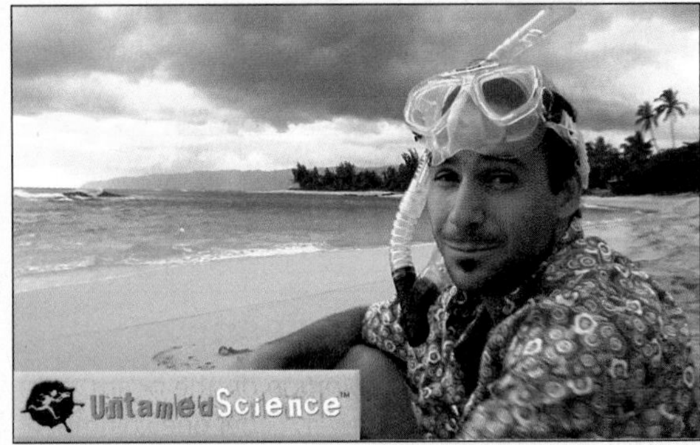

ART IN MOTION
An animated diagram highlights the relationship between photosynthesis and cellular respiration.

INTERACTIVE ART
In this short animation, students watch how glucose is broken down and energy is transferred during the process of cellular respiration.

ART REVIEW
Students explore the details of electron transport and ATP synthesis.

TUTOR TUBE
This short, online tutorial provides extra help on the electron transport chain and ATP production.

DATA ANALYSIS
Students analyze data to learn more about lactic acid and exercise.

LESSON 9.1

Getting Started

Objectives

9.1.1 Explain where organisms get the energy they need for life processes.

9.1.2 Define cellular respiration.

9.1.3 Compare photosynthesis and cellular respiration.

Student Resources

Study Workbooks A and B, 9.1 Worksheets

Spanish Study Workbook, 9.1 Worksheets

Lab Manual B, 9.1 Data Analysis Worksheet

Lesson Overview • Lesson Notes • Activity: Art in Motion • Assessment: Self-Test, Lesson Assessment

For corresponding lesson in the **Foundation Edition**, see pages 212–215.

Activate Prior Knowledge

Write the term *cellular respiration* on the board. Then, make a **T-Chart** below it. Label one column Facts and the other Questions. Have each student come up to the board and write either a fact they know or a question they have about cellular respiration. Discuss the T-Chart as a class. Answer any questions that students will need to know before reading the lesson.

Study Wkbks A/B, Appendix S30, T-Chart. **Transparencies,** GO15.

INDIANA ACADEMIC STANDARDS

For the full text of all standards, see the Course Overview in the front matter of this book.

B.3.1 Describe how some organisms capture the sun's energy through the process of photosynthesis by converting carbon dioxide and water into high energy compounds and releasing oxygen.

B.3.2 Describe how most organisms can combine and recombine the elements contained in sugar molecules into a variety of biologically essential compounds by utilizing the energy from cellular respiration.

Cellular Respiration: An Overview

B.3.1 Photosynthesis; B.3.2 Cellular respiration. Also covered: NoS.3, NoS.6, B.3.1.

Key Questions

Where do organisms get energy?

What is cellular respiration?

What is the relationship between photosynthesis and cellular respiration?

Vocabulary

calorie • cellular respiration • aerobic • anaerobic

Taking Notes

Preview Visuals Before you read, study **Figure 9–2** on page 252. Make a list of questions that you have about the diagram. As you read, write down the answers to the questions.

THINK ABOUT IT When you are hungry, how do you feel? If you are like most people, you might feel sluggish, a little dizzy, and—above all—weak. Weakness is a feeling triggered by a lack of energy. You feel weak when you are hungry because food serves as a source of energy. Weakness is your body's way of telling you that your energy supplies are low. But how does food get converted into a usable form of energy? Car engines have to burn gasoline in order to release its energy. Do our bodies burn food the way a car burns gasoline, or is there something more to it?

Chemical Energy and Food

Where do organisms get energy?

Food provides living things with the chemical building blocks they need to grow and reproduce. Recall that some organisms, such as plants, are autotrophs, meaning that they make their own food through photosynthesis. Other organisms are heterotrophs, meaning that they rely on other organisms for food. For all organisms, food molecules contain chemical energy that is released when their chemical bonds are broken. **Organisms get the energy they need from food.**

How much energy is actually present in food? Quite a lot, although it varies with the type of food. Energy stored in food is expressed in units of calories. A **calorie** is the amount of energy needed to raise the temperature of 1 gram of water 1 degree Celsius. The Calorie (capital C) that is used on food labels is a kilocalorie, or 1000 calories. Cells can use all sorts of molecules for food, including fats, proteins, and carbohydrates. The energy stored in each of these macromolecules varies because their chemical structures, and therefore their energy-storing bonds, differ. For example, 1 gram of the sugar glucose releases 3811 calories of heat energy when it is burned. By contrast, 1 gram of the triglyceride fats found in beef releases 8893 calories of heat energy when its bonds are broken. In general, carbohydrates and proteins contain approximately 4000 calories (4 Calories) of energy per gram, while fats contain approximately 9000 calories (9 Calories) per gram.

Cells, of course, don't simply burn food and release energy as heat. Instead, they break down food molecules gradually, capturing a little bit of chemical energy at key steps. This enables cells to use the energy stored in the chemical bonds of foods like glucose to produce compounds such as ATP that directly power the activities of the cell.

BUILD Vocabulary

PREFIXES The prefix *macro-* means "large" or "elongated." Macromolecules are made up of many smaller molecular subunits. Carbohydrates, proteins, and lipids are important macromolecules found in living things.

UbD Teach for Understanding

ENDURING UNDERSTANDING A cell is the basic unit of life; the processes that occur at the cellular level provide the energy and basic structure organisms need to survive.

GUIDING QUESTION Why do most organisms undergo the process of cellular respiration?

EVIDENCE OF UNDERSTANDING *At the end of the lesson, have students complete this assessment to show they understand the importance of cellular respiration for life on Earth.* Have students make a case for cellular respiration. Ask them to write a short persuasive argument that explains why cellular respiration is an important process on an individual organism level as well as on a global scale.

Analyzing Data MATH

NoS.3

You Are What You Eat

Organisms get energy from the food they eat, but the energy contained in foods varies greatly. Most foods contain a combination of proteins, carbohydrates, and fats. One gram of protein or a carbohydrate such as glucose contains roughly 4 Calories. One gram of fat, however, contains about 9 Calories. The accompanying table shows the approximate composition of one serving of some common foods.

Composition of Some Common Foods

Food	Protein (g)	Carbohydrate (g)	Fat (g)
Apple, 1 medium	0	22	0
Bacon, 2 slices	5	0	6
Chocolate, 1 bar	3	23	13
Eggs, 2 whole	12	0	9
2% milk, 1 cup	8	12	5
Potato chips, 15 chips	2	14	10
Skinless roasted turkey, 3 slices	11	3	1

1. **Interpret Data** Per serving, which of the foods included in the table has the most protein? Which has the most carbohydrates? Which has the most fat?
2. **Calculate** Approximately how many more Calories are there in 2 slices of bacon than there are in 3 slices of roasted turkey? Why is there a difference?
3. **Calculate** Walking at a moderate pace consumes around 300 Calories per hour. At that rate, how many minutes would you have to walk to burn the Calories in one chocolate bar? (*Hint:* Start by calculating the number of Calories consumed per minute by walking.)

Overview of Cellular Respiration

What is cellular respiration?

If oxygen is available, organisms can obtain energy from food by a process called **cellular respiration.** **Cellular respiration is the process that releases energy from food in the presence of oxygen.** Although cellular respiration involves dozens of separate reactions, an overall chemical summary of the process is remarkably simple:

In Symbols:

$$6O_2 + C_6H_{12}O_6 \longrightarrow 6CO_2 + 6H_2O + \text{Energy}$$

In Words:

Oxygen + Glucose ⟶ Carbon dioxide + Water + Energy

As you can see, cellular respiration requires oxygen and a food molecule such as glucose, and it gives off carbon dioxide, water, and energy. Do not be misled, however, by the simplicity of this equation. If cellular respiration took place in just one step, all of the energy from glucose would be released at once, and most of it would be lost in the form of light and heat. Clearly, a living cell has to control that energy. It can't simply start a fire—the cell has to release the explosive chemical energy in food molecules a little bit at a time. The cell needs to find a way to trap those little bits of energy by using them to make ATP.

FIGURE 9–1 A Controlled Release Cellular respiration involves a series of controlled reactions that slowly release the energy stored in food. If the energy were to be released too suddenly, most of it would be lost in the forms of light and heat—just as it is when a marshmallow catches fire.

In Your Notebook *Do plants undergo cellular respiration? What organelle(s) do they have that helps you determine the answer?*

Teach

Lead a Discussion

Make sure students understand the overall chemical summary for cellular respiration. Reinforce that the bolded reactions shown are simplifications, or summations, of many sub-reactions. Have students verify that the reaction shown is balanced by counting the molecules of each element on the right and left sides of the reaction.

DIFFERENTIATED INSTRUCTION

L1 Struggling Students Write the word form of the cellular respiration summary on the board. Then, read it aloud, pointing to each word and reaction symbol as you read. For example, you might say, "oxygen and glucose are converted into carbon dioxide and water and energy." As you say *oxygen,* point to the word; as you say *and,* point to the plus sign. Then, write the symbol form of the summary below it. Draw lines from each chemical formula to its corresponding name in the word form of the summary.

ELL Focus on ELL: Build Background

BEGINNING AND INTERMEDIATE SPEAKERS Distribute copies of a **BKWL Chart** to your students. Then, show students a short animation, video, or several drawings of the process of cellular respiration. Have them take notes on the visuals in the build background column. Write the words *obtain, release, extract, respiration,* and *energy* on the board. Have them copy the words and define each in the build background column. Then, have students fill out the K and W columns of the chart. As students read the lesson, have them fill in the L column.

Study Wkbks A/B, Appendix S27, BKWL Chart. **Transparencies,** GO12.

Analyzing Data

PURPOSE Students will examine and interpret data to find how the energy content in foods varies.

PLANNING Have a few of the foods listed in the table on hand, and display them for students before they do the activity. Ask students to predict which of the foods contain the most Calories, and have them explain their reasoning.

ANSWERS

1. Eggs have the most protein; chocolate has the most carbohydrates; chocolate has the most fat.
2. There are approximately 9 more Calories in 2 slices of bacon than in 3 slices of roast turkey. The primary difference is that the bacon contains so much more fat than the turkey.
3. a little over 44 minutes

Answers

IN YOUR NOTEBOOK Yes; they contain mitochondria.

Teach continued

Use Visuals

Use **Figure 9–2** to talk about the overall process of cellular respiration. Start by helping students make the connection between this visual and the chemical summary equations from the previous page. Point out where and how glucose and oxygen are used during the process and that water, carbon dioxide, and energy are released. Make sure students understand that cellular respiration can be divided into three basic stages. Tell them that they will learn more detailed information about each of these stages in later lessons.

DIFFERENTIATED INSTRUCTION

L1 Struggling Students Have students read the section, **Stages of Cellular Respiration,** in the text and look carefully at **Figure 9–2.** As a class, discuss the first pictured stage, glycolysis. Then, have students write a one-sentence summary of the discussion. For example, students might write, "During glycolysis, glucose is broken down into pyruvic acid and energy is released." Then, discuss and summarize each of the next two stages.

To help students answer the question, remind them that whales need to surface to breathe air. Make the connection between aerobic pathways and the whale's breathing. Ask them to speculate on how long the breath might last and how the whale might obtain energy once that air runs out. Students can go online to Biology.com to gather their evidence.

Address Misconceptions

Cellular Respiration v. Respiration Some of your students may have difficulty distinguishing between the concepts of cellular respiration and respiration as breathing. Have students read the first paragraph of the **Oxygen and Energy** section, research the connection between the two processes, and make a poster for the classroom wall that graphically shows the relationship.

Answers

FIGURE 9–2 the Krebs cycle and the electron transport chain

IN YOUR NOTEBOOK Flowcharts should accurately show the connections between glycolysis, the Krebs cycle, and the electron transport chain.

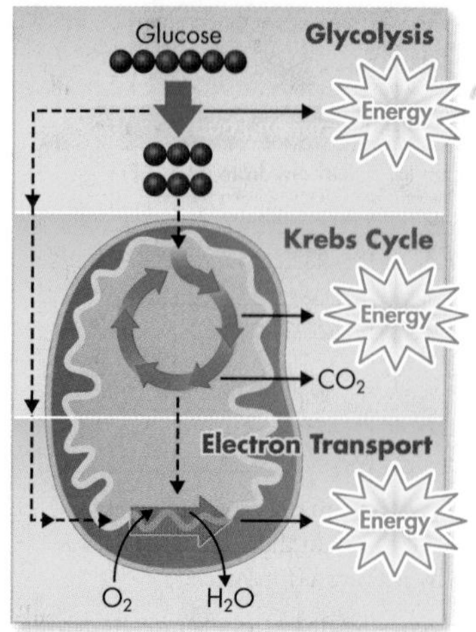

FIGURE 9–2 The Stages of Cellular Respiration There are three stages to cellular respiration: glycolysis, the Krebs cycle, and the electron transport chain. Interpret Visuals *Which stage(s) of cellular respiration occur in the mitochondrion?*

Stages of Cellular Respiration Cellular respiration captures the energy from food in three main stages—glycolysis, the Krebs cycle, and the electron transport chain. Although cells can use just about any food molecule for energy, we will concentrate on just one as an example—the simple sugar glucose. Glucose first enters a chemical pathway known as glycolysis (gly KAHL ih sis). Only a small amount of energy is captured to produce ATP during this stage. In fact, at the end of glycolysis, about 90 percent of the chemical energy that was available in glucose is still unused, locked in chemical bonds of a molecule called pyruvic (py ROO vik) acid.

How does the cell extract the rest of that energy? First, pyruvic acid enters the second stage of cellular respiration, the Krebs cycle, where a little more energy is generated. The bulk of the energy, however, comes from the final stage of cellular respiration, the electron transport chain. This stage requires reactants from the other two stages of the process, as shown by dashed lines in **Figure 9–2.** How does the electron transport chain extract so much energy from these reactants? It uses one of the world's most powerful electron acceptors—oxygen.

Oxygen and Energy Oxygen is required at the very end of the electron transport chain. Any time a cell's demand for energy increases, its use of oxygen increases, too. As you know, the word *respiration* is often used as a synonym for *breathing*. This is why we have used the term *cellular respiration* to refer to energy-releasing pathways within the cell. The double meaning of respiration points out a crucial connection between cells and organisms: Most of the energy-releasing pathways within cells require oxygen, and that is the reason we need to breathe, to respire.

Pathways of cellular respiration that require oxygen are said to be **aerobic** ("in air"). The Krebs cycle and electron transport chain are both aerobic processes. Even though the Krebs cycle does not *directly* require oxygen, it is classified as an aerobic process because it cannot run without the oxygen-requiring electron transport chain. Glycolysis, however, does not directly require oxygen, nor does it rely on an oxygen-requiring process to run. Glycolysis is therefore said to be **anaerobic** ("without air"). Even though glycolysis is anaerobic, it is considered part of cellular respiration because its final products are key reactants for the aerobic stages.

Recall that mitochondria are structures in the cell that convert chemical energy stored in food to usable energy for the cell. Glycolysis actually occurs in the cytoplasm of a cell, but the Krebs cycle and electron transport chain, which generate the majority of ATP during cellular respiration, take place inside the mitochondria. If oxygen is not present, another anaerobic pathway, known as fermentation, makes it possible for the cell to keep glycolysis running, generating ATP to power cellular activity. You will learn more about fermentation later in this chapter.

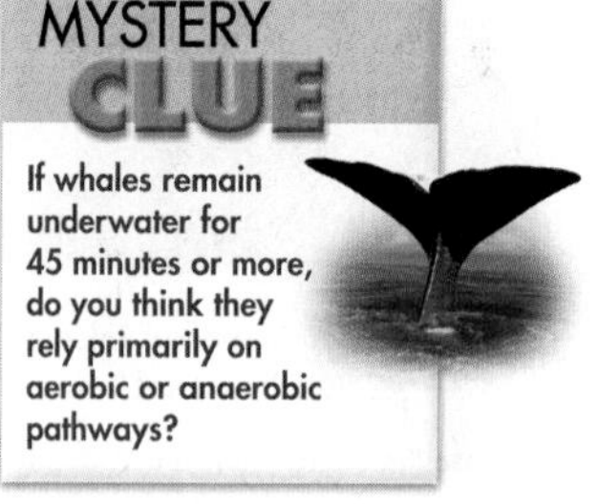

MYSTERY
CLUE
If whales remain underwater for 45 minutes or more, do you think they rely primarily on aerobic or anaerobic pathways?

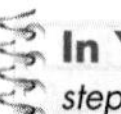

In Your Notebook *Make a flowchart that shows the different steps of cellular respiration.*

UbD Check for Understanding

INDEX CARD SUMMARIES

Give students each an index card, and ask them to write one important idea about cellular respiration that they understand on the front of the card. Then, have them write something about cellular respiration that they don't understand on the back of the card in the form of a question.

ADJUST INSTRUCTION

Read over students' cards to get a sense of which concepts they understand and which they are struggling with. If a question will be answered by reading the rest of the chapter, use that card when the time comes to emphasize a concept. If the answer to a question is necessary to move forward, review the topic as a class to allow students to hear the concept discussed in different ways.

Comparing Photosynthesis and Cellular Respiration

What is the relationship between photosynthesis and cellular respiration?

If nearly all organisms break down food by the process of cellular respiration, why doesn't Earth run out of oxygen? Where does all of the carbon dioxide waste product go? How does the chemical energy stored in food get replaced? As it happens, cellular respiration is balanced by another process: photosynthesis. The energy in photosynthesis and cellular respiration flows in opposite directions. Look at **Figure 9–3** and think of the chemical energy in carbohydrates as money in the Earth's savings account. Photosynthesis is the process that "deposits" energy. Cellular respiration is the process that "withdraws" energy. As you might expect, the equations for photosynthesis and cellular respiration are the reverse of each other.

On a global level, photosynthesis and cellular respiration are also opposites. **Photosynthesis removes carbon dioxide from the atmosphere, and cellular respiration puts it back. Photosynthesis releases oxygen into the atmosphere, and cellular respiration uses that oxygen to release energy from food.** The release of energy by cellular respiration takes place in nearly all life: plants, animals, fungi, protists, and most bacteria. Energy capture by photosynthesis, however, occurs only in plants, algae, and some bacteria.

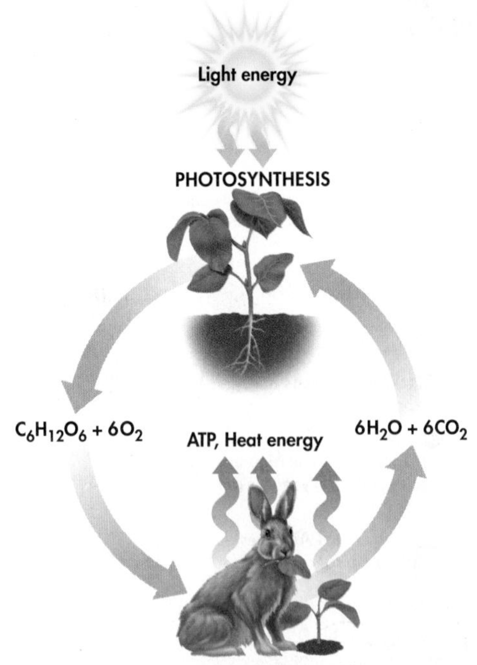

Light energy

PHOTOSYNTHESIS

$C_6H_{12}O_6 + 6O_2$

ATP, Heat energy

$6H_2O + 6CO_2$

CELLULAR RESPIRATION

FIGURE 9–3 Opposite Processes Photosynthesis and cellular respiration can be thought of as opposite processes. Compare and Contrast ***Exactly how is the equation for photosynthesis different from the equation for cellular respiration?***

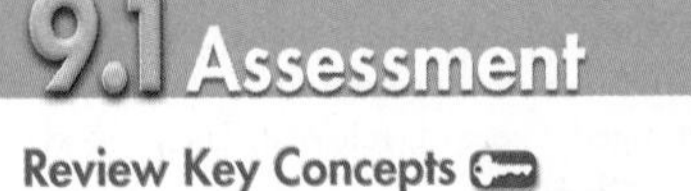

9.1 Assessment

IN NoS.6, B.3.2

Review Key Concepts

1. a. Review Why do all organisms need food?
   b. Relate Cause and Effect Why do macromolecules differ in the amount of energy they contain?
2. a. Review Write the overall reaction for cellular respiration.
   b. Apply Concepts How does the process of cellular respiration maintain homeostasis at the cellular level?
3. a. Review In what ways are cellular respiration and photosynthesis considered opposite processes?
   b. Use Analogies How is the chemical energy in glucose similar to money in a savings account?

BUILD VOCABULARY

4. The Greek word *glukus* means "sweet," and the Latin word *lysis* refers to a process of loosening or decomposing. Based on this information, write a definition for the word *glycolysis*.

BIOLOGY.com Search Lesson 9.1 GO  • Lesson Assessment • Self-Test • Art in Motion

BIOLOGY.com To better understand the relationship between photosynthesis and cellular respiration, students can watch the animation, **Art in Motion: Opposite Processes.**

Assess and Remediate

EVALUATE UNDERSTANDING

Have pairs of students use **Figure 9–3** to help them summarize the content of the lesson. For example, ask them to explain why both the rabbit and the plant are producing ATP and heat. Listen to their discussions to help you evaluate their grasp of lesson concepts. Then, have them complete the 9.1 Assessment.

REMEDIATION SUGGESTION

LPR Less Proficient Readers If students have trouble understanding **Question 2b,** suggest they use the Glossary at the back of this text to review the meaning of the term *homeostasis*.

BIOLOGY.com Students can check their understanding of lesson concepts with the **Self-Test** assessment. They can then take an online version of the **Lesson Assessment.**

Answers

FIGURE 9–3 The products of photosynthesis are the reactants of cellular respiration, and the reactants of cellular respiration are the products of photosynthesis.

Assessment Answers

1a. Food provides organisms with the energy they need to carry out life processes such as growth and reproduction.

1b. The amount of energy stored in macromolecules varies because their chemical structures, and therefore the energy contained in their chemical bonds, differ.

2a. $6O_2 + C_6H_{12}O_6 \rightarrow 6CO_2 + 6H_2O$ + Energy

2b. The process of cellular respiration provides the energy a cell needs to carry out basic cell processes, which, in turn, control the cell's internal conditions.

3a. Photosynthesis "deposits" energy, uses carbon dioxide and water, and produces oxygen and glucose. By contrast, cellular respiration "withdraws" energy, uses oxygen and glucose, and produces carbon dioxide and water.

3b. Chemical energy is stored in the chemical bonds of glucose, just as money is stored in a savings account.

BUILD VOCABULARY

4. Sample answer: a process that involves the breaking down of a sweet substance

Getting Started

Objectives

9.2.1 Describe what happens during glycolysis.

9.2.2 Describe what happens during the Krebs cycle.

9.2.3 Explain how high-energy electrons are used by the electron transport chain.

9.2.4 Identify how much ATP cellular respiration generates.

Student Resources

Study Workbooks A and B, 9.2 Worksheets

Spanish Study Workbook, 9.2 Worksheets

 Lesson Overview • Lesson Notes • Activities: InterActive Art, Art Review, Tutor Tube • Assessment: Self-Test, Lesson Assessment

 For corresponding lesson in the **Foundation Edition**, see pages 216–222.

Activate Prior Knowledge

Ask students to think about how they get to school every day. Have them break this process into several stages. For example, they might describe getting ready to leave home, taking the bus, and walking into school. Then, have them describe some of the smaller steps they make to accomplish these three stages. Discuss how this analogy relates to the process of cellular respiration.

IN INDIANA ACADEMIC STANDARDS

For the full text of all standards, see the Course Overview in the front matter of this book.

B.2.3 Explain that most cells contain mitochondria, the key sites of cellular respiration, where stored chemical energy is converted into useable energy for the cell and some cells, including many plant cells, contain chloroplasts, the key sites of photosynthesis, where the energy of light is captured for use in chemical work.

B.3.2 Describe how most organisms can combine and recombine the elements contained in sugar molecules into a variety of biologically essential compounds by utilizing the energy from cellular respiration.

9.2 The Process of Cellular Respiration

IN **B.2.3** Mitochondria and chloroplasts; **B.3.2** Cellular respiration. Also covered: **B.1.2.**

Key Questions

What happens during the process of glycolysis?

What happens during the Krebs cycle?

How does the electron transport chain use high-energy electrons from glycolysis and the Krebs cycle?

How much ATP does cellular respiration generate?

Vocabulary

glycolysis • NAD⁺ • Krebs cycle • matrix

Taking Notes

Compare/Contrast Table As you read, make a compare/contrast table showing the location, starting reactants, and end products of glycolysis, the Krebs cycle, and the electron transport chain. Also include how many molecules of ATP are produced in each step of the process.

THINK ABOUT IT

Food burns! It's true, of course, that many common foods (think of apples, bananas, and ground beef) have too much water in them to actually light with a match. However, foods with little water, including sugar and cooking oil, will indeed burn. In fact, flour, which contains both carbohydrates and protein, is so flammable that it has caused several explosions, including the one seen here at London's City Flour Mills in 1872 (which is why you're not supposed to store flour above a stove). So, plenty of energy is available in food, but how does a living cell extract that energy without setting a fire or blowing things up?

Glycolysis

What happens during the process of glycolysis?

The first set of reactions in cellular respiration is known as **glycolysis,** a word that literally means "sugar-breaking." Glycolysis involves many chemical steps that transform glucose. The end result is 2 molecules of a 3-carbon molecule called pyruvic acid. **During glycolysis, 1 molecule of glucose, a 6-carbon compound, is transformed into 2 molecules of pyruvic acid, a 3-carbon compound.** As the bonds in glucose are broken and rearranged, energy is released. The process of glycolysis can be seen in **Figure 9–4.**

ATP Production Even though glycolysis is an energy-releasing process, the cell needs to put in a little energy to get things going. At the pathway's beginning, 2 ATP molecules are used up. Earlier in this chapter, photosynthesis and respiration were compared, respectively, to a deposit to and a withdrawal from a savings account. Similarly, the 2 ATP molecules used at the onset of glycolysis are like an investment that pays back interest. In order to earn interest from a bank, first you have to put money into an account. Although the cell puts 2 ATP molecules into its "account" to get glycolysis going, glycolysis produces 4 ATP molecules. This gives the cell a net gain of 2 ATP molecules for each molecule of glucose that enters glycolysis.

UbD Teach for Understanding

ENDURING UNDERSTANDING A cell is the basic unit of life; the processes that occur at the cellular level provide the energy and basic structure organisms need to survive.

GUIDING QUESTION How do cells release energy from food in the presence of oxygen?

EVIDENCE OF UNDERSTANDING *At the end of this lesson, give students the following assessment to show they understand how cellular respiration provides organisms with a way to efficiently release energy from food.* Have students make a sketch of the overall process of cellular respiration. Ask them to make it as detailed as they can. Then, have them discuss with a partner why it makes sense that cellular respiration is a complex process involving many steps.

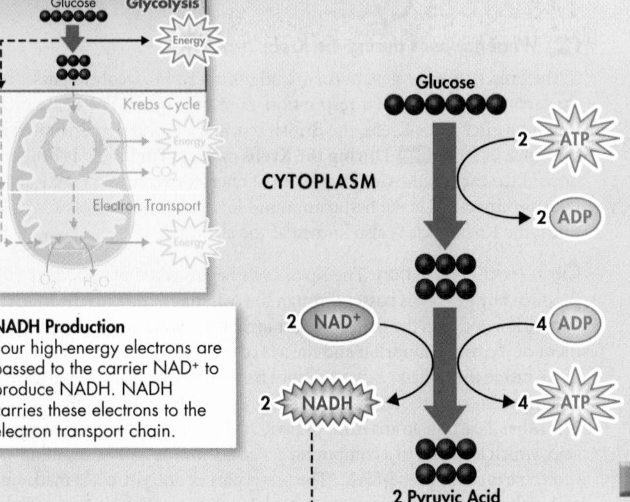

Glucose
Glycolysis
Energy
Krebs Cycle
Energy
CO_2
Electron Transport
Energy
O_2
H_2O
NADH Production
Four high-energy electrons are passed to the carrier NAD⁺ to produce NADH. NADH carries these electrons to the electron transport chain.
Glucose
CYTOPLASM
2 ATP
2 ADP
2 NAD⁺
4 ADP
2 NADH
4 ATP
2 Pyruvic Acid
To Electron Transport Chain
To Krebs Cycle
ATP Production
Two ATP molecules are "invested" to get the process of glycolysis going. Overall, 4 ATP molecules are produced, for a net gain of 2 ATP per molecule of glucose.

ZOOMING IN

GLYCOLYSIS

FIGURE 9–4 Glycolysis is the first stage of cellular respiration. During glycolysis, glucose is broken down into 2 molecules of pyruvic acid. ATP and NADH are produced as part of the process. **Interpret Visuals** ***How many carbon atoms are there in glucose? How many carbon atoms are in each molecule of pyruvic acid?***

NADH Production One of the reactions of glycolysis removes 4 electrons, now in a high-energy state, and passes them to an electron carrier called **NAD⁺,** or nicotinamide adenine dinucleotide. Like NADP⁺ in photosynthesis, each NAD⁺ molecule accepts a pair of high-energy electrons. This molecule, now known as NADH, holds the electrons until they can be transferred to other molecules. As you will see, in the presence of oxygen, these high-energy electrons can be used to produce even more ATP molecules.

The Advantages of Glycolysis In the process of glycolysis, 4 ATP molecules are synthesized from 4 ADP molecules. Given that 2 ATP molecules are used to start the process, there is a net gain of just 2 ATP molecules. Although the energy yield from glycolysis is small, the process is so fast that cells can produce thousands of ATP molecules in just a few milliseconds. The speed of glycolysis can be a big advantage when the energy demands of a cell suddenly increase.

Besides speed, another advantage of glycolysis is that the process itself does not require oxygen. This means that glycolysis can quickly supply chemical energy to cells when oxygen is not available. When oxygen is available, however, the pyruvic acid and NADH "outputs" generated during glycolysis become the "inputs" for the other processes of cellular respiration.

BUILD Vocabulary

ACADEMIC WORDS The verb **synthesize** means "to bring together as a whole." Therefore, a molecule of ATP is synthesized when a phosphate group combines with the molecule ADP, forming a high-energy bond.

In Your Notebook *In your own words, describe the advantages of glycolysis to the cell in terms of energy production.*

Quick Facts

BEGINNING WITH GLUCOSE

Why do biologists pay so much attention to glucose? It's because most other food molecules are broken down to release energy in much the same way. Proteins are broken down into individual amino acids, which are converted to compounds that can enter either glycolysis or the Krebs cycle. Carbohydrates are generally broken into simple sugars and then converted into glucose. Lipids are broken down into fatty acids and glycerol. These compounds enter the mitochondria where special enzymes cut them up, two carbon atoms at a time, to produce acetyl-CoA, which then enters the Krebs cycle. This means that literally any food can provide the chemical energy for cellular respiration—the body is a furnace that can run on any fuel.

Teach

ZOOMING IN

Suggest students look carefully at **Figure 9–4.** Then, use the figure to start a discussion on glycolysis. Call on students at random to answer questions about what they observe.

Ask What do the six dark balls at the top of the figure represent? *(the six carbon atoms in a molecule of glucose)*

Ask What does it mean to "invest" a molecule of ATP? *(The energy stored in ATP is released and used to help start the process of glycolysis.)*

Ask What are the products of glycolysis? *(2 NADH molecules, 2 pyruvic acid molecules, and 4 ATP molecules)*

Ask Where do these products go? *(The NADH goes to the electron transport chain, the pyruvic acid goes to the Krebs cycle, and the ATP gets used by cells.)*

DIFFERENTIATED INSTRUCTION

L1 Special Needs Have students work in pairs to make a model of glycolysis. Have them use pop beads to represent carbon molecules, and different-size paper clips to model ATP/ADP and NAD⁺/NADH. Have pairs discuss the process as they model it.

BIOLOGY.com For an overview of the processes covered in this chapter, suggest students watch **InterActive Art: Cellular Respiration and Fermentation.**

Address Misconceptions

Energy Some students may think that energy is somehow created during glycolysis and the other stages of cellular respiration. Remind students that energy cannot be created or destroyed. Reinforce the fact that the energy used in glycolysis to make ATP is stored in the chemical bonds of glucose. Suggest students investigate how energy is stored as potential energy in chemical bonds and make a presentation to the class of what they learn.

Answers

FIGURE 9–4 6 carbon atoms in glucose; 3 carbon atoms in each molecule of pyruvic acid

IN YOUR NOTEBOOK Students' descriptions should mention that there is a net gain of 2 ATP molecules, that the process is fast, and that it can supply energy to the cell when oxygen is not available.

Teach continued

Connect to Chemistry

An understanding of the three stages of cellular respiration depends on some knowledge of basic chemistry. Before students study the Krebs cycle, point out that the cycle is a series of chemical reactions mainly involving carbon compounds. Explain that the element carbon has a remarkable ability to easily combine with both itself and other atoms, and the result is a tremendous number of carbon compounds in living things. Point out that following the changing carbon compounds is key to understanding the Krebs cycle.

DIFFERENTIATED INSTRUCTION

L1 Struggling Students Some students may have a difficult time understanding how ATP stores energy. Tell students that a common analogy used for ATP is that its three phosphates are like a loaded spring. Losing one of the phosphates—the source of energy for a cell—is like relaxing the spring. Adding a phosphate to a molecule of ADP is like loading, or compressing, the spring again.

LPR Less Proficient Readers Struggling readers may stumble on the names of the compounds *pyruvic acid, acetyl-CoA,* and *citric acid.* Before students read, preview these terms by writing the names on the board and saying each name aloud. Have students repeat the words so they become comfortable reading and pronouncing them.

To help students answer the question, explain that *tolerance* means "able to withstand the effects of something without showing the usual unfavorable effects." Point out that some people, for example, are able to tolerate colder temperatures than others. Students can go online to **Biology.com** to gather their evidence.

Answers

IN YOUR NOTEBOOK The electron carriers involved in the Krebs cycle are NAD^+ and FAD. After they accept electrons, NAD^+ becomes NADH and FAD becomes $FADH_2$.

MYSTERY CLUE

The urge to surface and gasp for breath when underwater is a response to CO_2 buildup in the blood. The average human can hold his or her breath for only about a minute. Whales stay underwater for much longer. What does this suggest about a whale's tolerance of CO_2?

The Krebs Cycle

What happens during the Krebs cycle?

In the presence of oxygen, pyruvic acid produced in glycolysis passes to the second stage of cellular respiration, the **Krebs cycle.** The Krebs cycle is named after Hans Krebs, the British biochemist who demonstrated its existence in 1937. **During the Krebs cycle, pyruvic acid is broken down into carbon dioxide in a series of energy-extracting reactions.** Because citric acid is the first compound formed in this series of reactions, the Krebs cycle is also known as the citric acid cycle.

Citric Acid Production The Krebs cycle begins when pyruvic acid produced by glycolysis passes through the two membranes of the mitochondrion and into the matrix. The **matrix** is the innermost compartment of the mitochondrion and the site of the Krebs cycle reactions. Once inside the matrix, 1 carbon atom from pyruvic acid becomes part of a molecule of carbon dioxide, which is eventually released into the air. The other 2 carbon atoms from pyruvic acid rearrange and form acetic acid, which is joined to a compound called coenzyme A. The resulting molecule is called acetyl-CoA. (The acetyl part of acetyl-CoA is made up of 2 carbon atoms, 1 oxygen atom, and 3 hydrogen atoms.) As the Krebs cycle begins, acetyl-CoA adds the 2-carbon acetyl group to a 4-carbon molecule already present in the cycle, producing a 6-carbon molecule called citric acid.

Energy Extraction As the cycle continues, citric acid is broken down into a 4-carbon molecule, more carbon dioxide is released, and electrons are transferred to energy carriers. Follow the reactions in **Figure 9–5** and you will see how this happens. First, look at the 6 carbon atoms in citric acid. One is removed, and then another, releasing 2 molecules of carbon dioxide and leaving a 4-carbon molecule. Why is the Krebs cycle a "cycle"? Because the 4-carbon molecule produced in the last step is the same molecule that accepts the acetyl-CoA in the first step. The molecule needed to start the reactions of the cycle is remade with every "turn."

Next, look for ATP. For each turn of the cycle, a molecule of ADP is converted to a molecule of ATP. Recall that glycolysis produces 2 molecules of pyruvic acid from 1 molecule of glucose. So, each starting molecule of glucose results in two complete turns of the Krebs cycle and, therefore, 2 ATP molecules. Finally, look at the electron carriers, NAD^+ and FAD (flavine adenine dinucleotide). At five places, electron carriers accept a pair of high-energy electrons, changing NAD^+ to NADH and FAD to $FADH_2$. FAD and $FADH_2$ are molecules similar to NAD^+ and NADH, respectively.

What happens to each of these Krebs cycle products—carbon dioxide, ATP, and electron carriers? Carbon dioxide is not useful to the cell and is expelled every time you exhale. The ATP molecules are *very* useful and become immediately available to power cellular activities. As for the carrier molecules like NADH, in the presence of oxygen, the electrons they hold are used to generate huge amounts of ATP.

In Your Notebook *List the electron carriers involved in the Krebs cycle. Include their names before and after they accept the electrons.*

UbD Check for Understanding

ORAL QUESTIONING

Use the following prompts to gauge student understanding of the Krebs cycle:

- Why does glycolysis have to occur before the Krebs cycle can occur?
- For each turn of the Krebs cycle, what is produced that can immediately be used to power cell activities?
- How does the cell use the NADH and $FADH_2$ produced in the Krebs cycle?

ADJUST INSTRUCTION

Evaluate students' answers to get a sense of which concepts they understand and which concepts they are having trouble with. Because understanding the Krebs cycle is essential to understanding the whole process of cellular respiration, review difficult concepts as a class so students can hear events described in different ways.

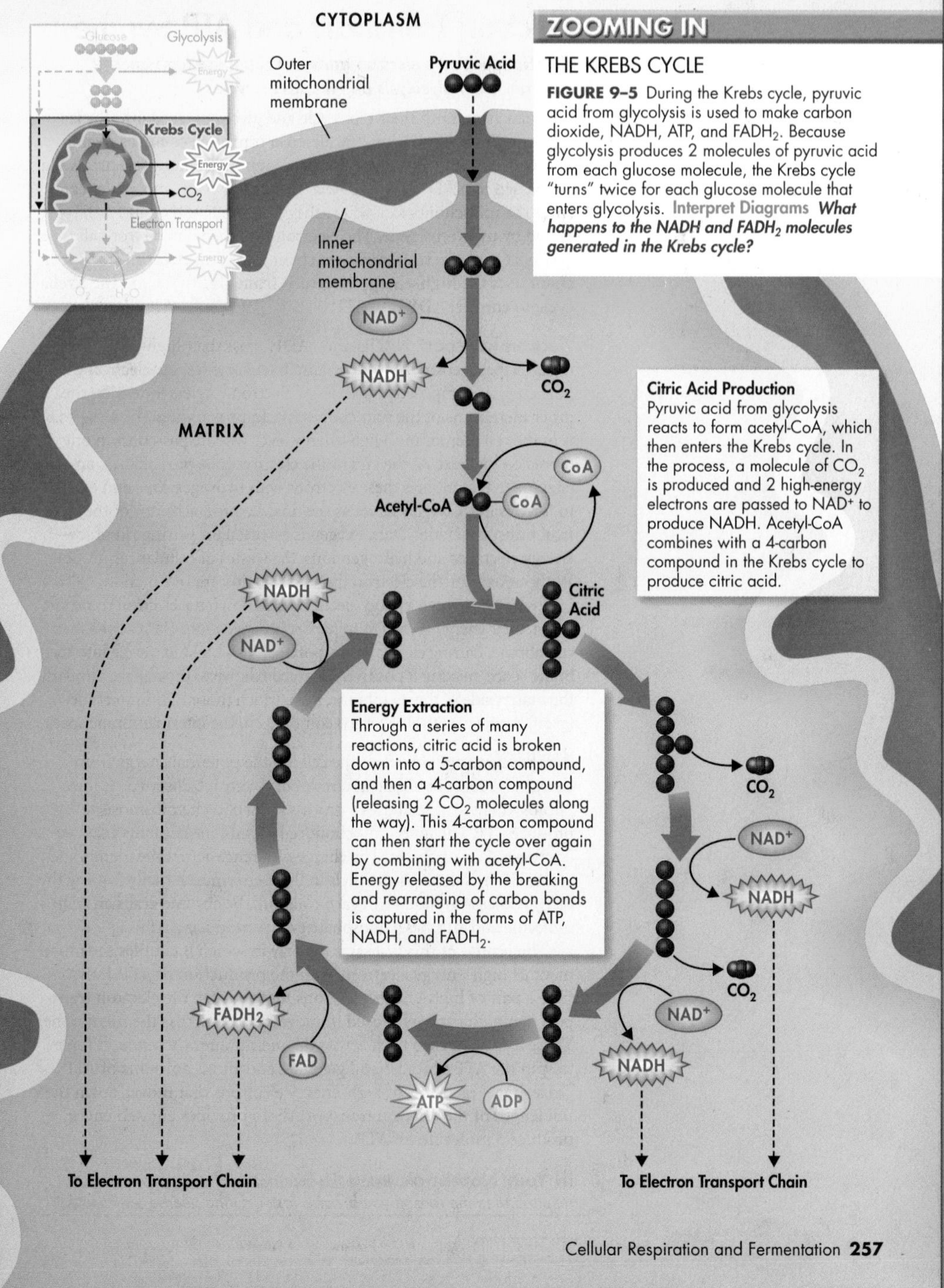
CYTOPLASM
Glucose
Glycolysis
Energy
Krebs Cycle
Energy
CO_2
Electron Transport
Energy
Outer mitochondrial membrane
Pyruvic Acid
Inner mitochondrial membrane
NAD^+
NADH
CO_2
MATRIX
CoA
Acetyl-CoA
CoA
Citric Acid Production
Pyruvic acid from glycolysis reacts to form acetyl-CoA, which then enters the Krebs cycle. In the process, a molecule of CO_2 is produced and 2 high-energy electrons are passed to NAD^+ to produce NADH. Acetyl-CoA combines with a 4-carbon compound in the Krebs cycle to produce citric acid.
NADH
NAD^+
Citric Acid
Energy Extraction
Through a series of many reactions, citric acid is broken down into a 5-carbon compound, and then a 4-carbon compound (releasing 2 CO_2 molecules along the way). This 4-carbon compound can then start the cycle over again by combining with acetyl-CoA. Energy released by the breaking and rearranging of carbon bonds is captured in the forms of ATP, NADH, and $FADH_2$.
CO_2
NAD^+
NADH
CO_2
$FADH_2$
FAD
NAD^+
NADH
ATP
ADP
To Electron Transport Chain
To Electron Transport Chain

ZOOMING IN

THE KREBS CYCLE

FIGURE 9–5 During the Krebs cycle, pyruvic acid from glycolysis is used to make carbon dioxide, NADH, ATP, and $FADH_2$. Because glycolysis produces 2 molecules of pyruvic acid from each glucose molecule, the Krebs cycle "turns" twice for each glucose molecule that enters glycolysis. Interpret Diagrams ***What happens to the NADH and $FADH_2$ molecules generated in the Krebs cycle?***

Cellular Respiration and Fermentation **257**

Biology In-Depth

ATP—OR GTP?

In the description and illustration of the Krebs cycle above, each turn of the cycle is said to produce 1 molecule of ATP. Designating ATP as a product of the Krebs cycle is done for the sake of simplicity. The triphosphate compound actually produced in the Krebs cycle is GTP (guanosine triphosphate) from GDP—not ATP from ADP. The amount of energy trapped in GTP is identical to that in ATP. When pools of ATP are low in the cell, the third phosphate of GTP is efficiently transferred, with the help of an enzyme, to ADP to produce ATP. This process provides more ATP for the cell to use and also leaves behind GDP, which can then accept another phosphate in the Krebs cycle.

ZOOMING IN

Divide the class into small groups, and ask students to study the illustration of the Krebs cycle. Have each group write five questions about the Krebs cycle, each on a separate note card. Questions should focus on information students think is essential to understanding what occurs in the Krebs cycle and why it is important to the cell. Then, have groups trade cards and write the answers to the questions on the back of each card. Call on each group to read the question that was most difficult to answer and discuss it as a class.

DIFFERENTIATED INSTRUCTION

L1 Special Needs Have students model the Krebs cycle using clay balls to represent carbon molecules and toothpicks. Start with a three-carbon chain to represent pyruvic acid. As they work through the cycle, have them add or subtract carbons as needed and discuss what occurs at each step.

ELL Focus on ELL: Access Content

ALL SPEAKERS Pair beginning and intermediate speakers with advanced or advanced high speakers. Have them use **Figure 9–5** to help them complete a **Think-Pair-Share** exercise. Write the questions below on the board. Have each student write or draw a short response. Then, ask students to discuss the answers as pairs. Encourage advanced and advanced high speakers to help their partners as necessary.

- What does the Krebs cycle produce?
- Why is the conversion of FAD to $FADH_2$ and NAD^+ to NADH important?
- What happens to the carbon dioxide that is produced?

Study Wkbks A/B, Appendix S14, Think-Pair-Share.

Answers

FIGURE 9–5 Both the NADH and $FADH_2$ molecules feed into the last step of cellular respiration, the electron transport chain.

Teach continued

Build Reading Skills

Explain that one way to organize information in a long reading passage is to create a graphic representation of the information. In this case, the reading describes a process—electron transport and ATP synthesis—that can be well represented by a flowchart. Ask students to help you construct a **Flowchart** of the process on the board. Begin with this first step: *NADH and $FADH_2$ from glycolysis and the Krebs cycle enter the electron transport chain.* Ask students to suggest the next step as well as further steps in the process. The last step should be production of ATP as hydrogen ions pass through ATP synthase.

Study Wkbks A/B, Appendix S25, Flowchart. **Transparencies,** GO8.

DIFFERENTIATED INSTRUCTION

LPR Less Proficient Readers In simplified language, paraphrase the most important concepts about **Electron Transport** and **ATP Production.** For example, write on the board:

Electron Transport:

- NADH and $FADH_2$ pass electrons to the electron transport chain.
- Electrons are then passed from one carrier to the next.
- Each time electrons are passed, hydrogen moves across the membrane.
- Hydrogen ions build up in the intermembrane space. This space becomes positively charged.
- Oxygen is the final electron acceptor.

Create a similar bulleted list for ATP production. Keep these lists on the board for students to refer to as they work through **Figure 9–6.**

Electron Transport and ATP Synthesis

How does the electron transport chain use high-energy electrons from glycolysis and the Krebs cycle?

Products from both the Krebs cycle and glycolysis feed into the last step of cellular respiration, the electron transport chain, as seen in **Figure 9–6.** Recall that glycolysis generates high-energy electrons that are passed to NAD^+, forming NADH. Those NADH molecules can enter the mitochondrion, where they join the NADH and $FADH_2$ generated by the Krebs cycle. The electrons are then passed from all those carriers to the electron transport chain. **The electron transport chain uses the high-energy electrons from glycolysis and the Krebs cycle to convert ADP into ATP.**

Electron Transport NADH and $FADH_2$ pass their high-energy electrons to the electron transport chain. In eukaryotes, the electron transport chain is composed of a series of electron carriers located in the inner membrane of the mitochondrion. In prokaryotes, the same chain is in the cell membrane. High-energy electrons are passed from one carrier to the next. At the end of the electron transport chain is an enzyme that combines these electrons with hydrogen ions and oxygen to form water. Oxygen serves as the final electron acceptor of the electron transport chain. Thus, oxygen is essential for getting rid of low-energy electrons and hydrogen ions, the wastes of cellular respiration. Without oxygen, the electron transport chain cannot function.

Every time 2 high-energy electrons pass down the electron transport chain, their energy is used to transport hydrogen ions (H^+) across the membrane. During electron transport, H^+ ions build up in the intermembrane space, making it positively charged relative to the matrix. Similarly, the matrix side of the membrane, from which those H^+ ions have been taken, is now negatively charged compared to the intermembrane space.

ATP Production How does the cell use the potential energy from charge differences built up as a result of electron transport? As in photosynthesis, the cell uses a process known as chemiosmosis to produce ATP. The inner mitochondrial membrane contains enzymes known as ATP synthases. The charge difference across the membrane forces H^+ ions through channels in these enzymes, actually causing the ATP synthases to spin. With each rotation, the enzyme grabs an ADP molecule and attaches a phosphate group, producing ATP.

The beauty of this system is the way in which it couples the movement of high-energy electrons with the production of ATP. Every time a pair of high-energy electrons moves down the electron transport chain, the energy is used to move H^+ ions across the membrane. These ions then rush back across the membrane with enough force to spin the ATP synthase and generate enormous amounts of ATP. On average, each pair of high-energy electrons that moves down the full length of the electron transport chain provides enough energy to produce 3 molecules of ATP.

In Your Notebook *Relate the importance of oxygen in cellular respiration to the reason you breathe faster during intense exercise.*

BIOLOGY.com Search Lesson 9.2 GO • Art Review • Tutor Tube

Quick Facts

ATP PRODUCTION IN THE ELECTRON TRANSPORT CHAIN

To produce 3 molecules of ATP, each pair of high-energy electrons must move down the full length of the electron transport chain. NADH molecules "drop off" their electrons at the start of the chain, and therefore these electrons power the production of about 3 molecules of ATP each. The electron carrier $FADH_2$, however, enters lower on the chain, and its electrons have a bit less energy. As a result, the electrons of each $FADH_2$ molecule provide only enough energy for the production of about 2 molecules of ATP.

Answers

IN YOUR NOTEBOOK Oxygen serves as the final electron acceptor of the electron transport chain. Without oxygen, the electron transport chain (and the Krebs cycle which depends on it) cannot function. During intense exercise, ATP is produced in great quantities by electron transport and ATP synthesis. Extra oxygen is needed to keep these processes going—no oxygen, no ATP by these processes.

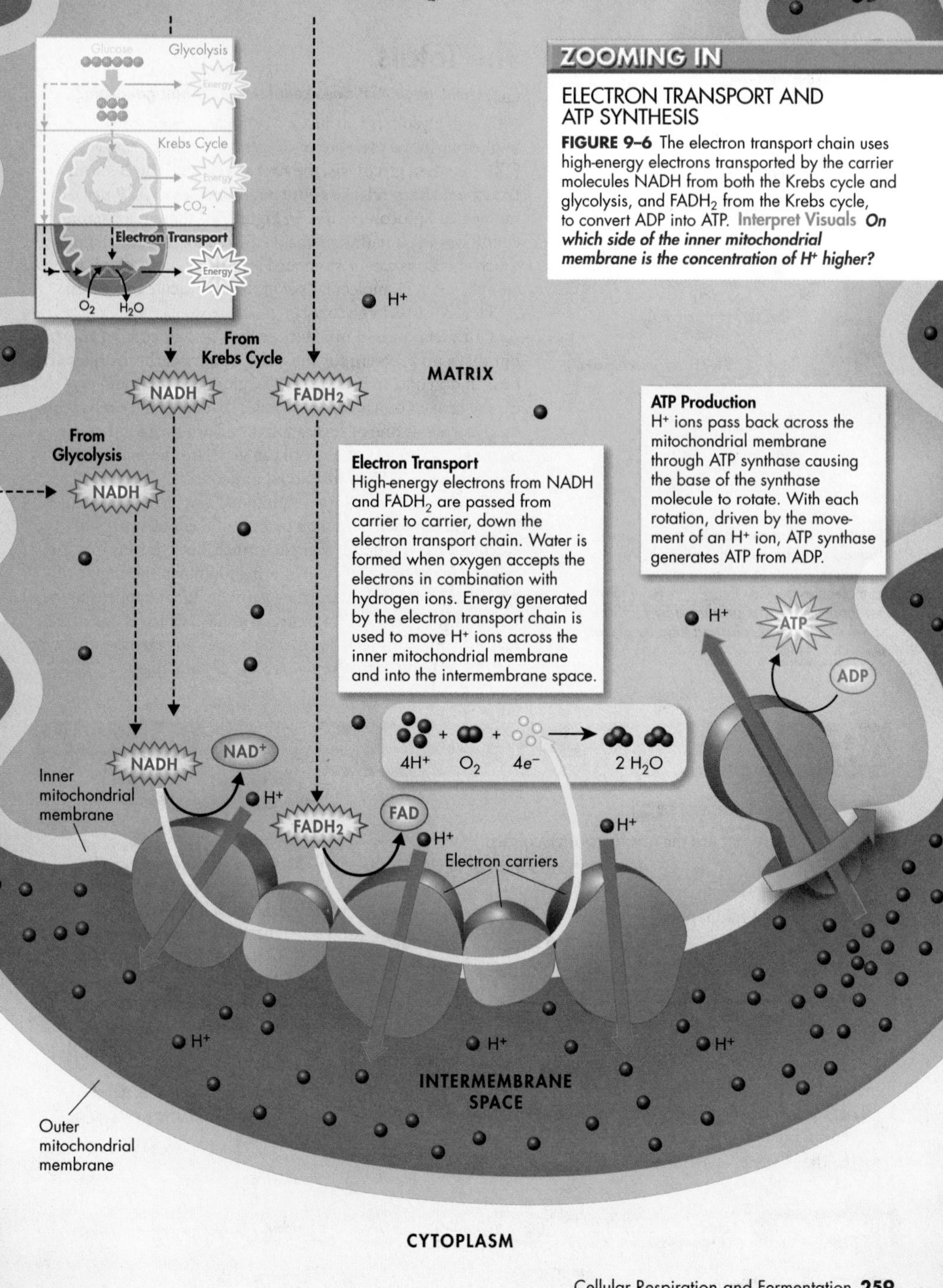
Glucose
Glycolysis
Energy
Krebs Cycle
Energy
CO2
Electron Transport
Energy
O2
H2O
From Krebs Cycle
NADH
FADH2
MATRIX
From Glycolysis
NADH
H+
Electron Transport
High-energy electrons from NADH and FADH2 are passed from carrier to carrier, down the electron transport chain. Water is formed when oxygen accepts the electrons in combination with hydrogen ions. Energy generated by the electron transport chain is used to move H+ ions across the inner mitochondrial membrane and into the intermembrane space.
ATP Production
H+ ions pass back across the mitochondrial membrane through ATP synthase causing the base of the synthase molecule to rotate. With each rotation, driven by the movement of an H+ ion, ATP synthase generates ATP from ADP.
ATP
ADP
4H+ O2 4e− 2 H2O
NADH
NAD+
Inner mitochondrial membrane
FADH2
FAD
Electron carriers
INTERMEMBRANE SPACE
Outer mitochondrial membrane
CYTOPLASM

ZOOMING IN

ELECTRON TRANSPORT AND ATP SYNTHESIS

FIGURE 9–6 The electron transport chain uses high-energy electrons transported by the carrier molecules NADH from both the Krebs cycle and glycolysis, and $FADH_2$ from the Krebs cycle, to convert ADP into ATP. **Interpret Visuals** ***On which side of the inner mitochondrial membrane is the concentration of H^+ higher?***

UbD Check for Understanding

DEPTH OF UNDERSTANDING

Ask students why each of the three stages of cellular respiration are necessary and integral parts of the process. *(Students with a superficial understanding of cellular respiration might simply say that each stage helps produce energy. They may also have difficulty connecting the stages in an overall process. Students with a sophisticated understanding of cellular respiration will be able to identify the relationships between each stage—how one stage produces molecules needed for the next step. They may also mention where in the cell each stage occurs and why location is important to each step in the process.)*

ADJUST INSTRUCTION

Have students create a simplified drawing of cellular respiration that just shows the reactants and products of each stage and how they relate to one another.

ZOOMING IN

Help orient students as they interpret **Figure 9–6.** Start by pointing out the electron carriers NADH from glycolysis and the Krebs cycle and $FADH_2$ from the Krebs cycle. Have students trace how these carriers move through the matrix to the first protein in the electron transport chain. Then, have them follow the electrons through the chain to oxygen.

Ask How do electron carriers use the energy generated by passing the electrons down the electron transport chain? *(to transport hydrogen ions across the inner mitochondrial membrane)*

Then, direct students' attention to the ATP synthase molecule shown at the lower right of the figure.

Ask What causes the production of ATP from ADP? *(As H^+ ions rush through ATP synthase, the base of the synthase rotates, generating ATP from ADP.)*

Ask What causes the H^+ ions to rush through the ATP synthase? *(the concentration gradient of H^+ across the inner mitochondrial membrane, which it cannot directly cross)*

DIFFERENTIATED INSTRUCTION

L1 Struggling Students Many students may find interpreting the figure difficult. To help these students, redraw the figure on the board in a simplified form. Start by sketching the electron transport chain. Draw a line to represent the membrane and five circles to represent the electron carrier proteins in the membrane. Then, draw an NADH molecule approaching the chain. Have students direct you as you draw the electrons from NADH entering the chain. Show how electrons move down the chain, continuing until they reach oxygen. Also, show how hydrogen ions move through the carrier proteins from the matrix into the intermembrane space.

Ask Which contains more hydrogen ions than it did before the process started, the intermembrane space or the matrix? *(the intermembrane space)*

Ask Which side has less? *(the matrix)*

Then, extend the line for the membrane and sketch an ATP synthase. Show an ion moving back through the synthase, producing ATP.

BIOLOGY.com For more on the electron transport chain, have students view **Art Review: Electron Transport and ATP Synthesis.** Suggest they watch **Tutor Tube: Oxygen as the Acceptor of Cellular Respiration Waste** for extra help with electron transport and ATP synthesis.

Answers

FIGURE 9–6 on the intermembrane space side

LESSON 9.2

Teach continued

Lead a Discussion

Explain to students that the number of ATP molecules produced by a molecule of glucose is variable and difficult to determine exactly. Point out that the actual number is likely in the range of 30–42 ATPs per glucose. Mention that a total of 36 ATPs, though, is reasonable since it assumes 2 ATPs per $FADH_2$ and 3 ATPs per NADH (with approximately 2 ATPs lost due to the cost of transporting NADH produced in the cytoplasm into the mitochondria for oxidation).

Assess and Remediate

EVALUATE UNDERSTANDING

Call on students at random to describe the main events in each stage of cellular respiration. Then, have students complete the 9.2 Assessment.

REMEDIATION SUGGESTION

L1 Struggling Students If students cannot identify the function of $NADP^+$ in **Question 1b,** advise them to look back to Lesson 8.3, where they learned about the electron carriers involved in photosynthesis.

BIOLOGY.com Students can check their understanding of lesson concepts with the **Self-Test** assessment. They can then take an online version of the **Lesson Assessment.**

Answers

FIGURE 9–7 18 times more energy

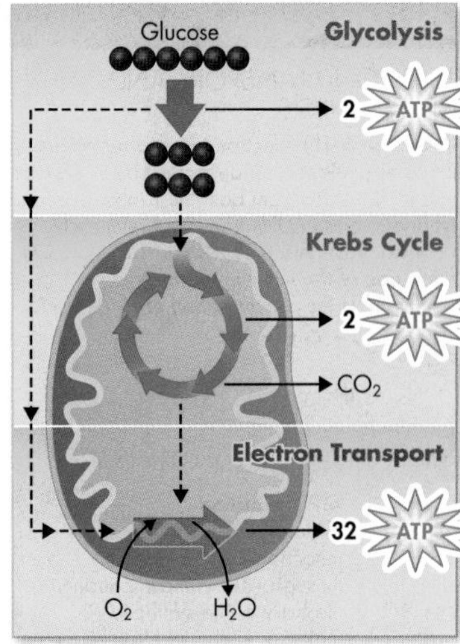

FIGURE 9–7 Energy Totals The complete breakdown of glucose through cellular respiration results in the production of 36 molecules of ATP. Calculate *How many times more energy is produced by all three stages of cellular respiration than by glycolysis alone?* MATH

The Totals

How much ATP does cellular respiration generate?

Although glycolysis nets just 2 ATP molecules per molecule of glucose, in the presence of oxygen, everything changes. **Together, glycolysis, the Krebs cycle, and the electron transport chain release about 36 molecules of ATP per molecule of glucose.** Notice in **Figure 9–7** that under aerobic conditions these pathways enable the cell to produce 18 times as much energy as can be generated by anaerobic glycolysis alone (roughly 36 ATP molecules per glucose molecule versus just 2 ATP molecules in glycolysis).

Our diets contain much more than just glucose, of course, but that's no problem for the cell. Complex carbohydrates are broken down to simple sugars like glucose. Lipids and proteins can be broken down into molecules that enter the Krebs cycle or glycolysis at one of several places. Like a furnace that can burn oil, gas, or wood, the cell can generate chemical energy in the form of ATP from just about any source.

How efficient is cellular respiration? The 36 ATP molecules generated represent about 36 percent of the total energy of glucose. That might not seem like much, but it means that the cell is actually more efficient at using food than the engine of a typical automobile is at burning gasoline. What happens to the remaining 64 percent? It is released as heat, which is one of the reasons your body feels warmer after vigorous exercise, and why your body temperature remains 37°C day and night.

9.2 Assessment

IN B.3.2

Review Key Concepts

1. a. Review What are the products of glycolysis?
   b. Compare and Contrast How is the function of NAD^+ similar to that of $NADP^+$?
2. a. Review What happens to pyruvic acid in the Krebs cycle?
   b. Interpret Visuals Look at **Figure 9–5** and list the products of the Krebs cycle. What happens to each of these products?
3. a. Review How does the electron transport chain use the high-energy electrons from glycolysis and the Krebs cycle?
   b. Relate Cause and Effect How does the cell use the charge differences that build up across the inner mitochondrial membrane during cellular respiration?
4. a. Review How many molecules of ATP are produced in the entire breakdown of glucose?
   b. Use Analogies How is the cell like a furnace?

Apply the Big idea

Cellular Basis of Life

5. As you have learned, cellular respiration is a process by which cells transform energy stored in the bonds of food molecules into the bonds of ATP. What does the body do with all of the ATP this process generates? Review the characteristics of life in Chapter 1 and explain why ATP is necessary for each life process.

BIOLOGY.com Search Lesson 9.2 GO • Self-Test • Lesson Assessment

Assessment Answers

1a. 2 molecules of pyruvic acid, 2 molecules of NADH, and a net gain of 2 ATP molecules

1b. Both molecules are electron carriers.

2a. Pyruvic acid is broken down into carbon dioxide through a series of energy-extracting reactions collectively called the Krebs cycle.

2b. The products are ATP, NADH, $FADH_2$, and CO_2. CO_2 is expelled in exhalation. The ATP molecules are used to power cellular activities. The NADH and $FADH_2$ molecules are used in the electron transport chain to generate ATP.

3a. to power the "pumping" of H^+ ions against a concentration gradient from the matrix to the intermembrane space

3b. The charge differences force protons through ATP synthase, which powers the conversion of ADP to ATP.

4a. about 36 molecules of ATP per molecule of glucose

4b. It can "burn" many different types of fuels, not just glucose. Also, a cell releases heat energy through the breakdown of glucose that heats the organism, just as a furnace releases energy to heat a building.

5. Big idea The body uses the ATP generated by cellular respiration to carry out basic life processes such as reproduction, growth, and development.

Biology & Society

Should Creatine Supplements Be Regulated?

ATP is the chemical compound that gives muscles the energy to contract, but the amount of ATP in most muscle cells is only enough for a few seconds of activity. Muscle cells have a chemical trick, however, that enables them to sustain maximum effort for several more seconds. They attach phosphate groups to a compound called creatine. As they contract, the cells quickly transfer phosphate from creatine to ADP, producing enough ATP to keep working. The creatine phosphate in skeletal muscles effectively doubles or triples the amount of ATP available for intense exercise.

If a little creatine is good, then more creatine would be even better, right? That's what many athletes think and that's why they take creatine supplements. Some studies do suggest that creatine may increase the body's capacity for strong, short-term muscle contractions. As a reason to regulate the use of creatine, however, critics point to potentially serious side effects—such as liver and kidney damage—when creatine is overused.

Because creatine occurs naturally in the body and in foods, testing for creatine use is nearly impossible; so, creatine is *not* banned in major sports leagues. However, due to a lack of long-term studies, the NCAA prohibits coaches from giving creatine to college athletes. Some schools argue that creatine should be banned altogether.

The Viewpoints

Creatine Supplements Should Not Be Regulated Taken in recommended doses, creatine helps build muscle strength and performance. Creatine supplements may help athletes train longer and build strength. No serious side effects have been reported in people who follow the instructions on container labels. Of course, anything can be harmful when abused, but creatine should not be treated any differently from other substances such as caffeine or sugar.

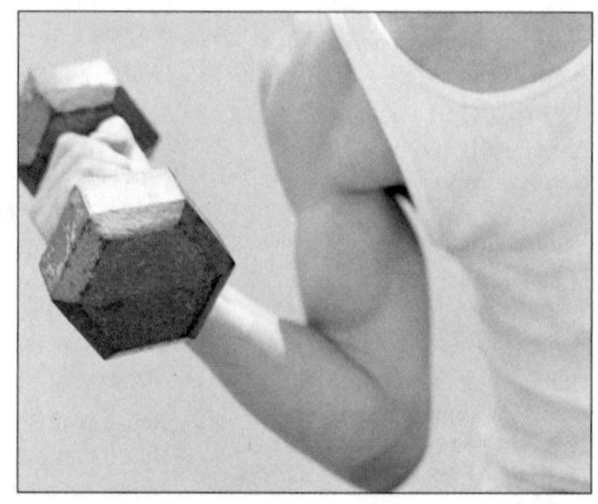

Creatine Supplements Should Be Regulated Scientists know that creatine can cause severe health problems when abused. But even when used properly, creatine is known to cause some problems, such as dehydration and stomach upset. There have been no adequate studies on creatine use by people younger than 18, and there are no good studies of its long-term effects. For these reasons, creatine supplements should be regulated like cigarettes and alcohol—no one under the age of 18 should be allowed to buy them, and schools should have the right to regulate or prohibit their use by athletes.

Research and Decide

1. Analyze the Viewpoints Learn more about this issue by consulting library or Internet resources. Then, list the key arguments of the proponents and critics of creatine use.

2. Form an Opinion Should creatine be regulated? Research examples of high schools or colleges that have banned creatine use by athletes. What were the reasons for these decisions? Do you agree with them?

Quick Facts

CREATINE

Creatine is an interesting compound. It is naturally produced in the body, primarily in the kidneys and liver, and then transported through the blood to muscles. Other interesting facts about creatine include:

- Creatine supplements are sold in several forms, including powder, tablets, energy bars, and drinks.
- Creatine supplements are not considered to be medicines, and therefore they are not regulated by the Federal Drug Administration (FDA).
- Creatine supplements first became widely popular among athletes in the 1990s.
- Researchers are investigating whether creatine might be helpful in treating such health conditions as heart failure, Huntington's disease, and muscular dystrophy.

Teach

Lead a Discussion

After students have read the feature, begin a discussion of creatine supplements. Divide the class in half and assign a viewpoint to each group. Tell students that even if they don't agree with the viewpoint they've been assigned, understanding the other side of the argument will help them more fully form their opinions. Then, have students debate the issue. Insist that any opinions given be backed up by logical arguments.

Answers

1. Answers may vary. Students should list the arguments included on this page as well as any they find through research. Sources should be cited.
2. Opinions may vary about the regulation of creatine. Students should cite specific instances of banning the use of creatine in high schools or colleges. The reasons for agreeing or not agreeing on such a ban should be logical and demonstrate an understanding of the issue.

Getting Started

Objectives

9.3.1 Explain how organisms get energy in the absence of oxygen.

9.3.2 Identify the pathways the body uses to release energy during exercise.

Student Resources

Study Workbooks A and B, 9.3 Worksheets

Spanish Study Workbook, 9.3 Worksheets

Lab Manual B, 9.3 Hands-On Activity Worksheet

 Lesson Overview • Lesson Notes • Activities: Data Analysis • Assessment: Self-Test, Lesson Assessment

For corresponding lesson in the **Foundation Edition**, see pages 223–225.

Activate Prior Knowledge

Have students examine a piece of bread from a leavened loaf and an unleavened loaf. Point out that yeast is added to dough to make it rise. Ask students what process they think yeast cells carry out to cause the characteristics of leavened bread.

Answers

IN YOUR NOTEBOOK Students' table should include that both processes are anaerobic ways to produce NAD^+ using pyruvic acid and NADH. Alcoholic fermentation produces alcohol and CO_2; lactic acid fermentation produces lactic acid.

9.3 Fermentation

Key Questions

How do organisms generate energy when oxygen is not available?

How does the body produce ATP during different stages of exercise?

Vocabulary

fermentation

Taking Notes

Outline Before you read, make an outline using the green and blue headings in the text. As you read, fill in notes under each heading.

THINK ABOUT IT We are air-breathing organisms, and we use oxygen to release chemical energy from the food we eat. But what if oxygen is not around? What happens when you hold your breath and dive under water, or use up oxygen so quickly that you cannot replace it fast enough? Do your cells simply stop working? And, what about microorganisms that live in places where oxygen is not available? Is there a pathway that allows cells to extract energy from food in the absence of oxygen?

Fermentation

How do organisms generate energy when oxygen is not available?

Recall from earlier in this chapter that two benefits of glycolysis are that it can produce ATP quickly and that it does not require oxygen. However, when a cell generates large amounts of ATP from glycolysis, it runs into a problem. In just a few seconds, all of the cell's available NAD^+ molecules are filled up with electrons. Without oxygen, the electron transport chain does not run, so there is nowhere for the NADH molecules to deposit their electrons. Thus, NADH does not get converted back to NAD^+. Without NAD^+, the cell cannot keep glycolysis going, and ATP production stops. That's where a process called fermentation comes in.

When oxygen is not present, glycolysis is followed by a pathway that makes it possible to continue to produce ATP without oxygen. The combined process of this pathway and glycolysis is called **fermentation.** **In the absence of oxygen, fermentation releases energy from food molecules by producing ATP.**

During fermentation, cells convert NADH to NAD^+ by passing high-energy electrons back to pyruvic acid. This action converts NADH back into the electron carrier NAD^+, allowing glycolysis to produce a steady supply of ATP. Fermentation is an anaerobic process that occurs in the cytoplasm of cells. Sometimes, glycolysis and fermentation are together referred to as anaerobic respiration. There are two slightly different forms of the process—alcoholic fermentation and lactic acid fermentation, as seen in **Figure 9–8.**

BUILD Vocabulary

RELATED WORD FORMS The noun **fermentation** and the verb *ferment* are related word forms. Dough that is beginning to ferment is just starting to undergo the process of fermentation.

In Your Notebook *Make a compare/contrast table in which you compare alcoholic fermentation to lactic acid fermentation.*

UbD Teach for Understanding

ENDURING UNDERSTANDING A cell is the basic unit of life; the processes that occur at the cellular level provide the energy and basic structure organisms need to survive.

GUIDING QUESTION How do cells release energy from food without oxygen?

EVIDENCE OF UNDERSTANDING *Give students this assessment at the end of the lesson to show they understand how cells react when they need to release energy from food without oxygen.* Ask each student to write a fictional account of a person running twice around the school's track at full speed (assume this takes at least 2 minutes). The story should describe how the runner's body reacts to this strenuous activity, including the runner's breathing and what happens within the body's cells as they react to the great demand for energy.

Alcoholic Fermentation Yeasts and a few other microorganisms use alcoholic fermentation, which produces ethyl alcohol and carbon dioxide. A summary of alcoholic fermentation after glycolysis is

$$\text{Pyruvic acid} + \text{NADH} \longrightarrow \text{Alcohol} + CO_2 + NAD^+$$

Alcoholic fermentation is used to produce alcoholic beverages. It is also the process that causes bread dough to rise. When yeast cells in the dough run out of oxygen, the dough begins to ferment, giving off tiny bubbles of carbon dioxide. These bubbles form the air spaces you see in a slice of bread. The small amount of alcohol produced in the dough evaporates when the bread is baked.

Lactic Acid Fermentation Most organisms carry out fermentation using a chemical reaction that converts pyruvic acid to lactic acid. Unlike alcoholic fermentation, lactic acid fermentation does not give off carbon dioxide. However, like alcoholic fermentation, lactic acid fermentation also regenerates NAD^+ so that glycolysis can continue. Lactic acid fermentation after glycolysis can be summarized as

$$\text{Pyruvic acid} + \text{NADH} \longrightarrow \text{Lactic acid} + NAD^+$$

Certain bacteria that produce lactic acid as a waste product during fermentation are important to industry. For example, prokaryotes are used in the production of a wide variety of foods and beverages—such as cheese, yogurt, buttermilk, and sour cream—to which the acid contributes the familiar sour taste. Pickles, sauerkraut, and kimchi are also produced using lactic acid fermentation.

Humans are lactic acid fermenters. During brief periods without oxygen, many of the cells in our bodies are capable of producing ATP by lactic acid fermentation. The cells best adapted to doing that, however, are muscle cells, which often need very large supplies of ATP for rapid bursts of activity.

FIGURE 9–8 Fermentation In alcoholic fermentation, pyruvic acid produced by glycolysis is converted into alcohol and carbon dioxide. Lactic acid fermentation converts the pyruvic acid to lactic acid. **Compare and Contrast** ***What reactants and products do the two types of fermentation have in common?***

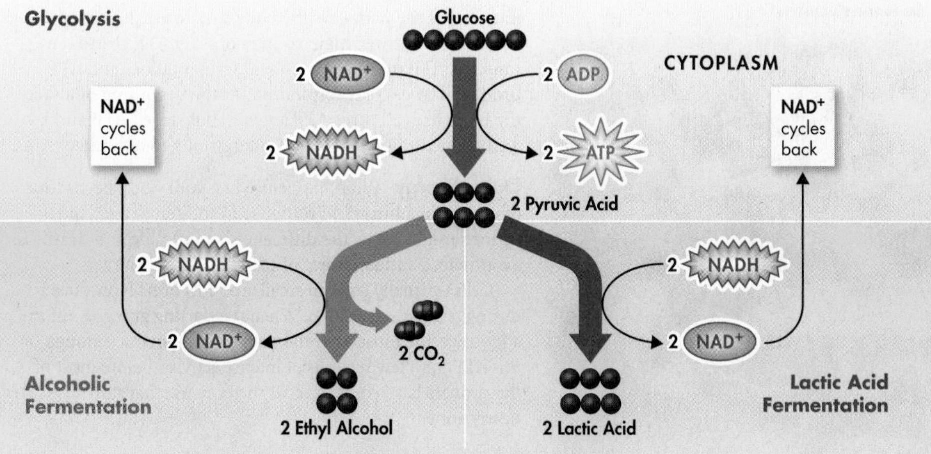

UbD Check for Understanding

ONE-MINUTE RESPONSE

Give students about a minute to respond to the following question.

- Explain why human cells' ability to carry out fermentation is important. *(Responses should mention that lactic acid fermentation helps us make energy quickly, and continue obtaining energy for activity when oxygen intake is inadequate.)*

ADJUST INSTRUCTION

If students' responses are incorrect, lead a short class discussion on the importance of fermentation. Point out that being able to carry out both cellular respiration and fermentation makes humans better adapted for intense activity. Cellular respiration produces more energy, but fermentation allows humans to continue producing energy even when oxygen is not present in adequate amounts.

Teach

Use Visuals

Point out to students that, while the figure shows both alcoholic and lactic acid fermentation, these processes do not normally occur at the same time in an organism. Most organisms carry out either one or the other. Explain that the figure shows pyruvic acid from glycolysis entering either alcoholic or lactic acid fermentation, not both at once.

Ask Why does a cell need NAD^+ to keep glycolysis going? *(The cell needs NAD^+ to accept electrons when glucose is broken down into pyruvic acid.)*

Ask What is missing from the illustration of fermentation that makes the process anaerobic? *(oxygen)*

Ask Which form of fermentation is carried out by your body? *(lactic acid fermentation)*

DIFFERENTIATED INSTRUCTION

L3 Advanced Students Ask interested students to investigate one of the processes in which fermentation is used in the production of a food or a beverage. Students may use the library or online resources in their research. Ask each student to prepare a written report on the food or beverage chosen and to share the report with the class.

ELL Focus on ELL: Extend Language

BEGINNING SPEAKERS Explain that the word *fermentation* is derived from a Latin word for "yeast." Point out that this process, then, was named after a microorganism that carries it out. Also, explain that an organism that carries out fermentation is called a *fermenter*. For example, the text calls humans "lactic acid fermenters." Divide the word *fermentation* into word parts. Have students pronounce each part separately and then pronounce the complete word.

Answers

FIGURE 9–8 Both alcoholic fermentation and lactic acid fermentation have the same two reactants, pyruvic acid and NADH. Both also have one product in common, NAD^+.

Teach continued

Connect to the Real World

Ask What do you think the effects of lactic acid buildup in an athlete's muscles might be? *(Sample answers: muscle cramping, soreness, and fatigue)*

Tell students that, until recently, many people thought that lactic acid buildup was responsible for muscle fatigue and soreness. Point out that researchers have since found that lactic acid can actually be used as a fuel by mitochondria to make energy.

DIFFERENTIATED INSTRUCTION

L3 Advanced Students Have advanced students write a story about a mountain climber who tries to reach the peak of a mountain in just a few hours. Ask students to include descriptions of the cellular processes used by the mountain climber for the energy needed to reach the peak.

Ask How might changes in altitude affect the energy-producing processes in the climber's body?

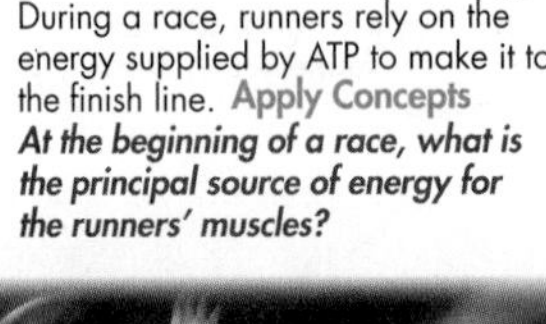

Have students use the **Data Analysis: Lactic Acid and Athletes** to find out more about lactic acid and exercise.

How Does Exercise Affect Disposal of Wastes From Cellular Respiration?

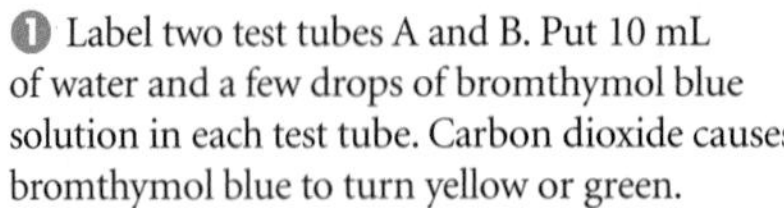

1. Label two test tubes A and B. Put 10 mL of water and a few drops of bromthymol blue solution in each test tube. Carbon dioxide causes bromthymol blue to turn yellow or green.
2. Your partner will time you during this step. When your partner says "go," slowly blow air through a straw into the bottom of test tube A. **CAUTION:** *Do not inhale through the straw.*
3. When the solution changes color, your partner should say "stop" and then record how long the color change took.
4. Jog in place for 2 minutes. **CAUTION:** *Do not do this if you have a medical condition that interferes with exercise. If you feel faint or dizzy, stop immediately and sit down.*
5. Repeat steps 2–4 using test tube B.
6. Trade roles with your partner. Repeat steps 1 through 5.

Analyze and Conclude

1. **Analyze Data** How did exercise affect the time it took the solution to change color?
2. **Infer** What process in your body produces carbon dioxide? How does exercise affect this process?

Energy and Exercise

How does the body produce ATP during different stages of exercise?

Bang! The starter's pistol goes off, and the runners push off their starting blocks and sprint down the track, as seen in **Figure 9–9.** The initial burst of energy soon fades, and the runners settle down to a steady pace. After the runners hit the finish line, they walk around slowly and breathe deeply to catch their breath.

Let's look at what happens at each stage of the race in terms of the pathways the body uses to release energy. Humans have three main sources of ATP: ATP already in muscles, ATP made by lactic acid fermentation, and ATP produced by cellular respiration. At the beginning of a race, the body uses all three ATP sources, but stored ATP and lactic acid fermentation can supply energy only for a limited time.

Quick Energy What happens when your body needs lots of energy in a hurry? In response to sudden danger, quick actions might make the difference between life and death. To an athlete, a sudden burst of speed might win a race.

Cells normally contain small amounts of ATP produced during cellular respiration. When the starting gun goes off in a footrace, the muscles of the runners contain only enough of this ATP for a few seconds of intense activity. Before most of the runners have passed the 50-meter mark, that store of ATP is nearly gone.

FIGURE 9–9 Exercise and Energy During a race, runners rely on the energy supplied by ATP to make it to the finish line. **Apply Concepts** ***At the beginning of a race, what is the principal source of energy for the runners' muscles?***

Answers

FIGURE 9–9 ATP that is already in the cell, then ATP produced by lactic acid fermentation

Quick Lab

PURPOSE Students investigate the relationship between exercise and the production of carbon dioxide, a byproduct of cellular respiration.

MATERIALS 2 small test tubes, glass-marking pencil, 10-mL graduated cylinder, bromthymol blue solution, straws, clock or watch with second indicator

SAFETY Caution students to handle glassware with care. Advise students to wear goggles and lab apron when performing the lab. Read and reinforce the cautionary notes before starting the lab. Have students wash their hands after completing the lab.

PLANNING Read the safety information for bromthymol blue before the lab, and warn students not to inhale or swallow the solution. If desired, have students slowly blow through a straw into a test tube that contains just water in order to practice the technique before starting the lab. For special needs students, model the lab in front of the class. Have them perform the role of your partner as you exercise and blow through the straw.

ANALYZE AND CONCLUDE

1. Students should find that the solution changed color more rapidly after exercise than before exercise.
2. Cellular respiration produces carbon dioxide. Exercise increases the rate of cellular respiration.

At this point, the runners' muscle cells are producing most of their ATP by lactic acid fermentation, which can usually supply enough ATP to last about 90 seconds. In a 200- or 300-meter sprint, this may be just enough to reach the finish line.

Fermentation produces lactic acid as a byproduct. When the race is over, the only way to get rid of lactic acid is in a chemical pathway that requires extra oxygen. For that reason, you can think of a quick sprint as building up an oxygen debt that a runner has to repay with plenty of heavy breathing after the race. An intense effort that lasts just 10 or 20 seconds may produce an oxygen debt that requires several minutes of huffing and puffing to clear. **For short, quick bursts of energy, the body uses ATP already in muscles as well as ATP made by lactic acid fermentation.**

MYSTERY CLUE

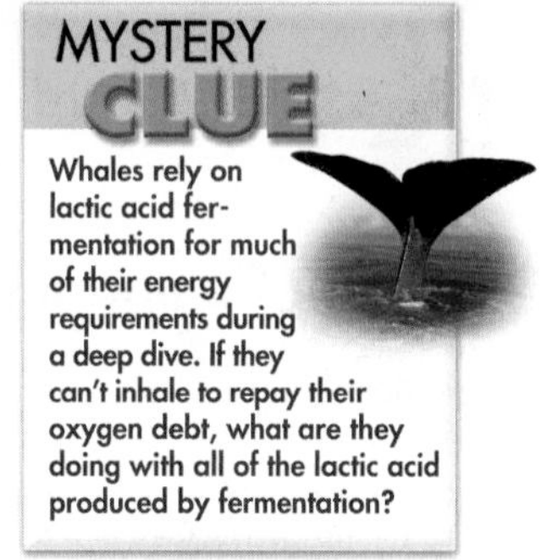

Whales rely on lactic acid fermentation for much of their energy requirements during a deep dive. If they can't inhale to repay their oxygen debt, what are they doing with all of the lactic acid produced by fermentation?

Long-Term Energy What happens if a race is longer? How does your body generate the ATP it needs to run 2 kilometers or more, or to play in a soccer game that lasts more than an hour? **For exercise longer than about 90 seconds, cellular respiration is the only way to continue generating a supply of ATP.** Cellular respiration releases energy more slowly than fermentation does, which is why even well-conditioned athletes have to pace themselves during a long race or over the course of a game. Your body stores energy in muscle and other tissues in the form of the carbohydrate glycogen. These stores of glycogen are usually enough to last for 15 or 20 minutes of activity. After that, your body begins to break down other stored molecules, including fats, for energy. This is one reason why aerobic forms of exercise such as running, dancing, and swimming are so beneficial for weight control. Some organisms, like the bear in **Figure 9–10,** count on energy stored in fat to get them through long periods without food.

FIGURE 9–10 Energy Storage Hibernating animals like this brown bear in Alaska rely on stored fat for energy when they sleep through the winter. Predict ***How will this bear look different when it wakes up from hibernation?***

9.3 Assessment

Review Key Concepts

1. a. Review Name the two main types of fermentation.
   b. Compare and Contrast How are alcoholic fermentation and lactic acid fermentation similar? How are they different?
2. a. Review Why do runners breathe heavily after a sprint race?
   b. Sequence List the body's sources of energy in the order in which they are used during a long-distance race.

PRACTICE PROBLEM

3. You have opened a bakery, selling bread made according to your family's secret recipe. Unfortunately, most customers find the bread too heavy. Review what you have learned about chemical reactions in Chapter 2 and make a list of factors such as temperature that might affect the enzyme-catalyzed fermentation reaction involved in baking bread. Predict how each factor will affect the rate of fermentation and propose a solution for making the bread lighter by adding more bubbles to your family bread recipe.

BIOLOGY.com Search Lesson 9.3 GO • Self-Test • Lesson Assessment • Data Analysis

MYSTERY CLUE Point out to students that whale cells carry out lactic acid fermentation when oxygen isn't available, just as human cells do. Explain that the lactic acid that builds up in human cells stays there until enough oxygen is available to clear the lactic acid away. Students can go online to Biology.com to gather their evidence.

Assess and Remediate

EVALUATE UNDERSTANDING

Ask students to write the chemical summaries for alcoholic fermentation and lactic acid fermentation. Then, have them complete the 9.3 Assessment.

REMEDIATION SUGGESTION

L1 **Struggling Students** If your students have trouble with the sequence called for in **Question 2b,** have pairs reread the subsections, **Quick Energy** and **Long-Term Energy.** Then, have them create a **Flowchart** that shows the body's sources of energy in the order that they are used.

Study Wkbks A/B, Appendix S25, Flowchart. **Transparencies,** GO8.

BIOLOGY.com Students can check their understanding of lesson concepts with the **Self-Test** assessment. They can then take an online version of the **Lesson Assessment.**

Answers

FIGURE 9–10 Sample answer: The bear will probably be thinner, because it will have used its stored fat for energy during hibernation.

Assessment Answers

1a. alcoholic fermentation and lactic acid fermentation

1b. Both forms provide energy to the cell in the absence of oxygen, and both produce NAD$^+$. They are different in that alcoholic fermentation produces alcohol and carbon dioxide, while lactic acid fermentation produces lactic acid.

2a. When the race is over, the only way to get rid of lactic acid is through a chemical pathway that requires extra oxygen.

2b. ATP already in muscles, ATP made by lactic acid fermentation, and ATP produced by cellular respiration

PRACTICE PROBLEM

3. Answers may vary. Students should demonstrate an understanding that the more alcoholic fermentation that occurs in baking the bread, the more CO_2 will be produced, the more bubbles will occur in the bread, and the lighter the bread will be. Factors that could affect the enzyme-catalyzed fermentation include temperature, amount of yeast added to the dough, the amount of sugar (yeast food) added to the dough, and the pH of the dough. Students should predict how each of these factors would affect the rate of fermentation and then propose a solution based on a prediction.

CHAPTER LAB

Pre-Lab

Introduce students to the concepts they will explore in the chapter lab by assigning the Pre-Lab questions.

Lab

Tell students they will perform the chapter lab *Comparing Fermentation Rates of Sugars* described in **Lab Manual A.**

 **Struggling Students** A simpler version of the chapter lab is provided in **Lab Manual B.**

SAFETY

Students should wear goggles and a lab apron while performing the lab. They should use care when working with the hot plate. When finished with the activity, students should wash their hands thoroughly.

Look online for **Editable Lab Worksheets.**

For corresponding pre-lab in the **Foundation Edition**, see page 226.

Real-World Lab

GUIDED INQUIRY

Pre-Lab: Comparing Fermentation Rates of Sugars

Problem How does the type of sugar affect the rate of fermentation?

Materials probe interface, gas pressure probe, hot plate, 400-mL beaker, thermometer, ring stand, test-tube clamp, medium test tube, test-tube rack, sugar solution, yeast suspension, pipettes, vegetable oil, 1-hole rubber stopper, plastic tubing with lock fitting

Lab Manual Chapter 9 Lab

Skills Focus Predict, Measure, Analyze Data, Infer

Connect to the Big idea In most cells, the pathways that release energy from food start with the conversion of glucose to pyruvic acid. This process does not require oxygen. When oxygen is present, however, pyruvic acid can react to form acetyl-CoA, which is used in the second stage of cellular respiration. When oxygen is not present, the pyruvic acid can be used in an anaerobic pathway. This alternate pathway from glucose to ATP is called fermentation. In this lab, you will use yeast to ferment sugars and compare the rates of fermentation.

Background Questions

a. Review What is the importance of the NAD^+ that is produced during the fermentation of pyruvic acid?

b. Review What other products are produced besides NAD^+ when yeast ferment sugar?

c. Compare and Contrast How are simple sugars different from disaccharides? (If needed, review Lesson 2.3 in your textbook.)

d. Use Analogies What do fermentation and a detour that drivers must use when roads are closed have in common?

Pre-Lab Questions

Preview the procedure in the lab manual.

1. Infer Why do you think you will add a layer of vegetable oil above the sugar and yeast mixture?
2. Relate Cause and Effect Explain why it is possible to compare the rates of fermentation by measuring gas pressure in the test tubes.
3. Predict Which of the sugars do you think will have the highest rate of fermentation, and why?

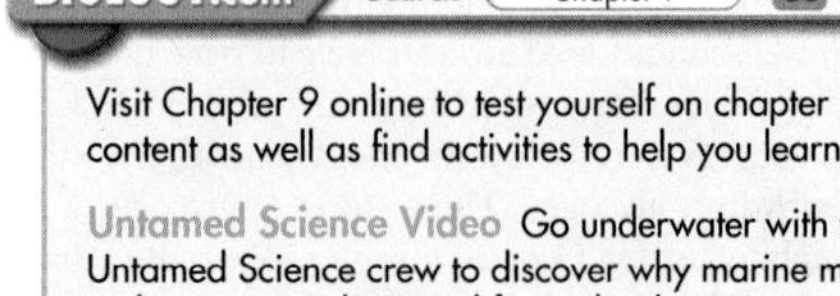

Visit Chapter 9 online to test yourself on chapter content as well as find activities to help you learn.

Untamed Science Video Go underwater with the Untamed Science crew to discover why marine mammals can stay submerged for such a long time.

Data Analysis Analyze the role of lactic acid in exercise and learn about its effects on athletic performance.

Tutor Tube Improve your understanding of respiration by working "backward" from a breath of oxygen.

Art Review Review the components of electron transport and ATP synthesis.

InterActive Art See glycolysis and the Krebs cycle in action.

Art in Motion See how matter and energy cycle between photosynthesis and respiration.

Pre-Lab Answers

BACKGROUND QUESTIONS

a. Without NAD^+, glycolysis will not be able to keep going and the production of ATP will stop.

b. Alcohol and carbon dioxide are produced.

c. Sample answer: Simple sugars are the smallest possible carbohydrate molecules. Disaccharides form when two simple sugar molecules join together and form one larger molecule.

d. Sample answer: Fermentation and a detour are both alternate routes, in one case to the release of energy and in the other case to a destination. (In both cases, the alternate route is less efficient.)

PRE-LAB QUESTIONS

1. Sample answer: The layer of vegetable oil will prevent oxygen from reaching the sugar and yeast mixture. In the presence of oxygen, fermentation will not take place.
2. One of the products of fermentation is carbon dioxide, which is a gas. The faster the reaction, the greater the amount of gas in the tube and the greater the pressure will be.
3. Students are likely to choose glucose because they know that the first step in fermentation is the conversion of glucose to pyruvic acid.

9 Study Guide

Big idea Cellular Basis of Life

Organisms obtain the energy they need from the breakdown of food molecules by cellular respiration and fermentation.

9.1 Cellular Respiration: An Overview

Organisms get the energy they need from food.

Cellular respiration is the process that releases energy from food in the presence of oxygen.

Photosynthesis removes carbon dioxide from the atmosphere, and cellular respiration puts it back. Photosynthesis releases oxygen into the atmosphere, and cellular respiration uses that oxygen to release energy from food.

calorie (250)
cellular respiration (251)
aerobic (252)
anaerobic (252)

9.2 The Process of Cellular Respiration

During glycolysis, 1 molecule of glucose, a 6-carbon compound, is transformed into 2 molecules of pyruvic acid, a 3-carbon compound.

During the Krebs cycle, pyruvic acid is broken down into carbon dioxide in a series of energy-extracting reactions.

The electron transport chain uses the high-energy electrons from glycolysis and the Krebs cycle to convert ADP into ATP.

Together, glycolysis, the Krebs cycle, and the electron transport chain release about 36 molecules of ATP per molecule of glucose.

glycolysis (254)
NAD^+ (255)
Krebs cycle (256)
matrix (256)

9.3 Fermentation

In the absence of oxygen, fermentation releases energy from food molecules by producing ATP.

For short, quick bursts of energy, the body uses ATP already in muscles as well as ATP made by lactic acid fermentation.

For exercise longer than about 90 seconds, cellular respiration is the only way to continue generating a supply of ATP.

fermentation (262)

Think Visually Using the information in this chapter, complete the following compare/contrast table about cellular respiration and fermentation:

Comparing Cellular Respiration and Fermentation

Characteristic	Cellular Respiration	Fermentation
Starting reactants	1	2
Pathways involved	3	4
End products	5	6
Number of ATP molecules produced	7	8

Study Online

REVIEW AND ASSESSMENT RESOURCES

Editable Worksheets Pages of Study Workbooks A and B, Lab Manuals A and B, and the Assessment Resources Book are available online. These documents can be easily edited using a word-processing program.

Lesson Overview Have students reread the Lesson Overviews to help them study chapter concepts.

Vocabulary Review The *Flash Cards* and *Match It* provide an interactive way to review chapter vocabulary.

Chapter Assessments Have students take online versions of the Chapter 9 Assessment.

Standardized Test Prep Students can take an online version of the Standardized Test Prep. You will receive their scores along with ideas for remediation.

Diagnostic and Benchmark Tests Use these tests to monitor your students' progress and supply remediation.

UbD Performance Tasks

SUMMATIVE TASK Have small groups of students write a screenplay that shows how energy is produced in a cell. For example, students might write about a miniature explorer observing the processes of fermentation and cellular respiration, or they might create the screenplay as a first-person account by a carbon atom.

TRANSFER TASK Have students keep an exercise journal for a week. Each time they exercise, have them write down the following:

- what type of exercise they performed
- how long they exercised
- how they felt after

Also have them note any changes in appetite on days when they exercised more than usual. Once the journals are complete, have them write a short essay describing how their entries relate to the content of this chapter.

Answers

THINK VISUALLY

1. glucose and oxygen
2. pyruvic acid and NADH
3. glycolysis, Krebs cycle, electron transport chain
4. glycolysis and either lactic acid or alcoholic fermentation
5. carbon dioxide, water, and energy
6. either carbon dioxide, alcohol, and NAD^+ or lactic acid and NAD^+
7. 36
8. 2

Lesson 9.1

UNDERSTAND KEY CONCEPTS

1. c **2.** d **3.** b

4. b **5.** d

6. A calorie is the amount of energy needed to raise the temperature of 1 gram of water 1 degree Celsius. High-calorie molecules are an energy source for cells.

7. $6O_2 + C_6H_{12}O_6 \rightarrow 6CO_2 + 6\ H_2O$ + Energy, or Oxygen + Glucose → Carbon dioxide + Water + Energy

8. about 10 percent

9. A process is anaerobic if it does not directly require oxygen. Glycolysis is anaerobic.

THINK CRITICALLY

10. Cellular respiration slowly releases energy through a series of controlled reactions. A fire releases energy more quickly.

11. Photosynthesis removes carbon dioxide from the atmosphere, and cellular respiration puts it back. Photosynthesis releases oxygen into the atmosphere, and cellular respiration uses that oxygen to release energy from food.

Lesson 9.2

UNDERSTAND KEY CONCEPTS

12. b **13.** c **14.** b

15. During glycolysis, 1 molecule of glucose is transformed into 2 molecules of pyruvic acid.

16. NAD^+ is an electron carrier. It provides high-energy electrons needed to produce ATP.

17. Pyruvic acid is broken down into carbon dioxide in a series of energy-extracting reactions. ATP is produced. In addition, high-energy electrons are carried to the electron transport chain by NADH and $FADH_2$.

18. H^+ ions pass across the mitochondrial membrane through ATP synthase, causing the base of the ATP synthase to spin. With each rotation, the enzyme grabs an ADP molecule and attaches a phosphate, producing ATP.

THINK CRITICALLY

19. Both are electron carriers that hold high-energy electrons until they can be transferred to other molecules.

20. It is found in the inner membrane of the mitochondrion in eukaryotes and in the cell membrane of prokaryotes.

21. Students' flowcharts should show that NADH produced in glycolysis and NADH and $FADH_2$ produced in the Krebs cycle carry high-energy electrons to the electron transport chain, which uses these electrons to produce ATP.

22. Students should show that glycolysis occurs in the cytoplasm, the Krebs cycle in the mitochondrial matrix, and the electron transport chain in the inner mitochondrial membrane.

Lesson 9.3

UNDERSTAND KEY CONCEPTS

23. b **24.** a **25.** b

26. Both processes begin with glycolysis and produce ATP.

27. Alcoholic fermentation: Pyruvic acid + NADH → Alcohol + CO_2 + NAD^+; lactic acid fermentation: Pyruvic acid + NADH → Lactic acid + NAD^+. Common reactants: pyruvic acid, NADH

9 Assessment

The numbers following the questions refer to Indiana Academic Standards for Biology I.

9.1 Cellular Respiration: An Overview

Understand Key Concepts

1. Cells use the energy available in food to make a final energy-rich compound called B.3.2
a. water. **c.** ATP.
b. glucose. **d.** ADP.

2. Each gram of glucose contains approximately how much energy?
a. 1 calorie **c.** 4 calories
b. 1 Calorie **d.** 4 Calories

3. The process that releases energy from food in the presence of oxygen is B.3.2
a. synthesis. **c.** ATP synthase.
b. cellular respiration. **d.** photosynthesis.

4. The first step in releasing the energy of glucose in the cell is known as
a. fermentation. **c.** the Krebs cycle.
b. glycolysis. **d.** electron transport.

5. Which of the following organisms perform cellular respiration? B.3.2

a. only C **c.** only B and D
b. only A and C **d.** all of the above

6. What is a calorie? Briefly explain how cells use a high-calorie molecule such as glucose. B.3.2

7. Write a chemical equation for cellular respiration. Label the molecules involved. B.3.2

8. What percentage of the energy contained in a molecule of glucose is captured in the bonds of ATP at the end of glycolysis? B.3.2

9. What does it mean if a process is "anaerobic"? Which part of cellular respiration is anaerobic?

Think Critically

10. **Use Analogies** Why is comparing cellular respiration to a burning fire a poor analogy? NoS.6

11. **Compare and Contrast** Why are cellular respiration and photosynthesis considered opposite reactions? B.3.1, B.3.2

9.2 The Process of Cellular Respiration

Understand Key Concepts

12. The net gain of energy from glycolysis is
a. 4 ATP molecules.
b. 2 ATP molecules.
c. 8 ADP molecules.
d. 3 pyruvic acid molecules.

13. The Krebs cycle takes place within the B.2.3
a. chloroplast. **c.** mitochondrion.
b. nucleus. **d.** cytoplasm.

14. The electron transport chain uses the high-energy electrons from the Krebs cycle to
a. produce glucose.
b. move H^+ ions across the inner mitochondrial membrane.
c. convert acetyl-CoA to citric acid.
d. convert glucose to pyruvic acid.

15. How is glucose changed during glycolysis? B.3.2

16. What is NAD^+? Why is it important?

17. Summarize what happens during the Krebs cycle. What happens to high-energy electrons generated during the Krebs cycle?

18. How is ATP synthase involved in making energy available to the cell? B.1.2

Think Critically

19. **Compare and Contrast** How is the function of NAD^+ in cellular respiration similar to that of $NADP^+$ in photosynthesis? B.1.2

20. **Compare and Contrast** Where is the electron transport chain found in a eukaryotic cell? Where is it found in a prokaryotic cell? B.2.3

21. **Sequence** Explain how the products of glycolysis and the Krebs cycle are related to the electron transport chain. Draw a flowchart that shows the relationships between these products and the electron transport chain.

22. **Use Models** Draw and label a mitochondrion surrounded by cytoplasm. Indicate where glycolysis, the Krebs cycle, and the electron transport chain occur in a eukaryotic cell. B.2.3

9.3 Fermentation

Understand Key Concepts

23. Because fermentation takes place in the absence of oxygen, it is said to be
    a. aerobic.
    b. anaerobic.
    c. cyclic.
    d. oxygen-rich.

24. The process carried out by yeast that causes bread dough to rise is
    a. alcoholic fermentation.
    b. lactic acid fermentation.
    c. cellular respiration.
    d. yeast mitosis.

25. During heavy exercise, the buildup of lactic acid in muscle cells results in
    a. cellular respiration.
    b. oxygen debt.
    c. fermentation.
    d. the Krebs cycle.

26. How are fermentation and cellular respiration similar?

27. Write equations to show how lactic acid fermentation compares with alcoholic fermentation. Which reactant(s) do they have in common?

Think Critically

28. **Infer** Certain types of bacteria thrive in conditions that lack oxygen. What does that fact indicate about the way they obtain energy?

29. **Infer** To function properly, heart muscle cells require a steady supply of oxygen. After a heart attack, small amounts of lactic acid are present. What does this evidence suggest about the nature of a heart attack?

30. **Predict** In certain cases, regular exercise causes an increase in the number of mitochondria in muscle cells. How might that situation improve an individual's ability to perform energy-requiring activities?

31. **Formulate Hypotheses** Yeast cells can carry out both fermentation and cellular respiration, depending on whether oxygen is present. In which case would you expect yeast cells to grow more rapidly? Explain.

32. **Apply Concepts** Carbon monoxide (CO) molecules bring the electron transport chain in a mitochondrion to a stop by binding to an electron carrier. Use this information to explain why carbon monoxide gas kills organisms.

solve the CHAPTER MYSTERY

DIVING WITHOUT A BREATH

To be able to sustain regular 45-minute intervals underwater, whales employ a number of special mechanisms. For example, whale blood is very tolerant of CO_2 buildup that results from the Krebs cycle. This allows whales to stay underwater for an extended period without triggering the reflex to surface. The Krebs cycle and electron transport rely on oxygen, of course. And once the oxygen is used—and it's used quickly!—whale muscles must rely on lactic acid fermentation to generate energy. In humans, lactic acid causes the pH of the blood to drop. If the blood gets too acidic, a dangerous condition called acidosis can occur. Whale muscles are extremely tolerant of lactic acid. The lactic acid remains in the muscles without causing acidosis. When whales resurface after a long dive, they inhale oxygen that clears away the lactic acid buildup.

1. **Relate Cause and Effect** Why must whales have blood that is tolerant of CO_2?
2. **Predict** Myoglobin, a molecule very similar to hemoglobin, stores oxygen in muscles. Would you expect to find more or less myoglobin than average in the muscle tissue of whales if you were to examine it under the microscope?
3. **Infer** How might being able to dive into very deep water be an advantage for whales such as the sperm whale?
4. **Connect to the Big idea** When swimming near the surface, whales breathe every time their heads break out of the water. How do you think the energy pathways used during this type of swimming differ from the ones used during long dives?

THINK CRITICALLY

28. These organisms likely obtain energy through the anaerobic process of fermentation.
29. During a heart attack, lactic acid fermentation must occur. Thus, a heart attack must somehow prevent oxygen from reaching cardiac cells which would in turn prevent the heart from functioning properly.
30. More mitochondria would mean more places for cellular respiration to occur, which would result in more production of ATP to be used in energy-requiring activities.
31. Yeast cells would grow more rapidly when oxygen is present because the aerobic process of cellular respiration produces more ATP than the anaerobic process of fermentation.
32. If CO binds to a cell's electron carriers, no high-energy electrons could be passed down the electron transport chain. The result is reduced production of ATP, the energy source for cells—cells and organisms cannot live without energy.

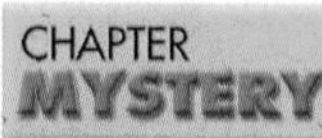

After students have read through the Chapter Mystery, discuss the topics of energy production and oxygen consumption.

Ask How does your body respond when it is low on oxygen? *(I breathe harder and my cells make energy without oxygen.)*

Ask Why does it make sense that whales have different adaptations that help them respond to low-oxygen conditions? *(Whales live in the ocean. They would have to surface each time they needed to "breathe harder" when they are low on oxygen. That would limit how active they can be underwater and how long they can stay underwater.)*

Ask Are whales the only ocean organisms that use oxygen to make energy? *(no)*

Ask Do you think all ocean organisms have the same adaptations for obtaining oxygen and producing energy as whales? Explain. *(Accept all reasonable responses. Sample answer: No, other organisms, like tuna, use gills to obtain oxygen directly from the water rather than the air.)*

CHAPTER MYSTERY ANSWERS

1. Carbon dioxide is one of the products of the Krebs cycle. In humans, a buildup of CO_2 triggers breathing (this is what makes you gasp if you hold your breath). If this happened in whales, they would need to surface or they would drown.
2. Students should predict that muscle tissue in whales would have more than the average amount of myoglobin, because whales need as much stored oxygen as possible in order to carry out cellular respiration during the long periods they are underwater. (In fact, 41 percent of the oxygen stored in the body during a dive is in the muscles of whales as compared to just 13 percent for humans.)
3. Answers may vary. Being able to dive into deep water is beneficial to whales, because they are able to hunt for food in a larger area of the ocean.
4. When swimming near the surface, the cells of whales can carry out cellular respiration, because the supply of oxygen is available for that process. During long dives, however, when oxygen is not available, cells must carry out lactic acid fermentation to produce ATP for energy.

For more on marine mammals and cellular respiration suggest students watch **Untamed Science: Take a Deep Breath.**

Connecting Concepts

USE SCIENCE GRAPHICS

33. On average, there are 9 Calories in 1 gram of a lipid, 4 Calories in 1 gram of a carbohydrate, and 4 Calories in 1 gram of a protein. The differences are a result of differences in their chemical structures.

34. 4.5 grams of protein

35. 1240 Calories; 62 percent

WRITE ABOUT SCIENCE

36. Answers may vary. For each of the three stages of cellular respiration, the reactants used in the chemical reactions of the stage should be analogized as "deposits" and the products should be analogized as "returns." The net return for the whole process of cellular respiration is 36 ATP molecules per deposit of 1 glucose molecule.

37. **Big idea** Sketches may vary, though they should accurately show the processes involved in breathing and cellular respiration. The two processes are related in that breathing brings into the body the oxygen needed to carry out cellular respiration and expels from the body carbon dioxide, a product of cellular respiration.

Connecting Concepts

Use Science Graphics NoS.3

Use the nutritional information below to answer questions 33–35.

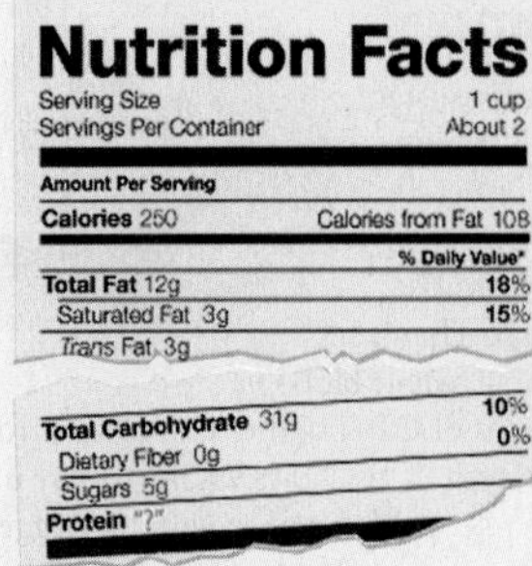

33. Apply Concepts On average, how many Calories are there in 1 gram of a lipid, carbohydrate, and protein? Why the differences?

34. Calculate How many grams of protein must there be in order to account for the number of Calories per serving indicated? MATH

35. Calculate Look at the percent daily value column on the food label. The percent daily value represents the proportion of a typical day's Calories that, on average, should be contributed from the category listed. For example, 31 g of carbohydrates is approximately 10 percent of a daily value. So, a typical person's daily diet should contain about 310 g of carbohydrates. How many Calories does this represent? What percentage of a typical 2000-Calories-per-day diet should therefore come from carbohydrates? MATH

Write About Science NoS.3

36. Explanation Expand the analogy of deposits and withdrawals of money that was used in the chapter to write a short paragraph that explains cellular respiration. (*Hint:* Think about what "inputs" or deposits are required and what "outputs" or returns are produced at each step.) NoS.6

37. Assess the Big idea Draw a sketch that shows respiration (breathing) at the organismal, or whole animal, level. Draw another sketch that shows the overall process of cellular respiration. How do your sketches show breathing and cellular respiration as related processes? B.3.2

Analyzing Data

IN NoS.3

The volume of oxygen uptake was measured in liters per minute (L/min). The scientist collecting the data was interested in how the volume of oxygen breathed in was affected as the difficulty level of the exercise (measured in watts) increased. The data are summarized in the accompanying graph.

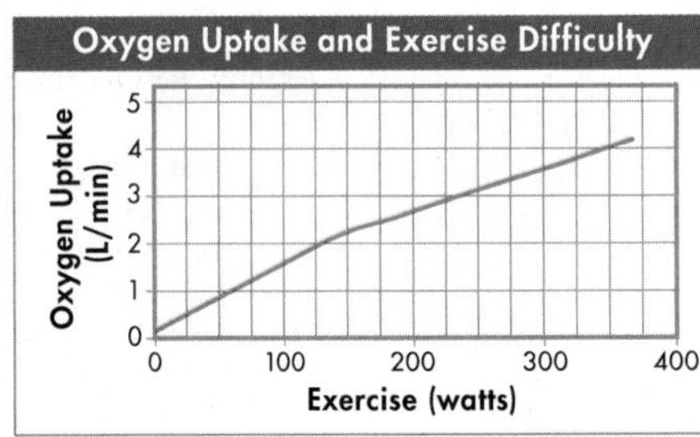

38. Interpret Graphs Based on the graph, at what level of exercise difficulty did oxygen uptake reach 3 L/min?

a. approximately 100 watts
b. approximately 200 watts
c. between 200 and 300 watts
d. between 300 and 400 watts

39. Formulate Hypotheses Which of the following is a valid hypothesis that explains the trend shown on the graph?

a. As exercise becomes more difficult, the body relies more and more on lactic acid fermentation.
b. Exercise below a level of 100 watts does not require increased oxygen uptake.
c. Difficult exercise requires additional oxygen intake in order to generate extra ATP for muscle cells.
d. The human body cannot maintain exercise levels above 500 watts.

Analyzing Data

PURPOSE Students will analyze data to understand the effect that exercise has on the body's oxygen uptake.

PLANNING Review with students the different parts of a graph, such as the horizontal and vertical axes and the labels. Elicit from students the observation that the line begins at 0 watts on the horizontal axis and about 0.2 L/min on the vertical axis. Point out that this is an indication of low oxygen uptake before exercise, when the body is at rest.

ANSWERS

38. c

39. c

Standardized Test Practice for Indiana

Multiple Choice

1. What raw materials are needed for cellular respiration?
   A glucose and carbon dioxide
   B glucose and oxygen
   C carbon dioxide and oxygen
   D oxygen and lactic acid B.3.2

2. During the Krebs cycle
   A hydrogen ions and oxygen form water.
   B the cell releases a small amount of energy through fermentation.
   C each glucose molecule is broken down into 2 molecules of pyruvic acid.
   D pyruvic acid is broken down into carbon dioxide in a series of reactions.

3. Which substance is needed to begin the process of glycolysis?
   A ATP C pyruvic acid
   B NADP D carbon dioxide B.1.2

4. In eukaryotic cells, MOST of cellular respiration takes place in the
   A nuclei. C mitochondria.
   B cytoplasm. D cell walls. B.2.3

5. Which substance is broken down during the process of glycolysis?
   A carbon C glucose
   B NAD^+ D pyruvic acid B.3.2

6. The human body can use all of the following as energy sources EXCEPT
   A ATP in muscles.
   B glycolysis.
   C lactic acid fermentation.
   D alcoholic fermentation.

7. During cellular respiration, which of the following are released as byproducts?
   A CO_2 and O_2
   B H_2O and O_2
   C O_2 and H_2O
   D CO_2 and H_2O B.3.2

8. Which of the following is an aerobic process?
   A the Krebs cycle C alcoholic fermentation
   B glycolysis D lactic acid fermentation

Questions 9 and 10

The graph below shows the rate of alcoholic fermentation for yeast at different temperatures.

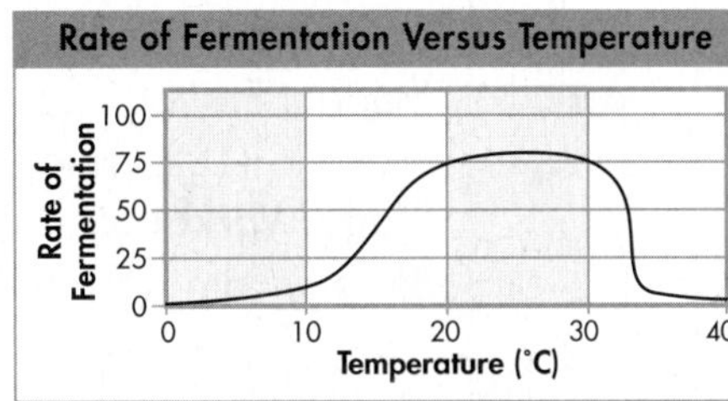

9. According to the graph, what is the relationship between the rate of fermentation and temperature?
   A The rate of fermentation continually increases as temperature increases.
   B The rate of fermentation continually decreases as temperature increases.
   C The rate of fermentation increases with temperature at first, and then it rapidly decreases.
   D The rate of fermentation decreases with temperature at first, and then it rapidly increases.

10. Which statement could explain the data shown in the graph?
    A The molecules that regulate fermentation perform optimally at temperatures above 30°C.
    B The yeast begins releasing carbon dioxide at 30°C.
    C The yeast cannot survive above 30°C.
    D The molecules that regulate fermentation perform optimally at temperatures below 10°C.

Open-Ended Response

11. Explain how a sprinter gets energy during a 30-second race. Is the process aerobic or anaerobic? How does it compare to a long-distance runner getting energy during a 5-kilometer race?

If You Have Trouble With . . .

Question	1	2	3	4	5	6	7	8	9	10	11
See Lesson	9.1	9.2	9.2	9.1	9.2	9.3	9.1	9.1	9.3	9.3	9.3

Test-Taking Tip

INTERPRET GRAPHS

When answering questions about a line graph, suggest students first take the time to analyze the graph before reading the questions. Begin by looking at the shape of the line. Then, identify the variables labeled on each of the graph's axes. Try to determine how the variables are related. That is, determine how one variable changes in response to changes in the other variable. Finally, look again at the line. After analyzing the graph, read and answer the questions that relate to the graph.

Answers

1. B
2. D
3. A
4. C
5. C
6. D
7. D
8. A
9. C
10. C
11. Sample answer: During a 30-second race, a runner gets energy from the small amounts of ATP already in the muscles and from ATP produced by lactic acid fermentation. This process does not depend on oxygen, and, therefore, is anaerobic. During a 5-kilometer race, the only way for the runner to continue generating a supply of ATP is through cellular respiration. Because cellular respiration occurs only in the presence of oxygen, this process is aerobic.

CHAPTER PLANNER 10

Cell Growth and Division

Chapter Contents	IN	Time	Core Resources
Chapter Preview			**Student Edition,** pp. 272–273 **Chapter Mystery,** p. 273
10.1 Cell Growth, Division, and Reproduction Limits to Cell Size • Cell Division and Reproduction	NoS.6, B.2.1	1 period 1/2 block	Student Edition, pp. 274–278 Inquiry 10.1 Quick Lab, p. 275 L2 **Study Workbook A** 10.1 Worksheets L2 Biology.com *Visual Analogy:* Growing Pains
10.2 The Process of Cell Division Chromosomes • The Cell Cycle • Mitosis • Cytokinesis	B.5.1, B.6.1	2 periods 1 block	**Student Edition,** pp. 279–285 Inquiry 10.2 Quick Lab, p. 283 L2 **Study Workbook A** 10.2 Worksheets L2 Biology.com *Art Review:* Eukaryotic Chromosome • *Data Analysis:* Timing the Cell Cycle • *InterActive Art:* Mitosis **Assessment Resources Book** Visual Quiz L2
10.3 Regulating the Cell Cycle Controls on Cell Division • Cancer: Uncontrolled Cell Growth • *Technology & Biology: Fluorescence Microscopy*	NoS.3, B.1.2, B.1.3, B.3.3, B.5.5	1 period 1/2 block	**Student Edition,** pp. 286–291 Inquiry 10.3 Analyzing Data, p. 288 L2 **Study Workbook A** 10.3 Worksheets L2 Biology.com *Art in Motion:* Growth of Cancer Cells • 10.3 Self-Test • 10.3 Lesson Assessment **Assessment Resources Book** Visual Quiz L2
10.4 Cell Differentiation From One Cell to Many • Stem Cells and Development • Frontiers in Stem Cell Research	NoS.3, B.1.3, B.3.3, B.6.3	1 period 1/2 block	**Student Edition,** pp. 292–297 Inquiry 10.4 Analyzing Data, p. 294 L2 **Study Workbook A** 10.4 Worksheets L2 Biology.com 10.4 Lesson Overview • 10.4 Lesson Notes • 10.4 Self-Test • 10.4 Lesson Assessment
Chapter Pre-Lab	NoS.1, NoS.4	1 period 1/2 block	**Student Edition,** p. 298 L2 **Lab Manual A** *Regeneration in Planaria* L2

Differentiated Instruction Tools

Study Workbook B includes worksheets with lesson-level differentiated instruction support and explanations of differentiated instruction teaching strategies.

Lab Manual B includes skills labs, simplified chapter labs, and hands-on activities.

ELL Handbook explains ways to make *Biology* more accessible to ELL students.

Spanish Study Workbook is a Spanish translation of Study Workbook A.

Multilingual Glossary is the glossary translated into ten languages.

Differentiated Instruction Key

- L1 Special Needs or Struggling Students
- ELL English Language Learners
- LPR Less Proficient Readers
- L2 On-Level Students
- L3 Advanced Students

Additional Resources

Biology.com Untamed Science Video • Vocabulary Flash Cards

Study Workbook B 10.1 Worksheets L1 ELL LPR
Spanish Study Workbook 10.1 Worksheets ELL
Biology.com 10.1 Lesson Overview • 10.1 Lesson Notes • 10.1 Self-Test • 10.1 Lesson Assessment

Study Workbook B 10.2 Worksheets L1 ELL LPR
Spanish Study Workbook 10.2 Worksheets ELL
Biology.com *Tutor Tube:* Unraveling Chromosome Vocabulary • 10.2 Lesson Overview • 10.2 Lesson Notes • 10.2 Self-Test • 10.2 Lesson Assessment

Study Workbook B 10.3 Worksheets L1 ELL LPR
Spanish Study Workbook 10.3 Worksheets ELL
Biology.com 10.3 Lesson Overview • 10.3 Lesson Notes

Study Workbook B 10.4 Worksheets L1 ELL LPR
Spanish Study Workbook 10.4 Worksheets ELL

Lab Manual B *Regeneration in Planaria* • Data Analysis: *The Rise and Fall of Cyclins, Cellular Differentiation of* C. elegans • Hands-On Activity: *Comparing Surface Area to Volume* L1 ELL LPR

Chapter Review

Student Edition Study Guide, p. 299 L2 • Unit Project, p. 304 L2
Study Workbook A Chapter 10 Vocabulary Review L2 • Chapter 10 Chapter Mystery/21st Century Skills Activity L2 L3
Transparencies, pp. 122–136 L1 ELL LPR L2
Biology.com Untamed Science Video • You're the Director • Editable Worksheets of Study Workbooks A and B and Lab Manuals A and B • Chapter 10 Flash Cards and Crossword Puzzle

Untamed Science DVD • Classroom Resources CD (includes lesson presentations and editable worksheets)

Chapter Assessment

Student Edition Assessment, pp. 300–303 L2
Study Workbook B Chapter 10 Chapter Review L1 ELL LPR • Chapter 10 Taking a Standardized Test L1 ELL LPR
Assessment Resources Book Chapter 10 Test A L2 • Chapter 10 Test B L1 ELL LPR • Unit 3 Test A L2 • Unit 3 Test B L1 ELL LPR
Biology.com Chapter 10 Assessment • Editable Worksheets of Chapter 10 Visual Quizzes, Chapter 10 Tests A and B, and Unit 3 Tests A and B

Exam*View* *Assessment Suite* • Classroom Resources CD (includes lesson presentations and editable worksheets)

Time: 1 period, 1/2 block

Pressed for Time?

Preview the Chapter Have students read the Key Questions for Lesson 10.2 and preview Figure 10–13.

Cover the Chapter Quickly Have students read *Limits to Cell Size* in Lesson 10.1 and go over Figure 10–2. Have them read all of Lesson 10.2, review Figures 10–7 and 10–13, and perform the Quick Lab on p. 283. Then, have them read *Controls on Cell Division* in Lesson 10.3 and *From One Cell to Many* in Lesson 10.4.

Assess Assign questions 1 and 3 in the 10.1 Assessment, the 10.2 Assessment, questions 1 and 3 in the 10.3 Assessment, and the Chapter 10 Standardized Test Prep except questions 2 and 6.

Connect to the Big Idea

Use the photo of embryonic whitefish cells to help students connect to concepts they will learn in this chapter. First, activate prior knowledge by asking them if they know how many cells an adult human body has. *(60–100 trillion)* Then, ask where those cells came from. *(a single fertilized cell)* Ask if that means that all the cells in their body are the same. *(No, they have differentiated.)*

Now have them study the false-colored micrograph of embryonic whitefish cells. Ask them to describe what they see. Focus their attention on the metaphase chromosomes in the cell at the center of the image. Ask how it differs from surrounding cells. *(chromosomes double, lined up for division)* Talk about how the rate of division for embryonic cells differs from that of cells in an adult. If cells in an embryo divide rapidly, ask what stops them from continuing to divide. *(internal, external regulation)* Ask them to anticipate the answer to the question, **How does a cell produce a new cell?** Ask what it means that cells are the basic unit of life.

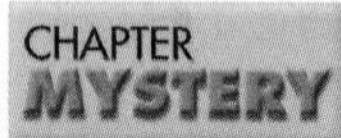

Have students read over the Chapter Mystery and predict what they think might happen to the salamander's limb. Use their predictions to help them start connecting the Chapter Mystery to the Big Idea of Growth, Development, and Reproduction.

BIOLOGY.com Have students preview the chapter vocabulary terms using the **Flash Cards.**

IN INDIANA ACADEMIC STANDARDS

For the full text of all standards, see the Course Overview in the front matter of this book.

Key standards: Chapter 10 covers key ideas from Standard 1: Cellular Chemistry, Standard 2: Cellular Structure, Standard 5: Molecular Basis of Heredity, and Standard 6: Cellular Reproduction and Gene Expression, including **B.5.1** DNA and chromosomes and **B.6.1** Mitosis.

10 Cell Growth and Division

Big idea Growth, Development, and Reproduction

Q: How does a cell produce a new cell?

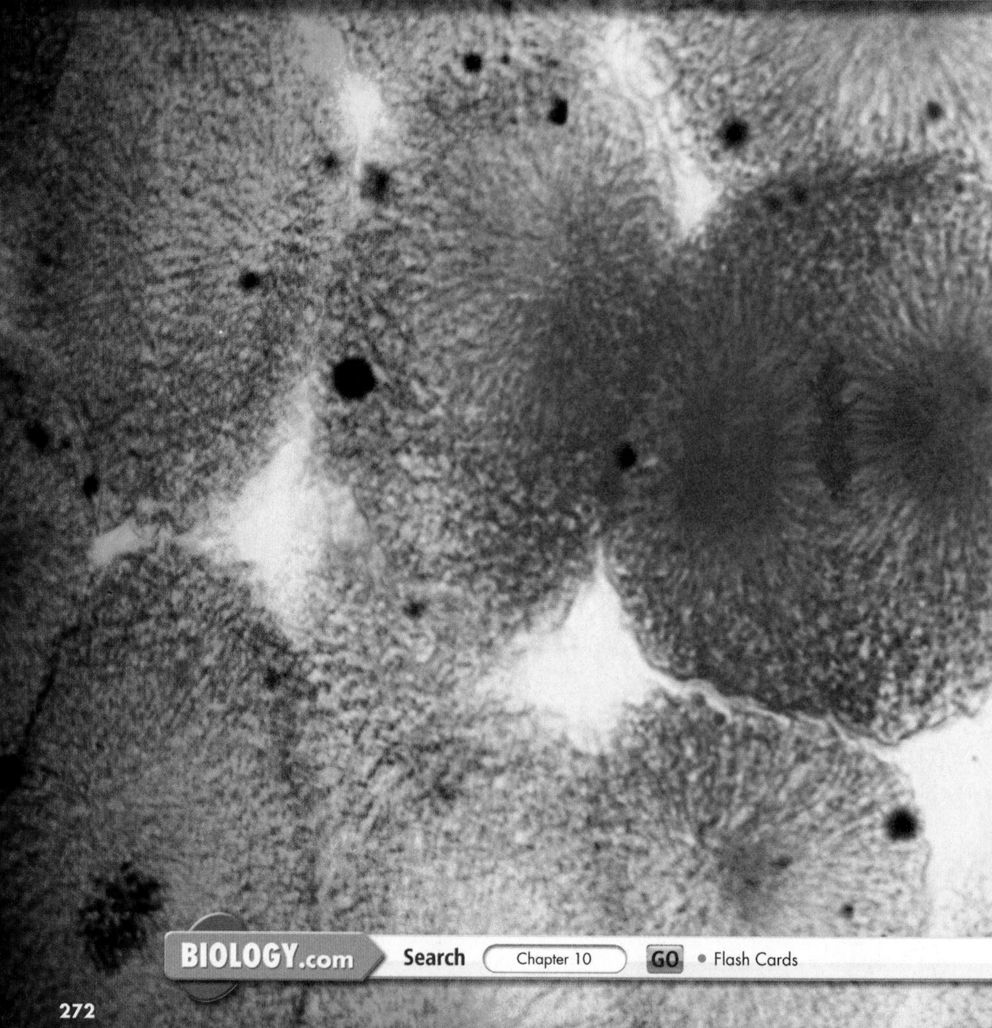

BIOLOGY.com Search Chapter 10 GO • Flash Cards

272

UbD Understanding by Design

In unit 3, students are building toward the Enduring Understanding of how *a cell is the basic unit of life; the processes that occur at the cellular level provide the energy and basic structure organisms need to survive.* In Chapter 10, they will explore cell size, cell division, and the process of differentiation. As shown in the graphic organizer at the right, a Big Idea, Essential Question, and lesson Guiding Questions help frame their exploration of how chapter content informs this Enduring Understanding.

PERFORMANCE GOALS

In Chapter 10, students will be able to express their knowledge of the cell cycle orally, in written words, and by modeling it with classroom objects. Students will apply their knowledge of cell regulation and differentiation by creating real-world analogies for both processes. They will also practice data analysis skills by interpreting cell regulation and differentiation data. At the end of the chapter, students will synthesize what they know by writing a memoir as if they were a cell that had just divided.

INDIANA ACADEMIC STANDARDS FOR SCIENCE

Nature of Science NoS.1, NoS.3, NoS.4, NoS.6, NoS.10; **Cellular Chemistry** B.1.2, B.1.3; **Cellular Structure** B.2.1; **Matter Cycles and Energy Transfer** B.3.3; **Molecular Basis of Heredity** B.5.1, B.5.5; **Cellular Reproduction and Gene Expression** B.6.1. See lessons for details.

Embryonic cells from a whitefish blastula (LM 1250×)

CHAPTER

PET SHOP ACCIDENT

Julia stared into the salamander tank in horror. As an assistant in a pet shop, Julia had mistakenly put a small salamander in the same tank as a large one. Just as she realized her error, the large salamander attacked and bit off one of the small salamander's limbs.

Acting quickly, Julia scooped up the injured salamander and put it in its own tank. She was sure it would die before her shift ended. But she was wrong! Days passed . . . then weeks. Every time Julia checked on the salamander, she was more amazed at what she saw. How did the salamander's body react to losing a limb? As you read this chapter, look for clues to help you predict the salamander's fate. Think about the cell processes that would be involved. Then, solve the mystery.

Never Stop Exploring Your World. Finding the solution to the Pet Shop mystery is only the beginning. Take a video field trip with the ecogeeks of Untamed Science to see where the mystery leads.

UntamedScience™

• Untamed Science Video • Chapter Mystery

Cell Growth and Division 273

Chapter 10 Big Idea: Growth, Development, and Reproduction

Chapter 10 EQ: How does a cell produce a new cell?

- **10.1 GQ:** Why do cells divide?
- **10.2 GQ:** How do cells divide?
- **10.3 GQ:** How does a cell control the process of cell division?
- **10.4 GQ:** How does a single undifferentiated cell lead to a complex multicellular organism?

What's Online

BIOLOGY.com Extend your reach by using these and other digital assets offered at Biology.com.

CHAPTER MYSTERY
Students use what they learn about cell division and differentiation to help them discover how salamanders are able to regrow limbs.

UNTAMED SCIENCE VIDEO
This short movie will take students on a field trip that starts with a hunt for salamanders in an American woodland and ends with scientists studying echinoderm regeneration in Sweden.

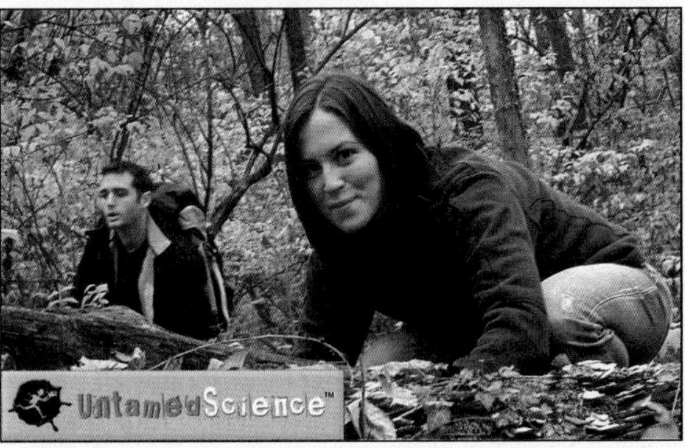

VISUAL ANALOGY
Animations and virtual comparisons of cell parts with town structures help students better understand limits on cell size.

ART REVIEW
Students explore the eukaryotic chromosome by labeling specific structures.

TUTOR TUBE
Short, online tutorials provide extra help on eukaryotic chromosome structure and the phases of the cell cycle.

DATA ANALYSIS
Students can gather data from a virtual sample of plant tissue to determine the relative durations of the different phases of the cell cycle.

INTERACTIVE ART
A short animation shows students that, while mitosis is broken into phases, cell division is a continuous process in which one phase leads to another.

ART IN MOTION
Students watch how cancer cells form a tumor and metastasize throughout the body.

LESSON 10.1

Getting Started

Objectives

10.1.1 Explain the problems that growth causes for cells.

10.1.2 Compare asexual and sexual reproduction.

Student Resources

Study Workbooks A and B, 10.1 Worksheets

Spanish Study Workbook, 10.1 Worksheets

Lab Manual A, 10.1 Quick Lab Worksheet

Lab Manual B, 10.1 Hands-On Activity Worksheet

Lesson Overview • Lesson Notes • Activity: Visual Analogy • Assessment: Self-Test, Lesson Assessment

For corresponding lesson in the **Foundation Edition**, see pages 234–238.

Activate Prior Knowledge

Have students come to the board, one by one, and build a **Cluster Diagram** that incorporates all they can remember about cell growth. Encourage them to include diagrams when appropriate. Refer back to this diagram as you work through the lesson.

Study Wkbks A/B, Appendix S19, Cluster Diagram. **Transparencies,** GO2.

IN INDIANA ACADEMIC STANDARDS

For the full text of all standards, see the Course Overview in the front matter of this book.

B.2.1 Describe features common to all cells that are essential for growth and survival, and explain their functions.

10.1 Cell Growth, Division, and Reproduction

IN B.2.1 Features common to all cells. Also covered: **NoS.6.**

Key Questions

What are some of the difficulties a cell faces as it increases in size?

How do asexual and sexual reproduction compare?

Vocabulary

cell division
asexual reproduction
sexual reproduction

Taking Notes

Outline As you read, create an outline about cell growth, division, and reproduction. As you read, fill in key phrases or sentences about each heading.

THINK ABOUT IT When a living thing grows, what happens to its cells? Does an organism get larger because each cell increases in size or because it produces more of them? In most cases, living things grow by producing more cells. What is there about growth that requires cells to divide and produce more of themselves?

Limits to Cell Size

What are some of the difficulties a cell faces as it increases in size?

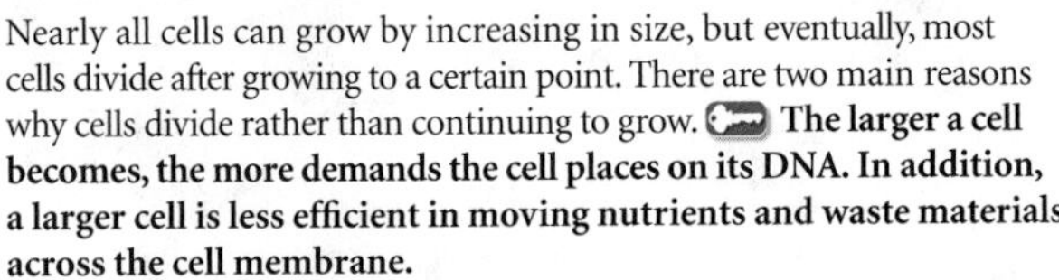

Nearly all cells can grow by increasing in size, but eventually, most cells divide after growing to a certain point. There are two main reasons why cells divide rather than continuing to grow. **The larger a cell becomes, the more demands the cell places on its DNA. In addition, a larger cell is less efficient in moving nutrients and waste materials across the cell membrane.**

Information "Overload" Living cells store critical information in a molecule known as DNA. As a cell grows, that information is used to build the molecules needed for cell growth. But as a cell increases in size, its DNA does not. If a cell were to grow too large, an "information crisis" would occur.

To get a better sense of information overload, compare a cell to a growing town. Suppose a small town has a library with a few thousand books. As more people move in, more people will borrow books. Sometimes, people may have to wait to borrow popular books. Similarly, a larger cell would make greater demands on its genetic "library." After a while, the DNA would no longer be able to serve the needs of the growing cell—it might be time to build a new library.

Exchanging Materials There is another critical reason why cell size is limited. Food, oxygen, and water enter a cell through its cell membrane. Waste products leave a cell in the same way. The rate at which this exchange takes place depends on the surface area of the cell, which is the total area of its cell membrane. The rate at which food and oxygen are used up and waste products are produced depends on the cell's volume. Understanding the relationship between a cell's surface area and its volume is the key to understanding why cells must divide rather than continue to grow.

UbD Teach for Understanding

ENDURING UNDERSTANDING A cell is the basic unit of life; the processes that occur at the cellular level provide the energy and basic structure organisms need to survive.

GUIDING QUESTION Why do cells divide?

EVIDENCE OF UNDERSTANDING *After completing the lesson, give students this assessment to ensure they understand how a small size helps cells survive and function efficiently.* Have students use classroom objects to model how DNA overload or material exchange limits the size of cells. For example, they might limit the number of pencils available to the class. As the class size gets bigger, fewer people can be writing compared to the number who do not have a pencil.

Ratio of Surface Area to Volume in Cells

	1 cm × 1 cm × 1 cm cube	2 cm × 2 cm × 2 cm cube	3 cm × 3 cm × 3 cm cube
Surface Area (length × width) × 6 sides	1 cm × 1 cm × 6 = 6 cm^2	2 cm × 2 cm × 6 = 24 cm^2	3 cm × 3 cm × 6 = 54 cm^2
Volume (length × width × height)	1 cm × 1 cm × 1 cm = 1 cm^3	2 cm × 2 cm × 2 cm = 8 cm^3	3 cm × 3 cm × 3 cm = 27 cm^3
Ratio of Surface Area to Volume	6 / 1 = 6 : 1	24 / 8 = 3 : 1	54 / 27 = 2 : 1

▶ ***Ratio of Surface Area to Volume*** Imagine a cell that is shaped like a cube, like those shown in **Figure 10–1**. The formula for area ($l \times w$) is used to calculate the surface area. The formula for volume ($l \times w \times h$) is used to calculate the amount of space inside. By using a ratio of surface area to volume, you can see how the size of the cell's surface area grows compared to its volume.

Notice that for a cell with sides that measure 1 cm in length, the ratio of surface area to volume is 6/1 or 6 : 1. Increase the length of the cell's sides to 2 cm, and the ratio becomes 24/8 or 3 : 1. What if the length triples? The ratio of surface area to volume becomes 54/27 or 2 : 1. Notice that the surface area is not increasing as fast as the volume increases. For a growing cell, a decrease in the relative amount of cell membrane available creates serious problems.

FIGURE 10–1 Ratio of Surface Area to Volume As the length of the sides increases, the volume increases more than the surface area. **Interpret Tables** ***What are the ratios comparing?***

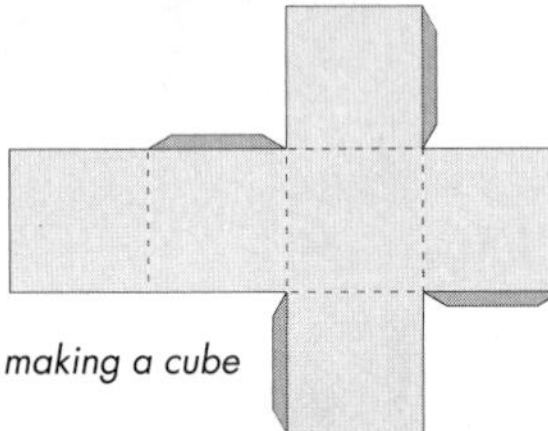

making a cube

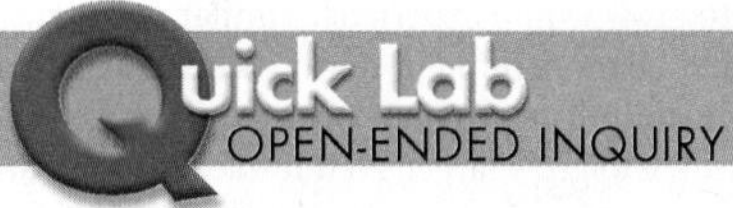

Modeling the Relationship Between Surface Area and Volume

1. Use the drawing and grid paper to make patterns for a 6-cm cube, a 5-cm cube, a 4-cm cube, and a 3-cm cube.
2. Cut out your patterns and fold them. Then use the tabs to tape or glue the sides together. Don't tape down the top side.
3. Construct a data table to compare the volume, the surface area, and the ratio of surface area to volume of each cube.
4. Use your data to calculate the number of 3-cm cubes that would fit in the same volume as the 6-cm cube. Also calculate the total surface area for the smaller cubes. MATH

Analyze and Conclude

1. Review Describe the function of a cell membrane and its relationship to what happens inside a cell.

2. Apply Concepts How does the surface area change when a large cell divides into smaller cells that have the same total volume?

Teach

Build Math Skills

Some students may have limited experience with ratios. Explain that a ratio is a comparison. In this case, it compares the amount of surface area a cell has to its volume. A ratio can be expressed as a proportion, such as 2:1, or as a fraction, such as $\frac{2}{1}$. In **Figure 10–1,** the ratios have been reduced to their simplest form to make it more obvious how the cube's surface area grows in relationship to its volume.

Ask What is the ratio of vowels to consonants in the alphabet? *(5:21 or $\frac{5}{21}$)*

DIFFERENTIATED INSTRUCTION

L1 Special Needs Use clay models to help students understand that a smaller surface area to volume ratio does not mean the cube is getting smaller. Both surface area and cube volume increase as the length of the side increases.

L1 Struggling Students Some students may have a difficult time understanding the information presented in the table. Point out that the cube directly above each column shows the "cell" that the calculations refer to. Then, explain that the first row shows how to find the surface area for each cubic "cell." Use a clay or plastic model of a cube to explain that, when students multiply length and width *($l \times w$),* they are finding the surface area of one face of the cube. They need to multiply this area by six, because the cube has six faces.

PURPOSE Students will explore the ratio of surface area to volume in different-sized cubes that fill an equal volume.

MATERIALS 1-cm grid paper, tape, scissors

PLANNING Suggest students choose side lengths that are multiples of one another and make enough small cubes to fill the larger cube.

ANALYZE AND CONCLUDE

1. The cell membrane provides the surface across which materials can be exchanged between a cell and its environment.
2. A growing cell requires more surface area because it carries out more activity than a smaller cell. A cell's volume cannot become so large that its cell membrane can no longer bring in enough nutrients or get rid of wastes.

Answers

FIGURE 10–1 the amount of surface area a cell has to its volume

LESSON 10.1

Teach continued

VISUAL ANALOGY

Explore the comparison of a cell to a town.

Ask What do the books and library represent? *(DNA and the nucleus)*

Ask What part of a town would be analogous to a cell membrane? *(the town's border)*

Ask What do the crowds and traffic suggest about activity in the town? *(Workers and materials are not getting where they need to go.)*

DIFFERENTIATED INSTRUCTION

L3 Advanced Students Give students five minutes to come up with other analogies for cell growth. Have them consider the idea of central control, as well as the ability to process materials efficiently.

BIOLOGY.com Students can further explore the visual analogy by watching the virtual city grow in **Visual Analogy: Growing Pains.**

Address Misconceptions

Cell Growth Students may think that cells get smaller and smaller with every successive cell division. Tell students that cells go through a period of growth after they divide. Remind students that cell division helps a cell avoid the problems of growing too large.

Answers

FIGURE 10–2 As a cell grows, it needs more materials to cross its membrane. Traffic is comparable to the movement of materials such as nutrients, water, oxygen, and waste across a cell's membrane. With a larger cell, the "lanes of traffic" are more crowded.

VISUAL ANALOGY

GROWING PAINS

FIGURE 10–2 Lots of growth can mean lots of trouble—both in a town and in a cell. **Use Analogies** ***How could cell growth create a problem that is similar to a traffic jam?***

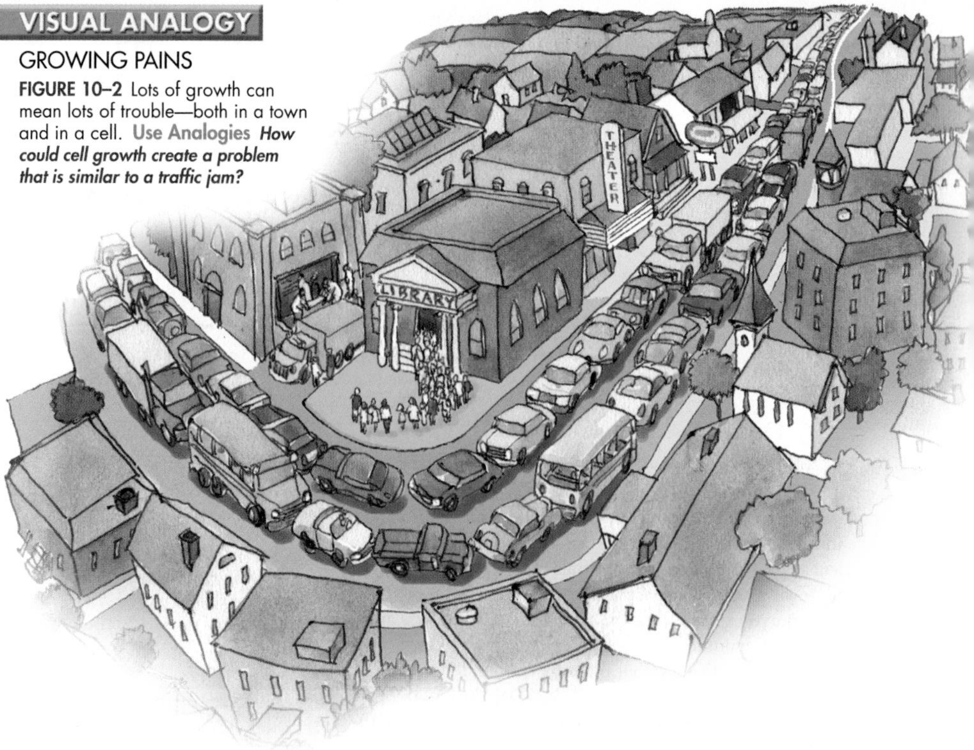

► ***Traffic Problems*** To use the town analogy again, suppose the town has just a two-lane main street leading to the center of town. As the town grows, more and more traffic clogs the main street. It becomes increasingly difficult to move goods in and out.

A cell that continues to grow would experience similar problems. If a cell got too large, it would be more difficult to get sufficient amounts of oxygen and nutrients in and waste products out. This is another reason why cells do not continue to grow larger even if the organism does.

Division of the Cell Before it becomes too large, a growing cell divides, forming two "daughter" cells. The process by which a cell divides into two new daughter cells is called **cell division.**

Before cell division occurs, the cell replicates, or copies all of its DNA. This replication of DNA solves the problem of information overload because each daughter cell gets one complete copy of genetic information. Cell division also solves the problem of increasing size by reducing cell volume. Cell division results in an increase in the ratio of surface area to volume for each daughter cell. This allows for the efficient exchange of materials within a cell.

UbD Check for Understanding

FOLLOW-UP PROBES

Ask What problem does cell division solve for a cell, both in terms of information overload and cellular traffic? Explain. *(Cell division keeps cells from growing too large, so the information stored in DNA can get to where it is needed in the cell. Also, with a smaller size, a cell can efficiently move materials across its membrane.)*

ADJUST INSTRUCTION

If students struggle to answer the question, have them review the sections, **Information "Overload"** and **Exchanging Materials,** in the student edition. Then, have pairs work together to write two short summary statements that explain why information overload and exchanging materials limit cell size.

Cell Division and Reproduction

How do asexual and sexual reproduction compare?

Reproduction, the formation of new individuals, is one of the most important characteristics of living things. For an organism composed of just one cell, cell division can serve as a perfectly good form of reproduction. You don't have to meet someone else, conduct a courtship, or deal with rivals. All you have to do is to divide, and *presto*—there are two of you!

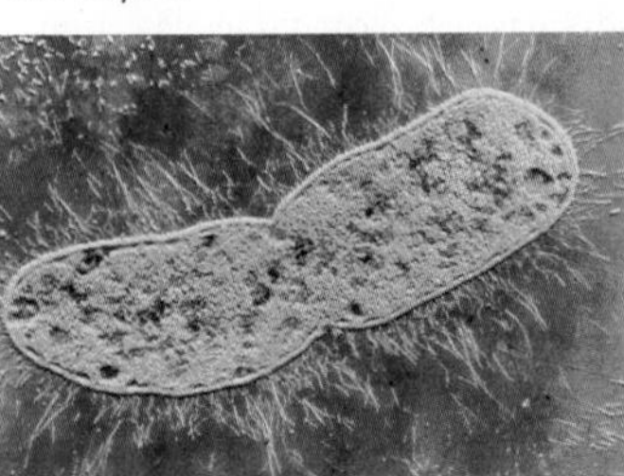

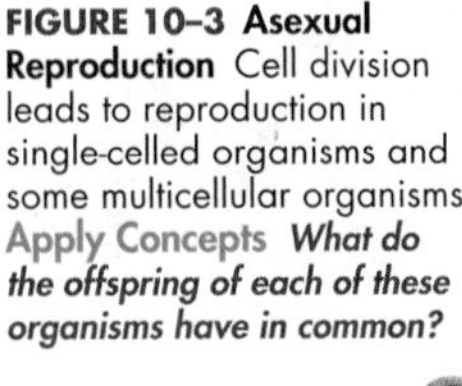

FIGURE 10–3 Asexual Reproduction Cell division leads to reproduction in single-celled organisms and some multicellular organisms. Apply Concepts ***What do the offspring of each of these organisms have in common?***

Asexual Reproduction For many single-celled organisms, such as the bacterium in **Figure 10–3,** cell division is the only form of reproduction. The process can be relatively simple, efficient, and effective, enabling populations to increase in number very quickly. In most cases, the two cells produced by cell division are genetically identical to the cell that produced them. This kind of reproduction is called **asexual reproduction.** **The production of genetically identical offspring from a single parent is known as asexual reproduction.**

Asexual reproduction also occurs in many multicellular organisms. The small bud growing off the hydra will eventually break off and become an independent organism, an example of asexual reproduction in an animal. Each of the small shoots or plantlets on the tip of the kalanchoe leaf may also grow into a new plant.

Sexual Reproduction Unlike asexual reproduction, where cells separate to form a new individual, **sexual reproduction** involves the fusion of two separate parent cells. In sexual reproduction, offspring are produced by the fusion of special reproductive cells formed by each of two parents. **Offspring produced by sexual reproduction inherit some of their genetic information from each parent.** Most animals and plants reproduce sexually, and so do some single-celled organisms. You will learn more about the form of cell division that produces reproductive cells in Chapter 11.

BUILD Vocabulary

PREFIXES The prefix *a-* in *asexual* means "without." **Asexual reproduction** is reproduction without the fusion of reproductive cells.

In Your Notebook *Use a Venn diagram to compare asexual and sexual reproduction.*

Quick Facts

CELL SIZE

While surface area to volume ratios limit the sizes of cells, not all cells are the same size. In fact, there are a surprising variety of cell sizes that exist in nature. For example, some tiny *Mycoplasma* bacteria measure a scant 0.3 micrometers in diameter. To put that in perspective, it can take hundreds of these bacteria, set end to end, to equal the width of a single human hair, about 50–200 micrometers. On the other extreme, giraffes have nerve cells that stretch for meters along the length of their necks.

Lead a Discussion

Talk about how cell division relates to the process of asexual reproduction. To reinforce students' knowledge, have them apply what they have learned to their everyday lives.

Ask Why do bacterial infections spread so quickly through a school? *(Bacteria can reproduce asexually. So, they can quickly reproduce in the right environment, such as a crowded school.)*

DIFFERENTIATED INSTRUCTION

LPR Less Proficient Readers List the Key Concepts on the board in simplified language. For example, write:

- Offspring of asexual reproduction have the same genetic information.
- Offspring of sexual reproduction have genetic information from both parents.

Suggest that students preview these Key Concepts and keep them in mind as they read the text.

ELL Focus on ELL: Access Content

BEGINNING SPEAKERS Show students how cells combine and divide during asexual and sexual reproduction by drawing these simple diagrams on the board:

Asexual Reproduction **Sexual Reproduction**

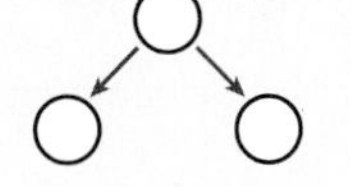

Parent Cells

Offspring

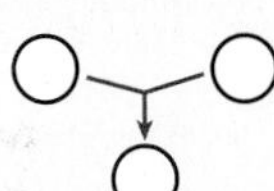

Color code the drawings of the parent cells and the label "Parent Cells," as well as the offspring cells and their label. Point to the diagrams as you explain why asexual reproduction results in genetically identical offspring while sexual reproduction produces offspring with a combination of genetic information from both parents.

Answers

FIGURE 10–3 The offspring share the same genetic material as their parent.

IN YOUR NOTEBOOK Venn diagrams should show the following characteristics: For both sexual and asexual reproduction: produces new organisms; For asexual reproduction only: quick, produces genetically identical offspring, one parent; For sexual reproduction only: offspring produced by the fusion of two cells, two parents

Teach continued

Discuss with students what they think starts to happen to the lost limb of the salamander after a few days. Suggest students look back at the hydra and kalanchoe in **Figure 10–3** for a hint. Students can go online at Biology.com to gather their evidence.

Assess and Remediate

EVALUATE UNDERSTANDING

Ask students to write a paragraph that explains why a cell in the human body never grows as large as a fist. Then, have them complete the 10.1 Assessment.

REMEDIATION SUGGESTION

L1 **Struggling Students** If your students have trouble with **Question 1a,** have them go back to the Key Concept on the first page of the lesson. Have them rewrite each part of the Key Concept in "if-then" form.

BIOLOGY.com Students can check their understanding of lesson concepts with the **Self-Test** assessment. They can then take an online version of the **Lesson Assessment.**

MYSTERY CLUE

As its wound heals, the salamander's body cells are dividing to repair the damage. In what way is this type of cell division similar to asexual reproduction?

Comparing Asexual and Sexual Reproduction You can see that each type of reproduction has its advantages and disadvantages when you look at each one as a strategy for survival. Species survive by reproducing. The better suited a species is to its environment, the greater its chance of survival.

For single-celled organisms, asexual reproduction is a survival strategy. When conditions are right, the faster they reproduce, the better their chance of survival over other organisms using the same resources. Having offspring that are genetically identical is also an advantage as long as conditions remain favorable. However, a lack of genetic diversity becomes a disadvantage when conditions change in ways that do not fit the characteristics of an organism.

Sexual reproduction is a different type of survival strategy. The process of finding a mate and the growth and development of offspring require more time. However, this can be an advantage for species that live in environments where seasonal changes affect weather conditions and food availability. Sexual reproduction also provides genetic diversity. If an environment changes, some offspring may have the right combination of characteristics needed to survive.

Some organisms reproduce both sexually and asexually. Yeasts, for example, are single-celled eukaryotes that use both strategies. They reproduce asexually most of the time. However, under certain conditions, they enter a sexual phase. The different advantages of each type of reproduction may help to explain why the living world includes organisms that reproduce sexually, those that reproduce asexually, and many organisms that do both.

10.1 Assessment

IN B.2.1, NoS.6

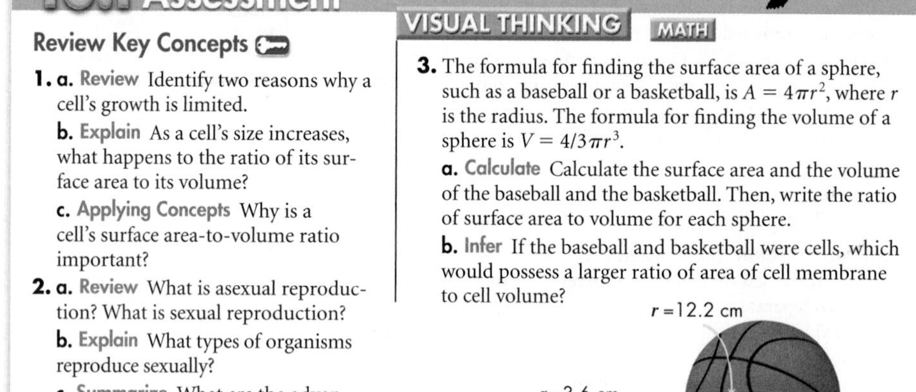

Review Key Concepts

1. a. **Review** Identify two reasons why a cell's growth is limited.
   b. **Explain** As a cell's size increases, what happens to the ratio of its surface area to its volume?
   c. **Applying Concepts** Why is a cell's surface area-to-volume ratio important?
2. a. **Review** What is asexual reproduction? What is sexual reproduction?
   b. **Explain** What types of organisms reproduce sexually?
   c. **Summarize** What are the advantages and disadvantages of both asexual and sexual reproduction?

VISUAL THINKING MATH

3. The formula for finding the surface area of a sphere, such as a baseball or a basketball, is $A = 4\pi r^2$, where r is the radius. The formula for finding the volume of a sphere is $V = 4/3\pi r^3$.
   a. **Calculate** Calculate the surface area and the volume of the baseball and the basketball. Then, write the ratio of surface area to volume for each sphere.
   b. **Infer** If the baseball and basketball were cells, which would possess a larger ratio of area of cell membrane to cell volume?

BIOLOGY.com Search Lesson 10.1 GO • Self-Test • Lesson Assessment

Assessment Answers

1a. The larger a cell becomes, the more demands it places on its DNA and the more trouble it has moving enough nutrients and wastes across the cell membrane.

1b. As a cell grows, its surface area-to-volume ratio decreases.

1c. As a cell's volume grows, its membrane needs more and more surface area to bring nutrients, oxygen, and water into the cell and move waste out. The cell's surface area-to-volume ratio shows how much area is available to move materials in and out of the cell compared to the cell's volume.

2a. Asexual reproduction is the production of offspring from only one parent. Sexual reproduction is the production of offspring from two parents.

2b. Most animals and plants reproduce sexually, as do some single-celled organisms.

2c. Asexual reproduction occurs rapidly, enabling a population to increase rapidly; however, the offspring are genetically identical and may not survive a change in the environment. Sexual reproduction takes longer, so a population does not grow fast; however, the offspring have a mix of genetic material from two parents that might help the population survive if the environment changes.

VISUAL THINKING

3a. baseball, 0.85:1; basketball, 0.25:1

3b. the baseball

10.2 The Process of Cell Division

B.5.1 Basic structure of DNA; B.6.1 Mitosis.

THINK ABOUT IT What role does cell division play in your life? You know from your own experience that living things grow, or increase in size, during particular stages of life or even throughout their lifetime. This growth clearly depends on the production of new cells through cell division. But what happens when you are finished growing? Does cell division simply stop? Think about what must happen when your body heals a cut or a broken bone. And finally, think about the everyday wear and tear on the cells of your skin, digestive system, and blood. Cell division has a role to play there, too.

Chromosomes

What is the role of chromosomes in cell division?

What do you think would happen if a cell were simply to split in two, without any advance preparation? The results might be disastrous, especially if some of the cell's essential genetic information wound up in one of the daughter cells, and not in the other. In order to make sure this doesn't happen, cells first make a complete copy of their genetic information before cell division begins.

Even a small cell like the bacterium *E. coli* has a tremendous amount of genetic information in the form of DNA. In fact, the total length of this bacterium's DNA molecule is 1.6 mm, roughly 1000 times longer than the cell itself. In terms of scale, imagine a 300-meter rope stuffed into a school backpack. Cells can handle such large molecules only by careful packaging. Genetic information is bundled into packages of DNA known as **chromosomes.**

Prokaryotic Chromosomes Prokaryotes lack nuclei and many of the organelles found in eukaryotes. Their DNA molecules are found in the cytoplasm along with most of the other contents of the cell. Most prokaryotes contain a single, circular DNA chromosome that contains all, or nearly all, of the cell's genetic information.

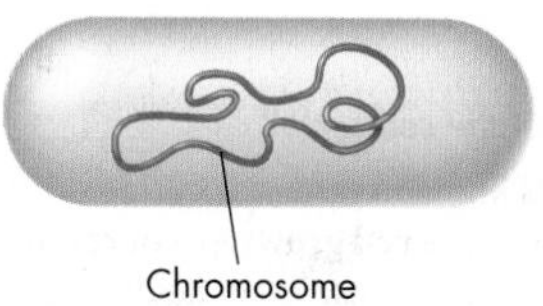

FIGURE 10–4 Prokaryotic Chromosome In most prokaryotes, a single chromosome holds most of the organism's DNA.

Key Questions

What is the role of chromosomes in cell division?

What are the main events of the cell cycle?

What events occur during each of the four phases of mitosis?

How do daughter cells split apart after mitosis?

Vocabulary

chromosome • chromatin • cell cycle • interphase • mitosis • cytokinesis • prophase • centromere • chromatid • centriole • metaphase • anaphase • telophase

Taking Notes

Two-Column Chart As you read, create a two-column chart. In the left column, make notes about what is happening in each stage of the cell cycle. In the right column, describe what the process looks like or draw pictures.

Teach for Understanding

ENDURING UNDERSTANDING A cell is the basic unit of life; the processes that occur at the cellular level provide the energy and basic structure organisms need to survive.

GUIDING QUESTION How do cells divide?

EVIDENCE OF UNDERSTANDING *Have students complete this assessment to show they understand how cell division helps a cell efficiently organize and transfer genetic information to its daughter cells.* Ask pairs of students to brainstorm various ways to equally divide a pile of several-sized rubber bands amongst themselves. Tell them to apply what they know about how a cell divides its genetic information to help them come up with the most efficient, even method for distributing the rubber bands. As a class, discuss and evaluate each pair's method.

Getting Started

Objectives

10.2.1 Describe the role of chromosomes in cell division.

10.2.2 Name the main events of the cell cycle.

10.2.3 Describe what happens during the four phases of mitosis.

10.2.4 Describe the process of cytokinesis.

Student Resources

Study Workbooks A and B, 10.2 Worksheets

Spanish Study Workbook, 10.2 Worksheets

Lesson Overview • Lesson Notes • Activities: Art Review, Tutor Tube, Data Analysis, InterActive Art • Assessment: Self-Test, Lesson Assessment

For corresponding lesson in the **Foundation Edition**, see pages 239–244.

Build Background

Have students think of as many words as they can that are associated with copying, for example, *duplicate, copy, reproduce, replica, replicate, pair.* Write the words on the board, and discuss which words are verbs and which are nouns. As students work through the lesson, encourage them to use the words from the list whenever possible.

IN INDIANA ACADEMIC STANDARDS

For the full text of all standards, see the Course Overview in the front matter of this book.

B.5.1 Describe the relationship between chromosomes and DNA along with their basic structure and function.

B.6.1 Describe the process of mitosis and explain that this process ordinarily results in daughter cells with a genetic make-up identical to the parent cells.

Teach

Use Visuals

Use **Figure 10–5** to start a discussion on the structure of eukaryotic chromosomes. Discuss the levels of organization within the chromosome structure.

Ask What are nucleosomes composed of? *(DNA wrapped around histone molecules)*

Ask Tightly-packed nucleosomes form what structure? *(coils)*

DIFFERENTIATED INSTRUCTION

ELL English Language Learners Model how the organized structure of eukaryotic chromosomes helps cells divide DNA efficiently. Cut 8 long pieces of string (40 cm each) and 8 shorter pieces of string (10 cm each). Combine 4 longer strands and 4 shorter strands in one tangled pile. Then, wind the remaining strands each around an individual pencil. Group this set of pencils and string as a second "genome." Have two volunteers race to divide each of the two genomes in half. Discuss the results of the race.

L3 Advanced Students Ask students to discuss why the eukaryotic chromosome structure makes sense. Suggest they think of different ways to pack a rope into a small bag, and discuss how compact each way is. Ask them to consider how easy it would be to find a specific spot on the rope for each packing suggestion.

BIOLOGY.com Have students further explore chromosome structure by viewing **Art Review: Eukaryotic Chromosome.**

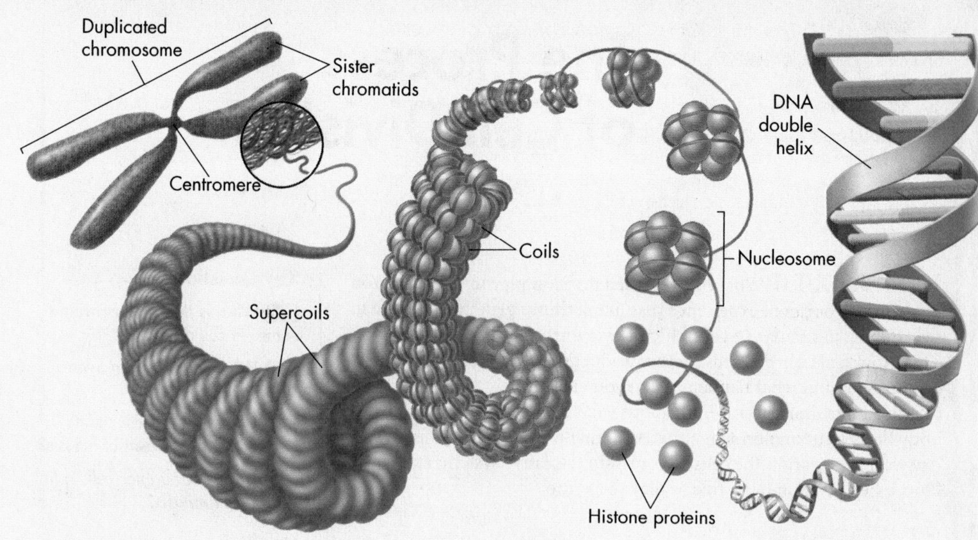

FIGURE 10–5 Eukaryotic Chromosome As a eukaryotic cell prepares for division, each chromosome coils more and more tightly to form a compact structure. Interpret Visuals *Which side of the diagram, left or right, shows the smallest structures, and which shows the largest?*

Eukaryotic Chromosomes Eukaryotic cells generally have much more DNA than prokaryotes have and, therefore, contain multiple chromosomes. Fruit flies, for example, have 8 chromosomes per cell, human cells have 46, and carrot cells have 18. The chromosomes in eukaryotic cells form a close association with histones, a type of protein. This complex of chromosome and protein is referred to as **chromatin.** DNA tightly coils around the histones, and together, the DNA and histone molecules form beadlike structures called nucleosomes. Nucleosomes pack together to form thick fibers, which condense even further during cell division. Usually the chromosome shape you see drawn is a duplicated chromosome with supercoiled chromatin, as shown in **Figure 10–5.**

Why do cells go to such lengths to package their DNA into chromosomes? One of the principal reasons is to ensure equal division of DNA when a cell divides. **Chromosomes make it possible to separate DNA precisely during cell division.**

In Your Notebook *Write instructions to build a eukaryotic chromosome.*

The Cell Cycle

What are the main events of the cell cycle?

Cells go through a series of events known as the **cell cycle** as they grow and divide. **During the cell cycle, a cell grows, prepares for division, and divides to form two daughter cells.** Each daughter cell then moves into a new cell cycle of activity, growth, and division.

UbD Check for Understanding

ONE-MINUTE RESPONSE

Write the following prompt on the board, and give students about a minute to write a quick response summarizing their understanding.

Explain why an organized chromosome structure is an important adaptation for eukaryotic organisms. *(Essays should mention that having an organized structure helps cells use and pass on large amounts of DNA in multiple strands exactly and efficiently.)*

ADJUST INSTRUCTION

If student responses are incorrect or incomplete, review the advantages of chromosome structure by comparing it to a spool of thread. Point out that it is easier to sort two spools of thread than two long, tangled threads. Have them use the analogy to help them explain how chromosome structure helps cells divide.

Answers

FIGURE 10–5 The right side shows the smallest structures. The left side shows the largest.

IN YOUR NOTEBOOK Check that students have traced the hierarchy of chromosome structure shown in **Figure 10–5** starting with DNA coiling around histone proteins to the condensed, supercoiled structure of a chromatid.

The Prokaryotic Cell Cycle The prokaryotic cell cycle is a regular pattern of growth, DNA replication, and cell division that can take place very rapidly under ideal conditions. Researchers are only just beginning to understand how the cycle works in prokaryotes, and relatively little is known about its details. It is known that most prokaryotic cells begin to replicate, or copy, their DNA chromosomes once they have grown to a certain size. When DNA replication is complete, or nearly complete, the cell begins to divide.

The process of cell division in prokaryotes is a form of asexual reproduction known as binary fission. Once the chromosome has been replicated, the two DNA molecules attach to different regions of the cell membrane. A network of fibers forms between them, stretching from one side of the cell to the other. The fibers constrict and the cell is pinched inward, dividing the cytoplasm and chromosomes between two newly formed cells. Binary fission results in the production of two genetically identical cells.

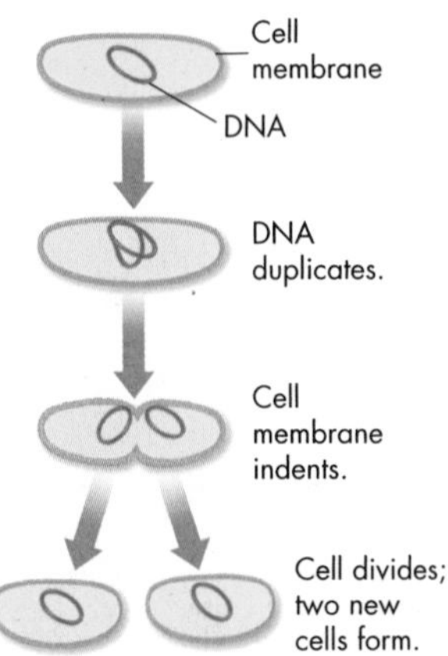

FIGURE 10–6 Binary Fission Cell division in a single-celled organism produces two genetically identical organisms.

The Eukaryotic Cell Cycle In contrast to prokaryotes, much more is known about the eukaryotic cell cycle. As you can see in **Figure 10–7**, the eukaryotic cell cycle consists of four phases: G_1, S, G_2, and M. The length of each part of the cell cycle—and the length of the entire cell cycle—varies depending on the type of cell.

At one time, biologists described the life of a cell as one cell division after another separated by an "in-between" period of growth called **interphase.** We now appreciate that a great deal happens in the time between cell divisions. Interphase is divided into three parts: G_1, S, and G_2.

▶ ***G_1 Phase: Cell Growth*** Cells do most of their growing during the G_1 phase. In this phase, cells increase in size and synthesize new proteins and organelles. The *G* in G_1 and G_2 stands for "gap," but the G_1 and G_2 phases are actually periods of intense growth and activity.

▶ ***S Phase: DNA Replication*** The G_1 phase is followed by the S phase. The *S* stands for "synthesis." During the S phase, new DNA is synthesized when the chromosomes are replicated. The cell at the end of the S phase contains twice as much DNA as it did at the beginning.

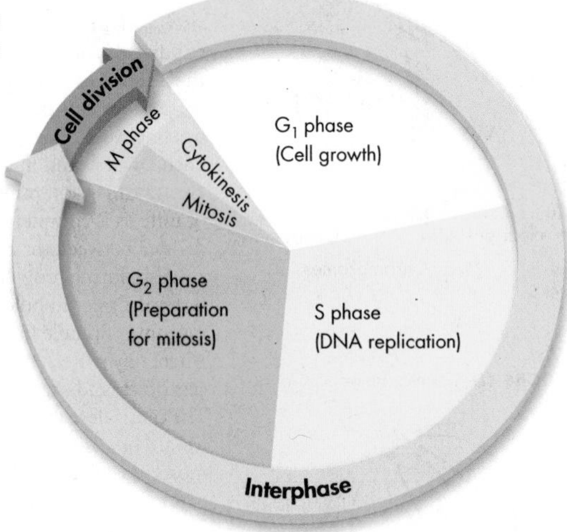

FIGURE 10–7 The Cell Cycle During the cell cycle, a cell grows, prepares for division, and divides to form two daughter cells. The cell cycle includes four phases—G_1, S, G_2, and M. **Infer** ***During which phase or phases would you expect the amount of DNA in the cell to change?***

How Science Works

HUMAN CELLS THAT KEEP DIVIDING

To study cell division for medical and other purposes, biologists need human cells that continue to divide in culture in the laboratory. Yet, finding such cells proved difficult. In 1951, researchers at Johns Hopkins University tried to culture a line of cells that would continue to live and multiply. Every cell sample they tried died out in a few weeks, because normal mammalian cells will divide only about 50 times in culture before cell division stops. Finally, cells from one sample kept dividing week after week, and eventually, year after year. These were called HeLa cells after their original source, a young Baltimore woman named Henrietta Lacks. The sample had been taken from a malignant tumor in her body. Unfortunately, she died a few months later, but HeLa cells have been grown since that time in laboratories around the world.

Use Visuals

Discuss binary fission. Talk about the importance of each step pictured in **Figure 10–6.**

Ask Why does the cell duplicate its DNA? *(The cell duplicates its DNA so that each daughter cell will have a complete copy of the original cell's DNA.)*

Ask What might happen if the membrane did not indent and pinch off? *(The cell would remain undivided, and no new cells would form.)*

Use **Figure 10–7** to discuss the main events of the eukaryotic cell cycle. Explain that this process is called a cycle because it is continuous through generations of cells and because one phase leads to the next.

Ask What are the four phases of the cell cycle? *(G_1 phase, S phase, G_2 phase, and M phase)*

Ask For each individual cell, when does the cell cycle begin? *(when two daughter cells form, after cytokinesis)*

DIFFERENTIATED INSTRUCTION

L1 Struggling Students Some students might have difficulty making the connection that **Figure 10–6** shows a prokaryotic cell cycle, even though it is not drawn as a cycle. To help these students better understand the visual, redraw the figure on the board as a four-stage cycle similar to the six-stage cycle shown in **Figure 10–13.**

Answers

FIGURE 10–7 the S phase and M phase

Teach continued

Use Visuals

Point out each of the labeled structures in **Figures 10–8** and **10–9.** Discuss the role each plays in mitosis.

Ask What does the spindle do? *(The spindle helps pull apart the duplicated chromosomes.)*

Ask What structures are joined at a centromere? *(sister chromatids)*

DIFFERENTIATED INSTRUCTION

ELL English Language Learners Divide the class into groups, and give each group a packet of pictures that contains images of cells in each phase of mitosis. Challenge each group to model how mitosis proceeds by placing the individual pictures in the correct sequence. Then, have groups present their sequences to the class.

LPR Less Proficient Readers Struggling readers may become overwhelmed by the amount of new vocabulary associated with mitosis. Have students make a quick sketch for each word to help them better understand the words.

BIOLOGY.com For more on the cell cycle have students complete the **Data Analysis: Timing the Cell Cycle.**

Address Misconceptions

Hereditary Information Students may think that hereditary information is passed on only through reproductive events. Reinforce that mitosis ensures the accurate and complete transfer of DNA, or hereditary information, from one cell to the next. Make sure students know that cells that are not directly involved in reproduction undergo mitosis on a regular basis.

▶ ***G_2 Phase: Preparing for Cell Division*** When DNA replication is completed, the cell enters the G_2 phase. G_2 is usually the shortest of the three phases of interphase. During the G_2 phase, many of the organelles and molecules required for cell division are produced. When the events of the G_2 phase are completed, the cell is ready to enter the M phase and begin the process of cell division.

▶ ***M Phase: Cell Division*** The M phase of the cell cycle, which follows interphase, produces two daughter cells. The M phase takes its name from the process of mitosis. During the normal cell cycle, interphase can be quite long. In contrast, the process of cell division usually takes place quickly.

In eukaryotes, cell division occurs in two main stages. The first stage of the process, division of the cell nucleus, is called **mitosis** (my TOH sis). The second stage, the division of the cytoplasm, is called **cytokinesis** (sy toh kih NEE sis). In many cells, the two stages may overlap, so that cytokinesis begins while mitosis is still taking place.

BUILD Vocabulary

WORD ORIGINS The prefix *cyto-* in **cytokinesis** refers to cells and derives from the Greek word *kytos,* meaning "a hollow vessel." *Cytoplasm* is another word that has the same root.

Mitosis

What events occur during each of the four phases of mitosis?

Biologists divide the events of mitosis into four phases: prophase, metaphase, anaphase, and telophase. Depending on the type of cell, mitosis may last anywhere from a few minutes to several days. **Figure 10–8** through **Figure 10–11** show mitosis in an animal cell.

FIGURE 10–8 Prophase

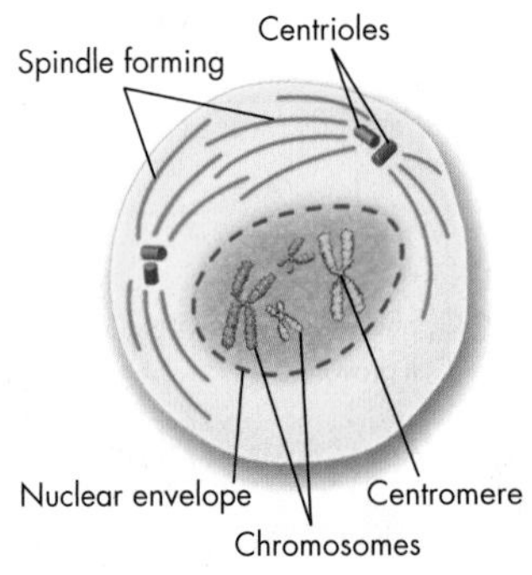

Prophase The first phase of mitosis, **prophase,** is usually the longest and may take up to half of the total time required to complete mitosis. **During prophase, the genetic material inside the nucleus condenses and the duplicated chromosomes become visible. Outside the nucleus, a spindle starts to form.**

The duplicated strands of the DNA molecule can be seen to be attached along their length at an area called the **centromere.** Each DNA strand in the duplicated chromosome is referred to as a **chromatid** (KROH muh tid), or sister chromatid. When the process of mitosis is complete, the chromatids will have separated and been divided between the new daughter cells.

Also during prophase, the cell starts to build a spindle, a fanlike system of microtubules that will help to separate the duplicated chromosomes. Spindle fibers extend from a region called the centrosome, where tiny paired structures called **centrioles** are located. Plant cells lack centrioles, and organize spindles directly from their centrosome regions. The centrioles, which were duplicated during interphase, start to move toward opposite ends, or poles, of the cell. As prophase ends, the chromosomes coil more tightly, the nucleolus disappears, and the nuclear envelope breaks down.

FIGURE 10–9 Metaphase

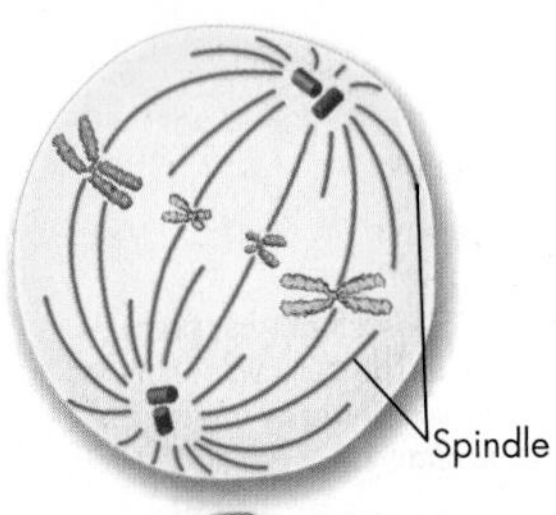

Metaphase The second phase of mitosis, **metaphase,** is generally the shortest. **During metaphase, the centromeres of the duplicated chromosomes line up across the center of the cell. Spindle fibers connect the centromere of each chromosome to the two poles of the spindle.**

 BIOLOGY.com Search Lesson 10.2 GO • Data Analysis

UbD Check for Understanding

INDEX CARD SUMMARIES

Give students each an index card. Ask them to write one big idea about cell division that they understand on the front of the card. Then, have them identify something about cell division that they don't understand and write it on the back in the form of a question.

ADJUST INSTRUCTION

Read over students' cards to get a sense of which concepts they understand well and which concepts they are struggling with. Choose several questions that represent areas of confusion shared by multiple students, and discuss them as a class.

Anaphase The third phase of mitosis, **anaphase,** begins when sister chromatids suddenly separate and begin to move apart. Once anaphase begins, each sister chromatid is now considered an individual chromosome. **During anaphase, the chromosomes separate and move along spindle fibers to opposite ends of the cell.** Anaphase comes to an end when this movement stops and the chromosomes are completely separated into two groups.

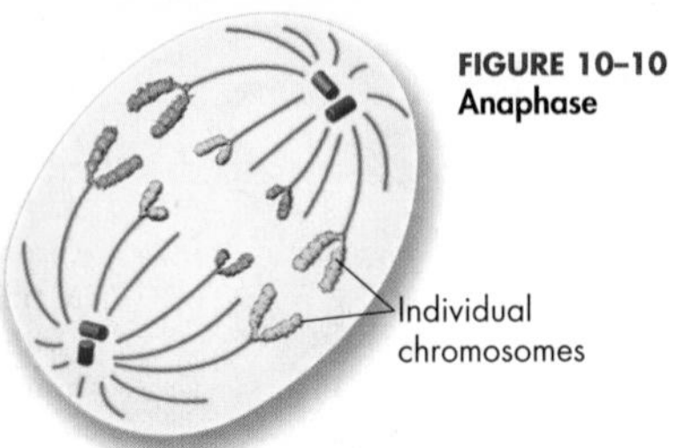

FIGURE 10–10
Anaphase

Telophase Following anaphase is **telophase,** the fourth and final phase of mitosis. **During telophase, the chromosomes, which were distinct and condensed, begin to spread out into a tangle of chromatin.** A nuclear envelope re-forms around each cluster of chromosomes. The spindle begins to break apart, and a nucleolus becomes visible in each daughter nucleus. Mitosis is complete. However, the process of cell division has one more step to go.

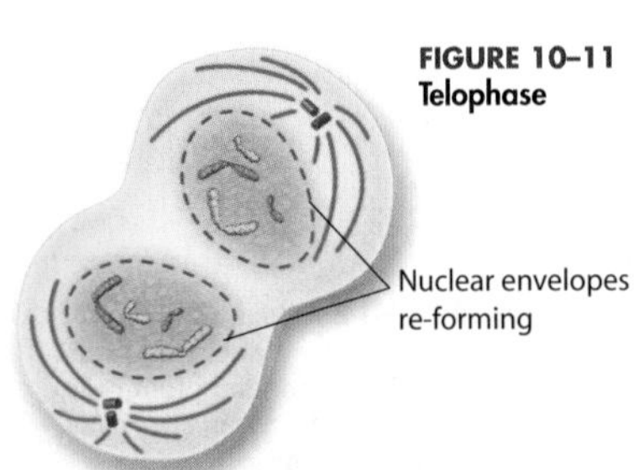

FIGURE 10–11
Telophase

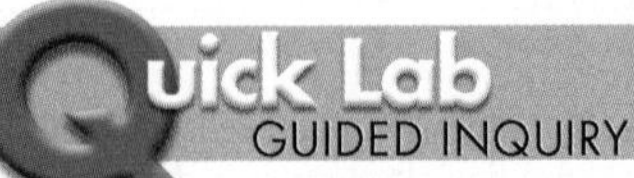

In Your Notebook *Create a chart that lists the important information about each phase of mitosis.*

Quick Lab
GUIDED INQUIRY

B.6.1

Mitosis in Action

1. Examine a slide of a stained onion root tip under a microscope. Viewing the slide under low power, adjust the stage until you find the boxlike cells just above the root tip.
2. Switch the microscope to high power and locate cells that are in the process of dividing.
3. Find and sketch cells that are in each phase of mitosis. Label each sketch with the name of the appropriate phase.

Analyze and Conclude

1. **Observe** In which phase of the cell cycle were most of the cells you observed? Why do you think this is?
2. **Draw Conclusions** What evidence did you observe that shows mitosis is a continuous process, not a series of separate events?
3. **Apply Concepts** Cells in the root divide many times as the root grows longer and thicker. With each cell division, the chromosomes are divided between two daughter cells, yet the number of chromosomes in each cell does not change. What processes ensure that the normal number of chromosomes is restored after each cell division?

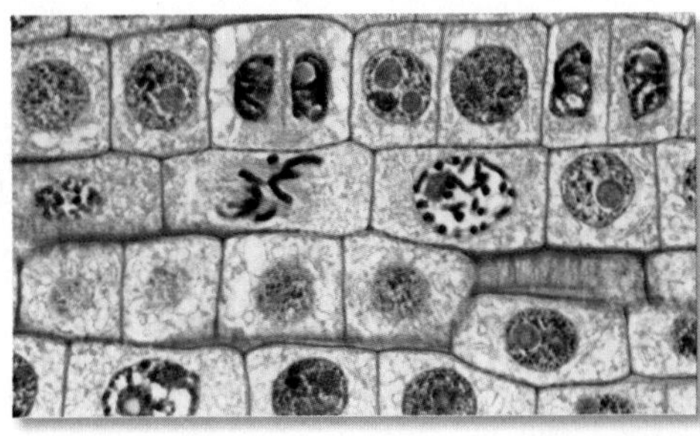

(LM 820×)

Use Visuals

Direct students attention to **Figures 10–10** and **10–11.** Use these visuals to discuss the main events of anaphase and telophase.

DIFFERENTIATED INSTRUCTION

ELL English Language Learners Have students read aloud the description of anaphase and telophase. Ask pairs or small groups of students to discuss how **Figures 10–10** and **10–11** each shows the main events of the phase.

L3 Advanced Students Challenge students to identify what might happen if specific events in mitosis failed to occur.

Ask Suppose the nuclear envelope did not re-form. What might be the result? *(The daughter cells would lack a defined nucleus and their genetic material would remain in the cytoplasm.)*

Answers

IN YOUR NOTEBOOK Students' charts should include the following information: Prophase: genetic material condenses, spindle starts to form, nuclear envelope starts to break down; Metaphase: centromeres line up, spindle fibers connect to centromeres; Anaphase: chromosomes separate and move to opposite ends of the cell; Telophase: chromosomes spread out, nuclear envelope reforms.

Quick Lab

PURPOSE Students will observe what the phases of the cell cycle look like in a typical plant cell.

MATERIALS microscope, prepared slides of onion root tips

SAFETY Remind students to handle the glass microscope slides with care.

PLANNING Have students read the procedure and discuss any questions they have about the materials and what they are to do. To save time, you may also want to set up individual microscope stations that show a cell in each stage of mitosis in the center of the field of vision. Have students rotate through the stations and identify which phase of mitosis is shown.

ANALYZE AND CONCLUDE

1. Most cells were in interphase. This is likely true because interphase is the longest phase of the cell cycle.
2. Some of the cells are in intermediate phases of mitosis rather than in one specific phase of mitosis.
3. The replication of chromosomes during the S phase of the cell cycle and the process of mitosis ensure that each daughter cell has the normal number of chromosomes after cell division.

Teach continued

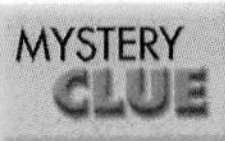

Discuss with students what they think might happen to the cell cycles of the cells surrounding the salamander's wound. Suggest students reread the information on the eukaryotic cell cycle and review **Figure 10–7.** Students can go online at **Biology.com** to gather their evidence.

Assess and Remediate

EVALUATE UNDERSTANDING

Have students look at **Figure 10–7.** Call on volunteers to describe the events in each phase of interphase and each phase of mitosis. Then, have them complete the 10.2 Assessment.

REMEDIATION SUGGESTION

L1 Struggling Students If your students have trouble comparing and contrasting in **Questions 1** and **4,** suggest that they create Venn diagrams to help them understand the similarities and differences between the cell processes they are comparing.

BIOLOGY.com Students can check their understanding of lesson concepts with the **Self-Test** assessment. They can then take an online version of the **Lesson Assessment.**

Answers

FIGURE 10–12 The cell's organelles and other materials in the cytoplasm will be divided between the two new cells.

MYSTERY CLUE

How might the cell cycles of the cells surrounding the salamander's wound be affected?

Cytokinesis

How do daughter cells split apart after mitosis?

As a result of mitosis, two nuclei—each with a duplicate set of chromosomes—are formed. All that remains to complete the M phase of the cycle is cytokinesis, the division of the cytoplasm itself. Cytokinesis usually occurs at the same time as telophase. **Cytokinesis completes the process of cell division—it splits one cell into two.** The process of cytokinesis differs in animal and plant cells.

Cytokinesis in Animal Cells During cytokinesis in most animal cells, the cell membrane is drawn inward until the cytoplasm is pinched into two nearly equal parts. Each part contains its own nucleus and cytoplasmic organelles.

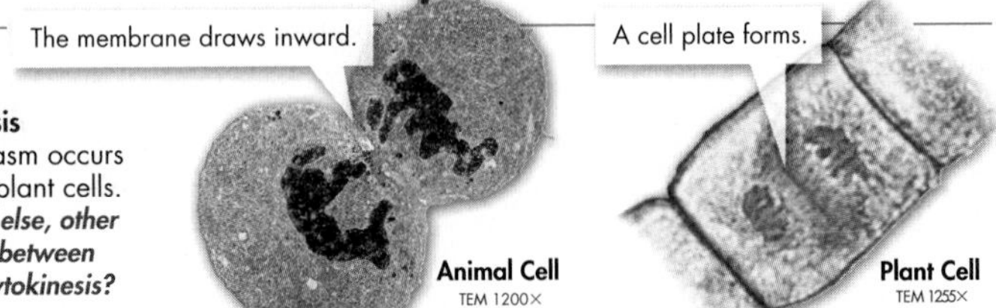

FIGURE 10–12 Cytokinesis The division of the cytoplasm occurs differently in animal and plant cells. **Draw Conclusions** *What else, other than cytoplasm, is divided between the two new cells during cytokinesis?*

Cytokinesis in Plant Cells Cytokinesis in plant cells proceeds differently. The cell membrane is not flexible enough to draw inward because of the rigid cell wall that surrounds it. Instead, a structure known as the cell plate forms halfway between the divided nuclei. The cell plate gradually develops into cell membranes that separate the two daughter cells. A cell wall then forms in between the two new membranes, completing the process.

10.2 Assessment

IN B.5.1, B.6.1

Review Key Concepts

1. a. Review What are chromosomes?
b. Compare and Contrast How does the structure of chromosomes differ in prokaryotes and eukaryotes?

2. a. Review What is the cell cycle?
b. Sequence During which phase of the cell cycle are chromosomes replicated?

3. a. Review What happens during each of the four phases of mitosis? Write one or two sentences for each phase.
b. Predict What do you predict would happen if the spindle fibers were disrupted during metaphase?

4. a. Review What is cytokinesis and when does it occur?
b. Compare and Contrast How does cytokinesis differ in animal and plant cells?

WRITE ABOUT SCIENCE

Summary

5. Summarize what happens during interphase. Be sure to include all three parts of interphase. *Hint:* Include all of the main details in your summary.

Assessment Answers

1a. Chromosomes are bundles of DNA that store most of a cell's genetic information.

1b. Prokaryotic chromosomes are composed of a single, circular strand of DNA. Eukaryotic chromosomes are made up of DNA that is tightly wound around histone molecules. These DNA and protein structures pack together to form condensed coils.

2a. a series of events that a cell goes through as it grows and divides

2b. the S phase

3a. During prophase, DNA in the nucleus condenses and the spindle begins to form. In metaphase, the chromosomes line up and the spindle fibers attach to the centromeres. The chromosomes then separate and move to opposite ends of the cell in anaphase. During telophase, the chromosomes begin to unwind and the spindle begins to break apart.

3b. The centromeres would not attach to the spindle, and the chromosomes could not be pulled apart during anaphase.

4a. Cytokinesis is the division of the cytoplasm and occurs at the end of cell division.

4b. In animal cells, the cell membrane pinches in half to form two cells. In plant cells, a cell plate forms that gradually develops into cell membranes separating the daughter cells. Eventually, a cell wall forms between the two daughter cells.

WRITE ABOUT SCIENCE

5. There are three main parts of interphase. During the G_1 phase, the cell grows and makes new proteins and organelles. In the S phase, the cell replicates its DNA. During the G_2 phase, the cell produces the organelles and molecules it needs to divide.

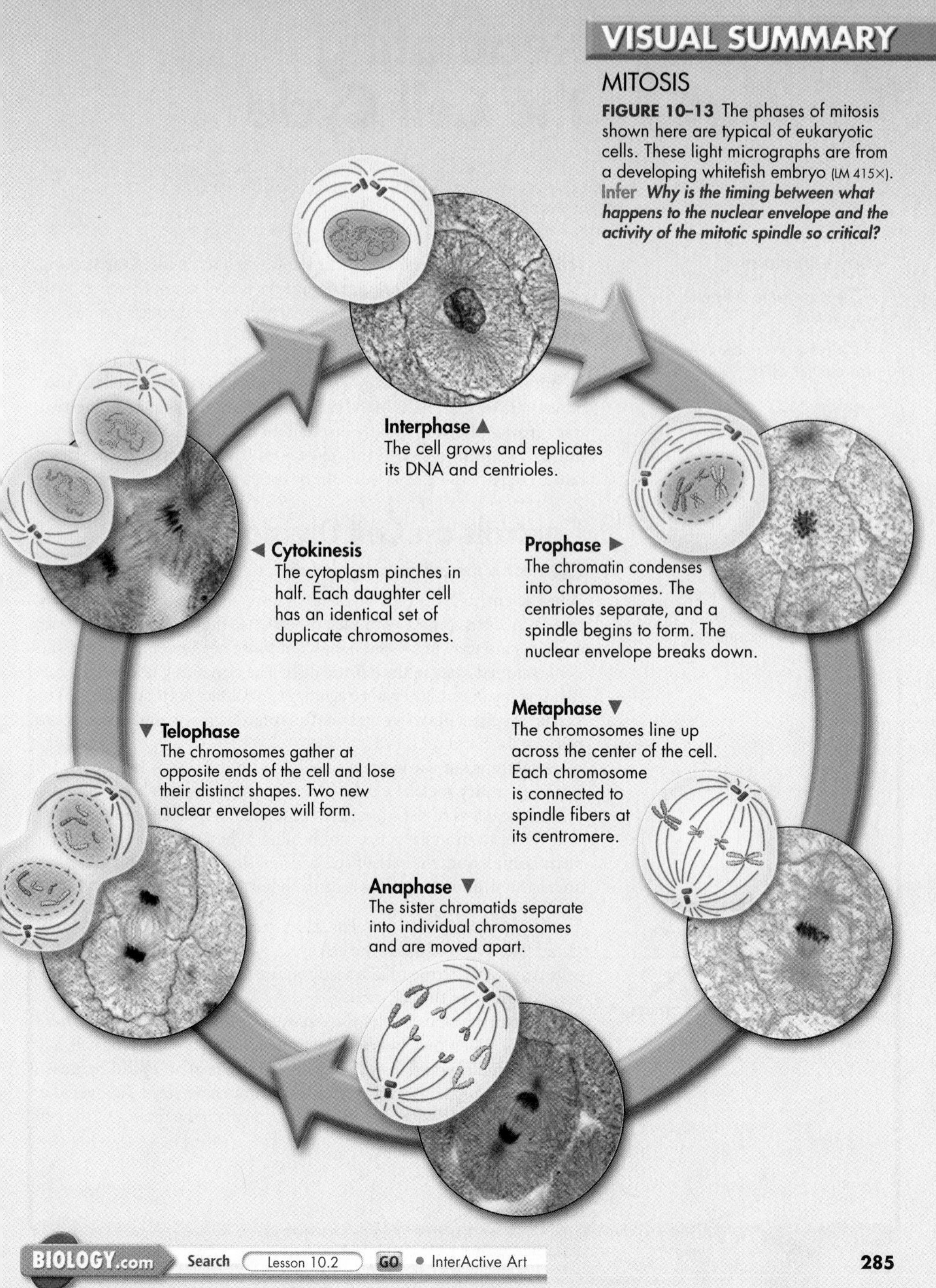

VISUAL SUMMARY
MITOSIS
Interphase ▲
The cell grows and replicates its DNA and centrioles.
Prophase ▶
The chromatin condenses into chromosomes. The centrioles separate, and a spindle begins to form. The nuclear envelope breaks down.
Metaphase ▼
The chromosomes line up across the center of the cell. Each chromosome is connected to spindle fibers at its centromere.
Anaphase ▼
The sister chromatids separate into individual chromosomes and are moved apart.
▼ Telophase
The chromosomes gather at opposite ends of the cell and lose their distinct shapes. Two new nuclear envelopes will form.
◀ Cytokinesis
The cytoplasm pinches in half. Each daughter cell has an identical set of duplicate chromosomes.
BIOLOGY.com Search Lesson 10.2 GO • InterActive Art
285

FIGURE 10–13 The phases of mitosis shown here are typical of eukaryotic cells. These light micrographs are from a developing whitefish embryo (LM 415×). **Infer** ***Why is the timing between what happens to the nuclear envelope and the activity of the mitotic spindle so critical?***

VISUAL SUMMARY

Have small groups of students work through the Visual Summary and discuss how each photo shows the stage of the cell cycle being described.

DIFFERENTIATED INSTRUCTION

L1 Special Needs Suggest students model the stages of the cell cycle with paper towel "cells" and six paper clip "chromosomes." Have them start with three clips on their towels. To model DNA replication, they can make pairs by clipping the remaining three clips to the ones on the towel. Then, have students perform the job of the spindle fibers by lining up the pairs, separating them, and moving them to the ends of their towels. They can then rip the towel in half to model cytokinesis.

ELL Focus on ELL: Extend Language

INTERMEDIATE SPEAKERS Have students use the content on the page and in this lesson to complete a peer-learning **Jigsaw Review** activity. Form students into study groups. Have each group focus on a different phase of the cell cycle: interphase, prophase, metaphase, anaphase, telophase, and cytokinesis. Study group members should work together to prepare a lesson on their phase.

Once the study groups have prepared and practiced their lessons, have students reorganize into learning circles composed of one member from each study group. Each student in the learning circle should then present his or her phase in the order in which it occurs in the cell cycle.

Study Wkbks A/B, Appendix S7, Jigsaw Review.

BIOLOGY.com Students can watch an animated version of the cell cycle in **InterActive Art: Mitosis.** Suggest they review chromosome vocabulary in **Tutor Tube: Unraveling Chromosome Vocabulary**.

UbD Check for Understanding

VISUAL REPRESENTATION

Draw a **Cycle Diagram** on the board with six circles to represent the phases of the cell cycle. Call on students to label each circle with the correct phase and then draw what happens during that phase. Then, ask other students to describe in words what is happening in the cell during each phase.

Study Wkbks A/B, Appendix S23 Cycle Diagram. **Transparencies,** GO6.

ADJUST INSTRUCTION

If students are having a difficult time identifying and describing the phases of the cell cycle, have them reread the sections, **The Cell Cycle** and **Mitosis,** in groups. Then, have them complete another Cycle Diagram.

Answers

FIGURE 10–13 During interphase, the nuclear envelope contains the genetic material. During mitosis, the spindle fibers pull the chromosomes to specific locations in the cell. Nuclear envelope degradation and spindle formation need to be synched.

LESSON 10.3

Getting Started

Objectives

10.3.1 Describe how the cell cycle is regulated.

10.3.2 Explain how cancer cells are different from other cells.

Student Resources

Study Workbooks A and B, 10.3 Worksheets

Spanish Study Workbook, 10.3 Worksheets

Lab Manual B, 10.3 Data Analysis Worksheet

Lesson Overview • Lesson Notes • Activity: Art in Motion • Assessment: Self-Test, Lesson Assessment

For corresponding lesson in the **Foundation Edition**, see pages 245–247.

Activate Prior Knowledge

Give students the following scenario: Two athletes are brought before an investigating committee because both tested positive for growth hormones. One athlete, a record holder, denies ever knowingly taking the growth hormone. The other recently had knee surgery and was taking the drugs prescribed by the doctor. Have students write a short response in which they speculate on how the growth hormones were being used by the athletes. As a class, discuss the question, What does the cell cycle have to do with this story?

10.3 Regulating the Cell Cycle

IN B.1.2 Molecules and cellular processes; B.1.3 Cell function and differentiation; B.5.5 Roles of proteins. Also covered: NoS.3, B.3.3.

Key Questions

How is the cell cycle regulated?

How do cancer cells differ from other cells?

Vocabulary

cyclin
growth factor
apoptosis
cancer
tumor

Taking Notes

Concept Map As you read, create a concept map to organize the information in this lesson.

THINK ABOUT IT How do cells know when to divide? One striking fact about cells in multicellular organisms is how carefully cell growth and cell division are controlled. Not all cells move through the cell cycle at the same rate.

In the human body, for example, most muscle cells and nerve cells do not divide at all once they have developed. In contrast, cells in the bone marrow that make blood cells and cells of the skin and digestive tract grow and divide rapidly throughout life. These cells may pass through a complete cycle every few hours. This process provides new cells to replace those that wear out or break down.

Controls on Cell Division

How is the cell cycle regulated?

When scientists grow cells in the laboratory, most cells will divide until they come into contact with each other. Once they do, they usually stop dividing and growing. What happens if those neighboring cells are suddenly scraped away in the culture dish? The remaining cells will begin dividing again until they once again make contact with other cells. This simple experiment shows that controls on cell growth and division can be turned on and off.

Something similar happens inside the body. Look at **Figure 10–14.** When an injury such as a cut in the skin or a break in a bone occurs, cells at the edges of the injury are stimulated to divide rapidly. New cells form, starting the process of healing. When the healing process nears completion, the rate of cell division slows, controls on growth are restored, and everything returns to normal.

BUILD Vocabulary

ACADEMIC WORDS The verb **regulate** means "to control or direct." Therefore, a substance that regulates the cell cycle controls when the cell grows and divides.

The Discovery of Cyclins For many years, biologists searched for a signal that might **regulate** the cell cycle—something that would "tell" cells when it was time to divide, duplicate their chromosomes, or enter another phase of the cell cycle.

In the early 1980s, biologists discovered a protein in cells that were in mitosis. When they injected the protein into a nondividing cell, a mitotic spindle would form. They named this protein **cyclin** because it seemed to regulate the cell cycle. Investigators have since discovered a family of proteins known as cyclins that regulate the timing of the cell cycle in eukaryotic cells.

IN INDIANA ACADEMIC STANDARDS

For the full text of all standards, see the Course Overview in the front matter of this book.

B.1.2 Understand that the shape of a molecule determines its role in the many different types of cellular processes including metabolism, homeostasis, growth and development, and heredity, and understand that the majority of these processes involve proteins that act as enzymes.

B.1.3 Explain and give examples of how the function and differentiation of cells is influenced by their external environment, including temperature, acidity and the concentration of certain molecules, and that changes in these conditions may affect how a cell functions.

UbD Teach for Understanding

ENDURING UNDERSTANDING A cell is the basic unit of life; the processes that occur at the cellular level provide the energy and basic structure organisms need to survive.

GUIDING QUESTION How does a cell control the process of cell division?

EVIDENCE OF UNDERSTANDING *At the end of the lesson, have students complete this assessment to show they understand why cell regulation is a necessary part of the healthy function and survival of an organism.* Break the class into small groups. Have each group develop a pamphlet to explain the regulation of cell division and how cancer cells have lost control of the cell cycle that normal cells have.

Regulatory Proteins The discovery of cyclins was just the start. Scientists have since identified dozens of other proteins that also help to regulate the cell cycle. **The cell cycle is controlled by regulatory proteins both inside and outside the cell.**

▶ ***Internal Regulators*** One group of proteins, internal regulatory proteins, respond to events occurring inside a cell. Internal regulatory proteins allow the cell cycle to proceed only when certain events have occurred in the cell itself. For example, several regulatory proteins make sure a cell does not enter mitosis until its chromosomes have replicated. Another regulatory protein prevents a cell from entering anaphase until the spindle fibers have attached to the chromosomes.

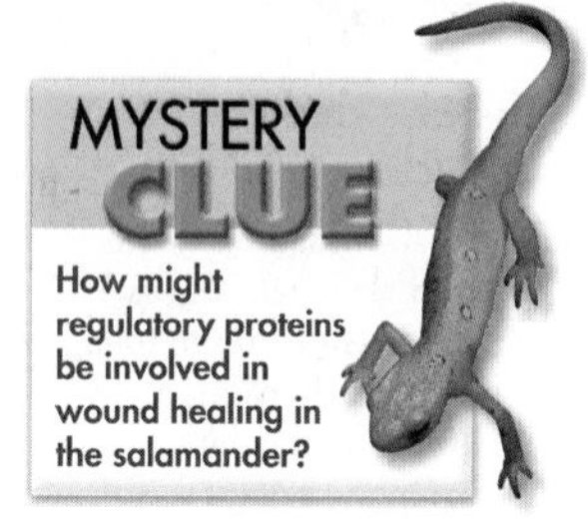

MYSTERY
CLUE
How might regulatory proteins be involved in wound healing in the salamander?

▶ ***External Regulators*** Proteins that respond to events outside the cell are called external regulatory proteins. External regulatory proteins direct cells to speed up or slow down the cell cycle.

One important group of external regulatory proteins is the group made up of the growth factors. **Growth factors** stimulate the growth and division of cells. These proteins are especially important during embryonic development and wound healing. Other external regulatory proteins on the surface of neighboring cells often have an opposite effect. They cause cells to slow down or stop their cell cycles. This prevents excessive cell growth and keeps body tissues from disrupting one another.

In Your Notebook *Use a cause-and-effect diagram to describe how internal and external regulators work together to control the cell cycle.*

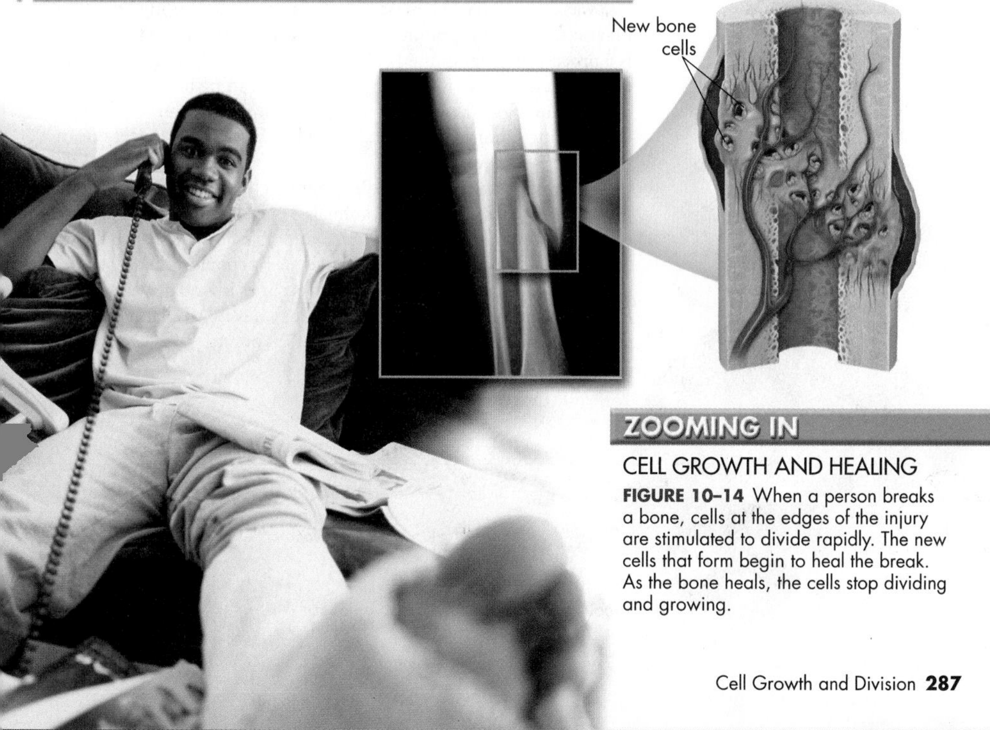

ZOOMING IN

CELL GROWTH AND HEALING

FIGURE 10–14 When a person breaks a bone, cells at the edges of the injury are stimulated to divide rapidly. The new cells that form begin to heal the break. As the bone heals, the cells stop dividing and growing.

Biology In-Depth

HEALING OF A BROKEN BONE

Several stages are involved in the healing of a broken bone. The stages reveal the complex nature of bone tissue, of which students are probably not aware. When a bone breaks, blood vessels are torn apart and a massive blood clot forms. Many bone cells die because they are cut off from oxygen and nutrients. Within a few days, a soft callus forms. New capillaries grow into the area and bring oxygen and nutrients to the repair site. Immune system cells begin to remove dead cells and other debris. Bone cells from surrounding areas move into the damaged area. These cells produce collagen fibers and bony substances that form a bridge between the ends of the broken bone. Soon, the soft callus hardens and forms a bony callus (shown in **Figure 10–14**). Even when all of the bone structures are re-formed, the healing is not complete. As the person resumes a normal activity level, the new bone tissue will react to mechanical stressors and alter its configuration.

Teach

Build Study Skills

Have students develop an analogy to grasp the importance of cell cycle regulation. Point out that many everyday tasks require a regulated system to be completed successfully. For example, to make a peanut butter and jelly sandwich, you need to lay out the bread before you put jelly on the knife. You also need to control how much peanut butter and jelly are used to make the sandwich.

Ask small groups to think of a daily task that requires a sequence of regulated steps. One student should present the group's analogy to the class. The presentation should include the steps involved and what could go wrong if regulation goes awry.

After the presentations, write the phases of the cell cycle on the board.

Ask What could go wrong if the cycle is not carefully regulated? *(Sample answer: DNA may not be divided evenly between the cells. Cells could divide when new cells are not needed by the organism.)*

DIFFERENTIATED INSTRUCTION

L1 Struggling Students Provide students with an activity analogy, such as riding a bike, and have them write down or say the steps that need to occur for the activity to be completed. Have them talk about how it is regulated.

ZOOMING IN

Ask students to compare the way a wound in the skin heals and the way a broken bone heals. Students should note that a skin wound also begins to heal at the edge of the wound.

Ask students which type of regulators—internal, external, or both—are likely involved in the salamander's wound healing. How do the regulators ensure that some types of tissue do not grow faster than others? Students can go online at Biology.com to gather their evidence.

Answers

IN YOUR NOTEBOOK Students' diagrams should show how events inside the cell trigger internal regulators while external regulators respond to events outside the cell. For example, a cause might be a wound whose effect would be growth factors speeding up the cell cycle.

Teach continued

Lead a Discussion

Make sure students understand that apoptosis is a normal cell process and is beneficial to many organisms. In fact, apoptosis is a necessary process for multicellular organisms. Apoptosis allows organisms to more fully control which cells continue to grow and divide and which do not. If a cell is old or damaged, apoptosis allows for this cell to be destroyed rather than continuing to grow, divide, and use the resources that other healthy cells need to survive.

DIFFERENTIATED INSTRUCTION

L1 Struggling Students Some students may think that apoptosis—programmed cell death—is always a sign of disease. Explain that apoptosis is an important event for the health of a multicellular organism. For example, old cells, such as skin cells, must be removed so that new cells have space to grow.

Ask If old skin cells did not die and shed, what would happen to a person's skin? *(The skin would become too thick and lose some of its properties.)*

ELL English Language Learners To encourage English language learners to use their language skills, pair them with native English speakers. Have pairs discuss why apoptosis is beneficial to multicellular organisms.

Analyzing Data

NoS.3, B.1.2, B.1.3, B.5.5

The Rise and Fall of Cyclins

Scientists measured cyclin levels in clam egg cells as the cells went through their first mitotic divisions after fertilization. The data are shown in the graph.

Cyclins are continually produced and destroyed within cells. Cyclin production signals cells to enter mitosis, while cyclin destruction signals cells to stop dividing and enter interphase.

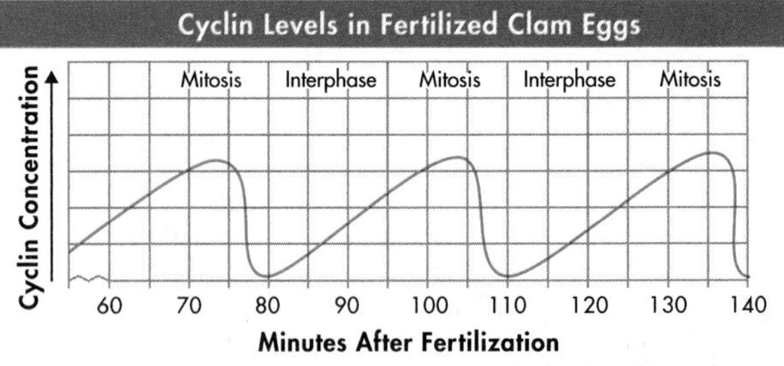

1. **Interpret Graphs** How long does cyclin production last during a typical cell cycle in fertilized clam eggs?
2. **Infer** During which part of the cell cycle does cyclin production begin? How quickly is cyclin destroyed?
3. **Predict** Suppose that the regulators that control cyclin production are no longer produced. What are two possible outcomes?

Apoptosis Just as new cells are produced every day in a multicellular organism, many other cells die. Cells end their life cycle in one of two ways. A cell may die by accident due to damage or injury, or a cell may actually be "programmed" to die. **Apoptosis** (AYP up TOH sis) is a process of programmed cell death. Once apoptosis is triggered, a cell undergoes a series of controlled steps leading to its self-destruction. First, the cell and its chromatin shrink, and then parts of the cell's membranes break off. Neighboring cells then quickly clean up the cell's remains.

Apoptosis plays a key role in development by shaping the structure of tissues and organs in plants and animals. For example, look at the photos of a mouse foot in **Figure 10–15.** Each foot of a mouse is shaped the way it is partly because cells between the toes die by apoptosis during tissue development. When apoptosis does not occur as it should, a number of diseases can result. For example, the cell loss seen in AIDS and Parkinson's disease can result if too much apoptosis occurs.

FIGURE 10–15 Apoptosis The cells between a mouse's toes undergo apoptosis during a late stage of development. **Predict** ***What is one way the pattern of apoptosis would differ in foot development for a duck?***

Analyzing Data

PURPOSE Students will examine and interpret data that show the rise and fall of cyclins during the cell cycle of developing clams.

PLANNING Walk through the different parts of the graph, such as the axis labels and title, to make sure students understand the information in the graph before they begin analyzing it. If students are confused by a graph that does not start at zero, explain that the jagged line before the 60-minute mark tells readers that some information has been condensed.

ANSWERS

1. about 25 minutes
2. interphase; within a few minutes
3. If a regulator that turns on cyclin production is no longer produced, a cell will not enter mitosis. If a regulator that turns off cyclin production is no longer produced, a cell will not be able to enter interphase.

Answers

FIGURE 10–15 Not all of the cells between a duck's toes would undergo apoptosis. Some of the cells would remain, causing a duck to have webbed feet.

Cancer: Uncontrolled Cell Growth

How do cancer cells differ from other cells?

Why is cell growth regulated so carefully? The principal reason may be that the consequences of uncontrolled cell growth in a multicellular organism are very severe. **Cancer,** a disorder in which body cells lose the ability to control growth, is one such example.

Cancer cells do not respond to the signals that regulate the growth of most cells. As a result, the cells divide uncontrollably. Cancer cells form a mass of cells called a **tumor.** However, not all tumors are cancerous. Some tumors are benign, or noncancerous. A benign tumor does not spread to surrounding healthy tissue or to other parts of the body. Cancerous tumors, such as the one in **Figure 10–16,** are malignant. Malignant tumors invade and destroy surrounding healthy tissue.

As the cancer cells spread, they absorb the nutrients needed by other cells, block nerve connections, and prevent the organs they invade from functioning properly. Soon, the delicate balances that exist in the body are disrupted, and life-threatening illness results.

What Causes Cancer? Cancers are caused by defects in the genes that regulate cell growth and division. There are several sources of such defects, including: smoking or chewing tobacco, radiation exposure, other defective genes, and even viral infection. All cancers, however, have one thing in common: The control over the cell cycle has broken down. Some cancer cells will no longer respond to external growth regulators, while others fail to produce the internal regulators that ensure orderly growth.

An astonishing number of cancer cells have a defect in a gene called p53, which normally halts the cell cycle until all chromosomes have been properly replicated. Damaged or defective p53 genes cause cells to lose the information needed to respond to signals that normally control their growth.

In Your Notebook *Use a two-column chart to compare the controls that regulate normal cell growth to the lack of control seen in cancer cells.*

FIGURE 10–16 Growth of Cancer Cells Normal cells grow and divide in a carefully controlled fashion. Cells that are cancerous lose this control and continue to grow and divide, producing tumors.

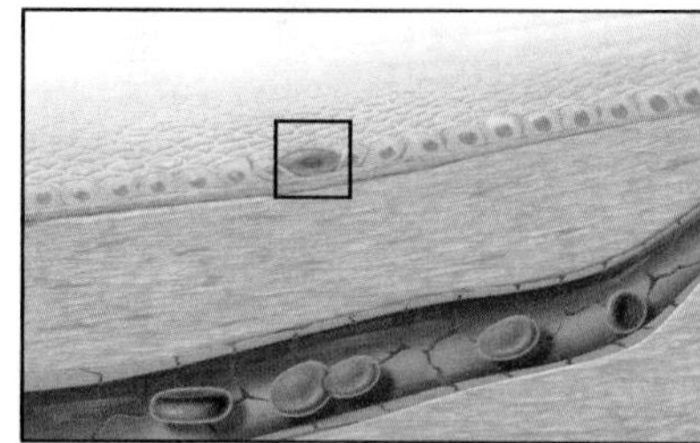

1 A cell begins to divide abnormally.

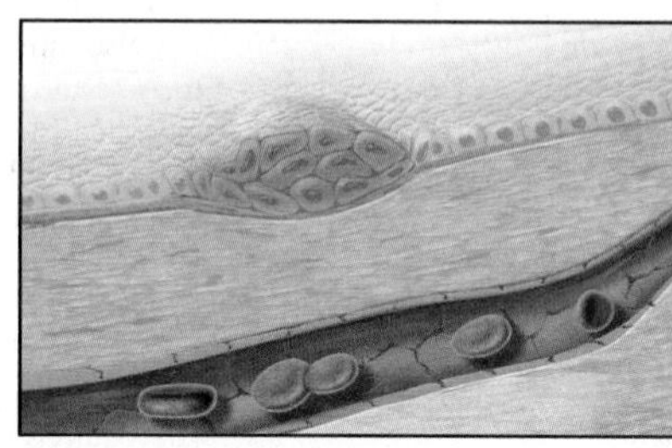

2 The cancer cells produce a tumor, which begins to displace normal cells and tissues.

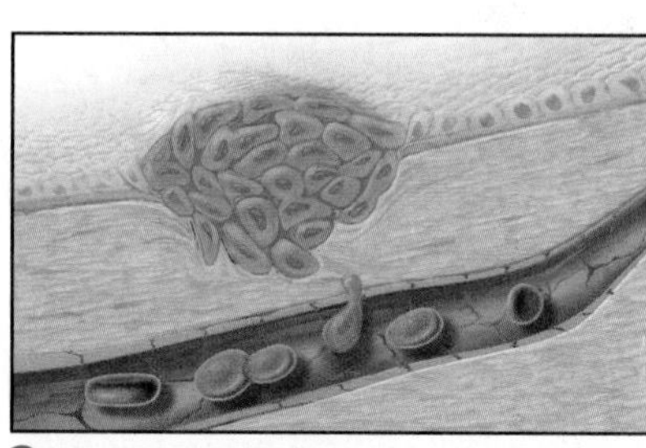

3 Cancer cells are particularly dangerous because of their tendency to spread once they enter the bloodstream or lymph vessels. The cancer then moves into other parts of the body and forms secondary tumors, a process called metastasis.

BIOLOGY.com Search Lesson 10.3 GO • Art in Motion

Use Visuals

Talk through the steps of **Figure 10–16** with the class.

Ask What makes cancer cells different from healthy cells? *(Cancer cells do not respond to the signals that regulate cell growth and division. They continue to divide, when healthy cells would stop.)*

Ask When researchers develop drugs to fight cancer, what characteristics of cancer cells do you think they target? *(Sample answer: They might target rapidly dividing cells.)*

DIFFERENTIATED INSTRUCTION

LPR Less Proficient Readers Ask students to read aloud the captions of the figure and look over each drawing. Then, have them summarize the meaning of each pictured step in their own words.

ELL Focus on ELL: Build Background

INTERMEDIATE SPEAKERS Since cancer is a common disorder, many English language learners may already be familiar with certain aspects of the disease. Engage students by asking them to discuss or write down what they already know about cancer in their native language. Have them translate the main points of their discussion or written response into a short list in English. You can use this list as a starting point to talk about the relationship between cancer and cell regulation.

BIOLOGY.com To see how cancer cells grow and divide, suggest students watch the animation **Art in Motion: Growth of Cancer Cells**.

UbD Check for Understanding

ORAL QUESTIONING

Use the following prompts to gauge students' understanding of lesson concepts.

- How does the growth of a tumor relate to normal cell growth and division?
- How does cancer relate to the Big Idea of Growth, Development, and Reproduction?
- What details from this lesson, and past lessons, could you add to the captions of **Figure 10–16** that further explain what is happening in each picture?

ADJUST INSTRUCTION

Help students make the connection between regulation and cancer by asking them to think about what might happen if different real-world controls, such as traffic signals, no longer worked. Reinforce that cancer is the result of uncontrolled cell division.

Answers

IN YOUR NOTEBOOK Students' two-column charts should show how normal cells respond to regulators and how these controls are lost in cancer cells. For example, some types of growth factors slow down the growth and division of normal cells. Certain cancer cells have lost their ability to respond to growth factors, so their growth is no longer slowed in the same way.

Assess and Remediate

EVALUATE UNDERSTANDING

Call on students at random to explain what regulates the cell cycle and why cancer cells are different from normal cells in the body. Then, have them complete the 10.3 Assessment.

REMEDIATION SUGGESTIONS

L1 Struggling Students If students have a difficult time with developing a hypothesis for **Question 1b,** suggest that they review the text on cyclins and the Analyzing Data feature in this lesson. Have them write down and discuss the role of cyclins in the cell cycle with a partner. Then, have pairs write a hypothesis together.

BIOLOGY.com Students can check their understanding of lesson concepts with the **Self-Test** assessment. They can then take an online version of the **Lesson Assessment.**

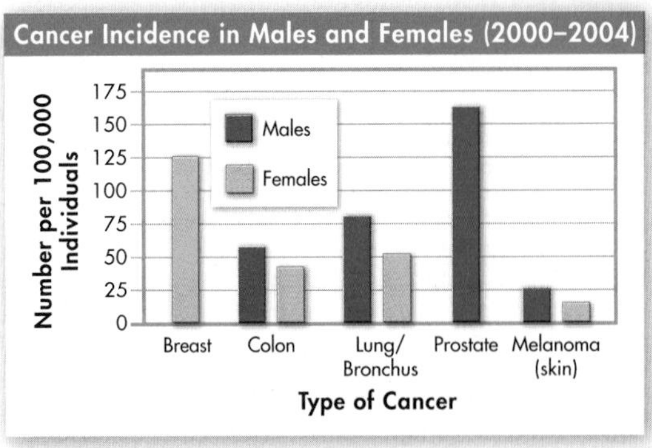

FIGURE 10–17 Cancer Incidence Cancer can affect almost every organ in the body. Interpret Graphs ***How many cases of breast cancer were reported compared to prostate cancer for the time period shown?***

Treatments for Cancer When a cancerous tumor is localized, it can often be removed by surgery. Skin cancer, the most common form of the disease, can usually be treated this way. Melanomas, the most serious form of skin cancer, can be removed surgically, but only if spotted very early.

Other forms of treatment make use of the fact that cancer cells grow rapidly and, therefore, need to copy their DNA more quickly than do most normal cells. This makes them especially vulnerable to damage from radiation. As a result, many tumors can be effectively treated with carefully targeted beams of radiation.

Medical researchers have worked for years to develop chemical compounds that would kill cancer cells, or at least slow their growth. The use of such compounds against cancer is known as chemotherapy. Great advances in chemotherapy have taken place in recent years and have even made it possible to cure some forms of cancer. However, because most chemotherapy compounds target rapidly dividing cells, they also interfere with cell division in normal, healthy cells. This produces serious side effects in many patients, and it is one of the reasons why scientists are so interested in gaining a better understanding of the role of cell cycle proteins in cancer. The goal of many researchers is to find highly specific ways in which cancer cells can be targeted for destruction while leaving healthy cells unaffected.

Cancer is a serious disease. Understanding and combating cancer remains a major scientific challenge, but scientists at least know where to start. Cancer is a disease of the cell cycle, and conquering cancer will require a much deeper understanding of the processes that control cell division.

10.3 Assessment

IN B.1.2, B.1.3, B.5.5

Review Key Concepts

1. a. Review Name the two types of proteins that regulate the cell cycle. How do these proteins work?
   b. Form a Hypothesis Write a hypothesis about what you think would happen if cyclin were injected into a cell during mitosis. How could you test your hypothesis?
2. a. Review Why is cancer considered a disease of the cell cycle?
   b. Compare and Contrast How are the growth of a tumor and the repair of a scrape on your knee similar? How are they different?

Apply the Big idea

Growth, Development, and Reproduction

3. Why do you think it is important that cells have a "control system" to regulate the timing of cell division?

BIOLOGY.com Search Lesson 10.3 GO • Self-Test • Lesson Assessment

Answers

FIGURE 10–17 Per 100,000 individuals, there were about 125 cases of breast cancer reported, compared to about 165 cases of prostate cancer.

Assessment Answers

1a. Internal and external regulators are two types of proteins that regulate the cell cycle. Internal regulators allow the cell cycle to proceed only after certain events occur. External regulators speed up or slow down the cell cycle.

1b. Sample answer: If cyclins were injected into cells during mitosis, then the cells would go through the cell cycle more quickly than cells that were not injected with cyclins. I would test my hypothesis by comparing a sample of injected cells with a control sample.

2a. Cancer is considered a disease of the cell cycle because it occurs when changes happen in a cell that prevent the cell from regulating how often it divides.

2b. They are similar because they involve rapid cell division. They are different because once a scrape is repaired, the rapid cell division will stop; however, in a tumor the rapid cell division does not stop.

3. Big idea There are so many steps involved with cell division that a system must be in place to make sure the proper steps have been completed before a cell moves into the next phase of cell division. Without this order, cells would not be able to divide successfully.

Technology & BIOLOGY

NoS.10 Scientific discoveries and new technologies.

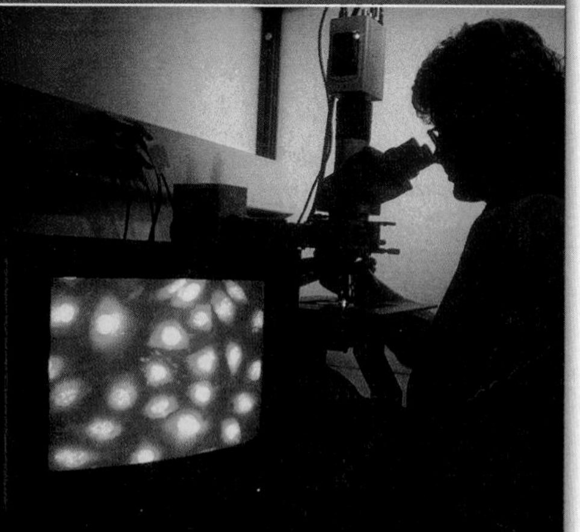

Fluorescence Microscopy

Imagine being able to "see" proteins at work inside a cell, or to track proteins from where they are made to where they go. Scientists can now do all of these things, thanks to advances in fluorescence microscopy. One advance came from the discovery that Pacific jellyfish, properly known as *Aequorea victoria*, produce a protein that glows. By fusing the gene for this protein to other genes, scientists can label different parts of the cell with fluorescence. Other advances include the development of additional highly specific fluorescent labels and the invention of powerful laser microscopes. As the images on this page show, the view is clearly amazing.

WRITING Suppose you are a cell biologist studying cell division and cancer. What might you use a fluorescence microscope to study? Describe your ideas in a paragraph.

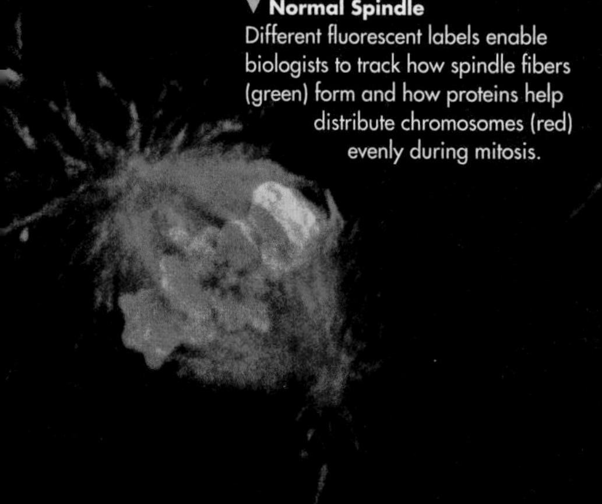

▲ **Viewing Labeled Specimens** In fluorescence microscopy, a specimen is labeled with a molecule that glows under a specific wavelength of light. Different fluorescent labels give off different colors. This way, biologists can easily see exactly where a protein is located within a cell or tissue.

▼ **Normal Spindle** Different fluorescent labels enable biologists to track how spindle fibers (green) form and how proteins help distribute chromosomes (red) evenly during mitosis.

▼ **Abnormal Spindle** Cell cycle control has gone awry in this cell, causing an abnormal mitotic spindle to form.

Teach

Lead a Discussion

In 2000, an artist named Eduardo Kac commissioned a laboratory to make "Alba"—a bunny containing the green fluorescence protein. Under blue light, Alba glowed in the dark. Kac planned to display Alba for a time in an art installation and then take her home to live with him and his family. But the lab decided not to release Alba to Kac, and the bunny remained in captivity.

Color photos of Alba are still available online. Consider bringing in photos to show your students. Use the questions below to start a discussion on the ethics involved with Alba.

Ask Is it right to alter genomes of animals just because the technology exists to do so?

Ask What types of social issues do you think could arise due to this technology?

Ask Can Alba be considered "art"?

DIFFERENTIATED INSTRUCTION

L3 Advanced Students Have students identify and discuss another technological advance that has raised ethical issues. Ask them to talk about why the technology was developed and how its use created an ethical debate.

How Science Works

USES OF FLUORESCENCE MICROSCOPY

Fluorescence microscopy has led to many breakthroughs in cell biology. Researchers can watch a hormone interact with a receptor on a cell membrane; they can watch calcium be released from a muscle cell; they can see which neurons in a brain fire in response to a particular stimulus. But fluorescence microscopy also has other interesting applications.

One group of researchers had discovered how to produce sterile male mosquitoes. They hoped that by releasing these sterile mosquitoes into the wild, they would be able to help control the mosquito population and malaria outbreaks. But the researchers had a difficult time differentiating between sterile male mosquito larvae and fertile female mosquito larvae. So, they used a fluorescence molecule to tag a protein produced only in the male larvae. Then, they examined larvae for the glowing protein and released only the males that glowed into the wild.

Answers

WRITING Answers will vary. Student responses may include suggestions such as labeling internal regulators in normal and cancerous cells.

INDIANA ACADEMIC STANDARDS

For the full text of all standards, see the Course Overview in the front matter of this book.

Getting Started

Objectives

10.4.1 Describe the process of differentiation.

10.4.2 Define stem cells and explain their importance.

10.4.3 Identify the possible benefits and issues relating to stem cell research.

Student Resources

Study Workbooks A and B, 10.4 Worksheets

Spanish Study Workbook, 10.4 Worksheets

Lab Manual B, 10.4 Data Analysis Worksheet

BIOLOGY.com Lesson Overview • Lesson Notes • Assessment: Self-Test, Lesson Assessment

For corresponding lesson in the **Foundation Edition**, see pages 248–251.

Build Background

Present the prefixes *toti-* (all), *pluri-* (most), and *multi-* (many) as a sequence that shows how each is progressively less inclusive. Write out the definitions of *totipotent, pluripotent,* and *multipotent* and talk about how each respective cell type is more limited in what it can develop into.

IN INDIANA ACADEMIC STANDARDS

For the full text of all standards, see the Course Overview in the front matter of this book.

B.1.3 Explain and give examples of how the function and differentiation of cells is influenced by their external environment, including temperature, acidity and the concentration of certain molecules, and that changes in these conditions may affect how a cell functions.

10.4 Cell Differentiation

IN B.1.3 Cell function and differentiation. Also covered: NoS.3, B.3.3.

Key Questions

How do cells become specialized for different functions?

What are stem cells?

What are some possible benefits and issues associated with stem cell research?

Vocabulary

embryo • differentiation • totipotent • blastocyst • pluripotent • stem cell • multipotent

Taking Notes

Compare/Contrast Table As you read, create a table comparing the ability of different cell types to differentiate.

THINK ABOUT IT The human body contains an estimated 100,000,000,000,000 (one hundred trillion) cells. That's a staggering number, but in one respect it's not quite as large as you might think. Why? Try to estimate how many times a single cell would have to divide through mitosis to produce that many cells. It may surprise you to learn that as few as 47 rounds of cell division can produce that many cells.

The results of those 47 cell cycles are truly amazing. The human body contains hundreds of distinctly different cell types, and every one of them develops from the single cell that starts the process. How do the cells get to be so different from each other?

From One Cell to Many

How do cells become specialized for different functions?

Each of us started life as just one cell. So, for that matter, did your pet dog, an earthworm, and the petunia on the windowsill. These living things pass through a developmental stage called an **embryo,** from which the adult organism is gradually produced. During the development process, an organism's cells become more and more differentiated and specialized for particular functions. **Figure 10–18** shows some of the specialized cells found in the roots, stems, and leaves of a plant.

FIGURE 10–18 Specialized Plant Cells

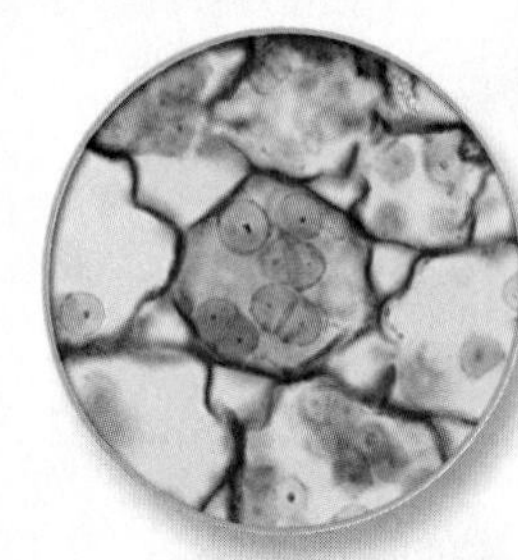

Cells that store sugar

Cells that transport materials

Cells that carry out photosynthesis

BIOLOGY.com Search Lesson 10.4 GO • Lesson Overview • Lesson Notes

UbD Teach for Understanding

ENDURING UNDERSTANDING A cell is the basic unit of life; the processes that occur at the cellular level provide the energy and basic structure organisms need to survive.

GUIDING QUESTION How does a single undifferentiated cell lead to a complex multicellular organism?

EVIDENCE OF UNDERSTANDING *At the end of the lesson, have students complete this assessment to show they understand the importance of differentiation in the proper function and survival of complex multicellular organisms.* Have students come up with real-world analogies for the process of differentiation. Tell them to make sure their analogies highlight the advantages of specialization. For example, students might suggest how medical doctors are specialized. Specialists are experts on how best to treat specific parts of the human body. Have students describe how their analogies connect to the process of differentiation.

Defining Differentiation The process by which cells become specialized is known as **differentiation** (dif ur en shee AY shun). **During the development of an organism, cells differentiate into many types of cells.** A differentiated cell has become, quite literally, different from the embryonic cell that produced it, and specialized to perform certain tasks, such as contraction, photosynthesis, or protection. Our bodies, and the bodies of all multicellular organisms, contain highly differentiated cells that carry out the jobs we need to perform to stay alive.

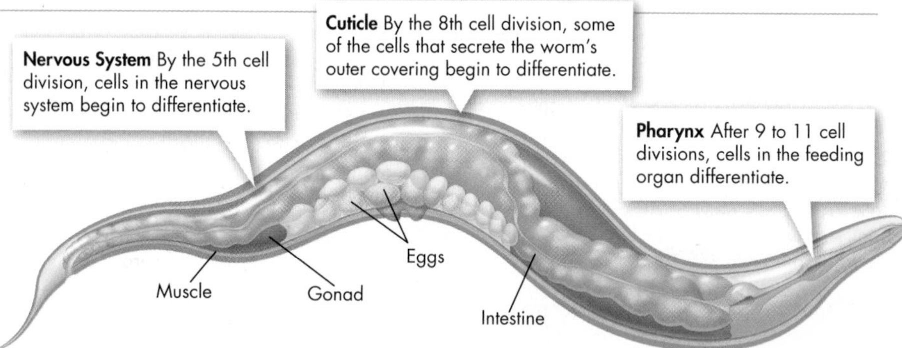

Cuticle By the 8th cell division, some of the cells that secrete the worm's outer covering begin to differentiate.
Nervous System By the 5th cell division, cells in the nervous system begin to differentiate.
Pharynx After 9 to 11 cell divisions, cells in the feeding organ differentiate.
Eggs
Muscle
Gonad
Intestine

FIGURE 10–19 Differentiation in *C. elegans* A fertilized egg develops into an adult worm after many cell divisions. Daughter cells from each cell division follow a specific path toward a role as a particular kind of cell.

Mapping Differentiation The process of differentiation determines a cell's ultimate identity, such as whether it will spend its life as a nerve cell or a muscle cell. In some organisms, a cell's role is rigidly determined at a specific point in the course of development. In the microscopic worm *Caenorhabditis elegans*, for example, biologists have mapped the outcome of each and every cell division from fertilized egg to adult.

The process of cell differentiation in *C. elegans* begins with the very first division and continues throughout embryonic development. **Figure 10–19** shows when some of the cells found in the adult begin to differentiate during development. Each and every time a new worm develops, the process is the same, resulting in 959 cells with precisely determined functions.

Differentiation in Mammals Other organisms, including mammals like us, go through a more flexible process in which cell differentiation is controlled by a number of interacting factors in the embryo, many of which are still not well understood. What is known, however, is that adult cells generally do reach a point at which their differentiation is complete—when they can no longer become other types of cells.

In Your Notebook *Starting with a single cell, calculate how many cells might result after 4, 8, and 10 cell divisions.*

Biology In-Depth

A GREAT LAB ANIMAL

Caenorhabditis elegans has become such a well-established laboratory animal that more is known about its biology than that of almost any other organism. Because it is only 1 mm long when mature, *C. elegans* can be raised in small laboratory dishes. It takes only 12 hours from fertilization of the egg to hatching of the juvenile worm. In that time, successive cell divisions produce 671 cells, of which 113 are programmed to die, leaving 558 in the worm that hatches. This "programmed-to-die" characteristic is valuable to researchers studying the aging process. The precise number of 959 cells in the mature worm is adequate for studying the development of complex organ systems, but the number is not so high that it is impossible to track the divisions of each cell. The pattern and number of cell divisions in *C. elegans* are unvarying, making it possible to study the effects of a single genetic mutation.

Teach

Build Math Skills

The discussion on this page and the diagram offer an opportunity to review exponents. Help students calculate how many cells are in the embryonic worm at the point when its nervous system begins to differentiate (2^5=32). Have them calculate the number of cells in the worm when the cuticle starts to differentiate (2^8=256).

DIFFERENTIATED INSTRUCTION

L1 Special Needs Students can cut a large piece of paper in half, those two pieces in half again, and so on, to understand how cell divisions double the number of total cells with each round of division. They will see how quickly cell numbers increase.

L3 Advanced Students Some students will point out that **Figure 10–19** says that pharynx cells are still differentiating at the 11th cell division, which would produce 2^{11} or 2048 cells. This is more than the number of cells in the adult. They may also point out that the final number of cells found in the adult worm (959) is not divisible by 2. Have them infer what process happens during the worm's development to create a final number of cells that is only 959. They will need to recall apoptosis from Lesson 10.3.

Address Misconceptions

Differentiation Students may think that cells differentiate by passing on different hereditary information when they divide. Remind students that, when cells divide, mitosis ensures that each daughter cell receives a complete set of genetic information from its parent cell.

Answers

IN YOUR NOTEBOOK 2^4 = 16; 2^8 = 256; 2^{10} = 1024

Teach continued

Lead a Discussion

Make sure students understand the difference between totipotent and pluripotent stem cells.

Ask What types of cells can totipotent stem cells form that pluripotent stem cells cannot? *(Totipotent cells can form tissues surrounding the embryo, while pluripotent cells cannot.)*

Point out that both totipotent and pluripotent stem cells can develop into all of the types of cells that make up an adult human body.

DIFFERENTIATED INSTRUCTION

LPR Less Proficient Readers Struggling readers may stumble over the vocabulary associated with stem cells. Take a few minutes to preview the vocabulary. Have them find the words on the page. Say the word aloud and use it in a sentence. Then, have students repeat the words so they are familiar and comfortable using them before they begin reading.

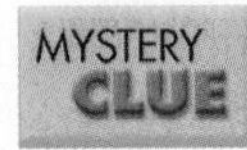

To help students arrive at the answer, remind them about what they already know: that the salamander in the story eventually grew a new limb.

Ask What kinds of tissues are found in a salamander limb? *(Bone, blood, and nerve tissue can be found in a salamander limb.)*

Help lead students to the conclusion that certain cells in the adult salamander must retain the ability to differentiate into these types of tissues. Students can go online at **Biology.com** to gather their evidence.

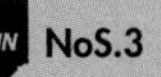

NoS.3

Cellular Differentiation of *C. elegans*

The adult microscopic worm *C. elegans* contains 959 cells. The data table shows some of the different cell types in this worm. Copy the data table into your notebook and answer the following questions.

1. Calculate Calculate the percentage of the total cell number represented by each tissue or organ listed by using this formula:

$$\frac{\text{Number of cells in adult}}{\text{Total number of cells}} \times 100$$

2. Calculate Find both the number of cells and the percentage of the total represented by cells in tissues or organs not listed ("other"). The category includes cells from, among other organs, the intestine. Record the results in your table. MATH

Cell Type	Number of Cells in Adult	Percent of Total
Cuticle	213	22%
Gonad (excluding germ line cells)	143	15
Mesoderm muscle	81	8
Pharynx	80	8
Other	442	46

3. Infer Why does *C. elegans* make an ideal model for studying cellular differentiation?

4. Infer Why would it be more difficult to map the differentiation patterns in a different organism, such as a mammal?

MYSTERY CLUE

Some adult salamander cells never completely differentiate. What ability do these cells retain?

Stem Cells and Development

What are stem cells?

One of the most important questions in biology is how all of the specialized, differentiated cell types in the body are formed from just a single cell. Biologists say that such a cell is **totipotent** (toh TIP uh tunt), literally able to do everything, to develop into any type of cell in the body (including the cells that make up the extraembryonic membranes and placenta). Only the fertilized egg and the cells produced by the first few cell divisions of embryonic development are truly totipotent. If there is a "secret" by which cells start the process of differentiation, these are the cells that know that secret.

Human Development After about four days of development, a human embryo forms into a **blastocyst,** a hollow ball of cells with a cluster of cells inside known as the inner cell mass. Even at this early stage, the cells of the blastocyst have begun to specialize. The outer cells form tissues that attach the embryo to its mother, while the inner cell mass becomes the embryo itself. The cells of the inner cell mass are said to be pluripotent (plu RIP uh tunt). Cells that are **pluripotent** can develop into most, but not all, of the body's cell types. They cannot form the tissues surrounding the embryo.

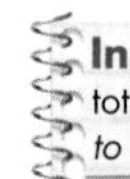

In Your Notebook *Look up the roots that form the words* totipotent, pluripotent, *and* multipotent. *How do the roots relate to each cell's ability to differentiate?*

PURPOSE Students will practice math skills using data from *C. elegans* research.

PLANNING Before students begin filling out the table, point out that most, but not all, the data they need to calculate the percentages are in the table. Remind them to read the introductory paragraph carefully to help them find the information they will need to complete the table.

ANSWERS

1. gonad 15%; mesoderm 8%; pharynx 8%
2. 442 cells; 46%. Note: If students add the percents in the table, they may notice that they total 99%, not 100%. Tell students that this discrepancy is a result of rounding.
3. *C. elegans* has a very limited number of cells in the adult organism and follows a rigid pattern of differentiation.
4. Other animals have a more flexible developmental pattern and have many more cells to keep track of than *C. elegans*.

Answers

IN YOUR NOTEBOOK Students should discover that the root "potent" comes from the Latin word *potens*, meaning "to be able." Using the meaning of the prefixes *toti-* (all), *pluri-* (most), and *multi-* (many), students should infer each cell type's respective ability to differentiate, from most flexible (totipotent) to most limited (multipotent).

Stem Cells **The unspecialized cells from which differentiated cells develop are known as stem cells.** As the name implies, **stem cells** sit at the base of a branching "stem" of development from which different cell types form. Because of their potential to develop into other cell types, stem cells are the subject of intense interest by researchers around the world.

▶ ***Embryonic Stem Cells*** As you have seen, the pluripotent stem cells of the inner cell mass eventually produce all of the cells of the body. Embryonic stem cells are pluripotent cells found in the early embryo. In 1998, researchers at the University of Wisconsin found a way to grow these embryonic stem cells in culture. Their experiments confirmed that such cells did indeed have the capacity to produce just about any cell type in the human body. In fact, scientists have managed to coax mouse embryonic stem cells to differentiate into nerve cells, muscle cells, and even into sperm and egg cells. Recently, sperm made from embryonic stem cells were used to generate live mice.

▶ ***Adult Stem Cells*** For years, biologists have suspected that adult organisms might also contain some types of stem cells. Cells in the blood and skin, for example, have a limited life span and must be constantly replaced. This suggests that the body contains pools of stem cells from which new skin and blood cells can be produced.

Adult stem cells are groups of cells that differentiate to renew and replace cells in the adult body. Because of their more limited potential, adult stem cells are referred to as **multipotent** (muhl TIP uh tunt), meaning that they can develop into many types of differentiated cells. Typically, stem cells of a given organ or tissue produce only the types of cells that are unique to that tissue. For example, adult stem cells in the bone marrow can develop into several different types of blood cells, while stem cells in the brain can produce neurons, or nerve cells.

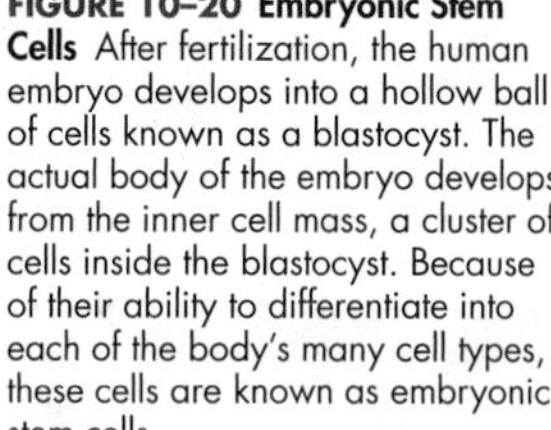

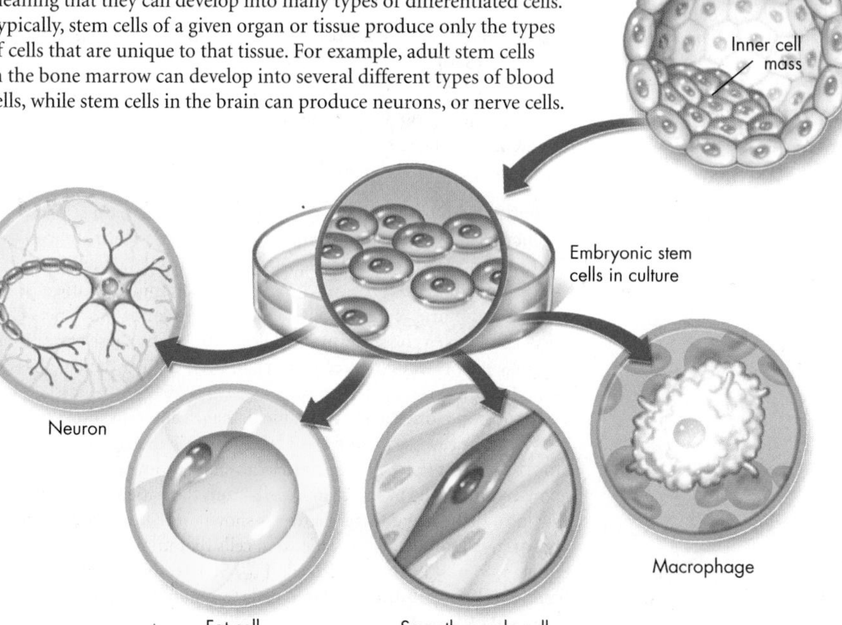

FIGURE 10–20 Embryonic Stem Cells After fertilization, the human embryo develops into a hollow ball of cells known as a blastocyst. The actual body of the embryo develops from the inner cell mass, a cluster of cells inside the blastocyst. Because of their ability to differentiate into each of the body's many cell types, these cells are known as embryonic stem cells.

How Science Works

BONE MARROW TRANSPLANTS

Students might be surprised to find out that doctors are already using adult stem cells to treat sick patients. In fact, bone marrow transplants are effectively stem cell transplants. Found inside bones, bone marrow is a soft tissue that contains hematopoietic stem cells. Hematopoietic cells differentiate into white blood cells, red blood cells, and platelets. Bone marrow transplants can be used to treat patients with certain blood disorders that cause the patients to produce abnormal blood cells. Bone marrow transplants can also be used to treat cancer patients whose own marrow has been damaged by high doses of chemotherapy or radiation.

Use Visuals

Some students may have trouble navigating the figure on this page. Show students how they can use the arrows to follow the process shown.

Ask What does the figure show happening to the inner cell mass? *(The cells are transferred into culture.)*

Ask What four types of cells do these cells in culture become? *(neuron, fat cell, smooth muscle cell, and macrophage)*

DIFFERENTIATED INSTRUCTION

L1 Special Needs Use physical models made of resin or plastic to help students see or feel the differences between the structure of a blastocyst and the structures of differentiated cells. Depending on ability, ask students to speak or write about the differences they observe.

ELL English Language Learners Give students two index cards and have them write True on one and False on the other. Question students with true/false statements to assess their comprehension of lesson content. For example,

- The blastocyst is a very early stage of embryo. (True)
- The cells in the inner cell mass are totipotent. (False)
- Multipotent cells can develop into many, but not all, types of cells. (True)

Have students react to the statements by holding up either their True or False card. Use their responses to identify areas of confusion.

LPR Less Proficient Readers Before they read, ask struggling readers to create a **KWL** chart. Ask them to fill out what they know in the first column and any questions they want to know the answer to in the second. Then, have them read the lesson text and fill out what they learned in the third column. As a class, discuss any questions students still have about stem cells.

Study Wkbks A/B, Appendix S27, KWL. **Transparencies,** GO11.

Teach continued

Lead a Discussion

Have students identify the potential benefits and issues associated with stem cell research. Use these points to start a discussion on the importance of considering both ethics and potential scientific advancement in research. You may want to talk about other areas of scientific inquiry that currently have ethical considerations. For example, you could discuss screening for genetic markers of disease such as the genes associated with breast cancer.

DIFFERENTIATED INSTRUCTION

L3 **Advanced Students** Stem cell research is frequently in the media. Using media can reinforce existing knowledge and add new insights, but it can also present biases and misinformation. Have students investigate how responsible use of media can help inform them about the stem cell debate.

Ask students to gather print articles, research online, and, if possible, take notes on radio or TV reports that cover stem cell research. Then, have students meet in small groups and analyze their sources. Write the following discussion prompts on the board:

- How do the sources vary?
- What are the qualities of each source?
- What kinds of stories are likely to be published by each source?
- What qualities do you think the editor was looking for, and how does this impact the coverage?
- What sources would you most likely use if doing a report on stem cell research in the United States?

Have students end the discussion by talking about any new stem cell information they learned from their articles. Have them comment on the credibility of the information.

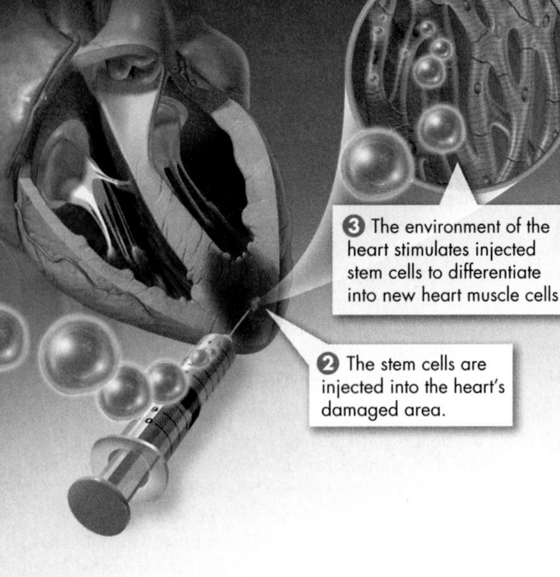

① Stem cells are filtered from bone marrow removed from a patient's hip.
② The stem cells are injected into the heart's damaged area.
③ The environment of the heart stimulates injected stem cells to differentiate into new heart muscle cells.

FIGURE 10–21 A Possible Future Treatment for Heart Disease? Stem cell research may lead to new ways to reverse the damage caused by a severe heart attack. The diagram shows one method currently being investigated. Infer ***How would the fate of the stem cells change after they are moved from the bone marrow to the heart?***

Frontiers in Stem Cell Research

What are some possible benefits and issues associated with stem cell research?

Understanding how stem cells retain the capacity to differentiate into so many cell types is an important unsolved problem in biology. Scientists would like to learn exactly which signals tell a cell to become specialized, and how other cells remain multipotent.

Potential Benefits Basic research on stem cells takes on a special urgency in light of the importance it might have for human health. There are many causes of damage to particular types of cells. Heart attacks destroy cells in the heart muscle, strokes injure brain cells, and spinal cord injuries cause paralysis by breaking connections between nerve cells. Given the suffering and death caused by these conditions, the prospect of using stem cells to repair such cellular damage has excited medical researchers.

Many hope to see a day when the damage caused by a severe heart attack can be reversed using stem cell therapy. Experiments using animals suggest that several approaches show promise of success. One approach might be to inject stem cells from the patient's bone marrow into the heart's damaged area, as shown in **Figure 10–21.** Another approach is to inject embryonic stem cells that might eventually differentiate into new heart muscle cells. **Stem cells offer the potential benefit of using undifferentiated cells to repair or replace badly damaged cells and tissues.**

UbD Check for Understanding

HAND SIGNALS

Present students with the following questions and ask them to show a thumbs-up sign if they understand, a thumbs-down sign if they are confused, or a waving-hand sign if they partially understand.

- Why is differentiation important to multicellular organisms?
- What are the three different types of stem cells and their respective potential to differentiate?
- What are the benefits and issues surrounding stem cell research?

ADJUST INSTRUCTION

If students are struggling with a particular question, have them review it in small groups. Then, have each group write a short answer and present it to the class.

Answers

FIGURE 10–21 They would become heart muscle cells rather than blood cells.

Ethical Issues Because adult stem cells can be obtained directly from the body of a willing donor, research with these cells has raised few ethical questions to date. This is not the case with embryonic stem cells, which are generally obtained from very early embryos.

Most techniques for harvesting embryonic stem cells cause the destruction of an embryo. For this reason, individuals who regard the embryo as entitled to the rights and protections of any human being object to such work. This concern has made government funding of embryonic stem cell research an important political issue. Groups seeking to protect embryos oppose such research as unethical. Other groups support such research as essential for saving human lives and argue that it would be unethical to restrict research. **Human embryonic stem cell research is controversial because the arguments for it and against it both involve ethical issues of life and death.**

It is possible, however, that in the not-too-distant future, both ethical concerns will be addressed with a technological solution. Some recent experiments have suggested that there may be ways to extract a small number of stem cells from an early embryo without damaging the embryo itself. Other experiments have shown that it is possible to switch "on" a small number of genes that reprogram adult cells to look and function like pluripotent embryonic stem cells. Such a technique would do away with the need to involve embryos at all. It also might make it possible to tailor specific therapies to the needs of each individual patient. Approaches like these, if successful, might allow potentially lifesaving research to go forward while avoiding any destruction of embryonic life.

In Your Notebook *Make a two-column chart that lists the benefits and issues related to stem cell research.*

BUILD Vocabulary

ACADEMIC WORDS The word **harvest** is the act or process of gathering. Scientists who harvest stem cells are gathering the cells.

10.4 Assessment

IN B.1.3

Review Key Concepts

1. a. Review What happens during differentiation?
   b. Apply Concepts What does "mapping" refer to in the process of cell differentiation?
2. a. Review What are stem cells?
   b. Compare and Contrast How are embryonic stem cells and adult stem cells alike? How are they different?
3. a. Review Summarize the potential benefits and issues of stem cell research.
   b. Form an Opinion How might technological advances help address the ethical concerns surrounding stem cell research?

Apply the Big idea

Cellular Basis of Life

4. Use what you learned in this lesson to discuss how cells become specialized for different functions. Include an explanation of how the potential for specialization varies with cell type and how it varies over the life span of an organism.

BIOLOGY.com Search Lesson 10.4  GO • Self-Test • Lesson Assessment

LESSON 10.4

Expand Vocabulary

Have students look up *harvest* in the dictionary and summarize its different meanings in their own words.

DIFFERENTIATED INSTRUCTION

ELL English Language Learners Explain that *harvest* is both a noun and a verb in English. Show students a picture of a harvest and a farmer harvesting so they can see the difference.

Assess and Remediate

EVALUATE UNDERSTANDING

Have students write a few paragraphs of a pamphlet that aims to educate the public on the science behind stem cell research. Then, have them complete the 10.4 Assessment.

REMEDIATION SUGGESTION

L1 Struggling Students If your students have trouble with **Question 1a,** have them review **Figure 10–19** and discuss it with a partner.

BIOLOGY.com Students can check their understanding of lesson concepts with the **Self-Test** assessment. They can then take an online version of the **Lesson Assessment.**

Answers

IN YOUR NOTEBOOK Answers will vary. Check that student lists include reasonable benefits and issues pertaining to stem cell research.

Assessment Answers

1a. During differentiation, a cell becomes specialized.

1b. Mapping refers to tracking the progress of a cell's differentiation.

2a. Stem cells are unspecialized cells from which different types of cells develop.

2b. Embryonic stem cells and adult stem cells both have the ability to differentiate into specific cell types. Embryonic stem cells are found in embryos. Adult stem cells are found in certain organs of adults and are more limited in their ability to differentiate than are embryonic stem cells.

3a. Sample answers: benefits: repair or regeneration of cells damaged by certain kinds of disease; issues: embryonic stem cells cannot be harvested without destroying the embryo.

3b. Sample answer: If adult stems cells could be coaxed into behaving like embryonic stem cells, then perhaps there would no longer be a desire by scientists to harvest and use embryonic stem cells.

4. Big idea Student responses should explain the process of differentiation in embryonic and adult organisms. Within this explanation, totipotent, pluripotent, and multipotent cells should each be defined and discussed.

CHAPTER LAB

Pre-Lab

Introduce students to the concepts they will explore in the chapter lab by assigning the Pre-Lab questions.

Lab

Tell students they will perform the chapter lab *Regeneration in Planaria* described in **Lab Manual A.**

 **Struggling Students** A simpler version of the chapter lab is provided in **Lab Manual B.**

SAFETY

Students should wear protective equipment and handle the scalpel and glassware with care.

 Look online for **Editable Lab Worksheets.**

 For corresponding pre-lab in the **Foundation Edition**, see page 252.

IN INDIANA ACADEMIC STANDARDS

For the full text of all standards, see the Course Overview in the front matter of this book.

Design Your Own Lab

OPEN-ENDED INQUIRY

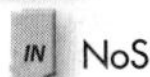 **NoS.1** Develop explanations; **NoS.4** Evaluate the work of peers.

Pre-Lab: Regeneration in Planaria

Problem How potent are the stem cells in planaria?

Materials fresh water or spring water, planarians, petri dishes, glass-marking pencil, forceps, scalpel, dissecting microscope, glass microscope slide, lens paper, pipette, small paintbrush, clear ruler

Lab Manual Chapter 10 Lab

Skills Focus Form a Hypothesis, Design an Experiment, Draw Conclusions

Connect to the Big idea All cells come from existing cells. When most cells in a multicellular organism divide, they produce cells just like themselves. However, some cells can differentiate to form different types of cells. These cells enable an organism to repair tissue after an injury or in some cases to regenerate body parts. In this lab, you will investigate the ability of planarians to regenerate body parts.

Background Questions

a. Compare and Contrast What is the difference between totipotent stem cells and multipotent stem cells?

b. Apply Concepts What type of stem cell enables your body to produce cells, such as skin and blood cells that are constantly replaced by the body?

c. Apply Concepts What type of stem cell enables a salamander to regenerate its tail?

d. Compare and Contrast In what way is regeneration of a body part similar to asexual reproduction? In what way is it different?

Pre-Lab Questions

Preview the procedure in the lab manual.

1. Apply Concepts What would you expect to observe if the stem cells in planarians are totipotent? What would you expect to observe if the stem cells are multipotent?
2. Control Variables What will you use as a control in your experiment? Explain why you need this control.
3. Infer Two planarians are cut at different locations. Regeneration occurs in one planarian, but not in the other. Based on these results, what might you infer about stem cells in planarians?

 Search Chapter 10 

Visit Chapter 10 online to test yourself on chapter content and to find activities to help you learn.

Untamed Science Video Journey with the Untamed Science crew to a research facility in Sweden to learn why scientists are studying regeneration in brittle stars.

Visual Analogy Compare a growing cell to a growing city to understand limits on cell size.

Data Analysis Learn how to time the cell cycle by counting cells in mitosis.

Art Review Test your knowledge of the structure of a eukaryotic chromosome.

Tutor Tube Sort out chromosome structure vocabulary with this simple tutorial video.

InterActive Art See the phases of mitosis in action.

Art in Motion See what happens when cancerous cells invade normal tissue.

Pre-Lab Answers

BACKGROUND QUESTIONS

a. Totipotent stem cells can form all types of cells in a body. Multipotent stem cells can form many, but not all, types of cells.

b. multipotent stem cells

c. totipotent stem cells

d. Sample answer: Asexual reproduction and regeneration are similar because they depend on cell division and differentiation. They are different because asexual reproduction always produces two organisms, but regeneration may result in a single repaired organism.

PRE-LAB QUESTIONS

1. Sample answer: If the stem cells are totipotent, a cut planarian should regenerate completely. If the cells are multipotent, regeneration should be incomplete.
2. Sample answer: I will use an uncut planarian. Growth that takes place in the uncut planarian can be compared with the growth that takes place during regeneration.
3. Sample answer: You might infer that stem cells are not found at every location in a planarian.

10 Study Guide

Big idea Growth, Development, and Reproduction

Cells undergo cell division to produce new cells. In eukaryotic cells, cell division is part of a highly regulated cycle known as the cell cycle.

10.1 Cell Growth, Division, and Reproduction

The larger a cell becomes, the more demands the cell places on its DNA. In addition, a larger cell is less efficient in moving nutrients and waste materials across the cell membrane.

Asexual reproduction is the production of genetically identical offspring from a single parent.

Offspring produced by sexual reproduction inherit some of their genetic information from each parent.

cell division (276)
asexual reproduction (277)
sexual reproduction (277)

10.2 The Process of Cell Division

Chromosomes make it possible to separate DNA precisely during cell division.

During the cell cycle, a cell grows, prepares for division, and divides to form two daughter cells.

During prophase, the genetic material inside the nucleus condenses. During metaphase, the chromosomes line up across the center of the cell. During anaphase, the chromosomes separate and move along spindle fibers to opposite ends of the cell. During telophase, the chromosomes, which were distinct and condensed, begin to spread out into a tangle of chromatin.

Cytokinesis completes the process of cell division—it splits one cell into two.

chromosome (279)
chromatin (280)
cell cycle (280)
interphase (281)
mitosis (282)
cytokinesis (282)
prophase (282)
centromere (282)
chromatid (282)
centriole (282)
metaphase (282)
anaphase (283)
telophase (283)

10.3 Regulating the Cell Cycle

The cell cycle is controlled by regulatory proteins both inside and outside the cell.

Cancer cells do not respond to the signals that regulate the growth of most cells. As a result, the cells divide uncontrollably.

cyclin (286)
growth factor (287)
apoptosis (288)
cancer (289)
tumor (289)

10.4 Cell Differentiation

During the development of an organism, cells differentiate into many types of cells.

The unspecialized cells from which differentiated cells develop are known as stem cells.

Stem cells offer the potential benefit of using undifferentiated cells to repair or replace badly damaged cells and tissues.

Human embryonic stem cell research is controversial because the arguments for it and against it both involve ethical issues of life and death.

embryo (292)
differentiation (293)
totipotent (294)
blastocyst (294)
pluripotent (294)
stem cell (295)
multipotent (295)

Think Visually Using the information in this chapter, complete the following cycle diagram of the cell cycle.

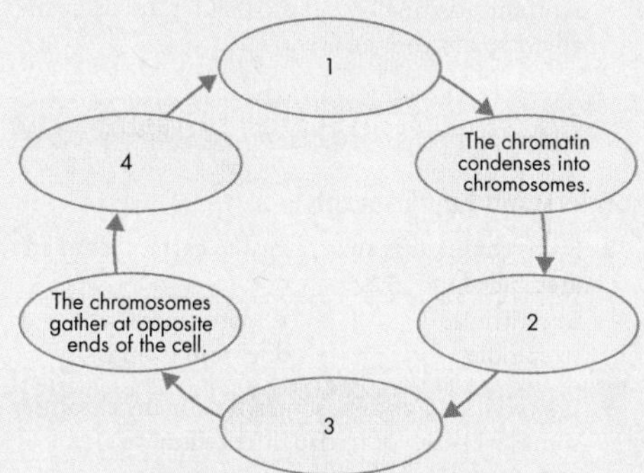
1
The chromatin condenses into chromosomes.
2
3
The chromosomes gather at opposite ends of the cell.
4

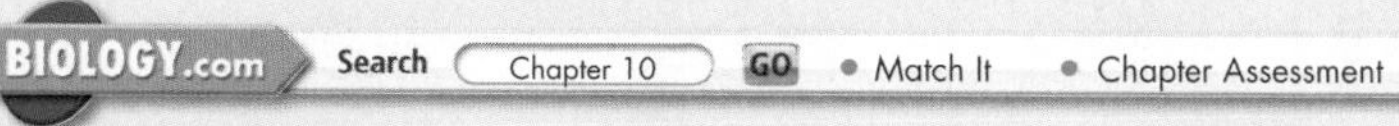

Study Online

REVIEW AND ASSESSMENT RESOURCES

Editable Worksheets Pages of Study Workbooks A and B, Lab Manuals A and B, and the Assessment Resources Book are available online. These documents can be easily edited using a word-processing program.

Lesson Overview Have students reread the Lesson Overviews to help them study chapter concepts.

Vocabulary Review The *Flash Cards* and *Crossword* provide an interactive way to review chapter vocabulary.

Chapter Assessments Have students take online versions of the Chapter 10 Assessment.

Standardized Test Prep Students can take an online version of the Standardized Test Prep. You will receive their scores along with ideas for remediation.

Diagnostic and Benchmark Tests Use these tests to monitor your students' progress and supply remediation.

Answers

THINK VISUALLY

1. The cell grows and replicates its DNA and centrioles.
2. The chromosomes line up across the middle of the cell.
3. The sister chromatids separate into individual chromosomes and move apart.
4. The cell membrane pinches the cytoplasm in half.

UbD Performance Tasks

SUMMATIVE TASK Have each student write a memoir as if he or she were a cell that had just divided. Write the following prompts on the board and tell students that they should mention each of these points in their memoir.

- Why did you decide to divide?
- What signals did you receive that told you it was time to divide? Describe how you divided. What happened? In what order?
- Talk about why each process you went through was important to you and your daughter cells.

TRANSFER TASK Ask each student to make a list of the types of cells and tissues humans can regrow, such as hair and nails. Have small groups of students compare lists and make a comprehensive group list. Then, have each group discuss the following questions:

- How is the regrowth of human hair and nails different than regeneration in salamanders and planarians?
- Why might humans be more limited in their potential to regenerate an entire leg than salamanders?
- Humans can regenerate liver tissue. How is this phenomenon similar to the regrowth of hair and nails? How is it different?
- Stem cells in human bone marrow can produce blood cells. How are stem cells related to regeneration?

10 Assessment

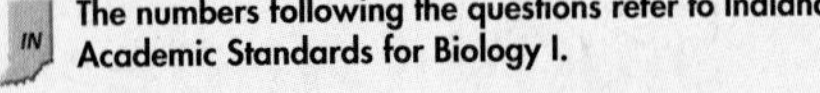
The numbers following the questions refer to Indiana's Academic Standards for Biology I.

10.1 Cell Growth, Division, and Reproduction

Understand Key Concepts

1. The rate at which materials enter and leave the cell depends on the cell's B.2.1
   a. volume. c. speciation.
   b. weight. d. surface area.
2. In order for a cell to divide successfully, the cell must first
   a. duplicate its genetic information.
   b. decrease its volume.
   c. increase its number of chromosomes.
   d. decrease its number of organelles.
3. The process that increases genetic diversity within a population is
   a. asexual reproduction. c. cell division.
   b. sexual reproduction. d. binary fission.
4. Describe what is meant by each of the following terms: *cell volume, cell surface area, ratio of surface area to volume.*
5. Describe asexual and sexual reproduction as survival strategies.

Think Critically

6. **Calculate** Calculate the ratio of surface area to volume of an imaginary cubic cell measuring 4 mm long on each side. MATH
7. **Form a Hypothesis** In a changing environment, which organisms have an advantage—those that reproduce asexually or those that reproduce sexually? Explain your answer.

10.2 The Process of Cell Division

Understand Key Concepts

8. Sister chromatids are attached to each other at an area called the B.5.1
   a. centriole. c. centromere.
   b. spindle. d. chromosome.
9. If a cell has 12 chromosomes, how many chromosomes will each of its daughter cells have after mitosis and cytokinesis? B.6.1
   a. 4 b. 6 c. 12 d. 24
10. Which of the illustrations below best represents metaphase of mitosis? B.6.1

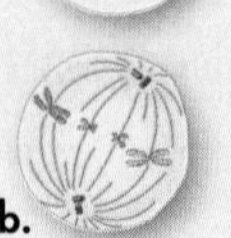
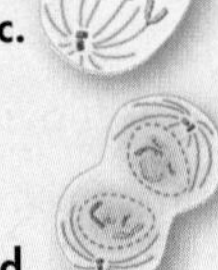

11. In plant cells, what forms midway between the divided nuclei during cytokinesis?
    a. nuclear membrane c. cell membrane
    b. centromere d. cell plate
12. Describe how a eukaryotic cell's chromosomes change as a cell prepares to divide. B.5.1
13. What is the relationship between interphase and cell division?
14. List the following stages of mitosis in the correct sequence, and describe what happens during each stage: anaphase, metaphase, prophase, and telophase. B.6.1

Think Critically

15. **Compare and Contrast** How is the process of cell division in prokaryotes different from cell division in eukaryotes?
16. **Form a Hypothesis** Some cells have several nuclei within their cytoplasm. Considering the events in a typical cell cycle, which phase of the cell cycle is not operating when such cells form? B.6.1
17. **Compare and Contrast** Describe the differences between cell division in an animal cell and cell division in a plant cell.
18. **Relate Cause and Effect** The nerve cells in the human nervous system seldom undergo mitosis. Based on this information, explain why complete recovery from injuries to the nervous system usually does not occur.
19. **Apply Concepts** A scientist treats cells with a chemical that prevents DNA synthesis. In which stage of the cell cycle will these cells remain?

Lesson 10.1

UNDERSTAND KEY CONCEPTS

1. d **2.** a **3.** b

4. Cell volume is the amount of material inside a cell. Cell surface area is the total area of the cell's membrane. Ratio of surface area to volume is the surface area compared to the volume.

5. Asexual reproduction allows populations to increase in number very quickly. Sexual reproduction provides genetic diversity.

THINK CRITICALLY

6. 2.25:1

7. sexually; genetic differences in a population may help the organisms better cope with environmental changes

Lesson 10.2

UNDERSTAND KEY CONCEPTS

8. c **9.** c **10.** b **11.** d

12. Well before cell division, each chromosome is replicated. At the beginning of cell division, the chromosomes condense, with each chromosome consisting of two identical sister chromatids joined at a centromere.

13. Interphase is the period of growth between cell divisions.

14. prophase, metaphase, anaphase, telophase; In prophase, chromosomes condense and the mitotic spindle starts to form. During metaphase, the duplicated chromosomes line up in the middle of the cell and the centromeres attach to the spindle. In anaphase, the chromosomes separate and move to opposite ends of the cell. During telophase, the chromosomes spread out and nuclear envelopes begin re-forming around the genetic material.

THINK CRITICALLY

15. Prokaryotes divide by binary fission: the DNA replicates and each DNA molecule attaches to a different part of the cell membrane. The cell pinches and divides. In eukaryotes, cell division occurs in two stages—mitosis and cytokinesis.

16. The presence of many nuclei indicates that mitosis has occurred repeatedly without cytokinesis having occurred.

17. Cell division is similar in animal and plant cells. Plant cells, though, do not have centrioles, as animal cells do. Plant cells organize their mitotic spindles from regions known as centrosomes. Also, during cytokinesis in most animal cells, the cell membrane moves inward until the cytoplasm is pinched into two nearly equal parts. In plant cells, a cell plate forms midway between the divided nuclei and gradually develops into separating membranes. A cell wall then appears in the cell plate.

18. Because nerve cells seldom undergo mitosis, the body is usually unable to repair damage to parts of the nervous system. Thus, complete recovery may not occur.

19. They will remain in the S phase of interphase.

20. a. metaphase **b.** It is an animal cell because centrioles are present. **c.** The two strands of the same chromosome contain identical genetic material. This is important because when the strands move to opposite ends and the cell splits, each daughter cell will have the same genetic material.

20. **Interpret Visuals** The diagram shows a phase of mitosis. Use the diagram to answer the following questions.

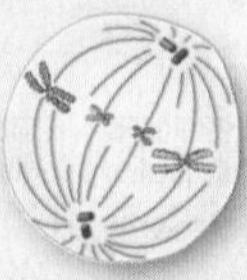

a. Identify the phase of mitosis shown in the diagram. B.6.1
b. Is this a plant or animal cell? How do you know?
c. The four chromosomes shown in the center of this cell each have two connected strands. Explain how the two strands on the same chromosome compare with regard to the genetic information they carry. In your answer, be sure to explain why this is important to the cell. B.5.1, B.6.1

10.3 Regulating the Cell Cycle

Understand Key Concepts

21. The timing in the cell cycle in eukaryotic cells is believed to be controlled by a group of closely related proteins known as B.1.2, B.1.3
a. chromatids.
b. cyclins.
c. centromeres.
d. centrioles.

22. In the cell cycle, external regulatory proteins direct cells to B.1.2, B.1.3
a. speed up or slow down the cell cycle.
b. remain unchanged.
c. proceed and then stop the cell cycle.
d. grow uncontrollably.

23. When some cells are removed from the center of a tissue culture, will new cells replace the cells that were removed? Explain.

24. Describe the role of cyclins. B.1.3, B.5.5

Think Critically

25. **Compare and Contrast** How do cancer cells differ from noncancerous cells? How are they similar? B.1.3

26. **Predict** A cell will usually undergo apoptosis if the cell experiences DNA damage that could lead to a tumor. Predict what may happen if a gene that controls apoptosis is damaged.

solve the CHAPTER MYSTERY

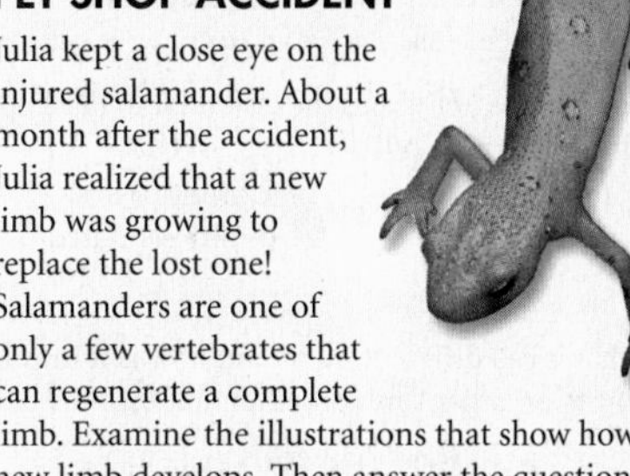

PET SHOP ACCIDENT

Julia kept a close eye on the injured salamander. About a month after the accident, Julia realized that a new limb was growing to replace the lost one! Salamanders are one of only a few vertebrates that can regenerate a complete limb. Examine the illustrations that show how a new limb develops. Then answer the questions.

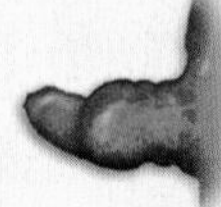

Week 1: Dedifferentiation
At first, cells in the injured limb undergo dedifferentiation. During this process, cells such as muscle cells and nerve cells lose the characteristics that make them specialized.

Week 3: Blastema Formation
The dedifferentiated cells migrate to the wounded area and form a blastema—a growing mass of undifferentiated cells.

Week 5: Redifferentiation
Cells in the blastema then redifferentiate and form the tissues needed for a mature limb. The limb will continue to grow until it is full size.

1. **Relate Cause and Effect** Why is dedifferentiation of the salamander's limb cells necessary before regeneration can occur?
2. **Classify** What type of cells do you think are contained in the blastema? Explain.
3. **Connect to the Big idea** Unlike salamanders, planarians contain undifferentiated cells throughout their adult bodies. How might the regeneration process in salamanders and planarians differ?

After students have read through the Chapter Mystery, discuss the topics of dedifferentiation and specialization.

Ask What is dedifferentiation? *(The process by which specialized cells lose their specialized characteristics.)*

Ask How did the process of dedifferentiation change the cells in the salamander's leg? *(The cells were no longer specialized.)*

Ask Name some types of specialized cells that are in both your legs and the salamander's limb. *(Sample answers: muscle, nerve, blood, skin, bone cells)*

Ask How does the regeneration of the salamander's limb differ from the healing of a broken human leg bone? *(For the salamander's limb, dedifferentiation results in unspecialized cells that can then differentiate into whatever type of cells are needed to build a whole new limb. When a human bone heals, bone cells can repair bone cells, but they cannot dedifferentiate to form new types of tissue.)*

CHAPTER MYSTERY ANSWERS

1. Dedifferentiation needs to occur to provide the undifferentiated cells necessary to form a new limb through regeneration.
2. Stem cells; the blastema contains unspecialized cells that differentiate into specific types of cells.
3.  Planarians would not need to go through dedifferentiation when they are injured.

Students can explore cell differentiation, with the Untamed Science crew in **A Tail of Cell Division.**

Lesson 10.3

UNDERSTAND KEY CONCEPTS

21. b 22. a
23. Yes, new cells will replace the removed cells because the process of cell division will continue until the new cells come in contact with other cells. When that occurs, cell division will stop.
24. Cyclins regulate the timing of the cell cycle in eukaryotic cells.

THINK CRITICALLY

25. Cancer cells do not respond to the signals that regulate the growth of most cells. As a result, they form tumors that can damage surrounding tissues. Cancer cells are similar to normal cells in that they are body cells that undergo cell division.
26. If the gene that controls apoptosis is damaged, a cell will not die when its DNA is damaged, and a tumor may result.

Lesson 10.4

UNDERSTAND KEY CONCEPTS

27. b **28.** a

29. a hollow ball of cells that contains the inner cell mass

30. Cell differentiation is the process by which cells become specialized. It is important because multicellular organisms consist of cells specialized for different functions.

31. There may be ways to obtain stem cells from an early embryo without damaging the embryo itself, or it may be possible to switch on genes that would cause adult cells to mimic pluripotent embryonic stem cells.

THINK CRITICALLY

32. Heart attack patients would be able to receive new heart cells to replace the damaged ones.

33. In *C. elegans*, each cell's role is rigidly determined at a specific point in the course of development. Mammals go through a more flexible process in which cell differentiation is controlled by a number of interacting factors in the embryo.

Connecting Concepts

USE SCIENCE GRAPHICS

34. Heart and spinal cord injuries are similar in that damaged cells won't be replaced. Because smooth muscle cells can divide, injuries to smooth muscle can likely be repaired by producing new cells.

35. Because cancer cells have lost the ability to control growth and, hence, divide uncontrollably, they would be listed as "long-lived" and "can divide" in the data table.

WRITE ABOUT SCIENCE

36. Students might mention that organisms are made of units called cells and that organisms grow and develop as their cells divide.

37. Big idea Because the growth and development of an organism is carefully controlled by internal and external regulators, changes to one cell can disrupt all the others around it. In the case of cancer, the damaged cell begins to divide uncontrollably and forms a tumor, which can then lead to disease in the entire organism.

10.4 Cell Differentiation

Understand Key Concepts

27. Bone marrow cells that produce blood cells are best categorized as
a. embryonic stem cells. **c.** pluripotent.
b. adult stem cells. **d.** totipotent cells.

28. Which type of cell has the potential to develop into any type of cell?
a. totipotent **c.** multipotent
b. pluripotent **d.** differentiated

29. What is a blastocyst?

30. What is cell differentiation and how is it important to an organism's development? B.1.3

31. Describe two ways that technology may address the ethical concerns related to stem cell research.

Think Critically

32. **Relate Cause and Effect** When researchers discovered how to make skin stem cells pluripotent, how did they apply their discovery to the treatment for heart attack patients?

33. **Compare and Contrast** How does embryonic development and cell differentiation in *C. elegans* differ from how these processes work in mammals? B.1.3

Connecting Concepts

Use Science Graphics NoS.3

Use the data table to answer questions 34 and 35.

Life Spans of Various Human Cells		
Cell Type	**Life Span**	**Cell Division**
Red blood cells	<120 days	Cannot divide
Cardiac (heart) muscle	Long-lived	Cannot divide
Smooth muscle	Long-lived	Can divide
Neuron (nerve cell)	Long-lived	Most do not divide

34. **Compare and Contrast** Based on the data, in what ways might injuries to the heart and spinal cord be similar? How might they differ from injuries to smooth muscles?

35. **Predict** If cancer cells were added to the table, predict what would be written in the Life Span and Cell Division columns. Explain.

Write About Science NoS.3

36. **Explanation** Recall what you learned about the characteristics of life in Chapter 1. Explain how cell division is related to two or more of those characteristics. B.1.2, B.3.3

37. **Assess the Big idea** How is cancer an example of how changes to a single cell can affect the health of an entire organism?

Analyzing Data

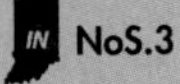
NoS.3

A scientist performed an experiment to determine the effect of temperature on the length of the cell cycle in onion cells. His data are summarized in the table below.

Effect of Temperature on Length of Onion Cell Cycle	
Temperature (°C)	**Length of Cell Cycle (hours)**
10	54.6
15	29.8
20	18.8
25	13.3

38. **Interpret Tables** On the basis of the data in the table, how long would you expect the cell cycle to be at 5°C?
a. less than 13.3 hours
b. more than 54.6 hours
c. between 29.8 and 54.6 hours
d. about 20 hours

39. **Draw Conclusions** Given this set of data, what is one valid conclusion the scientist could state?

PURPOSE Students will analyze data to understand the effects of temperature on the cell cycle of onion cells.

PLANNING Some students may have difficulty calculating the percent increase in temperature, since it is greater than 100%. For these students, write the following formula on the board and have them solve it.

$$\frac{\text{Temperature difference (final – original)}}{\text{Original temperature}} \times 100$$

ANSWERS

38. b

39. Sample answer: As the temperature decreases, the length of the cell cycle (in onions) takes longer.

Standardized Test Practice for Indiana

Multiple Choice

1. Which statement is true regarding a cell's surface area-to-volume ratio?
   A As the size of a cell increases, its volume decreases.
   B As the size of a cell decreases, its volume increases.
   C Larger cells will have a greater surface area-to-volume ratio.
   D Smaller cells will have a greater surface area-to-volume ratio.

2. Which of the following is NOT an advantage of asexual reproduction?
   A simple and efficient
   B produces large number of offspring quickly
   C increases genetic diversity
   D requires one parent

3. At the beginning of cell division, a chromosome consists of two
   A centromeres. C chromatids.
   B centrioles. D spindles. B.6.1

4. What regulates the timing of the cell cycle in eukaryotes?
   A chromosomes C nutrients
   B cyclins D DNA and RNA B.1.2

5. The period between cell divisions is called
   A interphase. C G_3 phase.
   B prophase. D cytokinesis.

6. Which of the following is TRUE about totipotent cells?
   A Embryonic stem cells are totipotent cells.
   B Totipotent cells are differentiated cells.
   C Totipotent cells can differentiate into any type of cell and tissue.
   D Adult stem cells are totipotent cells.

7. A cell enters anaphase before all of its chromosomes have attached to the spindle. This may indicate that the cell is not responding to
   A internal regulators. C growth factors.
   B mitosis. D apoptosis. B.1.2, B.6.1

Questions 8–10

The spindle fibers of a dividing cell were labeled with a fluorescent dye. At the beginning of anaphase, a laser beam was used to mark a region of the spindle fibers about halfway between the centrioles and the chromosomes. The laser beam stopped the dye from glowing in this region, as shown in the second diagram. The laser did not inhibit the normal function of the fibers.

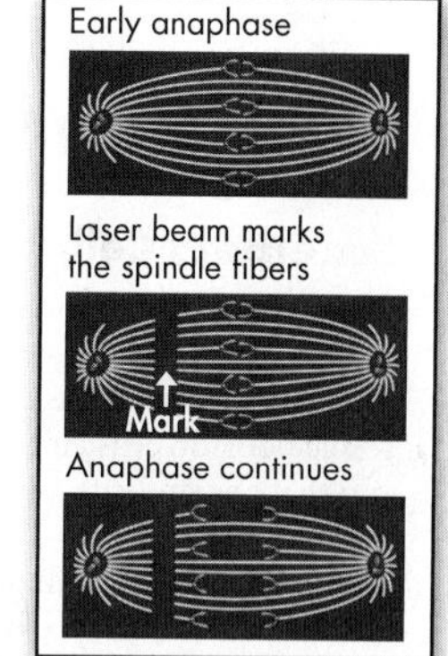

8. This experiment tests a hypothesis about
   A how chromosomes migrate during cell division.
   B how fluorescent dyes work in the cell.
   C the effect of lasers on cells.
   D why cells divide.

9. The diagrams show that chromosomes move to the poles of the cell as the spindle fibers
   A shorten on the chromosome side of the mark.
   B lengthen on the chromosome side of the mark.
   C shorten on the centriole side of the mark.
   D lengthen on the centriole side of the mark.

10. A valid conclusion that can be drawn from this experiment is that the spindle fibers break down
   A at the centrioles.
   B in the presence of dye.
   C when marked by lasers.
   D where they are attached to chromosomes.

Open-Ended Response

11. Explain why careful regulation of the cell cycle is important to multicellular organisms. B.1.2

If You Have Trouble With . . .

Question	1	2	3	4	5	6	7	8	9	10	11
See Lesson	10.1	10.1	10.2	10.3	10.2	10.4	10.3	10.2	10.2	10.2	10.3

Test-Taking Tip

INTERPRETING VISUALS

When answering questions that contain a visual prompt, remind students to look carefully at the visual and read through any descriptive text that goes with it. Then, suggest they read and answer the test questions. For students who struggle to answer questions with visual prompts, suggest that they make a quick mental summary of what the visual is showing before reading the test questions.

Answers

1. D
2. C
3. C
4. B
5. A
6. C
7. A
8. A
9. A
10. D
11. Careful regulation of the cell cycle ensures that each cell in a multicellular organism grows, divides, stops dividing, or dies appropriately. If cell cycle regulation goes awry, then diseases such as cancer can result.

UNIT 3

Plan Ahead

Have students read through the Unit 3 Project a few days in advance of writing their comic books to give them time to think about the task. Suggest they review differences between prokaryotic and eukaryotic cells, as well as differences between plant and animal cells. You may want to have several "superhero" comic books on hand to give students examples of how they might portray their "superhero cell."

Materials colored pencils or pens, paper

Monitor the Project

Tell students the comic book should have a minimum of four pages, but may have as many as they can create in the given time period, as long as each page is well done. As they work on their comic books, walk around the room and ask students questions that will help them focus both on the cell being portrayed and the story line of the comic book.

Ask What kind of cell is your superhero, and what structures and organelles does that kind of cell include?

Ask How does your story line provide insight into the way your particular cell works?

Project Assessment

Make sure students use the rubric and reflection questions to assess their work. Then, use the rubric to assign a final score. Note that it is important to value the creativity of students' work as well as the content when you score their projects. If desired, talk with students about any differences between their self-assessment scores and your assigned score.

Unit Project

Superhero Cell

Do you like reading comics? Have you ever designed a comic book of your own? Here's your chance! A high school teacher has contacted you asking for a comic book on cells and cell processes. She has told you that her students are just about to start studying cells and need a good introduction to the topic. You've been tasked with developing the story line and visuals that will provide the students with a basic understanding of cell structure and function. Remember that sometimes a picture can be worth a thousand words—so be creative!

Your Task Write a comic book about a "superhero cell" for an audience of high school students.

Be sure to
- incorporate important concepts and details about the structure and function of various organelles and cell processes.
- provide insight into the ways cells work and interact with their environment.
- be entertaining and creative.

Reflection Questions

1. **Score your project using the rubric below. What score did you give yourself?**
2. **What did you do well on this project?**
3. **What about your project needs improvement?**
4. **Exchange your comic book with a classmate and have him/her read it. What did your partner like about your comic book? What did he/she think could use improvement?**

Assessment Rubric

Score	Scientific Content	Quality of Comic Book
4	The comic book includes accurate details about the structures and functions of several organelles and cell processes. It provides exceptional insight into how a cell works and interacts with its environment.	The comic book is thoughtfully and creatively written and illustrated.
3	The comic book includes mostly accurate details about the structure and functions of organelles and cell processes. It provides good insight into how a cell works and interacts with its environment.	The comic book is well written and includes some creativity. Illustrations are clear.
2	The comic book includes a few details about the structure and functions of organelles and cell processes, with some inaccuracies. It provides some insight into how a cell works and interacts with its environment.	The comic book needs some edits and could use more creativity. Some parts of the story line and illustrations are difficult to follow.
1	The comic book includes vague and inaccurate information about the structure and functions of organelles and cell processes. It provides little insight into how a cell works and interacts with its environment.	The comic book needs significant edits and includes very little creativity. Story line and illustrations are unclear.

21st Century Skills

To be successful in the 21st century, students need skills and learning experiences that extend beyond subject area mastery. The Unit 3 Project helps students build the following 21st Century Skills: *Communication Skills; Creativity and Intellectual Curiosity; Interpersonal and Collaborative Skills; Self-Direction;* and *Accountability and Adaptability.*

FOCUS ON CRITICAL THINKING AND SYSTEMS THINKING Extend this Unit Project by having pairs of students work together to create a comic book that features a cell in a multicellular organism that is part of an organ or organ system, such as the digestive system or circulatory system. Explain that the story line should focus on how cells cooperate in a multicellular organism.

For more practice building 21st Century Skills, see The Chapter Mystery pages in **Study Workbook A.**

IN INDIANA ACADEMIC STANDARDS

B.2.1 Features common to all cells, **B.2.2** Cell membrane, **B.2.3** Mitochondria and chloroplasts, **B.2.4** Protein synthesis, **B.2.5** Protein structures, **B.2.6** Variation in cell structure and function. Also covered: **B.1.2, B.1.3**

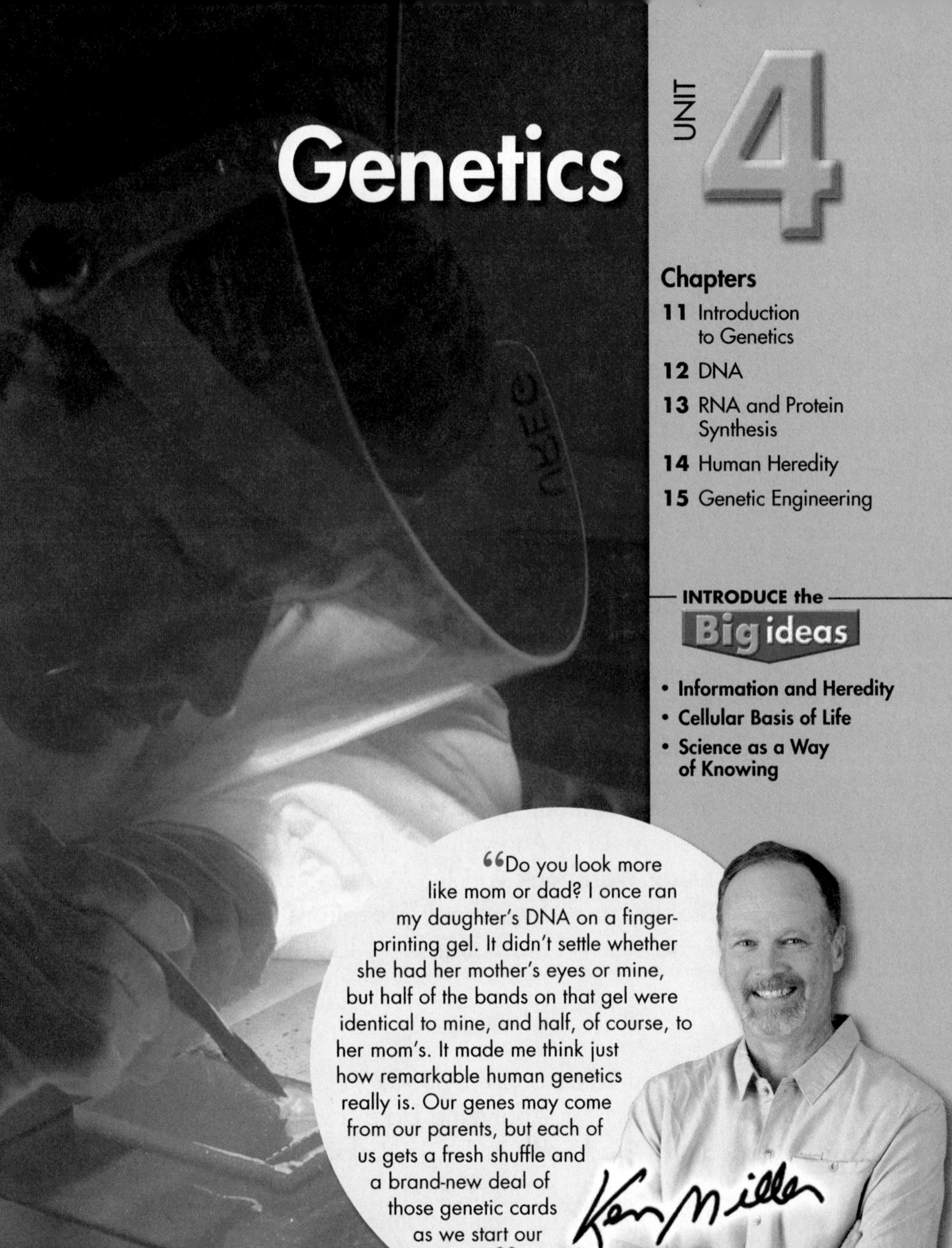

Genetics
UNIT 4
Chapters
11 Introduction to Genetics
12 DNA
13 RNA and Protein Synthesis
14 Human Heredity
15 Genetic Engineering
INTRODUCE the Big ideas
• Information and Heredity
• Cellular Basis of Life
• Science as a Way of Knowing
"Do you look more like mom or dad? I once ran my daughter's DNA on a fingerprinting gel. It didn't settle whether she had her mother's eyes or mine, but half of the bands on that gel were identical to mine, and half, of course, to her mom's. It made me think just how remarkable human genetics really is. Our genes may come from our parents, but each of us gets a fresh shuffle and a brand-new deal of those genetic cards as we start our lives."
305

UNIT 4

Dear Colleague,

A few months ago, I had the honor of speaking at a symposium in honor of Gregor Mendel. To prepare for my talk for the meeting, I read over Mendel's famous paper, a dry scientific report with the unassuming title of "Investigations of Plant Hybridization." As I turned the pages, I wondered if Mendel himself had any idea what he was starting. It would take decades, of course, but eventually his work led to a revolution in biology. Once, we naturalists were merely observers of life. Biologists today, of course, are active participants who study, shape, analyze, and even change living things.

What struck me most as I looked over Mendel's paper was not the way in which it laid out the basic principles of genetics. Mendel's great contribution, it seems to me, was his insistence that life itself could be studied, analyzed, and understood along systematic, rational lines. This attitude infuses every paragraph of his work, and it was picked up, almost unconsciously, by the scientists who rediscovered and extended that work at the beginning of the twentieth century.

Today, we have an opportunity to bring that sense of discovery to our students as never before. The rise of Mendelian genetics led to intense curiosity about the chemical nature of the gene. That, in turn, led to the identification of DNA as the genetic material, as well as the discovery of its double-helical structure. The result of all that curiosity, of course, is a new understanding of life that we can bring to all of our students. DNA carries the genetic code, and with it the fundamental instructions that operate our cells and interact with the environment to build our bodies. It's both our heritage and the legacy that we pass along to new generations. It's also something we share with every other living thing on this planet. That revolution in understanding may have begun with Gregor Mendel, but it hasn't stopped, even today. Indeed, the most important message we may be able to give our students is that the really interesting work is just beginning.

Introduction to Genetics

Chapter Contents	IN	Time	Core Resources
Chapter Preview			**Student Edition,** pp. 306–307 **Chapter Mystery,** p. 307
11.1 The Work of Gregor Mendel The Experiments of Gregor Mendel • Segregation	B.5.2, B.5.5, B.5.6, B.7.1, B.7.2, B.7.3	1/2 period 1/4 block	**Student Edition,** pp. 308–312 Inquiry 11.1 Quick Lab, p. 311 L2 **Study Workbook A** 11.1 Worksheets L2 **Biology.com** 11.1 Self-Test • 11.1 Lesson Assessment
11.2 Applying Mendel's Principles Probability and Punnett Squares • Independent Assortment • A Summary of Mendel's Principles	B.7.1, B.7.2, B.7.3	1 1/2 periods 3/4 block	**Student Edition,** pp. 313–318 Inquiry 11.2 Quick Lab, p. 315 L2 **Study Workbook A** 11.2 Worksheets L2 **Biology.com** *InterActive Art:* Punnett Squares **Assessment Resources Book** Visual Quiz L2
11.3 Other Patterns of Inheritance Beyond Dominant and Recessive Alleles • Genes and the Environment • *Careers & Biology: Forensic Scientist, Plant Breeder, Population Geneticist*	NoS.3, B.1.3, B.5.6, B.7.2, B.7.3	1/2 period 1/4 block	**Student Edition,** pp. 319–322 Inquiry 11.3 Analyzing Data, p. 320 L2 **Study Workbook A** 11.3 Worksheets L2 **Biology.com** *Art Review:* Exceptions to Mendel's Principles • 11.3 Self-Test • 11.3 Lesson Assessment
11.4 Meiosis Chromosome Number • Phases of Meiosis • Comparing Meiosis and Mitosis • Gene Linkage and Gene Maps	NoS.3, B.6.4, B.6.5	2 periods 1 block	**Student Edition,** pp. 323–329 Inquiry 11.4 Analyzing Data, p. 327 L2 **Study Workbook A** 11.4 Worksheets L2 **Biology.com** *Art in Motion:* Meiosis • *Tutor Tube:* Connecting Punnett Squares to Meiosis **Assessment Resources Book** Visual Quiz L2
Chapter Pre-Lab	NoS.6, B.6.4	1 period 1/2 block	**Student Edition,** p. 330 L2 **Lab Manual A** *Modeling Meiosis* L2 • *Independent Assortment and Gene Linkage* L2

Differentiated Instruction Tools

Study Workbook B includes worksheets with lesson-level differentiated instruction support and explanations of differentiated instruction teaching strategies.

Lab Manual B includes skills labs, simplified chapter labs, and hands-on activities.

ELL Handbook explains ways to make *Biology* more accessible to ELL students.

Spanish Study Workbook is a Spanish translation of Study Workbook A.

Multilingual Glossary is the glossary translated into ten languages.

Differentiated Instruction Key

- L1 Special Needs or Struggling Students
- ELL English Language Learners
- LPR Less Proficient Readers
- L2 On-Level Students
- L3 Advanced Students

Additional Resources

Biology.com Untamed Science Video • Vocabulary Flash Cards

Study Workbook B 11.1 Worksheets L1 ELL LPR
Spanish Study Workbook 11.1 Worksheets ELL
Biology.com 11.1 Lesson Overview • 11.1 Lesson Notes

Study Workbook B 11.2 Worksheets L1 ELL LPR
Spanish Study Workbook 11.2 Worksheets ELL
Biology.com 11.2 Lesson Overview • 11.2 Lesson Notes • 11.2 Self-Test • 11.2 Lesson Assessment

Study Workbook B 11.3 Worksheets L1 ELL LPR
Spanish Study Workbook 11.3 Worksheets ELL
Biology.com 11.3 Lesson Overview • 11.3 Lesson Notes

Study Workbook B 11.4 Worksheets L1 ELL LPR
Spanish Study Workbook 11.4 Worksheets ELL
Biology.com *Data Analysis:* Gene Location and Crossing-Over • 11.4 Lesson Overview • 11.4 Lesson Notes • 11.4 Self-Test • 11.4 Lesson Assessment

Lab Manual B *Modeling Meiosis* • Hands-On Activity: *How Are Dimples Inherited?* • Data Analysis: *Human Blood Types* • Data Analysis: *Calculating Haploid and Diploid Numbers* L1 ELL LPR

Chapter Review

Student Edition Study Guide, p. 331 L2
Study Workbook A Chapter 11 Vocabulary Review L2 • Chapter 11 Chapter Mystery/21st Century Skills Activity L2 L3
Transparencies, pp. 137–147 L1 ELL LPR L2
Biology.com Untamed Science Video • Editable Worksheets of Study Workbooks A and B and Lab Manuals A and B • Chapter 11 Flash Cards and Match It

Untamed Science DVD • Classroom Resources CD (includes lesson presentations and editable worksheets)

Chapter Assessment

Student Edition Assessment, pp. 332–335 L2
Study Workbook B Chapter 11 Chapter Review L1 ELL LPR • Chapter 11 Taking a Standardized Test L1 ELL LPR
Assessment Resources Book Chapter 11 Test A L2 • Chapter 11 Test B L1 ELL LPR
Biology.com Chapter 11 Assessment • Editable Worksheets of Chapter 11 Visual Quizzes and Chapter 11 Tests A and B

Exam*View* *Assessment Suite* • Classroom Resources CD (includes lesson presentations and editable worksheets)

Time: 1 period, 1/2 block

Pressed for Time?

Preview the Chapter Preview Figure 11–3 and introduce students to the vocabulary in Lesson 11.2.

Cover the Chapter Quickly Have students read *The Experiments of Gregor Mendel* in Lesson 11.1, all of Lesson 11.2, and *Beyond Dominant and Recessive Alleles* in Lesson11.3. Assign *Chromosome Number,* the introductory paragraph of *Phases of Meiosis,* and go over Figures 11–15 and 11–16 in Lesson 11.4.

Assess Assign question 1 in the 11.1 Assessment, the entire 11.2 Assessment, questions 1 and 2 in the 11.3 Assessment, and questions 1 and 2 in the 11.4 Assessment. In the Chapter 11 Assessment, assign questions 1–16, 19, 20, 22–24.

Connect to the Big Idea

Big idea Have students look at the photo and describe their observations. Ask students whether they think the dogs in the photo are related to one another. *(Students might say that they are all the same breed, so they could be from the same family.)* Explain that the colors of the dogs' coats are determined by heredity, or the passing of traits from parents to offspring. Then, have students read the question, **How does biological information pass from one generation to another?** Tell students that, in this chapter, they will learn how offspring can inherit information from both parents, yet show traits that do not appear in either parent.

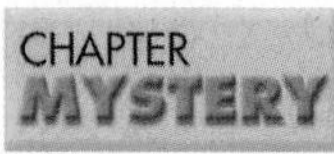

Have students read over the Chapter Mystery and brainstorm a list of reasons why none of the chicks look like their parents. As a hint, suggest students reread the chapter's Big Idea and Essential Question. Have students refer back to this list as they gather more evidence throughout the chapter.

BIOLOGY.com Have students preview the chapter vocabulary using the **Flash Cards.**

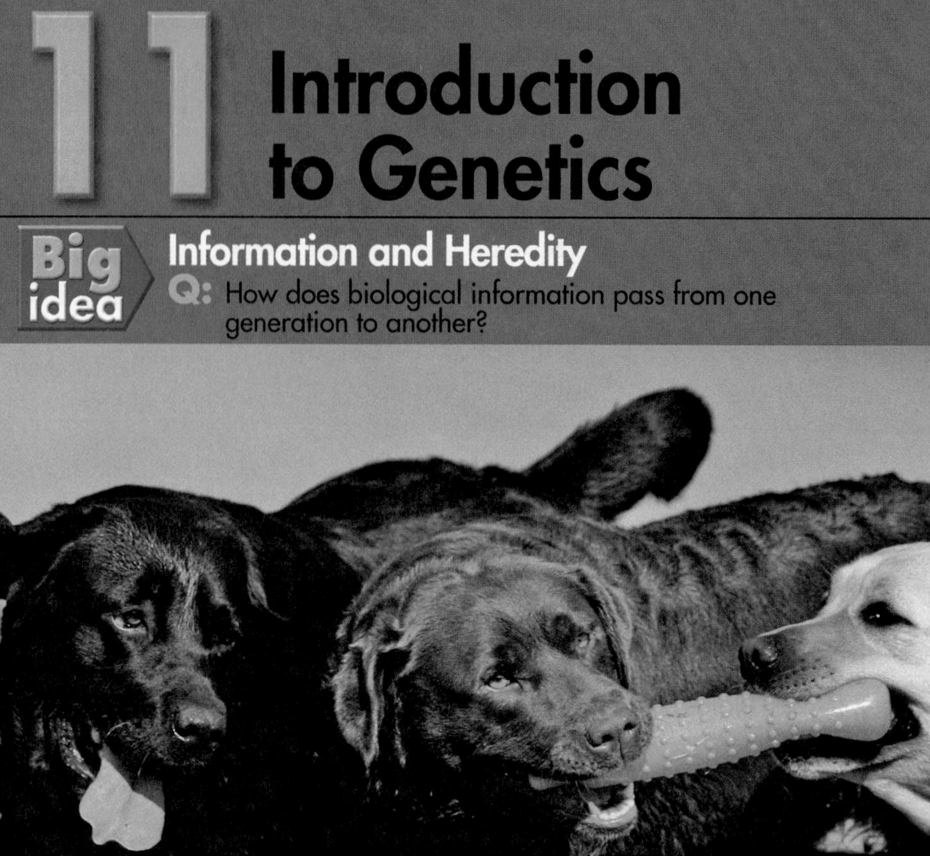

11 Introduction to Genetics

Big idea **Information and Heredity**

Q: How does biological information pass from one generation to another?

Genetics is the study of biological inheritance. The different coat colors of these Labrador retrievers are an example of the inherited characteristics that geneticists try to understand.

BIOLOGY.com Search Chapter 11 GO • Flash Cards

306

IN INDIANA ACADEMIC STANDARDS

For the full text of all standards, see the Course Overview in the front matter of this book.

Key standards: Chapter 11 covers key ideas from Standard 6: Cellular Reproduction and Gene Expression and Standard 7: Genetics, including **B.6.4** Meiosis, **B.6.5** Sorting and recombination of genes, **B.7.1** Dominant and recessive alleles, **B.7.2** Inheritance patterns, and **B.7.3** Traits.

UbD Understanding by Design

In Chapter 11, students discover how cellular information passes from one generation to another. The graphic organizer at right shows how chapter content frames their exploration of the Unit 4 Enduring Understanding: *DNA is the universal code for life; it enables an organism to transmit hereditary information and, along with the environment, determines an organism's characteristics.*

PERFORMANCE GOALS

In Chapter 11, students are introduced to many basic genetics concepts. Lesson assessments provide real-life genetics problems for students to solve using their knowledge of chapter concepts. At the end of the chapter, students will complete assessment tasks that require creative writing and critical thinking skills to synthesize knowledge of meiosis, patterns of inheritance, and gene linkage.

CHAPTER 11

INDIANA ACADEMIC STANDARDS FOR SCIENCE

Nature of Science NoS.3, NoS.6; **Cellular Chemistry** B.1.3; **Molecular Basis of Heredity** B.5.2, B.5.5, B.5.6; **Cellular Reproduction and Gene Expression** B.6.4, B.6.5; **Genetics** B.7.1, B.7.2, B.7.3. See lessons for details.

CHAPTER MYSTERY

GREEN PARAKEETS

Susan's birthday was coming up. Parakeets make great pets, so Susan's parents decided to give two birds to her as a birthday present. At the pet store, they selected two healthy green parakeets—one male and one female. They knew that green was Susan's favorite color.

Susan was delighted about her birthday present. She fed the birds and kept their cage clean. A few weeks later, Susan found three small eggs in the birds' nest. She couldn't wait to welcome three new green parakeets. When the eggs finally hatched, however, Susan was amazed. None of the chicks was green—one chick was white, one was blue, and one was yellow. Why weren't any of them green? What had happened to the green color of the birds' parents? As you read this chapter, look for clues to help you identify why the parakeet chicks were differently colored than their parents. Then, solve the mystery.

Never Stop Exploring Your World. Finding the solution to the green parakeet mystery is only the beginning. Take a video field trip with the ecogeeks of Untamed Science to see where the mystery leads.

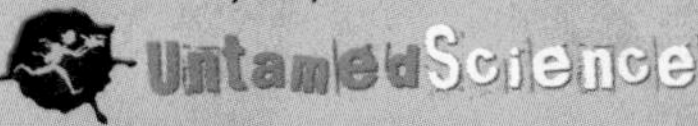

• Untamed Science Video • Chapter Mystery

What's Online

Extend your reach by using these and other digital assets offered at Biology.com.

CHAPTER MYSTERY
As students delve into the principles of heredity, they uncover clues that help them solve the seeming paradox of yellow, blue, and white offspring from green parents.

UNTAMED SCIENCE VIDEO
Take a trip back in time with the Untamed Science crew in **Genetics Takes Root** to see Mendel in action.

INTERACTIVE ART
Students can use this interactive activity to learn more about Punnett squares.

ART REVIEW
Students can use this drag-and-drop activity to review inheritance patterns using Punnett squares.

ART IN MOTION
This short animation shows students how genetic material is separated during meiosis.

TUTOR TUBE
To help students better understand the process of meiosis, the tutor makes connections between meiosis and Punnett squares.

DATA ANALYSIS
Students analyze the connection between crossing-over and gene location.

Chapter 11 Big Idea: Information and Heredity

Chapter 11 EQ: How does cellular information pass from one generation to another?

- **11.1 GQ:** How does an organism pass its characteristics on to its offspring?
- **11.2 GQ:** How can you predict the outcome of a genetic cross?
- **11.3 GQ:** How can interactions between alleles, genes, and the environment affect an organism's traits?
- **11.4 GQ:** How does a cell divide to create cells with exactly half of the original cell's genetic information?

LESSON 11.1

Getting Started

Objectives

11.1.1 Describe Mendel's studies and conclusions about inheritance.

11.1.2 Describe what happens during segregation.

Student Resources

Study Workbook A and B, 11.1 Worksheets

Spanish Study Workbook, 11.1 Worksheets

Lesson Overview • Lesson Notes • Assessment: Self-Test, Lesson Assessment

For corresponding lesson in the **Foundation Edition**, see pages 262–265.

Build Background

Show students a picture of a large family that includes at least two generations. Ask students to list some physical characteristics that the younger family members likely inherited from their parents or grandparents. Invite volunteers to share one or two items on their list. Then, encourage students to share their ideas about the inheritance of traits.

11.1 The Work of Gregor Mendel

B.5.6 Types of traits; B.7.1 Dominant and recessive alleles; B.7.2 Inheritance patterns; B.7.3 Traits. Also covered: B.5.2, B.5.5.

Key Questions

Where does an organism get its unique characteristics?

How are different forms of a gene distributed to offspring?

Vocabulary

genetics • fertilization • trait • hybrid • gene • allele • principle of dominance • segregation • gamete

Taking Notes

Two-Column Chart Before you read, draw a line down the center of a sheet of paper. On the left side, write the main ideas in this lesson. On the right side, note the details and examples that support each of those ideas.

THINK ABOUT IT What is an inheritance? To many people, it is money or property left to them by relatives who have passed away. That kind of inheritance matters, of course, but there is another kind that matters even more. It is something we each receive from our parents—a contribution that determines our blood type, the color of our hair, and so much more. Most people leave their money and property behind by writing a will. But what kind of inheritance makes a person's face round or their hair curly?

The Experiments of Gregor Mendel

Where does an organism get its unique characteristics?

Every living thing—plant or animal, microbe or human being—has a set of characteristics inherited from its parent or parents. Since the beginning of recorded history, people have wanted to understand how that inheritance is passed from generation to generation. The delivery of characteristics from parent to offspring is called heredity. The scientific study of heredity, known as **genetics,** is the key to understanding what makes each organism unique.

The modern science of genetics was founded by an Austrian monk named Gregor Mendel. Mendel, shown in **Figure 11–1,** was born in 1822 in what is now the Czech Republic. After becoming a priest, Mendel spent several years studying science and mathematics at the University of Vienna. He spent the next 14 years working in a monastery and teaching high school. In addition to his teaching duties, Mendel was in charge of the monastery garden. In this simple garden, he was to do the work that changed biology forever.

Mendel carried out his work with ordinary garden peas, partly because peas are small and easy to grow. A single pea plant can produce hundreds of offspring. Today we call peas a "model system." Scientists use model systems because they are convenient to study and may tell us how other organisms, including humans, actually function. By using peas, Mendel was able to carry out, in just one or two growing seasons, experiments that would have been impossible to do with humans and that would have taken decades—if not centuries—to do with pigs, horses, or other large animals.

FIGURE 11–1 Gregor Mendel

IN INDIANA ACADEMIC STANDARDS

For the full text of all standards, see the Course Overview in the front matter of this book.

B.7.1 Distinguish between dominant and recessive alleles and determine the phenotype that would result from the different possible combinations of alleles in an offspring.

B.7.2 Describe dominant, recessive, codominant, sex-linked, incompletely dominant, multiply allelic, and polygenic traits and illustrate their inheritance patterns over multiple generations.

B.7.3 Determine the likelihood of the appearance of a specific trait in an offspring given the genetic make-up of the parents.

UbD Teach for Understanding

ENDURING UNDERSTANDING DNA is the universal code for life; it enables an organism to transmit hereditary information and, along with the environment, determines an organism's characteristics.

GUIDING QUESTION How does an organism pass its characteristics on to its offspring?

EVIDENCE OF UNDERSTANDING *After completing the lesson, give students the following assessment to show they understand how Gregor Mendel contributed to our knowledge of how an organism passes its characteristics on to its offspring.* Have each student write a short story about Mendel's experiments using the first person point of view, as if Gregor Mendel was writing the story himself. Tell them that their stories should clearly explain Mendel's experiments and his conclusions.

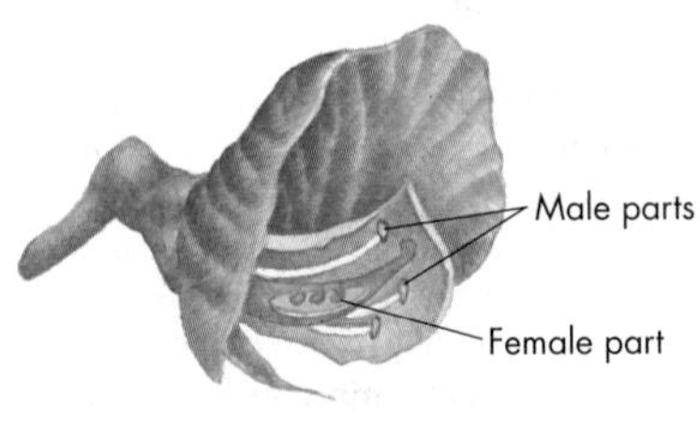

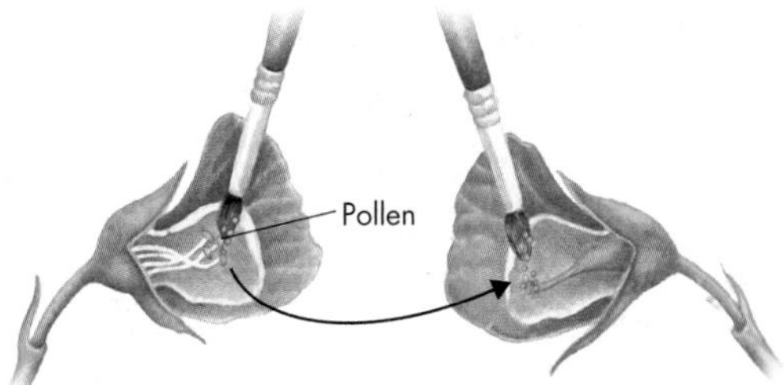

FIGURE 11–2 Cross-Pollination To cross-pollinate pea plants, Mendel cut off the male parts of one flower and then dusted the female part with pollen from another flower. **Apply Concepts** ***How did this procedure prevent self-pollination?***

The Role of Fertilization When Mendel began his experiments, he knew that the male part of each flower makes pollen, which contains the plant's male reproductive cells, called sperm. Similarly, Mendel knew that the female portion of each flower produces reproductive cells called eggs. During sexual reproduction, male and female reproductive cells join in a process known as **fertilization** to produce a new cell. In peas, this new cell develops into a tiny embryo encased within a seed.

Pea flowers are normally self-pollinating, which means that sperm cells fertilize egg cells from within the same flower. A plant grown from a seed produced by self-pollination inherits all of its characteristics from the single plant that bore it; it has a single parent.

Mendel's monastery garden had several stocks of pea plants. These plants were "true-breeding," meaning that they were self-pollinating, and would produce offspring identical to themselves. In other words, the traits of each successive generation would be the same. A **trait** is a specific characteristic, such as seed color or plant height, of an individual. Many traits vary from one individual to another. For instance, one stock of Mendel's seeds produced only tall plants, while another produced only short ones. One line produced only green seeds, another produced only yellow seeds.

To learn how these traits were determined, Mendel decided to "cross" his stocks of true-breeding plants—that is, he caused one plant to reproduce with another plant. To do this, he had to prevent self-pollination. He did so by cutting away the pollen-bearing male parts of a flower. He then dusted the pollen from a different plant onto the female part of that flower, as shown in **Figure 11–2.** This process, known as cross-pollination, produces a plant that has two different parents. Cross-pollination allowed Mendel to breed plants with traits different from those of their parents and then study the results.

Mendel studied seven different traits of pea plants. Each of these seven traits had two contrasting characteristics, such as green seed color or yellow seed color. Mendel crossed plants with each of the seven contrasting characteristics and then studied their offspring. The offspring of crosses between parents with different traits are called **hybrids.**

In Your Notebook *Explain, in your own words, what fertilization is.*

Teach

Build Science Skills

Explain that much of Mendel's success came from his choice of experimental organism. Pea plants are useful for genetic study because they have many contrasting characteristics, reproduce sexually, have easily controlled crosses, have short life cycles, produce a large number of offspring, and are also easy to grow.

Ask What other characteristics of pea plants made them useful for Mendel's studies? *(self-pollination and true-breeding)*

Emphasize that offspring from one plant continued to have the same traits because hereditary information came from only one parent.

Then, give students lilies, tulips, or other flowers with large stamens and pistils. Help them observe the intact flower with a hand lens and identify the male and female parts. Instruct them to cut off the stamens and pistils and examine these parts individually. Students may be able to observe pollen and egg cells with a compound microscope on low power. Then, have students draw a labeled diagram of their observations. Finally, have them write an explanation of how Mendel accomplished cross-pollination and how this procedure affected the information passed from parents to offspring.

DIFFERENTIATED INSTRUCTION

L1 Struggling Students Some students may have difficulty understanding how identical offspring can result during sexual reproduction. Explain that self-pollination can occur in the same flower or different flowers from the same plant. The offspring of self-pollinating, true-breeding plants get a combination of hereditary information from the egg cell and the sperm cell. But, because the hereditary information is the same in the egg and in the sperm, these combinations still result in the same traits.

How Science Works

METHODS OF MENDEL'S SUCCESS

Mendel was the first scientist of his time to obtain successful results from inheritance studies because of the methods he employed. He studied only one trait at a time. He also took the time to verify that the parent plants were true-breeding for the particular trait he was studying. He used a quantitative approach to analyze his results. He counted the number of offspring from every cross and used statistical analysis to interpret his numbers. Most important, Mendel formulated hypotheses to explain his results, and he developed experimental tests to support them. Many of his methods were so successful that they continue to be used today.

Answers

FIGURE 11–2 The flower with the female part intact no longer had its own source of pollen.

IN YOUR NOTEBOOK Explanations should include that male and female reproductive cells join to form a new cell.

Teach continued

Use Visuals

Use **Figure 11–3** to review the different forms of each trait in the peas Mendel studied. Explain that the traits in pea plants have two distinct forms. Direct students' attention to the trait of seed shape.

Ask What does it mean for the trait of roundness to be dominant in the F_1 generation? *(If a plant has one allele for round and one for wrinkled, the offspring will have a round seed shape.)*

DIFFERENTIATED INSTRUCTION

L1 Special Needs Check that students understand the symbols P and F_1 in **Figure 11–3.** Then, explain that the symbol × stands for "cross," and point out the example of a round-seeded plant crossed with a wrinkle-seeded plant. Draw the chart on the board in a new orientation with Trait, Parent 1, Parent 2, and Offspring as column heads. Start filling in the chart by writing × between Parent 1 and Parent 2 and → between Parent 2 and Offspring. Write "seed shape" under Trait, "round" under Parent 1, "wrinkled" under Parent 2, and "round" under Offspring. Have students complete the chart in this way for the rest of the traits from **Figure 11–3.**

ELL Focus on ELL: Access Content

ALL SPEAKERS Model how a recessive allele can be masked by a dominant allele. Start by tapping both of your pointer fingers on your desktop. Tell students that a tapping finger models the expression of a dominant allele. The recessive allele for this trait is modeled by a silent, still finger. Show two fingers tapping, for homozygous dominant, and then two still fingers, for homozygous recessive. Then, tap one finger while keeping the other still. Point out that you can still hear tapping, or the dominant allele, even though only one finger is moving. Suggest pairs of students come up with their own models of dominance. Then, have each pair share their model with the class.

MYSTERY CLUE Remind students that an allele is one form of a gene. Then, have them make predictions about the number of alleles there might be for feather color. Guide them to conclude that there is likely more than two alleles since there are four possible phenotypes. Students can go online to **Biology.com** to gather their evidence.

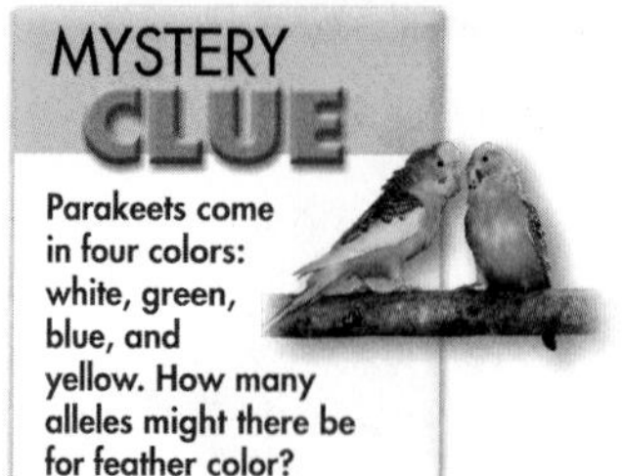

MYSTERY CLUE

Parakeets come in four colors: white, green, blue, and yellow. How many alleles might there be for feather color?

Genes and Alleles When doing genetic crosses, we call each original pair of plants the P, or parental, generation. Their offspring are called the F_1, or first filial, generation. (*Filius* and *filia* are the Latin words for "son" and "daughter.")

What were Mendel's F_1 hybrid plants like? To his surprise, for each trait studied, all the offspring had the characteristics of only one of its parents, as shown in **Figure 11–3.** In each cross, the nature of the other parent, with regard to each trait, seemed to have disappeared. From these results, Mendel drew two conclusions. His first conclusion formed the basis of our current understanding of inheritance. **An individual's characteristics are determined by factors that are passed from one parental generation to the next.** Today, scientists call the factors that are passed from parent to offspring **genes.**

Each of the traits Mendel studied was controlled by a single gene that occurred in two contrasting varieties. These variations produced different expressions, or forms, of each trait. For example, the gene for plant height occurred in one form that produced tall plants and in another form that produced short plants. The different forms of a gene are called **alleles** (uh LEELZ).

Dominant and Recessive Alleles Mendel's second conclusion is called the **principle of dominance.** This principle states that some alleles are dominant and others are recessive. An organism with at least one dominant allele for a particular form of a trait will exhibit that form of the trait. An organism with a recessive allele for a particular form of a trait will exhibit that form only when the dominant allele for the trait is not present. In Mendel's experiments, the allele for tall plants was dominant and the allele for short plants was recessive. Likewise, the allele for yellow seeds was dominant over the recessive allele for green seeds.

FIGURE 11–3 Mendel's F_1 Crosses When Mendel crossed plants with contrasting traits, the resulting hybrids had the traits of only one of the parents.

Mendel's Seven F_1 Crosses on Pea Plants

	Seed Shape	Seed Color	Seed Coat	Pod Shape	Pod Color	Flower Position	Plant Height
P	Round X Wrinkled	Yellow X Green	Gray X White	Smooth X Constricted	Green X Yellow	Axial X Terminal	Tall X Short
F_1	Round	Yellow	Gray	Smooth	Green	Axial	Tall

UbD Check for Understanding

QUESTION BOX

Establish a question box or email address where students may post questions about the concepts in this lesson they do not understand. Collect the questions at the end of each class session and review them. At the beginning of the next class session, discuss the questions and answers with the class.

ADJUST INSTRUCTION

If several students are having difficulty understanding a concept, set up small study groups that each include at least one student who understands the material and can communicate well with other members. Have groups meet for a few minutes at the beginning or end of class to go over difficult concepts.

Quick Lab
GUIDED INQUIRY

B.5.6, B.7.1, B.7.2, B.7.3

Classroom Variation

1. Copy the data table into your notebook.
2. Write a prediction of whether the traits listed in the table will be evenly distributed or if there will be more dominant than recessive traits.
3. Examine your features, using a mirror if necessary. Determine which traits you have for features A–E.
4. Interview at least 14 other students to find out which traits they have. Tally the numbers. Record the totals in each column.

Trait Survey				
Feature	Dominant Trait	Number	Recessive Trait	Number
A	Free ear lobes		Attached ear lobes	
B	Hair on fingers		No hair on fingers	
C	Widow's peak		No widow's peak	
D	Curly hair		Straight hair	
E	Cleft chin		Smooth chin	

Analyze and Conclude

1. **Calculate** Calculate the percentages of each trait in your total sample. How do these numbers compare to your prediction? MATH
2. **Form a Hypothesis** Why do you think recessive traits are more common in some cases?

In Your Notebook *Make a diagram that explains Mendel's principle of dominance.*

Segregation

How are different forms of a gene distributed to offspring?

Mendel didn't just stop after crossing the parent plants, because he had another question: Had the recessive alleles simply disappeared, or were they still present in the new plants? To find out, he allowed all seven kinds of F_1 hybrids to self-pollinate. The offspring of an F_1 cross are called the F_2 (second filial) generation. In effect, Mendel crossed the F_1 generation with itself to produce the F_2 offspring, as shown in **Figure 11–4.**

The F_1 Cross When Mendel compared the F_2 plants, he made a remarkable discovery: The traits controlled by the recessive alleles reappeared in the second generation. Roughly one fourth of the F_2 plants showed the trait controlled by the recessive allele. Why, then, did the recessive alleles seem to disappear in the F_1 generation, only to reappear in the F_2 generation?

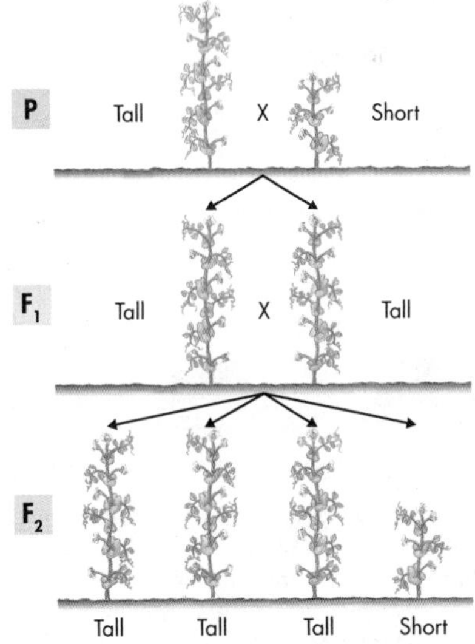

FIGURE 11–4 Results of the F_1 Cross When Mendel allowed the F_1 plants to reproduce by self-pollination, the traits controlled by recessive alleles reappeared in about one fourth of the F_2 plants in each cross. **Calculate** ***What proportion of the F_2 plants had a trait controlled by a dominant allele?*** MATH

Use Visuals

Walk students through the crosses shown in **Figure 11–4.** Make sure they understand that the short trait reappeared because the F_1 generation had both tall and short alleles.

Ask Why didn't the allele for shortness show in the F_1 generation? *(The short allele is recessive. It was masked by the dominant allele for tallness.)*

Ask Was the recessive allele for shortness lost in the F_1 generation? How do you know? *(No, it reappeared in the F_2 generation.)*

DIFFERENTIATED INSTRUCTION

LPR Less Proficient Readers Help struggling readers make connections between the text and **Figure 11–4.** Explain that the text on this page focuses primarily on the bottom two parts of the figure. Have student volunteers read the text on the page a couple of sentences at a time. After each volunteer finishes reading, discuss how the text he or she just read is shown by or relates to **Figure 11–4.**

L3 Advanced Students Challenge students to create a poster on which they identify Mendel's question and hypothesis and outline his experimental design.

Quick Lab

PURPOSE Students will make a prediction about whether dominant traits are more common than recessive traits and form a hypothesis about why recessive traits are more common in some cases.

MATERIALS mirror (optional)

SAFETY Caution students to handle glass mirrors with care.

PLANNING Bring mirrors to class, or invite students to bring mirrors from home. Tell students the traits shown by the class may vary from a larger population because of the small sample size.

ANALYZE AND CONCLUDE

1. Results and predictions will vary. Sample prediction: Dominant traits are more common than recessive traits. Results will likely indicate that a dominant trait is not necessarily more common than a recessive one.
2. Sample answer: Recessive alleles may be more common in the population.

Answers

FIGURE 11–4 Three-fourths of the F_2 plants had a trait controlled by a dominant allele.

IN YOUR NOTEBOOK Students' diagrams should have content similar to that in **Figure 11–3.**

Teach continued

Use Visuals

Make sure students understand the results of the F_2 generation in **Figure 11–5** by tracing the inheritance pattern. Point out how the F_1 gametes segregated to produce new combinations of alleles in the F_2 plants.

DIFFERENTIATED INSTRUCTION

ELL English Language Learners. Point out that, usually, the first letter of the dominant trait is used to represent a gene (*T* for Tall), though any letter could be used. Have students redraw **Figure 11–5** using the letter and word for tall in their native language.

Assess and Remediate

EVALUATE UNDERSTANDING

Assign students a trait in pea plants from **Figure 11–3.** Have them set up a cross to show the hybrid F1 and resulting F2 offspring. Then, have them complete the 11.1 Assessment.

REMEDIATION SUGGESTION

L1 Struggling Students If your students have trouble with **Question 2b,** choose a pea trait from **Figure 11–3** besides height. Draw the alleles and gametes for the P generation through the F_1 and F_2 generations. Walk through each step, using the terms *dominant, recessive, allele, gamete,* and *segregation.*

BIOLOGY.com Students can check their understanding of lesson concepts with the **Self-Test** assessment. They can then take an online version of the **Lesson Assessment.**

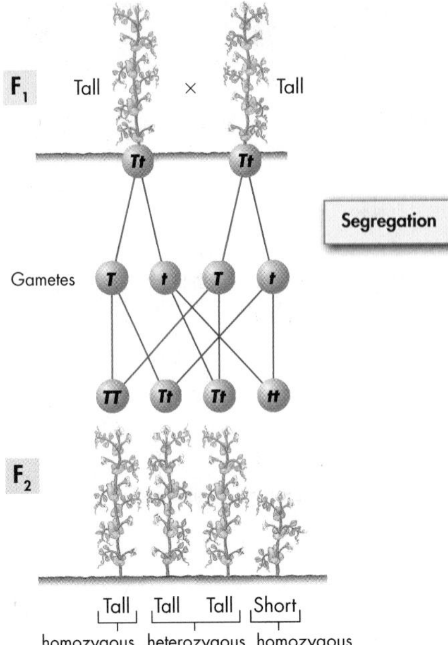

FIGURE 11–5 Segregation During gamete formation, alleles segregate from each other so that each gamete carries only a single copy of each gene. Each F_1 plant makes two types of gametes—those with the allele for tallness and those with the allele for shortness. The alleles are paired up again when gametes fuse during fertilization.

Explaining the F_1 Cross To begin with, Mendel assumed that a dominant allele had masked the corresponding recessive allele in the F_1 generation. However, the trait controlled by the recessive allele did show up in some of the F_2 plants. This reappearance indicated that, at some point, the allele for shortness had separated from the allele for tallness. How did this separation, or **segregation,** of alleles occur? Mendel suggested that the alleles for tallness and shortness in the F_1 plants must have segregated from each other during the formation of the sex cells, or **gametes** (GAM eetz). Did that suggestion make sense?

The Formation of Gametes Let's assume, as Mendel might have, that all the F_1 plants inherited an allele for tallness from the tall parent and one for shortness from the short parent. Because the allele for tallness is dominant, all the F_1 plants are tall. **During gamete formation, the alleles for each gene segregate from each other, so that each gamete carries only one allele for each gene.** Thus, each F_1 plant produces two kinds of gametes—those with the tall allele and those with the short allele.

Look at **Figure 11–5** to see how alleles separate during gamete formation and then pair up again in the F_2 generation. A capital letter represents a dominant allele. A lowercase letter represents a recessive allele. Now we can see why the recessive trait for height, *t*, reappeared in Mendel's F_2 generation. Each F_1 plant in Mendel's cross produced two kinds of gametes—those with the allele for tallness and those with the allele for shortness. Whenever a gamete that carried the *t* allele paired with the other gamete that carried the *t* allele to produce an F_2 plant, that plant was short. Every time one or both gametes of the pairing carried the *T* allele, a tall plant was produced. In other words, the F_2 generation had new combinations of alleles.

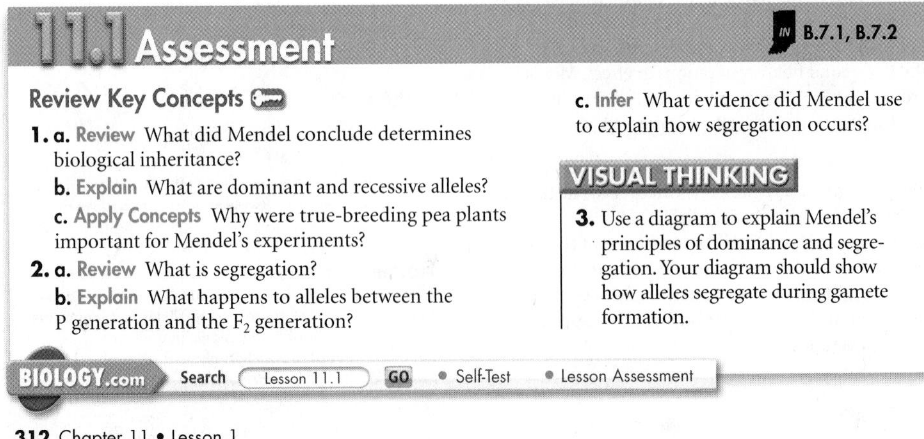

11.1 Assessment

IN B.7.1, B.7.2

Review Key Concepts

1. a. Review What did Mendel conclude determines biological inheritance?
b. Explain What are dominant and recessive alleles?
c. Apply Concepts Why were true-breeding pea plants important for Mendel's experiments?

2. a. Review What is segregation?
b. Explain What happens to alleles between the P generation and the F_2 generation?
c. Infer What evidence did Mendel use to explain how segregation occurs?

VISUAL THINKING

3. Use a diagram to explain Mendel's principles of dominance and segregation. Your diagram should show how alleles segregate during gamete formation.

BIOLOGY.com Search Lesson 11.1 GO • Self-Test • Lesson Assessment

Assessment Answers

1a. factors that are passed from one generation to the next

1b. dominant: form of an allele whose trait always shows up if it is present; recessive: form of an allele whose trait shows up only when the dominant allele is not present

1c. They have two identical alleles for a gene, so in a genetic cross, each parent contributes only one form of a gene, making inheritance patterns more detectable.

2a. separation of alleles

2b. The two alleles of the P generation separate during gamete formation. Each gamete carries only a single allele from each parent, which pairs at random in the F_1 generation. The process repeats when F_1 plants cross and produce F_2 plants. As a result, the F_2 generation has new combinations of alleles that may be different from those of preceding generations.

2c. A short plant appeared in the F_2 generation, indicating that this plant had only recessive alleles, so the alleles in the F_1 generation must have separated and then recombined when the plants were crossed.

VISUAL THINKING

3. Diagrams should be similar to **Figures 11–4** and **11–5** and clearly show single alleles, as well as which alleles are dominant and which are recessive.

11.2 Applying Mendel's Principles

 B.7.1 Dominant and recessive alleles; B.7.2 Inheritance patterns; B.7.3 Traits.

THINK ABOUT IT *Nothing in life is certain.* There's a great deal of wisdom in that old saying, and genetics is a fine example. If a parent carries two different alleles for a certain gene, we can't be sure which of those alleles will be inherited by any one of the parent's offspring. However, think carefully about the nature of inheritance and you'll see that even if we can't predict the exact future, we can do something almost as useful—we can figure out the odds.

Probability and Punnett Squares

How can we use probability to predict traits?

Whenever Mendel performed a cross with pea plants, he carefully categorized and counted the offspring. Consequently, he had plenty of data to analyze. For example, whenever he crossed two plants that were hybrids for stem height (*Tt*), about three fourths of the resulting plants were tall and about one fourth were short.

Upon analyzing his data, Mendel realized that the principles of probability could be used to explain the results of his genetic crosses. **Probability** is a concept you may have learned about in math class. It is the likelihood that a particular event will occur. As an example, consider an ordinary event, such as flipping a coin. There are two possible outcomes of this event: The coin may land either heads up or tails up. The chance, or probability, of either outcome is equal. Therefore, the probability that a single coin flip will land heads up is 1 chance in 2. This amounts to 1/2, or 50 percent.

If you flip a coin three times in a row, what is the probability that it will land heads up every time? Each coin flip is an independent event with a 1/2 probability of landing heads up. Therefore, the probability of flipping three heads in a row is:

$$1/2 \times 1/2 \times 1/2 = 1/8$$

As you can see, you have 1 chance in 8 of flipping heads three times in a row. The multiplication of individual probabilities illustrates an important point: Past outcomes do not affect future ones. Just because you've flipped three heads in a row does not mean that you're more likely to have a coin land tails up on the next flip. The probability for that flip is still 1/2.

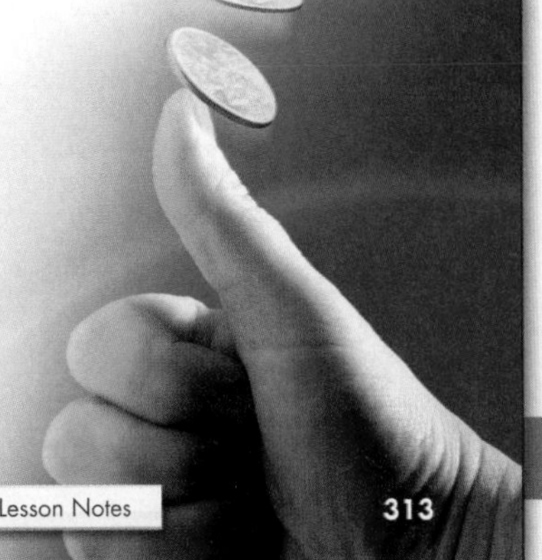

FIGURE 11–6 Probability Probability allows you to calculate the likelihood that a particular event will occur. The probability that the coin will land heads up is ½, or 50 percent.

Key Questions

How can we use probability to predict traits?

How do alleles segregate when more than one gene is involved?

What did Mendel contribute to our understanding of genetics?

Vocabulary

probability • homozygous • heterozygous • phenotype • genotype • Punnett square • independent assortment

Taking Notes

Preview Visuals Before you read, preview **Figure 11–7.** Try to infer the purpose of this diagram. As you read, compare your inference to the text. After you read, revise your statement if needed or write a new one about the diagram's purpose.

UbD Teach for Understanding

ENDURING UNDERSTANDING DNA is the universal code for life; it enables an organism to transmit hereditary information and, along with the environment, determines an organism's characteristics.

GUIDING QUESTION How can you predict the outcome of a genetic cross?

EVIDENCE OF UNDERSTANDING *After completing the lesson, give students the following assessment to show they understand how to predict the outcome of a genetic cross.* Have students create a "how-to" book based on lesson concepts. Their books should explain how to apply the principles of probability to predict outcomes of genetic crosses as well as how to construct and use Punnett squares.

Getting Started

Objectives

11.2.1 Explain how geneticists use the principles of probability to make Punnett squares.

11.2.2 Explain the principle of independent assortment.

11.2.3 Explain how Mendel's principles apply to all organisms.

Student Resources

Study Workbook A and B, 11.2 Worksheets

Spanish Study Workbook, 11.2 Worksheets

Lab Manual A, 11.2 Quick Lab Worksheet

Lab Manual B, 11.2 Hands-On Activity

BIOLOGY.com Lesson Overview • Lesson Notes • Activities: InterActive Art • Assessment: Self-Test, Lesson Assessment

For corresponding lesson in the **Foundation Edition**, see pages 266–270.

IN INDIANA ACADEMIC STANDARDS

For the full text of all standards, see the Course Overview in the front matter of this book.

B.7.1 Distinguish between dominant and recessive alleles and determine the phenotype that would result from the different possible combinations of alleles in an offspring.

B.7.2 Describe dominant, recessive, codominant, sex-linked, incompletely dominant, multiply allelic, and polygenic traits and illustrate their inheritance patterns over multiple generations.

B.7.3 Determine the likelihood of the appearance of a specific trait in an offspring given the genetic make-up of the parents.

LESSON 11.2

Teach

Connect to Math

To explain how probability principles work in genetic crosses, model the cross shown in **Figure 11–7.** Write *Tt* on the board, and draw a circle around it to represent the cell of one of the parents in the figure. Draw ten gamete circles under the parent cell. Then, draw an arrow from the parent cell to each gamete. To determine which allele (*T* or *t*) will go in each gamete circle, flip a coin. Tell students that heads represents the dominant allele (*T*) and tails represents the recessive allele (*t*). As you fill in each circle, flip the coin and repeat that the probability of a *T* or a *t* going to a gamete is one in two, or 1/2. Emphasize that each event is random and independent of the others and that probability predicts outcomes; it does not guarantee them. Then, do the same with another parent cell. Show two gametes joining, and explain that this event also is random and independent. Therefore, the probability of an F_2 cell having a particular combination of alleles is found by multiplying 1/2 × 1/2.

DIFFERENTIATED INSTRUCTION

LPR **Less Proficient Readers** If students have trouble understanding the subsection **Probabilities Predict Averages,** have each student toss a coin 20 times and record the outcomes. Then, combine the data from the entire class. As you add in each student's results, the overall data should get closer and closer to the expected ratio of one head to one tail.

ELL Focus on ELL: Extend Language

BEGINNING, INTERMEDIATE, AND ADVANCED SPEAKERS Have students construct a three-column chart to record lesson vocabulary terms and any other terms they may find difficult. Label column 1 Words I Understand, column 2 Words I Think I Understand, and column 3 Words I Have Never Seen. Ask students to write the definitions in their own words for columns 2 and 3. Allow beginning speakers to dictate their definitions as you record them. Intermediate and advanced speakers should write their own definitions. Use the information in the chart to focus ELL instruction.

Answers

FIGURE 11–7 All of the offspring would be tall (*TT* or *Tt*).

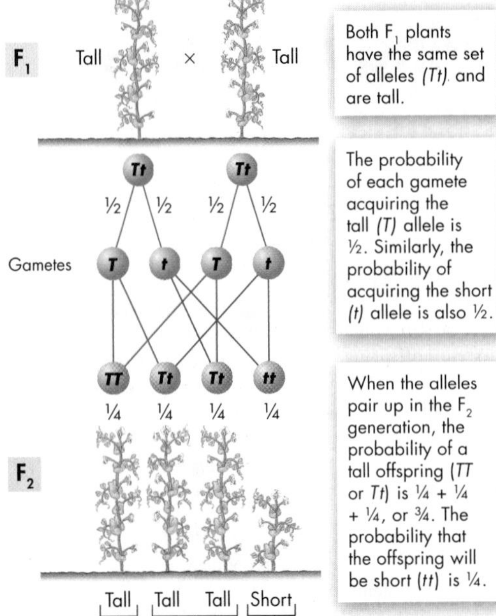

F_1
Tall
×
Tall
Both F_1 plants have the same set of alleles (*Tt*) and are tall.
Tt
Tt
½ ½ ½ ½
Gametes
T t T t
The probability of each gamete acquiring the tall (*T*) allele is ½. Similarly, the probability of acquiring the short (*t*) allele is also ½.
TT Tt Tt tt
¼ ¼ ¼ ¼
F_2
When the alleles pair up in the F_2 generation, the probability of a tall offspring (*TT* or *Tt*) is ¼ + ¼ + ¼, or ¾. The probability that the offspring will be short (*tt*) is ¼.
Tall Tall Tall Short
homozygous heterozygous homozygous

FIGURE 11–7 Segregation and Probability In this cross, the *TT* and *Tt* allele combinations produced three tall pea plants, while the *tt* allele combination produced one short plant. These quantities follow the laws of probability. **Predict** ***If you crossed a TT plant with a Tt plant, would the offspring be tall or short?***

Using Segregation to Predict Outcomes

The way in which alleles segregate during gamete formation is every bit as random as a coin flip. Therefore, the principles of probability can be used to predict the outcomes of genetic crosses.

Look again at Mendel's F_1 cross, shown in **Figure 11–7.** This cross produced a mixture of tall and short plants. Why were just 1/4 of the offspring short? Well, the F_1 plants were both tall. If each plant had one tall allele and one short allele (*Tt*), and if the alleles segregated as Mendel thought, then 1/2 of the gametes produced by the plants would carry the short allele (*t*). Yet, the *t* allele is recessive. The only way to produce a short (*tt*) plant is for two gametes, each carrying the *t* allele, to combine.

Like the coin toss, each F_2 gamete has a one in two, or 1/2, chance of carrying the *t* allele. There are two gametes, so the probability of both gametes carrying the *t* allele is 1/2 × 1/2 = 1/4. In other words, roughly one fourth of the F_2 offspring should be short, and the remaining three fourths should be tall. This predicted ratio—3 offspring exhibiting the dominant trait to 1 offspring exhibiting the recessive trait—showed up consistently in Mendel's experiments. For each of his seven crosses, about 3/4 of the plants showed the trait controlled by the dominant allele. About 1/4 showed the trait controlled by the recessive allele. Segregation did occur according to Mendel's model.

As you can see in the F_2 generation, not all organisms with the same characteristics have the same combinations of alleles. Both the *TT* and *Tt* allele combinations resulted in tall pea plants, but only one of these combinations contains identical alleles. Organisms that have two identical alleles for a particular gene—*TT* or *tt* in this example—are said to be **homozygous** (hoh moh ZY gus). Organisms that have two different alleles for the same gene—such as *Tt*—are **heterozygous** (het ur oh ZY gus).

Probabilities Predict Averages Probabilities predict the average outcome of a large number of events. If you flip a coin twice, you are likely to get one heads and one tails. However, you might also get two heads or two tails. To get the expected 50 : 50 ratio, you might have to flip the coin many times. The same is true of genetics.

The larger the number of offspring, the closer the results will be to the predicted values. If an F_2 generation contains just three or four offspring, it may not match Mendel's ratios. When an F_2 generation contains hundreds or thousands of individuals, the ratios usually come very close to matching predictions.

UbD Check for Understanding

HAND SIGNALS

Focus students' attention on **Figure 11–7,** and present them with the following statements. Ask them to show a thumbs-up sign if they understand, a thumbs-down sign if they are confused, or a waving-hand sign if they partially understand.

- A tall plant can be homozygous or heterozygous. A short plant must be homozygous.
- One-half of the F_2 generation is heterozygous and one-half is homozygous, but three-fourths are tall and one-fourth is short.

ADJUST INSTRUCTION

If students showed a thumbs-down or waving-hand sign, review the terms *homozygous* and *heterozygous*. Then, have small groups discuss why each statement is true.

Genotype and Phenotype One of Mendel's most revolutionary insights followed directly from his observations of F_1 crosses: Every organism has a genetic makeup as well as a set of observable characteristics. All of the tall pea plants had the same **phenotype,** or physical traits. They did not, however, have the same **genotype,** or genetic makeup. Look again at **Figure 11–7** and you will find three different genotypes among the F_2 plants: *TT, Tt,* and *tt.* The genotype of an organism is inherited, and the phenotype is largely determined by the genotype. Two organisms may share the same phenotype but have different genotypes.

Using Punnett Squares One of the best ways to predict the outcome of a genetic cross is by drawing a simple diagram known as a **Punnett square.**  **Punnett squares use mathematical probability to help predict the genotype and phenotype combinations in genetic crosses.** Constructing a Punnett square is fairly easy. You begin with a square. Then, following the principle of segregation, all possible combinations of alleles in the gametes produced by one parent are written along the top edge of the square. The other parent's alleles are then segregated along the left edge. Next, every possible genotype is written into the boxes within the square, just as they might appear in the F_2 generation. **Figure 11–8** on the next page shows step-by-step instructions for constructing Punnett squares.

In Your Notebook *In your own words, write definitions for the terms* homozygous, heterozygous, phenotype, *and* genotype.

BUILD Vocabulary

PREFIXES The prefix *pheno-* in **phenotype** comes from the Greek word *phainein,* meaning "to show." *Geno-,* the prefix in **genotype,** is derived from the Greek word *genus,* meaning "race, kind."

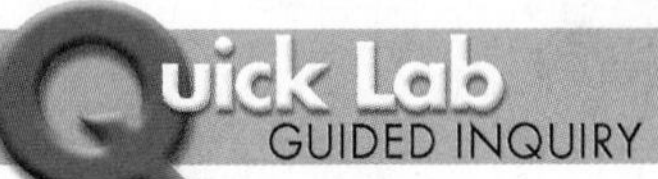

Quick Lab GUIDED INQUIRY

B.7.1, B.7.2, B.7.3

How Are Dimples Inherited?

1. Write the last four digits of any telephone number. These four random digits represent the alleles of a gene that determines whether a person will have dimples. Odd digits represent the allele for the dominant trait of dimples. Even digits represent the allele for the recessive trait of no dimples.
2. Use the first two digits to represent a father's genotype. Use the symbols *D* and *d* to write his genotype as shown in the example.
3. Use the last two digits the same way to find the mother's genotype. Write her genotype.
4. Use **Figure 11–8** on the next page to construct a Punnett square for the cross of these parents. Then, using the Punnett square, determine the probability that their child will have dimples.
5. Determine the class average of the percent of children with dimples.

Father's genotype is *dd* (2 even digits).

Mother's genotype is *Dd* (1 even digit and 1 odd digit).

46 38

Analyze and Conclude

1. **Apply Concepts** How does the class average compare with the result of a cross of two heterozygous parents?
2. **Draw Conclusions** What percentage of the children will be expected to have dimples if one parent is homozygous for dimples (*DD*) and the other is heterozygous (*Dd*)?

Lead a Discussion

Make sure students understand the difference between *phenotype* and *genotype.* Have students look at **Figure 11–7** and note that tall plants have one phenotype but two possible genotypes.

Ask What are the two possible genotypes of a tall plant? *(TT and Tt)*

Ask What is the phenotype of a plant that has two alleles for shortness? *(short)*

DIFFERENTIATED INSTRUCTION

LPR Less Proficient Readers Help students distinguish the terms *phenotype* and *genotype* by pointing out that *physical* and *phenotype* begin with *ph.* Explain that *genotype* shares the root *gen* with *gene.*

Address Misconceptions

Genotype and Phenotype Some students equate genotype and phenotype. Give them practice in distinguishing the two terms by making a **T-Chart** on the board. Label the left column Genotype and the right column Phenotype. List the possible allele combinations of a tall pea plant in the left column and the words *tall* or *short* in the right column beside the correct combinations. Explain the difference, and have students complete their own T-Charts with other traits of pea plants.

Study Wkbks A/B, Appendix S30, T-Chart. **Transparencies,** GO15.

Quick Lab

PURPOSE Students will be able to conclude how dimples are inherited.

MATERIALS calculator

PLANNING Students can use their own phone numbers. Tell them to count 0 as an even digit. Demonstrate the use of a 4-digit number to represent the genotypes of the parents in a genetic cross. Show students how to set up and use Punnett squares, if necessary.

Tell students that having dimples is a dominant trait.

ANALYZE AND CONCLUDE

1. Answers will vary, but class averages usually will be close to the results of a cross of two heterozygous parents, that is, 75 percent of the children having dimples.
2. 100 percent will have dimples, because the allele for dimples is dominant.

Answers

IN YOUR NOTEBOOK Sample answer: homozygous – an individual with two copies of the same allele of a gene; heterozygous – an individual with two different alleles for a gene; phenotype – the outward appearance of an individual; genotype – an individual's genetic makeup

Teach continued

VISUAL SUMMARY

Use **Figure 11–8** to help students learn how to construct, complete, and interpret a Punnett square. Walk them through the one-factor cross first. Have them identify the alleles each parent could pass on to offspring *(Bb* and *Bb).* Walk through each column and row to make sure they understand how the alleles combine. Point out that combinations are simply pairings of the male and female alleles from a particular row and column. In step 5, remind students that a Punnett square identifies possible gene combinations and that actual combinations could be different. Then, call on volunteers to explain each step in the two-factor cross. Give the class practice problems in making and completing both types of Punnett squares.

DIFFERENTIATED INSTRUCTION

L1 Struggling Students Students might need extra help figuring out the gametes in step 2 of the two-factor cross. Make sure they understand that each parent's genotype includes two genes and that gametes get only one allele for each gene. Thus, for *TtGg,* there are two choices for height: *T* or *t.* No matter which of these goes into a gamete, there are two choices for color: *G* or *g.* So the number of possible combinations is 4; 2 × 2 = 4. Tell students that one way to double-check their work in step 4 is to make sure the letter above each column appears in the cells below it. Similarly, the letter to the left of the rows must appear in each cell in that row.

ELL English Language Learners As you describe each step, use vocabulary terms as often as possible. For example, in step 4, point out that in the completed table on the right, *BB* is homozygous dominant, *bb* is homozygous recessive, and *Bb* is heterozygous. Phrase questions so that students answer using vocabulary terms.

BIOLOGY.com Students can learn more about Punnett squares in **InterActive Art: Punnett Squares.**

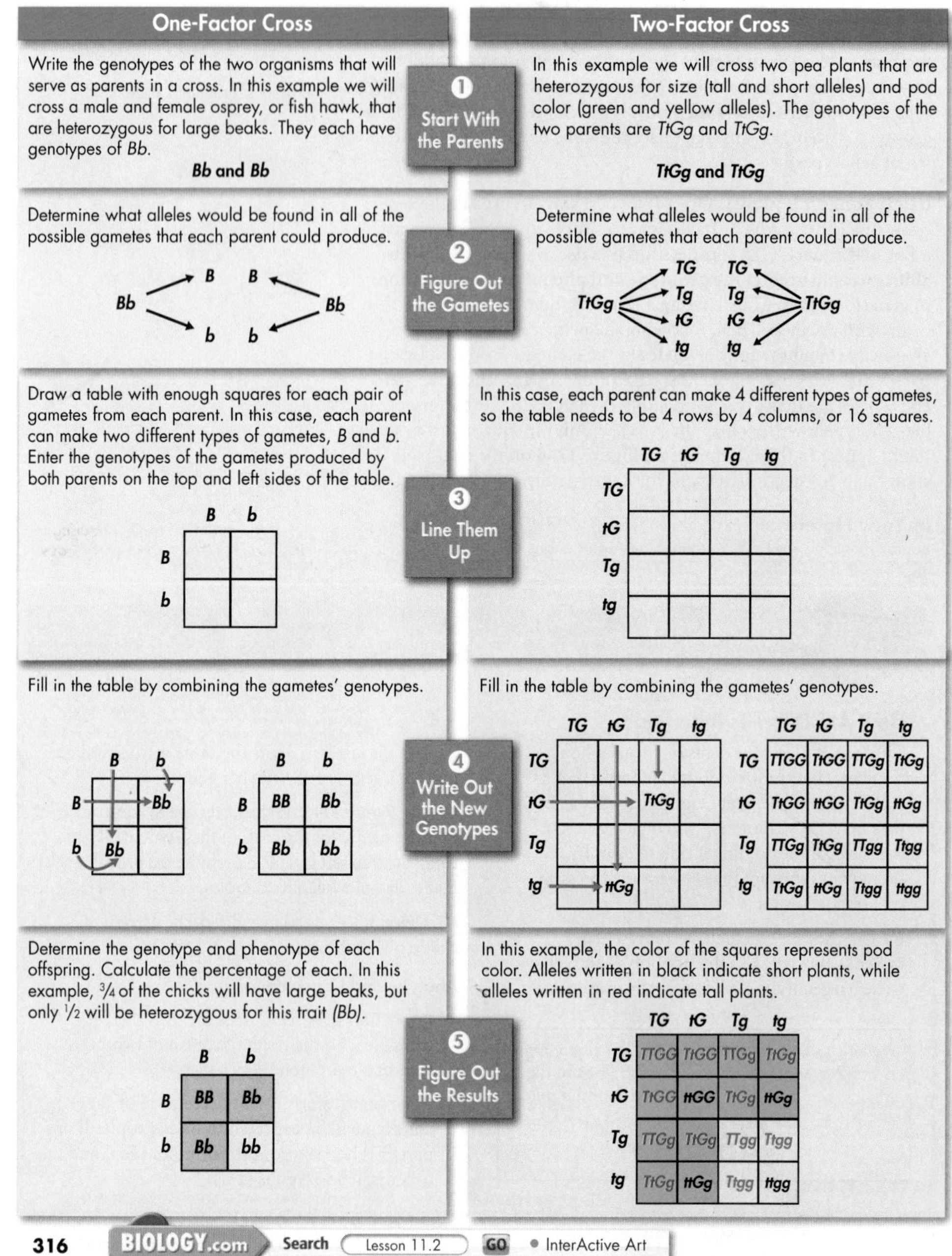

VISUAL SUMMARY

HOW TO MAKE A PUNNETT SQUARE

FIGURE 11–8 By drawing a Punnett square, you can determine the allele combinations that might result from a genetic cross.

One-Factor Cross | **Two-Factor Cross**

1 Start With the Parents

One-Factor Cross: Write the genotypes of the two organisms that will serve as parents in a cross. In this example we will cross a male and female osprey, or fish hawk, that are heterozygous for large beaks. They each have genotypes of *Bb*.

Bb* and *Bb

Two-Factor Cross: In this example we will cross two pea plants that are heterozygous for size (tall and short alleles) and pod color (green and yellow alleles). The genotypes of the two parents are *TtGg* and *TtGg*.

TtGg* and *TtGg

2 Figure Out the Gametes

One-Factor Cross: Determine what alleles would be found in all of the possible gametes that each parent could produce.

Bb → *B*, *b*; *Bb* → *B*, *b*

Two-Factor Cross: Determine what alleles would be found in all of the possible gametes that each parent could produce.

TtGg → *TG*, *Tg*, *tG*, *tg*; *TtGg* → *TG*, *Tg*, *tG*, *tg*

3 Line Them Up

One-Factor Cross: Draw a table with enough squares for each pair of gametes from each parent. In this case, each parent can make two different types of gametes, *B* and *b*. Enter the genotypes of the gametes produced by both parents on the top and left sides of the table.

	B	*b*
B		
b		

Two-Factor Cross: In this case, each parent can make 4 different types of gametes, so the table needs to be 4 rows by 4 columns, or 16 squares.

	TG	*tG*	*Tg*	*tg*
TG				
tG				
Tg				
tg				

4 Write Out the New Genotypes

One-Factor Cross: Fill in the table by combining the gametes' genotypes.

	B	*b*
B		*Bb*
b	*Bb*	

	B	*b*
B	*BB*	*Bb*
b	*Bb*	*bb*

Two-Factor Cross: Fill in the table by combining the gametes' genotypes.

	TG	*tG*	*Tg*	*tg*
TG				
tG			*TtGg*	
Tg				
tg		*ttGg*		

	TG	*tG*	*Tg*	*tg*
TG	*TTGG*	*TtGG*	*TTGg*	*TtGg*
tG	*TtGG*	*ttGG*	*TtGg*	*ttGg*
Tg	*TTGg*	*TtGg*	*TTgg*	*Ttgg*
tg	*TtGg*	*ttGg*	*Ttgg*	*ttgg*

5 Figure Out the Results

One-Factor Cross: Determine the genotype and phenotype of each offspring. Calculate the percentage of each. In this example, ¾ of the chicks will have large beaks, but only ½ will be heterozygous for this trait *(Bb)*.

	B	*b*
B	*BB*	*Bb*
b	*Bb*	*bb*

Two-Factor Cross: In this example, the color of the squares represents pod color. Alleles written in black indicate short plants, while alleles written in red indicate tall plants.

	TG	*tG*	*Tg*	*tg*
TG	*TTGG*	*TtGG*	*TTGg*	*TtGg*
tG	*TtGG*	*ttGG*	*TtGg*	*ttGg*
Tg	*TTGg*	*TtGg*	*TTgg*	*Ttgg*
tg	*TtGg*	*ttGg*	*Ttgg*	*ttgg*

316 BIOLOGY.com Search Lesson 11.2 GO • InterActive Art

How Science Works

INVENTOR OF THE PUNNETT SQUARE

Reginald Punnett (1875–1967) was an English geneticist at Cambridge University who, along with William Bateson, was one of the first scientists to use Mendelian experimentation on plants and animals. Punnett devised the Punnett square to graphically represent the results of hybrid crosses. He also wrote a textbook on the subject of genetics and, together with Bateson, co-founded the *Journal of Genetics,* which is still in print today.

Independent Assortment

How do alleles segregate when more than one gene is involved?

After showing that alleles segregate during the formation of gametes, Mendel wondered if the segregation of one pair of alleles affects another pair. For example, does the gene that determines the shape of a seed affect the gene for seed color? To find out, Mendel followed two different genes as they passed from one generation to the next. Because it involves two different genes, Mendel's experiment is known as a two-factor, or "dihybrid," cross. (Single-gene crosses are "monohybrid" crosses.)

The Two-Factor Cross: F_1 First, Mendel crossed true-breeding plants that produced only round yellow peas with plants that produced wrinkled green peas. The round yellow peas had the genotype *RRYY*, and the wrinkled green peas had the genotype *rryy*. All of the F_1 offspring produced round yellow peas. These results showed that the alleles for yellow and round peas are dominant. As the Punnett square in **Figure 11–9** shows, the genotype in each of these F_1 plants is *RrYy*. In other words, the F_1 plants were all heterozygous for both seed shape and seed color. This cross did not indicate whether genes assort, or segregate independently. However, it provided the hybrid plants needed to breed the F_2 generation.

The Two-Factor Cross: F_2 In the second part of this experiment, Mendel crossed the F_1 plants to produce F_2 offspring. Remember, each F_1 plant was formed by the fusion of a gamete carrying the dominant *RY* alleles with another gamete carrying the recessive *ry* alleles. Did this mean that the two dominant alleles would always stay together, or would they segregate independently, so that any combination of alleles was possible?

In Mendel's experiment, the F_2 plants produced 556 seeds. Mendel compared their variation. He observed that 315 of the seeds were round and yellow, while another 32 seeds were wrinkled and green—the two parental phenotypes. However, 209 seeds had combinations of phenotypes, and therefore combinations of alleles, that were not found in either parent. This clearly meant that the alleles for seed shape segregated independently of those for seed color. Put another way, genes that segregate independently (such as the genes for seed shape and seed color in pea plants) do not influence each other's inheritance.

Mendel's experimental results were very close to the 9 : 3 : 3 : 1 ratio that the Punnett square shown in **Figure 11–10** predicts. Mendel had discovered the principle of **independent assortment.** **The principle of independent assortment states that genes for different traits can segregate independently during the formation of gametes.** Independent assortment helps account for the many genetic variations observed in plants, animals, and other organisms—even when they have the same parents.

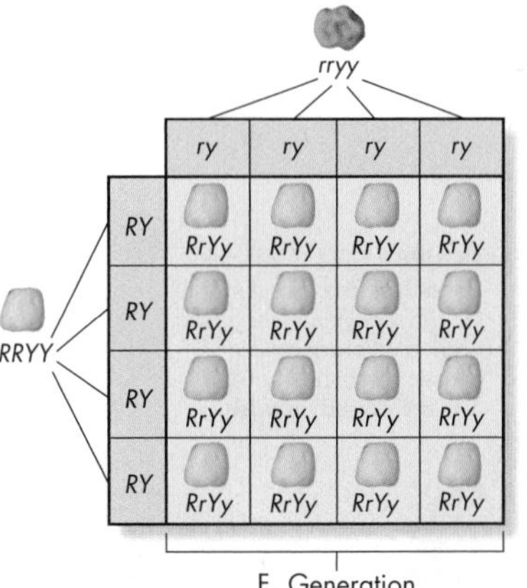

FIGURE 11–9 Two-Factor Cross: F_1 Mendel crossed plants that were homozygous dominant for round yellow peas with plants that were homozygous recessive for wrinkled green peas. All of the F_1 offspring were heterozygous dominant for round yellow peas. **Interpret Graphics** ***How is the genotype of the offspring different from that of the homozygous dominant parent?***

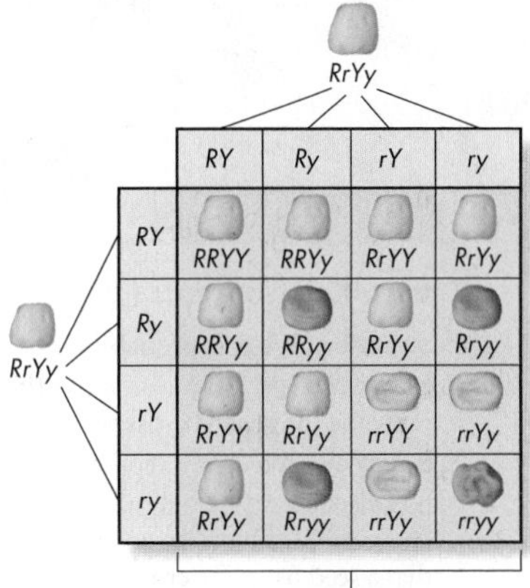

FIGURE 11–10 Two-Factor Cross: F_2 When Mendel crossed F_1 plants that were heterozygous dominant for round yellow peas, he found that the alleles segregated independently to produce the F_2 generation.

Use Visuals

Tell students the two-factor cross they learned about in **Figure 11–8** is called a "dihybrid cross" because it involves two different traits. Refer them to **Figure 11–9,** and discuss the results of the F_1 cross.

Ask Why didn't Mendel know, from the results of the first cross, whether two genes segregated independently? *(All the offspring had dominant alleles.)*

Ask What evidence did Mendel have that alleles segregated independently in the cross shown in **Figure 11–10?** *(All combinations of phenotypes resulted.)*

Ask What phenotypes would Mendel have observed if the alleles did not segregate independently—in other words, if the *RY* always stayed together and the *ry* always stayed together? *(round, yellow seeds and wrinkled, green seeds)*

DIFFERENTIATED INSTRUCTION

L1 Special Needs Help students who are overwhelmed by the symbols in the figures to write out the crosses using words. Use *ROUND* and *YELLOW* for the dominant alleles and *wrinkled* and *green* for the recessive ones. Tell students when a capitalized (dominant) word appears with a lowercase (recessive) word, the capitalized word is the trait that shows. Explain that with the symbols, the same letter is used for one gene, such as *Rr,* instead of *Rw,* because two alleles code for the same gene.

Quick Facts

CALCULATING PROBABILITIES WITHOUT PUNNETT SQUARES

You can obtain the outcomes of dihybrid or trihybrid crosses without setting up a Punnett square by multiplying probabilities. The ratio of dominant to recessive phenotypes in a monohybrid cross is 3:1. Using the example of seed color and shape, the chance of showing the dominant phenotype, having *YY* (or *RR*) or *Yy* (or *Ry*), in a monohybrid cross is 3/4. The chance of showing the recessive phenotype, having *yy* (or *rr*) is 1/4. You can find the chance of yellow, round peas by multiplying those two probabilities (3/4 × 3/4 = 9/16). If a third trait is added, for example, pod color, the same rules apply. Green pod color is dominant over yellow, so the chance of *GG* or *Gg* is 3/4 and the chance of *gg* is 1/4. For example, the probability of offspring with green, wrinkled peas and green pods is 3/64 (1/4 × 1/4 × 3/4).

Answers

FIGURE 11–9 The offspring are heterozygous for each trait (*RrYy*).

Assess and Remediate

EVALUATE UNDERSTANDING

Assign students different pea traits from **Figure 11–3.** Instruct them to set up a Punnett square to show a cross between two pea plants that are heterozygous for the trait. They should give both the genotypic and phenotypic ratio of the offspring. Then, have them complete the 11.2 Assessment.

REMEDIATION SUGGESTION

L1 **Struggling Students** If your students have trouble with **Question 4,** show them how to calculate that 29% (31/106) of the plants have white flowers. Explain that this is close to the 25% you would expect from a heterozygous cross, similar to the 3:1 ratio in the tall to short plants in the F_2 generation in **Figure 11–7.**

BIOLOGY.com Students can check their understanding of lesson concepts with the **Self-Test** assessment. They can then take an online version of the **Lesson Assessment.**

FIGURE 11–11 A Model Organism The common fruit fly, *Drosophila melanogaster,* is an ideal organism for genetic research. These fruit flies are poised on a lemon.

A Summary of Mendel's Principles

What did Mendel contribute to our understanding of genetics?

As you have seen, Mendel's principles of segregation and independent assortment can be observed through one- and two-factor crosses. **Mendel's principles of heredity, observed through patterns of inheritance, form the basis of modern genetics.** These principles are as follows:

- The inheritance of biological characteristics is determined by individual units called genes, which are passed from parents to offspring.
- Where two or more forms (alleles) of the gene for a single trait exist, some alleles may be dominant and others may be recessive.
- In most sexually reproducing organisms, each adult has two copies of each gene—one from each parent. These genes segregate from each other when gametes are formed.
- Alleles for different genes usually segregate independently of each other.

Mendel's principles don't apply only to plants. At the beginning of the 1900s, the American geneticist Thomas Hunt Morgan wanted to use a model organism of another kind to advance the study of genetics. He decided to work on a tiny insect that kept showing up, uninvited, in his laboratory. The insect was the common fruit fly, *Drosophila melanogaster,* shown in **Figure 11–11.** *Drosophila* can produce plenty of offspring—a single pair can produce hundreds of young. Before long, Morgan and other biologists had tested all of Mendel's principles and learned that they applied to flies and other organisms as well. In fact, Mendel's basic principles can be used to study the inheritance of human traits and to calculate the probability of certain traits appearing in the next generation. You will learn more about human genetics in Chapter 14.

11.2 Assessment

IN B.7.1, B.7.2, B.7.3

Review Key Concepts

1. a. Review What is probability?
   b. Use Models How are Punnett squares used to predict the outcomes of genetic crosses?
2. a. Review What is independent assortment?
   b. Calculate An F_1 plant that is homozygous for shortness is crossed with a heterozygous F_1 plant. What is the probability that a seed from the cross will produce a tall plant? Use a Punnett square to explain your answer and to compare the probable genetic variations in the F_2 plants. MATH
3. a. Review How did Gregor Mendel contribute to our understanding of inherited traits?
   b. Apply Concepts Why is the fruit fly an ideal organism for genetic research?

Apply the Big idea

Information and Heredity

4. Suppose you are an avid gardener. One day, you come across a plant with beautiful lavender flowers. Knowing that the plant is self-pollinating, you harvest its seeds and plant them. Of the 106 plants that grow from these seeds, 31 have white flowers. Using a Punnett square, draw conclusions about the nature of the allele for lavender flowers.

BIOLOGY.com Search (Lesson 11.2)  • Self-Test • Lesson Assessment

Assessment Answers

1a. the likelihood that a particular event will occur

1b. Punnett squares are used to show all of the combinations of alleles that might result from a cross and the likelihood that each might occur.

2a. During gamete formation, pairs of alleles for a gene segregate, or separate, independently of each other.

2b. 50 percent; the Punnett square should show a cross between a homozygous short plant (*tt*) and a heterozygous tall plant (*Tt*).

3a. The patterns of inheritance he observed form the basis of modern genetics.

3b. Fruit flies are small, easy to keep in the laboratory, and produce large numbers of offspring in a short period of time.

4. Big idea Of the 106 plants, 31 had white flowers; this is 29%, or approximately one-fourth, of the plants. To get an approximate 3:1 ratio of lavender to white flowers, the parent plant was heterozygous with the allele for lavender flowers being dominant. The Punnett square should show the self-pollination of a plant that is heterozygous for lavender flowers (*Ll*).

11.3 Other Patterns of Inheritance

B.5.6 Types of traits; B.7.2 Inheritance patterns. Also covered: NoS.3, B.1.3, B.7.3.

THINK ABOUT IT Mendel's principles offer a tidy set of rules with which to predict various patterns of inheritance. Unfortunately, biology is not a tidy science. There are exceptions to every rule, and exceptions to the exceptions. What happens if one allele is not completely dominant over another? What if a gene has several alleles?

Beyond Dominant and Recessive Alleles

What are some exceptions to Mendel's principles?

Despite the importance of Mendel's work, there are important exceptions to most of his principles. For example, not all genes show simple patterns of inheritance. In most organisms, genetics is more complicated, because the majority of genes have more than two alleles. Also, many important traits are controlled by more than one gene. Understanding these exceptions allows geneticists to predict the ways in which more complex traits are inherited.

Incomplete Dominance A cross between two four o'clock (*Mirabilis jalapa*) plants shows a common exception to Mendel's principles. **Some alleles are neither dominant nor recessive.** As shown in **Figure 11–12,** the F_1 generation produced by a cross between red-flowered (*RR*) and white-flowered (*WW*) *Mirabilis* plants consists of pink-colored flowers (*RW*). Which allele is dominant in this case? Neither one. Cases in which one allele is not completely dominant over another are called **incomplete dominance.** In incomplete dominance, the heterozygous phenotype lies somewhere between the two homozygous phenotypes.

Codominance A similar situation arises from **codominance,** in which the phenotypes produced by both alleles are clearly expressed. For example, in certain varieties of chicken, the allele for black feathers is codominant with the allele for white feathers. Heterozygous chickens have a color described as "erminette," speckled with black and white feathers. Unlike the blending of red and white colors in heterozygous four o'clocks, black and white colors appear separately in chickens. Many human genes, including one for a protein that controls cholesterol levels in the blood, show codominance, too. People with the heterozygous form of this gene produce two different forms of the protein, each with a different effect on cholesterol levels.

Key Questions

What are some exceptions to Mendel's principles?

Does the environment have a role in how genes determine traits?

Vocabulary

incomplete dominance • codominance • multiple allele • polygenic trait

Taking Notes

Outline Make an outline using the green and blue headings. As you read, write bulleted notes below each heading to summarize its topic.

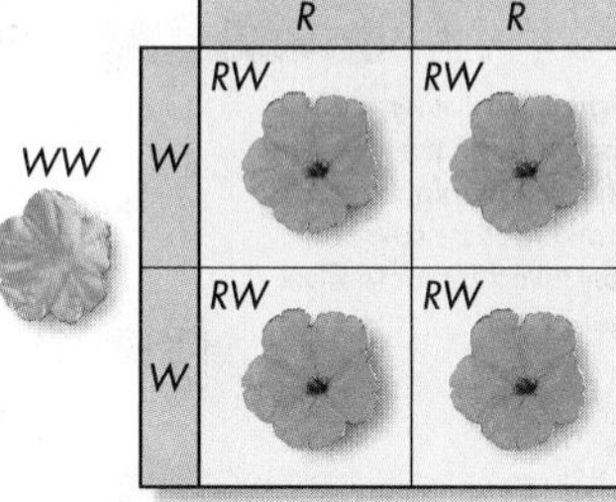

FIGURE 11–12 Incomplete Dominance In four o'clock plants, the alleles for red and white flowers show incomplete dominance. Heterozygous (*RW*) plants have pink flowers—a mix of red and white coloring.

BIOLOGY.com Search Lesson 11.3 GO • Lesson Overview • Lesson Notes • Art Review

319

UbD Teach for Understanding

ENDURING UNDERSTANDING DNA is the universal code for life; it enables an organism to transmit hereditary information and, along with the environment, determines an organism's characteristics.

GUIDING QUESTION How can interactions between alleles, genes, and the environment affect an organism's traits?

EVIDENCE OF UNDERSTANDING *After completing the lesson, give students the following assessment to show they understand different patterns of heredity.* Have students write a short poem or rap using the following lesson vocabulary terms: *incomplete dominance, codominance, multiple alleles,* and *polygenic traits.* Tell students their lyrics should show they understand what each term means. Have volunteers share their work with the class.

LESSON 11.3

Getting Started

Objectives

11.3.1 Describe the other inheritance patterns.

11.3.2 Explain the relationship between genes and the environment.

Student Resources

Study Workbook A and B, 11.3 Worksheets

Spanish Study Workbook, 11.3 Worksheets

Lab Manual B, 11.3 Data Analysis Worksheet

Lesson Overview • Lesson Notes • Activities: Art Review • Assessment: Self-Test, Lesson Assessment

For corresponding lesson in the **Foundation Edition**, see pages 271–274.

Activate Prior Knowledge

Tell students to think about all the different shades of hair color that humans have. Then, ask if they think that hair color is controlled by just one gene. Lead students to conclude that there is likely more than one gene responsible for the color of human hair.

BIOLOGY.com Students can drag and drop labels to correctly finish diagrams of three Punnett squares in the activity **Art Review: Exceptions to Mendel's Principles.**

IN INDIANA ACADEMIC STANDARDS

For the full text of all standards, see the Course Overview in the front matter of this book.

B.5.6 Recognize that traits can be structural, physiological or behavioral and can include readily observable characteristics at the organismal level or less recognizable features at the molecular and cellular level.

B.7.2 Describe dominant, recessive, codominant, sex-linked, incompletely dominant, multiply allelic, and polygenic traits and illustrate their inheritance patterns over multiple generations.

Teach continued

Lead a Discussion

Explain that there being more than two alleles for a gene is common in a population. Make sure students understand, though, that any given individual in this population will have only two of those alleles. To illustrate this point, write the symbols for four alleles for rabbit coat color on the board in order from the most dominant to the least dominant: *C* = full color, C^{ch} = chinchilla color, C^{h} = Himalayan color, *c* = albino (no color). Have students make up genetic crosses for coat color in rabbits. If desired, have them exchange their proposed crosses with a partner who can then use Punnett squares to solve the problems.

DIFFERENTIATED INSTRUCTION

LPR Less Proficient Readers Help struggling students better understand lesson concepts by completing a **Jigsaw Review** activity. Form small learning circles of four students each. Assign each group member a number from 1 to 4. Have students regroup into study groups according to number (for example, all 1s together). Assign each group one of the four sections of text with blue heads under **Beyond Dominant and Recessive Alleles.** Have groups review the topic and create a brief lesson on it. Then, instruct students to re-form their original learning circles, and have each member of a circle teach the other members about his or her topic. If you have more students, add **Genes and the Environment** as a topic.

Study Wkbks A/B, Appendix S7, Jigsaw Review.

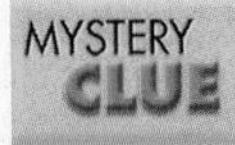

Have students discuss whether they think feather color is polygenic. Lead them to conclude that there are likely two genes controlling feather color, one for each pigment. Students can go online to **Biology.com** to gather their evidence.

Address Misconceptions

Polygenic Traits Many students think that one gene is always responsible for one trait. Explain that such a case is actually rare. Most traits—such as hair and eye color in humans—are influenced by multiple genes.

Answers

IN YOUR NOTEBOOK Students' descriptions should reflect that multiple alleles are more than two forms of the same gene in a population and polygenic traits have more than one gene contributing to the phenotype of an individual.

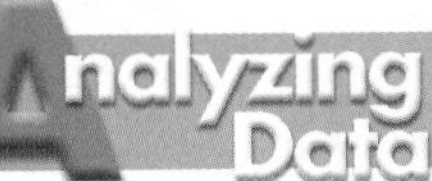

IN NoS.3, B.7.3

Human Blood Types

Red blood cells carry antigens, molecules that can trigger an immune reaction, on their surfaces. Human blood type A carries an A antigen, type B has a B antigen, type AB has both antigens, and type O carries neither antigen. The gene for these antigens has three alleles; A, B, and O.

For a transfusion to succeed, it must not introduce a new antigen into the body of the recipient. So, a person with type A blood may receive type O, but not vice versa.

Another gene controls a second type of antigen, known as Rh factor. Rh^+ individuals carry this antigen, while Rh^- ones don't. This chart of the U.S. population shows the percentage of each blood type.

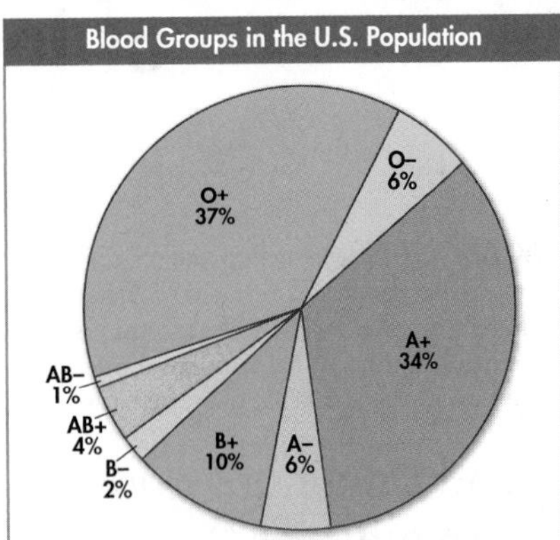

1. **Interpret Graphs** Which blood type makes up the greatest percentage of the U.S. population?
2. **Calculate** What percentage of the total U.S. population has a positive Rh factor? What percentage has a negative Rh factor?
3. **Infer** Which blood type can be used for transfusion into the largest percentage of individuals? Which type has the smallest percentage of possible donors available?
4. **Predict** Could a person with O^+ blood have two parents with O^- blood? Could that person have a daughter with AB^+ blood? Explain your answers.

MYSTERY CLUE

Green feathers don't actually contain green pigments. Rather, they contain a mixture of blue and yellow pigments. Could feather color be controlled by more than one gene?

Multiple Alleles So far, our examples have described genes for which there are only two alleles, such as *a* and *A*. In nature, such genes are the exception rather than the rule. **Many genes exist in several different forms and are therefore said to have multiple alleles.** A gene with more than two alleles is said to have **multiple alleles.** An individual, of course, usually has only two copies of each gene, but many different alleles are often found within a population. One of the best-known examples is coat color in rabbits. A rabbit's coat color is determined by a single gene that has at least four different alleles. The four known alleles display a pattern of simple dominance that can produce four coat colors. Many other genes have multiple alleles, including the human genes for blood type.

Polygenic Traits **Many traits are produced by the interaction of several genes.** Traits controlled by two or more genes are said to be **polygenic traits.** *Polygenic* means "many genes." For example, at least three genes are involved in making the reddish-brown pigment in the eyes of fruit flies. Polygenic traits often show a wide range of phenotypes. The variety of skin color in humans comes about partly because more than four different genes probably control this trait.

In Your Notebook *In your own words, describe multiple alleles and polygenic traits. How are they similar? How are they different?*

PURPOSE Students will analyze data to make an inference and a prediction about alleles for human blood types.

PLANNING Tell students that the A and B alleles are codominant. A and B are each dominant over O. Explain that the Rh factor is inherited independently of the blood type alleles. Rh^+ is dominant over Rh^-.

ANSWERS

1. O^+
2. 85% are Rh^+; 15% are Rh^-.
3. O^- can be used for 100% of individuals; AB^+ can be used for only 4%.
4. No, because both parents would be homozygous recessive for the Rh factor. They do not have any Rh^+ alleles to pass on. This person could not have an AB^+ daughter, because a person with O^+ blood has only O alleles to pass on.

Genes and the Environment

Does the environment have a role in how genes determine traits?

The characteristics of any organism—whether plant, fruit fly, or human being—are not determined solely by the genes that organism inherits. Genes provide a plan for development, but how that plan unfolds also depends on the environment. In other words, the phenotype of an organism is only partly determined by its genotype.

Consider the western white butterfly, *Pontia occidentalis*, shown in **Figure 11–13.** It is found throughout western North America. Butterfly enthusiasts had noted for years that western whites hatching in the summer (right) had different color patterns on their wings than those hatching in the spring (left). Scientific studies showed the reason—butterflies hatching in the shorter days of springtime had greater levels of pigment in their wings, making their markings appear darker than those hatching in the longer days of summer. In other words, the environment in which the butterflies develop influences the expression of their genes for wing coloration.  **Environmental conditions can affect gene expression and influence genetically determined traits.** An individual's actual phenotype is determined by its environment as well as its genes.

In the case of the western white butterfly, these changes in wing pigmentation are particularly important. In order to fly effectively, the body temperature of the butterfly must be 28°C–40°C (about 84°F–104°F). Since the spring months are cooler in the west, greater pigmentation helps them reach the body temperature needed for flight. Similarly, in the hot summer months, less pigmentation enables the moths to avoid overheating.

Environmental Temperature and Butterfly Needs

Temp. Needed for Flight	Average Spring Temp.	Average Summer Temp.
28–40°C	26.5°C	34.8°C

FIGURE 11–13 Temperature and Wing Color Western white butterflies that hatch in the spring have darker wing patterns than those that hatch in summer. The dark wing color helps increase their body heat. This trait is important because the butterflies need to reach a certain temperature in order to fly. **Calculate** ***What is the difference between the minimum temperature these butterflies need to fly and the average spring temperature? Would the same calculation apply to butterflies developing in the summer?*** MATH

11.3 Assessment

IN B.1.3, B.7.2, B.7.3

Review Key Concepts

1. **a. Review** What does *incomplete dominance* mean? Give an example.
   b. Design an Experiment Design an experiment to determine whether the pink flowers of petunia plants result from incomplete dominance.
2. **a. Review** What is the relationship between the environment and phenotype?
   b. Infer What might be the result of an exceptionally hot spring on wing pigmentation in the western white butterfly?

PRACTICE PROBLEM

3. Construct a genetics problem to be given as an assignment to a classmate. The problem must test incomplete dominance, codominance, multiple alleles, or polygenic traits. Your problem must have an answer key that includes all of your work.

BIOLOGY.com Search Lesson 11.3 GO • Self-Test • Lesson Assessment

Lead a Discussion

Point out that "environment" refers to internal factors, too. For example, both men and women can have the genes for male pattern baldness, but baldness shows up more often in men because male hormones trigger the expression of the gene.

DIFFERENTIATED INSTRUCTION

L3 Advanced Students Challenge students to design an experiment that shows how environment affects phenotype, using cuttings from a coleus plant.

Assess and Remediate

EVALUATE UNDERSTANDING

Ask volunteers to explain the four patterns of inheritance described in this lesson, as well as how environmental factors can influence phenotypes. Then, have students complete the 11.3 Assessment.

REMEDIATION SUGGESTION

L1 Struggling Students If your students have trouble with **Question 1b,** have them work in pairs or small groups to brainstorm possible experiments.

BIOLOGY.com Students can check their understanding of lesson concepts with the **Self-Test** assessment. They can then take an online version of the **Lesson Assessment.**

Answers

FIGURE 11–13 1.5°C; No, because the average summer temperature is greater than the minimum temperature the butterflies need to fly.

Assessment Answers

1a. In incomplete dominance, neither of two alleles is dominant. The phenotype is a blend of the two alleles, such as pink flowers from red and white parents.

1b. Sample answer: Cross two petunia plants with pink flowers. If some of the offspring have red, some have white, and others have pink flowers, the pink color is caused by incomplete dominance.

2a. The environment affects how genes are expressed and therefore influence an organism's phenotype.

2b. The higher temperatures of an unusually hot spring will likely result in lighter wing colors.

PRACTICE PROBLEM

3. Students' problems should follow the rules of genetics and include correct and complete answers.

Teach

Lead a Discussion

Point out that the featured scientist has combined the study of two fields of biology, genetics and immunology. Tell students that population geneticists look at the inheritance of traits in populations rather than in individuals. An immunologist conducts research on the immune system, which is a body system that defends against disease-causing organisms and cancer. Tell students that careers in both areas require advanced degrees with coursework in biology, math, chemistry, computers, and medicine. These careers also require critical thinking skills, complex problem solving, and the ability to communicate orally and in writing.

DIFFERENTIATED INSTRUCTION

L3 Advanced Students Suggest interested students find out more about the possible careers that a degree in genetics and immunology might prepare them for. If possible, have them interview a geneticist or immunologist about his or her field of study.

If you enjoy learning about genetics, you may want to pursue one of the careers listed below.

FORENSIC SCIENTIST
Do you enjoy solving puzzles? That's what forensic scientists do when they solve crimes. Local, state, and federal agencies employ forensic scientists to use scientific approaches that support criminal investigations. Criminalists are forensic scientists who specialize in the analysis of physical evidence, such as hair, fiber, DNA, fingerprints, and weapons. They are often called to testify in trials as expert witnesses.

PLANT BREEDER
Did you ever wonder how seedless watermelons become seedless? They are the product of a plant breeder. Plant breeders use genetic techniques to manipulate crops. Often, the goal is to make a crop more useful by increasing yield or nutritional value. Some breeders introduce new traits, such as pesticide resistance, to the plant's genetic makeup.

POPULATION GENETICIST
Why are certain populations more susceptible to particular diseases? This is the kind of question that population geneticists answer. Their goal is to figure out why specific traits of distinct groups of organisms occur in varying frequencies. The patterns they uncover can lead to an understanding of how gene expression changes as a population evolves.

CAREER CLOSE-UP:
Sophia Cleland, Population Geneticist and Immunologist

Sophia Cleland, a Ph.D. student in immunology at George Washington University, studies the molecular, cellular, and genetic mechanisms that contribute to autoimmune diseases. One of only a few Native Americans with an advanced degree in genetics, Ms. Cleland became interested in autoimmune diseases when she noticed that the frequencies of these illnesses, such as rheumatoid arthritis and lupus, were several times higher among her tribal communities (Lakota-Sioux and California Mission Indian) than among Caucasians. Furthermore, she observed that such diseases progressed more rapidly among these communities than in any other human group in the world. Because of the frequency and severity of these diseases among indigenous tribal groups, Ms. Cleland is spreading the word about the need for focused research in this area.

"A compromise is needed between the world views of indigenous tribal groups and modern scientific approaches to gathering knowledge. We will encounter difficulties, but by working together with an open mind to learn, balanced and just results are possible."

WRITING How do you think a high frequency of genetic illness can affect a population? Explain.

Answers

WRITING Students' explanations might include financial burdens, inadequate health care, and decreased quality of life.

Quick Facts

THE GENETICS OF LUPUS

Lupus presents in different forms, but the most common type damages joints, skin, blood vessels, and organs such as the kidneys and brain. The disease has no cure. Lupus has a complex inheritance pattern. It runs in families but is not solely a genetic disease, leading scientists to think lupus has a genetic susceptibility and is polygenic. The genes involved in lupus vary in populations. The prevalence of lupus is higher in African Americans, Latinos, Asians, and Native Americans. Because lupus is rare in Africa, some scientists think environmental risk factors that are common in the United States and Europe but rare in Africa might trigger the disease.

11.4 Meiosis

B.6.4 Meiosis; B.6.5 Sorting and recombination of genes. Also covered: NoS.3.

THINK ABOUT IT As geneticists in the early 1900s applied Mendel's principles, they wondered where genes might be located. They expected genes to be carried on structures inside the cell, but *which* structures? What cellular processes could account for segregation and independent assortment, as Mendel had described?

Chromosome Number

How many sets of genes are found in most adult organisms?

To hold true, Mendel's principles require at least two events to occur. First, an organism with two parents must inherit a single copy of every gene from each parent. Second, when that organism produces gametes, those two sets of genes must be separated so that each gamete contains just one set of genes. As it turns out, chromosomes—those strands of DNA and protein inside the cell nucleus—are the carriers of genes. The genes are located in specific positions on chromosomes.

Diploid Cells Consider the fruit fly that Morgan used, *Drosophila.* A body cell in an adult fruit fly has eight chromosomes, as shown in **Figure 11–14.** Four of the chromosomes come from its male parent, and four come from its female parent. These two sets of chromosomes are **homologous** (hoh MAHL uh gus), meaning that each of the four chromosomes from the male parent has a corresponding chromosome from the female parent. A cell that contains both sets of homologous chromosomes is said to be **diploid,** meaning "two sets." **The diploid cells of most adult organisms contain two complete sets of inherited chromosomes and two complete sets of genes.** The diploid number of chromosomes is sometimes represented by the symbol 2N. Thus, for *Drosophila,* the diploid number is 8, which can be written as 2N = 8, where N represents the single set of chromosomes found in a sperm or egg cell.

Haploid Cells Some cells contain only a single set of chromosomes, and therefore a single set of genes. Such cells are **haploid,** meaning "one set." The gametes of sexually reproducing organisms, including fruit flies and peas, are haploid. For *Drosophila* gametes, the haploid number is 4, which can be written as N = 4.

Key Questions

How many sets of genes are found in most adult organisms?

What events occur during each phase of meiosis?

How is meiosis different from mitosis?

How can two alleles from different genes be inherited together?

Vocabulary

homologous • diploid • haploid • meiosis • tetrad • crossing-over • zygote

Taking Notes

Compare/Contrast Table Before you read, make a compare/contrast table to show the differences between mitosis and meiosis. As you read, complete the table.

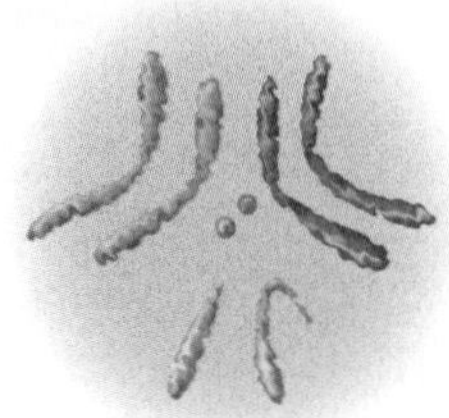

FIGURE 11–14 Fruit Fly Chromosomes These chromosomes are from a fruit fly. Each of the fruit fly's body cells is diploid, containing eight chromosomes.

UbD Teach for Understanding

ENDURING UNDERSTANDING DNA is the universal code for life; it enables an organism to transmit hereditary information and, along with the environment, determines an organism's characteristics.

GUIDING QUESTION How does a cell divide to create cells with exactly half of the original cell's genetic information?

EVIDENCE OF UNDERSTANDING *After completing the lesson, give students the following assessment to show they understand how a cell divides to create cells with exactly half of the original cell's genetic information.* Have students use colored pencils to draw their own labeled diagrams of the phases of meiosis. In their diagrams, have them show how genes assort independently. Suggest they use homozygous alleles *Y* and *y*.

LESSON 11.4

Getting Started

Objectives

11.4.1 Contrast the number of chromosomes in body cells and in gametes.

11.4.2 Summarize the events of meiosis.

11.4.3 Contrast meiosis and mitosis.

11.4.4 Describe how alleles from different genes can be inherited together.

Student Resources

Study Workbook A and B, 11.4 Worksheets

Spanish Study Workbook, 11.4 Worksheets

Lab Manual B, 11.4 Data Analysis Worksheet

BIOLOGY.com Lesson Overview • Lesson Notes • Activities: Art in Motion, Tutor Tube, Data Analysis • Assessment: Self-Test, Lesson Assessment

For corresponding lesson in the **Foundation Edition**, see pages 275–279.

Build Background

Create a class **Cluster Diagram** for *meiosis.* Write the term on the board, and have student volunteers add any facts, terms, or concepts they know to the diagram. Refer to the cluster diagram as you work through the lesson.

Study Wkbks A/B, Appendix S19, Cluster Diagram. **Transparencies,** GO2.

IN INDIANA ACADEMIC STANDARDS

For the full text of all standards, see the Course Overview in the front matter of this book.

B.6.4 Describe and model the process of meiosis and explain the relationship between the genetic make-up of the parent cell and the daughter cells (gametes).

B.6.5 Explain how, in sexual reproduction, crossing over, independent assortment, and random fertilization result in offspring that are genetically different from the parents.

Teach

Use Visuals

Use **Figure 11–15** to help students understand the process of meiosis I. Emphasize that before meiosis begins, every chromosome is copied, so the cell has four copies of each chromosome. Review the structures shown in the Prophase I cell and in the close-up of crossing-over. Have students identify those structures. Then, use the figure to walk students through meiosis I.

DIFFERENTIATED INSTRUCTION

L1 Struggling Students Some students might be confused by the number of chromosomes at each stage. Remind them that *haploid* and *diploid* refer to the number of sets of chromosomes in a cell. Help them understand that at the beginning of interphase, the cell is diploid or 2N. In this case, it contains two chromosomes. Emphasize that this is not shown in the figure. Explain that, during interphase, the chromosomes replicate and the cell becomes 4N (it has 8 chromatids, or 4 chromosomes). Have students verify that the cells are still 4N in the prophase, metaphase, and anaphase stages. When the cells divide in telophase I and cytokinesis, each cell has half the number of chromosomes, but it is not considered diploid because it contains only one duplicated set of chromosomes.

ELL Focus on ELL: Build Background

BEGINNING AND INTERMEDIATE SPEAKERS
Refer students to **Figure 11–15,** and have them identity the cell structures they learned about when they studied mitosis. Point out the centrioles, chromosomes, centromeres, and spindles. Use previously learned and new vocabulary terms frequently as you walk them through the visual and ask questions requiring them to use those terms. Then, have students draw and label their own diagrams of the phases of meiosis. Beginning speakers can use single words or phrases or their native language to write captions. Intermediate speakers should write complete sentences. Ask students to describe their diagrams to a partner.

Answers

FIGURE 11–15 During crossing-over, the alleles can be exchanged between chromatids of homologous chromosomes to produce new combinations of alleles.

FIGURE 11–15 Meiosis I During meiosis I, a diploid cell undergoes a series of events that results in the production of two daughter cells. Neither daughter cell has the same sets of chromosomes that the original diploid cell had. Interpret Graphics *How does crossing-over affect the alleles on a chromosome?*

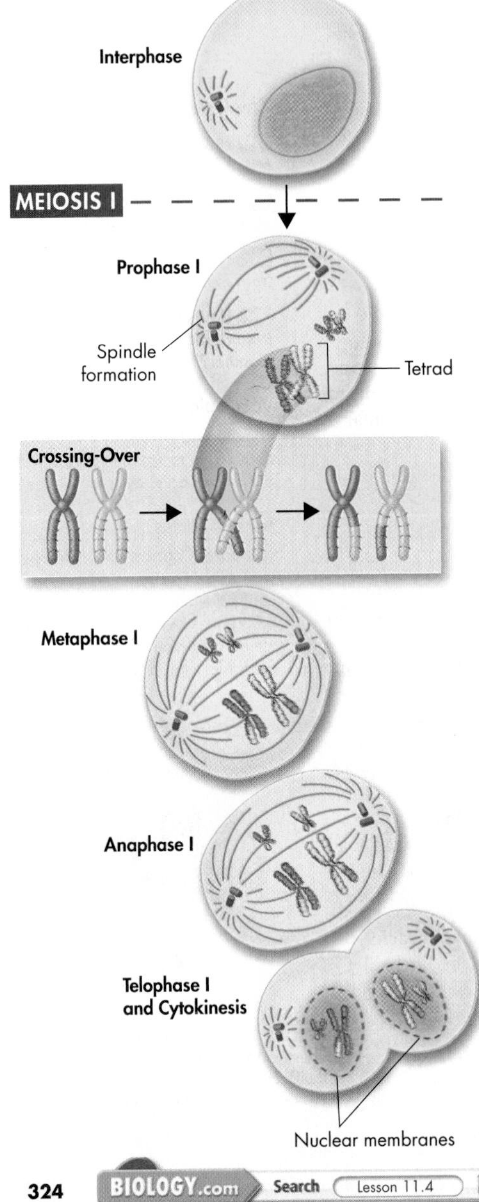

Phases of Meiosis

What events occur during each phases of meiosis?

How are haploid (N) gamete cells produced from diploid (2N) cells? That's where meiosis (my OH sis) comes in. **Meiosis** is a process in which the number of chromosomes per cell is cut in half through the separation of homologous chromosomes in a diploid cell. Meiosis usually involves two distinct divisions, called meiosis I and meiosis II. By the end of meiosis II, the diploid cell becomes four haploid cells. Let's see how meiosis takes place in a cell that has a diploid number of 4 (2N = 4).

Meiosis I Just prior to meiosis I, the cell undergoes a round of chromosome replication during interphase. As in mitosis, which was discussed in Chapter 10, each replicated chromosome consists of two identical chromatids joined at the center. Follow the sequence in **Figure 11–15** as you read about meiosis I.

▶ ***Prophase I*** After interphase I, the cell begins to divide, and the chromosomes pair up. **In prophase I of meiosis, each replicated chromosome pairs with its corresponding homologous chromosome.** This pairing forms a structure called a **tetrad,** which contains four chromatids. As the homologous chromosomes form tetrads, they undergo a process called **crossing-over.** First, the chromatids of the homologous chromosomes cross over one another. Then, the crossed sections of the chromatids—which contain alleles—are exchanged. Crossing-over therefore produces new combinations of alleles in the cell.

▶ ***Metaphase I and Anaphase I*** As prophase I ends, a spindle forms and attaches to each tetrad. **During metaphase I of meiosis, paired homologous chromosomes line up across the center of the cell.** As the cell moves into anaphase I, the homologous pairs of chromosomes separate. **During anaphase I, spindle fibers pull each homologous chromosome pair toward opposite ends of the cell.**

▶ ***Telophase I and Cytokinesis*** When anaphase I is complete, the separated chromosomes cluster at opposite ends of the cell. **The next phase is telophase I, in which a nuclear membrane forms around each cluster of chromosomes. Cytokinesis follows telophase I, forming two new cells.**

324 BIOLOGY.com Search Lesson 11.4 GO • Art in Motion

Biology In-Depth

GENETIC VARIATION IN MEIOSIS PHASES

Genetic variation occurs during meiosis in several phases. During prophase I crossing-over, sister chromatids become attached and swap sections at points called chiasmata. The sections are portions of adjacent DNA molecules. Neither chromatid gains or loses any genes. In humans (23 chromosomes), if only one cross-over event occurs in each tetrad (and it is usually two or three), over 70 trillion combinations are possible (4^{23}). During metaphase I, homologous pairs of chromosomes line up randomly with respect to orientation; each pair can line up in two different ways. The number of possible combinations is over 8 million (2^{23}). When those numbers are multiplied together and that result is multiplied by two because of fertilization, you can see why each person is unique!

Meiosis I results in two cells, called daughter cells. However, because each pair of homologous chromosomes was separated, neither daughter cell has the two complete sets of chromosomes that it would have in a diploid cell. Those two sets have been shuffled and sorted almost like a deck of cards. The two cells produced by meiosis I have sets of chromosomes and alleles that are different from each other and from the diploid cell that entered meiosis I.

Meiosis II The two cells now enter a second meiotic division. Unlike the first division, neither cell goes through a round of chromosome replication before entering meiosis II.

▶ ***Prophase II*** **As the cells enter prophase II, their chromosomes—each consisting of two chromatids—become visible.** The chromosomes do not pair to form tetrads, because the homologous pairs were already separated during meiosis I.

▶ ***Metaphase II, Anaphase II, Telophase II, and Cytokinesis*** During metaphase of meiosis II, chromosomes line up in the center of each cell. As the cell enters anaphase, the paired chromatids separate. **The final four phases of meiosis II are similar to those in meiosis I. However, the result is four haploid daughter cells.** In the example shown here, each of the four daughter cells produced in meiosis II receive two chromosomes. These four daughter cells now contain the haploid number (N)—just two chromosomes each.

Gametes to Zygotes The haploid cells produced by meiosis II are the gametes that are so important to heredity. In male animals, these gametes are called sperm. In some plants, pollen grains contain haploid sperm cells. In female animals, generally only one of the cells produced by meiosis is involved in reproduction. The female gamete is called an egg in animals and an egg cell in some plants. After it is fertilized, the egg is called a **zygote** (ZY goht). The zygote undergoes cell division by mitosis and eventually forms a new organism.

In Your Notebook *Describe the difference between meiosis I and meiosis II. How are the end results different?*

FIGURE 11–16 Meiosis II The second meiotic division, called meiosis II, produces four haploid daughter cells.

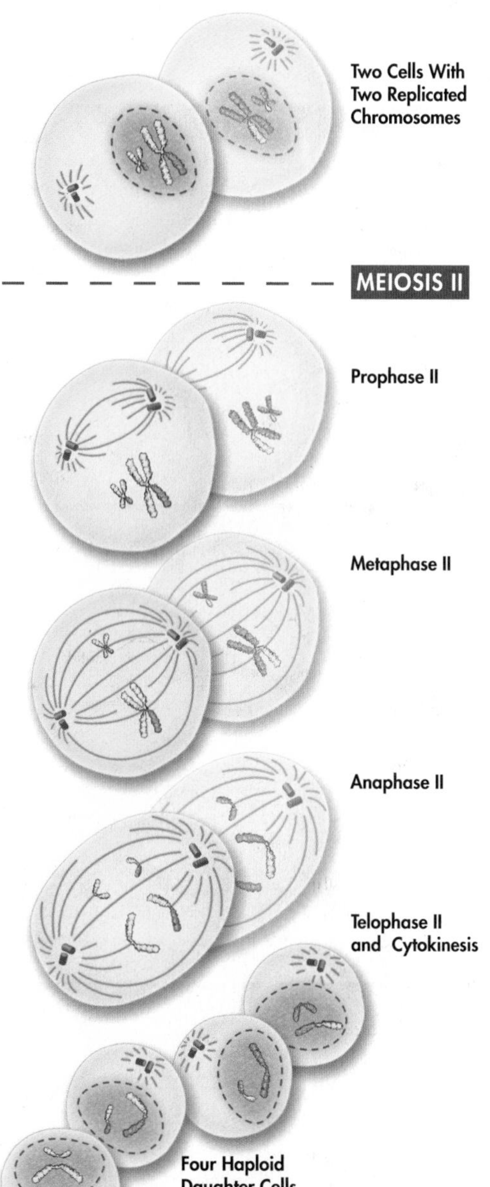

LESSON 11.4

Use Visuals

Draw students' attention to the two cells at the top of **Figure 11–16.** Reinforce that, while each has a 2N number of chromosomes, the cells are not considered diploid because the chromatid strands in the replicated chromosomes came from the same parent. Then, have volunteers use their own words to describe what occurs during each step of meiosis II.

Ask How many haploid (N) daughter cells are produced at the end of meiosis II? *(four)*

Ask What are some differences between meiosis I and meiosis II? *(Sample answer: homologous chromosomes separate during meiosis I but not during meiosis II. The centromeres and sister chromatids separate during meiosis II.)*

DIFFERENTIATED INSTRUCTION

L1 Special Needs Help students model the steps in meiosis using pipe cleaners of the same color to represent chromosome pairs, with different pairs having different colors. Monitor students to make sure they double each chromosome before meiosis begins by adding another pipe cleaner of the same color. They can use beads to hold the chromatids together or twist the pipe cleaners together in the middle. Make sure they separate the chromosome pairs during meiosis I and the chromatids during meiosis II.

LPR Less Proficient Readers Have students write an outline of meiosis in which each major step is a main heading. Suggest they include the information in the boldface Key Concepts as details.

BIOLOGY.com Students can view the phases of meiosis online in **Art in Motion: Meiosis.** For extra help, have students view **Tutor Tube: Connecting Punnett Squares to Meiosis.**

UbD Check for Understanding

USE VOCABULARY

Ask students to create a jingle, acronym, or other mnemonic to help them remember what happens in each phase of meiosis I and II. Suggest they use the vocabulary terms whenever possible. An example is a cheer: (for meiosis I) "Give me a P—paired chromosomes form a tetrad, give me an M—meet in the middle and line up, give me an A—away from the middle, give me a TC—two cells."

ADJUST INSTRUCTION

If students have difficulty creating the mnemonic or it is incorrect, have them reread the boldface statements under **Phases of Meiosis.** Tell them to focus on the movements of the chromosomes or what is happening to them. For example, for prophase II, have them focus on "become visible." Then, tell them to think of a memory device for that action. For a cheer, an example is "Give me a P—pops up."

Answers

IN YOUR NOTEBOOK Answers should include the following: Meiosis I involves chromosome replication, formation of tetrads, crossing-over, separation of paired homologous chromosomes, and division into two cells. Meiosis II includes separation of sister chromatids as each cell divides. The end result of meiosis I is two genetically different cells, each containing the same number of chromosomes as the original cell but recombined due to crossing-over. The end result of meiosis II is four different haploid cells.

LESSON 11.4

Teach continued

VISUAL SUMMARY

Have students compare and contrast mitosis and meiosis using **Figure 11–17.** Draw particular attention to phases in meiosis where genetic recombination occurs. For example, in prophase in mitosis, the replicated chromosomes do not pair up, whereas in prophase I in meiosis, the replicated chromosomes pair up with their homologues and the process of crossing-over occurs.

As you walk students through the Visual Summary, have them note differences in the lining up of chromosomes, the number of chromosomes each cell contains, and how chromosomes separate into new cells.

DIFFERENTIATED INSTRUCTION

L1 Special Needs Provide students with beads and pipe cleaners of different colors, and have them model the steps in mitosis. Help them to arrange this model next to the model they made of meiosis earlier. Then, ask them to explain what is happening in each phase of mitosis and tell how those phases are similar and different to those of meiosis. Suggest students glue their models to poster board to use as a study guide.

L1 Struggling Students Students who have difficulty understanding the Visual Summary might benefit from drawing diagrams that show only the chromosomes without the distraction of other structures, such as the spindle fibers. Help them draw circles for each phase of mitosis and meiosis and fill in only the chromosomes at each stage. Then, have them write simple captions that describe what is happening in each phase.

L3 Advanced Students To add detail to the students' comparisons of mitosis and meiosis, have them create a third column for **Figure 11–17** on a separate sheet of paper labeled Meiosis II. Have students use **Figure 11–16** as a model for drawing corresponding diagrams for prophase II, metaphase II, anaphase II, and telophase II. Then, have students use their extended visual summary to compare the two processes in more detail.

VISUAL SUMMARY

COMPARING MITOSIS AND MEIOSIS

FIGURE 11–17 Mitosis and meiosis both ensure that cells inherit genetic information. Both processes begin after interphase, when chromosome replication occurs. However, the two processes differ in the separation of chromosomes, the number of cells produced, and the number of chromosomes each cell contains.

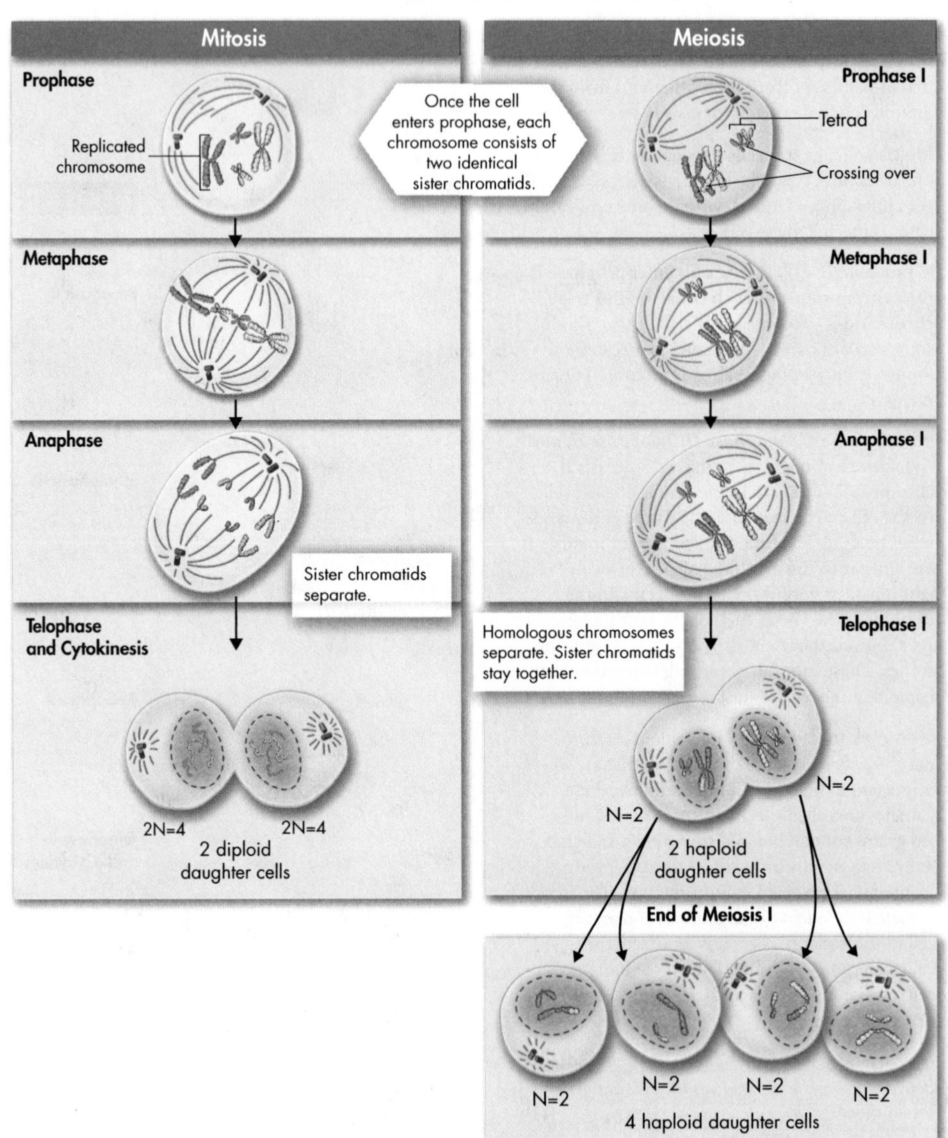

Biology In-Depth

POLAR BODIES

In many female animals, cytokinesis at the end of meiosis I and meiosis II is uneven. At the end of meiosis I, one of the cells receives most of the cytoplasm and is called a secondary oocyte. The cell that receives very little is the polar body. At the end of meiosis II, the secondary oocyte divides so that once again one cell receives most of the cytoplasm; this cell becomes the egg, and the other cell is another polar body. The polar body formed at the end of meiosis I divides into two polar bodies in meiosis II. The three polar bodies eventually die. The reason for the uneven divisions is the allotment of more materials in the egg cell to nourish the zygote.

Comparing Meiosis and Mitosis

How is meiosis different from mitosis?

The words *mitosis* and *meiosis* may sound similar, but the two processes are very different, as you can see in **Figure 11–17.** Mitosis can be a form of asexual reproduction, whereas meiosis is an early step in sexual reproduction. There are three other ways in which these two processes differ.

Replication and Separation of Genetic Material Mitosis and meiosis are both preceded by a complete copying, or replication, of the genetic material of chromosomes. However, the next steps differ dramatically. **In mitosis, when the two sets of genetic material separate, each daughter cell receives one complete set of chromosomes. In meiosis, homologous chromosomes line up and then move to separate daughter cells.** As a result, the two alleles for each gene are segregated, and end up in different cells. The sorting and recombination of genes in meiosis result in a greater variety of possible gene combinations than could result from mitosis.

Changes in Chromosome Number **Mitosis does not normally change the chromosome number of the original cell. This is not the case for meiosis, which reduces the chromosome number by half.** A diploid cell that enters mitosis with eight chromosomes will divide to produce two diploid daughter cells, each of which also has eight chromosomes. On the other hand, a diploid cell that enters meiosis with eight chromosomes will pass through two meiotic divisions to produce four haploid gamete cells, each with only four chromosomes.

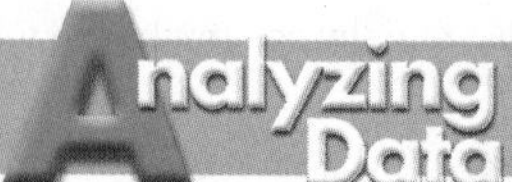

NoS.3

Calculating Haploid and Diploid Numbers

Haploid and diploid numbers are designated by the algebraic notations N and 2N, respectively. Either number can be calculated when the other is known. For example, if the haploid number (N) is 3, the diploid number (2N) is 2 × 3, or 6. If the diploid number (2N) is 12, the haploid number (N) is 12/2, or 6.

The table shows haploid or diploid numbers of a variety of organisms. Copy the table into your notebook and complete it. Then, use the table to answer the questions that follow.

Trait Survey

Organism	Haploid Number	Diploid Number
Amoeba	N=25	
Chimpanzee	N=24	
Earthworm	N=18	
Fern		2N=1010
Hamster	N=22	
Human		2N=46
Onion		2N=16

1. **Calculate** What are the haploid numbers for the fern and onion plants? MATH
2. **Interpret Data** In the table, which organisms' diploid numbers are closest to that of a human?
3. **Apply Concepts** Why is a diploid number always even?
4. **Evaluate** Which organism's haploid and diploid numbers do you find the most surprising? Why?

Lead a Discussion

After students have read through **Comparing Meiosis and Mitosis,** have pairs of students reread the three Key Concepts and discuss why each one is important. Then, have them share their ideas with the class.

DIFFERENTIATED INSTRUCTION

L1 Special Needs Provide students with three different pairs of items to represent three gene pairs. Each member of a pair should be different from the other. Examples are two differently shaped buttons, two differently colored pencils, and two different kinds of coins. Tell students to use these objects to contrast the results of mitosis and meiosis. *(After mitosis, a cell would have the same six items. After meiosis, a gamete could have any combination of button, pencil, and coin.)* Students should show the different possible combinations as a result of meiosis.

L3 Advanced Students Provide various art materials for students, and challenge them to illustrate what might happen if sex cells, or gametes, did not have half the number of chromosomes as body cells. Have them present their models to the class and explain why sex cells must have half the number of chromosomes as body cells.

PURPOSE Students will complete and interpret a data table to better understand diploid and haploid numbers.

PLANNING Review the vocabulary terms *haploid* and *diploid* with students.

ANSWERS

1. fern—505; onion—8
2. chimpanzee and hamster
3. Any number multiplied by 2 is always even.
4. Sample answer: A fern's numbers were most surprising, because the number of chromosomes is so large.

Teach continued

Use Models

Have students demonstrate why genes that are close together do not usually assort independently. Ask them to use two differently colored markers to draw two paired chromosomes. Have them place three symbols (in the same color as the chromosome) along each chromosome to indicate the relative positions of the genes for star eye, dumpy wing, and speck wing as indicated in **Figure 11–18.** Then, have another student point to the same spot on both chromosomes to identify a location for crossing-over. Have pairs redraw the chromosomes as if crossing-over occurred, using the two colors to show the parts of the chromosomes that have exchanged. Then, have them use the symbols to check for gene linkage.

Ask Which genes are most likely inherited together? Why? *(Star eye and dumpy wing. Because these genes are so close together on the chromosome, the chance that crossing-over would separate them is smaller.)*

DIFFERENTIATED INSTRUCTION

L1 Struggling Students Refer students who need extra help to the close-up image of crossing-over in **Figure 11–15.** Point out that chunks of the chromosomes, not individual genes, are exchanged between chromosomes. Have students model gene linkage in crossing-over by using different colors of modeling clay to represent each chromosome. Students can pull apart chunks of one color clay and attach them to the other color.

ELL English Language Learners Show students a road map, and point out how maps show where things such as cities and roads are located. Then, point to **Figure 11–18,** and tell them a gene map shows where genes are located.

BIOLOGY.com Students can analyze the connection between crossing-over and gene location in **Data Analysis: Gene Location and Crossing-Over.**

Number of Cell Divisions Mitosis is a single cell division, resulting in the production of two identical daughter cells. On the other hand, meiosis requires two rounds of cell division, and, in most organisms, produces a total of four daughter cells. **Mitosis results in the production of two genetically identical diploid cells, whereas meiosis produces four genetically different haploid cells.**

Gene Linkage and Gene Maps

How can two alleles from different genes be inherited together?

If you think carefully about Mendel's principle of independent assortment in relation to meiosis, one question might bother you. Genes that are located on different chromosomes assort independently, but what about genes that are located on the same chromosome? Wouldn't they generally be inherited together?

Gene Linkage The answer to this question, as Thomas Hunt Morgan first realized in 1910, is yes. Morgan's research on fruit flies led him to the principle of gene linkage. After identifying more than 50 *Drosophila* genes, Morgan discovered that many of them appeared to be "linked" together in ways that, at first glance, seemed to violate the principle of independent assortment. For example, Morgan used a fly with reddish-orange eyes and miniature wings in a series of test crosses. His results showed that the genes for those two traits were almost always inherited together. Only rarely did the genes separate from each other. Morgan and his associates observed so many genes that were inherited together that, before long, they could group all of the fly's genes into four linkage groups. The linkage groups assorted independently, but all of the genes in one group were inherited together. As it turns out, *Drosophila* has four linkage groups and four pairs of chromosomes.

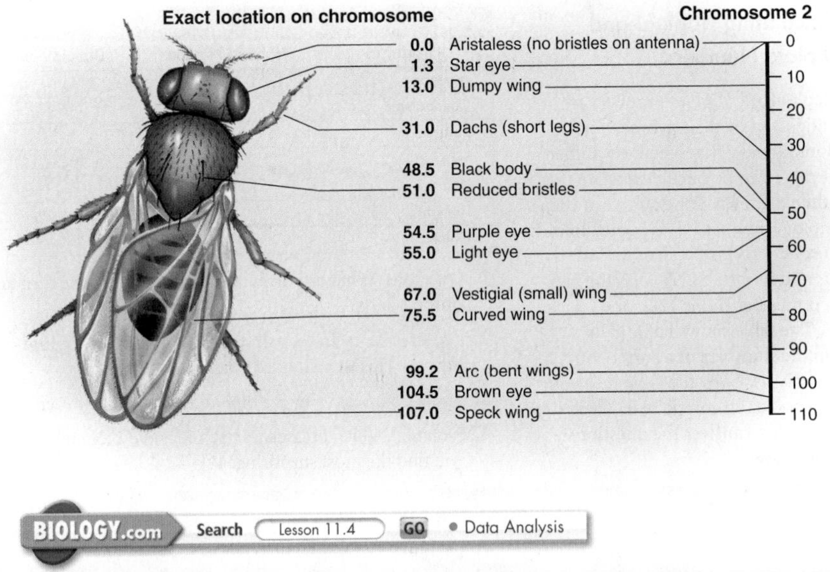

FIGURE 11–18 Gene Map This gene map shows the location of a variety of genes on chromosome 2 of the fruit fly. The genes are named after the problems that abnormal alleles cause, *not* after the normal structures. **Interpret Graphics** ***Where on the chromosome is the "purple eye" gene located?***

 BIOLOGY.com Search Lesson 11.4 GO • Data Analysis

UbD Check for Understanding

FOLLOW-UP PROBES

Ask students the following questions:

- Why are the alleles for reddish-orange eyes and miniature wings in fruit flies usually inherited together? *(The genes are located near each other on the same chromosome.)*
- Morgan found that fruit flies, with their four pairs of chromosomes, had four linkage groups. Why does this make sense? *(Each chromosome is a set of linked genes.)*

ADJUST INSTRUCTION

If students have difficulty answering the questions, have them reread the text on gene linkage and Morgan's work. Have pairs of students summarize Morgan's work. Ask several pairs to share their summaries with the class.

Answers

FIGURE 11–18 The "purple eye" gene is located at 54.5.

Morgan's findings led to two remarkable conclusions. First, each chromosome is actually a group of linked genes. Second, Mendel's principle of independent assortment still holds true. It is the chromosomes, however, that assort independently, not individual genes. **Alleles of different genes tend to be inherited together from one generation to the next when those genes are located on the same chromosome.**

How did Mendel manage to miss gene linkage? By luck, or design, several of the genes he studied are on different chromosomes. Others are so far apart that they also assort independently.

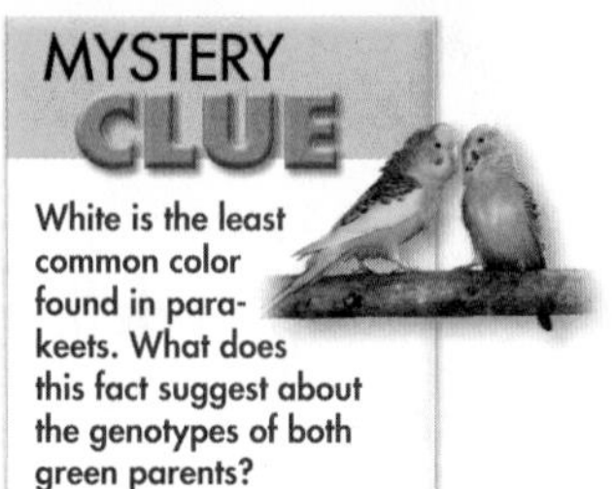

White is the least common color found in parakeets. What does this fact suggest about the genotypes of both green parents?

Gene Mapping In 1911, a Columbia University student was working part time in Morgan's lab. This student, Alfred Sturtevant, wondered if the frequency of crossing-over between genes during meiosis might be a clue to the genes' locations. Sturtevant reasoned that the farther apart two genes were on a chromosome, the more likely it would be that crossing-over would occur between them. If two genes are close together, then crossovers between them should be rare. If two genes are far apart, then crossovers between them should be more common. By this reasoning, he could use the frequency of crossing-over between genes to determine their distances from each other.

Sturtevant gathered up several notebooks of lab data and took them back to his room. The next morning, he presented Morgan with a gene map showing the relative locations of each known gene on one of the *Drosophila* chromosomes. Sturtevant's method has been used to construct gene maps, like the one in **Figure 11–18,** ever since this discovery.

MYSTERY CLUE Have students discuss their own experiences with parakeets. Ask them whether they have ever seen a parakeet that has only white feathers. Remind students that when a phenotype is coded for by recessive alleles, it is often less common in a population, especially if the dominant alleles occur frequently in the population. Lead students to conclude that white parakeets are likely homozygous recessive for both blue and white pigment genes, so both parents must be heterozygous for both pigments. Students can go online to Biology.com to gather their evidence.

LESSON 11.4

11.4 Assessment

IN B.6.4, B.6.5

Review Key Concepts

1. a. Review Describe the main results of meiosis.
   b. Calculate In human cells, 2N = 46. How many chromosomes would you expect to find in a sperm cell? How many would you expect to find in an egg cell? MATH
2. a. Review Write a summary of each phase of meiosis.
   b. Use Analogies Compare the chromosomes of a diploid cell to a collection of shoes in a closet. How are they similar? What would make the shoe collection comparable to the chromosomes of a haploid cell?
3. a. Review What are the principal differences between mitosis and meiosis?
   b. Apply Concepts Is there any difference between sister chromatids and homologous pairs of chromosomes? Explain.
4. a. Review How does the principle of independent assortment apply to chromosomes?
   b. Infer If two genes are on the same chromosome but usually assort independently, what does that tell you about how close together they are?

Apply the Big idea

Information and Heredity

5. In asexual reproduction, mitosis occurs but meiosis does not occur. Which type of reproduction—sexual or asexual—results in offspring with greater genetic variation? Explain your answer.

BIOLOGY.com Search Lesson 11.4 GO • Self-Test • Lesson Assessment

Assess and Remediate

EVALUATE UNDERSTANDING

Have students verbally list the stages of meiosis in order and describe in their own words what occurs during each stage. Then, have them complete the 11.4 Assessment.

REMEDIATION SUGGESTION

L1 **Struggling Students** If your students have trouble with **Question 3,** review with them the text of **Diploid Cells** and the first paragraph of **Meiosis I.** Then, have them draw diagrams to show how homologous chromosomes are formed from two parent cells joining and how sister chromatids are formed by replication within a single cell.

BIOLOGY.com Students can check their understanding of lesson concepts with the **Self-Test** assessment. They can then take an online version of the **Lesson Assessment.**

Assessment Answers

1a. Meiosis results in four haploid cells that are genetically different from one another and from the original cell.

1b. Each gamete cell has 23 chromosomes.

2a. Check that student answers include accurate summaries of interphase I, prophase I and II, metaphase I and II, anaphase I and II, telophase I and II, and cytokinesis I and II.

2b. Shoes are in pairs as are chromosomes in a diploid cell. A "haploid" shoe collection would have only one shoe of each kind.

3a. Mitosis produces two genetically identical diploid cells. Meiosis produces four genetically different haploid cells.

3b. The sister chromatids are identical, because one is a copy of the other. The homologous pairs are not identical; one chromosome comes from the mother and one comes from the father.

4a. It is the chromosomes that assort independently, not individual genes.

4b. The two genes are located very far apart from each other.

5. Big idea Sexual reproduction; during meiosis, the shuffling and separating of homologous chromosomes and crossing-over events produce gametes genetically different from each other and from the original cell. Fertilization with a gamete from a different parent further increases genetic variation.

CHAPTER LAB

Pre-Lab

Introduce students to the concepts they will explore in the chapter lab by assigning the Pre-Lab questions.

Lab

Tell students they will perform the chapter lab *Modeling Meiosis* described in **Lab Manual A.**

 **Struggling Students** A simpler version of the chapter lab is provided in **Lab Manual B.**

 Look online for **Editable Lab Worksheets.**

 For corresponding pre-lab in the **Foundation Edition**, see page 280.

IN INDIANA ACADEMIC STANDARDS

For the full text of all standards, see the Course Overview in the front matter of this book.

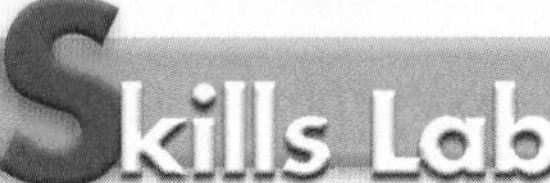

GUIDED INQUIRY

 NoS.6 Use analogies and models; B.6.4 Meiosis.

Pre-Lab: Modeling Meiosis

Problem How does meiosis increase genetic variation?

Materials pop-it beads, magnetic centromeres, large sheet of paper, colored pencils, scissors

Lab Manual Chapter 11 Lab

Skills Use Models, Sequence, Draw Conclusions

Connect to the Big idea Inherited traits are passed from parents to offspring in the form of genes. Offspring produced by sexual reproduction receive one set of genes from each parent when the reproductive cells, or gametes, combine. Meiosis is the process by which gametes are produced. During meiosis, new combinations of genes form when genes cross over from one homologous chromosome to the other. Also, the sorting of chromatids among gametes is random. Both crossing-over and sorting lead to greater diversity in the genes of a population.

In this lab, you will model the steps of meiosis and track what happens to alleles as they move from diploid cells to haploid gametes.

Background Questions

a. **Review** What are alleles?

b. **Sequence** What happens during prophase I of meiosis? What happens during metaphase I? What happens during anaphase I?

c. **Compare and Contrast** In what ways does meiosis differ from mitosis?

Pre-Lab Questions

Preview the procedure in the lab manual.

1. **Control Variables** Why must you use the same number of beads when you construct the second chromosome in Step 1?
2. **Infer** Why is the longer chromosome pair used to model crossing-over?
3. **Calculate** A diploid cell has two pairs of homologous chromosomes. How many different combinations of chromosomes could there be in the gametes? 

BIOLOGY.com Search Chapter 11 GO

Visit Chapter 11 online to test yourself on chapter content and to find activities to help you learn.

Untamed Science Video Travel back in time with the Untamed Science explorers as they prove Mendel was no pea brain!

Art in Motion View a short animation that brings the process of meiosis to life.

Art Review Review your understanding of multiple alleles, incomplete dominance, and other exceptions to Mendel's principles.

InterActive Art Build your understanding of Punnett squares with this animation.

Data Analysis Determine gene linkage and construct a gene map by examining the phenotypic frequencies of offspring.

Tutor Tube Tune into the tutor to review the connection between setting up Punnett squares and meiosis.

Pre-Lab Answers

BACKGROUND QUESTIONS

a. Alleles are different forms of the same gene.

b. During prophase I, homologous chromosomes form tetrads. The tetrads line up across the center of the cell during metaphase I and are pulled to opposite ends of the cells during anaphase I.

c. During meiosis, homologous chromosomes separate, two cell divisions occur, and daughter cells have half as many chromosomes. During mitosis, homologous chromosomes are not separated, only one cell division occurs, and the number of chromosomes per cell does not change.

PRE-LAB QUESTIONS

1. There must be an allele for each gene on each chromosome in the homologous pair.
2. Genes that are on the same chromosome are likely to be linked. The chances of crossing-over are greater on the longer chromosome.
3. There could be four different combinations (ignoring any variation due to crossing-over).

11 Study Guide

Big idea Information and Heredity

Genetic information passes from parent to offspring during meiosis when gametes, each containing one representative from each chromosome pair, unite.

11.1 The Work of Gregor Mendel

An individual's characteristics are determined by factors that are passed from one parental generation to the next.

During gamete formation, the alleles for each gene segregate from each other so that each gamete carries only one allele for each gene.

genetics (308)
fertilization (309)
trait (309)
hybrid (309)
gene (310)
allele (310)
principle of dominance (310)
segregation (312)
gamete (312)

11.2 Applying Mendel's Principles

Punnett squares use mathematical probability to help predict the genotype and phenotype combinations in genetic crosses.

The principle of independent assortment states that genes for different traits can segregate independently during the formation of gametes.

Mendel's principles of heredity, observed through patterns of inheritance, form the basis of modern genetics.

probability (313)
homozygous (314)
heterozygous (314)
phenotype (315)
genotype (315)
Punnett square (315)
independent assortment (317)

11.3 Other Patterns of Inheritance

Some alleles are neither dominant nor recessive. Many genes exist in several different forms and are therefore said to have multiple alleles. Many traits are produced by the interaction of several genes.

Environmental conditions can affect gene expression and influence genetically determined traits.

incomplete dominance (319)
codominance (319)
multiple allele (320)
polygenic trait (320)

11.4 Meiosis

The diploid cells of most adult organisms contain two complete sets of inherited chromosomes and two complete sets of genes.

In prophase I, replicated chromosomes pair with corresponding homologous chromosomes. At metaphase I, paired chromosomes line up across the center of the cell. In anaphase I, chromosome pairs move toward opposite ends of the cell. In telophase I, a nuclear membrane forms around each cluster of chromosomes. Cytokinesis then forms two new cells. As the cells enter prophase II, their chromosomes become visible. The final four phases of meiosis II result in four haploid daughter cells.

In mitosis, when the two sets of genetic material separate, each daughter cell receives one complete set of chromosomes. In meiosis, homologous chromosomes line up and then move to separate daughter cells. Mitosis does not normally change the chromosome number of the original cell. Meiosis reduces the chromosome number by half. Mitosis results in the production of two genetically identical diploid cells, whereas meiosis produces four genetically different haploid cells.

Alleles of different genes tend to be inherited together from one generation from the next when those genes are located on the same chromosome.

homologous (323)
diploid (323)
haploid (323)
meiosis (324)
tetrad (324)
crossing-over (324)
zygote (325)

Think Visually Use the following terms to create a concept map: *alleles, genes, chromosomes, dominant, traits, recessive.*

Study Online

REVIEW AND ASSESSMENT RESOURCES

Editable Worksheets Pages of Study Workbooks A and B, Lab Manuals A and B, and the Assessment Resources Book are available online. These documents can be easily edited using a word-processing program.

Lesson Overview Have students reread the Lesson Overviews to help them study chapter concepts.

Vocabulary Review The *Flash Cards* and *Match It* provide an interactive way to review chapter vocabulary.

Chapter Assessment Have students take an online version of the Chapter 11 Assessment.

Standardized Test Prep Students can take an online version of the Standardized Test Prep. You will receive their scores along with ideas for remediation.

Diagnostic and Benchmark Tests Use these tests to monitor your students' progress and supply remediation.

UbD Performance Tasks

SUMMATIVE TASK Have students write a story about a chromosome going through meiosis for the first time. Encourage them to use illustrations and to be creative, but they must give accurate information about the movement of chromosomes.

TRANSFER TASK Tell students to imagine they are dog breeders for a particular breed. Spotted coats are dominant over solid coats, and curly coats are dominant over straight coats. They mate two dogs with spotted, curly coats. Two puppies have spotted, curly coats, and two have solid, straight coats. Another breeder claims the phenotypes must be due to gene linkage and cannot be due to a two-factor cross in which the two genes are not linked. Have students explain how either explanation is plausible and draw diagrams to demonstrate their reasoning. Then, have them explain why it is important to a dog breeder to know whether the phenotypes are from a gene linkage or a dihybrid cross.

Answers

THINK VISUALLY

Students' concept maps should include that a gene has two alleles, genes are located on chromosomes, genes help determine traits, and alleles can be dominant or recessive.

ASSESSMENT

Lesson 11.1

UNDERSTAND KEY CONCEPTS

1. c **2.** c

3. True-breeding organisms self-fertilize to produce offspring like themselves.

4. Mendel removed the pollen-producing parts from the flowers of his pea plants so they would not self-pollinate.

THINK CRITICALLY

5. Cross the white ram with a number of black ewes. If any offspring are black, then the white ram is heterozygous.

6. The original genotypes and the crosses could have been *Tt* × *tt* or *Tt* × *Tt*. The genotype *TT* could not have been present; if it were, all the offspring would be tall.

Lesson 11.2

UNDERSTAND KEY CONCEPTS

7. a **8.** c **9.** c

10. (1) The inheritance of biological characteristics is determined by genes. (2) Where there are two or more forms (alleles) of the gene for a single trait, some forms of the gene may be dominant and others recessive. (3) In most sexually reproducing organisms, each adult has two copies of each gene, one from each parent. These genes are segregated when gametes form. (4) The alleles for different genes (actually, the chromosomes) usually segregate independently.

11. 1 *YY* : 2 *Yy* : 1 *yy*; the Punnett square should show a cross between two heterozygous plants (*Yy*).

THINK CRITICALLY

12. The result of each fertilization is independent of any previous fertilizations, so it is possible for all offspring to have smooth coats. Each offspring could receive a recessive allele from both its parents.

Lesson 11.3

UNDERSTAND KEY CONCEPTS

13. d **14.** a

15. A single gene has multiple alleles if it has more than two alleles. Two or more genes control polygenic traits.

16. Many different phenotypes are possible, because, while individuals only have two alleles each, there can be many different alleles present in the population. Different possible allele combinations can yield different phenotypes.

17. No, genes provide a plan for development, but how the plan unfolds depends on the environment.

THINK CRITICALLY

18. The color helps the ptarmigan hide from predators. In winter, its white coat color blends in with its snowy surroundings.

11 Assessment

IN The numbers following the questions refer to Indiana's Academic Standards for Biology I

11.1 The Work of Gregor Mendel

Understand Key Concepts

1. Different forms of a gene are called B.5.2
a. hybrids. **c.** alleles.
b. dominant factors. **d.** recessive factors.

2. Organisms that have two identical alleles for a particular trait are said to be
a. hybrid. **c.** homozygous.
b. heterozygous. **d.** dominant.

3. Mendel had many stocks of pea plants that were true-breeding. What is meant by this term?

4. Explain how Mendel kept his pea plants from self-pollinating.

Think Critically

5. Design an Experiment In sheep, the allele for white wool (*A*) is dominant over the allele for black wool (*a*). A ram is a male sheep. How would you determine the genotype of a white ram? B.7.1, B.7.3

6. Infer Suppose Mendel crossed two pea plants and got both tall and short offspring. What could have been the genotypes of the two original plants? What genotype could *not* have been present? B.7.1, B.7.3

11.2 Applying Mendel's Principles

Understand Key Concepts

7. A Punnett square is used to determine the B.7.3
a. probable outcome of a cross.
b. actual outcome of a cross.
c. result of incomplete dominance.
d. result of meiosis.

8. The physical characteristics of an organism are called its
a. genetics. **c.** phenotype.
b. heredity. **d.** genotype.

9. The probability of flipping a coin twice and getting two heads is
a. 1. **c.** 1/4.
b. 1/2. **d.** 3/4.

10. List the four basic principles of genetics that Mendel discovered in his experiments. Briefly describe each of these principles.

11. In pea plants, the allele for yellow seeds is dominant over the allele for green seeds. Predict the genotypic ratio of offspring produced by crossing two parents that are heterozygous for this trait. Draw a Punnett square to illustrate your prediction. B.7.1, B.7.2

Think Critically

12. Apply Concepts In guinea pigs, the allele for a rough coat (*R*) is dominant over the allele for a smooth coat (*r*). A heterozygous guinea pig (*Rr*) and a homozygous recessive guinea pig (*rr*) have a total of nine offspring. The Punnett square for this cross shows a 50 percent chance that any particular offspring will have a smooth coat. Explain how all nine offspring can have smooth coats. B.7.3

	R	*r*
r	*Rr*	*rr*
r	*Rr*	*rr*

11.3 Other Patterns of Inheritance

Understand Key Concepts

13. A situation in which a gene has more than two alleles is known as
a. complete dominance.
b. codominance.
c. polygenic dominance.
d. multiple alleles.

14. A pink-flowered *Mirabilis* plant (*RW*) is crossed with a white-flowered *Mirabilis* (*WW*). What is the chance that a seed from this cross will produce a red-flowered plant? B.7.2, B.7.3
a. 0 **c.** 1/2
b. 1/4 **d.** 1

15. What is the difference between multiple alleles and polygenic traits? B.5.6, B.7.2

16. Why can multiple alleles result in many different phenotypes for a trait? B.5.6, B.7.2

17. Are an organism's characteristics determined only by its genes? Explain. B.1.3

Think Critically

18. **Interpret Visuals** Genes that control hair or feather color in some animals are expressed differently in the winter than in the summer. How might such a difference be beneficial to the ptarmigan shown here?

11.4 Meiosis

Understand Key Concepts

19. The illustration below represents what stage of meiosis? B.6.4

a. prophase I
b. anaphase II
c. telophase I
d. metaphase I

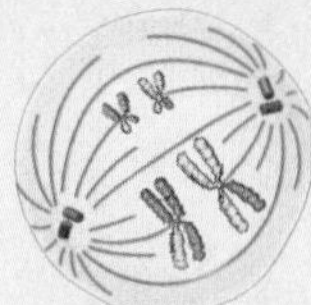

20. Unlike mitosis, meiosis in male mammals results in the formation of B.6.4

a. one haploid gamete.
b. three diploid gametes.
c. four diploid gametes.
d. four haploid gametes.

21. A gene map shows

a. the number of possible alleles for a gene.
b. the relative locations of genes on a chromosome.
c. where chromosomes are in a cell.
d. how crossing-over occurs.

22. Suppose that an organism has the diploid number 2N = 8. How many chromosomes do this organism's gametes contain?

23. Describe the process of meiosis. B.6.4

24. Explain why chromosomes, not individual genes, assort independently. B.6.4

Think Critically

25. **Compare and Contrast** Compare the phases of meiosis I with the phases of meiosis II in terms of number and arrangement of the chromosomes. B.6.4

solve the CHAPTER MYSTERY

GREEN PARAKEETS

After consulting with the owner of the pet store, Susan realized she had a rare gift. White parakeets are very uncommon. The pet shop owner told Susan that two genes control feather color. A dominant Y allele results in the production of a yellow pigment. The dominant B allele controls melanin production. If the genotype contains a capital Y (either YY or Yy) and a capital B, the offspring will be green. If the genotype contains two lowercase y alleles, and a capital B, the offspring will be blue. If the genotype contains two lowercase y's and two lowercase b's, the offspring will be white.

1. **Use Models** Draw a Punnett square that accounts for the inheritance of blue pigment.
2. **Use Models** Construct a Punnett square that explains the inheritance of a white pigment.
3. **Apply Concepts** Solve the mystery by determining the genotypes and phenotypes of the parents and offspring.
4. **Connect to the Big idea** What ratio of colored offspring would you expect if Susan breeds her original pair of parakeets in the years ahead? Would any offspring be green?

IN B.7.1, B.7.3

  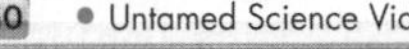 

Have students read through the Chapter Mystery. Ask them to identify which two pigments blend to form green. *(blue and yellow)* Then, have them recall an example they have studied in which colors blended and identify the inheritance pattern. *(incomplete dominance)* Lead students to hypothesize that incomplete dominance could have led to the green color of the parents. To test this idea, have students assume each parent has two dominant alleles, *B* (blue) and *Y* (yellow), similar to the plants in **Figure 11–12.** Ask them to draw a Punnett square and explain the phenotype of the offspring. *(1/4 would be blue, 1/2 would be green, and 1/4 would be yellow.)* Help students see that the genotypes of the parents cannot be simply *BY* and *BY*, because that does not account for the white offspring. Then, have them answer the questions, which will help them solve the mystery.

CHAPTER MYSTERY ANSWERS

1. Students' Punnett squares should show a two-factor cross between green parents that are heterozygous for both yellow and blue pigment. The offspring with *Bbyy* or *BByy* genotypes would account for the blue offspring.
2. Students' Punnett squares should show a two-factor cross between green parents that are heterozygous for both yellow and blue pigment. The offspring with *bbyy* genotypes would account for the white offspring.
3. Parents: genotype *BbYy*, phenotype green; Offspring: (1) genotype *BByy* or *Bbyy*, phenotype blue; (2) genotype *bbYY* or *bbYy*, phenotype yellow; (3) genotype *bbyy*, phenotype white
4. **Big idea** The ratios would reflect the probability of the different combinations in a two-factor heterozygous cross, 9:3:3:1, green:blue:yellow:white. 9/16 of the offspring could be expected to be green.

Follow the crew of Untamed Science in **Genetics Takes Root** as they go back in time to interview Mendel about his famous pea plant experiments that germinated modern genetics.

Lesson 11.4

UNDERSTAND KEY CONCEPTS

19. d **20.** d **21.** b

22. four

23. Meiosis is a process of cell division in which the number of chromosomes per cell is cut in half through the separation of homologous chromosomes.

24. It is the chromosomes that are separated during meiosis. The genes are located on the chromosomes.

THINK CRITICALLY

25. Sample answer: Meiosis I results in two daughter cells with 2N chromosomes each, while meiosis II results in four daughter cells with N chromosomes each. In Prophase I, replicated, homologous chromosomes pair up to form tetrads, while in Prophase II, the chromosomes do not replicate or form tetrads. In Metaphase I, homologous pairs of chromosomes separate, while in Metaphase II, paired chromatids separate. The final four phases of meiosis I and meiosis II are similar.

ASSESSMENT

Connecting Concepts

USE SCIENCE GRAPHICS

26. 66 smooth and 66 wrinkled

27. Yes, the observed numbers are close to the expected values. No other cross would predict a ratio close to 50 percent for each trait.

28. No, a similar outcome would result from a cross like this if wrinkled seeds were dominant.

WRITE ABOUT SCIENCE

29. Students' explanations should be clear and concise and include examples. They should explain that a gene has at least two alleles. Some alleles are dominant and others are recessive. An organism with a dominant allele will always exhibit that form of the trait. Recessive alleles are expressed only in the absence of dominant alleles.

30. Students' explanations should include that these two traits are located close together on the same chromosome. When alleles of different genes are close to each other, they are said to be linked. These genes tend to be inherited together. Diagrams should indicate the alleles' positions on one chromosome as being close together throughout meiosis.

31. Big idea Pairs of genes are found on pairs of chromosomes. The pairs of chromosomes and their genes separate during meiosis and gamete formation. Each gamete gets only one of each pair of chromosomes and one of each pair of genes. In fertilization, chromosome pairs and their genes come together from each parent to form new combinations.

Connecting Concepts

Use Science Graphics NoS.3

Seed coat was one trait that Mendel studied in pea plants. The coat, or covering, of the seed is either smooth or wrinkled. Suppose a researcher has two plants—one that makes smooth seeds and another that makes wrinkled seeds. The researcher crosses the wrinkled-seed plants and the smooth-seed plants, obtaining the following data. Use the data to answer questions 26–28.

Results of Seed Experiment

Phenotype	Number of Plants in the F_1 Generation	
	Expected	Observed
Smooth seeds		60
Wrinkled seeds		72

26. **Predict** Mendel knew that the allele for smooth (*R*) seeds was dominant over the allele for wrinkled (*r*) seeds. If this cross was $Rr \times rr$, what numbers would fill the middle column? B.7.1

27. **Analyze Data** Are the observed numbers consistent with the hypothesis that the cross is $Rr \times rr$? Explain your answer. B.7.1

28. **Draw Conclusions** Are the data from this experiment alone sufficient to conclude that the allele for smooth seeds is dominant over the allele for wrinkled seeds? Why or why not? B.7.1

Write About Science NoS.3

29. **Explain** Write an explanation of dominant and recessive alleles that would be appropriate to give to an eighth-grade science class. You can assume that the eighth-grade students already know the meanings of *gene* and *allele*. (*Hint*: Use examples to make your explanation clear.) B.7.1

30. **Cause and Effect** Explain why the alleles for reddish-orange eyes and miniature wings in *Drosophila* are usually inherited together. Describe the pattern of inheritance these alleles follow, and include the idea of gene linkage. (*Hint*: To organize your ideas, draw a cause-effect diagram that shows what happens to the two alleles during meiosis.)

31. **Assess the**  Explain why the gene pairs described by Mendel behave in a way that is consistent with the behavior of chromosomes during gamete formation, fertilization, and reproduction. B.6.4

Analyzing Data

IN NoS.3

A researcher studying fruit flies finds a mutant fly with brown-colored eyes. Almost all fruit flies in nature have bright red eyes. When the researcher crosses the mutant fly with a normal red-eyed fly, all of the F_1 offspring have red eyes. The researcher then crosses two of the F_1 red-eyed flies and obtains the following results in the F_2 generation.

Eye Color in the F_2 Generation	
Red eyes	37
Brown eyes	14

32. **Calculate** What is the ratio of red-eyed flies to brown-eyed flies? MATH

a. 1 : 1
b. 1 : 3
c. 3 : 1
d. 4 : 1

33. **Draw Conclusions** The allele for red eyes in fruit flies is B.7.1

a. dominant over brown eyes.
b. recessive to brown eyes.
c. codominant with the brown-eyed gene.
d. a multiple allele with the brown-eyed gene and others.

PURPOSE Students will analyze data to draw conclusions about the inheritance pattern of a trait in fruit flies.

PLANNING Have students review the terms *dominant, recessive, codominance,* and *multiple alleles.*

ANSWERS

32. c

33. a

Standardized Test Practice for Indiana

Multiple Choice

1. What happens to the chromosome number during meiosis?
   A It doubles.
   B It stays the same.
   C It halves.
   D It becomes diploid. B.6.4

2. Which ratio did Mendel find in his F_2 generation?
   A 3 : 1
   B 1 : 3 : 1
   C 1 : 2
   D 3 : 4 B.7.1

3. During which phase of meiosis is the chromosome number reduced?
   A anaphase I
   B metaphase I
   C telophase I
   D telophase II B.6.4

4. Two pink-flowering plants are crossed. The offspring flower as follows: 25% red, 25% white, and 50% pink. What pattern of inheritance does flower color in these flowers follow?
   A dominance
   B multiple alleles
   C incomplete dominance
   D polygenic traits B.7.1

5. Which of the following is used to construct a gene map?
   A chromosome number
   B mutation rate
   C rate of meiosis
   D recombination rate

6. Alleles for the same trait are separated from each other during the process of
   A cytokinesis.
   B meiosis I.
   C meiosis II.
   D metaphase II. B.6.4

7. Which of the following is NOT one of Gregor Mendel's principles?
   A The alleles for different genes usually segregate independently.
   B Some forms of a gene may be dominant.
   C The inheritance of characteristics is determined by factors (genes).
   D Crossing-over occurs during meiosis.

Questions 8–9

Genes A, B, C, and D are located on the same chromosome. After calculating recombination frequencies, a student determines that these genes are separated by the following map units: C–D, 25 map units; A–B, 12 map units; B–D, 20 map units; A–C, 17 map units.

8. How many map units apart are genes A and D?
   A 5
   B 8
   C 10
   D 12.5

9. Which gene map best reflects the student's data?

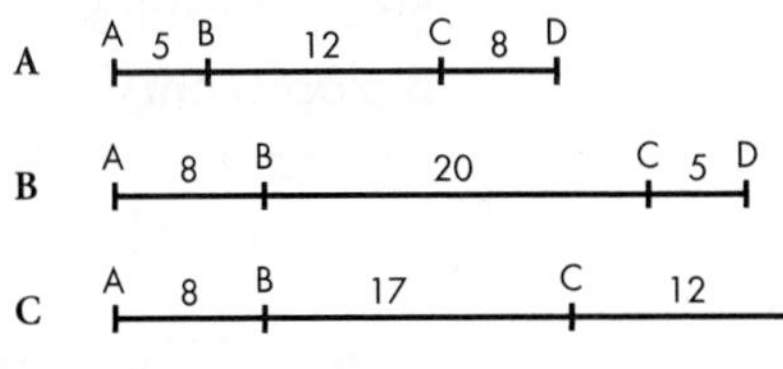

D C 5 B 12 A 8 D

Open-Ended Response

10. Explain why meiosis allows organisms to maintain their chromosome numbers from one generation to the next. B.6.4

If You Have Trouble With . . .										
Question	1	2	3	4	5	6	7	8	9	10
See Lesson	11.4	11.1	11.4	11.3	11.4	11.4	11.2	11.4	11.4	11.4

Test-Taking Tip

ANTICIPATE THE ANSWER

Tell students to read the question stem and try to anticipate what the answer will be. Then, have them read all the answer choices carefully to see which choice best matches the answer they anticipated. Reinforce that they should read all the answer choices before selecting one.

Answers

1. C
2. A
3. D
4. C
5. D
6. B
7. D
8. B
9. D
10. By reducing the number of chromosomes in gametes to one half of the diploid number, fertilization will restore the diploid number when the gametes fuse.

CHAPTER PLANNER 12 DNA

Chapter Contents	IN	Time	Core Resources
Chapter Preview			**Student Edition,** pp. 336–337 **Chapter Mystery,** p. 337
12.1 Identifying the Substance of Genes Bacterial Transformation • Bacterial Viruses • The Role of DNA	NoS.6, B.5.1, B.5.2	1 period 1/2 block	**Student Edition,** pp. 338–343 **Study Workbook A** 12.1 Worksheets L2 **Biology.com** *Art in Motion:* Hershey-Chase Experiment • *Visual Analogy:* The Main Functions of DNA and Books • 12.1 Self-Test • 12.1 Lesson Assessment
12.2 The Structure of DNA The Components of DNA • Solving the Structure of DNA • The Double-Helix Model • *Biology & History: Discovering the Role of DNA*	NoS.3, B.5.1	1 period 1/2 block	**Student Edition,** pp. 344–349 **Inquiry** 12.2 Analyzing Data, p. 345 L2 **Study Workbook A** 12.2 Worksheets L2 **Biology.com** *Tutor Tube:* Memory Tricks for Base Pairing • *Data Analysis:* Tracking Illegal Whaling **Assessment Resources Book** Visual Quiz L2
12.3 DNA Replication Copying the Code • Replication in Living Cells	B.1.2, B.7.4	1 period 1/2 block	**Student Edition,** pp. 350–353 **Inquiry** 12.3 Quick Lab, p. 352 L2 **Study Workbook A** 12.3 Worksheets L2 **Biology.com** *Art Review:* Eukaryotic and Prokaryotic DNA Replication **Assessment Resources Book** Visual Quiz L2
Chapter Pre-Lab		1 period 1/2 block	**Student Edition,** p. 354 L2 **Lab Manual A** *Extracting DNA* L2

Differentiated Instruction Tools

Study Workbook B includes worksheets with lesson-level differentiated instruction support and explanations of differentiated instruction teaching strategies.

Lab Manual B includes skills labs, simplified chapter labs, and hands-on activities.

ELL Handbook explains ways to make *Biology* more accessible to ELL students.

Spanish Study Workbook is a Spanish translation of Study Workbook A.

Multilingual Glossary is the glossary translated into ten languages.

Differentiated Instruction Key

- L1 Special Needs or Struggling Students
- ELL English Language Learners
- LPR Less Proficient Readers
- L2 On-Level Students
- L3 Advanced Students

Additional Resources

Biology.com Untamed Science Video • Vocabulary Flash Cards

Study Workbook B 12.1 Worksheets L1 ELL LPR
Spanish Study Workbook 12.1 Worksheets ELL
Biology.com 12.1 Lesson Overview • 12.1 Lesson Notes

Study Workbook B 12.2 Worksheets L1 ELL LPR
Spanish Study Workbook 12.2 Worksheets ELL
Biology.com 12.2 Lesson Overview • 12.2 Lesson Notes • 12.2 Self-Test • 12.2 Lesson Assessment

Study Workbook B 12.3 Worksheets L1 ELL LPR
Spanish Study Workbook 12.3 Worksheets ELL
Biology.com *InterActive Art:* DNA Replication • 12.3 Lesson Overview • 12.3 Lesson Notes • 12.3 Self-Test • 12.3 Lesson Assessment

Lab Manual B *Extracting DNA* • Data Analysis: *Base Percentages* • Hands-On Activity: *Modeling DNA Replication* L1 ELL LPR

Chapter Review

Student Edition Study Guide, p. 355 L2
Study Workbook A Chapter 12 Vocabulary Review L2 • Chapter 12 Chapter Mystery/21st Century Skills Activity L2 L3
Transparencies, pp. 148–156 L1 ELL LPR L2
Biology.com Untamed Science Video • Editable Worksheets of Study Workbooks A and B and Lab Manuals A and B • Chapter 12 Flash Cards and Match It

Untamed Science DVD • Classroom Resources CD (includes lesson presentations and editable worksheets)

Chapter Assessment

Student Edition Assessment, pp. 356–359 L2
Study Workbook B Chapter 12 Chapter Review L1 ELL LPR • Chapter 12 Taking a Standardized Test L1 ELL LPR
Assessment Resources Book Chapter 12 Test A L2 • Chapter 12 Test B L1 ELL LPR
Biology.com Chapter 12 Assessment • Editable Worksheets of Chapter 12 Visual Quizzes and Chapter 12 Tests A and B

Exam*View Assessment Suite* • Classroom Resources CD (includes lesson presentations and editable worksheets)

Time: 1 period, 1/2 block

Pressed for Time?

Preview the Chapter Preview Figure 12–5 and read the Key Questions for Lesson 12.2.

Cover the Chapter Quickly Have students read *The Role of DNA* in Lesson 12.1, all of Lesson 12.2, and *Copying the Code* in Lesson 12.3, focusing on Figure 12–8.

Assess Assign question 3 in the 12.1 Assessment, the entire 12.2 Assessment, question 1 in the 12.3 Assessment, and questions 9–17, 20–22, 24, and 25 in the Chapter 12 Assessment.

Connect to the Big Idea

Ask students to describe the sculpture shown on this page. *(Sample answer: circular, twisted, colorful)* Point out the caption, which explains that this sculpture models the structure of DNA, a molecule that carries genetic information in living things.

Explain that the structure of DNA was not determined until the 1950s. Tell students that an understanding of DNA's function gave some clues to its structure. Observations and experiments by many scientists also provided clues to DNA's structure. Suggest students note the relationship between DNA's structure and function as they read the chapter. Ask them to anticipate the answer to the question, **What is the structure of DNA, and how does it function in genetic inheritance?**

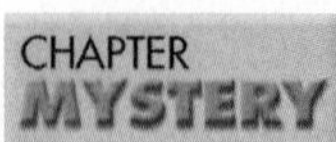

Have students read the Chapter Mystery. Ask them to make predictions about the relationship between UV light, cell damage, and skin cancer. After students have completed the chapter, have them compare their predictions to the information in the Chapter Mystery clues found throughout the chapter and online.

BIOLOGY.com Have students preview the chapter vocabulary terms using the **Flash Cards.**

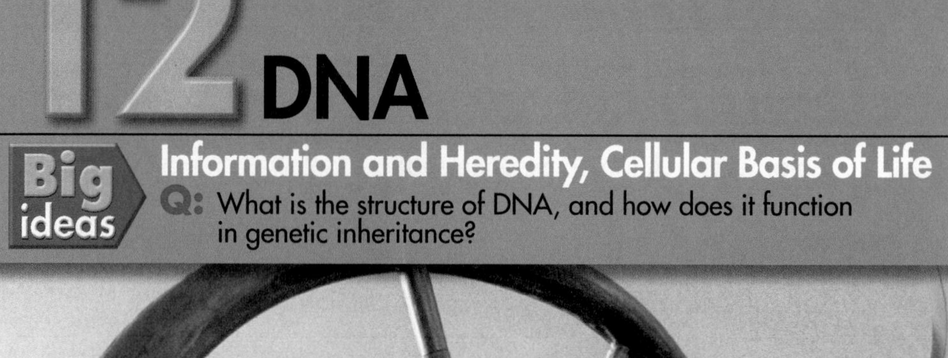
12 DNA
Big ideas
Information and Heredity, Cellular Basis of Life
Q: What is the structure of DNA, and how does it function in genetic inheritance?

BIOLOGY.com Search Chapter 12 GO • Flash Cards

336

IN INDIANA ACADEMIC STANDARDS

For the full text of all standards, see the Course Overview in the front matter of this book.

Key standards: Chapter 12 covers key ideas from Standard 5: Molecular Basis of Heredity and Standard 7: Genetics, including **B.5.1** DNA and chromosomes, **B.5.2** Genes, and **B.7.4** DNA: Duplication and damage.

UbD Understanding by Design

In Chapter 12, students learn about experiments that helped reveal the structure and function of DNA as well as how DNA replicates. Use the ideas and questions shown in the graphic organizer at the right to connect Chapter 12 content with the Unit 4 Enduring Understanding: *DNA is the universal code for life; it enables an organism to transmit hereditary information and, along with the environment, determines an organism's characteristics.*

PERFORMANCE GOALS

Students' mastery of Chapter 12 content will be demonstrated by their responses to discussion questions found in this Teacher's Edition and their completion of labs and data analysis activities. Additionally, the Performance Tasks require students to synthesize with chapter content by creating a chapter review software presentation and writing a letter from the point of view of Watson or Crick.

INDIANA ACADEMIC STANDARDS FOR SCIENCE

Nature of Science NoS.3, NoS.6; **Cellular Chemistry** B.1.2; **Molecular Basis of Heredity** B.5.1, B.5.2; **Genetics** B.7.4. See lessons for details.

This sculpture, outside the Lawrence Hall of Science at the University of California at Berkeley, models the structure of DNA—the substance that genes are made of.

- Untamed Science Video
- Chapter Mystery

CHAPTER MYSTERY

UV LIGHT

"Put on your sunscreen!" This familiar phrase can be heard at most beaches on a sunny day. It's an important directive, though, because sunlight—for all its beneficial effects—can readily damage the skin. The most dangerous wavelengths of sunlight are the ones we can't see: the ultraviolet (UV) region of the electromagnetic spectrum. Not only can excess exposure to UV light damage skin cells, it can cause a deadly form of skin cancer that kills nearly 10,000 Americans each year. Why is UV light so dangerous? How can these particular wavelengths of light damage our cells to the point of causing cell death and cancer? As you read this chapter, look for clues to help you solve the question of why UV light is so damaging to skin cells. Then, solve the mystery.

Never Stop Exploring Your World. Finding the connection between UV light and DNA is only the beginning. Take a video field trip with the ecogeeks of Untamed Science to see where the mystery leads.

Chapter 12 Big Idea: Information and Heredity, Cellular Basis of Life

Chapter 12 EQ: What is the structure of DNA, and how does it function in genetic inheritance?

- **12.1 GQ:** How did scientists determine that DNA is responsible for storing, copying, and transmitting genetic information?
- **12.2 GQ:** How was the basic structure of DNA discovered?
- **12.3 GQ:** How do cells copy their DNA?

What's Online

Extend your reach by using these and other digital assets offered at Biology.com.

CHAPTER MYSTERY
Students collect information about how UV light changes DNA and how DNA damage causes skin cancer to help them solve the mystery.

UNTAMED SCIENCE VIDEO
Follow the Untamed Science crew as they unlock the hidden information that can be found in DNA evidence from a crime scene.

ART IN MOTION
Students can watch an animated version of the experiment that convinced scientists DNA was the genetic material found in cells.

VISUAL ANALOGY
With this activity, students will watch the ways in which DNA can be compared to a "How-To" book.

DATA ANALYSIS
Students can analyze DNA data to assess the relatedness of different species.

TUTOR TUBE
This online tutorial offers some handy strategies for remembering which DNA bases pair together.

INTERACTIVE ART
Students can watch an animation of DNA replication and then drag-and-drop labels to test their understanding.

DATA ANALYSIS
Students analyze DNA sequences for the purpose of identifying illegally caught whales.

ART REVIEW
This drag-and-drop labeling activity helps students review the differences between prokaryotic and eukaryotic DNA replication.

LESSON 12.1

Getting Started

Objectives

12.1.1 Summarize the process of bacterial transformation.

12.1.2 Describe the role of bacteriophages in identifying genetic material.

12.1.3 Identify the role of DNA in heredity.

Student Resources

Study Workbooks A and B, 12.1 Worksheets

Spanish Study Workbook, 12.1 Worksheets

Lesson Overview • Lesson Notes
- Activities: Art in Motion, Visual Analogy
- Assessment: Self-Test, Lesson Assessment

For corresponding lesson in the **Foundation Edition**, see pages 288–291.

Activate Prior Knowledge

Have several volunteers describe how the information they learned in elementary and middle school prepared them for the academic work they are now doing in high school. Point out that, without the skills they learned earlier in life, they would be unable to carry out high-school level work. Explain that scientific knowledge grows in a similar way. Tell students this lesson will describe experiments that laid the groundwork for current work in the scientific field of genetics.

IN INDIANA ACADEMIC STANDARDS

For the full text of all standards, see the Course Overview in the front matter of this book.

B.5.2 Describe how hereditary information passed from parents to offspring is encoded in regions of DNA molecules called genes.

12.1 Identifying the Substance of Genes

IN B.5.2 Genes. Also covered: NoS.6, B.5.1.

Key Questions

What clues did bacterial transformation yield about the gene?

What role did bacterial viruses play in identifying genetic material?

What is the role of DNA in heredity?

Vocabulary

transformation
bacteriophage

Taking Notes

Flowchart As you read this section, make a flowchart that shows how scientists came to understand the molecule known as DNA.

THINK ABOUT IT How do genes work? To answer that question, the first thing you need to know is what genes are made of. After all, you couldn't understand how an automobile engine works without understanding what the engine is made of and how it's put together. So, how would you go about figuring out what molecule or molecules go into making a gene?

Bacterial Transformation

What clues did bacterial transformation yield about the gene?

In the first half of the twentieth century, biologists developed the field of genetics to the point where they began to wonder about the nature of the gene itself. To truly understand genetics, scientists realized they first had to discover the chemical nature of the gene. If the molecule that carries genetic information could be identified, it might be possible to understand how genes actually control the inherited characteristics of living things.

Like many stories in science, the discovery of the chemical nature of the gene began with an investigator who was actually looking for something else. In 1928, the British scientist Frederick Griffith was trying to figure out how bacteria make people sick. More specifically, Griffith wanted to learn how certain types of bacteria produce the serious lung disease known as pneumonia.

Griffith had isolated two very similar types of bacteria from mice. These were actually two different varieties, or strains, of the same bacterial species. Both strains grew very well in culture plates in Griffith's lab, but only one of them caused pneumonia. The disease-causing bacteria (S strain) grew into smooth colonies on culture plates, whereas the harmless bacteria (R strain) produced colonies with rough edges. The difference in appearance made the two strains easy to tell apart.

Griffith's Experiments When Griffith injected mice with disease-causing bacteria, the mice developed pneumonia and died. When he injected mice with harmless bacteria, the mice stayed healthy. Griffith wondered what made the first group of mice get pneumonia. Perhaps the S-strain bacteria produced a toxin that made the mice sick? To find out, he ran the series of experiments shown in **Figure 12–1.** First, Griffith took a culture of the S strain, heated the cells to kill them, then injected the heat-killed bacteria into laboratory mice. The mice survived, suggesting that the cause of pneumonia was not a toxin from these disease-causing bacteria.

Search Lesson 12.1

• Lesson Overview • Lesson Notes

UbD Teach for Understanding

ENDURING UNDERSTANDING DNA is the universal code for life; it enables an organism to transmit hereditary information and, along with the environment, determines an organism's characteristics.

GUIDING QUESTION How did scientists determine that DNA is responsible for storing, copying, and transmitting genetic information?

EVIDENCE OF UNDERSTANDING *After completing the lesson, give students the following assessment to show they understand how scientists identified the genetic material in cells.* Have students work in small groups to write a newspaper article describing the work of either Frederick Griffith, Oswald Avery, or Alfred Hershey and Martha Chase. Explain that newspaper articles usually provide answers to the following set of questions: *Who? What? Where? When?* and *Why?* Have each group share its completed newspaper article with the class.

In Griffith's next experiment, he mixed the heat-killed, S-strain bacteria with live, harmless bacteria from the R strain. This mixture he injected into laboratory mice. By themselves, neither type of bacteria should have made the mice sick. To Griffith's surprise, however, the injected mice developed pneumonia, and many died. When he examined the lungs of these mice, he found them to be filled not with the harmless bacteria, but with the disease-causing bacteria. How could that happen if the S-strain cells were dead?

Transformation Somehow, the heat-killed bacteria passed their disease-causing ability to the harmless bacteria. Griffith reasoned that, when he mixed the two types of bacteria together, some chemical factor transferred from the heat-killed cells of the S strain into the live cells of the R strain. This chemical compound, he hypothesized, must contain information that could change harmless bacteria into disease-causing ones. He called this process **transformation,** because one type of bacteria (the harmless form) had been changed permanently into another (the disease-causing form). Because the ability to cause disease was inherited by the offspring of the transformed bacteria, Griffith concluded that the transforming factor had to be a gene.

In Your Notebook *Write a summary of Griffith's experiments.*

FIGURE 12–1 Griffith's Experiments Griffith injected mice with four different samples of bacteria. When injected separately, neither heat-killed, disease-causing bacteria nor live, harmless bacteria killed the mice. The two strains injected together, however, caused fatal pneumonia. From this experiment, Griffith inferred that genetic information could be transferred from one bacterial strain to another. **Infer** ***Why did Griffith test to see whether the bacteria recovered from the sick mice in his last experiment would produce smooth or rough colonies in a petri dish?***

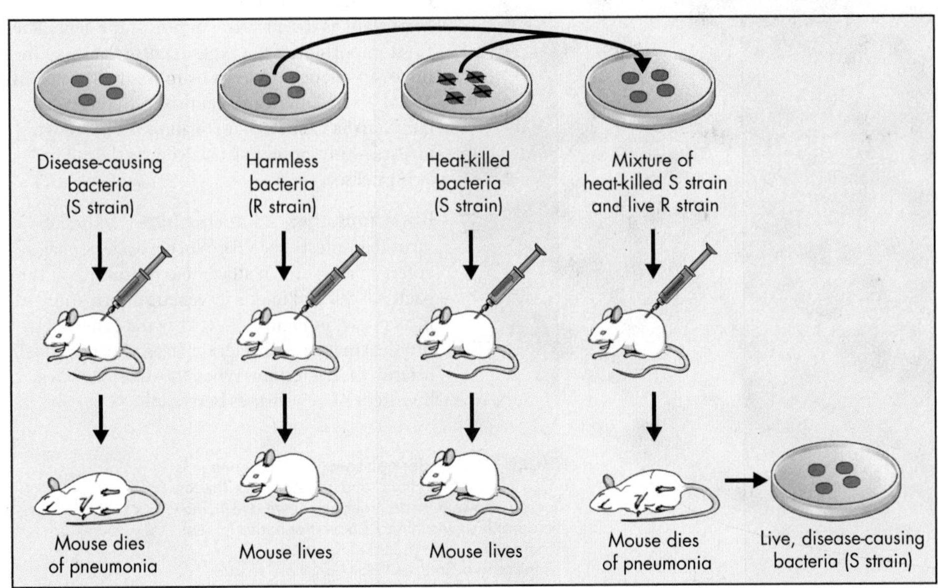

How Science Works

EARLY INVESTIGATION OF NUCLEIC ACIDS

Well before the work of Frederick Griffith, experiments had provided information about nucleic acids. In the late 1860s, Friedrich Miescher, a medical researcher, isolated a substance called nuclein while working with white blood cells. Miescher was able to determine that this substance, found in the nuclei of cells, was a complex of protein and an additional compound, which today is known to be nucleic acid, or DNA. He was also able to discover the chemical makeup of nuclein—hydrogen, oxygen, nitrogen, and phosphorus. These results were published in 1871.

Teach

Use Visuals

Tell students the word *transformation* means "change."

Ask Why is the word *transformation* a good description of what happened in Griffith's experiment? *(Sample answer: One strain of bacteria transformed, or changed, into another.)*

Ask Why did Griffith conclude that the transforming factor had to be a gene? *(The factor was inherited by offspring of the transformed bacteria.)*

DIFFERENTIATED INSTRUCTION

LPR Less Proficient Readers Have struggling readers use **Figure 12–1** to learn about Griffith's experiment. Point out and describe what happens in each vertical panel of the figure.

Ask In this experiment, which strain of bacteria caused disease? *(the S strain)*

Ask What happened when heat-killed S strain was injected into a mouse? *(It no longer caused disease.)*

Ask What happened when the heat-killed S strain was mixed with the harmless R-strain bacteria? *(The mouse got sick.)*

ELL Focus on ELL: Extend Language

INTERMEDIATE SPEAKERS To understand the content of this lesson, students need a working knowledge of terms such as *experiment, inferred, concluded,* and *observed.* As students read about the experiments in this lesson, have them locate these terms in the text. Ask students to find a definition for each term in a dictionary and to practice pronouncing each term aloud.

Answers

FIGURE 12–1 to determine whether the substance transferred from the heat-killed bacteria to the R strain was heritable

IN YOUR NOTEBOOK Students' summaries should include a description of the four different samples of bacteria Griffith injected into the mice, the fate of the mice injected with each strain, and the conclusion Griffith drew based on his results.

Teach continued

Lead a Discussion

Review with students the experimental design used by Avery and his team. Have students identify the manipulated, or independent, variable in the experiment. *(the type of enzyme used to treat the extract from heat-killed bacteria)* Make sure they realize that only one enzyme was used in each experiment. Then, have them identify the responding, or dependent, variable in this experiment. *(whether transformation occurred)* Have students state the conclusion that was reached using the results of these experiments. *(DNA stores and transmits genetic information.)*

DIFFERENTIATED INSTRUCTION

L1 Struggling Students Provide students with a visual representation of Avery's experiment. Start by drawing a cluster of heat-killed bacteria on the board. Then, draw an arrow from the bacteria to a test tube with liquid in it, while explaining that Avery extracted cellular materials from the bacteria. Draw protein-destroying enzymes being added to this test tube. Then, draw another arrow to a cluster of live R-strain bacteria, and tell students that Avery mixed the enzyme-treated material with the live R-strain bacteria. Finally, show another arrow pointing to live S-strain bacteria. Explain that transformation occurred. Repeat this drawing process to show the effects of an RNA-destroying enzyme. Finally, draw the process for a DNA-destroying enzyme. For this one, talk about why transformation did not occur and how Avery used this result to reach his conclusion that DNA is the transforming factor.

ELL English Language Learners Introduce students to the term *bacteriophage.* Tell students that the word part *-phage* is based on the Greek word *phagein,* meaning "to eat." Explain that when *-phage* is added to a noun, it signifies "one who eats." Have students apply this knowledge to *bacteriophage* and discuss its meaning. *(Students should conclude that bacteriophages "eat," or destroy, the bacteria they infect.)*

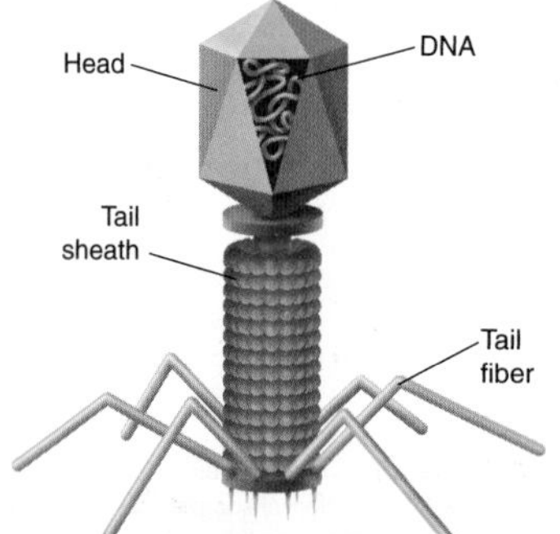

The Molecular Cause of Transformation In 1944, a group of scientists at the Rockefeller Institute in New York decided to repeat Griffith's work. Led by the Canadian biologist Oswald Avery, the scientists wanted to determine which molecule in the heat-killed bacteria was most important for transformation. They reasoned that if they could find this particular molecule, it might reveal the chemical nature of the gene.

Avery and his team extracted a mixture of various molecules from the heat-killed bacteria. They carefully treated this mixture with enzymes that destroyed proteins, lipids, carbohydrates, and some other molecules, including the nucleic acid RNA. Transformation still occurred. Clearly, since those molecules had been destroyed, none of them could have been responsible for transformation.

Avery's team repeated the experiment one more time. This time, they used enzymes that would break down a different nucleic acid—DNA. When they destroyed the DNA in the mixture, transformation did not occur. There was just one possible explanation for these results: *DNA was the transforming factor.* **By observing bacterial transformation, Avery and other scientists discovered that the nucleic acid DNA stores and transmits genetic information from one generation of bacteria to the next.**

Bacterial Viruses

What role did bacterial viruses play in identifying genetic material?

Scientists are a skeptical group. It usually takes several experiments to convince them of something as important as the chemical nature of the gene. The most important of the experiments relating to the discovery made by Avery's team was performed in 1952 by two American scientists, Alfred Hershey and Martha Chase. They collaborated in studying viruses—tiny, nonliving particles that can infect living cells.

Bacteriophages A **bacteriophage** is a kind of virus that infects bacteria. When a bacteriophage enters a bacterium, it attaches to the surface of the bacterial cell and injects its genetic information into it, as shown in **Figure 12–2.** The viral genes act to produce many new bacteriophages, which gradually destroy the bacterium. When the cell splits open, hundreds of new viruses burst out.

TEM 200,000×

FIGURE 12–2 Bacteriophages A bacteriophage is a type of virus that infects and kills bacteria. The top diagram shows a bacteriophage known as T4. The micrograph shows three T2 bacteriophages (green) invading an *E. coli* bacterium (gold).
Compare and Contrast ***How large are viruses compared with bacteria?***

UbD Check for Understanding

HAND SIGNALS

Ask students the following questions, and have them show a thumbs-up sign if they can answer a question, a thumbs-down sign if they cannot, or a waving-hand sign if they are unsure.

- What is bacterial transformation?
- What conclusion did Frederick Griffith draw from his experimental results?
- What conclusion did Oswald Avery draw from his experimental results?

ADJUST INSTRUCTION

If students are confused, have pairs work together to write a one-sentence response to each question.

Answers

FIGURE 12–2 Viruses are much smaller than bacteria.

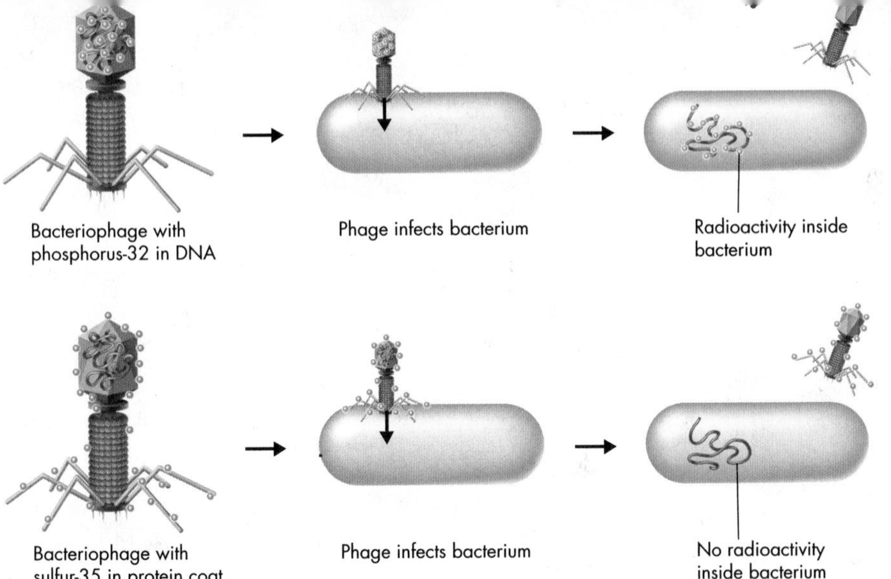

FIGURE 12–3 Hershey-Chase Experiment Alfred Hershey and Martha Chase used different radioactive markers to label the DNA and proteins of bacteriophages. The bacteriophages injected only DNA, not proteins, into bacterial cells.

The Hershey-Chase Experiment Hershey and Chase studied a bacteriophage that was composed of a DNA core and a protein coat. They wanted to determine which part of the virus—the protein coat or the DNA core—entered the bacterial cell. Their results would either support or disprove Avery's finding that genes were made of DNA.

The pair grew viruses in cultures containing radioactive isotopes of phosphorus-32 (^{32}P) and sulfur-35 (^{35}S). This was a clever strategy, because proteins contain almost no phosphorus, and DNA contains no sulfur. Therefore, these radioactive substances could be used as markers, enabling the scientists to tell which molecules actually entered the bacteria, carrying the genetic information of the virus. If they found radioactivity from ^{35}S in the bacteria, it would mean that the virus's protein coat had been injected into the bacteria. If they found ^{32}P, then the DNA core had been injected.

The two scientists mixed the marked viruses with bacterial cells. They waited a few minutes for the viruses to inject their genetic material. Next, they separated the viruses from the bacteria and tested the bacteria for radioactivity. **Figure 12–3** shows the steps in this experiment. What were the results? Nearly all the radioactivity in the bacteria was from phosphorus (^{32}P), the marker found in DNA. Hershey and Chase concluded that the genetic material of the bacteriophage was indeed DNA, not protein. **Hershey and Chase's experiment with bacteriophages confirmed Avery's results, convincing many scientists that DNA was the genetic material found in genes—not just in viruses and bacteria, but in all living cells.**

In Your Notebook *Identify the independent and dependent variables in the Hershey-Chase experiment, and list some possible control variables.*

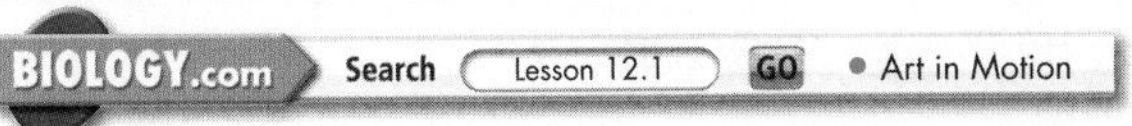
BIOLOGY.com Search Lesson 12.1 GO • Art in Motion

How Science Works

RADIOISOTOPES—A TOOL FOR BIOLOGISTS

Radioisotopes, or radioactive isotopes, are commonly used by biologists to study cell processes because they can be substituted into biochemical reactions without changing the chemistry of the reactions. Isotopes of an element contain the same number of protons but different numbers of neutrons in their nuclei. Radioisotopes are isotopes that have an unstable nucleus. For example, ^{32}P is an isotope of phosphorus. ^{32}P is not stable, so it "decays" into a more stable form. This decay is detected as radioactivity. Scientists studying a particular biochemical reaction that involves phosphorus can use ^{32}P to monitor the reaction. Radioisotopes of many other elements also exist, giving biologists a wide range of these "tools" to work with.

Lead a Discussion

Begin a discussion on the Hershey-Chase experiment.

Ask What happens when a bacteriophage infects a bacterium? *(The bacteriophage injects its genetic material into the bacterium.)*

Ask What did the bacteriophage used by Hershey and Chase consist of? *(protein and DNA)*

Ask What question did Hershey and Chase seek to answer with their experiment? *(Does DNA or protein transmit genetic information?)*

DIFFERENTIATED INSTRUCTION

L1 Struggling Students To help students understand the Hershey-Chase experiment, walk them through the steps of how a bacteriophage infects a bacterium. As a class, construct a **Flowchart** that shows these steps. First, the bacteriophage attaches to the surface of the bacterium and injects its genetic information. Next, the viral genes are replicated, and many new bacteriophages are produced. Last, the bacterium splits open, and new viruses burst out.

Study Wkbks A/B, Appendix S25, Flowchart. **Transparencies,** GO8.

BIOLOGY.com To help students better visualize the experiment, suggest they watch **Art in Motion: Hershey-Chase Experiment.**

Answers

IN YOUR NOTEBOOK The independent variable is the substance that was labeled, DNA or protein. The dependent variable is the presence of radioactivity in the infected cell. An example of a control variable is the amount of time Hershey and Chase waited for the viruses to infect the bacteria.

LESSON 12.1

Teach continued

VISUAL ANALOGY

Have students examine **Figure 12–4,** which uses the analogy of a book to describe the functions of DNA.

Ask Look at the title of the book. In what ways is DNA like a how-to book? *(It stores instructions.)*

Ask How does DNA store information? *(Sample answer: in its molecular structure)*

Ask Why is it important that DNA can be accurately copied? *(so that each daughter cell receives a complete and correct copy of the genetic material during cell division)*

DIFFERENTIATED INSTRUCTION

L1 Special Needs Make a bulleted list on the board of the three main functions of DNA presented in this lesson *(storing information, copying information, and transmitting information)*. Have students use this list to remind them of DNA's basic functions as they learn more about DNA's structure and replication in this chapter.

BIOLOGY.com Students can explore this analogy further by completing the online activity **Visual Analogy: The Main Functions of DNA and Books.**

Address Misconceptions

Genes Although most students are familiar with the word *gene*, many cannot describe the chemical basis of inheritance. As students are introduced to the function of DNA in this lesson, remind them that genes, which are made of DNA, carry a chemical code for biological processes. It is this chemical code that stores genetic information, is copied when a cell divides, and transmits information from one generation to the next.

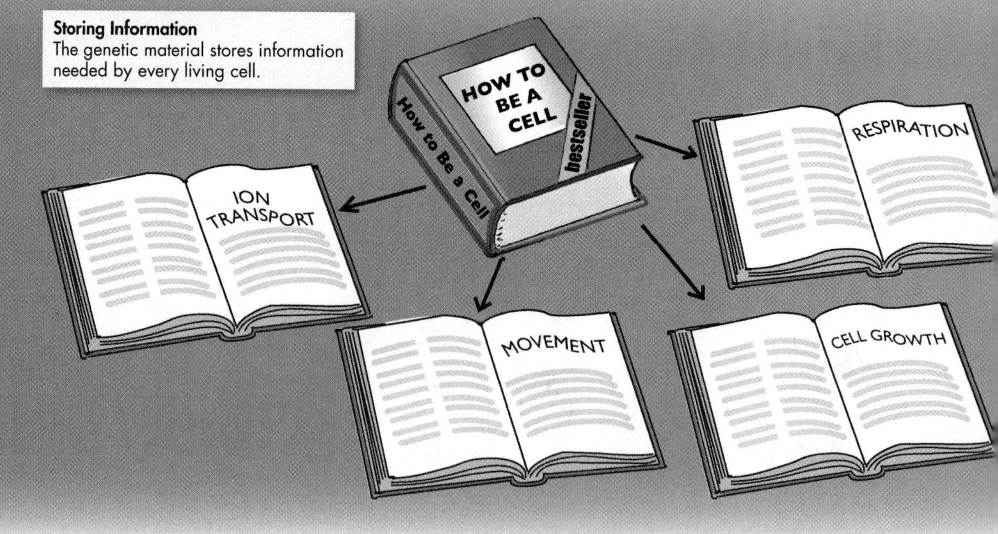

VISUAL ANALOGY

THE MAIN FUNCTIONS OF DNA

FIGURE 12–4 Like DNA, the book in this diagram contains coded instructions for a cell to carry out important biological processes, such as how to move or transport ions. The book, like DNA, can also be copied and passed along to the next generation. These three tasks—storing, copying, and transmitting information—are also the three main functions of DNA.

The Role of DNA

What is the role of DNA in heredity?

You might think that scientists would have been satisfied knowing that genes were made of DNA, but that was not the case at all. Instead, they wondered how DNA, or any molecule for that matter, could do the critical things that genes were known to do. The next era of study began with one crucial assumption. **The DNA that makes up genes must be capable of storing, copying, and transmitting the genetic information in a cell.** These three functions are analogous to the way in which you might share a treasured book, as pictured in **Figure 12–4.**

Storing Information The foremost job of DNA, as the molecule of heredity, is to store information. The genes that make a flower purple must somehow carry the information needed to produce purple pigment. Genes for blood type and eye color must have the information needed for their jobs as well, and other genes have to do even more. Genes control patterns of development, which means that the instructions that cause a single cell to develop into an oak tree, a sea urchin, or a dog must somehow be written into the DNA of each of these organisms.

Copying Information Before a cell divides, it must make a complete copy of every one of its genes. To many scientists, the most puzzling aspect of DNA was how it could be copied. The solution to this and other puzzles had to wait until the structure of the DNA molecule became known. Within a few weeks of this discovery, a copying mechanism for the genetic material was put forward. You will learn about this mechanism later in the chapter.

 BIOLOGY.com Search Lesson 12.1 GO • Visual Analogy

UbD Check for Understanding

ONE-MINUTE RESPONSE

Write the following prompt on the board, and give students about a minute to write a response summarizing their understanding.

What are the three functions of DNA, and why is each function important to living things? *(Responses should identify storing, copying, and transmitting information, and they should include an explanation of the importance of each function.)*

ADJUST INSTRUCTION

If responses show that students do not understand the three functions of DNA, divide the class into three groups. Assign one function to each group. Then, have each group develop and give a short, creative presentation, such as a rap or song, to help others remember the function.

Copying Information Before a cell divides, its genetic information must be copied.

Transmitting Information When a cell divides, each daughter cell must receive a complete copy of the genetic information.

Transmitting Information As Mendel's work had shown, genes are transmitted from one generation to the next. Therefore, DNA molecules must be carefully sorted and passed along during cell division. Such careful sorting is especially important during the formation of reproductive cells in meiosis. Remember, the chromosomes of eukaryotic cells contain genes made of DNA. The loss of any DNA during meiosis might mean a loss of valuable genetic information from one generation to the next.

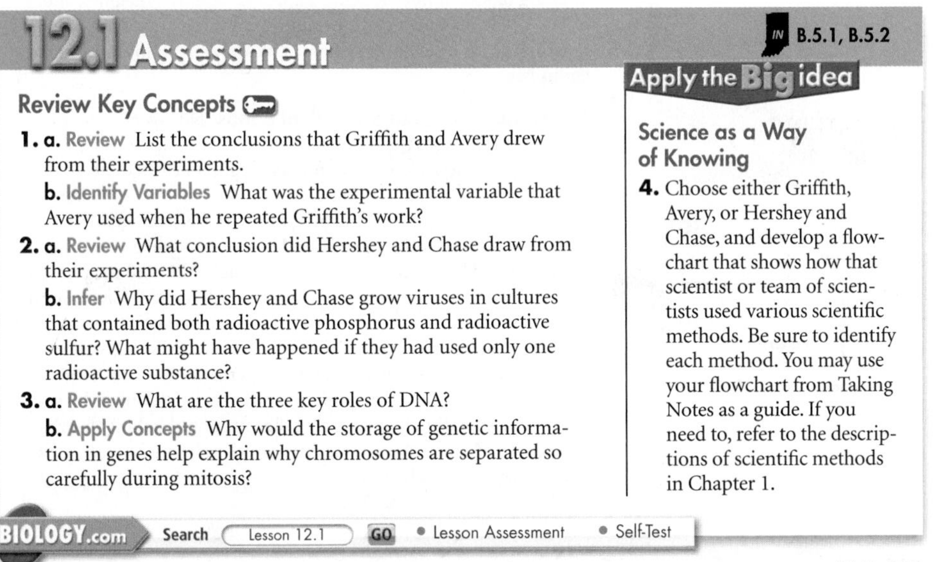

12.1 Assessment

IN B.5.1, B.5.2

Review Key Concepts

1. a. Review List the conclusions that Griffith and Avery drew from their experiments.
   b. Identify Variables What was the experimental variable that Avery used when he repeated Griffith's work?
2. a. Review What conclusion did Hershey and Chase draw from their experiments?
   b. Infer Why did Hershey and Chase grow viruses in cultures that contained both radioactive phosphorus and radioactive sulfur? What might have happened if they had used only one radioactive substance?
3. a. Review What are the three key roles of DNA?
   b. Apply Concepts Why would the storage of genetic information in genes help explain why chromosomes are separated so carefully during mitosis?

Apply the Big idea

Science as a Way of Knowing

4. Choose either Griffith, Avery, or Hershey and Chase, and develop a flowchart that shows how that scientist or team of scientists used various scientific methods. Be sure to identify each method. You may use your flowchart from Taking Notes as a guide. If you need to, refer to the descriptions of scientific methods in Chapter 1.

BIOLOGY.com Search Lesson 12.1 GO • Lesson Assessment • Self-Test

Assess and Remediate

EVALUATE UNDERSTANDING

Call on a student to name a scientist described in this lesson. Then, ask volunteers to describe that scientist's experiment and conclusion. Continue until students have described the work of Griffith, Avery, and Hershey and Chase. Then, have students complete the 12.1 Assessment.

REMEDIATION SUGGESTION

L1 Struggling Students If students have trouble with **Question 2,** ask them to write short paragraphs summarizing Hershey and Chase's experiment in their own words. Tell them that rephrasing the information in their own words promotes comprehension and can help them grasp concepts that are difficult to understand. Then, have students work in pairs to review and revise their paragraphs.

BIOLOGY.com Students can check their understanding of lesson concepts with the **Self-Test** assessment. They can then take an online version of the **Lesson Assessment.**

Assessment Answers

1a. Griffith concluded that a heritable substance transforms harmless bacteria into harmful bacteria. Avery found that this heritable substance is DNA.

1b. The experimental variable in Avery's experiment was the type of molecule-destroying enzyme he used.

2a. Hershey and Chase concluded that DNA is the genetic material found in genes.

2b. Growing viruses in separate cultures that contained both radioactive sulfur and radioactive phosphorus ensured that one sample of the virus had radioactive protein and the other sample had radioactive DNA. If only one type of molecule had been marked, they would not have been able to detect both types of molecule, and the results would not have been conclusive.

3a. storing, copying, and transmitting genetic information

3b. During mitosis, the cell's DNA is replicated, and each daughter cell receives a copy. If the chromosomes do not separate correctly, the information they carry in DNA might not be passed correctly to the daughter cells.

4.  Students' flowcharts should describe the work of Griffith, Avery, or Hershey and Chase, including their procedures and conclusions.

LESSON 12.2

Getting Started

Objectives

12.2.1 Identify the chemical components of DNA.

12.2.2 Discuss the experiments leading to the identification of DNA as the molecule that carries the genetic code.

12.2.3 Describe the steps leading to the development of the double-helix model of DNA.

Student Resources

Study Workbooks A and B, 12.2 Worksheets

Spanish Study Workbook, 12.2 Worksheets

Lab Manual B, 12.2 Data Analysis Worksheet

Lesson Overview • Lesson Notes
- Activities: Data Analysis, Tutor Tube
- Assessment: Self-Test, Lesson Assessment

For corresponding lesson in the **Foundation Edition**, see pages 292–295.

Activate Prior Knowledge

Explain that scientists often work much like detectives, and that the structure of DNA was an important "case" for scientists. The evidence included Griffith and Avery's work. Have students watch for other evidence for DNA structure as they read the lesson.

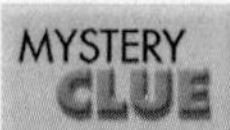
Guide students to infer that UV light may change the bonding in the DNA molecule. Students can go online to Biology.com to gather their evidence.

IN INDIANA ACADEMIC STANDARDS

For the full text of all standards, see the Course Overview in the front matter of this book.

B.5.1 Describe the relationship between chromosomes and DNA along with their basic structure and function.

12.2 The Structure of DNA

IN B.5.1 DNA and chromosomes. Also covered: **NoS.3.**

Key Questions

What are the chemical components of DNA?

What clues helped scientists solve the structure of DNA?

What does the double-helix model tell us about DNA?

Vocabulary

base pairing

Taking Notes

Outline As you read, find the key ideas for the text under each green heading. Write down a few key words from each main idea. Then, use these key words to summarize the information about DNA.

THINK ABOUT IT It's one thing to say that the molecule called DNA carries genetic information, but it would be quite another thing to explain how it could do this. DNA must not only specify how to assemble proteins, but how genes can be replicated and inherited. DNA has to be a very special molecule, and it's got to have a very special structure. As we will see, understanding the structure of DNA has been the key to understanding how genes work.

The Components of DNA

What are the chemical components of DNA?

Deoxyribonucleic acid, or DNA, is a unique molecule indeed. **DNA is a nucleic acid made up of nucleotides joined into long strands or chains by covalent bonds.** Let's examine each of these components more closely.

Nucleic Acids and Nucleotides As you may recall, nucleic acids are long, slightly acidic molecules originally identified in cell nuclei. Like many other macromolecules, nucleic acids are made up of smaller subunits, linked together to form long chains. Nucleotides are the building blocks of nucleic acids. **Figure 12–5** shows the nucleotides in DNA. These nucleotides are made up of three basic components: a 5-carbon sugar called deoxyribose, a phosphate group, and a nitrogenous base.

MYSTERY CLUE

The energy from UV light can excite electrons in the absorbing substance to the point where the electrons cause chemical changes. What chemical changes might occur in the nitrogenous bases of DNA?

Nitrogenous Bases and Covalent Bonds Nitrogenous bases, simply put, are bases that contain nitrogen. DNA has four kinds of nitrogenous bases: adenine (AD uh neen), guanine (GWAH neen), cytosine (SY tuh zeen), and thymine (THY meen). Biologists often refer to the nucleotides in DNA by the first letters of their base names: A, G, C, and T. The nucleotides in a strand of DNA are joined by covalent bonds formed between the sugar of one nucleotide and the phosphate group of the next. The nitrogenous bases stick out sideways from the nucleotide chain. The nucleotides can be joined together in any order, meaning that any sequence of bases is possible. These bases, by the way, have a chemical structure that makes them especially good at absorbing ultraviolet (UV) light. In fact, we can determine the amount of DNA in a solution by measuring the amount of light it absorbs at a wavelength of 260 nanometers (nm), which is in the UV region of the electromagnetic spectrum.

UbD Teach for Understanding

ENDURING UNDERSTANDING DNA is the universal code for life; it enables an organism to transmit hereditary information and, along with the environment, determines an organism's characteristics.

GUIDING QUESTION How was the basic structure of DNA discovered?

EVIDENCE OF UNDERSTANDING *After completing the lesson, give students the following assessment to show they understand the structure of DNA.* Have students work in pairs to sketch and label a section of a DNA molecule. Suggest they use colored pencils, crayons, or markers to distinguish different components of the molecule. Post the completed diagrams in the classroom.

If you don't see much in **Figure 12–5** that could explain the remarkable properties of DNA, don't be surprised. In the 1940s and early 1950s, the leading biologists in the world thought of DNA as little more than a string of nucleotides. They were baffled, too. The four different nucleotides, like the 26 letters of the alphabet, could be strung together in many different sequences, so it was possible they could carry coded genetic information. However, so could many other molecules, at least in principle. Biologists wondered if there were something more to the structure of DNA.

Solving the Structure of DNA

What clues helped scientists solve the structure of DNA?

Knowing that DNA is made from long chains of nucleotides was only the beginning of understanding the structure of this molecule. The next step required an understanding of the way in which those chains are arranged in three dimensions.

Chargaff's Rule One of the puzzling facts about DNA was a curious relationship between its nucleotides. Years earlier, Erwin Chargaff, an Austrian-American biochemist, had discovered that the percentages of adenine [A] and thymine [T] bases are almost equal in any sample of DNA. The same thing is true for the other two nucleotides, guanine [G] and cytosine [C]. The observation that [A] = [T] and [G] = [C] became known as "Chargaff's rule." Despite the fact that DNA samples from organisms as different as bacteria and humans obeyed this rule, neither Chargaff nor anyone else had the faintest idea why.

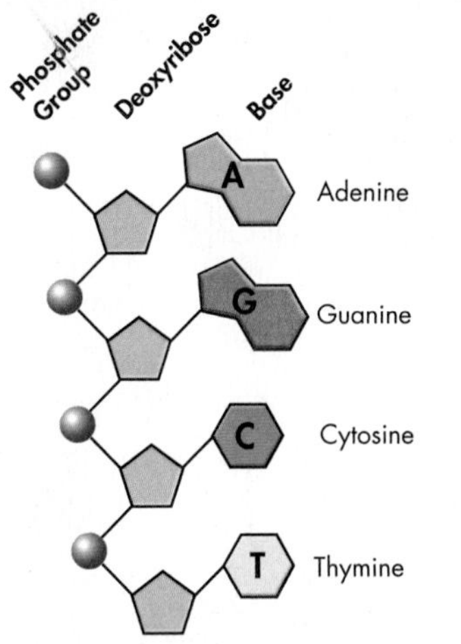

FIGURE 12–5 DNA Nucleotides DNA is made up of nucleotides, each with a deoxyribose molecule, a phosphate group, and a nitrogen-containing base. The four bases are adenine (A), guanine (G), cytosine (C), and thymine (T). Interpret Visuals *How are these four nucleotides joined together to form part of a DNA chain?*

Analyzing Data

IN NoS.3

Base Percentages

In 1949, Erwin Chargaff discovered that the relative amounts of A and T, and of G and C, are almost always equal. The table shows a portion of the data that Chargaff collected.

Percentages of Bases in Five Organisms

Source of DNA	A	T	G	C
Streptococcus	29.8	31.6	20.5	18.0
Yeast	31.3	32.9	18.7	17.1
Herring	27.8	27.5	22.2	22.6
Human	30.9	29.4	19.9	19.8
E.coli	24.7	23.6	26.0	25.7

1. Interpret Tables Which organism has the highest percentage of adenine?

2. Calculate If a species has 35 percent adenine in its DNA, what is the percentage of the other three bases? MATH

3. Draw Conclusions What did the fact that A and T, and G and C, occurred in equal amounts suggest about the relationship among these bases?

BIOLOGY.com Search Lesson 12.2 GO • Tutor Tube • Data Analysis

Analyzing Data

PURPOSE Students will analyze data to determine the percentages of the four nitrogenous bases in the DNA of four different organisms.

PLANNING Remind students that A, G, C, and T are the abbreviations often used by biologists for adenine, guanine, cytosine, and thymine. Point out that these four bases are the only nitrogenous bases found in DNA.

ANSWERS

1. yeast

2. 35% thymine and 15% each of guanine and cytosine

3. It suggested that A is paired with T and G with C in some way.

Teach

Expand Vocabulary

Write the following terms on the board: *nucleic acid, nucleotide, nitrogenous base, covalent bond.* Explain to students that an understanding of these terms is necessary to understand the structure of DNA. Have students write a one-sentence definition of each term. Then, ask them to make a diagram or drawing to represent each term, using **Figure 12–5** as a model. Have volunteers share their definitions and diagrams with the class.

DIFFERENTIATED INSTRUCTION

ELL English Language Learners Draw an enlarged, unlabeled copy of **Figure 12–5** on the board. Provide students with index cards on which are written: *covalent bond, nucleotide, phosphate group, deoxyribose, adenine, guanine, cytosine,* and *thymine.* Point to a structure in the diagram, and have students hold up the correct card. Then, have them pronounce the term aloud.

LPR Less Proficient Readers Help students locate the information in the text that describes nucleic acids, nucleotides, nitrogenous bases, and covalent bonds. Then, show students how **Figure 12–5** can be used to visualize each of these terms.

BIOLOGY.com Have students analyze DNA data to track illegally caught whales in **Data Analysis: Tracking Illegal Whaling.** If students need extra help remembering how DNA bases pair up, suggest they watch **Tutor Tube: Memory Tricks for Base Pairing.**

Answers

FIGURE 12–5 The nucleotides in a strand of DNA are joined by covalent bonds formed between their sugar and phosphate groups.

Teach continued

VISUAL SUMMARY

Have students examine **Figure 12–6,** and then divide the class into three groups. Assign one of the following scientists or teams to each group: Chargaff, Franklin, and Watson and Crick. Have each group prepare a short presentation describing the contribution of its assigned scientist(s). Ask each group to share its presentation with the class.

DIFFERENTIATED INSTRUCTION

L3 **Advanced Learners** As students are preparing the presentations described above, have advanced learners do additional research to prepare a short report about the Nobel Prize that was awarded to Watson, Crick, and Wilkins for their work on DNA's structure. Have them learn more about why Maurice Wilkins was included in the prize but Rosalind Franklin was not. Have students share this information when the group reports are presented.

ELL Focus on ELL: Access Content

ALL SPEAKERS Have students fold a sheet of paper into thirds to organize the information about Chargaff, Franklin, and Watson and Crick. At the top of each section, have students record the name of the scientist or scientist team. Then, suggest beginning and intermediate speakers make bulleted lists of words or phrases that will help them recall the contributions of each scientist or team. Encourage advanced students to record the information in complete sentences. Require advanced high students to write full, complex sentences that accurately summarize the scientists' work.

Rosalind Franklin

VISUAL SUMMARY

CLUES TO THE STRUCTURE OF DNA

FIGURE 12–6 Erwin Chargaff, Rosalind Franklin, James Watson, and Francis Crick were among the many scientists who helped solve the puzzle of DNA's molecular structure. Franklin's X-ray diffraction photograph shows the pattern that indicated the structure of DNA is helical.

Erwin Chargaff

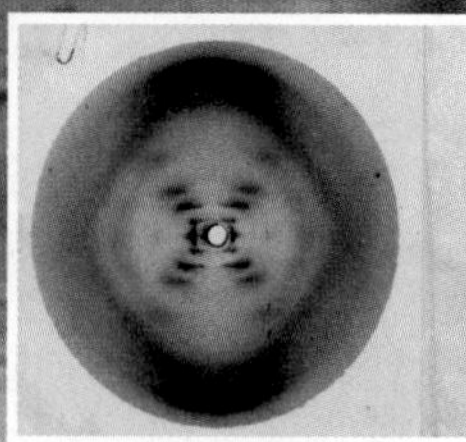

Franklin's X-ray diffraction photograph, May 1952

Franklin's X-Rays In the early 1950s, the British scientist Rosalind Franklin began to study DNA. Franklin used a technique called X-ray diffraction to get information about the structure of the DNA molecule. First, she purified a large amount of DNA, then stretched the DNA fibers in a thin glass tube so that most of the strands were parallel. Next, she aimed a powerful X-ray beam at the concentrated DNA samples and recorded the scattering pattern of the X-rays on film. Franklin worked hard to obtain better and better patterns from DNA until the patterns became clear. The result of her work is the X-ray photograph shown in **Figure 12–6,** taken in the summer of 1952.

By itself, Franklin's X-ray pattern does not reveal the structure of DNA, but it does carry some very important clues. The X-shaped pattern shows that the strands in DNA are twisted around each other like the coils of a spring, a shape known as a **helix.** The angle of the X suggests that there are two strands in the structure. Other clues suggest that the nitrogenous bases are near the center of the DNA molecule.

BUILD Vocabulary

ACADEMIC WORDS In biochemistry, the noun **helix** refers to an extended spiral chain of units in a protein, nucleic acid, or other large molecule. The plural term is *helices.*

The Work of Watson and Crick While Franklin was continuing her research, James Watson, an American biologist, and Francis Crick, a British physicist, were also trying to understand the structure of DNA. They built three-dimensional models of the molecule that were made of cardboard and wire. They twisted and stretched the models in various ways, but their best efforts did nothing to explain DNA's properties.

Then, early in 1953, Watson was shown a copy of Franklin's remarkable X-ray pattern. The effect was immediate. In his book *The Double Helix,* Watson wrote: "The instant I saw the picture my mouth fell open and my pulse began to race."

UbD Check for Understanding

FOLLOW-UP PROBES

Ask How is solving the puzzle of DNA's structure an example of a collection of discoveries by different scientists? *(Although Watson and Crick are remembered as the team that solved the structure of DNA, their work would not have been possible without the work of many other scientists, including those described in this lesson.)*

ADJUST INSTRUCTION

Use the following demonstration to help students understand the key roles played by scientists other than Watson and Crick to determine DNA's structure. Open a box containing the pieces of a jigsaw puzzle. Hand one piece of the puzzle to each of four or five students. Point out that the puzzle could not be completed without the pieces held by those students. In the same way, the puzzle of DNA's structure was solved because many individuals supplied a "piece of the puzzle."

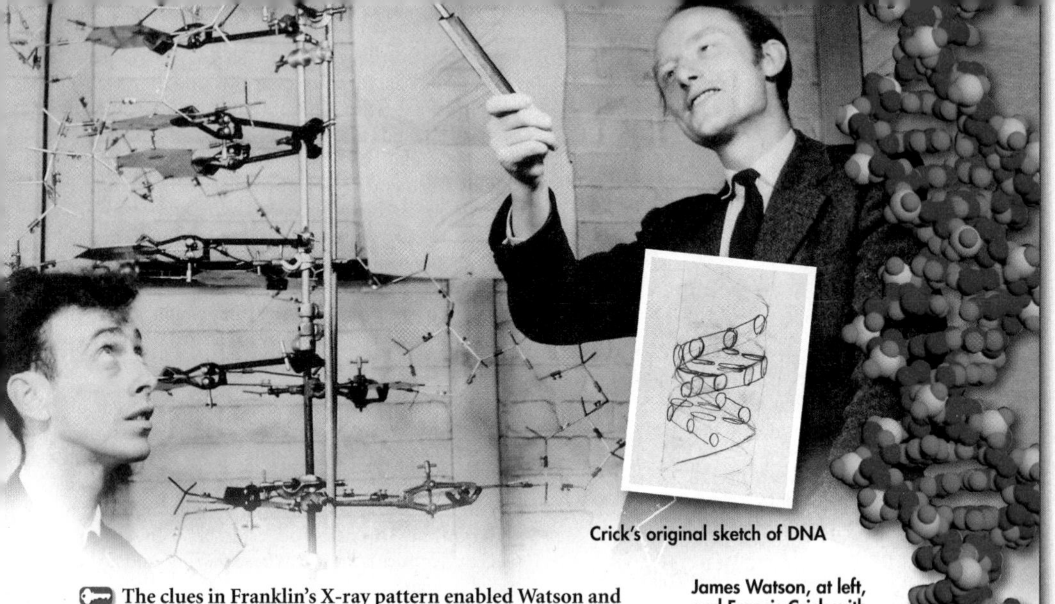

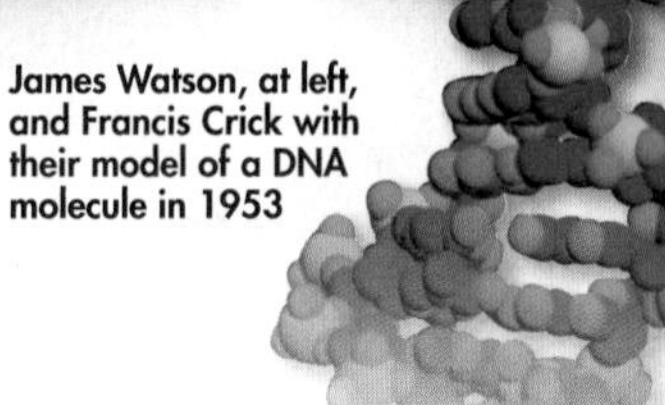

Crick's original sketch of DNA

James Watson, at left, and Francis Crick with their model of a DNA molecule in 1953

A computer model of DNA

The clues in Franklin's X-ray pattern enabled Watson and Crick to build a model that explained the specific structure and properties of DNA. The pair published their results in a historic one-page paper in April of 1953, when Franklin's paper describing her X-ray work was also published. Watson and Crick's breakthrough model of DNA was a double helix, in which two strands of nucleotide sequences were wound around each other.

The Double-Helix Model

What does the double-helix model tell us about DNA?

A double helix looks like a twisted ladder. In the double-helix model of DNA, the two strands twist around each other like spiral staircases. Watson and Crick realized that the double helix accounted for Franklin's X-ray pattern. Further still, it explained many of the most important properties of DNA. **The double-helix model explains Chargaff's rule of base pairing and how the two strands of DNA are held together.** This model can even tell us how DNA can function as a carrier of genetic information.

Antiparallel Strands One of the surprising aspects of the double-helix model is that the two strands of DNA run in opposite directions. In the language of biochemistry, these strands are "antiparallel." This arrangement enables the nitrogenous bases on both strands to come into contact at the center of the molecule. It also allows each strand of the double helix to carry a sequence of nucleotides, arranged almost like letters in a four-letter alphabet.

In Your Notebook *Draw and label your own model of the DNA double-helix structure.*

MYSTERY CLUE

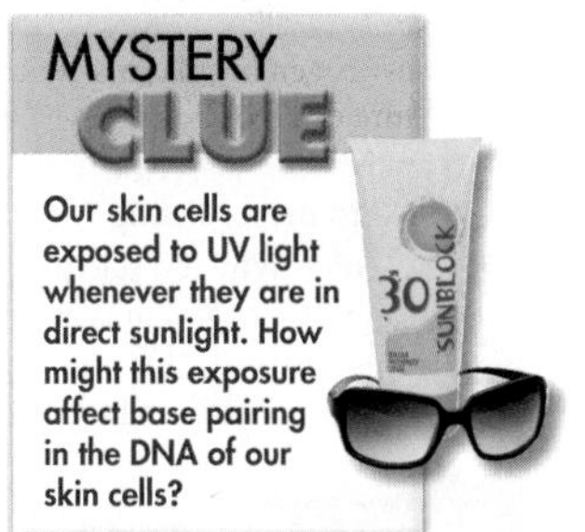

Our skin cells are exposed to UV light whenever they are in direct sunlight. How might this exposure affect base pairing in the DNA of our skin cells?

Use Models

Show the class a physical model of a DNA molecule. Point out to students that a double helix looks like a twisted ladder.

Ask If a twisted ladder is used as a model of DNA, which parts of a DNA molecule correspond to the sides of the ladder? *(the phosphate group and the 5-carbon sugar deoxyribose)*

Ask Which parts of a DNA molecule correspond to the rungs of the ladder? *(nitrogenous base pairs)*

DIFFERENTIATED INSTRUCTION

L1 Special Needs Draw a picture of a ladder on the board. Explain how the ladder can model the structure of DNA. Label the rungs of the ladder Nitrogenous Bases and the sides of the ladder Sugar and Phosphate Groups. Ask students to imagine what the ladder would look like if it were twisted. Then, show them a physical model of DNA. Help them make the connection between the ladder drawing and the DNA model by pointing out the nitrogenous bases, phosphate groups, and sugar molecules.

Students should infer that exposure to UV light may interfere with proper base pairing in the DNA of skin cells. Students can go online to Biology.com to gather their evidence.

Quick Facts

THE STRUCTURE OF DNA

When Watson and Crick were ready to announce their double-helix model in 1953, they made a drawing of DNA and sent it with a letter to *Nature*, a highly respected scientific journal. *Nature* routinely publishes "letters," which are much shorter than typical scientific papers. The second and third paragraphs of Watson and Crick's letter explained why they believed a triple-helix model of DNA, which was being developed by Linus Pauling and other researchers, was incorrect. The letter then proceeded to describe the double-helix model of DNA. They ended the letter by writing, "It has not escaped our notice that the specific pairing we have postulated immediately suggests a possible copying mechanism for the genetic material." Within a few weeks, *Nature* published Watson and Crick's description of the copying mechanism. Their classic paper, titled "A Structure for Deoxyribose Nucleic Acid," appeared in the April 25, 1953 issue of the journal.

Answers

IN YOUR NOTEBOOK Students' models should depict DNA as a double helix, with labels identifying the nitrogenous bases, deoxyribose, and phosphate groups.

LESSON 12.2

Assess and Remediate

EVALUATE UNDERSTANDING

Read the first Key Question for this lesson to the class. Then, ask a volunteer to provide an answer. Continue until each of the three Key Questions has been answered. Then, have students complete the 12.2 Assessment.

REMEDIATION SUGGESTION

L1 Struggling Students If students have difficulty answering **Question 1b,** remind them that hydrogen bonds are a type of weak chemical bond.

BIOLOGY.com Students can check their understanding of lesson concepts with the **Self-Test** assessment. They can then take an online version of the **Lesson Assessment.**

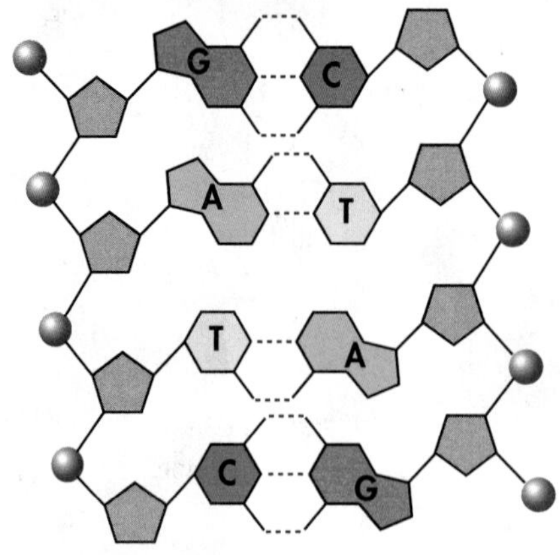

FIGURE 12–7 Base Pairing The two strands of DNA are held together by hydrogen bonds between the nitrogenous bases adenine and thymine, and between guanine and cytosine.

Hydrogen Bonding At first, Watson and Crick could not explain what forces held the two strands of DNA's double helix together. They then discovered that hydrogen bonds could form between certain nitrogenous bases, providing just enough force to hold the two strands together. As you may recall, hydrogen bonds are relatively weak chemical forces.

Does it make sense that a molecule as important as DNA should be held together by weak bonds? Indeed, it does. If the two strands of the helix were held together by strong bonds, it might well be impossible to separate them. As we will see, the ability of the two strands to separate is critical to DNA's functions.

Base Pairing Watson and Crick's model showed that hydrogen bonds could create a nearly perfect fit between nitrogenous bases along the center of the molecule. However, these bonds would form only between certain base pairs—adenine with thymine, and guanine with cytosine. This nearly perfect fit between A–T and G–C nucleotides is known as **base pairing,** and is illustrated in **Figure 12–7.**

Once they observed this process, Watson and Crick realized that base pairing explained Chargaff's rule. It gave a reason why [A] = [T] and [G] = [C]. For every adenine in a double-stranded DNA molecule, there has to be exactly one thymine. For each cytosine, there is one guanine. The ability of their model to explain Chargaff's observations increased Watson and Crick's confidence that they had come to the right conclusion, with the help of Rosalind Franklin.

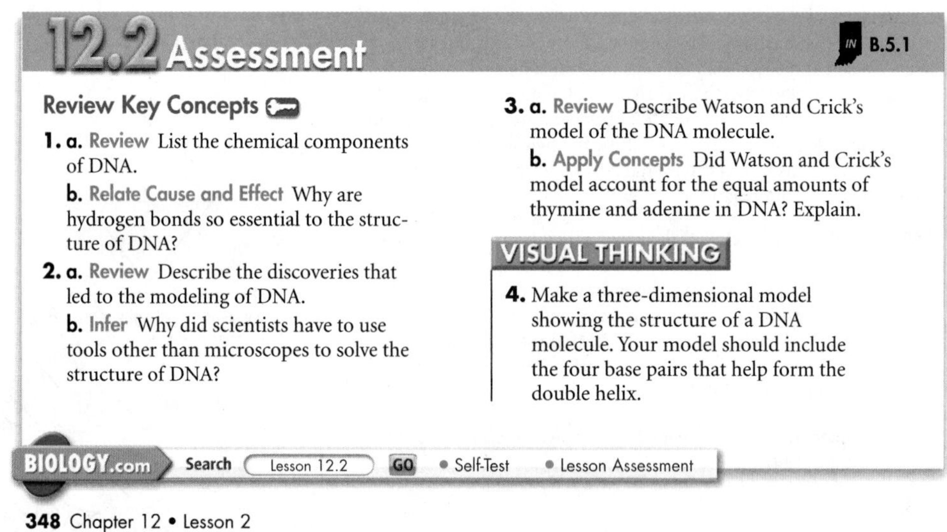

12.2 Assessment

IN B.5.1

Review Key Concepts

1. a. Review List the chemical components of DNA.

b. Relate Cause and Effect Why are hydrogen bonds so essential to the structure of DNA?

2. a. Review Describe the discoveries that led to the modeling of DNA.

b. Infer Why did scientists have to use tools other than microscopes to solve the structure of DNA?

3. a. Review Describe Watson and Crick's model of the DNA molecule.

b. Apply Concepts Did Watson and Crick's model account for the equal amounts of thymine and adenine in DNA? Explain.

VISUAL THINKING

4. Make a three-dimensional model showing the structure of a DNA molecule. Your model should include the four base pairs that help form the double helix.

BIOLOGY.com Search Lesson 12.2 GO • Self-Test • Lesson Assessment

Assessment Answers

1a. 5-carbon sugar molecules, phosphate groups, four different nitrogenous bases

1b. Hydrogen bonds hold the paired nitrogenous bases together. Because hydrogen bonds are weak bonds, the two strands of DNA are easily separated—a characteristic that is important to DNA's function.

2a. Chargaff determined that, in a double-stranded DNA molecule, adenine and thymine are present in equal proportions and guanine and cytosine are present in equal proportions. Franklin's X-ray photographs of DNA revealed a spiral structure. Both of these findings helped Watson and Crick understand DNA's double helix and complementary base pairing.

2b. DNA is too small to be examined with a light microscope—the only kind of microscope available at the time.

3a. Watson and Crick's model is composed of two antiparallel strands that are connected by hydrogen bonds between nitrogenous bases. Hydrogen bonds form between adenine and thymine and between cytosine and guanine.

3b. Watson and Crick's model depicted DNA as a double helix with adenine and thymine paired together. This pairing accounts for the equal amounts of thymine and adenine in DNA.

VISUAL THINKING

4. Students' models should show the structure of DNA as a double helix and include correct base pairing between adenine and thymine and between cytosine and guanine.

Discovering the Role of DNA **Genes and the principles of genetics were discovered before scientists identified the molecules that genes are made of. With the discovery of DNA, scientists have been able to explain how genes are replicated and how they function.**

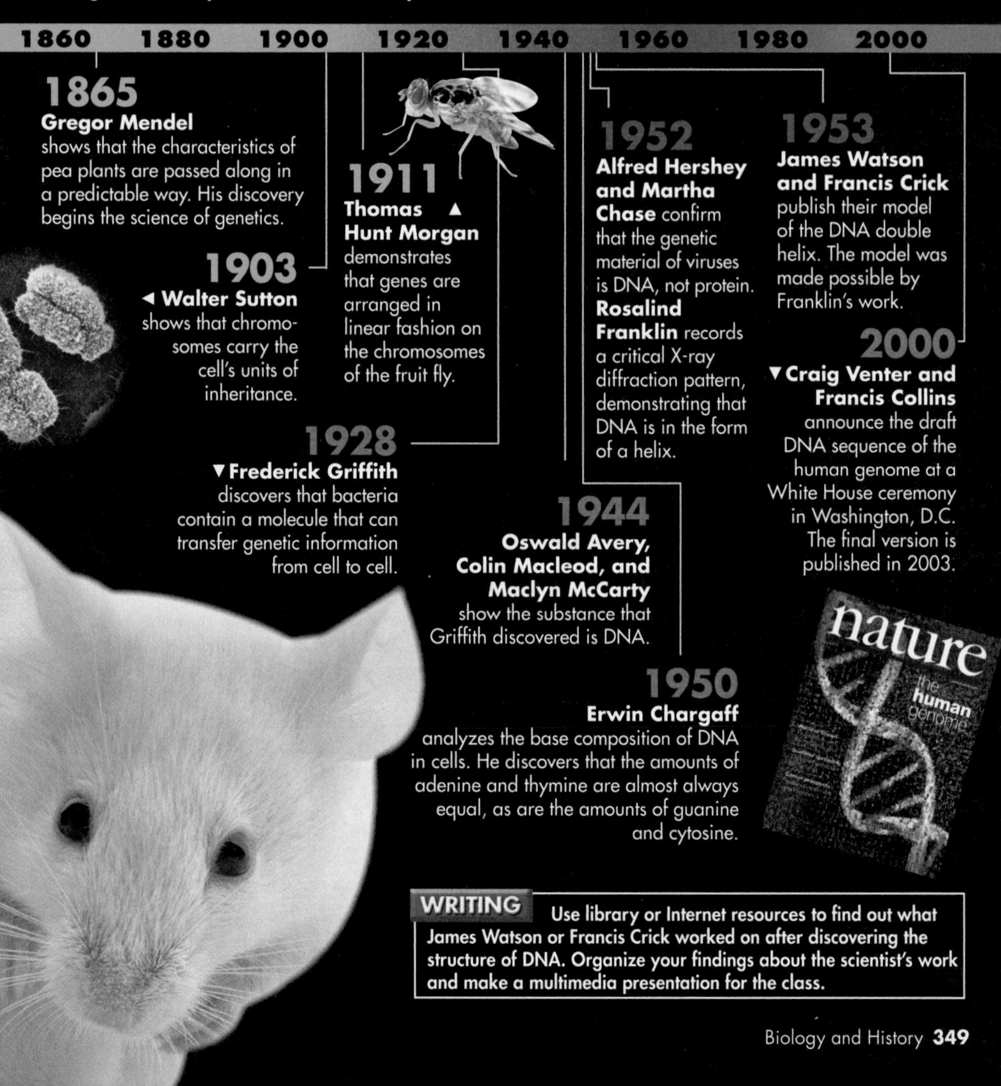

1860 1880 1900 1920 1940 1960 1980 2000
1865
Gregor Mendel shows that the characteristics of pea plants are passed along in a predictable way. His discovery begins the science of genetics.
1903
◄ Walter Sutton shows that chromosomes carry the cell's units of inheritance.
1911
Thomas Hunt Morgan ▲ demonstrates that genes are arranged in linear fashion on the chromosomes of the fruit fly.
1928
▼ Frederick Griffith discovers that bacteria contain a molecule that can transfer genetic information from cell to cell.
1944
Oswald Avery, Colin Macleod, and Maclyn McCarty show the substance that Griffith discovered is DNA.
1950
Erwin Chargaff analyzes the base composition of DNA in cells. He discovers that the amounts of adenine and thymine are almost always equal, as are the amounts of guanine and cytosine.
1952
Alfred Hershey and Martha Chase confirm that the genetic material of viruses is DNA, not protein. Rosalind Franklin records a critical X-ray diffraction pattern, demonstrating that DNA is in the form of a helix.
1953
James Watson and Francis Crick publish their model of the DNA double helix. The model was made possible by Franklin's work.
2000
▼ Craig Venter and Francis Collins announce the draft DNA sequence of the human genome at a White House ceremony in Washington, D.C. The final version is published in 2003.
nature
the human genome

WRITING **Use library or Internet resources to find out what James Watson or Francis Crick worked on after discovering the structure of DNA. Organize your findings about the scientist's work and make a multimedia presentation for the class.**

Teach

Lead a Discussion

Have students examine the time line to learn more about the history of genetics research. Ask them questions to make sure they understand the information presented on the page.

Ask How many years passed between the work of Mendel and the announcement of the draft of the human genome? *(135 years)*

Ask What did Walter Sutton find? *(Walter Sutton found that the chromosomes carry genes.)*

Ask How does Rosalind Franklin's work illustrate the connection between technology and science? *(Rosalind Franklin's work would not have been possible without X-ray diffraction technology.)*

DIFFERENTIATED INSTRUCTION

L1 Struggling Students Have students take turns reading aloud the time line entries, moving in chronological order. After each entry has been read, have a brief discussion of the significance of the discovery.

L3 Advanced Students Explain that the most recent entry on the time line, the sequencing of the human genome, is a project that built on all of the previous discoveries in the time line. Have students imagine a future entry for the time line, based on what they know about genetics and what they envision as future applications of genetics. Have each student share his or her imagined time line entry with the class.

How Science Works

SCIENTISTS ARE A SKEPTICAL BUNCH

Today, iit seems clear that Avery's results had shown without a doubt that DNA makes up genes. However, in 1944 the results were questionable. Then, inheritance in bacteria was just beginning to be studied. Scientists didn't know whether bacteria had genes like those in more complex organisms. And even if DNA were the heredity substance in bacteria, it might not be the hereditary substance in more complex organisms. DNA was still considered a very simple molecule. Scientists were more satisfied with Hershey and Chase's results with bacteriophages in 1952. By that time, genetic studies showed that bacteriophages had properties of heredity similar to those of more complex organisms. Also, experiments showed that DNA was more complex than originally thought.

Answers

WRITING

Students' responses will vary based on their research. Students might note that both Watson and Crick went on to research how DNA controls protein synthesis.

LESSON 12.3

Getting Started

Objectives

12.3.1 Summarize the events of DNA replication.

12.3.2 Compare DNA replication in prokaryotes with that of eukaryotes.

Student Resources

Study Workbooks A and B, 12.3 Worksheets

Spanish Study Workbook, 12.3 Worksheets

Lab Manual B, 12.2 Hands-On Activity

Lesson Overview • Lesson Notes
- Activities: InterActive Art, Art Review
- Assessment: Self-Test, Lesson Assessment

For corresponding lesson in the **Foundation Edition**, see pages 296–299.

Build Background

Have students suggest ways to make a copy of a page of the text. *(Sample answers: by hand, by using a copier)* Ask them why it is important to make an exact copy. *(so the information doesn't change)* Explain that cells copy DNA in a process called DNA replication.

Answers

IN YOUR NOTEBOOK Sample answer: DNA separates into two strands and produces two new complementary strands by the rules of base pairing.

IN INDIANA ACADEMIC STANDARDS

For the full text of all standards, see the Course Overview in the front matter of this book.

B.7.4 Explain the process by which a cell copies its DNA and identify factors that can damage DNA and cause changes in its nucleotide sequence.

12.3 DNA Replication

IN B.7.4 DNA duplication and damage. Also covered: B.1.2.

Key Questions

What role does DNA polymerase play in copying DNA?

How does DNA replication differ in prokaryotic cells and eukaryotic cells?

Vocabulary

replication
DNA polymerase
telomere

Taking Notes

Preview Visuals Before you read, study the diagram in **Figure 12–8.** Make a list of questions about the diagram. As you read, write down the answers to your questions.

BUILD Vocabulary

WORD ORIGINS The prefix *re-* means "back" or "again." *Plicare* is a Latin verb meaning "to fold." To replicate something is, in a sense, to repeat it, or to fold back again.

THINK ABOUT IT Before a cell divides, its DNA must first be copied. How might the double-helix structure of DNA make that possible? What might happen if one of the nucleotides were damaged or chemically altered just before the copying process? How might this affect the DNA inherited by each daughter cell after cell division?

Copying the Code

What role does DNA polymerase play in copying DNA?

When Watson and Crick discovered the structure of DNA, they immediately recognized one genuinely surprising aspect of the structure. Base pairing in the double helix explains how DNA can be copied, or replicated, because each base on one strand pairs with one—and only one—base on the opposite strand. Each strand of the double helix therefore has all the information needed to reconstruct the other half by the mechanism of base pairing. Because each strand can be used to make the other strand, the strands are said to be complementary.

The Replication Process Before a cell divides, it duplicates its DNA in a copying process called **replication.** This process, which occurs during late interphase of the cell cycle, ensures that each resulting cell has the same complete set of DNA molecules. During replication, the DNA molecule separates into two strands and then produces two new complementary strands following the rules of base pairing. Each strand of the double helix of DNA serves as a template, or model, for the new strand.

Figure 12–8 shows the process of DNA replication. The two strands of the double helix have separated, or "unzipped," allowing two replication forks to form. As each new strand forms, new bases are added following the rules of base pairing. If the base on the old strand is adenine, then thymine is added to the newly forming strand. Likewise, guanine is always paired to cytosine. For example, a strand that has the base sequence TACGTT produces a strand with the complementary base sequence ATGCAA. The result is two DNA molecules identical to each other and to the original molecule. Note that each DNA molecule resulting from replication has one original strand and one new strand.

In Your Notebook *In your own words, describe the process of DNA replication.*

UbD Teach for Understanding

ENDURING UNDERSTANDING DNA is the universal code for life; it enables an organism to transmit hereditary information and, along with the environment, determines an organism's characteristics.

GUIDING QUESTION How do cells copy their DNA?

EVIDENCE OF UNDERSTANDING *After completing the lesson, give students the following assessment to show they understand how cells copy their DNA.* Have students work in small groups to make a series of three diagrams. The first diagram should show a labeled 15-base section of double-stranded DNA. The second diagram should show what the DNA would look like during the replication process. The third diagram should show the results of replication. Remind students to label each nitrogenous base and to follow the rules of base pairing.

The Role of Enzymes DNA replication is carried out by a series of enzymes. These enzymes first "unzip" a molecule of DNA by breaking the hydrogen bonds between base pairs and unwinding the two strands of the molecule. Each strand then serves as a template for the attachment of complementary bases. You may recall that enzymes are proteins with highly specific functions. For this reason, they are often named for the reactions they catalyze. The principal enzyme involved in DNA replication is called **DNA polymerase** (PAHL ih mur ayz). **DNA polymerase is an enzyme that joins individual nucleotides to produce a new strand of DNA.** Besides producing the sugar-phosphate bonds that join nucleotides together, DNA polymerase also "proofreads" each new DNA strand, so that each molecule is a near-perfect copy of the original.

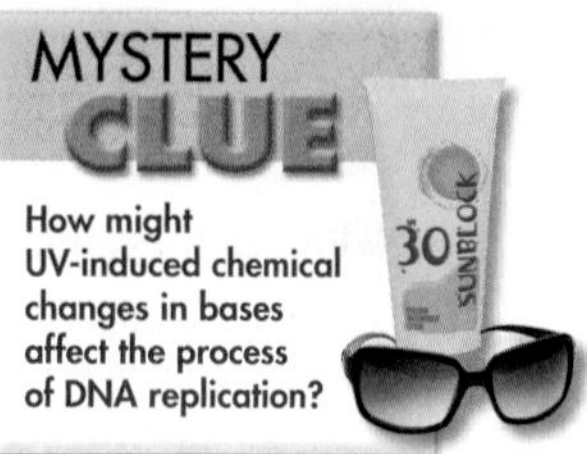

How might UV-induced chemical changes in bases affect the process of DNA replication?

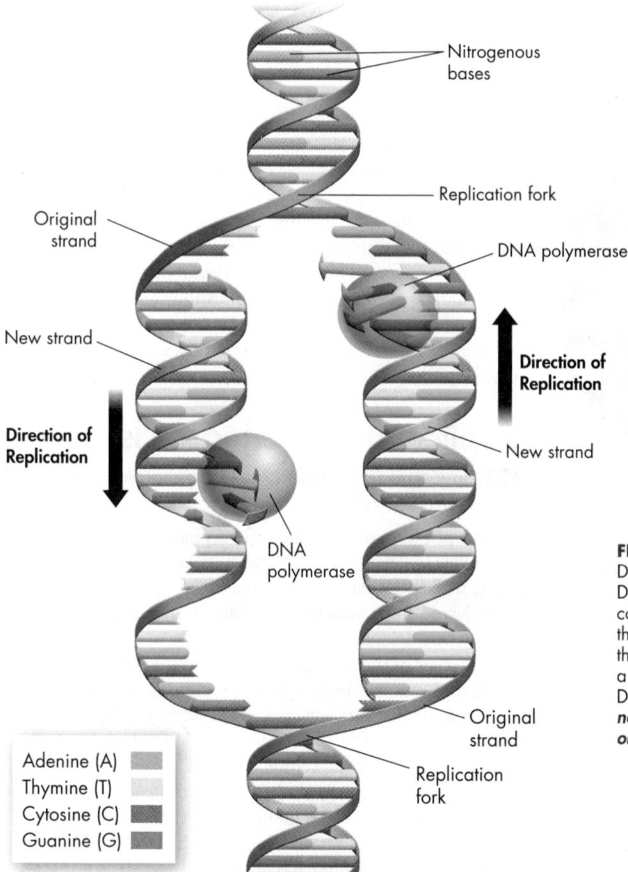

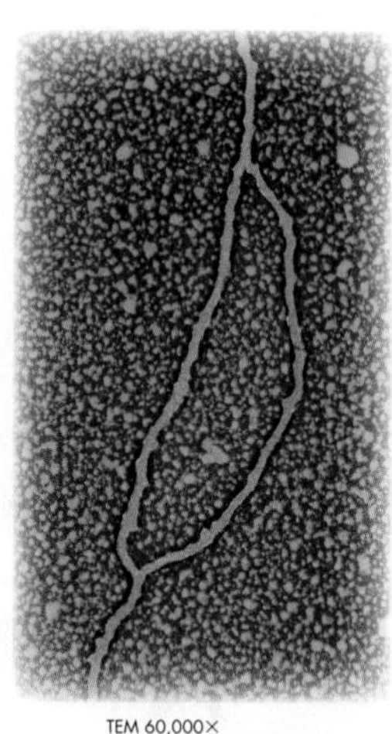

FIGURE 12–8 DNA Replication During DNA replication, the DNA molecule produces two new complementary strands. Each strand of the double helix serves as a template for the new strand. The micrograph shows a pair of replication forks in human DNA. **Apply Concepts** ***What makes the new DNA strand complementary to the original strand?***

How Science Works

THE DISCOVERY OF DNA POLYMERASE

In 1959, Arthur Kornberg, a researcher in the field of enzymology, won a Nobel Prize for the discovery of DNA polymerase. This groundbreaking work was summarized in two scientific papers. The first paper described the extraction and purification of DNA polymerase from bacteria; the second paper described an analysis of the substances required for DNA synthesis, including DNA polymerase. These two papers were submitted to the *Journal of Biological Chemistry* in 1957. Both papers were initially rejected. After intervention by a newly hired editor-in-chief, the papers were published in 1958.

Teach

Use Visuals

Have students use **Figure 12–8** to clarify the process of DNA replication.

Ask How is DNA unzipped at the replication forks? *(Hydrogen bonds are broken.)*

Ask What are the two roles of DNA polymerase in replication? *(DNA polymerase joins individual nucleotides to produce a new strand of DNA and proofreads the new strand.)*

DIFFERENTIATED INSTRUCTION

L1 Struggling Students Write the following sentence starters on the board.

- During replication, DNA polymerase . . .
- At the replication fork, . . .
- During replication, each original DNA strand . . .

Ask students to write a phrase to complete each sentence. Then, ask volunteers to share their responses with the class.

L3 Advanced Students Explain to advanced students that enzymes are critical to the process of DNA replication, just as they are to most chemical reactions in living things. Have students find the name of, and learn more about, the enzyme that unwinds and unzips DNA during replication. *(helicase)* Ask them to share their findings with the class.

MYSTERY CLUE Have students discuss what might happen if a UV-induced base change was copied during the process of DNA replication. Students can go online to **Biology.com** to gather their evidence.

BIOLOGY.com Students can watch an animated version of DNA replication by accessing **InterActive Art: DNA Replication**.

Answers

FIGURE 12–8 The new DNA strand is complementary to the original strand because its base sequence is determined by the rules of base pairing.

Teach continued

Build Reading Skills

Point out the head **Replication in Living Cells.** Have students use this head to start an outline of the material in this section. Show them how to incorporate the two subheads for prokaryotic and eukaryotic DNA replication. After students have completed their outlines, ask volunteers to share them with the class.

DIFFERENTIATED INSTRUCTION

LPR **Less Proficient Readers** Encourage struggling readers to work in small groups to prepare the outline of the information in this section, as described above. Students can divide the reading among members of the group and share what they learn to create the outline.

ELL Focus on ELL: Build Background

ALL SPEAKERS Divide students into four groups of mixed speaking levels. Then, have them complete a **Gallery Walk** activity. Ask the groups to rotate between four locations in the classroom where you have posted questions about lesson content, such as "What happens during DNA replication?" or "What does DNA polymerase do?" At each location, have an intermediate or advanced speaker read the question aloud. Then, ask beginning speakers to give a short oral response to the question. Have advanced high speakers prepare a written response in the form of at least one complete, complex sentence. Groups should also read, evaluate, and comment on any of the previous groups' answers.

Study Wkbks A/B, Appendix S6, Gallery Walk.

IN B.1.2, B.7.4

Modeling DNA Replication

1. Cut out small squares of white and yellow paper to represent phosphate and sugar molecules. Then, cut out small strips of blue, green, red, and orange paper to represent the four nitrogenous bases. Build a set of five nucleotides using your paper strips and tape. Look back at **Figure 12–5** if you need help.

2. Using your nucleotides, tape together a single strand of DNA. Exchange strands with a partner.

3. Model DNA replication by creating a strand that is complementary to your partner's original strand.

Analyze and Conclude

1. **Use Models** Taping together the nucleotides models the action of what enzyme?
2. **Evaluate** In what ways does this lab accurately represent DNA replication? How could you improve the lab to better show the steps of replication?

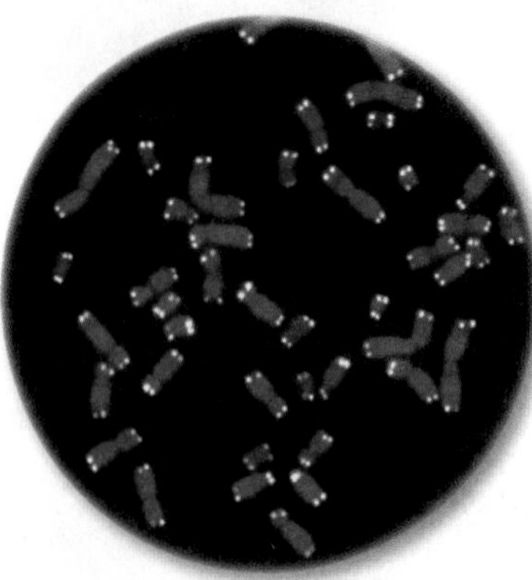

FIGURE 12–9 Telomeres The telomeres are the white (stained) part of the blue human chromosomes.

Telomeres DNA at the tips of chromosomes are known as **telomeres** (**Figure 12–9**). This DNA is particularly difficult to replicate. Cells use a special enzyme, called telomerase, to solve this problem by adding short, repeated DNA sequences to the telomeres. In rapidly dividing cells, such as stem cells and embryonic cells, telomerase helps to prevent genes from being damaged or lost during replication. Telomerase is often switched off in adult cells. In cancer cells, however, telomerase may be activated, enabling these cells to grow and proliferate rapidly.

Replication in Living Cells

How does DNA replication differ in prokaryotic cells and eukaryotic cells?

DNA replication occurs during the S phase of the cell cycle. As we saw in Chapter 10, replication is carefully regulated, along with the other critical events of the cycle so that it is completed before a cell enters mitosis or meiosis. But where, exactly, is DNA found inside a living cell?

The cells of most prokaryotes have a single, circular DNA molecule in the cytoplasm, containing nearly all the cell's genetic information. Eukaryotic cells, on the other hand, can have up to 1000 times more DNA. Nearly all of the DNA of eukaryotic cells is found in the nucleus, packaged into chromosomes. Eukaryotic chromosomes consist of DNA, tightly packed together with proteins to form a substance called chromatin. Together, the DNA and histone molecules form beadlike structures called nucleosomes, as described in Chapter 10. Histones, you may recall, are proteins around which chromatin is tightly coiled.

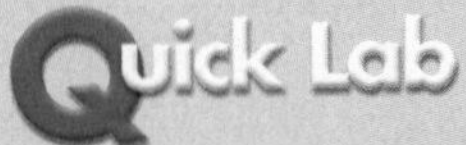

PURPOSE Students will model DNA replication.

MATERIALS colored paper, tape, scissors

PLANNING Have students review the structure of DNA before completing the Quick Lab. Suggest students tape together the individual nucleotides before taping the strand together.

ANALYZE AND CONCLUDE

1. DNA polymerase
2. Sample answer: This lab models how the bases in a sequence of DNA are paired with complementary bases. To better show the steps of replication, I would make lots more nucleotides and join two long strands of bases together to indicate that a DNA molecule is double-stranded. I would then be able to model how the two strands separate and how complementary bases are added, resulting in two new complementary strands.

Prokaryotic DNA Replication In most prokaryotes, DNA replication does not start until regulatory proteins bind to a single starting point on the chromosome. These proteins then trigger the beginning of the S phase, and DNA replication begins. **Replication in most prokaryotic cells starts from a single point and proceeds in two directions until the entire chromosome is copied.** This process is shown in **Figure 12–10.** Often, the two chromosomes produced by replication are attached to different points inside the cell membrane and are separated when the cell splits to form two new cells.

Eukaryotic DNA Replication Eukaryotic chromosomes are generally much bigger than those of prokaryotes. **In eukaryotic cells, replication may begin at dozens or even hundreds of places on the DNA molecule, proceeding in both directions until each chromosome is completely copied.** Although a number of proteins check DNA for chemical damage or base pair mismatches prior to replication, the system is not foolproof. Damaged regions of DNA are sometimes replicated, resulting in changes to DNA base sequences that may alter certain genes and produce serious consequences.

The two copies of DNA produced by replication in each chromosome remain closely associated until the cell enters prophase of mitosis. At that point, the chromosomes condense, and the two chromatids in each chromosome become clearly visible. They separate from each other in anaphase of mitosis, as described in Chapter 10, producing two cells, each with a complete set of genes coded in DNA.

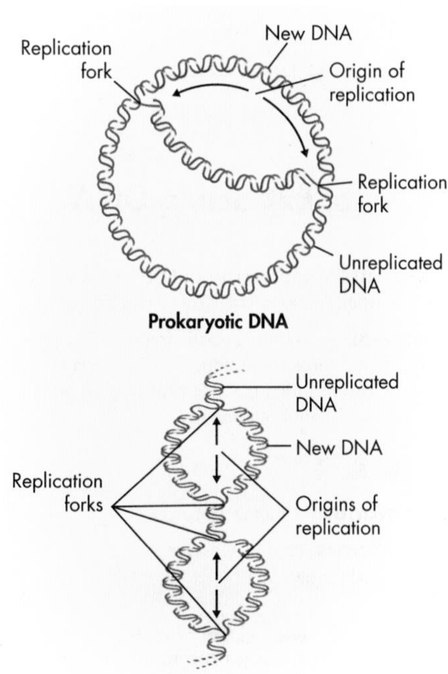

FIGURE 12–10 Differences in DNA Replication Replication in most prokaryotic cells (top) begins at a single starting point and proceeds in two directions until the entire chromosome is copied. In eukaryotic cells (bottom), replication proceeds from multiple starting points on individual chromosomes and ends when all the chromosomes are copied.

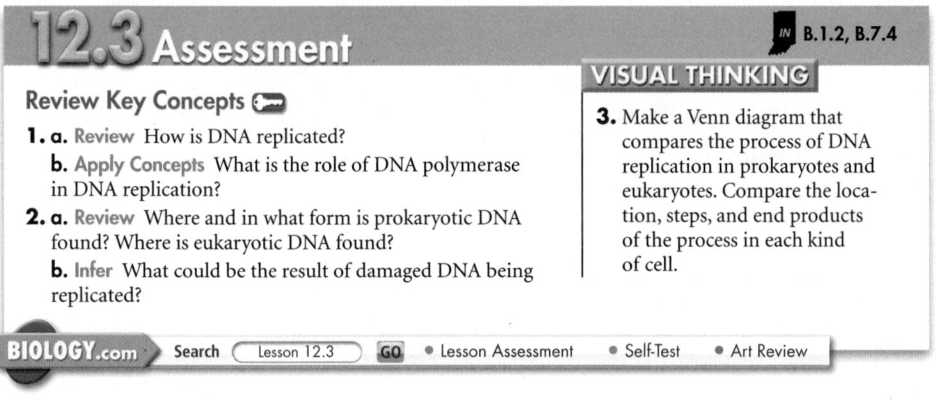

12.3 Assessment

IN B.1.2, B.7.4

Review Key Concepts

1. a. Review How is DNA replicated?

b. Apply Concepts What is the role of DNA polymerase in DNA replication?

2. a. Review Where and in what form is prokaryotic DNA found? Where is eukaryotic DNA found?

b. Infer What could be the result of damaged DNA being replicated?

VISUAL THINKING

3. Make a Venn diagram that compares the process of DNA replication in prokaryotes and eukaryotes. Compare the location, steps, and end products of the process in each kind of cell.

BIOLOGY.com Search Lesson 12.3 GO • Lesson Assessment • Self-Test • Art Review

LESSON 12.3

BIOLOGY.com Have students review and compare prokaryotic and eukaryotic DNA replication by completing the drag-and-drop labeling activity **Art Review: Eukaryotic and Prokaryotic DNA Replication.**

Assess and Remediate

EVALUATE UNDERSTANDING

Have students write a short paragraph explaining the process of DNA replication. Ask several students to share their paragraphs with the class. Then, have students complete the 12.3 Assessment.

REMEDIATION SUGGESTION

L1 **Struggling Students** If students have difficulty completing **Question 3,** have them fill in a **Compare/Contrast Table** with each type of replication in its own column and the following five rows: Location, Number of origins of replication, Replication proceeds in both directions, Involves DNA polymerase, and End products.

Study Wkbks A/B, Appendix S20, Compare/Contrast Table. **Transparencies,** GO3.

BIOLOGY.com Students can check their understanding of lesson concepts with the **Self-Test** assessment. They can then take an online version of the **Lesson Assessment.**

Assessment Answers

1a. The DNA molecule separates into two strands at the replication fork. Each individual strand is then used as a template for the attachment of complementary bases.

1b. DNA polymerase joins individual nucleotides to produce a new strand of DNA and proofreads each new strand.

2a. DNA in prokaryotic cells is found in the form of a single circular chromosome in the cytoplasm; DNA in eukaryotic cells is found in the nucleus, packaged into bigger, individual chromosomes.

2b. If damaged DNA is replicated, the cell that receives it may have altered genes, which could lead to serious consequences.

VISUAL THINKING

3. Students' Venn diagrams should include for prokaryotic replication only: occurs in the cytoplasm, DNA arranged in a single circular chromosome, starts at just one point and continues around the circle until it is completed; for eukaryotic replication only: occurs in the nucleus, begins at several points on the DNA molecule; for both: DNA polymerase joins nucleotides, new DNA strands are complementary to the strands they were made from.

CHAPTER LAB

Pre-Lab

Introduce students to the concepts they will explore in the chapter lab by assigning the Pre-Lab questions.

Lab

Tell students they will perform the chapter lab *Extracting DNA* described in **Lab Manual A.**

 **Struggling Students** A simpler version of the chapter lab is provided in **Lab Manual B.**

SAFETY

Students should wear safety goggles while performing this lab. Have students wash their hands when they complete the lab. Students should use caution with glassware and follow the lab instructions exactly.

BIOLOGY.com Look online for **Editable Lab Worksheets.**

For corresponding pre-lab in the **Foundation Edition**, see page 300.

GUIDED INQUIRY

Pre-Lab: Extracting DNA

Problem What properties of DNA can you observe when you extract DNA from cells?

Materials self-sealing plastic freezer bag, ripe strawberry, detergent solution, 25-mL graduated cylinder, cheesecloth, funnel, test tube, test tube rack, chilled ethanol, stirring rod

Lab Manual Chapter 12 Lab

Skills Focus Predict, Observe, Draw Conclusions

Connect to the Big idea Not surprisingly, the molecules that store genetic information are long molecules. If the DNA from a human cell were unfolded, the double helix structure would be about one meter long. Yet, most of a cell's DNA can be folded and tightly packed inside the cell's tiny nucleus. How can scientists remove DNA from the nucleus so that it can be studied and analyzed? In this lab, you will learn that extracting DNA from living tissue is not as difficult as you might think.

Background Questions

a. **Review** Describe the structure of a DNA molecule.

b. **Review** What type of bond holds the strands of DNA together?

c. **Apply Concepts** How does the strength of those bonds affect how DNA functions?

Pre-Lab Questions

Preview the procedure in the lab manual.

1. **Apply Concepts** Why do strawberry cells need DNA?
2. **Form a Hypothesis** If you observe a cell nucleus under a compound microscope, you will not see a molecule of DNA. Why will you be able to see the DNA you extract?
3. **Predict** Use what you know about DNA to predict some of the physical properties of DNA.
4. **Design an Experiment** How could you determine what percentage of a strawberry's mass is DNA?

Visit Chapter 12 online to test yourself on chapter content and to find activities to help you learn.

Untamed Science Video The Untamed Science CSI crew unravels the secrets of DNA left at the scene of a crime.

Art in Motion View an animation that re-creates the Hershey-Chase experiments.

Art Review Review your understanding of both prokaryotic and eukaryotic DNA replication.

InterActive Art Drag-and-drop base pairs to build your own strand of DNA while you practice the process of DNA replication.

Data Analysis Learn how analysis of DNA base sequences can be used to track animal poaching.

Tutor Tube Tune into the tutor to find out hints for remembering which bases pair together.

Visual Analogy Compare transcription and translation with the process of publishing a book.

Pre-Lab Answers

BACKGROUND QUESTIONS

a. In DNA nucleotides are joined together in long strands by covalent bonds. A double helix structure forms when two antiparallel strands twist around each other.

b. hydrogen bonds

c. Because hydrogen bonds are relatively weak, the strands of DNA can separate and be replicated.

PRE-LAB QUESTIONS

1. Sample answer: Strawberry cells need DNA to produce the proteins that control reactions within its cells.
2. The clump of DNA will contain DNA from many cells.
3. Sample answer: The solid DNA will be made up of thin long threads. The solid will be flexible rather than rigid.
4. Measure the mass of the strawberry and the mass of the extracted DNA. Divide the mass of the DNA by the mass of the strawberry.

12 Study Guide

Big ideas Information and Heredity, Cellular Basis of Life

DNA is a double-stranded protein molecule made up of nucleotide base pairs. DNA stores, copies, and transmits the genetic information in a cell.

12.1 Identifying the Substance of Genes

By observing bacterial transformation, Avery and other scientists discovered that the nucleic acid DNA stores and transmits genetic information from one generation of bacteria to the next.

Hershey and Chase's experiment with bacteriophages confirmed Avery's results, convincing many scientists that DNA was the genetic material found in genes—not just in viruses and bacteria, but in all living cells.

The DNA that makes up genes must be capable of storing, copying, and transmitting the genetic information in a cell.

transformation (339) bacteriophage (340)

12.2 The Structure of DNA

DNA is a nucleic acid made up of nucleotides joined into long strands or chains by covalent bonds.

The clues in Franklin's X-ray pattern enabled Watson and Crick to build a model that explained the specific structure and properties of DNA.

The double-helix model explains Chargaff's rule of base pairing and how the two strands of DNA are held together.

base pairing (348)

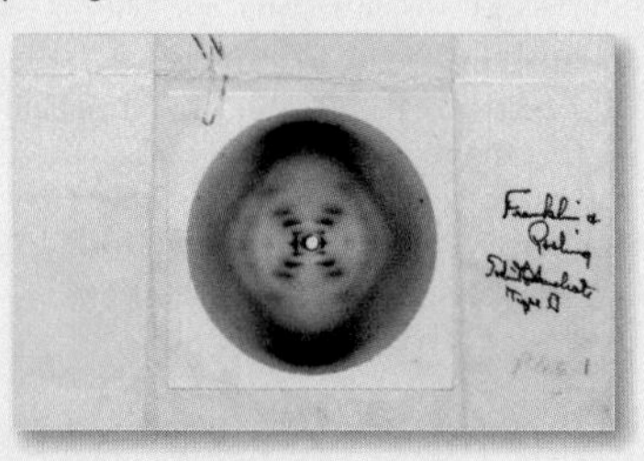

12.3 DNA Replication

DNA polymerase is an enzyme that joins individual nucleotides to produce a new strand of DNA.

Replication in most prokaryotic cells starts from a single point and proceeds in two directions until the entire chromosome is copied.

In eukaryotic cells, replication may begin at dozens or even hundreds of places on the DNA molecule, proceeding in both directions until each chromosome is completely copied.

replication (350) telomere (352)
DNA polymerase (351)

Think Visually Using the information in this chapter, complete the following concept map about DNA replication:

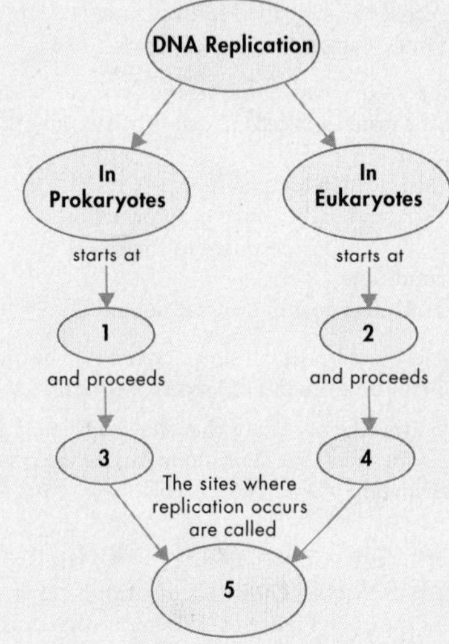

UbD Performance Tasks

SUMMATIVE TASK Tell students to imagine they have been hired as tutors to teach this chapter to a group of students. Have them work in small groups to create a slide presentation that could be used to teach chapter content. Each presentation should consist of at least ten slides of text and graphics. Tell students their presentation must convey information about each lesson Key Question. Have groups share their presentations with the class.

TRANSFER TASK Have students imagine they are either James Watson or Francis Crick. The year is 1953, and Watson and Crick have just submitted their paper describing DNA's structure to the journal *Nature*. In their role as Watson or Crick, have students write a letter to a friend explaining the model of DNA. The letter should also describe the work of at least three other scientists whose work influenced the development of the model.

Study Online

REVIEW AND ASSESSMENT RESOURCES

Editable Worksheets Pages of Study Workbooks A and B, Lab Manuals A and B, and the Assessment Resources Book are available online. These documents can be easily edited using a word-processing program.

Lesson Overview Have students reread the Lesson Overviews to help them study chapter concepts.

Vocabulary Review The *Flash Cards* and *Match It* provide an interactive way to review chapter vocabulary.

Chapter Assessment Have students take an online version of the Chapter 12 Assessment.

Standardized Test Prep Students can take an online version of the Standardized Test Prep. You will receive their scores along with ideas for remediation.

Diagnostic and Benchmark Tests Use these tests to monitor your students' progress and supply remediation.

Answers

THINK VISUALLY

1. a single point

2. dozens or even hundreds of places

3. in both directions

4. in both directions

5. replication forks

ASSESSMENT

Lesson 12.1

UNDERSTAND KEY CONCEPTS

1. b **2.** d **3.** c **4.** b

5. A chemical factor can be transferred from dead bacteria to living bacteria that can change the heritable characteristics of the living bacteria.

6. DNA contains phosphorus, but protein does not. Protein contains sulfur, but DNA does not. This allowed radioactive phosphorus and radioactive sulfur to identify each molecule specifically.

THINK CRITICALLY

7. Griffith heated a culture of a disease-causing strain of bacteria, which killed the bacteria but did not destroy the DNA. When he mixed the heat-killed, disease-causing bacteria with live, harmless bacteria, the DNA from the disease-causing bacteria was transferred to the live bacteria. These bacteria and their offspring caused pneumonia in the mice.

8. Avery and his team used enzymes to destroy various biological molecules. They showed that when DNA was destroyed, genetic information could not be transferred. Destroying other biological molecules did not have the same effect.

Lesson 12.2

UNDERSTAND KEY CONCEPTS

9. b **10.** a **11.** c

12. A nucleotide has three parts: a 5-carbon sugar called deoxyribose, a phosphate group, and a nitrogenous base.

13. Chargaff's rules of base pairing gave Watson and Crick confidence that their model was correct, because their model agreed with Chargaff's observations of the relative percentages of A, T, G, and C in DNA.

14. The scattering pattern of X-rays sent through a sample of DNA showed that the molecule was helical and consisted of two strands.

15. The two strands of DNA are antiparallel, which means that the bases can line up in the two strands and form hydrogen bonds between the A–T and G–C pairs.

THINK CRITICALLY

16. The model showed that hydrogen bonds could create a nearly perfect fit between nitrogenous bases along the center of the molecule. But the bonds could only form between adenine and thymine, and guanine and cytosine.

17. Adenine and guanine are larger than cytosine and thymine. The equal distance between the backbones suggested that a small base must always be paired with a large base.

12 Assessment

The numbers following the questions refer to Indiana's Academic Standards for Biology I

12.1 Identifying the Substance of Genes

Understand Key Concepts

1. The process by which one strain of bacterium is apparently changed into another strain is called
- **a.** transcription.
- **b.** transformation.
- **c.** duplication.
- **d.** replication.

2. Bacteriophages are
- **a.** a form of bacteria.
- **b.** enzymes.
- **c.** coils of DNA.
- **d.** viruses.

3. Which of the following researchers used radioactive markers in experiments to show that DNA was the genetic material in cells?
- **a.** Frederick Griffith
- **b.** Oswald Avery
- **c.** Alfred Hershey and Martha Chase
- **d.** James Watson and Francis Crick

4. Before DNA could definitively be shown to be the genetic material in cells, scientists had to show that it could B.5.2
- **a.** tolerate high temperatures.
- **b.** carry and make copies of information.
- **c.** be modified in response to environmental conditions.
- **d.** be broken down into small subunits.

5. Briefly describe the conclusion that could be drawn from the experiments of Frederick Griffith.

6. What was the key factor that allowed Hershey and Chase to show that DNA alone carried the genetic information of a bacteriophage?

Think Critically

7. Interpret Visuals Look back at Griffith's experiment shown in **Figure 12–1.** Describe the occasion in which the bacterial DNA withstood conditions that killed the bacteria. What happened to the DNA during the rest of the experiment?

8. Evaluate Avery and his team identified DNA as the molecule responsible for the transformation seen in Griffith's experiment. How did they control variables in their experiment to make sure that only DNA caused the effect?

12.2 The Structure of DNA

Understand Key Concepts

9. A nucleotide does NOT contain B.5.1
- **a.** a 5-carbon sugar.
- **b.** an amino acid.
- **c.** a nitrogen base.
- **d.** a phosphate group.

10. According to Chargaff's rule of base pairing, which of the following is true about DNA? B.5.1
- **a.** A = T, and C = G
- **b.** A = C, and T = G
- **c.** A = G, and T = C
- **d.** A = T = C = G

11. The bonds that hold the two strands of DNA together come from B.5.1
- **a.** the attraction of phosphate groups for each other.
- **b.** strong bonds between nitrogenous bases and the sugar-phosphate backbone.
- **c.** weak hydrogen bonds between nitrogenous bases.
- **d.** carbon-to-carbon bonds in the sugar portion of the nucleotides.

12. Describe the components and structure of a DNA nucleotide. B.5.1

13. Explain how Chargaff's rule of base pairing helped Watson and Crick model DNA. B.5.1

14. What important clue from Rosalind Franklin's work helped Watson and Crick develop their model of DNA? B.5.1

15. Why is it significant that the two strands of DNA are antiparallel? B.5.1

Think Critically

16. Use Models How did Watson and Crick's model of the DNA molecule explain base pairing? B.5.1

17. Infer Rosalind Franklin's X-ray pattern showed that the distance between the two phosphate-sugar backbones of a DNA molecule is the same throughout the length of the molecule. How did that information help Watson and Crick determine how bases are paired? B.5.1

Lesson 12.3

UNDERSTAND KEY CONCEPTS

18. c **19.** a **20.** a **21.** d

22. Base pairing is the principle that hydrogen bonds form only between certain base pairs: adenine and thymine, cytosine and guanine. In replication, base pairing ensures that the new complementary strands are identical to the original strands.

23. In a typical prokaryotic cell, DNA is found in the cytoplasm in a single circular chromosome.

24. DNA separates into two strands, then two new complementary strands are generated following the rules of base pairing. Each new DNA molecule has one strand from the original molecule and one newly synthesized strand, making each new DNA molecule an exact duplicate of the original.

12.3 DNA Replication

Understand Key Concepts

18. In prokaryotes, DNA molecules are located in the

a. nucleus. c. cytoplasm.
b. ribosomes. d. histones.

19. In eukaryotes, nearly all the DNA is found in the

a. nucleus. c. cytoplasm.
b. ribosomes. d. histones.

20. The diagram below shows the process of DNA B.7.4

a. replication. c. transformation.
b. digestion. d. transpiration.

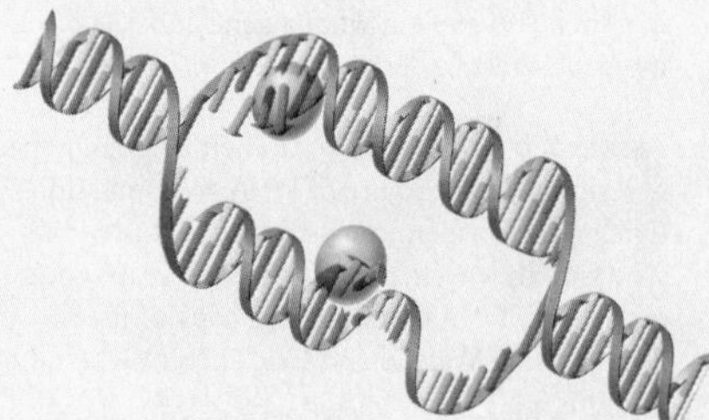

21. The main enzyme involved in linking individual nucleotides into DNA molecules is B.1.2

a. DNA protease. c. carbohydrase.
b. ribose. d. DNA polymerase.

22. What is meant by the term *base pairing*? How is base pairing involved in DNA replication?

23. Describe the appearance of DNA in a typical prokaryotic cell.

24. Explain the process of replication. When a DNA molecule is replicated, how do the new molecules compare to the original molecule? B.7.4

Think Critically

25. Use Analogies Is photocopying a document similar to DNA replication? Think of the original materials, the copying process, and the final products. Explain how the two processes are alike. Identify major differences. NoS.6

26. Compare and Contrast Describe the similarities and differences between DNA replication in prokaryotic cells and in eukaryotic cells. B.7.4

solve the CHAPTER MYSTERY

UV LIGHT

The nucleotides in DNA include the nitrogenous bases adenine, cytosine, guanine, and thymine (A, C, G, and T). The energy from UV light can produce chemical changes in these bases, damaging the DNA molecule and producing errors when DNA is replicated.

1. **Predict** Use your understanding of the structure of DNA to predict what sorts of problems excessive UV light might produce in the DNA molecule. How might these changes affect the functions of DNA?
2. **Infer** All cells have systems of enzymes that repair UV-induced damage to their DNA. Some cellular systems block DNA replication if there are base pairing problems in the double helix. Why are these systems important? How might they work?
3. **Relate Cause and Effect** Analyze the effects that UV light might have on skin cells. Why is UV light so dangerous? Why is the skin particularly vulnerable to it?
4. **Connect to the Big idea** Among humans who inherit genetic defects in their DNA-repair systems, the incidence of skin cancer is as much as 1000 times greater than average. Based on this information, what can you infer about the effect of UV light on DNA?

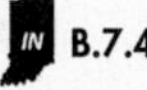 B.7.4

 Search  Chapter 12  GO  • Untamed Science Video • Chapter Mystery

THINK CRITICALLY

25. Photocopying a document is similar in some ways to DNA replication. In both processes, you start with one copy and end up with two identical copies. However, the copying process is different. In photocopying, the original is copied, so you end up with one original copy and one completely new copy. In DNA replication, the original molecule splits in half, so you end up with two copies that are half original and half new.

26. Similarities: DNA replication in both eukaryotes and prokaryotes proceeds in both directions and results in two identical strands of DNA. Differences: prokaryotic DNA replication occurs in the cytoplasm and begins at a single point on the chromosome; eukaryotic DNA replication occurs in the nucleus and begins in many places on a chromosome.

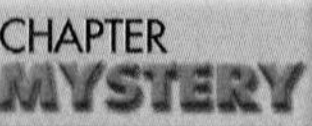 CHAPTER MYSTERY

After students have read through the Chapter Mystery, have a discussion about the connection between UV light and changes in DNA.

Ask What part of the DNA molecule is changed by exposure to UV light? *(the nitrogenous bases)*

Explain that UV light damages DNA by inducing changes in its structure, which consequently affect function. For example, UV light induces the formation of pyrimidine dimers (covalent linking between adjacent pyrimidine bases), which block normal DNA replication.

Ask How might exposure to UV light change DNA's ability to store, copy, or transmit information? *(Any change in the structure of DNA could lead to changes in stored information and could interfere with the accurate copying of the information. This might lead to incorrect information being transmitted to daughter cells during cell division.)*

Ask How could this information be used to inform others of the importance of wearing sunscreen? *(Describing how UV light damages DNA would allow you to use scientific information to support your argument that wearing sunscreen is a healthful action.)*

CHAPTER MYSTERY ANSWERS

1. Sample answer: The energy from UV light can cause chemical changes in the bases. It might cause the formation of new bonds or the breaking of old ones, preventing the DNA molecule from replicating properly.
2. Sample answer: They are important because they prevent damaged DNA from passing along incorrect information when it replicates. They might work by disabling DNA polymerase.
3. UV light is dangerous because it can cause chemical changes in DNA. The skin is particularly vulnerable because it covers and protects most of the body and is the organ that is subject to the greatest exposure to UV light.
4. Big idea Sample answer: The fact that people with genetic defects in their DNA repair systems have a higher incidence of skin cancer, and the fact that excessive exposure to UV light causes skin cancer, provides evidence that for the effect of UV light on DNA—UV light damages DNA, and DNA damage is associated with cancer. Students may be interested to know that xeroderma pigmentosum is the name of the genetic disorder described in this question.

Have students watch the short video **DNA Super Sleuth** to see how scientists use DNA to solve crimes.

ASSESSMENT

Connecting Concepts

USE SCIENCE GRAPHICS

27. about 260 nm

28. Ultraviolet light, particularly between 250 and 270 nm wavelengths, is harmful to living organisms.

29. Sample answer: As more ozone is destroyed, does the amount of UV radiation that reaches Earth's surface increase?

WRITE ABOUT SCIENCE

30. Answers will vary. In their letters to Mendel, students should describe the structure of a typical eukaryotic gene, the structure of DNA, and how genes are parts of chromosomes.

31. Big idea Sample answer: Two strands with paired bases held together by weak hydrogen bonds can be easily pulled apart. New bases lined up on the two strands by base-paring rules would generate two molecules with the same base sequence.

Connecting Concepts

Use Science Graphics NoS.3

A scientist studied the effect of exposing DNA to various wavelengths of ultraviolet light. The scientist determined the number of copying errors made after exposure to ultraviolet rays. The graph shows the results. Use the graph to answer questions 27 and 28.

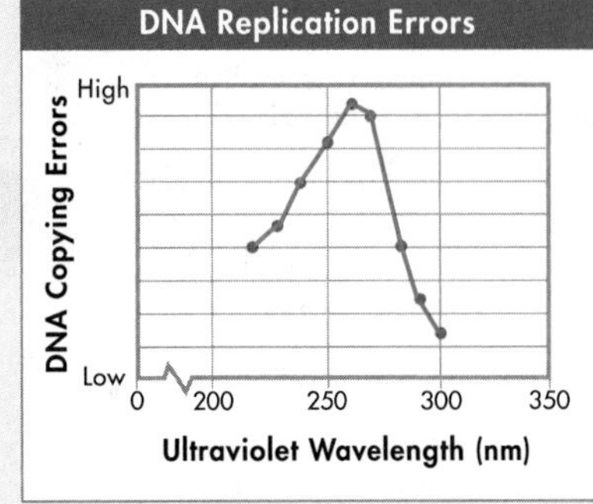

27. Interpret Graphs The most damaging effects of ultraviolet light on DNA replication occur at which wavelength?

28. Infer What conclusion would you draw from the graph about the effect of ultraviolet light on living organisms? B.7.4

29. Pose Questions Ozone is a molecule that is very effective at absorbing ultraviolet light from the sun. Evidence indicates that human activities have contributed to the destruction of ozone in the atmosphere. What question would you ask about the effect of removing ozone from the atmosphere?

Write About Science NoS.3

30. Explanation Recall that Gregor Mendel concluded that factors, which we now call genes, determine the traits that pass from one generation to the next. Imagine that you could send a letter backward in time to Mendel. Write a letter to him in which you explain what a gene consists of in molecular terms. B.5.2

31. Assess the Big idea In their original paper describing the structure of DNA, Watson and Crick noted in a famous sentence that the structure they were proposing immediately suggested how DNA could make a copy of itself. Explain what Watson and Crick meant when they said this. B.5.1

Analyzing Data

IN NoS.3

The following table shows the results of measuring the percentages of the four bases in the DNA of several different organisms. Some of the values are missing from the table.

	Nitrogenous Bases (%)			
Organism	**A**	**G**	**T**	**C**
Human		19.9	29.4	
Chicken	28.8			21.5
Bacterium (*S. lutea*)	13.4			

32. Predict Based on Chargaff's rule, the percentage of adenine bases in human DNA should be around
a. 30.9%.
b. 19.9%.
c. 21.5%.
d. 13.4%.

33. Calculate The value for the percent of guanine bases in the bacterium would be expected to be about MATH
a. 13.4%.
b. 28.8%.
c. 36.6%.
d. There is not enough information given.

34. Predict If the two DNA strands of the bacterium were separated and the base composition of just one of the strands was determined, you could expect
a. the amount of A to equal the amount of T.
b. the amount of C to equal the amount of G.
c. the amount of A to equal the amounts of T, C, and G.
d. the four nitrogenous bases to have any value.

PURPOSE Students will apply Chargaff's rules to determine the relationship between the percentages of nitrogenous bases in DNA from a few organisms.

PLANNING Remind students that, according to base pairing, adenine bonds with thymine and guanine bonds with cytosine.

ANSWERS

32. a

33. c

34. d

Standardized Test Practice for Indiana

Multiple Choice

1. During replication, which sequence of nucleotides would bond with the DNA sequence TATGA?
   A TATGA   C CACTA
   B ATACT   D AGTAT   B.5.1

2. The scientist(s) responsible for the discovery of bacterial transformation is (are)
   A Watson and Crick.   C Griffith.
   B Avery.   D Franklin.

3. Which of the following does NOT describe the structure of DNA?
   A double helix
   B nucleotide polymer
   C contains adenine-guanine pairs
   D sugar-phosphate backbone   B.5.1

4. What did Hershey and Chase's work show?
   A Genes are probably made of DNA.
   B Genes are probably made of protein.
   C Viruses contain DNA but not protein.
   D Bacteria contain DNA but not protein.   B.5.2

5. The two "backbones" of the DNA molecule consist of
   A adenines and sugars.
   B phosphates and sugars.
   C adenines and thymines.
   D thymines and sugars.   B.5.1

6. In eukaryotic chromosomes, DNA is tightly coiled around proteins called
   A DNA polymerase.
   B chromatin.
   C histones.
   D nucleotides.   B.5.1

7. When prokaryotic cells copy their DNA, replication begins at
   A one point on the DNA molecule.
   B two points on opposite ends of the DNA molecule.
   C dozens to hundreds of points along the molecule.
   D opposite ends of the molecule.   B.7.4

8. Compared to eukaryotic cells, prokaryotic cells contain
   A about 1000 times more DNA.
   B about one thousandth as much DNA.
   C twice as much DNA.
   D the same amount of DNA.

Questions 9–10

Under ideal conditions, a single bacterial cell can reproduce every 20 minutes. The graph shows how the total number of cells under ideal conditions can change over time.

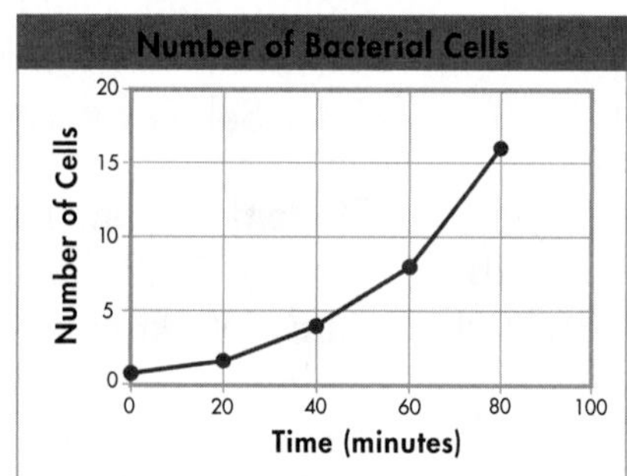

9. How many cells are present after 80 minutes?
   A 1   C 16
   B 2   D 32

10. If the DNA of this bacterium is 4 million base pairs in length, how many total molecules of A, T, C, and G are required for replication to be successful?
    A 2 million
    B 4 million
    C 8 million
    D 32 million

Open-Ended Response

11. Describe how eukaryotic cells are able to keep such large amounts of DNA in the small volume of the cell nucleus.

If You Have Trouble With . . .											
Question	1	2	3	4	5	6	7	8	9	10	11
See Lesson	12.3	12.1	12.2	12.1	12.2	12.3	12.3	12.3	12.3	12.3	12.3

Test-Taking Tip

USE SCRATCH PAPER

Tell students that when they are asked to find the solution to a problem, such as the complementary sequence of DNA, they should first solve the problem on scratch paper. They should then compare their answer with the options provided. This method will help them avoid answer choices that are very similar, but not identical to, the correct answer choice.

Answers

1. B
2. C
3. C
4. A
5. B
6. C
7. A
8. B
9. C
10. C
11. In eukaryotic cells, DNA is tightly wound and coiled around proteins and coiled again and again to form chromosomes. This means that a very large amount of DNA can be stored in a small space.

CHAPTER PLANNER 13 RNA and Protein Synthesis

Chapter Contents	IN	Time	Core Resources
Chapter Preview			**Student Edition,** pp. 360–361 **Chapter Mystery,** p. 361
13.1 RNA The Role of RNA • RNA Synthesis	NoS.6, B.1.2, B.5.3	1 period 1/2 block	**Student Edition,** pp. 362–365 **Study Workbook A** 13.1 Worksheets L2 **Biology.com** *Visual Analogy:* Master Plans and Blueprints • *Art in Motion:* RNA Processing • 13.1 Self-Test • 13.1 Lesson Assessment
13.2 Ribosomes and Protein Synthesis The Genetic Code • Translation • The Molecular Basis of Heredity	B.1.2, B.2.4, B.5.3, B.5.5, B.8.1	1 1/2 periods 3/4 block	**Student Edition,** pp. 366–371 **Inquiry** 13.2 Quick Lab, p. 367 L2 **Study Workbook A** 13.2 Worksheets L2 **Biology.com** *InterActive Art:* Transcription and Translation • *Tutor Tube:* Why Are Proteins So Important? **Assessment Resources Book** Visual Quiz L2
13.3 Mutations Types of Mutations • Effects of Mutations	B.5.3, B.5.4, B.5.5, B.7.4, B.7.5	1 period 1/2 block	**Student Edition,** pp. 372–376 **Inquiry** 13.3 Quick Lab, p. 374 L2 **Study Workbook A** 13.3 Worksheets L2 **Biology.com** *Art Review:* Types of Mutations **Assessment Resources Book** Visual Quiz L2
13.4 Gene Regulation and Expression Prokaryotic Gene Regulation • Eukaryotic Gene Regulation • Genetic Control of Development	NoS.3, B.1.2, B.1.3, B.5.5, B.6.2	1 1/2 periods 3/4 block	**Student Edition,** pp. 377–383 **Inquiry** 13.4 Analyzing Data, p. 381 L2 **Study Workbook A** 13.4 Worksheets L2 **Biology.com** *Data Analysis:* Identifying *Lac* Operon Mutants • 13.4 Self-Test • 13.4 Lesson Assessment
Chapter Pre-Lab	NoS.6, NoS.7, B.5.3	1 period 1/2 block	**Student Edition,** p. 384 L2 **Lab Manual A** *From DNA to Protein Synthesis* L2

Differentiated Instruction Tools

Study Workbook B includes worksheets with lesson-level differentiated instruction support and explanations of differentiated instruction teaching strategies.

Lab Manual B includes skills labs, simplified chapter labs, and hands-on activities.

ELL Handbook explains ways to make *Biology* more accessible to ELL students.

Spanish Study Workbook is a Spanish translation of Study Workbook A.

Multilingual Glossary is the glossary translated into ten languages.

Differentiated Instruction Key

- L1 Special Needs or Struggling Students
- ELL English Language Learners
- LPR Less Proficient Readers
- L2 On-Level Students
- L3 Advanced Students

Additional Resources

Biology.com Untamed Science Video • Vocabulary Flash Cards

Study Workbook B 13.1 Worksheets L1 ELL LPR
Spanish Study Workbook 13.1 Worksheets ELL
Biology.com 13.1 Lesson Overview • 13.1 Lesson Notes

Study Workbook B 13.2 Worksheets L1 ELL LPR
Spanish Study Workbook 13.2 Worksheets ELL
Biology.com *Data Analysis:* A Complicated Operon • 13.2 Lesson Overview • 13.2 Lesson Notes • 13.2 Self-Test • 13.2 Lesson Assessment

Study Workbook B 13.3 Worksheets L1 ELL LPR
Spanish Study Workbook 13.3 Worksheets ELL
Biology.com 13.3 Lesson Overview • 13.3 Lesson Notes • 13.3 Self-Test • 13.3 Lesson Assessment

Study Workbook B 13.4 Worksheets L1 ELL LPR
Spanish Study Workbook 13.4 Worksheets ELL
Biology.com 13.4 Lesson Overview • 13.4 Lesson Notes

Lab Manual B *From DNA to Protein Synthesis* L1 ELL LPR • Data Analysis: *The Discovery of RNA Interference* L1 ELL LPR

Chapter Review

Student Edition Study Guide, p. 385 L2
Study Workbook A Chapter 13 Vocabulary Review L2 • Chapter 13 Chapter Mystery/21st Century Skills Activity L2 L3
Transparencies, pp. 157–171 L1 ELL LPR L2
Biology.com Untamed Science Video • Editable Worksheets of Study Workbooks A and B and Lab Manuals A and B • Chapter 13 Flash Cards and Match It

Untamed Science DVD • Classroom Resources CD (includes lesson presentations and editable worksheets)

Chapter Assessment

Student Edition Assessment, pp. 386–389 L2
Study Workbook B Chapter 13 Chapter Review L1 ELL LPR • Chapter 13 Taking a Standardized Test L1 ELL LPR
Assessment Resources Book Chapter 13 Test A L2 • Chapter 13 Test B L1 ELL LPR
Biology.com Chapter 13 Assessment • Editable Worksheets of Chapter 13 Visual Quizzes and Chapter 13 Tests A and B

Exam*View* *Assessment Suite* • Classroom Resources CD (includes lesson presentations and editable worksheets)

Time: 1 period, 1/2 block

Pressed for Time?

Preview the Chapter Introduce the Lesson 13.1 vocabulary and discuss Figures 13–3 and 13–7.

Cover the Chapter Quickly Have students read *The Role of RNA* and the Transcription section of *RNA Synthesis* in Lesson 13.1. Assign *The Genetic Code and Translation* in Lesson 13.2, complete the Quick Lab on p. 367, and go over Figure 13–7. Assign *Types of Mutations* in Lesson 13.3.

Assess Assign questions 1, 2a, and 3 in the 13.1 Assessment, questions 1, 2, and 4 in the 13.2 Assessment, questions 1 and 3 in the 13.3 Assessment, and the Chapter 13 Standardized Test Prep except for questions 5, 6, and 9.

CHAPTER 13

Connect to the Big Idea

Have students look at the photograph and read the caption. Call on a volunteer to describe how the two tigers differ. *(One has orange and black fur, and the other has white and brown fur.)* Help students connect this observation with the Big Idea of Information and Heredity. Explain that genes carry the information needed by cells to produce proteins, and proteins determine traits such as fur color. Remind students that genes are contained within the nucleus. Add that proteins are made, or synthesized, in the cytoplasm. Then, have students anticipate the answer to the question, **How does information flow from DNA to RNA to direct the synthesis of proteins?**

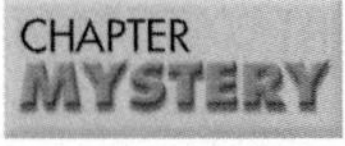

Have students read over the Chapter Mystery. Remind them that DNA is the universal code for life and that it helps determine an organism's characteristics. Stress the universality of the code to help students understand how a mouse gene inserted into a fruit fly could lead to a fruit fly with many eyes. Then, discuss with the class why scientists would want to transplant a mouse gene into a fruit fly. Challenge students to predict what scientists might learn by doing this.

BIOLOGY.com Have students preview the chapter vocabulary using the **Flash Cards.**

13 RNA and Protein Synthesis

Big idea **Information and Heredity**

Q: How does information flow from DNA to RNA to direct the synthesis of proteins?

BIOLOGY.com Search Chapter 13 GO • Flash Cards

360

IN INDIANA ACADEMIC STANDARDS

For the full text of all standards, see the Course Overview in the front matter of this book.

Key standards: Chapter 13 covers key ideas from Standard 5: Molecular Basis of Heredity and Standard 7: Genetics, including **B.5.3** DNA and protein production, **B.6.2** Gene expression and differentiation, **B.7.4** DNA: Duplication and damage, and **B.7.5** Gene alteration.

UbD Understanding by Design

Chapter 13 provides knowledge that is fundamental to the Unit 4 Enduring Understanding: *DNA is the universal code for life; it enables an organism to transmit hereditary information and, along with the environment, determines an organism's characteristics.* As shown in the graphic organizer at the right, the chapter explains how information encoded in DNA flows from the nucleus to the cytoplasm, where it directs protein synthesis.

PERFORMANCE GOALS

Students will analyze data, interpret diagrams, and use analogies to develop an understanding of how the information in DNA is used to direct protein synthesis and influence an organism's characteristics. At the end of the chapter, they will write a story about gene regulation and develop a research proposal about how RNA interference affects gene expression.

INDIANA ACADEMIC STANDARDS FOR SCIENCE

Nature of Science NoS.3, NoS.6, NoS.7; **Cellular Chemistry** B.1.2, B.1.3; **Cellular Structure** B.2.4; **Molecular Basis of Heredity** B.5.1, B.5.3, B.5.4, B.5.5; **Cellular Reproduction and Gene Expression** B.6.2; **Genetics** B.7.4, B.7.5; **Evolution** B.8.1. See lessons for details.

Two Bengal tigers—one with normal coloration and one with a genetic mutation that affects its coloring.

• Untamed Science Video • Chapter Mystery

CHAPTER MYSTERY

MOUSE-EYED FLY

It was definitely not a science fiction movie. The animal in the laboratory was real. Besides having two forward-looking eyes, it also had eyes on its knees and eyes on its hind legs. It even had eyes in the back of its head! Yet as strange as it looked, this animal was not a monster. It was simply a fruit fly with eyes in very strange places. These eyes looked like the fly's normal compound eyes, but a mouse gene transplanted into the fly's DNA had produced them. How could a mouse gene produce extra eyes in a fly?

As you read this chapter, look for clues to explain how a gene that normally controls the growth of eyes in mice could possibly cause a fly to grow extra eyes in unusual places. Then, solve the mystery.

Never Stop Exploring Your World. Finding the solution to the mouse-eyed fly is only the beginning. Take a video field trip with the ecogeeks of Untamed Science to see where this mystery leads.

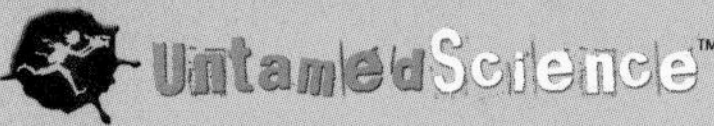

Chapter 13 Big Idea: Information and Heredity

Chapter 13 EQ: How does information flow from the cell nucleus to direct the synthesis of proteins in the cytoplasm?

13.1 GQ: What is RNA?

13.2 GQ: How do cells make proteins?

13.3 GQ: What happens when a cell's DNA changes?

13.4 GQ: How do cells regulate gene expression?

What's Online

Extend your reach by using these and other digital assets offered at **Biology.com.**

CHAPTER MYSTERY
Students can investigate how genes transplanted from a mouse are able to control the development of extra eyes in a fruit fly.

UNTAMED SCIENCE VIDEO
To further explore how mutations affect species, students can take a video field trip with Untamed Science.

VISUAL ANALOGY
Using master plans and blueprints as an analogy for DNA and RNA helps students comprehend the different roles of these two types of molecules.

INTERACTIVE ART
This animation of transcription and translation helps students make sense of the processes involved in protein synthesis.

ART IN MOTION
Students will have a better understanding of RNA editing by watching an animation that shows how it happens.

TUTOR TUBE
Students will hear about the importance of proteins in determining phenotype.

ART REVIEW
This drag-and-drop activity gives students a chance to review different types of mutations.

DATA ANALYSIS
Students can analyze and interpret data on mutations in the *lac* operon of *E. coli*.

LESSON 13.1

Getting Started

Objectives

13.1.1 Contrast RNA and DNA.

13.1.2 Explain the process of transcription.

Student Resources

Study Workbooks A and B, 13.1 Worksheets

Spanish Study Workbook, 13.1 Worksheets

 Lesson Overview • Lesson Notes • Activities: Visual Analogy, InterActive Art, Art in Motion • Assessment: Self-Test, Lesson Assessment

 For corresponding lesson in the **Foundation Edition**, see pages 308–310.

Activate Prior Knowledge

Have students complete a **Quick Write** for RNA. Give students five minutes to write down any facts or concepts they already know about RNA. Encourage them to write continuously for this time. If, at any point, they are stuck, encourage them to continue writing the same fact until they can think of a new one.

Study Wkbks A/B, Appendix S11, Quick Write.

IN INDIANA ACADEMIC STANDARDS

For the full text of all standards, see the Course Overview in the front matter of this book.

B.5.3 Describe the process by which DNA directs the production of protein within a cell.

13.1 RNA

IN B.5.3 DNA and protein production. Also covered: **NoS.6, B.1.2.**

Key Questions

How does RNA differ from DNA?

How does the cell make RNA?

Vocabulary

RNA
messenger RNA
ribosomal RNA
transfer RNA
transcription
RNA polymerase
promoter
intron
exon

Taking Notes

Preview Visuals Before you read, look at **Figure 13–3.** Write a prediction of how you think a cell makes RNA based on the figure. Then as you read, take notes on how a cell makes RNA. After you read, compare your notes and your prediction.

THINK ABOUT IT We know that DNA is the genetic material, and we know that the sequence of nucleotide bases in its strands must carry some sort of code. For that code to work, the cell must be able to understand it. What exactly do those bases code for? Where is the cell's decoding system?

The Role of RNA

How does RNA differ from DNA?

When Watson and Crick solved the double-helix structure of DNA, they understood right away how DNA could be copied. All a cell had to do was to separate the two strands and then use base pairing to make a new complementary strand for each. But the structure of DNA by itself did not explain how a gene actually works. That question required a great deal more research. The answer came from the discovery that another nucleic acid—ribonucleic acid, or RNA—was involved in putting the genetic code into action. **RNA,** like DNA, is a nucleic acid that consists of a long chain of nucleotides.

In a general way, genes contain coded DNA instructions that tell cells how to build proteins. The first step in decoding these genetic instructions is to copy part of the base sequence from DNA into RNA. RNA then uses these instructions to direct the production of proteins, which help to determine an organisms's characteristics.

Comparing RNA and DNA Remember that each nucleotide in DNA is made up of a 5-carbon sugar, a phosphate group, and a nitrogenous base. This is true for RNA as well. **But there are three important differences between RNA and DNA: (1) the sugar in RNA is ribose instead of deoxyribose, (2) RNA is generally single-stranded and not double-stranded, and (3) RNA contains uracil in place of thymine.** These chemical differences make it easy for enzymes in the cell to tell DNA and RNA apart.

You can compare the different roles played by DNA and RNA molecules in directing the production of proteins to the two type of plans builders use. A master plan has all the information needed to construct a building. But builders never bring a valuable master plan to the job site, where it might be damaged or lost. Instead, as **Figure 13–1** shows, they work from blueprints, inexpensive, disposable copies of the master plan.

UbD Teach for Understanding

ENDURING UNDERSTANDING DNA is the universal code of life; it enables an organism to transmit hereditary information and, along with the environment, determines an organism's characteristics.

GUIDING QUESTION What is RNA?

EVIDENCE OF UNDERSTANDING *After completing the lesson, assign students the following assessment to show they understand how mRNA is synthesized.* Have pairs of students make a two-part labeled diagram to show the process of mRNA synthesis. Tell them to represent DNA transcription in the first part of the diagram and RNA editing in the second part.

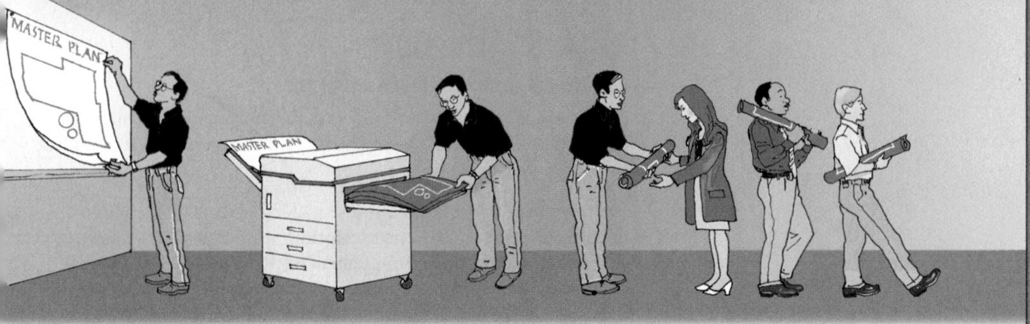

Similarly, the cell uses the vital DNA "master plan" to prepare RNA "blueprints." The DNA molecule stays safely in the cell's nucleus, while RNA molecules go to the protein-building sites in the cytoplasm—the ribosomes.

VISUAL ANALOGY

MASTER PLANS AND BLUEPRINTS

FIGURE 13–1 The different roles of DNA and RNA molecules in directing protein synthesis can be compared to the two types of plans used by builders: master plans and blueprints.

Functions of RNA You can think of an RNA molecule as a disposable copy of a segment of DNA, a working facsimile of a single gene. RNA has many functions, but most RNA molecules are involved in just one job—protein synthesis. RNA controls the assembly of amino acids into proteins. Like workers in a factory, each type of RNA molecule specializes in a different aspect of this job. **Figure 13–2** shows the three main types of RNA: messenger RNA, ribosomal RNA, and transfer RNA.

▶ ***Messenger RNA*** Most genes contain instructions for assembling amino acids into proteins. The RNA molecules that carry copies of these instructions are known as **messenger RNA** (mRNA). They carry information from DNA to other parts of the cell.

▶ ***Ribosomal RNA*** Proteins are assembled on ribosomes, small organelles composed of two subunits. These subunits are made up of several **ribosomal RNA** (rRNA) molecules and as many as 80 different proteins.

▶ ***Transfer RNA*** When a protein is built, a third type of RNA molecule transfers each amino acid to the ribosome as it is specified by the coded messages in mRNA. These molecules are known as **transfer RNA** (tRNA).

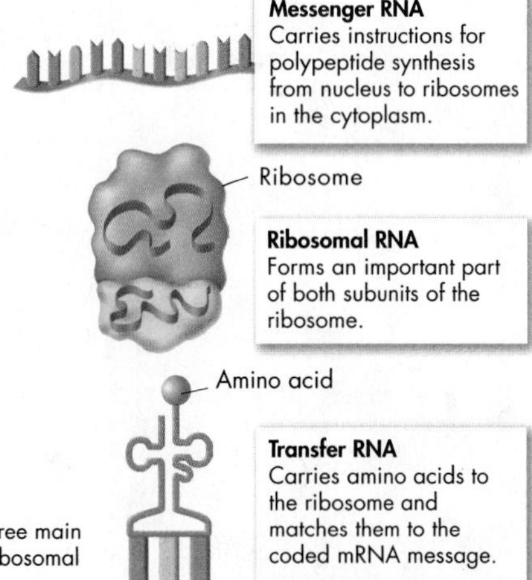

Messenger RNA
Carries instructions for polypeptide synthesis from nucleus to ribosomes in the cytoplasm.
Ribosome
Ribosomal RNA
Forms an important part of both subunits of the ribosome.
Amino acid
Transfer RNA
Carries amino acids to the ribosome and matches them to the coded mRNA message.

FIGURE 13–2 Types of RNA The three main types of RNA are messenger RNA, ribosomal RNA, and transfer RNA.

Teach

VISUAL ANALOGY

Refer to **Figure 13–1,** and ask students what the master plans and blueprints represent in the analogy. *(DNA and RNA, respectively)* Discuss with the class how builders use copies of blueprints at building sites so that they don't have to worry about the master blueprint being damaged. Likewise, cells use copies of DNA (in the form of RNA) rather than the original DNA molecule when proteins are synthesized. This prevents the threat of DNA being damaged at protein building sites. Ask students to think about what mechanisms in the nucleus might be represented by the copy machine in the analogy. Tell them they will read about these mechanisms later in the lesson.

DIFFERENTIATED INSTRUCTION

L3 Advanced Students Encourage advanced students to come up with additional analogies for the relationship between DNA and RNA. For example, a student might suggest a film negative for DNA and photographic prints of that negative for RNA. Then, have pairs or small groups of students discuss their analogies and choose a few that they think best model the roles of DNA and RNA. Ask students to share these analogies with the class.

BIOLOGY.com Students can further explore the analogy in **Figure 13–1** with **Visual Analogy: Master Plans and Blueprints.**

Address Misconceptions

Importance of RNA Students often fail to appreciate the importance of other genetic material besides DNA. Make sure they are aware that DNA is the inherited genetic material but RNA is the genetic material that carries out the instructions encoded in DNA. Without RNA, the instructions in DNA could not be used by cells.

Biology In-Depth

SNURPS AND SPLICEOSOMES

In addition to the three types of RNA described above, a fourth type of RNA is also at work in cells. This type of RNA, called small nuclear RNA (snRNA) is involved in the important role of editing mRNA before it leaves the nucleus. snRNA is only found in the nucleus in combination with certain proteins, called small ribonucleoproteins, or snRNP (snurps). Snurp-snRNA complexes are given the name spliceosomes. They have a role that is somewhat analogous to ribosomes in the cytoplasm. As ribosomes join together amino acids to form chains of polypeptides, spliceosomes splice together exons to form edited strands of mRNA.

Teach continued

Use Visuals

Make color copies of **Figure 13–3,** and give a copy to each student. As you discuss the process of transcription with the class, have students record their class notes on the diagram. Discuss the role of RNA polymerase in "unzipping" the two strands of DNA. Explain that RNA polymerase binds to DNA only at sites called promoters, which have specific base sequences. The promoters "tell" the enzyme where to start transcribing DNA. Point out how bases in the DNA strand are bound to complementary bases that will form the RNA strand. Ask students to label the bases in some of the base pairs with the letters A, C, G, T, or U. Remind them that uracil in RNA is complementary to adenine in DNA. State that transcription is just the first stage of RNA synthesis.

Ask What is the second stage of RNA synthesis? *(RNA editing)*

DIFFERENTIATED INSTRUCTION

LPR Less Proficient Readers Some students may be confused by the multiple steps of RNA synthesis. Suggest that they make a **Flowchart** showing the sequence of steps in the process. Their flowchart should include the steps of both DNA transcription and RNA editing. Encourage them to add simple sketches to the steps of their flowchart.

Study Wkbks A/B, Appendix S25, Flowchart. **Transparencies,** GO8.

ELL Focus on ELL: Extend Language

BEGINNING AND INTERMEDIATE SPEAKERS Have students divide a sheet of paper into four equal parts. In the upper left square, have them write the word *transcription*. In the upper right square, ask them to sketch the transcription process, using **Figure 13–3** as a guide. In the lower left square, ask them to write a definition of transcription, in their own words, based on the diagram. Then, tell them to write an original sentence about transcription in the lower right square. Give students a chance to share their work with other students.

BIOLOGY.com In **InterActive Art: Transcription and Translation,** students can explore transcription with an interactive version of **Figure 13–3.** This activity also covers translation, which students will learn in Lesson 13.2.

RNA Synthesis

How does the cell make RNA?

Cells invest large amounts of raw material and energy into making RNA molecules. Understanding how cells do this is essential to understanding how genes work.

Transcription Most of the work of making RNA takes place during **transcription.** **In transcription, segments of DNA serve as templates to produce complementary RNA molecules.** The base sequences of the transcribed RNA complement the base sequences of the template DNA.

In prokaryotes, RNA synthesis and protein synthesis take place in the cytoplasm. In eukaryotes, RNA is produced in the cell's nucleus and then moves to the cytoplasm to play a role in the production of protein. Our focus here is on transcription in eukaryotic cells.

Transcription requires an enzyme, known as **RNA polymerase,** that is similar to DNA polymerase. RNA polymerase binds to DNA during transcription and separates the DNA strands. It then uses one strand of DNA as a template from which to assemble nucleotides into a complementary strand of RNA, as shown in **Figure 13–3.** The ability to copy a single DNA sequence into RNA makes it possible for a single gene to produce hundreds or even thousands of RNA molecules.

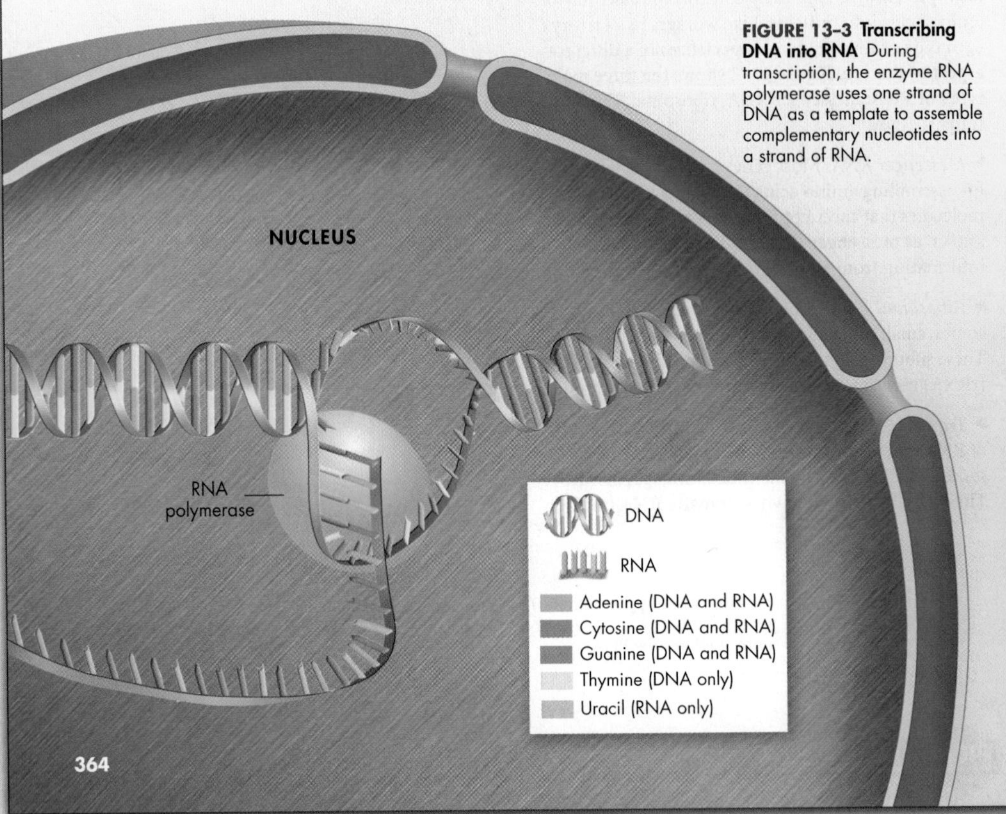

FIGURE 13–3 Transcribing DNA into RNA During transcription, the enzyme RNA polymerase uses one strand of DNA as a template to assemble complementary nucleotides into a strand of RNA.

UbD Check for Understanding

VISUAL REPRESENTATION

Ask students to make a **Concept Map** about RNA, with the term *RNA* in the center of the map. The concept map should include information about the general structure of RNA and the specific functions of the three main types of RNA.

Study Wkbks A/B, Appendix S21, Concept Map. **Transparencies,** GO4.

ADJUST INSTRUCTION

If students struggle to complete their concept maps, have them exchange their maps with a partner. Have partners discuss the concepts and relationships represented in the maps and revise them as necessary.

Promoters How does RNA polymerase know where to start and stop making a strand of RNA? The answer is that RNA polymerase doesn't bind to DNA just anywhere. The enzyme binds only to **promoters,** regions of DNA that have specific base sequences. Promoters are signals in the DNA molecule that show RNA polymerase exactly where to begin making RNA. Similar signals in DNA cause transcription to stop when a new RNA molecule is completed.

RNA Editing Like a writer's first draft, RNA molecules sometimes require a bit of editing before they are ready to be read. These pre-mRNA molecules have bits and pieces cut out of them before they can go into action. The portions that are cut out and discarded are called **introns.** In eukaryotes, introns are taken out of pre-mRNA molecules while they are still in the nucleus. The remaining pieces, known as **exons,** are then spliced back together to form the final mRNA, as shown in **Figure 13–4.**

Why do cells use energy to make a large RNA molecule and then throw parts of that molecule away? That's a good question, and biologists still don't have a complete answer. Some pre-mRNA molecules may be cut and spliced in different ways in different tissues, making it possible for a single gene to produce several different forms of RNA. Introns and exons may also play a role in evolution, making it possible for very small changes in DNA sequences to have dramatic effects on how genes affect cellular function.

FIGURE 13–4 Introns and Exons Before many mRNA molecules can be read, sections called introns are "edited out." The remaining pieces, called exons, are spliced together. Then, an RNA cap and tail are added to form the final mRNA molecule.

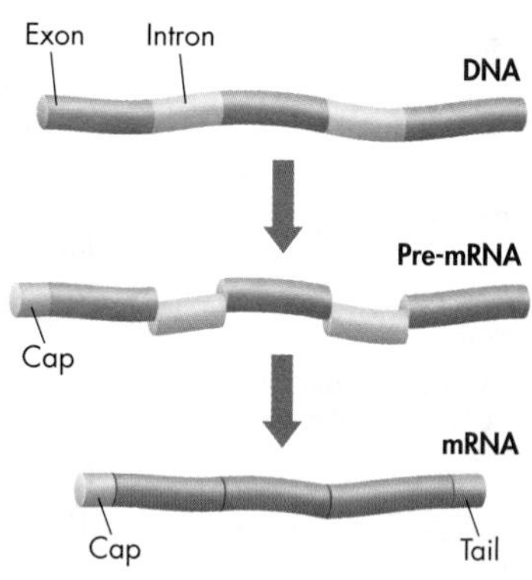

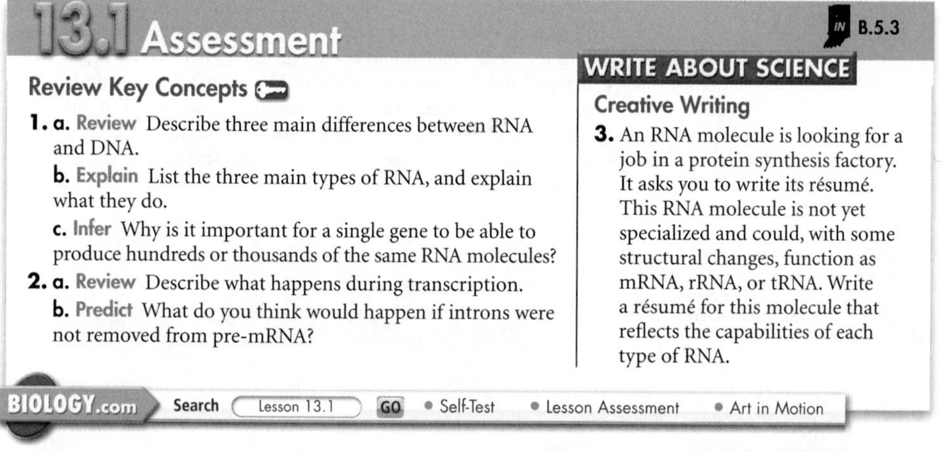

13.1 Assessment

IN B.5.3

Review Key Concepts

1. a. **Review** Describe three main differences between RNA and DNA.
   b. **Explain** List the three main types of RNA, and explain what they do.
   c. **Infer** Why is it important for a single gene to be able to produce hundreds or thousands of the same RNA molecules?
2. a. **Review** Describe what happens during transcription.
   b. **Predict** What do you think would happen if introns were not removed from pre-mRNA?

WRITE ABOUT SCIENCE

Creative Writing

3. An RNA molecule is looking for a job in a protein synthesis factory. It asks you to write its résumé. This RNA molecule is not yet specialized and could, with some structural changes, function as mRNA, rRNA, or tRNA. Write a résumé for this molecule that reflects the capabilities of each type of RNA.

BIOLOGY.com Search Lesson 13.1 GO • Self-Test • Lesson Assessment • Art in Motion

LESSON 13.1

BIOLOGY.com Students can view an animation of RNA being edited by watching **Art in Motion: RNA Processing.**

Assess and Remediate

EVALUATE UNDERSTANDING

Tell students to write sentences using lesson vocabulary terms. The sentences should show what the terms mean. Ask them to exchange their completed sentences with a partner and edit each other's sentences for factual errors. Then, have students complete the 13.1 Assessment.

REMEDIATION SUGGESTION

L1 Struggling Students If students have trouble with **Question 3,** have them reread the functions of RNA on page 363 and re-examine **Figure 13–2,** including the caption.

BIOLOGY.com Students can check their understanding of lesson concepts with the **Self-Test** assessment. They can then take an online version of the **Lesson Assessment.**

Assessment Answers

1a. RNA contains the sugar ribose instead of deoxyribose, is generally single-stranded rather than double-stranded, and contains uracil instead of thymine.

1b. Messenger RNA carries instructions for polypeptide synthesis from DNA in the nucleus to ribosomes in the cytoplasm. Ribosomal RNA forms an important part of both subunits of a ribosome, where proteins are assembled. Transfer RNA carries amino acids to a ribosome and matches them to the coded mRNA message.

1c. Sample answer: Proteins must be continuously synthesized in the cell, so the instructions coded in genes must be used over and over again. Therefore, a single gene must be able to produce hundreds or thousands of the same RNA molecules for protein synthesis.

2a. During transcription, the enzyme RNA polymerase binds to DNA and separates the DNA strands. It then uses one strand of DNA as a template to assemble nucleotides into a complementary strand of RNA.

2b. Sample answer: If introns were not removed, the instructions carried by mRNA for assembling amino acids into a protein might be incorrect, and the resulting protein might not function properly.

WRITE ABOUT SCIENCE

3. Answers will vary but should show that students understand the different functions of mRNA, rRNA, and tRNA in protein synthesis.

LESSON 13.2

Getting Started

Objectives

13.2.1 Identify the genetic code and explain how it is read.

13.2.2 Summarize the process of translation.

13.2.3 Describe the "central dogma" of molecular biology.

Student Resources

Study Workbooks A and B, 13.2 Worksheets

Spanish Study Workbook, 13.2 Worksheets

Lesson Overview • Lesson Notes
- Activities: InterActive Art, Tutor Tube
- Assessment: Self-Test, Lesson Assessment

For corresponding lesson in the **Foundation Edition**, see pages 311–315.

Build Background

Introduce the genetic code by giving the class an encoded message to translate. On the board, write:

9 3-1-14 18-5-1-4 20-8-9-19 3-15-4-5

Tell students that each number represents a letter (a = 1, b = 2, c = 3, and so on). After students have deciphered the message *(I can read this code)*, explain that RNA also contains a code.

Answers

FIGURE 13–5 AUG, AAC, and UCU

IN INDIANA ACADEMIC STANDARDS

For the full text of all standards, see the Course Overview in the front matter of this book.

B.2.4 Explain that all cells contain ribosomes, the key sites for protein synthesis, where genetic material is decoded in order to form unique proteins.

B.5.3 Describe the process by which DNA directs the production of protein within a cell.

B.5.5 Understand that proteins are responsible for the observable traits of an organism and for most of the functions within an organism.

13.2 Ribosomes and Protein Synthesis

B.2.4 Protein synthesis; **B.5.3** DNA and protein production; **B.5.5** Roles of proteins. Also covered: **B.1.2, B.8.1.**

Key Questions

What is the genetic code, and how is it read?

What role does the ribosome play in assembling proteins?

What is the "central dogma" of molecular biology?

Vocabulary

polypeptide • genetic code • codon • translation • anticodon • gene expression

Taking Notes

Outline Before you read, write down the green headings in this lesson. As you read, keep a list of the main points, and then write a summary for each heading.

THINK ABOUT IT How would you build a system to read the messages that are coded in genes and transcribed into RNA? Would you read the bases one at a time, as if the code were a language with just four words—one word per base? Perhaps you would read them, as we do in English, as individual letters that can be combined to spell longer words.

The Genetic Code

What is the genetic code, and how is it read?

The first step in decoding genetic messages is to transcribe a nucleotide base sequence from DNA to RNA. This transcribed information contains a code for making proteins. You learned in Chapter 2 that proteins are made by joining amino acids together into long chains, called **polypeptides.** As many as 20 different amino acids are commonly found in polypeptides.

The specific amino acids in a polypeptide, and the order in which they are joined, determine the properties of different proteins. The sequence of amino acids influences the shape of the protein, which in turn determines its function. How is the order of bases in DNA and RNA molecules translated into a particular order of amino acids in a polypeptide?

As you know from Lesson 13.1, RNA contains four different bases: adenine, cytosine, guanine, and uracil. In effect, these bases form a "language" with just four "letters": A, C, G, and U. We call this language the **genetic code.** How can a code with just four letters carry instructions for 20 different amino acids? **The genetic code is read three "letters" at a time, so that each "word" is three bases long and corresponds to a single amino acid.** Each three-letter "word" in mRNA is known as a **codon.** As shown in **Figure 13–5,** a codon consists of three consecutive bases that specify a single amino acid to be added to the polypeptide chain.

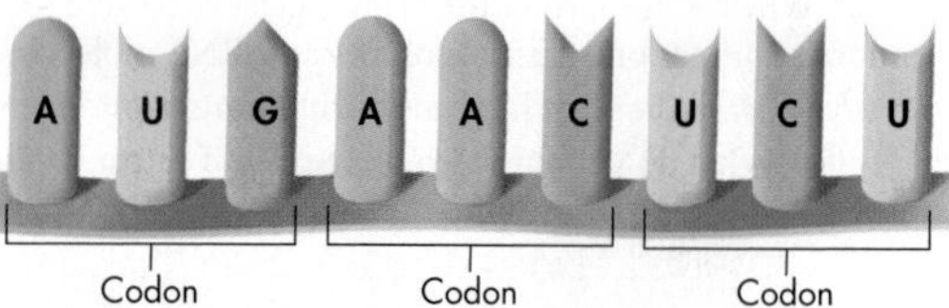

FIGURE 13–5 Codons A codon is a group of three nucleotide bases in messenger RNA that specifies a particular amino acid. **Observe** *What are the three-letter groups of the codons shown here?*

UbD Teach for Understanding

ENDURING UNDERSTANDING DNA is the universal code of life; it enables an organism to transmit hereditary information and, along with the environment, determines an organism's characteristics.

GUIDING QUESTION How do cells make proteins?

EVIDENCE OF UNDERSTANDING *After completing the lesson, assign students the following assessment to show they understand how cells make proteins.* Divide the class into groups, and ask members of each group to develop and present a short skit in which they play the parts of RNA, ribosomes, and amino acids. Allow them to use props and act out the way translation produces a polypeptide.

How to Read Codons Because there are four different bases in RNA, there are 64 possible three-base codons ($4 \times 4 \times 4 = 64$) in the genetic code. **Figure 13–6** shows these possible combinations. Most amino acids can be specified by more than one codon. For example, six different codons—UUA, UUG, CUU, CUC, CUA, and CUG—specify leucine. But only one codon—UGG—specifies the amino acid tryptophan.

Decoding codons is a task made simple by use of a genetic code table. Just start at the middle of the circle with the first letter of the codon, and move outward. Next, move out to the second ring to find the second letter of the codon. Find the third and final letter among the smallest set of letters in the third ring. Then read the amino acid in that sector.

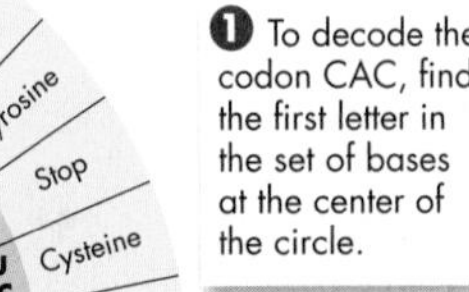

1 To decode the codon CAC, find the first letter in the set of bases at the center of the circle.

2 Find the second letter of the codon A, in the "C" quarter of the next ring.

3 Find the third letter, C, in the next ring, in the "C-A" grouping.

4 Read the name of the amino acid in that sector—in this case histidine.

FIGURE 13–6 Reading Codons This circular table shows the amino acid to which each of the 64 codons corresponds. To read a codon, start at the middle of the circle and move outward.

Start and Stop Codons Any message, whether in a written language or the genetic code, needs punctuation marks. In English, punctuation tells us where to pause, when to sound excited, and where to start and stop a sentence. The genetic code has punctuation marks, too. The methionine codon AUG, for example, also serves as the initiation, or "start," codon for protein synthesis. Following the start codon, mRNA is read, three bases at a time, until it reaches one of three different "stop" codons, which end translation. At that point, the polypeptide is complete.

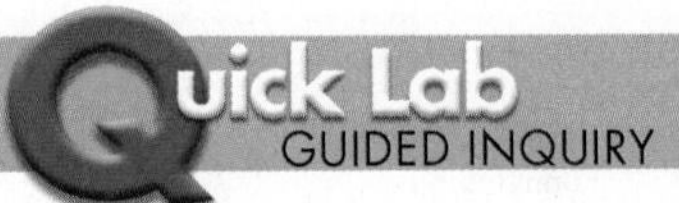

GUIDED INQUIRY

B.5.3

How Does a Cell Interpret Codons?

1 A certain gene has the following base sequence:

GACAAGTCCACAATC

Write this sequence on a separate sheet of paper.

2 From left to right, write the sequence of the mRNA molecule transcribed from this gene.

3 Using **Figure 13–6**, read the mRNA codons from left to right. Then write the amino acid sequence of the polypeptide.

4 Repeat step 2, reading the sequence of the mRNA molecule from right to left.

Analyze and Conclude

1. **Apply Concepts** Why did steps 3 and 4 produce different polypeptides?

2. **Infer** Do cells usually decode nucleotides in one direction only or in either direction?

Teach

Use Visuals

Explain how to use **Figure 13–6** to identify the amino acid that corresponds to a particular codon. Then, write several codons on the board, and call on students to name the amino acid each one represents. Reverse the process by writing the names of several amino acids and having students identify the codons that represent them. Finally, guide students in drawing conclusions about the genetic code.

Ask How many amino acids does each codon represent? *(one)*

Ask How many codons can code for a single amino acid? *(from one to six)*

Ask What else may codons represent? *(stop and start)*

Point out that the methionine codon, AUG, also means "start." Call on a volunteer to explain how the stop and start codons are interpreted during protein synthesis.

DIFFERENTIATED INSTRUCTION

L1 Special Needs Some students may find it difficult to understand and use **Figure 13–6.** Pair these students with students who have a good understanding of the material, and have partners work together to make index cards to represent the genetic code. Tell them to write the name of an amino acid on the front of each card and to list all of its corresponding codons on the back of the card. Let students use the index cards instead of **Figure 13–6** when they answer questions about the genetic code.

L1 Struggling Students Help students access genetic code content by presenting and discussing a visual representation of the code that differs from the diagram in **Figure 13–6.** For example, show students a rectangular matrix of the code. Have them take notes on the discussion and then use the notes to explain the alternative code representation to another student.

PURPOSE Students will translate codons to identify the correct sequence of amino acids in a protein.

PLANNING Point out that steps 2 and 3 represent the two major stages of protein synthesis. Step 2 represents transcription of the genetic code to form mRNA, and step 3 represents the translation of mRNA to amino acids in a protein.

ANALYZE AND CONCLUDE

1. The polypeptide produced in step 3 is leucine-phenylalanine-arginine-cysteine-stop. In step 4, the polypeptide produced is aspartic acid-cysteine-glycine-leucine-valine. They are different because the codons are read in the opposite direction.
2. Sample answer: Cells usually decode nucleotides in one direction only. Otherwise, the nucleotides could be reversed and code for a different sequence of amino acids.

Teach continued

VISUAL SUMMARY

As students examine **Figure 13–7,** ask volunteers to briefly describe transcription and the structure and function of ribosomes. Describe how a ribosome moves along an mRNA strand, like a bead sliding along a string, translating the strand of mRNA as it moves.

Ask What role does transfer RNA play in translation? *(It brings amino acids to the ribosome.)*

Ask If an mRNA codon has the bases CUA, what bases will the corresponding transfer RNA anticodon have? *(GAU)*

DIFFERENTIATED INSTRUCTION

ELL English Language Learners Instruct students to complete an **ELL Frayer Model** for the term *translation*. Tell them to define the term and to sketch the translation process, using **Figure 13–7** as a guide. For their example, they can write a sequence of codons and their matching anticodons and amino acids. Then, have students write a definition of the term *translation* into their own language, if possible.

Study Wkbks A/B, Appendix S26, ELL Frayer Model. **Transparencies,** GO10.

LPR Less Proficient Readers Use **Cloze Prompts** to help students focus on the most important points as they read about translation in the text. Copy important sentences from the passage, leaving a term out of each one. Then, have students fill in the blanks as they read.

Study Wkbks A/B, Appendix S2, Cloze Prompts.

BIOLOGY.com In **InterActive Art: Transcription and Translation,** students can explore translation with an interactive version of **Figure 13–7.** To help students understand how the products of translation—proteins—relate to phenotype, have them view **Tutor Tube: Why Are Proteins So Important?**

Address Misconceptions

Products of Translation Students frequently misidentify the products of translation as mRNA or amino acids. Stress that mRNA is the product of transcription, not translation, and that amino acids are already available in the cell—they just need to be joined together in the correct sequence to make a polypeptide.

Translation

What role does the ribosome play in assembling proteins?

The sequence of nucleotide bases in an mRNA molecule is a set of instructions that gives the order in which amino acids should be joined to produce a polypeptide. Once the polypeptide is complete, it then folds into its final shape or joins with other polypeptides to become a functional protein.

If you've ever tried to assemble a complex toy, you know that instructions alone don't do the job. You need to read them and then put the parts together. In the cell, a tiny factory—the ribosome—carries out both these tasks. **Ribosomes use the sequence of codons in mRNA to assemble amino acids into polypeptide chains.** The decoding of an mRNA message into a protein is a process known as **translation.**

Steps in Translation Transcription isn't part of the translation process, but it is critical to it. Transcribed mRNA directs that process. In a eukaryotic cell, transcription goes on in the cell's nucleus; translation is carried out by ribosomes after the transcribed mRNA enters the cell's cytoplasm. Refer to **Figure 13–7** as you read about translation. **A** Translation begins when a ribosome attaches to an mRNA molecule in the cytoplasm. As each codon passes through the ribosome, tRNAs bring the proper amino acids into the ribosome. One at a time, the ribosome then attaches these amino acids to the growing chain.

VISUAL SUMMARY

TRANSLATION

FIGURE 13–7 During translation, or protein synthesis, the cell uses information from messenger RNA to produce proteins.

Messenger RNA
Messenger RNA is transcribed in the nucleus and then enters the cytoplasm.

A Transfer RNA
Translation begins at AUG, the start codon. Each transfer RNA has an anticodon whose bases are complementary to the bases of a codon on the mRNA strand. The ribosome positions the start codon to attract its anticodon, which is part of the tRNA that binds methionine. The ribosome also binds the next codon and its anticodon.

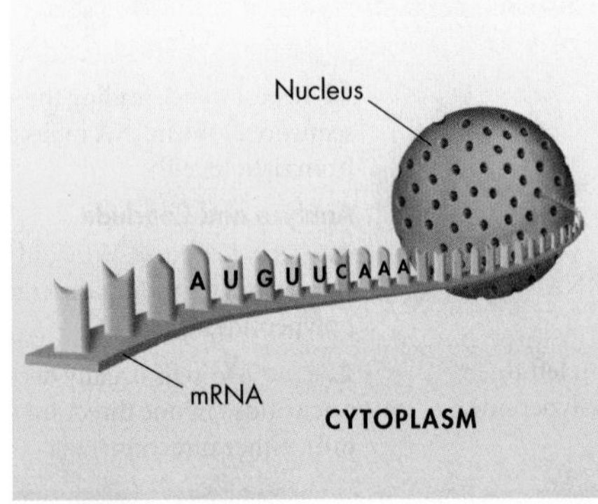

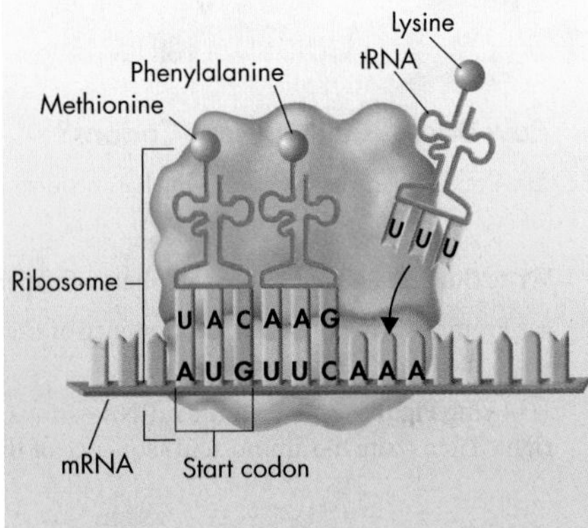

 BIOLOGY.com Search Lesson 13.2 GO • InterActive Art • Tutor Tube

UbD Check for Understanding

ORAL QUESTIONING

Call on students to answer the following questions about the genetic code and translation:

- How is a codon similar to a word? How is it different from a word?
- What are general characteristics of the genetic code?
- Describe the process of translation.

ADJUST INSTRUCTION

Discuss any questions that students answer incorrectly or incompletely. Then, ask if anyone still has questions. Call on volunteers to address any additional questions that students raise.

Each tRNA molecule carries just one kind of amino acid. In addition, each tRNA molecule has three unpaired bases, collectively called the **anticodon.** Each tRNA anticodon is complementary to one mRNA codon.

In the case of the tRNA molecule for methionine, the anticodon is UAC, which pairs with the methionine codon, AUG. The ribosome has a second binding site for a tRNA molecule for the next codon. If that next codon is UUC, a tRNA molecule with an AAG anticodon fits against the mRNA molecule held in the ribosome. That second tRNA molecule brings the amino acid phenylalanine into the ribosome.

B Like an assembly-line worker who attaches one part to another, the ribosome helps form a peptide bond between the first and second amino acids—methionine and phenylalanine. At the same time, the bond holding the first tRNA molecule to its amino acid is broken. That tRNA then moves into a third binding site, from which it exits the ribosome. The ribosome then moves to the third codon, where tRNA brings it the amino acid specified by the third codon.

C The polypeptide chain continues to grow until the ribosome reaches a "stop" codon on the mRNA molecule. When the ribosome reaches a stop codon, it releases both the newly formed polypeptide and the mRNA molecule, completing the process of translation.

In Your Notebook *Briefly summarize the three steps in translation.*

FIGURE 13–8 Molecular Model of a Ribosome This model shows ribosomal RNA and associated proteins as colored ribbons. The large subunit is blue, green, and purple. The small subunit is shown in yellow and orange. The three solid elements in the center are tRNA molecules.

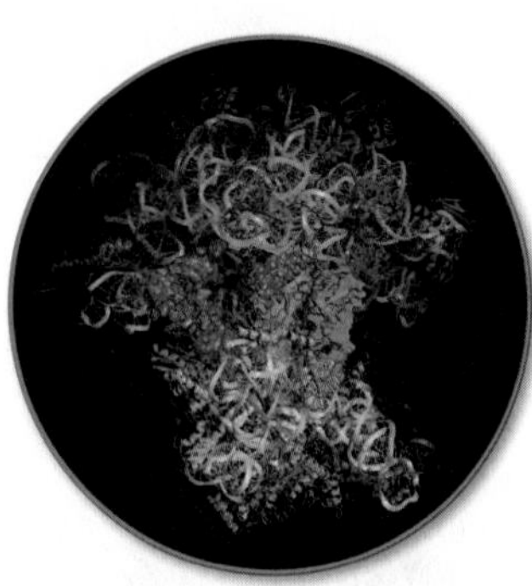

B The Polypeptide "Assembly Line"
The ribosome joins the two amino acids—methionine and phenylalanine—and breaks the bond between methionine and its tRNA. The tRNA floats away from the ribosome, allowing the ribosome to bind another tRNA. The ribosome moves along the mRNA, from right to left, binding new tRNA molecules and amino acids.

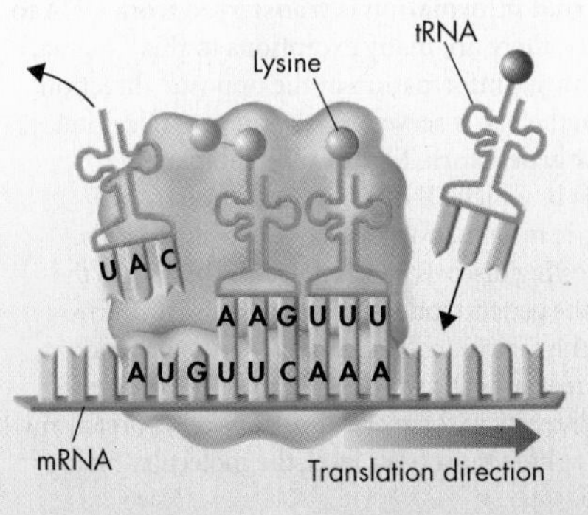

C Completing the Polypeptide
The process continues until the ribosome reaches one of the three stop codons. Once the polypeptide is complete, it and the mRNA are released from the ribosome.

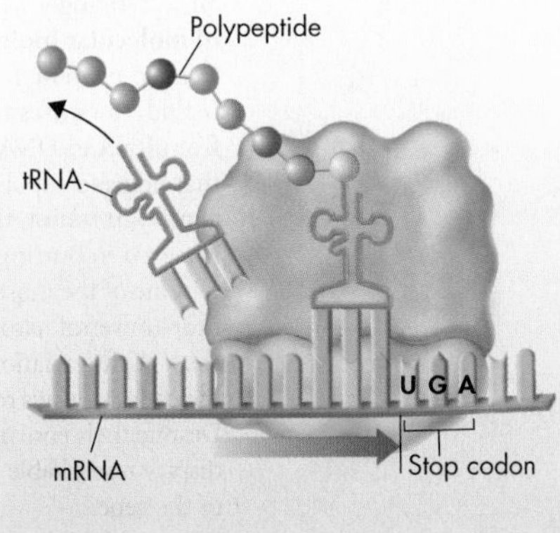

Quick Facts

ANTICODONS AND TRANSFER RNA

Individual transfer RNA anticodons sometimes recognize more than one mRNA codon. These are generally codons that differ only in their third base. This is because the binding attraction is relatively weak between the third base of a tRNA anticodon and the third base of an mRNA codon. This can result in mistakes in translation. For example, the tRNA anticodon GCC might bind to CGA instead of CGG. However, in this case, the same amino acid would still be inserted in the polypeptide, because CGA and CGG both code for arginine. In fact, because there are multiple codons for each amino acid, most of which differ only in their third base, such mistakes in translation often have no effect on the polypeptide.

Use Models

Ask groups of students to use materials of their choice to make a three-dimensional model representing the process of translation. Suitable materials might include modeling clay, craft sticks, various beads, dried pasta in different shapes and colors, chenille stems, string, or yarn. Remind students to include in their model a strand of mRNA, a ribosome, a few molecules of tRNA, and a short polypeptide. Give groups a chance to share their models with the class.

DIFFERENTIATED INSTRUCTION

L1 Special Needs Support special needs students by modeling the processes of transcription and translation as a class. Sit at your desk, and tell the class that you represent DNA in the nucleus of a cell and the classroom represents the cytoplasm of the cell. Assign a student to represent a ribosome, and place a handful of multicolored paper clip "amino acids" next to him or her. On a piece of paper, write the message, "Clip a yellow and white paper clip together." Ask another student to come to your desk, copy the message on a scrap of paper, and carry the copy to the "ribosome." After the "ribosome" student follows the instructions in the note, explain how the exercise models the way information encoded in DNA is carried from the nucleus to the cytoplasm and acted upon at a ribosome. Ask students if they know what the messenger student represents. *(mRNA)*

LPR Less Proficient Readers Use a more familiar meaning of the term *translation* as an analogy to help students understand the process of mRNA translation. On the board, write specific examples showing how words of one language can be translated into another language (e.g., *mother* to *madre*, *street* to *rue*). Ask English language learners or students who have studied a foreign language to translate a few words, as well. Then, explain that translation in genetics is a similar process. The codons of mRNA are like words of one language, and they are translated into amino acids, which are like words of another language.

Answers

IN YOUR NOTEBOOK The ribosome positions the start codon of mRNA to attract its anticodon, which is part of a tRNA molecule. The ribosome also binds the next codon and attracts its anticodon. Then, the ribosome joins the first two amino acids and breaks the bond between the first amino acid and its tRNA. The ribosome moves along the mRNA strand, repeating this process until the ribosome reaches a stop codon. Then, it releases the newly formed polypeptide and the mRNA strand.

Teach continued

Lead a Discussion

Write the following on the board:

DNA → RNA → Protein

Tell students this represents the central dogma of molecular biology. Call on several volunteers to express the central dogma in their own words. Then, lead a discussion about its implications and limitations.

Ask What does the central dogma imply about the role of RNA? *(Sample answer: It's the step between DNA and proteins.)*

Point out that the central dogma does have limitations. For example, it doesn't represent the other roles of RNA. Explain that many RNA molecules are not translated into proteins but still play important roles in gene expression. Tell students that other roles of RNA are discussed in Lesson 13.4.

DIFFERENTIATED INSTRUCTION

L3 Advanced Students Ask several students to choose sides and debate the issue of whether the central dogma of molecular biology is still useful despite its limitations. Give them a chance to find documentation to support their side of the issue and then to present their debate in class.

ELL Focus on ELL: Access Content

ALL SPEAKERS Have students review lesson concepts by participating in a **Core Concept Discussion.** Ask each student to write down one core concept from the lesson. Accept words or short phrases from beginning speakers. Then, have students form small groups that contain a mix of students with differing English proficiency. Group members should take turns discussing one another's core concepts. Discuss a few of the more difficult concepts as a class.

Study Wkbks A/B, Appendix S3, Core Concept Discussion.

MYSTERY CLUE Students are likely to explain that a mouse's gene works inside the cells of a fly because the genetic code is nearly universal. In almost all organisms, the same amino acids are assigned to particular codons, and the code is always read three bases at a time and in the same direction. Students can go online to **Biology.com** to gather their evidence.

The Roles of tRNA and rRNA in Translation All three major forms of RNA—mRNA, tRNA, and rRNA—come together in the ribosome during translation. The mRNA molecule, of course, carries the coded message that directs the process. The tRNA molecules deliver exactly the right amino acid called for by each codon on the mRNA. The tRNA molecules are, in effect, adaptors that enable the ribosome to "read" the mRNA's message accurately and to get the translation just right.

Ribosomes themselves are composed of roughly 80 proteins and three or four different rRNA molecules. These rRNA molecules help hold ribosomal proteins in place and help locate the beginning of the mRNA message. They may even carry out the chemical reaction that joins amino acids together.

The Molecular Basis of Heredity

What is the "central dogma" of molecular biology?

Gregor Mendel might have been surprised to learn that most genes contain nothing more than instructions for assembling proteins. He might have asked what proteins could possibly have to do with the color of a flower, the shape of a leaf, or the sex of a newborn baby. The answer is that proteins have everything to do with these traits. Remember that many proteins are enzymes, which catalyze and regulate chemical reactions. A gene that codes for an enzyme to produce pigment can control the color of a flower. Another gene produces proteins that regulate patterns of tissue growth in a leaf. Yet another may trigger the female or male pattern of development in an embryo. In short, proteins are microscopic tools, each specifically designed to build or operate a component of a living cell.

MYSTERY CLUE

What features of the genetic code make it possible for a mouse's gene to work inside the cells of a fly?

As you've seen, once scientists learned that genes were made of DNA, a series of other discoveries soon followed. Before long, with the genetic code in hand, a new scientific field called molecular biology had been established. Molecular biology seeks to explain living organisms by studying them at the molecular level, using molecules like DNA and RNA. One of the earliest findings came to be known, almost jokingly, as the field's "central dogma." **The central dogma of molecular biology is that information is transferred from DNA to RNA to protein.** In reality, there are many exceptions to this "dogma," including viruses that transfer information in the opposite direction, from RNA to DNA. Nonetheless, it serves as a useful generalization that helps to explain how genes work. **Figure 13–9** illustrates **gene expression,** the way in which DNA, RNA, and proteins are involved in putting genetic information into action in living cells.

One of the most interesting discoveries of molecular biology is the near-universal nature of the genetic code. Although some organisms show slight variations in the amino acids assigned to particular codons, the code is always read three bases at a time and in the same direction. Despite their enormous diversity in form and function, living organisms display remarkable unity at life's most basic level, the molecular biology of the gene.

How Science Works

CHALLENGES TO THE CENTRAL DOGMA

The central dogma of molecular biology was first postulated by Francis Crick in 1958. Over most of the next 50 years, it was the cornerstone of the field, focusing research on DNA segments that code for proteins. However, research shows that the central dogma is too simple and may be pointing research in the wrong direction. It now seems that RNA may play at least as important a role in genetics and evolution as DNA. For example, researchers have found that a single RNA molecule is probably responsible for many of the differences between human and chimpanzee brains. Other researchers, studying the human genome, have shown that so-called junk DNA that doesn't code for proteins may actually be transcribed into RNA and play important roles in cells, although most of these roles are still unknown.

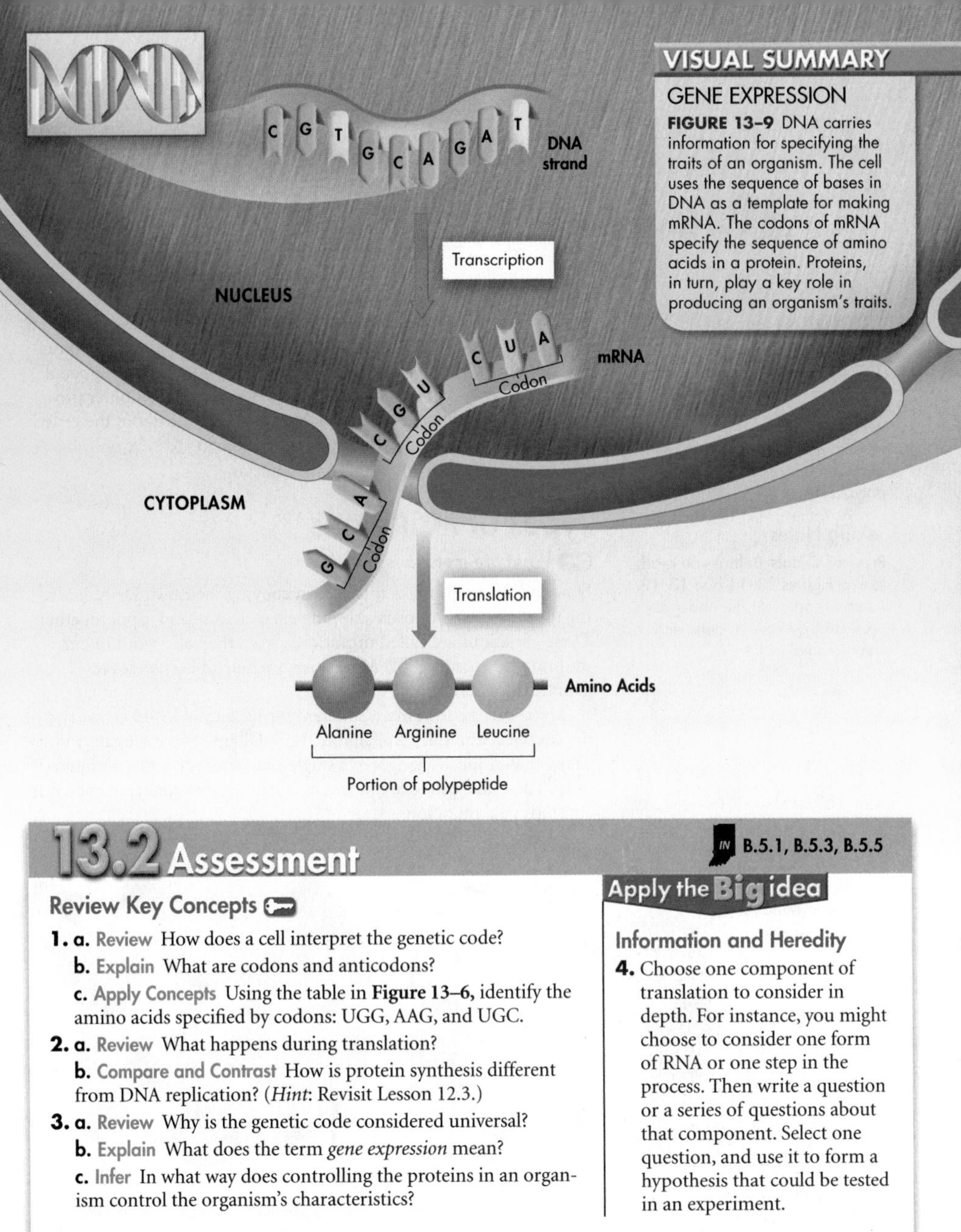

GENE EXPRESSION

FIGURE 13–9 DNA carries information for specifying the traits of an organism. The cell uses the sequence of bases in DNA as a template for making mRNA. The codons of mRNA specify the sequence of amino acids in a protein. Proteins, in turn, play a key role in producing an organism's traits.

13.2 Assessment

IN B.5.1, B.5.3, B.5.5

Review Key Concepts

1. a. Review How does a cell interpret the genetic code?
   b. Explain What are codons and anticodons?
   c. Apply Concepts Using the table in **Figure 13–6**, identify the amino acids specified by codons: UGG, AAG, and UGC.
2. a. Review What happens during translation?
   b. Compare and Contrast How is protein synthesis different from DNA replication? (*Hint*: Revisit Lesson 12.3.)
3. a. Review Why is the genetic code considered universal?
   b. Explain What does the term *gene expression* mean?
   c. Infer In what way does controlling the proteins in an organism control the organism's characteristics?

Apply the Big idea

Information and Heredity

4. Choose one component of translation to consider in depth. For instance, you might choose to consider one form of RNA or one step in the process. Then write a question or a series of questions about that component. Select one question, and use it to form a hypothesis that could be tested in an experiment.

BIOLOGY.com Search Lesson 13.2 GO • Self-Test • Lesson Assessment

RNA and Protein Synthesis 371

VISUAL SUMMARY

Suggest students review the process of transcription in **Figure 13–3** and the process of translation in **Figure 13–7,** so that they realize that **Figure 13–9** is a simplification. Then, relate the diagram in the figure to the central dogma of molecular biology. Have students point out the part of the diagram that relates to each part of the central dogma.

DIFFERENTIATED INSTRUCTION

L1 Struggling Students Make color copies of **Figure 13–9** without labels or the caption. Have students add labels to all the structures in the diagram, referring back to earlier diagrams as needed.

Assess and Remediate

EVALUATE UNDERSTANDING

Ask students to write a paragraph stating and explaining the central dogma of molecular biology. The explanation should include the role of transcription and translation in the central dogma. Then, have them complete the 13.2 Assessment.

REMEDIATION SUGGESTION

LPR Less Proficient Readers If students have trouble answering **Question 4,** model a suitable response by reading the sample answer below.

BIOLOGY.com Students can check their understanding of lesson concepts with the **Self-Test** assessment. They can then take an online version of the **Lesson Assessment.**

Assessment Answers

1a. The genetic code is read one codon, or three bases at a time; each codon, except the stop codon, codes for an amino acid.

1b. Codons are three-letter "words" in mRNA that specify amino acids. Anticodons are three unpaired bases in tRNA, complementary to mRNA codons.

1c. tryptophan, lysine, cysteine

2a. During translation, a ribosome uses the sequence of codons in mRNA to assemble amino acids into a polypeptide chain. The correct amino acids are brought to the ribosome by tRNA.

2b. Check that students' responses identify differences between protein synthesis and DNA replication.

3a. In all organisms the code is read three bases at a time and in the same direction. In most organisms the same amino acids are assigned to particular codons.

3b. It refers to the way in which DNA, RNA, and proteins are involved in putting genetic information into action in living cells.

3c. Proteins build or operate components of cells, so they play a key role in producing an organism's characteristics. For example, enzymes catalyze and regulate chemical reactions in cells, and other proteins regulate growth patterns or embryonic development.

4. Big idea Questions should pertain to a single component or step in translation, and one of the questions should be restated as a testable hypothesis. Sample answer: Question: What happens to mRNA after it has been translated by a ribosome? Hypothesis: After mRNA has been translated, it is released from the ribosome.

LESSON 13.3

Getting Started

Objectives

13.3.1 Define mutations and describe the different types of mutations.

13.3.2 Describe the effects mutations can have on genes.

Student Resources

Study Workbooks A and B, 13.3 Worksheets

Spanish Study Workbook, 13.3 Worksheets

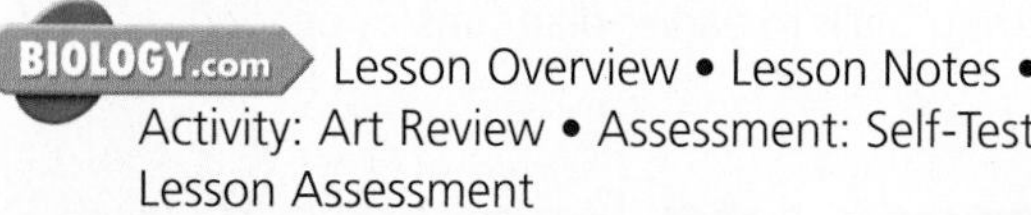

Lesson Overview • Lesson Notes • Activity: Art Review • Assessment: Self-Test, Lesson Assessment

For corresponding lesson in the **Foundation Edition**, see pages 316–319.

Build Background

Ask students if they ever played a game in which a message is whispered from one person to another around a circle until the message reaches the last person. Often, at least one person mishears the message and passes on an inaccurate version to the next person. As a result, the final message can be quite different than the original message. You may want to have the class play the game. Relate what happens in the game to how mistakes are introduced in genes as they are copied and passed on to offspring. Ask students if they know what mistakes in genes are called. *(mutations)*

IN INDIANA ACADEMIC STANDARDS

For the full text of all standards, see the Course Overview in the front matter of this book.

B.5.5 Understand that proteins are responsible for the observable traits of an organism and for most of the functions within an organism.

B.7.4 Explain the process by which a cell copies its DNA and identify factors that can damage DNA and cause changes in its nucleotide sequence.

B.7.5 Explain and demonstrate how inserting, substituting or deleting segments of a DNA molecule can alter a gene, which is then passed to every cell that develops from it and that the results may be beneficial, harmful or have little or no effect on the organism.

Mutations

B.5.5 Roles of proteins; **B.7.4** DNA: Duplication and damage; **B.7.5** Gene alteration. Also covered: **B.5.3, B.5.4.**

Key Questions

What are mutations?

How do mutations affect genes?

Vocabulary

mutation • point mutation • frameshift mutation • mutagen • polyploidy

Taking Notes

Preview Visuals Before you read, look at **Figures 13–11** and **13–12.** As you read, note the changes produced by various gene and chromosomal mutations.

THINK ABOUT IT The sequence of bases in DNA are like the letters of a coded message, as we've just seen. But what would happen if a few of those letters changed accidentally, altering the message? Could the cell still understand its meaning? Think about what might happen if someone changed at random a few lines of code in a computer program that you rely on. Knowing what you already do about the genetic code, what effects would you predict such changes to have on genes and the polypeptides for which they code?

Types of Mutations

What are mutations?

Now and then cells make mistakes in copying their own DNA, inserting the wrong base or even skipping a base as a strand is put together. These variations are called **mutations,** from the Latin word *mutare,* meaning "to change." **Mutations are heritable changes in genetic information.**

Mutations come in many different forms. **Figure 13–10** shows two of the countless examples. But all mutations fall into two basic categories: Those that produce changes in a single gene are known as gene mutations. Those that produce changes in whole chromosomes are known as chromosomal mutations.

FIGURE 13–10 Plant and Animal Mutations

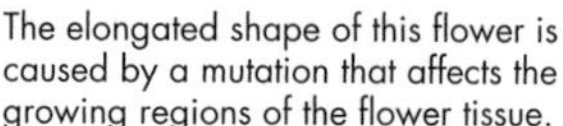
The elongated shape of this flower is caused by a mutation that affects the growing regions of the flower tissue.

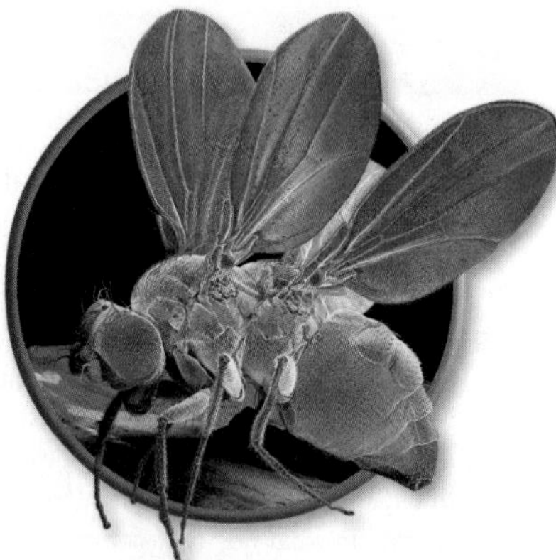
A mutation in the gene known as *bithorax* has produced an extra set of wings in this fruit fly. (SEM: 20×)

UbD Teach for Understanding

ENDURING UNDERSTANDING DNA is the universal code of life; it enables an organism to transmit hereditary information and, along with the environment, determines an organism's characteristics.

GUIDING QUESTION What happens when a cell's DNA changes?

EVIDENCE OF UNDERSTANDING *After completing the lesson, assign students the following assessment to show they understand mutations.* Have students write one paragraph each on the types, causes, and effects of mutations. Tell them to assume their paragraphs will be read by middle-school students who have no prior knowledge of biology.

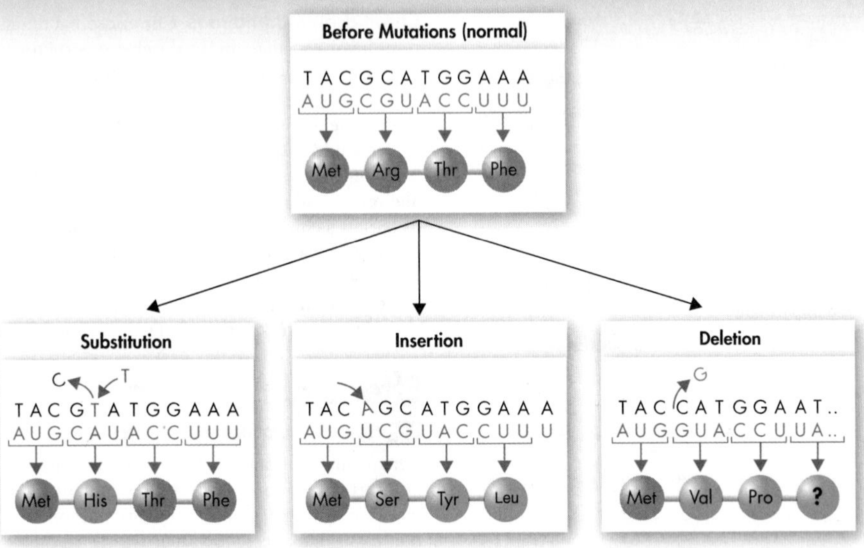

FIGURE 13–11 Point Mutations These diagrams show how changes in a single nucleotide can affect the amino acid sequence of proteins. Analyze Data ***Which type of mutations affects only a single amino acid in a protein? Which can affect more than one?***

Gene Mutations Gene mutations that involve changes in one or a few nucleotides are known as **point mutations** because they occur at a single point in the DNA sequence. Point mutations include substitutions, insertions, and deletions. They generally occur during replication. If a gene in one cell is altered, the alteration can be passed on to every cell that develops from the original one. Refer to **Figure 13–11** as you read about the different forms of point mutations.

▶ ***Substitutions*** In a substitution, one base is changed to a different base. Substitutions usually affect no more than a single amino acid, and sometimes they have no effect at all. For example, if a mutation changed one codon of mRNA from CCC to CCA, the codon would still specify the amino acid proline. But a change in the first base of the codon—changing CCC to ACC—would replace proline with the amino acid threonine.

▶ ***Insertions and Deletions*** Insertions and deletions are point mutations in which one base is inserted or removed from the DNA sequence. The effects of these changes can be dramatic. Remember that the genetic code is read three bases at a time. If a nucleotide is added or deleted, the bases are still read in groups of three, but now those groupings shift in every codon that follows the mutation.

Insertions and deletions are also called **frameshift mutations** because they shift the "reading frame" of the genetic message. By shifting the reading frame, frameshift mutations can change every amino acid that follows the point of the mutation. They can alter a protein so much that it is unable to perform its normal functions.

In Your Notebook *Use a cause/effect diagram to describe the different types of gene mutations.*

Teach

Use Visuals

Call on students to explain in their own words how the different types of gene mutations occur, based on the examples shown in **Figure 13–11.** Then, have students create their own examples of the three types of gene mutations.

DIFFERENTIATED INSTRUCTION

L1 Struggling Students On the board, write the following sentence:

Theboysawthetandogrun.

Tell students to read the sentence, three letters at a time. Then, insert the letter *x* after the first *The*, and give students the same instruction. Repeat, but this time, delete the letter *e* in *The*. Explain how inserting or deleting a letter is like a frameshift mutation.

ELL Focus on ELL: Build Background

BEGINNING AND INTERMEDIATE SPEAKERS Ask students to write the term *mutation* on a **Vocabulary Word Map.** Then, familiarize them with mutations by showing visuals of organisms with and without visible traits caused by mutations. Discuss how changes in a cell's DNA can produce these visible differences. Then, have them complete the map using the information on the page.

Study Wkbks A/B, Appendix S32, Vocabulary Word Map. **Transparencies,** GO17.

BIOLOGY.com The drag-and-drop activity, **Art Review: Point Mutations,** lets students review different types of mutations.

Quick Facts

TIMING AND FREQUENCY OF MUTATIONS

Mutations may occur at different times in the life cycle of an individual. Mutations that occur in gametes or just after fertilization affect all the cells of the organism. Mutations that occur during the embryonic stage, when cells and tissues are differentiating, cause mosaicism, in which only some cells of the organism have the mutation. Mutations that occur after an organism is fully formed affect only the cells in which they occur and their daughter cells. If these mutations occur in sex cells, they may be inherited by the organism's offspring. On the contrary, if mutations occur in somatic (body) cells, the mutations will leave the gene pool when the organism dies. At the population level, some mutations are fairly common. They are called polymorphisms if they have allele frequencies greater than 1 percent. Polymorphisms contribute to normal human genetic variation.

Answers

FIGURE 13–11 Substitutions affect only one amino acid; insertions and deletions affect more than one nucleotide.

IN YOUR NOTEBOOK Students' cause/effect diagrams may vary but should show they understand different types of gene mutations.

Teach continued

Expand Vocabulary

On the board, write the verbs *delete*, *duplicate*, and *invert*. Call on students to define each verb. *(Sample answers: Delete means "to erase," duplicate means "to copy," and invert means "to reverse.")* Have students look at the deletion, duplication, and inversion mutation examples shown in **Figure 13–12.** Call on volunteers to explain how the meanings of the verbs relate to the manner in which the mutations occur. Then, write the term *translocation* on the board, and divide it into its parts. Ask students if they know what the parts mean. *(Trans- means "across," and location means "place.")* Call on a volunteer to explain how the meaning of the term relates to what happens when a translocation mutation occurs.

DIFFERENTIATED INSTRUCTION

L1 Special Needs Have students model chromosomal mutations with strips of paper representing segments of chromosomes. Give them six strips of paper of the same length. On five of the strips, ask them to write the sequence of letters *A B C D E F*. Tell them to glue one of these strips across the top of a sheet of paper. Then, have them cut the remaining labeled strips into sections and rearrange them to illustrate each of the chromosomal mutations shown in **Figure 13–12.** Tell them to use the blank strip to make any extra parts they need for the mutations. Have students glue the rearranged strips below the original strip and label the type of mutation each rearrangement represents.

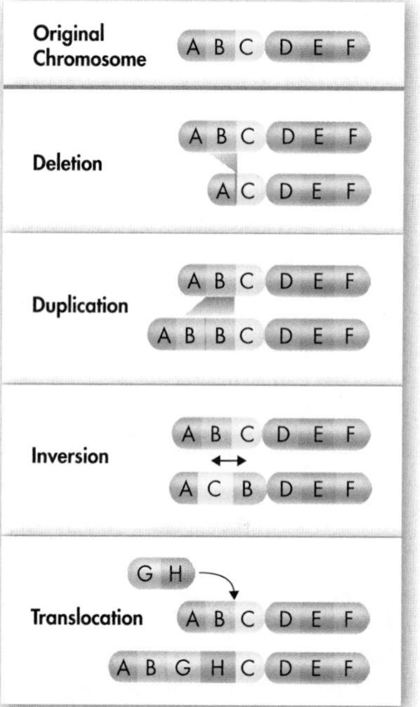

FIGURE 13–12 Chromosomal Mutations Four types of mutations cause changes in whole chromosomes. Use Diagrams ***What is the difference between inversion and translocation?***

Chromosomal Mutations Chromosomal mutations involve changes in the number or structure of chromosomes. These mutations can change the location of genes on chromosomes and can even change the number of copies of some genes.

Figure 13–12 shows four types of chromosomal mutations: deletion, duplication, inversion, and translocation. Deletion involves the loss of all or part of a chromosome; duplication produces an extra copy of all or part of a chromosome; and inversion reverses the direction of parts of a chromosome. Translocation occurs when part of one chromosome breaks off and attaches to another.

Effects of Mutations

How do mutations affect genes?

Genetic material can be altered by natural events or by artificial means. The resulting mutations may or may not affect an organism. And some mutations that affect individual organisms can also affect a species or even an entire ecosystem.

Many mutations are produced by errors in genetic processes. For example, some point mutations are caused by errors during DNA replication. The cellular machinery that replicates DNA inserts an incorrect base roughly once in every 10 million bases. But small changes in genes can gradually accumulate over time.

IN B.7.4, B.7.5

Modeling Mutations

Small mutations in DNA can cause huge changes in the proteins that are synthesized. Similarly, small changes in a word can dramatically alter its meaning. Look at the following sequence of words:

milk mile wile wise wisp wasp

Notice that each word differs from the previous word by just one letter and that none of the words is meaningless. Think of these changes as "point mutations" that affect word meaning.

Analyze and Conclude

1. Apply Concepts Start with the word *gene*, and change it letter by letter to make new words. Make sure each new word is an actual word but not a proper noun. Write at least four "point mutations" of the word *gene*.

2. Apply Concepts Show how you could use words to model a frameshift mutation. (*Hint*: You can use a sentence.)

3. Use Models Use the words in this sentence to model a substitution mutation.

PURPOSE Students will model substitution and frameshift mutations with words and sentences.

PLANNING Have students review the types of gene mutations in **Figure 13–11.** Then, ask them to identify the type of mutation that changes the word *milk* to *mile. (substitution)*

ANALYZE AND CONCLUDE

1. Sample answer: gene → gone → tone → tune → tuna

2. Answers will vary but should show that students understand that a frameshift mutation occurs when a base is inserted or deleted, which shifts the "reading frame." For example, they could write a sentence and then delete or insert a single letter so that the reading frame shifts and the letters no longer spell out recognizable words.

3. Sample answer: Changing *words* to *works* models a substitution mutation.

Answers

FIGURE 13–12 An inversion mutation reverses the direction of part of one chromosome. A translocation mutation attaches part of one chromosome to another chromosome.

Stressful environmental conditions may cause some bacteria to increase mutation rates. This can actually be helpful to the organism, since mutations may sometimes give such bacteria new traits, such as the ability to consume a new food source or to resist a poison in the environment.

Mutagens Some mutations arise from **mutagens,** chemical or physical agents in the environment. Chemical mutagens include certain pesticides, a few natural plant alkaloids, tobacco smoke, and environmental pollutants. Physical mutagens include some forms of electromagnetic radiation, such as X-rays and ultraviolet light. If these agents interact with DNA, they can produce mutations at high rates. Cells can sometimes repair the damage; but when they cannot, the DNA base sequence changes permanently. Some compounds interfere with base-pairing, increasing the error rate of DNA replication. Others weaken the DNA strand, causing breaks and inversions that produce chromosomal mutations.

BUILD Vocabulary

WORD ORIGINS The word **mutagen** is a Latin word that means "origin of change." Mutagens change an organism's genetic information.

In Your Notebook *Make a table to keep track of both the helpful and harmful results of mutations. As you read, fill it in.*

Harmful and Helpful Mutations As you've already seen, some mutations don't even change the amino acid specified by a codon, while others may alter a complete protein or even an entire chromosome. **The effects of mutations on genes vary widely. Some have little or no effect; and some produce beneficial variations. Some negatively disrupt gene function.** Many if not most mutations are neutral; they have little or no effect on the expression of genes or the function of the proteins for which they code. Whether a mutation is negative or beneficial depends on how its DNA changes relative to the organism's situation. Mutations are often thought of as negative, since they can disrupt the normal function of genes. However, without mutations, organisms could not evolve, because mutations are the source of genetic variability in a species.

▶***Harmful Effects*** Some of the most harmful mutations are those that dramatically change protein structure or gene activity. The defective proteins produced by these mutations can disrupt normal biological activities, and result in genetic disorders. Some cancers, for example, are the product of mutations that cause the uncontrolled growth of cells. Sickle cell disease is a disorder associated with changes in the shape of red blood cells. You can see its effects in **Figure 13–13.** It is caused by a point mutation in one of the polypeptides found in hemoglobin, the blood's principal oxygen-carrying protein. Among the symptoms of the disease are anemia, severe pain, frequent infections, and stunted growth.

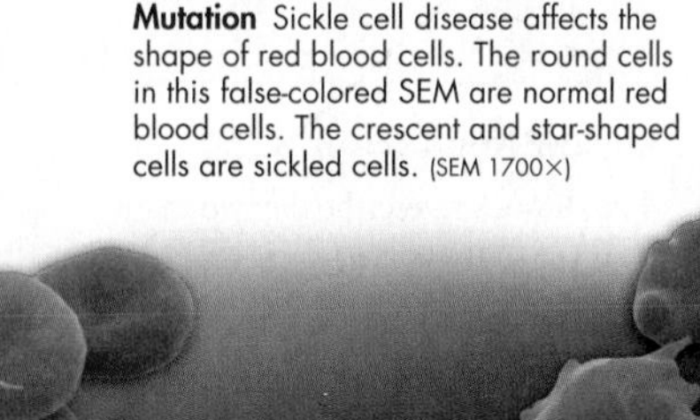

FIGURE 13–13 Effects of a Point Mutation Sickle cell disease affects the shape of red blood cells. The round cells in this false-colored SEM are normal red blood cells. The crescent and star-shaped cells are sickled cells. (SEM 1700×)

Connect to Health

Elaborate on sickle cell disease to illustrate how the effects of a mutation may depend on the environment. Explain that sickle cell disease occurs only in homozygotes for the sickle cell allele. Heterozygotes—those who have one sickle cell allele and one normal allele—do not have sickle cell disease, but may notice harmful effects at high altitudes. Both homozygotes and heterozygotes are resistant to the parasite that causes malaria. In areas like tropical Africa, where malaria is endemic, heterozygotes are more fit than people who are homozygous for the normal allele. This explains why the sickle cell allele is fairly common in some populations (including African and African-American populations), and why people in these populations have a relatively high risk of inheriting two copies of the mutant gene. Tell students they will learn more about sickle cell disease in Chapter 14.

DIFFERENTIATED INSTRUCTION

LPR Less Proficient Readers Suggest that students make a **Cluster Diagram** to organize the information about the effects of mutations. They should write Effects of Mutations in the center circle of the diagram. In the major surrounding circles they should write Neutral Effects, Harmful Effects, and Helpful Effects. Additional circles should be used to add information as students read the text.

Study Wkbks A/B, Appendix S19, Cluster Diagram. **Transparencies,** GO2.

MYSTERY CLUE Because they have not yet read about homeobox genes, students might assume that a major chromosomal mutation would be required to cause more eyes than normal to appear on a fly. Students can go online to Biology.com to gather their evidence.

UbD Check for Understanding

ANALOGY PROMPT

Ask students to complete the following analogy prompt:

A mutation is like _______ because ____________________. *(Sample answer: A mutation is like a typo because both are mistakes in "words" that may or may not change how messages are read.)*

ADJUST INSTRUCTION

Call on several students to read their analogies to the class. Discuss the merits of each analogy.

Answers

IN YOUR NOTEBOOK Helpful effects include proteins with useful altered or new functions and stronger organisms with enhanced abilities. Harmful effects include dramatically changed protein structure or gene activity, genetic disorders, and some cancers.

LESSON 13.3

Assess and Remediate

EVALUATE UNDERSTANDING

Give each student seven index cards. Tell students to write or draw an example of one type of gene or chromosomal mutation on the front of each card and its name on the back. Ask students to exchange cards with a partner and try to identify the types of mutations from the examples. Then, have students complete the 13.3 Assessment.

REMEDIATION SUGGESTION

ELL English Language Learners If students have trouble with **Question 2b,** explain that the term *significance* means "importance." Then, suggest that students reread the paragraphs about harmful and helpful mutations. As they do, they should look for information on how mutations are important to organisms and species.

BIOLOGY.com Students can check their understanding of lesson concepts with the **Self-Test** assessment. They can then take an online version of the **Lesson Assessment.**

Answers

IN YOUR NOTEBOOK Check that students have listed five examples of mutations and identified each as neutral, harmful, or helpful. For example, students may list a mutation that increases bone strength and density as a helpful mutation.

FIGURE 13–14 Polyploid Plants The fruit of the Tahiti lime is seedless, a result of polyploidy. Changes to the ploidy number of citrus plants can affect the size and strength of the trees as well as the quality and seediness of their fruit.

▶ ***Beneficial Effects*** Some of the variation produced by mutations can be highly advantageous to an organism or species. **Mutations often produce proteins with new or altered functions that can be useful to organisms in different or changing environments.** For example, mutations have helped many insects resist chemical pesticides. And some have enabled microorganisms to adapt to new chemicals in the environment.

Over the past 20 years, mutations in the mosquito genome have made many African mosquitoes resistant to the chemical pesticides once used to control them. This may be bad news for humans, but it is highly beneficial to the insects themselves. Beneficial mutations occur in humans, too, including ones that increase bone strength and density, making fractures less likely, and mutations that increase resistance to HIV, the virus that causes AIDS.

Plant and animal breeders often make use of "good" mutations. For example, when a complete set of chromosomes fails to separate during meiosis, the gametes that result may produce triploid (3N) or tetraploid (4N) organisms. The condition in which an organism has extra sets of chromosomes is called **polyploidy.** Polyploid plants are often larger and stronger than diploid plants. Important crop plants—including bananas and the limes shown in **Figure 13–14**—have been produced this way. Polyploidy also occurs naturally in citrus plants, often through spontaneous mutations.

In Your Notebook *List five examples of mutations. Classify each as neutral, harmful, or helpful, and explain your reasoning.*

13.3 Assessment

IN B.7.5

Review Key Concepts

1. a. Review Describe the two main types of mutations.

b. Explain What is a frameshift mutation? Give an example.

c. Infer The effects of a mutation are not always visible. Choose a species, and explain how a biologist might determine whether a mutation has occurred and, if so, what type of mutation it is.

2. a. Review List three effects mutations can have on genes.

b. Apply Concepts What is the significance of mutations to living things?

VISUAL THINKING

3. Make a compare/contrast table to organize your ideas about gene mutations and chromosomal mutations. Then use your table to write a paragraph comparing and contrasting these two kinds of mutations.

BIOLOGY.com Search (Lesson 13.3) GO • Self-Test • Lesson Assessment

Assessment Answers

1a. Gene mutations involve changes in one or a few nucleotides. Chromosomal mutations involve changes in the number or structure of chromosomes.

1b. A frameshift mutation is an insertion or deletion that shifts the "reading frame" of the genetic message. An example is the insertion of an extra U in AUGCUC to make AUGUCUC. Following AUG, the "reading frame" is shifted by one base.

1c. Sample answer: To identify a gene mutation, a biologist might compare DNA base sequences among members of the species. To identify a chromosomal mutation, the biologist might examine some karyotypes.

2a. Effects of mutations on genes can be harmful, beneficial, or they can have little or no effect at all.

2b. Mutations are a source of genetic variation for living things. Sometimes variation can help organisms adapt to different or changing environments. Mutations are also necessary for species to evolve.

VISUAL THINKING

3. Students' tables should contain much of the following information: Gene mutations involve changes in one or a few nucleotides. They include substitutions, insertions, and deletions. Insertions and deletions are called frameshift mutations because they change the "reading frame" of the genetic message. Gene mutations may or may not have major effects on an organism. Chromosomal mutations involve changes in the number or structure of chromosomes. They include deletions, duplications, inversions, and translocations. They can change the location of genes on chromosomes, and even the number of copies of genes. Chromosomal mutations generally have major effects on an organism.

13.4 Gene Regulation and Expression

B.1.3 Cell function and differentiation; B.5.5 Roles of proteins; B.6.2 Gene expression and differentiation. Also covered: NoS.3, B.1.2.

THINK ABOUT IT Think of a library filled with how-to books. Would you ever need to use all of those books at the same time? Of course not. If you wanted to know how to fix a leaky faucet, you'd open a book about plumbing but would ignore the one on carpentry. Now picture a tiny bacterium like *E. coli*, which contains more than 4000 genes. Most of its genes code for proteins that do everything from building cell walls to breaking down food. Do you think *E. coli* uses all 4000-plus volumes in its genetic library at the same time?

Prokaryotic Gene Regulation

How are prokaryotic genes regulated?

As it turns out, bacteria and other prokaryotes do not need to transcribe all of their genes at the same time. To conserve energy and resources, prokaryotes regulate their activities, using only those genes necessary for the cell to function. For example, it would be wasteful for a bacterium to produce enzymes that are needed to make a molecule that is readily available from its environment. By regulating gene expression, bacteria can respond to changes in their environment—the presence or absence of nutrients, for example. How? **DNA-binding proteins in prokaryotes regulate genes by controlling transcription.** Some of these regulatory proteins help switch genes on, while others turn genes off.

How does an organism know when to turn a gene on or off? One of the keys to gene transcription in bacteria is the organization of genes into operons. An **operon** is a group of genes that are regulated together. The genes in an operon usually have related functions. *E. coli,* shown in **Figure 13–15,** provides us with a clear example. The 4288 genes that code for proteins in *E. coli* include a cluster of 3 genes that must be turned on together before the bacterium can use the sugar lactose as a food. These three lactose genes in *E. coli* are called the *lac* operon.

Key Questions

How are prokaryotic genes regulated?

How are genes regulated in eukaryotic cells?

What controls the development of cells and tissues in multicellular organisms?

Vocabulary

operon
operator
RNA interference
differentiation
homeotic gene
homeobox gene
Hox gene

Taking Notes

Outline Before you read, use the headings in this lesson to make an outline. As you read, fill in the subtopics and smaller topics. Then add phrases or a sentence after each subtopic that provides key information.

FIGURE 13–15
Small Cell, Many Genes
This *E. coli* bacterium has been treated with an enzyme enabling its DNA, which contains more than 4000 genes, to spill out.

TEM 27,000×

BIOLOGY.com Search Lesson 13.4 GO • Lesson Overview • Lesson Notes

377

Getting Started

Objectives

13.4.1 Describe gene regulation in prokaryotes.

13.4.2 Explain how most eukaryotic genes are regulated.

13.4.3 Relate gene regulation to development in multicellular organisms.

Student Resources

Study Workbooks A and B, 13.4 Worksheets

Spanish Study Workbook, 13.4 Worksheets

Lab Manual B, 13.4 Data Analysis Worksheet

BIOLOGY.com Lesson Overview • Lesson Notes • Activity: Data Analysis • Assessment: Self-Test, Lesson Assessment

For corresponding lesson in the **Foundation Edition**, see pages 320–325.

Activate Prior Knowledge

Have students recall from Lesson 13.1 what happens to mRNA after it is transcribed. *(The mRNA is edited; introns are cut out and exons are spliced together.)* Next, call on a student to define gene expression, which was introduced in Lesson 13.2. *(the way that DNA, RNA, and proteins put genetic information into action in living cells)* Then, ask a volunteer to infer how mRNA editing affects gene expression. *(Sections of mRNA are cut out and not translated into proteins.)* Tell students they will read in this lesson about other ways gene expression is controlled.

UbD Teach for Understanding

ENDURING UNDERSTANDING DNA is the universal code of life; it enables an organism to transmit hereditary information and, along with the environment, determines an organism's characteristics.

GUIDING QUESTION How do cells regulate gene expression?

EVIDENCE OF UNDERSTANDING *After completing the lesson, assign students the following assessment to show they understand how eukaryotic cells regulate gene expression.* Ask students to use presentation software to create and present a series of slides showing how gene expression in eukaryotic cells is regulated by transcription factors and RNA interference. Their slides should include both text and visuals.

IN INDIANA ACADEMIC STANDARDS

For the full text of all standards, see the Course Overview in the front matter of this book.

B.1.3 Explain and give examples of how the function and differentiation of cells is influenced by their external environment, including temperature, acidity and the concentration of certain molecules, and that changes in these conditions may affect how a cell functions.

B.5.5 Understand that proteins are responsible for the observable traits of an organism and for most of the functions within an organism.

B.6.2 Understand that most cells of a multicellular organism contain the same genes, but develop from a single cell (e.g., a fertilized egg) in different ways due to differential gene expression.

LESSON 13.4

Teach

Use Visuals

Guide students in using **Figure 13–16** to learn about prokaryotic gene regulation. Ask them to locate and identify the function of each of the following elements in the figure: repressor, promoter, operator, *lac* genes, RNA polymerase, lactose, and mRNA. Make sure they know that each panel shows the same segment of DNA in an *E. coli* bacterium. Point out that lactose is absent in the second panel but present in the third panel.

Ask In the second panel, what happens because lactose is absent? *(The repressor binds to the operator, preventing RNA polymerase from binding to the promoter.)*

Ask In the third panel, what happens because lactose is present? *(Lactose binds to the repressor, preventing the repressor from binding to the promoter. This allows RNA polymerase to bind to the promoter.)*

DIFFERENTIATED INSTRUCTION

LPR Less Proficient Readers Have students fill in a **Flowchart** to sequence the events that occur during the process of prokaryote gene regulation, using the *lac* operon as an example. They should add to the flowchart a brief description and sketch of each event in the process as they read about it in the text.

Study Wkbks A/B, Appendix S25, Flowchart. **Transparencies,** GO8.

BIOLOGY.com In the **Data Analysis: A Complicated Operon,** students analyze results of growing bacteria with *lac* operon mutations to identify which genes contain the mutations.

The *Lac* Operon Why must *E. coli* be able to switch the *lac* genes on and off? Lactose is a compound made up of two simple sugars, galactose and glucose. To use lactose for food, the bacterium must transport lactose across its cell membrane and then break the bond between glucose and galactose. These tasks are performed by proteins coded for by the genes of the *lac* operon. This means, of course, that if the bacterium grows in a medium where lactose is the only food source, it must transcribe these genes and produce these proteins. If grown on another food source, such as glucose, it would have no need for these proteins.

Remarkably, the bacterium almost seems to "know" when the products of these genes are needed. When lactose is not present, the *lac* genes are turned off by proteins that bind to DNA and block transcription.

Promoters and Operators On one side of the operon's three genes are two regulatory regions. The first is a promoter (P), which is a site where RNA-polymerase can bind to begin transcription. The other region is called the **operator** (O). The O site is where a DNA-binding protein known as the *lac* repressor can bind to DNA.

▶***The* Lac *Repressor Blocks Transcription*** As **Figure 13–16** shows, when the *lac* repressor binds to the O region, RNA polymerase cannot reach the *lac* genes to begin transcription. In effect, the binding of the repressor protein switches the operon "off" by preventing the transcription of its genes.

▶***Lactose Turns the Operon "On"*** If the repressor protein is always present, how can the *lac* genes ever be switched on? Besides its DNA binding site, the *lac* repressor protein has a binding site for lactose itself. When lactose is added to the medium, it diffuses into the cell and attaches to the *lac* repressor. This changes the shape of the repressor protein in a way that causes it to fall off the operator. Now, with the repressor no longer bound to the O site, RNA polymerase can bind to the promoter and transcribe the genes of the operon. As a result, in the presence of lactose, the operon is automatically switched on.

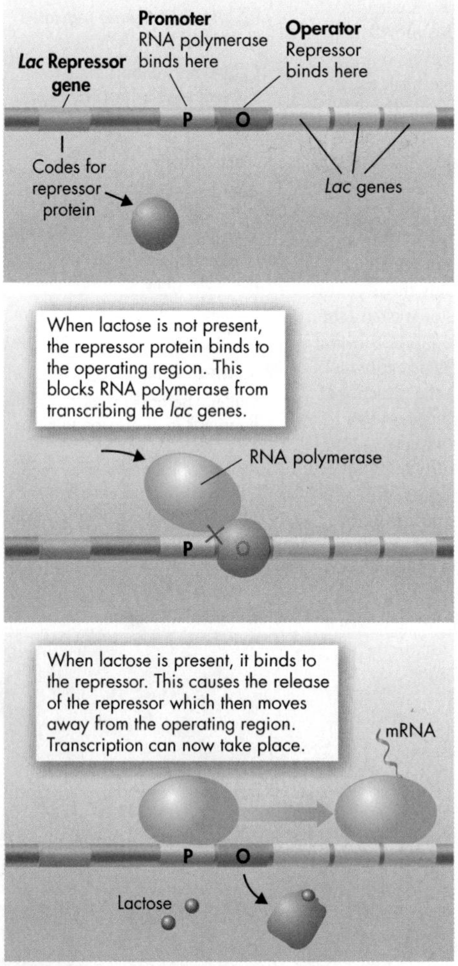

FIGURE 13–16 Gene Expression in Prokaryotes The *lac* genes in *E. coli* are turned off by *lac* repressors and turned on in the presence of lactose. Use Analogies ***How is the way lactose turns genes on and off similar to the way cold air signals a furnace to turn on or off?***

How Science Works

DISCOVERY OF THE *LAC* OPERON

The three French scientists who discovered the *lac* operon won the 1965 Nobel Prize in Physiology or Medicine for their work. Why was it considered such an important discovery? The *lac* operon is the first system of gene regulation ever discovered. It showed for the first time that structural genes, which code for proteins, are regulated by other genes. The existence of regulatory genes was unknown until then. The *lac* operon also provided a mechanism to explain how living cells could respond to environmental stimuli by controlling the expression of genes and thereby the enzymes and other proteins they code for.

Answers

FIGURE 13–16 Sample answer: Cold air causes a furnace to turn on. When the air is no longer cold, the warmer temperature causes the furnace to turn off. Lactose works in a similar way. The presence of lactose causes *lac* genes to turn on. When lactose is no longer present, the absence of lactose causes *lac* genes to turn off.

Eukaryotic Gene Regulation

How are genes regulated in eukaryotic cells?

The general principles of gene regulation in prokaryotes also apply to eukaryotes, although there are differences. Most eukaryotic genes are controlled individually and have more complex regulatory sequences than those of the *lac* repressor system.

Figure 13–17 shows several features of a typical eukaryotic gene. One of the most interesting is the TATA box, a short region of DNA, about 25 or 30 base pairs before the start of a gene, containing the sequence TATATA or TATAAA. The TATA box binds a protein that helps position RNA polymerase by marking a point just before the beginning of a gene.

Transcription Factors Gene expression in eukaryotic cells can be regulated at a number of levels. One of the most critical is the level of transcription, by means of DNA-binding proteins known as transcription factors. **By binding DNA sequences in the regulatory regions of eukaryotic genes, transcription factors control the expression of those genes.** Some transcription factors enhance transcription by opening up tightly packed chromatin. Others help attract RNA polymerase. Still others block access to certain genes, much like prokaryotic repressor proteins. In most cases, multiple transcription factors must bind before RNA polymerase is able to attach to the promoter region and start transcription.

Promoters have multiple binding sites for transcription factors, each of which can influence transcription. Certain factors activate scores of genes at once, dramatically changing patterns of gene expression in the cell. Other factors form only in response to chemical signals. Steroid hormones, for example, are chemical messengers that enter cells and bind to receptor proteins. These "receptor complexes" then act as transcription factors that bind to DNA, allowing a single chemical signal to activate multiple genes. Eukaryotic gene expression can also be regulated by many other factors, including the exit of mRNA molecules from the nucleus, the stability of mRNA, and even the breakdown of a gene's protein products.

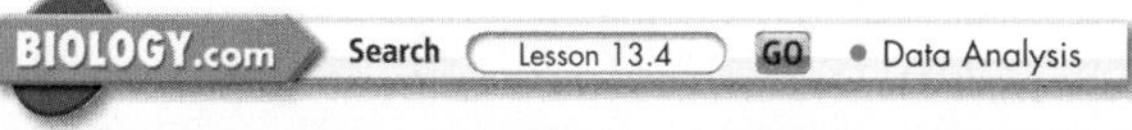

In Your Notebook *Compare gene regulation in single-cell organisms and multicellular organisms.*

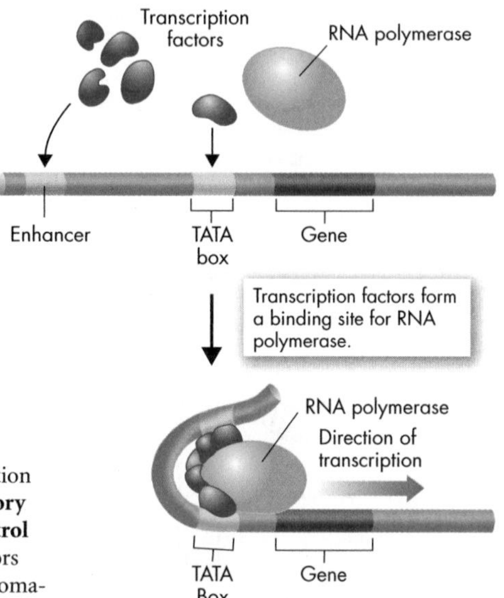

FIGURE 13–17 The TATA Box and Transcription Many eukaryotic genes include a region called the TATA box that helps position RNA polymerase.

MYSTERY CLUE

To make the mouse gene work inside the cells of a fly, researchers attached a new promoter sequence to the gene. Why do you think they did that?

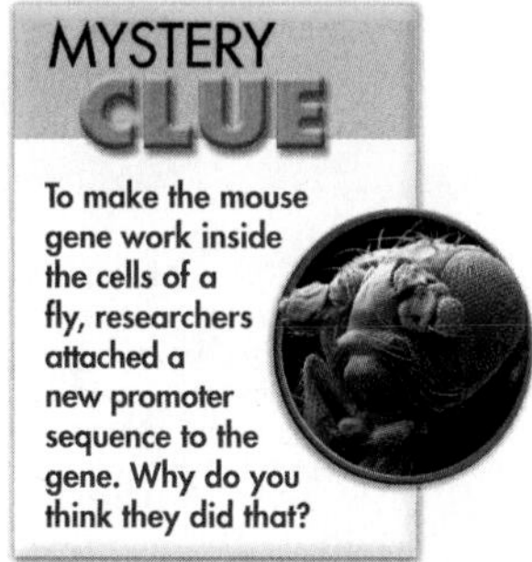

BIOLOGY.com Search Lesson 13.4 GO • Data Analysis

UbD Check for Understanding

QUESTION BOX

Establish an e-mail address for yourself. Give students the e-mail address and instruct them to send any questions they have about gene regulation. Suggest they check their understanding by trying to answer the two Key Questions about gene regulation first. If they are unsure of the answers, encourage them to identify specific questions they still have and send them to the e-mail address.

ADJUST INSTRUCTION

Read students' e-mail questions to the class, and ask for volunteers to answer them. Encourage students to raise any other questions they have.

Build Science Skills

Tell students that transcription promotion, which is shown in **Figure 13–17,** is just one way that eukaryotic genes can be regulated. They can also be regulated by transcription repression. Create a class diagram on the board that shows how repressor proteins could control transcription in eukaryotes. (The diagram should resemble the part of **Figure 13–16** that shows transcription repression in prokaryotes.)

DIFFERENTIATED INSTRUCTION

ELL English Language Learners Have students begin a **KWL Chart** about eukaryotic gene regulation before they start reading about it in the lesson. Ask them to make predictions about eukaryotic gene regulation based on what they already know about gene regulation in prokaryotes. Tell them to list their predictions in column K. In column W, they should write questions they would like to have answered. Have them try to find answers to the questions as they read and record their answers in column L.

Study Wkbks A/B, Appendix S27, KWL Chart. **Transparencies,** GO11.

MYSTERY CLUE Sample answer: The researchers attached a new promoter sequence to the mouse eye gene so that RNA polymerase would have a point to start transcription of the gene. Students can go online to **Biology.com** to gather their evidence.

Address Misconceptions

Control of Gene Expression Students often fail to understand the importance of regulatory genes in gene expression. Address this lack of understanding by pointing out that genes coding for repressor proteins and other regulatory proteins are an important part of the genome of even single-celled organisms such as bacteria. The *lac* operon is just one, well-studied example. Stress how the specialized cells of multicellular eukaryotes make gene regulation even more important.

Answers

IN YOUR NOTEBOOK In a single-celled organism, if a gene is turned on, it is turned on in the entire organism. In single-celled organisms, genes are usually regulated by repressor proteins that bind to operons or other substrates and prevent or allow the transcription of groups of genes. In a multicellular organism, cells are specialized. Each cell can have a unique set of genes that are turned on at any given moment.

Teach continued

Lead a Discussion

Tell students that it is easier to understand new material by relating it to something they already know. Point out that RNA interference depends on something they already know about: complementary base pairing. Call on volunteers to explain how base pairing works and to identify the processes in which it occurs. *(DNA replication, transcription, translation)* Then, discuss with the class how RNA interference depends on base pairing. Ask students to identify each step in the process of RNA interference in which complementary bases pair up.

DIFFERENTIATED INSTRUCTION

L1 Special Needs Guide students in finding online animations of RNA interference. Try to find animations that simplify the process described in the text. Watch the animations with students, and answer any questions they have.

FIGURE 13–18 Blocking Gene Expression Like tiny pieces of sticky tape, microRNAs attach to certain mRNA molecules and stop them from passing on their protein-making instructions.
Interpret Visuals *What happens to the mRNA sequence that is complementary to the bound miRNA?*

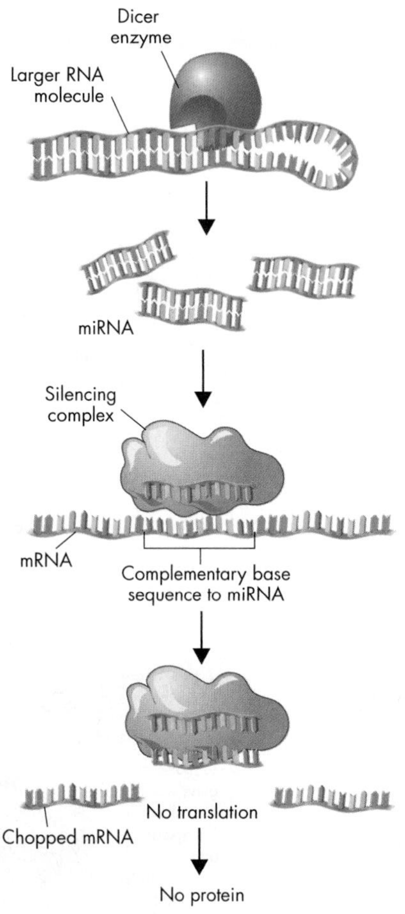

Cell Specialization Why is gene regulation in eukaryotes more complex than in prokaryotes? Think for a moment about the way in which genes are expressed in a multicellular organism. The genes that code for liver enzymes, for example, are not expressed in nerve cells. Keratin, an important protein in skin cells, is not produced in blood cells. Cell specialization requires genetic specialization, yet all of the cells in a multicellular organism carry the same genetic code in their nucleus. Complex gene regulation in eukaryotes is what makes specialization possible.

RNA Interference For years biologists wondered why cells contain lots of small RNA molecules, only a few dozen bases long, that don't belong to any of the major groups of RNA (mRNA, tRNA, or rRNA). In the last decade, a series of important discoveries has shown that these small RNA molecules play a powerful role in regulating gene expression. And they do so by interfering with mRNA.

As **Figure 13–18** shows, after they are produced by transcription, the small interfering RNA molecules fold into double-stranded hairpin loops. An enzyme called the "Dicer" enzyme cuts, or dices, these double-stranded loops into microRNA (miRNA), each about 20 base pairs in length. The two strands of the loops then separate. Next, one of the miRNA pieces attaches to a cluster of proteins to form what is known as a silencing complex. The silencing complex binds to and destroys any mRNA containing a sequence that is complementary to the miRNA. In effect, miRNA sticks to certain mRNA molecules and stops them from passing on their protein-making instructions.

The silencing complex effectively shuts down the expression of the gene whose mRNA it destroys. Blocking gene expression by means of an miRNA silencing complex is known as **RNA interference.** At first, RNA interference (RNAi) seemed to be a rare event, found only in a few plants and other species. It's now clear that RNA interference is found throughout the living world and that it even plays a role in human growth and development.

Biology In-Depth

TREATING DISEASE USING RNA INTERFERENCE

Soon after RNA interference was discovered, scientists began exploring ways that it might be used to treat or cure diseases. The aim was to develop artificial miRNA molecules that could turn off the expression of disease-causing genes. One of the first diseases to be studied was macular degeneration, which is the primary cause of adult blindness in the U.S. The disease occurs when a protein stimulates overgrowth of capillaries in the eye. An RNAi drug was developed that shuts down the expression of the gene coding for this protein. The drug can be injected directly into the eye. This is important because a drug injected into the blood might prevent the expression of this gene in parts of the body where it is needed. Researchers are also trying to find RNAi treatments for cancer, AIDS, hepatitis C, and Huntington's disease.

Answers

FIGURE 13–18 That mRNA sequence is destroyed and not translated.

Analyzing Data

IN NoS.3, B.1.2

The Discovery of RNA Interference

In 1998, Andrew Fire and Craig Mello carried out an experiment that helped explain the mechanism of RNA interference. They used RNA from a large gene called unc-22, which codes for a protein found in muscle cells. They prepared short mRNA fragments corresponding to two exon regions of the gene and injected them into egg cells of the worm *C. elegans.* Some of their results are shown in the table.

Injections of mRNA into *C. elegans* Eggs

Portion of Gene Used to Produce mRNA	Strand Injected	Result in Adult Worm
Unc-22 (exon 21–22)	Sense	Normal
	Antisense	Normal
	Sense + Antisense	Twitching
Unc-22 (exon 27)	Sense	Normal
	Antisense	Normal
	Sense + Antisense	Twitching

1. Draw Conclusions How did the adult worms' responses differ to injections of single-stranded mRNA (the "sense" strand), its complementary strand ("antisense"), and double-stranded RNA ("sense + antisense")?

2. Form a Hypothesis Twitching results from the failure of muscle cells to control their contractions. What does this suggest about the unc-22 protein in some of the worms? How would you test your hypothesis?

3. Infer The injected fragments came from two different places in the gene and were only a few hundred bases long. The unc-22 mRNA is thousands of bases long. What does this suggest about the mechanism of RNA interference?

The Promise of RNAi Technology The discovery of RNAi has made it possible for researchers to switch genes on and off at will, simply by inserting double-stranded RNA into cells. The Dicer enzyme then cuts this RNA into miRNA, which activates silencing complexes. These complexes block the expression of genes producing mRNA complementary to the miRNA. Naturally this technology is a powerful way to study gene expression in the laboratory. However, RNAi technology also holds the promise of allowing medical scientists to turn off the expression of genes from viruses and cancer cells, and it may provide new ways to treat and perhaps even cure diseases.

Genetic Control of Development

What controls the development of cells and tissues in multicellular organisms?

Regulating gene expression is especially important in shaping the way a multicellular organism, like the mouse embryo in **Figure 13–19,** develops. Each of the specialized cell types found in the adult originates from the same fertilized egg cell. Cells don't just grow and divide during embryonic development. As the embryo develops, different sets of genes are regulated by transcription factors and repressors. Gene regulation helps cells undergo **differentiation,** becoming specialized in structure and function. The study of genes that control development and differentiation is one of the most exciting areas in biology today.

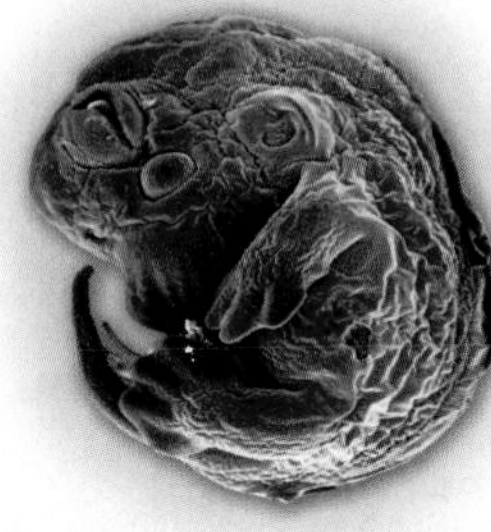

FIGURE 13–19 Differentiation This scanning electron micrograph shows a mouse embryo undergoing cell differentiation 13.5 days after conception.

Analyzing Data

PURPOSE Students will analyze data to infer how RNA interference works.

PLANNING Make sure students understand the role of double-stranded RNA in RNA interference by reviewing **Figure 13–18.**

ANSWERS

1. For both portions of the gene, injection of single-stranded mRNA produced adult worms with normal responses, whereas injection of double-stranded mRNA produced adult worms with twitching responses.
2. Sample answer: In worms with the twitching response, the unc-22 protein that controls muscle contractions was not produced. I would test this hypothesis by determining whether the protein was present in the worms with the twitching response.
3. Sample answer: RNA interference may prevent a gene from being expressed by interfering with just a small percentage of its bases.

Connect to Health

After students read about the promise of RNA interference technology, challenge them to explain how the technology could be used to treat a specific genetic disease. Explain that Huntington's disease is caused by a single autosomal dominant mutant gene. The gene produces a protein that causes brain abnormalities, which in turn interfere with coordination, speech, and mental abilities.

Ask How might RNA interference technology be used to treat Huntington's disease? *(An miRNA molecule complementary to the mutant gene that causes Huntington's disease might be injected into a person with the gene. The miRNA would prevent the expression of the gene so that its protein could not be produced. This would prevent the disease from developing.)*

DIFFERENTIATED INSTRUCTION

L1 Struggling Students Use a **Quick Write** strategy to check students' understanding of the difficult topics of RNA interference and RNA interference technology. Give them one or two minutes to write down everything they know about the topics. Then, read their responses and identify anything they don't understand. Clarify these issues before moving on to the next topic.

Study Wkbks A/B, Appendix S11, Quick Write.

L3 Advanced Students Assign one of the following diseases to each of five students: macular degeneration, cancer, AIDS, hepatitis C, or Huntington's disease. Tell them to find reports of research investigating the use of RNA interference to treat their assigned disease. Ask them to make a list of the most student-friendly research reports to share with the class.

Teach continued

Use Models

Use a simple model to help students understand how homeobox genes control development. Stand about 20 dominoes on end in a long row. The dominoes should be spaced so that knocking over the first domino will cause a cascade effect that knocks over the rest of the dominoes. Say that the first five dominoes represent a homeobox gene and the other dominoes represent genes that control the development of an organ. Have students observe what happens to the other dominoes when you knock over the first domino. Explain how this models the effects of a homeobox gene on genes that control development. Set up the dominoes again, and then remove the second through fifth dominoes from the row. Say that this represents a mutation in the homeobox gene. Demonstrate how knocking over the first domino no longer causes the cascade effect. Ask students to infer how a mutation in a homeobox gene might affect an organism's development.

DIFFERENTIATED INSTRUCTION

LPR Less Proficient Readers On the board, write the term *differentiation* and separate it into its parts (*different* and *-ation*). Explain that *-ation* means "process of."

Ask What do you think *differentiation* means? *(process of making things different)*

Ask What does *cell differentiation* mean? *(process of making cells different)*

Describe concrete examples of differentiated cells, such as skin and blood cells. Point out specific ways they differ. Then, explain how gene regulation is involved in the differentiation of cells.

MYSTERY CLUE Students are likely to infer that homeobox genes control the growth and development of eyes in flies and mice. Students can go online to **Biology.com** to gather their evidence.

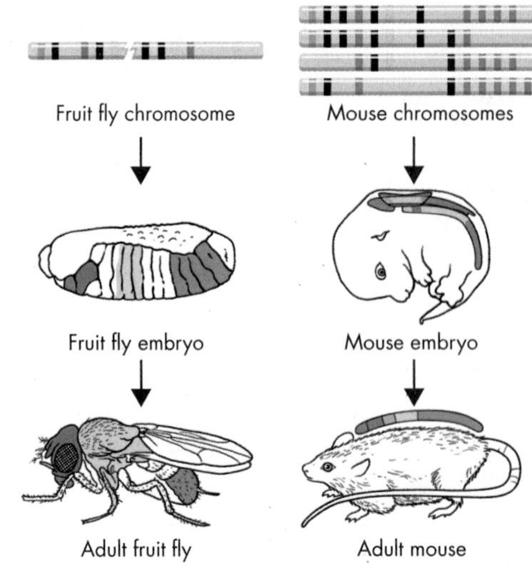

FIGURE 13–20 Hox Genes and Body Development In fruit flies, a series of Hox genes along a chromosome determines the basic body structure. Mice have similar genes on four different chromosomes. The colored areas on the fly and mouse show the approximate body areas affected by genes of the corresponding colors. **Interpret Visuals** ***What section of the bodies of flies and mice is coded by the genes shown in blue?***

Homeotic Genes The American biologist Edward B. Lewis was the first to show that a specific group of ger controls the identities of body parts in the embryo of common fruit fly. Lewis found that a mutation in one these genes actually resulted in a fly with a leg growing out of its head in place of an antenna! From Lewis's wor it became clear that a set of master control genes, know **homeotic genes,** regulates organs that develop in speci parts of the body.

Homeobox and Hox Genes Molecular studies of homeotic genes show that they share a very similar 18 base DNA sequence, which was given the name home box. **Homeobox genes** code for transcription factors activate other genes that are important in cell develop and differentiation. Homeobox genes are expressed in certain regions of the body, and they determine factor the presence of wings or legs.

In flies, a group of homeobox genes known as **Hox g** are located side by side in a single cluster, as shown in **Figure 13–20.** Hox genes determine the identities of eac segment of a fly's body. They are arranged in the exact in which they are expressed, from anterior to posterior. mutation in one of these genes can completely change organs that develop in specific parts of the body.

Remarkably, clusters of Hox genes exist in the DNA of other animals, including humans. These genes are arranged in the same way—from head to tail. The func of Hox genes in humans seems to be almost the same in fruit flies: They tell the cells of the body how to diffe tiate as the body grows. What this means, of course, is nearly all animals, from flies to mammals, share the sa basic tools for building the different parts of the body.

The striking similarity of master control genes—ge that control development—has a simple scientific exp tion. Common patterns of genetic control exist becau all these genes have descended from the genes of com ancestors. **Master control genes are like switches trigger particular patterns of development and diffe tiation in cells and tissues.** The details can vary from organism to another, but the switches are nearly ident Recent studies have shown that the very same Hox ger that triggers the development of hands and feet is also active in the fins of certain fish.

How Science Works

DISCOVERY OF HOMEOBOX GENES

The discovery of homeobox genes by Edward B. Lewis provided an explanation for something scientists had observed 200 years before but had never been able to explain: the similarity in basic body plans of animals as diverse as insects and humans. In the early 1800s, French zoologist Étienne Geoffroy Saint-Hilaire noted that vertebrates are basically arthropods turned upside down. Around the same time, German embryologist Karl Ernst von Baer demonstrated that vertebrate embryos were all virtually identical. When Lewis identified homeobox genes in fruit flies in the mid-1900s, these observations suddenly made sense. The evolution of gene sequencing technologies over the next few decades allowed scientists to sequence the homeobox genes. Since then, nearly identical homeobox genes have been found in many vertebrates, including humans. This discovery has had a profound influence on the study of evolution.

Answers

FIGURE 13–20 the back of the body (posterior portion of the abdomen of the fruit fly and rump of the mouse)

Environmental Influences You've seen how cell differentiation is controlled at least in part by the regulation of gene expression. Conditions in an organism's environment play a role too. In prokaryotes and eukaryotes, environmental factors like temperature, salinity, and nutrient availability can influence gene expression. One example: The *lac* operon in *E. coli* is switched on only when lactose is the only food source in the bacteria's environment.

Metamorphosis is another well-studied example of how organisms can modify gene expression in response to change in their environment. Metamorphosis involves a series of transformations from one life stage to another. It is typically regulated by a number of external (environmental) and internal (hormonal) factors. As organisms move from larval to adult stages, their body cells differentiate to form new organs. At the same time, old organs are lost through cell death.

Consider the metamorphosis of a tadpole into a bullfrog, as shown in **Figure 13–21.** Under less than ideal conditions—a drying pond, a high density of predators, low amounts of food—tadpoles may speed up their metamorphosis. In other words, the speed of metamorphosis is determined by various environmental changes that are translated into hormonal changes, with the hormones functioning at the molecular level. Other environmental influences include temperature and population size.

FIGURE 13–21 Metamorphosis Environmental factors can affect gene regulation. If the bullfrog's environment changes for the worse, its genes will direct the production of hormones to speed the transformation of the tadpole (top photo) to the adult bullfrog (bottom photo).

13.4 Assessment

IN B.1.2, B.1.3, B.5.5, B.6.2

Review Key Concepts

1. a. Review How is the *lac* operon regulated?
   b. Explain What is a promoter?
   c. Use Analogies Write an analogy that demonstrates how the *lac* repressor functions.
2. a. Review Describe how most eukaryotic genes are controlled.
   b. Compare and Contrast How is gene regulation in prokaryotes and eukaryotes similar? How is it different?
3. a. Review What genes control cell differentiation during development?
   b. Compare and Contrast How is the way Hox genes are expressed in mice similar to the way they are expressed in fruit flies? How is it different?

PRACTICE PROBLEM

4. A hormone is a chemical that is produced in one part of the body, travels through the blood, and affects cells in other parts of the body. Many hormones are proteins. How might the production of a hormone affect the expression of genes in a eukaryotic cell? Write a hypothesis that could be tested to answer this question. (*Hint*: Include promoters in your hypothesis.)

BIOLOGY.com Search  Lesson 13.4 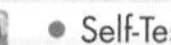 GO • Self-Test • Lesson Assessment

LESSON 13.4

Assess and Remediate

EVALUATE UNDERSTANDING

Ask students to write a list of steps that occur in eukaryote gene regulation. Have them compare lists with a partner and discuss any discrepancies. Then, have students complete the 13.4 Assessment.

REMEDIATION SUGGESTION

L1 Struggling Students If students have trouble with **Question 4,** review the role of repressors and transcription factors in gene regulation. Remind students that repressors, transcription factors, and hormones are proteins.

BIOLOGY.com Students can check their understanding of lesson concepts with the **Self-Test** assessment. They can then take an online version of the **Lesson Assessment.**

Assessment Answers

1a. The *lac* operon is regulated by a repressor protein that binds to the *lac* operon site in the absence of lactose. In the presence of lactose, the repressor protein falls off the *lac* operon site, so that the *lac* genes can be transcribed.

1b. a site where RNA polymerase can bind

1c. Answers will vary but should show that students understand how the *lac* repressor functions.

2a. Most eukaryotic genes are controlled by a TATA box. The TATA box binds a protein that helps position RNA polymerase so transcription can begin. Eukaryotic genes are also regulated by transcription factors that bind to regulatory regions of DNA. RNA interference also controls gene expression in eukaryotes.

2b. Prokaryote gene regulation typically involves a repressor protein that prevents transcription of groups of genes. Eukaryote gene regulation is based on the same general principle: transcription is controlled by proteins that bind to regulatory sites. However, most eukaryotic genes are controlled individually, and have more complex regulatory sequences.

3a. homeobox genes

3b. In fruit flies and mice, Hox genes are expressed from anterior (front) to posterior (back). The expression of Hox genes differs in the specific structures and processes the genes control.

PRACTICE PROBLEM

4. Sample answer: A hormone can bind with regulatory regions of genes and allow RNA polymerase to attach to promoters.

CHAPTER LAB

Pre-Lab

Introduce students to the concepts they will explore in the chapter lab by assigning the Pre-Lab questions.

Lab

Tell students they will perform the chapter lab *From DNA to Protein Synthesis* described in **Lab Manual A.**

L1 Struggling Students A simpler version of the chapter lab is provided in **Lab Manual B.**

Look online for **Editable Lab Worksheets.**

For corresponding pre-lab in the **Foundation Edition**, see page 326.

INDIANA ACADEMIC STANDARDS

For the full text of all standards, see the Course Overview in the front matter of this book.

Skills Lab

GUIDED INQUIRY

NoS.6 Use analogies and models; **B.5.3** DNA and protein production. Also covered: **NoS.7.**

Pre-Lab: From DNA to Protein Synthesis

Problem What are the steps involved in making a protein?

Lab Manual Chapter 13 Lab

Skills Focus Use Models, Sequence

Connect to the Big idea One of the most important tasks in a cell is the assembly of proteins from amino acids. This task always begins on ribosomes that are located throughout a cell's cytoplasm. The directions for the assembly of proteins are stored in DNA molecules. The information is carried to the ribosomes by a form of RNA called messenger RNA, or mRNA. In this lab, you will model the transcription of DNA and the translation of mRNA.

Background Questions

a. Review Is the following sequence from a DNA or mRNA molecule? How can you tell?

CUAAUGCCCUAGGGCACU

b. Compare and Contrast How are transcription and translation similar? How are they different?

c. Sequence List the following molecules in the order in which they take part in protein synthesis: amino acid, DNA, mRNA, tRNA.

Pre-Lab Questions

Preview the procedure in the lab manual.

1. Sequence Describe briefly the process you will use to decode the messages.

2. Compare and Contrast What role do stop codons play in protein synthesis? What are they used for in the coded messages?

3. Predict Which six letters will not appear in the coded messages? Give a reason for your answer.

BIOLOGY.com Search Chapter 13 GO

Visit Chapter 13 online to test yourself on chapter content and to find activities to help you learn.

Untamed Science Video Watch the Untamed Science explorers as they search for examples of how mutations have benefitted a species.

Art in Motion Watch how RNA is processed to make mRNA.

Art Review Review your understanding of different types of mutations with this drag-and-drop activity.

InterActive Art Build your understanding of transcription and translation with these animations.

Visual Analogy Compare DNA and RNA to the master plans and blueprints of a builder.

Data Analysis Analyze the results of growing bacteria with mutations in the *lac* operon in order to identify which gene contains the mutation.

Tutor Tube Tune into the tutor to find out why proteins are so important!

Pre-Lab Answers

BACKGROUND QUESTIONS

a. mRNA, because the sequence contains uracil instead of thymine.

b. Sample answer: During both transcription and translation, large molecules are synthesized from smaller units. During transcription, nucleotides are assembled into complementary mRNA molecules. During translation, amino acids are assembled into proteins.

c. DNA, mRNA, tRNA, amino acid

PRE-LAB QUESTIONS

1. Transcribe the DNA to mRNA; translate the mRNA to amino acids, find the single-letter abbreviation for each amino acid.

2. In protein synthesis, a stop codon is used to mark the end of a protein synthesis. In the coded messages, stop codons are used to represent spaces between words.

3. The letters B, J, O, U, X, and Z will not appear in the messages because these letters are not used as single-letter abbreviations for amino acids.

13 Study Guide

Big idea Information and Heredity

Messenger RNA, transfer RNA, and ribosomal RNA work together in prokaryotic and eukaryotic cells to translate DNA's genetic code into functional proteins. These proteins, in turn, direct the expression of genes.

13.1 RNA

The main differences between RNA and DNA are that (1) the sugar in RNA is ribose instead of deoxyribose; (2) RNA is generally single-stranded, not double-stranded; and (3) RNA contains uracil in place of thymine.

In transcription, segments of DNA serve as templates to produce complementary RNA molecules.

RNA (362)
messenger RNA (363)
ribosomal RNA (363)
transfer RNA (363)
transcription (364)
RNA polymerase (364)
promoter (365)
intron (365)
exon (365)

13.2 Ribosomes and Protein Synthesis

The genetic code is read three "letters" at a time, so that each "word" is three bases long and corresponds to a single amino acid.

Ribosomes use the sequence of codons in mRNA to assemble amino acids into polypeptide chains.

The central dogma of molecular biology is that information is transferred from DNA to RNA to protein.

polypeptide (366)
genetic code (366)
codon (366)
translation (368)
anticodon (369)
gene expression (370)

13.3 Mutations

Mutations are heritable changes in genetic information.

The effects of mutations on genes vary widely. Some have little or no effect; some produce beneficial variations. Some negatively disrupt gene function.

Mutations often produce proteins with new or altered functions that can be useful to organisms in different or changing environments.

mutation (372)
point mutation (373)
frameshift mutation (373)
mutagen (375)
polyploidy (376)

13.4 Gene Regulation and Expression

DNA-binding proteins in prokaryotes regulate genes by controlling transcription.

By binding DNA sequences in the regulatory regions of eukaryotic genes, transcription factors control the expression of those genes.

Master control genes are like switches that trigger particular patterns of development and differentiation in cells and tissues.

operon (377)
operator (378)
RNA interference (380)
differentiation (381)
homeotic gene (382)
homeobox gene (382)
Hox gene (382)

Think Visually

Using the information in this chapter, complete the following flowchart about protein synthesis:

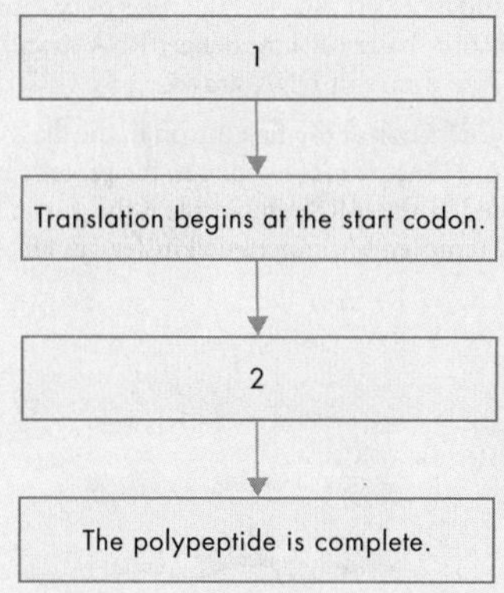

1
Translation begins at the start codon.
2
The polypeptide is complete.

Study Online

REVIEW AND ASSESSMENT RESOURCES

Editable Worksheets Pages of Study Workbooks A and B, Lab Manuals A and B, and the Assessment Resources Book are avilable online. These documents can be easily edited using a word-processing program.

Lesson Overview Have students reread the Lesson Overviews to help them study chapter concepts.

Vocabulary Review The *Flash Cards* and *Match It* provide an interactive way to review chapter vocabulary.

Chapter Assessment Have students take an online version of the Chapter 13 Assessment.

Standardized Test Prep Students can take an online version of the Standardized Test Prep. You will receive their scores along with ideas for remediation.

Diagnostic and Benchmark Tests Use these tests to monitor your students' progress and supply remediation.

UbD Performance Tasks

SUMMATIVE TASK Ask students to write a newspaper story reporting on a "case" of gene regulation. All the factors involved in gene regulation (genes, transcription factors, repressor proteins, RNA polymerase, regulatory sites) should appear as characters in the story. The story should be a journalistic-style account of events and describe what happens to the characters as the events unfold.

TRANSFER TASK Have groups of students write a research proposal about RNA interference technology and a particular genetic disease. The proposal should have the following sections: Research Question, Literature Review, Research Hypothesis, Research Plan, What the Research Will Show, and Why the Research Is Important. Make sure students do an actual literature review before they write their proposal.

Answers

THINK VISUALLY

1. Sample answer: mRNA is transcribed and edited in the nucleus and then goes to a ribosome in the cytoplasm.
2. Sample answer: As the ribosome reads each codon, tRNA brings the correct amino acid to the ribosome, where it is attached to other amino acids in a growing polypeptide. This continues until a "stop" codon is reached.

Lesson 13.1

UNDERSTAND KEY CONCEPTS

1. b **2.** b

3. Messenger RNA carries the instructions for protein synthesis from DNA to the cytoplasm. Ribosomal RNA makes up ribosomes, where proteins are made. Transfer RNA carries amino acids to the ribosome and matches them to the coded mRNA message.

4. The enzyme knows to start transcribing DNA at a promoter, which is a region of DNA that has specific base sequences.

5. Introns are sections of mRNA that are not needed for protein synthesis. Exons are sections of mRNA that are needed for protein synthesis.

THINK CRITICALLY

6. UGGCAGUG

7. If the intron were not removed, its codons would be translated and become part of a protein. As a result, the protein might not function properly.

Lesson 13.2

UNDERSTAND KEY CONCEPTS

8. c **9.** d **10.** c **11.** c

12. a three-base code "word" in the genetic code that specifies a particular amino acid, start, or stop

13. At the ribosome, anticodons in tRNA form bonds with the complementary codons in mRNA, and tRNA adds its amino acid to the polypeptide chain.

14. mRNA: GAU; tRNA: CUA

15. Proteins determine the characteristics of organisms because they are like microscopic tools, each specifically designed to build or operate a component of a living cell. Therefore, controlling the proteins in an organism controls the organism's characteristics.

THINK CRITICALLY

16. Transcription in genetics means to "write out" the genetic code in DNA in the form of a strand of mRNA. The message in mRNA is still in the same "language," the genetic code. Translation in genetics means to express the codons in mRNA in a different "language," that is, as a chain of amino acids instead of as a string of codons.

13 Assessment

The numbers following the questions refer to Indiana's Academic Standards for Biology I.

13.1 RNA

Understand Key Concepts

1. The process by which the genetic code of DNA is copied into a strand of RNA is called B.1.2, B.5.3

a. translation. **c.** transformation.
b. transcription. **d.** replication.

2. Which of the following describes RNA?

a. RNA is usually double-stranded and contains the base thymine.
b. RNA is usually single-stranded and contains the base uracil.
c. RNA is longer than DNA and uses five bases to encode information.
d. RNA is made in the nucleus of eukaryotic cells and stays there to carry out its functions.

3. Describe the function of each of the three types of RNA. B.1.2

4. How does the enzyme that makes RNA know where to start transcribing the DNA? B.1.2

5. Compare introns and exons.

Think Critically

6. Apply Concepts Suppose you start with the DNA strand ACCGTCAC. Use the rules of base pairing to list the bases on a messenger RNA strand transcribed from this DNA strand.

7. Predict Look at the first intron in the diagram below. What would happen to the protein produced by the mRNA molecule if the intron were not removed but functioned instead as an exon?

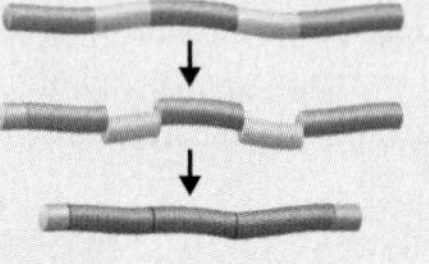

13.2 Ribosomes and Protein Synthesis

Understand Key Concepts

8. In messenger RNA, each codon specifies a particular

a. nucleotide. **c.** amino acid.
b. enzyme. **d.** promoter.

9. The number of codons in the genetic code is B.5.3

a. 3. **b.** 4. **c.** 20. **d.** 64.

10. Which of the following statements about the genetic code is true? B.5.3

a. A codon can specify more than one amino acid.
b. Every codon specifies a different amino acid.
c. Some codons specify the same amino acid.
d. Some codons have no function at all.

11. The process of making proteins on the ribosome based on instructions from messenger RNA is called B.2.4

a. transcription. **c.** translation.
b. transformation. **d.** molecular biology.

12. What is a codon?

13. How do anticodons function? B.5.3

14. If a code on a DNA molecule for a specific amino acid is CTA, what would the messenger RNA codon be? The transfer RNA codon? B.5.3

15. Explain why controlling the proteins in an organism controls the organism's characteristics. B.5.3

Think Critically

16. Use Analogies The word *transcribe* means "to write out." The word *translate* means "to express in another language." Review the meanings of *transcription* and *translation* in genetics. How do the technical meanings of these words relate to the everyday meanings of the words? NoS.3

17. Predict A researcher identifies the nucleotide sequence AAC in a long strand of RNA inside a nucleus. In the genetic code, AAC codes for the amino acid asparagine. When that RNA becomes involved in protein synthesis, will asparagine necessarily appear in the protein? Explain your answer. B.5.3

17. The appearance of the sequence AAC does *not* necessarily mean that asparagine will appear in the protein. That nucleotide sequence could be part of an intron and edited out of the RNA before it leaves the nucleus and becomes involved in protein synthesis. Or, the nucleotide sequence AAC could appear in a long strand of RNA and could be divided over two codons (such as, GGA-ACC).

Lesson 13.3

UNDERSTAND KEY CONCEPTS

18. b **19.** d **20.** b

21. Sample answer: gene mutations and chromosomal mutations. An example of a gene mutation is an insertion mutation, in which an extra base is inserted into a codon. An example of a chromosomal mutation is an inversion, in which part of a chromosome is reversed. Gene mutations affect a single gene; whereas chromosomal mutations affect all or part of a chromosome.

13.3 Mutations

Understand Key Concepts

18. Changes in DNA sequences that affect genetic information are known as B.7.5

a. replications. **c.** transformations.
b. mutations. **d.** translations.

19. A single-base mutation in a messenger RNA molecule could transcribe the DNA sequence CAGTAT into B.7.5

a. GTCATA. **c.** GTCUTU.
b. GUCAUA. **d.** GUAAUA.

20. A substance that can cause a change in the DNA code of an organism is called a B.7.4

a. toxin. **c.** nitrogenous base.
b. mutagen. **d.** nucleotide.

21. Name and give examples of two major types of mutations. What do they have in common? How are they different? B.7.5

22. How does a deletion mutation differ from a substitution mutation? B.7.5

23. Can mutations have a positive effect? B.7.5

Think Critically

24. Compare and Contrast How does the possible impact of a chromosomal mutation that occurs during meiosis differ from that of a similar event that occurs during mitosis of a body cell that is not involved in reproduction? B.7.5

25. Apply Concepts A mutation in the DNA of an organism changes one base sequence in a protein-coding region from CAC to CAT. What is the effect of the mutation on the final protein? Explain your answer. B.5.3

13.4 Gene Regulation and Expression

Understand Key Concepts

26. An expressed gene B.5.3

a. functions as a promoter.
b. is transcribed into RNA.
c. codes for just one amino acid.
d. is made of mRNA.

solve the CHAPTER MYSTERY

MOUSE-EYED FLY

Years ago geneticists discovered a fly gene they called eyeless. Mutations that inactivate this gene cause flies to develop without eyes. Geneticists later discovered a mouse gene, called *Pax6,* that was homologous to eyeless. Transplanting an activated Pax6 gene into a fruit fly can cause the fly to grow eyes in odd places. This happens despite the fact that mouse eyes and fly eyes are very different. In fact the only reason we describe them as "eyes" is because they make vision possible.

How can the Pax6 gene perform the same role in such diverse animals? It probably began very early in the history of life, when eyes were just patches of light-sensitive cells on the skin of the common ancestors of all animals. As those organisms evolved and diversified, master control genes like Pax6 kept working, but with altered functions. Many genes like Pax6 are shared, not only by insects, but by all animals, including worms, sea urchins, and humans.

1. Compare and Contrast How are fly eyes and mouse eyes different? Similar?

2. Infer The Pax6 and eyeless genes code for transcription factors, not for parts of the actual eye. Why does this make sense in light of the effect of Pax6 when it is inserted into a fly?

3. Connect to the Big idea What feature of the genetic code makes it possible for a mouse gene to work inside the cell of a fly? B.8.1

 B.7.5

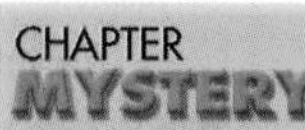

After students have read through the Chapter Mystery, ask them what the *Pax6* gene controls in both mice and fruit flies. *(development of eyes)* Then, ask them to infer what type of gene *Pax6* likely is. *(It is likely a homeobox gene, because it controls other genes that are responsible for development of major body structures.)*

CHAPTER MYSTERY ANSWERS

1. Fly eyes and mouse eyes look very different and have different structures. However, both types of eyes have the same function. They sense light and make vision possible.

2. If the *Pax6* gene coded for parts of the actual eye, then the fly would develop mouse eyes in addition to normal fly eyes when the gene was inserted. Instead, *Pax6* causes the fly to develop extra fly eyes. This makes sense if *Pax6* codes for transcription factors that turn on other genes in the fly, which in turn code for the parts of the actual fly eye.

3. Big idea A mouse gene can work inside the cell of a fly because the genetic code is nearly universal. In virtually all organisms, codons are read three bases at a time and in the same order, and the codons code for the same amino acids.

In the **Untamed Science Video: Tales of a Mutant Leopard,** the crew leads students on a field trip to see how some species benefit from mutations.

22. A deletion mutation occurs when a base is lost from a codon. This shifts the "reading frame," so all the codons after the point of deletion are affected. A substitution mutation occurs when a single base is replaced by a different base. This does not shift the "reading frame."

23. Yes, a mutation could produce a protein with a new or altered function that might be useful to an organism in a changing environment.

THINK CRITICALLY

24. A chromosomal mutation that occurs during meiosis will be carried by some of the organism's gametes and possibly to the organism's offspring. A mutation that occurs during mitosis in a body cell will be passed on to that cell's daughter cells but not to the organism's offspring.

25. The mutation in the DNA changes the codon in mRNA from GUG to GUA. Both of these codons code for the amino acid valine, so the final protein would not be affected.

ASSESSMENT

Lesson 13.4

UNDERSTAND KEY CONCEPTS

26. b **27.** b **28.** a **29.** c

30. DNA-binding proteins regulate genes by helping switch genes on or off before transcription.

31. The term *cell specialization* means the adaptation of eukaryotic cells for specialized functions by the regulation of gene expression.

32. A TATA box is usually found just before a gene. It binds transcription factor proteins that help position RNA polymerase at the point where transcription should begin. When transcription factors bind to the TATA box, they form a binding site for RNA polymerase, which can then start transcription.

33. A homeobox gene is a gene that codes for a transcription factor that activates other genes important to cell development and differentiation.

THINK CRITICALLY

34. Sample answer: In prokaryotes, genes are organized into operons, where groups of genes are regulated together. In eukaryotes, most genes are controlled individually and have more complex sequences. Gene expression in eukaryotes can also be regulated at many levels, and is more complicated in multicellular organisms, where there is cell specialization. Then there are microRNAs that can block gene expression through RNA interference.

Connecting Concepts

USE SCIENCE GRAPHICS

35. no effect

36. Sample answer: Substituting a C for a G in the first base of a codon that codes for valine would replace it with leucine. Substituting a C for a U in the second base of a codon that codes for valine would replace it with alanine. These substitutions may alter the function of the resulting protein.

WRITE ABOUT SCIENCE

37. Student explanations should address neutral, harmful, and beneficial mutations and explain ways in which each may occur.

38. 

DNA is transcribed to form mRNA. After the mRNA is edited, it leaves the nucleus and enters the cytoplasm. A ribosome containing rRNA attaches to the mRNA strand and translates it to form a polypeptide. In translation, tRNA molecules bring the correct amino acids to the ribosome to add to the polypeptide.

27. A group of genes that are regulated together is called a(n)
a. promoter.
b. operon.
c. intron.
d. allele.

28. To turn on the lactose-digesting enzymes of *E. coli*, the lactose must first B.1.2
a. bind to the repressor.
b. bind to the DNA of the bacterium.
c. separate from the repressor.
d. initiate the synthesis of messenger RNA.

29. Blocking gene expression in eukaryotes with microRNA strands is called RNA B.1.2
a. transcription.
b. translation.
c. interference.
d. digestion.

30. How is gene expression controlled in prokaryotes? B.1.2, B.5.5

31. What is meant by the term *cell specialization*? How is cell specialization controlled? B.6.2

32. Describe how a TATA box helps position RNA polymerase in a eukaryotic cell.

33. What is a homeobox gene?

Think Critically

34. Apply Concepts The number of promoter sequences, enhancer sites, and the TATA box in eukaryotes makes gene regulation in these organisms far more complex than regulation in prokaryotes. Why is regulation in eukaryotes so much more sophisticated? B.6.2

Connecting Concepts

Use Science Graphics NoS.3

Use the data table to answer questions 35 and 36.

Codon Translation	
Amino Acid	**mRNA Codons**
Alanine (Ala)	GCA, GCG, GCU, GCC
Valine (Val)	GUA, GUG, GUU, GUC
Leucine (Leu)	CUA, CUG, CUU, CUC, UUA, UUG

35. Relate Cause and Effect The table shows RNA codons for three amino acids. How would a substitution mutation in the third nucleotide position of the codons for alanine and valine affect the resulting protein? B.7.5

36. Infer The three amino acids shown in the table have very similar—though not identical—properties. What substitution mutations could result in switching one of these amino acids for another? What might be the result? B.7.5

Write About Science NoS.3

37. Explanation Write a paragraph explaining why the effect of mutations can vary widely—from neutral to harmful to beneficial. B.7.5

38. Assess the Big idea Explain the roles of the three types of RNA in taking the information in DNA and using it to make proteins. B.1.2

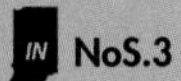
NoS.3

RNA is the genetic material of many viruses. Scientists analyzed RNA from four different types of viruses. The content of the four nitrogenous bases is shown below.

Base Percentages in Four Viruses				
Virus	**A**	**U**	**C**	**G**
A	26.3	29.3	20.6	23.8
B	x	x	17.6	17.5
C	21.9	12.8	34.3	31.1
D	29.8	26.3	18.5	25.3

39. Interpret Graphics Which of the four types of viruses is most likely to use double-stranded RNA as its genetic material?
a. Virus A
b. Virus B
c. Virus C
d. Virus D

40. Infer The values in the two boxes labeled with an *x* would most likely be about
a. 32.5 % A and 32.5% U.
b. 17.5% A and 17.5% U.
c. 26.3% A and 29.3% U.
d. 32.5% A and 17.5% U.

388 Chapter 13 • Assessment

PURPOSE Students will interpret a data table to infer the specific nitrogenous bases in a virus.

PLANNING Before students begin the activity, ask them to explain why double-stranded RNA would have the same percentage of C bases as G bases and the same percentage of A bases as U bases.

ANSWERS

39. b

40. a

Standardized Test Practice for Indiana

Multiple Choice

1. How does RNA differ from DNA?
   - A RNA contains uracil and deoxyribose.
   - B RNA contains ribose and thymine.
   - C RNA contains uracil and ribose.
   - D RNA contains adenine and ribose.

2. How would the DNA sequence GCTATA be transcribed to mRNA?
   - A GCUAUA
   - B CGATAT
   - C CGAUAU
   - D GCUTUT

   B.5.3

Questions 3–4

Use the chart below to answer the questions.

First Base in Code Word	Third Base in Code Word	Second Base in Code Word: A	G	U	C
A	A	Lys	Arg	Ile	Thr
A	G	Lys	Arg	Met	Thr
A	U	Asn	Ser	Ile	Thr
A	C	Asn	Ser	Ile	Thr
G	A	Glu	Gly	Val	Ala
G	G	Glu	Gly	Val	Ala
G	U	Asp	Gly	Val	Ala
G	C	Asp	Gly	Val	Ala
U	A	"Stop"	"Stop"	Leu	Ser
U	G	"Stop"	Trp	Leu	Ser
U	U	Tyr	Cys	Phe	Ser
U	C	Tyr	Cys	Phe	Ser
C	A	Gln	Arg	Leu	Pro
C	G	Gln	Arg	Leu	Pro
C	U	His	Arg	Leu	Pro
C	C	His	Arg	Leu	Pro

3. Which of the following codons signifies the end of translation?
   - A CAA
   - B UGA
   - C AUC
   - D CCA

4. Which of the chains of amino acids corresponds to the nucleotide sequence UCAAGCGUA?
   - A glu-cys-pro
   - B glu-asp-"stop"
   - C thr-arg-met
   - D ser-ser-val

5. In eukaryotes, functional messenger RNA molecules are made from
   - A exons spliced together after introns are removed.
   - B introns spliced together after exons are removed.
   - C exons spliced together with introns.
   - D long pieces of RNA shortened by the Dicer enzyme.

   B.1.2

6. Promoters are
   - A genes that code for individual proteins.
   - B proteins that bind with DNA and prevent transcription.
   - C DNA sequences near operons that regulate transcription.
   - D small molecules that bind with repressor proteins.

Questions 7–8

Use the diagrams below to answer the questions.

Normal Chromosome M N O P Q R S

Mutant 1 M P O N Q R S

Mutant 2 M N N O P Q R S

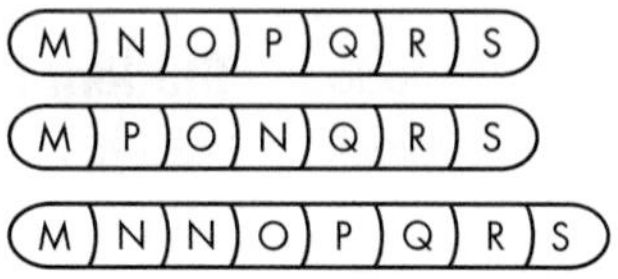

7. Mutant 1 is a(n)
   - A deletion.
   - B translocation.
   - C inversion.
   - D duplication.

   B.7.5

8. Mutant 2 is a(n)
   - A deletion.
   - B translocation.
   - C inversion.
   - D duplication.

   B.7.5

Open-Ended Response

9. What is the function of the *lac* repressor system in *E. coli*?

   B.1.2

If You Have Trouble With . . .									
Question	1	2	3	4	5	6	7	8	9
See Lesson	13.1	13.1	13.2	13.2	13.1	13.1	13.3	13.3	13.4

Answers

1. C
2. C
3. B
4. D
5. A
6. C
7. C
8. D
9. The *lac* repressor system controls the production of enzymes needed to digest lactose. When lactose is absent and the enzymes are not needed, repressor proteins turn off the genes, so that the enzymes are not produced. When lactose is present and the enzymes are needed, lactose prevents the repressor proteins from turning off the genes, so that the enzymes are produced.

Test-Taking Tip

USE SCRATCH PAPER

Tell students that it is a good idea to use scratch paper when they are asked to find solutions to problems, even on multiple-choice tests. For example, when they are asked to identify complementary RNA sequences or to translate a series of RNA codons into amino acids, they should first solve the problem on scratch paper. Then, they can compare their answer with the options provided. This will reduce their chances of making mistakes.

CHAPTER PLANNER 14

Human Heredity

Chapter Contents	IN	Time	Core Resources
Chapter Preview			**Student Edition,** pp. 390–391 **Chapter Mystery,** p. 391
14.1 Human Chromosomes Karyotypes • Transmission of Human Traits • Human Pedigrees	NoS.6, B.5.1, B.5.6, B.7.2, B.7.3	1 period 1/2 block	**Student Edition,** pp. 392–397 Inquiry 14.1 Quick Lab, p. 395 L2 **Study Workbook A** 14.1 Worksheets L2 **Biology.com** *Art Review:* A Human Karyotype • *Data Analysis:* Blood Types and Cholera • *InterActive Art:* Pedigrees **Assessment Resources Book** Visual Quiz L2
14.2 Human Genetic Disorders From Molecule to Phenotype • Chromosomal Disorders • *Biology & Society: Are Laws Protecting Genetic Privacy Necessary?*	NoS.3, B.1.2, B.5.2, B.5.4, B.5.5, B.5.6, B.7.5	1/2 period 1/4 block	**Student Edition,** pp. 398–402 Inquiry 14.2 Analyzing Data, p. 400 L2 **Study Workbook A** 14.2 Worksheets L2 **Biology.com** *Art in Motion:* Nondisjunction Disorders • 14.2 Self-Test • 14.2 Lesson Assessment
14.3 Studying the Human Genome Manipulating DNA • The Human Genome Project	NoS.6, NoS.10	1 period 1/2 block	**Student Edition,** pp. 403–409 Inquiry 14.3 Quick Lab, p. 405 L2 **Study Workbook A** 14.3 Worksheets L2 **Assessment Resources Book** Visual Quiz L2
Chapter Pre-Lab	NoS.6, NoS.7, B.7.3	1 period 1/2 block	**Student Edition,** p. 410 L2 **Lab Manual A** *Using DNA to Identify Human Remains* L2

Differentiated Instruction Tools

Study Workbook B includes worksheets with lesson-level differentiated instruction support and explanations of differentiated instruction teaching strategies.

Lab Manual B includes skills labs, simplified chapter labs, and hands-on activities.

ELL Handbook explains ways to make *Biology* more accessible to ELL students.

Spanish Study Workbook is a Spanish translation of Study Workbook A.

Multilingual Glossary is the glossary translated into ten languages.

Differentiated Instruction Key

- L1 Special Needs or Struggling Students
- ELL English Language Learners
- LPR Less Proficient Readers
- L2 On-Level Students
- L3 Advanced Students

Additional Resources

Biology.com Untamed Science Video • Vocabulary Flash Cards

Study Workbook B 14.1 Worksheets L1 ELL LPR
Spanish Study Workbook 14.1 Worksheets ELL
Biology.com *Tutor Tube:* Skipping a Generation • 14.1 Lesson Overview • 14.1 Lesson Notes • 14.1 Self-Test • 14.1 Lesson Assessment

Study Workbook B 14.2 Worksheets L1 ELL LPR
Spanish Study Workbook 14.2 Worksheets ELL
Biology.com 14.2 Lesson Overview • 14.2 Lesson Notes

Study Workbook B 14.3 Worksheets L1 ELL LPR
Spanish Study Workbook 14.3 Worksheets ELL
Biology.com 14.3 Lesson Overview • 14.3 Lesson Notes • 14.3 Self-Test • 14.3 Lesson Assessment

Lab Manual B *Using DNA to Identify Human Remains* • Data Analysis: *The Geography of Malaria* • Hands-On Activity: *Modeling Restriction Enzymes* L1 ELL LPR

Chapter Review

Student Edition Study Guide, p. 411 L2
Study Workbook A Chapter 14 Vocabulary Review L2 • Chapter 14 Chapter Mystery/21st Century Skills Activity L2 L3
Transparencies, pp. 172–181 L1 ELL LPR L2
Biology.com Untamed Science Video • Editable Worksheets of Study Workbooks A and B and Lab Manuals A and B • Chapter 14 Flash Cards and Crossword Puzzle

Untamed Science DVD • Classroom Resources CD (includes lesson presentations and editable worksheets)

Chapter Assessment

Student Edition Assessment, pp. 412–415 L2
Study Workbook B Chapter 14 Chapter Review L1 ELL LPR • Chapter 14 Taking a Standardized Test L1 ELL LPR
Assessment Resources Book Chapter 14 Test A L2 • Chapter 14 Test B L1 ELL LPR
Biology.com Chapter 14 Assessment • Editable Worksheets of Chapter 14 Visual Quizzes and Chapter 14 Tests A and B

Exam*View Assessment Suite* • Classroom Resources CD (includes lesson presentations and editable worksheets)

Time: 1 period, 1/2 block

Pressed for Time?

Preview the Chapter Preview Figures 14–1 and 14–7 and introduce the Lesson 14.1 vocabulary.

Cover the Chapter Quickly Have students read all of Lesson 14.1 and go over Figure 14–7. Have students read *Manipulating DNA* in Lesson 14.3.

Assess Assign the 14.1 Assessment and questions 1–7, 18, 20, 21, 25, and 27–29 from the Chapter 14 Assessment.

Connect to the Big Idea

Big idea Have students examine the photo and discuss the ways the people look different from one another and the ways they look similar. Help students connect the caption to the Big Idea of Information and Heredity by asking them to recall the role of DNA and its significance in heredity. *(DNA carries the complete blueprint of an organism. Genetic information is passed from one generation to the next in the form of genes, which are coded segments of DNA.)* Remind students that organisms resulting from sexual reproduction inherit a unique combination of genes. Point out that the chapter specifically covers the genetics of humans. Then, ask students to offer reasons for studying human inheritance. *(They will probably mention the value of studying inherited diseases to try to find cures.)* Read aloud the question, **How can we use genetics to study human inheritance?** Have students anticipate an answer. Then, tell them to keep the question in mind as they study the chapter.

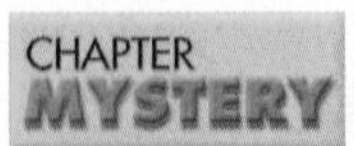

Have students read over the Chapter Mystery and make predictions about how sickle cell disease is inherited. Have them discuss how Ava might use genetics to help her find out if she is at risk for sickle cell disease.

BIOLOGY.com Have students preview the chapter vocabulary using the **Flash Cards.**

IN INDIANA ACADEMIC STANDARDS

For the full text of all standards, see the Course Overview in the front matter of this book.

Key standards: Chapter 14 covers key ideas from Standard 7: Genetics, including **B.7.2** Inheritance patterns and **B.7.3** Traits.

14 Human Heredity

Big idea **Information and Heredity**

Q: How can we use genetics to study human inheritance?

UbD Understanding by Design

In Unit 4, students are building toward the Enduring Understanding that *DNA is the universal code for life; it enables an organism to transmit hereditary information and, along with the environment, determines an organism's characteristics.* The graphic organizer at the right shows how chapter content informs the Enduring Understanding.

PERFORMANCE GOALS

In Chapter 14, students learn about patterns of human heredity and how genetics is used to study human inheritance. Students will apply their knowledge of human genetics by constructing models, writing explanations, and developing analogies to show they understand key concepts. At the end of the chapter, students will develop a comprehensive interview with a geneticist and write a letter expressing an opinion about genetic testing.

INDIANA ACADEMIC STANDARDS FOR SCIENCE

Nature of Science NoS.3, NoS.6, NoS.7, NoS.10; **Cellular Chemistry** B.1.2; **Molecular Basis of Heredity** B.5.1, B.5.2, B.5.4, B.5.5, B.5.6; **Genetics** B.7.1, B.7.2, B.7.3, B.7.5. See lessons for details.

One thing to notice about this group of students is that none of them looks alike. The diversity of traits among the human race stems from one microscopic molecule—DNA.

• Untamed Science Video • Chapter Mystery

CHAPTER MYSTERY

THE CROOKED CELL

When Ava visited her Uncle Eli in the hospital, he appeared tired and pale. He complained of sharp pains in his bones. "I've got sickle cell disease," Uncle Eli explained, short of breath. "I just hope it doesn't run in your side of the family."

That evening, Ava searched the Internet for information about her uncle's disease. She saw photos of red blood cells shaped like the letter *C*—a far cry from the healthy, round blood cells of a normal individual. Ava learned that these sickle-shaped cells are rigid and sticky. In blood vessels, they form clumps that can block blood flow and even cause organ damage. "Am I at risk?" Ava wondered. To find out, she would need to investigate her family history—and her own cells. As you read this chapter, look for clues that would help Ava discover whether she might carry sickle cell trait. Then, solve the mystery.

Never Stop Exploring Your World. Finding out about Ava's risk of sickle cell disease is only the beginning. Take a video field trip with the ecogeeks of Untamed Science to see where the mystery leads.

Chapter 14 Big Idea: Information and Heredity

Chapter 14 EQ: How can we use genetics to study human inheritance?

14.1 GQ: How does studying the human genome help us draw conclusions about the inheritance of traits?

14.2 GQ: What causes some human genetic disorders?

14.3 GQ: How do we study the human genome, and what have we learned so far?

What's Online

Extend your reach by using these and other digital assets offered at Biology.com.

CHAPTER MYSTERY
As a young woman probes into her family history to ascertain her risk of sickle cell trait, students use their knowledge of human heredity to find the answer along with her.

UNTAMED SCIENCE VIDEO
Take a trip with the crew of Untamed Science into the microscopic world of chromosomes to find out how colorblindness is inherited.

ART REVIEW
Drag-and-drop items allow students to construct a karyotype.

DATA ANALYSIS
Students analyze the connection between blood type O and a higher susceptibility to cholera.

INTERACTIVE ART
Students can interact with pedigrees online.

TUTOR TUBE
Short, online tutorial shows how pedigrees help students understand how a trait can "skip a generation."

ART IN MOTION
Students watch an animation that shows how non-disjunction occurs during meiosis.

LESSON 14.1

Getting Started

Objectives

14.1.1 Identify the types of human chromosomes in a karyotype.

14.1.2 Describe the patterns of the inheritance of human traits.

14.1.3 Explain how pedigrees are used to study human traits.

Student Resources

Study Workbooks A and B, 14.1 Worksheets

Spanish Study Workbook, 14.1 Worksheets

Lesson Overview • Lesson Notes • Activities: Art Review, Data Analysis, InterActive Art, Tutor Tube • Assessment: Self-Test, Lesson Assessment

For corresponding lesson in the **Foundation Edition**, see pages 334–338.

Activate Prior Knowledge

Ask students if they know what a dog pedigree is or if any of them owns a dog with a pedigree. *(A pedigree is a record of the family tree, usually back at least three generations.)* Explain that a pedigree is often used to show a dog is a purebred, and it gives information about the dog's background and any hereditary health problems in its blood line. Tell them that human pedigrees also are used to show information about a person's background, most commonly to trace genetic disorders.

IN INDIANA ACADEMIC STANDARDS

For the full text of all standards, see the Course Overview in the front matter of this book.

B.5.6 Recognize that traits can be structural, physiological or behavioral and can include readily observable characteristics at the organismal level or less recognizable features at the molecular and cellular level.

B.7.2 Describe dominant, recessive, codominant, sex-linked, incompletely dominant, multiply allelic, and polygenic traits and illustrate their inheritance patterns over multiple generations.

B.7.3 Determine the likelihood of the appearance of a specific trait in an offspring given the genetic make-up of the parents.

14.1 Human Chromosomes

IN B.5.6 Types of traits; B.7.2 Inheritance patterns; B.7.3 Traits. Also covered: NoS.6, B.5.1.

Key Questions

What is a karyotype?

What patterns of inheritance do human traits follow?

How can pedigrees be used to analyze human inheritance?

Vocabulary

genome • karyotype • sex chromosome • autosome • sex-linked gene • pedigree

Taking Notes

Outline Before you read, make an outline of the major headings in the lesson. As you read, fill in main ideas and supporting details for each heading.

THINK ABOUT IT If you had to pick an ideal organism for the study of genetics, would you choose one that produced lots of offspring? How about one that was easy to grow in the lab? Would you select one with a short life span in order to do several crosses per month? How about all of the above? You certainly would not choose an organism that produced very few offspring, had a long life span, and could not be grown in a lab. Yet, when we study human genetics, this is exactly the sort of organism we deal with. Given all of these difficulties, it may seem a wonder that we know as much about human genetics as we do.

Karyotypes

What is a karyotype?

What makes us human? We might try to answer that question by looking under the microscope to see what is inside a human cell. Not surprisingly, human cells look much like the cells of other animals. To find what makes us uniquely human, we have to look deeper, into the genetic instructions that build each new individual. To begin this undertaking, we have to explore the human genome. A **genome** is the full set of genetic information that an organism carries in its DNA.

The study of any genome starts with chromosomes—those bundles of DNA and protein found in the nuclei of eukaryotic cells. To see human chromosomes clearly, cell biologists photograph cells in mitosis, when the chromosomes are fully condensed and easy to view. Scientists then cut out the chromosomes from the photographs and arrange them in a picture known as a **karyotype** (kar ee uh typ). **A karyotype shows the complete diploid set of chromosomes grouped together in pairs, arranged in order of decreasing size.**

FIGURE 14–1 A Human Karyotype A typical human cell has 23 pairs of chromosomes. These chromosomes have been cut out of a photograph and arranged to form a karyotype.

UbD Teach for Understanding

ENDURING UNDERSTANDING DNA is the universal code for life; it enables an organism to transmit hereditary information and, along with the environment, determines an organism's characteristics.

GUIDING QUESTION How does studying the human genome help us draw conclusions about the inheritance of traits?

EVIDENCE OF UNDERSTANDING *At the end of the lesson, give students the following assessment to show they understand how chromosomes and genes are related to the inheritance of traits.* Provide pairs of students with white, red, and green pipe cleaners to represent X and Y chromosomes that do not have the trait for colorblindness and X chromosomes that do. Ask them to model all six possible pairings between males and females with different genotypes for the trait of colorblindness and to construct Punnett squares showing the possible genotype outcomes for the male and female offspring (carrier, normal vision, or colorblind).

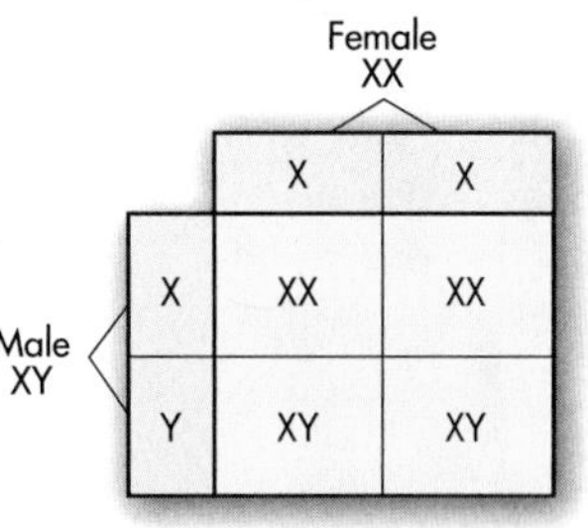

FIGURE 14–2 Sex Ratios Human egg cells contain a single X chromosome. Sperm cells contain either one X chromosome or one Y chromosome. Interpret Tables ***What does this Punnett square suggest about the sex ratio of the human population?***

The karyotype in **Figure 14–1** is from a typical human cell, which contains 46 chromosomes, arranged in 23 pairs. Why do our chromosomes come in pairs? Remember that we begin life when a haploid sperm, carrying just 23 chromosomes, fertilizes a haploid egg, also with 23 chromosomes. The resulting diploid cell develops into a new individual and carries the full complement of 46 chromosomes—two sets of 23.

Sex Chromosomes Two of the 46 chromosomes in the human genome are known as **sex chromosomes,** because they determine an individual's sex. Females have two copies of the X chromosome. Males have one X chromosome and one Y chromosome. As you can see in **Figure 14–2,** this is the reason why males and females are born in a roughly 50 : 50 ratio. All human egg cells carry a single X chromosome (23,X). However, half of all sperm cells carry an X chromosome (23,X) and half carry a Y chromosome (23,Y). This ensures that just about half the zygotes will be males and half will be females.

More than 1200 genes are found on the X chromosome, some of which are shown in **Figure 14–3.** Note that the human Y chromosome is much smaller than the X chromosome and contains only about 140 genes, most of which are associated with male sex determination and sperm development.

Autosomal Chromosomes To distinguish them from the sex chromosomes, the remaining 44 human chromosomes are known as autosomal chromosomes, or **autosomes.** The complete human genome consists of 46 chromosomes, including 44 autosomes and 2 sex chromosomes. To quickly summarize the total number of chromosomes present in a human cell—both autosomes and sex chromosomes—biologists write 46,XX for females and 46,XY for males.

In Your Notebook *Describe what makes up a human karyotype.*

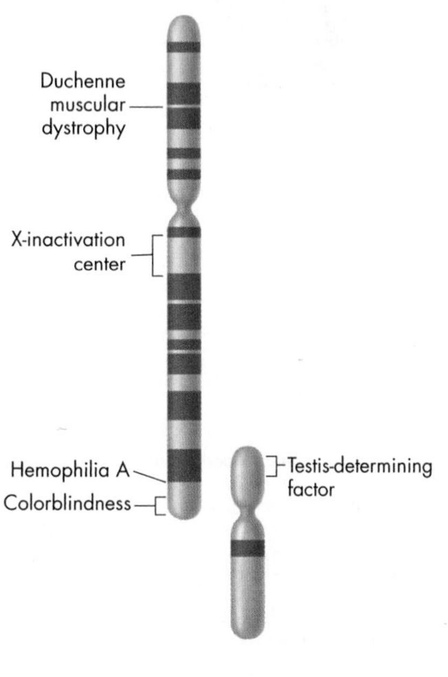

FIGURE 14–3 X and Y Chromosomes The human Y chromosome is smaller and carries fewer genes than the human X chromosome.

Quick Facts

DUCHENNE MUSCULAR DYSTROPHY

Duchenne muscular dystrophy is the most common form of the more than thirty kinds of muscular dystrophy. It is caused by a mutation in a gene on the X chromosome that codes for a muscle protein called dystrophin. The mutated gene causes defects in muscle proteins, leading to muscle degeneration. Because the gene is inherited in an X-linked recessive pattern, the disease affects mainly boys. Many children with the disease cannot walk and require respirators to breathe. Most do not live beyond their 30s. Researchers are experimenting with several approaches to a cure, including gene therapy that involves injecting children with altered viruses that can introduce normal genes to affected cells.

Teach

Use Visuals

Use **Figure 14–2** to have students identify the chromosomes that determine an individual's sex. Ask students to identify which boxes in the figure represent sperm cells. (*the two left-most boxes that contain either a single "X" or a single "Y"*) Point out that the sperm determines the sex of the child. Have students note the difference in size of the X and Y chromosomes in **Figure 14–3.** The sex chromosomes are the only pair of chromosomes that do not match in size and gene content. Then, ask students to identify the person's sex in **Figure 14–1.** (*male*)

DIFFERENTIATED INSTRUCTION

L1 **Struggling Students** Have students draw two simple diagrams of meiosis, contrasting the formation of sex cells in males and in females. Have them examine the diagrams to identify pairings of sex cells that would result in a male or a female offspring. Ask how the pairings show that the sperm determines the sex of the child. *(Male sex cells contain an X or a Y chromosome, whereas all female sex cells contain only an X chromosome.)*

ELL Focus on ELL: Build Background

ADVANCED AND ADVANCED HIGH SPEAKERS Help students make connections between the real world and what they will study by bringing to class current articles on human genetics from newspapers, magazines, or online news sources. Read aloud parts of the articles, and show visuals. Provide students with copies of the articles, and have them work in pairs to identify any science terms they recognize and any terms that they do not know. Invite students to comment on the articles and share any knowledge about the topic. Ask simple questions to give them an opportunity to practice their oral English.

BIOLOGY.com Students can drag and drop items to construct a karyotype in **Art Review: A Human Karyotype.**

Answers

FIGURE 14–2 It suggests that about half the population is male and about half is female.

IN YOUR NOTEBOOK A human karyotype is made up of the complete diploid set of chromosomes in a cell.

Teach continued

Build Science Skills

Ask students to recall what they know about simple inheritance patterns. Draw a blank Punnett square on the board. Ask them how to label the columns and rows and fill out the cells to show a cross between two people who are both heterozygous for the Rh factor. Have students explain how the results show a pattern of simple dominance. Then, use **Figure 14–5** to discuss codominant and multiple alleles. Have students work out crosses between different genotypes to see how different blood types can be inherited.

DIFFERENTIATED INSTRUCTION

L1 Struggling Students Make sure students understand that the superscripts in **Figure 14–5** are not exponents or additional alleles but labels that distinguish the two codominant alleles. Have them make a simpler version of the second column in the chart by rewriting the I^A, I^B, and *i* alleles as *A, B,* and *O,* respectively.

BIOLOGY.com Have students determine the connection between blood type O and a higher susceptibility to cholera in the activity **Data Analysis: Blood Types and Cholera.**

Address Misconceptions

Frequencies of Dominant and Recessive Traits Some students think that dominant traits are more common in a population. This might stem from their observation that 75 percent of offspring in a heterozygous cross show the dominant trait. Use Punnett squares to show a cross between two homozygous recessive parents and a cross between two heterozygous parents. Point out that a Punnett square shows the phenotype frequencies for a specific cross, not for an entire population. Most individuals in a population will show a recessive trait if the population has many recessive alleles and therefore has more incidents of crosses involving homozygous recessive parents. Emphasize that allele frequencies can be high or low regardless of how the allele is expressed.

Answers

FIGURE 14–5 The allele for no antigens, *i*, is recessive to I^A and I^B, so it is hidden by the I^A and I^B genes. Thus, two different genotypes—I^AI^A and I^Ai—result in the A phenotype, and two other genotypes—I^BI^B and I^Bi—result in the B phenotype.

FIGURE 14–4 Recessive Alleles Some of the recessive alleles of the *MC1R* gene cause red hair. An individual with red hair usually has two of these recessive alleles.

Transmission of Human Traits

What patterns of inheritance do human traits follow?

It has not been easy studying our species using traditional genetic techniques. Despite the difficulties, human genetics has progressed rapidly, especially in recent years, with the use of molecular techniques to study human DNA. What have these studies shown? Human genes follow the same Mendelian patterns of inheritance as the genes of other organisms.

Dominant and Recessive Alleles **Many human traits follow a pattern of simple dominance.** For instance, a gene known as *MC1R* helps determine skin and hair color. Some of *MC1R*'s recessive alleles produce red hair. An individual with red hair usually has two of these recessive alleles, inheriting a copy from each parent. Dominant alleles for the *MC1R* gene help produce darker hair colors.

Another trait that displays simple dominance is the Rhesus, or Rh blood group. The allele for Rh factor comes in two forms: Rh^+ and Rh^-. Rh^+ is dominant, so an individual with both alleles (Rh^+/Rh^-) is said to have Rh positive blood. Rh negative blood is found in individuals with two recessive alleles (Rh^-/Rh^-).

Codominant and Multiple Alleles **The alleles for many human genes display codominant inheritance.** One example is the ABO blood group, determined by a gene with three alleles: I^A, I^B, and *i*. Alleles I^A and I^B are codominant. They produce molecules known as antigens on the surface of red blood cells. As **Figure 14–5** shows, individuals with alleles I^A and I^B produce both A and B antigens, making them blood type AB. The *i* allele is recessive. Individuals with alleles I^AI^A or I^Ai produce only the A antigen, making them blood type A. Those with I^BI^B or I^Bi alleles are type B. Those homozygous for the *i* allele (*ii*) produce no antigen and are said to have blood type O. If a patient has AB-negative blood, it means the individual has I^A and I^B alleles from the ABO gene and two Rh^- alleles from the Rh gene.

FIGURE 14–5 Human Blood Groups This table shows the relationship between genotype and phenotype for the ABO blood group. It also shows which blood types can safely be transfused into people with other blood types. **Apply Concepts** ***How can there be four different phenotypes even though there are six different genotypes?***

Blood Groups

Phenotype (Blood Type)	Genotype	Antigen on Red Blood Cell	Safe Transfusions	
			To	From
A	I^AI^A or I^Ai	A	A, AB	A, O
B	I^BI^B or I^Bi	B	B, AB	B, O
AB	I^AI^B	A and B	AB	A, B, AB, O
O	*ii*	None	A, B, AB, O	O

Biology In-Depth

BLOOD TYPES AND TRANSFUSIONS

Knowing a person's blood group is critical because using the wrong type of blood for a transfusion can be fatal. Type A and type B red blood cells have antigens for their respective type on their surface. The immune system of a person with type B blood would recognize type A cells as foreign and produce antibodies against the type A antigen, and vice versa. The immune system of a person with type O blood would recognize both A and B cells as foreign and produce antibodies against both type A and type B antigens. People with type AB blood have both type A and type B antigens, so they do not produce antibodies against these types of blood. They are called "universal recipients" because they can receive all types of blood in a transfusion. People with type O blood are called "universal donors" because their red blood cells have no antigens to elicit an antibody response, and thus, their blood can be safely donated to people of all blood types.

Sex-Linked Inheritance  **Because the X and Y chromosomes determine sex, the genes located on them show a pattern of inheritance called sex-linkage.** A **sex-linked gene** is a gene located on a sex chromosome. As you might expect, genes on the Y chromosome are found only in males and are passed directly from father to son. Genes located on the X chromosome are found in both sexes, but the fact that men have just one X chromosome leads to some interesting consequences.

For example, humans have three genes responsible for color vision, all located on the X chromosome. In males, a defective allele for any of these genes results in colorblindness, an inability to distinguish certain colors. The most common form, red-green colorblindness, occurs in about 1 in 12 males. Among females, however, colorblindness affects only about 1 in 200. Why is there such a difference? In order for a recessive allele, like colorblindness, to be expressed in females, it must be present in two copies—one on each of the X chromosomes. This means that the recessive phenotype of a sex-linked genetic disorder tends to be much more common among males than among females.

MYSTERY CLUE

The presence of two sickle cell alleles is needed to produce sickle cell disease. Males and females develop sickle cell disease in equal frequencies. What do these statements suggest about the location of the gene responsible for the disorder?

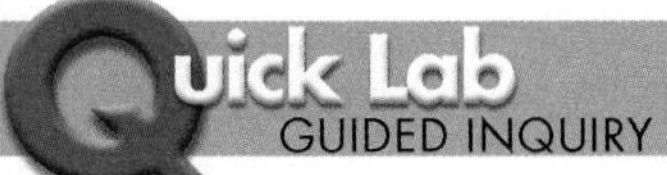

Quick Lab GUIDED INQUIRY

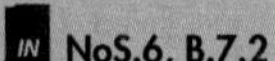
NoS.6, B.7.2

How Is Colorblindness Transmitted?

1. Make a data table with the column headings Trial, Colors, Sex of Individual, and Number of X-Linked Alleles. Draw ten rows under the headings and fill in the numbers 1 through 10 in the Trial column. Label one plastic cup Mother and a second plastic cup Father.
2. The white beans represent X chromosomes. Use a black marker to make a dot on 1 white bean to represent the X-linked allele for colorblindness. Place this bean, plus 1 unmarked white bean, into the cup labeled Mother.
3. Mark a black dot on 1 more white bean. Place this bean, plus 1 red bean, into the cup labeled Father. The red bean represents a Y chromosome.

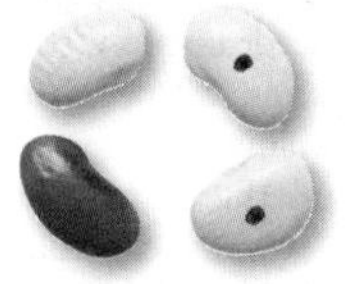

4. Close your eyes and pick one bean from each cup to represent how each parent contributes to a sex chromosome and a fertilized egg.
5. In your data table, record the color of each bean and the sex of an individual who would carry this pair of sex chromosomes. Also record how many X-linked alleles the individual has. Put the beans back in the cups they came from.
6. Determine whether the individual would have colorblindness.
7. Repeat steps 4 to 6 for a total of 10 pairs of beans.

Analyze and Conclude

1. **Draw Conclusions** How do human sex chromosomes keep the numbers of males and females roughly equal?
2. **Calculate** Calculate the class totals for each data column. How many females were colorblind? How many males? Explain these results. MATH
3. **Use Models** Evaluate your model. How accurately does it represent the transmission of colorblindness in a population? Why?

Build Science Skills

Help students explore sex-linked inheritance by examining a specific cross involving colorblindness. Have students construct a Punnett square to show a cross between a father with normal vision and a mother who is a carrier of the colorblindness trait. Tell them to use the symbols X^B to represent the dominant allele on the X chromosome and X^b for the recessive one. Refer them to **Figure 14–2** for help in constructing the cross.

Ask What percent of the children have normal vision? *(75%)*

Ask Are both daughters carriers? Explain. *(No, only one daughter has the X^b allele.)*

DIFFERENTIATED INSTRUCTION

L3 Advanced Students Challenge students to infer whether a trait controlled by a dominant allele on the X chromosome is more common in male offspring. *(A trait controlled by a dominant allele is not more common in males because females, like males, would need to inherit just one dominant allele to have the trait.)* Have students make a Punnett square to show how a sex-linked dominant allele would be passed to offspring.

If students need help answering the question, have them reread the last paragraph under **Sex-Linked Inheritance** and think about the number of alleles needed to cause disease in a sex-linked disease. Guide them to infer that the location of the sickle cell allele is not on a sex chromosome. Students can go online to **Biology.com** to gather their evidence.

PURPOSE Students will model how colorblindness is transmitted and draw conclusions about frequencies of inheritance of the disorder.

MATERIALS 2 plastic cups, black marker, 3 white beans, 1 red bean

PLANNING Remind students to keep their eyes closed while picking the beans so they choose randomly.

ANALYZE AND CONCLUDE

1. Only the father's chromosome will determine sex. The chance is 50/50 a child will receive an X chromosome from the father, and 50/50 a child will receive a Y chromosome from the father.
2. About 50 percent of the females and 50 percent of the males will be colorblind. The mother is heterozygous, which means her sons have a 50 percent chance of inheriting the X chromosome that carries the allele for colorblindness. The father is colorblind, which means the daughters have a 50 percent chance of inheriting an X chromosome from each parent that carries the allele for colorblindness.
3. The model represents only one type of cross within a population. In an actual human population, the ratio of colorblind to non-colorblind people will be much lower, because not all parents carry the allele for colorblindness.

Teach continued

Use Visuals

Use **Figure 14–7** to explain that a pedigree helps trace inheritance patterns by looking at known phenotypes for a single trait. Copy the pedigree on the board. Have volunteers identify what each of the symbols means. Then, walk students through the pedigree. Remind them that the allele for the white forelock trait is dominant, and given this information, have them identify the phenotype and possible genotypes for each individual as you write them beside the appropriate symbols.

Then, ask students to consider the phenotypes as if the allele for the white forelock trait was recessive rather than dominant. Have them point out where the pedigree shows that this is not possible. (*The gene cannot be recessive because if it were, the parents in the second generation who both show the phenotype would be homozygous recessive and could not have a child who shows the opposite phenotype.*) Reinforce that pedigree analysis provides information on the nature of genes and alleles. Ask students to infer a reason for constructing a pedigree chart. (*to trace the inheritance of genetic disorders*)

DIFFERENTIATED INSTRUCTION

L1 Struggling Students For students who are having difficulty understanding how a pedigree can help show how traits are inherited, draw a pedigree showing a wife with a genetic disorder and a husband without it who have a daughter with the disorder and a son without it. Ask students whether they can tell if the trait is controlled by a dominant or a recessive allele. (*no*) Extend the pedigree back one generation by adding two parents without the disorder for the wife. Then, ask the same question. (*The trait must be recessive; otherwise, at least one of the wife's parents would also have the trait.*) Point out that often, the more generations a pedigree has, the more obvious the pattern of inheritance is.

FIGURE 14–6 X-Chromosome Inactivation Female calico cats are tri-colored. The color of spots on their fur is controlled by a gene on the X chromosome. Spots are either orange or black, depending on which X chromosome is inactivated in different patches of their skin.

X-Chromosome Inactivation If just one X chromosome is enough for cells in males, how does the cell "adjust" to the extra X chromosome in female cells? The answer was discovered by the British geneticist Mary Lyon. In female cells, most of the genes in one of the X chromosomes are randomly switched off, forming a dense region in the nucleus known as a Barr body. Barr bodies are generally not found in males because their single X chromosome is still active.

The same process happens in other mammals. In cats, for example, a gene that controls the color of coat spots is located on the X chromosome. One X chromosome may have an allele for orange spots and the other X chromosome may have an allele for black spots. In cells in some parts of the body, one X chromosome is switched off. In other parts of the body, the other X chromosome is switched off. As a result, the cat's fur has a mixture of orange and black spots, like those in **Figure 14–6.** Male cats, which have just one X chromosome, can have spots of only one color. Therefore, if the cat's fur has three colors—white with orange and black spots, for example—you can almost be certain that the cat is female.

In Your Notebook *Write three quiz questions about the transmission of human traits and answer them.*

Human Pedigrees

How can pedigrees be used to analyze human inheritance?

Given the complexities of genetics, how would you go about determining whether a trait is caused by a dominant or recessive allele and whether the gene for that trait is autosomal or sex-linked? The answers, not surprisingly, can be found by applying Mendel's basic principles of genetics.

To analyze the pattern of inheritance followed by a particular trait, you can use a chart that shows the relationships within a family. Such a chart is called a **pedigree.** A pedigree shows the presence or absence of a trait according to the relationships between parents, siblings, and offspring. It can be used for any species, not just humans.

The pedigree in **Figure 14–7** shows how one human trait—a white lock of hair just above the forehead—passes through three generations of a family. The allele for the white forelock trait is dominant. At the top of the chart is a grandfather who had the white forelock trait. Two of his three children inherited the trait. Three grandchildren have the trait, but two do not.

BUILD Vocabulary

WORD ORIGINS The word **pedigree** combines the Latin words *pedem*, meaning "foot," and *gruem*, meaning "crane." A crane is a long-legged waterbird. On old manuscripts, a forked sign resembling a crane's footprint indicated a line of ancestral descent.

BIOLOGY.com Search Lesson 14.1 GO • InterActive Art • Tutor Tube • Data Analysis

UbD Check for Understanding

VISUAL REPRESENTATION

Ask students to work in pairs to construct a pedigree that shows the inheritance of a single recessive allele, starting with the first generation having genotypes *Aa* × *Aa* and producing three children that represent all three genotypes that could result from a heterozygous cross. Then, have students extend the pedigree to show the members of a third generation, who represent the possible genotypes produced if each member of the second generation crossed with a person having the genotype *Aa*. Discuss the resulting pedigree as a class.

ADJUST INSTRUCTION

If students have trouble identifying the genotypes that result from a cross, draw Punnett squares to show the possibilities. If students are confusing symbols and shading, review **Figure 14–7.**

Answers

IN YOUR NOTEBOOK Answers will vary. Check that students have written three questions and that their answers are accurate. Consider having students work in pairs to quiz each other.

A circle represents a female.

A square represents a male.

A horizontal line connecting a male and a female represents a marriage.

A vertical line and a bracket connect the parents to their children.

A circle or square that is not shaded indicates that a person does not express the trait.

A shaded circle or square indicates that a person expresses the trait.

■● = presence of white forelock trait

□○ = no forelock trait

FIGURE 14–7 Pedigree Example This diagram shows what the symbols in a pedigree represent. Interpret Visuals ***What are the genotypes of both parents on the left in the second row? How do you know?***

By analyzing a pedigree, we can often infer the genotypes of family members. For example, because the white forelock trait is dominant, all the family members in **Figure 14–7** lacking this trait must have homozygous recessive alleles. One of the grandfather's children lacks the white forelock trait, so the grandfather must be heterozygous for this trait.

With pedigree analysis, it is possible to apply the principles of Mendelian genetics to humans. **The information gained from pedigree analysis makes it possible to determine the nature of genes and alleles associated with inherited human traits.** Based on a pedigree, you can often determine if an allele for a trait is dominant or recessive, autosomal or sex-linked.

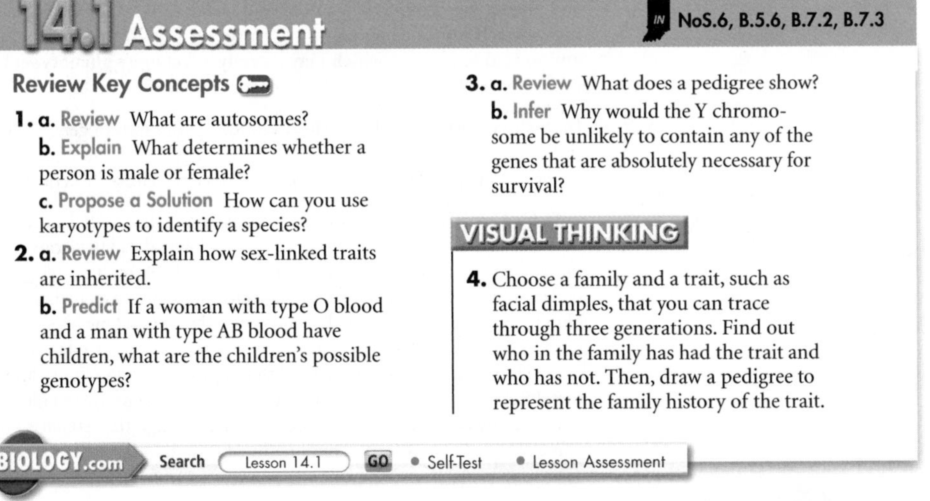

14.1 Assessment

NoS.6, B.5.6, B.7.2, B.7.3

Review Key Concepts

1. a. Review What are autosomes?
   b. Explain What determines whether a person is male or female?
   c. Propose a Solution How can you use karyotypes to identify a species?
2. a. Review Explain how sex-linked traits are inherited.
   b. Predict If a woman with type O blood and a man with type AB blood have children, what are the children's possible genotypes?
3. a. Review What does a pedigree show?
   b. Infer Why would the Y chromosome be unlikely to contain any of the genes that are absolutely necessary for survival?

VISUAL THINKING

4. Choose a family and a trait, such as facial dimples, that you can trace through three generations. Find out who in the family has had the trait and who has not. Then, draw a pedigree to represent the family history of the trait.

BIOLOGY.com Search (Lesson 14.1) GO • Self-Test • Lesson Assessment

BIOLOGY.com Students can interact with a pedigree online in **InterActive Art: Pedigrees.** For more help with pedigrees, access **Tutor Tube: Skipping a Generation.**

Assess and Remediate

EVALUATE UNDERSTANDING

Tell students to make up a word problem about human genetics that can be solved using a Punnett square or a pedigree. Have students solve a partner's word problem. Then, have students complete the 14.1 Assessment.

REMEDIATION SUGGESTION

L1 Struggling Students If students have trouble with **Question 3b,** turn the question around and ask them to assume the Y chromosome has all the genes necessary for survival. Then, have them look at **Figure 14–2.** Ask whether all children receive the Y chromosome. *(no)* Ask what would happen to the children who do not have the Y chromosome. *(They would die.)*

BIOLOGY.com Students can check their understanding of lesson concepts with the **Self-Test** assessment. They can then take an online version of the **Lesson Assessment.**

Answers

FIGURE 14–7 Both are heterozygous, because they have a child with the recessive phenotype who must have received two copies of the recessive allele.

Assessment Answers

1a. Autosomes are chromosomes that are not sex chromosomes.

1b. Females have two X chromosomes; males have one X chromosome and one Y chromosome.

1c. Sample answer: A karyotype shows the complete set of chromosomes in a cell, and they are displayed in order by size. The number and size of chromosomes varies from one species to the next.

2a. A sex-linked trait is controlled by a recessive allele on the X chromosome. Because males have only one X chromosome, they will show the trait when they inherit an X chromosome with the allele. For a female to show the trait, both of her X chromosomes must have the allele for the trait.

2b. $I^{A}i$ and $I^{B}i$

3a. A pedigree shows the presence or absence of a trait over several generations within a family. It can be used to determine inheritance patterns or the possibility of inheritance for a future generation.

3b. A female child would not survive because females do not have a Y chromosome.

VISUAL THINKING

4. If students have difficulty finding a family to use for the pedigree, allow them to make up one. Answers will vary but pedigrees should use the standard pedigree symbols and include a key. Students may choose other traits besides facial dimples, such as having a widow's peak, having attached earlobes, or having a cleft chin.

LESSON 14.2

Getting Started

Objectives

14.2.1 Explain how small changes in DNA cause genetic disorders.

14.2.2 Summarize the problems caused by nondisjunction.

Student Resources

Study Workbooks A and B, 14.2 Worksheets

Spanish Study Workbooks, 14.2 Worksheets

Lab Manual B, 14.2 Data Analysis Worksheet

BIOLOGY.com Lesson Overview • Lesson Notes • Activities: Art in Motion • Assessment: Self-Test, Lesson Assessment

For corresponding lesson in the **Foundation Edition**, see pages 339–341.

Activate Prior Knowledge

Give students one minute to list the different ways mutations can occur, and then ask volunteers to share their list with the class. Lists might include base substitutions, insertions, deletions, and changes in the number or structure of chromosomes. Remind students that most mutations have little or no effect on an organism, but some can result in serious disorders. Invite students to name genetic disorders they have heard about.

IN INDIANA ACADEMIC STANDARDS

For the full text of all standards, see the Course Overview in the front matter of this book.

B.5.4 Explain how the unique shape and activity of each protein is determined by the sequence of its amino acids.

B.5.6 Recognize that traits can be structural, physiological or behavioral and can include readily observable characteristics at the organismal level or less recognizable features at the molecular and cellular level.

B.7.5 Explain and demonstrate how inserting, substituting or deleting segments of a DNA molecule can alter a gene, which is then passed to every cell that develops from it and that the results may be beneficial, harmful or have little or no effect on the organism.

14.2 Human Genetic Disorders

IN **B.1.2** Molecules and cellular processes; **B.5.4** Sequence of amino acids: protein shape and activity; **B.5.5** Roles of proteins; **B.5.6** Types of traits; **B.7.5** Gene alteration. Also covered: **NoS.3, B.5.2.**

Key Questions

How do small changes in DNA molecules affect human traits?

What are the effects of errors in meiosis?

Vocabulary

nondisjunction

Taking Notes

Two-Column Chart Before you read, make a two-column chart. In the first column, write three questions you have about genetic disorders. As you read, fill in answers to your questions in the second column. When you have finished, research the answers to your remaining questions.

THINK ABOUT IT Have you ever heard the expression "It runs in the family"? Relatives or friends might have said that about your smile or the shape of your ears, but what could it mean when they talk of diseases and disorders? What, exactly, is a genetic disorder?

From Molecule to Phenotype

How do small changes in DNA molecules affect human traits?

We know that genes are made of DNA and that they interact with the environment to produce an individual organism's characteristics, or phenotype. However, when a gene fails to work or works improperly, serious problems can result.

Molecular research techniques have shown us a direct link between genotype and phenotype. For example, the wax that sometimes builds up in our ear canals can be one of two forms: wet or dry. People of African and European ancestry are more likely to have wet earwax—the dominant form. Those of Asian or Native American ancestry most often have the dry form, which is recessive. A single DNA base in the gene for a membrane-transport protein is the culprit. A simple base change from guanine (G) to adenine (A) causes this protein to produce dry earwax instead of wet earwax.

The connection between molecule and trait, and between genotype and phenotype, is often that simple, and just as direct. **Changes in a gene's DNA sequence can change proteins by altering their amino acid sequences, which may directly affect one's phenotype.** In other words, there is a molecular basis for genetic disorders.

Disorders Caused by Individual Genes Thousands of genetic disorders are caused by changes in individual genes. These changes often affect specific proteins associated with important cellular functions.

▶ ***Sickle Cell Disease*** This disorder is caused by a defective allele for beta-globin, one of two polypeptides in hemoglobin, the oxygen-carrying protein in red blood cells. The defective polypeptide makes hemoglobin a bit less soluble, causing hemoglobin molecules to stick together when the blood's oxygen level decreases. The molecules clump into long fibers, forcing cells into a distinctive sickle shape, which gives the disorder its name.

Sickle-shaped cells are more rigid than normal red blood cells, and, therefore, they tend to get stuck in the capillaries—the narrowest blood vessels in the body. If the blood stops moving through the capillaries, damage to cells, tissues, and even organs can result.

UbD Teach for Understanding

ENDURING UNDERSTANDING DNA is the universal code for life; it enables an organism to transmit hereditary information and, along with the environment, determines an organism's characteristics.

GUIDING QUESTION What causes some human genetic disorders?

EVIDENCE OF UNDERSTANDING *After completing the lesson, give students the following assessment to show they understand how changes in individual genes can cause disorders.* Have students imagine they are a genetic counselor who must explain to prospective parents how the genes for sickle cell disease, cystic fibrosis, or Huntington's disease are inherited and how they cause disease. Students should choose one disorder and write a summary of what they would say to the parents. The language they use should be conversational and easily understood by people who have no specialized background in genetics.

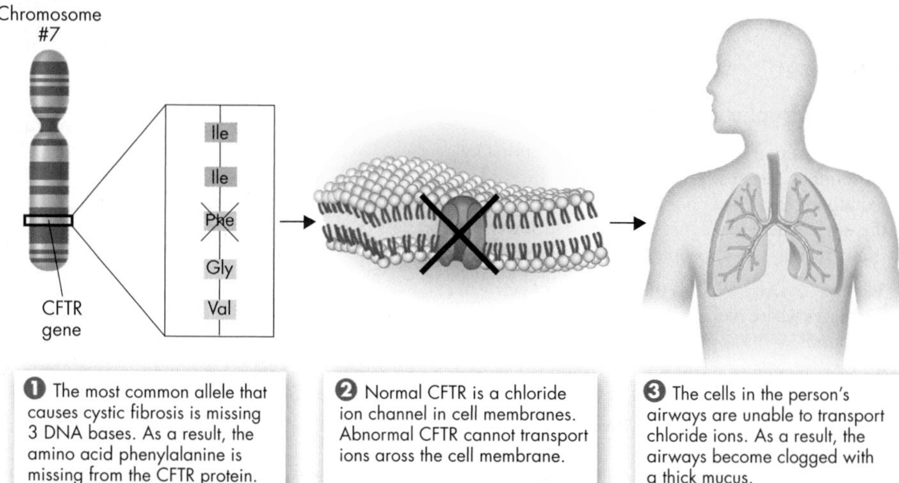

❶ The most common allele that causes cystic fibrosis is missing 3 DNA bases. As a result, the amino acid phenylalanine is missing from the CFTR protein.

❷ Normal CFTR is a chloride ion channel in cell membranes. Abnormal CFTR cannot transport ions aross the cell membrane.

❸ The cells in the person's airways are unable to transport chloride ions. As a result, the airways become clogged with a thick mucus.

▶ ***Cystic Fibrosis*** Known as CF for short, cystic fibrosis is most common among people of European ancestry. CF is caused by a genetic change almost as small as the earwax allele. Most cases result from the deletion of just three bases in the gene for a protein called cystic fibrosis transmembrane conductance regulator (CFTR). CFTR normally allows chloride ions (Cl^-) to pass across cell membranes. The loss of these bases removes a single amino acid—phenylalanine—from CFTR, causing the protein to fold improperly. The misfolded protein is then destroyed. With cell membranes unable to transport chloride ions, tissues throughout the body malfunction.

People with one normal copy of the CF allele are unaffected by CF, because they can produce enough CFTR to allow their cells to work properly. Two copies of the defective allele are needed to produce the disorder, which means the CF allele is recessive. Children with CF have serious digestive problems and produce thick, heavy mucus that clogs their lungs and breathing passageways.

▶ ***Huntington's Disease*** Huntington's disease is caused by a dominant allele for a protein found in brain cells. The allele for this disease contains a long string of bases in which the codon CAG—coding for the amino acid glutamine—repeats over and over again, more than 40 times. Despite intensive study, the reason why these long strings of glutamine cause disease is still not clear. The symptoms of Huntington's disease, namely mental deterioration and uncontrollable movements, usually do not appear until middle age. The greater the number of codon repeats, the earlier the disease appears, and the more severe are its symptoms.

FIGURE 14–8 Mutations Cause Cystic Fibrosis CF is usually caused by the deletion of three bases in the DNA of a single gene. As a result, the body does not produce normal CFTR, a protein needed to transport chloride ions. **Infer** ***Why isn't the cause of CF considered a frameshift mutation?***

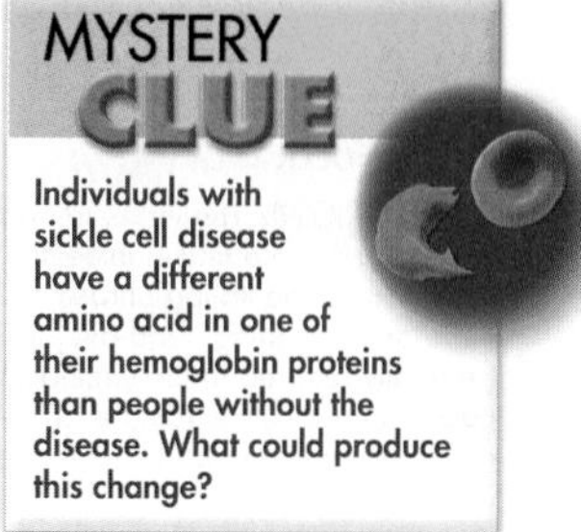

Individuals with sickle cell disease have a different amino acid in one of their hemoglobin proteins than people without the disease. What could produce this change?

Teach

Use Visuals

Walk through **Figure 14–8** with students to help them understand the biochemistry of cystic fibrosis. Discuss how a deletion mutation can affect protein folding. Ask students how protein folding relates to protein function. (*If proteins do not fold properly, they sometimes cannot function.*) Ask students to infer whether chloride ions can cross cell membranes by simply passing through the lipid bilayer without the aid of a protein. (*They must not be able to cross on their own, because a lack of the CFTR proteins results in a disease.*)

DIFFERENTIATED INSTRUCTION

L1 Special Needs Demonstrate how a deletion can cause a protein to not function. Model protein folding by wrapping a long pipe cleaner (representing a polypeptide chain) around a thick marker. Remove the marker so that the pipe-cleaner coils form a tube shape (representing the final folded protein). Demonstrate that the model protein is a functioning ion channel by passing a marble (representing a chloride ion) through the tube. Model the mutation of the protein by folding one of the coils inward so that it blocks the passage of the marble through the tube.

ELL Focus on ELL: Access Content

ALL SPEAKERS Pair beginning and intermediate speakers with advanced or advanced high speakers. Give them a few minutes to preview the lesson, reading the headings and boldface Key Concepts, and looking at the diagrams and maps. Then, ask them to predict what they think they will learn. The pairs should discuss their predictions orally and then record them. Beginning and intermediate speakers may draw pictures or write in words or phrases.

Quick Facts

FOUNDER EFFECT AND HUNTINGTON'S DISEASE

One of the highest known frequencies of Huntington's disease is found in the Afrikaner population of South Africa. Researchers have discovered that the affected persons are descendants of a settler from the Netherlands who arrived there in the 1600s. This phenomenon of one or a few individuals with a genetic abnormality causing the establishment of a new population is known as the founder effect. The founder effect is most likely to occur in remote areas where the total population is relatively small. (The founder effect is discussed in Chapter 17.)

Guide students to understand that a substitution in one or more of the nucleotides that code for an amino acid can cause that codon to code for a different amino acid. Students can go online to **Biology.com** to gather their evidence.

Answers

FIGURE 14–8 Exactly one codon (three nucleotide bases) has been deleted, so the rest of the reading frame has not been affected.

Teach continued

Lead a Discussion

Discuss with students the idea that location and other environmental factors can determine whether an allele is beneficial or harmful for a population. For example, for people who live in areas where malaria is common, a gene pool that contains the sickle cell allele is beneficial. In these areas, the "fittest" people are those with one sickle cell allele.

Ask Why is having no copies or two copies of the abnormal allele a disadvantage? *(The people with two normal alleles are more likely to get malaria, and the ones with two abnormal alleles are more likely to have sickle cell disease.)*

Ask How would displacing members of the population to areas where malaria is not present change whether the allele is a genetic advantage? *(In areas where malaria does not exist, it is no longer an advantage to be a carrier. It is only a disadvantage in that you could have children with the disease.)* Then, have students identify how changes in public sanitation might have changed how a population may or may not benefit from having individuals that carry one CF allele. *(As sanitation improves and typhoid becomes less common, the population benefits less from having the CF allele.)*

DIFFERENTIATED INSTRUCTION

L1 Struggling Students Some students may have difficulty reconciling the evolutionary benefit of protection against malaria with the drawback of a fatal disease. Tell them that about 100,000 people worldwide die annually of sickle cell disease, but malaria kills about 1,500,000. Thus, from a population perspective, the benefit of having the allele outweighs the drawback. Have them speculate how those numbers might change if the sickle cell allele did not exist.

L3 Advanced Students Challenge students to hypothesize how the sickle cell allele became so common among the ancestors of African Americans who lived in central Africa. *(After the mutated allele appeared in the population, those individuals who inherited a copy of that allele were more likely to survive malaria and pass the allele on to their children. Individuals without the allele and individuals with both alleles were more likely to die, either from malaria or from sickle cell disease.)* Have students construct a Punnett square to show the different phenotypes that can result from various pairings of individuals with the different genotypes for the sickle cell trait.

IN NoS.3, B.7.5

The Geography of Malaria

Malaria is a potentially fatal disease transmitted by mosquitoes. Its cause is a parasite that lives inside red blood cells. The upper map shows the parts of the world where malaria is common. The lower map shows regions where people have the sickle cell allele.

1. Analyze Data What is the relationship between the places where malaria and the sickle cell allele are found?

2. Infer In 1805, a Scottish explorer named Mungo Park led an expedition of European geographers to find the source of the Niger River in Africa. The journey began with a party of 45 Europeans. During the expedition, most of these men perished from malaria. Why do you think their native African guides survived?

3. Form a Hypothesis As the map shows, the sickle cell allele is not found in African populations that are native to southern Africa. Propose an explanation for this discrepancy.

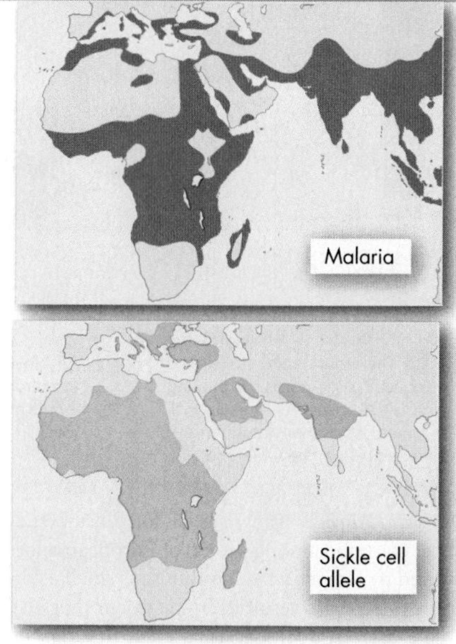

Genetic Advantages Disorders such as sickle cell disease and CF are still common in human populations. In the United States, the sickle cell allele is carried by approximately 1 person in 12 of African ancestry, and the CF allele is carried by roughly 1 person in 25 of European ancestry. Why are these alleles still around if they can be fatal for those who carry them? The answers may surprise you.

Most African Americans today are descended from populations that originally lived in west central Africa, where malaria is common. Malaria is a mosquito-borne infection caused by a parasite that lives inside red blood cells. Individuals with just one copy of the sickle cell allele are generally healthy and are also highly resistant to the parasite. This resistance gives them a great advantage against malaria, which even today claims more than a million lives every year.

More than 1000 years ago, the cities of medieval Europe were ravaged by epidemics of typhoid fever. Typhoid is caused by a bacterium that enters the body through cells in the digestive system. The protein produced by the CF allele helps block the entry of this bacterium. Individuals heterozygous for CF would have had an advantage when living in cities with poor sanitation and polluted water, and—because they also carried a normal allele—these individuals would not have suffered from cystic fibrosis.

BUILD Vocabulary

WORD ORIGINS The term *malaria* was coined in the mid-eighteenth century from the Italian phrase, *mala aria*, meaning "bad air." It originally referred to the unpleasant odors caused by the release of marsh gases, to which the disease was initially attributed.

PURPOSE Students will analyze map data to understand the relationship between sickle cell disease and malaria.

PLANNING Remind students that the sickle cell allele is beneficial in heterozygous persons because it confers resistance to malaria.

ANSWERS

1. The areas where malaria is common and the areas where people have the sickle cell allele overlap.
2. They likely carried one allele for the sickle cell trait, so they were healthy and highly resistant to malaria.
3. Malaria is not common in southern Africa, so people who carry the sickle cell allele would not have a reproductive advantage over people who do not carry the sickle cell allele.

Chromosomal Disorders

What are the effects of errors in meiosis?

Most of the time, the process of meiosis works perfectly and each human gamete gets exactly 23 chromosomes. Every now and then, however, something goes wrong. The most common error in meiosis occurs when homologous chromosomes fail to separate. This mistake is known as **nondisjunction,** which means "not coming apart." **Figure 14–9** illustrates the process.

If nondisjunction occurs during meiosis, gametes with an abnormal number of chromosomes may result, leading to a disorder of chromosome numbers. For example, if two copies of an autosomal chromosome fail to separate during meiosis, an individual may be born with three copies of that chromosome. This condition is known as a trisomy, meaning "three bodies." The most common form of trisomy, involving three copies of chromosome 21, is Down syndrome, which is often characterized by mild to severe mental retardation and a high frequency of certain birth defects.

Nondisjunction of the X chromosomes can lead to a disorder known as Turner's syndrome. A female with Turner's syndrome usually inherits only one X chromosome. Women with Turner's syndrome are sterile, which means that they are unable to reproduce. Their sex organs do not develop properly at puberty.

In males, nondisjunction may cause Klinefelter's syndrome, resulting from the inheritance of an extra X chromosome, which interferes with meiosis and usually prevents these individuals from reproducing. There have been no reported instances of babies being born without an X chromosome, indicating that this chromosome contains genes that are vital for the survival and development of the embryo.

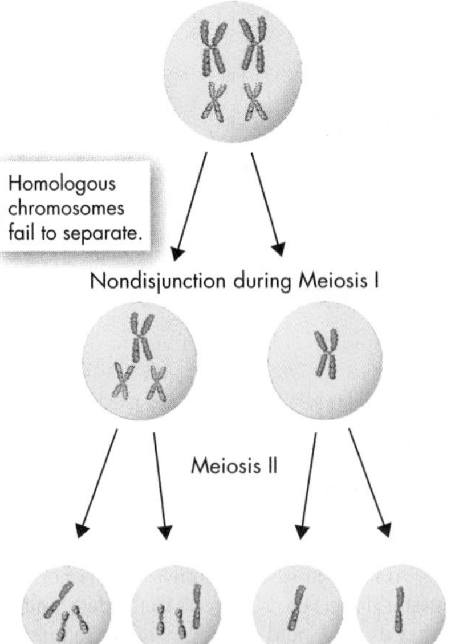

FIGURE 14–9 Nondisjunction This failure of meiosis causes gametes to have an abnormal number of chromosomes. Apply Concepts ***Which phase of meiosis is shown in the first cell?***

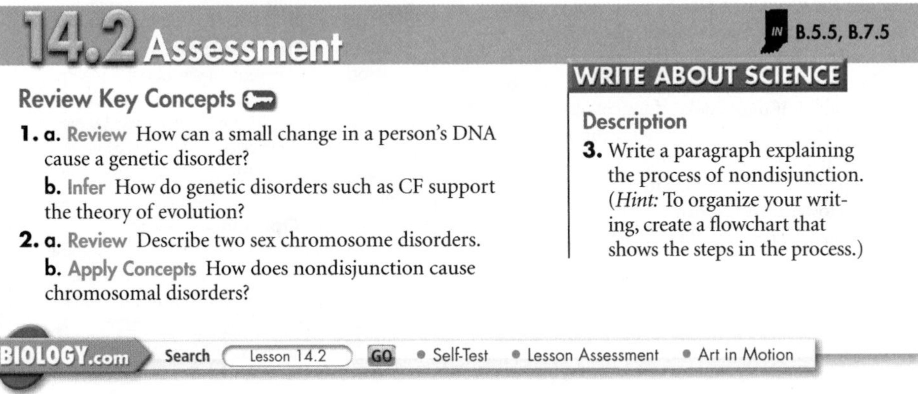

14.2 Assessment

B.5.5, B.7.5

Review Key Concepts

1. **a.** Review How can a small change in a person's DNA cause a genetic disorder?
   b. Infer How do genetic disorders such as CF support the theory of evolution?
2. **a.** Review Describe two sex chromosome disorders.
   b. Apply Concepts How does nondisjunction cause chromosomal disorders?

WRITE ABOUT SCIENCE

Description

3. Write a paragraph explaining the process of nondisjunction. (*Hint:* To organize your writing, create a flowchart that shows the steps in the process.)

BIOLOGY.com Search Lesson 14.2 GO • Self-Test • Lesson Assessment • Art in Motion

Assessment Answers

1a. It can affect the structure and function of a protein, which may cause a disorder.

1b. Sample answer: People with one CF allele have an advantage of being less likely to contract typhoid fever. This helped them survive and pass the trait to their offspring.

2a. A female with Turner's syndrome has only one X chromosome, and is sterile. A male with Klinefelter's syndrome has one or more extra X chromosomes and is usually sterile.

2b. Chromosomes fail to separate, causing gametes to have abnormal numbers of chromosomes.

WRITE ABOUT SCIENCE

3. Paragraphs should explain how a pair of homologous chromosomes can fail to separate during anaphase I or how a pair of chromatids can fail to separate during anaphase II.

Use Visuals

Walk through the two different divisions of meiosis shown in **Figure 14–9** to explain how nondisjunction occurs. If necessary, review meiosis so students remember that in meiosis I, homologous chromosomes separate to produce a haploid cell and in meiosis II, sister chromatids separate.

Ask How could Down syndrome result from the type of nondisjunction shown in the figure? (*Down syndrome could result if one of the two cells on the left met up with a normal sex cell and the resulting individual had a trisomy for chromosome 21.*) Relate **Figure 14–9** to **Figure 14–1** by having students draw a human karyotype for a person with Down syndrome.

DIFFERENTIATED INSTRUCTION

L1 Struggling Students Ask students to look at **Figure 14–1.** Point out that in the trisomy resulting in Down syndrome, the karyotype would show three chromosomes at the 21 position.

BIOLOGY.com Students can watch **Art in Motion: Nondisjunction Disorders** to see how nondisjunction occurs during meiosis.

Assess and Remediate

EVALUATE UNDERSTANDING

Have students make a **Compare/Contrast Table** of sickle-cell disease, cystic fibrosis, and Huntington's disease. Each column should represent a disease, and each row should represent one of the following characteristics: Cause, Effect, and Protein/Amino Acid Affected. Then, have them complete the 14.2 Assessment.

Study Wkbks A/B, Appendix S20, Compare/Contrast Table. **Transparencies,** GO3.

REMEDIATION SUGGESTION

L1 Struggling Students If students have trouble with **Question 3,** have them make a diagram that shows the steps in meiosis I and II when the processes occur normally.

BIOLOGY.com Students can check their understanding of lesson concepts with the **Self-Test** assessment. They can then take an online version of the **Lesson Assessment.**

Answers

FIGURE 14–9 The first cell shows metaphase I.

Teach

Lead a Discussion

Have students read the feature. Then, explain that all citizens, not just scientists, need to have some knowledge of the human genome because the way data from genetic testing are used can affect everyone. Point out that they may be called upon as voters or jurors to decide on issues or cases related to access of data from genetic testing.

Divide the class into small groups, and have students discuss their viewpoints on regulating genetic data. One member of each group should record the group's positions. Then, tell each group to devise a set of guidelines for the use of genetic data. Have each group share with the class its guidelines and the reasoning behind them.

Biology & Society

Are Laws Protecting Genetic Privacy Necessary?

The rapid development of new tools and techniques to analyze DNA makes it possible to test for alleles related to thousands of medical conditions. In theory, the results of genetic testing should benefit everyone. Accurate genetic data helps physicians select the proper treatments for patients. It may allow people with genes that place them at risk of certain conditions to minimize those risks.

At issue, however, is individual privacy. Once a test is done, who has access to the data, and how can they use it? Could employers refuse to hire people who might drive up their medical costs? Might insurance companies refuse to renew the policies of individuals with genes for certain disorders? These are not hypothetical questions. In 2005, managers of a professional basketball team asked one of its players to be tested for a gene linked to heart ailments. When he refused, they traded the player to another team. Dr. Francis Collins, director of the National Human Genome Research Institute, worries that "the public is afraid of taking advantage of genetic testing." Is he correct? Should genetic data be protected by law, or should it be open to public view?

The Viewpoints

Genetic Privacy Does Not Need Legal Protection
Other laws already protect individuals from discrimination on the basis of medical disability. Employers and insurance companies are nonetheless allowed to ask individuals if they smoke, use alcohol, or have a history of medical problems. Having this information allows employers to make intelligent choices about whom to hire. It also helps insurance companies maintain lower rates for their healthiest clients. Free access to genetic data should be a public right.

Many commercial laboratories test human DNA for genetic disorders.

Genetic Privacy Should Be Protected by Law
The Genetic Information Nondiscrimination Act (GINA) went into effect in 2009, and it provides important protections to personal privacy. Individuals may not take advantage of today's advances in genetic medicine if they fear their personal information might be used to deny them employment or insurance. We need such laws to realize the full benefits of modern medicine and to protect otherwise healthy individuals from genetic discrimination.

Research and Decide

1. Analyze the Viewpoints To make an informed decision, learn more about genetic testing by consulting library or Internet resources. Then, list the key arguments expressed by the proponents and critics of both points of view. Find out if laws preventing genetic discrimination have been proposed or passed in your state.

2. Form an Opinion Should access and use of genetic data be regulated? Weigh both sides of the issue. Who will benefit from the sharing of genetic data? Will anyone suffer? Do some arguments outweigh others? If so, which ones? Explain your answers.

Answers

1. Answers will vary. Check that students have investigated state laws regarding genetic discrimination. Sample answer: Proponents argue that genetic testing could lead to treatment of a health condition before symptoms appear. Critics argue that genetic testing could prevent some people from getting health insurance.
2. Accept all reasonable answers. Opinions should include reasonable explanations.

Quick Facts

GENETIC DISCRIMINATION

Genetic discrimination is treating people differently because they are found to have differences in their DNA that increase their risk of developing a certain disease or disorder. For some diseases, such as diabetes or Alzheimer's disease, a genetic predisposition for a disease does not mean the person will develop the disease, only that the risk is greater. Anti-genetic-discrimination legislation aims to prevent these people from being treated differently than other healthy individuals. The Genetic Information Nondiscrimination Act (GINA) prohibits genetic discrimination by health insurers and employers. However, GINA does not protect against discrimination from insurers of life, disability, and long-term care policies.

14.3 Studying the Human Genome

NoS.10 Scientific discoveries and new technologies. Also covered: NoS.6.

THINK ABOUT IT Just a few decades ago, computers were gigantic machines found only in laboratories and universities. Today, many of us carry small, powerful computers to school and work every day. Decades ago, the human genome was unknown. Today, we can see our entire genome on the Internet. How long will it be before having a copy of your own genome is as ordinary as carrying a cellphone in your pocket?

Manipulating DNA

What techniques are used to study human DNA?

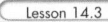

Since discovering the genetic code, biologists have dreamed of a time when they could read the DNA sequences in the human genome. For a long time, it seemed impossible. DNA is a huge molecule—even the smallest human chromosome contains nearly 50 million base pairs. Manipulating such large molecules is extremely difficult. In the late 1960s, however, scientists found they could use natural enzymes in DNA analysis. From this discovery came many useful tools. **By using tools that cut, separate, and then replicate DNA base by base, scientists can now read the base sequences in DNA from any cell.** Such techniques have revolutionized genetic studies of living organisms, including humans.

Cutting DNA Nucleic acids are chemically different from other macromolecules such as proteins and carbohydrates. This difference makes DNA relatively easy to extract from cells and tissues. However, DNA molecules from most organisms are much too large to be analyzed, so they must first be cut into smaller pieces. Many bacteria produce enzymes that do exactly that. Known as **restriction enzymes,** these highly specific substances cut even the largest DNA molecule into precise pieces, called restriction fragments, that are several hundred bases in length. Of the hundreds of known restriction enzymes, each cuts DNA at a different sequence of nucleotides.

In Your Notebook *Make a flowchart that shows the processes scientists use to analyze DNA.*

Key Questions

What techniques are used to study human DNA?

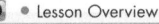

What were the goals of the Human Genome Project, and what have we learned so far?

Vocabulary

restriction enzyme
gel electrophoresis
bioinformatics
genomics

Taking Notes

Preview Visuals Before you read, look at **Figure 14–10,** and write down three questions you have about the figure. As you read, find answers to your questions.

Getting Started

Objectives

14.3.1 Summarize the methods of DNA analysis.

14.3.2 State the goals of the Human Genome Project and explain what we have learned so far.

Student Resources

Study Workbooks A and B, 14.3 Worksheets

Spanish Study Workbook, 14.3 Worksheets

Lab Manual B, 14.3 Hands-On Activity Worksheet

BIOLOGY.com Lesson Overview • Lesson Notes • Assessment: Self-Test, Lesson Assessment

For corresponding lesson in the **Foundation Edition**, see pages 342–345.

Build Background

Show students a thick telephone directory and say how many pages are in it. Tell them the number of pages needed to hold the equivalent of the DNA sequence in the human genome is 200,000. Emphasize that every cell in the body contains a copy of this information encoded in the DNA base pairs.

Answers

IN YOUR NOTEBOOK The main processes should include cutting, separating, and reading DNA. Sample answer: DNA molecules are cut into small pieces → DNA pieces are separated by gel electrophoresis → DNA pieces are sequenced

IN INDIANA ACADEMIC STANDARDS

For the full text of all standards, see the Course Overview in the front matter of this book.

NoS.10 Describe how scientific discoveries lead to the development of new technologies, and conversely how technological advances can lead to scientific discoveries through new experimental methods and equipment.

UbD Teach for Understanding

ENDURING UNDERSTANDING DNA is the universal code for life; it enables an organism to transmit hereditary information and, along with the environment, determines an organism's characteristics.

GUIDING QUESTION How do we study the human genome, and what have we learned so far?

EVIDENCE OF UNDERSTANDING *After completing the lesson, give students the following assessment to show they understand the principles behind the techniques biologists use to study DNA.* Have students work in small groups to develop an analogy for the manipulation and study of the human genome. For example, they might compare DNA to a language with a four-letter alphabet and describe sequencing the DNA molecule in terms of using a software program with search and editing functions. Have each group share its analogy with the class and explain the comparison.

Teach

VISUAL SUMMARY

Use **Figure 14–10** to walk students through the steps of manipulating DNA. Provide a visual comparison for each step of the process to help students understand what is happening on the molecular level. Explain that in the first step, restriction enzymes are used like "pinking shears" to cut a DNA molecule so that its tab-shaped cut ends can be matched up exactly with other ends that have been cut by the same "shears."

In the second step, the DNA fragments are run through gel electrophoresis. Tell them to imagine that the gel is like a yard of grass and the DNA fragments are like leaves of different sizes. When a leaf blower blows the leaves across the grass, the smaller, lighter-weight ones are able to tumble faster and farther than the larger, heavier leaves.

Ask In the yard analogy, what does the wind from the leaf blower represent? *(the electric current that draws the DNA strands across the gel)*

Encourage students to come up with a third visual comparison or expand upon the first two for the final step of manipulating DNA.

DIFFERENTIATED INSTRUCTION

LPR **Less Proficient Readers** Have students make their own labeled drawings of the steps involved in manipulating DNA. Ask them to write in their own words what is happening in each step.

ELL Focus On ELL: Extend Language

ALL SPEAKERS Give students practice using gene sequencing terminology by providing **Cloze Prompts.** Distribute a modified paragraph that describes the steps shown in **Figure 14–10** but leaves some strategic words blank. An example is "The enzyme that copies DNA is _____." *(DNA polymerase)* Provide a word bank for beginning speakers. For intermediate speakers, omit the word bank. Advanced and advanced high speakers can make up their own sentences and then switch with another student to fill in the blanks.

Study Wkbks A/B, Appendix S2, Cloze Prompts.

Cutting DNA
A restriction enzyme is like a key that fits only one lock. The *Eco*RI restriction enzyme can only recognize the base sequence GAATTC. It cuts each strand of DNA between the G and A bases, leaving single-stranded overhangs with the sequence AATT. The overhangs are called "sticky ends" because they can bond, or "stick," to a DNA fragment with the complementary base sequence.

Separating DNA
Gel electrophoresis is used to separate DNA fragments. After being cut by restriction enzymes, the fragments are put into wells on a gel that is similar to a slice of gelatin. An electric voltage moves them across the gel. Shorter fragments move faster than longer fragments. Within an hour or two, the fragments all separate, each appearing as a band on the gel.

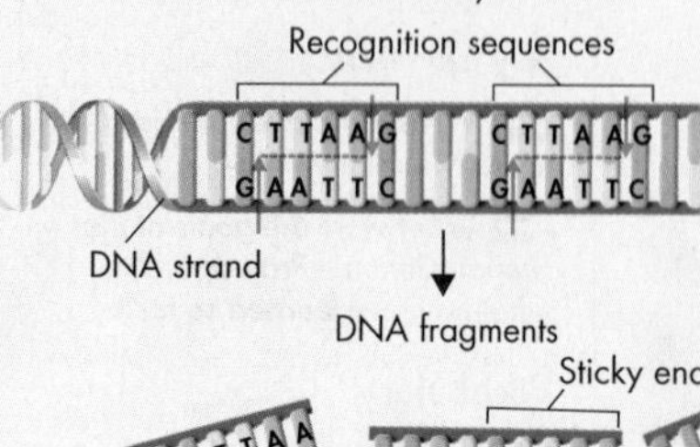

VISUAL SUMMARY

HOW SCIENTISTS MANIPULATE DNA

FIGURE 14–10 By using tools that cut, separate, and replicate DNA, scientists can read the base sequences in DNA from any cell. Knowing the sequence of an organism's DNA allows us to study specific genes.

Separating DNA Once DNA has been cut by restriction enzymes, scientists can use a technique known as **gel electrophoresis** to separate and analyze the differently sized fragments. **Figure 14–10** illustrates this simple, yet effective, method. A mixture of DNA fragments is placed at one end of a porous gel. When an electric voltage is applied to the gel, DNA molecules—which are negatively charged—move toward the positive end of the gel. The smaller the DNA fragment, the faster and farther it moves. The result is a pattern of bands based on fragment size. Specific stains that bind to DNA make these bands visible. Researchers can then remove individual restriction fragments from the gel and study them further.

Reading DNA After the DNA fragments have been separated, researchers use a clever chemical "trick" to read, or sequence, them. The single-stranded DNA fragments are placed in a test tube containing DNA polymerase—the enzyme that copies DNA—along with the four nucleotide bases, A, T, G, and C. As the enzyme goes to work, it uses the unknown strand as a template to make one new DNA strand after another. The tricky part is that researchers also add a small number of bases that have a chemical dye attached. Each time a dye-labeled base is added to a new DNA strand, the synthesis of that strand stops. When DNA synthesis is completed, the result is a series of color-coded DNA fragments of different lengths. Researchers can then separate these fragments, often by gel electrophoresis. The order of colored bands on the gel tells the exact sequence of bases in the DNA. The entire process can be automated and controlled by computers, so that DNA sequencing machines can read thousands of bases in a matter of seconds.

UbD Check for Understanding

HAND SIGNALS

Present students with the following questions and ask them to show a thumbs-up sign if they can answer the question, a thumbs-down sign if they definitely cannot, or a waving-hand sign if they are not sure.

- Why are restriction enzymes used to cut DNA?
- How do DNA fragments separate from each other in an electrophoresis gel?
- Why is DNA polymerase used in sequencing DNA?

ADJUST INSTRUCTION

If students showed a thumbs-down or waving-hand sign for any questions, pair students and have them reread the text on this and the previous page and study **Figure 14–10.** Give student pairs a few minutes to discuss the answers.

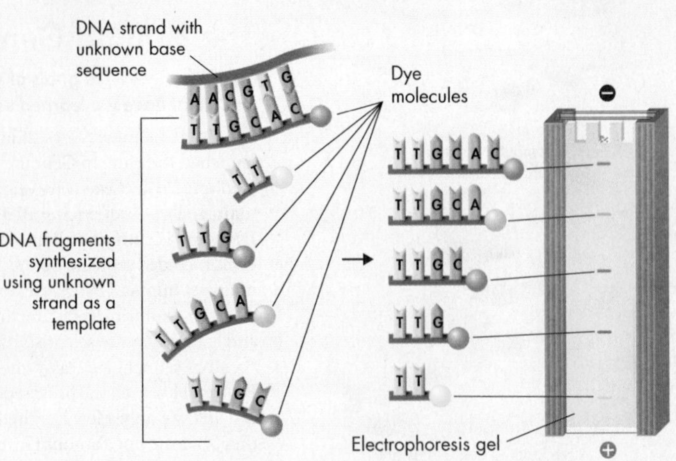

Reading DNA A small proportion of dye-labeled nucleotides are used to make a complementary DNA strand. Each time a labeled nucleotide is added to the strand, DNA replication stops. Because each base was labeled with a different color, the result is color-coded DNA fragments of different lengths. When gel electrophoresis is used to separate the fragments, scientists can "read" the DNA sequence directly from the gel.

Base sequence as "read" from the order of the bands on the gel from bottom to top: **T G C A C**

Quick Lab
GUIDED INQUIRY

NoS.6

Modeling Restriction Enzymes

1. Write a 50-base, double-stranded DNA sequence using the bases A, C, G, and T in random order. Include each sequence shown below at least once in the sequence you write.
2. Make three copies of your double-stranded sequence on three different-colored strips of paper.
3. Use the drawings below to see how the restriction enzyme *Eco*RI would cut your DNA sequence. Use scissors to cut one copy of the sequence as *Eco*RI would.

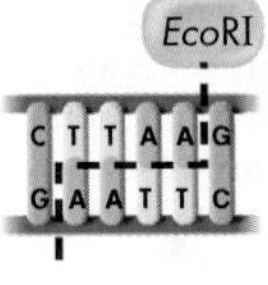

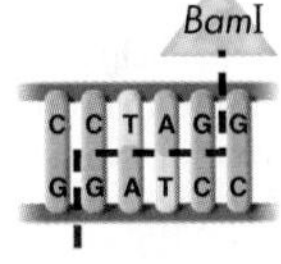

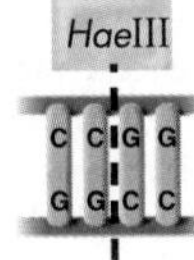

4. Use the procedure in Step 3 to cut apart another copy of your sequence as the restriction enzyme *Bam*I would. Then, cut the third copy as the restriction enzyme *Hae*III would.
5. Tape the single-stranded end of one of your DNA fragments to a complementary, single-stranded end of a classmate's fragment. This will form a single, double-stranded DNA molecule.

Analyze and Conclude

1. **Observe** Which restriction enzyme produced the most pieces? The fewest pieces?
2. **Evaluate** How well did your model represent the actual process of using restriction enzymes to cut DNA? (*Hint:* Contrast the length of your model DNA sequence to the actual length of a DNA molecule.)

Quick Lab

PURPOSE Students will model how restriction enzymes cut DNA.

MATERIALS construction paper, scissors, transparent tape

PLANNING To increase the chance of students finding a matching cut site, provide them with several additional 50-base sequences that include one or more cut sites.

ANALYZE AND CONCLUDE

1. Answers will vary.
2. Sample answer: The model well represents the action of restriction enzymes and the "sticky ends" they create, but the number of fragments produced is much smaller than would be produced by a DNA molecule.

Lead a Discussion

Discuss as a class how scientists read DNA. Have students read the annotation and study the illustration in **Figure 14–10.** Using a short nucleotide sequence of five bases, draw a more complete diagram of the process on the board. In your drawing, emphasize the large numbers of each kind of molecule present in the replication mixture. Make sure students realize that there are several copies of the original DNA strand in the test tube. Show them that all four nucleotides required to form the complementary strand are in the test tube as well. However, only a small percentage of them are marked with the chemical dye. Reinforce that a complementary sequence of every length, from one nucleotide to the complete sequence, is produced in the replication reaction.

DIFFERENTIATED INSTRUCTION

L1 Special Needs Check for understanding by asking questions such as "Why are four different colors used?" *(There are four different bases.)* and "Why do the fragments line up from bottom to top in size?" *(The smaller pieces are moving faster toward the positive end of the gel.)* Then, have students model the sequencing of DNA using crafts materials, such as yarn, beads, and color construction paper.

L3 Advanced Students Challenge students to explain how a power source is set up to create a circuit with a current that moves the DNA molecules across the gel during the sequencing process. *(The power source has positive and negative electrodes connected to either end of the gel. The positive electrode is attached on the end away from the wells so that the negatively charged DNA moves toward it.)* Have them make a sketch of a power setup with labels of all charges and arrows to indicate how the fragments move.

Teach continued

Use Models

Review the steps in shotgun sequencing shown in **Figure 14–11.** Explain that the term *shotgun sequencing* is an analogy to the random pattern that shot makes when fired from a shotgun. Then, model shotgun sequencing with the following activity. Tell students that they will be identifying the sequence of an unknown strand of DNA using fragments of identical strands. The unknown strand has 28 base pairs, and there are four known markers found in the following order on the strand: **GTAC, TTT, CCCC,** and **TCTG.**

Have students copy the following six fragments of the DNA strand onto separate strips of paper: TA**CCCC**CCAA, **TAC**A**TTT,** A**TTT**A**CCCC**, CAAT**TCT-GCCG,** G**GTAC**A, **TCTG**CCGGG. Then, tell them to work together to match up the markers using shotgun sequencing to determine the sequence of the unknown DNA strand. *(The solution: G**GTAC**A**TTT**A**CCCC**CCAAT**TCTG**CCGGG)*

Ask What problem did scientists solve by using shotgun sequencing? *(Sample answer: The human genome is so large that sequencing only a few hundred nucleotides at a time would take a very long time. Shotgun sequencing shortened the task of sequencing all three billion base pairs of DNA.)*

DIFFERENTIATED INSTRUCTION

L1 Special Needs Model shotgun sequencing as above, only use strips of paper with colored dots or stickers, pieced fabric of differing textures or color, or lengths of colored yarn.

ELL English Language Learners Have students incorporate the information about sequencing base pairs and identifying genes into a **Main Ideas and Details Chart.** Encourage them to use their own words. Beginning and intermediate speakers may use single words or short phrases. *(Sample answer: Main Idea—shotgun sequencing; Details—cut DNA; sort DNA, etc.)* Advanced and advanced high speakers should use complete sentences.

Study Wkbks A/B, Appendix S28, Main Ideas and Details Chart, **Transparencies,** GO13.

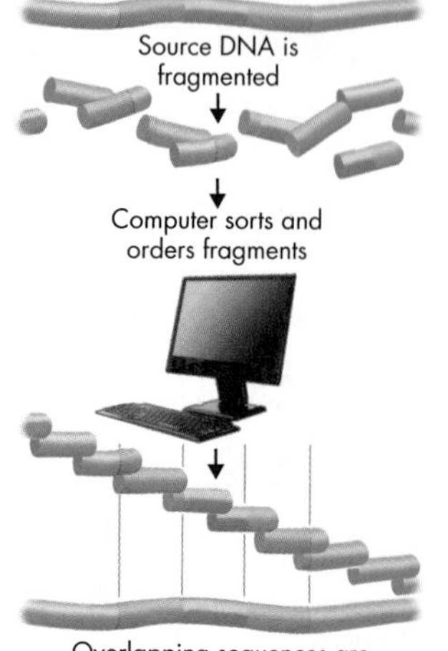

FIGURE 14–11 Shotgun Sequencing This method rapidly sorts DNA fragments by overlapping base sequences.

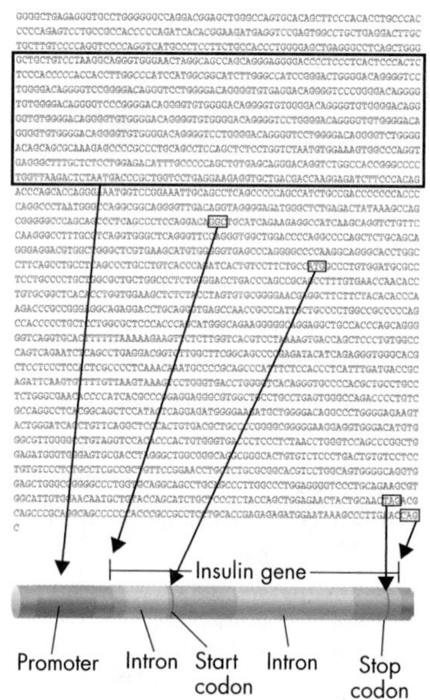

FIGURE 14–12 Locating a Gene A typical gene, such as that for insulin, has several DNA sequences that can serve as locators. These include the promoter, sequences between introns and exons, and start and stop codons.

The Human Genome Project

What were the goals of the Human Genome Project, and what have we learned so far?

In 1990, the United States, along with several other countries, launched the Human Genome Project. **The Human Genome Project was a 13-year, international effort with the main goals of sequencing all 3 billion base pairs of human DNA and identifying all human genes.** Other important goals included sequencing the genomes of model organisms to interpret human DNA, developing technology to support the research, exploring gene functions, studying human variation, and training future scientists.

DNA sequencing was at the center of the Human Genome Project. However, the basic sequencing method you saw earlier can analyze only a few hundred nucleotides at a time. How, then, can the huge amount of DNA in the human genome be sequenced quickly? First, researchers must break up the entire genome into manageable pieces. By determining the base sequences in widely separated regions of a DNA strand, they can use the regions as markers, not unlike the mile markers along a road that is thousands of miles long. The markers make it possible for researchers to locate and return to specific locations in the DNA.

Sequencing and Identifying Genes Once researchers have marked the DNA strands, they can use the technique of "shotgun sequencing." This rapid sequencing method involves cutting DNA into random fragments, then determining the base sequence in each fragment. Computer programs take the sequencing data, find areas of overlap between fragments, and put the fragments together by linking the overlapping areas. The computers then align these fragments relative to the known markers on each chromosome, as shown in **Figure 14–11.** The entire process is like putting a jigsaw puzzle together, but instead of matching shapes, the computer matches DNA base sequences.

Reading the DNA sequence of a genome is not the same as understanding it. Much of today's research explores the vast amount of data from the Human Genome Project to look for genes and the DNA sequences that control them. By locating sequences known to be promoters—binding sites for RNA polymerase—scientists can identify many genes. Shortly after a promoter, there is usually an area called an open reading frame, which is a sequence of DNA bases that will produce an mRNA sequence. Other sites that help to identify genes are the sequences that separate introns from exons, and stop codons located at the ends of open reading frames. **Figure 14–12** shows these sites on a typical gene.

UbD Check for Understanding

QUESTION BOX

Establish a question box or an email address where students may submit questions about DNA manipulation or the Human Genome Project. Encourage students who are uncomfortable admitting publicly that they do not understand a concept to submit their questions anonymously.

ADJUST INSTRUCTION

Address questions by posting questions and answers on a bulletin board, calling on volunteers in a class discussion, or by sending out a weekly email to the class. Identify where students might find answers to their questions in the textbook, at the library, or through online resources.

Comparing Sequences If you were to compare the genomes of two unrelated individuals, you would find that most—but not all—of their DNA matches base-for-base with each other. On average, one base in 1200 will not match between two individuals. Biologists call these single base differences SNPs (pronounced "snips"), which stands for single nucleotide polymorphisms. Researchers have discovered that certain sets of closely linked SNPs occur together time and time again. These collections of linked SNPs are called haplotypes—short for haploid genotypes. To locate and identify as many haplotypes in the human population as possible, the International HapMap Project began in 2002. The aim of the project is to give scientists a rapid way to identify haplotypes associated with various diseases and conditions and to pave the way to more effective life-saving medical care in the future.

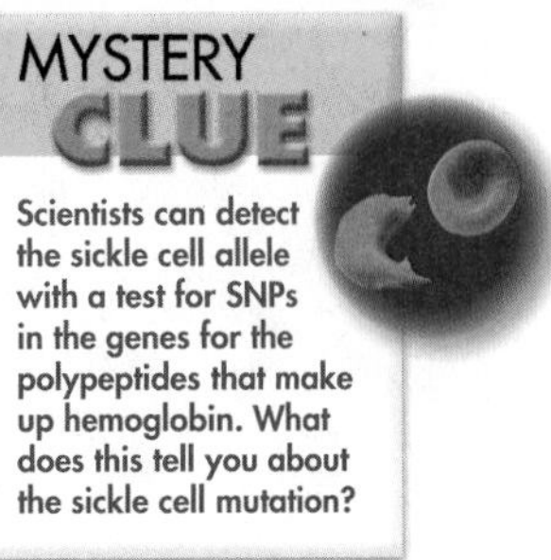

Scientists can detect the sickle cell allele with a test for SNPs in the genes for the polypeptides that make up hemoglobin. What does this tell you about the sickle cell mutation?

Sharing Data The Human Genome Project was completed in 2003. Copies of the human genome DNA sequence, and those of many other organisms, are now freely available on the Internet. Online computer access enables researchers and students to browse through databases of human DNA and study its sequence. More data from the human genome, and the genomes of other organisms, are added to these databases every day.

One of the key research areas of the Human Genome Project was a new field of study called **bioinformatics.** The root word, *informatics,* refers to the creation, development, and operation of databases and other computing tools to collect, organize, and interpret data. The prefix *bio-* refers to life sciences—specifically, molecular biology. Assembling the bits and pieces of the human genome would have been impossible without sophisticated computer programs that could recognize overlapping sequences and place them in the proper order, or immense databases where such information could be stored and retrieved. Without the tools of bioinformatics shown in **Figure 14–13,** the wealth of information gleaned from the Human Genome Project would hardly be useful. Bioinformatics also launched a more specialized field of study known as **genomics**—the study of whole genomes, including genes and their functions.

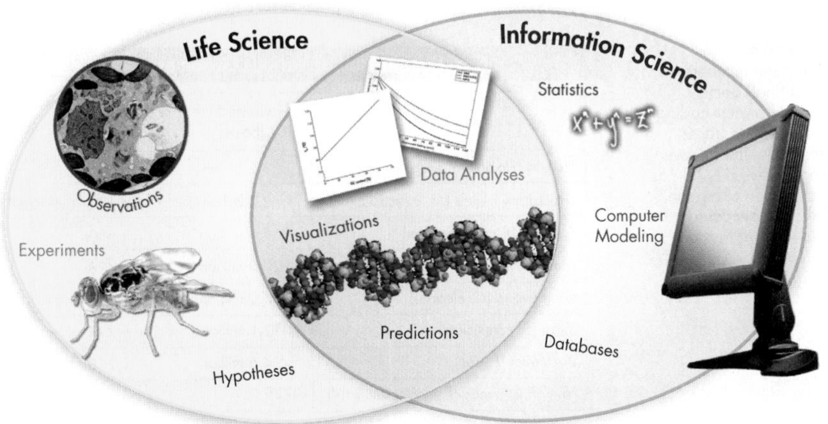

FIGURE 14–13 Bioinformatics Bioinformatics is a new field that combines molecular biology with information science. It is critical to studying and understanding the human genome.

Build Reading Skills

Help students understand the content under the green heading, **The Human Genome Project,** by summarizing the main ideas and supporting details. Model how to do this using the paragraph with the blue heading, **Comparing Sequences.** Explain that they should first carefully read the paragraph and identify the main idea in their own words—for example, "When comparing two unrelated people's genomes, small differences in the sequence can tell scientists a lot about the individuals."

Next, they should identify important supporting details—for example, "SNPs are single base differences between two unrelated individuals," "A haplotype is a collection of linked SNPs," and "The HapMap project helps scientists identify haplotypes associated with various diseases." Direct students to repeat this process for each paragraph in the section. Remind them to focus on the most important concepts, omitting minor details and examples.

DIFFERENTIATED INSTRUCTION

L1 **Struggling Students** Have students work in pairs to create an outline that summarizes the concepts under the green heading, **The Human Genome Project.** Explain that a good way to start an outline is to use the headings themselves as the framework. Tell students that they can also use Key Concept statements, highlighted vocabulary terms, and figure titles as guides for determining the important concepts. Have them refer back to their outlines when completing the lesson assessment.

If students need help answering the question, have them reread **Comparing Sequences** and identify the characteristics of a haplotype. Then, guide them to use this information to infer that the sickle cell mutation affects the formation of the protein hemoglobin. Students can go online to **Biology.com** to gather their evidence.

How Science Works

MORE ABOUT HAPMAPS

The HapMap Project is of particular interest to scientists in medical fields because haplotypes—as opposed to single SNPs—are more likely to be associated with diseases such as cancer, heart disease, and diabetes, which involve multiple genes. Searching for key disease-related haplotypes would be currently less expensive and less time-consuming than comparing the complete genetic sequences of healthy individuals with those of individuals who have a particular disease. Scientists hope to use the HapMap not only to identify regions of the human genome that are associated with diseases but also to study susceptibility to infection and sensitivity to environmental factors, drugs, and vaccines.

LESSON 14.3

Teach continued

Lead a Discussion

Have students identify characteristics scientists discovered about the human genome as you list them on the board.

Ask What information did scientists find surprising about the human genome? (*Chromosomes have large regions that contain very few genes.*)

Ask What inference can be made about the similarities between coded proteins in humans and other organisms? *(Humans and other organisms have a common evolutionary origin.)*

Finally, have students discuss how scientists might use their knowledge of the location of sequences for diseases and disorders.

DIFFERENTIATED INSTRUCTION

L3 **Advanced Students** Have students search the Internet and scientific journals for the latest findings on a disease or disorder associated with gene sequences identified through the Human Genome Project. Have students present their findings to the class by giving an oral report.

Address Misconceptions

Single Gene vs. Multifactorial Diseases Students may think that inheriting DNA sequences for any disease means the person will definitely develop the disease. Review how single gene disorders, such as CF, are passed through families in such a way that offspring who inherit the mutated gene will develop the disease. Highlight the fact that, in such cases, environment does not affect whether the person develops disease. Explain that most genetic diseases, such as heart disease and most cancers, are multifactorial—a combination of factors determines whether disease will develop. A person who inherits these genes is at higher risk of developing the disease, but may never actually develop it, due to environmental and behavioral factors. For example, a person who inherits genes for heart disease can greatly decrease his or her risk of developing the disease by avoiding tobacco smoke, maintaining a healthy weight, and eating a healthy diet.

Answers

FIGURE 14–15 Sample answer: I could use an Internet search engine to search for articles by entering the key phrase "size comparison of genomes." To make sure that the information was current, I could check the dates of the articles that result from the search.

FIGURE 14–14 Announcements The first details of the human genome appeared in two well-known scientific journals in February 2001.

What We Have Learned In June 2000, scientists announced that a working copy of the human genome was complete. The first details appeared in the February 2001 issues of the journals *Nature* and *Science*. The full reference sequence was completed in April 2003, marking the end of the Human Genome Project—two years ahead of the original schedule. Coincidentally, that was also the fiftieth anniversary of Watson and Crick's publication of DNA structure that launched the era of molecular biology!

Besides finding that the human genome in its haploid form contains three billion nucleotide bases, the Human Genome Project uncovered a wealth of interesting, and sometimes surprising, information. For instance, only about 2 percent of our genome encodes instructions for the synthesis of proteins, and many chromosomes contain large areas with very few genes. As much as half of our genome is made up of DNA sequences from viruses and other genetic elements within human chromosomes. During the project, investigators completed the genomes of several other organisms, including unicellular ones. They found that more than 40 percent of the proteins coded for by our genome have strong similarity to proteins in many of those organisms, including fruit flies, worms, and even yeast. **Figure 14–15** compares the human genome with these and other model organisms.

By any standard, the Human Genome Project has been a great scientific success. **The Human Genome Project pinpointed genes and associated particular sequences in those genes with numerous diseases and disorders. It also identified about three million locations where single-base DNA differences occur in humans.** This information may help us find DNA sequences associated with diabetes, cancer, and other health problems. The Human Genome Project also transferred important new technologies to the private sector, including agriculture and medicine. By doing so, the project catalyzed the U.S. biotechnology industry and fostered the development of new medical applications.

FIGURE 14–15 Genome Size Comparisons The gene numbers in this table are not final. Some estimates include only protein-coding genes, while others include genes that code only for RNA. The discovery of small interfering RNAs (siRNAs) has complicated the definition of a gene. **Propose a Solution** ***How could you find updated information on genome sizes?***

Size Comparison of Various Genomes

Organism	Genome Size (bases)	Estimated Genes
Human (*Homo sapiens*)	3.2 billion	25,000
Laboratory mouse (*M. musculus*)	2.5 billion	24,174
Fruit fly (*D. melanogaster*)	165.0 million	13,600
Mustard weed (*A. thaliana*)	120.0 million	25,498
Roundworm (*C. elegans*)	97.0 million	19,000
Yeast (*S. cerevisiae*)	12.1 million	6,294
Bacterium (*E. coli*)	4.6 million	4,288
Human immunodeficiency virus (HIV)	9749.0	9

Quick Facts

GENES ASSOCIATED WITH OBESITY

Obesity, a major health issue that, in recent decades, has reached epidemic proportions in many populations, is associated with more than 400 genes to date. While the condition has a strong association with genes, it is a multifactorial trait resulting also from environmental and lifestyle influences. Researchers in Canada have developed the Human Obesity Gene Map, an online database that contains information on genes associated with obesity. By studying these genes and their interactions with the environment, researchers hope to better address the obesity problem through prevention and intervention.

New Questions Throughout its duration, the Human Genome Project worked to identify and address ethical, legal, and social issues surrounding the availability of human genome data and its powerful new technologies. The issues, including privacy, fairness in the use of and access to genomic information, medical issues, and commercialization, are complex. For example, who owns and controls genetic information? Is genetic privacy different from medical privacy? Who should have access to personal genetic information, and how will it be used? Right now, these questions are hypothetical, but they may not be for long. In May 2008, President George Bush signed into law the Genetic Information Nondiscrimination Act, which prohibits U.S. insurance companies and employers from discriminating on the basis of information derived from genetic tests. Other protective laws may soon follow.

What's Next? Many more sequencing projects are underway, helped along by powerful new technologies. You can expect an ever-growing database of information from microbial, animal, and plant genomes in the years ahead. Each of these will have its own mysteries to be explored, not to mention the fact that we still don't fully understand the functions of as many as 50 percent of the human genes thus far discovered.

The 1000 Genomes Project, launched in 2008, will study the genomes of 1000 people in an effort to produce a detailed catalogue of human variation. Data from the project will be used in future studies of development and disease, and the information may hold the key to successful research on new drugs and therapies to save human lives and preserve health.

Perhaps the most important challenge that lies ahead is to understand how all the "parts" of cells—genes, proteins, and many other molecules—work together to create complex living organisms. Future efforts may provide a deeper understanding of the molecular processes underlying life and may influence how we view our own place in the global ecosystem.

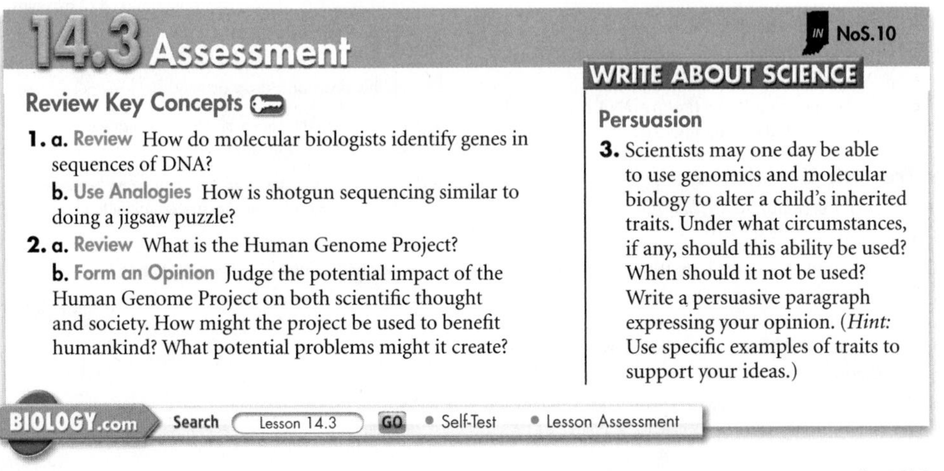

14.3 Assessment

IN NoS.10

Review Key Concepts

1. **a. Review** How do molecular biologists identify genes in sequences of DNA?
   b. Use Analogies How is shotgun sequencing similar to doing a jigsaw puzzle?
2. **a. Review** What is the Human Genome Project?
   b. Form an Opinion Judge the potential impact of the Human Genome Project on both scientific thought and society. How might the project be used to benefit humankind? What potential problems might it create?

WRITE ABOUT SCIENCE

Persuasion

3. Scientists may one day be able to use genomics and molecular biology to alter a child's inherited traits. Under what circumstances, if any, should this ability be used? When should it not be used? Write a persuasive paragraph expressing your opinion. (*Hint:* Use specific examples of traits to support your ideas.)

BIOLOGY.com Search Lesson 14.3 GO • Self-Test • Lesson Assessment

Assess and Remediate

EVALUATE UNDERSTANDING

Have students verbally summarize the information displayed in each figure in the lesson. Then, have them complete the 14.3 Assessment.

REMEDIATION SUGGESTION

L1 **Struggling Students** If students have trouble with **Question 2b,** review with them the last paragraph in **What We Have Learned,** and brainstorm specific examples of how gene technology might be used in the future. Then, have them reread **New Questions** and suggest answers to each question.

BIOLOGY.com Students can check their understanding of lesson concepts with the **Self-Test** assessment. They can then take an online version of the **Lesson Assessment.**

Assessment Answers

1a. They look for promoters, open reading frames, the sequences that separate introns from exons, and stop codons.

1b. In a jigsaw puzzle, shapes are matched to recreate the puzzle. In shotgun sequencing, DNA base sequences are matched to recreate the genome.

2a. The Human Genome Project is an international effort to sequence all 3 billion base pairs of human DNA and to identify all human genes.

2b. Sample answer: The project might benefit humankind by helping scientists learn about the causes of genetic disorders. Potential problems include deciding who owns and controls genetic information.

WRITE ABOUT SCIENCE

3. Answers will vary, but opinions should be fully developed and supported by examples. Sample answer: A child's inherited traits should be altered if those traits relate to disease. Traits should not be altered to change a child's appearance.

Pre-Lab

Introduce students to the concepts they will explore in the chapter lab by assigning the Pre-Lab questions.

Lab

Tell students they will perform the chapter lab *Using DNA to Identify Human Remains* described in **Lab Manual A.**

L1 Struggling Students A simpler version of the chapter lab is provided in **Lab Manual B.**

Look online for **Editable Lab Worksheets.**

For corresponding pre-lab in the **Foundation Edition**, see page 346.

IN INDIANA ACADEMIC STANDARDS

For the full text of all standards, see the Course Overview in the front matter of this book.

GUIDED INQUIRY

NoS.6 Use analogies and models; **NoS.7** Develop explanatory models; **B.7.3** Traits.

Pre-Lab: Using DNA to Identify Human Remains

Problem How can pedigrees help scientists identify human remains?

Lab Manual Chapter 14 Lab

Skills Focus Analyze Data, Draw Conclusions

Connect to the Big idea The nucleus is not the only location in a cell where DNA can be found. DNA is also found in the mitochondria of cells. This mitochondrial DNA, or mtDNA, exists as small loops, rather than long strands. Unlike nuclear DNA, mtDNA is inherited only from the mother. Thus, except for mutations, the sequence of nucleotides in mtDNA remains constant over many generations.

Less than one percent of a cell's DNA is mtDNA, but in that percentage are many copies of the small mtDNA molecules. So when forensic scientists cannot collect a suitable sample of nuclear DNA, they look for mtDNA. Usable mtDNA can often be found even after a body decays or is burned. In this lab, you will explore how mtDNA was used to help confirm the identity of bones that scientists thought belonged to members of the Romanov family.

The Romanovs ruled Russia for 300 years until the Bolshevik Revolution of 1918 resulted in the execution of Tsar Nicholas II and his family.

Background Questions

a. Review What is a pedigree?

b. Explain In a pedigree, what does a circle represent? What does a square represent?

c. Infer How do you know that mtDNA isn't sorted and recombined during meiosis?

Pre-Lab Questions

Preview the procedure in the lab manual.

1. Infer The tsar and tsarina had five children. Did all seven family members have the same mtDNA? Give a reason for your answer.

2. Predict To confirm that bones belonged to the tsar's children, which living relative would be more useful—a relative of the tsar or a relative of the tsarina? Why?

3. Infer If two people have the same mtDNA, what can you infer about their biological relationship?

BIOLOGY.com Search Chapter 14 GO

Visit Chapter 14 online to test yourself on chapter content and to find activities to help you learn.

Untamed Science Video The Untamed Science crew identifies the chromosomes that carry genes for colorblindness.

Art in Motion View a short animation that explains nondisjunction.

Art Review Review your understanding of karyotypes with this drag-and-drop activity.

InterActive Art Learn all about pedigrees and how to make them with this animation.

Data Analysis Analyze the connection between type O blood and an increased susceptibility to cholera.

Tutor Tube Why do traits sometimes "skip a generation"? Tune in to the tutor to find out.

Pre-Lab Answers

BACKGROUND QUESTIONS

a. A pedigree is a chart that is used to analyze the pattern of inheritence of a trait across several generations.

b. In a pedigree, a circle represents a female and a square represents a male.

c. Sample answer: The sequence of nucleotides in mtDNA remains constant over many generations. (All the daughter cells must have identical mtDNA.)

PRE-LAB QUESTIONS

1. The tsarina and the children had the same mtDNA because the children inherited their mtDNA from the tsarina. The tsar had different mtDNA, which he inherited from his mother.

2. A living relative of the tsarina would be more useful because that relative would have the same mtDNA as the children.

3. Sample answer: The two people have a common ancestor on the maternal side of their family trees.

14 Study Guide

Big idea Information and Heredity

Humans have 23 pairs of chromosomes, including one pair of sex chromosomes, that follow the same patterns of Mendelian inheritance as do other organisms. Scientists study human heredity using karyotypes, pedigrees, and Punnett squares, but they also use the tools of molecular biology and bioinformatics to study DNA and gene expression. The Human Genome Project has revolutionized the study of human heredity.

14.1 Human Chromosomes

A karyotype shows the complete diploid set of chromosomes grouped together in pairs, arranged in order of decreasing size.

Human genes follow the same Mendelian patterns of inheritance as the genes of other organisms. Many human traits follow a pattern of simple dominance. The alleles for other human genes display codominant inheritance. Because the X and Y chromosomes determine sex, the genes located on them show a pattern of inheritance called sex-linkage.

The information gained from pedigree analysis makes it possible to determine the nature of genes and alleles associated with inherited human traits.

genome (392)
karyotype (392)
sex chromosome (393)
autosome (393)
sex-linked gene (395)
pedigree (396)

14.2 Human Genetic Disorders

Changes in a gene's DNA sequence can change proteins by altering their amino acid sequences, which may directly affect one's phenotype.

If nondisjunction occurs during meiosis, gametes with an abnormal number of chromosomes may result, leading to a disorder of chromosome numbers.

nondisjunction (401)

14.3 Studying the Human Genome

By using tools that cut, separate, and then replicate DNA base by base, scientists can now read the base sequences in DNA from any cell.

The Human Genome Project was a 13-year, international effort with the main goals of sequencing all 3 billion base pairs of human DNA and identifying all human genes.

The Human Genome Project pinpointed genes and associated particular sequences in those genes with numerous diseases and disorders. It also identified about three million locations where single-base DNA differences occur in humans.

restriction enzyme (403)
gel electrophoresis (404)
bioinformatics (407)
genomics (407)

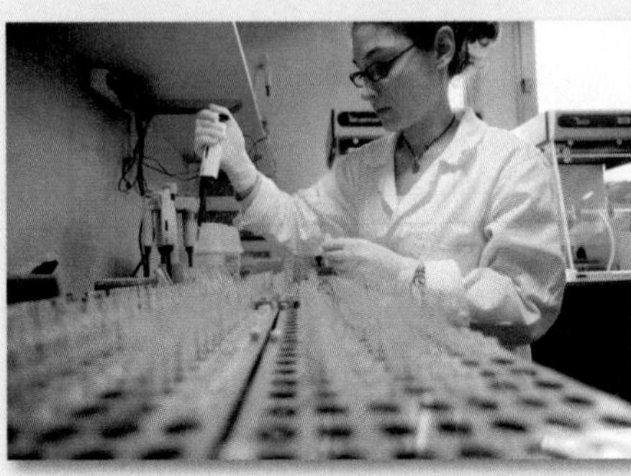

Think Visually
Create a concept map using the following terms: nondisjunction, autosomes, sex chromosomes, Down syndrome, Turner's syndrome, and Klinefelter's syndrome.

 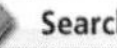 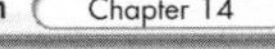  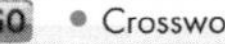 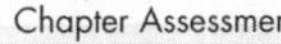

BIOLOGY.com Search Chapter 14 GO • Crossword • Chapter Assessment

STUDY GUIDE

Study Online

REVIEW AND ASSESSMENT RESOURCES

Editable Worksheets Pages of Study Workbooks A and B, Lab Manuals A and B, and the Assessment Resources Book are available online. These documents can be easily edited using a word-processing program.

Lesson Overview Have students reread the Lesson Overviews to help them study chapter concepts.

Vocabulary Review The *Flash Cards* and *Crossword* provide an interactive way to review chapter vocabulary.

Chapter Assessment Have students take an online version of the Chapter 14 Assessment.

Standardized Test Prep Students can take an online version of the Standardized Test Prep. You will receive their scores along with ideas for remediation.

Diagnostic and Benchmark Tests Use these tests to monitor your students' progress and supply remediation.

Answers

THINK VISUALLY

Students' concept maps should show that heritable disorders can be caused by nondisjunction of autosomes (in the case of Down syndrome) or sex chromosomes (in the case of Turner's syndrome and Klinefelter's syndrome).

UbD Performance Tasks

SUMMATIVE TASK Have students work in pairs to write and perform a short skit in which a newscaster interviews a geneticist about Huntington's disease. In their script, they must include information about the pattern of inheritance, a sample pedigree showing the trait, how the allele causes disease, and a summary of the techniques scientists might use to locate the allele on the human genome. They should write the scripts for a general adult audience with high school knowledge of biology.

TRANSFER TASK Tell students that several companies market genetic tests directly to consumers, who send in a saliva sample to be tested for particular genes. Some tests tell whether a person is at higher risk for a disease, such as Alzheimer's, heart disease, and some cancers. As a class, discuss the following questions:

- Would you want to know your risk of certain diseases? If so, which ones and why? If not, why not?
- If you choose to know, what would you do, if anything, with the data? For example, would you change your lifestyle?
- Would you share your data with anyone, for example, your doctor or a prospective marriage partner? Explain.

After the discussion, have individuals write a fictional letter to a friend or family member persuading him or her to use or avoid using a mail-order genetics test for a certain disease. In their letters, they should support their arguments with information learned from the chapter.

ASSESSMENT

Lesson 14.1

UNDERSTAND KEY CONCEPTS

1. b **2.** a **3.** b

4. The sex chromosomes, X and Y, determine an individual's sex; the remaining 22 pairs of chromosomes are autosomal.

5. No, the I^A and I^B alleles are codominant. When both alleles are present in an individual, that person has blood type AB.

THINK CRITICALLY

6. The father's genotype could be X^CY or X^cY because he contributes to his sons only the Y chromosome, which does not determine colorblindness. The mother's genotype must be X^CX^c (a carrier of the gene for colorblindness) or X^cX^c (colorblind and homozygous for the gene for colorblindness).

7. Answers will vary but may include a cross between a diseased female and a normal male. If the gene is sex-linked, the disease will appear only in male offspring.

Lesson 14.2

UNDERSTAND KEY CONCEPTS

8. d **9.** b **10.** d

11. It is the karyotype of a person with Down syndrome, because it has three copies of chromosome 21.

12. A chromosomal disorder is a disorder caused by nondisjunction during meiosis, resulting in gametes with an abnormal number of chromosomes.

13. A female with Turner's syndrome has only one X chromosome and is sterile. A male with Klinefelter's syndrome has one or more extra X chromosomes and is usually sterile.

THINK CRITICALLY

14. No, cystic fibrosis is caused by a gene mutation. Karyotypes can detect abnormalities only in chromosome number.

15. The incidence of Down syndrome increases with the age of the mother.

14 Assessment

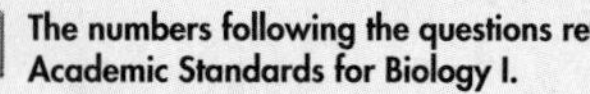
The numbers following the questions refer to Indiana's Academic Standards for Biology I.

14.1 Human Chromosomes

Understand Key Concepts

1. A normal human diploid zygote contains
- **a.** 23 chromosomes.
- **b.** 46 chromosomes.
- **c.** 44 chromosomes.
- **d.** XXY chromosomes.

2. A chart that traces the inheritance of a trait in a family is called a(n) NoS.6
- **a.** pedigree.
- **b.** karyotype.
- **c.** genome.
- **d.** autosome.

3. An example of a trait that is determined by multiple alleles is B.5.6, B.7.2
- **a.** cystic fibrosis.
- **b.** ABO blood groups.
- **c.** Down syndrome.
- **d.** colorblindness.

4. What is the difference between autosomes and sex chromosomes?

5. Is it possible for a person with blood type alleles I^A and I^B to have blood type A? Explain your answer. (Refer to **Figure 14–5**). B.7.2

Think Critically

6. Predict What are the possible genotypes of the parents of a male child who is colorblind? B.7.3

7. Design an Experiment Fruit fly sex is determined by X and Y chromosomes, just as it is in humans. Researchers suspect that a certain disease is caused by a recessive allele in a gene located on the X chromosome in fruit flies. Design an experiment to test this hypothesis.

14.2 Human Genetic Disorders

Understand Key Concepts

8. A mutation involving a change in a single DNA base pair B.7.5
- **a.** will definitely result in a genetic disease.
- **b.** will have no effect on the organism's phenotype.
- **c.** will produce a positive change.
- **d.** may have an effect on the organism's phenotype.

9. Cystic fibrosis is caused by B.7.5
- **a.** nondisjunction of an autosome.
- **b.** a change of three base pairs in DNA.
- **c.** nondisjunction of a sex chromosome.
- **d.** deletion of an entire gene from a chromosome.

10. Malaria is a disease caused by a
- **a.** gene mutation.
- **b.** defect in red blood cells.
- **c.** bacterium found in water.
- **d.** parasite carried by mosquitoes.

11. Analyze the human karyotype below. Identify the chromosomal disorder that it shows.

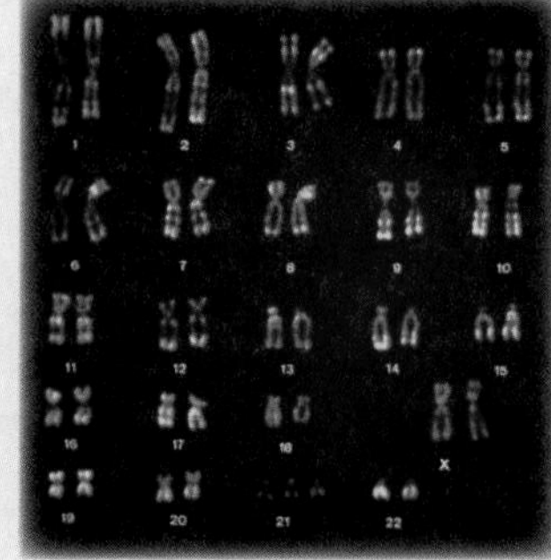

12. What is a chromosomal disorder?

13. Describe two sex-chromosome disorders.

Think Critically

14. Infer Can a genetic counselor use a karyotype to identify a carrier of cystic fibrosis? Explain.

15. Interpret Graphs What can you infer about the relationship between the age of the mother and the incidence of Down syndrome? NoS.3

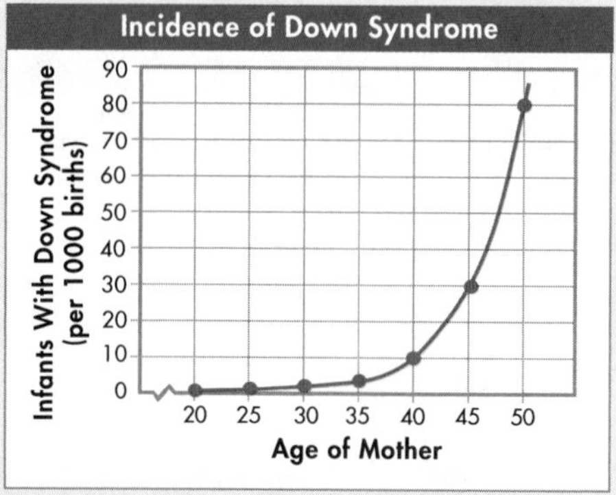

14.3 Studying the Human Genome

Understand Key Concepts

16. The human genome consists of approximately how many DNA base pairs?
a. 30,000 **c.** 300,000,000
b. 3,000,000 **d.** 3,000,000,000

17. The fraction of the human genome that actually codes for proteins is about
a. 2%. **c.** 98%.
b. 20%. **d.** 100%.

18. Cutting DNA into small pieces that can be sequenced is accomplished by
a. restriction enzymes.
b. DNA polymerase.
c. gel electrophoresis.
d. RNA polymerase.

19. If you sequence short pieces of DNA and then use a computer to find overlapping sequences that map to a much longer DNA fragment, you are using NoS.10
a. genomics.
b. hapmaps.
c. shotgun sequencing.
d. open reading frame analysis.

20. Describe the tools and processes that scientists use to manipulate human DNA. NoS.10

21. Explain why restriction enzymes are useful tools in sequencing DNA. NoS.10

solve the CHAPTER MYSTERY

THE CROOKED CELL

When Ava inquired about her family's medical history, she found out that Uncle Eli's mother (Ava's grandmother) also had sickle cell disease, but Uncle Eli's father did not. One of her uncle's four children also had the disease. However, Ava's father, who is Eli's only sibling, did not have sickle cell disease, nor did Ava's mother. Ava's two siblings showed no signs of the disease, either.

1. Apply Concepts In general, what pattern of heredity does the sickle cell trait follow? Cite evidence from the chapter and its clues to support your conclusion.

2. Draw Conclusions Based on your answer to question 1, what can you conclude about the inheritance of sickle cell disease in Ava's family? What might be Ava's chances of being a carrier of the sickle cell trait?

3. Classify What kind of medical test could Ava request that would help determine whether or not she has the sickle cell trait? Explain your answer.

4. Infer The restriction enzyme *Mst* II, which cuts normal DNA at a particular site, will not recognize (and, therefore, will not cut) DNA that contains the sickle cell mutation. If Uncle Eli's DNA is cut with *Mst* II, will the restriction fragments be identical to those from his brother, Ava's father? Explain.

5. Focus on the Big idea Which technique(s) that you have read about in this chapter could be used to perform the kind of test described in question 4? Which technique could be used to analyze the results? NoS.10

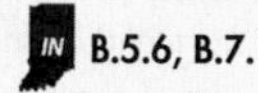
B.5.6, B.7.1

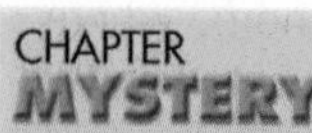

After students read through the Chapter Mystery, ask them to work in pairs to construct a pedigree to illustrate how sickle cell disease and the trait have been passed in Ava's family. Tell students to use the pedigree to infer each individual's possible genotype and label it using *S* for the normal allele and *s* for the defective allele. Make sure students have drawn the correct pedigree by asking the following questions.

Ask What is the genotype of Ava's grandmother? Explain. *(ss because she has the disease)*

Ask What is the genotype of Ava's grandfather? Explain. *(Ss because neither he nor Ava's father have the disease; Ava's father must have inherited a normal allele from his father, and Ava's uncle must have inherited a recessive allele from him.)*

Ask What are the possible genotypes for Ava's mother? *(SS and Ss)*

CHAPTER MYSTERY ANSWERS

1. Students should recognize that the sickle cell alleles are inherited in a dominant-recessive pattern. Sickle cell disease is autosomal (not X-linked) recessive. A person must inherit two recessive alleles for sickle cell disease to develop.

2. Ava's grandfather must be heterozygous for the trait, because Ava's grandmother is homozygous recessive but Ava's father does not have the disease. Her father had to have received one normal allele from her grandfather. Ava has 50% chance of being a carrier of the sickle cell trait.

3. Sample answer: Protein amino-acid sequencing of beta-globin or DNA analysis of the gene that codes for that protein would show whether Ava is a carrier of the defective allele, because the allele that causes sickle cell disease is known.

4. The fragments from Uncle Eli will be longer than some of his brother's, because the enzyme will not recognize (and therefore will not cut) the DNA that contains the sickle cell mutation.

5. Big idea Students should recognize that the test could be performed using restriction enzymes to cut DNA at specific sites and include gel electrophoresis and DNA sequencing as techniques to analyze the results.

Suggest students follow the Untamed Science crew in **What Color Are My Genes?** to find out how colorblindness is inherited.

Lesson 14.3

UNDERSTAND KEY CONCEPTS

16. d **17.** a **18.** a **19.** c

20. Answers should include descriptions of restriction enzymes, gel electrophoresis, and the use of colored labels in sequencing DNA.

21. Restriction enzymes can cut DNA into short fragments at predictable locations. The short fragments can be more easily sequenced.

22. An SNP is a place in the human genome where a single DNA base does not match between two unrelated individuals.
23. Bioinformatics is the creation, development, and operation of databases and other tools to collect, organize, and interpret biological data.

THINK CRITICALLY

24. It is likely that protein coding genes are located in open reading frames that follow promoter sequences.
25. DNA is negatively charged.
26. *Bam*HI, *Hind*III, and *Eco*RI are the three restriction enzymes that produce sticky ends. All the restriction enzyme recognition sites are sequences that read the same in both directions.

Connecting Concepts

USE SCIENCE GRAPHICS

27. In fruit flies, maleness and femaleness are determined by the number of X chromosomes (one for male, two for female). In humans, maleness requires a Y chromosome.
28. Genes on the Y chromosome are not necessary for survival.

WRITE ABOUT SCIENCE

29. Students' explanations should include a description of the inheritance of a sex-linked gene, an explanation as to why it is more common in males, and at least one example of genotypes in two parents that would result in a child with colorblindness. Females must receive both defective copies of the allele to be colorblind, while males must receive just one copy (from their mothers) to be colorblind.
30. Big idea Students' explanations should include a description of nondisjunction (how chromosomes fail to separate in meiosis) and the combinations of chromosomes in gametes that result in each of the disorders. Down syndrome is trisomy 21, Turner's syndrome is a female having only one X chromosome, and Klinefelter's syndrome is a male having more than one X chromosome.

22. What is an SNP (single nucleotide polymorphism)?
23. What is bioinformatics? NoS.10

Think Critically

24. **Draw Conclusions** Scientists have searched the human genome database to find possible promoter sequences. What is likely to be found near a promoter sequence?
25. **Infer** Why does DNA move toward the positive end of the gel during gel electrophoresis?
26. **Observe** The table below shows the DNA sequences that are recognized by five different restriction enzymes and the locations where those enzymes cut. Which enzymes produce DNA fragments with "sticky ends"? What is the common feature of the sequences cut by these enzymes?

DNA Sequences Cut by Enzymes

Enzyme	Recognition Sequence
*Alu*I	A G↓C T T C↑G A
*Hae*III	G G↓C C C C↑G G
*Bam*HI	G↓G A T C C C C T A G↑G
*Hind*III	A↓A G C T T T T C G A↑A
*Eco*RI	G↓A A T T C C T T A A↑G

Connecting Concepts

Use Science Graphics NoS.3

Use the data table to answer questions 27 and 28.

Chromosomes and Phenotypes

Sex Chromosomes	Fruit Fly Phenotype	Human Phenotype
XX	Female	Female
XY	Male	Male
X	Male	Female
XXY	Female	Male

27. **Interpret Tables** What differs in the sex-determining mechanism of the two organisms?
28. **Draw Conclusions** What can you logically conclude about the genes on the sex chromosomes of fruit flies and humans?

Write About Science NoS.3

29. **Explanation** Write a paragraph that tells how colorblindness is inherited. Describe the condition and explain why it is much more common in males. (*Hint*: Begin your paragraph with a topic sentence that expresses the paragraph's main idea.) B.7.2
30. **Assess the Big idea** Explain the relationship between meiosis and Down syndrome, Turner's syndrome, and Klinefelter's syndrome.

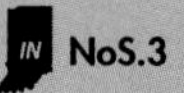

NoS.3

Hemophilia is an example of a sex-linked disorder. Two genes carried on the X chromosome help control blood clotting. A recessive allele in either of these two genes may produce hemophilia. The pedigree shows the transmission of hemophilia through three generations of a family.

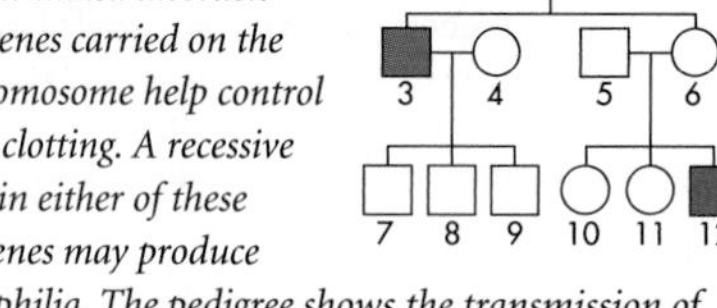

31. **Interpret Diagrams** Which mothers are definite carriers of the gene? NoS.6
32. **Apply Concepts** Why did the sons of Person 3 not inherit the trait? B.7.2, B.7.3
33. **Apply Concepts** How could Person 12 have hemophilia if neither of his parents had hemophilia? B.7.2, B.7.3

PURPOSE Students will interpret a diagram and apply concepts of human inheritance to explain how hemophilia is passed through a family.

PLANNING Have students review the symbols used in a pedigree.

ANSWERS

31. Person 1 and Person 6
32. Person 3 can pass his affected X chromosome only to his daughters; his sons inherit a copy of his Y chromosome and an X chromosome from their mother.
33. Person 12 inherited the allele for hemophilia on the X chromosome he got from his mother, Person 6, who is a carrier.

Standardized Test Practice for Indiana

Multiple Choice

1. Which of the following disorders can be observed in a human karyotype?
   A colorblindness
   B trisomy 21
   C cystic fibrosis
   D sickle cell disease

2. Which of the following disorders is a direct result of nondisjunction?
   A sickle cell disease
   B Turner's syndrome
   C Huntington's disease
   D cystic fibrosis

3. A woman is homozygous for A^- blood type. A man has AB^- blood type. What is the probability that the couple's child will have type B^- blood?
   A 0%　C 75%
   B 50%　D 100%　B.7.3

4. Cystic fibrosis is a genetic disorder caused by a
   A single base substitution in the gene for hemoglobin.
   B deletion of an amino acid from a chloride channel protein.
   C defective gene found on the X chromosome.
   D trisomy of chromosome 21.　B.5.5, B.7.5

5. The technique used to separate DNA strands of different lengths is
   A gel electrophoresis.
   B shotgun sequencing.
   C restriction enzyme digestion.
   D bioinformatics.　NoS.10

6. The study of whole genomes, including genes and their functions, is called
   A bioinformatics.
   B information science.
   C life science.
   D genomics.　NoS.10

7. DNA can be cut into shorter sequences by proteins known as
   A haplotypes.　C restriction enzymes.
   B polymerases.　D restriction fragments.

Questions 8–9

A student traced the recurrence of a widow's peak hairline in her family. Based on her interviews and observations, she drew the pedigree shown below.

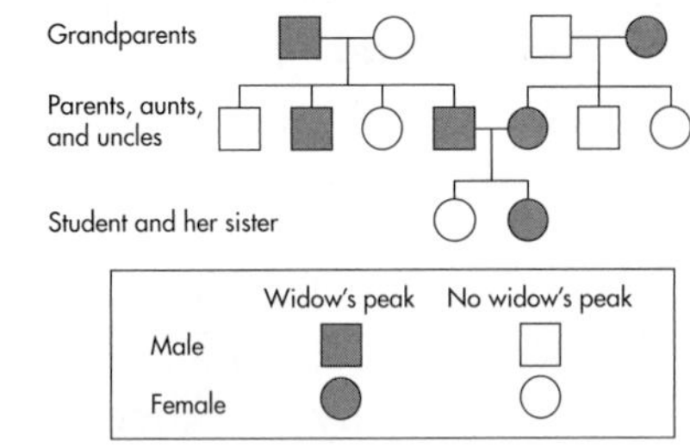

8. Which pattern of inheritance is consistent with the pedigree?
   A sex-linked inheritance
   B complete dominance
   C codominance
   D multiple alleles　B.7.2

9. What are the probable genotypes of the student's parents?
   A Mother—*Ww*; Father—*ww*
   B Mother—*ww*; Father—*ww*
   C Mother—*WW*; Father—*Ww*
   D Mother—*Ww*; Father—*Ww*

Open-Ended Response

10. Explain how the allele for sickle cell disease, which is a harmful allele when a person is homozygous, can be beneficial when a person is heterozygous.　B.5.6, B.7.5

If You Have Trouble With . . .										
Question	1	2	3	4	5	6	7	8	9	10
See Lesson	14.1	14.2	14.1	14.2	14.3	14.3	14.3	14.1	14.1	14.2

Answers

1. B
2. B
3. A
4. B
5. A
6. D
7. C
8. B
9. D
10. It is harmful in homozygous individuals because all of their hemoglobin has the defective form of the protein and the resulting defective red blood cells do not function normally, causing clots that can damage tissues. It is beneficial in heterozygous individuals because they are generally healthy and being carriers of the trait makes them resistant to the malaria parasite.

Test-Taking Tip

READ ALL THE ANSWER CHOICES

Tell students to take the time to read each question completely, including all of the answer choices. They should consider each possible choice before determining which answer is the best.

CHAPTER PLANNER 15

Genetic Engineering

Chapter Contents	IN	Time	Core Resources
Chapter Preview			**Student Edition,** pp. 416–417 **Chapter Mystery,** p. 417
15.1 Selective Breeding Selective Breeding • Increasing Variation	B.7.5	1/2 period 1/4 block	**Student Edition,** pp. 418–420 **Study Workbook A** 15.1 Worksheets L2 **Biology.com** 15.1 Lesson Overview • 15.1 Lesson Notes • 15.1 Self-Test • 15.1 Lesson Assessment
15.2 Recombinant DNA Copying DNA • Changing DNA • Transgenic Organisms	NoS.10	1 period 1/2 block	**Student Edition,** pp. 421–427 Inquiry 15.2 Quick Lab, p. 425 L2 **Study Workbook A** 15.2 Worksheets L2 **Biology.com** *Art in Motion:* Plasmid DNA Transformation **Assessment Resources Book** Visual Quiz L2
15.3 Applications of Genetic Engineering Agriculture and Industry • Health and Medicine • Personal Identification • *Technology & Biology: Artifical Life?*	NoS.3, NoS.10, NoS.11	1/2 period 1/4 block	**Student Edition,** pp. 428–435 Inquiry 15.3 Analyzing Data, p. 429 L2 **Study Workbook A** 15.3 Worksheets L2 **Biology.com** *Art Review:* Identifying Individuals **Assessment Resources Book** Visual Quiz L2
15.4 Ethics and Impacts of Biotechnology Profits and Privacy • Safety of Transgenics • Ethics of the New Biology	NoS.11	1/2 period 1/4 block	**Student Edition,** pp. 436–439 Inquiry 15.4 Quick Lab, p. 438 L2 **Study Workbook A** 15.4 Worksheets L2 **Biology.com** *Data Analysis:* Who Sees Your DNA? Privacy and Genetic Data • 15.4 Self-Test • 15.4 Lesson Assessment
Chapter Pre-Lab	NoS.1	1 period 1/2 block	**Student Edition,** p. 440 L2 **Lab Manual A** *Using DNA to Solve Crimes* L2

Differentiated Instruction Tools

Study Workbook B includes worksheets with lesson-level differentiated instruction support and explanations of differentiated instruction teaching strategies.

Lab Manual B includes skills labs, simplified chapter labs, and hands-on activities.

ELL Handbook explains ways to make *Biology* more accessible to ELL students.

Spanish Study Workbook is a Spanish translation of Study Workbook A.

Multilingual Glossary is the glossary translated into ten languages.

Differentiated Instruction Key

- L1 Special Needs or Struggling Students
- ELL English Language Learners
- LPR Less Proficient Readers
- L2 On-Level Students
- L3 Advanced Students

Additional Resources

Biology.com Untamed Science Video • Vocabulary Flash Cards

Study Workbook B 15.1 Worksheets L1 ELL LPR
Spanish Study Workbook 15.1 Worksheets ELL

Study Workbook B 15.2 Worksheets L1 ELL LPR
Spanish Study Workbook 15.2 Worksheets ELL
Biology.com 15.2 Lesson Overview • 15.2 Lesson Notes • 15.2 Self-Test • 15.2 Lesson Assessment

Study Workbook B 15.3 Worksheets L1 ELL LPR
Spanish Study Workbook 15.3 Worksheets ELL
Biology.com 15.3 Lesson Overview • 15.3 Lesson Notes • 15.3 Self-Test • 15.3 Lesson Assessment

Study Workbook B 15.4 Worksheets L1 ELL LPR
Spanish Study Workbook 15.4 Worksheets ELL
Biology.com 15.4 Lesson Overview • 15.4 Lesson Notes

Lab Manual B *Using DNA to Solve Crimes* • Data Analysis: *Genetically Modified Crops in the United States* • Hands-On Activity: *Crime Scene DNA* L1 ELL LPR

Chapter Review

Student Edition Study Guide, p. 441 L2 • Unit Project, p. 446 L2
Study Workbook A Chapter 15 Vocabulary Review L2 • Chapter 15 Chapter Mystery/21st Century Skills Activity L2 L3
Transparencies, pp. 182–192 L1 ELL LPR L2
Biology.com Untamed Science Video • You're the Director • Editable Worksheets of Study Workbooks A and B and Lab Manuals A and B • Chapter 15 Flash Cards and Crossword Puzzle

Untamed Science DVD • Classroom Resources CD (includes lesson presentations and editable worksheets)

Chapter Assessment

Student Edition Assessment, pp. 442–445 L2
Study Workbook B Chapter 15 Chapter Review L1 ELL LPR • Chapter 15 Taking a Standardized Test L1 ELL LPR
Assessment Resources Book Chapter 15 Test A L2 • Chapter 15 Test B L1 ELL LPR • Unit 4 Test A L2 • Unit 4 Test B L1 ELL LPR
Biology.com Chapter 15 Assessment • Editable Worksheets of Chapter 15 Visual Quizzes, Chapter 15 Tests A and B, and Unit 4 Tests A and B

Exam*View* *Assessment Suite* • Classroom Resources CD (includes lesson presentations and editable worksheets)

Time: 1 period, 1/2 block

Pressed for Time?

Preview the Chapter Introduce students to the Lesson 15.1 and 15.3 vocabulary.

Cover the Chapter Quickly Assign students to read *Increasing Variation* in Lesson 15.1 and all of Lesson 15.3.

Assess Assign questions 2a, 2b, and 3 in the 15.1 Assessment, the 15.3 assessment, and questions 4, 5, and 17–22 in the Chapter 15 Assessment.

Connect to the Big Idea

Big idea Have students look at the photographs of the cats and read the caption. Explain that the researchers who developed the cat that glows in the dark hope experiments like these will help scientists understand genetic diseases in animals and humans. Ask students how they think the researchers were able to modify the cat's genes to make it glow red in the dark. *(Sample answer: The researchers were somehow able to place a "glowing" gene into the cat's DNA.)* Ask how they think the technology and processes used to modify the cat's genome could be used to benefit people. *(Answers will vary. Some students might suggest this technology could be used to cure diseases or improve crops.)* In discussing the modification of genes in these cats, have students anticipate the answer to the question, **How and why do scientists manipulate DNA in living cells?**

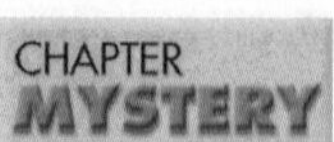

Have students read through the introduction to the Chapter Mystery and predict how the police figured out they had the wrong suspect. Use their predictions to help them start connecting the Chapter Mystery to the Big Idea of Science as a Way of Knowing.

BIOLOGY.com Have students preview the chapter vocabulary terms using the **Flash Cards.**

IN INDIANA ACADEMIC STANDARDS

For the full text of all standards, see the Course Overview in the front matter of this book.

Key standards: Chapter 15 covers key ideas from The Nature of Science and Standard 7: Genetics, including **NoS.10** Scientific discoveries and new technologies, **NoS.11** Scientific knowledge: environmental and social issues, and **B.7.5** Gene alteration.

15 Genetic Engineering

Big idea Science as a Way of Knowing

Q: How and why do scientists manipulate DNA in living cells?

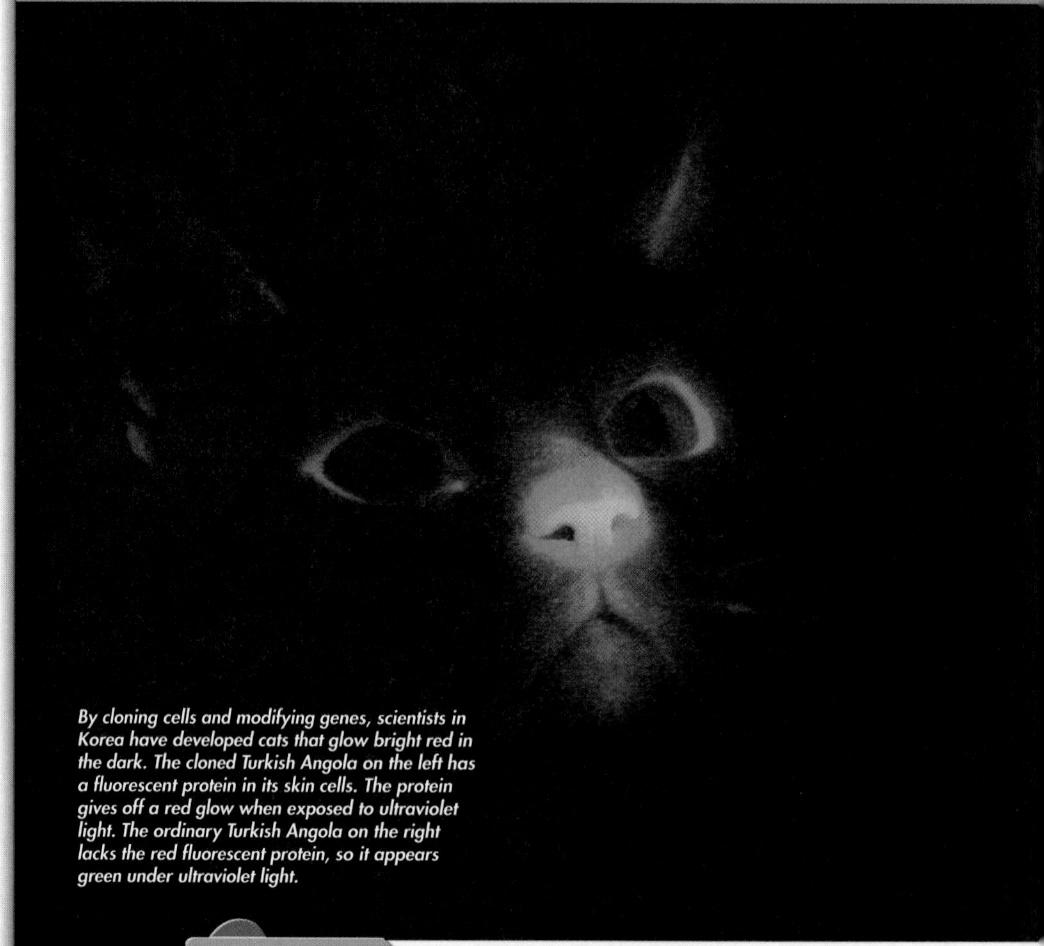

By cloning cells and modifying genes, scientists in Korea have developed cats that glow bright red in the dark. The cloned Turkish Angola on the left has a fluorescent protein in its skin cells. The protein gives off a red glow when exposed to ultraviolet light. The ordinary Turkish Angola on the right lacks the red fluorescent protein, so it appears green under ultraviolet light.

BIOLOGY.com Search Chapter15 GO • Flash Cards

UbD Understanding by Design

In Chapter 15, students examine genetic engineering and further explore the Unit 4 Enduring Understanding that *DNA is the universal code for life; it enables an organism to transmit hereditary information and, along with the environment, determines an organism's characteristics.* The Big Idea, Essential Question, and Guiding Questions, shown at the right, help frame their exploration.

PERFORMANCE GOALS

In Chapter 15, students will interpret information in figures that show biotechnology processes, model the insertion of genetic markers in DNA, analyze GM crop adoption data, and conduct a survey about genetic engineering. At the end of the chapter, they will create a teleplay about a detective learning the process of DNA fingerprinting.

INDIANA ACADEMIC STANDARDS FOR SCIENCE

Nature of Science NoS.1, NoS.3, NoS.10, NoS.11; **Genetics** B.7.5. See lessons for details.

CHAPTER MYSTERY

A CASE OF MISTAKEN IDENTITY

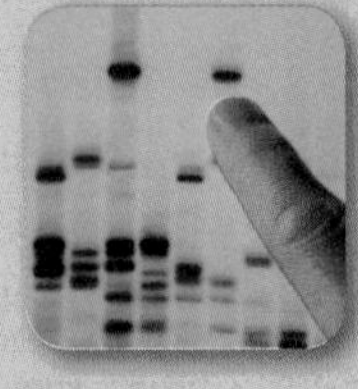

In the summer of 1998, an elderly Indiana woman was brutally assaulted. In the predawn darkness, she didn't get a look at her assailant's face.

At first light, police found a man only a few blocks from the victim's house. He was unconscious, his clothing was stained with blood, and there were scratches on his forearms. The man claimed that he had passed out following a drunken brawl. He couldn't remember what had happened afterward. The blood type of the stains on his clothing matched the victim's blood type. The police thought they had their man.

Hours later, the police knew they had the wrong suspect. They resumed their search for the real attacker, who was subsequently caught, tried, and convicted. As you read this chapter, look for clues to help you determine how the police knew they had the wrong suspect. Then, solve the mystery.

Never Stop Exploring Your World. Finding the solution to the case of mistaken identity is only the beginning. Take a video field trip with the ecogeeks of Untamed Science to see where the mystery leads.

• Untamed Science Video • Chapter Mystery

What's Online

Extend your reach by using these and other digital assets offered at Biology.com.

CHAPTER MYSTERY
Students determine how police concluded that a suspect in a crime could not have committed the crime.

UNTAMED SCIENCE VIDEO
Watch and see how pigeon breeding helps the Untamed Science crew unravel the mysteries of genetic engineering.

ART IN MOTION
In this animation, students can observe the steps of DNA transformation.

ART REVIEW
In this drag-and-drop activity, students label electrophoresis gels to identify individuals.

DATA ANALYSIS
Students explore how genetically modified crop plants can help prevent nutrient deficiencies.

Chapter 15 Big Idea: Science as a Way of Knowing

Chapter 15 EQ: How and why do scientists manipulate DNA in living cells?

- **15.1 GQ:** How do humans take advantage of naturally occurring variation among organisms?
- **15.2 GQ:** How do scientists study and work with specific genes?
- **15.3 GQ:** How do humans use genetic engineering?
- **15.4 GQ:** What are some of the ethical issues raised by genetic engineering?

LESSON 15.1

Getting Started

Objectives

15.1.1 Explain the purpose of selective breeding.

15.1.2 Explain how people increase genetic variation.

Student Resources

Study Workbooks A and B, 15.1 Worksheets

Spanish Study Workbook, 15.1 Worksheets

Lesson Overview • Lesson Notes • Assessment: Self-Test, Lesson Assessment

For corresponding lesson in the **Foundation Edition**, see pages 354–356.

Activate Prior Knowledge

Show students photos of two or three familiar breeds of dogs, such as German shepherds and golden retrievers. Ask them to identify the breeds, and then ask how they think these breeds are maintained. *(Sample answer: The breeds are maintained by having only dogs of the same breed mate with one another.)*

IN INDIANA ACADEMIC STANDARDS

For the full text of all standards, see the Course Overview in the front matter of this book.

B.7.5 Explain and demonstrate how inserting, substituting or deleting segments of a DNA molecule can alter a gene, which is then passed to every cell that develops from it and that the results may be beneficial, harmful or have little or no effect on the organism.

Selective Breeding

IN B.7.5 Gene alteration.

Key Questions

What is selective breeding used for?

How do people increase genetic variation?

Vocabulary

selective breeding
hybridization
inbreeding
biotechnology

Taking Notes

Outline Before you read this lesson, start an outline. Use the green headings in the lesson as first-level entries. Use the blue headings as second-level entries, leaving space after each entry. As you read, summarize the key ideas below your entries.

THINK ABOUT IT You've enjoyed popcorn at the movies, you've probably made it at home, and you've certainly seen it in stores. Where does it come from? Would you be surprised to learn that popcorn is one of the earliest examples of human efforts to select and improve living organisms for our benefit? Corn as we know it was domesticated at least 6000 years ago by Native Americans living in Mexico. A tiny kernel of popped corn found in a cave in New Mexico is more than 5000 years old!

Selective Breeding

What is selective breeding used for?

Visit a dog show, and what do you see? Striking contrasts are everywhere—from a tiny Chihuahua to a massive Great Dane, from the short coat of a Labrador retriever to the curly fur of a poodle, from the long muzzle of a wolfhound to the pug nose of a bulldog. The differences among breeds of dogs, like the ones in **Figure 15–1,** are so great that someone might think they are different species. They're not, of course, but where did these obvious differences come from?

The answer is that we did it. Humans have kept and bred dogs for thousands of years, always looking to produce animals that are better hunters, better retrievers, or better companions. We've done so by **selective breeding,** allowing only those animals with wanted characteristics to produce the next generation. **Humans use selective breeding, which takes advantage of naturally occurring genetic variation, to pass wanted traits on to the next generation of organisms.**

FIGURE 15–1 Dog Breeds There are more than 150 dog breeds, and many new breeds are still being developed.

UbD Teach for Understanding

ENDURING UNDERSTANDING DNA is the universal code for life; it enables an organism to transmit hereditary information and, along with the environment, determines an organism's characteristics.

GUIDING QUESTION How do humans take advantage of naturally occurring variation among organisms?

EVIDENCE OF UNDERSTANDING *After completing this lesson, assign students the following assessment to show their understanding of hybridization and inbreeding.* Have students work in pairs to create a poster showing how hybridization and inbreeding can be used to develop a plant variety or animal breed with desired characteristics.

For thousands of years, we've produced new varieties of cultivated plants and nearly all domestic animals—including horses, cats, and cows—by selectively breeding for particular traits. Long before Europeans came to the New World, Native Americans had selectively bred teosinte (tee oh SIN tee), a wild grass native to central Mexico, to produce corn, a far more productive and nutritious plant. **Figure 15–2** shows both plants. Corn is now one of the world's most important crops. There are two common methods of selective breeding—hybridization and inbreeding.

Hybridization American botanist Luther Burbank may have been the greatest selective breeder of all time. During his lifetime (1849–1926), he developed more than 800 varieties of plants. As one of his tools, Burbank used **hybridization,** crossing dissimilar individuals to bring together the best of both organisms. Hybrids—the individuals produced by such crosses—are often hardier than either of the parents. Many of Burbank's hybrid crosses combined the disease resistance of one plant with the food-producing capacity of another. The result was a new line of plants that had the traits farmers needed to increase food production. **Figure 15–3** shows a type of peach developed using Burbank's methods.

Inbreeding To maintain desirable characteristics in a line of organisms, breeders often use a technique known as inbreeding. **Inbreeding** is the continued breeding of individuals with similar characteristics. The many breeds of dogs—from beagles to poodles—are maintained using this practice. Inbreeding helps ensure that the characteristics that make each breed unique are preserved. Although inbreeding is useful in preserving certain traits, it can be risky. Most of the members of a breed are genetically similar, which increases the chance that a cross between two individuals will bring together two recessive alleles for a genetic defect.

In Your Notebook *Compare and contrast hybridization and inbreeding.*

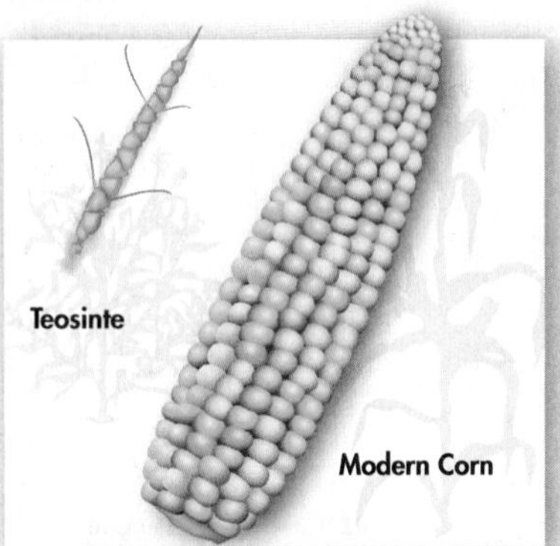

FIGURE 15–2 Corn From Teosinte Modern corn was selectively bred from teosinte at least 6000 years ago. During its domestication, corn lost the ability to survive in the wild but gained valuable agricultural traits. For example, the hard case around the kernel disappeared over time, leaving the rows of soft corn kernels we enjoy today. Observe ***What other differences can you see between the two plants?***

FIGURE 15–3 Selectively Bred Fruit Luther Burbank used hybridization—a form of selective breeding—to develop a variety of plants. These July Elberta peaches, *Prunus persica*, are among his most successful varieties.

Increasing Variation

How do people increase genetic variation?

Selective breeding would be nearly impossible without the wide variation found in natural populations of plants and animals. But sometimes breeders want more variation than exists in nature. **Breeders can increase the genetic variation in a population by introducing mutations, which are the ultimate source of biological diversity.**

When scientists manipulate the genetic makeup of an organism, they are using biotechnology. **Biotechnology** is the application of a technological process, invention, or method to living organisms. Selective breeding is one form of biotechnology important in agriculture and medicine, but there are many others.

Teach

Lead a Discussion

Talk about how both hybridization and inbreeding have been used by humans for thousands of years to make domestic crops and animals more useful. Review the example of Luther Burbank crossing plants to produce desired hybrids.

Ask What process did Burbank use to produce a variety of plants with the characteristics he wanted? *(hybridization)*

DIFFERENTIATED INSTRUCTION

LPR **Less Proficient Readers** To help students understand selective breeding, make a **Vocabulary Word Map** on the board. Begin with the top oval, and fill in Selective Breeding**.** Then, ask students to name the two common methods of selective breeding. *(hybridization and inbreeding)* Draw lines down from the top oval, and write those terms in their own ovals. Call on students to find details of each method in the text, and add those in ovals below.

Study Wkbks A/B, Appendix S32, Vocabulary Word Map. **Transparencies,** GO17.

ELL Focus on ELL: Extend Language

ALL SPEAKERS Provide each English language learner with four note cards, one for each of the lesson's vocabulary terms. Ask students to write a vocabulary term on the front of a card and its definition and a sentence using the term on the back. Students can also make drawings on the cards to help them remember the term's meaning. Then, pair beginning and intermediate speakers with advanced and advanced high speakers, and have pairs work on pronouncing the terms and improving or correcting the definitions and sentences.

Quick Facts

A COMBINATION OF METHODS

In practice, the two common methods of hybridization and inbreeding are often used together. For example, plant growers may inbreed selected plants for several generations to produce plants with desired characteristics. After the growers have established two lines with different desired characteristics through inbreeding, they then cross plants from the two different varieties to produce hybrids with both characteristics.

Answers

FIGURE 15–2 Sample answer: An ear of modern corn is much larger than an ear of teosinte, and the kernels of modern corn are yellow compared to the greenish kernels of teosinte.

IN YOUR NOTEBOOK Both are methods of selective breeding. They are different in that hybridization is the crossing of dissimilar individuals to bring together the best of both organisms, while inbreeding is the breeding of individuals with similar characteristics.

Teach continued

Use Visuals

Use **Figure 15–4** to discuss ways in which scientists can manipulate the genetic makeup of an organism by inducing mutations with radiation or chemicals and by inducing polyploidy with drugs. Make sure students understand that all these techniques are examples of biotechnology.

DIFFERENTIATED INSTRUCTION

L1 Struggling Students Help students understand the information in the table in **Figure 15–4.** For example, explain that the haploid number for domestic oat, 7, is the number of a single set of chromosomes in a gamete. The chromosome number, 42, is the number of chromosomes in a gamete of a polyploid domestic oat. The polyploid crop has 6 sets, or 6N, because 42 ÷ 7 = 6.

Assess and Remediate

EVALUATE UNDERSTANDING

Call on students to explain how hybridization is used to improve plants, how inbreeding is used to maintain dog breeds, and what biotechnology is. Then, have students complete the 15.1 Assessment.

REMEDIATION SUGGESTION

L1 Struggling Students If students have difficulty answering **Question 1b,** have them reread the information on hybridization. Then, call on students to describe what a sunflower looks like and how crosses could be used to produce a sunflower with a shorter stem and red petals.

BIOLOGY.com Students can check their understanding of lesson concepts with the **Self-Test** assessment. They can then take an online version of the **Lesson Assessment.**

Answers

FIGURE 15–4 sugar cane

Polyploid Crops

Plant	Probable Ancestral Haploid Number	Chromosome Number	Ploidy Level
Domestic oat	7	42	6N
Peanut	10	40	4N
Sugar cane	10	80	8N
Banana	11	22, 33	2N, 3N
Cotton	13	52	4N

FIGURE 15–4 Ploidy Numbers Because polyploid plants are often larger than other plants, many farmers deliberately grow polyploid varieties of crops like those listed above. Interpret Tables ***Which plant has undergone the most dramatic changes in chromosome number?***

Bacterial Mutations Mutations—heritable changes in DNA—occur spontaneously, but breeders can increase the mutation rate of an organism by using radiation or chemicals. Many mutations are harmful to the organism. With luck and perseverance, however, breeders can often produce a few mutants—individuals with mutations—with useful characteristics that are not found in the original population. This technique has been particularly useful with bacteria. Because they are small, millions of bacteria can be treated with radiation or chemicals at the same time, which increases the chances of producing a useful mutant. This technique has allowed scientists to develop hundreds of useful bacterial strains. For instance, we have known for decades that certain strains of oil-digesting bacteria are effective for cleaning up oil spills. Today scientists are working to produce bacteria that can clean up radioactive substances and metal pollution in the environment.

Polyploid Plants Drugs that prevent the separation of chromosomes during meiosis are very useful in plant breeding. These drugs can produce cells that have many times the normal number of chromosomes. Plants grown from these cells are called polyploid because they have many sets of chromosomes. Polyploidy is usually fatal in animals. But, for reasons that are not clear, plants are much better at tolerating extra sets of chromosomes. Polyploidy can quickly produce new species of plants that are larger and stronger than their diploid relatives. A number of important crop plants, including bananas and many varieties of citrus fruits, have been produced in this way. **Figure 15–4** lists several examples of polyploid plants.

15.1 Assessment

IN B.7.5

Review Key Concepts

1. a. Review Give an example of selective breeding.
   b. Compare and Contrast Suppose you are a geneticist trying to develop a sunflower with red petals and a short stem. As you compare the sunflowers you have on hand, what genetic variations would you look for? What kinds of plants would you select for crossing?
2. a. Review What is the relationship between genetic variations and mutations?
   b. Explain How can breeders introduce mutations?
   c. Draw Conclusions How is selective breeding a form of biotechnology?

WRITE ABOUT SCIENCE

Explanation

3. Write a paragraph in which you suggest ways that plants could be genetically altered to improve the world's food supply. (*Hint*: The first sentence in your paragraph should express the paragraph's main idea.)

BIOLOGY.com Search Lesson 15.1 GO • Self-Test • Lesson Assessment

Assessment Answers

1a. Sample answer: Corn was produced from selectively bred teosinte.

1b. You would look for reddish petals and shorter stems. You would select plants with shorter stems and plants with red pigment in their flowers for crossing.

2a. the more mutations, the greater the genetic variation

2b. with radiation and chemicals

2c. Sample answer: Biotechnology is the application of a technological process to living organisms. Since selective breeding is a technological process that helps humans breed organisms with desired traits, it is a form of biotechnology.

WRITE ABOUT SCIENCE

3. Answers will vary. Students might suggest genetically altering plants to increase yield, calorie or vitamin content, or resistance to disease and agricultural pests.

15.2 Recombinant DNA

NoS.10 Scientific discoveries and new technologies.

THINK ABOUT IT Suppose you have an electronic game you want to change. Knowing that the game depends on a coded program in a computer microchip, how would you set about rewriting the program? First you'd need a way to get the existing program out of the microchip. Then you'd have to read the program, make the changes you want, and put the modified code back into the microchip. What does this scenario have to do with genetic engineering? Just about everything.

Copying DNA

How do scientists copy the DNA of living organisms?

Until recently plant and animal breeders could only work with variations that already exist in nature. Even when breeders tried to add variation by introducing mutations, the changes they produced were unpredictable. Today genetic engineers can transfer certain genes at will from one organism to another, designing new living things to meet specific needs.

Recall from Chapter 14 that it is relatively easy to extract DNA from cells and tissues. The extracted DNA can be cut into fragments of manageable size using restriction enzymes. These restriction fragments can then be separated according to size using gel electrophoresis or another similar technique. That's the easy part. The tough part comes next: How do you find a specific gene?

The problem is huge. If we were to cut DNA from a bacterium like *E. coli* into restriction fragments averaging 1000 base pairs in length, we would have 4000 restriction fragments. In the human genome, we would have 3 million restriction fragments. How do we find the DNA of a single gene among millions of fragments? In some respects, it's the classic problem of finding a needle in a haystack—we have an enormous pile of hay and just one needle.

Actually, there is a way to find a needle in a haystack. We can toss the hay in front of a powerful magnet until something sticks. The hay won't stick, but a needle made of iron or steel will. Believe it or not, similar techniques can help scientists identify specific genes.

Key Questions

How do scientists copy the DNA of living organisms?

How is recombinant DNA used?

How can genes from one organism be inserted into another organism?

Vocabulary

polymerase chain reaction
recombinant DNA
plasmid
genetic marker
transgenic
clone

Taking Notes

Preview Visuals Before you read, preview **Figure 15–7** and write down any questions you may have about the figure. As you read, find answers to your questions.

MYSTERY CLUE

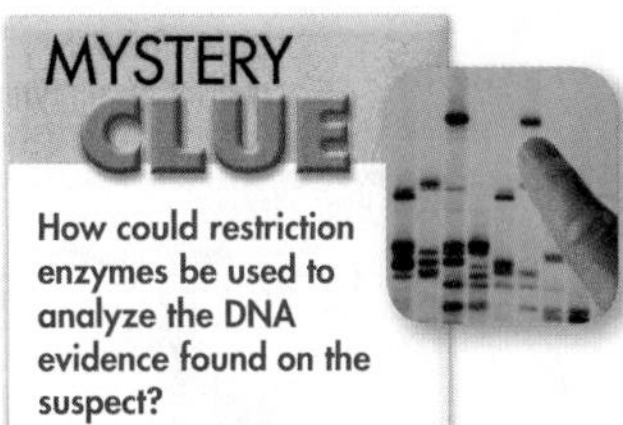

How could restriction enzymes be used to analyze the DNA evidence found on the suspect?

Getting Started

Objectives

15.2.1 Explain how scientists manipulate DNA.

15.2.2 Describe the importance of recombinant DNA.

15.2.3 Define *transgenic* and describe the usefulness of some transgenic organisms to humans.

Student Resources

Study Workbooks A and B, 15.2 Worksheets

Spanish Study Workbook, 15.2 Worksheets

Lab Manual A, 15.2 Quick Lab Worksheet

 Lesson Overview • Lesson Notes • Activities: Tutor Tube, Art in Motion • Assessment: Self-Test, Lesson Assessment

For corresponding lesson in the **Foundation Edition**, see pages 357–361.

Activate Prior Knowledge

Call on students to review how scientists use restriction enzymes to cut DNA and the process of gel electrophoresis to separate and analyze DNA fragments.

Discuss restriction enzymes with students. Then, talk about how DNA might be used in evaluating suspects in a crime. Students can go online to **Biology.com** to gather their evidence.

LESSON 15.2

Teach for Understanding

ENDURING UNDERSTANDING DNA is the universal code for life; it enables an organism to transmit hereditary information and, along with the environment, determines an organism's characteristics.

GUIDING QUESTION How do scientists study and work with specific genes?

EVIDENCE OF UNDERSTANDING *After completing this lesson, assign students the following assessment to show their understanding of plasmid DNA transformation.* Ask students to write instructions for inserting a human gene into bacterial DNA. Tell them their instructions should be written like a cooking recipe. You might provide samples of recipes for students to examine. Have volunteers share their "recipes" with the class.

IN INDIANA ACADEMIC STANDARDS

For the full text of all standards, see the Course Overview in the front matter of this book.

NoS.10 Describe how scientific discoveries lead to the development of new technologies, and conversely how technological advances can lead to scientific discoveries through new experimental methods and equipment.

Teach

Lead a Discussion

Talk about Douglas Prasher's investigation of the protein GFP.

Ask Why did Prasher want to determine the mRNA base sequence that coded for GFP? *(because the sequence of bases gives the instructions for the protein)*

Ask Why was finding the gene for GFP important to genetic engineering? *(GFP can be used to link to a specific protein so scientists could study how the linked protein was being made in a cell.)*

DIFFERENTIATED INSTRUCTION

LPR Less Proficient Readers To help struggling readers better understand Prasher's work, create a **Flowchart** on the board that outlines his process. Start with the step: Used the GFP amino acid sequence to predict an mRNA sequence. Discuss this step with students to make sure they understand what Prasher did. If necessary, have students review **The Genetic Code** from Lesson 13.2. Then, list the second step: Made a complementary base sequence to attract GFP mRNA. Again, discuss this step as a class before moving on to the next.

Study Wkbks A/B, Appendix S25, Flowchart. **Transparencies,** GO8.

ELL Focus on ELL: Access Content

BEGINNING AND INTERMEDIATE SPEAKERS

Before students read the lesson, give them each an empty **T-Chart.** In the left column, have them write the lesson's green headings: **Copying DNA, Changing DNA,** and **Transgenic Organisms.** As students read, they can fill in the right column with vocabulary terms, definitions, and details of the processes, as well as translations into their native language. Suggest that beginning speakers draw illustrations to help them remember the meaning of each term or concept.

Study Wkbks A/B, Appendix S30, T-Chart. **Transparencies,** GO15.

FIGURE 15–5 A Fluorescent Gene The Pacific Ocean jellyfish, *Aequoria victoria,* emits a bluish glow. A protein in the jellyfish absorbs the blue light and produces green fluorescence. This protein, called GFP, is now widely used in genetic engineering.

Finding Genes In 1987, Douglas Prasher, a biologist at Woods Hole Oceanographic Institute in Massachusetts, wanted to find a specific gene in a jellyfish. The gene he hoped to identify is the one that codes for a molecule called green fluorescent protein, or GFP. This natural protein, found in the jellyfish shown in **Figure 15–5,** absorbs energy from light and makes parts of the jellyfish glow. Prasher thought that GFP from the jellyfish could be used to report when a protein was being made in a cell. If he could somehow link GFP to a specific protein, it would be a bit like attaching a light bulb to that molecule.

To find the GFP gene, Prasher studied the amino acid sequence of part of the GFP protein. By comparing this sequence to a genetic code table, he was able to predict a probable mRNA base sequence that would have coded for this sequence of amino acids. Next, Prasher used a complementary base sequence to "attract" an mRNA that matched his prediction and would bind to that sequence by base pairing. After screening a genetic "library" with thousands of different mRNA sequences from the jellyfish, he found one that bound perfectly.

After Prasher located the mRNA that produced GFP, he set out to find the actual gene. Taking a gel in which restriction fragments from the jellyfish genome had been separated, he found that one of the fragments bound tightly to the mRNA. That fragment contained the actual gene for GFP, which is now widely used to label proteins in living cells. The method he used, shown in **Figure 15–6,** is called Southern blotting. Today it is often quicker and less expensive for scientists to search for genes in computer databases where the complete genomes of many organisms are available.

FIGURE 15–6 Southern Blotting Southern blot analysis, named after its inventor Edwin Southern, is a research technique for finding specific DNA sequences, among dozens. A labeled piece of nucleic acid serves as a probe among the DNA fragments.

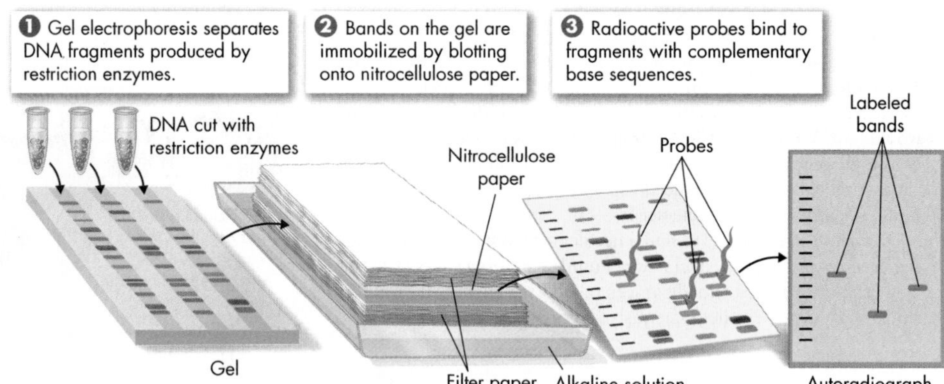

1 Gel electrophoresis separates DNA fragments produced by restriction enzymes.
2 Bands on the gel are immobilized by blotting onto nitrocellulose paper.
3 Radioactive probes bind to fragments with complementary base sequences.
DNA cut with restriction enzymes
Gel
Nitrocellulose paper
Filter paper
Alkaline solution
Probes
Labeled bands
Autoradiograph

How Science Works

FINDING GFP IN A JELLYFISH

The bioluminescence, or glow, in the jellyfish *Aequoria victoria* is produced by two proteins. One, called aequorin, produces a blue light. The other, called green fluorescent protein (GFP), absorbs the blue light and re-emits it as a green fluorescence. GFP was discovered in 1962 by a Princeton scientist, Osamu Shimomura. During the summers, Shimomura would collect thousands of these jellyfish per day from a harbor on the coast of Washington State. From those organisms, he was able to isolate both proteins in the lab. At first, the protein aequorin received the most attention. It wasn't until years later that Prasher discovered the gene that coded for GFP. That protein has proved useful for studies in genetic engineering.

Polymerase Chain Reaction Once they find a gene, biologists often need to make many copies of it. A technique known as **polymerase chain reaction** (PCR) allows them to do exactly that. At one end of the original piece of DNA, a biologist adds a short piece of DNA that complements a portion of the sequence. At the other end, the biologist adds another short piece of complementary DNA. These short pieces are known as primers because they prepare, or prime, a place for DNA polymerase to start working.

As **Figure 15–7** suggests, the idea behind the use of PCR primers is surprisingly simple. **The first step in using the polymerase chain reaction method to copy a gene is to heat a piece of DNA, which separates its two strands. Then, as the DNA cools, primers bind to the single strands. Next, DNA polymerase starts copying the region between the primers. These copies can serve as templates to make still more copies.** In this way, just a few dozen cycles of replication can produce billions of copies of the DNA between the primers.

Where did Kary Mullis, the American scientist who invented PCR, find a DNA polymerase enzyme that could stand repeated cycles of heating and cooling? Mullis found it in bacteria from the hot springs of Yellowstone National Park in the northwestern United States—a powerful example of the importance of biodiversity to biotechnology!

In Your Notebook *List the steps in the PCR method.*

Changing DNA

How is recombinant DNA used?

Just as they were beginning to learn how to read and analyze DNA sequences, scientists began wondering if it might be possible to change the DNA of a living cell. As many of them realized, this feat had already been accomplished decades earlier. Do you remember Griffith's experiments on bacterial transformation? During transformation, a cell takes in DNA from outside the cell, and that added DNA becomes a component of the cell's own genome. Today biologists understand that Griffith's extract of heat-killed bacteria contained DNA fragments. When he mixed those fragments with live bacteria, a few of them took up the DNA molecules, transforming them and changing their characteristics. Griffith, of course, could only do this with DNA extracted from other bacteria.

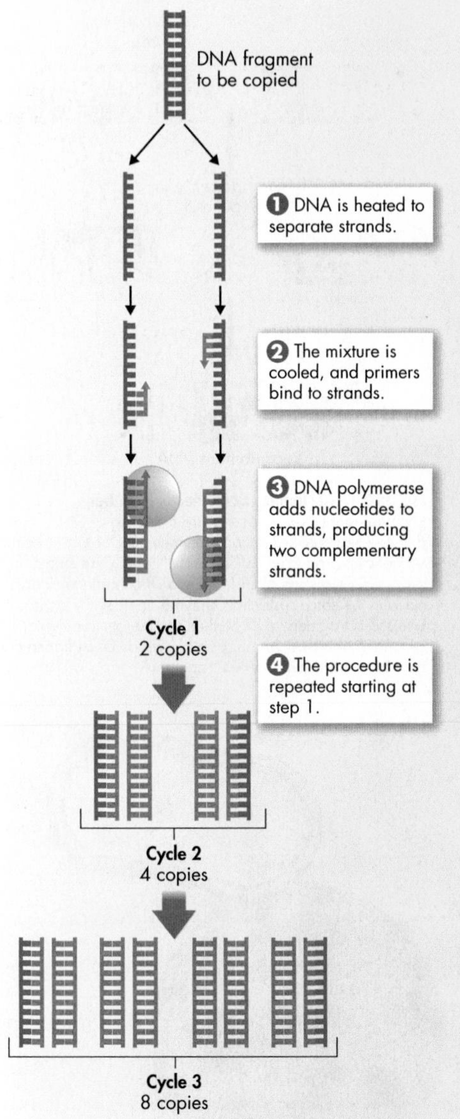

DNA fragment to be copied
1 DNA is heated to separate strands.
2 The mixture is cooled, and primers bind to strands.
3 DNA polymerase adds nucleotides to strands, producing two complementary strands.
4 The procedure is repeated starting at step 1.
Cycle 1
2 copies
Cycle 2
4 copies
Cycle 3
8 copies

FIGURE 15–7 The PCR Method Polymerase chain reaction is used to make multiple copies of a gene. This method is particularly useful when only tiny amounts of DNA are available. **Calculate** ***How many copies of the DNA fragment will there be after six PCR cycles?*** MATH

LESSON 15.2

Use Visuals

Have students examine **Figure 15–7,** which shows the steps in the PCR method. Point out that this method starts a chain reaction, which means it continues over and over again.

Ask What is a primer? *(A primer is a short piece of DNA that complements a portion of the original DNA sequence.)*

Ask Why does the DNA polymerase used in PCR need to be able to withstand repeated cycles of heating and cooling? *(The process of PCR involves many cycles of copying DNA. Each cycle has a step in which the mixture is heated and a step in which it is cooled.)*

Ask What is the purpose of PCR? *(to make many copies of a gene)*

DIFFERENTIATED INSTRUCTION

L1 Struggling Students Make sure students understand the process of PCR by working through each numbered step on **Figure 15–7,** one-by-one.

Ask Why is it important to separate the strands of DNA in step 1? *(The strands need to be separated so they can each be used as a template to make new copies of the gene.)*

Ask In step 2, what happens as the mixture cools? *(The primers bind to the DNA strands.)*

Then, talk about how scientists use PCR.

Ask Why is this technique especially useful when only small amounts of the original DNA are available? *(It allows scientists to make many copies of a gene from a relatively small sample.)*

UbD Check for Understanding

ORAL QUESTIONING

Use the following prompts to gauge students' understanding of PCR.

- Why do scientists use PCR?
- What is the purpose of adding primers to the DNA?
- What does DNA polymerase do?
- How are the first two copies of DNA used to further the process?

ADJUST INSTRUCTION

Evaluate students' answers to get a sense of what they understand about PCR and what they are having trouble with. Review the process as a class so students can hear the steps described in different ways.

Answers

FIGURE 15–7 64

IN YOUR NOTEBOOK (1) DNA is heated to separate strands. (2) The mixture is cooled, and primers bind to strands. (3) DNA polymerase adds nucleotides to strands, producing two complementary strands. (4) The procedure is repeated, starting at step 1.

Teach continued

Build Reading Skills

Explain that one way to understand difficult material is by making an outline. Begin an outline on the board with the following title and two primary heads:

Changing DNA in Cells

I Combining DNA Fragments

II Plasmids and Genetic Markers

Ask students to complete the outline on their own by adding details under each primary head. Point out that they may have more than one level under each primary head. After students have completed their outlines, divide the class into small groups. Have group members compare their outlines and discuss concepts they found difficult to understand.

DIFFERENTIATED INSTRUCTION

ELL English Language Learners Before students make their outline, have an English language learner read the boldface Key Concept on this page about recombinant-DNA technology. Then, pair beginning and intermediate speakers with advanced and advanced high speakers, and ask each pair to discuss any words they don't understand. Encourage the more proficient speakers to help the less proficient speakers summarize the Key Concept in their own words.

L3 Advanced Students Ask students who have a firm grasp of the concepts related to recombinant DNA to act as "visiting resources" for the other students. Have them go from group to group to answer questions and clarify misconceptions. Ask them to write down any questions they cannot answer, and then discuss these questions as a class.

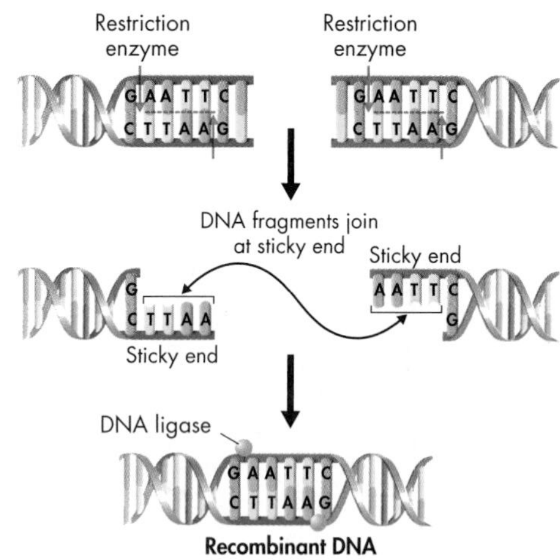

FIGURE 15–8 Joining DNA Pieces Together Recombinant DNA molecules are made up of DNA from different sources. Restriction enzymes cut DNA at specific sequences, producing "sticky ends," which are single-stranded overhangs of DNA. If two DNA molecules are cut with the same restriction enzyme, their sticky ends will bond to a fragment of DNA that has the complementary sequence of bases. An enzyme known as DNA ligase can then be used to join the two fragments.

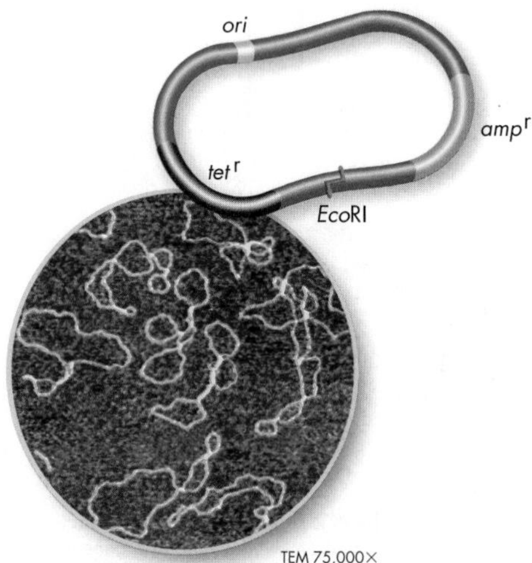

FIGURE 15–9 A Plasmid Map Plasmids used for genetic engineering typically contain a replication start signal, called the origin of replication (*ori*), and a restriction enzyme cutting site, such as *Eco*RI. They also contain genetic markers, like the antibiotic resistance genes tet^r and amp^r shown here.

Combining DNA Fragments With today's technologies, scientists can produce custom-built DNA molecules in the lab and then insert those molecules—along with the genes they carry—into living cells. The first step in this sort of genetic engineering is to build a DNA sequence with the gene or genes you'd like to insert into a cell. Machines known as DNA synthesizers can produce short pieces of DNA, up to several hundred bases in length. These synthetic sequences can then be joined to natural sequences using DNA ligase or other enzymes that splice DNA together. These same enzymes make it possible to take a gene from one organism and attach it to the DNA of another organism, as shown in **Figure 15–8.** The resulting molecules are called **recombinant DNA.** This technology relies on the fact that any pair of complementary sequences tends to bond, even if each sequence comes from a different organism. **Recombinant-DNA technology—joining together DNA from two or more sources—makes it possible to change the genetic composition of living organisms.** By manipulating DNA in this way, scientists can investigate the structure and functions of genes.

Plasmids and Genetic Markers Scientists working with recombinant DNA soon discovered that many of the DNA molecules they tried to insert into host cells simply vanished because the cells often did not copy, or replicate, the added DNA. Today scientists join recombinant DNA to another piece of DNA containing a replication "start" signal. This way, whenever the cell copies its own DNA, it copies the recombinant DNA too.

In addition to their own chromosomes, some bacteria contain small circular DNA molecules known as **plasmids.** Plasmids, like those shown in **Figure 15–9,** are widely used in recombinant DNA studies. Joining DNA to a plasmid, and then using the recombinant plasmid to transform bacteria, results in the replication of the newly added DNA along with the rest of the cell's genome.

Plasmids are also found in yeasts, which are single-celled eukaryotes that can be transformed with recombinant DNA as well. Biologists working with yeasts can construct artificial chromosomes containing centromeres, telomeres, and replication start sites. These artificial chromosomes greatly simplify the process of introducing recombinant DNA into the yeast genome.

Biology In-Depth

PLASMIDS

Plasmids, which are found in almost all bacterial cells, are nonchromosomal DNA molecules scattered within the bacterial cytoplasm. The DNA in plasmids is helical and double stranded, just as chromosomal DNA is, though in plasmids the DNA forms a circle, with the two ends of the molecule covalently bonded together. A plasmid may contain from just a few genes to 20 or more genes. Plasmids are not necessary for the growth of bacteria, although some plasmids can code for enzymes that make the bacteria resistant to antibiotics. The ability of some plasmids to move into and out of bacterial chromosomes makes them extremely useful in genetic engineering.

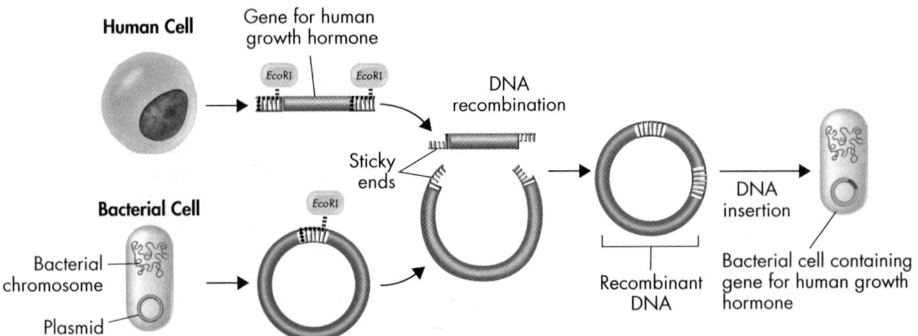

FIGURE 15–10 Plasmid DNA Transformation Scientists can insert a piece of DNA into a plasmid if both the plasmid and the target DNA have been cut by the same restriction enzymes to create sticky ends. With this method, bacteria can be used to produce human growth hormone. First, a human gene is inserted into bacterial DNA. Then, the new combination of genes is returned to a bacterial cell, which replicates the recombinant DNA over and over again. Infer ***Why might scientists want to copy the gene for human growth hormone?***

Figure 15–10 shows how bacteria can be transformed using recombinant plasmids. First, the DNA being used for transformation is joined to a plasmid. The plasmid DNA contains a signal for replication, helping to ensure that if the DNA does get inside a bacterial cell, it will be replicated. In addition, the plasmid also has a genetic marker, such as a gene for antibiotic resistance. A **genetic marker** is a gene that makes it possible to distinguish bacteria that carry the plasmid from those that don't. Using genetic markers, researchers can mix recombinant plasmids with a culture of bacteria, add enough DNA to transform just one cell in a million, and still locate that one cell. After transformation, the culture is treated with an antibiotic. Only those rare cells that have been transformed survive, because only they carry the resistance gene.

In Your Notebook *Write a summary of the process of plasmid DNA transformation.*

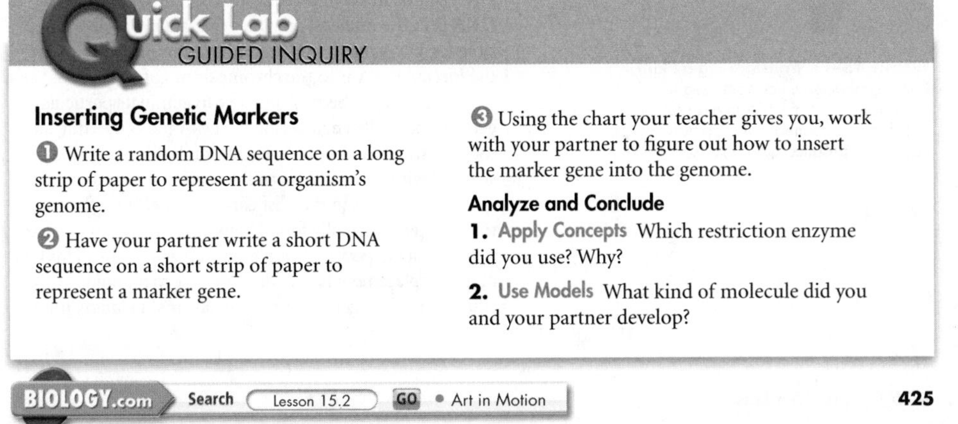

Quick Lab
GUIDED INQUIRY

Inserting Genetic Markers

1. Write a random DNA sequence on a long strip of paper to represent an organism's genome.
2. Have your partner write a short DNA sequence on a short strip of paper to represent a marker gene.
3. Using the chart your teacher gives you, work with your partner to figure out how to insert the marker gene into the genome.

Analyze and Conclude

1. **Apply Concepts** Which restriction enzyme did you use? Why?
2. **Use Models** What kind of molecule did you and your partner develop?

Use Visuals

Have students examine **Figure 15–10.**

Ask What allows the gene from the human cell to be inserted into the plasmid? *(The same restriction enzymes have been used to cut both the human DNA and the plasmid, producing "sticky ends" on each.)*

Ask Why would scientists make sure the plasmid inserted with a human gene contains a genetic marker? *(so they can distinguish bacteria that carry the plasmid from bacteria that don't)*

DIFFERENTIATED INSTRUCTION

L1 Special Needs Have students work in small groups to make a model of bacterial transformation. Group special needs students with students who have a good understanding of how bacteria can be transformed using recombinant plasmids. Provide each group with lengths of plastic or rubber tubing to represent parts of plasmids and genes. Students can cover the tubing with tape of different colors to represent genes, and plastic bags can represent bacterial cells. After groups have had time to manipulate these materials, have each group demonstrate how a gene can be inserted into a plasmid with a genetic marker, which is then inserted into a bacterial cell.

BIOLOGY.com To view an animated version of transformation using recombinant plasmids, have students watch **Art in Motion: Plasmid DNA Transformation.**

Quick Lab

PURPOSE Students will model the insertion of a genetic marker in a DNA sequence to develop recombinant DNA.

PLANNING Divide the class into pairs to do the lab. Provide students with a chart of restriction enzymes, showing where they cut DNA sequences.

ANALYZE AND CONCLUDE

1. Answers will depend on students' sequences.
2. a molecule of recombinant DNA

Answers

FIGURE 15–10 Sample answer: By copying that gene, scientists can mass produce the hormone, perhaps for use as a medicine.

IN YOUR NOTEBOOK Sample answer: In plasmid DNA transformation, a desired gene sequence is inserted into a plasmid, using restriction enzymes to create sticky ends. The recombinant plasmid, which contains a genetic marker so that it can easily be selected for, is then returned to a bacterial cell. The bacterial cell replicates the recombinant DNA over and over again, producing vast amounts of the desired protein.

LESSON 15.2

Teach continued

Build Study Skills

Divide the class into small groups, and ask each group to discuss transgenic plants, transgenic animals, and cloning. First, have groups discuss **Figures 15–11** and **15–12,** and make sure all group members understand how transgenic organisms and clones are produced. Have each group write ten questions about lesson content on a sheet of paper and the answers to the questions on another sheet of paper. Tell groups to trade questions and answer the new set of questions. Then, have groups share answer sheets. As a class, discuss any differences between groups' answers.

DIFFERENTIATED INSTRUCTION

ELL **English Language Learners** Help students understand the meaning of the term *transgenic.* Point out that *trans-* means "transferred" and *-genic* refers to "genes." Therefore, a transgenic plant is a plant whose cells have "transferred genes" from other organisms.

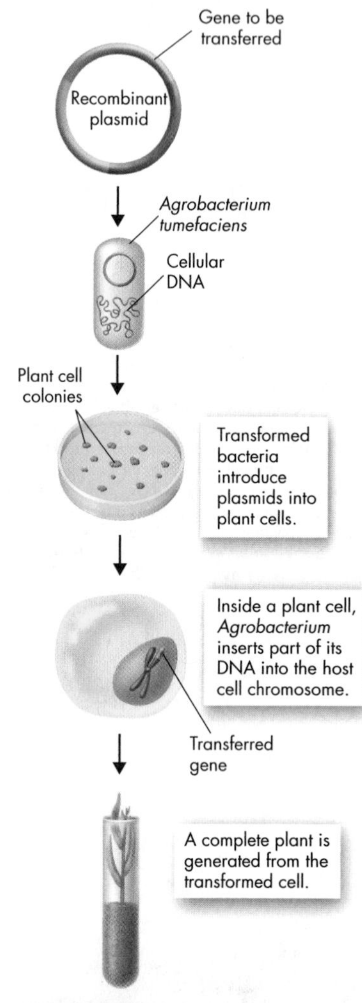

FIGURE 15–11 Transforming a Plant Cell *Agrobacterium* can be used to introduce bacterial DNA into a plant cell. The transformed cells can be cultured to produce adult plants.

Transgenic Organisms

How can genes from one organism be inserted into another organism?

The universal nature of the genetic code makes it possible to construct organisms that are **transgenic,** containing genes from other species. **Transgenic organisms can be produced by the insertion of recombinant DNA into the genome of a host organism.** Like bacterial plasmids, the DNA molecules used for transformation of plant and animal cells contain genetic markers that help scientists identify which cells have been transformed.

Transgenic technology was perfected using mice in the 1980s. Genetic engineers can now produce transgenic plants, animals, and microorganisms. By examining the traits of a genetically modified organism, it is possible to learn about the function of the transferred gene. This ability has contributed greatly to our understanding of gene regulation and expression.

Transgenic Plants Many plant cells can be transformed using *Agrobacterium.* In nature this bacterium inserts a small DNA plasmid that produces tumors in a plant's cells. Scientists can deactivate the plasmid's tumor-producing gene and replace it with a piece of recombinant DNA. The recombinant plasmid can then be used to infect and transform plant cells, as shown in **Figure 15–11.**

There are other ways to produce transgenic plants as well. When their cell walls are removed, plant cells in culture will sometimes take up DNA on their own. DNA can also be injected directly into some cells. If transformation is successful, the recombinant DNA is integrated into one of the plant cell's chromosomes.

Transgenic Animals Scientists can transform animal cells using some of the same techniques used for plant cells. The egg cells of many animals are large enough that DNA can be injected directly into the nucleus. Once the DNA is in the nucleus, enzymes that are normally responsible for DNA repair and recombination may help insert the foreign DNA into the chromosomes of the injected cell.

Recently it has become possible to eliminate particular genes by carefully engineering the DNA molecules that are used for transformation. The DNA molecules can be constructed with two ends that will sometimes recombine with specific sequences in the host chromosome. Once they do, the host gene normally found between those two sequences may be lost or specifically replaced with a new gene. This kind of gene replacement has made it possible to pinpoint the specific functions of genes in many organisms, including mice.

 Check for Understanding

INDEX CARD SUMMARIES

Give each student an index card, and ask students to write one concept about recombinant DNA, plasmid DNA transformation, or transgenic organisms that they understand on the front of the card. Then, have them write a major question they still have about one of these concepts on the back of the card.

ADJUST INSTRUCTION

Evaluate students' cards to get a sense of which concepts most students understand and which they are struggling with. If a majority of students are having trouble with the same concept, review the topic as a class. Read several of the questions aloud, and invite volunteers to provide answers. After an answer has been given, encourage other students to add details or clarifications.

An egg cell is taken from an adult female sheep.

Egg Cell

The nucleus of the egg cell is removed.

A donor cell is taken from a sheep's udder.

Donor Nucleus

The two cells are fused using an electric shock.

Fused Cell

The fused cell begins dividing normally.

Embryo

The embryo is placed in the uterus of a foster mother.

Foster Mother

The embryo develops into a lamb—Dolly.

Cloned Lamb

FIGURE 15–12 Cloning Animals Animal cloning uses a procedure called nuclear transplantation. The process combines an egg cell with a donor nucleus to produce an embryo. Apply Concepts ***Why won't the cloned lamb resemble its foster mother?***

Cloning A **clone** is a member of a population of genetically identical cells produced from a single cell. The technique of cloning uses a single cell from an adult organism to grow an entirely new individual that is genetically identical to the organism from which the cell was taken.

Cloned colonies of bacteria and other microorganisms are easy to grow, but this is not always true of multicellular organisms, especially animals. Clones of animals were first produced in 1952 using amphibian tadpoles. In 1997, Scottish scientist Ian Wilmut stunned biologists by announcing that he had produced a sheep, called Dolly, by cloning.

Figure 15–12 shows the basic steps by which an animal can be cloned. First, the nucleus of an unfertilized egg cell is removed. Next, the egg cell is fused with a donor cell that contains a nucleus, taken from an adult. The resulting diploid egg develops into an embryo, which is then implanted in the uterine wall of a foster mother, where it develops until birth. Cloned cows, pigs, mice, and even cats have since been produced using similar techniques.

15.2 Assessment

IN NoS.10

Review Key Concepts

1. a. Review Describe the process scientists use to copy DNA.
   b. Infer Why would a scientist want to know the sequence of a DNA molecule?
2. a. Review How do scientists use recombinant DNA?
   b. Use Analogies How is genetic engineering like computer programming?
3. a. Review What is a transgenic organism?
   b. Compare and Contrast Compare the transformation of a plant cell with the transformation of an animal cell.

PRACTICE PROBLEM

4. Design an experiment to find a way to treat disorders caused by a single gene. State your hypothesis and list the steps you would follow. (*Hint*: Think about the uses of recombinant DNA.)

BIOLOGY.com Search Lesson 15.2 GO • Self-Test • Lesson Assessment

Assess and Remediate

EVALUATE UNDERSTANDING

Call on a volunteer to summarize the polymerase chain reaction method. Call on other volunteers to outline the steps of PCR. Use the same process to evaluate students' understanding of plasmid DNA transformation and cloning. Then, have students complete the 15.2 Assessment.

REMEDIATION SUGGESTION

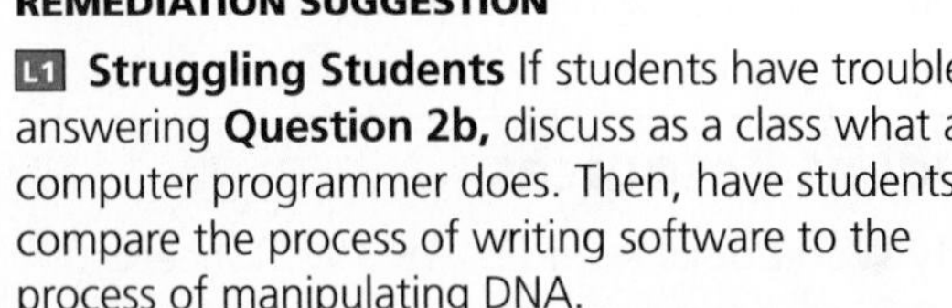

L1 Struggling Students If students have trouble answering **Question 2b,** discuss as a class what a computer programmer does. Then, have students compare the process of writing software to the process of manipulating DNA.

BIOLOGY.com Students can check their understanding of lesson concepts with the **Self-Test** assessment. They can then take an online version of the **Lesson Assessment.**

Answers

FIGURE 15–12 The cloned lamb has the DNA of the donor cell nucleus, not that of the foster mother.

Assessment Answers

1a. The first step is to heat the DNA, which separates its two strands. Then, as the DNA cools, primers bind to the single strands. Next, DNA polymerase starts copying the region between the primers. These copies can serve as templates to make more copies.

1b. Knowing the sequence allows scientists to find individual genes.

2a. to change the genetic composition of living organisms and investigate the structure and function of genes

2b. Sample answer: In computer programming, a programmer writes a program that produces a specific output. In genetic engineering, a scientist engineers genes to produce desired gene products.

3a. an organism that contains genes from other species

3b. Transforming a plant cell can involve the use of *Agrobacterium* to introduce bacterial DNA into the plant cell. Also, if plant cell walls are removed, plant cells in culture will sometimes take up DNA on their own. Scientists can transform animal cells using some of the same techniques used to transform plant cells. Transforming animal cells can also involve injecting DNA directly into an animal cell nucleus or using specially designed DNA molecules.

PRACTICE PROBLEM

4. Experimental designs will vary. A possible design might involve using a transgenic organism to insert recombinant DNA into the affected organism to replace the gene that causes the disorder.

LESSON 15.3

Getting Started

Objectives

15.3.1 Describe the benefits of genetic engineering as they relate to agriculture and industry.

15.3.2 Explain how recombinant DNA technology can improve human health.

15.3.3 Summarize the process of DNA fingerprinting and explain its uses.

Student Resources

Study Workbooks A and B, 15.3 Worksheets

Spanish Study Workbook, 15.3 Worksheets

Lab Manual B, 15.3 Data Analysis Worksheet, Hands-On Activity Worksheet

Lesson Overview • Lesson Notes • Activity: Art Review • Assessment: Self-Test, Lesson Assessment

For corresponding lesson in the **Foundation Edition**, see pages 362–366.

15.3 Applications of Genetic Engineering

NoS.10 Scientific discoveries and new technologies; NoS.11 Scientific knowledge: environmental and social issues. Also covered: NoS.3.

Key Questions

How can genetic engineering benefit agriculture and industry?

How can recombinant-DNA technology improve human health?

How is DNA used to identify individuals?

Vocabulary

gene therapy
DNA microarray
DNA fingerprinting
forensics

Taking Notes

Outline Make an outline of this lesson by using the green and blue headings. As you read, take notes on the different applications of genetic engineering.

THINK ABOUT IT Have you eaten any genetically modified food lately? Don't worry if you're not sure how to answer that question. In the United States and many other countries, this kind of food doesn't have to be labeled in grocery stores or markets. But if you've eaten corn, potatoes, or soy products in any of your meals this week, chances are close to 100 percent that you've eaten foods modified in some way by genetic engineering.

Agriculture and Industry

How can genetic engineering benefit agriculture and industry?

Everything we eat and much of what we wear come from living organisms. Not surprisingly, then, researchers have used genetic engineering to try to improve the products we get from plants and animals. **Ideally, genetic modification could lead to better, less expensive, and more nutritious food as well as less-harmful manufacturing processes.**

GM Crops Since their introduction in 1996, genetically modified (GM) plants, like the soybeans in **Figure 15–13,** have become an important component of our food supply. In 2007, GM crops made up 92 percent of soybeans, 86 percent of cotton, and 80 percent of corn grown in the United States. One type of modification, which has already proved particularly useful to agriculture, uses bacterial genes that produce a protein known as Bt toxin. While this toxin is harmless to humans and most other animals, enzymes in the digestive systems of insects convert Bt to a form that kills the insects. Plants with the Bt gene, then, do not have to be sprayed with pesticides. In addition, they produce higher yields of crops.

Resistance to insects is just one useful characteristic being engineered into crops. Others include resistance to herbicides, which are chemicals that destroy weeds, and resistance to viral infections. Some transgenic plants may soon produce foods that are resistant to rot and spoilage. And engineers are currently developing GM plants that may produce plastics for the manufacturing industry.

FIGURE 15–13 GM Soybeans Genetically modified soybeans are a popular crop in the United States.

IN INDIANA ACADEMIC STANDARDS

For the full text of all standards, see the Course Overview in the front matter of this book.

NoS.10 Describe how scientific discoveries lead to the development of new technologies, and conversely how technological advances can lead to scientific discoveries through new experimental methods and equipment.

NoS.11 Explain how scientific knowledge can be used to guide decisions on environmental and social issues.

UbD Teach for Understanding

ENDURING UNDERSTANDING DNA is the universal code for life; it enables an organism to transmit hereditary information and, along with the environment, determines an organism's characteristics.

GUIDING QUESTION How do humans use genetic engineering?

EVIDENCE OF UNDERSTANDING *After completing this lesson, assign students the following assessment to show their understanding of an application of genetic engineering.* Have each student write an article for the local newspaper describing how researchers at a local university are using genetic engineering to develop a new product for agriculture, industry, or medicine. Students should describe the product as well as the process by which it is made, using language the general population will understand.

Analyzing Data

NoS.3, NoS.10

Genetically Modified Crops in the United States

U.S. farmers have adopted GM crops widely since their introduction in 1996. Soybeans, cotton, and corn have been modified to tolerate herbicides and resist insect damage. The graph at the right summarizes the extent to which these crops were adopted between 1996 and 2007. The modified traits shown here include herbicide tolerance (HT) and insect resistance (Bt).

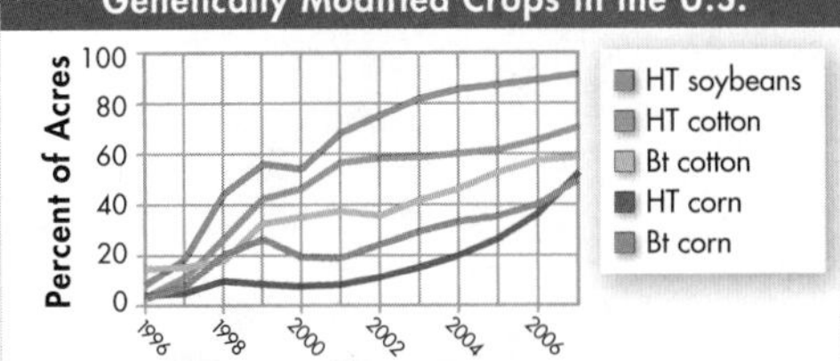

Source: U.S. Department of Agriculture Economic Research Service Data Sets

1. **Analyze Data** Which two crops were most widely and rapidly adopted?
2. **Draw Conclusions** Why do you think the levels of adoption fell at certain points over the period?
3. **Predict** What do you think will happen to HT soybeans and HT corn over the next few years? Why? Use the graph to support your prediction.
4. **Infer** Why do you think an increasing number of farmers have chosen to grow crops with herbicide tolerance?

GM Animals Transgenic animals are also becoming more important to our food supply. For example, about 30 percent of the milk in U.S. markets comes from cows that have been injected with hormones made by recombinant-DNA techniques to increase milk production. Pigs can be genetically modified to produce more lean meat or high levels of healthy omega-3 acids. Using growth-hormone genes, scientists have developed transgenic salmon that grow much more quickly than wild salmon. This effort makes it practical to grow these nutritious fish in captive aquaculture facilities that do not threaten wild populations.

When scientists in Canada combined spider genes into the cells of lactating goats, the goats began to manufacture silk along with their milk. By extracting polymer strands from the milk and weaving them into thread, we can create a light, tough, and flexible material that could be used in such applications as military uniforms, medical sutures, and tennis racket strings. Scientists are now using human genes to develop antibacterial goat milk.

Researchers hope that cloning will enable them to make copies of transgenic animals, which would increase the food supply and could even help save endangered species. In 2008, the U.S. government approved the sale of meat and milk from cloned animals. Many farmers and ranchers hope that cloning technology will allow them to duplicate the best qualities of prize animals without the time and complications of traditional breeding.

FIGURE 15–14 Antibacterial Goat Milk Scientists are working to combine a gene for lysozyme—an antibacterial protein found in human tears and breast milk—into the DNA of goats. Milk from these goats may help prevent infections in young children who drink it. **Apply Concepts** ***What action do scientists hope the lysozyme gene will take in genetically modified goats?***

In Your Notebook *Describe the ways in which GM organisms can benefit agriculture and industry.*

Teach

Build Study Skills

Tell students that studying with a partner may be helpful. Ask students to read the section, **Agriculture and Industry,** and write down any questions they have. Then, have pairs of students discuss the section and find answers in the text to the questions. Lead a class discussion to resolve any unanswered questions.

DIFFERENTIATED INSTRUCTION

L3 Advanced Students Pair students, and ask each pair to choose one of the transgenic plants or animals mentioned in the text and create a **Flowchart** showing how this organism may have been produced. Display flowcharts in the classroom.

Study Wkbks A/B, Appendix S25, Flowchart. **Transparencies,** GO8.

Analyzing Data

PURPOSE Students will analyze data of genetically modified crops in the U.S. to infer why farmers grow GM crops.

ANSWERS

1. HT soybeans and HT cotton
2. Sample answer: Perhaps the price of seed for these GM crops was higher than the expected increase in profit from growing the seed.
3. Sample answer: The percent of acres of HT soybeans will probably level off, because that crop is already grown on about 90 percent of the acreage. The percent of acres of HT corn may rise, because it is now grown on only about 50 percent of the acreage.
4. Sample answer: Those crops aren't affected by the herbicides farmers use to kill weeds. With fewer weeds, more of the fertilizer and soil nutrients can be used by the crop plants, so the crop yield is greater per acre.

Answers

FIGURE 15–14 produce antibacterial lysozyme in the goats' milk

IN YOUR NOTEBOOK Sample answer: Plants can be engineered to kill pests and resist herbicides, viruses, and spoilage. GM plants may be developed to produce plastics. GM animals can produce more milk or leaner meat and grow faster. GM goats may produce silk or antibacterial milk.

Teach continued

Lead a Discussion

Talk about the different ways in which recombinant-DNA technology has been used and might be used in the future to improve human health. Explain that each of the subsections on this page and the next two pages focus on different ways that genetic engineering can be used in medicine and to improve human health. Use the blue heads to focus your discussion on recent advances in the prevention and treatment of disease.

DIFFERENTIATED INSTRUCTION

LPR **Less Proficient Readers** For each of the subsections under **Health and Medicine,** list the main ideas on the board in simplified language. For example, for **Preventing Disease,** list:

- Golden rice is a GM plant that contains an important nutrient for humans.
- Scientists are trying to make GM plants and animals that can produce human antibodies.
- Some GM animals make human proteins. Many of these proteins could help prevent human disease.

Have students write these main ideas in their notebook. Then, ask them to identify and record the main ideas for each of the remaining four subsections.

Address Misconceptions

Genetic Engineering and Disease Students may have the misconception that medical researchers routinely focus on recombinant-DNA technology to cure various diseases, moving from one disease to the next. In reality, researchers often work for years on a specific disease, trying to determine what genes are involved in the disease, how those genes are regulated, and what environmental factors are involved. Explain that treating diseases with recombinant-DNA technology is a science in its infancy.

FIGURE 15–15 Vitamin-Rich Rice Golden rice is a GM plant that contains increased amounts of provitamin A, or beta-carotene. Two genes engineered into the rice genome help the grains produce and accumulate beta-carotene. The intensity of the golden color indicates the concentration of beta-carotene in the edible part of the rice seed.

Health and Medicine

How can recombinant-DNA technology improve human health?

Biotechnology, in its broadest sense, has always been part of medicine. Early physicians extracted substances from plants and animals to cure their patients. Twentieth-century medicine saw the use of vaccination to save countless lives. **Today, recombinant-DNA technology is the source of some of the most important and exciting advances in the prevention and treatment of disease.**

Preventing Disease One interesting development in transgenic technology is golden rice, shown in **Figure 15–15.** This rice contains increased amounts of provitamin A, also known as beta-carotene—a nutrient that is essential for human health. Provitamin A deficiencies produce serious medical problems, including infant blindness. There is hope that provitamin A-rich golden rice will help prevent these problems. Other scientists are developing transgenic plants and animals that produce human antibodies to fight disease.

In the future, transgenic animals may provide us with an ample supply of our own proteins. Several laboratories have engineered transgenic sheep and pigs that produce human proteins in their milk, making it easy to collect and refine the proteins. Many of these proteins can be used in disease prevention.

Medical Research Transgenic animals are often used as test subjects in medical research. In particular they can simulate human diseases in which defective genes play a role. Scientists use models based on these simulations to follow the onset and progression of diseases and to construct tests of new drugs that may be useful for treatment. This approach has been used to develop models for disorders like Alzheimer's disease and arthritis.

Treating Disease When recombinant-DNA techniques were developed for bacteria, biologists realized almost immediately that the technology held the promise to do something that had never been done before—to make important proteins that could prolong and even save human lives. For example, human growth hormone, which is used to treat patients suffering from pituitary dwarfism, was once scarce. Human growth hormone is now widely available because it is mass-produced by recombinant bacteria. Other products now made in genetically engineered bacteria include insulin to treat diabetes, blood-clotting factors for hemophiliacs, and potential cancer-fighting molecules such as interleukin-2 and interferon.

How Science Works

GENETIC ENGINEERING AND HUMAN GROWTH HORMONE

Fifty years ago, the only practical source of human growth hormone was human cadavers. So little hormone is present in any one person's pituitary gland, however, that thousands of cadavers were required to produce small batches of the hormone. To make matters worse, the use of cadavers placed recipients of the hormone at high risk for infection by pathogens that affect the central nervous system. Recombinant-DNA technology changed all that. The gene for the hormone was identified, isolated, and inserted into bacteria. Huge numbers of transformed bacteria made large amounts of the hormone, which was then available for those who needed it.

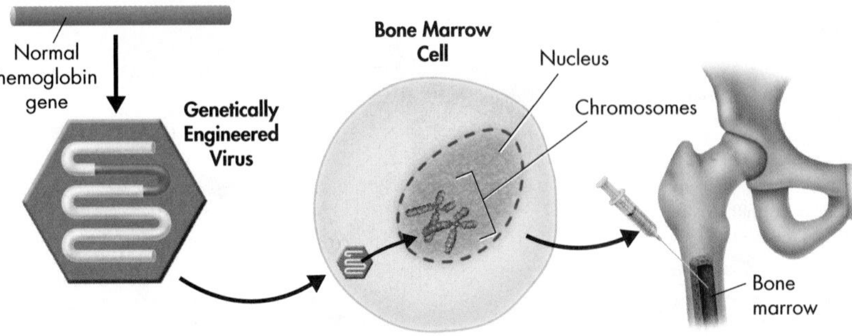

FIGURE 15–16 How Gene Therapy Can Be Used Gene therapy uses normal genes to add to or replace defective genes or to boost a normal function like immunity. Interpret Visuals *How is the virus in this diagram being used?*

If an individual is suffering from a missing or defective gene, can we replace that gene with a healthy one and fix the problem? The experimental field of gene therapy is attempting to answer that question. **Gene therapy** is the process of changing a gene to treat a medical disease or disorder. In gene therapy, an absent or faulty gene is replaced by a normal, working gene. This process allows the body to make the protein or enzyme it needs, which eliminates the cause of the disorder.

The idea of using gene therapy to cure disease arose from the major advances in molecular biology made in the past 20 years, including the Human Genome Project. **Figure 15–16** shows one of the ways in which researchers have attempted to carry out gene therapy. To deliver the correct, or therapeutic, gene to the affected, or target, cells, researchers first engineer a virus that cannot reproduce or cause harmful effects. They place DNA containing the therapeutic gene into the modified virus, and then they infect the patient's cells with it. In theory the virus will insert the healthy gene into the target cell and correct the defect. The challenge, however, is to deliver a gene that works correctly over the long term. For all the promise it holds, in most cases gene therapy remains a high-risk experimental procedure. For gene therapy to become an accepted treatment, we need more reliable ways to insert working genes and to ensure that the DNA used in the therapy does no harm.

Genetic Testing If two prospective parents suspect they are carrying the alleles for a genetic disorder such as cystic fibrosis (CF), how could they find out for sure? Because the CF allele has slightly different DNA sequences from its normal counterpart, genetic tests using labeled DNA probes can distinguish it. Like many genetic tests, the CF test uses specific DNA sequences that detect the complementary base sequences found in the disease-causing alleles. Other genetic tests search for changes in cutting sites of restriction enzymes. Some use PCR to detect differences between the lengths of normal and abnormal alleles. Genetic tests are now available for diagnosing hundreds of disorders.

FIGURE 15–17 A Brave Volunteer Gene therapy can be risky. In 1999, 18-year-old Jesse Gelsinger volunteered for a gene therapy experiment designed to treat a genetic disorder of his liver. He suffered a massive reaction from the viruses used to carry genes into his liver cells, and he died a few days later. Jesse's case makes clear that experiments with gene therapy must be done with great caution.

Quick Facts

THE SAD CASE OF JESSE GELSINGER

Jesse Gelsinger suffered from a genetic disease called ornithine transcarbamylase deficiency, which is a disorder that prevents the liver from breaking down ammonia. The buildup of ammonia that results can be fatal. Jesse had controlled his illness by maintaining a strict diet. He volunteered to take part in the gene therapy experiment because he thought he could help others with the disease who were not as successful as he was at controlling it. The virus used to carry a replacement gene was a modified version of the virus that causes the common cold. Jesse died when the virus caused a massive immune response, leading to organ failure and brain death.

Use Visuals

Make sure students understand that the process shown in **Figure 15–16** is just one example of gene therapy. Ask students to generalize from this example a broad description of what occurs in gene therapy. *(Sample answer: A normal gene is inserted into a genetically engineered virus, which is then used to carry the gene to a target cell.)*

DIFFERENTIATED INSTRUCTION

L1 Struggling Students To help students understand the process in **Figure 15–16** and connect the figure to the text, write the following sentence starters on the board.

- A normal hemoglobin gene is inserted . . . *(into a genetically engineered virus)*
- This virus has been modified so that it cannot . . . *(reproduce or cause harmful effects)*
- In this case, the target cell for the virus is a . . . *(bone marrow cell)*
- When the genetically engineered virus enters the bone marrow cell, it carries a normal gene that will replace . . . *(defective genes)*

Ask students to write a phrase to complete each sentence. Then, call on volunteers to share their responses with the class.

L3 Advanced Students Have interested students investigate the case of Jesse Gelsinger to find out how his death caused changes in the way candidates for gene therapy are accepted. Have them report their findings to the class.

ELL Focus on ELL: Access Content

BEGINNING AND INTERMEDIATE SPEAKERS
Give students an **ELL Frayer Model,** and have them write the term *gene therapy* in the center of the model. Then, have them add a definition of the term in the upper left box, a drawing in the upper right box, examples in the lower left box, and a translation of the definition (if possible) in the lower right box.

Study Wkbks A/B, Appendix S26, ELL Frayer Model. **Transparencies,** GO10.

Answers

FIGURE 15–16 The virus is being used to deliver therapeutic genes to bone marrow cells.

Teach continued

Use Visuals

Focus students' attention on **Figure 15–18,** and then call on a student to read aloud annotation 1a. Point out that the process starts with mRNA, which is involved in DNA transcription. That should indicate to students that the procedure outlined by this figure is related to gene expression. Ask if anyone has a question. Repeat this procedure with each remaining step.

Ask Why are single strands, not double strands, of DNA attached to wells in a microarray plate? *(Single strands are used so they will bind to the single-stranded DNA labeled with fluorescent colors.)*

Make sure that students understand that the labeled cDNA fragments compete for binding sites in the microarray wells. So, if one of the labeled samples expresses the given gene more than the other, it will have more cDNA fragments than the other sample. Therefore, one of the samples will outcompete the other, bind to the complementary DNA in the well, and turn the spot either green or red.

Ask Which spot in step 3 will turn yellow? What does that mean? *(The spot in front will turn yellow. It means that both labeled samples express the given gene equally.)*

DIFFERENTIATED INSTRUCTION

L1 Struggling Students Make a **Flowchart** on the board of the process involved in DNA microarray technology. Use simple sentences to clarify the process. For example:

1. Isolate mRNA from cancer cells and normal cells.
2. Use enzymes to copy the mRNA base sequence to DNA with fluorescent labels.
3. Mix those DNA samples with DNA samples on a microarray.
4. Analyze the samples to see which genes are active in the cancer cell.

Study Wkbks A/B, Appendix S25, Flowchart. **Transparencies,** GO8.

LPR Less Proficient Readers If students have a hard time understanding the description of microarrays, have them focus on the big picture: Microarrays are a way for scientists to study gene expression in cells.

1 Preparing the cDNA Probe

a mRNA samples are isolated from two different types of cells or tissues, such as cancer cells and normal cells.

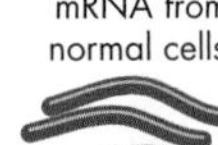

b Enzymes are used to prepare complementary DNA molecules (cDNA) from both groups of mRNA. Contrasting fluorescent labels are attached to both groups of cDNA (red to one, green to the other).

cDNA from cancer cells

cDNA from normal cells

2 Preparing the Microarray

a DNA fragments corresponding to different genes are bound to the wells in a microarray plate.

b Single strands of DNA are attached to wells in the plate.

3 Combining the Probe and Microarray Samples

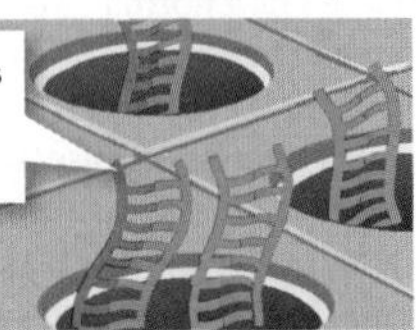

Labeled cDNA molecules bind to complementary sequences on the plate.

FIGURE 15–18 Analyzing Gene Activity DNA microarrays help researchers explore the underlying genetic causes of many human diseases.

Examining Active Genes Even though all of the cells in the human body contain identical genetic material, the same genes are not active in every cell. By studying which genes are active and which are inactive in different cells, scientists can understand how the cells function normally and what happens when genes don't work as they should. Today, scientists use **DNA microarray** technology to study hundreds or even thousands of genes at once to understand their activity levels. A DNA microarray is a glass slide or silicon chip to which spots of single-stranded DNA have been tightly attached. Typically each spot contains a different DNA fragment. Different colored tags are used to label the source of DNA.

Suppose, for example, that you want to compare the genes abnormally expressed in cancer cells with genes in normal cells from the same tissue. After isolating mRNA from both types of cells, you would use an enzyme to copy the mRNA base sequence into single-stranded DNA labeled with fluorescent colors—red for the cancer cell and green for the normal cell. Next you would mix both samples of labeled DNA together and let them compete for binding to the complementary DNA sequences already in the microarray. If the cancer cell produces more of a particular form of mRNA, then more red-labeled molecules will bind at the spot for that gene, turning it red. Where the normal cell produces more mRNA for another gene, that spot will be green. Where there is no difference between the two cell types, the spot will be yellow because it contains both colors. **Figure 15–18** shows how a DNA microarray is constructed and used.

UbD Check for Understanding

DEPTH OF UNDERSTANDING

To gauge students' understanding of DNA microarrays, ask them the purpose of doing a DNA microarray. *(Students with a superficial understanding might say it is to see which genes in cells are active and which are not. Students with a sophisticated understanding might say it can show scientists how gene expression is involved in normal functioning and in disorders.)*

ADJUST INSTRUCTION

If most students show superficial understanding, explore how DNA microarrays might help researchers better understand a disease with a genetic component, such as Type 1 diabetes, by focusing their attention on certain genes that are expressed differently in healthy and affected people.

1 Chromosomes contain many regions with repeated DNA sequences that do not code for proteins. These vary from person to person. Here, one sample has 12 repeats between genes A and B, while the second sample has 9 repeats between the same genes.

2 Restriction enzymes are used to cut the DNA into fragments containing genes and repeats. Note that the repeat fragments from these two samples are of different lengths.

3 The restriction fragments are separated according to size using gel electrophoresis. The DNA fragments containing repeats are then labeled using radioactive probes. This labeling produces a series of bands–the DNA fingerprint.

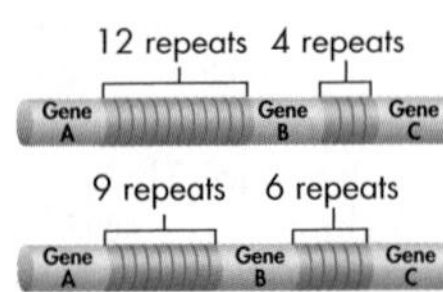

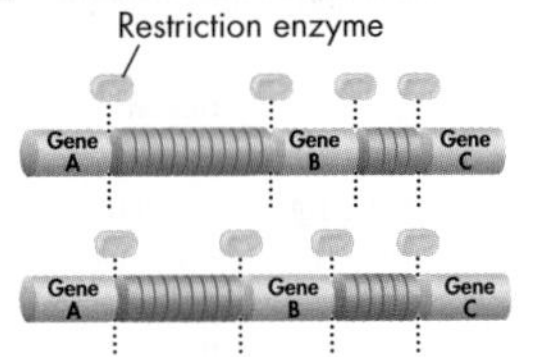

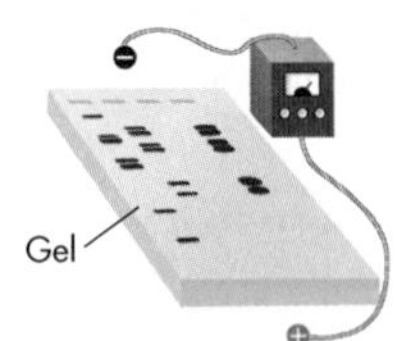

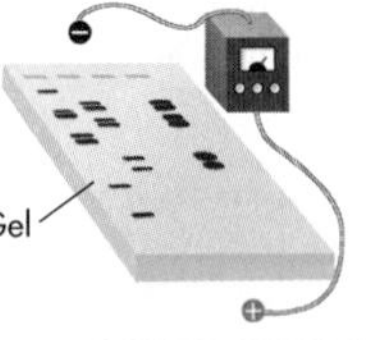

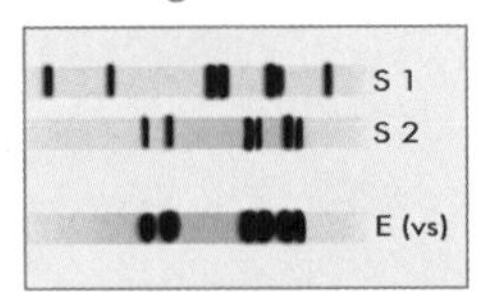

DNA fingerprint

Personal Identification

How is DNA used to identify individuals?

The complexity of the human genome ensures that no individual is exactly like any other genetically—except for identical twins, who share the same genome. Molecular biology has used this fact to develop a powerful tool called **DNA fingerprinting** for use in identifying individuals. **DNA fingerprinting analyzes sections of DNA that may have little or no function but that vary widely from one individual to another.** This method is shown in **Figure 15–19.** First, restriction enzymes cut a small sample of human DNA. Next, gel electrophoresis separates the restriction fragments by size. Then, a DNA probe detects the fragments that have highly variable regions, revealing a series of variously sized DNA bands. If enough combinations of enzymes and probes are used, the resulting pattern of bands can be distinguished statistically from that of any other individual in the world. DNA samples can be obtained from blood, sperm, or tissue—even from a hair strand if it has tissue at the root.

FIGURE 15–19 Identifying Individuals DNA fingerprinting can be used to determine a person's identity. It is especially useful in solving crimes. The diagram above shows how scientists match DNA evidence from a crime scene with two possible suspects. Interpret Graphics ***Does the DNA fingerprint above match suspect 1 (S1) or suspect 2 (S2)? How can you tell?***

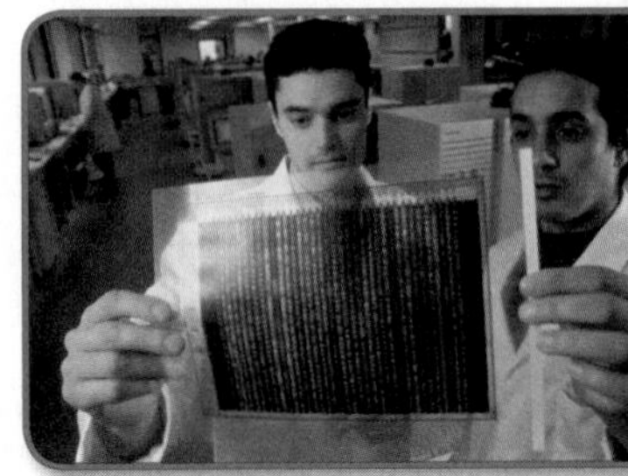

Forensic Science DNA fingerprinting has been used in the United States since the late 1980s. Its precision and reliability have revolutionized **forensics**—the scientific study of crime scene evidence. DNA fingerprinting has helped solve crimes, convict criminals, and even overturn wrongful convictions. To date, DNA evidence has saved more than 110 wrongfully convicted prisoners from death sentences.

DNA forensics is used in wildlife conservation as well. African elephants are a highly vulnerable species. Poachers, who slaughter the animals mainly for their precious tusks, have reduced their population dramatically. To stop the ivory trade, African officials now use DNA fingerprinting to identify the herds from which black-market ivory has been taken.

In Your Notebook *Describe the process of DNA fingerprinting.*

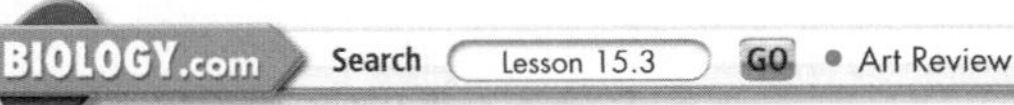

Connect to the Real World

After students have read about DNA fingerprinting and examined **Figure 15–19,** discuss ways this technology could be used to solve everyday problems.

Ask In what sorts of crimes would DNA fingerprinting help in identifying the criminal or exonerating someone innocent? *(in cases where blood, other body fluids, or body tissues were left behind, such as in rape or murder)*

Ask What process would investigators use to collect evidence against people who illegally sold tusks of protected African elephants? *(They would make a DNA fingerprint of each tusk for sale, and then compare those fingerprints to those of elephants from specific, protected African herds.)*

DIFFERENTIATED INSTRUCTION

L1 Special Needs Help visually impaired students better understand DNA fingerprinting by asking volunteers to make a model of a DNA fingerprint. Materials could include yarn, posterboard, and glue. Have students construct a DNA fingerprint similar to the one shown in **Figure 15–19.** They should make sure the yarn is all the same length, with some pieces close together to model the pattern of bands in a DNA fingerprint. Have visually impaired students scan the model manually as volunteers read the annotations in the figure.

BIOLOGY.com Have students explore DNA fingerprinting with the drop-and-drag activity **Art Review: Identifying Individuals.**

Biology In-Depth

METHODS OF DNA FINGERPRINTING

According to the U.S. Human Genome Project, only 0.1 percent of human DNA differs from one person to another. Several methods are used for DNA fingerprinting, including the following.

- Restriction Fragment Length Polymorphism (RFLP), which is a method for analyzing the variable lengths of DNA fragments
- PCR Analysis, which uses a polymerase chain reaction to make copies of extremely small DNA samples
- Short Tandem Repeat (STR) Analysis, which involves analysis of specific regions of DNA

Answers

FIGURE 15–19 suspect 2, because that suspect's DNA fingerprint is a close match to the DNA evidence (E) from the crime scene

IN YOUR NOTEBOOK First, restriction enzymes cut a small sample of human DNA. Next, gel electrophoresis separates the restriction fragments by size. Then, a DNA probe detects the fragments containing repeated sequences that have highly variable regions, revealing a series of variously sized DNA bands. If enough combinations of enzymes and probes are used, the resulting pattern of bands can be matched against DNA evidence from a crime.

Teach continued

Discuss the kind of evidence investigators collect at crime scenes, such as hair, blood, sweat, and saliva samples. Suggest students review the process of DNA fingerprinting to understand how this evidence could be used. Students can go online to **Biology.com** to gather their evidence.

Assess and Remediate

EVALUATE UNDERSTANDING

Read aloud the three boldfaced Key Concepts in the lesson. After reading each one, ask volunteers to provide supporting details from the text. Then, have students complete the 15.3 Assessment.

REMEDIATION SUGGESTION

L1 **Struggling Students** If students have difficulty answering **Question 3b,** remind them that each restriction enzyme cuts DNA at specific sequences of nucleotides. Help them infer that the more restriction enzymes that are used, the more DNA fragments there will be to separate and analyze.

BIOLOGY.com Students can check their understanding of lesson concepts with the **Self-Test** assessment. They can then take an online version of the **Lesson Assessment.**

MYSTERY CLUE

What kind of evidence do you think investigators collected at the crime scene? What kinds of tests would they have run on this evidence? What would the tests have to show before the suspect was released?

Establishing Relationships In cases of disputed paternity, how does our justice system determine the rightful father of a child? DNA fingerprinting makes it easy to find alleles carried by the child that do not match those of the mother. Any such alleles must come from the child's biological father, and they will show up in his DNA fingerprint. The probability that those alleles will show up in a randomly picked male is less than 1 in 100,000. This means the likelihood that a given male is the child's father must be higher than 99.99 percent to confirm his paternity.

When genes are passed from parent to child, genetic recombination scrambles the molecular markers used for DNA fingerprinting, so ancestry can be difficult to trace. There are two ways to solve this problem. The Y chromosome never undergoes crossing over, and only males carry it. Therefore, Y chromosomes pass directly from father to son with few changes. The same is true of the small DNA molecules found in mitochondria. These are passed, with very few changes, from mother to child in the cytoplasm of the egg cell.

Because mitochondrial DNA (mtDNA) is passed directly from mother to child, your mtDNA is the same as your mother's mtDNA, which is the same as her mother's mtDNA. This means that if two people have an exact match in their mtDNA, then there is a very good chance that they share a common maternal ancestor. Y-chromosome analysis has been used in the same way and has helped researchers settle longstanding historical questions. One such question—did President Thomas Jefferson father the child of a slave?—may have been answered in 1998. DNA testing showed that descendants of the son of Sally Hemings, a slave on Jefferson's Virginia estate, carried his Y chromosome. This result suggests Jefferson was the child's father, although the Thomas Jefferson Foundation continues to challenge that conclusion.

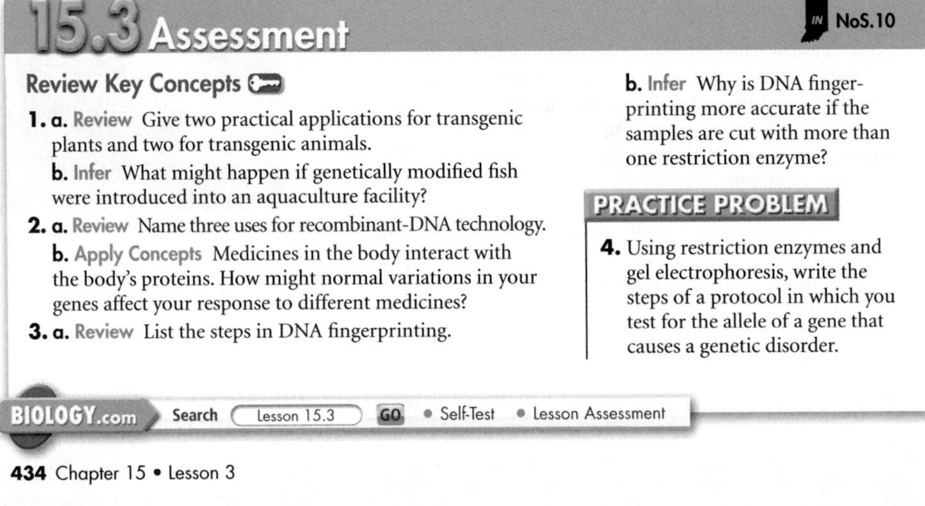

15.3 Assessment

IN NoS.10

Review Key Concepts

1. a. Review Give two practical applications for transgenic plants and two for transgenic animals.
   b. Infer What might happen if genetically modified fish were introduced into an aquaculture facility?
2. a. Review Name three uses for recombinant-DNA technology.
   b. Apply Concepts Medicines in the body interact with the body's proteins. How might normal variations in your genes affect your response to different medicines?
3. a. Review List the steps in DNA fingerprinting.
   b. Infer Why is DNA fingerprinting more accurate if the samples are cut with more than one restriction enzyme?

PRACTICE PROBLEM

4. Using restriction enzymes and gel electrophoresis, write the steps of a protocol in which you test for the allele of a gene that causes a genetic disorder.

BIOLOGY.com Search Lesson 15.3 GO • Self-Test • Lesson Assessment

Assessment Answers

1a. Sample answer: Plants: higher yields, resistance to herbicides; animals: increased milk production, leaner meat

1b. Sample answer: If genetically modified fish were introduced into an aquaculture facility, the fish populations might crossbreed and produce offspring with new characteristics.

2a. Sample answer: preventing disease, medical research, treating disease

2b. Variation in genes results in variation in proteins, because genes direct the building of proteins. As a result, the interaction of medicines with proteins varies from person to person.

3a. Restriction enzymes cut a small sample of human DNA. Gel electrophoresis separates the restriction fragments by size. A DNA probe detects the fragments that have highly variable regions, revealing a series of variously sized DNA bands that can be matched to another sample.

3b. Each restriction enzyme cuts DNA at a specific sequence of nucleotides. The more restriction enzymes that are used, the more DNA fragments will be produced. The more fragments there are to separate and analyze, the easier it will be to match the resulting DNA fingerprint to another sample.

PRACTICE PROBLEM

4. Protocols will vary in details, but students should accurately describe the use of restriction enzymes and gel electrophoresis in testing for the allele.

Technology & BIOLOGY

IN **NoS.10** Scientific discoveries and new technologies.

Artificial Life?

In 2008, scientists at the J. Craig Venter Institute in Rockville, Maryland, produced a synthetic genome with more than half a million DNA base pairs. It may not be long before artificial cells containing similar genomes can be grown in the laboratory. How? First a complete DNA molecule, containing the minimum set of the genetic information needed to keep a cell alive, is produced in the laboratory. Then, that molecule is inserted into a living cell to replace the cell's DNA. The result is a cell whose genome is entirely synthetic. Scientists hope this technique can help them design cells for specific purposes, like capturing solar energy or manufacturing biofuels.

Synthetic genome is synthesized in a lab.

...AGACCCGCCGGGA
CCACCCCCTGCTC
GGTCAGGTGCACT...

Synthetic genome is inserted into bacterium.

One daughter cell contains the synthetic genome.

▲ **Synthesizing a Genome**
One way to synthesize life is to replace a cell's genome with an artificial DNA molecule. As a result, cell division may produce a daughter cell containing only the human-made genome.

WRITING **What are the ethical issues in producing synthetic organisms? If you were a scientist working on the latest breakthroughs, how would you address those issues? Describe your ideas in an essay.**

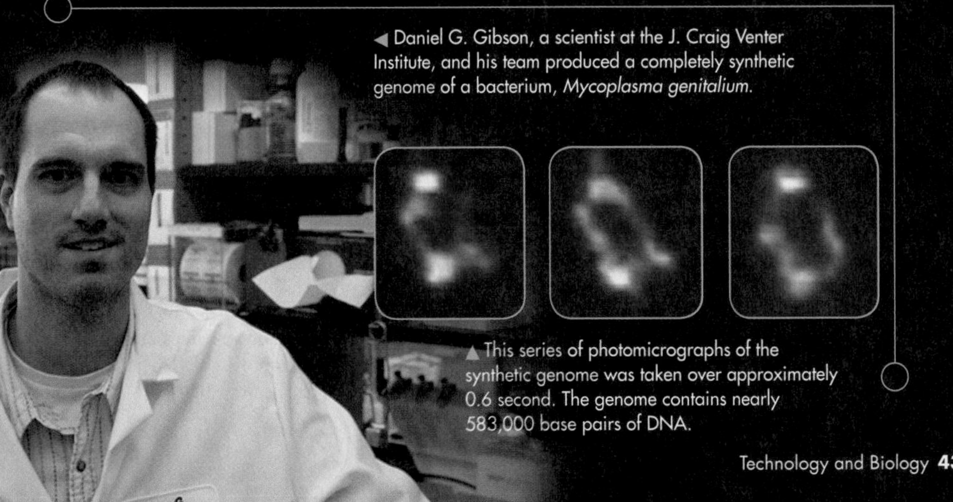

◀ Daniel G. Gibson, a scientist at the J. Craig Venter Institute, and his team produced a completely synthetic genome of a bacterium, *Mycoplasma genitalium.*

▲ This series of photomicrographs of the synthetic genome was taken over approximately 0.6 second. The genome contains nearly 583,000 base pairs of DNA.

Teach

Use Visuals

Focus students' attention on the figure in the top right of the page. Point out that the figure shows something that has not yet been done successfully. Rather, it shows how scientists might be able to produce a cell that contains a synthetic genome.

Ask How might a synthetic genome be inserted into a bacterial cell? *(Sample answer: Possibly, a virus could be used to insert the gene, as is done in gene therapy. Or perhaps it could be injected directly into the cell, similar to the way DNA is injected into cells to produce transgenic animals.)*

Point out that after the cell divides, one of the daughter cells is left with only the synthetic genome. Scientists hope that this cell will then be able to divide.

Ask Why is getting the cell containing the synthetic genome to divide an important step in the process shown? *(To have practical applications, scientists must be able to easily produce large quantities of bacteria carrying the synthetic genome. The easiest way to accomplish that is to get the cells to divide.)*

DIFFERENTIATED INSTRUCTION

L3 **Advanced Students** Challenge students to write a synopsis for a movie about a scientist who creates synthetic life. Explain that sometimes movies are made with alternative endings. For this movie, ask students to write two endings, one in which the synthetic life proves to be a great boon for humanity, and another in which the synthetic life causes terrible, unintended consequences. Give students the opportunity to present their synopses to the class.

Biology In-Depth

A THREE-STEP PROCESS

The production of a synthetic genome in 2008 by scientists at the J. Craig Venter Institute was the second step in a projected three-step process to create synthetic life. The first step, accomplished the year before by the same team, was transplanting a chromosome from one organism into another organism. The team was successful in transplanting the genome of one species of *Mycoplasma* into a cell of another *Mycoplasma* species. The second step was producing a synthetic genome, which they did by copying the DNA of the smallest-known free-living bacterium, *Mycoplasma genitalium.* That genome contains about 485 genes. The third step, which is seen as much more difficult, is to replace a bacteria's genome with a synthetic genome and get the cell to divide.

Answers

WRITING Essays will vary. Students might suggest scientists need to be extremely careful not to synthesize an organism that could cause a disease or otherwise be harmful. Students might also suggest measures to ensure that the synthetic organism could not escape from the lab.

IN INDIANA ACADEMIC STANDARDS

For the full text of all standards, see the Course Overview in the front matter of this book.

LESSON 15.4

Getting Started

Objectives

15.4.1 Describe some of the issues that relate to biotechnology.

15.4.2 Identify some of the pros and cons of genetically modified food.

15.4.3 Describe some of the ethical issues relating to biotechnology.

Student Resources

Study Workbooks A and B, 15.4 Worksheets

Spanish Study Workbook, 15.4 Worksheets

Lesson Overview • Lesson Notes • Activity: Data Analysis • Assessment: Self-Test, Lesson Assessment

For corresponding lesson in the **Foundation Edition**, see pages 367–369.

Build Background

Have students turn back to **Figure 15–15** and examine the GM rice that contains increased amounts of provitamin A. Explain that this product was kept off the market for years in a dispute over who owned the patent for it and had the right to profits from its sale. Ask students whether they think it is ethical to keep healthful products off the market because of disputes over patents and profits. Then, ask whether they think it would be ethical to keep a cure for cancer off the market for the same reasons. Encourage diverse opinions.

IN INDIANA ACADEMIC STANDARDS

For the full text of all standards, see the Course Overview in the front matter of this book.

NoS.11 Explain how scientific knowledge can be used to guide decisions on environmental and social issues.

15.4 Ethics and Impacts of Biotechnology

IN NoS.11 Scientific knowledge: environmental and social issues.

Key Questions

What privacy issues does biotechnology raise?

Are GM foods safe?

Should genetic modifications to humans and other organisms be closely regulated?

Taking Notes

Two-Column Chart As you read, write down the opposing viewpoints on each ethical issue.

THINK ABOUT IT Years ago a science fiction movie titled *Gattaca* speculated about a future world in which genetics determines people's ability to get ahead in life. In the movie, schooling, job prospects, and legal rights are rigidly determined by an analysis of the individual's DNA on the day he or she is born. Are we moving closer to this kind of society?

Profits and Privacy

What privacy issues does biotechnology raise?

Private biotechnology and pharmaceutical companies do much of the research involving GM plants and animals. Their goal is largely to develop profitable new crops, drugs, tests, or other products. Like most inventors, they protect their discoveries and innovations with patents. A patent is a legal tool that gives an individual or company the exclusive right to profit from its innovations for a number of years.

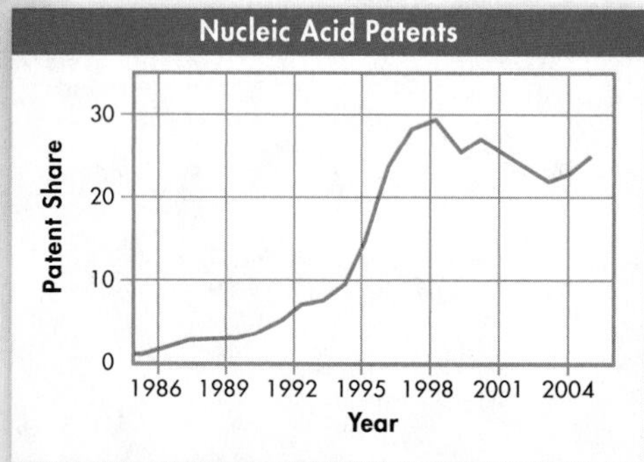

FIGURE 15–20 Patenting Nucleic Acids This graph shows the rise in the number of nucleic-acid patents between 1985 and 2005.

Patenting Life When you think about patents, you probably think about an inventor protecting a new machine or device. But molecules and DNA sequences can be patented, too. In fact, roughly one fifth of the known genes in the human genome are now patented commercially. Even laboratory techniques like PCR have been patented. When a scientist wants to run a PCR test, he or she must pay a fee for the license to use this process.

The ability to patent is meant to spur discovery and advancements in medicine and industry. After all, patent holders stand a good chance of reaping large financial rewards. Sometimes, though, patent holders demand high fees that block other scientists from exploring certain lines of research. That was the case in developing provitamin A-enriched golden rice, a GM plant described in Lesson 15.3. Even after the rice was developed, patent disputes kept it out of the hands of farmers for years.

Now consider the information held in your own genome. **Do you have exclusive rights to your DNA? Should you, like patent holders, be able to keep your genetic information confidential?** When it comes to your own DNA, how much privacy are you entitled to?

UbD Teach for Understanding

ENDURING UNDERSTANDING DNA is the universal code for life; it enables an organism to transmit hereditary information and, along with the environment, determines an organism's characteristics.

GUIDING QUESTION What are some of the ethical issues raised by genetic engineering?

EVIDENCE OF UNDERSTANDING *After completing this lesson, assign students the following assessment to show their understanding of privacy issues related to genetic engineering.* Ask students to draft a letter to a member of Congress or a state legislator about the use of information gathered from people's DNA. Students should take a position on the issue and support it with logical reasoning and sound, scientific arguments. Have volunteers read their letters to the class. Ask other students whether they agree or disagree with the positions presented.

Genetic Ownership One of the most hallowed sites in the United States is the one shown in **Figure 15–21.** It is the Tomb of the Unknowns in Arlington National Cemetery, near Washington, D.C. Buried here are the remains of unidentified American soldiers who fought our nation's wars. The tomb also serves as a focal point for the honor and remembrance of those service members lost in combat whose bodies have never been recovered.

Biotechnology offers hope that there will never be another unknown soldier. The U.S. military now requires all personnel to give a DNA sample when they begin their service. Those DNA samples are kept on file and used, if needed, to identify the remains of individuals who perish in the line of duty. In many ways, this practice is a comfort to military families, who can be assured that the remains of a loved one can be properly identified for burial.

But what if the government wants to use an individual's DNA sample for another purpose, in a criminal investigation or a paternity suit? What if health-insurance providers manage their healthcare policies based on a genetic predisposition to disease? For example, suppose that, years after giving a DNA sample, an individual is barred from employment or rejected for health insurance because of a genetic defect detected in the sample. Would this be a fair and reasonable use of genetic information?

After considering this issue for years, United States Congress passed the Genetic Information Nondiscrimination Act, which became law in 2008. This act protects Americans against discrimination based on their genetic information. Physicians and ethicists hope this will lead to more effective use of personal genetic information, without fear of prejudice in obtaining health insurance or employment.

FIGURE 15–21 Unknown Identities The Tomb of the Unknowns in Arlington National Cemetery holds the remains of unknown American soldiers from World Wars I and II, the Korean War, and, until 1998, the Vietnam War. **Form an Opinion** ***Should DNA testing be used to identify the remaining soldiers buried here? Why or why not?***

Safety of Transgenics

Are GM foods safe?

Much controversy exists concerning foods that have had their DNA altered through genetic engineering. The majority of GM crops today are grown in the United States, although farmers around the world have begun to follow suit. Are the foods from GM crops the same as those prepared from traditionally bred crops?

Pros of GM Foods The companies producing seeds for GM crops would say that GM plants are actually better and safer than other crops. Farmers choose them because they produce higher yields, reducing the amount of land and energy that must be devoted to agriculture and lowering the cost of food for everyone.

Insect-resistant GM plants need little, if any, insecticide to grow successfully, reducing the chance that chemical residues will enter the food supply and lessening damage to the environment. In addition, GM foods have been widely available for more than a decade. **Careful studies of such foods have provided no scientific support for concerns about their safety, and it does seem that foods made from GM plants are safe to eat.**

What privacy considerations, if any, should investigators have taken into account when obtaining the DNA evidence?

Quick Facts

GM FOODS AROUND THE WORLD

Here are a few quick facts about genetically modified foods grown around the world.

- In 2006, 252 million acres of GM crops were planted worldwide.
- The United States grew over half of the world's GM crops in 2006, with 53 percent. Argentina was the next closest, with 17 percent.
- Most of the GM crops grown around the world in 2006 were herbicide-resistant or insect-resistant soybeans, corn, cotton, canola, and alfalfa.

Teach

Lead a Discussion

Have students review the information on transgenic safety on this page and the next. Then, discuss the issue as a class, using the open-ended questions below. Make sure students support their opinions with logic and reason.

Ask Which argument do you find more convincing, the argument for GM foods or the argument against?

Ask Would you be concerned if you found out that some of the food you eat regularly is genetically modified?

Ask Do you think farmers and food manufacturers should have to label their products if they are genetically modified?

DIFFERENTIATED INSTRUCTION

LPR Less Proficient Readers Before leading a discussion on the safety of transgenics, have students organize the information about the pros and cons of GM foods in a **T-Chart.** Tell students to use the blue headings in their text as the chart's column heads, making the left column, Pros of GM Foods, and the right column, Cons of GM Foods. They should list opposing arguments in the two columns. Have students work with a partner to check their charts, and then use their charts during class discussion.

Study Wkbks A/B, Appendix S30, T-Chart. **Transparencies,** GO15.

Lead a discussion about the constitutional rights of citizens of the U.S., including privacy rights. Read aloud Amendment IV of the Bill of Rights to the U.S. Constitution, and discuss whether students think collecting DNA from people would violate their right against "unreasonable searches and seizures." Students can go online to **Biology.com** to gather their evidence.

BIOLOGY.com Have students analyze nutrition and genetic data to learn how genetically modified crops can help improve nutrition in **Data Analysis: Genetic Engineering for Nutrition**.

Answers

FIGURE 15–21 Opinions may vary. Accept any opinion that is supported by logical reasoning.

Teach continued

Connect to the Real World

After students have read the section, **Ethics of the New Biology,** divide the class in half. Assign one half to take the position that strong government regulations are needed to control the development and use of biotechnology. Assign the other half to take the position that the field of biotechnology should remain free of regulation, which would only stifle new developments. Have groups meet, make a list of points that support their position, and choose two or three representatives to speak for the group. Then, have the representatives from each group debate the issue.

DIFFERENTIATED INSTRUCTION

L3 **Advanced Students** In anticipation of the debate described above, ask a few students in each group to search online for arguments for and against regulation of GM foods and other uses of genetic engineering. Give students a day or two of research time before holding the debate.

ELL Focus on ELL: Build Background

ALL SPEAKERS Have students fill in a **Cluster Diagram** for the topic of *ethics.* Have them brainstorm a list of words and phrases that relate to ethics, and write them on the board. For each word, call on advanced or advanced high speakers to pronounce the word correctly and use it in a sentence. Have beginning and intermediate speakers repeat the correct pronunciation. After discussion, have students choose the words from the list that they will include in their cluster diagram.

Study Wkbks A/B, Appendix S19, Cluster Diagram. **Transparencies,** GO2.

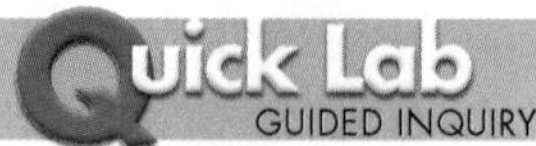

Survey Biotechnology Opinions

1. Select three safety, legal, or ethical issues related to genetic engineering.
2. Design a survey to ask people their opinions on these issues.
3. Find 15 people to answer your survey.
4. Collect the surveys and tabulate the answers.

Analyze and Conclude

1. **Analyze Data** Did all respondents agree on any issue? If so, which one(s)?
2. **Draw Conclusions** If you had surveyed more people, do you think you would have found more or less agreement in the responses? Why or why not?
3. **Evaluate** How informed about biotechnology issues were the people you surveyed? If you were a politician or government official, how would you act on the results of your survey?

Cons of GM Foods Critics acknowledge some benefits of genetically modified foods, but they also point out that no long-term studies have been made of the hazards these foods might present. **Even if GM food itself presents no hazards, there are many serious concerns about the unintended consequences that a shift to GM farming and ranching may have on agriculture.** Some worry that the insect resistance engineered into GM plants may threaten beneficial insects, killing them as well as crop pests. Others express concerns that use of plants resistant to chemical herbicides may lead to overuse of these weed-killing compounds.

Another concern is that the patents held on GM seeds by the companies that produce them may prove costly enough to force small farmers out of business, especially in the developing world. It is not clear whether any of these concerns should block the wider use of these new biotechnologies, but it is certain that they will continue to prove controversial in the years ahead.

In the United States, current federal regulations treat GM foods and non-GM foods equally. As a result, GM foods are not required to undergo special safety testing before entering the market. No additional labeling is required to identify a product as genetically modified unless its ingredients are significantly different from its conventional counterpart. The possibility that meat from GM animals may soon enter the food supply has heightened concerns about labeling. As a result, some states have begun to consider legislation to require the labeling of GM foods, thereby providing consumers with an informed choice.

In Your Notebook *List the pros and cons of GM foods.*

Ethics of the New Biology

Should genetic modifications to humans and other organisms be closely regulated?

"Know yourself." The ancient Greeks carved this good advice in stone, and it has been guiding human behavior ever since. Biotechnology has given us the ability to know ourselves more and more. With this knowledge, however, comes responsibility.

You've seen how easy it is to move genes from one organism to another. For example, the GFP gene can be extracted from a jellyfish and spliced onto genes coding for important cellular proteins. This ability has led to significant new discoveries about how cells function.

The same GFP technology was used to create the fluorescent zebra fish shown in **Figure 15–22.** These fish—along with fluorescent mice, tadpoles, rabbits, and even cats—have all contributed to our understanding of cells and proteins. But the ability to alter life forms for any purpose, scientific or nonscientific, raises important questions. **Just because we have the technology to modify an organism's characteristics, are we justified in doing so?**

Answers

IN YOUR NOTEBOOK Pros: crops produce higher yields, lowering the cost of food; insect-resistant varieties require little pesticide, reducing the chance of chemical residues in the food supply and reducing pesticides in the environment; they seem to be safe to eat. Cons: no long-term studies have been made concerning potential hazards; there may be possible unintended consequences to agriculture; engineered insect resistance may threaten beneficial insects; use of herbicide-resistant plants may lead to increased herbicide use; higher cost of seeds may force small farmers out of business.

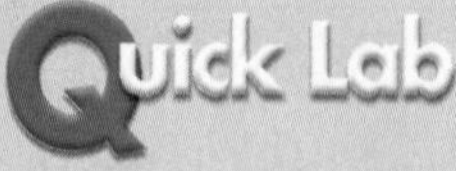

PURPOSE Students will design and conduct a survey on genetic engineering and draw conclusions from the results.

PLANNING Suggest students limit answers to responses such as Strongly Agree, Agree, Disagree, Strongly Disagree, Don't Know. Recommend students survey people of varying ages and backgrounds.

ANALYZE AND CONCLUDE

1. Answers will vary. Students should cite specific questions and provide evidence from the survey results.
2. Sample answer: Surveying more people may have yielded less agreement, because the sample might be more diverse.
3. Answers may vary, depending on survey results.

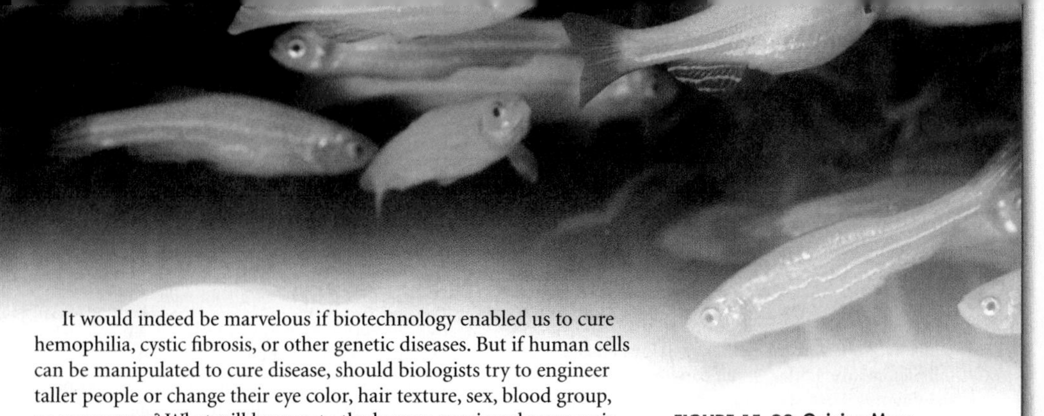

It would indeed be marvelous if biotechnology enabled us to cure hemophilia, cystic fibrosis, or other genetic diseases. But if human cells can be manipulated to cure disease, should biologists try to engineer taller people or change their eye color, hair texture, sex, blood group, or appearance? What will happen to the human species when we gain the opportunity to design our bodies or those of our children? What will be the consequences if biologists develop the ability to clone human beings by making identical copies of their cells? These are questions with which society must come to grips.

The goal of biology is to gain a better understanding of the nature of life. As our knowledge increases, however, so does our ability to manipulate the genetics of living things, including ourselves. In a democratic nation, all citizens—not just scientists—are responsible for ensuring that the tools science has given us are used wisely. This means that you should be prepared to help develop a thoughtful and ethical consensus of what should and should not be done with the human genome. To do anything less would be to lose control of two of our most precious gifts: our intellect and our humanity.

FIGURE 15–22 Gaining More Understanding These fluorescent zebra fish were originally bred to help scientists detect environmental pollutants. Today, studying fluorescent fish is helping us understand cancer and other diseases. The fish are also sold to the public at a profit.

15.4 Assessment

IN NoS.11

Review Key Concepts 

1. a. Review What is a patent?
   b. Apply Concepts How could biotechnology affect your privacy?
2. a. Review What are genetically modified foods?
   b. Form an Opinion Should a vegetarian be concerned about eating a GM plant that contains DNA from a pig gene? Support your answer with details from the text.
3. a. Review What are the main concerns about genetic engineering discussed in this lesson or elsewhere in the chapter?
   b. Pose Questions Write three specific questions about the ethical, social, or legal implications of genetic engineering that do not appear in this lesson. For example, how does personal genetic information affect self-identity?

WRITE ABOUT SCIENCE

Persuasion

4. Biologists may one day be able to use genetic engineering to alter a child's inherited traits. Under what circumstances, if any, should this ability be used? Write a persuasive paragraph expressing your opinion.

BIOLOGY.com Search Lesson 15.4 GO • Self-Test • Lesson Assessment

Assess and Remediate

EVALUATE UNDERSTANDING

Ask students to write a paragraph describing the ethical issue from this lesson that they found to be the most important. Have them include an explanation of why they feel that particular issue needs to be resolved. Then, have students complete the 15.4 Assessment.

REMEDIATION SUGGESTION

L1 **Struggling Students** If students have difficulty answering **Question 1b,** remind them that many illnesses with a genetic component show up in a person's genes before the person gets ill. Suggest students consider a situation in which an insurance company knows of a person's genetic predisposition to an illness before the person knows.

BIOLOGY.com Students can check their understanding of lesson concepts with the **Self-Test** assessment. They can then take an online version of the **Lesson Assessment.**

Assessment Answers

1a. a legal tool that gives an individual or company the exclusive right to profit from its innovations for a number of years

1b. Sample answer: It could be used to analyze my DNA and bar me from employment or health insurance, based on genetic information.

2a. Genetically modified foods are foods that contain ingredients from organisms that have had their DNA altered.

2b. Answers may vary but should show an understanding of how plants are genetically modified with animal genes.

3a. Sample answer: whether genetic engineering will be used wisely and ethically

3b. Sample answer: How will genetically modified plants and animals affect other organisms in their ecosystem? If a company has a patent on a gene, can that company deny its therapeutic use to people who are too poor to pay? Are there any long-term health effects of eating GM foods?

WRITE ABOUT SCIENCE

4. Answers will vary. Some students might suggest that genetically altering a child's inherited traits would be ethical to ensure the child doesn't develop an inherited disease later in life, but would not be ethical simply to make the person more attractive or a better athlete.

CHAPTER LAB

Pre-Lab

Introduce students to the concepts they will explore in the chapter lab by assigning the Pre-Lab questions.

Lab

Tell students they will perform the chapter lab *Using DNA to Solve Crimes* described in **Lab Manual A.**

 Struggling Students A simpler version of the chapter lab is provided in **Lab Manual B.**

SAFETY

In addition to wearing aprons, protective eyewear, and gloves, students should take care to avoid electrical shocks and wash their hands after the procedure is completed.

 Look online for **Editable Lab Worksheets.**

For corresponding pre-lab in the **Foundation Edition**, see page 370.

IN INDIANA ACADEMIC STANDARDS

For the full text of all standards, see the Course Overview in the front matter of this book.

Forensics Lab

GUIDED INQUIRY

IN NoS.1 Develop explanations.

Pre-Lab: Using DNA to Solve Crimes

Problem How can DNA samples be used to connect a suspect to a crime scene?

Materials gel block, electrophoresis chamber, buffer solution, 250-mL beaker, metric ruler, DNA samples, micropipettes, 9-volt batteries, electric cords, staining tray, DNA stain, 100-mL graduated cylinder, clock or timer

Lab Manual Chapter 15 Lab

Skills Focus Measure, Compare and Contrast, Draw Conclusions

Connect to the Big idea Scientists who worked on the Human Genome Project had to develop methods for sequencing and identifying genes. Those methods have since been used for many other applications. For example, genetically altered bacteria are used to produce large amounts of life-saving drugs. Another example is the use of DNA evidence to solve crimes. In this lab, you will prepare and compare DNA "fingerprints," or profiles.

Background Questions

a. **Review** What characteristic of the human genome makes DNA a powerful tool for solving crimes?

b. **Review** What do the segments of DNA that are used to make DNA profiles have in common?

c. **Apply Concepts** When forensic scientists want to determine whether two DNA samples come from the same person, they analyze more than one section of DNA. Why would the results be less reliable if the scientists compared only one section of DNA?

Pre-Lab Questions

Preview the procedure in the lab manual.

1. **Control Variables** Why must you use a new pipette to load each DNA sample?
2. **Relate Cause and Effect** Why will the DNA samples separate into bands as they move through the gel?
3. **Infer** Why is purple tracking dye added to the DNA samples?

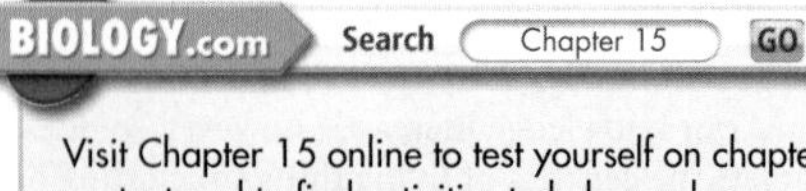

Visit Chapter 15 online to test yourself on chapter content and to find activities to help you learn.

Untamed Science Video Pigeon breeding helps the Untamed Science crew unravel the mysteries of genetic engineering.

Art in Motion View a short animation that brings bacterial transformation to life.

Art Review Review your understanding of DNA fingerprinting with this drag-and-drop activity.

Data Analysis Analyze nutrition and genetic data on nutrient deficiencies and crops genetically engineered to improve nutrition.

Pre-Lab Answers

BACKGROUND QUESTIONS

a. Except for identical twins, each individual has unique DNA.

b. The segments are regions with repeated DNA sequences that do not code for proteins.

c. Sample answer: The results would be less reliable because the probability of two people having an identical sequence in only one DNA section is much greater than the probability of two people having identical sequences in multiple sections.

PRE-LAB QUESTIONS

1. Using the same pipette would cause all samples to be contaminated, except the first sample.
2. The DNA samples contain fragments of different lengths. Shorter fragments will travel through the gel faster than longer fragments.
3. Because the DNA will not be visible until it is stained, the dye provides a visual indicator of when to stop the electrophoresis.

15 Study Guide

Big idea Science as a Way of Knowing

Genetic engineering allows scientists to manipulate the genomes of living things. Scientists can use bacteria to insert the DNA of one organism into another organism. Recombinant DNA has applications for agriculture, industry, medicine, and forensics. At the same time, there are ethical, legal, safety, and social issues surrounding the use of genetic engineering.

15.1 Selective Breeding

Humans use selective breeding, which takes advantage of naturally occurring genetic variation, to pass wanted traits on to the next generation of organisms.

Breeders can increase the genetic variation in a population by introducing mutations, which are the ultimate source of biological diversity.

selective breeding (418)
hybridization (419)
inbreeding (419)
biotechnology (419)

15.2 Recombinant DNA

The first step in using the polymerase chain reaction method to copy a gene is to heat a piece of DNA, which separates its two strands. Then, as the DNA cools, primers bind to the single strands. Next, DNA polymerase starts copying the region between the primers. These copies can serve as templates to make still more copies.

Recombinant-DNA technology—joining together DNA from two or more sources—makes it possible to change the genetic composition of living organisms.

Transgenic organisms can be produced by the insertion of recombinant DNA into the genome of a host organism.

polymerase chain reaction (423)
recombinant DNA (424)
plasmid (424)
genetic marker (425)
transgenic (426)
clone (427)

15.3 Applications of Genetic Engineering

Ideally, genetic modification could lead to better, less expensive, and more nutritious food as well as less-harmful manufacturing processes.

Recombinant-DNA technology is advancing the prevention and treatment of disease.

DNA fingerprinting analyzes sections of DNA that vary widely from one individual to another.

gene therapy (431)
DNA microarray (432)
DNA fingerprinting (433)
forensics (433)

15.4 Ethics and Impacts of Biotechnology

Should you, like patent holders, be able to keep your genetic information confidential?

Careful studies of GM foods have provided no scientific support for concerns about their safety.

There are many concerns about unintended consequences that a shift to GM farming and ranching may have on agriculture.

Just because we have the technology to modify an organism's characteristics, are we justified in doing so?

Think Visually
Complete the following concept map.

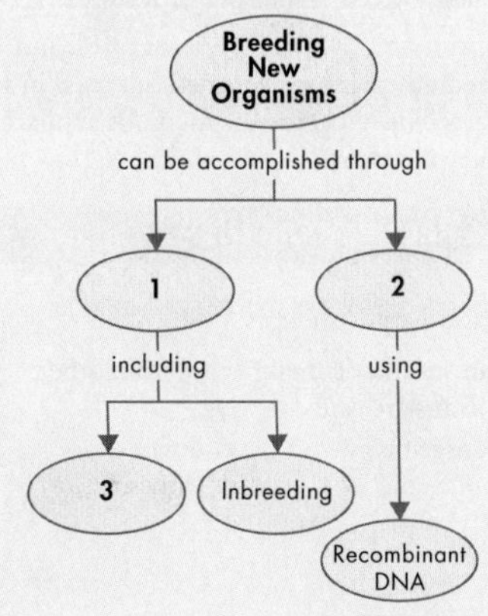

Search
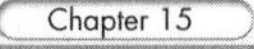

• Crossword • Chapter Assessment

Study Online

REVIEW AND ASSESSMENT RESOURCES

Editable Worksheets Pages of Study Workbooks A and B, Lab Manuals A and B, and the Assessment Resources Book are available online. These documents can be easily edited using a word-processing program.

Lesson Overview Have students reread the Lesson Overviews to help them study chapter concepts.

Vocabulary Review The *Flash Cards* and *Crossword* provide an interactive way to review chapter vocabulary.

Chapter Assessment Have students take an online version of the Chapter 15 Assessment.

Standardized Test Prep Students can take an online version of the Standardized Test Prep. You will receive their scores along with ideas for remediation.

Diagnostic and Benchmark Tests Use these tests to monitor your students' progress and supply remediation.

Answers

THINK VISUALLY

1. Selective breeding
2. Genetic engineering
3. Hybridization

UbD Performance Tasks

SUMMATIVE TASK Have students work in small groups to plan a Web site that future biology students could use to learn about genetic engineering. Tell groups they should design at least five Web pages that cover these topics: selective breeding, recombinant DNA and how it is used, GM crops and animals, recombinant DNA in health and medicine, DNA fingerprinting, and the ethics and safety of genetic engineering. If possible, have groups design their pages electronically. Otherwise, groups can display their Web page designs on large pieces of paper or poster board.

TRANSFER TASK Have students work in pairs to write a scene for a TV show in which a lab technician explains the process of DNA fingerprinting to a detective. Tell students they can use characters from a favorite TV show or make up their own characters. In this scene, the detective has a weak science background. So, the lab technician must explain what DNA and genes are, what samples can be used, how restriction enzymes and gel electrophoresis work, and what the results of DNA fingerprinting mean. Ask the authors of the best scenes to film them or act them out for the class.

ASSESSMENT

Lesson 15.1

UNDERSTAND KEY CONCEPTS

1. c **2.** a **3.** a

4. To produce organisms with new traits, breeders can induce mutations (usually in bacteria) using radiation or chemicals, or they can create polyploid plants.

5. Polyploidy describes an organism with multiple sets of chromosomes. It can be useful to produce new species of plants that are larger and stronger than their diploid relatives.

THINK CRITICALLY

6. Sample answer: Cross the pink and yellow roses until a thornless plant with sweet-smelling flowers is obtained. Then, cross that plant with the plant with scentless purple flowers until a thornless plant with sweet-smelling purple flowers is obtained.

7. They are similar in that both involve selective breeding that takes advantage of naturally occurring genetic variation to produce wanted characteristics in the next generation. They are different in that hybridization crosses dissimilar individuals to bring together the best of both organisms, while inbreeding involves breeding together individuals of similar characteristics.

Lesson 15.2

UNDERSTAND KEY CONCEPTS

8. a **9.** b **10.** c

11. c **12.** a

13. The first step is to heat a piece of DNA, which separates its two strands. Then, as the DNA cools, primers bind to the single strands. Next, DNA polymerase starts copying the region between the primers. These copies can serve as templates to make still more copies.

14. A genetic marker is a gene that makes it possible to distinguish bacteria that carry a plasmid from those that do not. Genetic markers are inserted into plasmids so that scientists can identify cells that have been transformed.

15. A transgenic plant contains genes from other species, while a hybrid plant contains genes from only the parent plants.

15 Assessment

The numbers following the questions refer to Indiana's Academic Standards for Biology I.

15.1 Selective Breeding

Understand Key Concepts

1. Crossing dissimilar individuals to bring together their best characteristics is called
a. domestication. **c.** hybridization.
b. inbreeding. **d.** polyploidy.

2. Crossing individuals with similar characteristics so that those characteristics will appear in their offspring is called
a. inbreeding. **c.** recombination.
b. hybridization. **d.** polyploidy.

3. Taking advantage of naturally occurring variations in organisms to pass wanted traits on to future generations is called
a. selective breeding. **c.** hybridization.
b. inbreeding. **d.** mutation.

4. How do breeders produce genetic variations that are not found in nature? B.7.5

5. What is polyploidy? When is this condition useful?

Think Critically

6. Propose a Solution Suppose a plant breeder has a thornless rose bush with scentless pink flowers, a thorny rose bush with sweet-smelling yellow flowers, and a thorny rose bush with scentless purple flowers. How might this breeder develop a pure variety of thornless, sweet-smelling purple roses?

7. Compare and Contrast Hybridization and inbreeding are important methods used in selective breeding. How are the methods similar? How are they different?

15.2 Recombinant DNA

Understand Key Concepts

8. Organisms that contain genes from other organisms are called
a. transgenic. **c.** donors.
b. mutagenic. **d.** clones.

9. What process is shown below? NoS.10
a. cloning
b. transformation
c. hybridization
d. polymerase chain reaction

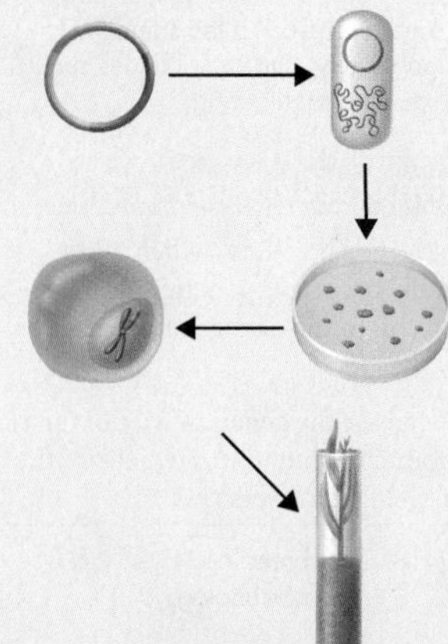

10. When cell transformation is successful, the recombinant DNA
a. undergoes mutation.
b. is treated with antibiotics.
c. becomes part of the transformed cell's genome.
d. becomes a nucleus.

11. Bacteria often contain small circular molecules of DNA known as
a. clones. **c.** plasmids.
b. chromosomes. **d.** hybrids.

12. A member of a population of genetically identical cells produced from a single cell is a
a. clone. **c.** mutant.
b. plasmid. **d.** sequence.

13. Describe what happens during a polymerase chain reaction.

14. Explain what genetic markers are and describe how scientists use them. NoS.10

15. How does a transgenic plant differ from a hybrid plant?

THINK CRITICALLY

16. Sample answer: One advantage of producing insulin or other proteins through genetic engineering is that huge cultures of bacteria can be cheaply grown, so large supplies of insulin can be made much more inexpensively than taking insulin from mammals. Also, recombinant DNA can be used to make human insulin, rather than having to rely on insulin made by other animals, which may be different and cause reactions in some people.

17. Sample answer: Because the genetic code is universal, it doesn't matter which organism a particular DNA sequence came from.

Think Critically

16. **Apply Concepts** Describe one or more advantages of producing insulin and other proteins through genetic engineering. NoS.11

17. **Apply Concepts** Bacteria and human beings are very different organisms. Why is it sometimes possible to combine their DNA and use a bacterium to make a human protein? NoS.11

15.3 Applications of Genetic Engineering

Understand Key Concepts

18. Which of the following characteristics is often genetically engineered into crop plants?
    a. improved flavor
    b. resistance to herbicides
    c. shorter ripening times
    d. thicker stems

19. A substance that has been genetically engineered into transgenic rice has the potential to treat NoS.10
    a. cancer.
    b. high blood pressure.
    c. vitamin A deficiency.
    d. malaria.

20. Physicians can screen for a genetic disorder using NoS.11
    a. a DNA microarray.
    b. PCR.
    c. restriction enzyme analysis.
    d. DNA sequencing.

21. Describe how a DNA microarray might be used to distinguish normal cells from cancer cells. NoS.10

22. Describe two important uses for DNA fingerprinting. NoS.11

Think Critically

23. **Infer** If a human patient's bone marrow was removed, altered genetically, and reimplanted, would the change be passed on to the patient's children? Explain your answer.

solve the CHAPTER MYSTERY

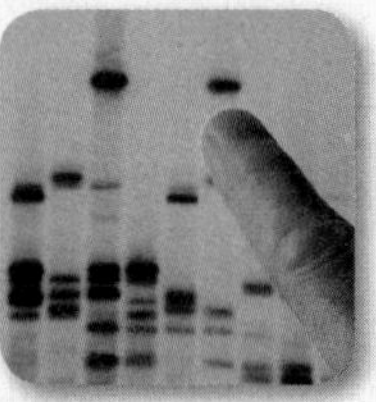

A CASE OF MISTAKEN IDENTITY

The first suspect was lucky: Twenty years earlier, it would have been an open-and-shut case. But by 1998, DNA fingerprinting was widely available. After the police took the suspect into custody, forensic scientists tested the DNA in the bloodstains on his shirt. Within a few hours, they knew they had the wrong suspect. Before long, the police caught the real attacker, who was subsequently tried and convicted of the crime.

1. **Infer** How did the investigators determine that the person they took into custody was not guilty of this crime? NoS.10

2. **Apply Concepts** Did the DNA evidence from the bloodstains come from the red blood cells, the white blood cells, or both? Explain your answer. NoS.10

3. **Predict** What if the initial suspect was related to the victim? Would that have changed the result? Why or why not?

4. **Connect to the Big idea** What might have happened if this crime were committed before DNA fingerprinting was discovered? Describe the series of events that might have taken place after police took in the first suspect.

 NoS.11

BIOLOGY.com Search Chapter 15 GO • Untamed Science Video • Chapter Mystery

443

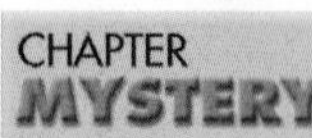

After students have read through the Chapter Mystery, review with them the evidence that suggested the man was guilty of the crime. *(His clothing was stained with blood that matched the blood type of the victim, there were scratches on his arms, and he couldn't remember what he did after a brawl.)* Then, discuss the process investigators used to exonerate him.

Ask How would investigators have tested the blood on his clothing for DNA? *(They would have used DNA fingerprinting.)*

Call on students to describe details of the DNA fingerprinting process.

Ask In reaching the conclusion that he was the wrong suspect, what would investigators have compared the results of that DNA fingerprint to? *(They would have compared the DNA fingerprint of the blood on his clothing to the DNA fingerprint of the victim.)*

CHAPTER MYSTERY ANSWERS

1. Through DNA fingerprinting, investigators discovered that the blood on his clothing didn't match the victim's blood.
2. The DNA evidence from the bloodstains came from the white blood cells, because red blood cells don't have nuclei, so they don't have DNA. When enough probes are used, DNA fingerprinting can distinguish samples of even the closest relatives.
3. It probably wouldn't have changed the result, because members of the same family have similar, but not identical, DNA.
4. Big idea Sample answer: The man might have been arrested and tried. After he was arrested, investigators would have discovered that the blood type of the blood on his clothing matched the victim's blood type. In an interrogation, the suspect wouldn't have been able to present an alibi, because he couldn't remember what happened the night before. With those two pieces of evidence, jurors would likely have convicted him in a trial.

Students can see the Untamed Science crew unravel the mysteries of genetic engineering in animals by watching **Untamed Science: Designer Pigeons.**

Lesson 15.3

UNDERSTAND KEY CONCEPTS

18. b **19.** c **20.** c

21. DNA microarrays allow scientists to compare the gene expression patterns of different cells. This kind of comparison can be used to distinguish cancer cells from normal cells.
22. DNA fingerprinting can be used to help solve crimes by matching DNA evidence from a crime scene with possible suspects. It can also be used to establish familial relationships, such as in cases of disputed paternity, by finding alleles in a child that are not carried by the mother and then matching them to the father's fingerprint.

THINK CRITICALLY

23. The change would not be passed on because genetically altering bone marrow would not affect the DNA in gametes involved in reproduction.

ASSESSMENT

ASSESSMENT

Lesson 15.4

UNDERSTAND KEY CONCEPTS

24. c **25.** b

26. Sample answer: Sometimes patent holders demand high fees that block other scientists from exploring lines of research.

27. Sample answer: Expensive GM seeds may force small farmers out of business, especially in the developing world.

THINK CRITICALLY

28. Sample answer: Transgenic microorganisms might be used to produce substances that can fight cancer. Transgenic animals might provide humans with sources of human proteins. Transgenic plants might produce foods that contain all necessary vitamins.

29. Sample answer: Hypothetically, because the genetic code is universal, it may one day be possible to create an animal with a frog's body and a bat's wings. However, in reality, this would be very difficult (if not impossible), because there are so many genes needed to code for a single body structure. Also, scientists would need reasons to do their experiments, and there doesn't appear to be a good reason to do this. So this is not really a reasonable statement.

Connecting Concepts

USE SCIENCE GRAPHICS

30. Complementary strand: TACTCTAGATGCCTTAAGAGTTGAACTTAGC on the original strand, *Bgl*III will cut after the fourth nucleotide and *ECO*RI will cut after the thirteenth nucleotide. *Hind*III will not cut the strand.

WRITE ABOUT SCIENCE

31. Students may either support or oppose the editorial stand. In their letters, students should demonstrate an understanding of both selective breeding and genetic engineering and the advantages and disadvantages of each.

32. The first step is to find the human gene by using gel electrophoresis to separate DNA fragments, and then identifying the gene with radioactive probes. PCR may be used to make copies of the gene. The next step is to insert the human gene into a plasmid that has been cut with the same restriction enzyme to create sticky ends. The resulting recombinant DNA can be inserted into a bacterial cell by mixing recombinant plasmids with a culture of bacteria. Bacterial cells that take up the recombinant plasmid can be identified if the plasmid also has a genetic marker, such as a gene for antibiotic resistance.

15.4 Ethics and Impacts of Biotechnology

Understand Key Concepts

24. The right to profit from a new genetic technology is protected by
a. getting a copyright for the method.
b. discovering a new gene.
c. obtaining a patent.
d. publishing its description in a journal.

25. Which of the following is most likely to be used in a court case to determine who the father of a particular child is? NoS.11
a. microarray analysis **c.** gene therapy
b. DNA fingerprinting **d.** genetic engineering

26. Give an example of a disadvantage associated with patenting genes.

27. What is one argument used by critics of genetically modified foods? NoS.11

Think Critically

28. Predict List three ways in which genetically engineered organisms might be used in the future. NoS.11

29. Evaluate Your friend suggests that genetic engineering makes it possible for biologists to produce an organism with any combination of characteristics—an animal with the body of a frog and the wings of a bat, for example. Do you think this is a reasonable statement? Explain your answer.

Connecting Concepts

Use Science Graphics NoS.3

Use the table below to answer question 30.

DNA Restriction Enzymes

Enzyme	Recognition Sequence
*Bgl*III	A↓G A T C T T C T A G↑A
*Eco*RI	G↓A A T T C C T T A A↑G
*Hind*III	A↓A G C T T T T C G A↑A

30. Apply Concepts Copy the following DNA sequence and write its complementary strand.

ATGAGATCTACGGAATTCTCAAGCTTGAATCG

Where will each restriction enzyme in the table cut the DNA strand?

Write About Science NoS.3

31. Explanation Your local newspaper has published an editorial against using genetic modification. It asserts that GM is still too new, and traditional selective breeding can accomplish the same things as GM. Write a letter to the editor supporting or opposing this position. NoS.11

32. Assess the Big idea Briefly describe the major steps involved in inserting a human gene into a bacterium.

Analyzing Data

NoS.3

Questions 33–35 refer to the diagram, which shows the results of a criminal laboratory test.

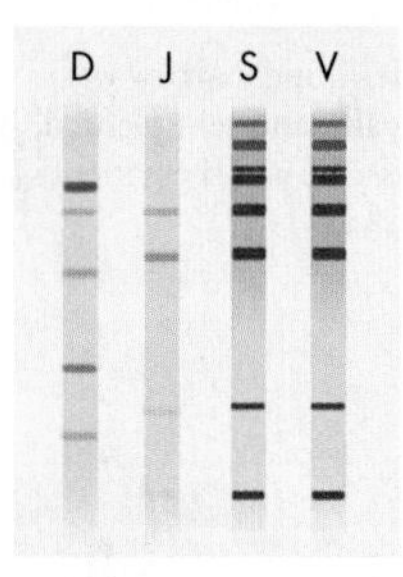

D = Defendant's blood
J = Blood from defendant's jeans
S = Blood from defendant's shirt
V = Victim's blood

33. Infer Briefly describe the biotechnological methods that would have been used to produce the results shown at the right. NoS.10

34. Compare and Contrast How are the bands from the jeans and the shirt similar? How are they different?

35. Draw Conclusions Based on the results shown, what conclusions might a prosecutor present to a jury during a criminal trial?

Analyzing Data

PURPOSE Students will analyze results from DNA fingerprinting that could help solve a crime.

PLANNING Review with students the steps used in DNA fingerprinting and how this method is used in forensics.

ANSWERS

33. Students should describe the steps of DNA fingerprinting.

34. The bands from the jeans match the bands from the shirt, though not all the bands on the shirt show up on the jeans.

35. Sample answer: DNA fingerprinting conclusively shows that blood from the victim was found on the defendant's shirt.

Standardized Test Practice for Indiana

Multiple Choice

1. Polyploidy may instantly produce new types of organisms that are larger and stronger than their diploid relatives in
   A animals. C bacteria.
   B plants. D fungi.

2. Which of the following characteristics does NOT apply to a plasmid?
   A made of DNA
   B found in bacterial cells
   C has circular loops
   D found in animal cells

3. To separate DNA fragments from one another, scientists use
   A polymerase chain reaction.
   B DNA microarrays.
   C gel electrophoresis.
   D restriction enzymes. NoS.10

4. Restriction enzymes cut DNA molecules
   A into individual nucleotides.
   B at random locations.
   C at short sequences specific to each type of enzyme.
   D into equal-sized pieces.

5. The expression of thousands of genes at one time can be followed using
   A polymerase chain reaction.
   B plasmid transformation.
   C restriction enzymes.
   D DNA microarrays. NoS.10

6. Genetically engineered crop plants can benefit farmers by
   A reducing the amount of land that is required to grow them.
   B introducing chemicals into the environment.
   C increasing an animal's resistance to antibiotics.
   D changing the genomes of other crop plants. NoS.11

7. Genetic markers allow scientists to
   A clone animals.
   B separate strands of DNA.
   C synthesize antibiotics.
   D identify transformed cells. NoS.10

Questions 8–9

The graph below shows the number of accurate copies of DNA produced by polymerase chain reaction.

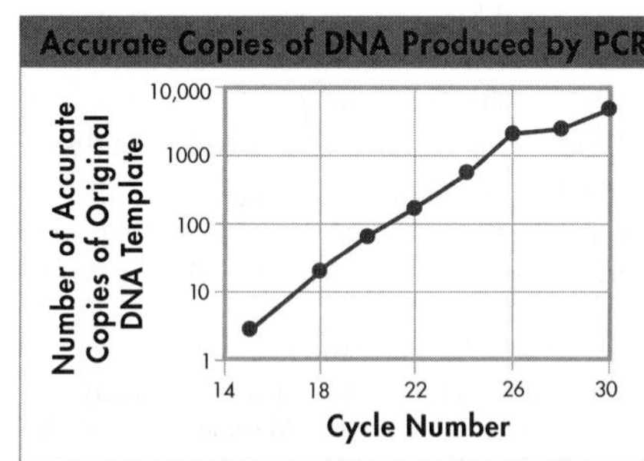

8. What can you conclude about cycles 18 through 26?
   A PCR produced accurate copies of template DNA at an exponential rate.
   B The amount of DNA produced by PCR doubled with each cycle.
   C The DNA copies produced by PCR were not accurate copies of the original DNA template.
   D The rate at which PCR produced accurate copies of template DNA fell in later cycles.

9. Based on the graph, which of the following might have happened between cycles 26 and 28?
   A PCR stopped producing accurate copies of the template.
   B The rate of reaction increased.
   C All of the template DNA was used up.
   D A mutation occurred.

Open-Ended Response

10. Why are bacteria able to make human proteins when a human gene is inserted in them with a plasmid?

If You Have Trouble With . . .

Question	1	2	3	4	5	6	7	8	9	10
See Lesson	15.1	15.2	15.2	15.2	15.3	15.4	15.2	15.2	15.2	15.3

Answers

1. B
2. D
3. C
4. C
5. D
6. A
7. D
8. A
9. A
10. Bacteria are able to make human proteins when a human gene is inserted into them because the genetic code is universal. Proteins are made up of amino acids, and DNA codes for the amino acids of a protein. A DNA sequence, such as ATG, specifies a certain amino acid. It doesn't matter if the cell is a bacterial cell or a human cell; it will interpret the code the same way.

Test-Taking Tip

ELIMINATE INCORRECT ANSWERS

If students are confused by a question on a multiple-choice test, suggest they start by eliminating each answer choice that they know is not correct. After eliminating incorrect choices, they can read over the remaining choices and choose the best answer.

Plan Ahead

Have students preview the Unit 4 Project a few days before making the collage. Suggest that they start collecting magazine, newspaper, and Internet images and articles that they want to use. You may also want to gather additional source materials that students can use the day they create their collages.

Materials magazines and newspapers, posterboard, glue or tape, scissors, colored markers or pens, additional art materials

Monitor the Project

Suggest students start by laying out the basic images and text in their collages before pasting or taping them down. As they work, walk around the classroom and ask students questions that will help them organize and design their collages.

Ask How does this image show why DNA is important to a cell?

Ask How can you show in pictures and words how DNA and genetics influence society?

Remind students to address all three central questions in their collages.

Project Assessment

Make sure students use the rubric and reflection questions to assess their work. Then, use the rubric to assign a final score. Note that it is important to value the creativity of students' work as well as the content when you score their projects. If desired, talk with students about any differences between their self-assessment scores and your assigned score.

Unit Project

Genetics Collage

Genetics is a fascinating field of study and is becoming increasingly important to society. A local genetics laboratory in your town wants to increase public awareness of the importance of genetics. To do so, it has decided to hold a scholarship competition. The scholarship will go to the student(s) who create the best educational collage related to topics in genetics.

Your Task Using magazine and newspaper clippings, Internet sources, and art materials to make a colorful collage. The images should relate to three central questions.

1) Why is DNA important to a cell?
2) Why is DNA important to you, as a human being?
3) Why is DNA important to society as a whole?

Be sure to

- communicate answers to the above questions in the images, words and phrases you choose.
- carefully design your collage so that it is clear and organized.

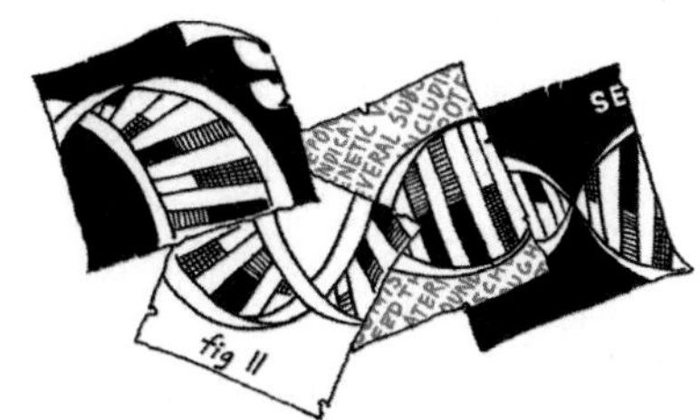

Reflection Questions

1. Score your collage using the rubric below. What score did you give yourself?
2. What did you do well in this project?
3. What about your collage needs improvement?
4. What could a person who didn't know much about DNA learn from your collage?

Assessment Rubric

Score	Scientific Content	Quality of Collage
4	Collage includes many important and thoughtful images related to the three central questions. Student demonstrates a deep understanding of genetics topics.	The collage is clear, organized, and creative.
3	Collage includes important images related to the three central questions. Student demonstrates an adequate understanding of genetics topics.	The collage is well designed and organized.
2	Collage is missing some important ideas and/or includes several insignificant ideas. Student demonstrates a limited level of understanding of genetics topics.	The collage could be better designed and organized.
1	Collage is missing several important ideas. Student demonstrates significant misunderstandings.	The collage is unclear and lacks a solid design.

IN INDIANA ACADEMIC STANDARDS

B.5.1 DNA and chromosomes, **B.5.2** Genes, **B.5.3** DNA and protein production, **B.6.2** Gene expression and differentiation

21st Century Skills

To be successful in the 21st century, students need skills and learning experiences that extend beyond subject area mastery. The Unit 4 Project helps students build the following 21st Century Skills: *Information and Media Literacy; Creativity and Intellectual Curiosity; Self-Direction;* and *Accountability and Adaptability.*

FOCUS ON INFORMATION AND MEDIA LITERACY Extend this Unit Project by having small groups of students evaluate the scientific accuracy of the media sources they used when making their collages. Then, ask them to consider the articles and images they chose (as well as the ones they did not) and discuss the intended audience of this information. Suggest students also discuss how the source's point of view may have influenced the information they presented.

For more practice building 21st Century Skills, see The Chapter Mystery pages in **Study Workbook A.**

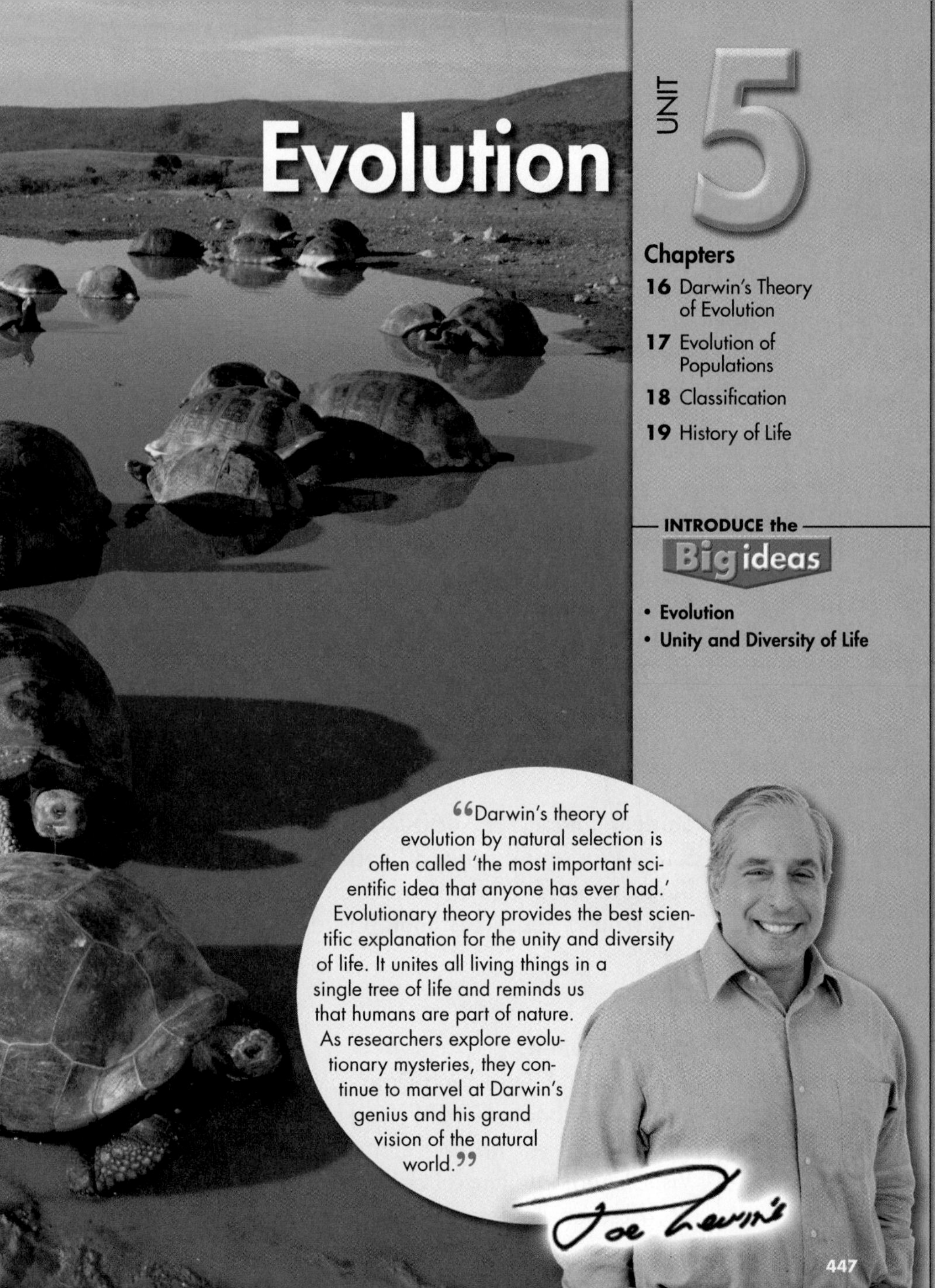

Evolution
UNIT 5
Chapters
16 Darwin's Theory of Evolution
17 Evolution of Populations
18 Classification
19 History of Life
INTRODUCE the Big ideas
• Evolution
• Unity and Diversity of Life
"Darwin's theory of evolution by natural selection is often called 'the most important scientific idea that anyone has ever had.' Evolutionary theory provides the best scientific explanation for the unity and diversity of life. It unites all living things in a single tree of life and reminds us that humans are part of nature. As researchers explore evolutionary mysteries, they continue to marvel at Darwin's genius and his grand vision of the natural world."
447

UNIT 5

Dear Colleague,

In 1992, a doctor at Tufts Medical School published a book entitled The Antibiotic Paradox, *explaining how bacteria are becoming resistant to nearly all known antibiotics. The author of the book, Stuart Levy, has argued that medicine and public health would be much better off if medical students were taught as much about Darwin as they are about Pasteur.*

Huh? Why should doctors learn so much about Darwin? Because bacteria evolve under pressure from natural selection—just as Darwin proposed. Once humans made antibiotics part of the environment, bacteria evolved resistance to those drugs.

Darwin's theory of evolution has been described as "the most important scientific idea that anyone has ever had." Ever since Darwin, new branches of science have appeared and matured, gathering information about the living world beyond Darwin's wildest dreams. Any of that evidence—from biochemistry, molecular genetics, geology, and physics—could have confirmed or negated Darwin's work. Astonishingly, all those new data supported, strengthened, and expanded Darwin's insights. Evolutionary theory now informs every aspect of biological thought, from global ecology to medicine.

But, evolutionary theory does more than just describe these phenomena; it enables us to predict how organisms will respond to events around them. Evolutionary theory informs new treatments for AIDS, new approaches to the production and use of antibiotics, and new strategies for using insecticides. These and other applications explain why understanding evolution is vital to making informed judgments about many issues in the modern world.

The goal of this unit is to help students understand the evolutionary worldview. As scientists and teachers, we believe very strongly that the purpose of education is to promote understanding, not to compel belief. That applies to evolution, too, which, if properly taught, should never threaten the beliefs of students. As biologists, we genuinely feel, as Darwin wrote, "There is grandeur in this view of life . . ." We hope you agree.

CHAPTER PLANNER 16

Darwin's Theory of Evolution

Chapter Contents	IN	Time	Core Resources
Chapter Preview			**Student Edition,** pp. 448–449 **Chapter Mystery,** p. 449
16.1 Darwin's Voyage of Discovery Darwin's Epic Journey • Observations Aboard the *Beagle*		1/2 period 1/4 block	**Student Edition,** pp. 450–453 **Inquiry** 16.1 Quick Lab, p. 451 L2 **Study Workbook A** 16.1 Worksheets L2 **Biology.com** 16.1 Self-Test • 16.1 Lesson Assessment
16.2 Ideas That Shaped Darwin's Thinking An Ancient, Changing Earth • Lamarck's Evolutionary Hypotheses • Population Growth • Artificial Selection • *Biology & History: Origins of Evolutionary Thought*	NoS.9	1 period 1/2 block	**Student Edition,** pp. 454–459 **Inquiry** 16.2 Quick Lab, p. 457 L2 **Study Workbook A** 16.2 Worksheets L2 **Biology.com** *Art in Motion:* The Ladder of Life • 16.2 Self-Test • 16.2 Lesson Assessment
16.3 Darwin Presents His Case Evolution by Natural Selection • Common Descent	B.8.5	1 period 1/2 block	**Student Edition,** pp. 460–464 **Study Workbook A** 16.3 Worksheets L2 **Biology.com** *Data Analysis:* Natural Selection **Assessment Resources Book** Visual Quizzes L2
16.4 Evidence of Evolution Biogeography • The Age of Earth and Fossils • Comparing Anatomy and Embryology • Genetics and Molecular Biology • Testing Natural Selection	NoS.3, NoS.6, B.8.3, B.8.4, B.8.5	1 1/2 periods 3/4 block	**Student Edition,** pp. 465–473 **Inquiry** 16.4 Analyzing Data, p. 470 L2 **Study Workbook A** 16.4 Worksheets L2 **Biology.com** *Art Review:* Homologous and Analogous • *Visual Analogy:* Finch Beak Tools • 16.4 Self-Test • 16.4 Lesson Assessment
Chapter Pre-Lab	NoS.2, NoS.4, B.8.2, B.8.3, B.8.4	1 period 1/2 block	**Student Edition,** p. 474 L2 **Lab Manual A** *Amino Acid Sequences: Indicators of Evolution* L2

Additional Resources

Biology.com Untamed Science Video • Vocabulary Flash Cards

Study Workbook B 16.1 Worksheets L1 ELL LPR
Spanish Study Workbook 16.1 Worksheets ELL
Biology.com 16.1 Lesson Overview • 16.1 Lesson Notes

Study Workbook B 16.2 Worksheets L1 ELL LPR
Spanish Study Workbook 16.2 Worksheets ELL
Biology.com 16.2 Lesson Overview • 16.2 Lesson Notes

Study Workbook B 16.3 Worksheets L1 ELL LPR
Spanish Study Workbook 16.3 Worksheets ELL
Biology.com 16.3 Lesson Overview • 16.3 Lesson Notes • 16.3 Self-Test • 16.3 Lesson Assessment

Study Workbook B 16.4 Worksheets L1 ELL LPR
Spanish Study Workbook 16.4 Worksheets ELL
Biology.com 16.4 Lesson Overview • 16.4 Lesson Notes

Lab Manual B *Amino Acid Sequences: Indicators of Evolution* • Data Analysis: *Molecular Homology in* Hoxc8 • Hands-On Activity: *Comparing Bones* L1 ELL LPR

Chapter Review

Student Edition Study Guide, p. 475 L2
Study Workbook A Chapter 16 Vocabulary Review L2 • Chapter 16 Chapter Mystery/21st Century Skills Activity L2 L3
Transparencies, pp. 193–202 L1 ELL LPR L2
Biology.com Untamed Science Video • Editable Worksheets of Study Workbooks A and B and Lab Manuals A and B • Chapter 16 Flash Cards and Crossword Puzzle

Untamed Science DVD • Classroom Resources CD (includes lesson presentations and editable worksheets)

Chapter Assessment

Student Edition Assessment, pp. 476–479 L2
Study Workbook B Chapter 16 Chapter Review L1 ELL LPR • Chapter 16 Taking a Standardized Test L1 ELL LPR
Assessment Resources Book Chapter 16 Test A L2 • Chapter 16 Test B L1 ELL LPR
Biology.com Chapter 16 Assessment • Editable Worksheets of Chapter 16 Visual Quizzes and Chapter 16 Tests A and B

Exam*View Assessment Suite* • Classroom Resources CD (includes lesson presentations and editable worksheets)

Time: 1 period, 1/2 block

Pressed for Time?

Preview the Chapter Preview Figures 16–9 and 16–10, and introduce the Key Questions for Lessons 16.3 and 16.4.

Cover the Chapter Quickly Have students read *Darwin's Epic Journey* in Lesson 16.1 and all of Lesson 16.3. Discuss Figure 16–10. Assign *Biogeography, The Age of Earth and Fossils, Comparing Anatomy and Embryology,* and *Genetics and Molecular Biology* in Lesson 16.4 and discuss Figures 16–13 and 16–14.

Assess Assign question 1a in the 16.1 Assessment, the 16.3 Assessment, questions 1–4 and 6 in the 16.4 Assessment, and the Chapter 16 Standardized Test Prep, except questions 2–4.

Connect to the Big Idea

Have students look at the photograph, and point out some of the ways the shells of the Cuban tree snails vary. Connect the image with the Big Idea of Evolution by explaining that the occurrence of natural variations such as these is a critical part of Charles Darwin's theory of evolution by natural selection. Encourage students to anticipate the answer to the question, **What is natural selection?**

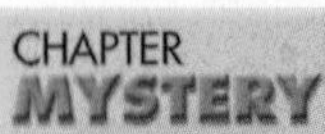

Ask students to read over the Chapter Mystery. Have a few students find online images of different species of Hawaiian honeycreepers and share them with the class. Explain that a bird's beak suits the type of food it normally eats. Ask students to infer what type of food each pictured species eats. Connect the Chapter Mystery to the Big Idea of Evolution by stating that all these varied honeycreepers came about through evolution by natural selection.

BIOLOGY.com Have students preview the chapter vocabulary terms using the **Flash Cards.**

IN INDIANA ACADEMIC STANDARDS

For the full text of all standards, see the Course Overview in the front matter of this book.

Key standards: Chapter 16 covers key ideas from Standard 8: Evolution, including **B.8.3** Evolutionary relationships and **B.8.5** Survival and reproduction.

16 Darwin's Theory of Evolution

Big idea **Evolution**

Q: What is natural selection?

BIOLOGY.com Search Chapter 16 GO • Flash Cards

448

UbD Understanding by Design

Chapter 16 introduces students to the Unit 5 Enduring Understanding: *The diversity of life is the result of ongoing evolutionary change. Species alive today have evolved from ancient common ancestors.* As the graphic organizer at the right shows, the chapter explains how Darwin developed his theory of evolution by natural selection. It describes his own observations while traveling aboard the *Beagle,* other influences on his thinking, and the main lines of evidence that support his theory.

PERFORMANCE GOALS

In Chapter 16, students will interpret visuals, analyze data, and apply concepts to demonstrate comprehension of the unit Enduring Understanding. At the end of the chapter, students will predict how a particular species might adapt to changes on Earth. They will also write an argument in support of evolution.

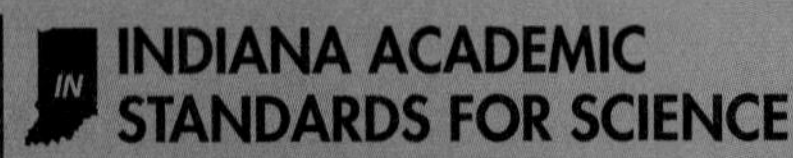

INDIANA ACADEMIC STANDARDS FOR SCIENCE

Nature of Science NoS.2, NoS.3, NoS.4, NoS.6, NoS.9; **Evolution** B.8.2, B.8.3, B.8.4, B.8.5. See lessons for details.

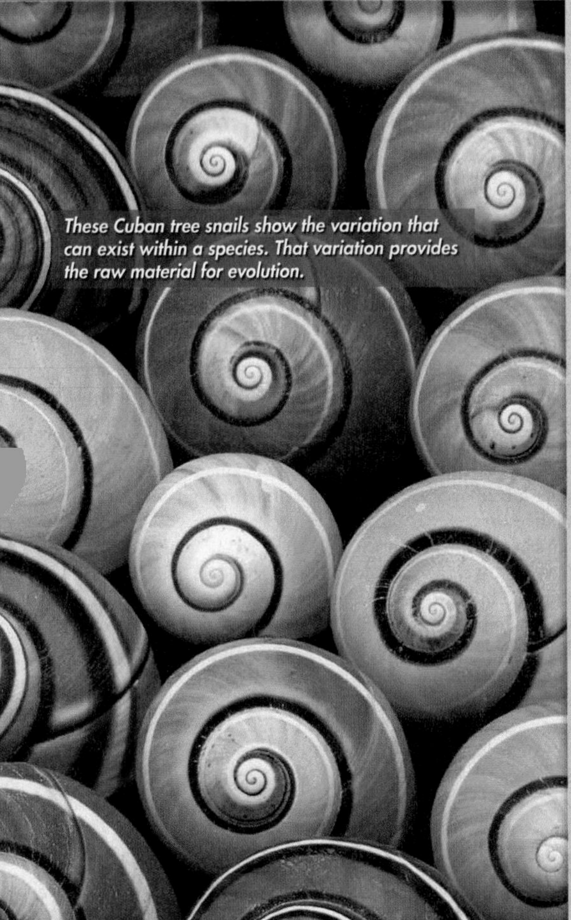

These Cuban tree snails show the variation that can exist within a species. That variation provides the raw material for evolution.

- Untamed Science Video
- Chapter Mystery

CHAPTER MYSTERY

SUCH VARIED HONEYCREEPERS

The misty rain forests on the Hawaiian island of Kauai are home to birds found nowhere else on Earth. Hiking at dawn, you hear them before you see them. Their songs fill the air with beautiful music. Then you spot a brilliant red bird with black wings called an 'i'iwi. As you watch, it uses its long, curved beak to probe for nectar deep in the flowers of 'ohi'a trees.

The 'i'iwi is just one of a number of species of Hawaiian honeycreepers, all of which are related to finches. Various honeycreeper species feed on nectar, insects, seeds, or fruits. Many Hawaiian honeycreepers, however, feed only on the seeds or nectar of unique Hawaiian plants.

How did all these birds get to Hawaii? How did some of them come to have such specialized diets? As you read the chapter, look for clues that help explain the number and diversity of Hawaiian honeycreepers. Then, solve the mystery.

Never Stop Exploring Your World. Finding the solution to the honeycreepers mystery is only the beginning. Take a video field trip to Hawaii with the ecogeeks of Untamed Science to see where the mystery leads.

Darwin's Theory of Evolution **449**

Chapter 16 Big Idea: Evolution

Chapter 16 EQ: What is natural selection?

16.1 GQ: What patterns of biodiversity did Darwin observe while traveling aboard the *Beagle*?

16.2 GQ: How did other scientists' work help Darwin develop his theory of natural selection?

16.3 GQ: What is Darwin's theory of evolution by natural selection?

16.4 GQ: What are the main lines of scientific evidence that support Darwin's theory of evolution by natural selection?

What's Online

BIOLOGY.com Extend your reach by using these and other digital assets offered at Biology.com.

CHAPTER MYSTERY
Students can study the case of Hawaiian honeycreepers and hypothesize how natural selection led to their diversity.

UNTAMED SCIENCE VIDEO
Take a trip to Hawaii with the Untamed Science crew to find out why these tiny islands hold big potential for evolution.

ART IN MOTION
An animation of canyon formation shows how fossil layers accumulate and are later exposed.

DATA ANALYSIS
Students collect population data to see how variation in a population of grasshoppers changes over time due to natural selection.

ART REVIEW
Students identify homologous and analogous structures in this drag-and-drop activity.

VISUAL ANALOGY
Simple animations show how the functions of specialized pliers and finch beak shapes are similar.

LESSON 16.1

Getting Started

Objectives

16.1.1 State Charles Darwin's contribution to science.

16.1.2 Describe the three patterns of biodiversity noted by Darwin.

Student Resources

Study Workbooks A and B, 16.1 Worksheets

Spanish Study Workbook, 16.1 Worksheets

 Lesson Overview • Lesson Notes • Assessment: Self-Test, Lesson Assessment

 For corresponding lesson in the **Foundation Edition,** see pages 380–383.

Activate Prior Knowledge

Most students will have some familiarity with Charles Darwin from previous science courses. Play a free-association word game to activate their prior knowledge. Call on students at random to say the first word that comes to mind when you say each of the following terms: Charles Darwin, *Beagle,* Galápagos Islands. Relate student responses to Darwin's voyage as an introduction to the lesson.

Answers

IN YOUR NOTEBOOK Sample answer: When Earth changes, life forms need to adapt to new environmental conditions to survive.

16.1 Darwin's Voyage of Discovery

Key Questions

What was Charles Darwin's contribution to science?

What three patterns of biodiversity did Darwin note?

Vocabulary

evolution
fossil

Taking Notes

Preview Visuals Before you read, look at **Figure 16–1.** Briefly summarize the route the *Beagle* took.

BUILD Vocabulary

RELATED WORD FORMS In biology, the noun **evolution** means "the process by which organisms have changed over time." The verb *evolve* means "to change over time."

THINK ABOUT IT If you'd met young Charles Darwin, you probably wouldn't have guessed that his ideas would change the way we look at the world. As a boy, Darwin wasn't a star student. He preferred bird-watching and reading for pleasure to studying. His father once complained, "You will be a disgrace to yourself and all your family." Yet Charles would one day come up with one of the most important scientific theories of all time—becoming far from the disgrace his father feared he would be.

Darwin's Epic Journey

What was Charles Darwin's contribution to science?

Charles Darwin was born in England on February 12, 1809—the same day as Abraham Lincoln. He grew up at a time when the scientific view of the natural world was shifting dramatically. Geologists were suggesting that Earth was ancient and had changed over time. Biologists were suggesting that life on Earth had also changed. The process of change over time is called **evolution.** **Darwin developed a scientific theory of biological evolution that explains how modern organisms evolved over long periods of time through descent from common ancestors.**

Darwin's journey began in 1831, when he was invited to sail on the HMS *Beagle*'s five-year voyage along the route shown in **Figure 16–1.** The captain and his crew would be mapping the coastline of South America. Darwin planned to collect specimens of plants and animals. No one knew it, but this would be one of the most important scientific voyages in history. Why? Because the *Beagle* trip led Darwin to develop what has been called the single best idea anyone has ever had.

If you think evolution is just about explaining life's ancient history, you might wonder why it's so important. But Darwin's work offers vital insights into today's world by showing how the living world is constantly changing. That perspective helps us understand modern phenomena like drug-resistant bacteria and newly emerging diseases like avian flu.

In Your Notebook *Using what you know about ecology, explain how the ideas of a changing Earth and evolving life forms might be related.*

UbD Teach for Understanding

ENDURING UNDERSTANDING *The diversity of life is the result of ongoing evolutionary change. Species alive today have evolved from ancient common ancestors.*

GUIDING QUESTION What patterns of biodiversity did Darwin observe while traveling aboard the *Beagle?*

EVIDENCE OF UNDERSTANDING *After completing the lesson, give students the following assessment to show their understanding of the patterns of biodiversity Darwin observed.* Have small groups of students find pictures of organisms online or in magazines and use printouts and/or clippings to create a poster that illustrates the patterns of biodiversity Darwin observed while aboard the *Beagle.*

Observations Aboard the *Beagle*

What three patterns of biodiversity did Darwin note?

A collector of bugs and shells in his youth, Darwin had always been fascinated by biological diversity. On his voyage, the variety and number of different organisms he encountered dazzled him. In a single day's trip into the Brazilian forest, he collected 68 species of beetles, and he wasn't particularly looking for beetles!

Darwin filled his notebooks with observations about the characteristics and habitats of the different species he saw. But Darwin wasn't content just to describe biological diversity. He wanted to explain it in a scientific way. He kept his eyes and mind open to larger patterns into which his observations might fit. As he traveled, Darwin noticed three distinctive patterns of biological diversity: (1) Species vary globally, (2) species vary locally, and (3) species vary over time.

Species Vary Globally Darwin visited a wide range of habitats on the continents of South America, Australia, and Africa and recorded his observations. For example, Darwin found flightless, ground-dwelling birds called rheas living in the grasslands of South America. Rheas look and act a lot like ostriches. Yet rheas live only in South America, and ostriches live only in Africa. When Darwin visited Australia's grasslands, he found another large flightless bird, the emu. **Darwin noticed that different, yet ecologically similar, animal species inhabited separated, but ecologically similar, habitats around the globe.**

Darwin also noticed that rabbits and other species living in European grasslands were missing from the grasslands of South America and Australia. What's more, Australia's grasslands were home to kangaroos and other animals that were found nowhere else. What did these patterns of geographic distribution mean? Why did different flightless birds live in similar grasslands across South America, Australia, and Africa, but not in the Northern Hemisphere? Why weren't there rabbits in Australian habitats that seemed ideal for them? And why didn't kangaroos live in England?

Darwin's Voyage

1. Using a world map and **Figure 16–1,** count the number of lines of 10° latitude the *Beagle* crossed.
2. Using the biome map from Chapter 4 as a reference, identify three different biomes Darwin visited on his voyage.

Analyze and Conclude

1. Infer How did the geography of Darwin's voyage give him far greater exposure to species variability than his fellow scientists back home had?

FIGURE 16–1 Darwin's Voyage On a five-year voyage aboard the *Beagle,* Charles Darwin visited several continents and many remote islands. Draw Conclusions ***Why is it significant that many of the stops the Beagle made were in tropical regions?***

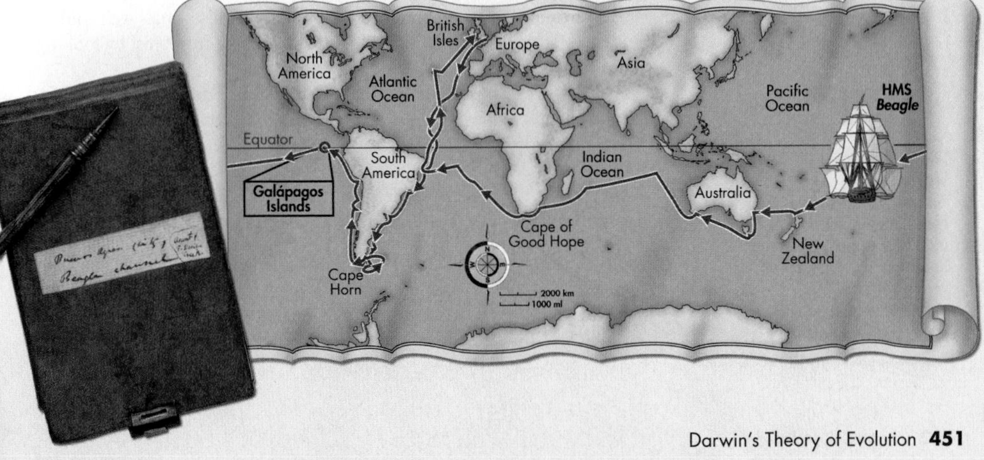

Teach

Build Science Skills

Discuss in greater detail the example of rheas, ostriches, and emus described in the text. Show the class visuals of the three types of birds and their habitats, and call on students to point out how the birds are adapted to their environments. Ask students to infer why large, flightless birds are found in grassland habitats around the globe.

DIFFERENTIATED INSTRUCTION

L1 Special Needs Pair special needs students with other students in the class, and have special needs students trace Darwin's voyage on the map in **Figure 16–1** while their partners read aloud about the voyage. Then, ask partners to find visuals of some of the places and organisms that Darwin saw and use them to make a scrapbook of his voyage.

ELL Focus on ELL: Build Background

BEGINNING AND INTERMEDIATE SPEAKERS
Guide students in using the visuals in the lesson to fill in a **BKWL Chart** about Darwin. Using the maps and photographs, summarize for students Darwin's voyage and observations. Have them take notes in column B as you do. Then, tell them to make inferences about Darwin, based on their notes, and list them in column K. In column W, have them record any questions they have about Darwin. They can look for answers to their questions as they read the lesson, and then write the answers in column L.

Study Wkbks A/B, Appendix S27, BKWL Chart. **Transparencies,** GO12.

Quick Lab

PURPOSE Students will identify the biomes Darwin visited and explain how this exposed him to greater species variability than other scientists experienced.

MATERIALS world map

PLANNING Remind students which lines on the map represent latitude. When they come to step 2, suggest they try to match places where the *Beagle* landed, which are shown in **Figure 16–1,** with the same locations on the world biome map in **Figure 4–18,** page 111.

ANALYZE AND CONCLUDE

1. Darwin crossed 11 lines of 10° latitude in his voyage (from London, 51° 25′ N to Cape Horn, 55° 90′ S). This gave him a chance to observe how species had adapted to different biomes and also how species had adapted to the same biomes in different parts of the world. As such, Darwin was exposed to much more variability than were his fellow scientists.

Answers

FIGURE 16–1 The relatively warm and wet climate of the tropics tends to correlate with high biodiversity. Being in tropical regions exposed Darwin to countless interesting and unfamiliar species.

Darwin's Theory of Evolution **451**

LESSON 16.1

Teach continued

Use Visuals

Call on students to describe differences between the two tortoises shown in **Figure 16–2.** Discuss how the differences between the tortoises are related to the differences in their environments. Challenge students to infer, based on the discussion, why groups of islands like the Galápagos are good places to study evolution.

Ask What other groups of islands might be good places to study evolution? *(Sample answers: the Hawaiian Islands, the islands of the Caribbean)*

DIFFERENTIATED INSTRUCTION

LPR **Less Proficient Readers** Suggest students use **Cornell Notes** to organize the information pertaining to Darwin's observations. Tell them to include as key words any terms that pertain to the main ideas, not just the lesson vocabulary terms.

Study Wkbks A/B, Appendix S22, Cornell Notes. **Transparencies,** GO5.

L3 **Advanced Students** Have students obtain a copy of Darwin's book, *On the Origin of Species,* and find passages in which Darwin describes his observations of plants and animals on the Galápagos Islands. Ask them to put some of the observations in their own words and share them with the class in an oral report. Have them illustrate their report with copies of Darwin's original drawings.

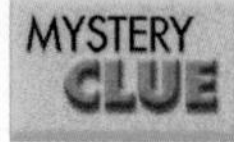

Students may say that the varied habitats on the Hawaiian Islands required honeycreepers to exploit different food sources, depending on which island they inhabited. This, in turn, may have led to the evolution of different traits on different islands. Students can go online to Biology.com to gather their evidence.

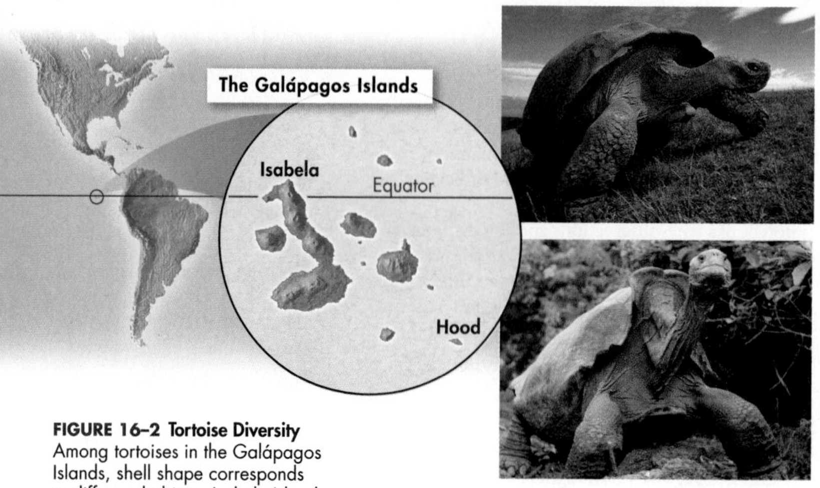

Isabela Island Tortoise Tortoises from Isabela Island have dome-shaped shells and short necks. Vegetation on this island is abundant and close to the ground.

Hood Island Tortoise The shells of Hood Island tortoises are curved and open around their long necks and legs. This enables them to reach the island's sparse, high vegetation.

FIGURE 16–2 Tortoise Diversity Among tortoises in the Galápagos Islands, shell shape corresponds to different habitats. Isabela Island has high peaks, is rainy, and has abundant vegetation. Hood Island, in contrast, is flat, dry, and has sparse vegetation.

Species Vary Locally There were other puzzles, too. For example, Darwin found two species of rheas living in South America. One lived in Argentina's grasslands and the other in the colder, harsher grass and scrubland to the south. **Darwin noticed that different, yet related, animal species often occupied different habitats within a local area.**

Other examples of local variation came from the Galápagos Islands, about 1000 km off the Pacific coast of South America. These islands are close to one another, yet they have different ecological conditions. Several islands were home to distinct forms of giant land tortoises. Darwin saw differences among the tortoises but didn't think much about them. In fact, like other travelers, Darwin ate several tortoises and tossed their remains overboard without studying them closely! Then Darwin learned from the islands' governor that the tortoises' shells varied in predictable ways from one island to another, as shown in **Figure 16–2.** Someone who knew the animals well could identify which island an individual tortoise came from, just by looking at its shell.

Darwin also observed that different islands had different varieties of mockingbirds, all which resembled mockingbirds that Darwin had seen in South America. Darwin also noticed several types of small brown birds on the islands with beaks of different shapes. He thought that some were wrens, some were warblers, and some were blackbirds. He didn't consider these smaller birds to be unusual or important—at first.

MYSTERY CLUE

Like the small brown birds on the Galápagos, Hawaiian honeycreepers live on islands with slightly different habitats. How might these varied habitats have affected the evolution of honeycreeper species?

Species Vary Over Time In addition to collecting specimens of living species, Darwin also collected **fossils,** which scientists already knew to be the preserved remains or traces of ancient organisms. Some fossils didn't look anything like living organisms, but others did.

UbD Check for Understanding

ONE-MINUTE RESPONSE

Ask students to write a one-minute response to the following:

Contrast the pattern Darwin observed among the large, flightless birds and the pattern he observed among the tortoises. *(The large, flightless birds lived far apart, yet their environments were similar, and the birds looked similar. The tortoises lived close to one another, yet they had differences that seemed to correspond to differences in their environments.)*

ADJUST INSTRUCTION

Call on volunteers to read their response aloud. If students have trouble distinguishing these patterns, tell them that similar environments seem to result in similarities among organisms. Different environments seem to result in differences among organisms.

Darwin noticed that some fossils of extinct animals were similar to living species. One set of fossils unearthed by Darwin belonged to the long-extinct glyptodont, a giant armored animal. Currently living in the same area was a similar animal, the armadillo. You can see in **Figure 16–3** that the armadillo appears to be a smaller version of the glyptodont. Darwin said of the organisms: "This wonderful relationship in the same continent between the dead and the living, will, I do not doubt, hereafter throw more light on the appearance of organic beings on our earth, and their disappearance from it, than any other class of facts." So, why had glyptodonts disappeared? And why did they resemble armadillos?

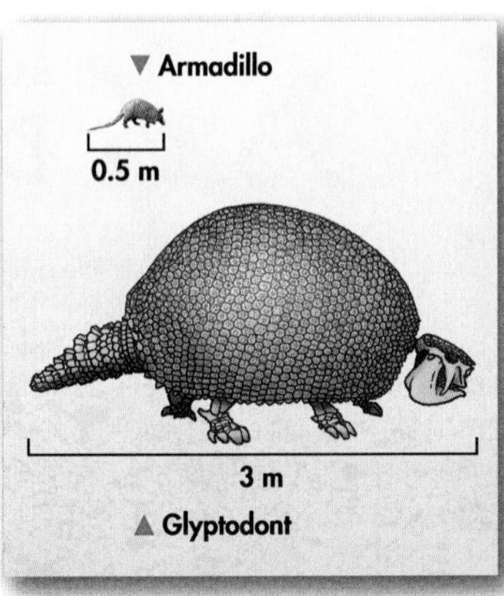

FIGURE 16–3 Related Organisms? Despite their obvious differences, Darwin wondered if the armadillo might be related to the ancient glyptodont. Compare and Contrast ***What similarities and differences do you see between these two animals?***

Putting the Pieces of the Puzzle Together On the voyage home, Darwin thought about the patterns he'd seen. The plant and animal specimens he sent to experts for identification set the scientific community buzzing. The Galápagos mockingbirds turned out to belong to three separate species found nowhere else! And the little brown birds that Darwin thought were wrens, warblers, and blackbirds were actually all species of finches! They, too, were found nowhere else, though they resembled a South American finch species. The same was true of Galápagos tortoises, marine iguanas, and many plants that Darwin collected on the islands.

Darwin was stunned by these discoveries. He began to wonder whether different Galápagos species might have evolved from South American ancestors. He spent years actively researching and filling notebooks with ideas about species and evolution. The evidence suggested that species are not fixed and that they could change by some natural process.

16.1 Assessment

Review Key Concepts 

1. a. Review What is evolution?
   b. Apply Concepts What ideas were changing in the scientific community at the time of Darwin's travels? How might those new ideas have influenced Darwin?
2. a. Review What three kinds of variations among organisms did Darwin observe during the voyage of the *Beagle?*
   b. Infer Darwin found fossils of many organisms that did not resemble any living species. How might this finding have affected his understanding of life's diversity?

Apply the Big idea

Interdependence in Nature

3. You have learned that both biotic and abiotic factors affect ecosystems. Give some examples of each, and explain how biotic and abiotic factors could have affected the tortoises that Darwin observed on the Galápagos Islands.

BIOLOGY.com Search (Lesson 16.1) GO • Self-Test • Lesson Assessment

Assess and Remediate

EVALUATE UNDERSTANDING

Ask students to write four fill-in, true-false, or multiple-choice questions based on the Key Concepts in the lesson. Have them exchange questions with a partner and try to answer the partner's questions. Then, have students complete the 16.1 Assessment.

REMEDIATION SUGGESTION

L1 Struggling Students If students have difficulty with **Question 3,** suggest they review biotic and abiotic factors in Chapter 3.

BIOLOGY.com Students can check their understanding of lesson concepts with the **Self-Test** assessment. They can then take an online version of the **Lesson Assessment.**

Answers

FIGURE 16–3 Sample answer: The armadillo is much smaller than the glyptodont, but the two organisms have similar shells, tails, and body shapes.

Assessment Answers

1a. the process of change over time

1b. Geologists were suggesting that Earth was ancient and had changed over time. Biologists were suggesting that life on Earth had changed over time, as well. These ideas might have influenced Darwin to develop a theory about how organisms had changed over long periods of time.

2a. Darwin observed that organisms vary globally, locally, and over time.

2b. Sample answer: This finding might have helped him understand that many species go extinct, while others evolve into different species. Darwin might have inferred that Earth's current diversity is less than the total diversity of living things that have ever existed.

3.  Sample answer: Biotic factors are any living component of the environment with which individuals interact, such as the plants they eat for food or the predators they try to avoid. Abiotic factors are nonliving parts of an organism's environment, such as precipitation and soil type. Variation in abiotic and biotic factors on different Galápagos Islands might explain the different traits of tortoises on the islands. For example, Hood Island is dry and has sparse vegetation, whereas Isabela Island is rainy and has dense vegetation. The necks and shells of tortoises suit them for the abiotic and biotic factors on the particular island they inhabit.

LESSON 16.2

Getting Started

Objectives

16.2.1 Identify the conclusions drawn by Hutton and Lyell about Earth's history.

16.2.2 Describe Lamarck's hypothesis of evolution.

16.2.3 Describe Malthus's view of population growth.

16.2.4 Explain the role of inherited variation in artificial selection.

Student Resources

Study Workbooks A and B, 16.2 Worksheets

Spanish Study Workbook, 16.2 Worksheets

Lesson Overview • Lesson Notes • Activities: Art in Motion • Assessment: Self-Test, Lesson Assessment

For corresponding lesson in the **Foundation Edition,** see pages 384–387.

Build Background

Describe a husband and wife who exercise regularly at the gym, build up their muscles, and then later have a baby. Ask students if the big muscles of the parents will be passed on to their child. *(Students are likely to say no.)* Tell them an early nineteenth-century scientist named Lamarck thought traits organisms developed during their life could be passed on to their offspring. Explain that they will read about Lamarck in this lesson, because his ideas influenced Darwin.

IN INDIANA ACADEMIC STANDARDS

NoS.9 Recognize that new scientific discoveries often lead to a re-evaluation of previously accepted scientific knowledge and of commonly held ideas.

16.2 Ideas That Shaped Darwin's Thinking

NoS.9 Scientific discoveries affect prior ideas.

Key Questions

What did Hutton and Lyell conclude about Earth's history?

How did Lamarck propose that species evolve?

What was Malthus's view of population growth?

How is inherited variation used in artificial selection?

Vocabulary

artificial selection

Taking Notes

Outline Make an outline of this lesson using the green headings as main topics and the blue headings as subtopics. As you read, fill in details under each heading.

THINK ABOUT IT All scientists are influenced by the work of other scientists, and Darwin was no exception. The *Beagle*'s voyage came during one of the most exciting periods in the history of science. Geologists, studying the structure and history of Earth, were making new observations about the forces that shape our planet. Naturalists were investigating connections between organisms and their environments. These and other new ways of thinking about the natural world provided the foundation on which Darwin built his ideas.

An Ancient, Changing Earth

What did Hutton and Lyell conclude about Earth's history?

Many Europeans in Darwin's day believed Earth was only a few thousand years old, and that it hadn't changed much. By Darwin's time, however, the relatively new science of geology was providing evidence to support different ideas about Earth's history. Most famously, geologists James Hutton and Charles Lyell formed important hypotheses based on the work of other researchers and on evidence they uncovered themselves. **Hutton and Lyell concluded that Earth is extremely old and that the processes that changed Earth in the past are the same processes that operate in the present.** In 1785, Hutton presented his hypotheses about how geological processes have shaped the Earth. Lyell, who built on the work of Hutton and others, published the first volume of his great work, *Principles of Geology,* in 1830.

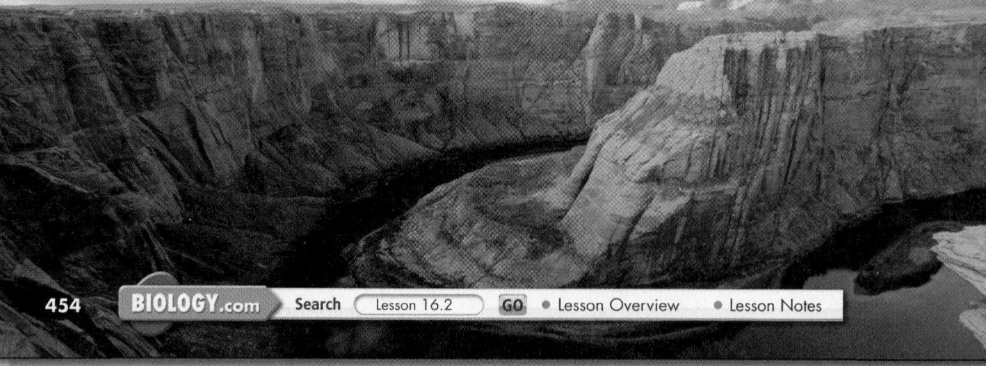

FIGURE 16–4 Ancient Rocks These rock layers in the Grand Canyon were laid down over millions of years and were then slowly washed away by the river, forming a channel.

UbD Teach for Understanding

ENDURING UNDERSTANDING *The diversity of life is the result of ongoing evolutionary change. Species alive today have evolved from ancient common ancestors.*

GUIDING QUESTION How did other scientists' work help Darwin develop his theory of natural selection?

EVIDENCE OF UNDERSTANDING *After completing the lesson, give students the following assessment to show their understanding of how other scientists contributed to Darwin's theory of evolution by natural selection.* In groups of five, have students assume the roles of Hutton, Lyell, Lamarck, Malthus, and Darwin. Ask group members to collaborate on creating and presenting a brief skit in which Hutton, Lyell, Lamarck, and Malthus present their ideas to Darwin, and Darwin responds by stating how the ideas influenced his theory of evolution by natural selection.

Hutton and Geological Change Hutton recognized the connections between a number of geological processes and geological features, like mountains, valleys, and layers of rock that seemed to be bent or folded. Hutton realized, for example, that certain kinds of rocks are formed from molten lava. He also realized that some other kinds of rocks, like those shown in **Figure 16–4,** form very slowly, as sediments build up and are squeezed into layers.

Hutton also proposed that forces beneath Earth's surface can push rock layers upward, tilting or twisting them in the process. Over long periods, those forces can build mountain ranges. Mountains, in turn, can be worn down by rain, wind, heat, and cold. Most of these processes operate very slowly. For these processes to have produced Earth as we know it, Hutton concluded that our planet must be much older than a few thousand years. He introduced a concept called *deep time*—the idea that our planet's history stretches back over a period of time so long that it is difficult for the human mind to imagine—to explain his reasoning.

Lyell's *Principles of Geology* Lyell argued that laws of nature are constant over time and that scientists must explain past events in terms of processes they can observe in the present. This way of thinking, called *uniformitarianism,* holds that the geological processes we see in action today must be the same ones that shaped Earth millions of years ago. Ancient volcanoes released lava and gases, just as volcanoes do now. Ancient rivers slowly dug channels, like the one in **Figure 16–5,** and carved canyons in the past, just as they do today. Lyell's theories, like those of Hutton before him, relied on there being enough time in Earth's history for these changes to take place. Like Hutton, Lyell argued that Earth was much, much older than a few thousand years. Otherwise, how would a river have enough time to carve out a valley?

Darwin had begun to read Lyell's books during the voyage of the *Beagle*, which was lucky. Lyell's work helped Darwin appreciate the significance of an earthquake he witnessed in South America. The quake was so strong that it threw Darwin onto the ground. It also lifted a stretch of rocky shoreline more than 3 meters out of the sea—with mussels and other sea animals clinging to it. Sometime later, Darwin observed fossils of marine animals in mountains thousands of feet above sea level.

Those experiences amazed Darwin and his companions. But only Darwin turned them into a startling scientific insight. He realized that he had seen evidence that Lyell was correct! Geological events like the earthquake, repeated many times over many years, could build South America's Andes Mountains—a few feet at a time. Rocks that had once been beneath the sea could be pushed up into mountains. Darwin asked himself, If Earth can change over time, could life change too?

BUILD Vocabulary

ACADEMIC WORDS The noun **process** means "a series of actions or changes that take place in a definite manner." The processes that shape Earth are the series of geological actions that do things such as build mountains and carve valleys.

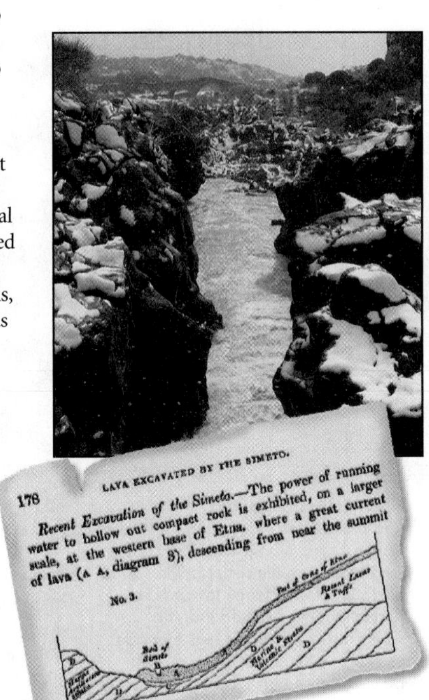

FIGURE 16–5 A woodcut from Lyell's *Principles of Geology* shows geological features near Italy's Mount Etna. Among them is a deep channel, labeled "B," carved into a bed of lava. The channel, shown in the photo, was formed gradually by the movement of water in the Simeto River.

LESSON 16.2

Teach

Connect to Geology

Have students examine the photographs shown in **Figures 16–4** and **16–5.** Point out that there is running water in both photographs. Call on volunteers to infer how geological processes produced the Grand Canyon and the deep channel of the Simeto River in Italy. *(Moving water gradually eroded rock layers.)* Discuss how long it took the Grand Canyon to form. *(Geologists estimate that the Grand Canyon formed over 6 million years.)* Ask students to infer how knowledge of such processes influenced Darwin.

DIFFERENTIATED INSTRUCTION

LPR **Less Proficient Readers** Give students one minute to write down everything they know about geology. Then, ask students to review **An Ancient, Changing Earth.** As they read, students should add details from the text to their brainstorm sheet.

ELL Focus on ELL: Extend Language

ADVANCED AND ADVANCED HIGH SPEAKERS As students read the lesson, have them write their own definition of each of the following concepts, based on the information in the text: *geological change*, *uniformitarianism*, *inheritance of acquired characteristics*, *population growth*, and *artificial selection*. When you review the lesson, ask students to read their definitions to the class.

BIOLOGY.com Have students view the **Art in Motion: The Ladder of Life** to see an animation of canyon formation, showing how fossil layers accumulate and are later exposed.

How Science Works

PATRICK MATTHEW AND HIS THEORY OF EVOLUTION

Most people have heard of Charles Darwin's theory of evolution by natural selection, but how many people have heard of Patrick Matthew's theory of evolution? Very few, although Matthew thought his name should be associated with the theory of evolution, not Charles Darwin's. Matthew was born in 1790 in Scotland, where he lived most of his life. He owned and managed a large fruit orchard. Although he wasn't a scientist, he wrote about evolution and described a mechanism similar to what we today call natural selection. Matthew's work appeared almost 30 years before Darwin published *On the Origin of Species*. Did Darwin steal Matthew's ideas? It seems unlikely, because Matthew's theories were "hidden" in obscure publications that Darwin claimed never to have read. Matthew's theory also differed from Darwin's in several important ways. It should also be noted that Matthew, unlike Darwin, did not spend decades gathering evidence for his theory.

Darwin's Theory of Evolution **455**

Teach continued

Build Science Skills

Challenge small groups of students to design an experiment to test Lamarck's hypothesis that acquired characteristics can be passed from parents to offspring. Their experimental design should include a hypothesis, a procedure, possible outcomes, and an explanation of how the outcomes would or would not support their hypothesis. Give groups a chance to share their experimental designs.

DIFFERENTIATED INSTRUCTION

L3 Advanced Students Suggest students research the ideas of Georges Cuvier and Georges-Louis Leclerc, Comte de Buffon—two naturalists whose ideas preceded Darwin's. Have students prepare a 5- to 10-minute class presentation in which they summarize the work of these two men and suggest how their work may have influenced Darwin.

Address Misconceptions

Selection for Perfection A common student misconception is that evolution produces perfect organisms. In the next lesson, this is addressed in detail, but take the opportunity here to introduce this misconception. Explain that the *tendency toward perfection* is one of the great flaws of Lamarck's ideas. No organism is perfectly adapted. In fact, the variations that make us less than perfect may also save us if our environment changes.

Lamarck's Evolutionary Hypotheses

How did Lamarck propose that species evolve?

Darwin wasn't the first scientist to suggest that characteristics of species could change over time. Throughout the eighteenth century, a growing fossil record supported the idea that life somehow evolved. Ideas differed, however, about just *how* life evolved. The French naturalist Jean-Baptiste Lamarck proposed two of the first hypotheses. **Lamarck suggested that organisms could change during their lifetimes by selectively using or not using various parts of their bodies. He also suggested that individuals could pass these acquired traits on to their offspring, enabling species to change over time.** Lamarck published his ideas in 1809, the year Darwin was born.

FIGURE 16–6 Acquired Characteristics? According to Lamarck, this black-necked stilt's long legs were the result of the bird's innate tendency toward perfection. He claimed that if a water bird needs long legs to wade in deep water, it can acquire them by making an effort to stretch and use its legs in new ways. He also claimed that the bird can then pass the trait on to its offspring.

Lamarck's Ideas Lamarck proposed that all organisms have an inborn urge to become more complex and perfect. As a result, organisms change and acquire features that help them live more successfully in their environments. He thought that organisms could change the size or shape of their organs by using their bodies in new ways. According to Lamarck, for example, a water bird could have acquired long legs because it began to wade in deeper water looking for food. As the bird tried to stay above the water's surface, its legs would grow a little longer. Structures of individual organisms could also change if they were not used. If a bird stopped using its wings to fly, for example, its wings would become smaller. Traits altered by an individual organism during its life are called *acquired characteristics.*

Lamarck also suggested that a bird that acquired a trait, like longer legs, during its lifetime could pass that trait on to its offspring, a principle referred to as *inheritance of acquired characteristics.* Thus, over a few generations, birds like the one in **Figure 16–6** could evolve longer and longer legs.

Evaluating Lamarck's Hypotheses Today, we know that Lamarck's hypotheses were incorrect in several ways. For one thing, organisms don't have an inborn drive to become more perfect. Evolution does not mean that over time a species becomes "better" somehow, and evolution does not progress in a predetermined direction. We now also know that traits acquired by individuals during their lifetime cannot be passed on to offspring. However, Lamarck was one of the first naturalists to suggest that species are not fixed. He was among the first to try to explain evolution scientifically using natural processes. He also recognized that there is a link between an organism's environment and its body structures. So, although Lamarck's explanation of evolutionary change was wrong, his work paved the way for later biologists, including Darwin.

In Your Notebook *Why are Lamarck's ideas called scientific hypotheses and not scientific theories?*

UbD Check for Understanding

DEPTH OF UNDERSTANDING

Ask students to respond in writing to the following question: How did Lamarck influence Darwin's thinking? *(Students with a superficial understanding might respond incorrectly that Lamarck gave Darwin the idea that individuals could develop new traits during their life and pass them to their offspring. Students with a sophisticated understanding should respond that Lamarck influenced Darwin with his ideas that natural processes can explain evolution and that species are influenced by their environments.)*

ADJUST INSTRUCTION

Collect and read students' responses. Select several of the more sophisticated responses, and share them with the class. To ensure understanding, ask a few students to rephrase various answers.

Answers

IN YOUR NOTEBOOK Hypotheses, unlike theories, are statements that are not necessarily supported by evidence, and Lamarck's ideas were not supported by evidence.

Population Growth

What was Malthus's view of population growth?

In 1798, English economist Thomas Malthus noted that humans were being born faster than people were dying, causing overcrowding, as shown in **Figure 16–7. Malthus reasoned that if the human population grew unchecked, there wouldn't be enough living space and food for everyone.** The forces that work against population growth, Malthus suggested, include war, famine, and disease.

Darwin realized that Malthus's reasoning applied even more to other organisms than it did to humans. A maple tree can produce thousands of seeds each summer. One oyster can produce millions of eggs each year. If all the descendants of almost any species survived for several generations, they would overrun the world. Obviously, this doesn't happen. Most offspring die before reaching maturity, and only a few of those that survive manage to reproduce.

Why was this realization so important? Darwin had become convinced that species evolved. But he needed a mechanism—a scientific explanation based on a natural process—to explain how and why evolution occurred. When Darwin realized that most organisms don't survive and reproduce, he wondered which individuals survive ... and why.

FIGURE 16–7 Overcrowding in London A nineteenth-century engraving shows the crowded conditions in London during Darwin's time. **Relate Cause and Effect** ***According to Malthus, what would happen if the population of London continued to grow?***

Artificial Selection

How is inherited variation used in artificial selection?

To find an explanation for change in nature, Darwin studied change produced by plant and animal breeders. Those breeders knew that individual organisms vary—that some plants bear larger or smaller fruit than average for their species, that some cows give more or less milk than others in their herd. They told Darwin that some of this variation could be passed from parents to offspring and used to improve crops and livestock.

Quick Lab — GUIDED INQUIRY

Variation in Peppers

1. Obtain a green, yellow, red, or purple bell pepper.
2. Slice open the pepper and count the number of seeds it contains.
3. Compare your data with the data of other students who have peppers of a different color.

Analyze and Conclude

1. **Calculate** Find the average (mean) number of seeds in your class's peppers. Then determine by how much the number of seeds in each pepper differs from the mean number. MATH
2. **Pose Questions** Think of the kinds of variations among organisms that Darwin observed. If Darwin had seen your data, what questions might he have asked?

BIOLOGY.com Search    Lesson 16.2 GO • Art in Motion

Connect to Math

Malthus believed populations of organisms increase exponentially, while the resources they need increase linearly. Tell students that his model of population growth can be expressed by the equation:

$$P_n = (1 + r)^n P_0$$

where n = number of years, r = rate of population growth per year, P_0 = size of the original population, and P_n = size of the population after n years. Starting with n = 0 and P_0 = 100, and assuming that r is constant at 0.2, work with students to find the values of P_n for n = 1 to 10. Then, have them graph the values. They should plot the values of n on the *x*-axis and the corresponding values of P_n on the *y*-axis. *(Their graphs should resemble a parabola.)* On the same graph, ask them to draw a straight line passing from the origin to the right at a 45° angle (i.e., a graph of $y = x$). Tell them this line represents a linear increase in resources. Discuss how and why the line representing population differs from the line representing resources. Also, discuss the implications of the lines for real populations.

DIFFERENTIATED INSTRUCTION

ELL English Language Learners After students have finished reading the lesson, have them get together for a **Core Concept Discussion.** Each student in the group should contribute one core concept from the lesson (such as Lamarck's ideas or Hutton and Lyell's conclusions), then other group members take turns discussing it.

Study Wkbks A/B, Appendix S3, Core Concept Discussion.

Quick Lab

PURPOSE Students will analyze variation in traits and infer questions Darwin might have posed about the data.

MATERIALS bell peppers of different colors, knife

SAFETY Remind students to wear goggles and handle the knife carefully. Make sure they wash their hands after finishing the lab.

PLANNING Provide each student with a pepper. Use several colors of peppers if possible. Be sure to use bell peppers, not hot peppers.

ANALYZE AND CONCLUDE

1. Answers will vary depending on class data.
2. Sample answer: Darwin might have asked whether variation in seed number was associated with other variables, such as growth conditions or pepper color. He may have wondered if the variation correlated to a pepper color's success in its environment.

Answers

FIGURE 16–7 There wouldn't be enough living space and food for everyone, which might increase the chances of war, famine, disease, and other population-limiting phenomena.

Teach continued

Assess and Remediate

EVALUATE UNDERSTANDING

Have students make an acrostic based on *Darwin*. Each letter in the term should be the first letter in a sentence describing an influence on Darwin. Then, have students complete the 16.2 Assessment.

REMEDIATION SUGGESTION

L1 Struggling Students If students have trouble with **Question 4b,** suggest they reread the Key Concept about artificial selection.

BIOLOGY.com Students can check their understanding of lesson concepts with the **Self-Test** assessment. They can then take an online version of the **Lesson Assessment.**

FIGURE 16–8 Artificial Selection Darwin used artificial selection in breeding fancy pigeons at his home outside London.

Farmers would select for breeding only trees that produced the largest fruit or cows that produced the most milk. Over time, this selective breeding would produce more trees with even bigger fruit and cows that gave even more milk. Darwin called this process **artificial selection.** **In artificial selection, nature provides the variations, and humans select those they find useful.** Darwin put artificial selection to the test by raising and breeding plants and fancy pigeon varieties, like those in **Figure 16–8.**

Darwin had no idea how heredity worked or what caused heritable variation. But he did know that variation occurs in wild species as well as in domesticated plants and animals. Before Darwin, scientists thought variations among individuals in nature were simply minor defects. Darwin's breakthrough was in recognizing that natural variation was very important because it provided the raw material for evolution. Darwin had all the information he needed. His scientific explanation for evolution was now formed—and when it was published, it would change the way people understood the living world.

16.2 Assessment

Review Key Concepts

1. a. Review What were Hutton's and Lyell's ideas about the age of Earth and the processes that shape the planet?
   b. Apply Concepts How would Hutton and Lyell explain the formation of the Grand Canyon?
2. a. Review What is an acquired characteristic? What role did Lamarck think acquired characteristics played in evolution?
   b. Evaluate What parts of Lamarck's hypotheses have been proved wrong? What did Lamarck get right?
3. a. Review According to Malthus, what factors limit human population growth?
   b. Draw Conclusions How did Malthus influence Darwin?
4. a. Review What is artificial selection?
   b. Infer Could artificial selection occur without inherited variation? Explain your answer.

WRITE ABOUT SCIENCE

Creative Writing

5. Imagine you are Thomas Malthus and the year is 1798. Write a newspaper article that explains your ideas about the impact of a growing population on society and the environment.

 Search Lesson 16.2 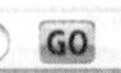 • Self-Test • Lesson Assessment

Assessment Answers

1a. Hutton thought geological processes, such as mountain building, take a very long time, so Earth must be much older than most people believed. Lyell expanded on Hutton's idea by suggesting that the same geological processes that changed Earth in the past are still at work today.

1b. Hutton and Lyell would explain that the Grand Canyon formed over millions of years as the running water of the Colorado River gradually wore away rocks—just as it does today.

2a. An acquired characteristic is a trait altered during an organism's life. Lamarck thought acquired characteristics could be passed on to offspring.

2b. Lamarck's idea about the inheritance of acquired characteristics and an organism's tendency toward perfection have been proven wrong. However, he was right that species are not fixed but change in response to their environment.

3a. living space and food

3b. Malthus got Darwin thinking about overproduction of offspring. The idea that many more organisms are produced than can survive led Darwin to suggest a mechanism that explains *which* organisms survive to reproduce.

4a. the process of allowing only organisms with desirable traits to reproduce in order to increase the number of individuals with those traits

4b. No, there would be nothing to select if all the members of a species were identical.

WRITE ABOUT SCIENCE

5. Answers will vary but should show that students understand Malthus's ideas about population growth and its potential negative consequences, such as war and disease.

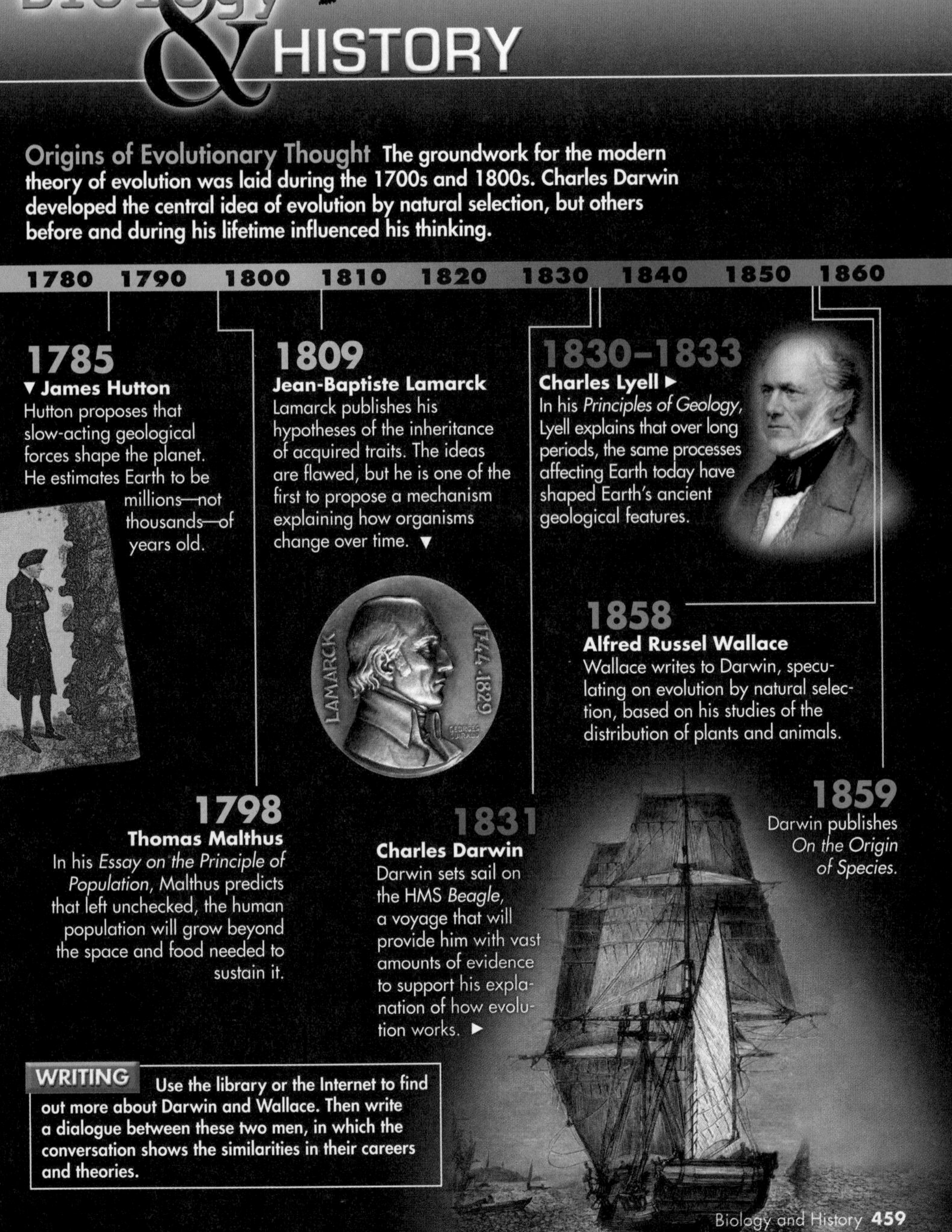

Biology & HISTORY
NoS.9 Scientific discoveries affect prior ideas.
Origins of Evolutionary Thought The groundwork for the modern theory of evolution was laid during the 1700s and 1800s. Charles Darwin developed the central idea of evolution by natural selection, but others before and during his lifetime influenced his thinking.
1780 1790 1800 1810 1820 1830 1840 1850 1860
1785
▼ James Hutton
Hutton proposes that slow-acting geological forces shape the planet. He estimates Earth to be millions—not thousands—of years old.
1809
Jean-Baptiste Lamarck
Lamarck publishes his hypotheses of the inheritance of acquired traits. The ideas are flawed, but he is one of the first to propose a mechanism explaining how organisms change over time. ▼
1830–1833
Charles Lyell ▶
In his Principles of Geology, Lyell explains that over long periods, the same processes affecting Earth today have shaped Earth's ancient geological features.
LAMARCK
1744-1829
1858
Alfred Russel Wallace
Wallace writes to Darwin, speculating on evolution by natural selection, based on his studies of the distribution of plants and animals.
1798
Thomas Malthus
In his Essay on the Principle of Population, Malthus predicts that left unchecked, the human population will grow beyond the space and food needed to sustain it.
1831
Charles Darwin
Darwin sets sail on the HMS Beagle, a voyage that will provide him with vast amounts of evidence to support his explanation of how evolution works. ▶
1859
Darwin publishes On the Origin of Species.
WRITING Use the library or the Internet to find out more about Darwin and Wallace. Then write a dialogue between these two men, in which the conversation shows the similarities in their careers and theories.
Biology and History 459

Teach

Lead a Discussion

By the end of Lesson 16.2, students should be familiar with all of the individuals in the time line except for Alfred Russel Wallace. You may want to provide additional background on him. (See Quick Facts below.) Tell students Wallace's letter influenced Darwin to publish *On the Origin of Species* more quickly than he otherwise would have. Discuss how the social climate of Darwin's time made him reluctant to publish his ideas about evolution and why he needed the extra impetus from Wallace to publish them when he did.

DIFFERENTIATED INSTRUCTION

ELL English Language Learners Match beginning or intermediate speakers with more advanced speakers, and ask pairs to discuss how each individual in the time line influenced Darwin to develop his theory of evolution by natural selection. Then, have partners collaborate to write a sentence about each individual that states the nature of his influence.

Quick Facts

ALFRED RUSSEL WALLACE

Alfred Russel Wallace is best remembered for developing a theory of evolution that is very similar to that of Darwin. However, this is just one reason why, by 1900, Wallace was among the world's most widely known and well-respected scientists. Other reasons include Wallace's concept of polymorphism and early contributions to the understanding of mimicry. Further, he authored the most famous book ever written on the Malay Archipelago and established himself as the world's authority on Indonesia. In addition, he discovered the "Wallace Effect" (selection for reproductive isolation). Throughout his life, Wallace defended natural selection while developing his own ideas—many of which were cited in Darwin's own works. In fact, historians believe the two men greatly influenced and challenged each other.

Answers

WRITING Dialogues will vary but should include similar statements by Darwin and Wallace about how plants and animals vary and how they evolve by natural selection. Dialogues should also reveal the two men's similar experiences as naturalists.

LESSON 16.3

Getting Started

Objectives

16.3.1 Describe the conditions under which natural selection occurs.

16.3.2 Explain the principle of common descent.

Student Resources

Study Workbooks A and B, 16.3 Worksheets

Spanish Study Workbook, 16.3 Worksheets

Lesson Overview • Lesson Notes • Activity: Data Analysis • Assessment: Self-Test, Lesson Assessment

For corresponding lesson in the **Foundation Edition,** see pages 388–391.

Build Background

Print a blank family tree (readily available online), and share it with the class. Explain how the tree can be used to show an individual's descent from his or her ancestors. Discuss how a family tree is similar to an evolutionary tree. Tell students Charles Darwin created the first known evolutionary tree, which they will read about in this lesson.

Darwin Presents His Case

B.8.5 Survival and reproduction.

Key Questions

Under what conditions does natural selection occur?

What does Darwin's mechanism for evolution suggest about living and extinct species?

Vocabulary

adaptation
fitness
natural selection

Taking Notes

Preview Visuals Before you read this lesson, look at **Figure 16–10.** Read the information in the figure, and then write three questions you have about it. As you read, answer your questions.

THINK ABOUT IT Soon after reading Malthus and thinking about artificial selection, Darwin worked out the main points of his theory about natural selection. Most of his scientific friends considered Darwin's arguments to be brilliant, and they urged him to publish them. But although he wrote up a complete draft of his ideas, he put the work aside and didn't publish it for another 20 years. Why? Darwin knew that many scientists, including some of Darwin's own teachers, had ridiculed Lamarck's ideas. Darwin also knew that his own theory was just as radical, so he wanted to gather as much evidence as he could to support his ideas before he made them public.

Then, in 1858, Darwin reviewed an essay by Alfred Russel Wallace, an English naturalist working in Malaysia. Wallace's thoughts about evolution were almost identical to Darwin's! Not wanting to get "scooped," Darwin decided to move forward with his own work. Wallace's essay was presented together with some of Darwin's observations at a scientific meeting in 1858. The next year, Darwin published his first complete work on evolution: *On the Origin of Species.*

Evolution by Natural Selection

Under what conditions does natural selection occur?

Darwin's great contribution was to describe a process in nature—a scientific mechanism—that could operate like artificial selection. In *On the Origin of Species,* he combined his own thoughts with ideas from Malthus and Lamarck.

The Struggle for Existence After reading Malthus, Darwin realized that if more individuals are produced than can survive, members of a population must compete to obtain food, living space, and other limited necessities of life. Darwin described this as *the struggle for existence.* But which individuals come out on top in this struggle?

Variation and Adaptation Here's where individual variation plays a vital role. Darwin knew that individuals have natural variations among their heritable traits. He hypothesized that some of those variants are better suited to life in their environment than others. Members of a predatory species that are faster or have longer claws or sharper teeth can catch more prey. And members of a prey species that are faster or better camouflaged can avoid being caught.

IN INDIANA ACADEMIC STANDARDS

For the full text of all standards, see the Course Overview in the front matter of this book.

B.8.5 Describe how due to genetic variations, environmental forces, and reproductive pressures, organisms with beneficial traits are more likely to survive, reproduce, and pass on their genetic information.

UbD Teach for Understanding

ENDURING UNDERSTANDING *The diversity of life is the result of ongoing evolutionary change. Species alive today have evolved from ancient common ancestors.*

GUIDING QUESTION What is Darwin's theory of evolution by natural selection?

EVIDENCE OF UNDERSTANDING *After completing the lesson, give students the following assessment to show their understanding of Darwin's theory of evolution by natural selection.* Ask students to apply the concepts in the lesson by writing an explanation of how bacteria could evolve the ability to resist a particular antibiotic through the process of natural selection.

Any heritable characteristic that increases an organism's ability to survive and reproduce in its environment is called an **adaptation.** Adaptations can involve body parts or structures, like a tiger's claws; colors, like those that make camouflage or mimicry possible; or physiological functions, like the way a plant carries out photosynthesis. Many adaptations also involve behaviors, such as the complex avoidance strategies prey species use. Examples of adaptations are shown in **Figure 16–9.**

BUILD Vocabulary

RELATED WORD FORMS The verb *inherited* and the adjective *heritable* are related word forms. Inherited traits are passed on to offspring from their parents. They are described as *heritable* (or sometimes *inheritable*) characteristics.

Survival of the Fittest Darwin, like Lamarck, recognized that there must be a connection between the way an organism "makes a living" and the environment in which it lives. According to Darwin, differences in adaptations affect an individual's fitness. **Fitness** describes how well an organism can survive and reproduce in its environment.

Individuals with adaptations that are well suited to their environment can survive and reproduce and are said to have high fitness. Individuals with characteristics that are not well suited to their environment either die without reproducing or leave few offspring and are said to have low fitness. This difference in rates of survival and reproduction is called *survival of the fittest.* Note that *survival* here means more than just staying alive. In evolutionary terms, *survival* means reproducing and passing adaptations on to the next generation.

In Your Notebook *If an organism produces many offspring, but none of them reach maturity, do you think the organism has high or low fitness? Explain your answer.*

VISUAL SUMMARY

ADAPTATIONS

FIGURE 16–9 Adaptations take many forms.

A. The scarlet king snake (bottom) is exhibiting mimicry—an adaptation in which an organism copies, or mimics, a more dangerous organism. Although the scarlet king snake is harmless, it looks like the poisonous eastern coral snake (top), so predators avoid it, too.

B. A scorpionfish's coloring is an example of camouflage—an adaptation that allows an organism to blend into its background and avoid predation.

C. Adaptations often involve many systems and even behavior. Here, a crane is displaying defensive behavior in an effort to scare off the nearby fox.

461

Teach

Expand Vocabulary

Make sure students understand the terms *adaptation* and *fitness,* because these terms are basic to their comprehension of the process of natural selection. After students read about the terms in context on this page, have them apply the concepts to specific cases. Ask them to describe examples of adaptations and explain how they increase the fitness of the organisms in which they occur.

DIFFERENTIATED INSTRUCTION

LPR Less Proficient Readers Suggest students make an outline of the lesson, using the green headings for the main topics and the blue headings for the subtopics. As they read the lesson, they can add details to their outline.

VISUAL SUMMARY

Call on students to identify each adaptation shown in **Figure 16–9.** Discuss how adaptations increase an individual's fitness. Describe additional examples of the same types of adaptations, such as viceroy butterflies that mimic poisonous monarch butterflies, stick insects that use camouflage to blend in with twigs, and dogs that growl defensively to warn off strangers. Then, challenge students to think of other types of adaptations that help organisms survive.

LESSON 16.3

How Science Works

STEPHEN JAY GOULD AND THE PANDA'S THUMB

Few scientists have reached as wide an audience on the subject of evolution as paleontologist Stephen Jay Gould. His essays appeared in 300 consecutive issues of *Natural History* between 1974 and 2001, and his award-winning books have sold more than a million copies. He was fond of describing "jury-rigged" adaptations as examples that defy intelligent design. For example, the giant panda has a modified wrist bone that it uses as a thumb to grasp bamboo. "The…thumb wins no prize in an engineer's derby," Gould said, "but it does its job and excites our imagination all the more because it builds on such improbable foundations." Along with his colleague Niles Eldredge, Gould also developed the theory of punctuated equilibrium, which posits that evolution often occurs in bursts of rapid change interspersed with long periods of little change.

Answers

IN YOUR NOTEBOOK If an organism produces many offspring, but none of them reach maturity, then it has low fitness, because its offspring will not pass on their traits to the next generation.

Teach continued

VISUAL SUMMARY

Have students read each step in the natural selection of the hypothetical grasshopper population shown in **Figure 16–10.** Extend the example by having students apply the same concepts to somewhat different conditions. For each step in the figure, describe an alternative situation, and ask students to explain how natural selection would be affected. For example, ask them to explain how selection might be different if there were brown grasshoppers in addition to yellow and green grasshoppers.

DIFFERENTIATED INSTRUCTION

L1 Special Needs Guide students in creating a hands-on model of the example in **Figure 16–10.** Have them trace and cut out insect shapes from yellow and green construction paper so there are equal numbers of each color. Then, have them place the "insects" on a sheet of green construction paper to represent a grassy environment. Ask students why the yellow insects would have lower fitness in this situation. *(Predators would be more likely to spot and catch the yellow insects.)* Then, ask them how they could use their model to simulate yellow insects having lower fitness than green insects. *(by removing some of the yellow insect shapes from the "population")*

BIOLOGY.com In **Data Analysis: Natural Selection,** students collect data to see how variation in a grasshopper poulation changes over several generations due to natural selection.

Address Misconceptions

Rate of Evolution Students commonly have the misconception that challenges to Darwin's view of evolution as a slow, steady process mean that natural selection is no longer accepted by scientists. Make sure students understand that evolution by natural selection is not in dispute. Rather, it has just been extended to include the possibility of evolution occurring at a relatively rapid rate under certain conditions. (See note about Stephen Jay Gould on preceding page.) In other words, Darwin's theory has been modified and improved, but his basic principles remain unchallenged within the scientific community.

Answers

FIGURE 16–10 body color

VISUAL SUMMARY

NATURAL SELECTION

FIGURE 16–10 This hypothetical population of grasshoppers changes over time as a result of natural selection. **Interpret Visuals** ***In the situation shown here, what characteristic is affecting the grasshoppers' fitness?***

1 The Struggle for Existence Organisms produce more offspring than can survive. Grasshoppers can lay over 200 eggs at a time. Only a small fraction of these offspring survive to reproduce.

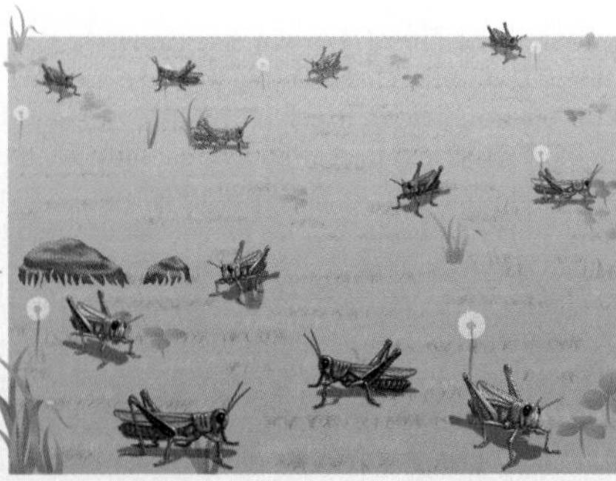

2 Variation and Adaptation There is variation in nature, and certain heritable variations—called adaptations—increase an individual's chance of surviving and reproducing. In this population of grasshoppers, heritable variation includes yellow and green body color. Green coloration is an adaptation: Green grasshoppers blend into their environment and so are less visible to predators.

3 Survival of the Fittest Because their green color serves to camouflage them from predators, green grasshoppers have a higher fitness than yellow grasshoppers. This means that green grasshoppers survive and reproduce more often than do yellow grasshoppers in this environment.

4 Natural Selection Green grasshoppers become more common than yellow grasshoppers in this population over time because: (1) more grasshoppers are born than can survive, (2) individuals vary in color and color is a heritable trait, and (3) green individuals have a higher fitness in their current environment.

Quick Facts

OBSERVING NATURAL SELECTION

A recent article published in the journal *Science* documents a case of selection at work in a natural population. The study not only adds support to Darwin's theory of evolution by natural selection, it also demonstrates that natural selection can occur very rapidly when selective pressures are especially strong. The study focused on a species of Samoan butterfly. The butterflies were infected with bacteria that killed males before they hatched. Although females were not affected by the bacteria, the almost total decimation of males threatened the entire population. Then, a mutation occurred (or was introduced) that gave males the ability to resist the bacteria and survive. Within just one year, or ten generations, the percentage of males in the butterfly population increased from a mere 1 percent to almost 40 percent, and all of the surviving males had the mutation. The researchers noted that this may be the fastest evolutionary change ever observed.

Natural Selection Darwin named his mechanism for evolution *natural selection* because of its similarities to artificial selection. **Natural selection** is the process by which organisms with variations most suited to their local environment survive and leave more offspring. In both artificial and natural selection, only certain individuals in a population produce new individuals. But in natural selection, the environment—not a farmer or animal breeder—influences fitness.

When does natural selection occur? **Natural selection occurs in any situation in which more individuals are born than can survive (the struggle for existence), there is natural heritable variation (variation and adaptation), and there is variable fitness among individuals (survival of the fittest).** Well-adapted individuals survive and reproduce. From generation to generation, populations continue to change as they become better adapted, or as their environment changes. **Figure 16–10** uses a hypothetical example to show the process of natural selection. Notice that natural selection acts only on inherited traits because those are the only characteristics that parents can pass on to their offspring.

Natural selection does not make organisms "better." Adaptations don't have to be perfect—just good enough to enable an organism to pass its genes to the next generation. Natural selection also doesn't move in a fixed direction. There is no one, perfect way of doing something, as demonstrated by **Figure 16–11.** Natural selection is simply a process that enables species to survive and reproduce in a local environment. If local environmental conditions change, some traits that were once adaptive may no longer be useful, and different traits may become adaptive. And if environmental conditions change faster than a species can adapt to those changes, the species may become extinct. Of course, natural selection is not the only mechanism driving evolution. You will learn about other evolutionary mechanisms in the next chapter.

In Your Notebook *Give at least two reasons why the following statement is NOT true: "The goal of natural selection is to produce perfect organisms."*

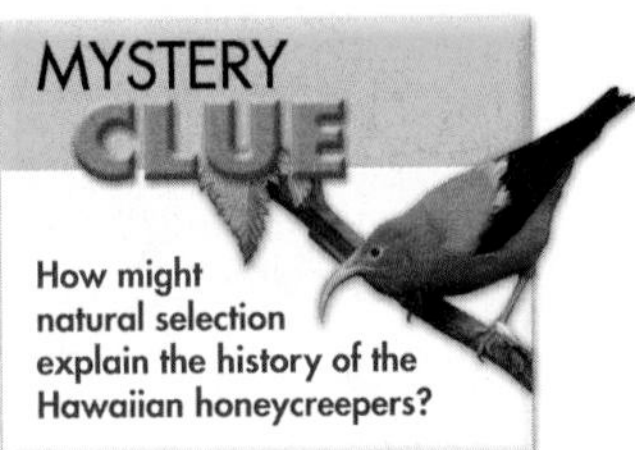

MYSTERY
CLUE
How might natural selection explain the history of the Hawaiian honeycreepers?

FIGURE 16–11 No Such Thing as Perfect Many different styles of pollination have evolved among flowering plants. Oak tree flowers (right) are pollinated by wind. Apple tree flowers (left) are pollinated by insects. Neither method is "better" than the other. Both kinds of pollination work well enough for these plants to survive and reproduce in their environments.

Build Science Skills

Point out the two different styles of pollination pictured in **Figure 16–11.** Have students look closely at the flowers and describe any structures that might be adaptations for pollination. *(Sample answer: The brightly colored blossoms of the apple tree flowers might be an adaptation that attracts insects.)* Ask students to explain how natural selection led to these adaptations. Use their answers to start a general discussion of why reproductive traits such as these are under strong selective pressure.

DIFFERENTIATED INSTRUCTION

L1 Struggling Students Point out that Darwin called his mechanism for evolution by the term *natural selection* because the process resembles artificial selection. Make sure students understand the similarities and differences between artificial and natural selection. Have them complete a **Venn Diagram** that compares and contrasts the two processes.

Study Wkbks A/B, Appendix S33, Venn Diagram. **Transparencies,** GO18.

ELL Focus on ELL: Extend Language

BEGINNING AND INTERMEDIATE SPEAKERS
Assign each of three groups of students one of the terms *adaptation, fitness,* or *selection.* Give group members a large sheet of paper, and have them write the assigned term, its component parts, and its definition. Also have them make a drawing to illustrate the term. When groups finish, ask them to present their work to the class, and then post their work in a **Word Wall.**

Study Wkbks A/B, Appendix S17, Word Wall.

Sample answer: Honeycreepers faced different environmental pressures depending on which island they inhabited, so different traits would have been selected for on different islands. This would explain how different species of honeycreepers evolved. Students can go online to Biology.com to gather their evidence.

UbD Check for Understanding

QUESTION BOX

Evolution by natural selection is one of the central organizing concepts in biology—it is also one of the most commonly misunderstood. Establish a secure box in your classroom where students can leave anonymous questions. As an assignment, have everyone in the class write at least one question.

ADJUST INSTRUCTION

Collect and review students' questions regularly. Go over the questions with the class. If an important question does *not* get asked, take the opportunity to raise it. Be sure to cover the common misconception that organisms evolve traits for a purpose as in, "birds evolved wings to fly." That is not correct. Rather, birds have wings that, today, enable them to fly.

Answers

IN YOUR NOTEBOOK Sample answer: Because natural selection is a natural process, it cannot have goals. Further, natural selection could never produce "perfect" organisms because environments change, and no organism is "better" or "more perfect" than any other in adjusting to future changes.

Teach continued

Address Misconceptions

Natural Selection and Evolution Natural selection and evolution are often used interchangeably—but they are not the same thing. Natural selection is a mechanism of evolution. Make sure students understand that organisms can evolve in other ways, too—through random mutation, lateral gene transfer, genetic drift, and gene shuffling in sexual reproduction.

Assess and Remediate

EVALUATE UNDERSTANDING

Ask students to write definitions, in their own words, for the lesson vocabulary terms. Tell them to read their definitions to a partner, and have the partner identify the terms from the definitions. Then, have students complete the 16.3 Assessment.

REMEDIATION SUGGESTION

ELL **English Language Learners** If students have trouble with **Question 1b,** make sure they understand that the term *fitness* has a different meaning in the context of natural selection than it does in common usage. In biology, fitness is a measure of an organism's ability to produce offspring as well as to survive.

BIOLOGY.com Students can check their understanding of lesson concepts with the **Self-Test** assessment. They can then take an online version of the **Lesson Assessment.**

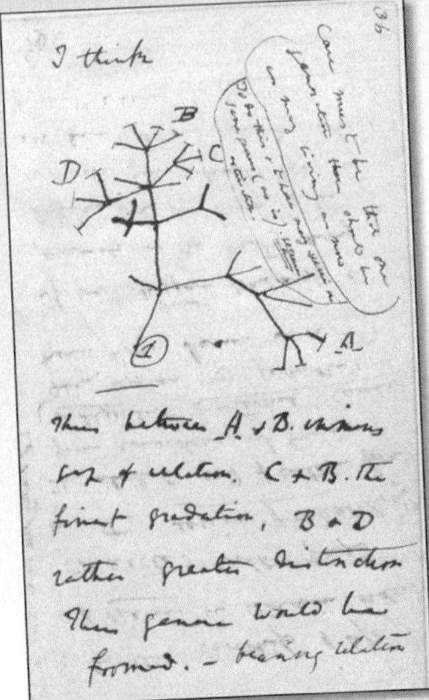

FIGURE 16–12 Descent With Modification This page from one of Darwin's notebooks shows the first evolutionary tree ever drawn. This sketch shows Darwin's explanation for how descent with modification could produce the diversity of life. Note that, just above the tree, Darwin wrote, "I think."

Common Descent

What does Darwin's mechanism for evolution suggest about living and extinct species?

Natural selection depends on the ability of organisms to reproduce, which means to leave descendants. Every organism alive today is descended from parents who survived and reproduced. Those parents descended from their parents, and so forth back through time.

Just as well-adapted individuals in a species survive and reproduce, well-adapted species survive over time. Darwin proposed that, over many generations, adaptation could cause successful species to evolve into new species. He also proposed that living species are descended, with modification, from common ancestors—an idea called *descent with modification.* Notice that this aspect of Darwin's theory implies that life has been on Earth for a very long time—enough time for all this descent with modification to occur! This is Hutton and Lyell's contribution to Darwin's theory: Deep time gave enough time for natural selection to act. For evidence of descent with modification over long periods of time, Darwin pointed to the fossil record.

Darwin based his explanation for the diversity of life on the idea that species change over time. To illustrate this idea, he drew the very first evolutionary tree, shown in **Figure 16–12.** This "tree-thinking" implies that all organisms are related. Look back in time, and you will find common ancestors shared by tigers, panthers, and cheetahs. Look farther back, and you will find ancestors that these felines share with dogs, then horses, and then bats. Farther back still is the common ancestor that all mammals share with birds, alligators, and fish. Far enough back are the common ancestors of all living things. **According to the principle of common descent, all species—living and extinct—are descended from ancient common ancestors.** A single "tree of life" links all living things.

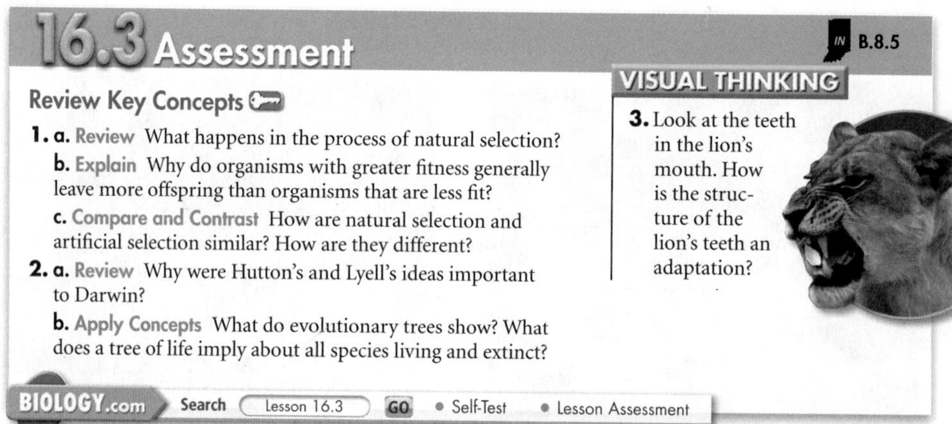

16.3 Assessment

IN B.8.5

Review Key Concepts

1. a. Review What happens in the process of natural selection?
   b. Explain Why do organisms with greater fitness generally leave more offspring than organisms that are less fit?
   c. Compare and Contrast How are natural selection and artificial selection similar? How are they different?
2. a. Review Why were Hutton's and Lyell's ideas important to Darwin?
   b. Apply Concepts What do evolutionary trees show? What does a tree of life imply about all species living and extinct?

VISUAL THINKING

3. Look at the teeth in the lion's mouth. How is the structure of the lion's teeth an adaptation?

BIOLOGY.com Search Lesson 16.3 GO • Self-Test • Lesson Assessment

464 Chapter 16 • Lesson 3

Assessment Answers

1a. Natural selection is the process by which organisms with variations most suited to their environment (adaptations) survive and leave more offspring than individuals without the adaptations.

1b. Individuals with high fitness have adaptations that make them better suited for their environment, so they survive and reproduce more often than individuals who are less fit.

1c. In both artificial and natural selection, certain individuals in a population disproportionately pass on their traits to the next generation, resulting in changes to the population. However, in natural selection the environment—not a farmer or animal breeder—determines which individuals pass on their traits.

2a. Hutton and Lyell thought Earth was very old. This was important to Darwin, because it allowed enough time for natural selection to work.

2b. Evolutionary trees show ancestor-descendant relationships among groups of related organisms. A tree of life implies that all species living and extinct are descended from ancient common ancestors.

VISUAL THINKING

3. Sample answer: The large pointed teeth of the lion are an adaptation, because they increase the lion's ability to kill prey and tear meat.

16.4 Evidence of Evolution

IN B.8.3 Evolutionary relationships; B.8.4 Evidence for evolutionary relationships; B.8.5 Survival and reproduction. Also covered: NoS.3, NoS.6.

THINK ABOUT IT Darwin's theory depended on assumptions that involved many scientific fields. Scientists in some fields, including geology, physics, paleontology, chemistry, and embryology, did not have the technology or understanding to test Darwin's assumptions during his lifetime. And other fields, like genetics and molecular biology, didn't exist yet! In the 150 years since Darwin published *On the Origin of Species*, discoveries in all these fields have served as independent tests that could have supported or refuted Darwin's work. Astonishingly, every scientific test has supported Darwin's basic ideas about evolution.

Biogeography

How does the geographic distribution of species today relate to their evolutionary history?

Darwin recognized the importance of patterns in the distribution of life—the subject of the field called biogeography. **Biogeography** is the study of where organisms live now and where they and their ancestors lived in the past. **Patterns in the distribution of living and fossil species tell us how modern organisms evolved from their ancestors.** Two biogeographical patterns are significant to Darwin's theory. The first is a pattern in which closely related species differentiate in slightly different climates. The second is a pattern in which very distantly related species develop similarities in similar environments.

Closely Related but Different To Darwin, the biogeography of Galápagos species suggested that populations on the island had evolved from mainland species. Over time, natural selection on the islands produced variations among populations that resulted in different, but closely related, island species.

Distantly Related but Similar On the other hand, similar habitats around the world are often home to animals and plants that are only distantly related. Darwin noted that similar ground-dwelling birds inhabit similar grasslands in Europe, Australia, and Africa. Differences in body structures among those animals provide evidence that they evolved from different ancestors. Similarities among those animals, however, provide evidence that similar selection pressures had caused distantly related species to develop similar adaptations.

Key Questions

- *How does the geographic distribution of species today relate to their evolutionary history?*
- *How do fossils help to document the descent of modern species from ancient ancestors?*
- *What do homologous structures and similarities in embryonic development suggest about the process of evolutionary change?*
- *How can molecular biology be used to trace the process of evolution?*
- *What does recent research on the Galápagos finches show about natural selection?*

Vocabulary

biogeography
homologous structure
analogous structure
vestigial structure

Taking Notes

Concept Map Construct a concept map that shows the kinds of evidence that support the theory of evolution.

MYSTERY CLUE

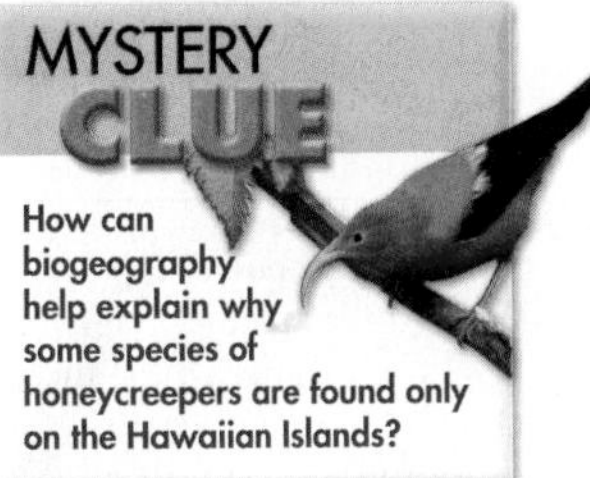

How can biogeography help explain why some species of honeycreepers are found only on the Hawaiian Islands?

Teach for Understanding

ENDURING UNDERSTANDING *The diversity of life is the result of ongoing evolutionary change. Species alive today have evolved from ancient common ancestors.*

GUIDING QUESTION What are the main lines of scientific evidence that support Darwin's theory of evolution by natural selection?

EVIDENCE OF UNDERSTANDING *After completing the lesson, give students the following assessment to show their understanding of the evidence that supports Darwin's theory of evolution.* Ask pairs of students to create and present an oral presentation with visuals outlining the main lines of evidence that support Darwin's theory of evolution by natural selection. Students should include examples of each line of evidence.

Getting Started

Objectives

16.4.1 Explain how geologic distribution of species relates to their evolutionary history.

16.4.2 Explain how fossils and the fossil record document the descent of modern species from ancient ancestors.

16.4.3 Describe what homologous structures and embryology suggest about the process of evolutionary change.

16.4.4 Explain how molecular evidence can be used to trace the process of evolution.

16.4.5 Explain the results of the Grants' investigation of adaptation in Galápagos finches.

Student Resources

Study Workbooks A and B, 16.4 Worksheets

Spanish Study Workbook, 16.4 Worksheets

Lab Manual B, 16.4 Data Analysis Worksheet, Hands-On Activity Worksheet

Lesson Overview • Lesson Notes
- Activities: Art Review, Visual Analogy
- Assessment: Self-Test, Lesson Assessment

For corresponding lesson in the **Foundation Edition,** see pages 392–397.

Students might infer the reason to be Hawaii's isolation from other landmasses. Students can go online to Biology.com to gather their evidence.

IN INDIANA ACADEMIC STANDARDS

For the full text of all standards, see the Course Overview in the front matter of this book.

B.8.3 Use anatomical and molecular evidence to establish evolutionary relationships between organisms.

B.8.4 Understand that molecular evidence supports the anatomical evidence for these evolutionary relationships and provides additional information about the order in which different lines of descent branched.

B.8.5 Describe how due to genetic variations, environmental forces, and reproductive pressures, organisms with beneficial traits are more likely to survive, reproduce, and pass on their genetic information.

LESSON 16.4

Teach continued

VISUAL SUMMARY

After students have examined **Figure 16–13,** put the evolution of whales in perspective. Explain that scientists since Darwin puzzled over how this transition occurred until the recent discovery of intermediate forms like *Ambulocetus*. Then, guide students in interpreting the evolutionary changes shown in the figure. Call on volunteers to identify possible advantages of specific changes. For example, ask why it might have been an advantage for *Ambulocetus* to be able to swim as well as walk or for *Dorudon* to have reduced hindlimbs and a streamlined body. Make sure students understand that each of the animals shown represents a branch in the evolutionary history of whales.

DIFFERENTIATED INSTRUCTION

L1 Special Needs Students may have a better understanding of fossils after doing this simple simulation. Have them place a small seashell at the bottom of a beaker that is about half full of water and then add a couple handfuls of soil to the beaker. Tell them to observe as the soil gradually settles to the bottom and covers the shell. Relate this to how dead organisms sink to the bottom of the ocean and become buried with sediments. Explain that the pressure of the water and additional sediments very slowly turns the dead organisms into fossils.

The Age of Earth and Fossils

How do fossils help to document the descent of modern species from ancient ancestors?

Two potential difficulties for Darwin's theory involved the age of Earth and gaps in the fossil record. Data collected since Darwin's time have answered those concerns and have provided dramatic support for an evolutionary view of life.

The Age of Earth Evolution takes a long time. If life has evolved, then Earth must be very old. Hutton and Lyell argued that Earth was indeed very old, but technology in their day couldn't determine just how old. Half a century after Darwin published his theory, however, physicists discovered radioactivity. Geologists now use radioactivity to establish the age of certain rocks and fossils. This kind of data could have shown that Earth is young. If that had happened, Darwin's ideas would have been refuted and abandoned. Instead, radioactive dating indicates that Earth is about 4.5 billion years old—plenty of time for evolution by natural selection to take place.

VISUAL SUMMARY

EVIDENCE FROM FOSSILS

FIGURE 16–13 Recently, researchers have found more than 20 related fossils that document the evolution of modern whales from ancestors that walked on land. Several reconstructions based on fossil evidence are shown below in addition to the modern mysticete and odontocete. **Infer** ***Which of the animals shown was probably the most recent to live primarily on land?***

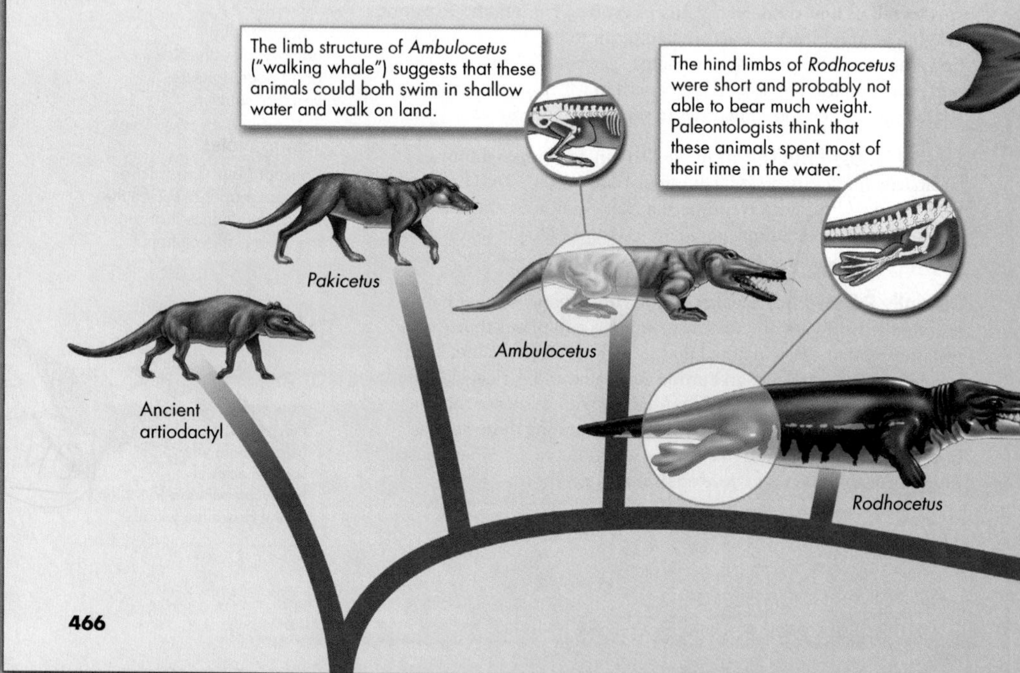

The limb structure of *Ambulocetus* ("walking whale") suggests that these animals could both swim in shallow water and walk on land.
The hind limbs of *Rodhocetus* were short and probably not able to bear much weight. Paleontologists think that these animals spent most of their time in the water.
Pakicetus
Ambulocetus
Ancient artiodactyl
Rodhocetus

466

Biology In-Depth

THE EVOLUTION OF WHALES

Fossils that provide evidence for the transition from land to water show that the transition took only 10 million years, which is a very short time in evolutionary terms. *Pakicetus* was first discovered in 1979 by paleontologist Philip Gingerich in Pakistan. In 1994, Gingerich's former student, J. Thewissen found *Ambulocetus*—a whale that lived about 50 million years ago and was probably amphibious. *Rodhocetus*, discovered by Gingerich in the 1990s, lived about 45 million years ago and was the earliest known completely aquatic mammal in the whale lineage. It is the ankle bone anatomy of *Rodhocetus* and another whale ancestor called *Artiocetus*, however, that proved to be the most important. The particular shape of the ancient whales' ankle bones allowed Gingerich to pinpoint their ancestry to artiodactyls—not to a group of extinct carnivores called mesonychids as previously thought.

Answers

FIGURE 16–13 *Ambulocetus*

Recent Fossil Finds Darwin also struggled with what he called the "imperfection of the geological record." Darwin's study of fossils had convinced him and other scientists that life evolved. But paleontologists in 1859 hadn't found enough fossils of intermediate forms of life to document the evolution of modern species from their ancestors. **Many recently discovered fossils form series that trace the evolution of modern species from extinct ancestors.**

Since Darwin, paleontologists have discovered hundreds of fossils that document intermediate stages in the evolution of many different groups of modern species. One recently discovered fossil series documents the evolution of whales from ancient land mammals, as shown in **Figure 16–13.** Other recent fossil finds connect the dots between dinosaurs and birds, and between fish and four-legged land animals. In fact, so many intermediate forms have been found that it is often hard to tell where one group begins and another ends. All historical records are incomplete, and the history of life is no exception. The evidence we do have, however, tells an unmistakable story of evolutionary change.

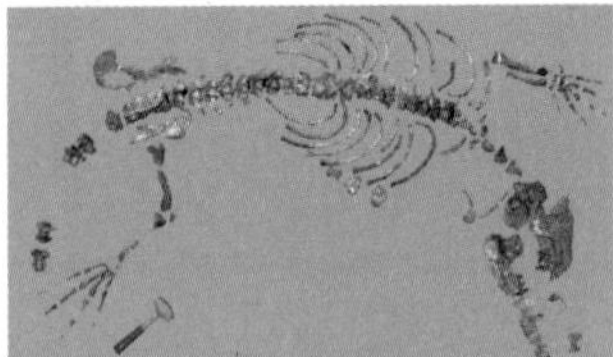

Fossil of the Eocene whale *Ambulocetus natans* (about 49 million years old)

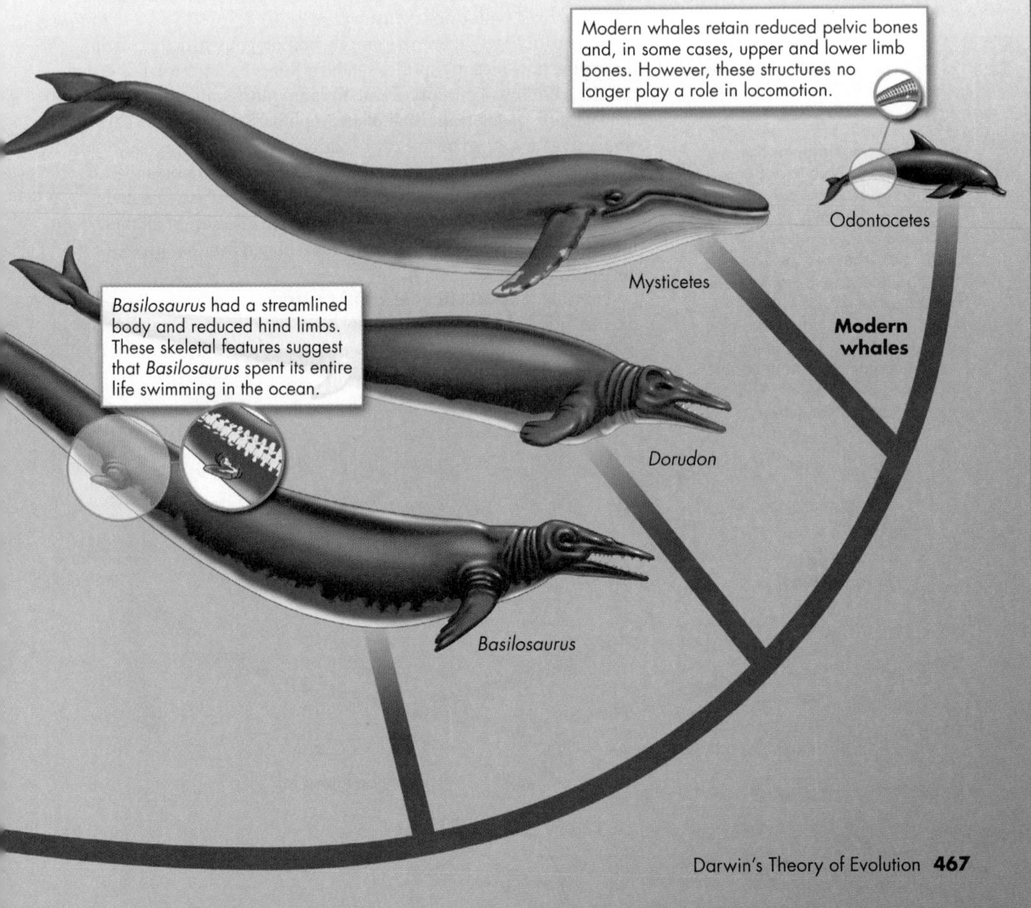

Modern whales retain reduced pelvic bones and, in some cases, upper and lower limb bones. However, these structures no longer play a role in locomotion.
Odontocetes
Mysticetes
Modern whales
Basilosaurus had a streamlined body and reduced hind limbs. These skeletal features suggest that Basilosaurus spent its entire life swimming in the ocean.
Dorudon
Basilosaurus

How Science Works

MINI DINOSAUR PROVIDES MISSING LINK

For decades, one of the most significant pieces of "missing" data for the evolution of birds from nonflying dinosaurs was evidence for a reduction in body size. Dinosaurs were generally large animals, and a relatively small body is a necessary prerequisite for flight. An 80-million-year-old fossil dinosaur found in China's Gobi Desert in 2007, named *Mahakala omnogovae,* provided the missing evidence. This diminutive dinosaur was only 70 centimeters long. It was the first known dinosaur that would have been small enough to fly. It also had winglike limbs, and probably had feathers.

Lead a Discussion

Tell students fossils of whale ancestors have been found in places that are no longer covered by water. For example, fossils of *Ambulocetus* and *Rodhocetus* were found in desert regions of Pakistan.

Ask How could fossils for amphibious or aquatic organisms be found in a desert? *(The environment changed since the organisms represented by the fossils lived there.)*

Use this example to start a general discussion of how environmental change is related to natural selection.

DIFFERENTIATED INSTRUCTION

ELL English Language Learners Use a **Question-Answer Relationships** strategy to help students glean the most important information from the passage, **Recent Fossil Finds.** Write the following questions on the board, and before students answer them, have them decide whether each question is a Right There, Think and Search, Author and You, or On My Own question:

- What was Darwin convinced of from his study of fossils? *(Right There)*
- Why did Darwin struggle with the "imperfection of the geological record"? *(Think and Search)*
- What traits do you think a species would have that was intermediate between dinosaurs and birds? *(On My Own)*

Study Wkbks A/B, Appendix S10, Question-Answer Relationships.

Address Misconceptions

Gaps in the Fossil Record Students commonly presume that missing intermediate fossils disprove Darwin's theory of evolution by natural selection. Stress how rare it is for fossils to form in the first place, let alone to be found by paleontologists! Then, describe some of the many intermediate fossils that have been found since Darwin's time, such as fossils showing that land animals descended from aquatic animals (Lesson 26.2), that whales descended from land-living ancestors, or that birds descended from nonflying dinosaurs.

Teach continued

Use Visuals

In **Figure 16–14,** have students find the blue-colored bones (the finger bones, or phalanges) of the ancient fish ancestor of modern vertebrates. Then, have them find the same bones in each of the vertebrate descendants shown in the figure. Call on students to describe how the bones differ in relative size and shape among the modern vertebrates. (Note: the images are NOT to scale.) Ask them to infer how each of the modern forms is adapted to its function. *(Sample answer: The long single finger of the horse elongates the arm, enabling faster running without much weight gain or air resistance.)*

DIFFERENTIATED INSTRUCTION

LPR Less Proficient Readers Homologous and analogous structures are readily confused, but it's important for students to be able to distinguish between them because of their different evolutionary implications. Guide students in filling in a **Compare/ Contrast Table** for the two types of structures. For column headings, tell them to use Homologous Structure and Analogous Structure. For row headings, have them use: What is it? What does it mean? What is an example? Students can complete the table as they read about the structures in the text.

Study Wkbks A/B, Appendix S20, Compare/ Contrast Table. **Transparencies,** GO3.

BIOLOGY.com Students can review homologous and analogous structures in the drag-and-drop activity, **Art Review: Homologous and Analogous.**

Comparing Anatomy and Embryology

What do homologous structures and similarities in embryonic development suggest about the process of evolutionary change?

By Darwin's time, scientists had noted that all vertebrate limbs had the same basic bone structure, as shown in **Figure 16–14.** Yet, some were used for crawling, some for climbing, some for running, and others for flying. Why should the same basic structures be used over and over again for such different purposes?

Homologous Structures Darwin proposed that animals with similar structures evolved from a common ancestor with a basic version of that structure. Structures that are shared by related species and that have been inherited from a common ancestor are called **homologous structures. Evolutionary theory explains the existence of homologous structures adapted to different purposes as the result of descent with modification from a common ancestor.** Biologists test whether structures are homologous by studying anatomical details, the way structures develop in embryos, and the pattern in which they appeared over evolutionary history.

Similarities and differences among homologous structures help determine how recently species shared a common ancestor. For example, the front limbs of reptiles and birds are more similar to each other than either is to the front limb of an amphibian or mammal. This similarity—among many others—indicates that the common ancestor of reptiles and birds lived more recently than the common ancestor of reptiles, birds, and mammals. So birds are more closely related to crocodiles than they are to bats! The common ancestor of all these four-limbed animals was an ancient lobe-finned fish that lived over 380 million years ago.

Homologous structures aren't just restricted to animals. Biologists have identified homologies in many other organisms. Certain groups of plants, for example, share homologous stems, roots, and flowers.

BUILD Vocabulary

WORD ORIGINS The word **homologous** comes from the Greek word *homos,* meaning "same." Homologous structures may not look exactly the same, but they share certain characteristics and a common ancestor.

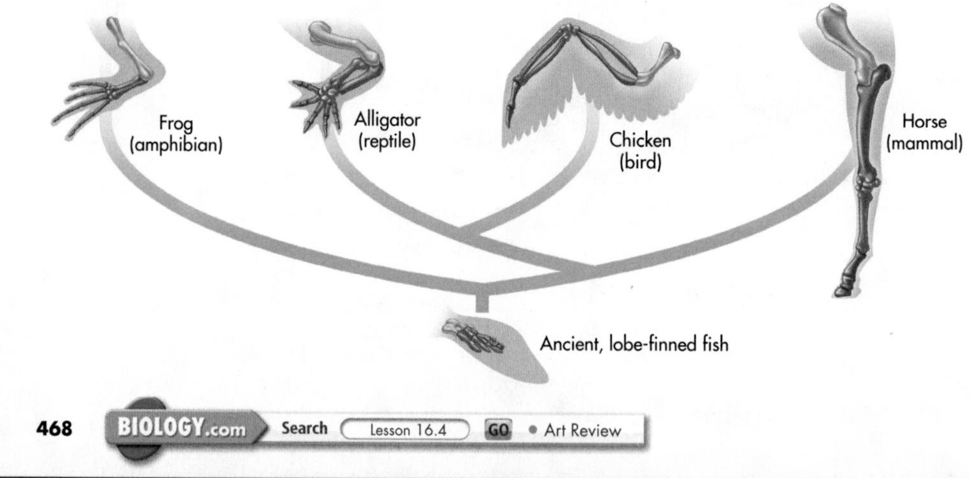

FIGURE 16–14 Homologous Limb Bones Homologous bones, as indicated by color-coding, support the differently shaped front limbs of these modern vertebrates. These limbs evolved, with modifications, from the front limbs of a common ancestor whose bones resembled those of an ancient fish. If these animals had no recent common ancestor, they would be unlikely to share so many common structures.

Quick Facts

VESTIGIAL STRUCTURES AND PROCESSES IN HUMANS

Classical examples of vestigial structures in humans include the appendix, which is an extension of the cecum of the large intestine. It plays an important role in digestion in some mammals but appears—although this is debated—to have little function in humans. Other vestigial structures in humans are the tailbones at the base of the spine. They are miniature remnants of bones that form the tail in many other animals. Try to use the muscles in your head to move your ears like a dog or cat, and the most you're likely to manage is a slight twitch. That's because the muscles that control ear movement are also vestigial structures in humans. Physiological processes, as well as structures, may be vestigial. Getting goosebumps when we are cold is an example. When this occurs, body hairs stand on end. This helps retain body heat in animals with thick body hair but has no effect in relatively hairless humans.

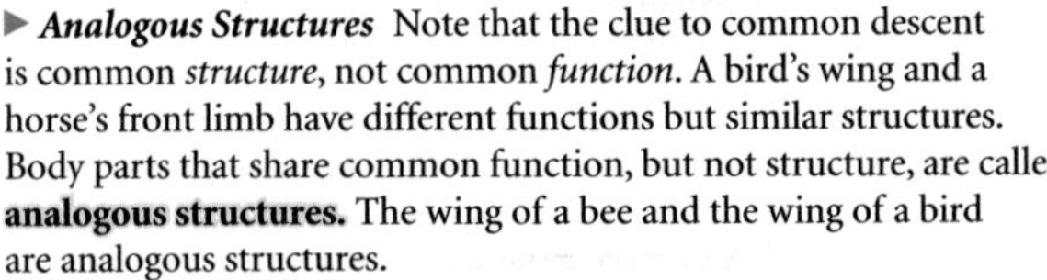
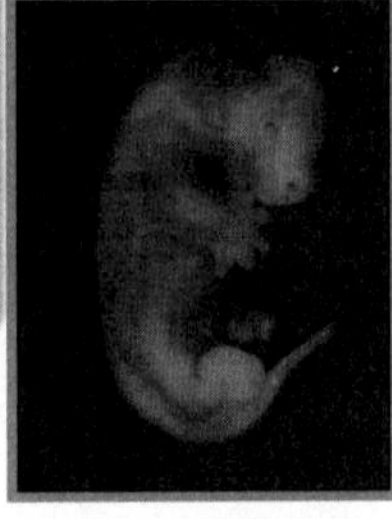

FIGURE 16–15 Vestigial Organs and Embryology
A. The wings of the flightless cormorant and the legs of the Italian three-toed skink are vestigial structures. **B.** Because the early stages of development among vertebrates are so similar, it would take an expert to identify this as an opossum embryo. Infer ***Looking at the legs of the skink, do you think its ancestors had functioning legs? Explain your answer.***

▶ ***Analogous Structures*** Note that the clue to common descent is common *structure*, not common *function*. A bird's wing and a horse's front limb have different functions but similar structures. Body parts that share common function, but not structure, are called **analogous structures.** The wing of a bee and the wing of a bird are analogous structures.

In Your Notebook *Do you think the shell of a clam and the shell of a lobster are homologous or analogous structures? Explain.*

▶ ***Vestigial Structures*** Not all homologous structures have important functions. **Vestigial structures** are inherited from ancestors but have lost much or all of their original function due to different selection pressures acting on the descendant. For example, the hipbones of the bottlenose dolphin, shown on page 467, are vestigial structures. In their ancestors, hipbones played a role in terrestrial locomotion. However, as the dolphin lineage adapted to life at sea, this function was lost. Why do dolphins and the organisms in **Figure 16–15** retain structures with little or no function? One possibility is that the presence of the structure does not affect an organism's fitness, and, therefore, natural selection does not act to eliminate it.

Embryology Researchers noticed a long time ago that the early developmental stages of many animals with backbones (called vertebrates) look very similar. Recent observations make clear that the same groups of embryonic cells develop in the same order and in similar patterns to produce many homologous tissues and organs in vertebrates. For example, despite the very different adult shapes and functions of the limb bones in **Figure 16–14,** all those bones develop from the same clumps of embryonic cells. Evolutionary theory offers the most logical explanation for these similarities in patterns of development. **Similar patterns of embryological development provide further evidence that organisms have descended from a common ancestor.**

Darwin realized that similar patterns of development offer important clues to the ancestory of living organisms. He could not have anticipated, however, the incredible amount of evidence for his theory that would come from studying the genes that control development—evidence from the fields of genetics and molecular biology.

Lead a Discussion

After students read about vestigial structures, lead a discussion about why vestigial structures persist in organisms.

Ask In terms of natural selection, what must be true about vestigial structures if they remain in a population? *(They must not be strongly selected against in the current environment.)*

Clarify that the term vestigial is *not* synonymous with "useless." Explain that sometimes, a vestigial structure can have a non-obvious function. For example, the vestigial hipbones of large whales seem to play a role in male reproduction.

Ask How does a secondary function, as in the hipbones of some large whales, help to explain why vestigial structures remain? *(If the structure has a function, then it's more likely that it is selected for in terms of natural selection. For example, if the whale needs the vestigial hipbones to reproduce, individuals without the vestigial bones will have a very low fitness.)*

DIFFERENTIATED INSTRUCTION

L3 Advanced Students Have interested students explore recent scientific findings involving the human appendix. Though still often referred to as a vestigial organ, the appendix is now thought by some scientiests to serve as a "safe house" for good bacteria in the human digestive tract. Have students write a paragraph explaining what they found and how it ties in with the discussion of how some structures take on secondary functions.

Biology In-Depth

EMBRYOLOGICAL SIMILARITIES

For more than a hundred years, biologists have been fascinated by the fact that organisms as dissimilar as chickens, snakes, and dogs show striking similarities in their early development. For example, in reptiles and birds, a sac grows around the large amount of yolk that is stored to support the embryo's growth. Placental mammals, on the other hand, depend upon the bodies of their mothers for nourishment—therefore, their eggs contain very little yolk. Nonetheless, mammalian embryos still form a large and recognizable yolk sac, although it is completely empty. Why? Evolutionary biology answers that question—because mammals are descended from animals (reptiles) that once required the yolk sac, they still produce the sac even though today it has no yolk to surround.

Answers

FIGURE 16–15 Sample answer: I think the skink's ancestors had functioning legs, because the skink's legs look like vestigial structures. They probably declined in size due to different selection pressures in the descendants.

IN YOUR NOTEBOOK The shell of a clam and the shell of a lobster are probably analogous, because they have a common function (protection, support), but not a common structure.

Teach continued

Lead a Discussion

Ask students which type of evidence for evolution they think is more informative, fossil evidence or genetic evidence. After several students have weighed in on the issue, discuss what can and cannot be learned from each type of evidence. For example, molecular data can indicate how long living organisms have been evolving separately. However, unlike fossils, molecular evidence does not give any indication of what extinct organisms looked like, how they moved, or what they ate.

DIFFERENTIATED INSTRUCTION

L1 Struggling Students Use a **Directed Reading-Thinking Activity** to help students comprehend the passage, **Genetics and Molecular Biology.** Have them skim the passage by examining the headings, Key Concept, and **Figure 16–16.** Ask them to predict what the passage will be about and explain why they think so. Then, when they read, have them pause after each paragraph to evaluate what they just learned.

Study Wkbks A/B, Appendix S5, Directed Reading-Thinking Activity.

Genetics and Molecular Biology

How can molecular biology be used to trace the process of evolution?

The most troublesome "missing information" for Darwin had to do with heredity. Darwin had no idea how heredity worked, and he was deeply worried that this lack of knowledge might prove fatal to his theory. As it happens, some of the strongest evidence supporting evolutionary theory comes from genetics. A long series of discoveries, from Mendel to Watson and Crick to genomics, helps explain how evolution works. **At the molecular level, the universal genetic code and homologous molecules provide evidence of common descent.** Also, we now understand how mutation and the reshuffling of genes during sexual reproduction produce the heritable variation on which natural selection operates.

Life's Common Genetic Code One dramatic example of molecular evidence for evolution is so basic that by this point in your study of biology you might take it for granted. All living cells use information coded in DNA and RNA to carry information from one generation to the next and to direct protein synthesis. This genetic code is nearly identical in almost all organisms, including bacteria, yeasts, plants, fungi, and animals. This is powerful evidence that all organisms evolved from common ancestors that shared this code.

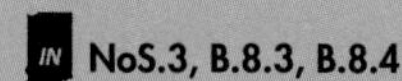

Molecular Homology in *Hoxc8*

Molecular homologies can be used to infer relationships among organisms. The diagram below shows a small portion of the DNA for the same gene, *Hoxc8*, in three animals—a mouse, a baleen whale, and a chicken.

1. Calculate What percentage of the nucleotides in the baleen whale's DNA are different from those of the mouse? (*Hint*: First count the number of DNA nucleotides in one entire sequence. Then count the nucleotides in the whale DNA that differ from those in the mouse DNA. Finally, divide the number of nucleotides that are different by the total number of nucleotides, and multiply the result by 100.) MATH

2. Calculate What percentage of the nucleotides in the chicken are different from those of the mouse? MATH

3. Draw Conclusions Do you think a mouse is more closely related to a baleen whale or to a chicken? Explain your answer.

4. Evaluate Do you think that scientists can use small sections of DNA, like the ones shown here, to infer evolutionary relationships? Why or why not?

Animal	Sequence of Bases in Section of *Hoxc8*
Mouse	C A G A A A T G C C A C T T T T A T G G C C C T G T T T G T C T C C C T G C T C
Baleen whale	C **C** G A A A T G C C **T** C T T T T A T G G C **G** C T G T T T G T C T C C C T G C **G** C
Chicken	**A** A **A** A A A T G C C **G** C T T T T A **C** **A** G C **T** C T G T T T G T C T C **T** C T G C T **A**

PURPOSE Students will calculate the percentage of shared nucleotides in related organisms and based on their calculations, conclude how closely related the organisms are.

PLANNING Review how to calculate percentages.

ANSWERS

1. 10 percent
2. 20 percent
3. Sample answer: I think a mouse is more closely related to a baleen whale than to a chicken, because it shares a greater percentage of nucleotides with the whale.
4. Sample answer: Scientists probably prefer not to use small sections of DNA to infer evolutionary relationships, because chance could play too big a role in the results. They probably try to use larger sections of DNA in their analyses.

Homologous Molecules In Darwin's day, biologists could only study similarities and differences in structures they could see. But physical body structures can't be used to compare mice with yeasts or bacteria. Today, we know that homology is not limited to physical structures. As shown in **Figure 16–16,** homologous proteins have been found in some surprising places. Homologous proteins share extensive structural and chemical similarities. One homologous protein is cytochrome c, which functions in cellular respiration. Remarkably similar versions of cytochrome c are found in almost all living cells, from cells in baker's yeast to cells in humans.

There are many other kinds of homologies at the molecular level. Genes can be homologous, too, which makes sense given the genetic code that all plants and animals share. One spectacular example is a set of ancient genes that determine the identities of body parts. Known as the Hox genes, they help to determine the head-to-tail axis in embryonic development. In vertebrates, sets of homologous Hox genes direct the growth of front and hind limbs. Small changes in these genes can produce dramatic changes in the structures they control. So, relatively minor changes in an organism's genome can produce major changes in an organism's structure and the structure of its descendants. At least some homologous Hox genes are found in almost all multicellular animals, from fruit flies to humans. Such profound biochemical similarities are best explained by Darwin's conclusion: Living organisms evolved through descent with modification from a common ancestor.

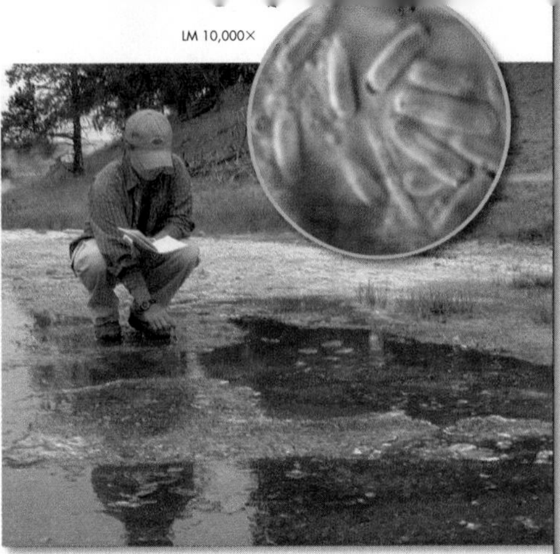

FIGURE 16–16 Similar Genes Bacteria in this hot spring live in near-boiling water—an inhospitable environment to animals. Their cells even look different from animal cells. Yet many of their genes, and therefore the proteins coded by those genes, are similar to those of animals. This is more evidence that all organisms share an ancient common ancestor.

Testing Natural Selection

What does recent research on the Galápagos finches show about natural selection?

One way to gather evidence for evolutionary change is to observe natural selection in action. But most kinds of evolutionary change we've discussed so far took place over millions of years—which makes it tough to see change actually happening. Some kinds of evolutionary change, however, have been observed and studied repeatedly in labs and in controlled outdoor environments. Scientists have designed experiments involving organisms from bacteria to guppies to test Darwin's theories. Each time, the results have supported Darwin's basic ideas. But one of the best examples of natural selection in action comes from observations on animals living in their natural environment. Fittingly, those observations focused on Galápagos finches.

A Testable Hypothesis Remember that when Darwin first saw the Galápagos finches, he thought they were wrens, warblers, and blackbirds because they looked so different from one another. Once Darwin learned that the birds were all finches, he hypothesized that they had descended from a common ancestor.

UbD Check for Understanding

INDEX CARD SUMMARIES/QUESTIONS

Distribute index cards to your students, and ask them to write an idea from the lesson that they fully understand on one side and something from the lesson that is unclear on the other side. Collect and review the cards.

ADJUST INSTRUCTION

Have volunteers explain to the class the ideas they best understand. Hopefully, many of the topics that were identified as unclear on the cards will be covered in this way. Then, review with the class any additional topics that students were unclear about.

Connect to the Real-World

Explain to students that one of the most striking examples of a small change in Hox gene expression resulting in a major change to an organism is the snake. Pythons have hundreds of vertebrae. Unlike many reptiles, which show regionalization of their backbone into neck, chest, back, and tail regions, each vertebra (except the atlas) anterior to the hindlimbs in pythons (which appear as tiny vestigial buds in development) resembles a chest vertebra. Research first published in 1999 suggests that broadened expression of two Hox genes accounts for both the loss of front limbs and the incredibly elongated thoracic (chest) region of the python.

DIFFERENTIATED INSTRUCTION

L3 Advanced Students Challenge students to predict how assumptions about neutral mutation rates and data on homologous molecules in two different species could be used to estimate the time since the two species shared a common ancestor. Tell students to check their prediction by reading about molecular clocks in Lesson 17.4.

ELL Focus on ELL: Access Content

ALL SPEAKERS Divide students into four study groups for a **Jigsaw Review** of the material in this lesson. Assign each group one of the following sources of evolution evidence: the age of the Earth and fossils, comparative anatomy and embryology, genetics and molecular biology, and testing natural selection in nature. Have each study group review their material together. Then, form four new groups, mixing up members from each group who will serve as the "expert" in the learning circles on their topic in the new group. Have these new groups discuss the contents of the lesson and record any remaining questions they have. These questions can be addressed when the class reforms.

Study Wkbks A/B, Appendix S7, Jigsaw Review.

Teach continued

VISUAL ANALOGY

Explain why beak size and shape are crucial to the fitness of Darwin's finches and why the Grants focused on these traits in their research. Then, extend the analogy by sharing the maxim, "the right tool for the job." Help students appreciate the importance of using the right tool for the job by having them imagine painting an entire house with a very small brush or driving a small nail into a delicate piece of furniture with a sledge hammer. Point out that each of the finches in the figure has the right beak for the job. Have students consider how difficult it would be for the finches to eat if they did not have a beak that was well suited for their food source. For example, if the *Geospiza* finch had a thin, narrow beak like the *Certhidea* finch, it would be like using delicate forceps to crack hard nutshells.

DIFFERENTIATED INSTRUCTION

ELL **English Language Learners** Use the **Stop and Answer** strategy to help students understand the Grants' research. For each passage with a blue heading, write a question on the board. For example, for the first passage on this page, you might write, What two specific hypotheses did the Grants test? After students have read each passage, have them stop and answer the question orally. Make sure students can answer all of the questions before they continue reading.

Study Wkbks A/B, Appendix S13, Stop and Answer.

Address Misconceptions

Observing Evolution Students commonly think that evolution cannot be observed, so it cannot be proved. Explain that, although most major evolutionary changes happen too slowly to be observed directly, there are many examples—including the Grants' research—that show evolution in "real time."

BIOLOGY.com Have students explore the analogy of finch beaks to tools by completing the **Visual Analogy: Finch Beak Tools** activity.

VISUAL ANALOGY

FINCH BEAK TOOLS

FIGURE 16–17 Finches use their beaks as tools to pick up and handle food. Different types of foods are most easily handled with beaks of different sizes and shapes.

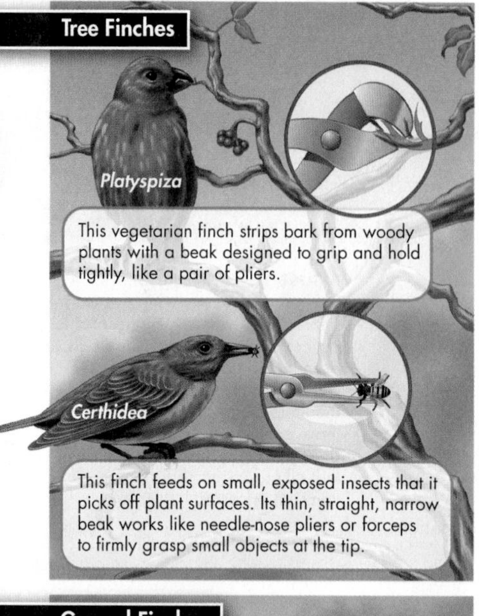

Tree Finches
Platyspiza
This vegetarian finch strips bark from woody plants with a beak designed to grip and hold tightly, like a pair of pliers.
Certhidea
This finch feeds on small, exposed insects that it picks off plant surfaces. Its thin, straight, narrow beak works like needle-nose pliers or forceps to firmly grasp small objects at the tip.

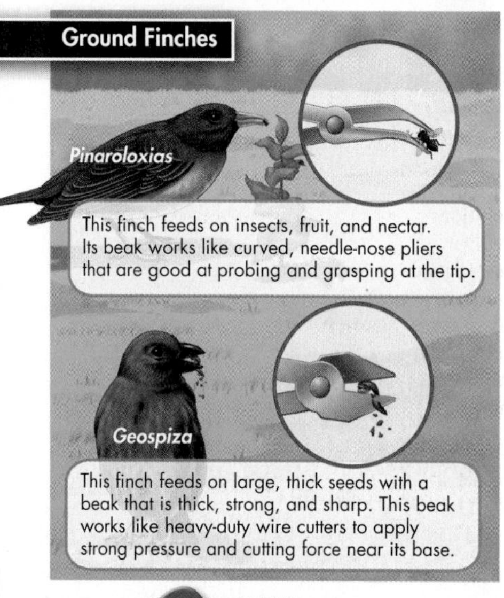

Ground Finches
Pinaroloxias
This finch feeds on insects, fruit, and nectar. Its beak works like curved, needle-nose pliers that are good at probing and grasping at the tip.
Geospiza
This finch feeds on large, thick seeds with a beak that is thick, strong, and sharp. This beak works like heavy-duty wire cutters to apply strong pressure and cutting force near its base.

Darwin noted that several finch species have beaks of very different sizes and shapes. Each species uses its beak like a specialized tool to pick up and handle its food, as shown in **Figure 16–17.** Darwin proposed that natural selection had shaped the beaks of different bird populations as they became adapted to eat different foods. That was a reasonable hypothesis. But was there any way to test it? No one thought there was a way until Peter and Rosemary Grant of Princeton University came along.

The Grants have spent more than 35 years studying Galápagos finches. They realized that Darwin's hypothesis rested on two testable assumptions. First, for beak size and shape to evolve, there must be enough heritable variation in those traits to provide raw material for natural selection. Second, differences in beak size and shape must produce differences in fitness.

The Grants have tested these hypotheses on the medium ground finch (*Geospiza*) on the island of Daphne Major. This island is large enough to support good-sized finch populations, yet small enough to allow the Grants to catch, tag, and identify nearly every bird of the species.

During their study, the Grants periodically recapture the birds. They record which individuals are alive and which have died, which have reproduced and which have not. For each individual, the Grants record anatomical characteristics like wing length, leg length, beak length, beak depth, beak color, feather colors, and total mass. The data the Grants have recorded show that there is indeed great variation of heritable traits among Galápagos finches.

Natural Selection The Grants' data have shown that individual finches with different-size beaks have better or worse chances of surviving both seasonal droughts and longer dry spells. When food becomes scarce during dry periods, birds with the largest beaks are more likely to survive, as shown in **Figure 16–18.** As a result, average beak size in this finch population has increased dramatically. **The Grants have documented that natural selection takes place in wild finch populations frequently, and sometimes rapidly.** Changes in food supply created selection pressure that caused finch populations to evolve within decades. This evolutionary change occurred much faster than many researchers thought possible.

How Science Works

SIGNIFICANCE OF THE GRANTS' RESEARCH

The Galápagos research of Peter and Rosemary Grant is widely acknowledged to be the most important field study of evolutionary processes that has been undertaken in the last three decades. The work has had a major influence on several fields of biology, including ecology, evolution, and population biology. The Grants began their research with finches on the Galápagos Islands in 1973. Since then, they have studied almost 20,000 individual birds over 25 generations. The evidence they have gathered has documented mechanisms of evolutionary change that, until their research, had only been postulated. The Grants truly took over where Darwin left off.

Not only have the Grants documented natural selection in nature, their data also confirm that competition and environmental change drive natural selection. Traits that don't matter much under one set of environmental conditions became adaptive as the environment changes during a drought. **The Grants' work shows that variation within a species increases the likelihood of the species' adapting to and surviving environmental change.** Without heritable variation in beak sizes, the medium ground finch would not be able to adapt to feeding on larger, tougher seeds during a drought.

Evaluating Evolutionary Theory Advances in many fields of biology, along with other sciences, have confirmed and expanded most of Darwin's hypotheses. Today, evolutionary theory—which includes natural selection—offers insights that are vital to all branches of biology, from research on infectious disease to ecology. That's why evolution is often called the grand unifying theory of the life sciences.

Like any scientific theory, evolutionary theory is constantly reviewed as new data are gathered. Researchers still debate important questions such as precisely how new species arise and why species become extinct. And there is also significant uncertainty about exactly how life began. However, any questions that remain are about *how* evolution works—not *whether* evolution occurs. To scientists, evolution is the key to understanding the natural world.

FIGURE 16–18 Survival and Beak Size This graph shows the survival rate of one species of ground finch, the medium ground finch, *Geospiza fortis*, during a drought period. **Interpret Graphs** *What trend does the graph show?*

16.4 Assessment

IN B.8.3, B.8.4, B.8.5

Review Key Concepts

1. a. **Review** What is biogeography?
   b. **Relate Cause and Effect** Why do distantly related species in very different places sometimes share similar traits?
2. a. **Review** Why are fossils important evidence for evolution?
   b. **Interpret Visuals** Use **Figure 16–13** to describe how a modern mysticete whale is different from *Ambulocetus*.
3. a. **Review** How do vestigial structures provide evidence for evolution?
   b. **Compare and Contrast** Explain the difference between homologous and analogous structures. Which are more important to evolutionary biologists? Why?
4. a. **Explain** What is the relationship between Hox genes and embryological development?
   b. **Draw Conclusions** Organisms A and B have very similar Hox genes, and their embryos, in the earliest stages of development, are also very similar. What do these similarities indicate about the ancestry of organisms A and B?
5. a. **Explain** What hypothesis have the Grants been testing?
   b. **Draw Conclusions** How do the Grants' data show that genetic variation is important in the survival of a species?

WRITE ABOUT SCIENCE

Explanation

6. In your own words, write a paragraph that explains how evidence since Darwin's time has strengthened his theories.

BIOLOGY.com Search Lesson 16.4  • Self-Test • Lesson Assessment

Assess and Remediate

EVALUATE UNDERSTANDING

Divide the class into teams, and play a quiz game in which teams compete by answering the most questions correctly. For questions, read the Key Concepts from the lesson, leaving blank important terms for students to fill in. Then, have students complete the 16.4 Assessment.

REMEDIATION SUGGESTION

L1 Struggling Students If students have trouble with **Question 4a,** review Hox genes and how they control development. You may also want to have students reread the information about Hox genes in Chapter 13.

BIOLOGY.com Students can check their understanding of lesson concepts with the **Self-Test** assessment. They can then take an online version of the **Lesson Assessment.**

Answers

FIGURE 16–18 The graph shows that during the drought period, a higher percentage of birds with larger beaks survived than those with smaller beaks.

Assessment Answers

1a. the study of where organisms live now and where they and their ancestors lived in the past

1b. because they evolved similar adaptations to the same environmental conditions in different places

2a. Fossils provide direct evidence of extinct organisms and allow scientists to trace the evolution of modern species from extinct ancestors.

2b. Sample answer: A modern mysticete whale has a large, streamlined body with fins and a tail but lacks legs. *Ambulocetus* had a smaller, four-legged body with a tail but no fins.

3a. Vestigial structures offer clues about the ancestors of organisms, because they are the remnants of structures with once important functions.

3b. Homologous structures share a common ancestry, but not necessarily a common function. Analogous structures share a common function, but do not share a common ancestry. Generally, homologous structures are more important to evolutionary biologists, because they provide evidence of evolutionary relationships.

4a. Hox genes control the timing of development and growth in embryos.

4b. The similarities indicate that organisms A and B likely share a recent common ancestor.

5a. Natural selection shaped the beaks of different bird populations .

5b. Their data show that variation within a species increases the likelihood of the species adapting to and surviving environmental change.

WRITE ABOUT SCIENCE

6. Students' answers should include mention of biogeography, the age of Earth and fossil finds, homologous structures and embryology, and observations of natural selection.

CHAPTER LAB

Pre-Lab

Introduce students to the concepts they will explore in the chapter lab by assigning the Pre-Lab questions.

Lab

Tell students they will perform the chapter lab *Amino Acid Sequences: Indicators of Evolution* described in **Lab Manual A.**

 **Struggling Students** A simpler version of the chapter lab is provided in **Lab Manual B.**

BIOLOGY.com Look online for **Editable Lab Worksheets.**

For corresponding pre-lab in the **Foundation Edition,** see page 398.

IN INDIANA ACADEMIC STANDARDS

For the full text of all standards, see the Course Overview in the front matter of this book.

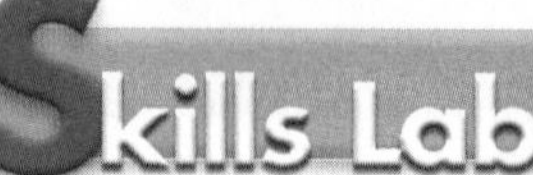
Skills Lab

GUIDED INQUIRY

IN B.8.2 Classification; B.8.3 Evolutionary relationships; B.8.4 Evidence of evolutionary relationships. Also covered: NoS.2, NoS.4.

Pre Lab: Amino Acid Sequences: Indicators of Evolution

Problem How can you use proteins to determine how closely organisms are related?

Materials light-colored highlighting pen; graph paper

Lab Manual Chapter 16 Lab

Skills Analyze Data, Graph, Draw Conclusions

Connect to the Big idea For years, scientists who studied evolution had to rely on only visible differences among organisms. Then a new source of evidence emerged. Biochemists were able to unravel the sequences of bases in DNA and amino acids in proteins. Scientists are able to use these data to confirm relationships based on anatomy. They also use the data to show that some species that appear very different are in fact more closely related than had been thought.

Biologists can compare the sequences of amino acids in a protein for two species. In general, when the total number of differences is small, the species are closely related. When the total number of differences is large, the species are more distantly related.

In this lab, you will compare amino acid sequences for one protein and analyze the results of a similar comparison for another protein. You will use both sets of data to predict relatedness among organisms.

Background Questions

a. Review What are homologous molecules?

b. Explain Why might scientists use molecules instead of anatomy to figure out how closely rabbits and fruit flies are related?

c. Relate Cause and Effect Amino acid sequences in the proteins of two species are similar. What can you conclude about the DNA in those species, and why?

Pre-Lab Questions

Preview the procedure in the lab manual.

1. **Predict** Based only on their anatomy, rank gorillas, bears, chimpanzees, and mice from most recent common ancestor with humans to least recent.
2. **Use Analogies** You tell a story to a second person who tells it to a third person, and so on. As the story is retold, changes are introduced. Overtime, the number of changes increases. How is this process an analogy for what happens to DNA over time?
3. **Infer** Hemoglobin from two species is compared. On the long protein chains, there are three locations where the amino acids are different. Where would you place the common ancestor of the two species on the "tree of life," and why?

BIOLOGY.com Search Chapter 16 GO

Visit Chapter 16 online to test yourself on chapter content and to find activities to help you learn.

Untamed Science Video Islands are rich environments for evolution, as you will find out with the Untamed Science crew.

Art in Motion This animation shows how fossil layers accumulate and are later exposed.

Art Review Review homologous and analogous structures in vertebrates.

Visual Analogy See how different types of finch beaks function like tools.

Data Analysis Collect population data for several generations of grasshoppers and then analyze how the population changed due to natural selection.

Pre-Lab Answers

BACKGROUND QUESTIONS

a. Homologous molecules have extensive similarities in structure and in chemistry.

b. Sample answer: Because rabbits and fruit flies are distantly related, they don't have many visible structures that can be used to establish their relatedness.

c. The order of bases in the related segment of DNA must be similar in both organisms because the sequence of bases in a gene controls the sequence of amino acids in the protein.

PRE-LAB QUESTIONS

1. Students are likely to say that chimpanzees and gorillas have a more recent common ancestor with humans than do bears and mice.
2. Students can compare retelling the story to the replication of DNA and the changes in the story to mutations. Despite the differences in time frame, with both the story and the DNA the number of changes will increase with time.
3. The common ancestor should be placed relatively recently along the tree based on the limited differences between the proteins and the time required for mutations to occur.

16 Study Guide

Big idea Evolution

Natural selection is a natural process through which life evolves. It acts on populations whose individuals must struggle for existence and that have both heritable variation in traits and variable fitness among individuals.

16.1 Darwin's Voyage of Discovery

Darwin developed a scientific theory of biological evolution that explains how modern organisms evolved over long periods of time through descent from common ancestors.

Darwin noticed that (1) different, yet ecologically similar, animal species inhabited separated, but ecologically similar, habitats around the globe; (2) different, yet related, animal species often occupied different habitats within a local area; and (3) some fossils of extinct animals were similar to living species.

evolution (450) fossil (452)

16.2 Ideas That Shaped Darwin's Thinking

Hutton and Lyell concluded that Earth is extremely old and that the processes that changed Earth in the past are the same processes that operate in the present.

Lamarck suggested that organisms could change during their lifetimes by selectively using or not using various parts of their bodies. He also suggested that individuals could pass these acquired traits on to their offspring, enabling species to change over time.

Malthus reasoned that if the human population grew unchecked, there wouldn't be enough living space and food for everyone.

In artificial selection, nature provides the variations, and humans select those they find useful.

artificial selection (458)

16.3 Darwin Presents His Case

Natural selection occurs in any situation in which more individuals are born than can survive, there is natural heritable variation, and there is variable fitness among individuals.

According to the principle of common descent, all species—living and extinct—are descended from ancient common ancestors.

adaptation (461) natural selection (463)
fitness (461)

16.4 Evidence of Evolution

Patterns in the distribution of living and fossil species tell us how modern organisms evolved from their ancestors.

Many recently discovered fossils form series that trace the evolution of modern species from extinct ancestors.

Evolutionary theory explains the existence of homologous structures adapted to different purposes as the result of descent with modification from a common ancestor.

The universal genetic code and homologous molecules provide evidence of common descent.

The Grants have documented that natural selection takes place in wild Galápagos finch populations frequently, and sometimes rapidly, and that variation within a species increases the likelihood of the species adapting to and surviving environmental change.

biogeography (465) analogous structure (469)
homologous structure (468) vestigial structure (469)

Think Visually

Using the information in this chapter, create a concept map that links the following terms: *adaptation, artificial selection, biogeography, camouflage, Charles Darwin, Charles Lyell, evolution, fitness, fossil, homology, James Hutton, Jean-Baptiste Lamarck, mimicry, natural selection,* and *Thomas Malthus.*

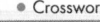

UbD Performance Tasks

SUMMATIVE TASK Divide the class into small groups, and instruct each group to brainstorm ways Earth might change over the next one million years. Then, have each group select a species living today and predict how populations descended from that species might evolve to adapt to the changes. Groups should describe and sketch specific adaptations in the species they select.

TRANSFER TASK Tell students to assume that a newspaper has published an article questioning whether evolution occurs. Ask them to write a letter to the editor of the newspaper in which they argue that evolution does occur, using evidence from the chapter to support their argument.

Study Online

BIOLOGY.com **REVIEW AND ASSESSMENT RESOURCES**

Editable Worksheets Pages of Study Workbooks A and B, Lab Manuals A and B, and the Assessment Resources Book are available online. These documents can be easily edited using a word-processing program.

Lesson Overview Have students reread the Lesson Overviews to help them study chapter concepts.

Vocabulary Review The *Flash Cards* and *Crossword* provide an interactive way to review chapter vocabulary.

Chapter Assessment Have students take an online version of the Chapter 16 Assessment.

Standardized Test Prep Students can take an online version of the Standardized Test Prep. You will receive their scores along with ideas for remediation.

Diagnostic and Benchmark Tests Use these tests to monitor your students' progress and supply remediation.

Answers

THINK VISUALLY

Students' concept maps may vary but should show the following relationships: Hutton, Lamarck, and Malthus influenced the development of Darwin's theory of evolution by natural selection; natural selection occurs when organisms in a population differ in fitness, and it leads to adaptations such as camouflage and mimicry; evidence for evolution includes fossils, artificial selection, homologies, and biogeography.

ASSESSMENT

Lesson 16.1

UNDERSTAND KEY CONCEPTS

1. c **2.** a

3. Darwin observed that each of these distantly related large, flightless birds found in a different but ecologically similar habitat around the globe shared many similarities in form and function.

4. Closely related Galápagos tortoises exhibited different traits depending on the environment of the island where they lived.

THINK CRITICALLY

5. Sample answer: *Evolution* means change over time. An example of evolution is the change over time in some bacteria that allows them to resist drugs.

6. Darwin's trip allowed him to observe, in a variety of habitats, patterns of biodiversity that result from evolution by natural selection.

7. because some Australian habitats seemed to be ideal for rabbits, and similar grasslands in Europe had rabbits

Lesson 16.2

UNDERSTAND KEY CONCEPTS

8. a **9.** d

10. Geological processes uplifted a former sea bed to form mountains.

11. Lyell proposed that Earth is extremely old and processes that changed Earth in the past are still at work today. This allowed for the great time span Darwin believed was necessary for evolution to occur. It also provided a geological analogy for biological evolution.

12. According to Malthus, population growth is limited by overcrowding and lack of food, which in turn lead to war, famine, and disease. His ideas apply to other organisms better than to humans, because other organisms can produce many more offspring over their lifetimes than humans.

13. Artificial selection is the process of selectively breeding plants and animals to have the traits desired by breeders or farmers. Artificial selection showed Darwin how heritable traits of organisms could change over time.

THINK CRITICALLY

14. Like many other organisms, sunflowers produce far more seeds than can survive and grow into mature plants. Most of the seeds will not germinate or the plants they develop into will die before they reach maturity.

15. Lamarck was one of the first naturalists to suggest that species are not fixed, and he tried to explain evolution scientifically using natural processes. He also recognized that there is a link between an organism's environment and its body structures.

Lesson 16.3

UNDERSTAND KEY CONCEPTS

16. b **17.** a

18. Variation is necessary if some organisms are to have greater fitness than others and to have a greater chance of passing on their traits to the next generation.

19. The statement means that living species are descended, with modification, from common ancestors. This implies that all organisms are related if you go back far enough in time. In other words, a single "tree of life" links all living things.

20. For natural selection to occur, there must be overproduction of offspring and variation among the heritable traits in organisms, and these variations must correlate to differences in fitness.

16 Assessment

IN The numbers following the questions refer to Indiana's Academic Standards for Biology I.

16.1 Darwin's Voyage of Discovery

Understand Key Concepts

1. Who observed variations in the characteristics of plants and animals on different islands of the Galápagos?

a. James Hutton **c.** Charles Darwin
b. Charles Lyell **d.** Thomas Malthus

2. In addition to observing living organisms, Darwin studied the preserved remains of ancient organisms called

a. fossils. **c.** homologies.
b. adaptations. **d.** vestigial structures.

3. What pattern of variation did Darwin observe among rheas, ostriches, and emus?

4. What connection did Darwin make between the Galápagos tortoises and their environments?

Think Critically

5. **Apply Concepts** Explain what the term *evolution* means, and give an example.

6. **Relate Cause and Effect** Why was Darwin's trip aboard the *Beagle* so important to his development of the theory of natural selection?

7. **Infer** Why was Darwin puzzled by the fact that there were no rabbits in Australia?

16.2 Ideas That Shaped Darwin's Thinking

Understand Key Concepts

8. Which of the following ideas proposed by Lamarck was later found to be incorrect?

a. Acquired characteristics can be inherited.
b. All species are descended from other species.
c. Living things change over time.
d. There is a relationship between an organism and its environment.

9. Which of the following would an animal breeder use to increase the number of cows that give the most milk?

a. overproduction **c.** acquired characteristics
b. genetic isolation **d.** artificial selection

10. What accounts for the presence of marine fossils on mountaintops?

11. How did Lyell's *Principles of Geology* influence Darwin?

12. According to Malthus, what factors limit population growth? Why did Malthus's ideas apply to other organisms better than they did to humans?

13. What is artificial selection? How did this concept influence Darwin's thinking?

Think Critically

14. **Relate Cause and Effect** A sunflower produces many seeds. Will all the seeds grow into mature plants? Explain your answer.

15. **Evaluate** Explain why Lamarck made a significant contribution to science even though his explanation of evolution was wrong.

16.3 Darwin Presents His Case

Understand Key Concepts

16. An inherited characteristic that increases an organism's ability to survive and reproduce in its specific environment is called a(n) B.8.5

a. vestigial structure. **c.** speciation.
b. adaptation. **d.** analogous structure.

17. How well an organism survives and reproduces in its environment can be described as its B.8.5

a. fitness. **c.** common descent.
b. homologies. **d.** analogies.

476 Chapter 16 • Assessment

18. How does natural variation affect evolution? B.8.5

19. Explain the following statement: "Descent with modification explains the diversity of life we see today." B.8.5

20. Describe the conditions necessary for natural selection to occur. B.8.5

Think Critically

21. **Apply Concepts** How would Darwin explain the long legs of the water bird in **Figure 16–6**? How would Darwin's explanation differ from Lamarck's explanation? B.8.5

22. **Compare and Contrast** Distinguish between fitness and adaptation. How are the two concepts related? B.8.5

23. **Infer** How does the process of natural selection account for the diversity of organisms that Darwin observed on the Galápagos Islands? B.8.5

24. **Infer** Many species of birds build nests in which they lay eggs and raise the newly hatched birds. How might nest-building behavior be an adaptation that ensures reproductive fitness? B.8.5

16.4 Evidence of Evolution

Understand Key Concepts

25. Structures that have different mature forms but develop from the same embryonic tissue are called
    a. analogous. c. homologous.
    b. adaptations. d. fossils.

26. Intermediate fossil forms are important evidence of evolution because they show B.8.3
    a. how organisms changed over time.
    b. how animals behaved in their environments.
    c. how the embryos of organisms develop.
    d. molecular homologies.

27. How does the geographic distribution of organisms support the theory of evolution? B.8.3

28. How do vestigial structures indicate that present-day organisms are different from their ancient ancestors? B.8.3

29. How do DNA and RNA provide evidence for common descent? B.8.3, B.8.4

solve the CHAPTER MYSTERY

SUCH VARIED HONEYCREEPERS

The 'i'iwi and other Hawaiian honeycreepers resemble Galápagos finches in a number of ways. They are species of small birds found nowhere else on Earth. They live on islands that are separated from one another by stretches of open sea and that are hundreds of miles from the nearest continent. They are also related to finches!

There are more than 20 known species of Hawaiian honeycreeper. Like the species of Galápagos finches, the honeycreeper species are closely related to one another. This is an indication that they are all descended, with modification, from a relatively recent common ancestor. Experts think the ancestor colonized the islands between 3 million and 4 million years ago. Many honeycreepers have specialized diets, evolutionary adaptations to life on the particular islands they call home. Today, habitat loss is endangering most of the honeycreepers. In fact, many species of honeycreeper are thought to have become extinct since humans settled on the islands.

1. **Infer** Suppose a small group of birds, not unlike the modern honeycreepers, landed on one of Hawaii's islands millions of years ago and then reproduced. Do you think all the descendants would have stayed on that one island? Explain your answer.

2. **Infer** Do you think that the climate and other environmental conditions are exactly the same everywhere on the Hawaiian Islands? How might environmental conditions have affected the evolution of honeycreeper species?

3. **Form a Hypothesis** Explain how the different species of honeycreepers in Hawaii today might have evolved from one ancestral species.

4. **Connect to the Big idea** Why are islands often home to species that exist nowhere else on Earth?

 B.8.5

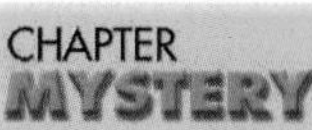

CHAPTER MYSTERY After students have read through the Chapter Mystery, encourage them to draw parallels between the honeycreepers on the Hawaiian Islands and the finches on the Galápagos Islands.

Ask Do you think Darwin would have drawn the same conclusions about evolution and natural selection if he had visited the Hawaiian Islands instead of the Galápagos Islands? *(Sample answer: yes, because he would have observed similar patterns of variation)*

CHAPTER MYSTERY ANSWERS

1. Sample answer: I think some of the descendants would have moved to other islands. If a small group of birds managed to travel far across the ocean to reach one of the islands, then it is likely their descendants would be able to travel to other, nearby islands.

2. Sample answer: I think there is variation in climate and other environmental conditions on the Hawaiian Islands. When the environment varies, different traits may be selected for. This would explain why there are now so many different species of honeycreepers on the Hawaiian Islands and why Hawaiian honeycreepers are different from related birds found elsewhere in the world.

3. Sample answer: An ancestral species might have made its way to one of the Hawaiian Islands. A few members of this species may have eventually reached other islands in the group. If environments differed on these other islands, each island's honeycreeper population might have evolved into a different species.

4. **Big idea** Islands are often home to species that exist nowhere else on Earth, because they are isolated by water. If a species manages to reach a group of islands, it may evolve by adapting to conditions on the islands and become a new species. Because of the isolation of the islands, the new species may never travel to other places.

THINK CRITICALLY

21. Darwin would explain the long legs of the water bird as an adaptation that evolved through natural selection. Lamarck would explain the long legs of the bird as an adaptation that evolved through the inheritance of acquired characteristics.

22. Fitness refers to how well an individual can survive and reproduce in its environment relative to other individuals of the same species. Adaptation refers to any heritable characteristic that increases an organism's fitness.

23. The Galápagos Islands varied in their environments, so organisms with different traits were better suited for different islands. Over time, natural selection for different traits on each island led to variation in the species.

24. Sample answer: Nest-building behavior might be an adaptation that ensures reproductive fitness, because it would help protect eggs and newly hatched birds. As a result, the offspring of nest-building birds would be more likely to survive.

Students can take a field trip with **Untamed Science: It Happened in Hawaii** and learn more about the Hawaiian honeycreeper mystery.

ASSESSMENT

Lesson 16.4

UNDERSTAND KEY CONCEPTS

25. c **26.** a

27. Sample answer: Patterns in the distribution of living and fossil species show how modern organisms evolved from their ancestors.

28. because these features are remnants of structures that functioned in the organism's ancestors

29. The universal genetic code in DNA and RNA shows that all living species descended from an ancient common ancestor.

THINK CRITICALLY

30. A cat, because cats and dogs shared a common ancestor more recently than did crickets and dogs.

31. The fact that the same molecule carries oxygen in the blood of all vertebrates indicates that all vertebrates have a common ancestor.

32. Sample answer: I think that some species of snake might have vestigial hip and leg bones, because snakes are reptiles and other reptiles have hips and legs inherited from an ancient vertebrate ancestor.

Connecting Concepts

USE SCIENCE GRAPHICS

33. Sample answer: Brown mice, because they blend in better with their background.

34. Sample answer: The coloring of the brown mice is an adaptation, because it increases the fitness of the mice in their environment. Other adaptations might include the ability to run fast.

WRITE ABOUT SCIENCE

35. Sample answer: Most examples of evolution must have occurred over a very long time period to bring about the great diversity of living and fossil species. Therefore, an ancient age for Earth supports the theory of evolution.

36. Natural selection occurs when there are more organisms born than can survive and variation among the heritable traits of organisms that results in some organisms having greater fitness than others. Check that students identify three lines of evidence that support evolution.

37. Big idea Answers will vary. Students should correctly explain Darwin's theory of evolution by natural selection.

38. Big idea Sample answer: If there was a drought, the grass might turn yellow. As a result, the number of green grasshoppers would decline, while the number of yellow grasshoppers would increase.

Think Critically

30. Infer Which animal—a cricket or a cat—would you expect to have cytochrome c more similar to that of a dog? Explain your answer. B.8.3, B.8.4

31. Infer In all animals with backbones, oxygen is carried in blood by a molecule called hemoglobin. What could this physiological similarity indicate about the evolutionary history of vertebrates (animals with backbones)? B.8.3, B.8.4

32. Apply Concepts Do you think some species of snake might have vestigial hip and leg bones? Explain your answer. B.8.3

Connecting Concepts

Use Science Graphics NoS.3

Use the illustration below to answer questions 33 and 34.

33. Infer Based on what you can see, which mice—white or brown—are better adapted to their environment? Explain your answer.

34. Apply Concepts In what way is the coloring of the brown mice an adaptation? What other adaptations besides coloring might affect the mice's ability to survive and reproduce? B.8.5

Write About Science NoS.3

35. Explanation Write a paragraph that explains how the age of Earth supports the theory of evolution.

36. Summary Summarize the conditions under which natural selection occurs. Then, describe three lines of evidence that support the theory of evolution by natural selection. B.8.5

37. Assess the Big idea Write a newspaper article about the meeting at which Darwin's and Wallace's hypotheses of evolution were first presented. Explain the theory of evolution by natural selection for an audience that knows nothing about the subject. B.8.5

38. Assess the Big idea Look back at **Figure 16–10** on page 462. Explain how conditions could change so that yellow coloring becomes adaptive. What would happen to the relative numbers of green and yellow grasshoppers in the population? B.8.5

Analyzing Data

IN NoS.3

Cytochrome c is a small protein involved in cellular respiration. The table compares the cytochrome c of various organisms to that of chimpanzees. The left column indicates the organism, and the right column indicates the number of amino acids that are different from those in chimpanzee cytochrome c.

Organism	Number of Amino Acids That Are Different From Chimpanzee Cytochrome c
Dog	10
Moth	24
Penguin	11
Yeast	38

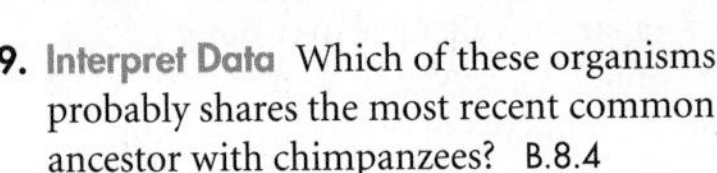

39. Interpret Data Which of these organisms probably shares the most recent common ancestor with chimpanzees? B.8.4

a. dog **c.** penguin
b. moth **d.** yeast

40. Calculate The primary structure of cytochrome c contains 104 amino acids. Approximately how many of these amino acids are the same in the chimpanzee and moth? MATH B.8.4

a. 10 **c.** 80
b. 24 **d.** 128

478 Chapter 16 • Assessment

Analyzing Data

PURPOSE Students will interpret data on homologous proteins and conclude which of four organisms shares the most recent common ancestor with chimpanzees.

PLANNING Remind students that cytochrome c is found in virtually all multicellular organisms (and many unicellular organisms, too) and differs very little from one species to another.

ANSWERS

39. a

40. c

Standardized Test Practice for Indiana

Multiple Choice

1. Which scientist formulated the theory of evolution through natural selection?
A Charles Darwin
B Thomas Malthus
C James Hutton
D Jean-Baptiste Lamarck

2. Lamarck's ideas about evolution were wrong because he proposed that
A species change over time.
B species descended from other species.
C acquired characteristics can be inherited.
D species are adapted to their environments.

3. Lyell's *Principles of Geology* influenced Darwin because it explained how
A organisms change over time.
B adaptations occur.
C the surface of Earth changes over time.
D the Galápagos Islands formed.

4. A farmer's use of the best livestock for breeding is an example of
A natural selection.
B artificial selection.
C extinction.
D adaptation.

5. The ability of an individual organism to survive and reproduce in its natural environment is called
A natural selection.
B evolution.
C descent with modification.
D fitness. B.8.5

6. Which of the following is an important concept in Darwin's theory of evolution by natural selection?
A descent with modification
B homologous molecules
C processes that change the surface of Earth
D the tendency toward perfection

7. Which of the following does NOT provide evidence for evolution?
A fossil record
B natural variation within a species
C geographical distribution of living things
D homologous structures of living organisms

8. DNA and RNA provide evidence of evolution because
A all organisms have nearly identical DNA and RNA.
B no two organisms have exactly the same DNA.
C each RNA codon specifies just one amino acid.
D in most organisms, the same codons specify the same amino acids. B.8.3, B.8.4

9. A bird's wings are homologous to a(n)
A fish's tailfin.
B alligator's claws.
C dog's front legs.
D mosquito's wings.

Questions 10 and 11

The birds shown below are 2 of the species of finches Darwin found on the Galápagos Islands.

Woodpecker Finch

Large Ground Finch

10. What process produced the two different types of beaks shown?
A artificial selection
B natural selection
C geographical distribution
D disuse of the beak B.8.5

11. The large ground finch obtains food by cracking seeds. Its short, strong beak is an example of
A the struggle for existence.
B the tendency toward perfection.
C an adaptation.
D a vestigial organ.

Open-Ended Response

12. Compare and contrast the processes of artificial selection and natural selection. B.8.5

If You Have Trouble With . . .

Question	1	2	3	4	5	6	7	8	9	10	11	12
See Lesson	16.1	16.2	16.2	16.2	16.3	16.3	16.4	16.4	16.4	16.3	16.3	16.3

Answers

1. A
2. C
3. C
4. B
5. D
6. A
7. B
8. A
9. C
10. B
11. C
12. Both artificial and natural selection change the heritable traits of a population or species over time. In both cases, organisms with certain traits are more likely to survive and reproduce than organisms with other traits. In artificial selection, a breeder or farmer decides which organisms reproduce. In natural selection, environmental conditions determine which organisms reproduce.

Test-Taking Tip

READ ALL THE ANSWER CHOICES

Tell students that it is a good idea to read all the answer choices for multiple choice questions before choosing the correct answer. Explain that wrong choices are often intentionally written to seem as though they could be correct. Therefore, without reading all of the choices, it is easy to make a mistake by selecting the first choice that appears to be correct.

CHAPTER PLANNER 17 Evolution of Populations

Chapter Contents	IN	Time	Core Resources
Chapter Preview			**Student Edition,** pp. 480–481 **Chapter Mystery,** p. 481
17.1 Genes and Variation Genetics Joins Evolutionary Theory • Sources of Genetic Variation • Single-Gene and Polygenic Traits	B.5.2, B.5.6, B.6.5, B.7.5, B.8.5, B.8.6	1 period 1/2 block	**Student Edition,** pp. 482–486 **Study Workbook A** 17.1 Worksheets L2 **Biology.com** *Art Review:* Frequency and Dominance **Assessment Resources Book** Visual Quiz L2
17.2 Evolution as Genetic Change in Populations How Natural Selection Works • Genetic Drift • Evolution Versus Genetic Equilibrium • *Biology & Society: Should Antibiotic Use Be Restricted?*	NoS.3, NoS.6, B.8.5	1 1/2 periods 3/4 block	**Student Edition,** pp. 487–493 Inquiry 17.2 Quick Lab, p. 491 L2 **Study Workbook A** 17.2 Worksheets L2 **Biology.com** *Art in Motion:* Natural Selection **Assessment Resources Book** Visual Quiz L2
17.3 The Process of Speciation Isolating Mechanisms • Speciation in Darwin's Finches	B.8.5	1/2 period 1/4 block	**Student Edition,** pp. 494–497 **Study Workbook A** 17.3 Worksheets L2 **Biology.com** *Tutor Tube:* Organizing the Vocabulary of Speciation • *Data Analysis:* Galápagos Finches: Evolution in Action • 17.3 Self-Test • 17.3 Lesson Assessment
17.4 Molecular Evolution Timing Lineage Splits: Molecular Clocks • Gene Duplication • Developmental Genes and Body Plans	NoS.3, B.6.5, B.7.5, B.8.3, B.8.4, B.8.6	1 period 1/2 block	**Student Edition,** pp. 498–501 Inquiry 17.4 Analyzing Data, p. 500 L2 **Study Workbook A** 17.4 Worksheets L2 **Biology.com** 17.4 Self-Test • 17.4 Lesson Assessment
Chapter Pre-Lab	NoS.1, NoS.6, B.8.5	1 period 1/2 block	**Student Edition,** p. 502 L2 **Lab Manual A** *Competing for Resources* L2 • *Ecosystems and Speciation* L2

Differentiated Instruction Tools

Study Workbook B includes worksheets with lesson-level differentiated instruction support and explanations of differentiated instruction teaching strategies.

Lab Manual B includes skills labs, simplified chapter labs, and hands-on activities.

ELL Handbook explains ways to make *Biology* more accessible to ELL students.

Spanish Study Workbook is a Spanish translation of Study Workbook A.

Multilingual Glossary is the glossary translated into ten languages.

Differentiated Instruction Key

- L1 Special Needs or Struggling Students
- ELL English Language Learners
- LPR Less Proficient Readers
- L2 On-Level Students
- L3 Advanced Students

Additional Resources

Biology.com Untamed Science Video • Vocabulary Flash Cards

Study Workbook B 17.1 Worksheets L1 ELL LPR
Spanish Study Workbook 17.1 Worksheets ELL
Biology.com 17.1 Lesson Overview • 17.1 Lesson Notes • 17.1 Self-Test • 17.1 Lesson Assessment

Study Workbook B 17.2 Worksheets L1 ELL LPR
Spanish Study Workbook 17.2 Worksheets ELL
Biology.com 17.2 Lesson Overview • 17.2 Lesson Notes • 17.2 Self-Test • 17.2 Lesson Assessment

Study Workbook B 17.3 Worksheets L1 ELL LPR
Spanish Study Workbook 17.3 Worksheets ELL
Biology.com 17.3 Lesson Overview • 17.3 Lesson Notes

Study Workbook B 17.4 Worksheets L1 ELL LPR
Spanish Study Workbook 17.4 Worksheets ELL
Biology.com 17.4 Lesson Overview • 17.4 Lesson Notes

Lab Manual B *Competing for Resources* • Data Analysis: *Allele Frequency* • Hands-On Activity: *Modeling Natural Selection* L1 ELL LPR

Chapter Review

Student Edition Study Guide, p. 503 L2
Study Workbook A Chapter 17 Vocabulary Review L2 • Chapter 17 Chapter Mystery/21st Century Skills Activity L2 L3
Transparencies, pp. 203–214 L1 ELL LPR L2
Biology.com Untamed Science Video • Editable Worksheets of Study Workbooks A and B and Lab Manuals A and B • Chapter 17 Flash Cards and Match It

Untamed Science DVD • Classroom Resources CD (includes lesson presentations and editable worksheets)

Chapter Assessment

Student Edition Assessment, pp. 504–507 L2
Study Workbook B Chapter 17 Chapter Review L1 ELL LPR • Chapter 17 Taking a Standardized Test L1 ELL LPR
Assessment Resources Book Chapter 17 Test A L2 • Chapter 17 Test B L1 ELL LPR
Biology.com Chapter 17 Assessment • Editable Worksheets of Chapter 17 Visual Quizzes and Chapter 17 Tests A and B

Exam*View Assessment Suite* • Classroom Resources CD (includes lesson presentations and editable worksheets)

Time: 1 period, 1/2 block

Pressed for Time?

Preview the Chapter Introduce students to the first Key Question for each lesson and preview Figures 17–2 and 17–6.

Cover the Chapter Quickly Have students read Lesson 17.1 and go over Figure 17–2. For Lesson 17.2, have them read *How Natural Selection Works* and *Genetic Drift* focusing on Figures 17–6 and 17–7. Then, have students read *Isolating Mechanisms* in Lesson 17.3 and *Timing Lineage Splits: Molecular Clocks* in Lesson 17.4. Discuss Figure 17–18.

Assess Assign the 17.1 Assessment, questions 1 and 2 from the 17.2 Assessment, question 1 from the 17.4 Assessment, and questions 1–17, 23, 24, 26, 27, and 29 in the Chapter 17 Assessment.

Connect to the Big Idea

Have students look closely at the two butterflies in the photograph. Ask them to identify ways they differ. *(Sample answer: Their spots are slightly different in color and location.)* Activate prior knowledge by asking students to state the relationship between genes and traits such as these. *(Genes contain genetic information. Genetic information, in combination with environmental factors, determines how genes are expressed.)* Remind students of the relationship between variation in traits and evolution of species. Have students synthesize these two relationships by inferring how genes are related to evolution. *(There must be variation in genes for organisms to vary in their traits, so variation in genes must also be needed for evolution to occur.)* Then, have students anticipate the answer to the question, **How can populations evolve to form new species?**

After having students read over the Chapter Mystery, remind them of the characteristics of life discussed in Chapter 1. Point out that viruses are not classified as living things because they cannot reproduce outside of a host, nor do they grow, develop, use energy, or respond to the environment. However, like living things, viruses carry genetic information in the form of DNA or RNA. Connect the Chapter Mystery to the Big Idea of Evolution by asking students to predict whether viruses evolve in the same ways that living things do.

BIOLOGY.com Have students preview the chapter vocabulary terms using the **Flash Cards.**

IN INDIANA ACADEMIC STANDARDS

For the full text of all standards, see the Course Overview in the front matter of this book.

Key standards: Chapter 17 covers key ideas from Standard 6: Cellular Reproduction and Gene Expression; Standard 7: Genetics; and Standard 8: Genetics, including **B.6.5** Sorting and recombination of genes, **B.7.5** Gene alteration, **B.8.3** Evolutionary relationships, and **B.8.5** Survival and reproduction.

17 Evolution of Populations

Big idea **Evolution**

Q: How can populations evolve to form new species?

Poised on a flower, the two common blue butterflies (Polyommatus icarus) appear identical. However, if you look closely, you can see that the patterns on their wings are slightly different. Variations among individual members of a population provide the raw material for evolution and sometimes for the formation of new species.

BIOLOGY.com Search Chapter 17 GO • Flash Cards

480

UbD Understanding by Design

Chapter 17 advances students' comprehension of the Enduring Understanding for Unit 5: *The diversity of life is the result of ongoing evolutionary change. Species alive today have evolved from ancient common ancestors.* The graphic organizer at the right shows how chapter content frames their explanation of this Enduring Understanding.

PERFORMANCE GOALS

In Chapter 17, students will use models, graphs, and data to learn how changes in allele frequencies lead to speciation. The Chapter Mystery provides a real-world example of evolution: the evolution of new strains of flu viruses. At the end of the chapter, students will create a poster to illustrate how evolution leads to diversity of life through speciation.

INDIANA ACADEMIC STANDARDS FOR SCIENCE

Nature of Science NoS.1, NoS.3, NoS.6, NoS.10; **Molecular Basis of Heredity** B.5.2, B.5.6; **Cellular Reproduction and Gene Expression** B.6.5; **Genetics** B.7.5; **Evolution** B.8.3, B.8.4, B.8.5, B.8.6. See lessons for details.

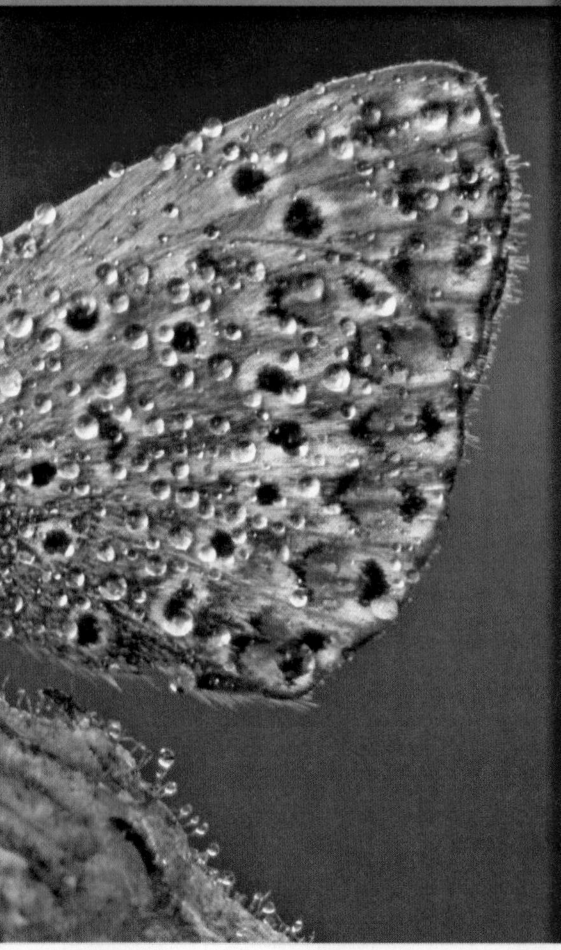

CHAPTER MYSTERY

EPIDEMIC

In 1918, an epidemic began that would go on to kill more than 40 million people. A doctor wrote: "Dead bodies are stacked about the morgue like cordwood."

What was this terrible disease? It was a variety of the same influenza virus that causes "the flu" you catch again and again. How did this strain of a common virus become so deadly? And could that kind of deadly flu epidemic happen again?

The answers to those questions explain why we can't make a permanent vaccine against the flu, as we can against measles or smallpox. They also explain why public health officials worry so much about something you may have heard referred to as "bird flu." As you read this chapter, look for evolutionary processes that might help explain how new strains of influenza virus appear all the time. Then, solve the mystery.

Never Stop Exploring Your World. Finding the solution to the epidemic mystery is only the beginning. Take a video field trip with the ecogeeks of Untamed Science to see where the mystery leads.

- Untamed Science Video
- Chapter Mystery

Chapter 17 Big Idea: Evolution

Chapter 17 EQ: How can populations evolve to form new species?

- **17.1 GQ:** How do genes make evolution possible?
- **17.2 GQ:** What causes a population's gene pool to change?
- **17.3 GQ:** How do new species form?
- **17.4 GQ:** What can genes tell us about an organism's evolutionary history?

What's Online

BIOLOGY.com Extend your reach by using these and other digital assets offered at **Biology.com.**

CHAPTER MYSTERY
The mystery of the 1918 flu epidemic allows students to investigate how mutations and other evolutionary processes lead to new strains of flu virus.

UNTAMED SCIENCE VIDEO
Students explore speciation mechanisms in Hawaii, where geographic isolation contributes to evolutionary patterns similar to those in Darwin's finches.

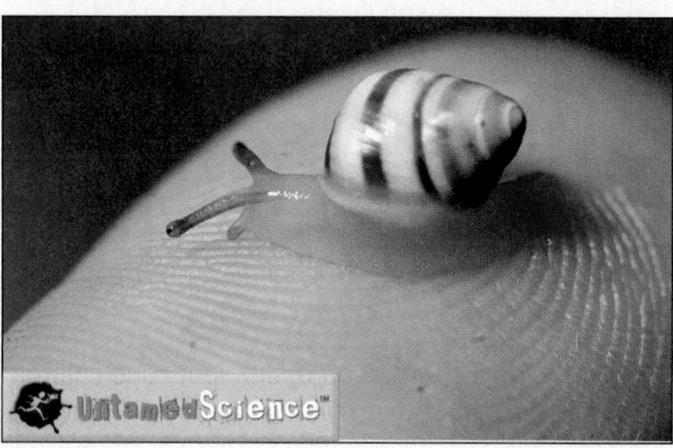

ART REVIEW
Drag-and-drop labels give students a chance to apply the concepts of dominance and allele frequency to additional gene pools.

ART IN MOTION
Students explore how the composition of a population changes under different types of natural selection pressure.

DATA ANALYSIS
Students can analyze data from the Grants' study of Darwin's finches.

TUTOR TUBE
The tutorial shows students how to use a concept map to distinguish the concepts of selection, adaptation, speciation, and evolution.

LESSON 17.1

Getting Started

Objectives

17.1.1 Define evolution in genetic terms.

17.1.2 Identify the main sources of genetic variation in a population.

17.1.3 State what determines the number of phenotypes for a trait.

Student Resources

Study Workbooks A and B, 17.1 Worksheets

Spanish Study Workbook, 17.1 Worksheets

Lesson Overview • Lesson Notes • Activity: Art Review • Assessment: Self-Test, Lesson Assessment

For corresponding lesson in the **Foundation Edition,** see pages 406–408.

Activate Prior Knowledge

Make a **T-Chart** on the board, and label one column *Genotype* and the other column *Phenotype*. Have each student add a descriptive term, fact, or example to the chart under one of the headings. Discuss the finished chart as a class. Make sure students understand how genotype and phenotype are related.

Study Wkbks A/B, Appendix S30, T-Chart. **Transparencies,** GO15.

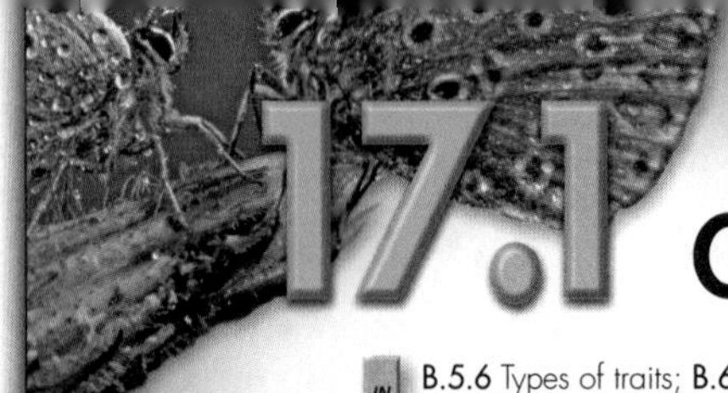

IN INDIANA ACADEMIC STANDARDS

For the full text of all standards, see the Course Overview in the front matter of this book.

B.6.5 Explain how, in sexual reproduction, crossing over, independent assortment, and random fertilization result in offspring that are genetically different from the parents.

B.8.5 Describe how due to genetic variations, environmental forces, and reproductive pressures, organisms with beneficial traits are more likely to survive, reproduce, and pass on their genetic information.

B.8.6 Explain how genetic variation within a population (a species) can be attributed to mutations as well as a random assortment of existing genes.

17.1 Genes and Variation

IN B.5.6 Types of traits; B.6.5 Sorting and recombination of genes; B.8.5 Survival and reproduction; B.8.6 Genetic variation within a species. Also covered: B.5.2, B.7.5.

Key Questions

How is evolution defined in genetic terms?

What are the sources of genetic variation?

What determines the number of phenotypes for a given trait?

Vocabulary

gene pool
allele frequency
single-gene trait
polygenic trait

Taking Notes

Concept Map As you read about sources of genetic variation, construct a concept map to describe the sources.

THINK ABOUT IT Darwin developed his theory of natural selection without knowing how heredity worked. Mendel's studies on inheritance in peas were published during Darwin's lifetime, but no one (including Darwin) realized how important that work was. So Darwin had no idea how heritable traits pass from one generation to the next. What's more, although Darwin based his theory on heritable variation, he had no idea where that variation came from. What would happen when genetics answered those questions?

Genetics Joins Evolutionary Theory

How is evolution defined in genetic terms?

After Mendel's work was rediscovered around 1900, genetics took off like a rocket. Researchers discovered that heritable traits are controlled by genes that are carried on chromosomes. They learned how changes in genes and chromosomes generate variation.

All these discoveries in genetics fit perfectly into evolutionary theory. Variation is the raw material for natural selection, and finally scientists could study how and why variation occurs. Today, techniques of molecular genetics are used to form and test many hypotheses about heritable variation and natural selection. Modern genetics enables us to understand, better than Darwin ever could, how evolution works.

Genotype and Phenotype in Evolution Typical plants and animals contain two sets of genes, one contributed by each parent. Specific forms of a gene, called alleles, may vary from individual to individual. An organism's genotype is the particular combination of alleles it carries. An individual's genotype, together with environmental conditions, produces its phenotype. Phenotype includes all physical, physiological, and behavioral characteristics of an organism, such as eye color or height. Natural selection acts directly on phenotype, not genotype. In other words, natural selection acts on an organism's characteristics, not directly on its alleles.

FIGURE 17–1 Genes and Variation Why do biological family members resemble each other, yet also look so different? Similarities come from shared genes. Most differences come from gene shuffling during reproduction and environmental influences. A few differences may be caused by random mutations.

UbD Teach for Understanding

ENDURING UNDERSTANDING The diversity of life is the result of ongoing evolutionary change. Species alive today have evolved from ancient common ancestors.

GUIDING QUESTION How do genes make evolution possible?

EVIDENCE OF UNDERSTANDING *After completing the lesson, give students the following assessment to show they understand that evolution is a change in the relative frequency of alleles in a population's gene pool.* Provide small groups of students with scissors and sheets of paper of different colors. Tell students to cut the paper into small squares to represent alleles. Then have groups use their squares to model how evolution occurs in genetic terms. Give each group a chance to explain its model to the class.

How does that work? In any population, some individuals have phenotypes that are better suited to their environment than are the phenotypes of other individuals. The better-suited individuals produce more offspring than the less fit individuals do. Therefore, organisms with higher fitness pass more copies of their genes to the next generation.

Natural selection never acts directly on genes. Why? Because it is an entire organism—not a single gene—that either survives and reproduces or dies without reproducing.

In Your Notebook *Describe how natural selection affects genotypes by acting on phenotypes.*

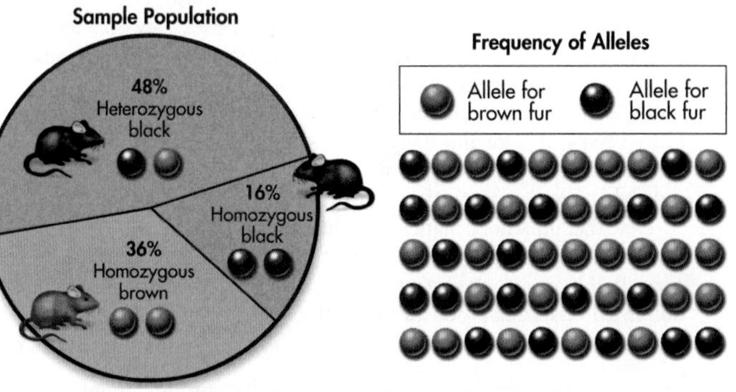

Frequency of Alleles

Allele for brown fur | Allele for black fur

FIGURE 17–2 Alleles in a Population When scientists try to determine whether a population is evolving, they study its allele frequencies. This diagram shows allele frequencies for fur color in a mouse population. **Calculate** ***Here, in a total of 50 alleles, 20 alleles are*** **B** ***(black) and 30 are*** **b** ***(brown). How many of each allele would be present in a total of 100 alleles?*** MATH

Populations and Gene Pools Genetic variation and evolution are both studied in populations. A population is a group of individuals of the same species that mate and produce offspring. Because members of a population interbreed, they share a common group of genes called a gene pool. A **gene pool** consists of all the genes, including all the different alleles for each gene, that are present in a population.

Researchers study gene pools by examining the numbers of different alleles they contain. **Allele frequency** is the number of times an allele occurs in a gene pool, compared to the total number of alleles in that pool for the same gene. For example, in the mouse population in **Figure 17–2,** the allele frequency of the domiant *B* allele (black fur) is 40 percent, and the allele frequency of the recessive *b* allele (brown fur) is 60 percent. The allele frequency of an allele has nothing to do with whether the allele is dominant or recessive. In this mouse population, the recessive allele occurs more frequently than the dominant allele.

Evolution, in genetic terms, involves a change in the frequency of alleles in a population over time. For example, if the frequency of the *B* allele in **Figure 17–2** drops to 30 percent, the population is evolving. It's important to note that populations, not individuals, evolve. Natural selection operates on individual organisms, but the changes it causes in allele frequency show up in the population as a whole.

BUILD Vocabulary

MULTIPLE MEANINGS Perhaps the most common definition of the noun *pool* is a large man-made body of water in which you can swim. However, a *pool* can also refer to an available supply of a resource. In the case of a **gene pool,** the resource is genetic information.

BIOLOGY.com Search Lesson 17.1 GO • Art Review

Teach

Use Visuals

Use **Figure 17–2** to help students see how a population's genotype frequencies relate to allele frequencies in its gene pool. Ask students to calculate the number of mice with each genotype, assuming that there are 25 individuals in the population, since **Figure 17–2** shows a total of 50 alleles. (*heterozygous black—12; homozygous black—4; homozygous brown—9*) Then, ask students to calculate the number of *B* and *b* alleles each genotype contributes to the gene pool. (*heterozygous black—12* B, *12* b; *homozygous black—8* B; *homozygous brown—18* b) Have students add the numbers of each type of allele and check that the totals match the number of allele icons in the matrix.

Ask If the current generation of homozygous brown mice had no offspring, how would this affect the allele frequency of the *b* allele in the next generation? *(The frequency would decline.)*

DIFFERENTIATED INSTRUCTION

L1 Special Needs Give students 20 pennies and 30 paper clips to represent the *B* and *b* alleles, respectively, in the mouse gene pool in **Figure 17–2.** Challenge students to arrange the items in groups of two to represent the numbers of genotypes in the mouse population.

BIOLOGY.com In **Art Review: Frequency and Dominance** students can use drag-and-drop labels and representations of alleles to help them distinguish between allele dominance and allele frequency.

How Science Works

A 20TH-CENTURY INTERPRETER OF DARWIN

By the early 1900s, scientists were aware of both Darwin's theory of evolution by natural selection and Mendel's laws of inheritance. Researchers were also rapidly accumulating data in the fields of genetics, taxonomy, and paleontology. However, it wasn't until the 1930s that anyone managed to synthesize all of these sources of theory and information into a single, coherent modern theory of evolution. The synthesizer was the Russian-born U.S. geneticist Theodosius Dobzhansky, and the landmark work that launched modern evolutionary theory was his 1937 book, *Genetics and the Origin of Species*. Dobzhansky amassed a huge amount of field and laboratory data in support of his synthesis. His famous genetics studies of the fruit fly *Drosophila* went on for almost half a century.

Answers

FIGURE 17–2 In a total of 100 alleles, 40 alleles would be *B (black)* and 60 alleles would be *b (brown)*.

IN YOUR NOTEBOOK Genotype largely determines phenotype. Phenotype directly affects how an organism interacts with its environment. Organisms with adaptive phenotypes are more likely to pass their alleles, and therefore their genotypes, on to the next generation.

Teach continued

Build Math Skills

Remind students that evolution depends on genetic diversity. Help them appreciate how much genetic diversity is created by independent assortment. Tell them that the number of different possible combinations of chromosomes in gametes is 2^n, where n is the haploid number. In humans, n = 23, so the number of possible chromosome combinations in a human gamete is $2^{23} = 8{,}388{,}608$. Remind students that any of these combinations in one parent's gamete may unite with any of the 8,388,608 combinations in the second parent's gamete.

Ask How many different combinations are possible in a species with a haploid number of 3? *(2^3, or 8)*

DIFFERENTIATED INSTRUCTION

L1 Struggling Students Use pipe cleaners of different lengths and colors to model the different combinations of chromosomes that can result in the offspring of two parent organisms that have the diploid number of 6 chromosomes. The pipe cleaners that represent each homologous chromosome pair should be the same length, so there will be three different lengths. Each chromosome should be a different color. Model for students the different kinds of combinations that gametes can have, and then model the different combinations that the offspring can have.

Students should infer that high mutation rates increase variation in the viral gene pool. Ask students to consider how high mutation rates might be related to the frequent appearance of new virus strains. Students can go online to **Biology.com** to gather their evidence.

Address Misconceptions

Mutations Students may hold the misconception that all mutations are harmful, making it hard for them to understand why mutations are needed for evolution. Address this misconception by giving them examples of mutations that are beneficial to the organisms in which they occur, such as those that let bacteria resist antibiotics and adult humans digest lactose.

Answers

IN YOUR NOTEBOOK Most diversity in a gene pool is due to sexual reproduction, not mutations, because millions of gene combinations can be produced through independent assortment and crossing-over.

FIGURE 17–3 Genetic Variation Genetic variation may produce visible variations in phenotype, such as the different-colored kernels in these ears of maize. Other kinds of genetic variation, such as resistance to disease, may not be visible, even though they are more important to evolutionary fitness.

Sources of Genetic Variation

What are the sources of genetic variation?

Genetics enables us to understand how heritable variation is produced. **Three sources of genetic variation are mutation, genetic recombination during sexual reproduction, and lateral gene transfer.**

Mutations A mutation is any change in the genetic material of a cell. Some mutations involve changes within individual genes. Other mutations involve changes in larger pieces of chromosomes. Some mutations—called neutral mutations—do not change an organism's phenotype.

Mutations that produce changes in phenotype may or may not affect fitness. Some mutations, such as those that cause genetic diseases, may be lethal. Other mutations may lower fitness by decreasing an individual's ability to survive and reproduce. Still other mutations may improve an individual's ability to survive and reproduce.

How common are mutations? Recent estimates suggest that each of us is born with roughly 300 mutations that make parts of our DNA different from that of our parents. Most of those mutations are neutral. One or two are potentially harmful. A few may be beneficial.

Note that mutations matter in evolution only if they can be passed from generation to generation. For that to happen, mutations must occur in the germ line cells that produce either eggs or sperm. A mutation in skin cells that produces a nonlethal skin cancer, for example, will not be passed to the next generation.

Genetic Recombination in Sexual Reproduction Mutations are not the only source of heritable variation. You do not look exactly like your biological parents, even though they gave you all your genes. You probably look even less like any brothers or sisters you may have. Yet no matter how you feel about your relatives, mutant genes are not primarily what makes them look so different from you. Most heritable differences are due not to mutations, but to genetic recombination during sexual reproduction. Remember that each chromosome in a pair moves independently during meiosis. In humans, who have 23 pairs of chromosomes, this process can produce 8.4 million gene combinations!

Crossing-over is another way in which genes are recombined. Recall that crossing-over occurs during meiosis. In this process, paired chromosomes often swap lengths of DNA at random. Crossing-over further increases the number of new genotypes created in each generation. You can now understand why, in species that reproduce sexually, no two siblings (except identical twins) ever look exactly alike. With all that independent assortment and crossing-over, you can easily end up with your mother's eyes, your father's nose, and hair that combines qualities from both your parents. You can also now understand why, as Darwin noted, individual members of a species differ from one another.

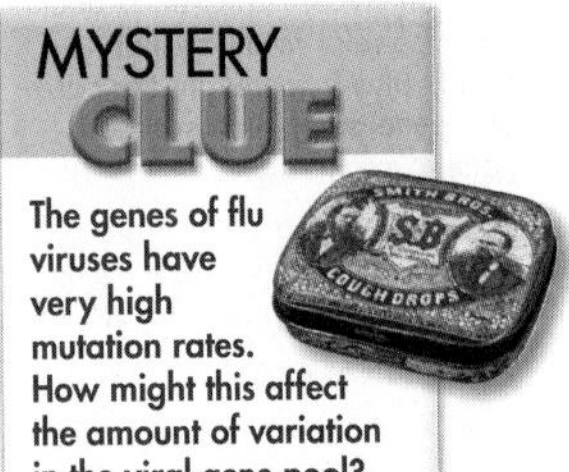

MYSTERY CLUE

The genes of flu viruses have very high mutation rates. How might this affect the amount of variation in the viral gene pool?

In Your Notebook *Which source of variation brings more diversity into a gene pool—mutation or sexual reproduction? Explain.*

UbD Check for Understanding

HAND SIGNALS

Ask students the following questions about sources of genetic variation. For each question, have them respond with a thumbs-up sign if they understand, a thumbs-down sign if they do not understand, and a waving-hand sign if they are uncertain.

- Why must mutations occur in germ line cells to affect evolution?
- How does sexual reproduction increase genetic variation?
- How does lateral gene transfer increase genetic variation?

ADJUST INSTRUCTION

For any question students do not understand, have them reread the relevant text and then prepare a brief written answer. Call on volunteers to read their answers to the class. If any answers are incorrect, explain the correct answers in detail.

Lateral Gene Transfer Most of the time, in most eukaryotic organisms, genes are passed only from parents to offspring (during sexual or asexual reproduction). Some organisms, however, pass genes from one individual to another, or even from individuals of one species to another. Recall, for example, that many bacteria swap genes on plasmids as though the genes were trading cards. This passing of genes from one organism to another organism that is not its offspring is called lateral gene transfer. Lateral gene transfer can occur between organisms of the same species or organisms of different species.

Lateral gene transfer can increase genetic variation in any species that picks up the "new" genes. This process is important in the evolution of antibiotic resistance in bacteria. Lateral gene transfer has been common, and important, in single-celled organisms during the history of life.

Single-Gene and Polygenic Traits

What determines the number of phenotypes for a given trait?

Genes control phenotype in different ways. In some cases, a single gene controls a trait. Other times, several genes interact to control a trait. **The number of phenotypes produced for a trait depends on how many genes control the trait.**

Single-Gene Traits In the species of snail shown below, some snails have dark bands on their shells, and other snails don't. The presence or absence of dark bands is a **single-gene trait**—a trait controlled by only one gene. The gene that controls shell banding has two alleles. The allele for a shell without bands is dominant over the allele for a shell with dark bands. All genotypes for this trait have one of two phenotypes—shells with bands or shells without bands. Single-gene traits may have just two or three distinct phenotypes.

The bar graph in **Figure 17–4** shows the relative frequency of phenotypes for this single gene in one population of snails. This graph shows that the presence of dark bands on the shells may be more common in a population than the absence of bands. This is true even though the allele for shells without bands is the dominant form. In populations, phenotypic ratios are determined by the frequency of alleles in the population as well as by whether the alleles are dominant or recessive.

FIGURE 17–4 Two Phenotypes In this species of snail, a single gene with two alleles controls whether or not a snail's shell has bands. The graph shows the percentages, in one population, of snails with bands and snails without bands.

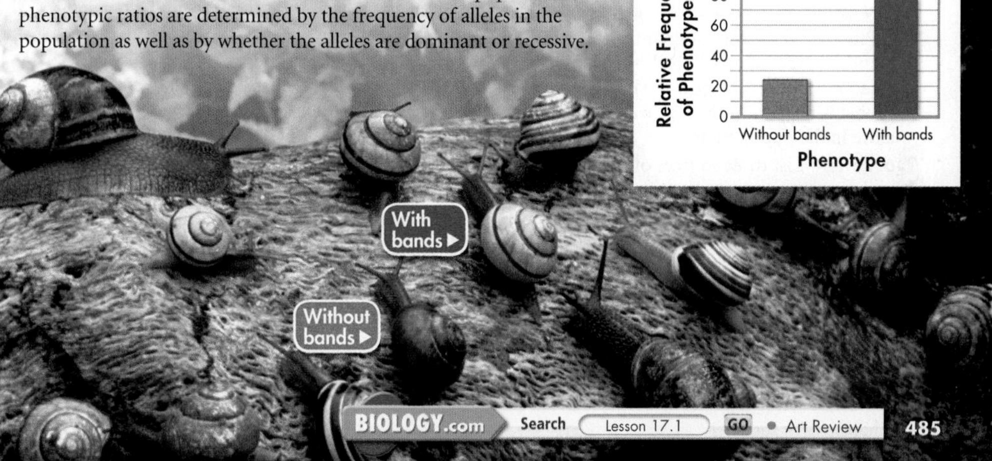

Biology In-Depth

SOURCES OF LATERAL GENE TRANSFER

Bacterial transformation by horizontal gene transfer is a primary factor in the spread of antibiotic resistance. Bacteria with antibiotic resistance can easily transfer the gene from organism to organism, quickly spreading the trait. Over the history of life there have been other sources of lateral gene transfer. One prominent source is endosymbiosis. (The endosymbiotic origin of mitochondria and possibly other organelles is discussed in Chapter 19.) Endosymbiosis occurred at least once in the evolution of eukaryotic cells. It probably occurred several other times during the evolution of plants, accounting for different types of chloroplasts in various groups of algae and in green plants.

Use Models

Help students appreciate how many more genotypes are possible for polygenic traits than single-gene traits by having groups of students model the possible genotypes for a single-gene trait and a two-gene (polygenic) trait. All genes should have two alleles. Students can represent alleles with letters or small objects such as coins or slips of paper. Ask groups to compare their models. Did they all arrive at the correct number of genotypes? *(3 for the single-gene trait, 9 for the two-gene trait)* Tell students that 64 genotypes are possible for a three-gene trait with two alleles per gene.

Ask How would the number of genotypes be affected if each gene had more than two alleles? *(It would be much greater.)*

DIFFERENTIATED INSTRUCTION

LPR Less Proficient Readers Graphs can be thought of as models that show trends. Use the graphs in **Figure 17–4** and **Figure 17–5** to help less proficient readers differentiate the number of phenotypes for single-gene and polygenic traits. Call students' attention to the patterns shown by the two graphs.

Ask What is the graph for the single-gene trait like? *(two distinct bars of different heights)* What is the graph for the polygenic trait like? *(a curve)* What does this tell you about the difference between single-gene and polygenic phenotypes? *(For single-gene traits, there are often only two distinct phenotypes. For polygenic traits, there is usually a range of phenotypes.)*

ELL Focus on ELL: Access Content

ALL SPEAKERS Ask students to create a **T-Chart** of lesson vocabulary terms. On the left side of the chart, have them list the terms. On the right side, have them list characteristics of each term and a symbol that will help them remember the term. Have intermediate speakers also add a sentence that will help them remember each term. Advanced speakers can write two or more sentences that define each term, using information from the text.

When students have finished their charts, pair advanced and advanced high speakers with intermediate and beginning speakers. Members of each pair should compare their charts. Advanced speakers should help beginning and intermediate speakers understand the meanings of the vocabulary terms.

Study Wkbks A/B, Appendix S30, T-Chart. **Transparencies,** GO15.

Assess and Remediate

EVALUATE UNDERSTANDING

Call on students to explain why populations, rather than individuals, evolve. *(Evolution occurs due to the change of the relative frequency of alleles in a population over time. The alleles in an individual organism do not change during the organism's lifetime.)* Then, have students complete the 17.1 Assessment.

REMEDIATION SUGGESTION

LPR **Less Proficient Readers** If students have trouble with **Question 3c,** have them compare the graphs in **Figure 17–4** and **Figure 17–5.** Ask how many phenotypes are shown in each graph. Then, ask how many different phenotypes are described in **Question 3c.**

BIOLOGY.com Students can check their understanding of lesson concepts with the **Self-Test** assessment. They can then take an online version of the **Lesson Assessment.**

Answers

FIGURE 17–5 The shape of the graph indicates that there is a range of heights in the population. Few people are very short or very tall—most are in the middle of the range.

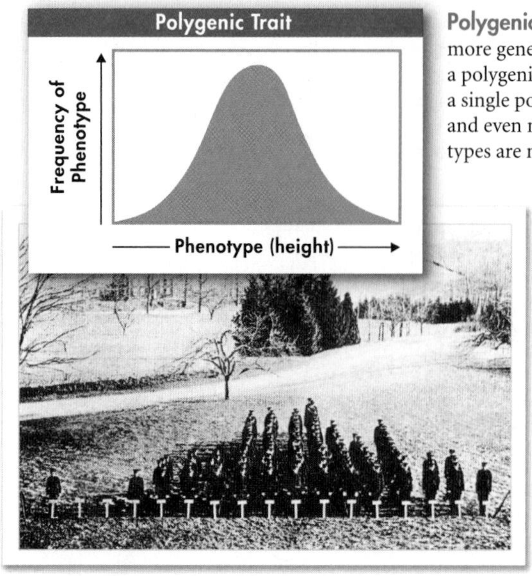

Polygenic Trait

Frequency of Phenotype

Phenotype (height)

Polygenic Traits Many traits are controlled by two or more genes and are called **polygenic traits.** Each gene of a polygenic trait often has two or more alleles. As a result, a single polygenic trait often has many possible genotypes and even more different phenotypes. Often those phenotypes are not clearly distinct from one another.

Height in humans is one example of a polygenic trait. Height varies from very short to very tall and everywhere in between. You can sample phenotypic variation in this trait by measuring the height of all the students in your class. You can then calculate average height for this group. Many students will be just a little taller or shorter than average. Some, however, will be very tall or very short. If you graph the number of individuals of each height, you may get a graph similar to the one in **Figure 17–5.** The symmetrical bell-like shape of this curve is typical of polygenic traits. A bell-shaped curve is also called a normal distribution.

FIGURE 17–5 A Range of Phenotypes The graph above shows the distribution of phenotypes that would be expected for a trait if many genes contributed to the trait. The photograph shows the actual distribution of heights in a group of young men. Interpret Graphs ***What does the shape of the graph indicate about height in humans?***

17.1 Assessment

IN B.5.2, B.5.6, B.6.5, B.7.5, B.8.5, B.8.6

Review Key Concepts

1. a. Review Define the terms *gene pool* and *allele frequency*.

b. Explain In genetic terms, what indicates that evolution is occurring in a population?

c. Predict Suppose a dominant allele causes a plant disease that usually kills the plant before it can reproduce. Over time, what would probably happen to the frequency of that allele in the population?

2. a. Review List three sources of genetic variation.

b. Explain How does genetic recombination result in genetic variation?

c. Relate Cause and Effect Why does sexual reproduction provide more opportunities for genetic variation than asexual reproduction?

3. a. Review What is a single-gene trait? What is a polygenic trait?

b. Explain How does the range of phenotypes for single-gene traits differ from the range for polygenic traits?

c. Infer A black guinea pig and a white guinea pig mate and have offspring. All the offspring are black. Is the trait of coat color probably a single-gene trait or a polygenic trait? Explain.

WRITE ABOUT SCIENCE

Explanation

4. Explain how mutations are important in the process of biological evolution. (*Hint:* How does mutation affect genetic variation?)

BIOLOGY.com Search Lesson 17.1 GO • Self-Test • Lesson Assessment

Assessment Answers

1a. A gene pool consists of all the genes, including all the different alleles for each gene, that are present in a population. The allele frequency is the number of times that the allele occurs in a gene pool, compared with the number of times other alleles for the same gene occur.

1b. change in the relative frequency of alleles in the population's gene pool over time

1c. The frequency would probably decrease.

2a. mutations, genetic recombination in sexual reproduction, and lateral gene transfer

2b. Gene shuffling results in different combinations of genes and alleles through independent assortment and crossing over.

2c. Sexual reproduction combines alleles from different parents to produce offspring with different genotypes than the parents. Asexual reproduction produces offspring with the same genotype as the parent.

3a. A single-gene trait is a trait controlled by only one gene. A polygenic trait is a trait controlled by two or more genes.

3b. Single-gene traits have just a few distinct phenotypes. Polygenic traits have many possible phenotypes, which often are not clearly distinct from one another.

3c. It is probably a single-gene trait because it has two distinct phenotypes. If it were a polygenic trait, the offspring's coat color would have more variation.

WRITE ABOUT SCIENCE

4. Mutations are a source of genetic variation in gene pools. Genetic variation is needed for biological evolution to occur. There must be variation in order for some organisms to be better-suited to their environment and thereby pass on more copies of their genes.

17.2 Evolution as Genetic Change in Populations

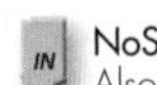

NoS.6 Use analogies and models; B.8.5 Survival and reproduction. Also covered: NoS.3.

THINK ABOUT IT Ever since humans began farming, they have battled insects that eat crops. Many farmers now use chemicals called pesticides to kill crop-destroying insects. When farmers first used modern pesticides such as DDT, the chemicals killed most insects. But after a few years, many pesticides stopped working. Today, farmers fight an ongoing "arms race" with insects. Scientists constantly search for new chemicals to control pests that old chemicals no longer control. How do insects fight back? By evolving.

At first, individual pesticides kill almost all insects exposed to them. But a few individual insects usually survive. Why? Because insect populations often contain enough genetic variation that a few individuals, just by chance, are resistant to a particular pesticide. By killing most of the susceptible individuals, farmers increase the relative fitness of the few individuals that can resist the poison. Those insects survive and reproduce, passing their resistance on to their offspring. After a few generations, the descendants of the original, resistant individuals dominate the population.

To understand completely how pesticide resistance develops, you need to know the relationship between natural selection and genetics.

How Natural Selection Works

How does natural selection affect single-gene and polygenic traits?

Pesticide-resistant insects have a kind of fitness that protects them from a harmful chemical. In genetic terms, what does *fitness* mean? Each time an organism reproduces, it passes copies of its genes on to its offspring. We can, therefore, view evolutionary fitness as success in passing genes to the next generation. In the same way, we can view an evolutionary adaptation as any genetically controlled trait that increases an individual's ability to pass along its alleles.

Key Questions

How does natural selection affect single-gene and polygenic traits?

What is genetic drift?

What conditions are required to maintain genetic equilibrium?

Vocabulary

directional selection
stabilizing selection
disruptive selection
genetic drift
bottleneck effect
founder effect
genetic equilibrium
Hardy-Weinberg principle
sexual selection

Taking Notes

Preview Visuals Before you read, look at **Figure 17–6.** What evolutionary trend does it seem to show?

Getting Started

Objectives

17.2.1 Explain how natural selection affects single-gene and polygenic traits.

17.2.2 Describe genetic drift.

17.2.3 Explain how different factors affect genetic equilibrium.

Student Resources

Study Workbooks A and B, 17.2 Worksheets

Spanish Study Workbook, 17.2 Worksheets

Lab Manual B, 17.2 Data Analysis Worksheet, Hands-On Activity Worksheet

BIOLOGY.com Lesson Overview • Lesson Notes • Activity: Art in Motion • Assessment: Self-Test, Lesson Assessment

For corresponding lesson in the **Foundation Edition,** see pages 409–413.

Activate Prior Knowledge

Based on what they learned in Chapter 16 about Darwin's theory of evolution, have several students in turn state a fact about, or give an example of, natural selection.

Ask If Darwin had known what you know about genes, how do you think he would have defined fitness? *(Sample answers: possession of genes that enhance survivability; ability of an individual to pass copies of its genes to its offspring)*

UbD Teach for Understanding

ENDURING UNDERSTANDING The diversity of life is the result of ongoing evolutionary change. Species alive today have evolved from ancient common ancestors.

GUIDING QUESTION What causes a population's gene pool to change?

EVIDENCE OF UNDERSTANDING *After the lesson, give students the following assessment to determine whether they understand the role of chance events in the evolution of small populations.* Have pairs of students use coin tosses to simulate the effects of chance on the allele frequencies in a population of 10 individuals. In the first generation, there are 10 "heads" alleles and 10 "tails" alleles. Students should assume that there are 10 individuals in the next generation. Students should toss the coin twice for each individual in the next generation and record the outcomes of the tosses. After pairs compare their new allele frequencies, have each student write a brief explanation of whether genetic drift has occurred.

IN INDIANA ACADEMIC STANDARDS

For the full text of all standards, see the Course Overview in the front matter of this book.

NoS.6 Use analogies and models (mathematical and physical) to simplify and represent systems that are difficult to understand or directly experience due to their size, time scale, or complexity, and recognize the limitations of analogies and models.

B.8.5 Describe how due to genetic variations, environmental forces, and reproductive pressures, organisms with beneficial traits are more likely to survive, reproduce, and pass on their genetic information.

LESSON 17.2

Teach

Build Reading Skills

Suggest that students preview the headings of the lesson to identify the topics covered, and then write a question about each topic. For example, for the subhead **Natural Selection on Single-Gene Traits,** students might write the question, "How does natural selection affect allele frequencies for a gene that controls a single trait?" As students read the lesson, they should read to find answers to their questions. Discuss any unanswered questions as a class.

DIFFERENTIATED INSTRUCTION

LPR **Less Proficient Readers** Help students use the answers to their questions from the activity described above to create or fill in a **Concept Map** for the information in **How Natural Selection Works.**

Study Wkbks A/B, Appendix S21, Concept Map. **Transparencies,** GO4.

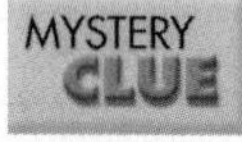

Explain that a person's immune system recognizes viruses by their surface proteins. A virus with a protein a person has already been exposed to is quickly detected by the immune system. However, a virus with a mutation that causes a new surface protein may escape detection. Have students predict how such a mutation would affect the fitness of the virus carrying it. Students can go online to Biology.com to gather their evidence.

Answers

FIGURE 17–6 Red lizards have been selected against because they are more visible to predators, while black lizards have been selected for because they can move faster and avoid predators. As a result, red lizards have been eliminated and black lizards have become more common.

IN YOUR NOTEBOOK Directional selection shifts the range of phenotypes toward one end of the curve because phenotypes at this end are most fit. Stabilizing selection narrows the curve without shifting it from the center because phenotypes at the center of the curve are most fit. Disruptive selection causes the curve to split into a higher and lower peak because phenotypes at both ends of the curve are more fit.

MYSTERY CLUE

Normally, our immune systems kill or disable disease-causing viruses. What might happen if one flu virus had a mutation that enabled it to escape the body's defenses?

Natural Selection on Single-Gene Traits Recall that evolution is any change over time in the allele frequency in a population. This process works somewhat differently for single-gene traits than for polygenic traits. **Natural selection on single-gene traits can lead to changes in allele frequencies and, thus, to changes in phenotype frequencies.** For example, imagine that a population of lizards experiences mutations in one gene that determines body color. The normal color of the lizards is brown. The mutations produce red and black forms, as shown in **Figure 17–6.** What happens to the new alleles? If red lizards are more visible to predators, they might be less likely to survive and reproduce. Therefore, the allele for red coloring might not become common.

Black lizards, on the other hand, might absorb more sunlight and warm up faster on cold days. If high body temperature allows the lizards to move faster to feed and avoid predators, they might produce more offspring than brown forms produce. The allele for black color might increase in frequency. The black phenotype would then increase in frequency. If color change has no effect on fitness, the allele that produces it will not be under pressure from natural selection.

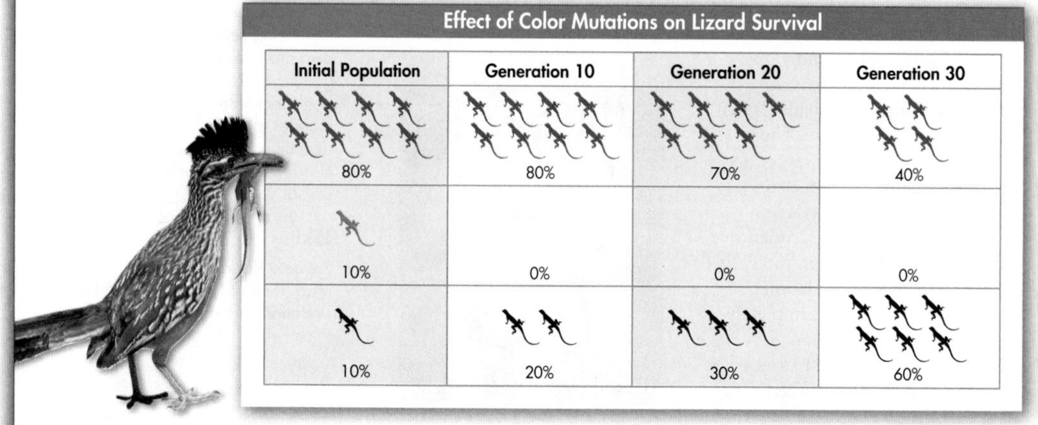

Effect of Color Mutations on Lizard Survival

Initial Population	Generation 10	Generation 20	Generation 30
80%	80%	70%	40%
10%	0%	0%	0%
10%	20%	30%	60%

FIGURE 17–6 Selection on a Single-Gene Trait Natural selection on a single-gene trait can lead to changes in allele frequencies and, thus, to evolution. **Interpret Visuals** ***What has happened to produce the population shown in Generation 30?***

Natural Selection on Polygenic Traits When traits are controlled by more than one gene, the effects of natural selection are more complex. As you saw earlier, polygenic traits such as height often display a range of phenotypes that form a bell curve. The fitness of individuals may vary from one end of such a curve to the other. Where fitness varies, natural selection can act. **Natural selection on polygenic traits can affect the relative fitness of phenotypes and thereby produce one of three types of selection: directional selection, stabilizing selection, or disruptive selection.** These types of selection are shown in **Figure 17–7.**

In Your Notebook *As you read the text on the following page, summarize each of the three types of selection.*

Biology In-Depth

BALANCING SELECTION

Balancing selection is a type of selection on a single-gene trait that is similar to stabilizing selection on a polygenic trait. In balancing selection, the heterozygous genotype has the highest fitness. An example is sickle cell hemoglobin in human populations that live in areas where malaria is endemic, such as sub-Saharan Africa. Heterozygotes for sickle cell disease have both normal and sickle cell hemoglobin. They are resistant to malaria but do not have full-blown sickle cell disease. In these populations, homozygotes for normal hemoglobin have reduced fitness, relative to heterozygotes, because they do not have resistance to malaria. Homozygotes for sickle cell hemoglobin are also resistant to malaria, but they have reduced fitness because they have sickle cell disease. Alleles for both types of hemoglobin have persisted at relatively stable frequencies for many generations in these populations.

▶ ***Directional Selection*** When individuals at one end of the curve have higher fitness than individuals in the middle or at the other end, **directional selection** occurs. The range of phenotypes shifts because some individuals are more successful at surviving and reproducing than are others.

Consider how limited resources, such as food, can affect individuals' fitness. Among seed-eating birds such as Darwin's finches, birds with bigger, thicker beaks can feed more easily on larger, harder, thicker-shelled seeds. Suppose the supply of small and medium-size seeds runs low, leaving only larger seeds. Birds with larger beaks would have an easier time feeding than would small-beaked birds. Big-beaked birds would therefore be more successful in surviving and passing genes to the next generation. Over time, the average beak size of the population would probably increase.

▶ ***Stabilizing Selection*** When individuals near the center of the curve have higher fitness than individuals at either end, **stabilizing selection** takes place. This situation keeps the center of the curve at its current position, but it narrows the curve overall.

For example, the mass of human infants at birth is under the influence of stabilizing selection. Very small babies are likely to be less healthy and, thus, less likely to survive. Babies who are much larger than average are likely to have difficulty being born. The fitness of these smaller or larger babies is, therefore, lower than that of more average-size individuals.

▶ ***Disruptive Selection*** When individuals at the outer ends of the curve have higher fitness than individuals near the middle of the curve, **disruptive selection** occurs. Disruptive selection acts against individuals of an intermediate type. If the pressure of natural selection is strong and lasts long enough, this situation can cause the single curve to split into two. In other words, disruptive selection creates two distinct phenotypes.

Suppose a bird population lives in an area where medium-size seeds become less common and large and small seeds become more common. Birds with unusually small or large beaks would have higher fitness. As shown in the graph, the population might split into two groups: one with smaller beaks and one with larger beaks.

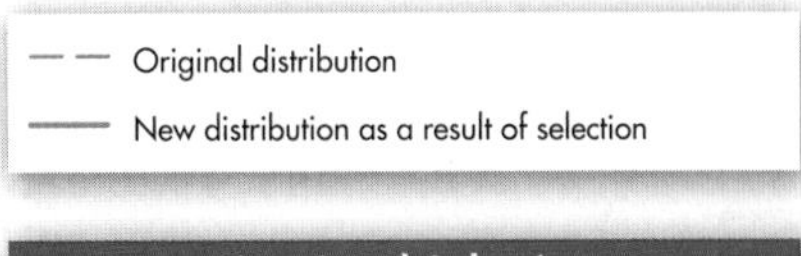

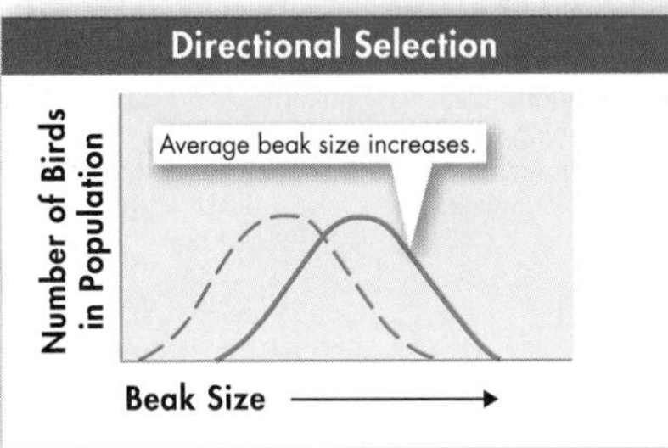

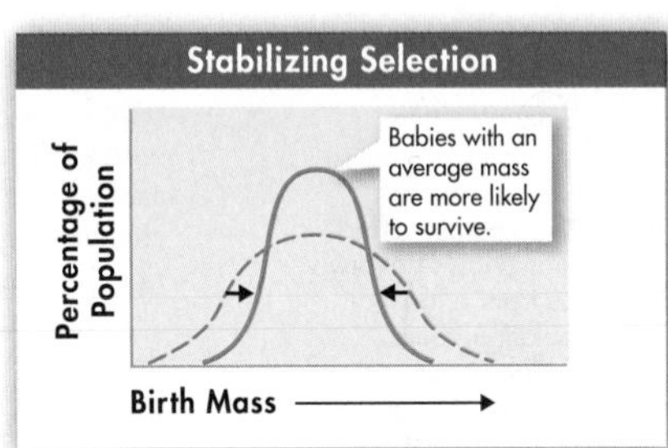

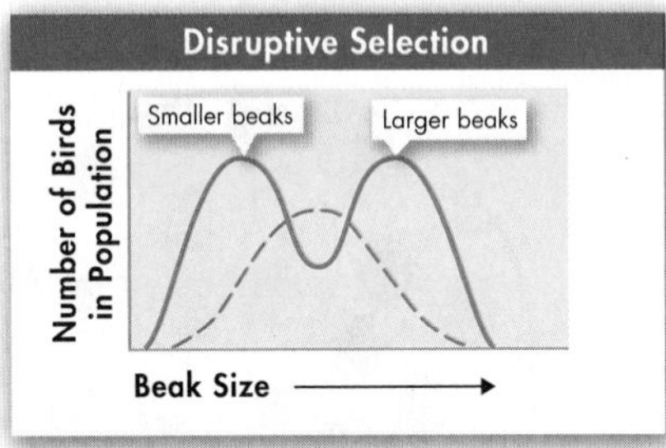

FIGURE 17–7 Selection on Polygenic Traits Natural selection on polygenic traits has one of three patterns—directional selection, stabilizing selection, or disruptive selection.

BIOLOGY.com Search Lesson 17.2 GO • Art in Motion

Use Visuals

After students have studied the three graphs in **Figure 17–7,** ask them to describe how each graph would look if fitness parameters changed. This will require students to apply what they learned about selection on polygenic traits.

Ask If large seeds became scarce and there were more small seeds available, how would this affect the curve for directional selection? *(The curve would probably shift to the left.)*

Ask If medical advances led to large babies having a better chance of surviving, how would this affect the curve for stabilizing selection? *(The curve would shift to the right.)*

Ask If more medium-sized seeds became available and small and large seeds became scarce, how would this affect the curve for disruptive selection? *(The curve would shift back to having one central peak.)*

DIFFERENTIATED INSTRUCTION

L1 **Struggling Students** To help students differentiate between the three types of selection, carefully go over each graph with them. Make sure that students understand how to interpret the different lines and the graph axes. Call attention to the key at the top of **Figure 17–7.**

Ask What does the dashed line show? *(the original distribution of phenotypes)* What does the solid line show? *(the distribution that resulted from selection)* Then discuss what the horizontal and vertical axes show in each graph.

Ask In each of the graphs, what does the arrow along the horizontal axis indicate? *(an increase in size)*

BIOLOGY.com Students can see how directional, stabilizing, and disruptive selection change the distribution of phenotypes for a polygenic trait over time in **Art in Motion: Natural Selection.**

UbD Check for Understanding

ANALOGY PROMPT

Ask small groups of students to complete this analogy: *Directional selection is like a car that moves in one direction because* ___________________. Give students several minutes to brainstorm ideas, and then ask groups to turn in their responses. *(Sample answer: Directional selection is like a car moving in one direction because the range of phenotypes shifts in one direction.)*

ADJUST INSTRUCTION

If students do not understand the analogy, have them look carefully at the graph showing directional selection. Ask them how the movement of the curve is like the movement of a car traveling in one direction.

Teach continued

Connect to Environmental Science

Explain that the founder effect may be especially likely to occur following a major change in the environment, such as a forest fire, landslide, volcanic eruption, or human destruction of a habitat. Challenge students to describe a scenario in which an environmental change such as this leads to the founder effect. *(Sample answer: a fire might isolate a few mice in a small remnant of forest.)*

DIFFERENTIATED INSTRUCTION

L1 Special Needs Adapt the Connect to Environmental Science activity for hearing-impaired students. Write the examples of environmental change on the board or show pictures to illustrate them. When you discuss the disasters and ask students to describe how they might lead to the founder effect, be sure to face students when you speak. For example, don't speak as you are writing on the board. Also avoid standing with your back to a window so your face is not in shadow. Give students the option of putting their descriptions in writing.

Address Misconceptions

Mechanisms of Evolution A common misconception about natural selection is that it is the only mechanism of evolution. Be sure to clear up this misconception, or students might not appreciate that genetic drift can also be a potent force of evolution. Make certain students understand that genetic drift can lead to evolution of a population entirely independent of natural selection.

Answers

FIGURE 17–8 The two populations of descendants are different because they were founded by small subgroups of the original population that were, by chance, genetically very different from one another.

Genetic Drift

What is genetic drift?

Natural selection is not the only source of evolutionary change. In small populations, an allele can become more or less common simply by chance. **In small populations, individuals that carry a particular allele may leave more descendants than other individuals leave, just by chance. Over time, a series of chance occurrences can cause an allele to become more or less common in a population.** This kind of random change in allele frequency is called **genetic drift.**

BUILD Vocabulary

ACADEMIC WORDS The adjective **random** means "lacking a pattern" or "happening by chance." A random change is a change that happens by chance.

Genetic Bottlenecks Sometimes, a disaster, such as disease, can kill many individuals in a population. Just by chance, the smaller population's gene pool may have allele frequencies that are different from those of the original gene pool. If the reduced population later grows, its alleles will be different in frequency from the original population's. The **bottleneck effect** is a change in allele frequency following a dramatic reduction in the size of a population. A severe bottleneck effect can sharply reduce a population's genetic diversity.

The Founder Effect Genetic drift may also occur when a few individuals colonize a new habitat. These founding individuals may carry alleles that differ in relative frequencies from those of the main population, just by chance. The new gene pool may therefore start out with allele frequencies different from those of the parent gene pool, as shown in **Figure 17–8.** This situation, in which allele frequencies change as a result of the migration of a small subgroup of a population, is known as the **founder effect.**

One example of the founder effect is the evolution of several hundred species of fruit flies on different Hawaiian islands. All those species descended from the same mainland fruit fly population. However, species on different islands have allele frequencies that are different from those of the original species.

FIGURE 17–8 Founder Effect This illustration shows how two small groups from a large, diverse population could produce new populations that differ from the original group. **Compare and Contrast** ***Explain why the two populations of descendants are so different from one another.***

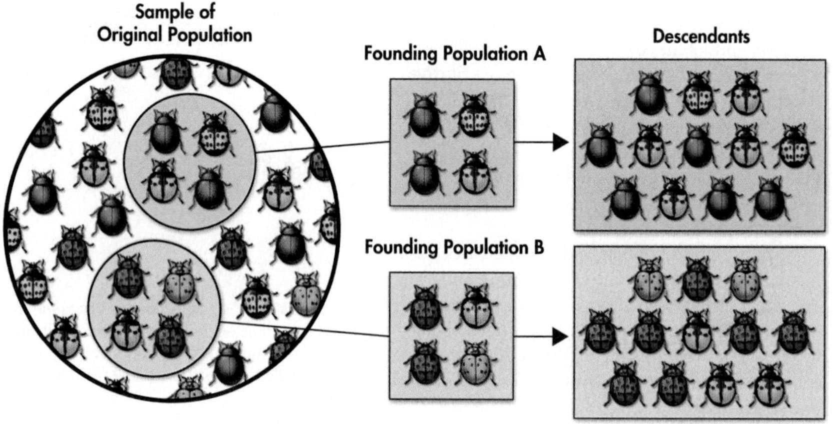

490 Chapter 17 • Lesson 2

Quick Facts

TRISTAN DA CUNHA

The tiny island of Tristan da Cunha in the South Atlantic provides an interesting example of the founder effect in humans. The island was originally settled by about 15 English immigrants in the early 1800s, and only a small number of people immigrated to the island after that. Today, the island has a population of about 250 people, and virtually all of them are related to one another, as evidenced by the fact that there are only seven different surnames on the island. One of the founders of the population apparently carried a recessive allele for a type of blindness called retinitis pigmentosa. This genetic disease is very rare in the English parent population but has a relatively high frequency in the population of Tristan da Cunha. This shows how the founder effect can lead to major changes in allele frequencies.

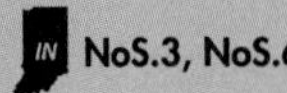

Analyzing Data MATH

IN NoS.3, NoS.6

Allele Frequency

The Hardy-Weinberg principle can be used to predict the frequencies of certain genotypes if you know the frequency of other genotypes.

Imagine, for example, that you know of a genetic condition, controlled by two alleles *S* and *s*, which follow the rule of simple dominance at a single locus. The condition affects only homozygous recessive individuals. (The heterozygous phenotype shows no symptoms.) The population you are studying has a population size of 10,000 and there are 36 individuals affected by the condition ($q^2 = 0.0036$). Based on this information, use the Hardy-Weinberg equations to answer the following questions.

1. Calculate What are the frequencies of the *S* and *s* alleles?

2. Calculate What are the frequencies of the *SS*, *Ss*, and *ss* genotypes?

3. Calculate What percentage of people, in total, is likely to be carrying the *s* allele, whether or not they know it?

Evolution Versus Genetic Equilibrium

What conditions are required to maintain genetic equilibrium?

One way to understand how and why populations evolve is to imagine a model of a hypothetical population that does not evolve. If a population is not evolving, allele frequencies in its gene pool do not change, which means that the population is in **genetic equilibrium.**

Sexual Reproduction and Allele Frequency Gene shuffling during sexual reproduction produces many gene combinations. But a century ago, researchers realized that meiosis and fertilization, by themselves, do not change allele frequencies. So hypothetically, a population of sexually reproducing organisms could remain in genetic equilibrium.

The Hardy-Weinberg Principle The **Hardy-Weinberg principle** states that allele frequencies in a population should remain constant unless one or more factors cause those frequencies to change. The Hardy-Weinberg principle makes predictions like Punnett squares—but for populations, not individuals. Here's how it works. Suppose that there are two alleles for a gene: *A* (dominant) and *a* (recessive). A cross of these alleles can produce three possible genotypes: *AA*, *Aa*, and *aa*. The frequencies of genotypes in the population can be predicted by these equations, where *p* and *q* are the frequencies of the dominant and recessive alleles:

In symbols:

$$p^2 + 2pq + q^2 = 1 \text{ and } p + q = 1$$

In words:

(frequency of *AA*) + (frequency of *Aa*) + (frequency of *aa*) = 100% and (frequency of *A*) + (frequency of *a*) = 100%

Suppose that, in one generation, the frequency of the *A* allele is 40 percent ($p = 0.40$) and the frequency of the *a* allele is 60 percent ($q = 0.60$).

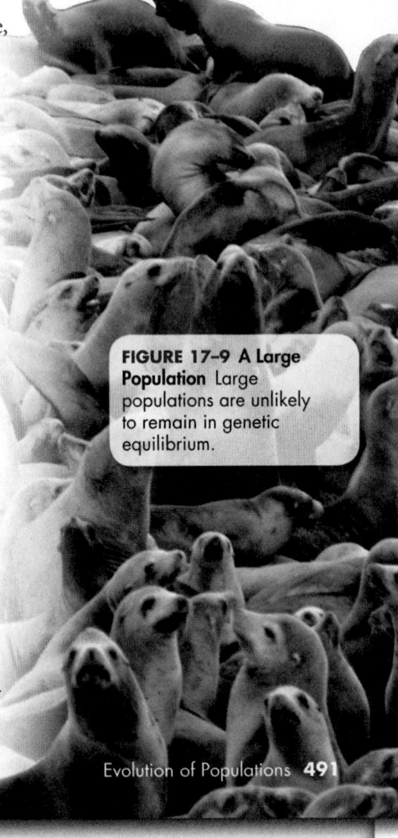

FIGURE 17–9 A Large Population Large populations are unlikely to remain in genetic equilibrium.

Analyzing Data

PURPOSE Students will apply the Hardy-Weinberg principle to calculate the allele and genotype frequencies for a hypothetical genetic condition.

PLANNING To make the numbers easier to work with, suggest students convert the information to decimals. Then, convert those decimals back to percentages to express the frequencies.

ANSWERS

1. frequency of $S = p = 94\%$ (0.94); frequency of $s = q = 6\%$ (0.06)

SS frequency $= p^2 = 0.8836 = 88.36\%$
Ss frequency $= 2pq = 0.1128 = 11.28\%$
ss frequency $= q^2 = 0.0036 = 0.36\%$

2. Percentage of people carrying the allele = percentage of asymptomatic carriers (heterozygotes) + percentage of homozygotes $= 2pq + q^2 = 11.64\%$

Expand Vocabulary

Genetic equilibrium is an important concept in evolution, so students should have a good understanding of the term. Begin with the word *equilibrium*. Tell students that the prefix *equi-* means "equal," and the rest of the term comes from the Latin word *libra*, which means "weight."

Have students make a **Cause and Effect Diagram** to show the five conditions that lead to genetic equilibrium, or *no* change in allele frequencies.

Study Wkbks A/B, Appendix S18, Cause and Effect Diagram. **Transparencies,** GO1.

DIFFERENTIATED INSTRUCTION

L1 Struggling Students To help students understand the concept of genetic equilibrium, draw a seesaw with a child at each end. Point out that if the children are equal in weight, the seesaw will be balanced. Ask students to volunteer a definition of *equilibrium* based on this analogy. *(state of balance)* Then ask them what the term *genetic equilibrium* means. *(state in which the allele frequencies in a population are in balance)* Have students compare their definitions with the definition in the text.

LESSON 17.2

Assess and Remediate

EVALUATE UNDERSTANDING

Ask students to draw, without looking back at **Figure 17–7,** a graph line to demonstrate how each pattern of natural selection (directional, stabilizing, disruptive) affects the distribution of phenotypes for a polygenic trait. Then, have them complete the 17.2 Assessment.

REMEDIATION SUGGESTION

ELL **English Language Learners** If students have difficulty answering **Question 2b,** tell them to go back to **Figure 17–8** and compare founding population A with the original population. Ask them to identify ways the founding population differs from the original population.

BIOLOGY.com Students can check their understanding of lesson concepts with the **Self-Test** assessment. They can then take an online version of the **Lesson Assessment.**

FIGURE 17–10 Choosing a Mate Random mating is one condition required to maintain genetic equilibrium in a population. However, in many species, mating is not random. Female peacocks, for example, choose mates on the basis of physical characteristics such as brightly patterned tail feathers. This is a classic example of sexual selection.

If this population is in genetic equilibrium, chances of an individual in the next generation having genotype *AA* would be 16% ($p^2 = 0.40^2 = 0.16$ or 16%). The probability of genotype *aa* would be 36% ($q^2 = 0.60^2 = 0.36$). The probability of genotype *Aa* would be 48% ($2pq = 2\ (0.40)\ (0.60) = 0.48$). If a population doesn't show these predicted phenotype frequencies, evolution is taking place. **The Hardy-Weinberg principle predicts that five conditions can disturb genetic equilibrium and cause evolution to occur: (1) nonrandom mating; (2) small population size; and (3) immigration or emigration; (4) mutations; or (5) natural selection.**

▶ ***Nonrandom Mating*** In genetic equilibrium, individuals must mate with other individuals at random. But in many species, individuals select mates based on heritable traits, such as size, strength, or coloration, a practice known as **sexual selection.** When sexual selection is at work, genes for the traits selected for or against are not in equilibrium.

▶ ***Small Population Size*** Genetic drift does not usually have major effects in large populations, but can affect small populations strongly. Evolutionary change due to genetic drift thus happens more easily in small populations.

▶ ***Immigration or Emigration*** Individuals who join a population may introduce new alleles into the gene pool, and individuals who leave may remove alleles. Thus, any movement of individuals into (immigration) or out of (emigration) a population can disrupt genetic equilibrium, a process called *gene flow*.

▶ ***Mutations*** Mutations can introduce new alleles into a gene pool, thereby changing allele frequencies and causing evolution to occur.

▶ ***Natural Selection*** If different genotypes have different fitness, genetic equilibrium will be disrupted, and evolution will occur.

One or more of these conditions usually holds for real populations. So, most of the time, in most species, evolution happens.

17.2 Assessment

IN B.8.5

Review Key Concepts

1. a. Review How does natural selection affect a single-gene trait?
   b. Compare and Contrast Compare directional selection and disruptive selection.
2. a. Review Define genetic drift.
   b. Relate Cause and Effect How can the founder effect lead to changes in a gene pool?
3. a. Review What five conditions are necessary to maintain genetic equilibrium?
   b. Infer Why is genetic equilibrium uncommon in actual populations?

Apply the Big idea

Evolution

4. Do you think populations stay in genetic equilibrium after the environment has changed significantly? Explain your answer.

BIOLOGY.com Search Lesson 17.2 GO • Self-Test • Lesson Assessment

Assessment Answers

1a. Natural selection can lead to changes in the frequencies of the alleles for a single-gene trait and, thus, to changes in phenotype frequencies.

1b. Directional selection shifts the distribution of phenotypes toward one end of the range because phenotypes at this end are most fit. Disruptive selection results when phenotypes at both ends of the range are more fit than phenotypes in the middle, or average, range.

2a. Genetic drift is a random change in allele frequency that occurs in small populations due to chance occurrences.

2b. A small number of individuals from a parent population may found a new population. Just by chance, these individuals may carry alleles in different relative frequencies than the parent population. The new gene pool will start out with different allele frequencies from the parent gene pool.

3a. The population must be very large; there can be no mutations; there must be random mating; there can be no movement into or out of the population; there can be no natural selection.

3b. Actual populations are unlikely to meet all five conditions that are required to maintain genetic equilibrium.

4. Big idea No, because under new environmental conditions, organisms with different characteristics will be more likely to survive and reproduce. The frequency of the alleles that produce these traits will likely increase.

Biology & Society

Should Antibiotic Use Be Restricted?

Natural selection and evolution aren't just about fossils and finches. Many disease-causing bacteria are evolving resistance to antibiotics—drugs intended to kill them or interfere with their growth.

During your lifetime, antibiotics have always been available and effective. So it is probably hard for you to imagine what life was like before antibiotics were discovered. It wasn't pleasant. During the 1930s, it was not unusual for half of all children in a family to die from bacterial infections that are considered trivial today.

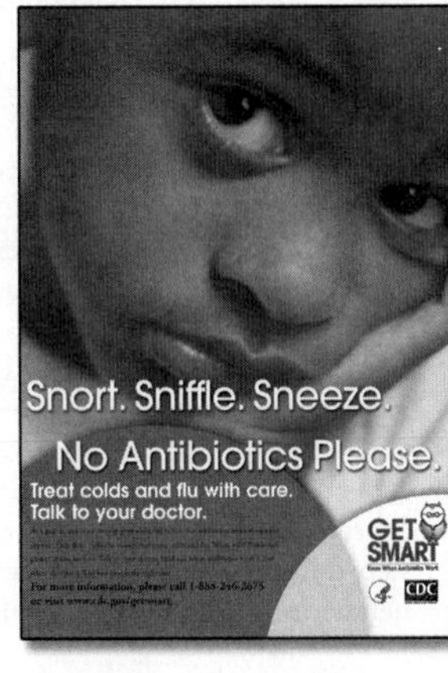

When antibiotics were developed, they rapidly became one of medicine's greatest weapons. Antibiotics saved thousands of lives during World War II by controlling bacterial infections among wounded soldiers. Soon, many bacterial diseases, such as pneumonia, posed much less of a threat. That's why antibiotics were called "magic bullets" and "wonder drugs." But the magic is fading as bacteria evolve.

Bacterial populations have always contained a few individuals with mutations that enabled them to destroy, inactivate, or eliminate antibiotics. But those individuals didn't have higher fitness, so those mutant alleles didn't become common.

Then, doctors began prescribing antibiotics widely, and farmers started feeding antibiotics to farm animals to prevent infections. As a result, antibiotics have become a regular part of the environment for bacteria.

In this new environment, individuals with resistance alleles have higher fitness, so the resistance alleles increase in frequency. Also, resistance alleles can be transferred from one bacterial species to another on plasmids. Thus, disease-causing bacteria can pick up resistance from harmless strains. Many bacteria, including those that cause tuberculosis and certain forms of staph infections, are evolving resistance to not just one antibiotic, but to almost all medicines known. Many doctors are terrified. They fear the loss of one of the vital weapons against bacterial disease. Given this problem, should government agencies restrict antibiotic use?

The Viewpoints

Restrict Antibiotic Use Some people think that the danger of an incurable bacterial epidemic is so high that the government must take action. Doctors overuse antibiotics because patients demand them. The livestock industry likes using antibiotics and will not change their practice unless forced to do so.

Don't Restrict Use Other people think that the doctors and the livestock industry need the freedom to find solutions that work best for them. Researchers are constantly developing new drugs. Some of these drugs can be reserved for human use only.

Research and Decide

1. Analyze the Viewpoints Learn more about this issue by consulting library and Internet resources. Then, list the advantages and disadvantages of restricting antibiotic use.

2. Form Your Opinion Should antibiotics be restricted? Would regulations be more appropriate in some situations than in others?

Teach

Lead a Discussion

Show students an example of the label that is always affixed to antibiotic prescription bottles, warning patients to take all of the medication. Tell students that, despite these warning labels, patients often discontinue antibiotics when they start feeling better.

Ask How might this practice help bacteria evolve antibiotic resistance? *(Some bacteria survive in the patient's body even after the patient starts feeling better. The surviving bacteria are likely to be resistant to the antibiotic. They multiply when the patient stops taking the medicine and may evolve into a new, antibiotic-resistant strain.)*

Ask How can patients help prevent antibiotic resistance from becoming more prevalent? *(by finishing any antibiotics that are prescribed for them)*

Quick Facts

MRSA

You have probably heard about MRSA in the news. It stands for methicillin-resistant *Staphylococcus aureus*, a strain of bacteria that has evolved resistance to most antibiotics. MRSA causes serious skin infections. It may also cause pneumonia or infections of other vital organs besides the lungs, with a high fatality rate. Until recently, most MRSA infections occurred in hospitals and nursing homes, but infections outside of these settings are becoming increasingly common. In community settings, young children and people who play contact sports are at greatest risk.

Answers

RESEARCH AND DECIDE

1. Advantages of restricting antibiotic use include a reduced risk of bacteria becoming resistant to antibiotics and therefore less danger of people succumbing to a disease caused by antibiotic-resistant bacteria or of epidemics of diseases caused by antibiotic-resistant bacteria. Disadvantages include a possible reduction in the food supply because of an increase in infections in farm animals, and a decrease in the options that doctors and farmers have to treat and prevent disease.
2. Accept any answers that are supported by facts and logical opinions.

Getting Started

Objectives

17.3.1 Identify the types of isolation that can lead to the formation of new species.

17.3.2 Describe the current hypothesis about Galápagos finch speciation.

Student Resources

Study Workbooks A and B, 17.3 Worksheets

Spanish Study Workbook, 17.3 Worksheets

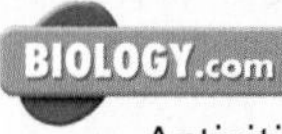
Lesson Overview • Lesson Notes • Activities: Data Analysis, Tutor Tube • Assessment: Self-Test, Lesson Assessment

For corresponding lesson in the **Foundation Edition,** see pages 414–416.

Activate Prior Knowledge

Remind students of some of the techniques for selective breeding and increasing genetic variation they learned about in Lesson 15.1. Many of the steps in these processes, such as preventing particular organisms from breeding and introducing mutations, are similar to what occurs naturally during the process of speciation.

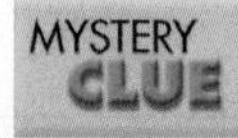
Students may infer that the isolation might lead to the emergence of new virus strains. Students can go online to Biology.com to gather their evidence.

INDIANA ACADEMIC STANDARDS

For the full text of all standards, see the Course Overview in the front matter of this book.

B.8.5 Describe how due to genetic variations, environmental forces, and reproductive pressures, organisms with beneficial traits are more likely to survive, reproduce, and pass on their genetic information.

17.3 The Process of Speciation

B.8.5 Survival and reproduction.

Key Questions

What types of isolation lead to the formation of new species?

What is a current hypothesis about Galápagos finch speciation?

Vocabulary

species
speciation
reproductive isolation
behavioral isolation
geographic isolation
temporal isolation

Taking Notes

Compare/Contrast Table
In a compare/contrast table, describe the three mechanisms of reproductive isolation.

THINK ABOUT IT How does one species become two? Natural selection and genetic drift can change allele frequencies, causing a population to evolve. But a change in allele frequency by itself does not lead to the development of a new species.

Isolating Mechanisms

What types of isolation lead to the formation of new species?

Biologists define a **species** as a population or group of populations whose members can interbreed and produce fertile offspring. Given this genetic definition of species, what must happen for one species to divide or give rise to a new species? The formation of a new species is called **speciation.**

Interbreeding links members of a species genetically. Any genetic changes can spread throughout the population over time. But what happens if some members of a population stop breeding with other members? The gene pool can split. Once a population has thus split into two groups, changes in one of those gene pools cannot spread to the other. Because these two populations no longer interbreed, **reproductive isolation** has occurred. **When populations become reproductively isolated, they can evolve into two separate species. Reproductive isolation can develop in a variety of ways, including behavioral isolation, geographic isolation, and temporal isolation.**

MYSTERY CLUE

A population of viruses inside a host's body is isolated from other viral populations. How might this isolation affect viral evolution?

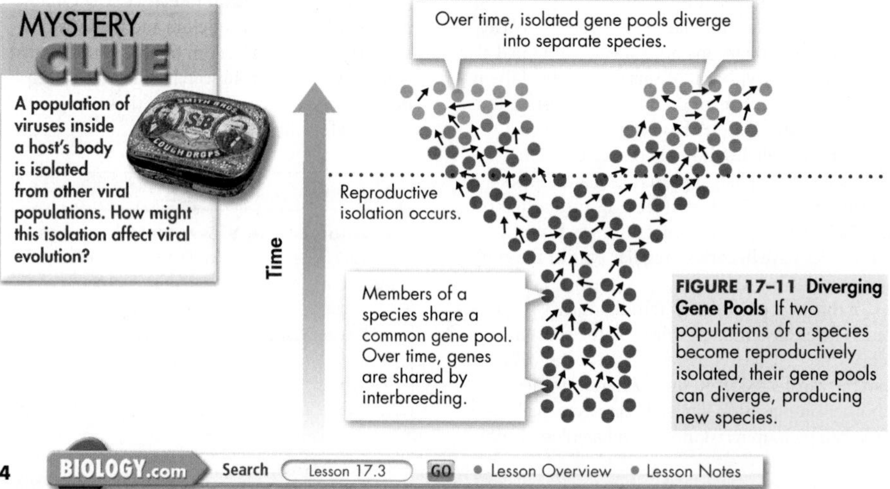
Over time, isolated gene pools diverge into separate species.
Reproductive isolation occurs.
Time
Members of a species share a common gene pool. Over time, genes are shared by interbreeding.

FIGURE 17–11 Diverging Gene Pools If two populations of a species become reproductively isolated, their gene pools can diverge, producing new species.

UbD Teach for Understanding

ENDURING UNDERSTANDING The diversity of life is the result of ongoing evolutionary change. Species alive today have evolved from ancient common ancestors.

GUIDING QUESTION How do new species form?

EVIDENCE OF UNDERSTANDING *After completing the lesson, give students the following assessment to evaluate whether they understand how new species form from an ancestor species.* Have students write on separate note cards a brief summary of each step in the speciation of Darwin's finches. Then have them shuffle the cards and try to put them back in the correct order.

Behavioral Isolation Suppose two populations that are capable of interbreeding develop differences in courtship rituals or other behaviors. **Behavioral isolation** can then occur. For example, eastern and western meadowlarks are similar birds whose habitats overlap. But, members of the two species will not mate with each other, partly because they use different songs to attract mates. Eastern meadowlarks don't respond to western meadowlark songs, and vice versa.

Geographic Isolation When two populations are separated by geographic barriers such as rivers, mountains, or bodies of water, **geographic isolation** occurs. The Abert's squirrel in **Figure 17–12,** for example, lives in the Southwest. About 10,000 years ago, a small population became isolated on the north rim of the Grand Canyon. Separate gene pools formed. Genetic changes that appeared in one group were not passed to the other. Natural selection and genetic drift worked separately on each group and led to the formation of a distinct subspecies, the Kaibab squirrel. The Abert's and Kaibab squirrels are very similar, indicating that they are closely related. However, the Kaibab squirrel differs from the Abert's squirrel in significant ways, such as fur coloring.

Geographic barriers do not always guarantee isolation. Floods, for example, may link separate lakes, enabling their fish populations to mix. If those populations still interbreed, they remain a single species. Also, a geographic barrier may separate certain organisms but not others. A large river may keep squirrels and other small rodents apart but probably won't isolate bird populations.

FIGURE 17–12 Geographic Isolation Abert's squirrel and the Kaibab squirrel are distinct subspecies within the same species. Their gene pools are separate. **Interpret Visuals** ***What geographic barrier separates the two populations of squirrels?***

Temporal Isolation A third isolating mechanism, known as **temporal isolation,** happens when two or more species reproduce at different times. For example, suppose three similar species of orchids live in the same rain forest. Each species has flowers that last only one day and must be pollinated on that day to produce seeds. Because the species bloom on different days, they cannot pollinate one another.

In Your Notebook *Explain how temporal isolation can lead to speciation.*

Biology In-Depth

POSTMATING ISOLATING MECHANISMS

The three types of reproductive isolating mechanisms described on this page prevent mating between organisms of different species. They are referred to generally as premating mechanisms. Other isolating mechanisms, called postmating mechanisms, occur at some point after mating occurs. For example, male gametes may be unable to reach female gametes because of differences in the anatomy of the reproductive organs. If male gametes do reach female gametes, they may be unable to fertilize them due to genetic differences in the gametes. If fertilization takes place and offspring are produced, the offspring may not survive, may be unable to reproduce, or may produce offspring of their own that are nonviable or infertile.

Teach

Lead a Discussion

Challenge students to infer the reproductive characteristics of species that are isolated by different mechanisms.

Ask What can you infer about species that are isolated by behavioral isolation? *(They are likely to have complex mating behaviors, such as courtship rituals.)*

Ask What can you infer about species that are isolated by temporal isolation? *(Their reproductive behavior is likely to be limited to certain times of day or days of the year.)*

DIFFERENTIATED INSTRUCTION

LPR Less Proficient Readers Suggest students make a **Concept Map** to show the types of isolating mechanisms that lead to speciation.

Study Wkbks A/B, Appendix S21, Concept Map. **Transparencies,** GO4.

ELL Focus on ELL: Build Background

BEGINNING SPEAKERS Help students understand that visuals often provide clues to the meaning of text. Call students' attention to the photos in **Figure 17–12.** Have an English-proficient student who speaks the beginners' native language ask the beginners what the photographs show. *(two different kinds of squirrels separated by the Grand Canyon)* Ask the English-proficient student to explain the concept of geographic isolation to the beginning students, and to relate the concept to the map and the photos.

Then point with your finger to the title of the figure, **Geographic Isolation.** With gestures, help students see that the title of the figure is the same as the blue heading and also the same as a yellow-highlighted vocabulary term. Help students understand that **Figure 17–12** is a visual representation of the text explanation of geographic isolation. Later in the lesson, when you discuss the process of speciation, reinforce the idea that visuals usually help clarify concepts explained in the written text.

Answers

FIGURE 17–12 the Grand Canyon

IN YOUR NOTEBOOK When organisms reproduce at different times, they cannot interbreed. For example, when flowers bloom at different times, they cannot pollinate one another.

LESSON 17.3

Teach continued

Lead a Discussion

Discuss the role of the founder effect and natural selection in the speciation of Darwin's finches.

Ask How might the founder effect have contributed to genetic variation in finch populations on different islands? *(Only a few finches are likely to have crossed to other islands from the first island the finches inhabited. Their allele frequencies could have differed, by chance, from those of finches on the first island.)*

Ask Why did selection increase genetic variation among finches on the different islands? *(Different traits were selected for, because the islands had different environments.)*

Ask How did selection lead to speciation? *(Selection led to different beak sizes, and differences in beak size prevented finches from mating. Therefore, the populations were reproductively isolated. Once populations have become reproductively isolated, they are separate species.)*

DIFFERENTIATED INSTRUCTION

LPR Less Proficient Readers Have students make a **Flowchart** showing how the process of speciation occurred in Darwin's finches.

Study Wkbks A/B, Appendix S25, Flowchart. **Transparencies,** GO8.

L3 Advanced Students The Chapter 16 Mystery described a similar process of speciation that occurred on the Hawaiian Islands several million years ago in birds called honeycreepers. Ask interested students to learn about speciation in Hawaiian honeycreepers and then use maps of the islands to explain to the class what happened. Have them point out similarities and differences between speciation in the honeycreepers and Darwin's finches.

BIOLOGY.com Have students use **Data Analysis: Galápagos Finches: Evolution in Action** to explore the data from the Grants' study of Darwin's finches. Then, have students use **Tutor Tube: Organizing the Vocabulary of Speciation** to help them organize what they have learned about the mechanisms of speciation.

Speciation in Darwin's Finches

What is a current hypothesis about Galápagos finch speciation?

Recall that Peter and Rosemary Grant spent years on the Galápagos islands studying changes in finch populations. The Grants measured and recorded anatomical characteristics such as beak length of individual medium ground finches. Many of the characteristics appeared in bell-shaped distributions typical of polygenic traits. As environmental conditions changed, the Grants documented directional selection among the traits. When drought struck the island of Daphne Major, finches with larger beaks capable of cracking the thickest seeds survived and reproduced more often than others. Over many generations, the proportion of large-beaked finches increased.

We can now combine these studies by the Grants with evolutionary concepts to form a hypothesis that answers a question: How might the founder effect and natural selection have produced reproductive isolation that could have led to speciation among Galápagos finches? **According to this hypothesis, speciation in Galápagos finches occurred by founding of a new population, geographic isolation, changes in the new population's gene pool, behavioral isolation, and ecological competition.**

FIGURE 17–13

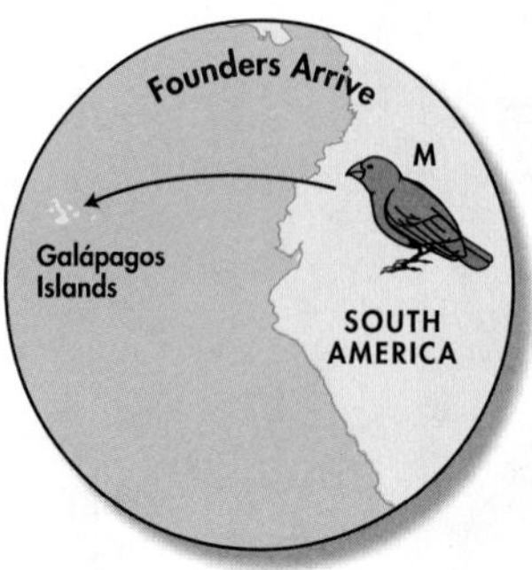

Founders Arrive Many years ago, a few finches from South America—species M—arrived on one of the Galápagos islands, as shown in **Figure 17–13.** These birds may have gotten lost or been blown off course by a storm. Once on the island, they survived and reproduced. Because of the founder effect, allele frequencies of this founding finch population could have differed from allele frequencies in the original South American population.

FIGURE 17–14

Geographic Isolation The island's environment was different from the South American environment. Some combination of the founder effect, geographic isolation, and natural selection enabled the island finch population to evolve into a new species—species A. Later, a few birds from species A crossed to another island. Because these birds do not usually fly over open water, they move from island to island very rarely. Thus, finch populations on the two islands were geographically isolated from each other and no longer shared a common gene pool.

FIGURE 17–15

Changes in Gene Pools Over time, populations on each island adapted to local environments. Plants on the first island may have produced small, thin-shelled seeds, whereas plants on the second island may have produced larger, thick-shelled seeds. On the second island, directional selection would have favored individuals with larger, heavier beaks. These birds could crack open and eat the large seeds more easily. Thus, birds with large beaks would be better able to survive on the second island. Over time, natural selection would have caused that population to evolve larger beaks, forming a distinct population, B, characterized by a new phenotype.

UbD Check for Understanding

ORAL QUESTIONING

Ask students to respond to the following question on a piece of paper: In the speciation in Darwin's finches, why did geographic isolation have to occur before changes happened in the two gene pools? *(If geographic isolation hadn't happened first, there would not have been two distinct populations with separated gene pools.)*

ADJUST INSTRUCTION

If students do not understand the sequence, refer them to **Figure 17–11.** Use this diagram to show how two distinct gene pools develop after populations become isolated from one another.

Behavioral Isolation Now, imagine that a few birds from the second island cross back to the first island. Will population-A birds breed with population-B birds? Probably not. These finches choose mates carefully. During courtship, they closely inspect a potential partner's beak. Finches prefer to mate with birds that have the same-size beak as they do. Big-beaked birds prefer to mate with other big-beaked birds, and smaller-beaked birds prefer to mate with other smaller-beaked birds. Because the populations on the two islands have evolved differently sized beaks, they would probably not mate with each other.

Thus, differences in beak size, combined with mating behavior, could lead to reproductive isolation. The gene pools of the two bird populations remain isolated—even when individuals live in the same place. The populations have now become two distinct species.

FIGURE 17–16

Competition and Continued Evolution As these two new species live together on the first island, they compete for seeds. During the dry season, birds that are most different from each other have the highest fitness. That is because the more specialized birds have less competition for certain kinds of seeds and other foods. Over time, species evolve in a way that increases the differences between them. The species-B birds on the first island may evolve into a new species, C.

The combined processes of geographic isolation on different islands, genetic change, and behavioral isolation could have repeated itself again and again across the Galápagos chain. Over many generations, the process could have produced the 13 different finch species found there today.

FIGURE 17–17

In Your Notebook *Explain how natural selection and behavioral isolation may have lead to reproductive isolation in Darwin's finches.*

17.3 Assessment

IN B.8.5

Review Key Concepts

1. a. Review What is geographic isolation?

b. Predict A newly formed lake divides a population of a beetle species into two groups. What other factors besides isolation might lead to the two groups becoming separate species?

2. a. Review What types of reproductive isolation may have been important in Galápagos finch speciation? Explain.

b. Apply Concepts Explain how the vegetarian tree finch, which feeds on fruit, might have evolved.

BUILD VOCABULARY

3. *Temporal* comes from the Latin word *tempus*, meaning "time." How is time a factor in temporal isolation?

4. *Isolation* is related to the Latin word *insula*, meaning "island." After reading about isolating mechanisms in this lesson, does the common origin of these two words make sense? Explain your answer.

BIOLOGY.com Search Lesson 17.3  GO  • Data Analysis • Self-Test • Lesson Assessment

Assess and Remediate

EVALUATE UNDERSTANDING

Give students a copy of **Figure 17–11** without the labels or caption. Ask them to add labels and text to the figure so that it explains how speciation occurs. Then, have students complete the 17.3 Assessment.

REMEDIATION SUGGESTION

L1 **Struggling Students** If students have difficulty answering **Question 1b,** ask them to list the factors that led to speciation in Darwin's finches. *(founder effect, differences in environment that caused differences in selection)* Then, have them consider whether these factors might apply to the situation described in the question.

BIOLOGY.com Students can check their understanding of lesson concepts with the **Self-Test** assessment. They can then take an online version of the **Lesson Assessment.**

Answers

IN YOUR NOTEBOOK Populations on different islands evolved differently sized beaks. Because finches prefer to mate with birds that have similarly sized beaks, this results in differences in mating behavior. Over time, this leads to reproductive isolation because the populations stay distinct even though they live in the same place.

Assessment Answers

1a. Geographic isolation is the situation in which two populations cannot interbreed because they are separated by geographic barriers, such as rivers.

1b. Sample answer: the founder effect and varied selection pressures in different environments

2a. Geographic isolation may have been important initially as populations of finches became separated on different islands, because they would no longer share a common gene pool. Later, if different species lived in the same place, behavioral isolation may have been important. The birds now had different-sized beaks and would not mate with each other, so their gene pools remained isolated.

2b. Finches that ate seeds or insects may have arrived on an island where fruit was available. Birds with beak variations that made them better-suited for eating fruit would have been favored by selection. Eventually, selection might have led to the evolution of a new species of fruit-eating finches.

BUILD VOCABULARY

3. Temporal isolation occurs when two or more species reproduce at different times, such as different times of day or days of the year.

4. Yes, because organisms on an island are geographically isolated from organisms that do not live on the same island.

LESSON 17.4

Getting Started

Objectives

17.4.1 Explain how molecular clocks are used.

17.4.2 Explain how new genes evolve.

17.4.3 Describe how Hox genes may be involved in evolutionary change.

Student Resources

Study Workbooks A and B, 17.4 Worksheets

Spanish Study Workbook, 17.4 Worksheets

Lesson Overview • Lesson Notes • Assessment: Self-Test, Lesson Assessment

For corresponding lesson in the **Foundation Edition,** see pages 417–419.

Build Background

On the board, draw a short section of DNA. Call on a student to sketch the same section of DNA on the board with a single point mutation. Call on another student to sketch the section of DNA with an additional point mutation. Tell students they will learn how DNA mutations like these reveal how species are related.

Answers

IN YOUR NOTEBOOK A neutral mutation is more likely to persist in a population than a negative one, because a negative mutation is likely to be eliminated by natural selection.

IN INDIANA ACADEMIC STANDARDS

For the full text of all standards, see the Course Overview in the front matter of this book.

B.7.5 Explain and demonstrate how inserting, substituting or deleting segments of a DNA molecule can alter a gene, which is then passed to every cell that develops from it and that the results may be beneficial, harmful or have little or no effect on the organism.

B.8.3 Use anatomical and molecular evidence to establish evolutionary relationships between organisms.

B.8.4 Understand that molecular evidence supports the anatomical evidence for these evolutionary relationships and provides additional information about the order in which different lines of descent branched.

17.4 Molecular Evolution

IN B.7.5 Gene alteration; **B.8.3** Evolutionary relationships; **B.8.4** Evidence of evolutionary relationships. Also covered: **NoS.3, B.6.5, B.8.6.**

Key Questions

What are molecular clocks?

Where do new genes come from?

How may Hox genes be involved in evolutionary change?

Vocabulary
molecular clock

Taking Notes
Outline As you read, make an outline of this lesson. Use the green headings as the main topics and the blue headings as the subtopics.

BUILD Vocabulary
ACADEMIC WORDS The word **sequence** means "the order in which parts are put together." The sequence of DNA is the order in which its molecules are arranged.

THINK ABOUT IT Recall that an organism's genome is its complete set of genetic information. Thousands of ongoing projects are analyzing the genomes of organisms ranging from viruses to humans. The analysis of genomes enables us to study evolution at the molecular level. By comparing DNA sequences from all of these organisms, we can often solve important evolutionary puzzles. For example, DNA evidence may indicate how two species are related to one another, even if their body structures don't offer enough clues.

Timing Lineage Splits: Molecular Clocks

What are molecular clocks?

When researchers use a **molecular clock,** they compare stretches of DNA to mark the passage of evolutionary time. **A molecular clock uses mutation rates in DNA to estimate the time that two species have been evolving independently.**

Neutral Mutations as "Ticks" To understand molecular clocks, think about old-fashioned pendulum clocks. They mark time with a swinging pendulum. A molecular clock also relies on a repeating process to mark time—mutation. As you've learned, simple mutations occur all the time, causing slight changes in the sequence of DNA. Some mutations have a major positive or negative effect on an organism's phenotype. These types of mutations are under powerful pressure from natural selection.

Many mutations, however, have no effect on phenotype. These neutral mutations tend to accumulate in the DNA of different species at about the same rate. Researchers can compare such DNA sequences in two species. The comparison can reveal how many mutations have occurred independently in each group, as shown in **Figure 17–18.** The more differences there are between the DNA sequences of the two species, the more time has elapsed since the two species shared a common ancestor.

In Your Notebook *Which kind of mutation—neutral or negative—will most likely persist in a population over time? Explain.*

UbD Teach for Understanding

ENDURING UNDERSTANDING The diversity of life is the result of ongoing evolutionary change. Species alive today have evolved from ancient common ancestors.

GUIDING QUESTION What can genes tell us about an organism's evolutionary history?

EVIDENCE OF UNDERSTANDING *After completing the lesson, give students the following assessment to show they understand how living things change over time through the accumulation of changes in DNA.* Ask each student to create a simple evolutionary tree, like the one in **Figure 17–18,** showing short DNA sequences for three related species. Have them copy each DNA sequence on a different note card, shuffle the cards, and exchange cards with a partner. Then ask students to try to arrange their partner's cards to reconstruct the evolutionary tree.

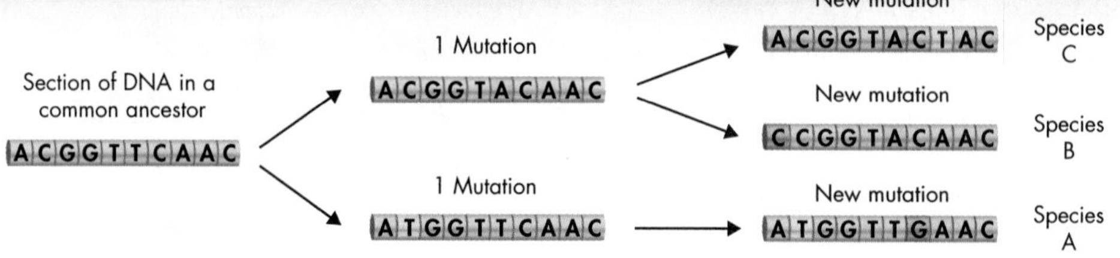

FIGURE 17–18 Molecular Clock
By comparing the DNA sequences of two or more species, biologists estimate how long the species have been separated. **Analyze Data** ***What evidence indicates that species C is more closely related to species B than to species A?***

Calibrating the Clock The use of molecular clocks is not simple, because there is not just one molecular clock in a genome. There are many different clocks, each of which "ticks" at a different rate. This is because some genes accumulate mutations faster than others. These different clocks allow researchers to time different evolutionary events. Think of a conventional clock. If you want to time a brief event, you use the second hand. To time an event that lasts longer, you use the minute hand or the hour hand. In the same way, researchers choose a different molecular clock to compare great apes than to estimate when mammals and fishes shared a common ancestor.

Researchers check the accuracy of molecular clocks by trying to estimate how often mutations occur. In other words, they estimate how often the clock they have chosen "ticks." To do this, they compare the number of mutations in a particular gene in species whose age has been determined by other methods.

Gene Duplication

Where do new genes come from?

Where did the roughly 25,000 working genes in the human genome come from? Modern genes probably descended from a much smaller number of genes in the earliest life forms. But how could that have happened? **One way in which new genes evolve is through the duplication, and then modification, of existing genes.**

Copying Genes Most organisms carry several copies of various genes. Sometimes organisms carry two copies of the same gene. Other times there may be thousands of copies. Where do those extra copies come from, and what happens to them?

Remember that homologous chromosomes exchange DNA during meiosis in a process called crossing-over. Sometimes crossing-over involves an unequal swapping of DNA. In other words, one chromosome in the pair gets extra DNA. That extra DNA can carry part of a gene, a full gene, or a longer length of chromosome. Sometimes, in different ways, an entire genome can be duplicated.

Biology In-Depth

MOLECULAR CLOCKS AND VIRAL EVOLUTION

Molecular clocks are particularly useful for studying viruses. After all, viruses do not leave fossils, so there is no tangible record of their appearance. Discovering when particular strains of viruses evolved may help explain the origins of important human diseases. Until recently, for example, some researchers speculated that human immunodeficiency virus (HIV) evolved from simian deficiency virus (SIV), when primate tissues contaminated with SIV were used in the manufacture of the oral polio vaccine. If this were true, HIV in humans would have originated in the 1950s, when the vaccine was administered. However, molecular clock data suggest that HIV probably diverged from SIV around 1800 and emerged in humans around 1930. Although the molecular data do not show how HIV evolved, they indicate that the production of the polio vaccine was not the origin.

Teach

Lead a Discussion

Use **Figure 17–8** to discuss molecular clocks.

Ask Why are neutral mutations, and not negative or positive mutations, used in molecular clocks? *(Neutral mutations, unlike positive and negative mutations, are not under pressure from natural selection. Therefore, changes among the genes in which these mutations are found will accumulate at a fairly steady rate.)*

DIFFERENTIATED INSTRUCTION

L1 **Struggling Students** Pair struggling students to carry out a **Think-Pair-Share** activity. Ask students to think about why negative and positive mutations do not tend to accumulate at a constant rate in organisms. Have them confer with their partner and present their ideas to the class.

Study Wkbks A/B, Appendix S14, Think-Pair-Share.

ELL Focus on ELL: Extend Language

INTERMEDIATE SPEAKERS Explain that some words have different meanings depending on context. Point out that in everyday usage, a clock is a device for keeping track of time in hours, minutes, and seconds. However, a molecular clock keeps track of the time in which two species have been evolving independently, and the time is measured in millions of years. Point out that the word *molecular* indicates that this type of clock depends on differences between molecules of DNA.

Use this example as a springboard for discussing multiple-meaning words in general. In the first paragraph on this page, for example, *tick* indicates the sound that a clock makes. *Tick* can also indicate a tiny animal with eight legs that is related to a spider. Encourage students to share words in their native languages that have more than one meaning.

Answers

FIGURE 17–18 Species B and C differ from one another by just two mutations, and they both differ from species A by four mutations.

Teach continued

Build Study Skills

Tell students that, if they can't explain a topic and make it understandable to another person, they probably do not understand it themselves. Therefore, a useful study skill is to try to explain to someone else what they have read. Give students a chance to practice this skill. Divide the class into pairs, and have partners take turns explaining to one another how duplicate genes evolve. Any students who are unable to provide clear explanations should reread the passage for greater understanding.

DIFFERENTIATED INSTRUCTION

L3 Advanced Students Pair advanced students with struggling students. Have the advanced students work with the struggling students to help the latter understand how genes become duplicated and then evolve into genes with new functions. Advanced students should use **Figure 17–19** as well as the text explanation. Also encourage them to use the analogy (an essay that is reconfigured for a different purpose) to clarify the process of gene evolution.

IN NoS.3, B.8.3, B.8.4

Fishes in Two Lakes

A research team studied two lakes in an area that sometimes experiences flooding. Each lake contained two types of similar fishes: a dull brown form and an iridescent gold form. The team wondered how all the fishes were related, and they considered the two hypotheses diagrammed on the right.

Hypothesis A

Lake 1: A → B, A → G

Lake 2: A → B, A → G

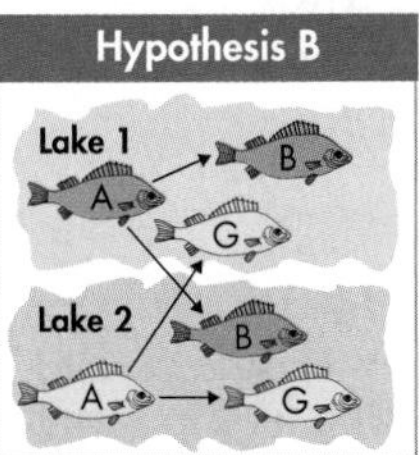

A = Possible ancestor
B = Contemporary brown form
G = Contemporary gold form
→ Shows possible line of descent

1. Interpret Visuals Study the two diagrams. What does hypothesis A indicate about the ancestry of the fishes in Lake 1 and Lake 2? What does hypothesis B indicate?

2. Compare and Contrast According to the two hypotheses, what is the key difference in the way the brown and gold fish populations might have formed?

3. Draw Conclusions A DNA analysis showed that the brown and gold fishes from Lake 1 are the most closely related. Which hypothesis does this evidence support?

Original gene

Duplication in ancestor

Mutation in one copy

New gene evolves new function.

Original gene keeps original function.

FIGURE 17–19 Gene Duplication In this diagram, a gene is first duplicated, and then one of the two resulting genes undergoes mutation.

Duplicate Genes Evolve What's so important about gene duplication? Think about using a computer to write an essay for English class. You then want to submit a new version of the essay to your school newspaper. So, you make an extra copy of the original file and edit it for the newspaper.

Duplicate genes can work in similar ways. Sometimes, extra copies of a gene undergo mutations that change their function. The original gene is still around, just like the original copy of your English essay. So, the new genes can evolve without affecting the original gene function or product. **Figure 17–19** shows how this happens.

Gene Families Multiple copies of a duplicated gene can turn into a group of related genes called a gene family. Members of a gene family typically produce similar, yet slightly different, proteins. Your body, for example, produces a number of molecules that carry oxygen. Several of these compounds—called globins—are hemoglobins. The globin gene family that produces them evolved, after gene duplication, from a single ancestral globin gene. Some of the most important evolution research focuses on another gene family—Hox genes.

Developmental Genes and Body Plans

How may Hox genes be involved in evolutionary change?

One exciting new research area is nicknamed "evo-devo" because it studies the relationship between evolution and embryological development. Darwin himself had a hunch that changes in the growth of embryos could transform adult body shape and size. Researchers now study how small changes in Hox gene activity could produce the kinds of evolutionary changes we see in the fossil record.

Analyzing Data

PURPOSE Students will draw conclusions from DNA about evolutionary relationships among fish species.

PLANNING Tell students to study the diagrams of hypotheses A and B carefully, paying close attention to the arrows and the colors of the fishes. Also have them look at the key below the diagram.

ANSWERS

1. Hypothesis A indicates that fishes B and G evolved twice from the same ancestor, once in Lake 1 and once in Lake 2. Hypothesis B indicates that fish B evolved from a brown ancestor in Lake 1 and fish G from a gold ancestor in Lake 2.
2. In hypothesis A, brown (B) and gold (G) fish populations each evolved independently. In hypothesis B, the brown (B) fish populations in both lakes evolved from fish type A in Lake 1, and the gold (G) fish populations in both lakes evolved from Fish type A in Lake 2.
3. This evidence supports hypothesis A in which the brown and gold fish share a recent common ancestor.

Hox Genes and Evolution As you read in Chapter 13, Hox genes determine which parts of an embryo develop arms, legs, or wings. Groups of Hox genes also control the size and shape of those structures. In fact, homologous Hox genes shape the bodies of animals as different as insects and humans—even though those animals last shared a common ancestor no fewer than 500 million years ago!

Small changes in Hox gene activity during embryological development can produce large changes in adult animals. For example, insects and crustaceans are related to ancient common ancestors that possessed dozens of legs. Today's crustaceans, including shrimp and lobsters, still have large numbers of paired legs, but insects have just 3 pairs of legs. What happened to those extra legs? Recent studies have shown that mutations in a single Hox gene, known as *Ubx*, turns off the growth of legs in the abdominal regions of insects. Thus, a change in one Hox gene accounts for a major evolutionary difference between two important animal groups.

Timing Is Everything Each part of an embryo starts to grow at a certain time, grows for a specific time, and stops growing at a specific time. Small changes in starting and stopping times can make a big difference in organisms. For example, small timing changes can make the difference between long, slender fingers and short, stubby toes. No wonder "evo-devo" is one of the hottest areas in evolutionary biology!

FIGURE 17–20 Change in a Hox Gene Insects such as fruit flies and crustaceans such as brine shrimp are descended from a common ancestor that had many legs. Due to mutations in the activity of a single Hox gene that happened millions of years ago, modern insects have fewer legs than do modern crustaceans. In the illustration, the legs of the fruit fly and the legs of the brine shrimp are the same color (red) because a variant of the same Hox gene, *Ubx*, directs the development of the legs of both animals.

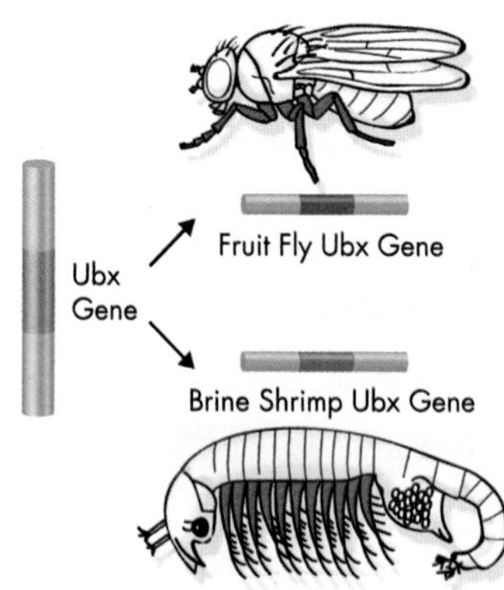

17.4 Assessment

B.7.5, B.8.3, B.8.4

Review Key Concepts

1. a. **Review** What is a molecular clock?
   b. **Explain** Why do molecular clocks use mutations that have no effect on phenotype?
2. a. **Review** How can crossing-over result in gene duplication?
   b. **Explain** Describe how duplicate genes form.
   c. **Relate Cause and Effect** Why is gene duplication important in evolution?
3. a. **Review** Use the evolution of the insect body plan to explain the significance of Hox genes in evolution.
   b. **Infer** In evolution, why have small changes in Hox genes had a great impact?

VISUAL THINKING

4. The colored bands in the diagrams below represent mutations in a segment of DNA in species A, B, and C. Which two of the three species probably share the most recent common ancestor?

Species A	Species B	Species C
C	C	C
T	G	T
A	A	A
A	G	G
C	C	C
G	G	G
T	T	T
T	T	C
G	A	G
C	C	C

BIOLOGY.com Search Lesson 17.4 GO • Self-Test • Lesson Assessment

Assess and Remediate

EVALUATE UNDERSTANDING

Ask students to use the text and **Figure 17–20** to explain why fruit flies and brine shrimp have different numbers of legs. Then, have students complete the 17.4 Assessment.

REMEDIATION SUGGESTION

L1 Struggling Students If students have difficulty answering **Question 4,** suggest they reread the information about molecular clocks and then carefully compare the order of the bases for Species A, B, and C.

BIOLOGY.com Students can check their understanding of lesson concepts with the **Self-Test** assessment. They can then take an online version of the **Lesson Assessment.**

Assessment Answers

1a. a model that uses mutation rates in DNA to estimate the time that two species have been evolving independently

1b. Mutations that have no effect on phenotype accumulate in the DNA of different species at about the same rate. Other mutations are under pressure from natural selection and accumulate at faster or slower rates.

2a. Crossing-over sometimes involves an unequal swapping of DNA. If the extra DNA carries a gene, gene duplication has occurred.

2b. Duplicate genes may form during crossing over, if there is an unequal swapping of DNA.

2c. because new genes can form without affecting the original gene function or product

3a. Insects are descended from an ancestor that had many legs. Because a mutation in a single Hox gene "turns off" the growth of some pairs of legs, modern insects have only three pairs of legs.

3b. because they caused major evolutionary differences between important groups of organisms

VISUAL THINKING

4. Species A and C probably share the most recent common ancestor because they differ by two mutations, whereas Species A and B and Species C and B differ by three mutations.

Pre-Lab

Introduce students to the concepts they will explore in the chapter lab by assigning the Pre-Lab questions.

Lab

Tell students they will perform the chapter lab *Competing For Resources* described in **Lab Manual A.**

L1 **Struggling Students** A simpler version of the chapter lab is provided in **Lab Manual B.**

SAFETY

Students should be careful when using sharp objects and handling seeds. Be aware of any allergies students may have to nuts or seeds.

BIOLOGY.com Look online for **Editable Lab Worksheets.**

For corresponding pre-lab in the **Foundation Edition,** see page 420.

IN INDIANA ACADEMIC STANDARDS

For the full text of all standards, see the Course Overview in the front matter of this book.

Skills Lab

GUIDED INQUIRY

IN B.8.5 Survival and reproduction. Also covered: NoS.1, NoS.6.

Pre-Lab: Competing For Resources

Problem How can competition lead to speciation?

Materials assorted tools, large and small seeds, large and small paper plates, timer or clock with second hand

Lab Manual Chapter 17 Lab

Skills Focus Use Models, Predict, Apply Concepts

Connect to the Big idea Speciation is not easy to see in nature. Usually, new phenotypes take years to emerge or become common enough to be noticed. Also, new phenotypes can be difficult to track in a complex environment. For scientists who want to study speciation, islands can provide an ideal environment.

Peter and Rosemary Grant spent years studying finches on the Galápagos Islands. They measured and recorded the traits and diets of hundreds of birds. During a year with a severe drought, the Grants were able to observe natural selection in action as food became scarce. In this lab you will model variation in bird beaks and diet to demonstrate the impact of competition on survival and speciation.

Background Questions

a. Review What is speciation?

b. Relate Cause and Effect How did geographic isolation lead to speciation among the Galápagos finches?

c. Compare and Contrast How does an adaptation differ from other inherited traits?

Pre-Lab Questions

Preview the procedure in the lab manual.

1. Use Models In this lab, what do the different types of tools represent?

2. Predict Which tools do you think will work best for picking up small seeds? Which will work best for picking up large seeds?

3. Design an Experiment Why will the time you have to collect seeds be limited?

BIOLOGY.com Search Chapter 17 GO

Visit Chapter 17 online to test yourself on chapter content and to find activities to help you learn.

Untamed Science Video Climb the cliffs of Hawaii with the Untamed Science crew to discover how geographic isolation can result in a new species.

Data Analysis Find out what happened to Galápagos finches during a drought by comparing data on finches and their food sources.

Art Review Review your understanding of alleles and allele frequencies in a population.

Art in Motion Watch how different types of selection change the types of individuals that comprise a population.

Tutor Tube Learn more about the mechanisms of speciation from the tutor.

Pre-Lab Answers

BACKGROUND QUESTIONS

a. Speciation is the formation of a new species.

b. Sample answer: Over time, populations of finches on different islands no longer shared the same gene pool.

c. An adaptation is a trait that increases an organism's ability to survive and reproduce in its environment.

PRE-LAB QUESTIONS

1. The tools represent different types of beaks.

2. Answers will vary with the types of tools. Tweezers or small spoons might work well with small seeds. Pliers or ice tongs might work well with large seeds.

3. Sample answer: Limiting the time gives an advantage to those with tools that are better adapted to pick up a certain type of seed.

17 Study Guide

Big idea Evolution

A new species can form when a population splits into two groups that are isolated from one another. The gene pools of the two groups may become so different that the groups can no longer interbreed.

17.1 Genes and Variation

Evolution is a change in the frequency of alleles in a population over time.

Three sources of genetic variation are mutation, genetic recombination during sexual reproduction, and lateral gene transfer.

The number of phenotypes produced for a trait depends on how many genes control the trait.

gene pool (483)
allele frequency (483)
single-gene trait (485)
polygenic trait (486)

17.2 Evolution as Genetic Change in Populations

Natural selection on single-gene traits can lead to changes in allele frequencies and, thus, to changes in phenotype frequencies.

Natural selection on polygenic traits can affect the relative fitness of phenotypes and thereby produce one of three types of selection: directional selection, stabilizing selection, or disruptive selection.

In small populations, individuals that carry a particular allele may leave more descendants than other individuals leave, just by chance. Over time, a series of chance occurrences can cause an allele to become more or less common in a population.

The Hardy-Weinberg principle predicts that five conditions can disturb genetic equilibrium and cause evolution to occur: (1) nonrandom mating; (2) small population size; and (3) immigration or emigration; (4) mutations; or (5) natural selection.

directional selection (489)
stabilizing selection (489)
disruptive selection (489)
genetic drift (490)
bottleneck effect (490)
founder effect (490)
genetic equilibrium (491)
Hardy-Weinberg principle (491)
sexual selection (492)

17.3 The Process of Speciation

When populations become reproductively isolated, they can evolve into two separate species. Reproductive isolation can develop in a variety of ways, including behavioral isolation, geographic isolation, and temporal isolation.

Speciation in Galápagos finches most likely occurred by founding of a new population, geographic isolation, changes in the new population's gene pool, behavioral isolation, and ecological competition.

species (494)
speciation (494)
reproductive isolation (494)
behavioral isolation (495)
geographic isolation (495)
temporal isolation (495)

17.4 Molecular Evolution

A molecular clock uses mutation rates in DNA to estimate the time that two species have been evolving independently.

One way in which new genes evolve is through the duplication, and then modification, of existing genes.

Small changes in Hox gene activity during embryological development can produce large changes in adult animals.

molecular clock (498)

Think Visually

Construct a concept map explaining the sources of genetic variation.

  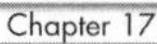   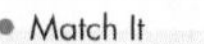

BIOLOGY.com Search Chapter 17 GO • Match It • Chapter Assessment

UbD Performance Tasks

SUMMATIVE TASK Have students work in small groups to create a poster illustrating how a hypothetical species splits to form two new species. Groups should use graphs, matrices, or other visuals to represent genes, genotypes, or phenotypes of the original species and its descendant species. They should also identify factors—for example, mutations, founder effect, geographic isolation, and selection—that are responsible for speciation occurring.

TRANSFER TASK Ask each student to write a short science-fiction story about a population of imaginary organisms on a planet in space. In their story, students should describe how the organisms evolve and come to have different phenotypes after several generations. The story should include details about conditions such as genetic bottlenecks or severe environmental stresses that cause the population to undergo genetic change.

Study Online

REVIEW AND ASSESSMENT RESOURCES

Editable Worksheets Pages of Study Workbooks A and B, Lab Manuals A and B, and the Assessment Resources Book are available online. These documents can be easily edited using a word-processing program.

Lesson Overview Have students reread the Lesson Overviews to help them study chapter concepts.

Vocabulary Review The *Flash Cards* and *Match It* provide an interactive way to review chapter vocabulary.

Chapter Assessment Have students take an online version of the Chapter 17 Assessment.

Standardized Test Prep Students can take an online version of the Standardized Test Prep. You will receive their scores along with ideas for remediation.

Diagnostic and Benchmark Tests Use these tests to monitor your students' progress and supply remediation.

Answers

THINK VISUALLY

Students' concept maps should show that there are three sources of genetic variation: mutation, genetic recombination in sexual reproduction, and lateral gene transfer.

ASSESSMENT

17 Assessment

The numbers following the questions refers to Indiana's Academic Standards for Biology I.

17.1 Genes and Variation

Understand Key Concepts

1. The combined genetic information of all members of a particular population forms a
   a. gene pool.
   b. niche.
   c. phenotype.
   d. population.

2. Mutations that improve an individual's ability to survive and reproduce are B.7.5
   a. harmful.
   b. neutral.
   c. beneficial.
   d. chromosomal.

3. Traits, such as human height, that are controlled by more than one gene are known as B.5.6
   a. single-gene traits.
   b. polygenic traits.
   c. recessive traits.
   d. dominant traits.

4. Explain what the term *allele frequency* means. Include an example illustrating your answer.

5. Explain why sexual reproduction is a source of genetic variation. B.6.5, B.8.6

6. Explain what determines the number of phenotypes for a given trait. B.5.6

7. What is *lateral gene transfer*?

8. Define evolution in genetic terms. B.8.5

Think Critically

9. **Compare and Contrast** Which kind of mutation has the greater potential to affect the evolution of a population: a mutation to a body cell or a mutation in an egg cell? Explain. B.7.5

10. **Apply Concepts** Explain how natural selection is related to phenotypes and genotypes. B.8.5

11. **Apply Concepts** Explain how natural selection is related to individuals and populations. B.8.5

12. **Relate Cause and Effect** How does genetic recombination affect genetic variation? B.6.5, B.8.6

17.2 Evolution as Genetic Change in Populations

Understand Key Concepts

13. The type of selection in which individuals of average size have greater fitness than small or large individuals have is called B.8.5
    a. disruptive selection.
    b. stabilizing selection.
    c. directional selection.
    d. neutral selection.

14. If coat color in a rabbit population is a polygenic trait, which process might have produced the graph below? B.8.4

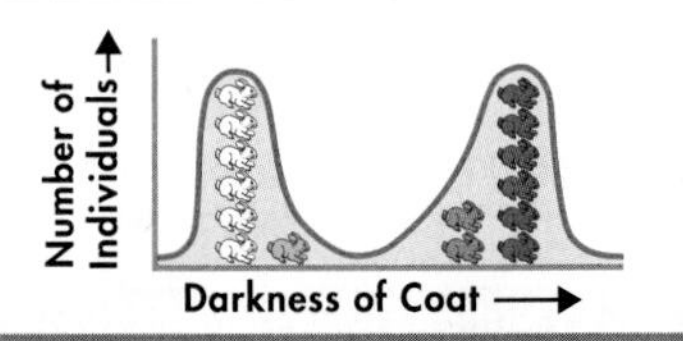

    a. disruptive selection
    b. stabilizing selection
    c. directional selection
    d. genetic equilibrium

15. A random change in a small population's allele frequency is known as
    a. a gene pool
    b. genetic drift
    c. variation
    d. fitness

16. What is *fitness* in genetic terms? B.8.5

17. How do stabilizing selection and disruptive selection differ? B.8.5

18. What is genetic equilibrium? In what kinds of situations is it likely to occur?

Think Critically

19. **Compare and Contrast** Distinguish between the ways in which natural selection affects single-gene traits and the ways in which it affects polygenic traits. How are phenotype frequencies altered in each case? B.8.5

20. **Infer** In a certain population of plants, flower size is a polygenic trait. What kind of selection is likely to occur if environmental conditions favor small flowers? B.8.5

Lesson 17.1

UNDERSTAND KEY CONCEPTS

1. a **2.** c **3.** b

4. Allele frequency is the number of times an allele occurs in a gene pool, compared with the total number of times all alleles for the same gene occur. For example, in a mouse population, the allele frequency of the allele for black fur might be 40 percent, compared with an allele frequency of 60 percent for the allele for brown fur color.

5. Each chromosome in a pair moves independently during meiosis, producing millions of possible gene combinations in gametes. Crossing-over creates an even greater number of possible gene combinations.

6. The number of phenotypes depends on how may genes control the trait. A single-gene trait with two alleles has at most three phenotypes. A polygenic trait can have many phenotypes.

7. the passing of genes from one organism to another organism that is not its offspring

8. any change in the relative frequency of alleles in the gene pool of a population over time

THINK CRITICALLY

9. a mutation in an egg cell, because it may be passed on to offspring and become part of the gene pool

10. Natural selection acts directly on phenotypes, not genotypes. However, phenotypes depend partly on genotypes, so natural selection may affect allele frequencies in gene pools.

11. Natural selection acts directly on individuals, but the resulting changes in allele frequencies show up at the population level. Populations, rather than individuals, evolve.

12. It increases genetic variation.

Lesson 17.2

UNDERSTAND KEY CONCEPTS

13. b **14.** a **15.** b

16. success in passing genes to the next generation

17. Stabilizing selection occurs when individuals near the center of the distribution of phenotypes have higher fitness than individuals at either end. It keeps the center of the distribution in the same place but narrows the overall curve. Disruptive selection occurs when individuals at both ends of the distribution have higher fitness than those near the center. It causes the curve to have a peak at both ends and a low point in the center.

18. Genetic equilibrium is the situation in which allele frequencies in a population remain the same. It occurs when the population is very large, there are no mutations, there is random mating, there is no movement into or out of the population, and there is no natural selection.

THINK CRITICALLY

19. For single-gene traits, natural selection leads to a change in frequency of one or a few distinct phenotypes. For polygenic traits, natural selection leads to changes in the frequency distribution of many, slightly different phenotypes. Natural selection on polygenic traits can lead to directional selection, stabilizing selection, or disruptive selection.

20. directional selection

21. no, because there has not been a change in allele frequencies

22. Only insects that were resistant to DDT survived. The small population of survivors had a high frequency of the allele for resistance. With repeated exposure to DDT, natural selection led to the evolution of insect populations with greater DDT resistance.

21. Infer A road built through a forest splits a population of frogs into two large groups. The allele frequencies of the two groups are identical. Has genetic drift occurred? Why or why not?

22. Form a Hypothesis DDT is an insecticide that was first used in the 1940s to kill mosquitoes and stop the spread of malaria. As time passed, people began to notice that DDT became less effective. Explain, in genetic terms, how the insects became resistant to the pesticide. B.8.5

17.3 The Process of Speciation

Understand Key Concepts

23. Temporal isolation occurs when two different populations
  a. develop different mating behaviors.
  b. become geographically separated.
  c. reproduce at different times.
  d. interbreed.

24. When two populations no longer interbreed, what is the result?
  a. genetic equilibrium
  b. reproductive isolation
  c. stabilizing selection
  d. artificial selection

25. Explain how the different species of Galápagos finches may have evolved. B.8.5

Think Critically

26. Relate Cause and Effect Explain why reproductive isolation usually must occur before a population splits into two distinct species.

27. Form a Hypothesis A botanist identifies two distinct species of violets growing in a field, as shown in the left of the illustration below. Also in the field are several other types of violets that, although somewhat similar to the two known species, appear to be new species. Develop a hypothesis explaining how the new species may have originated. B.8.5

solve the CHAPTER MYSTERY

EPIDEMIC

The genes of flu viruses mutate often, and different strains can swap genes if they infect the same host at the same time. These characteristics produce genetic diversity that enables the virus to evolve.

Flu viruses also undergo natural selection. Think of our bodies as the environment for viruses. Our immune system attacks viruses by "recognizing" proteins on the surface of the viruses. Viruses whose proteins our bodies can recognize and destroy have low fitness. Viruses our bodies can't recognize have higher fitness.

Influenza Virus

Viral evolution regularly produces slightly different surface proteins that our immune systems can't recognize right away. These strains evade the immune system long enough to make people sick. That's why you can catch the flu every winter, and why new flu vaccines must be made every year.

But now and then, influenza evolution produces radically new molecular "disguises" that our immune systems can't recognize *at all*. These can be deadly, like the 1918 strain. If a strain like that were to appear today, it could kill many people. That's why researchers are worried about "bird flu"—a strain of flu that can pass from birds, such as chickens, to humans.

1. Connect to the Big idea Explain why mutation and natural selection make developing new flu vaccines necessary every year.
2. Infer People do not need to receive a new measles vaccination every year. What does this suggest about a difference between flu viruses and the measles virus?
3. Apply Concepts Can you think of any other issues in public health that relate directly to evolutionary change?

IN NoS.10, B.8.5

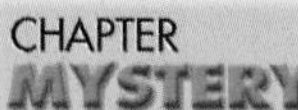

After students have read through the Chapter Mystery, discuss the characteristics of evolution in flu viruses that allow them quickly to evolve new strains that can evade the host's immune system.

Ask Besides a high rate of mutation, what other mechanism increases genetic diversity in viruses? *(Different strains can swap genes if they infect the same host at the same time.)*

Ask What is the major selective pressure in a flu virus's environment? *(the host's immune system)*

Ask How do new surface proteins increase a virus's fitness? *(They allow the virus to multiply repeatedly before being detected by the host's immune system.)*

Ask If a bird flu virus infected a human host, why would it be likely to cause a serious, even fatal, disease? *(The virus would probably have surface proteins the human immune system had never been exposed to and could not detect.)*

CHAPTER MYSTERY ANSWERS

1.  High mutation rates in flu viruses and the strong selective pressure of the human immune system lead to rapid evolution of new surface proteins that the immune system cannot detect. Therefore, with each new flu season, a new vaccine must be developed that can immunize against different surface proteins.
2. This suggests that the measles virus does not have as high a rate of mutation as the flu virus does.
3. Sample answer: Other issues include the problem of bacteria evolving antibiotic resistance and the difficulty of developing a vaccine for HIV because it also evolves quickly.

Students can explore speciation mechanisms at work in Hawaiian snails by watching **Evolution at a Snail's Pace.**

Lesson 17.3

UNDERSTAND KEY CONCEPTS

23. c 24. b

25. Some combination of the founder effect, geographic isolation, and natural selection enabled the finch populations on different Galápagos islands to evolve into new species.

THINK CRITICALLY

26. If populations are not reproductively isolated, genetic changes continue to spread among individuals through interbreeding. Only after reproductive isolation can genetic changes cause a divergence between gene pools and, therefore, speciation.

27. Sample answer: The new species originated from the two known species by becoming reproductively isolated, perhaps by flowering at different times, and then had different mutations and selective pressures.

ASSESSMENT

Lesson 17.4

UNDERSTAND KEY CONCEPTS

28. d **29.** c

30. During meiosis, crossing-over may involve an unequal swapping of DNA so that one chromosome in the pair gets an extra copy of a gene.

31. mutations that have no effect on phenotype

32. The study of "evo-devo" is the study of the relationship between evolution and embryological development. "Evo-devo" researchers study how small changes in Hox genes produce major evolutionary changes.

THINK CRITICALLY

33. Sample answer: Can we identify the specific changes in genes that determine precisely where an organism's eyes, limbs, etc., are located?

34. The more recently two species shared a common ancestor, the more similar their genes are likely to be.

Connecting Concepts

USE SCIENCE GRAPHICS

35. The frequency of Allele *B* steadily decreased over time, while the frequency of Allele *b* steadily increased over time.

36. In their current environment, individuals with allele *b* were more likely to survive and reproduce than individuals with allele *B*.

WRITE ABOUT SCIENCE

37. A mutation may have occurred in one or more Hox genes controlling the development of legs. The mutated gene might "turn off" the growth of some pairs of legs.

38. Big idea Ecology is the scientific study of interactions among organisms and between organisms and their environment. These same interactions also determine the nature of natural selection in populations. For example, predator-prey relationships or availability of food plants may favor certain phenotypes, which are more likely to pass copies of their genes to the next generation. Ecological conditions change through time, leading to changes in selective pressures and the evolution of populations.

17.4 Molecular Evolution

Understand Key Concepts

28. A group of related genes that resulted from the duplication and modification of a single gene is called a B.7.5, B.8.3

a. gene pool. **c.** lateral gene transfer.
b. molecular clock. **d.** gene family.

29. Each "tick" of a molecular clock is an occurrence of B.7.5

a. genetic drift. **c.** DNA mutation.
b. crossing-over. **d.** mitosis.

30. How do chromosomes gain an extra copy of a gene during meiosis? B.6.5

31. What are neutral mutations? B.6.5, B.7.5

32. What is the study of "evo-devo," and how is it related to evolution? B.7.5

Think Critically

33. **Pose Questions** What kinds of questions would scientists who are studying the evolution of Hox genes most likely be asking?

34. **Apply Concepts** Describe the relationship between evolutionary time and the similarity of genes in two species. B.7.5, B.8.4

Connecting Concepts

Use Science Graphics NoS.3

Use the data table to answer questions 35 and 36.

Frequency of Alleles		
Year	Frequency of Allele *B*	Frequency of Allele *b*
1910	0.81	0.19
1930	0.49	0.51
1950	0.25	0.75
1970	0.10	0.90

35. **Interpret Tables** Describe the trend shown by the data in the table.

36. **Form a Hypothesis** What might account for the trend shown by the data? B.8.5

Write About Science NoS.3

37. **Explanation** Explain the process that may have caused fruit flies to have fewer legs than their ancestors had. B.8.5

38. **Assess the Big idea** Sometimes, biologists say, "Evolution is ecology over time." Explain that statement. B.8.5

Analyzing Data

NoS.3

The graph shows data regarding the lengths of the beaks of three finch species. The percentage of individuals in each category of beak length is given.

Beak Length in Three Finch Species

Species A Species B Species C
Birds Observed (%): 0, 10, 20, 30, 40, 50
Beak Length (mm): 6, 8, 10, 12, 14, 16, 18, 20, 22

39. **Interpret Graphs** What is the shortest beak length observed in species A?

a. 3 mm **c.** 9 mm
b. 6 mm **d.** 12 mm

40. **Analyze Data** Which of the following is a logical interpretation of the data?

a. Species B eats the smallest seeds.
b. About 50 percent of species C eats seeds that are 20 mm long.
c. Species C eats the largest seeds.
d. All three species eat seeds of the same size.

PURPOSE Students interpret graphs to draw logical conclusions about data.

PLANNING Make sure students understand that each of the three curves is a frequency distribution of phenotypes for a polygenic trait (beak length). Relate the curves to the frequency distribution in **Figure 17–5.**

ANSWERS

39. b

40. c

Standardized Test Practice for Indiana

Multiple Choice

1. Which of the following conditions is MOST likely to result in changes in allele frequencies in a population?
   A random mating
   B small population size
   C no migrations into or out of a population
   D absence of natural selection NoS.6

2. Mutations and the genetic recombination that occurs during sexual reproduction are both sources of
   A genetic variation.
   B stabilizing selection.
   C genetic equilibrium.
   D genetic drift. B.6.5, B.8.6

3. In a population of lizards, the smallest and largest lizards are more easily preyed upon than medium-size lizards. What kind of natural selection is MOST likely to occur in this situation?
   A genetic drift C stabilizing selection
   B sexual selection D directional selection B.8.5

4. Populations of antibiotic-resistant bacteria are the result of the process of
   A natural selection. C genetic drift.
   B temporal isolation. D artificial selection. B.8.5

5. If species A and B have very similar genes and proteins, what is probably true?
   A Species A and B share a relatively recent common ancestor.
   B Species A evolved independently of species B for a long period.
   C Species A is younger than species B.
   D Species A is older than species B. B.8.4

6. When two species reproduce at different times, the situation is called
   A genetic drift.
   B temporal selection.
   C temporal isolation.
   D lateral gene transfer.

7. The length of time that two taxa have been evolving separately can be estimated using
   A genetic drift. C a molecular clock.
   B gene duplication. D Hox genes. B.7.5

Questions 8–9

The graphs below show the changes in crab color at one beach.

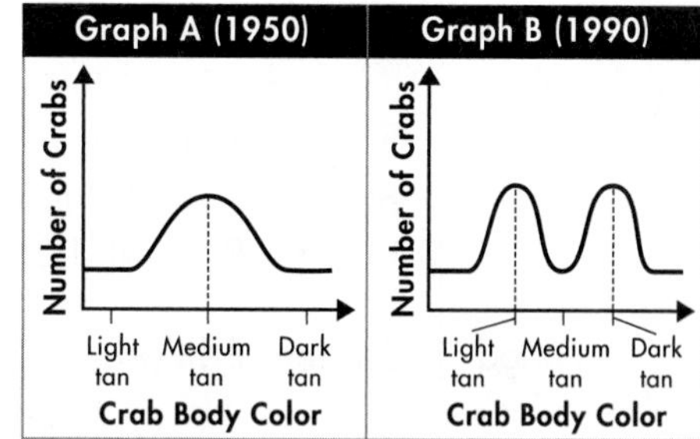

8. What process occurred over the 40-year period?
   A artificial selection C stabilizing selection
   B directional selection D disruptive selection B.8.5

9. Which of the following is MOST likely to have caused the change in the distribution?
   A A new predator arrived that preferred dark-tan crabs.
   B A new predator arrived that preferred light-tan crabs.
   C A change in beach color made medium-tan crabs the least visible to predators.
   D A change in beach color made medium-tan crabs the most visible to predators. B.8.5

Open-Ended Response

10. How does evolution change the relative frequency of alleles in a gene pool? Why does this happen? B.7.5, B.8.5

If You Have Trouble With . . .

Question	1	2	3	4	5	6	7	8	9	10
See Lesson	17.3	17.1	17.2	17.2	17.4	17.3	17.4	17.2	17.2	17.1

Answers

1. B
2. A
3. C
4. A
5. A
6. C
7. C
8. D
9. D
10. Evolution causes some alleles to become more common in a gene pool and other alleles to become less common. This changes the relative frequency of the alleles in the gene pool. This may happen due to natural selection or genetic drift.

Test-Taking Tip

INTERPRET GRAPHS

When answering questions about a graph, students should consider what type of graph it is, because different types of graphs are used for different purposes. For example, a circle graph (pie chart) is used to show the percentages that make up a whole. A bar graph is usually used to show the numbers of people or items in discrete categories. A line graph is used to show how one variable changes relative to another.

Help students understand how to interpret the graph on this page. For example, discuss what the arrows on the axes mean. Some students may be confused by the fact that there are no numbers on either axis. Point out that in some graphs, such as this one, the important point is the overall trend shown, not absolute quantities.

Classification

Chapter Contents	IN	Time	Core Resources
Chapter Preview			**Student Edition,** pp. 508–509 **Chapter Mystery,** p. 509
18.1 Finding Order in Diversity Why Classify? • Assigning Scientific Names • Linnaean Classification System	NoS.9, B.8.2	1 period 1/2 block	**Student Edition,** pp. 510–515 Inquiry 18.1 Quick Lab, p. 512 L2 **Study Workbook A** 18.1 Worksheets L2 **Biology.com** *Art in Motion:* Using a Dichotomous Key • 18.1 Self-Test • 18.1 Lesson Assessment
18.2 Modern Evolutionary Classification Evolutionary Classification • Cladograms • DNA in Classification	NoS.9, NoS.6, B.8.2, B.8.3, B.8.4	1 period 1/2 block	**Student Edition,** pp. 516–522 Inquiry 18.2 Quick Lab, p. 520 L2 **Study Workbook A** 18.2 Worksheets L2 **Biology.com** *InterActive Art:* Cladograms • *Data Analysis:* A Friend for Lonesome George **Assessment Resources Book** Visual Quiz L2
18.3 Building the Tree of Life Changing Ideas About Kingdoms • The Tree of All Life • *Technology & Biology: Bar-Coding Life*	NoS.3, NoS.6, NoS.9, B.8.2, B.8.3, B.8.4	1 period 1/2 block	**Student Edition,** pp. 523–529 Inquiry 18.3 Analyzing Data, p. 524 L2 **Study Workbook A** 18.3 Worksheets L2 **Biology.com** *Art Review:* Three Domains • *Data Analysis:* Bar-Coding Life • 18.3 Self-Test • 18.3 Lesson Assessment
Chapter Pre-Lab	NoS.6	1 period 1/2 block	**Student Edition,** p. 530 L2 **Lab Manual A** *Dichotomous Keys* L2

Differentiated Instruction Tools

Study Workbook B includes worksheets with lesson-level differentiated instruction support and explanations of differentiated instruction teaching strategies.

Lab Manual B includes skills labs, simplified chapter labs, and hands-on activities.

ELL Handbook explains ways to make *Biology* more accessible to ELL students.

Spanish Study Workbook is a Spanish translation of Study Workbook A.

Multilingual Glossary is the glossary translated into ten languages.

Differentiated Instruction Key

- L1 Special Needs or Struggling Students
- ELL English Language Learners
- LPR Less Proficient Readers
- L2 On-Level Students
- L3 Advanced Students

Additional Resources

Biology.com Untamed Science Video • Vocabulary Flash Cards

Study Workbook B 18.1 Worksheets L1 ELL LPR
Spanish Study Workbook 18.1 Worksheets ELL
Biology.com 18.1 Lesson Overview • 18.1 Lesson Notes

Study Workbook B 18.2 Worksheets L1 ELL LPR
Spanish Study Workbook 18.2 Worksheets ELL
Biology.com 18.2 Lesson Overview • 18.2 Lesson Notes • 18.2 Self-Test • 18.2 Lesson Assessment

Study Workbook B 18.3 Worksheets L1 ELL LPR
Spanish Study Workbook 18.3 Worksheets ELL
Biology.com 18.3 Lesson Overview • 18.3 Lesson Notes

Lab Manual B *Dichotomous Keys* • Hands-On Activity: *Classifying Cerealites* • Data Analysis: *Comparing the Domains* L1 ELL LPR

Chapter Review

Student Edition Study Guide, p. 531 L2
Study Workbook A Chapter 18 Vocabulary Review L2 • Chapter 18 Chapter Mystery/21st Century Skills Activity L2 L3
Transparencies, pp. 215–225 L1 ELL LPR L2
Biology.com Untamed Science Video • Editable Worksheets of Study Workbooks A and B and Lab Manuals A and B • Chapter 18 Flash Cards and Crossword Puzzle

Untamed Science DVD • Classroom Resources CD (includes lesson presentations and editable worksheets)

Chapter Assessment

Student Edition Assessment, pp. 532–535 L2
Study Workbook B Chapter 18 Chapter Review L1 ELL LPR • Chapter 18 Taking a Standardized Test L1 ELL LPR
Assessment Resources Book Chapter 18 Test A L2 • Chapter 18 Test B L1 ELL LPR
Biology.com Chapter 18 Assessment • Editable Worksheets of Chapter 18 Visual Quiz and Chapter 18 Tests A and B

Exam*View* *Assessment Suite* • Classroom Resources CD (includes lesson presentations and editable worksheets)

Time: 1 period, 1/2 block

Pressed for Time?

Preview the Chapter Preview Figures 18–4 and 18–9.

Cover the Chapter Quickly Have students read *Assigning Scientific Names* and *Linnaean Classification System* in Lesson 18.1. Assign *Evolutionary Classification* and *Cladograms* in Lesson 18.2, and go over Figure 18–7. Have students read *Changing Ideas About Kingdoms* in Lesson 18.3 and discuss Figure 18–14.

Assess Assign questions 2–4 in the 18.1 Assessment, questions 1, 2, and 4 in the 18.2 Assessment, and question 1 in the 18.3 Assessment. In the Chapter 18 Assessment, assign questions 2–6, 8, 9, 12, 13–16, 22–25, 29, and 33.

CHAPTER 18

Connect to the Big Idea

Big idea Have students look at the photograph of the collection of bird species at the National Museum of Natural History. Ask them how they think this collection might be used by biologists. *(Sample answer: Biologists could study each sample to identify physical characteristics of each type of bird. The samples could also be used to classify birds into species and other related groups.)* Then, have students brainstorm a list of characteristics that biologists could use to classify birds into groups. *(Sample answer: color, beak shape, wing shape, feet shape, markings, flying ability, swimming ability)* If students haven't already mentioned DNA, ask them how the genetic makeup of birds could be used to classify them into groups. Use their answers to help them anticipate the answer to the question, **What is the goal of biologists who classify living things?**

Have students read through the introduction of the Chapter Mystery and make predictions about whether polar bears and brown bears are members of the same species or not. Use their predictions to help them start connecting the Chapter Mystery to the Big Idea of Unity and Diversity of Life.

BIOLOGY.com Have students preview the chapter vocabulary terms using the **Flash Cards.**

IN INDIANA ACADEMIC STANDARDS

For the full text of all standards, see the Course Overview in the front matter of this book.

Key standards: Chapter 18 covers key ideas from Standard 8: Evolution, including **B.8.2** Classification and **B.8.3** Evolutionary relationships.

18 Classification

Big idea Unity and Diversity of Life

Q: What is the goal of biologists who classify living things?

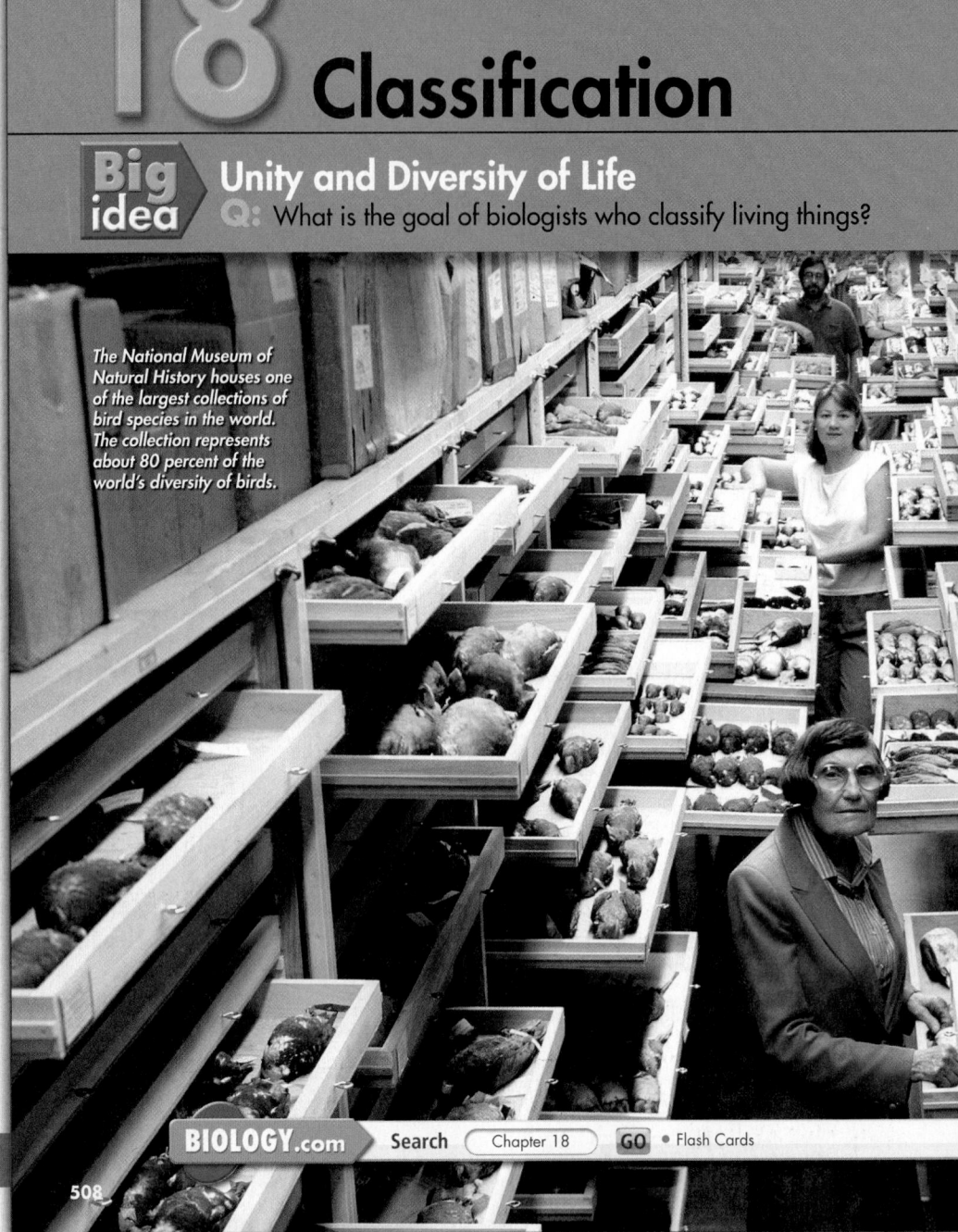

The National Museum of Natural History houses one of the largest collections of bird species in the world. The collection represents about 80 percent of the world's diversity of birds.

BIOLOGY.com Search Chapter 18 GO • Flash Cards

508

UbD Understanding by Design

In Chapter 18, students explore traditional classification, modern evolutionary classification, and the tree of life. As shown in the graphic organizer at the right, the Big Idea, Essential Question, and Guiding Questions help frame their exploration of how chapter content informs the Unit 5 Enduring Understanding that *the diversity of life is the result of ongoing evolutionary change. Species alive today have evolved from ancient common ancestors.*

PERFORMANCE GOALS

In Chapter 18, students will gain understanding of modern evolutionary classification by constructing and interpreting information in cladograms. At the end of the chapter, students will apply their learning to the development of a booklet that classifies organisms in their own neighborhood.

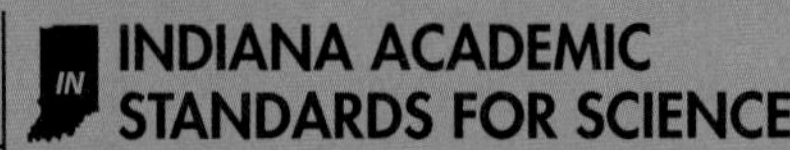

INDIANA ACADEMIC STANDARDS FOR SCIENCE

Nature of Science NoS.3, NoS.6, NoS.9, NoS.10; **Evolution** B.8.2, B.8.3, B.8.4. See lessons for details.

• Untamed Science Video • Chapter Mystery

CHAPTER MYSTERY

GRIN AND BEAR IT

If you simply looked at a polar bear and brown bear, you would probably never doubt that they are members of different species. Polar bears grow much larger than brown bears, and their paws have adapted to swimming long distances and to walking on snow and ice. Their white fur camouflages them, but the coats on brown bears are, well, brown—and their paws aren't adapted to water.

Clearly polar bears and brown bears are very different physically. But do physical characteristics tell the whole story? Remember the definition of *species:* "a group of similar organisms that can breed and produce fertile offspring." Well, polar bears and brown bears can mate and produce fertile offspring. They must be members of the same species, then. But are they? As you read this chapter, look for clues to whether polar bears are a separate species. Then, solve the mystery.

Never Stop Exploring Your World. Solving the mystery of scientific classification is only the beginning. Take a video field trip with the ecogeeks of Untamed Science to see where the mystery leads.

Chapter 18
Big Idea: Unity and Diversity of Life

Chapter 18 EQ: What is the goal of biologists who classify living things?

18.1 GQ: Why do scientists classify organisms?

18.2 GQ: How do evolutionary relationships affect the way scientists classify organisms?

18.3 GQ: What are the major groups within which all organisms are currently classified?

What's Online

BIOLOGY.com Extend your reach by using these and other digital assets offered at Biology.com.

CHAPTER MYSTERY
Students determine whether polar bears and brown bears should be classified in the same species.

UNTAMED SCIENCE VIDEO
Join the crew of Untamed Science as they investigate the classification of a new fish species.

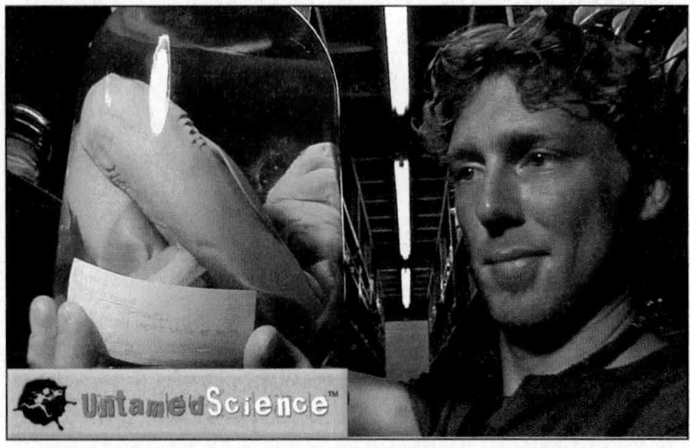

ART IN MOTION
This short animation can help students understand how to use a dichotomous key.

INTERACTIVE ART
Students can practice using cladograms.

ART REVIEW
Use this drag-and-drop activity to help students review the characteristics of the three domains.

DATA ANALYSIS
Students compare geographic relationships to genetic relationships to try to find a mate for Lonesome George, a Galápagos tortoise.

LESSON 18.1

Getting Started

Objectives

18.1.1 Describe the goals of binomial nomenclature and systematics.

18.1.2 Identify the taxa in the classification system devised by Linnaeus.

Student Resources

Study Workbooks A and B, 18.1 Worksheets

Spanish Study Workbook, 18.1 Worksheets

Lab Manual B, 18.1 Hands-On Activity Worksheet

Lesson Overview • Lesson Notes
- Activity: Art in Motion
- Assessment: Self-Test, Lesson Assessment

For corresponding lesson in the **Foundation Edition**, see pages 428–432.

Build Background

Show students a field guide used by bird watchers to identify birds in the wild. Point out that to help the birder in identification, a field guide is organized with similar birds together, with groupings of ducks, hawks, owls, finches, warblers, and so on. Have students look through the field guide, and ask on what basis they think birds have been grouped in the book. *(Sample answer: physical similarities)* Then, point out that the entry for each kind of bird includes a Latinate name in italics. Ask students if they know the significance of this name in italics. *(This is the scientific name for the genus and species of the bird.)*

IN INDIANA ACADEMIC STANDARDS

For the full text of all standards, see the Course Overview in the front matter of this book.

NoS.9 Recognize that new scientific discoveries often lead to a re-evaluation of previously accepted scientific knowledge and of commonly held ideas.

B.8.2 Explain how organisms are classified and named based on their evolutionary relationships into taxonomic categories.

18.1 Finding Order in Diversity

IN NoS.9 Scientific discoveries affect prior ideas; B.8.2 Classification.

Key Questions

What are the goals of binomial nomenclature and systematics?

How did Linnaeus group species into larger taxa?

Vocabulary

binomial nomenclature • genus • systematics • taxon • family • order • class • phylum • kingdom

Taking Notes

Preview Visuals Before you read, look at **Figure 18–5.** Notice all the levels of classification. As you read, refer to the figure again.

THINK ABOUT IT Scientists have been trying to identify, name, and find order in the diversity of life for a long time. The first scientific system for naming and grouping organisms was set up long before Darwin. In recent decades, biologists have been completing a changeover from that older system of names and classification to a newer strategy that is based on evolutionary theory.

Assigning Scientific Names

What are the goals of binomial nomenclature and systematics?

The first step in understanding and studying diversity is to describe and name each species. To be useful, each scientific name must refer to one and only one species, and everyone must use the same name for that species. But what kind of name should be used? Common names can be confusing, because they vary among languages and from place to place. The animal in **Figure 18–1,** for example, can be called a cougar, a puma, a panther, or a mountain lion. Furthermore, different species may share a common name. In the United Kingdom, the word *buzzard* refers to a hawk, whereas in the United States, *buzzard* refers to a vulture.

Back in the eighteenth century, European scientists recognized that these kinds of common names were confusing, so they agreed to assign Latin or Greek names to each species. Unhappily, that didn't do much to clear up the confusion. Early scientific names often described species in great detail, so the names could be long. For example, the English translation of the scientific name of a tree might be "Oak with deeply divided leaves that have no hairs on their undersides and no teeth around their edges." It was also difficult to standardize these names, because different scientists focused on different characteristics. Many of these same characteristics can still be used to identify organisms when using dichotomous keys, as you can see in **Figure 18–2.**

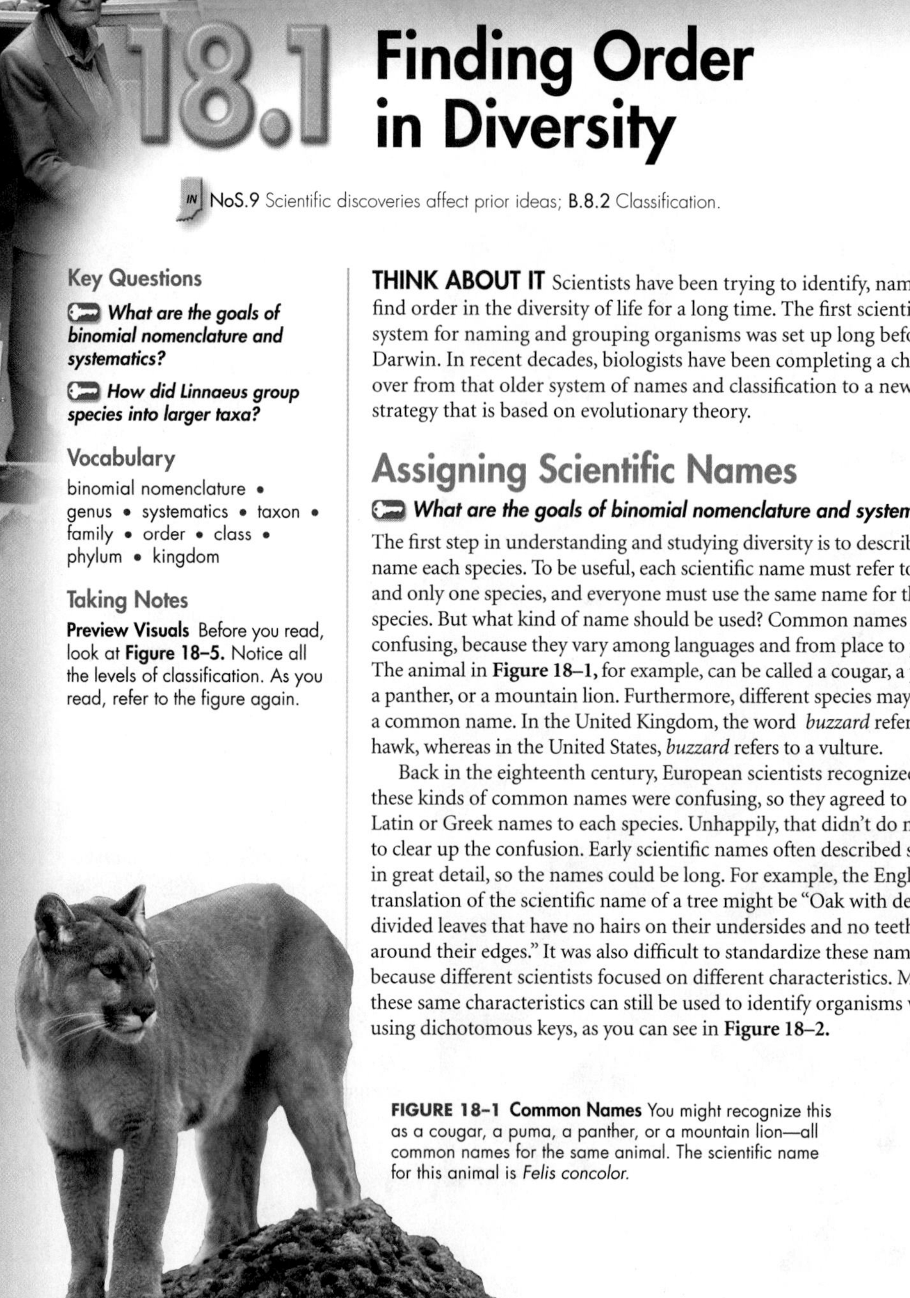

FIGURE 18–1 Common Names You might recognize this as a cougar, a puma, a panther, or a mountain lion—all common names for the same animal. The scientific name for this animal is *Felis concolor.*

UbD Teach for Understanding

ENDURING UNDERSTANDING The diversity of life is the result of ongoing evolutionary change. Species alive today have evolved from ancient common ancestors.

GUIDING QUESTION Why do scientists classify organisms?

EVIDENCE OF UNDERSTANDING *After completing the lesson, give students the following assessment to show they understand Linnaean classification.* Choose a familiar organism, such as a grasshopper, and have students work in pairs to arrange its Linnaean classification levels in the correct order. Give each pair a sheet of paper that has the names of each level in the Linnaean classification for the chosen organism, labeled with it's taxon, in scrambled order. For example, you might list phylum Arthropoda first. Have students, without looking at their textbooks, put the taxonomic levels for the organism in the proper order, beginning with species and ending with kingdom.

USING A DICHOTOMOUS KEY

FIGURE 18–2 A dichotomous key is used to identify organisms. It consists of a series of paired statements or questions that describe alternative possible characteristics of an organism. The paired statements usually describe the presence or absence of certain visible characteristics or structures. Each set of choices is arranged so that each step produces a smaller subset.

Suppose you found a leaf that you wanted to identify. The leaf looks like the one shown here. Use the key to identify this leaf.

Step	Leaf Characteristics	Tree
1a	Compound leaf (leaves divided into leaflets) . . . go to Step 2	
1b	Simple leaf (leaf not divided into leaflets) . . . go to Step 4	
2a	Leaflets all attached at a central point	Buckeye
2b	Leaflets attached at several points . . . go to Step 3	
3a	Leaflets tapered with pointed tips	Pecan
3b	Leaflets oval with rounded tips	Locust
4a	Veins branched out from one central point . . . go to Step 5	
4b	Veins branched off main vein in middle of the leaf . . . go to Step 6	
5a	Heart-shaped leaf	Redbud
5b	Star-shaped leaf	Sweet gum
6a	Leaf with jagged edges	Birch
6b	Leaf with smooth edges	Magnolia

Because your leaf is a simple leaf, you skip ahead to Step 4.

Continue reading the statements until you determine the identity of your leaf.

Because your leaf has jagged edges, you determine that it's from a birch tree.

BIOLOGY.com Search Lesson 18.1 GO • Art In Motion

511

Use Visuals

Begin an exploration of the dichotomous key in **Figure 18–2** by having a student read aloud the caption. Make sure students closely examine the leaf to the right of the caption, noting its physical characteristics. Then, walk through the steps on the key, calling on students to determine the choice, and the reason for the choice, at each step. Make sure students understand that dichotomous keys are tools for identification—not classification.

DIFFERENTIATED INSTRUCTION

L1 **Struggling Students** If possible, provide a leaf from a birch tree for students to examine as they work through the dichotomous key. To give students further practice using the key, draw and cut out the shapes of each of the pictured leaves, making sure to draw the correct vein pattern on each leaf. Then, have students classify each leaf cut-out using the key.

L3 **Advanced Students** For advanced students, collect several different types of plant leaves, and have them create their own dichotomous keys for these leaves. Then, have pairs of students exchange keys and use them to identify the leaves.

BIOLOGY.com Use **Art in Motion: Using a Dichotomous Key** to walk students through the process of using a dichotomous key.

UbD Check for Understanding

INDEX CARD SUMMARIES

Give students each an index card, and ask them to write one central concept from the lesson on the front of the card. This concept could be about naming or grouping organisms, assigning scientific names, the Linnaean classification system, or using a dichotomous key. Then, ask them to list a concept that they don't understand on the back of the card in the form of a question.

ADJUST INSTRUCTION

Read over the cards to determine which concepts students understand and which they are having trouble with. For concepts that students don't understand, call on volunteers to answer the questions from the back of the cards.

Teach

Lead a Discussion

Students should understand the difference between naming organisms and classifying them. Binomial nomenclature is a naming system in which every species gets a unique two-part name. Classification is the practice of putting things into groups. Binomial nomenclature and classification intersect with systematics—the science of naming and grouping organisms. The scientific name for an organism represents part of its classification since similar species are classified together in a genus.

Ask What is the scientific name for human beings? *(Homo sapiens)*

Ask The scientific name for the domestic cat is *Felis catus.* What genus is the domestic cat a member of, and what is its species? *(The genus is* Felis, *and* catus *designates the species within the genus.)*

DIFFERENTIATED INSTRUCTION

L1 Struggling Students Help struggling students understand binomial nomenclature by writing on the board the title, Binomial Nomenclature, and the scientific name for polar bears, *Ursus maritimus.* Draw a pointer from *Ursus* and write Genus, and draw a pointer from *maritimus* and write Species. Then, write on the board *Ursus arctos.* Explain that this is the scientific name for a grizzly bear.

Ask Are grizzly bears and polar bears part of the same genus and species? *(No. They belong to the same genus, but not the same species.)*

Ask Are grizzly bears and polar bears closely related? How do you know? *(Yes, because they belong to the same genus.)*

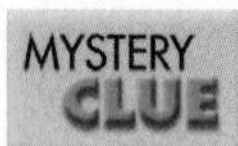

The fact that polar bears and brown bears interbreed and produce fertile offspring in zoos indicates that they have a close evolutionary relationship. Students can go online to Biology.com to gather their evidence.

Answers

IN YOUR NOTEBOOK In binomial nomenclature, each species is assigned a two-part scientific name—genus and species.

MYSTERY CLUE

Polar bears and brown bears interbreed and produce fertile hybrids in zoos, but they very rarely interbreed in nature. What do you think this means about the relationship between them?

Binomial Nomenclature In the 1730s, Swedish botanist Carolus Linnaeus, developed a two-word naming system called **binomial nomenclature.** **In binomial nomenclature, each species is assigned a two-part scientific name.** Scientific names are written in italic. The first word begins with a capital letter, and the second word is lowercased.

The polar bear in **Figure 18–3** is called *Ursus maritimus.* The first part of the name—*Ursus*—is the genus to which the organism belongs. A **genus** (plural: genera, JEN ur uh) is a group of similar species. The genus *Ursus* contains five other species of bears, including *Ursus arctos,* the brown bear or "grizzly."

The second part of a scientific name—in these examples, *maritimus* or *arctos*—is unique to each species. A species, remember, is generally defined as a group of individuals capable of interbreeding and producing fertile offspring. The species name is often a description of an important trait or the organism's habitat. The Latin word *maritimus,* refers to the sea, because polar bears often live on pack ice that floats in the sea.

In Your Notebook *The word* binomial *means "having two names." How does this meaning apply to binomial nomenclature?*

FIGURE 18–3 Binomial Nomenclature The scientific name of the polar bear is *Ursus maritimus,* which means "marine bear." The scientific name of the red maple is *Acer rubrum.* The genus *Acer* consists of all maple trees. The species *rubrum* describes the red maple's color.

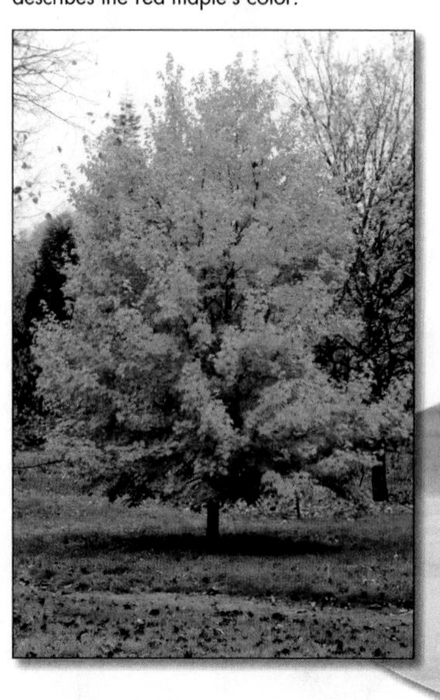

Classifying Species Into Larger Groups In addition to naming organisms, biologists also try to organize, or classify, living and fossil species into larger groups that have biological meaning. In a useful classification system, organisms in a particular group are more similar to one another than they are to organisms in other groups. The science of naming and grouping organisms is called **systematics** (sis tuh MAT iks). **The goal of systematics is to organize living things into groups that have biological meaning.** Biologists often refer to these groups as **taxa** (singular: taxon).

Whether you realize it or not, you use classification systems all the time. You may, for example, talk about "teachers" or "mechanics." Sometimes you refer to a smaller, more specific group, such as "biology teachers" or "auto mechanics." When you do this, you refer to these groups using widely accepted names and characteristics that many people understand. In the same way, when you hear the word *bird,* you immediately think of an animal with wings and feathers.

How Science Works

CAROLUS LINNAEUS

In 1735, the Swedish naturalist Carolus Linnaeus (1707–1778) published *Systema Naturae,* his classification of living things. His main interest at first was in classifying plants. As a university student, Linnaeus tended a botanical garden and became very interested in identifying and naming the garden's plants. His system of plant classification was based on the number and arrangement of a flower's reproductive parts, the stamens (male) and the pistils (female). A plant's class depended on the stamens its flower had; its order depended on the pistils. His system soon became outdated. The legacy of Linnaeus continues in his development of both binomial nomenclature and hierarchical classification.

Quick Lab
GUIDED INQUIRY

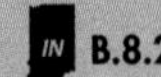
B.8.2

Classifying Fruits 

1. Obtain five different fruits.
2. Use a knife to cut each fruit open and examine its structure. **CAUTION:** *Be careful with sharp instruments. Do not eat any of the cut fruits.*
3. Construct a table with five rows and four columns. Label each row with the name of a different fruit.
4. Examine the fruits, and choose four characteristics that help you tell the fruits apart. Label the columns in your table with the names of these characteristics.
5. Record a description of each fruit in the table.

Analyze and Conclude

1. Classify Based on your table, which fruits most closely resemble one another?

The Linnaean Classification System

How did Linnaeus group species into larger taxa?

In addition to creating the system of binomial nomenclature, Linnaeus also developed a classification system that organized species into taxa that formed a hierarchy or set of ordered ranks. Linnaeus's original system had just four levels. **Over time, Linnaeus's original classification system expanded to include seven hierarchical taxa: species, genus, family, order, class, phylum, and kingdom.**

We've already discussed the two smallest categories, species and genus. Now let's work our way up to the rank of kingdom by examining how camels are classified. The scientific name of a camel with two humps is *Camelus bactrianus.* (Bactria was an ancient country in Asia.) As you can see in **Figure 18–5,** the genus *Camelus* also includes another species, *Camelus dromedarius,* the dromedary, which has only one hump. In deciding how to place organisms into these larger taxa, Linnaeus grouped species according to anatomical similarities and differences.

FIGURE 18–4 Carolus Linnaeus

▶ ***Family*** The South American llama bears some resemblance to Bactrian camels and dromedaries. But the llama is more similar to other South American species than it is to European and Asian camels. Therefore, llamas are placed in a different genus, *Lama;* their species name is *Lama glama.* Several genera that share many similarities, like *Camelus* and *Lama,* are grouped into a larger category, the **family**—in this case, Camelidae.

▶ ***Order*** Closely related families are grouped into the next larger rank—an **order.** Camels and llamas (family Camelidae) are grouped with several other animal families, including deer (family Cervidae) and cattle (family Bovidae), into the order Artiodactyla, hoofed animals with an even number of toes.

BUILD Vocabulary

MULTIPLE MEANINGS The words **family, order, class,** and **kingdom** all have different meanings in biology than they do in common usage. For example, in systematics, a *family* is a group of genera. In everyday usage, a *family* is a group of people who are related to one another. Use a dictionary to find the common meanings of *order, class,* and *kingdom.*

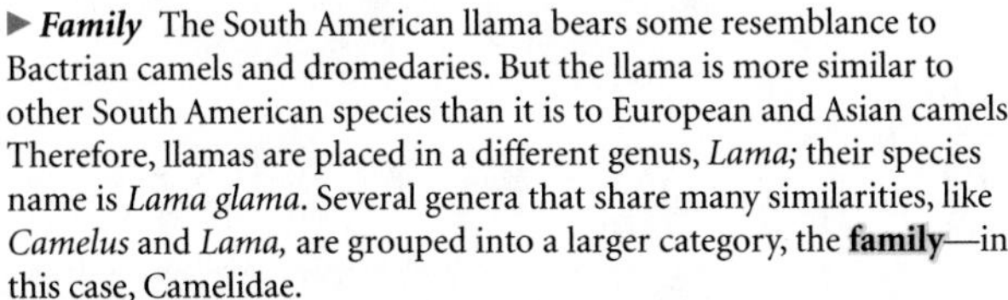

Quick Lab

PURPOSE Students will classify fruits according to observable characteristics.

MATERIALS knife, cutting board, 5 different fruits, such as apple, orange, pear, lemon, and banana

SAFETY Caution students always to direct the sharp edge and point of the knife away from themselves and others. Emphasize that they should not eat any of the fruits. Have students wash their hands after handling the fruit.

PLANNING Obtain fresh fruits from a supermarket. Make sure the knives are sharp enough to cut through the selected fruits. Make sure students understand that scientists might use different criteria than students use to classify fruits.

ANALYZE AND CONCLUDE

1. Answers will vary depending on the fruits students examine. Student classifications should be logical and based on observable characteristics of the five fruits.

Build Science Skills

Explain that classifying is a basic skill for scientists to learn. Give students practice in this skill by having them develop a hierarchical classification system similar to the Linnaean system to classify a selection of common items. For example, they might classify a collection that includes a hair clip, bobby pin, safety pin, rubber band, binder clip, button, zipper, and paper clip. Groups might identify all the items as a kind of fastener. Further, they might group hair clips and bobby pins together as fasteners of hair. Groups should create a name for each level of classification in the system. Have groups share their systems with the class.

DIFFERENTIATED INSTRUCTION

L1 Special Needs Modify the classification activity described above by giving special needs students common objects that are larger and easier to handle and manipulate. For example, you might present them with a collection of sports equipment, such as a baseball, basketball, baseball bat, tennis racquet, and so on. Have small groups of students work together to create a classification scheme using these objects. If time allows, suggest they start again and create a second classification scheme using the same objects.

Address Misconceptions

Classification by Habitat Some students may think that plants and animals can be classified by habitat rather than by structure or by evolutionary relationships. Explain that grouping animals, for example, by whether they live in forests or in the ocean can be useful for some biologists, such as ecologists, but habitat is not a characteristic that is used to classify organisms by systematists.

Teach continued

Use Visuals

After students have read the section, **Linnaean Classification System,** use **Figure 18–5** to discuss the system's seven taxa. Make sure students understand that the pyramid shows the taxonomic categories for one species, *Camelus bactrianus,* and that the more inclusive taxa include many more organisms than shown.

Ask What basic body feature, mentioned in the text, do all members of the phylum Chordata share? *(a nerve cord along the back)*

Ask What are four kinds of animals in the order Artiodactyla? *(Sample answer: Bactrian camel, dromedary, llama, and giraffe)*

DIFFERENTIATED INSTRUCTION

L1 Struggling Students Tell students that for remembering a squence of terms, it is often helpful to use a mnemonic. For example, a mnemonic to help remember the sequence of taxa, from most inclusive to least inclues, is: Kids Prefer Cheese Over Fresh Green Spinach. Ask small groups to create their own mnemonics and present their best mnemonic to the class.

ELL Focus on ELL: Build Background

BEGINNING SPEAKERS On the board, diagram an example of a familiar hierarchical classification system. For example, write the word *supermarket,* and draw a diagram showing how the products in a supermarket are arranged in hierarchical order; e.g., the entire supermarket is divided into the produce department and other departments, fruits are a subdivision within produce, etc. The diagram should be similar in organization to **Figure 18–5;** i.e., the word *supermarket* should be at the bottom of the diagram, *produce department* should be written above *supermarket, fruits* above *produce,* etc. Then, point to **Figure 18–5** and compare the hierarchical diagram of the supermarket to hierarchical Linnaean classification.

Answers

FIGURE 18–5 Chordata

► ***Class*** Similar orders, in turn, are grouped into the next larger rank, a **class.** The order Artiodactyla is placed in the class Mammalia, which includes all animals that are warmblooded, have body hair, and produce milk for their young.

► ***Phylum*** Classes are grouped into a **phylum.** A phylum includes organisms that are different but share important characteristics. The class Mammalia is grouped with birds (class Aves), reptiles (class Reptilia), amphibians (class Amphibia), and all classes of fish into the phylum Chordata. These organisms share important body-plan features, among them a nerve cord along the back.

► ***Kingdom*** The largest and most inclusive of Linnaeus's taxonomic categories is the **kingdom.** All multicellular animals are placed in the kingdom Animalia.

FIGURE 18–5 From Species to Kingdom This illustration shows how a Bactrian camel, *Camelus bactrianus,* is grouped within each taxonomic category. Only some representative organisms are illustrated for each taxon above the genus level. Interpret Visuals ***What phylum does Camelus bactrianus belong to?***

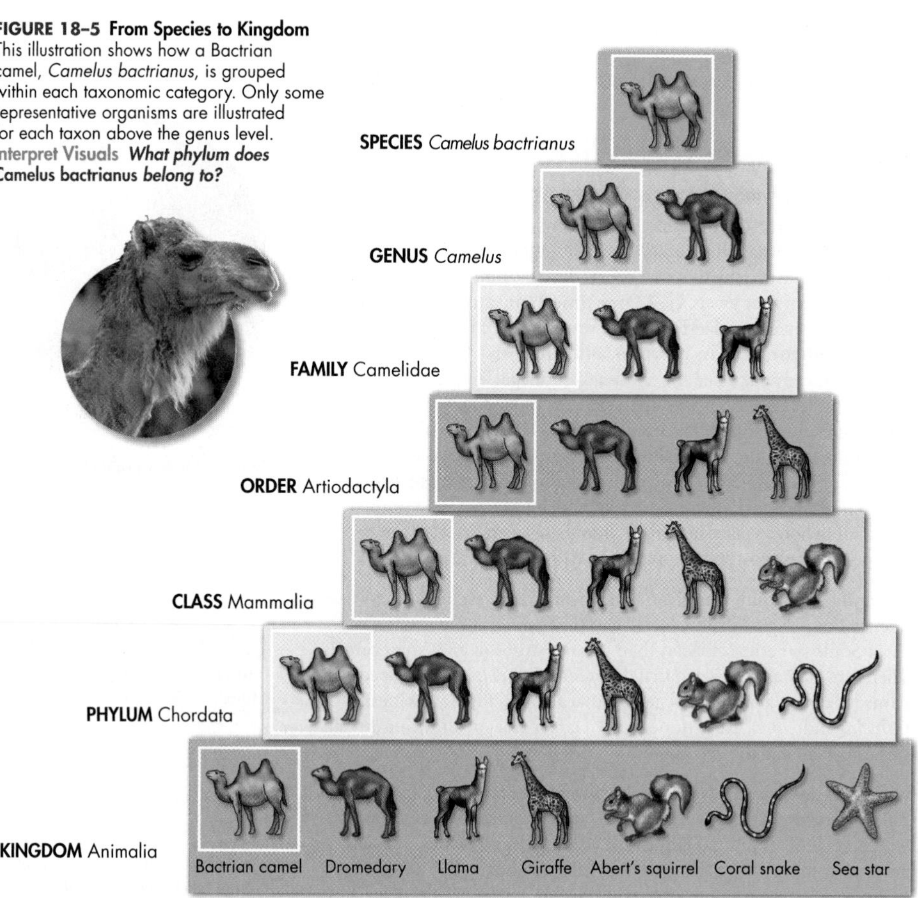

Biology In-Depth

CAMEL SPECIES

There are two living species of camels, the two-humped Bactrian camel *(Camelus bactrianus)* and the one-humped Arabian camel *(Camelus dromedaries),* or dromedary. Nearly all of the 2.5 million Bactrian camels alive today are domesticated. They are widely bred in Mongolia and China, with small wild populations of a few hundred restricted to parts of the Gobi Desert. The wild species of Bactrian camel, which is considered by the IUCN under the name *Camelus ferus,* is listed as Critically Endangered. DNA testing has shown the feral populations to be genetically distinct from the domesticated population. About 14 million Arabian camels exist, found in the arid regions of Southwest Asia and North Africa. Arabian camels are also found in Australia, where they were introduced and where a feral population now exists. Although they are classified as two distinct species, the Bactrian camel and Arabian camel have been bred in captivity with the production of fertile offspring.

Problems With Traditional Classification In a sense, members of a species determine which organisms belong to that species by deciding with whom they mate and produce fertile offspring. There is thus a "natural" definition of species. Researchers, on the other hand, define Linnaean ranks above the level of species. Because, over time, systematists have emphasized a variety of characteristics, some of these groups have been defined in different ways at different times.

For example, Linnaeus's strategy of classifying organisms according to visible similarities and differences seems simple at first. But how should scientists decide which similarities and differences are most important? If you lived in Linnaeus's time, for example, how would you have classified the animals shown in **Figure 18–6**? Adult barnacles and limpets live attached to rocks and have similar-looking shells. Adult crabs look quite unlike both barnacles and limpets. Based on these features, would you place limpets and barnacles together, and crabs in a different group? As biologists attempted to classify more organisms over time, these kinds of questions arose frequently.

Linnaeus was a good scientist, and he chose his characteristics carefully. Many of his groups are still valid under modern classification schemes. But Linnaeus worked more than a century before Darwin published his ideas about descent with modification. Modern systematists apply Darwin's ideas to classification and try look beyond simple similarities and differences to ask questions about evolutionary relationships. Linnaeus grouped organisms strictly according to similarities and differences. Scientists today try to assign species to a larger group in ways that reflect how closely members of those groups are related to each other.

FIGURE 18–6 Barnacles, Limpets, and Crabs Problems can arise when species are classified based on easily observed traits. Look closely at the barnacles (top), the limpets (bottom), and the crab (left). Notice their similarities and differences. **Compare and Contrast** ***Which animals seem most alike? Why?***

18.1 Assessment

IN B.8.2

Review Key Concepts

1. a. **Review** Identify two goals of systematics.
   b. **Explain** Why do the common names of organisms—like *daisy* or *mountain lion*—often cause problems for scientists?
   c. **Classify** The scientific name of the sugar maple is *Acer saccharum*. What does each part of the name designate?
2. a. **Review** List the ranks in the Linnaean system of classification, beginning with the smallest.
   b. **Explain** In which group of organisms are the members more closely associated—all of the organisms in the same kingdom or all of the organisms in the same order? Explain your answer.
   c. **Apply Concepts** What do scientists mean when they say that species is the only "natural" rank in classification?

Apply the Big idea

Unity and Diversity of Life

3. Which category has more biological meaning—all brown birds or all birds descended from a hawklike ancestor? Why?

BIOLOGY.com Search Lesson 18.1 GO • Self-Test • Lesson Assessment

Assessment Answers

1a. to assign each species a unique, universally accepted name; to organize living things into groups that have biological meaning

1b. Common names vary among languages and from place to place.

1c. *Acer* designates the genus name, and *saccharum* designates the species.

2a. species, genus, family, order, class, phylum, kingdom

2b. organisms in the same order

2c. Species is the only Linnaean rank not defined by scientists. A species is defined by a natural process—mating to produce fertile offspring.

3.  "All birds descended from a hawklike ancestor" has more biological meaning, because not all brown birds are closely related based on evolutionary relationships.

Lead a Discussion

Discuss with students the problems with traditional, or Linnaean, classification.

Ask What did Linnaeus—and traditional classification since his time—depend on to classify organisms? *(overall similarities and differences)*

Ask volunteers to explain why classification of dolphins might have been a problem with traditional classification.

DIFFERENTIATED INSTRUCTION

L3 Advanced Students Students can do research on the current classification of dolphins, from kingdom to species, and contrast that classification with the classification of a typical bony fish, such as tuna. Students can present their findings to the class in a diagram or table.

Assess and Remediate

EVALUATE UNDERSTANDING

Ask students to write a paragraph explaining the system of binomial nomenclature and why this system is useful. Then, have students complete the 18.1 Assessment.

REMEDIATION SUGGESTION

L1 Struggling Students If students struggle to answer **Question 1b,** call on an English language learner to say in his or her native language what the common name for *daisy* is. Point out that a scientific name must be understood by scientists from all countries around the world.

BIOLOGY.com Students can check their understanding of lesson concepts with the **Self-Test** assessment. They can then take an online version of the **Lesson Assessment.**

Answers

FIGURE 18–6 Answers may vary. Superficially, the barnacle and the limpet seem most alike, because they live attached to rocks and have similar-looking shells.

LESSON 18.2

Getting Started

Objectives

18.2.1 Explain the difference between evolutionary classification and Linnaean classification.

18.2.2 Describe how to make and interpret a cladogram.

18.2.3 Explain the use of DNA sequences in classification.

Student Resources

Study Workbook A and B, 18.2 Worksheets

Spanish Study Workbook, 18.2 Worksheets

Lesson Overview • Lesson Notes
- Activities: InterActive Art, Data Analysis
- Assessment: Self-Test, Lesson Assessment

For corresponding lesson in the **Foundation Edition**, see pages 433–437.

Answers

IN YOUR NOTEBOOK A monophyletic clade includes a single ancestor and all of its descendants. If any descendants are "missing" from the clade, it is called paraphyletic.

IN INDIANA ACADEMIC STANDARDS

For the full text of all standards, see the Course Overview in the front matter of this book.

NoS.6 Use analogies and models (mathematical and physical) to simplify and represent systems that are difficult to understand or directly experience due to their size, time scale, or complexity, and recognize the limitations of analogies and models.

B.8.2 Explain how organisms are classified and named based on their evolutionary relationships into taxonomic categories.

B.8.3 Use anatomical and molecular evidence to establish evolutionary relationships between organisms.

18.2 Modern Evolutionary Classification

IN **NoS.6** Use analogies and models; **NoS.9** Scientific discoveries affect prior ideas; **B.8.2** Classification; **B.8.3** Evolutionary relationships; **B.8.4** Evidence for evolutionary relationships.

Key Questions

What is the goal of evolutionary classification?

What is a cladogram?

How are DNA sequences used in classification?

Vocabulary

phylogeny
clade
monophyletic group
cladogram
derived character

Taking Notes

Outline Make an outline of this lesson using the green headings as the main topics and the blue headings as subtopics. As you read, fill in details under each heading.

THINK ABOUT IT Darwin's ideas about a "tree of life" suggests a new way to classify organisms—not just based on similarities and differences, but instead based on evolutionary relationships. Under this system, taxa are arranged according to how closely related they are. When organisms are rearranged in this way, some of the old Linnaean ranks fall apart. For example, the Linnaean class reptilia isn't valid unless birds are included—which means birds are reptiles! And not only are birds reptiles, they're also dinosaurs! Wondering why? To understand, we need to look at the way evolutionary classification works.

Evolutionary Classification

What is the goal of evolutionary classification?

The concept of descent with modification led to the study of **phylogeny** (fy LAHJ uh nee)—the evolutionary history of lineages. Advances in phylogeny, in turn, led to phylogenetic systematics. **The goal of phylogenetic systematics, or evolutionary classification, is to group species into larger categories that reflect lines of evolutionary descent, rather than overall similarities and differences.**

Common Ancestors Phylogenetic systematics places organisms into higher taxa whose members are more closely related to one another than they are to members of any other group. The larger a taxon is, the farther back in time all of its members shared a common ancestor. This is true all the way up to the largest taxa.

Clades Classifying organisms according to these rules places them into groups called clades. A **clade** is a group of species that includes a single common ancestor and all descendants of that ancestor—living and extinct. How are clades different from Linnaean taxa? A clade must be a monophyletic (mahn oh fy LET ik) group. A **monophyletic group** includes a single common ancestor and *all* of its descendants.

Some groups of organisms defined before the advent of evolutionary classification are monophyletic. Some, however, are paraphyletic, meaning that the group includes a common ancestor but excludes one or more groups of descendants. These groups are invalid under evolutionary classification.

BUILD Vocabulary

WORD ORIGINS The word **cladogram** comes from two Greek words: *klados*, meaning "branch," and *gramma*, meaning "something that is written or drawn." A cladogram is an evolutionary diagram with a branching pattern.

In Your Notebook *In your own words, explain what makes a clade monophyletic or paraphyletic.*

UbD Teach for Understanding

ENDURING UNDERSTANDING The diversity of life is the result of ongoing evolutionary change. Species alive today have evolved from ancient common ancestors.

GUIDING QUESTION How do evolutionary relationships affect the way scientists classify organisms?

EVIDENCE OF UNDERSTANDING *After students have studied the lesson, give them the following assessment to show they understand cladograms.* Have students work in small groups. Each group should prepare a brief presentation on how to make and interpret a cladogram. Tell students the target audience should be students who have never before heard of cladograms. Have each group make their presentation to the class. After all the presentations are concluded, discuss what strategies best explained cladograms.

Cladograms

What is a cladogram?

Modern evolutionary classification uses a method called cladistic analysis. Cladistic analysis compares carefully selected traits to determine the order in which groups of organisms branched off from their common ancestors. This information is then used to link clades together into a diagram called a **cladogram.** **A cladogram links groups of organisms by showing how evolutionary lines, or lineages, branched off from common ancestors.**

Building Cladograms To understand how cladograms are constructed, think back to the process of speciation. A speciation event, in which one ancestral species splits into two new ones, is the basis of each branch point, or node, in a cladogram. That node represents the last point at which the two new lineages shared a common ancestor. As shown in part 1 of **Figure 18–7,** a node splits a lineage into two separate lines of evolutionary ancestry.

Each node represents the last point at which species in lineages above the node shared a common ancestor. The bottom, or "root" of a cladogram, represents the common ancestor shared by all of the organisms in the cladogram. A cladogram's branching patterns indicate degrees of relatedness among organisms. Look at part 2 of **Figure 18–7.** Because lineages 3 and 4 share a common ancestor more recently with each other than they do with lineage 2, you know that lineages 3 and 4 are more closely related to each other than either is to lineage 2. The same is true for lineages 2, 3, and 4. In terms of ancestry, they are more closely related to each other than any of them is to lineage 1. Look at the cladogram shown in part 3 of **Figure 18–7.** Does it surprise you that amphibians are more closely related to mammals than they are to ray-finned fish? In terms of ancestry, it's true!

FIGURE 18–7 Building a Cladogram A cladogram shows relative degrees of relatedness among lineages.

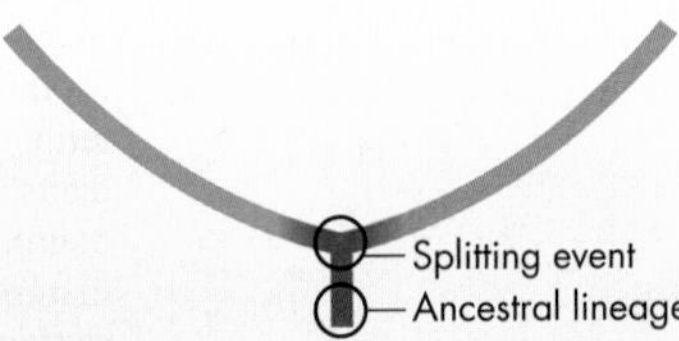

❶ Cladograms are diagrams showing how evolutionary lines, or lineages, split from each other over time. This diagram shows a single ancestral lineage splitting into two. The point of splitting is called a "node" in the cladogram.

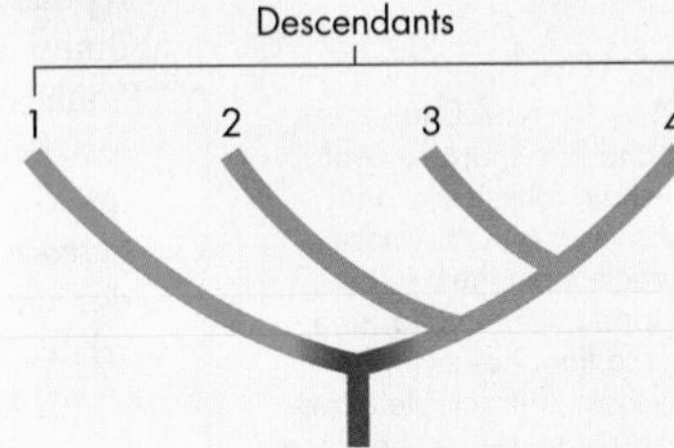

❷ How recently lineages share a common ancestor reflect how closely the lineages are related to one another. Here, lineages 3 and 4 are each more closely related to each other than any of them is to any other lineage.

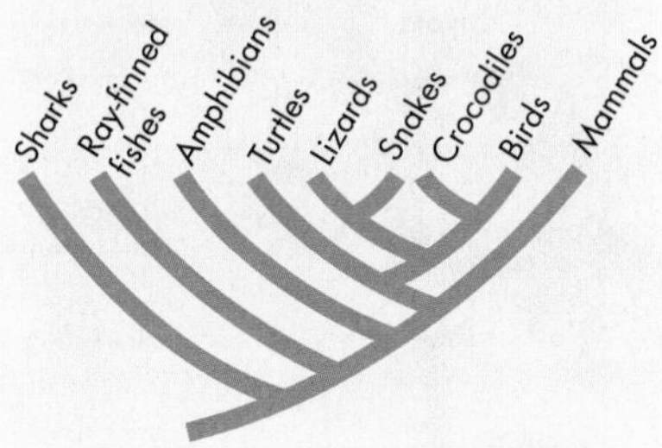

❸ This cladogram shows the evolutionary relationships among vertebrates, animals with backbones.

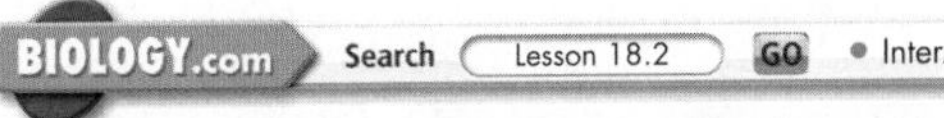

Search Lesson 18.2 GO • InterActive Art

How Science Works

CLADISTICS AND THE CLASSIFICATION OF BIRDS

Cladistic analysis has caused evolutionary systematists to rethink the classification of birds. In traditional Linnaean classification, birds form a class by themselves—class Aves—within subphylum Vertebrata, and separate from class Reptilia. Compelling fossil evidence and certain structural characteristics of modern birds indicate that birds descended from a group of dinosaurs called theropods. Modern birds, therefore, make up a clade within the larger clade of dinosaurs. Dinosaurs, in turn, are within the clade of reptiles. Therefore, systematists now consider birds to be a type of reptile. To illustrate this, see **Figure 18–10.**

Teach

Use Visuals

Use **Figure 18–7** to introduce how cladograms are built and interpreted.

Ask In Step 1, the ancestral lineage splits into two new lineages. On a cladogram, what is this place, where a split like this occurs, called? *(a node)*

Ask In Step 2, what does the node on the right side represent for lineages 3 and 4? *(the last point at which lineages 3 and 4 shared a common ancestor)*

Explain that the cladogram in Step 3 represents how lineages branched over time from the first branch in Step 1.

DIFFERENTIATED INSTRUCTION

L1 Special Needs Some students may better understand cladograms through modeling. Have small groups use colored pipe cleaners to build models of the final cladogram in **Figure 18–7.** Students could use tape and slips of paper to add labels.

ELL Focus on ELL: Extend Language

ADVANCED AND ADVANCED HIGH SPEAKERS Write the words *clade* and *cladogram* on the board. Ask students what the words have in common. *(Both words contain the root word* clad- *or* clade.*)* Remind students that words with the same root word often have related meanings; the specific definitions depend on how the root word is modified by additions, such as prefixes and suffixes, and combinations with other root words. Call attention to the Build Vocabulary on page 516. Ask how the meaning of the root *clad-* is modified by the addition of the word part *-ogram. (The addition of* -ogram *changes the meaning of* clade *from "a group of species with a common ancestor" to "a diagram showing the relationships among such groups.")*

Then, ask students to look at the list of lesson vocabulary and identify two other terms that share the same root word. (*phylogeny* and *monophyletic*) Have students use dictionaries to learn the Greek origins of both words and how the meanings of the words are modified by the suffix *-geny* and the prefix *mono-*.

BIOLOGY.com Students can practice interpreting and building cladograms with **InterActive Art: Cladograms.**

LESSON 18.2

Teach continued

Lead a Discussion

Make sure students understand that derived characters are used in cladograms to explain the branching of lineages. Explain to students that when considering whether a given character is derived, scientists use an "outgroup" for comparison.

An outgroup is an organism, or group of organisms, that evolved before the clade being analyzed. For example, reptiles are an outgroup for clade Mammalia. Likewise, amphibians are an outgroup for clade Reptilia. In **Figure 18–8,** members of the clade Carnivora are being compared. One possible outgroup for this clade are marsupials, such as the kangaroo as shown in **Figure 18–9.** Help students understand why kangaroos are considered an outgroup for the clade Carnivora by asking the following questions.

Ask Does a kangaroo have hair? *(yes)*

Ask If a kangaroo has hair, can hair be a derived trait for the clade Carnivora? *(No. If hair were a derived trait for Carnivora, then only carnivores would have hair, which is not true.)*

Ask Specialized shearing teeth are used by carnivores to eat meat. Kangaroos are herbivores. Are they likely to have specialized shearing teeth, then? *(no)*

Explain that since the outgroup for the clade does not have specialized shearing teeth, that trait is likely to be derived for clade Carnivora.

Using dogs and their relatives as the outgoup for clade Felidae, you can follow a similar process to illustrate that retractable claws is a derived trait for that clade.

DIFFERENTIATED INSTRUCTION

ELL English Language Learners Explain that *derived* means "received from a specified source." In this context, the term *character* means a "trait or characteristic." A *derived character,* then, means a trait or characteristic received from an ancestor. In **Figure 18–8,** the derived character of retractable claws is a characteristic the lion received from an ancestor.

Derived Characters In contrast to Linnaean taxonomy, cladistic analysis focuses on certain kinds of characters, called derived characters, when assigning organisms into clades. A **derived character** is a trait that arose in the most recent common ancestor of a particular lineage and was passed along to its descendants.

Whether or not a character is derived depends on the level at which you're grouping organisms. Here's what we mean. **Figure 18–8** shows several traits that are shared by coyotes and lions, both members of the clade Carnivora. Four limbs is a derived character for the entire clade Tetrapoda because the common ancestor of all tetrapods had four limbs, and this trait was passed to its descendants. Hair is a derived character for the clade Mammalia. But for mammals, four limbs is *not* a derived character—if it were, only mammals would have that trait. Nor is four limbs or hair a derived character for clade Carnivora. Specialized shearing teeth, however, is. What about retractable claws? This trait is found in lions but not in coyotes. Thus, retractable claws is a derived character for the clade Felidae—also known as cats.

Losing Traits Notice above that four limbs is a derived character for clade Tetrapoda. But what about snakes? Snakes are definitely reptiles, which are tetrapods. But snakes certainly don't have four limbs! The *ancestors* of snakes, however, did have four limbs. Somewhere in the lineage leading to modern snakes, that trait was lost. Because distantly related groups of organisms can sometimes lose the same character, systematists are cautious about using the *absence* of a trait as a character in their analyses. After all, whales don't have four limbs either, but snakes are certainly more closely related to other reptiles than they are to whales.

FIGURE 18–8 Derived Characters The coyote and lion share several characters—hair, four limbs, and specialized shearing teeth. These shared characters put them in the clades Tetrapoda, Mammalia, and Carnivora. The lion, however, has retractable claws. Retractable claws is the derived character for the clade Felidae.

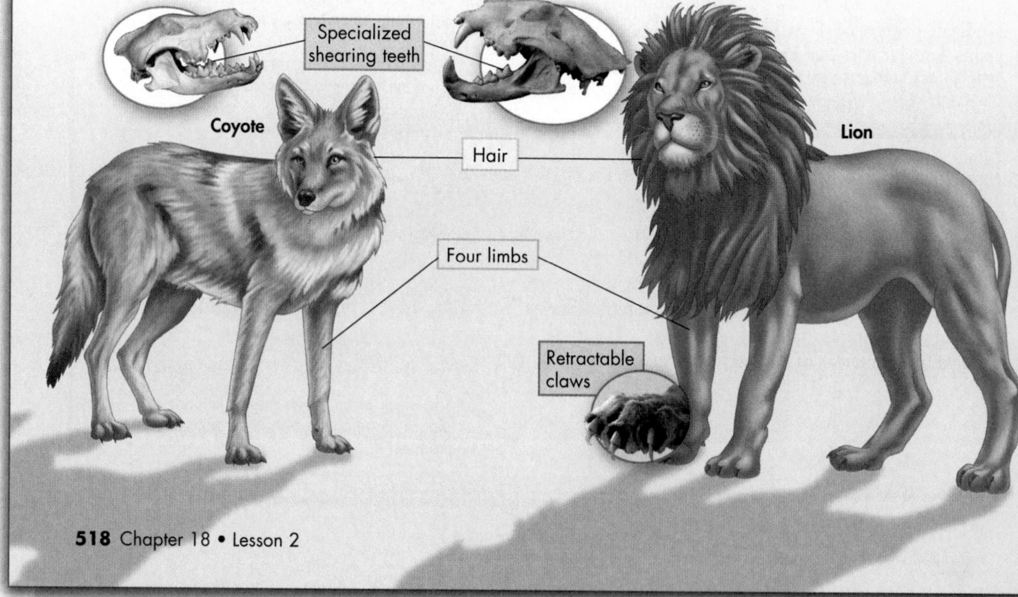

Biology In-Depth

PRIMITIVE AND DERIVED CHARACTERS

A primitive character, also called a plesiomorphy, is a character possessed by the members of a particular clade but that evolved before the branching of the clade being defined. For example, in **Figure 18–9,** a backbone is a primitive character for all the clades in the cladogram. (A synapomorphy is a derived character shared by two or more groups.) In contrast, a derived character, also called an apomorphy, is the character that is the evolutionary novelty for a particular clade. Whether a character is primitive or derived depends on which part of a cladogram you focus on. In **Figure 18–9,** the derived character noted for clade Mammalia is hair. For clade Felidae, however, hair is a primitive character.

VISUAL SUMMARY

INTERPRETING A CLADOGRAM

FIGURE 18–9 This cladogram shows the evolutionary history of cats. In a cladogram, all organisms in a clade share a set of derived characters. Notice that smaller clades are nested within larger clades. Interpret Visuals ***For which clade in this cladogram is an amniotic egg a derived character?***

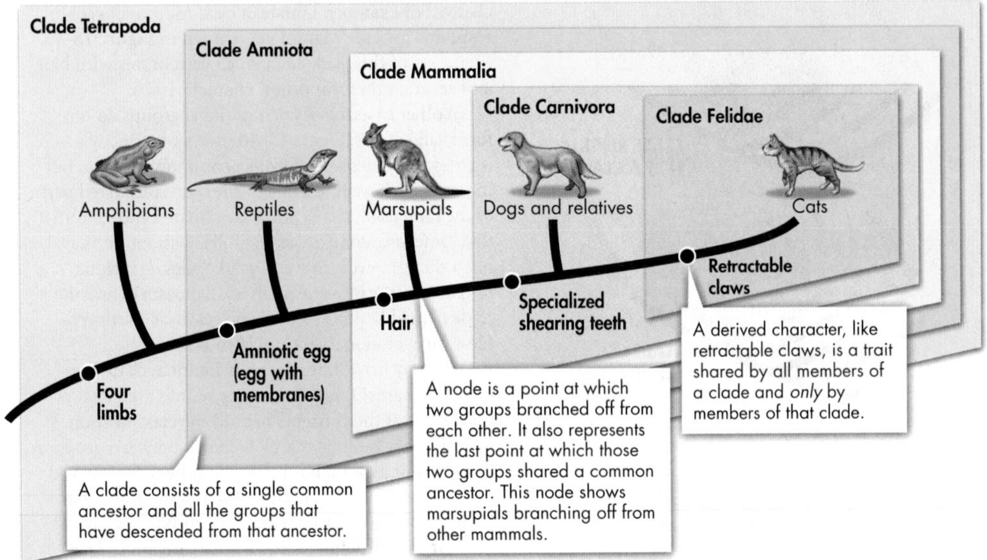

Clade Tetrapoda
Clade Amniota
Clade Mammalia
Clade Carnivora
Clade Felidae
Amphibians
Reptiles
Marsupials
Dogs and relatives
Cats
Four limbs
Amniotic egg (egg with membranes)
Hair
Specialized shearing teeth
Retractable claws
A clade consists of a single common ancestor and all the groups that have descended from that ancestor.
A node is a point at which two groups branched off from each other. It also represents the last point at which those two groups shared a common ancestor. This node shows marsupials branching off from other mammals.
A derived character, like retractable claws, is a trait shared by all members of a clade and *only* by members of that clade.

Interpreting Cladograms We can now put this information together to "read" a cladogram. **Figure 18–9** shows a simplified phylogeny of the cat family. The lowest node represents the last common ancestor of all four-limbed animals—members of the clade Tetrapoda. The forks in this cladogram show the order in which various groups branched off from the tetrapod lineage over the course of evolution. The positions of various characters in the cladogram reflect the order in which those characteristics arose in this lineage. In the lineage leading to cats, for example, specialized shearing teeth evolved before retractable claws. Furthermore, each derived character listed along the main trunk of the cladogram defines a clade. Hair, for example, is a defining character for the clade Mammalia. Retractable claws is a derived character shared only by the clade Felidae. Derived characters that occur "lower" on the cladogram than the branch point for a clade are not derived for that particular clade. Hair, for example, is not a derived character for the clade Carnivora.

In Your Notebook *List the derived characters in **Figure 18–9** and explain which groups in the cladogram have those characters.*

VISUAL SUMMARY

After students have read the information following the head **Interpreting Cladograms,** divide the class into small groups for discussion of the text and the visual summary in **Figure 18–9.** Point out that the cladogram in **Figure 18–9** is related to the explanation of a derived character in **Figure 18–8.** Ask each group to generate a list of questions about concepts that members find difficult to understand. In class discussion, ask a group to read aloud one of its questions. Have members of other groups respond. Continue until all groups' questions have been answered.

DIFFERENTIATED INSTRUCTION

L1 Struggling Students Struggling students may not understand the significance of the location of derived characters on a cladogram. On the board, write the first derived character of four limbs. Then, underneath that character write all the kinds of animals that share that trait. *(amphibians, reptiles, marsupials, dogs and their relatives, cats)* Call on students to help you make a similar list under each of the other four derived characters.

L3 Advanced Students Ask each student to write an analysis of what the cladogram shows about the evolution of cats. Explain that students should identify the derived characters and the different clades within clades. Ask volunteers to share their analyses with the class.

UbD Check for Understanding

FOLLOW-UP PROBES

Ask Why is "four limbs" a derived character for clade Tetrapoda, but a primitive character for all other clades in **Figure 18–9?** *("Four limbs" is a derived character for clade Tetrapoda, because only Tetrapods have four limbs. It is a primitive character for clades Amniota, Mammalia, Carnivora, and Felidae, because it isn't true that only reptiles, or that only marsupials, or only dogs or cats, have four limbs.)*

ADJUST INSTRUCTION

If students' responses indicate that they are confused by the definition and role of a derived character in cladistic analysis, suggest that they reread the section **Derived Characters** on the previous page. Have them write a short paragraph that defines a derived character and describes how they are used to define clades. Also have them include a "test" that can help them determine if a character is derived or primitive.

Answers

FIGURE 18–9 clades Amniota, Mammalia, Carnivora, and Felidae

IN YOUR NOTEBOOK four limbs—all clades; amniotic egg—Amniota, Mammalia, Carnivora, and Felidae; hair—Mammalia, Carnivora, and Felidae; specialized shearing teeth—Carnivora and Felidae; retractable claws—Felidae

LESSON 18.2

Teach continued

Use Visuals

One way to help your students understand clades is by using "the snip test." Have students imagine that they have a pair of scissors and can "snip" above any node on a cladogram. What would fall off is a monophyletic group, or clade. So, if students snipped above the node where amphibians branch off, a tree containing turtles, lizards, snakes, crocodiles, birds, and mammals would fall off. These groups form a monophyletic group called clade Amniota.

Have students recognize that you can snip the cladogram shown in **Figure 18–10** to get the two groups of organisms shaded in blue, but you cannot snip anywhere to get class Reptilia, the group of organisms shaded in green. That is because class Reptilia is not a clade, it's a paraphyletic group because it excludes birds, a descendant group of the common ancestor shared by the other organisms.

Ask Where would you snip on the cladogram to get clade Aves to fall off? *(right above the node that separates crocodiles from birds)*

Ask Do lizards and snakes form a clade? How do you know? *(Yes; you can snip above the node where lizards and snakes branch off from crocodiles and birds to get a tree that includes only snakes and lizards.)*

DIFFERENTIATED INSTRUCTION

L1 Struggling Students Some students may have difficulty interpreting the cladograms in **Figure 18–10.** Make sure they understand that all the cladograms show the same information regarding evolutionary relationships among the animal groups shown. Explain that the only difference in the three cladograms is the shading, which indicates the grouping of animals.

Ask What color highlights a group of animals that do not form a clade? *(green)*

Answers

FIGURE 18–10 Clade Reptilia plus amphibians would form a paraphyletic group because it excludes mammals, a descendant group of the common ancestor shared by amphibians and reptiles.

FIGURE 18–10 Clade or Not? A clade includes an ancestral species and all its descendants. Linnaean class Reptilia is not a clade because it does not include modern birds. Because it leaves this descendant group out, the class is paraphyletic. Clades Reptilia and Aves, however, are monophyletic and, therefore, valid clades. Apply Concepts ***Would a group that included all of clade Reptilia plus amphibians be monophyletic or paraphyletic? Explain.***

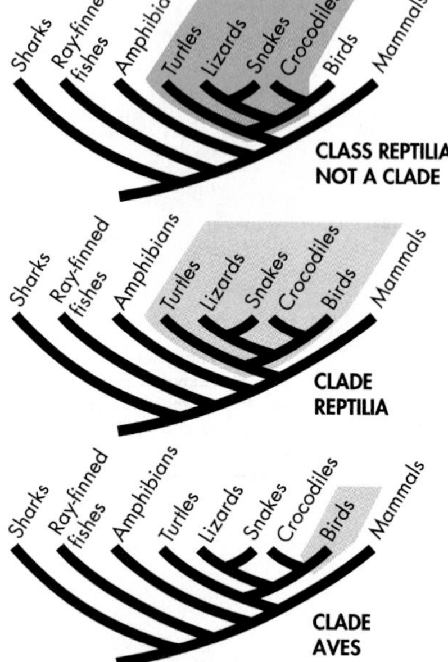

Clades and Traditional Taxonomic Groups Which of the Linnaean groupings form clades, and which do not? Remember that a true clade must be monophyletic, which means that it contains an ancestral species and *all* of its descendants—it can't leave any out. It also cannot include any species which are not descendants of that original ancestor. Cladistic analysis shows that many traditional taxonomic groups do form valid clades. For example, Linnaean class Mammalia corresponds to clade Mammalia (shown in **Figure 18–9**). Members of this clade include all vertebrates with hair and several other important characteristics.

In other cases, however, traditional groups do not form valid clades. **Figure 18–10** shows why. Today's reptiles are all descended from a common ancestor. But birds, which have traditionally not been considered part of the Linnaean class Reptilia, are also descended from that same ancestor. So, class Reptilia, without birds, is not a clade. However, several valid clades *do* include birds: Aves (the birds themselves), Dinosauria, and the clade named Reptilia. So, is it correct to call birds reptiles? An evolutionary biologist would say yes!

You may be wondering: class Reptilia, clade Reptilia, who cares? But the resulting names aren't as important as the concepts behind the classification. Evolutionary biologists look for links between groups, figuring out how each is related to others. So the next time you see a bird, thinking of it as a member of a clade or class isn't as important as thinking about it not just as a bird, but also as a dinosaur, a reptile, a tetrapod, and a chordate.

Quick Lab GUIDED INQUIRY

IN NoS.6, B.8.2, B.8.3

Constructing a Cladogram

1. Identify the organism in the table that is least closely related to the others.
2. Use the information in the table to construct a cladogram of these animals.

Derived Characters in Organisms			
Organism	Derived Character		
	Backbone	Legs	Hair
Earthworm	Absent	Absent	Absent
Trout	Present	Absent	Absent
Lizard	Present	Present	Absent
Human	Present	Present	Present

Analyze and Conclude

1. Interpret Tables What trait separates the least closely related animal from the other animals?

2. Apply Concepts Do you have enough information to determine where a frog should be placed on the cladogram? Explain your answer.

3. Draw Conclusions Does your cladogram indicate that lizards and humans share a more recent common ancestor than either does with an earthworm? Explain your answer.

Quick Lab

PURPOSE Students will construct a cladogram to classify a group of animals.

PLANNING Have students review how to build a cladogram as shown in **Figure 18–7.**

ANALYZE AND CONCLUDE

1. a backbone

2. No. A frog would be inserted somewhere between the trout and the human, since a frog has a backbone and legs but lacks hair. However, without another derived character, it's impossible to know if the frog lineage branched off before or after the lizard lineage.

3. Yes, lizards and humans share a more recent ancestor, because the branching point between them is farther up on the cladogram than the branching point between humans, lizards, and earthworms. Also, lizards and humans share the derived characters of legs and a backbone.

DNA in Classification

How are DNA sequences used in classification?

The examples of cladistic analysis we've discussed so far are based largely on physical characteristics like skeletons and teeth. But the goal of modern systematics is to understand the evolutionary relationships of all life on Earth—from bacteria to plants, snails, and apes. How can we devise hypotheses about the common ancestors of organisms that appear to have no physical similarities?

Genes as Derived Characters Remember that all organisms carry genetic information in their DNA passed on from earlier generations. A wide range of organisms share a number of genes and show important homologies that can be used to determine evolutionary relationships. For example, all eukaryotic cells have mitochondria, and all mitochondria have their own genes. Because all genes mutate over time, shared genes contain differences that can be treated as derived characters in cladistic analysis. For that reason, similarities and differences in DNA can be used to develop hypotheses about evolutionary relationships. **In general, the more derived genetic characters two species share, the more recently they shared a common ancestor and the more closely they are related in evolutionary terms.**

New Techniques Suggest New Trees The use of DNA characters in cladistic analysis has helped to make evolutionary trees more accurate. Consider, for example, the birds in **Figure 18–11.** The African vulture in the top photograph looks a lot like the American vulture in the middle photograph. Both were traditionally classified in the falcon clade. But American vultures have a peculiar behavior: When they get overheated, they urinate on their legs, relying on evaporation to cool them down. Storks share this behavior, while African vultures do not. Could the behavior be a clue to the real relationships between these birds?

Biologists solved the puzzle by analyzing DNA from all three species. Molecular analysis showed that the DNA from American vultures is more similar to the DNA of storks than to the DNA of African vultures. DNA evidence therefore suggests that American vultures and storks share a more recent common ancestor than the American and African vultures do. Molecular analysis is a powerful tool that is now routinely used by taxonomists to supplement data from anatomy and answer questions like these.

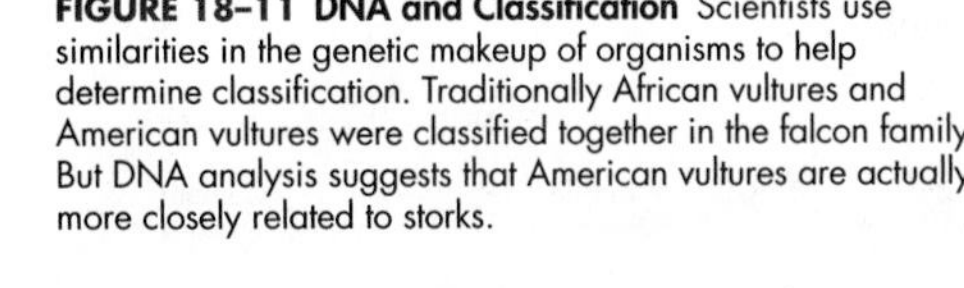

FIGURE 18–11 DNA and Classification Scientists use similarities in the genetic makeup of organisms to help determine classification. Traditionally African vultures and American vultures were classified together in the falcon family. But DNA analysis suggests that American vultures are actually more closely related to storks.

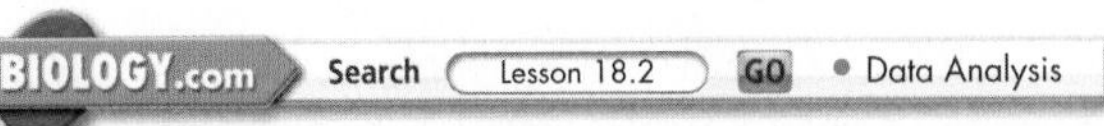

Lead a Discussion

Review with students what they learned about mitochondria in Chapter 7 and about mutations in Chapter 13. Then, discuss with students genes as derived characters.

Ask If a gene mutates and is passed along to offspring, how are those offspring different from other offspring within the species? *(The offspring with the mutated DNA will have a different genetic makeup than other offspring within the species.)*

Point out that the mutated form of the gene may be passed to each generation thereafter. DNA analysis can be used to determine whether a species is more closely related to one ancestor than to another by comparing the different forms of genes present in each species.

DIFFERENTIATED INSTRUCTION

L3 **Advanced Students** Have students make a cladogram similar to **Figure 18–10.** For this cladogram, though, have them use the example of American vultures, African vultures, and storks. Ask students to present their cladogram to the class and answer questions from other students about what it shows.

BIOLOGY.com Students can explore the case of finding a breeding partner for a sole surviving member of a Galápagos tortoise species in **Data Analysis: A Friend for Lonesome George.**

How Science Works

ARE WHALES CLOSELY RELATED TO HIPPOS?

DNA analysis is being used more and more in systematics. But, for some scientists, results from DNA analysis have to be confirmed by other types of evidence before evolutionary relationships among groups are accepted. For example, DNA studies as well as other biochemical evidence suggested that whales are closely related to animals in the order Artiodactyla, which includes camels, giraffes, pigs, and hippos. Some scientists doubted the connection, though, until fossils of whale "ankle bones" were discovered that are very similar to artiodactyl ankle bones. Together, DNA evidence and fossil evidence suggest that whales and hippos are closely related in evolutionary terms.

LESSON 18.2

Teach continued

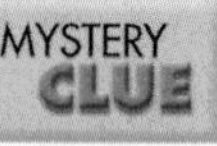

Guide students to suggest that, because some brown bears share a more recent common ancestor with polar bears than with other brown bears, brown bears and polar bears could be classified as one species. Students can go online to **Biology.com** to gather their evidence.

Assess and Remediate

EVALUATE UNDERSTANDING

Call on students to explain what a cladogram is, what a node is, what a derived character is, and what a clade is. If students have trouble explaining, call on volunteers for clarification. Then, have students complete the 18.2 Assessment.

REMEDIATION SUGGESTION

L1 Struggling Students If your students have difficulty answering **Questions 4a** and **4b,** draw the first cladogram in **Figure 18–9** on the board and suggest that, to help them answer the question, they think of species X as cats, Y as dogs, and Z as marsupials. Have pairs of students work through the questions again.

BIOLOGY.com Students can check their understanding of lesson concepts with the **Self-Test** assessment. They can then take an online version of the **Lesson Assessment.**

MYSTERY CLUE

DNA comparisons show that some populations of brown bears are more closely related to polar bears than they are to other brown bears. What do you think this means for the classification of polar bears?

Often, scientists use DNA evidence when anatomical traits alone can't provide clear answers. Giant pandas and red pandas, for example, have given taxonomists a lot of trouble. These two species share anatomical similarities with both bears and raccoons, and both of them have peculiar wrist bones that work like a human thumb. DNA analysis revealed that the giant panda shares a more recent common ancestor with bears than with raccoons. DNA places red pandas, however, outside the bear clade. So pandas have been reclassified, placed with other bears in the clade Ursidae, as shown in **Figure 18–12.** What happened to the red panda? It is now placed in a different clade that also includes raccoons and other organisms such as seals and weasels.

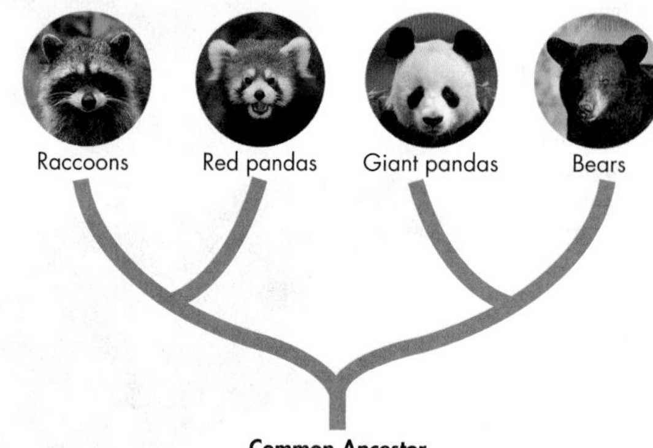

FIGURE 18–12 Classification of Pandas Biologists used to classify the red panda and the giant panda together. However, cladistic analysis using DNA suggests that the giant panda shares a more recent common ancestor with bears than with either red pandas or raccoons.

18.2 Assessment

IN NoS.6, B.8.2, B.8.3, B.8.4

Review Key Concepts

1. a. **Explain** How does evolutionary classification differ from traditional classification?
   b. **Apply Concepts** To an evolutionary taxonomist, what determines whether two species are in the same genus?
2. a. **Explain** What is a derived character?
   b. **Interpret Diagrams** Along any one lineage, what do the locations of derived characters on a cladogram show? In your answer, use examples from **Figure 18–9.**
3. a. **Review** How do taxonomists use the DNA sequences of species to determine how closely two species are related?
   b. **Relate Cause and Effect** Explain why the classification of American vultures has changed.

VISUAL THINKING

4. Examine the cladogram.
   a. **Interpret Diagrams** Which groups—X and Y, or X , Y, and Z—have the most recent common ancestor?
   b. **Infer** Which species—X and Y, or X and Z—share more derived characters?

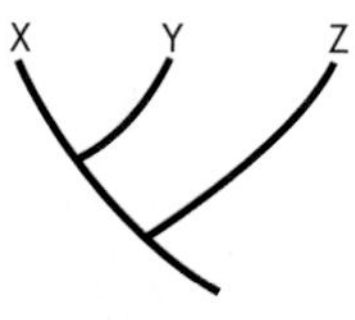

BIOLOGY.com Search Lesson 18.2 GO • Self-Test • Lesson Assessment

522 Chapter 18 • Lesson 2

Assessment Answers

1a. Traditional classification grouped organisms according to overall similarities and differences. Evolutionary classification groups species into larger categories that reflect hypotheses about lines of evolutionary descent.

1b. whether the two species share a more recent common ancestor with one another than they share with members of any other group

2a. a trait that arose in the common ancestor of a particular lineage and was passed along to its descendants

2b. Sample answer: Along any one lineage, the locations of derived characters show the order in which the characteristics arose in that lineage. For example, the cladogram in **Figure 18–9** shows that the trait of four limbs appeared before the trait of hair.

3a. In general, the more derived genetic characters shared by two species, the more recently they shared a common ancestor, and, therefore, the more closely they are related in evolutionary terms.

3b. American vultures used to be classified in the same family as African vultures. DNA evidence suggests that American vultures are more closely related to storks.

VISUAL THINKING

4a. X and Y

4b. X and Y

18.3 Building the Tree of Life

 B.8.2 Classification. Also covered: NoS.3, NoS.6, B.8.3, B.8.4.

THINK ABOUT IT The process of identifying and naming all known organisms, living and extinct, is a huge first step toward the goal of systematics. Yet naming organisms is only part of the work. The real challenge is to group everything, from bacteria to dinosaurs to blue whales, in a way that reflects their evolutionary relationships. Over the years, new information and ways of studying organisms have produced major changes in Linnaeus's original scheme for organizing living things.

Changing Ideas About Kingdoms

What are the six kingdoms of life as they are now identified?

During Linnaeus's time, the only known differences among living things were the fundamental characteristics that separated animals from plants. Animals were organisms that moved from place to place and used food for energy. Plants were green organisms that generally did not move and got their energy from the sun.

As biologists learned more about the natural world, they realized that Linnaeus's two kingdoms—Animalia and Plantae—did not reflect the full diversity of life. Classification systems have changed dramatically since Linnaeus's time, as shown in **Figure 18–13.** And hypotheses about relationships among organisms are still changing today as new data are gathered.

Key Questions

What are the six kingdoms of life as they are now identified?

What does the tree of life show?

Vocabulary

domain • Bacteria • Archaea • Eukarya

Taking Notes

Concept Map As you read, construct a concept map describing the characteristics of the three domains.

Kingdoms of Life, 1700s–1990s

First Introduced	Names of Kingdoms					
1700s	Plantae					Animalia
Late 1800s	Protista			Plantae		Animalia
1950s	Monera		Protista	Fungi	Plantae	Animalia
1990s	Eubacteria	Archaebacteria	Protista	Fungi	Plantae	Animalia

FIGURE 18–13 From Two to Six Kingdoms This diagram shows some of the ways in which organisms have been classified into kingdoms since the 1700s.

Getting Started

Objectives

18.3.1 Name the six kingdoms of life as they are currently identified.

18.3.2 Explain what the tree of life represents.

Student Resources

Study Workbook A and B, 18.3 Worksheets

Spanish Workbook, 18.3 Worksheets

Lab Manual B, 18.3 Data Analysis Worksheet

BIOLOGY.com Lesson Overview • Lesson Notes
- Activity: Art Review
- Assessment: Self-Test, Lesson Assessment

For corresponding lesson in the **Foundation Edition**, see pages 438–441.

Activate Prior Knowledge

Show students pictures of a variety of organisms, beginning with familiar plants and animals. In each case, ask them to identify the kingdom to which the organism belongs. After an initial few, mix in images of fungi, bacteria, and various protists, including amoeba, paramecium, and euglena. Challenge students to identify the kingdom each is a member of.

UbD Teach for Understanding

ENDURING UNDERSTANDING The diversity of life is the result of ongoing evolutionary change. Species alive today have evolved from ancient common ancestors.

GUIDING QUESTION What are the major groups within which all organisms are currently classified?

EVIDENCE OF UNDERSTANDING *After students have studied the lesson, give them the following assessment to show they understand the tree of life.* Ask each student to write a one-paragraph description of the tree of life, as shown in **Figure 18–18.** Explain that students do not have to describe everything shown in the tree, but they should include main ideas and important terms. Have students share their paragraphs with the class.

IN INDIANA ACADEMIC STANDARDS

For the full text of all standards, see the Course Overview in the front matter of this book.

B.8.2 Explain how organisms are classified and named based on their evolutionary relationships into taxonomic categories.

Teach

Lead a Discussion

Have students identify the difference between the kingdoms of the five-kingdom system and the kingdoms of the three-domain system. *(In the five-kingdom system, all bacteria were included in one kingdom, Monera. In the three-domain system, bacteria are split into two kingdoms, Eubacteria and Archaebacteria.)* Discuss how advanced technology, such as DNA analysis, is providing new information that has caused biologists to rethink how organisms should be classified. Then, call on volunteers to name organisms that are members of each of the six kingdoms.

DIFFERENTIATED INSTRUCTION

L1 Struggling Students For students who have a difficult time understanding how organisms are classified into kingdoms, provide them with more specific, guiding questions. Start by focusing their attention on **Figure 18–14.**

Ask Which kingdoms include eukaryotes? *("Protista," Fungi, Plantae, Animalia)*

Ask Which kingdoms include heterotrophs? *(all except Plantae)*

Ask What are examples of fungi? *(mushrooms, yeasts)*

ELL Focus on ELL: Access Content

ALL SPEAKERS Call students' attention to the table in **Figure 18–14.** Explain that a table is a way of presenting important information in shortened form. People who are learning English may find it easier to understand tables than text explanations. Point out the blue heading, **Six Kingdoms,** in the text. Show how the information in the boldface sentence corresponds to the second row of the table. Have students work with native or advanced high English speakers to read the text while referring to the table. The advanced speakers should help the beginning and intermediate speakers understand the words in the table, where necessary.

Use **Art Review: Three Domains** to reinforce the three-domain system of classification.

Comparing the Domains

The table in **Figure 18–14** compares the three domains and six kingdoms. Use the information in the table to answer the following questions.

1. Interpret Tables Which kingdom has cells that lack cell walls?

2. Interpret Tables Which domain contains multicellular organisms?

3. Compare and Contrast On the basis of information in the table, how are the members of domain Archaea similar to those of domain Bacteria? How are organisms in domain Archaea similar to those in domain Eukarya?

IN NoS.3, B.8.2

Five Kingdoms As researchers began to study microorganisms, they discovered that single-celled organisms were significantly different from plants and animals. At first all microorganisms were placed in their own kingdom, named Protista. Then yeasts and molds, along with mushrooms, were placed in their own kingdom, Fungi.

Later still, scientists realized that bacteria lack the nuclei, mitochondria, and chloroplasts found in other forms of life. All prokaryotes (bacteria) were placed in yet another new kingdom, Monera. Single-celled eukaryotic organisms remained in the kingdom Protista. This process produced five kingdoms: Monera, Protista, Fungi, Plantae, and Animalia.

Six Kingdoms By the 1990s, researchers had learned a great deal about the genetics and biochemistry of bacteria. That knowledge made clear that the organisms in kingdom Monera were actually two genetically and biochemically different groups. As a result, the monerans were separated into two kingdoms, Eubacteria and Archaebacteria, bringing the total number of kingdoms to six. **The six-kingdom system of classification includes the kingdoms Eubacteria, Archaebacteria, Protista, Fungi, Plantae, and Animalia.** This system of classification is shown in the bottom row of **Figure 18–13** on the previous page.

FIGURE 18–14 Three Domains Today organisms are grouped into three domains and six kingdoms. This table summarizes the key characteristics used to classify organisms into these major taxonomic groups.

Classification of Living Things

DOMAIN	Bacteria	Archaea	Eukarya			
KINGDOM	Eubacteria	Archaebacteria	"Protista"	Fungi	Plantae	Animalia
CELL TYPE	Prokaryote	Prokaryote	Eukaryote	Eukaryote	Eukaryote	Eukaryote
CELL STRUCTURES	Cell walls with peptidoglycan	Cell walls without peptidoglycan	Cell walls of cellulose in some; some have chloroplasts	Cell walls of chitin	Cell walls of cellulose; chloroplasts	No cell walls or chloroplasts
NUMBER OF CELLS	Unicellular	Unicellular	Most unicellular; some colonial; some multicellular	Most multicellular; some unicellular	Most multicellular: some green algae unicellular	Multicellular
MODE OF NUTRITION	Autotroph or heterotroph	Autotroph or heterotroph	Autotroph or heterotroph	Heterotroph	Autotroph	Heterotroph
EXAMPLES	*Streptococcus, Escherichia coli*	Methanogens, halophiles	*Amoeba, Paramecium,* slime molds, giant kelp	Mushrooms, yeasts	Mosses, ferns, flowering plants	Sponges, worms, insects, fishes, mammals

PPURPOSE Students will interpret information in a table to compare and contrast members of the three domains.

PLANNING Review with students the key characteristics of the members of each of the three domains.

ANSWERS

1. Animalia

2. Eukarya

3. Members of both Bacteria and Archaea are prokaryotes and unicellular, and members of both can be either autotrophs or heterotrophs. Members of both Archaea and Eukarya may be either autotrophs or heterotrophs. Some members of Eukarya and all members of Archaea are unicellular. Some members of Eukarya have cell walls, and all members of Archaea have cell walls.

Three Domains Genomic analysis has revealed that the two main prokaryotic groups are even more different from each other, and from eukaryotes, than previously thought. So biologists established a new taxonomic category—the domain. A **domain** is a larger, more inclusive category than a kingdom. Under this system, there are three domains—domain Bacteria (corresponding to the kingdom Eubacteria); domain Archaea (which corresponds to the kingdom Archaebacteria); and domain Eukarya (kingdoms Fungi, Plantae, and Animalia, and the "Protista").

Why do we put quotations around about the old kingdom Protista? Well, scientists now recognize that this is a paraphyletic group. This means that there is no way to put all unicellular eukaryotes into a clade that contains a single common ancestor, all of its descendants, and only those descendants. Since only monophyletic groups are valid under evolutionary classification, we use quotations to show that this is not a true clade. A summary of the three-domain system is shown in **Figure 18–14.**

The Tree of All Life

What does the tree of life show?

Remember that modern evolutionary classification is a rapidly changing science with a difficult goal—to present all life on a single evolutionary tree. As evolutionary biologists study relationships among taxa, they regularly change not only the way organisms are grouped, but also sometimes the names of groups. Remember that cladograms are visual presentations of hypotheses about relationships, and not hard and fast facts. **The tree of life shows current hypotheses regarding evolutionary relationships among the taxa within the three domains of life.**

Domain Bacteria Members of the domain **Bacteria** are unicellular and prokaryotic. Their cells have thick, rigid walls that surround a cell membrane. The cell walls contain a substance known as peptidoglycan (PEP tih doh gly kun). These bacteria are ecologically diverse, ranging from free-living soil organisms to deadly parasites. Some photosynthesize, while others do not. Some need oxygen to survive, while others are killed by oxygen. This domain corresponds to the kingdom Eubacteria.

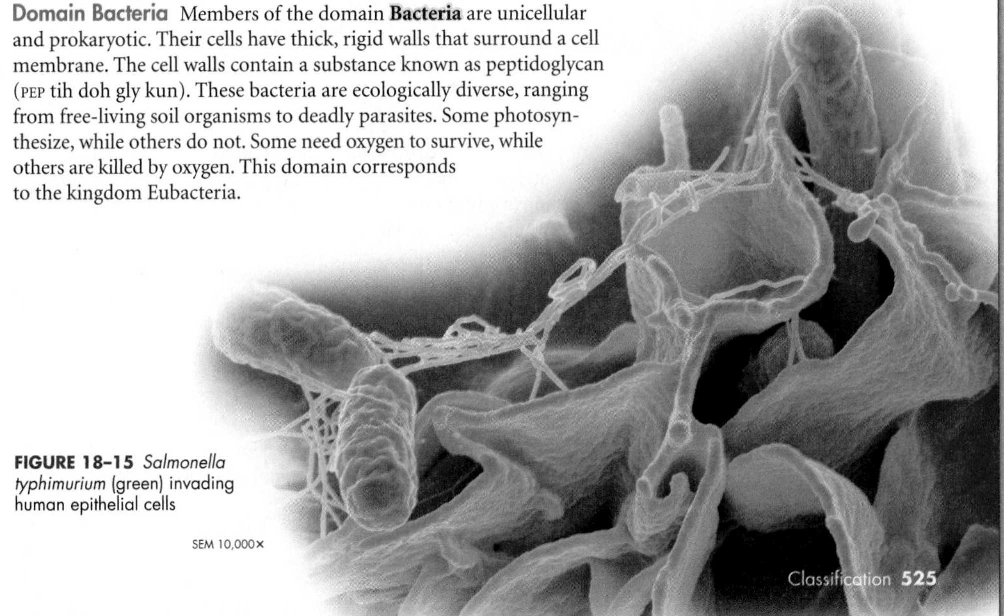

FIGURE 18–15 *Salmonella typhimurium* (green) invading human epithelial cells

SEM 10,000×

Build Reading Skills

Suggest students outline the text following the heading, **The Tree of All Life.** Start the outline on the board with these first-level entries: Domain Bacteria, Domain Archaea, Domain Eukarya. Tell students that the second level under the first three entries should be details from the text that explain or support the first level. For the last first-level entry, Domain Eukarya, students can use the subheadings: The "Protists," Fungi, Plantae, Animalia. Under each of these second-level entries, students should add details from the text.

DIFFERENTIATED INSTRUCTION

LPR **Less Proficient Readers** Help struggling readers by walking through the first part of the outline as a class. As students read through the section, write the following partial outline on the board:

Tree of Life

A. Domain Bacteria

1. members are unicellular and prokaryotic
2. members have cell walls containing peptidoglycan
3. members ecologically diverse
4. corresponds to kingdom Eubacteria

Have them work in pairs or small groups to complete the outline for **Domain Archaea** and **Domain Eukarya.**

Biology In-Depth

CHANGING CLASSIFICATION SYSTEMS

This text and many other modern sources use the three-domain, six-kingdom system. Because evolutionary classification is a rapidly changing science, students may encounter other systems when doing research. Some sources may use the three-domain system but with many more than six kingdoms. In some systems, the domains Bacteria and Archaea include several kingdoms each. Another system proposed by systematists includes six kingdoms, or supergroups, within the domain Eukarya. Students may encounter the name *Protoctista* in place of *Protista* in some systems. They may also see the term *division* instead of *phylum* as the taxon just below kingdom, especially in the classification of bacteria and plants.

Teach continued

Use Visuals

Use **Figure 18–18** to reinforce the three-domain system of classification. Make sure students understand that the blue, purple, and peach shading represents the domains while the actual color of the lines on the cladogram show which kingdom each lineage of organisms belong to.

Ask How can you tell by looking at the cladogram that each of the domains is its own clade? *(All of the organisms in each domain share a common ancestor.)*

DIFFERENTIATED INSTRUCTION

ELL English Language Learners Provide each student with an **ELL Frayer Model** to complete for the term *domain.* Have students write the word in the center box. Then, have them complete the page by writing a definition in the upper-right area, making a drawing to help them remember the definition in the upper-left area, writing the names of the three domains in the lower-left area, and, in the lower right, translating a description of the domains in their own language or in English, to the best of their ability.

Study Wkbks A/B, Appendix S26, ELL Frayer Model. **Transparencies,** GO10.

LPR Less Proficient Readers To help students visualize the three-domain system, make a **Concept Map** on the board, with an oval at the top containing Living Things. Beneath the title, write the word *include.* Then, draw three lines from that word to ovals containing the names of the domains: Bacteria, Archaea, and Eukarya. Add linking words and ovals for the characteristics of each domain. Have students copy the concept map into their notebooks.

Study Wkbks A/B, Appendix S21, Concept Map. **Transparencies,** GO4.

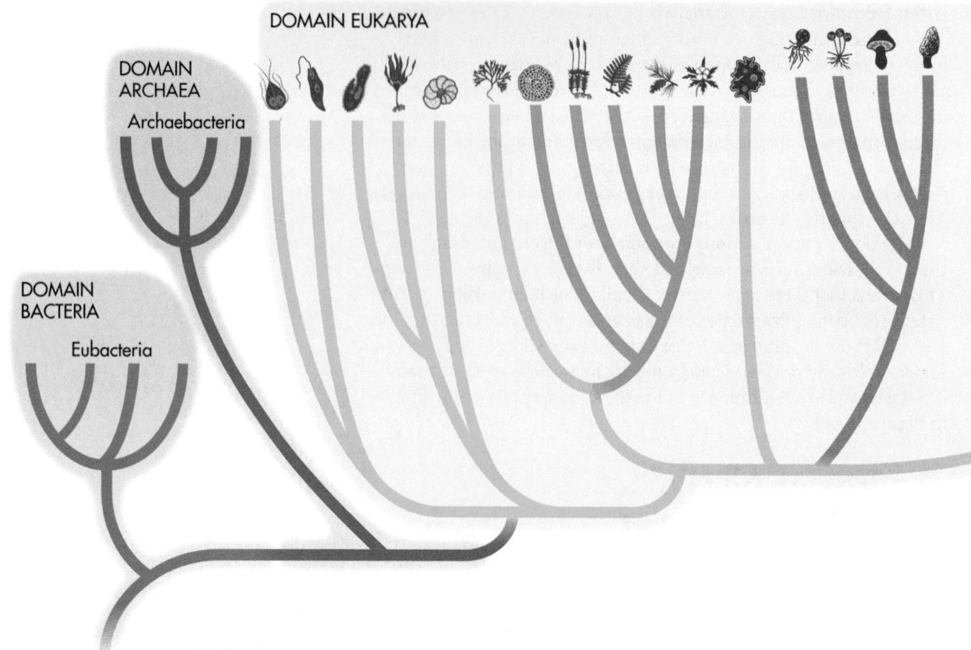

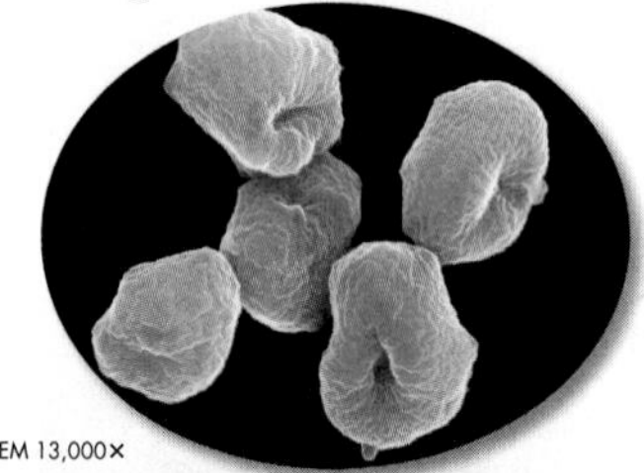
SEM 13,000×

FIGURE 18–16 ***Sulfolobus*** This member of the domain Archaea is found in hot springs and thrives in acidic and sulfur-rich environments.

Domain Archaea Also unicellular and prokaryotic, members of the domain **Archaea** (ahr KEE uh) live in some of the most extreme environments you can imagine—in volcanic hot springs, brine pools, and black organic mud totally devoid of oxygen. Indeed, many of these bacteria can survive only in the absence of oxygen. Their cell walls lack peptidoglycan, and their cell membranes contain unusual lipids that are not found in any other organism. The domain Archaea corresponds to the kingdom Archaebacteria.

Domain Eukarya The domain **Eukarya** consists of all organisms that have a nucleus. It comprises the four remaining major groups of the six-kingdom system: "Protista," Fungi, Plantae, and Animalia.

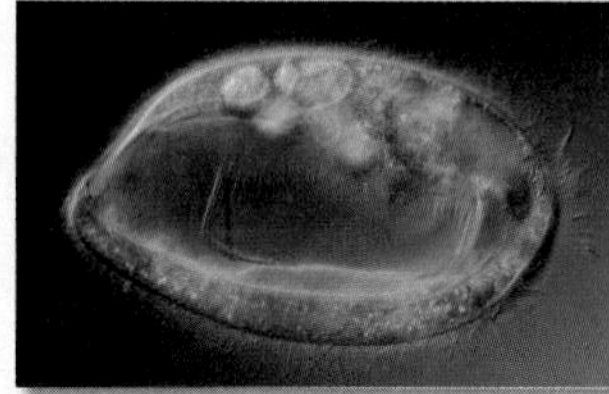
LM 900×

FIGURE 18–17 "Protists" "Protists" can live just about anywhere. This *Lembadion* is a freshwater ciliate.

▶ ***The "Protists": Unicellular Eukaryotes*** Recall that we are using quotations with this group to indicate that it is a paraphyletic group. Although some people still use the name "protists" to refer to these organisms, scientists who work with them have known for years that they do not form a valid clade. **Figure 18–18** reflects current cladistic analysis, which divides these organisms into at least five clades. The positions of these groups on the cladogram reflect its paraphyletic nature.

How Science Works

THE TREE OF LIFE WEB PROJECT

The Tree of Life Web Project is a database on the Internet that provides information about the evolutionary tree of life and other information about the diversity of life in the biosphere. The project was begun in the mid-1990s. The goal of the project is to have a Web page with information and images for every species and every group of organisms, both living and extinct. Hundreds of scientists from around the world have contributed to the database. The project includes information intended for both biologists and nonscientists. Connections from page to page are made by following phylogenetic branching patterns, similar to the branches of a cladogram. Users can move through the branches to find information about thousands of organisms.

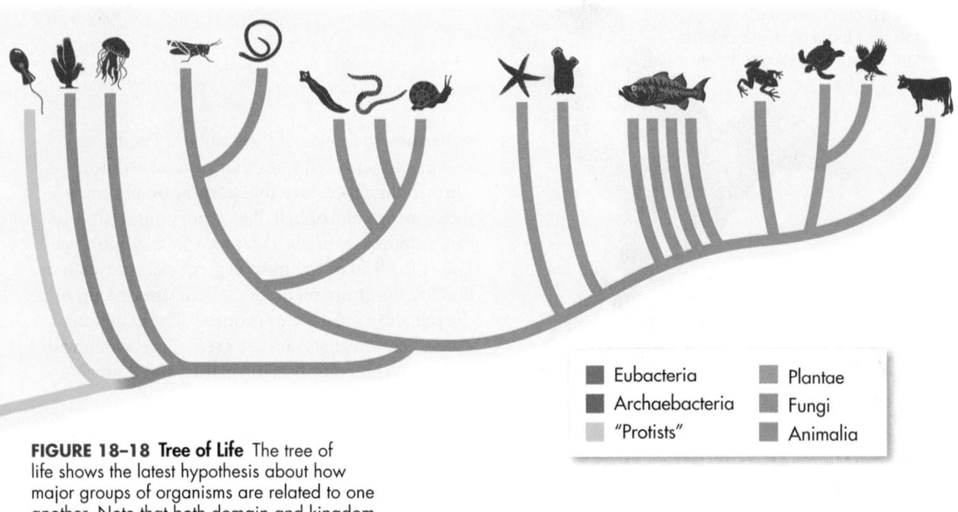

FIGURE 18–18 Tree of Life The tree of life shows the latest hypothesis about how major groups of organisms are related to one another. Note that both domain and kingdom designations are shown. Classify ***Which of the six kingdoms contains organisms that are not all in the same clade?***

Each group of "the eukaryotes formerly known as protists" is separate, and each shares closest common ancestors with other groups, rather than with each other. Most are unicellular, but one group, the brown algae, is multicellular. Some are photosynthetic, while others are heterotrophic. Some display characters that most closely resemble those of plants, fungi, or animals.

▶ ***Fungi*** Members of the kingdom Fungi are heterotrophs with cell walls containing chitin. Most feed on dead or decaying organic matter. Unlike other heterotrophs, fungi secrete digestive enzymes into their food source. After the digestive enzymes have broken down the food into smaller molecules, the fungi absorb the small molecules into their bodies. Mushrooms and other recognizable fungi are multicellular. Some fungi—yeasts, for example—are unicellular.

In Your Notebook *Explain why kingdom Protista is not valid under evolutionary classification.*

FIGURE 18–19 Ghost Fungus

Classification **527**

Lead a Discussion

Take the time to make sure students understand that, while the three domains each represent a clade, only five of the six kingdoms are clades. Explain that members of the kingdom Protista belong to different clades—and are thus not considered by biologists to be a true group. Despite this anomaly, the six kingdoms are often still used to group organisms, and students are likely to encounter the "kingdom Protista" in their studies. Be sure they understand the difference between classifying organisms by kingdoms and by clades, and how this book will often use quotation marks to indicate that Protista is not a group in cladistic classification.

DIFFERENTIATED INSTRUCTION

L1 Special Needs Use a model of the tree of life to help special needs students see or feel the way the tree branches. Ask volunteers to paste string, yarn, pipe cleaners, beads, thread, and shoelaces onto a poster board, using a different material for each kingdom and matching the branches on the model to the branches in **Figure 18–18.** A key can be made on a separate, smaller board that identifies each material with raised letters spelling out the kingdoms.

UbD Check for Understanding

ONE-MINUTE RESPONSE

Give students a minute to write a response to the following:

- What is the difference between the five-kingdom system of classification and the system of classification used in the tree of life shown in **Figure 18–18?** *(The five-kingdom system classified organisms into the five kingdoms Monera, Protista, Fungi, Plantae, and Animalia, while the system used in the tree of life includes the three domains, Bacteria, Archaea, and Eukarya, and six kingdoms, Eubacteria, Archaebacteria, Protista, Fungi, Plantae, and Animalia.)*

ADJUST INSTRUCTION

If students' responses are incorrect or incomplete, review the difference between domains and kingdoms and the differences in the two classification systems.

Answers

FIGURE 18–18 "Protists"

IN YOUR NOTEBOOK Members of the kingdom Protista fall into at least five clades that are *not* more closely related to each other than they are to other groups. In other words, they do not form a monophyletic clade, and only monophyletic groups are valid under evolutionary classification.

Assess and Remediate

EVALUATE UNDERSTANDING

Call on students at random to name the three domains and the six kingdoms in the three-domain system. After a kingdom is named, call on other students to identify examples of organisms in that kingdom. Then, have students complete the 18.3 Assessment.

REMEDIATION SUGGESTION

L1 Struggling Students If students have difficulty answering **Question 2c,** have them look again at **Figure 18–13.** Point out the changes in thinking that have occurred since the 1700s. Ask them to use the trend they can see to predict what will probably occur in the future.

BIOLOGY.com Students can check their understanding of lesson concepts with the **Self-Test** assessment. They can then take an online version of the **Lesson Assessment.**

FIGURE 18–20 Plants and Animals A sabre-wing hummingbird feeds on a pollinating ginger flower.

▶***Plantae*** Members of the kingdom Plantae are autotrophs with cell walls that contain cellulose. Autotrophic plants are able to carry on photosynthesis using chlorophyll. Plants are nonmotile—they cannot move from place to place. In this book, we follow the lead of the most current cladistic analysis, making the entire plant kingdom a sister group to the red algae, which are "protists." The plant kingdom, therefore, includes the green algae, along with mosses, ferns, cone-bearing plants, and flowering plants.

▶***Animalia*** Members of the kingdom Animalia are multicellular and heterotrophic. Animal cells do not have cell walls. Most animals can move about, at least for some part of their life cycle. As you will see in later chapters, there is incredible diversity within the animal kingdom, and many species of animals exist in nearly every part of the planet.

18.3 Assessment

IN NoS.3, B.8.2, B.8.3, B.8.4

Review Key Concepts

1. a. Review What are the six kingdoms of life as they are now identified?

b. Explain Why did systematists establish the domain?

c. Classify What were the monerans? Why did systematists split them into two kingdoms?

2. a. Review What are the three domains of life?

b. Explain Why are quotes used when describing the kingdom "Protista"?

c. Predict Do you think the tree of life cladogram will always stay the same as it is in **Figure 18–18?** Explain your answer.

ANALYZING DATA

3. The table compares some molecular characteristics of organisms in the three domains.

a. Interpret Tables Which domains have unbranched lipids in their cell membranes?

b. Interpret Tables Which domain has just one type of RNA polymerase?

c. Analyze Data On the basis of this table, how are archaea different from bacteria?

Molecular Characteristic	Domain		
	Bacteria	Archaea	Eukarya
Introns (parts of genes that do not code)	Rare	Sometimes present	Present
RNA polymerase	One type	Several types	Several types
Histones found with DNA	Not present	Present	Present
Lipids in cell membrane	Unbranched	Some branched	Unbranched

 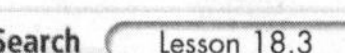  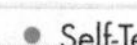

BIOLOGY.com Search Lesson 18.3 GO • Self-Test • Lesson Assessment

Assessment Answers

1a. Eubacteria, Archaebacteria, "Protista," Fungi, Plantae, Animalia

1b. Because genomic analysis revealed that the two main prokaryotic groups (eubacteria and archaebacteria) are more different from each other, and from eukaryotes, than previously thought.

1c. In the five-kingdom system, the Monera included all prokaryotes. Prokaryotes were split into two kingdoms because organisms in Monera are actually two genetically and biochemically different groups.

2a. Bacteria, Archaea, Eukarya

2b. Quotes are used to acknowledge that the kingdom Protista is paraphyletic, and therefore invalid under evolutionary classification.

2c. It will probably not stay the same. Through further research, biologists will likely discover new relationships among organisms that will lead to different classifications.

ANALYZING DATA

3a. In domains Bacteria and Eukarya, all lipids are unbranched; in Archaea, some are unbranched.

3b. Bacteria

3c. Introns are sometimes present in Archaea but rarely in Bacteria. Bacteria have only one type of RNA polymerase, while there are several types in Archaea. Histones are present in Archaea but not in Bacteria. There are only unbranched lipids in Bacteria; some lipids are branched in Archaea.

Technology & BIOLOGY

B.8.2 Classification. Also covered: NoS.10.

Bar-Coding Life

Until recently, classification has been a time-consuming process. A new project hopes to make identifying species as simple as scanning a supermarket bar code. It combines DNA sequencing with miniature computers, data processing, and the Internet.

To make this work, researchers picked a segment of DNA that all animals carry, the mitochondrial cytochrome oxidase (CO1) gene. (A chloroplast gene will probably be used for plants). Each base in the DNA sequence of CO1 is shown as a color-coded stripe, making it easy to spot differences between the barcodes of two specimens. The results are stored in a database.

Closely related species have similar bar codes. Species that are not closely related have bar codes that are very different from one another.

In the future, a researcher will be able to take a tiny sample of tissue or hair, analyze it using a portable device, and get a report on closest matches. Recent versions of this software even use maps to show where similar specimens have been collected before.

WRITING Learn more about DNA bar-coding on the Internet. Then write a paragraph describing another possible use for the DNA bar-coding technology.

▶ The bar code on the left belongs to the hermit thrush and the bar code on the right belongs to the American robin. Differences between the two bar codes, shown as lines in the middle column, show the genetic distance between the two species.

▶ Hermit Thrush

▶ American Robin

Quick Facts

BAR-CODING SPECIES

The bar-coding of all species on Earth will have many uses for scientists. For example:

- A bar code can be used to identify a member of a species at any stage of life, from larva to adulthood.
- Some species look very similar to other species, and bar codes will aid in telling the difference in such cases. For example, certain mosquitoes carry disease, while look-alike species are harmless.
- Bar codes will help in identifying new species, because the DNA sequence of a newly discovered species will not match any other bar-coded sequence.
- Bar-coding all the species identified with binomial names will provide a wealth of information about living things and help in building the tree of life.

Teach

Lead a Discussion

Direct students' attention to the two bar codes illustrated on the page. Have them compare the two, noting differences in the pattern of colors at many places along the codes, as indicated by lines in the middle column. Make sure students understand that these bar codes have been developed from the DNA of the two birds.

Ask What DNA do these bar codes show? *(a stretch of DNA in a mitochondrial gene in each bird)*

Ask Why would analyzing DNA in organisms be a good method for identifying them? *(Each species has a unique genetic makeup, both in nuclear DNA and in mitochondrial DNA.)*

DIFFERENTIATED INSTRUCTION

L1 **Struggling Students** For students who have trouble understanding DNA bar-coding technology, show the bar codes on different products, such as cereal or pasta. Have students use a hand lens to observe the differences in the bar codes. Explain that just as the price of different products can be identified by reading bar codes, the differences in DNA among organisms can be identified once bar codes are developed for different species.

Ask What do scientists use to make bar codes for different organisms? *(stretches of DNA)*

Answers

WRITING Answers will vary depending on the results of students' research. Possible uses for DNA bar-coding technology include protecting endangered species by making sure their meat or hides are not used in making commercial products, exploring the biodiversity of the deep parts of the ocean, identifying agricultural pests around the world, and identifying mosquitoes that carry diseases.

IN INDIANA ACADEMIC STANDARDS

For the full text of all standards, see the Course Overview in the front matter of this book.

CHAPTER LAB

Pre-Lab

Introduce students to the concepts they will explore in the chapter lab by assigning the Pre-Lab questions.

Lab

Tell students they will perform the chapter lab *Dichotomous Keys* described in **Lab Manual A.**

L1 **Struggling Students** A simpler version of the chapter lab is provided in **Lab Manual B.**

 Look online for **Editable Lab Worksheets.**

 For corresponding pre-lab in the **Foundation Edition**, see page 442.

Design Your Own Lab

OPEN-ENDED INQUIRY

 NoS.6 Use analogies and models.

Pre-Lab: Dichotomous Keys

Problem Can you construct a dichotomous key that can be used to identify organisms?

Materials reference materials

Lab Manual Chapter 18 Lab

Skills Focus Observe, Classify, Compare and Contrast, Sequence

Connect to the Big idea Given the enormous variety of life on Earth, not even experts can identify every organism they observe. Both experts and amateurs use dichotomous keys to identify organisms. These keys are based on the appearance of organisms. A key is a series of paired statements. Readers select the statement that best describes an organism at each step until the organism is identified and named. In this lab, you will practice using a dichotomous key. Then you will construct your own key for a group of organisms.

Background Questions

a. Review Why do biologists prefer to identify an organism by its scientific name?

b. Compare and Contrast Explain how the way modern biologists group species into larger categories is different from the system that Linnaeus used.

c. Review How many choices does a dichotomous key provide at each step?

Pre-Lab Questions

Preview the procedure in the lab manual.

1. Observe Name three different physical traits that are used in the shark dichotomous key.

2. Classify Do all the sharks you will try to identify belong to the same genus? Explain your answer.

3. Apply Concepts After you make a list of physical traits that you can use in your dichotomous key, how will you decide which trait to pick for the first step?

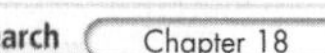 Search Chapter 18 GO

Visit Chapter 18 online to test yourself on chapter content and to find activities to help you learn.

Untamed Science Video Hop on board with the Untamed Science crew to find out how organisms are classified.

Art in Motion View a short animation that explains how to use a dichotomous key.

Art Review How well do you know the characteristics of the three domains? Test yourself in this activity.

InterActive Art Build your understanding of cladograms with this animation.

Data Analysis Investigate the problems involved in finding a mate for Lonesome George—the sole living member of his Galápagos tortoise species.

Pre-Lab Answers

BACKGROUND QUESTIONS

a. An organism can have many different common names. By using a scientific name, biologists can be sure that they are discussing the same organism.

b. Sample answer: Linnaeus based his groupings on easily observed traits. Modern biologists base their groupings on how recently organisms shared a common ancestor.

c. There are two choices at each step.

PRE-LAB QUESTIONS

1. Answers may include number of fins, body shape, mouth placement, and presence or absence of spines.

2. No, because the first word in each of their scientific names is different.

3. Sample answer: I will pick a trait that divides all the species into two smaller groups.

IN INDIANA ACADEMIC STANDARDS

For the full text of all standards, see the Course Overview in the front matter of this book.

18 Study Guide

Big idea Unity and Diversity of Life

The goal of biologists who classify organisms is to construct a tree of life that shows how all organisms are related to one another.

18.1 Finding Order in Diversity

In binomial nomenclature, each species is assigned a two-part scientific name.

The goal of systematics is to organize living things into groups that have biological meaning.

Over time, Linnaeus's original classification system expanded to include seven hierarchical taxa: species, genus, family, order, class, phylum, and kingdom.

binomial nomenclature (512)
genus (512)
systematics (512)
taxon (512)
family (513)
order (513)
class (514)
phylum (514)
kingdom (514)

18.2 Modern Evolutionary Classification

The goal of phylogenetic systematics, or evolutionary classification, is to group species into larger categories that reflect lines of evolutionary descent, rather than overall similarities and differences.

A cladogram links groups of organisms by showing how evolutionary lines, or lineages, branched off from common ancestors.

In general, the more derived genetic characters two species share, the more recently they shared a common ancestor and the more closely they are related in evolutionary terms.

phylogeny (516)
clade (516)
monophyletic group (516)
cladogram (517)
derived character (518)

18.3 Building the Tree of Life

The six-kingdom system of classification includes the kingdoms Eubacteria, Archaebacteria, Protista, Fungi, Plantae, and Animalia.

The tree of life shows current hypotheses regarding evolutionary relationships among the taxa within the three domains of life.

domain (525)
Bacteria (525)
Archaea (526)
Eukarya (526)

Think Visually Using the information in this chapter, complete the following Venn diagram comparing members of kingdom Plantae and kingdom Fungi.

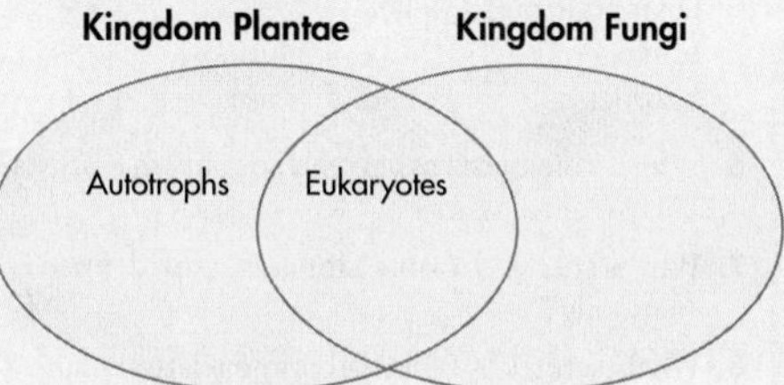

UbD Performance Tasks

SUMMATIVE TASK Have each student write a letter to the editor as if he or she were an organism being classified by systematists. The letter should take the perspective that being classified is an odd and perhaps disorienting experience. Write the following questions on the board to help students get started with their letters: How is being classified different in modern evolutionary classification as compared to the Linnaean system? What domain, kingdom, and other taxa is the organism classified in, and why?

TRANSFER TASK Have students work in small groups to create a booklet entitled *Organisms in the Neighborhood* that classifies at least 25 familiar organisms into domains, kingdoms, and other taxa, if possible. These organisms could include dogs, cats, specific birds, specific reptiles, trees, flowers, microorganisms in local streams or rivers, and so on. Students can use the classification section in the **Diversity Handbook** as well as any other reliable sources to help them in their classifications.

Study Online

BIOLOGY.com **REVIEW AND ASSESSMENT RESOURCES**

Editable Worksheets Pages of Study Workbooks A and B, Lab Manuals A and B, and the Assessment Resources Book are available online. These documents can be easily edited using a word-processing program.

Lesson Overview Have students reread the Lesson Overviews to help them study chapter concepts.

Vocabulary Review The *Flash Cards* and *Crossword* provide an interactive way to review chapter vocabulary.

Chapter Assessment Have students take an online version of the Chapter 18 Assessment.

Standardized Test Prep Students can take an online version of the Standardized Test Prep. You will receive their scores along with ideas for remediation.

Diagnostic and Benchmark Tests Use these tests to monitor your students' progress and supply remediation.

Answers

THINK VISUALLY

Heterotrophs (in kingdom Fungi oval). For an additional similarity, students might note that cell walls are present in both kingdoms. Additional differences the Venn diagram should show include the following: Plants have cell walls made of cellulose, while fungi have cell walls made of chitin; plants have chloroplasts, while fungi do not.

18 Assessment

The numbers following the questions refer to Indiana's Academic Standards for Biology I.

18.1 Finding Order in Diversity

Understand Key Concepts

1. The science of naming and grouping organisms is called
   a. anatomy.
   b. systematics.
   c. botany.
   d. paleontology.
2. Solely from its name, you know that *Rhizopus nigricans* must be
   a. a plant.
   b. an animal.
   c. in the genus *Nigricans.*
   d. in the genus *Rhizopus.*
3. A useful classification system does NOT
   a. show relationships.
   b. reveal evolutionary trends.
   c. use different scientific names for the same organism.
   d. change the taxon of an organism based on new data.
4. In Linnaeus's system of classifying organisms, orders are grouped together into
   a. classes.
   b. species.
   c. families.
   d. genera.
5. The largest and most inclusive of the Linnaean taxonomic ranks is the
   a. kingdom.
   b. order.
   c. phylum.
   d. domain.
6. Why do biologists assign each organism a universally accepted name?
7. Why is species the only Linnaean rank defined "naturally"?
8. What features of binomial nomenclature make it useful for scientists of all nations?
9. What is a taxon?

Think Critically

10. **Apply Concepts** What is a major problem with traditional classification? Give an example that demonstrates this problem. B.8.2
11. **Use Analogies** Why is it important for a supermarket to have a classification scheme for displaying the foods that it sells? NoS.6
12. **Classify** Venn diagrams can be used to make models of hierarchical classification schemes. A Venn diagram is shown below. Four groups are represented by circular regions—A, B, C, and D. Each region represents a collection of organisms or members of a taxonomic level. Regions that overlap, or intersect, share common members. Regions that do not overlap do not have members in common. Use the following terms to label the regions shown in the diagram: *kingdom Animalia, phylum Chordata, class Insecta,* and *class Mammalia.* NoS.6

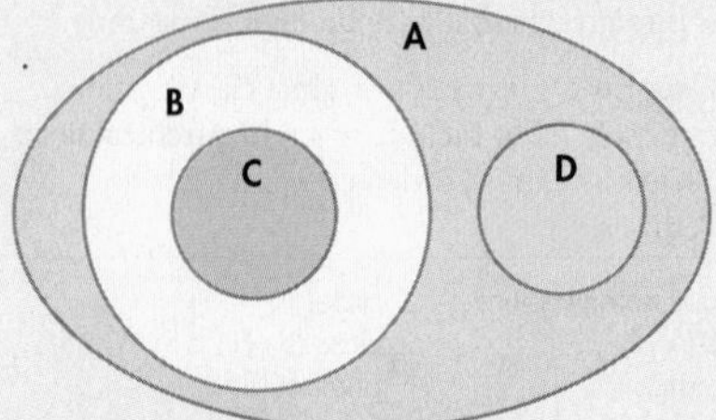

18.2 Modern Evolutionary Classification

Understand Key Concepts

13. A group that is limited to a common ancestor and all of its descendants is called a
    a. taxon.
    b. phylogeny.
    c. tree of life.
    d. monophyletic group.
14. A specific trait that is used to construct a cladogram is called a B.8.2
    a. taxon.
    b. structural feature.
    c. clade.
    d. derived character.
15. A branch of a cladogram that consists of a single common ancestor and all the descendants of that ancestor is called
    a. cladistics.
    b. a kingdom.
    c. a clade.
    d. a class.
16. What does each individual node in a cladogram represent?
17. Why can differences in mitochondrial DNA be used as derived characters? B.8.2, B.8.4
18. What is phylogeny?

Lesson 18.1

UNDERSTAND KEY CONCEPTS

1. b **2.** d **3.** c **4.** a

5. a

6. Referring to organisms by common names is confusing since they can vary from place to place.

7. Reproduction to form fertile offspring defines a species, but all of the other Linnaean ranks are defined by scientists.

8. Names are standardized under binomial nomenclature.

9. a classification group with biological meaning

THINK CRITICALLY

10. Sample answer: A major problem is that classifying according to overall similarities can be misleading. For example, dolphins could be misclassified as fishes because they have fins, but dolphins are mammals, not fishes.

11. Sample answer: so customers know where to find the items they want to buy

12. A: kingdom Animalia; B: phylum Chordata; C: class Mammalia; D: class Insecta

Lesson 18.2

UNDERSTAND KEY CONCEPTS

13. d **14.** d **15.** c

16. the last common ancestor shared by members of the branches above that node

17. Different forms of mitochondrial genes are found in all eukaryotic organisms. Because all genes mutate over time, shared genes contain differences that can be treated as derived characters in cladistic analysis.

18. the study of how living and extinct organisms are related to one another

THINK CRITICALLY

19. Sample answer: By analyzing which derived characters both snakes and worms share; this could be done by comparing internal structures and DNA sequences.

20. Linnaeus would ask about the physical differences or similarities between organisms. A modern systematist would ask how closely related an organism is to other organisms based on shared derived characters.

21. If the DNA of beetle A and the DNA of beetle B are more similar to each other than to the DNA of beetle C, then beetle A is likely more closely related to beetle B than to beetle C.

22. Sample answer: Natural selection results in the evolution of derived characteristics used to determine phylogeny.

23. Only members of clade Mammalia have hair, but many groups have four limbs. Four limbs did not evolve in the most recent common ancestor of all mammals, but evolved further back in the ancestor of all tetrapods. Four limbs is therefore a derived character for clade Tetrapoda.

Lesson 18.3

UNDERSTAND KEY CONCEPTS

24. c **25.** b

26. A kingdom is the largest and most inclusive category of the Linnaean classification system. A domain, used in modern evolutionary classification, is a larger, more inclusive category than a kingdom.

27. The organism is a prokaryote, has cell walls with peptidoglycan, and is unicellular.

Think Critically

19. Apply Concepts Both snakes and worms are tubular, with no legs. How could you determine whether their similarity in shape means that they share a recent common ancestor? B.8.2

20. Pose Questions What questions would Linnaeus ask to determine a classification? What questions would a modern systematist ask? B.8.2

21. Apply Concepts You are a biologist who is searching for new species in the Amazon jungle. You find two new species of beetles, beetle A and beetle B, that resemble each other closely but have somewhat different markings on their wings. In addition, both beetle A and beetle B resemble beetle C, a species that has already been identified. How could DNA similarities be used to help determine whether beetle A and beetle B are more closely related to each other or to beetle C? B.8.2

22. Infer What is the relationship between natural selection and phylogeny?

23. Apply Concepts Explain why hair is a derived character for clade Mammalia but having four limbs is not. For which clade is four limbs a derived character? B.8.2

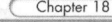

18.3 Building the Tree of Life

Understand Key Concepts

24. The three domains are
- **a.** Animalia, Plantae, and Archaebacteria.
- **b.** Plantae, Fungi, and Eubacteria.
- **c.** Bacteria, Archaea, and Eukarya.
- **d.** Protista, Bacteria, and Animalia.

25. Which of the following kingdoms includes only heterotrophs?
- **a.** Protista
- **b.** Fungi
- **c.** Plantae
- **d.** Eubacteria

26. How do domains and kingdoms differ?

27. What characteristics are used to place an organism in the domain Bacteria? B.8.2

solve the CHAPTER MYSTERY

GRIN AND BEAR IT

Most biologists classify the polar bear, *Ursus maritimus,* as a separate species from the brown bear, *Ursus arctos.* The teeth, body shape, metabolism, and behavior of polar bears are very different from those of brown bears. But some systematists are now questioning that classification.

Are polar bears and brown bears two distinct species? The answer depends on what a species is. The usual definition of *species* is "a group of similar organisms that can breed and produce fertile offspring." Polar bears and brown bears can, in fact, mate and produce offspring that are fertile. However, in the natural environment, polar bears and brown bears almost never mate.

The question is complicated by DNA analysis. There are different populations of brown bears, and these different populations have somewhat different genetic makeups. DNA analysis has shown that some populations of brown bears are more closely related to polar bears than they are to other populations of brown bears. According to DNA analysis, if polar bears are indeed a separate species, brown bears by themselves do not form a single clade.

1. Classify List the evidence that supports classifying polar bears and brown bears into two different species. Then list the evidence that indicates that polar bears and brown bears belong to the same species.

2. Infer What evidence indicates that different populations of brown bears belong to different clades?

3. Connect to the Big idea Do you think that the classic definition of *species*—"a group of similar organisms that can breed and produce fertile offspring"—is still adequate? Why or why not?

IN B.8.2, B.8.4

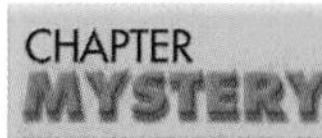

After students have read through the Chapter Mystery, discuss the difficulties in classifying polar bears and brown bears.

Ask Why have polar bears and brown bears traditionally been classified into different species in the Linnaean system? *(Linnaean classification groups organisms using observable similarities and differences. The differences between polar bears and brown bears—including color, teeth, body shape, metabolism, and behavior—determined their classification into different species.)*

Ask Why don't brown bears by themselves form a separate clade? *(A clade is a group of organisms that includes a single common ancestor and all descendants of that ancestor. DNA analysis shows that some brown bears are more closely related to polar bears than to other brown bears. Therefore, for all brown bears to be in a single clade, that clade would have to include polar bears.)*

CHAPTER MYSTERY ANSWERS

1. Evidence supporting separation: Polar bears and brown bears are different colors and different sizes. The teeth, body shape, metabolism, and behavior of the two types of bears are very different. In the natural environment, polar bears and brown bears almost never mate. Evidence indicating they belong to the same species: Polar bears and brown bears can mate and produce fertile offspring. DNA analysis shows that some populations of brown bears are more closely related to polar bears than to other brown bears.

2. Different populations of brown bears are more closely related to polar bears than to one another.

3. Big idea Sample answer: The classic definition of species is still valid, because it is still useful in many cases. Many organisms can be classified into separate species if they cannot or do not successfully mate and produce fertile offspring. This definition can help scientists determine evolutionary relationships, even if it doesn't hold true in all cases.

Students can learn more about the classification of new organisms by watching **Finned Kin.**

28. Archaea
29. Students should describe the defining characteristics of the kingdoms "Protista," Fungi, Plantae, and Animalia.
30. The main difference is that fungi are eukaryotic organisms, while eubacteria are prokaryotic organisms. Most fungi are multicellular, while all eubacteria are unicellular. All fungi are heterotrophs, while some eubacteria are autotrophs.
31. evolutionary relationships among groups

THINK CRITICALLY

32. Protists don't form a single clade. Current cladistic analysis divides these organisms into at least five distinct and only distantly related groups.
33. Organism A: Animal; Organism B: Archaea; Organism C: Fungi

Connecting Concepts

USE SCIENCE GRAPHICS

34. groups B and C
35. the last common ancestor shared by members of groups B and C
36. group A

WRITE ABOUT SCIENCE

37. Sample answer: Similarities and differences in DNA can be used to develop hypotheses about evolutionary relationships. In general, the more similar the DNA sequences of two species, the more recently they shared a common ancestor, and the more closely they are related in evolutionary terms. For example, the genetic makeup of the American vulture and the stork are similar, and that suggests these birds are more closely related than previously thought.
38. Big idea Students should explain that the tree of life shows systematists' latest hypothesis about how the major groups of organisms, represented by the branches, are related to one another. The base represents the first organisms that gave rise to all other organisms. Students might suggest research may discover evolutionary relationships that were unknown before, and, as a result, change the structure of the tree of life.

28. Which domain consists of prokaryotes whose cell walls lack peptidoglycan? B.8.2
29. Describe the four kingdoms that make up the domain Eukarya. B.8.2
30. What characteristic(s) differentiate the kingdom Fungi from the kingdom Eubacteria? B.8.2
31. What do the branches of the tree of life try to show? B.8.2

Think Critically

32. **Classify** In terms of cladistic analysis, what is the problem with placing all members of kingdom Protista into the same clade? B.8.3, B.8.4
33. **Classify** Study the descriptions of the following organisms, and place them in the correct kingdom.
Organism A: Multicellular eukaryote without cell walls
Organism B: Its cell walls lack peptidoglycan, and its cell membranes contain certain lipids that are not found in other organisms. It lives in an extreme environment and can survive only in the absence of oxygen.
Organism C: Unicellular eukaryote with cell walls of chitin B.8.2

Connecting Concepts

Use Science Graphics NoS.3

The cladogram below shows the relationships among three imaginary groups of organisms—groups A, B, and C. Use the cladogram to answer questions 34–36.

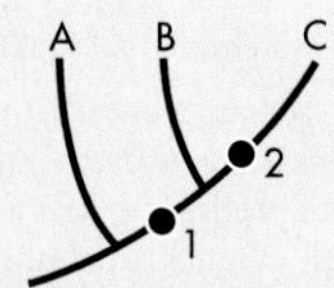

34. **Interpret Visuals** Which groups share derived character 1? B.8.2
35. **Apply Concepts** What does the node, or fork, between groups B and C represent? B.8.2
36. **Apply Concepts** Which group split off from the other groups first? B.8.2

Write About Science NoS.3

37. **Explanation** Write a short explanation of the way in which taxonomists use similarities and differences in DNA to help classify organisms and infer evolutionary relationships. (*Hint:* Use a specific example to help clarify your explanation.) B.8.3, B.8.4
38. **Assess the Big idea** Explain what the tree of life is and what its various parts represent. Also explain why the tree of life probably will change. (*Hint:* When you explain what the various parts represent, use the terms *base* and *branches*.) B.8.2, B.8.3

NoS.3

Use the table to answer questions 39–41.

	Turtle	Lamprey	Frog	Fish	Cat
Hair	No	No	No	No	Yes
Amniotic egg	Yes	No	No	No	Yes
Four legs	Yes	No	Yes	No	Yes
Jaw	Yes	No	Yes	Yes	Yes
Vertebrae	Yes	Yes	Yes	Yes	Yes

39. **Interpret Tables** The first column lists derived characters that can be used to make a cladogram of vertebrates. Which characteristic is shared by the most organisms? Which by the fewest? B.8.2
40. **Sequence** From the information given, place the animals in sequence from the most recently evolved to the most ancient. B.8.2, B.8.3
41. **Draw Conclusions** Of the following pairs—lamprey-turtle, fish-cat, and frog-turtle—which are probably most closely related? B.8.2, B.8.3

PURPOSE Students will analyze data in a table and draw conclusions about the sequence of evolution of selected animals.

PLANNING Review with students what derived characters are and how derived characters are used in constructing a cladogram.

ANSWERS

39. Presence of vertebrae is the derived character shared by the most; hair is the derived character shared by the fewest.
40. cat, turtle, frog, fish, lamprey
41. frog and turtle

Standardized Test Practice for Indiana

Multiple Choice

1. Which of the following is NOT a characteristic of Linnaeus's system for naming organisms?
   A two-part name
   B multipart name describing several traits
   C name that identifies the organism's genus
   D name that includes the organism's species identifier

2. In which of the following are the Linnaean ranks in correct order?
   A phylum, kingdom, species
   B genus, order, family
   C kingdom, phylum, class
   D order, class, family

3. In the six-kingdom system of classifying living things, which kingdoms contain unicellular organisms?
   A Eubacteria only
   B Eubacteria and "Protista" only
   C Archaebacteria only
   D Eubacteria, Archaebacteria, Plantae, and "Protista" B.8.2

4. If species A and B have very similar genes, which of the following statements is probably true?
   A Species A and B shared a relatively recent common ancestor.
   B Species A evolved independently of species B for a long period.
   C Species A and species B are the same species.
   D Species A is older than species B. B.8.3, B.8.4

5. The taxon called Eukarya is a(n)
   A order. C kingdom.
   B phylum. D domain.

6. Members of the kingdom "Protista" are classified into
   A two domains. C three species.
   B three domains. D three kingdoms.

Questions 7–9

The cladogram below shows the evolutionary relationships among four groups of plants.

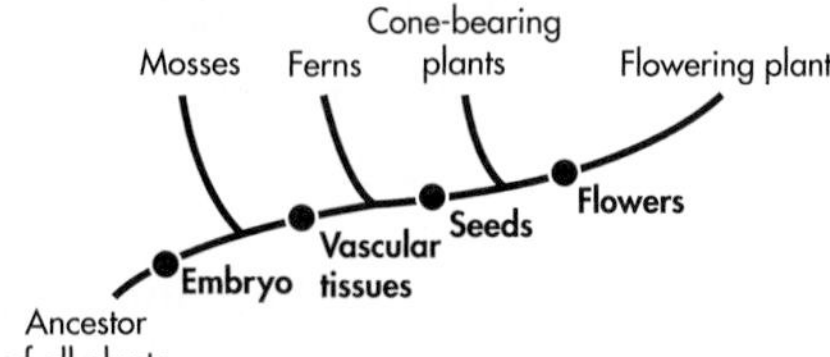

7. Which of the following groups, taken by themselves, do NOT form a clade?
   A cone-bearing plants and flowering plants
   B ferns, cone-bearing plants, and flowering plants
   C mosses and ferns
   D mosses, ferns, cone-bearing plants, and flowering plants B.8.2

8. Which of the following groups share the most recent common ancestor?
   A cone-bearing plants and flowering plants
   B mosses and ferns
   C mosses and cone-bearing plants
   D ferns and flowering plants B.8.2, B.8.3

9. Which derived character appeared first during the course of the plants' evolution?
   A seeds
   B flowers
   C embryo
   D vascular tissues B.8.3, B.8.4

Open-Ended Response

10. Why have biologists changed many of Linnaeus's original classifications of organisms? B.8.2

If You Have Trouble With . . .

Question	1	2	3	4	5	6	7	8	9	10
See Lesson	18.1	18.1	18.3	18.2	18.3	18.3	18.2	18.2	18.2	18.2

ASSESSMENT

Answers

1. B
2. C
3. D
4. A
5. D
6. A
7. C
8. A
9. C
10. Sample answer: Linnaeus based his classification on observable similarities and differences among organisms. Modern evolutionary classification groups species into larger categories that reflect lines of evolutionary descent. Also, modern systematists use biochemical similarities to determine classification.

Test-Taking Tip

USE TIME WISELY

Tell students that when they take a test, they need to pay attention to the time that they are spending on sections of the test and on individual questions. If students do not know the answer to a multiple-choice question, they should skip it and come back to it later, if time permits. If the test contains a constructed-response question that requires a long answer, students need to allocate time to plan their responses as well as to write them.

CHAPTER PLANNER 19 History of Life

Chapter Contents	IN	Time	Core Resources
Chapter Preview			**Student Edition,** pp. 536–537 **Chapter Mystery,** p. 537
19.1 The Fossil Record Fossils and Ancient Life • Dating Earth's History • Geologic Time Scale • Processes Affecting Life's History	NoS.6	1 period 1/2 block	**Student Edition,** pp. 538–545 Inquiry 19.1 Quick Lab, p. 541 L2 **Study Workbook A** 19.1 Worksheets L2 Biology.com *Art in Motion:* Fossil Formation • *Visual Analogy:* Geologic Time as a Clock **Assessment Resources Book** Visual Quiz L2
19.2 Patterns and Processes of Evolution Speciation and Extinction • Rate of Evolution • Adaptive Radiation and Convergent Evolution • Coevolution	NoS.3, B.8.5	1 period 1/2 block	**Student Edition,** pp. 546–552 Inquiry 19.2 Analyzing Data, p. 548 L2 **Study Workbook A** 19.2 Worksheets L2 Biology.com *Data Analysis:* Explaining Extinctions • 19.2 Self-Test • 19.2 Lesson Assessment
19.3 Earth's Early History The Mysteries of Life's Origins • Origin of Eukaryotic Cells • Sexual Reproduction and Multicellularity • *Careers & Biology: Fossil Preparator, Museum Guide, Paleontologist*	NoS.3, B.6.5, B.8.1, B.8.6, B.8.7	1 period 1/2 block	**Student Edition,** pp. 553–563 Inquiry 19.3 Analyzing Data, p. 556 L2 **Study Workbook A** 19.3 Worksheets L2 Biology.com *Art Review:* Conditions on the Early Earth **Assessment Resources Book** Visual Quiz L2
Chapter Pre-Lab	NoS.6	1 period 1/2 block	**Student Edition,** p. 564 L2 **Lab Manual A** *Using Index Fossils* L2

Differentiated Instruction Tools

Study Workbook B includes worksheets with lesson-level differentiated instruction support and explanations of differentiated instruction teaching strategies.

Lab Manual B includes skills labs, simplified chapter labs, and hands-on activities.

ELL Handbook explains ways to make *Biology* more accessible to ELL students.

Spanish Study Workbook is a Spanish translation of Study Workbook A.

Multilingual Glossary is the glossary translated into ten languages.

Differentiated Instruction Key

- L1 Special Needs or Struggling Students
- ELL English Language Learners
- LPR Less Proficient Readers
- L2 On-Level Students
- L3 Advanced Students

Additional Resources

Biology.com Untamed Science Video • Vocabulary Flash Cards

Study Workbook B 19.1 Worksheets L1 ELL LPR
Spanish Study Workbook 19.1 Worksheets ELL
Biology.com 19.1 Lesson Overview • 19.1 Lesson Notes • 19.1 Self-Test • 19.1 Lesson Assessment

Study Workbook B 19.2 Worksheets L1 ELL LPR
Spanish Study Workbook 19.2 Worksheets ELL
Biology.com 19.2 Lesson Overview • 19.2 Lesson Notes

Study Workbook B 19.3 Worksheets L1 ELL LPR
Spanish Study Workbook 19.3 Worksheets ELL
Biology.com 19.3 Lesson Overview • 19.3 Lesson Notes • 19.3 Self-Test • 19.3 Lesson Assessment

Lab Manual B *Using Index Fossils* • Data Analysis: *Extinctions Through Time* • Hands-On Activity: *Stepping Through Time* L1 ELL LPR

Chapter Review

Student Edition Study Guide, p. 565 L2 • Unit Project, p. 520
Study Workbook A Chapter 19 Vocabulary Review L2 • Chapter 19 Chapter Mystery/21st Century Skills Activity L2 L3
Transparencies, pp. 226–239 L1 ELL LPR L2
Biology.com Untamed Science Video • You're the Director • Editable Worksheets of Study Workbooks A and B and Lab Manuals A and B • Chapter 19 Flash Cards and Crossword

Untamed Science DVD • Classroom Resources CD (includes lesson presentations and editable worksheets)

Chapter Assessment

Student Edition Assessment, pp. 566–569 L2
Study Workbook B Chapter 19 Chapter Review L1 ELL LPR • Chapter 19 Taking a Standardized Test L1 ELL LPR
Assessment Resources Book Chapter 19 Test A L2 • Chapter 19 Test B L1 ELL LPR • Unit 5 Test A L2 • Unit 5 Test B L1 ELL LPR
Biology.com Chapter 19 Assessment • Editable Worksheets of Chapter 19 Visual Quizzes, Chapter 19 Tests A and B, and Unit 5 Tests A and B

Exam*View Assessment Suite* • Classroom Resources CD (includes lesson presentations and editable worksheets)

Time: 1 period, 1/2 block

Pressed for Time?

Preview the Chapter Introduce students to the chapter with the first two Key Questions for Lessons 19.1 and 19.2. Preview the pictures on pp. 560–563 and discuss how living things have changed over time.

Cover the Chapter Quickly Assign students to read *Fossils and Ancient Life* and *Dating Earth's History* in Lesson 19.1. Go over Figures 19–2 and 19–3. Assign all of Lesson 19.2 and *The Mysteries of Life's Origins* in Lesson19.3.

Assess Assign questions 1, 2, and 5 in the 19.1 Assessment, the 19.2 Assessment, and question 1 in the 19.3 Assessment. In the Chapter 19 Assessment, assign questions 1–4, 6, 7, 10–22, 24–27, 29, and 31–36.

CHAPTER 19

Connect to the Big Idea

Call attention to the fossilized ichthyosaur shown in the photograph. Ask students to describe the ichthyosaur by looking at the fossil. *(Sample answer: It had flipperlike appendages, a tail, and a pointed beak.)* Explain that everything scientists know about these organisms has been derived from studying their fossils. Ask students to predict what a fossil might reveal about an organism. *(its size and structure, the environment it lived in, what it might have eaten, whether or not it gave birth to live young)* Ask what the presence of fossils like these large marine reptiles in places like Kansas and South Dakota suggests about the environment in ancient times. *(Sample answer: It suggests that these areas were underwater at one time.)* Have students anticipate an answer to the question, **How do fossils help biologists understand the history of life on Earth?**

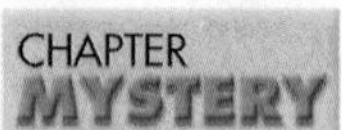

After students have read over the Chapter Mystery, explain that the Permian extinction is one of five well-documented mass extinctions in Earth's history. The best known is the extinction at the end of the Mesozoic that included the dinosaurs. The Permian extinction, however, was far more devastating, and far more mysterious. Ask students to think about the kinds of evidence scientists might look for to figure out what caused the Permian extinction.

BIOLOGY.com Have students preview the chapter vocabulary terms using the **Flash Cards.**

IN INDIANA ACADEMIC STANDARDS

For the full text of all standards, see the Course Overview in the front matter of this book.

Key standards: Chapter 19 covers key ideas from Standard 8: Evolution, including **B.8.1** History of life on Earth, **B.8.4** Survival and reproduction, and **B.8.7** Origins of life on Earth.

19 History of Life

Big idea Evolution

Q: How do fossils help biologists understand the history of life on Earth?

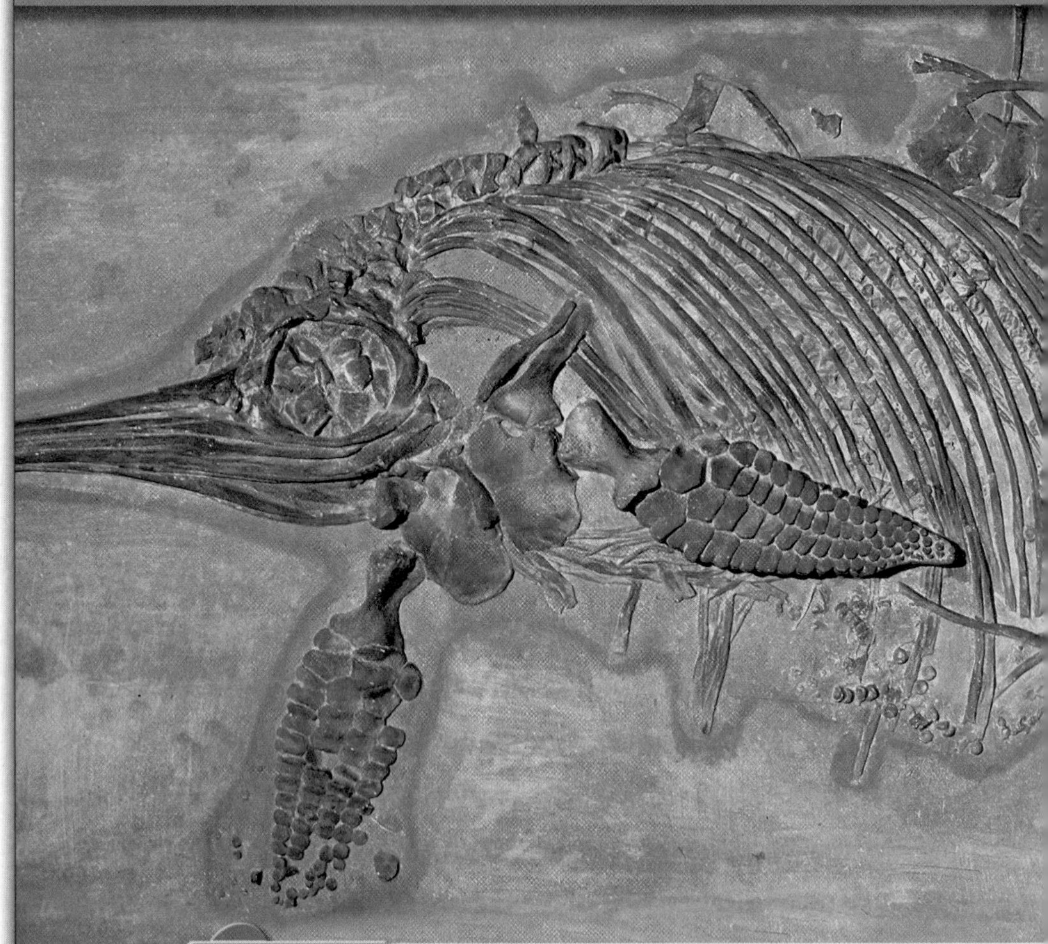

BIOLOGY.com Search Chapter 19 GO • Flash Cards

536

UbD Understanding by Design

Chapter 19 further explores the Big Idea of Evolution. Students explore fossil evidence for evolution, the geologic time scale, macroevolution patterns, and what's known about early Earth and the origin of life. The graphic organizer at the right shows how these ideas are connected to the chapter Essential Question and lesson Guiding Questions. These ideas and questions relate to the Unit 5 Enduring Understanding that *the diversity of life is the result of ongoing evolutionary change. Species alive today have evolved from ancient common ancestors.*

PERFORMANCE GOALS

In Chapter 19, students infer causes of the Permian extinction, summarize what they learned about Earth's history in a visual presentation, and predict the distribution of fossils based on organisms that exist today.

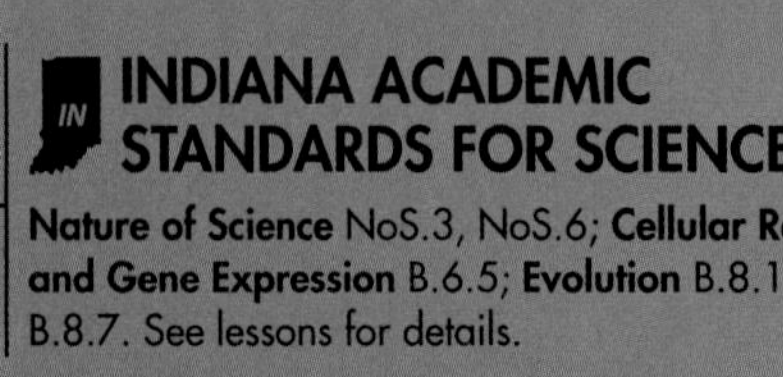

INDIANA ACADEMIC STANDARDS FOR SCIENCE

Nature of Science NoS.3, NoS.6; **Cellular Reproduction and Gene Expression** B.6.5; **Evolution** B.8.1, B.8.4, B.8.6, B.8.7. See lessons for details.

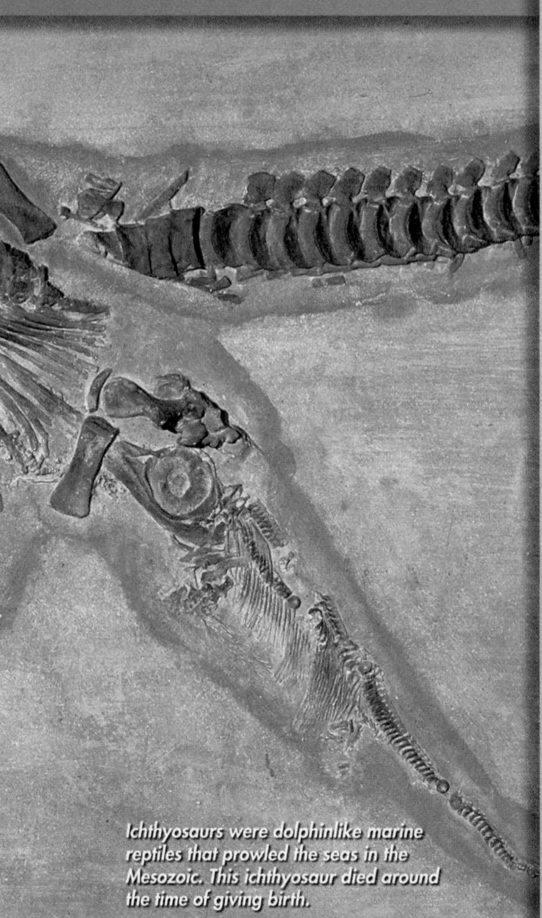

Ichthyosaurs were dolphinlike marine reptiles that prowled the seas in the Mesozoic. This ichthyosaur died around the time of giving birth.

• Untamed Science Video • Chapter Mystery

CHAPTER MYSTERY

MURDER IN THE PERMIAN

Just over 250 million years ago, during the Permian Period, life on Earth came as close as it has ever come to being wiped out. The Permian extinction may be the greatest murder mystery in the history of the world. Whatever happened back then killed off over 55 percent of all families on Earth, including about 96 percent of marine species and 70 percent of terrestrial vertebrate species. Ancient ecosystems were so completely disrupted that it took millions of years for them to be restored.

Researchers once thought that this "great dying" took place over a long time. But new fossil data suggest that it took no more than 200,000 years and possibly less. In geological terms, that's a short time. As you read this chapter, look for clues as to what could have killed so many different forms of life. Then, solve the mystery.

Never Stop Exploring Your World. Finding the solution to this mystery is only the beginning. Take a video field trip with the ecogeeks of Untamed Science to see where the mystery leads.

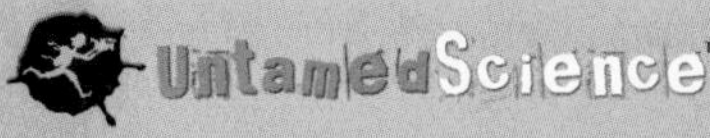

Chapter 19 Big Idea: Evolution

Chapter 19 EQ: How do fossils help biologists understand the history of life on Earth?

19.1 GQ: How do scientists use fossils to study Earth's history?

19.2 GQ: What are some patterns in which evolution has occurred?

19.3 GQ: What happened during Earth's early history?

What's Online

Extend your reach by using these and other digital assets offered at **Biology.com.**

CHAPTER MYSTERY
Students investigate the ultimate cold case. Why did such a large majority of species become extinct 250 million years ago?

UNTAMED SCIENCE VIDEO
What do fossils tell us? Students can answer this question by taking a trip back in time with the Untamed Science crew.

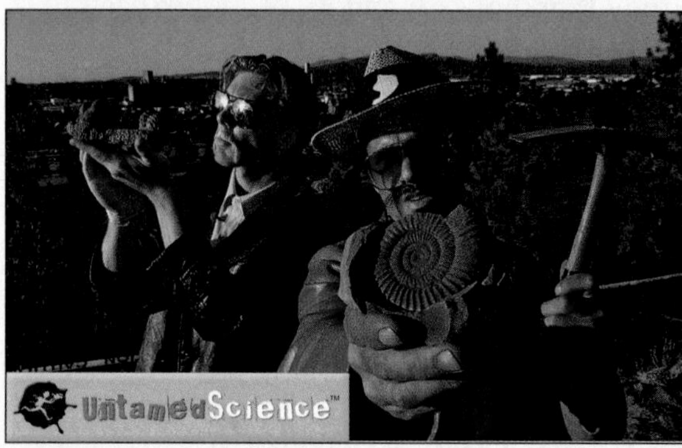

ART IN MOTION
Students can use this activity to see an animation of fossil formation.

VISUAL ANALOGY
This activity expands on the analogy of geologic time as a clock.

DATA ANALYSIS
Students can use data to infer likely causes of extinction events.

ART REVIEW
This drag-and-drop activity allows students to explore conditions on early Earth.

LESSON 19.1

Getting Started

Objectives

19.1.1 Explain what information fossils can reveal about ancient life.

19.1.2 Differentiate between relative dating and radiometric dating.

19.1.3 Identify the divisions of the geologic time scale.

19.1.4 Describe how environmental processes and living things have shaped life on Earth.

Student Resources

Study Workbooks A and B, 19.1 Worksheets

Spanish Study Workbook, 19.1 Worksheets

Lesson Overview • Lesson Notes
- Activities: Art in Motion, Visual Analogy
- Assessment: Self-Test, Lesson Assessment

For corresponding lesson in the **Foundation Edition**, see pages 450–455.

Activate Prior Knowledge

Ask students what they already know about fossils, and write their ideas on the board. *(Sample answers: fossils are ancient; most fossil organisms are extinct; fossils show organisms' structures.)*

Then, provide three or four photos or models of fossils for students to handle and inspect. Tell students they will learn more about fossils in this lesson.

IN INDIANA ACADEMIC STANDARDS

For the full text of all standards, see the Course Overview in the front matter of this book.

NoS.6 Use analogies and models (mathematical and physical) to simplify and represent systems that are difficult to understand or directly experience due to their size, time scale, or complexity, and recognize the limitations of analogies and models.

19.1 The Fossil Record

IN NoS.6 Use analogies and models.

Key Questions

What do fossils reveal about ancient life?

How do we date events in Earth's history?

How was the geologic time scale established, and what are its major divisions?

How have our planet's environment and living things affected each other to shape the history of life on Earth?

Vocabulary

extinct • paleontologist • relative dating • index fossil • radiometric dating • half-life • geologic time scale • era • period • plate tectonics

Taking Notes

Outline Make an outline using the green and blue headings in this lesson. Fill in details as you read to help you organize the information in the lesson.

THINK ABOUT IT Fossils, the preserved remains or traces of ancient life, are priceless treasures. They tell of life-and-death struggles and of mysterious worlds lost in the mists of time. Taken together, the fossils of ancient organisms make up the history of life on Earth called the fossil record. How can fossils help us understand life's history?

Fossils and Ancient Life

What do fossils reveal about ancient life?

Fossils are the most important source of information about extinct species. An **extinct** species is one that has died out. Fossils vary enormously in size, type, and degree of preservation, and they form only under certain conditions. For every organism preserved as a fossil, many died without leaving a trace, so the fossil record is not complete.

Types of Fossils Fossils can be as large and perfectly preserved as an entire animal, complete with skin, hair, scales, or feathers. They can also be as tiny as bacteria, developing embryos, or pollen grains. Many fossils are just fragments of an organism—teeth, pieces of a jawbone, or bits of leaf. Sometimes an organism leaves behind trace fossils—casts of footprints, burrows, tracks, or even droppings. Although most fossils are preserved in sedimentary rocks, some are preserved in other ways, like the insect shown in **Figure 19–1.**

FIGURE 19–1 Diversity of Fossils There are all different types of fossils. A fossil can be a single bone, some footprints, or entire organisms.

▲ Dimetrodon footprints

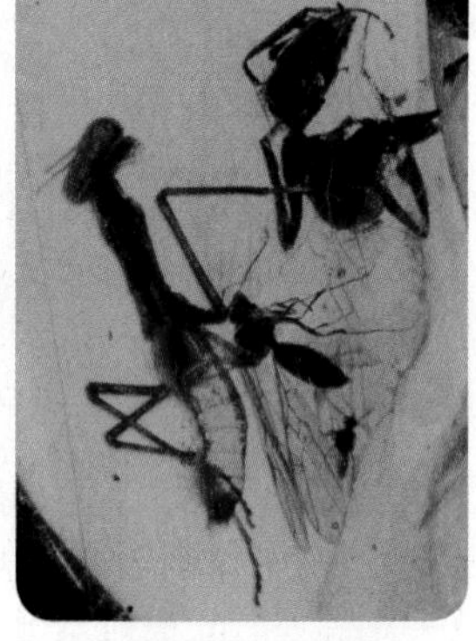
▲ Insect preserved in amber

UbD Teach for Understanding

ENDURING UNDERSTANDING The diversity of life is the result of ongoing evolutionary change. Species alive today have evolved from ancient common ancestors.

GUIDING QUESTION How do scientists use fossils to study Earth's history?

EVIDENCE OF UNDERSTANDING *After completing the lesson, give students the following assessment to show whether they understand one way scientists use fossils to study Earth's history.* Divide the class into small groups to design and build a model showing how index fossils in sedimentary rock layers are used to determine the relative ages of those layers and to correlate the ages of rock layers in different locations. Provide slabs of modeling clay or other materials to mimic rock layers. Also, provide leaves, bones, and small objects that students can embed in the "rock layers." Have each group explain how its model shows the use of index fossils.

Fossils in Sedimentary Rock Most fossils are preserved in sedimentary rock. **Figure 19–2** shows how. ❶ Sedimentary rock usually forms when small particles of sand, silt, clay, or lime muds settle to the bottom of a river, lake, ocean, or other body of water. Sedimentary rock can also form from compacted desert sands. ❷ As sediments build up, they bury dead organisms that have sunk to the bottom. If the remains of these organisms are buried relatively quickly, they may not be scattered by scavengers. Usually, soft body structures decay quickly after death, so only wood, shells, bones, or teeth remain. These hard structures can be preserved if they are saturated or replaced with mineral compounds. Sometimes, however, organisms are buried so quickly that soft tissues are protected from aerobic decay. When this happens, fossils may preserve incredibly detailed imprints of soft-bodied animals and structures like skin or feathers.

❸ As layers of sediment continue to build up over time, the remains are buried deeper and deeper. Over many years, water pressure gradually compresses the lower layers. This pressure, along with chemical activity, can turn the sediments into rock.

What Fossils Can Reveal Although the fossil record is incomplete, it contains an enormous amount of information for **paleontologists** (pay lee un TAHL uh jists), researchers who study fossils to learn about ancient life. **From the fossil record, paleontologists learn about the structure of ancient organisms, their environment, and the ways in which they lived.** By comparing body structures in fossils—a backbone, for example—to body structures in living organisms, researchers can infer evolutionary relationships and form hypotheses about how body structures and species have evolved. Bone structure and footprints can indicate how animals moved. Fossilized plant leaves and pollen suggest whether an area was a swamp, a lake, a forest, or a desert. Also, when different kinds of fossils are found together, researchers can sometimes reconstruct entire ancient ecosystems.

In Your Notebook *Construct a flowchart to explain how the remains of a snail might become fossilized in sedimentary rock.*

Fossil fish *Diplomystus dentatus* (about 50 million years old)

BUILD Vocabulary

WORD ORIGINS The words paleontology and **paleontologist** come from the Greek word *palaios*, meaning "ancient." A paleontologist studies the remains of ancient life.

❶

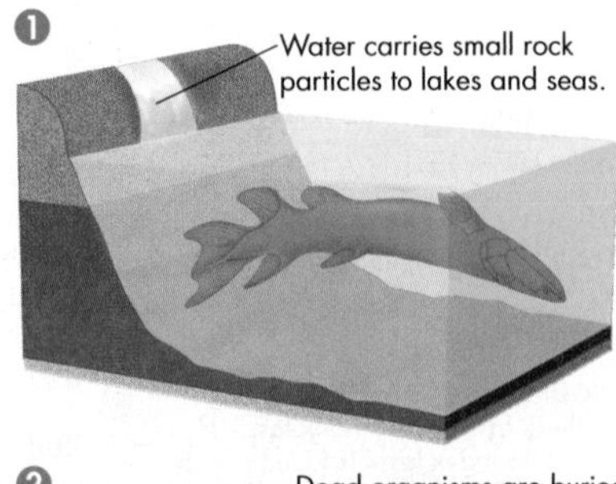

Water carries small rock particles to lakes and seas.

❷

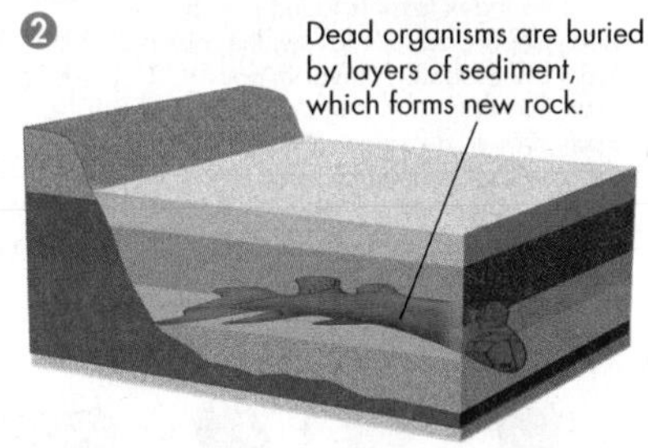

Dead organisms are buried by layers of sediment, which forms new rock.

❸

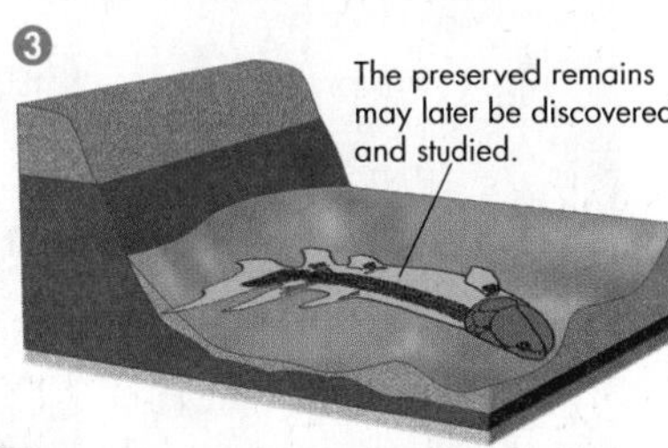

The preserved remains may later be discovered and studied.

FIGURE 19–2 Fossil Formation Most fossils, like the fish shown here, form in sedimentary rock. Interpret Photos ***What part of the fish has been preserved as a fossil?***

BIOLOGY.com Search Lesson 19.1 GO • Art in Motion

Teach

LESSON 19.1

Use Visuals

Have students use **Figure 19–2** to follow the process by which fossils form in sedimentary rock.

Ask Which body structures are most likely to become fossilized? *(hard structures such as shells, bones, or teeth)* Why? *(Hard structures are less susceptible to decay than soft tissues are.)*

Ask What turns layers of sediments into rock? *(Pressure and chemical activity turn sediment to rock.)*

Ask What can paleontologists infer from fossils? *(Sample answers: how body structures or species evolved, what an ancient ecosystem was like)*

DIFFERENTIATED INSTRUCTION

LPR Less Proficient Readers Divide the class into groups, and have a member of each group read aloud the internal captions in **Figure 19–2.** Instruct each group to write three questions about the process of fossil formation. Each group should then swap questions with another group and answer the new set of questions. Then, use the groups' questions for a review of the fossilization process.

ELL Focus on ELL: Extend Language

BEGINNING AND INTERMEDIATE SPEAKERS
Have ELL students work in pairs or small groups to complete an **ELL Frayer Model** for five of the lesson vocabulary terms. Students should start with the term's definition, then add a drawing or visual representation, examples, and, finally, a translation of the definition into their native language. At the conclusion of the lesson, ask each pair or group to choose one completed ELL Frayer Model to share with the class.

Study Wkbks A/B, Appendix S26, ELL Frayer Model. **Transparencies,** ELL Frayer Model GO10.

How Science Works

PLINY'S FOOTPRINTS

The first dinosaur footprints ever discovered in the U.S. were found in 1802 by 12-year-old Pliny Moody in a field on his family's farm in western Massachusetts. While plowing, Pliny turned up a flat stone with footprints on it that resembled bird footprints. However, they were too large to have been made by any known living bird. Crowds came to see the footprints, and some people speculated that the prints had been made by giant ravens released by Noah from the ark. Prompted by Pliny's discovery, Edward Hitchcock, president of Amherst College in Massachusetts, began a 30-year search for more prints. Hitchcock was convinced that the tracks had been made by large, ostrichlike birds, and he called the prints ornithichites, which means "stony bird tracks." He called his new field of science ornithichnology, shortened to ichnology, the study of tracks and traces left by organisms.

BIOLOGY.com Students can use the **Art in Motion: Fossil Formation** animation to learn more about fossil formation.

Answers

FIGURE 19–2 bones

IN YOUR NOTEBOOK Flowcharts should be based on the steps in **Figure 19–2.** They might indicate that soft parts of the snail decayed quickly and the hard shell was replaced by minerals as it was buried.

Teach continued

Use Visuals

Use **Figure 19–3** to explore some strengths and weaknesses of using index fossils for relative dating.

Ask Which index fossil is found in all three locations? *(D)*

Ask At Location 2, what likely happened to the first layer seen in Location 1? *(It eroded.)*

DIFFERENTIATED INSTRUCTION

L1 Struggling Students Help students understand the concept of relative dating by using the analogy of a messy desk. Tell students that on a desk at home, there is a teacup on top of a half-written essay, which is on top of an open geology textbook, which is on top of a birthday card from a friend. Finally, at the very bottom of the pile, is a graded math test. You may wish to draw these "layers" on the board.

Ask Which happened first, the student drank a cup of tea or started the essay? *(The student started the essay.)* How do you know? *(because the teacup was on top of the essay)*

Ask What could you infer about the date of the student's birthday? *(It happened sometime after the math test, but sometime before the student read from the geology book.)*

Dating Earth's History

How do we date events in Earth's history?

The fossil record wouldn't be as useful without a time scale to tell us what happened when. Researchers use several techniques to date rocks and fossils.

Relative Dating Since sedimentary rock is formed as layers of sediment are laid on top of existing sediments, lower layers of sedimentary rock, and fossils they contain, are generally older than upper layers. **Relative dating** places rock layers and their fossils in a temporal sequence, as shown in **Figure 19–3.** **Relative dating allows paleontologists to determine whether a fossil is older or younger than other fossils.**

To help establish the relative ages of rock layers and their fossils, scientists use index fossils. **Index fossils** are distinctive fossils used to establish and compare the relative ages of rock layers and the fossils they contain. A useful index fossil must be easily recognized and will occur only in a few rock layers (meaning the organism lived only for a short time), but these layers will be found in many places (meaning the organism was widely distributed). Trilobites, a large group of distinctive marine organisms, are often used as index fossils. There are more than 15,000 recognized species of trilobite. Together, they can be used to establish the relative dates of rock layers spanning nearly 300 million years.

Radiometric Dating Relative dating is important, but provides no information about a fossil's absolute age in years. One way to date rocks and fossils is radiometric dating. **Radiometric dating** relies on radioactive isotopes, which decay, or break down, into stable isotopes at a steady rate. A **half-life** is the time required for half of the radioactive atoms in a sample to decay. After one half-life, half of the original radioactive atoms have decayed, as shown in **Figure 19–4.**

FIGURE 19–3 Index Fossils Each of these fossils is an index fossil. If the same index fossil is found in two widely separated rock layers, the rock layers are probably similar in age. **Draw Conclusions** ***Using the index fossils shown, determine which layers are "missing" from each location. Layers may be missing because they were never formed, or because they were eroded.***

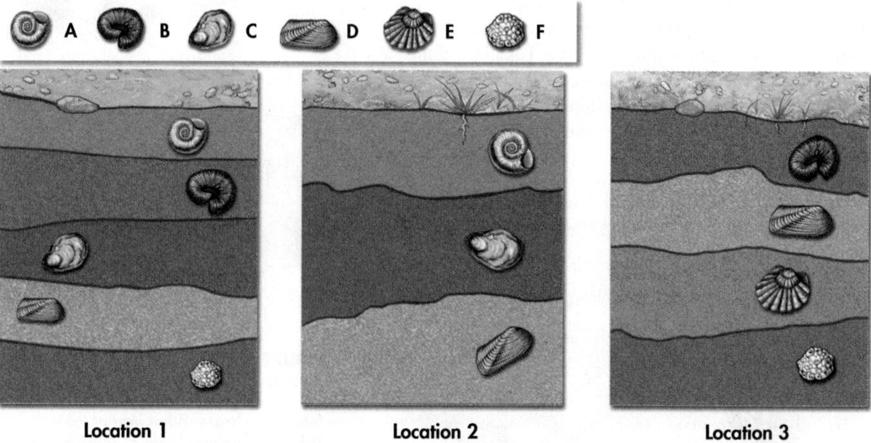

UbD Check for Understanding

FOLLOW-UP PROBES

Check students' understanding of relative dating and radiometric dating.

Ask Why would a paleontologist use radiometric dating instead of relative dating? *(to determine absolute age rather than relative age)*

ADJUST UNDERSTANDING

If students struggle with distinguishing between relative and absolute age, give them familiar examples, such as: Sam is younger than his parents. *(relative age)* Sam is 14 years old. *(absolute age)* Then, ask students to come up with a pair of examples on their own. Read some of the best examples to the class.

Answers

FIGURE 19–3 In Location 1, the layer with index fossil E is missing. Location 2 is missing the layers with index fossils B, E, and F. Location 3 is missing the layers with index fossils A and C.

After another half-life, another half of the remaining radioactive atoms will have decayed. **Radiometric dating uses the proportion of radioactive to stable isotopes to calculate the age of a sample.**

Different radioactive isotopes decay at different rates, so they have different half-lives. Elements with short half-lives are used to date recent fossils. Elements with long half-lives are used for dating older fossils. To understand this, think of timing sports events. For a 50-yard dash, a coach depends on the fast-moving second hand of a stopwatch. To time a marathon, slower-moving hour and minute hands are also important.

A number of radioactive isotopes are used to determine the ages of rocks and fossils. An isotope known as carbon-14 is particularly useful for directly dating organisms that lived in the recent past. Carbon-14 is produced at a steady rate in the upper atmosphere, so air generally contains a tiny amount of it, in addition to the much more common stable, nonradioactive form, carbon-12. Plants take carbon-14 in when they absorb carbon dioxide during photosynthesis, and animals acquire it when they eat plants or other animals. Once an organism dies, it no longer takes in this isotope, so its age can be determined by the amount of carbon-14 still remaining in tissues such as bone, hair, or wood. Carbon-14 has a half-life of roughly 5730 years, so its use is limited to organisms that lived in the last 60,000 years.

Older fossils can be dated indirectly by dating the rock layers in which they are found. Isotopes with much longer half-lives are used for this purpose, including potassium-40 (half-life: 1.26 billion years, shown in **Figure 19–4**), uranium-238 (4.5 billion years), and rubidium-87 (48.8 billion years). Over many years, geologists have combined the use of these and other isotope methods to make increasingly accurate estimates of the ages of geological formations. These studies have provided direct physical evidence for the ages of the index fossils used to identify periods of Earth history.

In Your Notebook *Explain why carbon-14 can't be used to estimate the age of very old fossils.*

Quick Lab — GUIDED INQUIRY

Modeling Half-Life

1. Construct a data table or spreadsheet with two columns and five rows. Label the columns Spill Number and Number of Squares Returned. Take a sheet of paper, and cut out 100 1-cm squares. Place an *X* on each square, and put all the squares in a cup.
2. Mix the squares in the cup, and spill them out.
3. Remove all the squares that have an *X* showing. Count the squares left, record the number, and return the remaining squares to the cup.
4. Repeat steps 2 and 3 until there are five or fewer squares left. Make a graph of your results with the number of spills on the *x*-axis and the number of squares remaining after each spill on the *y*-axis.

Analyze and Conclude

1. **Analyze Data** How many spills did you need to remove half the squares? To remove three fourths?
2. **Calculate** If each spill represents one year, what is the half-life of the squares? MATH

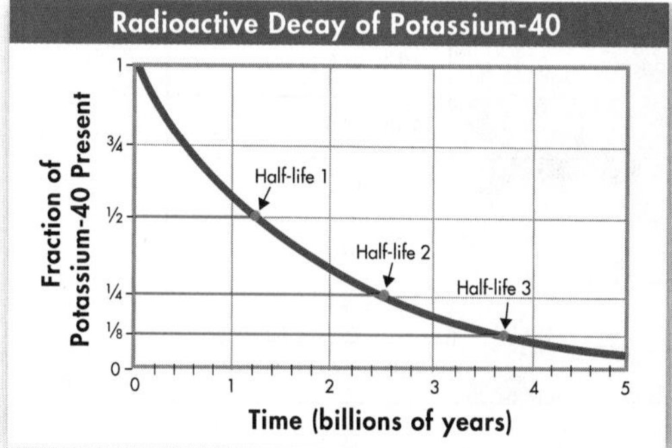

FIGURE 19–4 Radioactive Decay A half-life is the time it takes half the radioactive atoms in a sample to decay. The half-life of potassium-40 is 1.26 billion years.

Quick Lab

PURPOSE Students will analyze data and calculate the half-life of a model radioactive element.

MATERIALS 1-cm grid paper, scissors, plastic or paper cup

PLANNING Explain that, on average, about half of the remaining squares will be removed each time that step 3 is repeated.

ANALYZE AND CONCLUDE

1. About half the squares will be removed in one spill; about three fourths of the squares will be removed in two spills.
2. one year

Connect to Earth Science

Many students will not understand why scientists need to use relative dating. Explain that while radiometric dating provides an absolute age, it is far more complicated than simply running a test on a fossil. Unless the fossil sample is fairly young and can be carbon-14 dated, it cannot be dated directly. Geologists must radiometricly date the rock in which the fossil sits. But that, too, is complicated because most fossils occur in sedimentary rock and dating sedimentary rock will give you the age of the rock that served as the source for the sediment—not the age of the sedimentary rock itself. The only rock that can be dated reliably is igneous rock (rock formed from lava). In most situations, geologists use a mix of absolute dating of igneous rock and relative dating of layers to estimate fossil ages.

Ask If a fossil sits in sedimentary rock that is directly below a layer of 15-million-year-old igneous rock, what can be inferred about the fossil's age? (*The fossil is older than 15 million years.)*

DIFFERENTIATED INSTRUCTION

L3 Advanced Students Have your advanced students make a graph similar to **Figure 19–4** that shows the radioactive decay of carbon-14. The *x*-axis should be in thousands of years, with points at 5730 (half-life 1), 11,460 (half-life 2), 17,190 (half-life 3), and 22,920 (half-life 4).

Ask If a fossil is 20,000 years old, how much C-14 would you expect to be left in the sample? *(between 1/4 and 1/8)*

Ask Why would a scientist need to rely on other dating methods if a fossil is much older than 60,000 years? *(There would be no detectable amount of C-14 left in the fossil.)*

Answers

IN YOUR NOTEBOOK Carbon-14 has a relatively short half-life of 5730 years. After about 60,000 years, so little carbon-14 remains in fossils that it cannot be used to accurately assess the age of the fossils.

Teach continued

Use Visuals

Use **Figure 19–5** to introduce students to the geologic time scale. Check that they understand how to read the table and calculate the lengths of individual periods.

Ask What is the name of the oldest time interval on the scale? *(Precambrian Time)*

Ask What are the periods of the Paleozoic Era, from oldest to most recent? *(Cambrian, Ordovician, Silurian, Devonian, Carboniferous, Permian)*

Ask When did the Cretaceous Period end? *(65.5 million years ago)*

DIFFERENTIATED INSTRUCTION

L1 Special Needs Some students may need help understanding that periods make up an era and eras make up an eon. Work with them to complete sentences such as: The Paleogene, Neogene, and Quaternary Periods make up the *(Cenozoic)* Era. The Mesozoic Era is made up of the *(Triassic, Jurassic, and Cretaceous)* Periods.

LPR Less Proficient Readers Pair less-proficient readers with students who can read proficiently. Have students in each pair work together using the **Think-Pair-Share** strategy to answer questions that require interpreting the geologic time scale.

Ask Calculate the length of the Cretaceous Period. *(146–65.5 = 80.5 million years)*

Ask When did the Paleozoic Era begin, and when did it end? *(It began 542 million years ago, and it ended 251 million years ago.)*

Ask In what period do we live? *(Quaternary)*

Study Wkbks A/B, Appendix S14, Think-Pair-Share.

Geologic Time Scale

How was the geologic time scale established, and what are its major divisions?

Geologists and paleontologists have built a time line of Earth's history called the **geologic time scale.** The most recent version is shown in **Figure 19–5. The geologic time scale is based on both relative and absolute dating. The major divisions of the geologic time scale are eons, eras, and periods.**

Establishing the Time Scale By studying rock layers and index fossils, early paleontologists placed Earth's rocks and fossils in order according to their relative age. As they worked, they noticed major changes in the fossil record at boundaries between certain rock layers. Geologists used these boundaries to determine where one division of geologic time ended and the next began. Years later, radiometric dating techniques were used to assign specific ages to the various rock layers. This time scale is constantly being tested, verified, and adjusted.

FIGURE 19–5 Geologic Time Scale The basic divisions of the geologic time scale are eons, eras, and periods. Precambrian time was the name originally given to all of Earth's history before the Phanerozoic Eon. Note that the Paleogene and Neogene are sometimes called the Tertiary period. However, this term is generally considered outdated.

Geologic Time Scale

	Eon	Era	Period	Time (millions of years ago)
	Phanerozoic	Cenozoic	Quaternary	1.8–present
			Neogene	23–1.8
			Paleogene	65.5–23
		Mesozoic	Cretaceous	146–65.5
			Jurassic	200–146
			Triassic	251–200
		Paleozoic	Permian	299–251
			Carboniferous	359–299
			Devonian	416–359
			Silurian	444–416
			Ordovician	488–444
			Cambrian	542–488
Precambrian Time	Proterozoic			2500–542
	Archean			4000–2500
	Hadean			About 4600–4000

How Science Works

WILLIAM SMITH AND RELATIVE DATING

William Smith was born in 1769 at a period of great industrial development in England. By 1793, Smith had become a surveyor and was one of many at work digging canals to transport coal throughout England to feed its industries. Smith observed many fossils during canal excavations and noticed that certain fossils were always in a particular order. In time, he made a connection between the ages of rocks and the fossils buried in them. He also determined that rocks contained fossils in a specific sequence (the principle of faunal succession). His observations were a foundation for what would eventually become the geologic time scale. Smith went on to draw and publish the first map that showed the detailed geological stratification of England.

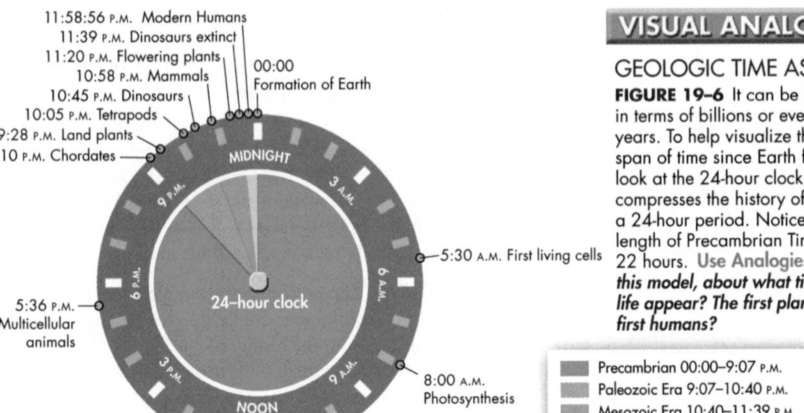

VISUAL ANALOGY

GEOLOGIC TIME AS A CLOCK

FIGURE 19–6 It can be hard to think in terms of billions or even millions of years. To help visualize the enormous span of time since Earth formed, look at the 24-hour clock here. It compresses the history of Earth into a 24-hour period. Notice the relative length of Precambrian Time—almost 22 hours. **Use Analogies** ***Using this model, about what time did life appear? The first plants? The first humans?***

Divisions of the Geologic Time Scale Divisions of geologic time have different lengths. The Cambrian Period, for example, began 542 million years ago and continued until 488 million years ago, which makes it 54 million years long. The Cretaceous Period was 80 million years long.

Geologists now recognize four eons. The Hadean Eon, during which the first rocks formed, spans the time from Earth's formation to about 4 billion years ago. The Archean Eon, during which life first appeared, followed the Hadean. The Proterozoic Eon began 2.5 billion years ago and lasted until 542 million years ago. The Phanerozoic (fan ur uh ZOH ic) Eon began at the end of the Proterozoic and continues to the present.

Eons are divided into **eras.** The Phanerozoic Eon, for example, is divided into the Paleozoic, Mesozoic, and Cenozoic Eras. And eras are subdivided into **periods,** which range in length from nearly 100 million years to just under 2 million years. The Paleozoic Era, for example, is divided into six periods, including the Permian Period.

Naming the Divisions Divisions of the geologic time scale were named in different ways. The Cambrian Period, for example, was named after Cambria—an old name for Wales, where rocks from that time were first identified. The Carboniferous ("carbon-bearing") Period is named for large coal deposits that formed during that time.

Geologists started to name divisions of the time scale before any rocks older than the Cambrian Period had been identified. For this reason, all of geologic time before the Cambrian was simply called Precambrian Time. Precambrian Time, however, actually covers about 90 percent of Earth's history, as shown in **Figure 19–6.**

MYSTERY CLUE

Paleontologists discovered dramatic changes in the fossil record at the end of the Permian Period. What methods do you think they used to date that change at 251 million years ago?

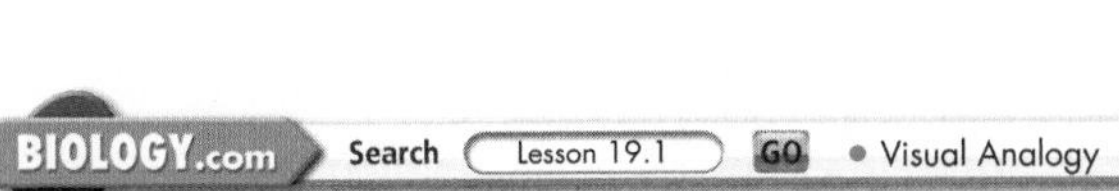

VISUAL ANALOGY

Use **Figure 19–6** to reinforce the concept of geologic time. Have students look at the parts of the clock face and the time intervals.

Ask How does this clock differ from most clocks in everyday use? *(A regular clock shows 12 hours; this clock shows 24 hours. Regular clocks do not include the geologic time scale.)*

Ask How does the clock model geologic time? *(It compares the length of geologic time to a 24-hour day.)*

Divide the class into small groups to look closely at the color key and the events of the 24-hour clock. Challenge each group to write two questions. Use the questions to start a class discussion. Have students compare the clock model to the geologic time scale shown in **Figure 19–5.**

DIFFERENTIATED INSTRUCTION

L1 Special Needs Many students have difficulty with scale or magnitude, especially understanding billions and millions of years. Getting them to envision what a billion years is like can help visual learners in particular. A football field of 100 yards can be marked off by having students stand at intervals representing each division of the geologic time scale. Each yard represents approximately 46 million years.

L1 Struggling Students If students struggle with the 24-hour clock analogy for geologic time, have them work with a partner to make a **Timeline** with the same intervals and labels that are on the clock model. Make sure students label the left end of the timeline *Formation of Earth.* When finished, they should understand that the greater the space between markings on the timeline, the longer the time between geologic events.

Study Wkbks A/B, Appendix S15, Timeline.

BIOLOGY.com Have students further explore the analogy by using **Visual Analogy: Geologic Time as a Clock.**

UbD Check for Understanding

ORAL QUESTIONING

Allow students to refer to **Figures 19–5** and **19–6** to answer these questions.

- Using the table model, which eon lasted from 4000 million years ago to 2500 million years ago? *(the Archean Eon)*
- Using the clock model, which event occurred more recently, sexual reproduction or the formation of oxygen from photosynthesis? *(sexual reproduction)*
- Which eon do we live in? *(the Phanerozoic Eon)*

ADJUST INSTRUCTION

If students have difficulty answering these questions, ask more direct questions for which they can give an answer by pointing to a location on one of the time scales.

MYSTERY CLUE Paleontologists would have used radiometric dating. If students seem uncertain about the answer, have them compare the limitations of relative dating and radiometric dating. Students can go online to **Biology.com** to gather their evidence.

Answers

FIGURE 19–6 life: 5:30 A.M.; first land plants: 9:28 P.M.; humans: 11:58:56 P.M.

Teach continued

Lead a Discussion

Read aloud the Key Question, and ask students to respond. *(Students should point out that geological forces have changed organisms' habitats throughout history, and living things themselves act on the land, water, and atmosphere of Earth.)* Write the headings *Physical Forces* and *Biological Forces* on the board, and ask students to provide examples of these forces. List their examples under the appropriate forces. Then, for each example, challenge students to infer how it affected the history of life on Earth.

DIFFERENTIATED INSTRUCTION

L1 Struggling Students Some students may have difficulty understanding how organisms are affected when their environments change. Refer students to **Figure 19–7.** First, help students locate the equator and the South Pole on the first map and find what is now South America. Remind students about the climates at the equator and the South Pole. Then, have students find South America in the subsequent maps and note how that continent moved in relation to the equator and the South Pole.

Ask How do you think the climate of South America changed as that continent moved? *(It became warmer.)*

Ask What effect do you think the climate change would have had on the plants and animals in South America over time? *(Organisms with adaptations enabling them to survive in the changed climate would have become predominant.)*

L3 Advanced Students Have a small group of students prepare a short "refresher course" on plate tectonics and continental drift and present it to the class. Ask the students to include visuals in their presentation.

FIGURE 19–7 The Changing Face of Earth Over the last 225 million years, the face of the Earth has changed dramatically.

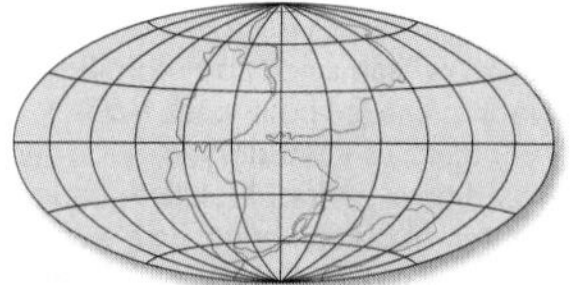

End of Permian Period At the end of the Permian Period, Earth's continents collided to form one giant landmass called Pangaea.

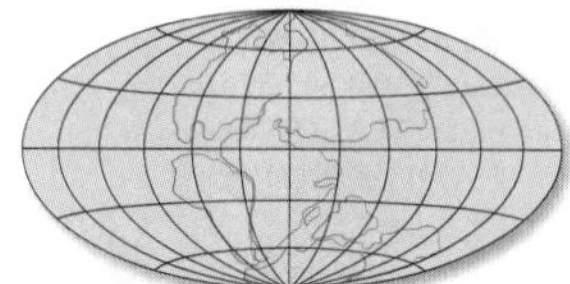

Triassic Period During the Triassic Period, Pangaea started to break apart and form separate land masses.

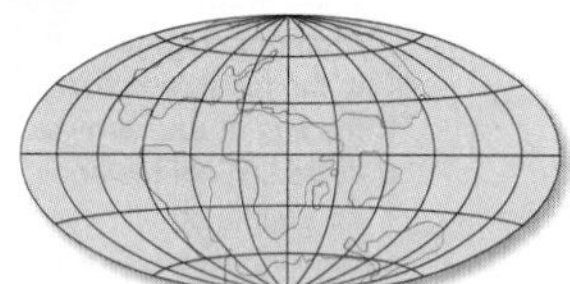

End of Cretaceous Period By the end of the Cretaceous Period, the continents as we know them began to drift apart.

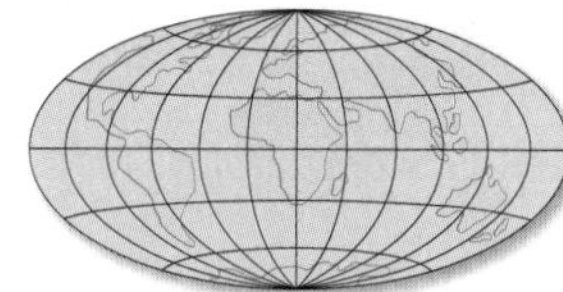

Present Day

Life on a Changing Planet

How have our planet's environment and living things affected each other to shape the history of life on Earth?

Today, it's easy to think of places on Earth where the environment is relatively constant from year to year. Arizona is dry, coastal Washington State is wet, Antarctica is cold, and the Sahara is hot. But this was not always the case. Earth's physical environment has undergone striking changes in its history, and many of these changes have affected life in dramatic ways.

Physical Forces Climate is one of the most important aspects of the physical environment, and Earth's climate has been anything but constant over the history of life. Many of these changes were triggered by fairly small shifts in global temperature. For example, during the global "heat wave" of the Mesozoic era, average global temperatures were only 6°C to 12°C higher than they were in the twentieth century. During the great ice ages, which swept across the globe as recently as 10,000 years ago, temperatures were only about 5°C cooler than they are now. Yet, these temperature shifts had far-reaching effects on living things.

Geological forces have also transformed life on Earth, building mountains and even moving whole continents. Remember that local climates are influenced by the interactions of wind and ocean currents with geological features like mountains and plains. Volcanic forces have altered landscapes over much of Earth, even producing entire islands that provide new habitats. The Hawaiian Islands, home to scores of unique plant and animal species, are a perfect example of how volcanic islands can alter the course of evolution. **Building mountains, opening coastlines, changing climates, and geological forces have altered habitats of living organisms repeatedly throughout Earth history.**

Over the long term, the process of continental drift has produced even more dramatic changes in Earth's biological landscape. As shown in **Figure 19–7,** continents have collided to form "super continents," and then drifted apart again, profoundly changing the flow of ocean currents. Continental drift has also affected the distribution of fossils and living organisms worldwide. For example, the continents of Africa and South America are now separated by the Atlantic Ocean. But fossils of *Mesosaurus*, an aquatic reptile, have been found in Africa and South America. The presence of these fossils on both continents reflects the fact that both were joined at one time. The theory of **plate tectonics** explains these movements as the result of solid "plates" moving slowly, as little as 3 cm a year, over Earth's mantle.

How Science Works

ALFRED WEGENER AND CONTINENTAL DRIFT

Not every new observation in science gains acceptance overnight. Alfred Wegener was greeted with some hostility in 1912 when he presented his hypothesis of continental displacement, or drift, before the Geological Association in Frankfurt, Germany. Wegener was trained as a meteorologist, but his curiosity opened him to a multidisciplinary interest in Earth as a whole. He observed that the shapes of continents look like pieces of a puzzle that might have fit together at one time. The presence of similar fossils on widely separated continents had also been observed. He hypothesized that Earth's landmasses had been connected and then separated, in a process called continental drift. At the time, however, he could not explain how these changes had occurred. Wegener died in 1930. It wasn't until the 1960s that the theory of plate tectonics proposed how continental drift could take place.

Forces from space have even altered Earth's physical environment. There is strong evidence that comets and large meteors have crashed into Earth many times in the past. Some of these impacts may have been so violent that they kicked enough dust and debris in the atmosphere to cause, or contribute to, worldwide extinctions of organisms on land and in the water.

Biological Forces Although we think of life as reacting to Earth's physical environment, in many cases life actually plays a major role in shaping that environment. Iron deposits in ancient sedimentary rock indicate that Earth's early oceans contained large amounts of soluble iron and little oxygen. The first photosynthetic organisms began absorbing carbon dioxide and releasing large amounts of oxygen. Our planet has never been the same since then. Earth cooled as carbon dioxide levels dropped. The iron content of the oceans fell, as iron ions reacted with oxygen to form insoluble compounds that settled to the ocean floor. These changes affected climate and ocean chemistry in many ways. **The actions of living organisms over time have changed conditions in the land, water, and atmosphere of planet Earth.**

Even today, organisms shape the landscape as they build soil from rock and sand. Plants, animals, and microorganisms are active players in global cycles of key elements, including carbon, nitrogen, and oxygen. Earth is a living planet, and its physical environment reflects that fact.

19.1 Assessment

Review Key Concepts

1. a. **Explain** What can a paleontologist learn from fossils?
   b. **Relate Cause and Effect** Why have so few organisms become fossilized?
2. a. **Review** What are the two ways in which geologists determine the age of fossils?
   b. **Draw Conclusions** Many more fossils have been found since Darwin's day, giving us a more complete record of life's history. How would this information make relative dating more accurate?
3. a. **Explain** How are eras and periods related?
   b. **Interpret Visuals** Use **Figure 19–5** to determine when the Silurian Period began and how long it lasted.
4. a. **Review** Describe three processes that have affected the history of life on Earth.
   b. **Relate Cause and Effect** Describe two ways in which continental drift has affected organisms.

VISUAL THINKING

5. Look at the fossil bat in the photograph below. Describe the fossil. What can you infer about how the organism moved? Explain your answer.

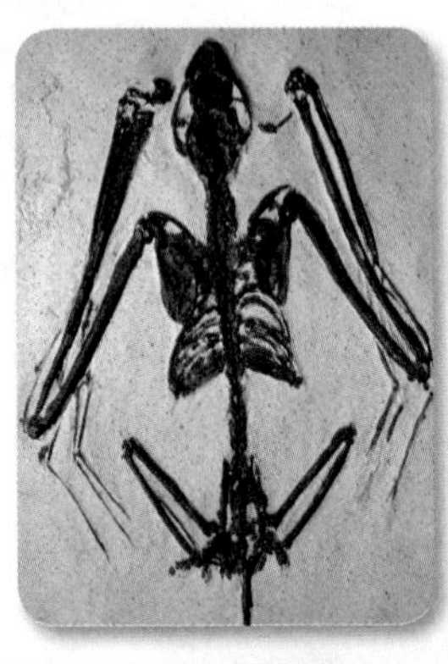

BIOLOGY.com Search Lesson 19.1 GO • Self-Test • Lesson Assessment

Assess and Remediate

EVALUATE UNDERSTANDING

Call on students to define vocabulary terms used in this lesson. After each term has been defined, call on another student to explain how it is related to fossils or the fossil record. Then, have students complete the 19.1 Assessment.

REMEDIATION SUGGESTION

L1 **Struggling Students** If students have trouble answering **Question 2b,** restate the question as, How would finding more fossils in rock layers make relative dating more accurate?

BIOLOGY.com Students can check their understanding of lesson concepts with the **Self-Test** assessment. They can then take an online version of the **Lesson Assessment.**

LESSON 19.1

Assessment Answers

1a. A paleontologist can learn about the structure of ancient organisms, their environment, and the way they lived.

1b. Fossils form only under highly specific and relatively rare conditions, such as the rapid burial of organisms in sediments. Further, organisms with hard parts fossilize far more often than organisms without.

2a. relative dating, based on the placement of fossils in rock layers; and radiometric dating using radioactive elements

2b. Sample answer: More fossils would make relative dating more accurate, because a greater number and variety of fossils could be compared to index fossils.

3a. Eras are divided into periods.

3b. It began 444 million years ago and lasted about 28 million years.

4a. Earth's plates have moved and carried organisms with them; collisions with giant asteroids tossed up dust and blocked the sun's energy; production of oxygen by photosynthetic bacteria and removal of carbon dioxide changed the atmosphere.

4b. When landmasses collide and mountain ranges rise, new climates and niches are created and species are redistributed.

VISUAL THINKING

5. Sample answer: The fossil appears to be a vertebrate, has a tail, and has forelimbs longer and sturdier than its hind limbs. It probably depended on its forelimbs to move about, possibly by flying.

LESSON 19.2

Getting Started

Objectives

19.2.1 Identify the processes that influence survival or extinction of a species or clade.

19.2.2 Contrast gradualism and punctuated equilibrium.

19.2.3 Name two important patterns in macroevolution.

19.2.4 Explain the evolutionary characteristics of coevolving organisms.

Student Resources

Study Workbooks A and B, 19.2 Worksheets

Spanish Study Workbook, 19.2 Worksheets

Lab Manual B, 19.2 Data Analysis Worksheet

Lesson Overview • Lesson Notes • Activity: Data Analysis • Assessment: Self-Test, Lesson Assessment

For corresponding lesson in the **Foundation Edition**, see pages 456–461.

Answers

IN YOUR NOTEBOOK Macroevolution is evolutionary change that occurs over a long period of time and across many species. Comparison of fossils over time can show general trends within and among clades.

IN INDIANA ACADEMIC STANDARDS

For the full text of all standards, see the Course Overview in the front matter of this book.

B.8.5 Describe how due to genetic variations, environmental forces, and reproductive pressures, organisms with beneficial traits are more likely to survive, reproduce, and pass on their genetic information.

19.2 Patterns and Processes of Evolution

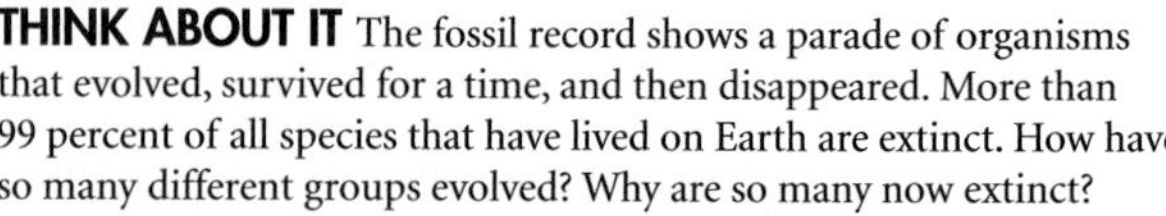

IN B.8.5 Survival and reproduction. Also covered: NoS.3.

Key Questions

What processes influence whether species and clades survive or become extinct?

How fast does evolution take place?

What are two patterns of macroevolution?

What evolutionary characteristics are typical of coevolving species?

Vocabulary

macroevolutionary patterns
background extinction
mass extinction
gradualism
punctuated equilibrium
adaptive radiation
convergent evolution
coevolution

Taking Notes

Concept Map Construct a concept map that includes the patterns of macroevolution shown in this lesson.

FIGURE 19–8 Paleontologists at Work The white covering protects the fossils until they can reach a museum.

THINK ABOUT IT The fossil record shows a parade of organisms that evolved, survived for a time, and then disappeared. More than 99 percent of all species that have lived on Earth are extinct. How have so many different groups evolved? Why are so many now extinct?

Speciation and Extinction

What processes influence whether species and clades survive or become extinct?

The study of life's history leaves no doubt that life has changed over time. Many of those changes occurred within species, but others occurred in larger clades and over longer periods of time. These grand transformations in anatomy, phylogeny, ecology, and behavior, which usually take place in clades larger than a single species, are known as **macroevolutionary patterns.** The ways new species emerge through speciation, and the ways species disappear through extinction, are among the simplest macroevolutionary patterns. The emergence, growth, and extinction of larger clades, such as dinosaurs, mammals, or flowering plants are examples of larger macroevolutionary patterns.

Macroevolution and Cladistics Paleontologists study fossils to learn about patterns of macroevolution and the history of life. Part of this process involves classifying fossils. Fossils are classified using the same cladistic techniques, based on shared derived characters, that are used to classify living species. In some cases, fossils are placed in clades that contain only extinct organisms. In other cases, fossils are classified into clades that include living organisms.

Remember that cladograms illustrate hypotheses about how closely related organisms are. Hypothesizing that a fossil species is *related* to a living species is not the same thing as claiming that the extinct organism is a direct *ancestor* of that (or any other) living species. For example, **Figure 19–9** does not suggest that any of the extinct species shown are direct ancestors of modern birds. Instead, those extinct species are shown as a series of species that descended, over time, from a line of common ancestors.

In Your Notebook *Explain what macroevolution is and how fossils can show macroevolutionary trends.*

UbD Teach for Understanding

ENDURING UNDERSTANDING The diversity of life is the result of ongoing evolutionary change. Species alive today have evolved from ancient common ancestors.

GUIDING QUESTION What are some patterns in which evolution has occurred?

EVIDENCE OF UNDERSTANDING *After completing the lesson, give students the following assessment to show whether they understand the difference between gradualism and punctuated equilibrium.* Divide the class into small groups, and have each group model either gradualism or punctuated equilibrium using familiar objects that have changed over time, such as automobiles, athletic shoes, or modes of communication. Each group's final product should include a poster that uses pictures to show how the objects have changed over time and annotations that describe the changes and whether the changes best model gradualism or punctuated equilibrium.

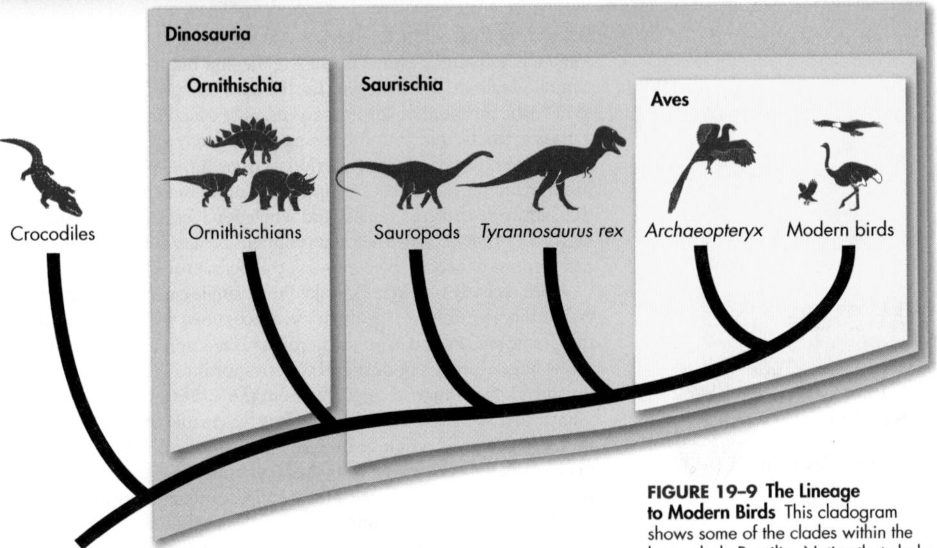

FIGURE 19–9 The Lineage to Modern Birds This cladogram shows some of the clades within the large clade Reptilia. Notice that clade Dinosauria is represented today by modern birds. Classify ***What are the two major clades of dinosaurs?***

Adaptation and Extinction Throughout the history of life, organisms have faced changing environments. When environmental conditions change, processes of evolutionary change enable some species to adapt to new conditions and thrive. Species that fail to adapt eventually become extinct. Interestingly, the rates at which species appear, adapt, and become extinct vary among clades, and from one period of geologic time to another.

Why have some clades produced many successful species that survived over long periods of time, while other clades gave rise to only a few species that vanished due to extinction? Paleontologists have tried to answer this question by studying macroevolutionary patterns of speciation and extinction in different clades over time.

One way to think about this process is in terms of species diversity. The emergence of new species with different characteristics can serve as the "raw material" for macroevolutionary change within a clade over long periods. In some cases, the more varied the species in a particular clade are, the more likely the clade is to survive environmental change. This is similar to the way in which genetic variation serves as raw material for evolutionary change for populations within a species. **If the rate of speciation in a clade is equal to or greater than the rate of extinction, the clade will continue to exist. If the rate of extinction in a clade is greater than the rate of speciation, the clade will eventually become extinct.**

The clade Reptilia (part of which is shown in **Figure 19–9**) is one example of a highly successful clade. It not only includes living organisms like snakes, lizards, turtles and crocodiles, but also dinosaurs that thrived for tens of millions of years. As you know, most species in the clade Dinosauria are now extinct. But the clade itself survived, because it produced groups of new species that successfully adapted to changing conditions. One of those groups survives and thrives today—we call them birds.

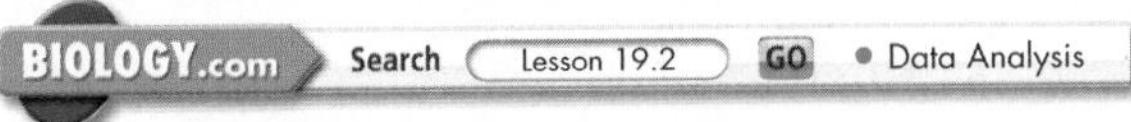

Biology In-Depth

ARCHAEOPTERYX

The first specimen of *Archaeopteryx* was discovered in 1860, just one year after Darwin published *On the Origin of Species*. As skeletal details emerged, it seemed like the perfect "missing link" between reptiles and birds. *Archaeopteryx* had a number of reptilian features including the presence of claws on its fingers, teeth, and a long, bony tail. It also had a number of avian characteristics, like feathers, a backwards-facing big toe, and a wishbone. There are eight known specimens of *Archaeopteryx* today, all dating to the late Jurassic, about 150 million years ago. It is widely accepted as the oldest known bird, though scientists continue to find new specimens and to refine the origin and evolution of birds and flight.

Teach

Lead a Discussion

Have students read about and discuss macroevolutionary patterns, speciation, and extinction.

Ask What are macroevolutionary patterns? *(grand, large-scale transformations that usually occur in clades larger than one species)*

Ask What does speciation result in? *(new species)*

Ask What does extinction result in? *(the disappearance of a species or clade)*

Ask How do the relative rates of speciation and extinction within a clade determine the fate of the clade as a whole? *(If the rate of speciation exceeds the rate of extinction, the clade will continue to exist. If the rate of extinction exceeds the rate of speciation, the clade will eventually become extinct.)*

DIFFERENTIATED INSTRUCTION

L1 Struggling Students If students have trouble understanding the idea of the extinction of clades, refer to **Figure 19–9.**

Ask What is the only group of dinosaurs in the diagram that is not extinct? *(modern birds)* Point out that, if modern birds were extinct, the entire clade shown in the diagram would be extinct. Since modern birds are not extinct, the clade is still surviving.

LPR Less Proficient Readers Have students work in groups of five. In each group, assign a different student to each of the four questions above. Have the student locate in the text the answer to his or her assigned question. Then, have each student state for his or her group the assigned question, the answer to the question, and the location of the answer in the text.

Address Misconceptions

Evolution—Ever Unfolding Some students may have the idea that in order for the theory of evolution by natural selection to be valid, evidence of a complete unbroken chain of fossil organisms will have to be pieced together one day. Explain that a current description of evolution is not limited to studying fossils. Rather, it is the combined results of research in genetics, cladistics, ecology, chemistry, and geology. We will never have an unbroken chain of fossils, but that in no way invalidates evolution by natural selection.

Answers

FIGURE 19–9 Ornithischia and Saurischia

LESSON 19.2

Teach continued

Build Reading Skills

To be proficient readers, students need to learn how to compare and contrast topics they read about. Have students read about patterns of extinction, and then have each student write a short paragraph comparing and contrasting background extinction and mass extinction. Remind students to include both similarities and differences in their paragraphs. Then, have several students share their paragraphs with the class and compile a list of similarities and a list of differences on the board, based on the content of their paragraphs.

DIFFERENTIATED INSTRUCTION

L1 **Struggling Students** Students who would have difficulty preparing a written paragraph comparing and contrasting background extinction and mass extinction should instead prepare a bulleted list of words and phrases that describe how background extinction and mass extinction are similar to one another and another bulleted list describing how they are different.

ELL Focus on ELL: Access Content

ALL SPEAKERS Have students use the **Think-Pair-Share** strategy to help them understand extinction. Pair beginning and intermediate speakers with advanced and advanced high speakers. Have students take turns reading aloud the information about patterns of extinction, one paragraph at a time. As students finish reading each paragraph, ask them a question about the content of the paragraph. Have each pair discuss a response and then share the response with other pairs. Follow up by having each pair of students develop a written question about patterns of extinction. Have one student in each pair read aloud his or her prepared question, and then call on another student to answer.

Study Wkbks A/B, Appendix S14, Think-Pair-Share.

MYSTERY CLUE Because most organisms need oxygen, a sharp reduction in oxygen would have killed many living things. Students can go online to **Biology.com** to gather their evidence.

BIOLOGY.com Have students use data to infer causes of extinction events in **Data Analysis: Explaining Extinctions.**

Patterns of Extinction Species are always evolving and competing—and some species become extinct because of the slow but steady process of natural selection. Paleontologists use the term **background extinction** to describe this kind of "business as usual" extinction. In contrast, a **mass extinction** is an event during which many species become extinct over a relatively short period of time. A mass extinction isn't just a small increase in background extinction. In a mass extinction, entire ecosystems vanish, and whole food webs collapse. Species become extinct because their environment breaks down and the ordinary process of natural selection can't compensate quickly enough.

Until recently researchers looked for a single cause for each mass extinction. For example, geologic evidence shows that at the end of the Cretaceous Period, a huge asteroid crashed into Earth. The impact threw huge amounts of dust and water vapor into the atmosphere, causing global climate change. At about the same time, dinosaurs and many other species became extinct. It is reasonable to infer, then, that the asteroid played a significant role in this mass extinction. Many mass extinctions, however, were probably caused by several factors, working in combination: volcanic eruptions, moving continents, *and* changing sea levels, for example.

After a mass extinction, biodiversity is dramatically reduced. But this is not bad for all organisms. Extinction offers new opportunities to survivors. And as speciation and adaptation produce new species to fill empty niches, biodiversity recovers. But this recovery takes a long time—typically between 5 and 10 million years. Some groups of organisms survive a mass extinction, while other groups do not.

MYSTERY CLUE

Evidence indicates that before the Permian extinction, the oceans lost most of their oxygen. What effect do you think the loss of oxygen had on most organisms?

NoS.3

Extinctions Through Time

The graph shows how the rate of extinction has changed over time. Study the graph, and then answer the questions.

1. **Interpret Graphs** What is plotted on the *y*-axis?
2. **Analyze Data** Which mass extinction killed off the highest percentage of genera?
3. **Draw Conclusions** Describe the overall pattern of extinction shown on the graph.
4. **Infer** What evidence is this graph probably based on?

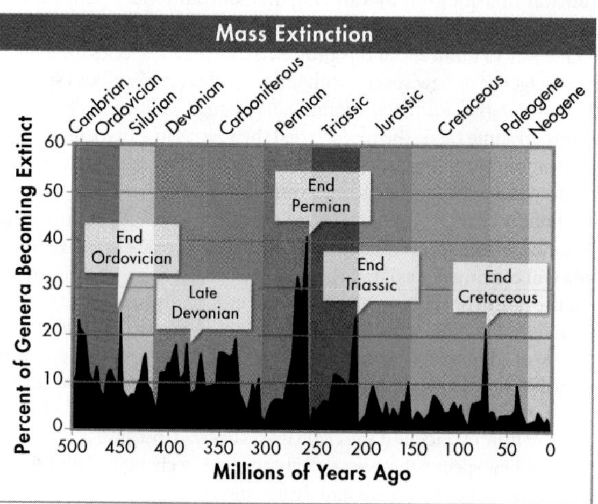

PURPOSE Students will interpret a graph about rates of extinction over time.

PLANNING Remind students to read all the labels on the graph. Discuss what the vertical color bars indicate. *(periods of the geologic time scale)*

ANSWERS

1. percent of genera becoming extinct
2. the extinction at the end of the Permian Period (about 41 percent)
3. According to the graph, extinctions have occurred throughout the history of life, with the percentage of extinctions fluctuating.
4. The graph is probably based on evidence from the fossil record.

Rate of Evolution

How fast does evolution take place?

How quickly does evolution operate? Does it always take place at the same speed? **Evidence shows that evolution has often proceeded at different rates for different organisms at different times over the long history of life on Earth.** Two models of evolution—gradualism and punctuated equilibrium—are shown in **Figure 19–10.**

Gradualism Darwin was impressed by the slow, steady pace of geologic change. He suggested that evolution also needed to be slow and steady, an idea known as **gradualism.** The fossil record shows that many organisms have indeed changed gradually over time.

Punctuated Equilibrium However, numerous examples in the fossil record indicate that the pattern of slow, steady change does not always hold. Horseshoe crabs, for example, have changed little in structure from the time they first appeared in the fossil record. Much of the time, these species are said to be in a state of equilibrium. This means that their structures do not change much even though they continue to evolve genetically.

Every now and then something happens to upset this equilibrium for some species. **Punctuated equilibrium** is the term used to describe equilibrium that is interrupted by brief periods of more rapid change. (Remember that we use *rapid* here relative to the geologic time scale. For geologists, rapid change can take thousands of years!) The fossil record does reveal periods of relatively rapid change in particular groups of organisms. In fact, some biologists suggest that most new species are produced during periods of rapid change.

Rapid Evolution After Equilibrium There are several reasons why evolution may proceed at different rates for different organisms at different times. Rapid evolution may occur after a small population becomes isolated from the main population. This small population can evolve faster than the larger one because genetic changes spread more quickly among fewer individuals. Rapid evolution may also occur when a small group of organisms migrates to a new environment. That's what happened with the Galápagos finches. In addition, mass extinctions open many ecological niches, creating new opportunities for those organisms that survive. It's not surprising, then, that groups of organisms that survive mass extinctions evolve rapidly in the several million years after the extinction.

In Your Notebook *In your own words, describe gradualism and punctuated equilibrium.*

FIGURE 19–10 Models of Evolution Biologists have considered two different patterns for the rate of evolution, gradualism and punctuated equilibrium. These illustrations are simplified to show the general trend of each model. Interpret Visuals ***How do the diagrams illustrate these two models?***

Gradualism

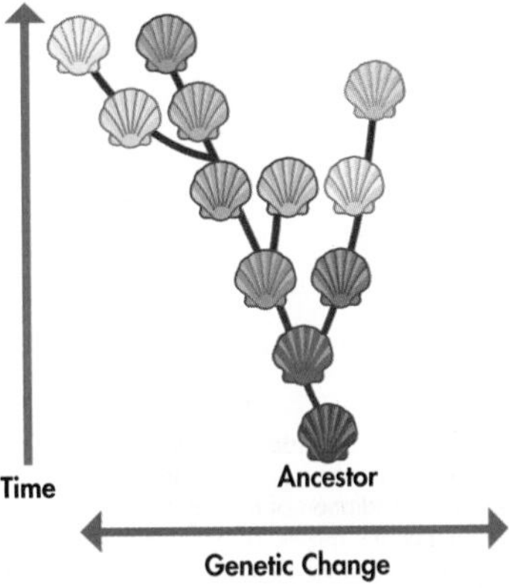

Gradualism involves a slow, steady change in a particular line of descent.

Punctuated Equilibrium

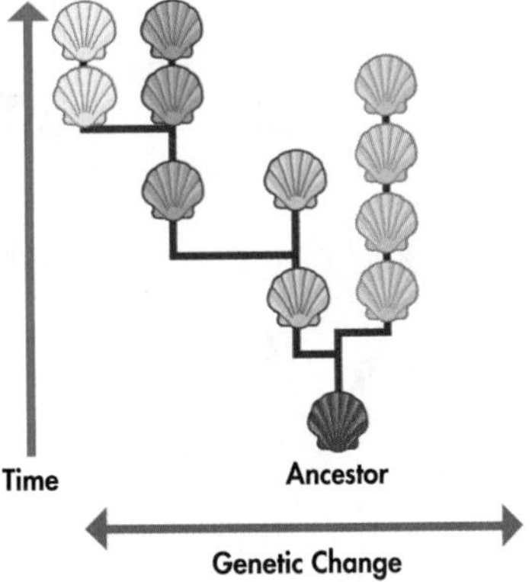

Punctuated equilibrium involves stable periods interrupted by rapid changes.

Build Study Skills

Before students read the text following the heading **Rate of Evolution,** have them preview the information. Write the following questions on the board to help them think about the main points.

- Why did Darwin think evolution was a gradual process? *(He thought biologic change happened like the slow, steady pace of geologic change.)*
- Why are horseshoe crabs an example of a species in a state of equilibrium? *(The species has not changed for a very long time.)*
- How is punctuated equilibrium different from gradualism? *(Gradualism consists of slow, steady change in species. Punctuated equilibrium consists of rapid change in species following a period of equilibrium.)*
- When might rapid evolution take place? *(after a small population becomes isolated; when a small group migrates to a new environment; after a mass extinction)*

After students have completed their preview, ask them to read the text. Follow up by asking volunteers to provide oral responses to the questions above.

DIFFERENTIATED INSTRUCTION

LPR Less Proficient Readers Help struggling readers understand the difference between gradualism and punctuated equilibrium by studying **Figure 19–10.** Point out that the number and final positions of the shells in both diagrams are the same. The only difference is how they got there.

Ask In the diagrams, what is indicated by a horizontal shift in the placement of a shell? *(a color change)*

Ask The paths of the shells in the top diagram are slightly curved. What kind of change does this indicate? *(gradual change)*

Ask The paths of the shells in the bottom diagram are made of straight lines. What do straight horizontal lines indicate? *(sudden change)* What do straight vertical lines indicate? *(periods of no change)*

How Science Works

PUNCTUATED EQUILIBRIUM

Stephen J. Gould and Niles Eldredge proposed the idea of punctuated equilibrium in 1972. Calling their idea a "novel interpretation" as opposed to a new discovery, Gould and Eldredge reasoned that there must be an explanation for why sudden appearances and disappearances of species in the fossil record are so common. While Darwin and others pointed to the incomplete fossil record to explain the lack of intermediates, Gould and Eldredge interpreted "stasis as data"—remarking that the fact species don't seem to change in the fossil record is important in itself and not just the artifact of an imperfect fossil record.

Answers

FIGURE 19–10 The diagram representing gradualism shows a slow, steady change in shell color in a particular line of descent; the diagram representing punctuated equilibrium shows stable periods interrupted by rapid changes.

IN YOUR NOTEBOOK Sample answer: Gradualism is a pattern of slow and steady change from one form to another. Punctuated equilibrium is a pattern of sudden, rapid changes in form between long periods of little change.

Teach continued

Expand Vocabulary

Write the term *adaptive radiation* on the board. Tell students that an understanding of each word that makes up this term will help make the meaning of the term clear. Tell students that *adaptive* means "having a capacity for or tendency toward adaptation," and *radiation* means "the action of spreading around as if from a center."

Ask How does the definition of the word *adaptive* relate to the term *adaptive radiation*? *(Adaptive radiation cannot occur in the absence of adaptation, which, in evolution, designates genetically determined characteristics that enhance fitness.)*

Ask How does the definition of the word *radiation* relate to the term *adaptive radiation*? *("Spreading as if from a center" describes the evolution of several species from a single or small group of species.)*

DIFFERENTIATED INSTRUCTION

L1 Special Needs Have students work with a partner to complete a **Vocabulary Word Map** for the term *adaptive radiation.* Have students write the term in the top box and then list attributes in the bottom boxes. Circulate among the pairs as they work, asking questions about the attributes identified in their vocabulary word maps.

Study Wkbks A/B, Appendix S32, Vocabulary Word Map. **Transparencies,** GO17.

Adaptive Radiation and Convergent Evolution

What are two patterns of macroevolution?

As paleontologists study the fossil record, they look for patterns. **Two important patterns of macroevolution are adaptive radiation and convergent evolution.** As you'll see, Darwin noted both patterns while aboard the *Beagle.*

Adaptive Radiation Studies of fossils and living organisms often show that a single species or small group of species has diversified over time into a clade containing many species. These species display variations on the group's ancestral body plan, and often occupy different ecological niches. These differences are the product of an evolutionary process called adaptive radiation. **Adaptive radiation** is the process by which a single species or a small group of species evolves over a relatively short time into several different forms that live in different ways. An adaptive radiation may occur when species migrate to a new environment or when extinction clears an environment of a large number of inhabitants. In addition, a species may evolve a new feature that enables it to take advantage of a previously unused environment.

▶ ***Adaptive Radiations in the Fossil Record*** Dinosaurs—one of several spectacular adaptive radiations of reptiles—flourished for about 150 million years during the Mesozoic. The fossil record documents that in the dinosaurs' heyday, mammals diversified but remained small. After most dinosaurs became extinct, however, an adaptive radiation of mammals began. That radiation, part of which is shown in **Figure 19–11,** produced the great diversity of mammals of the Cenozoic Era.

FIGURE 19–11 Adaptive Radiation This diagram shows part of the adaptive radiation of mammals. Note how the groups of animals shown have adapted to many different ways of life—including two groups which have become aquatic. Interpret Visuals ***According to this diagram, which mammal group is most closely related to elephants? Does this surprise you? Explain.***

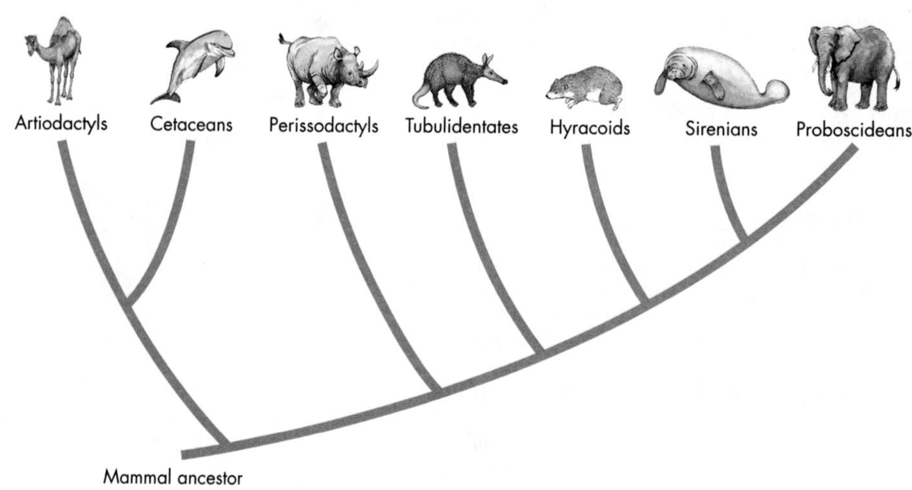

UbD Check for Understanding

FOLLOW-UP PROBES

Ask During a particular geologic period, land areas rose, draining shallow seas and creating moist tropical habitats. Explain why you would expect adaptive radiation to have taken place after these events. *(Adaptive radiation often occurs after major changes in environments. New niches form, which provide opportunities for new species to evolve.)*

ADJUST INSTRUCTION

If students have difficulty responding to the question, use an analogy. Ask them to think about what happens when an apartment building is built on newly cleared land. *(The organisms that lived on the land move or die, and many people move in.)* Explain how the new homes or apartments are like new niches.

Answers

FIGURE 19–11 sirenians; Yes, it is surprising because sirenians are aquatic and look nothing like elephants, which are terrestrial.

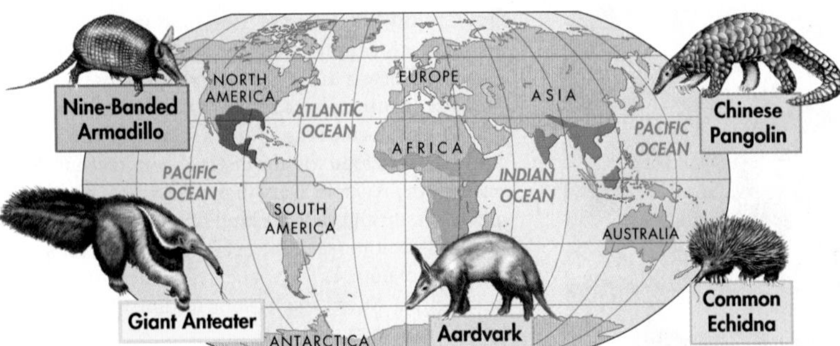

FIGURE 19–12 Convergent Evolution Mammals that feed on ants and termites evolved independently five times. Although each species is unique, each has evolved powerful front claws, a long hairless snout, and a tongue covered with sticky saliva. These adaptations are useful for hunting and eating insects.

▶ ***Modern Adaptive Radiations*** Galápagos finches and Hawaiian honeycreepers are two examples of adaptive radiations in modern organisms. In each of these cases, numerous species evolved from a single founding species. Both finches and honeycreepers evolved different beaks and behaviors that enable each of them to eat different kinds of food.

Convergent Evolution Sometimes, groups of organisms evolve in different places or at different times, but in similar environments. These organisms start out with different structures on which natural selection can operate. But they face similar selection pressures. In these situations, natural selection may mold different body structures in ways that perform similar functions. Because they perform similar functions, these body structures may look similar. Evolution produces similar structures and characteristics in distantly related organisms through the process of **convergent evolution.** Convergent evolution has occurred often in both plants and animals. For example, mammals that feed on ants and termites evolved not once, but five times, in different regions as shown in **Figure 19–12.** Remember how Darwin noted striking similarities among large, distantly related grassland birds? Emus, rheas, and ostriches are another example of convergent evolution.

Coevolution

What evolutionary characteristics are typical of coevolving species?

Sometimes the life histories of two or more species are so closely connected that they evolve together. Many flowering plants, for example, can reproduce only if their flowers attract a specific pollinator species. Pollinators, in turn, may depend on the flowers of certain plants for food in the form of pollen or nectar. The process by which two species evolve in response to changes in each other over time is called **coevolution.** **The relationship between two coevolving organisms often becomes so specific that neither organism can survive without the other. Thus, an evolutionary change in one organism is usually followed by a change in the other organism.**

Biology In-Depth

THE BIRDS AND THE BEES

An unusual example of coevolution occurs between certain orchids and insects. These plants are pollinated by species of insects in which the males emerge in the spring before the females. The orchid flowers have evolved shapes and odors that mimic the stimuli presented by the female insects. The males fly around in search of female insects. In doing so, the males encounter the insect-mimicking orchid flowers and try to mate with them. In the process, they pollinate the orchids. Some plants and their pollinators are so highly adapted to each other that only one species is able to pollinate a given plant. For example, in Hawaii, *Brighamia* flowers can be pollinated only by nectar-feeding birds called Hawaiian honeycreepers. However, the birds have declined in number, and now the plants also face extinction.

Lead a Discussion

Draw students' attention to the subsection **Convergent Evolution.** Explain that convergent evolution describes situations in which unrelated organisms evolve similar structures and traits due to similar environmental pressures.

Ask What similar structures evolved in the animals shown in **Figure 19–12?** *(powerful front claws, a long snout, and a tongue covered with sticky saliva)*

Ask What do these adaptations allow each of these animals to do? *(eat ants)*

Ask What structures do birds and bats have in common that can be attributed to convergent evolution? *(wings)*

DIFFERENTIATED INSTRUCTION

L1 Struggling Students Have students use a **Main Ideas and Details Chart** to organize information about convergent evolution. Have them enter the term *convergent evolution* as the main idea in their charts. Then, ask students to work in pairs to brainstorm details related to this main idea and enter them in their charts. Call on students to read aloud details they have included in their charts. Use their responses to identify any misconceptions students have about this topic, and address those in a discussion to increase the depth of students' understanding.

Study Wkbks A/B, Appendix S28, Main Ideas and Details Chart. **Transparencies,** GO13.

ELL English Language Learners Use the color coding in **Figure 19–12** to help ELL students understand convergent evolution. Begin by pointing to the illustration of the nine-banded armadillo and its label. Then move your finger to the continent of North America on the map. With the aid of an advanced speaker, explain that the border of the label box and the area of the animal's range are the same color. Then, point to the common echidna and link it to the continent of Australia on the map. Repeat the process for all the animals shown. The advanced speaker can also help you explain the process of convergent evolution and clarify the idea that all the animals have similar adaptations for feeding on ants.

LESSON 19.2

Teach continued

Lead a Discussion

Ask students to read about coevolution.

Ask What is coevolution? *(two species evolving in response to changes in each other)*

Ask How do the organisms in **Figure 19–13** demonstrate coevolution? *(Monarch caterpillars have evolved a tolerance for milkweed toxin.)*

DIFFERENTIATED INSTRUCTION

L3 **Advanced Students** Have students research the relationship between the yucca moth and the yucca plant. Ask them to share their findings with the class.

Assess and Remediate

EVALUATE UNDERSTANDING

Call on students to explain why evolution might proceed rapidly in some circumstances and slowly in others. Then, have students complete the 19.2 Assessment.

REMEDIATION SUGGESTION

L1 **Struggling Students** If some students struggle to answer **Question 2b,** point out that when organisms move from one place to another, their new environment may have significantly different conditions than their old one.

BIOLOGY.com Students can check their understanding of lesson concepts with the **Self-Test** assessment. They can then take an online version of the **Lesson Assessment.**

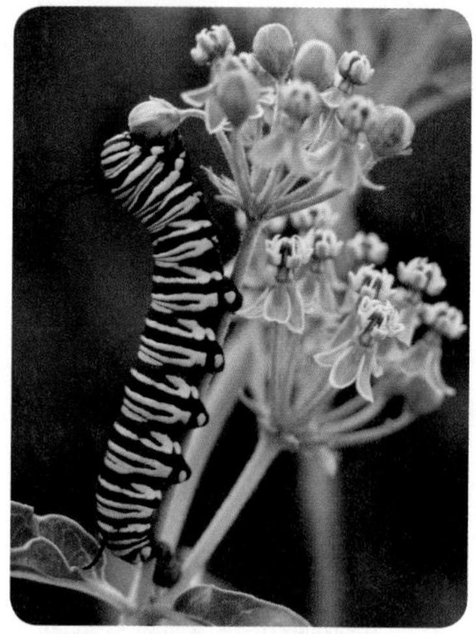

FIGURE 19–13 Plants and Herbivorous Insects Milkweed plants produce toxic chemicals. But monarch caterpillars not only can tolerate this toxin, they also can store it in their body tissues to use as a defense against *their* predators.

Flowers and Pollinators Coevolution of flowers and pollinators is common and can lead to unusual results. For example, Darwin discovered an orchid whose flowers had a long structure called a spur. Way down at the bottom of that 40-centimeter-long spur is a supply of nectar, which could serve as food for any insect able to reach it. But what insect could reach it? Darwin predicted that some pollinating insect must have some kind of feeding structure that would allow it to reach the nectar. Darwin never saw that insect. But about 40 years later, researchers discovered a moth with a 40-centimeter-long feeding tube that matched Darwin's prediction!

Plants and Herbivorous Insects Plants and herbivorous insects also demonstrate close, albeit less "friendly," coevolutionary relationships. Insects have been feeding on flowering plants since both groups emerged. Over time, many plants evolved bad-tasting or poisonous compounds that discourage insects from eating them. Some of the most powerful natural poisons are compounds developed by plants in response to insect attacks. But once plants began to produce poisons, natural selection on herbivorous insects favored any variants that could alter, inactivate, or eliminate those poisons. Time and again, a group of insects, like the caterpillar in **Figure 19–13,** evolved a way to deal with the particular poisons produced by a certain group of plants.

19.2 Assessment

IN B.8.5

Review Key Concepts

1. a. Review How does variation within a clade affect the clade's chance of surviving environmental change?
b. Compare and Contrast How is mass extinction different from background extinction?

2. a. Review Explain how punctuated equilibrium is different from gradualism.
b. Relate Cause and Effect Why would evolution speed up when a small group of organisms migrates to a new environment?

3. a. Review What is adaptive radiation?
b. Relate Cause and Effect When might adaptive radiation result in convergent evolution?

4. a. Review What is coevolution?
b. Apply Concepts Describe an example of coevolution.

Apply the Big idea

Evolution

5. What role does the environment play in convergent evolution?

BIOLOGY.com Search Lesson 19.2 GO • Self-Test • Lesson Assessment

Assessment Answers

1a. In general, it increases the chance of surviving environmental changes.

1b. In a mass extinction, many species become extinct over a relatively short period of time because their environment breaks down and natural selection cannot compensate quickly enough. Background extinction is a continuous process because some species are always becoming extinct by the slow, steady process of natural selection.

2a. Punctuated equilibrium consists of brief periods of rapid change that interrupt periods of little change. Gradualism is a slow, steady pace of change in species.

2b. Genetic changes spread more quickly through a small population; there may be new opportunities (niches) for the newly arrived organisms.

3a. Adaptive radiation is the process by which a single species or small group of species evolves over a relatively short time into several different forms with different ways of life.

3b. Adaptive radiation may result in convergent evolution as unrelated organisms face similar environments and evolve similar structures.

4a. process by which two species evolve in response to changes in each other

4b. Sample answer: evolution in monarch caterpillars of tolerance to milkweed toxins

5. Big idea Sample answer: The environment in one place can be similar to the environment in another place. Similar environments exert similar pressures on different species and may result in adaptations of structures to perform similar functions.

19.3 Earth's Early History

IN B.8.1 History of life on Earth; B.8.7 Origins of life on Earth. Also covered: NoS.3, B.6.5, B.8.6.

THINK ABOUT IT How did life on Earth begin? What were the earliest forms of life? How did life and the biosphere interact? Origin-of-life research is a dynamic field. But even though some current hypotheses likely will change, our understanding of other aspects of the story is growing.

The Mysteries of Life's Origins

What do scientists hypothesize about early Earth and the origin of life?

Geological and astronomical evidence suggests that Earth formed as pieces of cosmic debris collided with one another. While the planet was young, it was struck by one or more huge objects, and the entire globe melted. For millions of years, violent volcanic activity shook Earth's crust. Comets and asteroids bombarded its surface. About 4.2 billion years ago, Earth cooled enough to allow solid rocks to form and water to condense and fall as rain. Earth's surface became stable enough for permanent oceans to form.

This infant planet was very different from Earth today. **Earth's early atmosphere contained little or no oxygen. It was principally composed of carbon dioxide, water vapor, and nitrogen, with lesser amounts of carbon monoxide, hydrogen sulfide, and hydrogen cyanide.** If you had been there, a few deep breaths would have killed you! Because of the gases in the atmosphere, the sky was probably pinkish-orange. And because the oceans contained lots of dissolved iron, they were probably brown. This was the Earth on which life began.

Key Questions

What do scientists hypothesize about early Earth and the origin of life?

What theory explains the origin of eukaryotic cells?

What is the evolutionary significance of sexual reproduction?

Vocabulary

endosymbiotic theory

Taking Notes

Flowchart Construct a flowchart that shows what scientists hypothesize are the major steps from the origin of Earth to the appearance of eukaryotic cells.

FIGURE 19–14 Early Earth Violent volcanic eruptions helped shape Earth's early history.

Teach for Understanding

ENDURING UNDERSTANDING The diversity of life is the result of ongoing evolutionary change. Species alive today have evolved from ancient common ancestors.

GUIDING QUESTION What happened during Earth's early history?

EVIDENCE OF UNDERSTANDING *After completing the lesson, give students the following assessment to show whether they understand the major events in Earth's early history.* Divide the class into four groups. Provide each group with a length of table paper, and have students create an illustrated wall chart that tracks the major events thought to have occurred around the time of the origin of life on Earth.

LESSON 19.3

Getting Started

Objectives

19.3.1 Identify some of the hypotheses about early Earth and the origin of life.

19.3.2 Explain the endosymbiotic theory.

19.3.3 Explain the significance of sexual reproduction in evolution.

Student Resources

Study Workbooks A and B, 19.3 Worksheets

Spanish Study Workbook, 19.3 Worksheets

Lab Manual B, 19.3 Hands-On Activity Worksheet

Lesson Overview • Lesson Notes
- Activity: Art Review
- Assessment: Self-Test, Lesson Assessment

For corresponding lesson in the **Foundation Edition**, see pages 462–469.

Build Background

Ask students if they have ever learned about something without actually seeing it happen. For example, what if they awoke in the morning to find tree branches broken and the power out? Ask how they could determine what might have happened. *(by looking at the evidence, e.g., fallen trees and weather reports)* Ask how scientists have figured out the process by which Earth may have formed. *(by looking at the evidence)* Direct students to keep a list of evidence described in this lesson that scientists used to learn about Earth's early history.

IN INDIANA ACADEMIC STANDARDS

For the full text of all standards, see the Course Overview in the front matter of this book.

B.8.1 Explain how anatomical and molecular similarities among organisms that suggest life on earth began as simple, one-celled organisms about 4 billion years ago and multicellular organisms evolved later.

B.8.7 Describe the modern scientific theory of the origins of life on earth, and evaluate the evidence that supports it.

Teach

Use Visuals

Ask a volunteer to read aloud the numbered steps in **Figure 19–15.**

Then, use the following questions to enhance students' understanding of the Miller-Urey experiment.

Ask How did Miller and Urey model conditions that existed on early Earth in their experiment? *(They used water to simulate the oceans; water vapor, methane, ammonia, and hydrogen to simulate Earth's early atmosphere; and sparks of electricity to simulate lightning.)*

Ask What question did Miller and Urey's experiment seek to answer? *(Could organic molecules assemble under the conditions that existed on early Earth?)*

Ask What were the results of their experiment? *(Amino acids and other organic compounds could have assembled under the conditions that existed on early Earth.)*

DIFFERENTIATED INSTRUCTION

LPR **Less Proficient Readers** Emphasize that illustrations such as **Figure 19–15** usually go along with written text and help readers understand the text. Begin by having students read the text following the heading **The First Organic Molecules.** Then, go over each step in the illustration. After you read each internal caption aloud, have students find the corresponding description in the text. Once you have finished this process for all the steps, have students construct a **Flowchart** that summarizes the steps in the Miller-Urey experiment. (To help them, point out that their flowcharts will show five steps; the fifth step will be the collection of organic compounds.)

Study Wkbks A/B, Appendix S25, Flowchart. **Transparencies,** GO8.

BIOLOGY.com Have students find out more about early Earth by using **Art Review: Conditions on the Early Earth.**

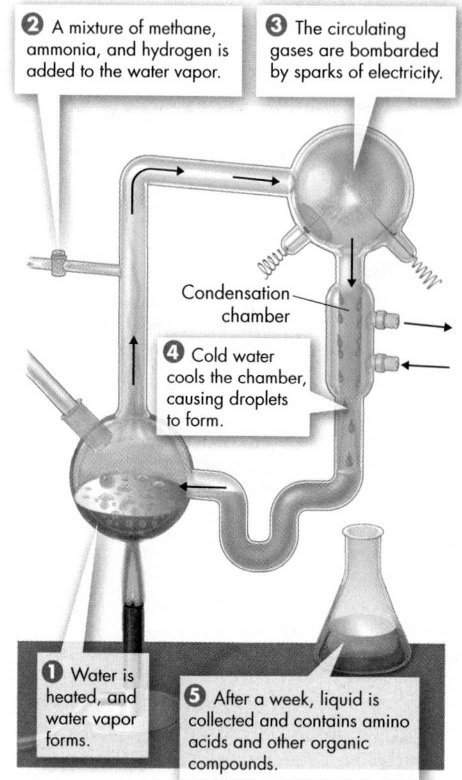

2 A mixture of methane, ammonia, and hydrogen is added to the water vapor.
3 The circulating gases are bombarded by sparks of electricity.
Condensation chamber
4 Cold water cools the chamber, causing droplets to form.
1 Water is heated, and water vapor forms.
5 After a week, liquid is collected and contains amino acids and other organic compounds.

FIGURE 19–15 Miller-Urey Experiment Miller and Urey produced amino acids, which are needed to make proteins, by passing sparks through a mixture of hydrogen, methane, ammonia, and water vapor. Evidence now suggests that the composition of Earth's early atmosphere was different from their 1953 experiment. However, more recent experiments with different mixtures of gases have produced similar results.

The First Organic Molecules Could organic molecules assemble under conditions on early Earth? In 1953, chemists Stanley Miller and Harold Urey tried to answer that question. They filled a sterile flask with water, to simulate the oceans, and boiled it. To the water vapor, they added methane, ammonia, and hydrogen, to simulate what they thought had been the composition of Earth's early atmosphere. Then, as shown in **Figure 19–15,** they passed the gases through electrodes, to simulate lightning. Next, they passed the gases through a condensation chamber, where cold water cooled them, causing drops to form. The liquid circulated through the experimental apparatus for a week. The results were spectacular: They produced 21 amino acids—building blocks of proteins. **Miller and Urey's experiment suggested how mixtures of the organic compounds necessary for life could have arisen from simpler compounds on a primitive Earth.**

We now know that Miller and Urey's ideas on the composition of the early atmosphere were incorrect. But new experiments based on current ideas of the early atmosphere have also produced organic compounds. In fact, in 1995, one of Miller's more accurate mixtures produced cytosine and uracil, two bases found in RNA.

Formation of Microspheres A stew of organic molecules is a long way from a living cell, and the leap from nonlife to life is the greatest gap in scientific hypotheses of life's early history. Geological evidence suggests that during the Archean Eon, 200 to 300 million years after Earth cooled enough to carry liquid water, cells similar to bacteria were common. How might these cells have originated?

Large organic molecules form tiny bubbles called proteinoid microspheres under certain conditions. Microspheres are not cells, but they have some characteristics of living systems. Like cells, they have selectively permeable membranes through which water molecules can pass. Microspheres also have a simple means of storing and releasing energy. Several hypotheses suggest that structures similar to proteinoid microspheres acquired the characteristics of living cells as early as 3.8 billion years ago.

Evolution of RNA and DNA Another unanswered question is the origin of RNA and DNA. Remember that cells are controlled by information stored in DNA, which is transcribed into RNA and then translated into proteins. How could this complex biochemical machinery have evolved?

Biology In-Depth

POLYMERS ON EARLY EARTH

After small organic molecules appeared on prebiotic Earth, the second major chemical step before life could appear was most likely polymerization, or the formation of organic polymers from monomers. Polymers are usually synthesized by dehydration reactions. In living cells, specific enzymes catalyze these reactions. However, polymerization can also take place in laboratory situations without enzymes, as when dilute solutions of organic monomers are dripped onto hot sand, clay, or rock. The heat vaporizes the water and concentrates the monomers on the underlying substance. Some of the monomers spontaneously bond in chains, forming polymers. In a similar way, on early Earth, rain and waves could have splashed dilute solutions of organic monomers onto fresh lava or other hot surfaces and then rinsed the proteinoids and other polymers into the sea after they formed on the hot surfaces.

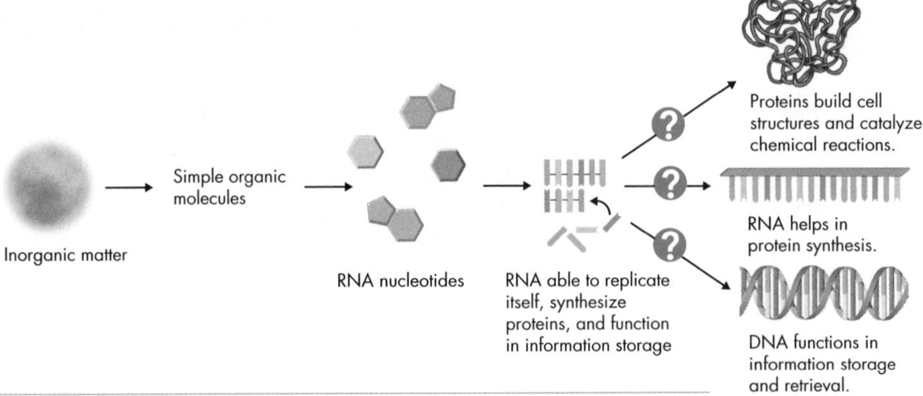
Inorganic matter
Simple organic molecules
RNA nucleotides
RNA able to replicate itself, synthesize proteins, and function in information storage
Proteins build cell structures and catalyze chemical reactions.
RNA helps in protein synthesis.
DNA functions in information storage and retrieval.

FIGURE 19–16 Origin of RNA and DNA The "RNA world" hypothesis about the origin of life suggests that RNA evolved before DNA. Scientists have not yet demonstrated the later stages of this process in a laboratory setting. Interpret Visuals ***How would RNA have stored genetic information?***

Scientists haven't solved this puzzle, but molecular biologists have generated intriguing hypotheses. A number of experiments that simulated conditions on early Earth suggest that small sequences of RNA could have formed from simpler molecules. Why is that interesting? It is interesting because we now know that, under the right conditions, some RNA sequences help DNA replicate. Other RNA sequences process messenger RNA after transcription. Still other RNA sequences catalyze chemical reactions, and some RNA molecules even grow and replicate on their own. **The "RNA world" hypothesis proposes that RNA existed by itself before DNA. From this simple RNA-based system, several steps could have led to DNA-directed protein synthesis.** This hypothesis, shown in **Figure 19–16,** is still being tested.

Production of Free Oxygen Microscopic fossils, or microfossils, of prokaryotes that resemble bacteria have been found in Archean rocks more than 3.5 billion years old. Those first life forms evolved in the absence of oxygen because at that time Earth's atmosphere contained very little of that highly reactive gas.

During the early Proterozoic Eon, photosynthetic bacteria became common. By 2.2 billion years ago, these organisms were churning out oxygen. At first, the oxygen combined with iron in the oceans, producing iron oxide, or rust. Iron oxide, which is not soluble in water, sank to the ocean floor, forming great bands of iron that are the source of most iron ore mined today. Without iron, the oceans changed color from brown to blue-green.

Next, oxygen gas began to accumulate in the atmosphere. The ozone layer began to form, and the skies turned their present shade of blue. Over several hundred million years, oxygen concentrations rose until they reached today's levels. In a sense, this increase in oxygen created the first global "pollution" crisis. To the first cells, which evolved in the absence of oxygen, this reactive gas was a deadly poison! The rise of oxygen in the atmosphere drove some early life forms to extinction. Some organisms, however, evolved new metabolic pathways that used oxygen for respiration. These organisms also evolved ways to protect themselves from oxygen's powerful reactive abilities.

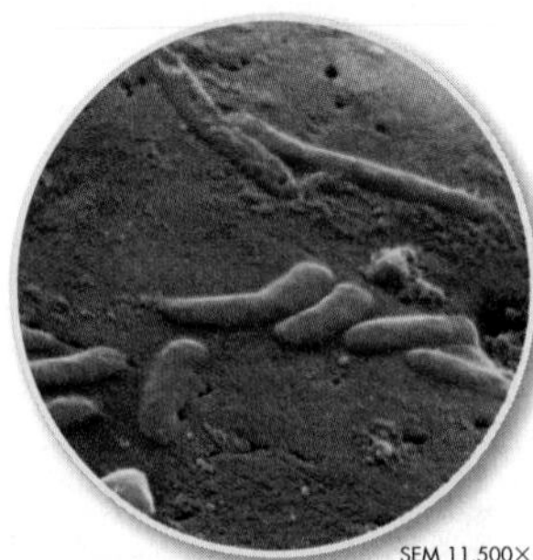
SEM 11,500×

FIGURE 19–17 Fossilized Bacteria Fossilized bacteria are the earliest evidence of life on Earth. These rod-shaped bacterial cells (red) are seen calcified on the shell of a single-celled protozoan.

Build Study Skills

Help students understand that oxygen has not always been available to organisms the way it is today. Have them read the passage headed **Production of Free Oxygen.** Then, as a class, create a **Timeline** on the board to help all students follow the sequence in the development of an oxygenated atmosphere.

Study Wkbks A/B, Appendix S15, Timeline.

DIFFERENTIATED INSTRUCTION

L1 Struggling Students Have students work in pairs to restate the timeline from above as a numbered list of events. Ask students to restate each entry on the timeline in their own words. Circulate among the pairs of students to answer questions or help students sequence the information.

L3 Advanced Students Challenge students to find out more about Earth's early atmosphere and how the atmosphere changed over time. Students can present the results of their research to the class. The following are some specific questions that students might research:

- What techniques have scientists used to estimate the amount of oxygen in the early atmosphere? Also, what inferences have scientists made, and on what observations have they based their inferences?
- What would have happened to lighter gases, such as hydrogen and helium, in the early atmosphere?
- Besides changing the amount of oxygen in the atmosphere, how else might early microbes have affected the atmosphere?
- What are oxidation-reduction reactions, and how were they significant in the early development of Earth's atmosphere?

UbD Check for Understanding

ONE-MINUTE RESPONSE

Write the following prompt on the board, and give students about one minute to write a response that summarizes their understanding.

- How would Earth be different today if photosynthesis had not evolved? *(Responses should indicate that Earth's atmosphere would not contain the amount of oxygen it does today and the oceans would still contain large amounts of iron. As a result, organisms would be very different than they are today.)*

ADJUST INSTRUCTION

If some students have difficulty answering the question, remind them that photosynthesis is the primary process through which oxygen is produced. So, the question could be rephrased as: How would Earth be different if its atmosphere contained no oxygen?

Answers

FIGURE 19–16 RNA would have stored genetic information in its nucleotide sequences.

LESSON 19.3

Teach continued

Lead a Discussion

Review eukaryotic and prokaryotic cells by calling on students at random to describe characteristics they recall about each type of cell. Show or draw examples of each type on the board, and label the parts as students mention individual organelles. Ask volunteers to describe the functions of the main organelles, particularly mitochondria and chloroplasts. Then, introduce the term *endosymbiotic theory*.

Ask What evidence do scientists use to support the endosymbiotic theory? *(similarity of the membranes around mitochondria and chloroplasts to the cell membranes of prokaryotes; similarity of the DNA in mitochondria and chloroplasts to bacterial DNA; similarity of ribosomes in mitochondria and chloroplasts to bacterial ribosomes; the fact that mitochondria and chloroplasts reproduce by binary fission, as do bacteria)*

DIFFERENTIATED INSTRUCTION

ELL English Language Learners Explain to ELL students that the prefix *endo-* means "inside, within." Remind students the *symbiotic* means "a close relationship between two organisms." So, *the endosymbiotic theory* has to do with two organisms, one within the other, that have a close relationship. Ask students to come up with and define three other words that use the prefix *endo-*.

LPR Less Proficient Readers As students read about the endosymbiotic theory, have them make a bulleted list of the evidence scientists use to support this theory. After they finish, have students compare lists. Ask each student to revise or add to his or her list, based on the comparison.

NoS.3

Comparing Atmospheres

Many scientists think that Earth's early atmosphere may have been similar to the gases released by a volcano today. The graphs show the composition of the atmosphere today and the composition of gases released by a volcano.

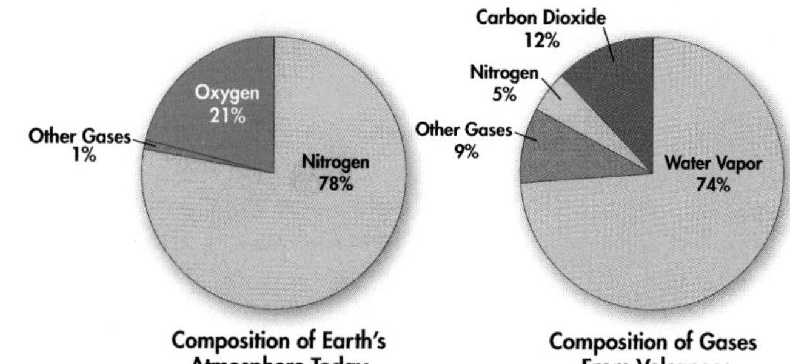

Composition of Earth's Atmosphere Today

Composition of Gases From Volcanoes

1. Interpret Graphs Which gas is most abundant in Earth's atmosphere today? What percentage of that gas may have been present in the early atmosphere?

2. Interpret Graphs Which gas was probably most abundant in the early atmosphere?

3. Infer Where did the water in today's oceans probably come from?

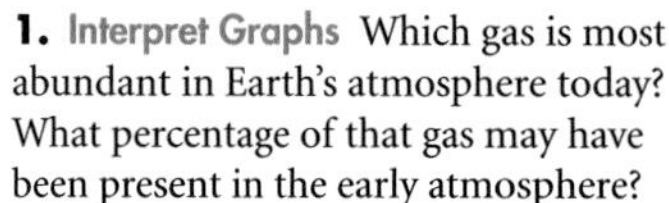

Origin of Eukaryotic Cells

What theory explains the origin of eukaryotic cells?

One of the most important events in the history of life was the evolution of eukaryotic cells from prokaryotic cells. Remember that eukaryotic cells have nuclei, but prokaryotic cells do not. Eukaryotic cells also have complex organelles. Virtually all eukaryotes have mitochondria, and both plants and algae also have chloroplasts. How did these complex cells evolve?

BUILD Vocabulary

PREFIXES The prefix *endo-* in **endosymbiotic theory** means "within" or "inner." The endosymbiotic theory involves a symbiotic relationship between eukaryotic cells and the prokaryotes within them.

Endosymbiotic Theory Researchers hypothesize that about 2 billion years ago, some ancient prokaryotes began evolving internal cell membranes. These prokaryotes were the ancestors of eukaryotic organisms. Then, according to **endosymbiotic** (en doh sim by AHT ik) **theory,** prokaryotic cells entered those ancestral eukaryotes. These intruders didn't infect their hosts, as parasites would have done, and the host cells didn't digest them, as they would have digested prey. Instead, the small prokaryotes began living inside the larger cells, as shown in **Figure 19–18.** **The endosymbiotic theory proposes that a symbiotic relationship evolved over time, between primitive eukaryotic cells and the prokaryotic cells within them.** This idea was proposed more than a century ago. At that time, microscopists saw that the membranes of mitochondria and chloroplasts resembled the cell membranes of free-living prokaryotes. This observation led to two related hypotheses.

PURPOSE Students will interpret graphs that compare the composition of Earth's atmosphere today with the composition of gases from volcanoes.

PLANNING Explain that circle graphs can be used to compare the parts of a whole. Review the structure of a circle graph and how it can be divided. Remind students that a circle is 360°. Any pie-shaped part, or sector, of the circle graph is a percentage of 360°.

ANSWERS

1. nitrogen; 5 percent

2. water vapor

3. The water in today's oceans probably came from water vapor in the early atmosphere that condensed into liquid form.

One hypothesis proposes that mitochondria evolved from endosymbiotic prokaryotes that were able to use oxygen to generate energy-rich ATP. Inside primitive eukaryotic cells, these energy-generating prokaryotes evolved into mitochondria that now power the cells of all multicellular organisms. Mitochondria enabled cells to metabolize oxygen. Without this ability, cells would have been killed by the free oxygen in the atmosphere.

Another hypothesis proposes that chloroplasts evolved from endosymbiotic prokaryotes that had the ability to photosynthesize. Over time, these photosynthetic prokaryotes evolved within eukaryotic cells into the chloroplasts of plants and algae.

Modern Evidence During the 1960s, Lynn Margulis of Boston University gathered evidence that supported the endosymbiotic theory. Margulis noted first that mitochondria and chloroplasts contain DNA similar to bacterial DNA. Second, she noted that mitochondria and chloroplasts have ribosomes whose size and structure closely resemble those of bacteria. Third, she found that mitochondria and chloroplasts, like bacteria, reproduce by binary fission when cells containing them divide by mitosis. Mitochondria and chloroplasts, then, share many features of free-living bacteria. These similarities provide strong evidence of a common ancestry between free-living bacteria and the organelles of living eukaryotic cells.

In Your Notebook *Describe two hypotheses relating to the endosymbiotic theory.*

FIGURE 19–18 The Endosymbiotic Theory The endosymbiotic theory proposes that eukaryotic cells arose from living communities formed by prokaryotic organisms. Ancient prokaryotes may have entered primitive eukaryotic cells, remained there, and evolved into organelles. **Infer** ***Is it likely that nonphotosynthetic prokaryotes could have evolved into chloroplasts? Explain your answer.***

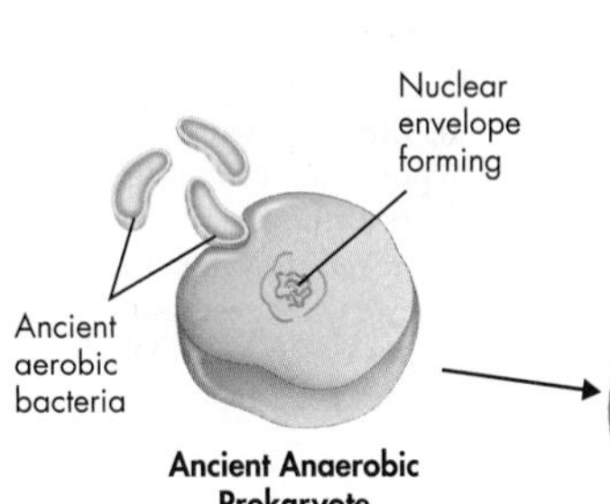

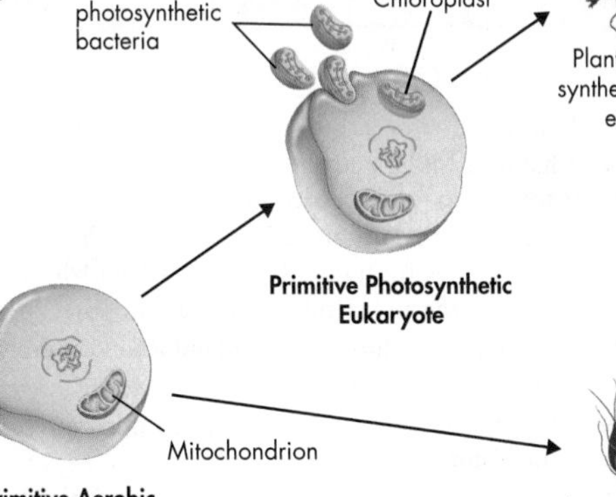

Use Visuals

Have the class spend 5 minutes in small groups to study and discuss **Figure 19–18.**

After studying the figure, have all groups come together to discuss the evidence offered by Lynn Margulis to support the endosymbiotic theory.

DIFFERENTIATED INSTRUCTION

L1 Struggling Students Help students understand the events described in **Figure 19–18** by having them work with a partner to read and paraphrase the caption and labels. Then, have the members of each pair work together to describe, in their own words, each event shown in the figure.

ELL Focus on ELL: Build Background

ALL SPEAKERS Ask students to explain what the following words mean: *events, complex, ancestral, digest, proposes, generate,* and *features.* If necessary, ask them to find the words in the passage and use context clues.

Then, assign students to small groups that include a mix of levels of speakers. Present each group with a written copy of the following discussion topics:

- How did ancient anaerobic prokaryotes benefit from a symbiotic relationship with bacteria?
- How did bacteria benefit from the relationship?

Allow groups about 10 minutes to discuss the topics. Then, have one member of each group share an oral response with the class.

UbD Check for Understanding

INDEX CARD SUMMARIES

Give students each an index card. Ask students to write one concept about the endosymbiotic theory that they understand on the front of the card. Then, have them identify something about the endosymbiotic theory they do not understand and write it on the back of the card in the form of a question.

ADJUST INSTRUCTION

Read students' cards to identify concepts that are well understood and those that are causing confusion. Choose several representative questions to discuss with the class.

Answers

FIGURE 19–18 No, chloroplasts have the ability to carry out photosynthesis.

IN YOUR NOTEBOOK Mitochondria evolved from endosymbiotic prokaryotes that could use oxygen to generate ATP. Chloroplasts evolved from endosymbiotic prokaryotes that could photosynthesize.

Teach continued

Lead a Discussion

Ask How did the development of sexual reproduction impact the amount of genetic variation in populations? *(It increased genetic variation.)*

Ask How is the pace of evolution affected by an increase in genetic variation? *(It increases.)*

DIFFERENTIATED INSTRUCTION

LPR Less Proficient Readers Have students use a **Cause and Effect Diagram** to clarify the effect that the development of sexual reproduction had on the rate of evolution. Then, ask students to explain why sexual reproduction increases the rate of evolution. *(It increases genetic variation.)*

Study Wkbks A/B, Appendix S18, Cause and Effect Diagram. **Transparencies,** GO1.

Assess and Remediate

EVALUATE UNDERSTANDING

Have students work with a partner to ask and answer each of the Key Questions. Then, have students complete the 19.3 Assessment.

REMEDIATION SUGGESTION

L1 Struggling Students If students have trouble with **Question 2b,** suggest they review **Figure 19–18.**

BIOLOGY.com Students can check their understanding of lesson concepts with the **Self-Test** assessment. They can then take an online version of the **Lesson Assessment.**

Sexual Reproduction and Multicellularity

What is the evolutionary significance of sexual reproduction?

Sometime after eukaryotic cells arose, they began to reproduce sexually. **The development of sexual reproduction sped up evolutionary change because sexual reproduction increases genetic variation.**

Significance of Sexual Reproduction When prokaryotes reproduce asexually, they duplicate their genetic material and pass it on to daughter cells. This process is efficient, but it yields daughter cells whose genomes duplicate their parent's genome. Genetic variation is basically restricted to mutations in DNA.

In contrast, when eukaryotes reproduce sexually, offspring receive genetic material from two parents. Meiosis and fertilization shuffle and reshuffle genes, generating lots of genetic diversity. That's why the offspring of sexually reproducing organisms are never identical to either their parents or their siblings (except for identical twins). The more heritable variation, the more "raw material" natural selection has to work on. Genetic variation increases the likelihood of a population's adapting to new or changing environmental conditions.

Multicellularity Multicellular organisms evolved a few hundred million years after the evolution of sexual reproduction. Early multicellular organisms underwent a series of adaptive radiations, resulting in great diversity.

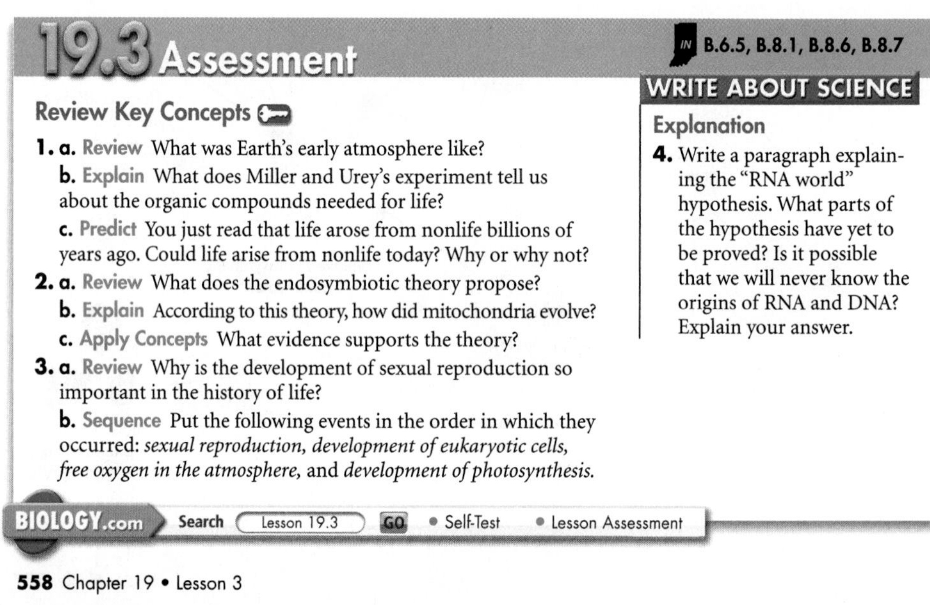

19.3 Assessment

IN B.6.5, B.8.1, B.8.6, B.8.7

Review Key Concepts

1. a. Review What was Earth's early atmosphere like?
   b. Explain What does Miller and Urey's experiment tell us about the organic compounds needed for life?
   c. Predict You just read that life arose from nonlife billions of years ago. Could life arise from nonlife today? Why or why not?
2. a. Review What does the endosymbiotic theory propose?
   b. Explain According to this theory, how did mitochondria evolve?
   c. Apply Concepts What evidence supports the theory?
3. a. Review Why is the development of sexual reproduction so important in the history of life?
   b. Sequence Put the following events in the order in which they occurred: *sexual reproduction, development of eukaryotic cells, free oxygen in the atmosphere,* and *development of photosynthesis.*

WRITE ABOUT SCIENCE

Explanation

4. Write a paragraph explaining the "RNA world" hypothesis. What parts of the hypothesis have yet to be proved? Is it possible that we will never know the origins of RNA and DNA? Explain your answer.

BIOLOGY.com Search Lesson 19.3 GO • Self-Test • Lesson Assessment

Assessment Answers

1a. It was made up mainly of carbon dioxide, water vapor, and nitrogen, and had little or no oxygen.

1b. In the environmental conditions of early Earth, simple compounds could have given rise to mixtures of organic compounds.

1c. Sample answer: probably not, because the same conditions no longer exist on Earth, and oxygen in the atmosphere would destroy organic molecules

2a. A symbiotic relationship evolved between ancient eukaryotic cells and prokaryotic cells within them.

2b. Mitochondria evolved from endosymbiotic prokaryotes that were able to use oxygen to generate ATP.

2c. Mitochondria and chloroplasts share many features of free-living bacteria. They contain similar DNA and ribosomes. They also reproduce by binary fission.

3a. Sexual reproduction increases genetic variation, which gives natural selection more raw material to work on.

3b. development of photosynthesis, free oxygen in the atmosphere, development of eukaryotic cells, sexual reproduction

WRITE ABOUT SCIENCE

4. Sample answer: One RNA hypothesis suggests that RNA evolved before DNA. Under certain conditions, RNA molecules can help DNA replicate, catalyze chemical reactions, and replicate themselves. Therefore, it is likely that RNA existed before DNA. Scientists have not yet been able to show how RNA led to DNA-directed protein synthesis, and we may never know.

More than 99 percent of the species that ever lived are now extinct. If studying past life interests you, you might consider one of the following careers.

FOSSIL PREPARATOR

If you believe what you see in the movies, fossils are usually found perfectly preserved and intact. But the truth is that fossils are almost always found jumbled and encased in rock. Using microscopes and delicate hand tools, fossil preparators remove fossils from the surrounding rock. Preparators carefully reconstruct damaged pieces and record information about fossil position and rock composition.

MUSEUM GUIDE

Museum guides are educators. But instead of using books to teach, they use museum exhibits. A museum guide at a natural history museum, for example, might have fossils that visitors can touch and manipulate. Museum guides also perform demonstrations and give informal talks.

PALEONTOLOGIST

Paleontologists study extinct and ancient life. It is not all about fossils, however. Today paleontolgists use everything from biochemistry to computer modeling to understand the evolutionary relationships among organisms. Living animals are also sometimes used to study movement, behavior, or development.

CAREER CLOSE-UP:

Dr. Kristi Curry Rogers, Curator of Paleontology, Science Museum of Minnesota

Dr. Curry Rogers' work is big—very big. Dr. Curry Rogers is a paleontologist who studies how the giant long-necked sauropod dinosaurs grew. How can you study how an extinct animal grew over 65 million years ago? By studying microscopic bone structure, Dr. Curry Rogers can estimate how long it took the animal to reach full size. This kind of research can help scientists understand how dinosaurs regulated their body temperature. In addition to questions about sauropod growth, Dr. Curry Rogers is also investigating how different sauropods are related.

"Unlike many kids who go through a 'fossil phase,' I never grew out of it!"

WRITING Choose one of the careers described here. Explain why this career is important to understanding the history of life.

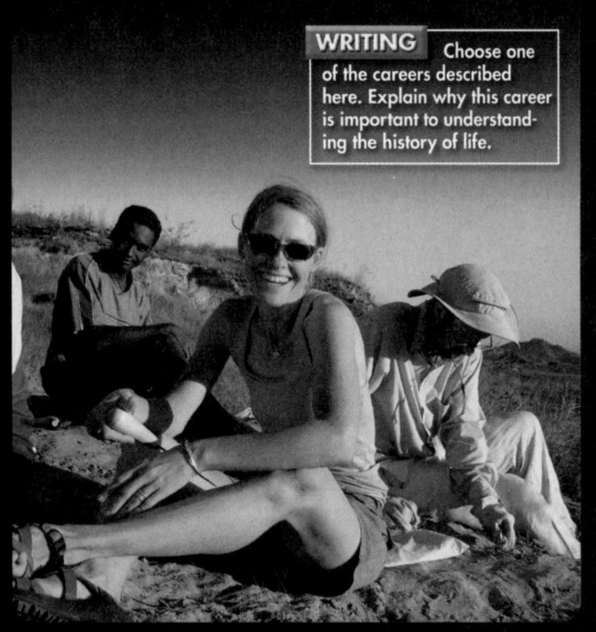

Biology In-Depth

CAREERS IN EARTH'S HISTORY

Fossil preparators collect, clean, reconstruct, and prepare fossil specimens for research or exhibit. A four-year degree in biology or geology is required for many positions.

A museum guide is often an unpaid, trained volunteer. Some guides also teach classes at museums. A degree in science is not required but is helpful. Guides receive training about the exhibits they show or the classes they teach.

Many paleontologists conduct research or teach at universities. They generally have a master's degree or doctorate in some aspect of geology or paleontology. Paleontologists are also employed by companies that drill for oil.

Teach

Lead a Discussion

Ask How do you think paleontologists determine where to find fossils? *(They determine the type and age of rock most likely to provide the kind of fossils they're interested in. Then, they go to a place where this kind of rock is exposed.)*

Ask Looking at the photo of Dr. Curry Rogers, you'll notice that the paleontologist doesn't appear to be digging. Do you think paleontologists dig, or look for fossils exposed to the surface? *(exposed at the surface)* What does this suggest about the types of places paleontologists go to look for fossils? *(they go where rock is exposed)*

Then, focus students' attention on the careers of museum guide and fossil preparator.

Ask Could the work of paleontologists happen without the work of fossil preparators? *(no, because fossil preparators carefully remove fossils from rock, enabling paleontologists to study the fossils in three dimensions)*

Ask How do museum guides help the work of scientists? *(They inform the public about the work in ways that nonscientists can understand.)*

DIFFERENTIATED INSTRUCTION

L3 **Advanced Students** Have a small group of students find out what kinds of fossils are found locally or in their state. Ask them to create a map showing the locations, types of fossils, and geologic periods from which the fossils come. Encourage students to include drawings or photos of the fossils.

Answers

WRITING

Sample answer: Paleontologists are important to understanding the history of life because they study the fossils and biochemistry of ancient organisms. Paleontologists work to understand the evolutionary relationships that existed between ancient organisms, and between ancient organisms and their modern descendants. They can help people understand what these organisms and their environments were like.

Teach

Use Visuals

Use the following strategy to help students organize the information presented in this four-page feature on the geologic time scale. Have them read and take notes about each period, including the eon and era during which each period occurred. Then, after students have finished reading the information on all four pages, have them review their notes. Finally, call on volunteers to explain how the example organism shown for each period reflects the characteristics of the period.

DIFFERENTIATED INSTRUCTION

ELL **English Language Learners** Have students work in pairs, and assign each pair two geologic periods for which to create a **Cluster Diagram.** Each cluster diagram should include specific characteristics of the assigned geologic period. Call on students to share their diagrams as each period is discussed.

Study Wkbks A/B, Appendix S19, Cluster Diagram. **Transparencies,** GO2.

LPR **Less Proficient Readers** Help students understand the organization of information on these four pages. Point out the three-tiered band across the top of each page, identifying the eon, era, and periods. Have students connect the colors used for these bands to the colors used in the time scale in Lesson 19.1. Then, show students how the vertical lines connect to detailed information about each period.

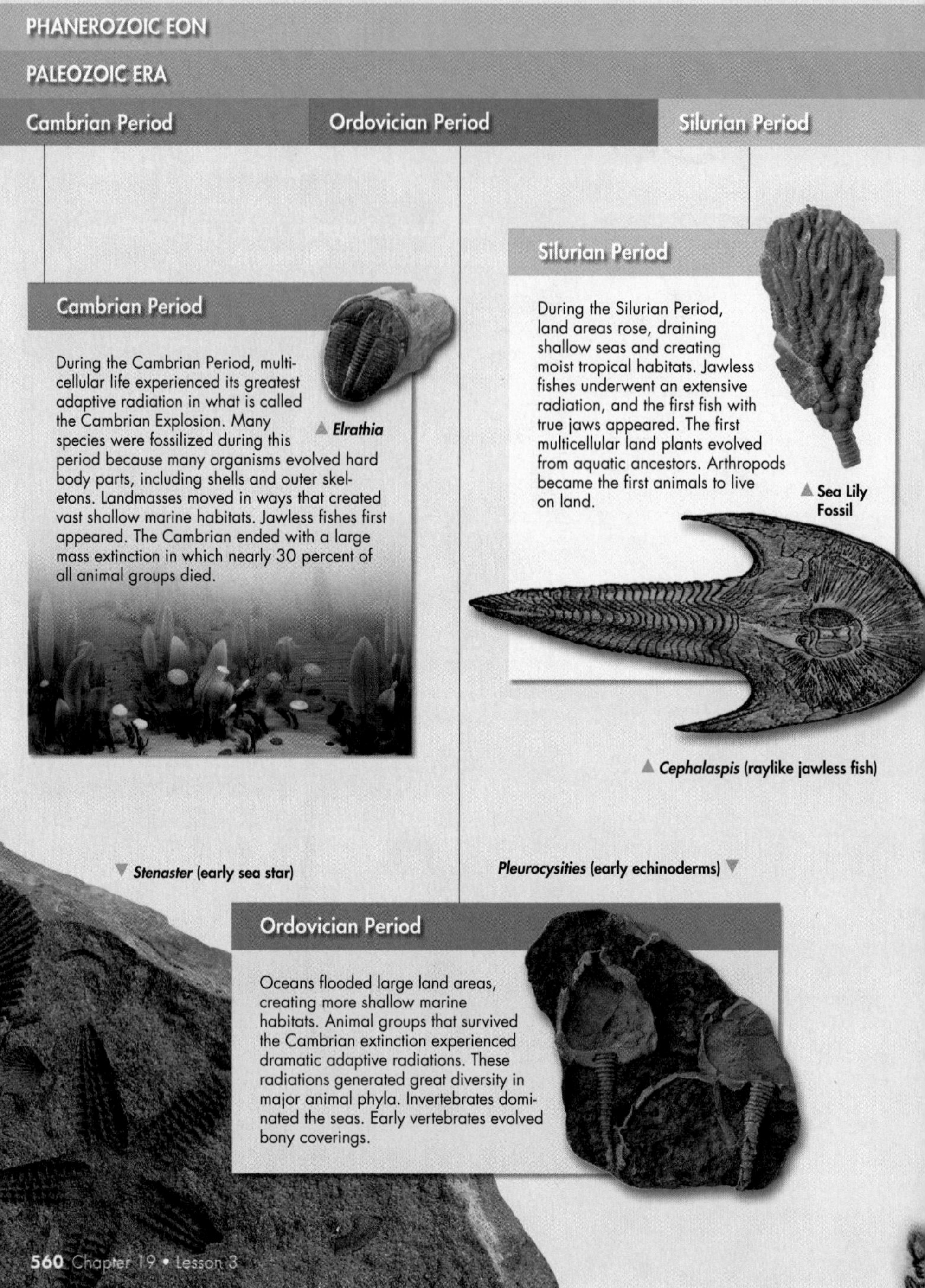

PHANEROZOIC EON

PALEOZOIC ERA

Cambrian Period | Ordovician Period | Silurian Period

Cambrian Period

During the Cambrian Period, multicellular life experienced its greatest adaptive radiation in what is called the Cambrian Explosion. Many species were fossilized during this period because many organisms evolved hard body parts, including shells and outer skeletons. Landmasses moved in ways that created vast shallow marine habitats. Jawless fishes first appeared. The Cambrian ended with a large mass extinction in which nearly 30 percent of all animal groups died.

▲ *Elrathia*

Silurian Period

During the Silurian Period, land areas rose, draining shallow seas and creating moist tropical habitats. Jawless fishes underwent an extensive radiation, and the first fish with true jaws appeared. The first multicellular land plants evolved from aquatic ancestors. Arthropods became the first animals to live on land.

▲ Sea Lily Fossil

▲ *Cephalaspis* (raylike jawless fish)

▼ *Stenaster* (early sea star)

Pleurocysities (early echinoderms) ▼

Ordovician Period

Oceans flooded large land areas, creating more shallow marine habitats. Animal groups that survived the Cambrian extinction experienced dramatic adaptive radiations. These radiations generated great diversity in major animal phyla. Invertebrates dominated the seas. Early vertebrates evolved bony coverings.

560 Chapter 19 • Lesson 3

Quick Facts

THE BURGESS SHALE

One of the most significant collections of fossils in the world is the Burgess Shale in British Columbia, Canada. The shale contains perfectly preserved fossils of organisms from the "Cambrian explosion"—a period of rapid adaptive radiation among multicellular organisms. The site was discovered in 1909 by Charles Walcott, then the Secretary of the Smithsonian Institution. Walcott amassed a collection of more than 60,000 specimens, most now housed at the Smithsonian Institution in Washington, D.C.

The significance of the fossils is in how well they were preserved and in the tremendous variety of the organisms. Soft body parts rarely survive the decay process, but some of the Burgess fossils show evidence of muscles and gut contents.

Permian Period

During the Permian Period, invertebrates, vertebrates, and land plants continued to expand over Earth's continents. Reptiles experienced the first of several major adaptive radiations, which produced the ancestors of modern reptiles, dinosaurs, and mammals. The Permian Period ended with the biggest mass extinction of all time. More than 50 percent of terrestrial animal families and more than 95 percent of marine species became extinct.

▲ Crinoid

Early Amphibian ▼

Devonian Period

During the Devonian Period, invertebrates and vertebrates thrived in the seas. Fishes evolved jaws, bony skeletons, and scales. Sharks began their adaptive radiation. Certain groups of fishes evolved leglike fins, and some of these evolved into the first amphibians. Some land plants, such as ferns, adapted to drier areas. Insects began to radiate on land.

◄ Fossil Fern From Carboniferous Period

Carboniferous Period

During the Carboniferous Period, mountain building created a wide range of habitats, from swampy lowlands to drier upland areas. Giant ferns, club mosses, and horsetails formed vast swampy forests. Amphibians, insects, and land plants experienced major adaptive radiations. Winged insects evolved into many forms, including huge dragonflies and cockroaches. For early vertebrates, insects were food; for plants, insects were predators. The first reptiles evolved from ancient amphibians.

UbD Check for Understanding

ONE-MINUTE RESPONSE

Have students select one period from these two pages, and give them about a minute to write a sentence describing the geological changes that occurred during the period and the response of organisms living at that time to those changes.

ADJUST INSTRUCTION

If some students cannot distinguish the information on geology and the responses of organisms, simplify the directions to read: Describe what happened to the land during that period. Describe what happened to the plants and animals after the land changed.

Lead a Discussion

Divide the class into three groups, and give each group an index card. Assign each group one of the geologic periods on this page. Give students a few minutes to skim the description of the period and write two questions on their index card. Encourage them to write one direct, factual question and one that begins with *why* or *what may have caused.* Collect the cards, and use them as a basis for a class discussion regarding the Devonian, Carboniferous, and Permian Periods.

DIFFERENTIATED INSTRUCTION

L1 Struggling Students Draw a **Main Ideas and Details Chart** on the board. Model for students how this format can be used to organize information about geologic time periods by completing the chart on the board, using the Devonian Period as the main idea. Ask students to identify details, and write the details that students mention in the chart. Explain that students can use this format for any of the periods described in this feature. Encourage each student to complete at least one main ideas and details chart about a period other than the Devonian.

Study Wkbks A/B, Appendix S28, Main Ideas and Details Chart. **Transparencies,** GO13.

Teach continued

Lead a Discussion

Help students understand the information on this page using the following questions.

Ask What three periods are part of the Mesozoic Era? *(Triassic, Jurassic, Cretaceous)*

Ask During which period did *Archaeopteryx* evolve? *(Jurassic)*

Ask During which period did the first dinosaurs evolve? *(Triassic)*

Ask During which period did the first mammals evolve? *(Triassic)*

Ask During which period did flowering plants evolve? *(Cretaceous)*

DIFFERENTIATED INSTRUCTION

L3 **Advanced Students** Have students work in a small group to develop a set of mnemonic devices that other class members can use to remember main ideas about each period described on this page. After allowing time for the group to develop their mnemonic devices, have these students teach a short lesson in which they share the mnemonic devices with the class.

Address Misconceptions

Dinosaur Success Some students might think dinosaurs were not very successful in evolutionary terms because they became extinct at the end of the Cretaceous Period. Point out that dinosaurs lived on Earth for about 150 million years, while hominids have been in existence for less than 10 million years. Further, you can remind students that dinosaurs still live today—as birds!

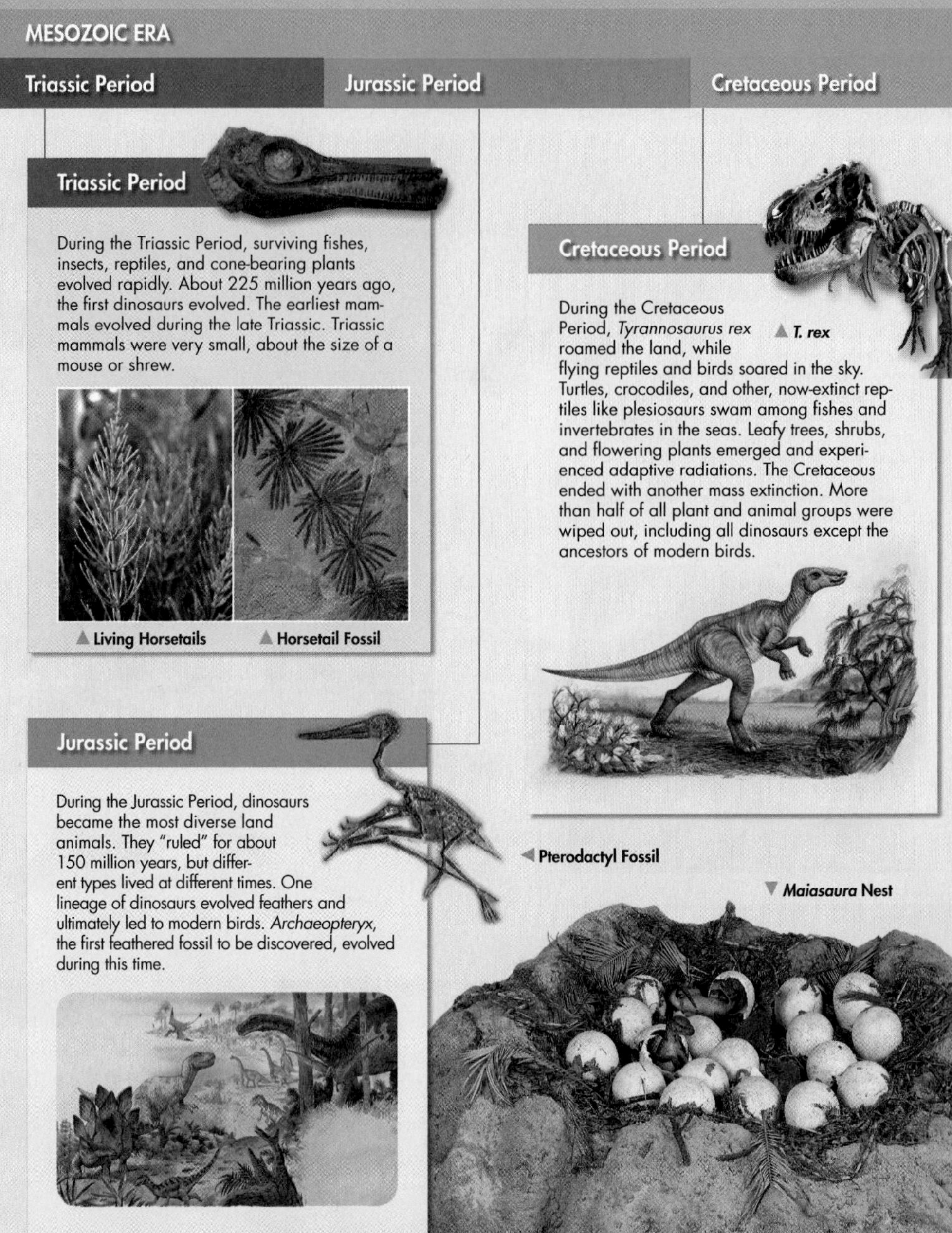

PHANEROZOIC EON

MESOZOIC ERA

Triassic Period | Jurassic Period | Cretaceous Period

Triassic Period

During the Triassic Period, surviving fishes, insects, reptiles, and cone-bearing plants evolved rapidly. About 225 million years ago, the first dinosaurs evolved. The earliest mammals evolved during the late Triassic. Triassic mammals were very small, about the size of a mouse or shrew.

▲ Living Horsetails ▲ Horsetail Fossil

Jurassic Period

During the Jurassic Period, dinosaurs became the most diverse land animals. They "ruled" for about 150 million years, but different types lived at different times. One lineage of dinosaurs evolved feathers and ultimately led to modern birds. *Archaeopteryx*, the first feathered fossil to be discovered, evolved during this time.

◀ Pterodactyl Fossil

Cretaceous Period

During the Cretaceous Period, *Tyrannosaurus rex* roamed the land, while flying reptiles and birds soared in the sky. Turtles, crocodiles, and other, now-extinct reptiles like plesiosaurs swam among fishes and invertebrates in the seas. Leafy trees, shrubs, and flowering plants emerged and experienced adaptive radiations. The Cretaceous ended with another mass extinction. More than half of all plant and animal groups were wiped out, including all dinosaurs except the ancestors of modern birds.

▲ *T. rex*

▼ *Maiasaura* Nest

562 Chapter 19 • Lesson 3

Biology In-Depth

THE K/T EXTINCTION

The extinction at the end of the Mesozoic is often abbreviated as K/T after the symbols used for the Cretaceous (K) and Tertiary (T) Periods. (Note that the Tertiary Period is now an outdated term.) The cause of the K/T extinction is widely agreed upon. Approximately 65 million years ago, a 10-kilometer wide asteroid hit Earth in the present-day Gulf of Mexico. Scientists have found the crater, called Chicxulub, buried under 65 million years of accumulated sediment. Around the world, a layer of iridium (an element common in asteroids but rare on Earth) and shocked quartz (a form of quartz found only near meteor/asteroid impact sites and nuclear bomb test sites) marks the time of the impact and the beginning of the mass extinction.

CENOZOIC ERA

Paleogene Period	Neogene Period	Quaternary Period

Paleogene Period

During the Paleogene Period, climates changed from warm and moist to cool and dry. Flowering plants, grasses, and insects flourished. After the dinosaurs and giant marine reptiles went extinct, mammals underwent a major adaptive radiation. As climates changed, forests were replaced by open woods and grasslands. Large mammals—ancestors of cattle, deer, and sheep and other grazers—evolved and spread across the grasslands. In the sea, the first whales evolved.

▲ Early Mammal

Neogene Period

During the Neogene Period, colliding continents pushed up modern mountain ranges, including the Alps in Europe and the Rockies, Cascades, and Sierra Nevadas in North America. As mountains rose, ice and snow built up at high elevations and in the Arctic. Falling sea levels and colliding continents created connections between North and South America, and between Africa, Europe, and Asia. Those connections led to great movements of land animals between continents. Climates continued a cooling and drying trend, and grasslands continued to expand. Modern grazing animals continued to coevolve with grasses, evolving specialized digestive tracts to deal with tough, low-nutrient grass tissue.

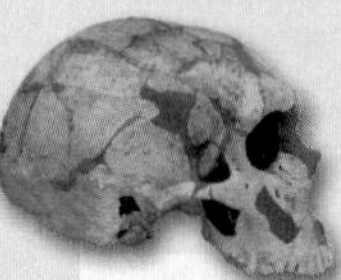

◄ Neanderthal Skull

Quaternary Period

During the Quaternary Period, Earth cooled. A series of ice ages saw thick glaciers advance and retreat over parts of Europe and North America. So much water was frozen in glaciers that sea levels fell by more than 100 meters. Then, about 20,000 years ago, Earth's climate began to warm. Over thousands of years, glaciers melted, and sea levels rose. In the oceans, algae, coral, mollusks, fishes, and mammals thrived. Insects and birds shared the skies. Land mammals—among them bats, cats, dogs, cattle, and mammoths—became common. Between 6 and 7 million years ago, one group of mammals began an adaptive radiation that led to the ancestors and close relatives of modern humans.

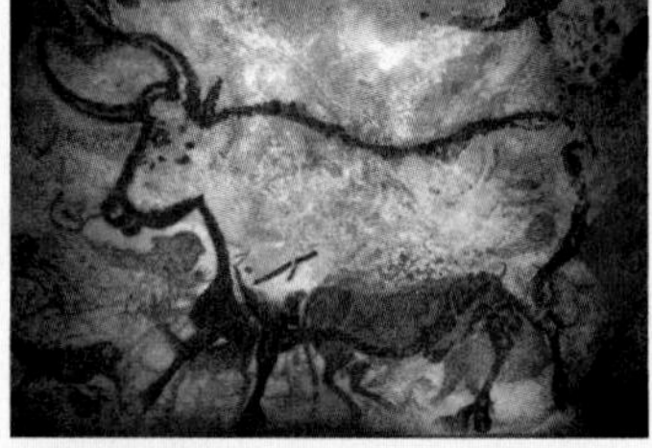

▲ Cave paintings

Quick Facts

ADAPTIVE ADVANTAGE OF FRUITS

The development of fruits and seeds was a major evolutionary advance in the reproduction of plants, and many animals became agents for spreading seeds. However, if animals eat immature fruit, the seeds are not able to germinate. Natural selection appears to have solved this problem in an interesting and not so sweet way. Many unripe fruits are green and contain bitter-tasting chemical compounds. This discourages animals from eating them. In addition, the green color makes the unripe fruits more difficult to see among plant leaves. The unappetizing features of the fruits appear to benefit the seeds by giving them time to mature. As the bitter-tasting compounds break down, the seeds mature, and the fruits become laden with sugars. Simultaneously, many fruits change color from green to more visible shades of red, orange, yellow, or purple. This makes the fruits easier to see against the leafy green background.

Lead a Discussion

Give students about 5 minutes to meet in small groups to prepare for a review of characteristics of all the periods described in this feature using a round-robin discussion format. For example, you might begin by saying, "During the Cambrian Period, there was a great radiation of multicellular organisms." Call on students to provide statements that logically follow the previous statement. Continue until all the periods have been covered.

DIFFERENTIATED INSTRUCTION

ELL English Language Learners Students may have difficulty with a round-robin discussion format. Provide these students with a written copy of several statements you could use to start a round-robin discussion. Have students read these statements, look at the text, and develop written or spoken statements that logically follow the starter statements you have provided. Call on students to share their responses.

Pre-Lab

Introduce students to the concepts they will explore in the chapter lab by assigning the Pre-Lab questions.

Lab

Tell students they will perform the chapter lab *Using Index Fossils* described in **Lab Manual A.**

L1 Struggling Students A simpler version of the chapter lab is provided in **Lab Manual B.**

SAFETY

Caution students to direct the pointed end of the scissors away from themselves and others.

BIOLOGY.com Look online for **Editable Lab Worksheets.**

For corresponding pre-lab in the **Foundation Edition**, see page 470.

IN INDIANA ACADEMIC STANDARDS

For the full text of all standards, see the Course Overview in the front matter of this book.

Forensics Lab

GUIDED INQUIRY

IN NoS.6 Use analogies and models.

Pre-Lab: Using Index Fossils

Problem How can fossils be used to determine the relative ages of rock layers?

Materials scissors

Lab Manual Chapter 19 Lab

Skills Focus Interpret Visuals, Sequence, Draw Conclusions

Connect to the Big idea When detectives work on a case, they may look for items with a time stamp, such as parking tickets and credit card slips. Such items can help detectives piece together a sequence of events. Events related to a crime usually occur within a relatively short period of time. In contrast, the events that paleontologists study will have occurred over millions of years. Placing these events in their proper order can be challenging. The clues that a paleontologist uses to sequence events in the history of life are fossils buried in rock layers. In this lab, you will use fossils to place rock layers in order from oldest to youngest.

Background Questions

a. Review What is a fossil? What are the characteristics of a good index fossil?

b. Explain What characteristic of radioactive decay allows scientists to assign specific ages to rock layers?

c. Classify How do fossils help geologists decide where one division of geologic time should end and another division begin?

Pre-Lab Questions

Preview the procedure in the lab manual.

1. Organize Data After you cut out the drawings of the rock layers, how will you begin the process of sorting the layers by age?

2. Infer *Desmatosuchus* was a crocodile relative that lived only during the Triassic Period. Horsetails are plants that first appeared in the Triassic Period and still exist. Which of these organisms would be more useful as an index fossil for the Triassic Period? Why?

3. Use Analogies Luke found a box of photos labeled 1970–1995. Each photo shows his entire extended family. No dates appear on the photos. Luke knows that his grandmother died in 1985 and his uncle was born in 1975. Luke's sister was born in 1990. How can Luke use this information to sort the photos into four batches? How are Luke's relatives similar to index fossils?

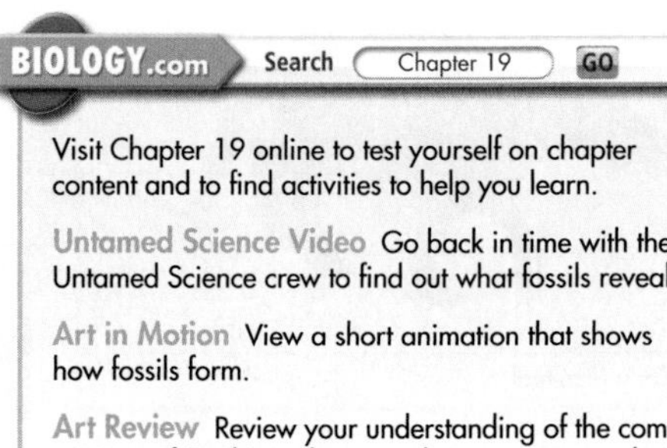

BIOLOGY.com Search Chapter 19 GO

Visit Chapter 19 online to test yourself on chapter content and to find activities to help you learn.

Untamed Science Video Go back in time with the Untamed Science crew to find out what fossils reveal.

Art in Motion View a short animation that shows how fossils form.

Art Review Review your understanding of the composition of Earth's early atmosphere as compared with the composition of Earth's current atmosphere.

Visual Analogy Compare geologic time to a 24-hour clock.

Data Analysis Correlate data on extinction events with other types of data to identify likely causes of extinction.

564 Chapter 19 • Pre-Lab

Pre-Lab Answers

BACKGROUND QUESTIONS

a. A fossil is the preserved remains of an ancient (usually extinct) organism. A good index fossil must be easy to identify. It must also come from a species that existed for a relatively short time over a wide geographic range.

b. Radioactive decay occurs at a steady rate over time.

c. Geologists noticed that major changes in the fossil record occurred at boundaries between certain rock layers. Those boundaries were used to divide geologic time into eons, eras, and periods.

PRE-LAB QUESTIONS

1. Sample answer: I will use the Key to Fossils to identify the fossils in each layer.

2. The crocodile relative would be more useful as an index fossil for the Triassic Period because it would not occur in rock layers from other periods.

3. Sample answer: Possible batches are photos with (1) grandmother only from 1970–1975, (2) grandmother and uncle from 1975–1985, (3) uncle only from 1985–1990, and (4) uncle and sister from 1990–1995. The people are like index fossils because they exist in specific time ranges relative to the overall range of the photos.

19 Study Guide

Big idea Evolution

Paleontologists use fossils to learn about the structure and environments of ancient organisms. Fossils also give clues to events that happened during Earth's history.

19.1 The Fossil Record

From the fossil record, paleontologists learn about the structure of ancient organisms, their environment, and the ways in which they lived.

Relative dating allows paleontologists to determine whether a fossil is older or younger than other fossils. Radiometric dating uses the proportion of radioactive to stable isotopes to calculate the age of a sample.

The geologic time scale is based on both relative and absolute dating. The major divisions of the geologic time scale are eons, eras, and periods.

Building mountains, opening coastlines, changing climates, and geological forces have altered habitats of living organisms repeatedly throughout Earth history. In turn, the actions of living organisms over time have changed conditions in the land, water, and atmosphere of planet Earth.

extinct (538)
paleontologist (539)
relative dating (540)
index fossil (540)
radiometric dating (540)
half-life (540)
geologic time scale (542)
era (543)
period (543)
plate tectonics (544)

19.2 Patterns and Processes of Evolution

If the rate of speciation in a clade is equal to or greater than the rate of extinction, the clade will continue to exist. If the rate of extinction in a clade is greater than the rate of speciation, the clade will eventually become extinct.

Evidence shows that evolution has often proceeded at different rates for different organisms at different times over the long history of life on Earth.

Two important patterns of macroevolution are adaptive radiation and convergent evolution. Adaptive radiation occurs when a single species or a small group of species evolves over a relatively short time into several different forms that live in different ways. Convergent evolution occurs when unrelated organisms evolve into similar forms.

The relationship between two coevolving organisms often becomes so specific that neither organism can survive without the other. Thus, an evolutionary change in one organism is usually followed by a change in the other organism.

macroevolutionary patterns (546)
background extinction (548)
mass extinction (548)
gradualism (549)
punctuated equilibrium (549)
adaptive radiation (550)
convergent evolution (551)
coevolution (551)

19.3 Earth's Early History

Earth's early atmosphere contained little or no oxygen. It was principally composed of carbon dioxide, water vapor, and nitrogen, with lesser amounts of carbon monoxide, hydrogen sulfide, and hydrogen cyanide.

Miller and Urey's experiment suggested how mixtures of the organic compounds necessary for life could have arisen from simpler compounds on a primitive Earth.

The "RNA world" hypothesis proposes that RNA existed by itself before DNA. From this simple RNA-based system, several steps could have led to DNA-directed protein synthesis.

The endosymbiotic theory proposes that a symbiotic relationship evolved over time between primitive eukaryotic cells and the prokaryotic cells within them.

The development of sexual reproduction sped up evolutionary change because sexual reproduction increases genetic variation.

endosymbiotic theory (556)

Think Visually Construct a table comparing the Paleozoic, Mesozoic, and Cenozoic eras. Include the approximate time periods for each era and identify the characteristic organisms.

BIOLOGY.com Search   • Crossword • Chapter Assessment

UbD Performance Tasks

SUMMATIVE TASK Divide the class into groups of three, and assign one lesson of the chapter to each group member. Ask group members to work together to create a condensed, visual version of the chapter. Students can draw sketches, use computer graphics, or copy illustrations from the text and display them with labels on a poster board; or they can create a slideshow with presentation software.

TRANSFER TASK Have students use what they have learned about fossils, evolution, and geologic time to write about a fossil excavation in the future in which paleontologists uncover fossils of organisms living today. Tell them to include answers to these questions in their report: Where will the paleontologists find fossils? What was preserved as fossils? What evidence might these fossils provide about environmental change?

Study Online

REVIEW AND ASSESSMENT RESOURCES

Editable Worksheets Pages of Study Workbooks A and B, Lab Manuals A and B, and the Assessment Resources Book are available online. These documents can be easily edited using a word-processing program.

Lesson Overview Have students reread the Lesson Overviews to help them study chapter concepts.

Vocabulary Review The *Flash Cards* and *Crossword* provide an interactive way to review chapter vocabulary.

Chapter Assessment Have students take an online version of the Chapter 19 Assessment.

Standardized Test Prep Students can take an online version of the Standardized Test Prep. You will receive their scores along with ideas for remediation.

Diagnostic and Benchmark Tests Use these tests to monitor your students' progress and supply remediation.

Answers

THINK VISUALLY

Students can use the information in **Figure 19–5** and in the time line pages to complete their table.

ASSESSMENT

19 Assessment

The numbers following the questions refer to Indiana's Academic Standards for Biology I.

19.1 The Fossil Record

Understand Key Concepts

1. Scientists who specialize in the study of fossils are called
   a. biologists. b. paleontologists. c. zoologists. d. geologists.
2. Sedimentary rocks usually form when layers of small particles are compressed
   a. in the atmosphere. b. in a snow field. c. in mountains. d. under water.
3. Using C–14 to analyze rock layers
   a. is a method of estimating absolute age.
   b. is a method of estimating relative age.
   c. can only be used on extremely ancient rock layers.
   d. is impossible because rock layers do not contain carbon.
4. Half-life is the time required for half the atoms in a radioactive sample to
   a. decay. b. double. c. expand. d. be created.
5. According to the theory of plate tectonics,
   a. Earth's climate has changed many times.
   b. Earth's continents move very slowly.
   c. evolution occurs at different rates.
   d. giant asteroids crashed into Earth in the past.
6. How does relative dating enable paleontologists to estimate a fossil's age?
7. Explain how radioactivity is used to date rocks.
8. What is the geologic time scale, and how was it developed?
9. How have the activities of organisms affected Earth's environment?

Think Critically

10. **Calculate** The half-life of carbon-14 is 5730 years. What is the age of a fossil containing 1/16 the amount of carbon-14 of living organisms? Explain your calculation. MATH
11. **Apply Concepts** Evolutionary biologists say that there is a good reason for gaps in the fossil record. Can you explain why some extinct animals and plants were never fossilized?

19.2 Patterns and Processes of Evolution

Understand Key Concepts

12. The process that produces similar-looking structures in unrelated groups of organisms is
    a. adaptive radiation. b. coevolution. c. convergent evolution. d. mass extinction.
13. The general term for large-scale evolutionary changes that take place over long periods of time is called
    a. macroevolution.
    b. coevolution.
    c. convergent evolution.
    d. geologic time.
14. Cladograms that are based on the fossil record always show
    a. which organisms are direct ancestors of the others.
    b. relationships based on shared derived characteristics.
    c. that clades are made up only of extinct species.
    d. relative ages of organisms in the clade.
15. Explain and give an example of the process of adaptive radiation. B.8.5
16. Explain the model of evolution known as punctuated equilibrium.
17. Use an example to explain the concept of coevolution.

Think Critically

18. **Infer** Major geologic changes often go hand in hand with mass extinctions. Why do you think this is true? B.8.5
19. **Apply Concepts** Why is rapid evolution especially likely to occur in a small population that has been separated from the main population? B.8.5
20. **Apply Concepts** What is the role of natural selection in adaptive radiation? How do these processes lead to diversity? B.8.5

Lesson 19.1

UNDERSTAND KEY CONCEPTS

1. b **2.** d **3.** a

4. a **5.** b

6. The age of a fossil is estimated by comparing its placement in rock layers with the placement of other fossils in other rock layers.

7. Radioactive elements decay at a steady rate, measured in units called half-lives. Radiometric dating uses half-lives to determine the age of rocks. Scientists calculate the age of rocks based on the amount of remaining radioactive isotopes they contain.

8. The geologic time scale is a timeline of Earth's history. It was developed by studying the boundaries between rock layers and by using both relative and absolute dating.

9. Sample answer: An example of how the activities of organisms have affected Earth's environment is the impact photosynthetic organisms had on the composition of the atmosphere during the Proterozoic Eon. These organisms added oxygen and removed carbon dioxide from the atmosphere.

THINK CRITICALLY

10. The fossil is 22,920 years old. At 1/16 the carbon-14 of living organisms, it has gone through four half-lives of carbon-14. (5730 yrs × 4 = 22,920 yrs)

11. Sample answer: Some organisms never fossilized because their remains never became part of sedimentary rock. For example, many organisms had soft bodies. With no hard body parts, such as bones or scales, they decayed without being fossilized. Some gaps are the result of erosion erasing the rock layers.

Lesson 19.2

UNDERSTAND KEY CONCEPTS

12. c **13.** a **14.** b

15. In adaptive radiation, a single species or small group of species evolves over a relatively short time into several different forms that live in different ways. An example of adaptive radiation is the evolution of Galápagos finches.

16. Punctuated equilibrium is a pattern of evolution in which long periods of time with little or no evolutionary change are interrupted by brief periods of rapid change.

17. Sample answer: Coevolution occurs when the relationship between two organisms becomes so specific that neither organism can survive without the other. As a result, an evolutionary change in one organism may be followed by a change in the other organism. An example is the evolution of flowers and their specific pollinators.

THINK CRITICALLY

18. Geological changes, such as volcanic eruptions and meteorite collisions, can quickly change the climate and environmental conditions. When the environment changes in an extreme way, many organisms in that environment lack adaptations that enable them to survive.

19. Once separated, a small population can evolve faster than a larger one because genetic changes spread more quickly among fewer individuals.

20. Natural selection leads to adaptive radiation. Living things respond to changes in their environments, and when they enter a new environment, they are faced with a new set of selective pressures. Those organisms with adaptive characteristics will survive and reproduce.

Understand Key Concepts

21. Earth's early atmosphere contained little or no
    a. water vapor. c. nitrogen.
    b. carbon dioxide. d. oxygen.

22. In their experiment that modeled conditions on ancient Earth, Miller and Urey used electric sparks to simulate
    a. temperature.
    b. sunlight.
    c. atmospheric gases.
    d. lightning.

23. Outlines of ancient cells that are preserved well enough to identify them as prokaryotes are B.8.7
    a. microfossils. c. autotrophs.
    b. heterotrophs. d. phototrophic.

24. What hypotheses have scientists proposed to explain Earth's early atmosphere and the way the oceans formed?

25. The diagram below shows the apparatus that Miller and Urey used in their experiment. Explain both what water and gases were meant to represent and what Miller and Urey were hoping to accomplish. B.8.7

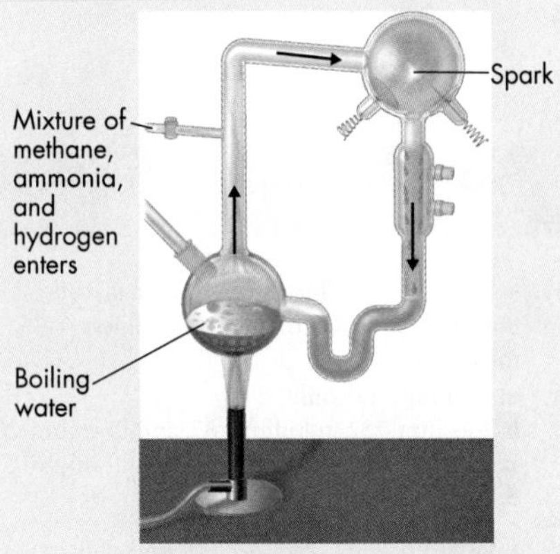

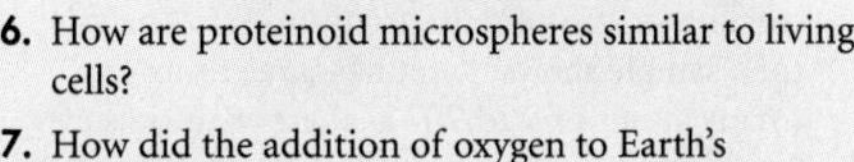

26. How are proteinoid microspheres similar to living cells?

27. How did the addition of oxygen to Earth's atmosphere affect the evolution of life? B.8.7

28. According to the endosymbiotic theory, how did mitochondria originate? B.8.1

solve the CHAPTER MYSTERY

MURDER IN THE PERMIAN

Solving a 250-million-year-old murder mystery isn't easy! In recent years, scientists have studied the chemistry of Permian rocks and changes in the fossil record. Some researchers determined that enormous and long-lasting volcanic eruptions in Siberia vented carbon dioxide into the atmosphere, causing a massive change in global climate. This put species and ecosystems under great environmental stress.

Other researchers used geochemical analyses to show that atmospheric oxygen levels dropped to roughly half of what they are today. Huge parts of the oceans lost all oxygen. Because of the reduction in available oxygen, land animals near sea level might have been gasping for breath as you would on top of Mount Everest.

Finally, there is evidence that an asteroid hit Earth! To this day, paleontologists are testing competing hypotheses that try to explain which of the events that occurred at this time caused the mass extinction. However, these hypotheses are constantly changing and have probably changed since this book was written.

1. **Compare and Contrast** How do current hypotheses about the Permian extinction compare with the predominant theory about the Cretaceous extinction?
2. **Form a Hypothesis** From the information in this book, suggest an explanation for the Permian mass extinction.
3. **Pose Questions** What questions could you ask to find out whether your hypothesis is correct? What evidence would answer those questions?
4. **Connect to the Big idea** What role have mass extinctions played in the history of life?

CHAPTER MYSTERY After students have read through the Chapter Mystery, have them discuss as a class factors that could have contributed to the Permian extinction.

Ask Is it possible that factors identified in all three competing hypotheses contributed to the extinction? *(Students' responses should include a well-reasoned argument for or against this possibility.)*

Ask What is one thing the three hypotheses have in common? *(All three hypotheses are related to major environmental change.)*

Ask In spite of the extinction, there were survivors. What kinds of opportunities were there for the survivors? How did they probably respond? *(New niches opened up. With little competition, there was probably adaptive radiation resulting in new species.)*

CHAPTER MYSTERY ANSWERS

1. Current hypotheses propose that the Permian extinction had multiple causes, while the Cretaceous extinction may have had only one major cause—the effects of an asteroid impact on Earth's climate.
2. Sample answer: Volcanic eruptions and the impact of an asteroid made environmental conditions become so harsh that many species could not survive.
3. Sample answer: Is there geological evidence of multiple volcanic eruptions? Is there an impact crater that dates to this time? Materials from volcanic and asteroid fallout in sedimentary rocks might provide an answer.
4. Big idea Sample answer: Mass extinctions have occurred at least five times. Each time, the process of adaptive radiation resulted in new organisms that were able to take advantage of new environments.

Students can explore fossils with the Untamed Science crew by watching **Stories in Stone.**

Lesson 19.3

UNDERSTAND KEY CONCEPTS

21. d **22.** d **23.** a

24. When Earth was young, a collision with a very large object produced enough heat to melt Earth. Elements then rearranged themselves by density. The least dense elements, including hydrogen and nitrogen, formed the first atmosphere. About 4.2 billion years ago, Earth cooled enough for water to condense. Rain fell, and permanent oceans formed.

25. The water was meant to simulate the ocean. The gases were meant to simulate Earth's early atmosphere. Miller and Urey were trying to show that early Earth conditions could have produced organic compounds.

26. Proteinoid microspheres are similar to cells because they have a selectively permeable membrane across which water and nutrients can travel and a means of storing and releasing energy.

27. The addition of oxygen to the atmosphere caused some organisms to become extinct or restricted to oxygen-free habitats because they had evolved in an oxygen-free atmosphere. Some organisms, however, evolved new metabolic pathways that used oxygen for respiration.

28. Mitochondria may have evolved from endosymbiotic prokaryotes that were able to use oxygen to generate energy-rich ATP molecules.

THINK CRITICALLY

29. Condensing water vapor represents rain. Rain would have carried many chemicals from the atmosphere into the primitive oceans. The oceans were probably the site of the first steps in chemical evolution.

30. When cells engulfed bacteria that evolved into mitochondria they obtained a way to get energy from food molecules. When engulfed bacteria evolved into chloroplasts, cells obtained a way to make food molecules (photosynthesis).

Connecting Concepts

USE SCIENCE GRAPHICS

31. Fossils in layer C are probably older. Layer C is buried more deeply than layer A.

32. None of the rock layers in Location 2 are the same age as layer C in Location 1.

33. Useful index fossils are easily identified and occur in only a few rock layers, but the rock layers will be found in many places.

WRITE ABOUT SCIENCE

34. Answers will vary but should include the following ideas: Volcanic activity was very common on early Earth but is now relatively rare. The atmosphere on early Earth was made mainly of carbon dioxide, nitrogen, and water vapor. Now it is mainly nitrogen and oxygen. The temperatures on early Earth were much hotter, and Earth was bombarded by asteroids.

35. Sample answer: Sharks, dolphins, and penguins belong to three different groups of animals—fish, mammals, and birds. However, they all live in an aquatic environment. Because of the similar selection pressures experienced, all three animals, though distantly related, developed similarities in body shape such as streamlined bodies and fins or flippers. This is an example of convergent evolution.

36. Big idea Students' responses should include the fact that sedimentary rock usually forms as mud, silt, and sand gradually fall to the bottom of a body of water, covering the bodies of organisms that also fell to the bottom. The deepest layers of sediment are the oldest, and, therefore, fossils found in the deepest layers are the oldest. Fossil organisms in layers near the top of the formation are younger and more recently evolved than those in the deeper layers.

37. Big idea Sample answer: Gould and Eldredge were acknowledging that in the history of life, lack of change (stasis) can be just as important as change. Their model of punctuated equilibrium described a pattern of evolution in which long periods of equilibrium are interrupted by short bursts of change.

Think Critically

29. **Use Models** What part of Miller and Urey's apparatus represents rain? What important role would rain play in chemical evolution? B.8.7

30. **Relate Cause and Effect** How do you think the cells that took in the ancestors of mitochondria and chloroplasts benefited from the relationship? B.8.1

Connecting Concepts

Use Science Graphics NoS.3

The diagram shows rock layers in two different places. Use the diagram to answer questions 31 and 32.

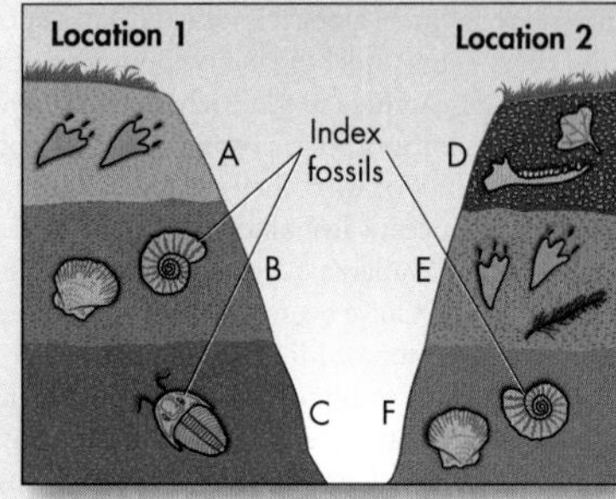

31. Which fossils are probably older—those in layer A or those in layer C? How do you know?

32. Which rock layer in location 2 is probably about the same age as layer C in location 1? How do you know?

33. What are the characteristics of a useful index fossil?

Write About Science NoS.3

34. **Explanation** Write a paragraph comparing conditions on early Earth with those on modern Earth.

35. **Description** Use the example of body shape in sharks, dolphins, and penguins to explain convergent evolution.

36. **Assess the Big idea** Explain how the formation of sedimentary rock gives paleontologists information about the sequence in which life forms appeared on Earth.

37. **Assess the Big idea** When describing their theory of punctuated equilibrium, Stephen Jay Gould and Niles Eldredge often used the motto "stasis is data." Stasis is another word for equilibrium. Explain what Gould and Eldredge meant.

Analyzing Data

IN NoS.3

The table below compares the half-life of several radioactive atoms. Use the table to answer questions 38 and 39.

Isotope and Decay Product	Half-Life (years)
Rubidium-87 ⟶ Strontium-87	48.8 billion
Thorium-232 ⟶ Lead-208	14.0 billion
Uranium-235 ⟶ Lead-207	704.0 million
Uranium-238 ⟶ Lead-206	4.5 billion

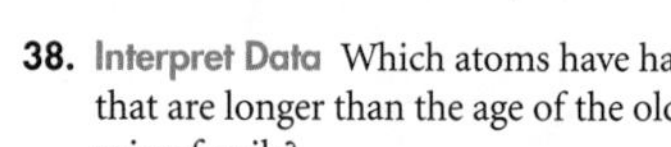

38. **Interpret Data** Which atoms have half-lives that are longer than the age of the oldest microfossils?

a. uranium-235 only
b. thorium-232, rubidium-87, and uranium-235
c. rubidium-87, thorium-232, and uranium-238
d. uranium-235 and rubidium-87

39. **Apply Concepts** Lead-207 is found only in rocks that also contain uranium-235. Analysis of a sample shows that it has three times as many atoms of lead-207 as there are atoms of uranium-235. How many half-lives have passed since this rock formed?

a. one **b.** two **c.** three **d.** four

PURPOSE Students will analyze data to demonstrate an understanding of isotope decay and half-life.

PLANNING Have students review half-lives using the Lesson 19.1 **Quick Lab.** Point out that information about the age of the oldest microfossils is found in Lesson 19.3.

ANSWERS

38. c

39. b

Standardized Test Practice for Indiana

Multiple Choice

1. Useful index fossils are found
   A in a small area for a short time.
   B in a small area for a long time.
   C over a large area for a short time.
   D over a large area for a long time.

2. What happens if the rate of extinction in a clade is greater than the rate of speciation?
   A The clade will eventually become extinct.
   B The clade will continue to exist.
   C The species in the clade will become more varied.
   D The number of species in the clade will stay the same.

3. Which of the following is evidence for the endosymbiotic theory?
   A Mitochondria and chloroplasts contain DNA similar to bacterial DNA.
   B Mitochondria and chloroplasts have similar functions in the cell.
   C Mitochondria and chloroplasts have no DNA of their own.
   D Mitochondria and chloroplasts can live independently when removed from the eukaryotic cell.
   B.8.1

4. Carbon–14 is NOT useful for dating most fossils because
   A it has a very long half-life.
   B it has a very short half-life.
   C most organisms contain more potassium than carbon.
   D it is found only in certain rock layers.

5. The movement of continents has played a significant role in evolution because
   A continents move rapidly and some organisms cannot adjust.
   B without the movement of continents, there would be no water on Earth.
   C the movement of continents has caused environments to change.
   D all mass extinctions are the result of continental drift.
   B.8.5

Questions 6 and 7

The graph shows the decay of radioactive isotopes. Use the information in the graph to answer the questions that follow.

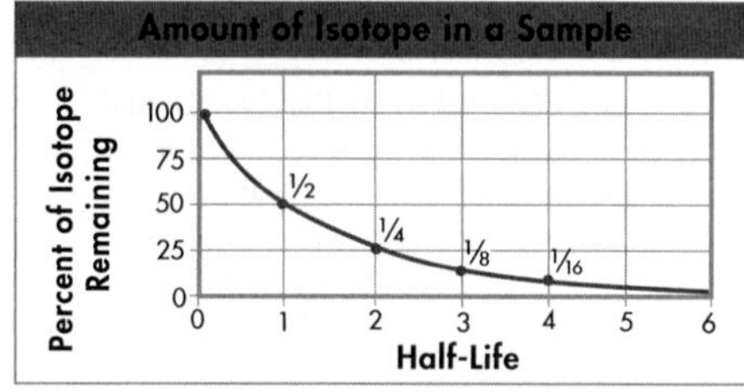

6. The half-life of thorium-230 is 75,000 years. How long will it take for $\frac{7}{8}$ of the original amount of thorium-230 in a sample to decay?
   A 75,000 years
   B 225,000 years
   C 25,000 years
   D 150,000 years

7. The half-life of potassium-40 is about 1.3 billion years. After four half-lives have passed, how much of the original sample will be left?
   A $\frac{1}{16}$
   B $\frac{1}{16} \times 1300$ million grams
   C $\frac{1}{4}$
   D $\frac{1}{4} \times 1300$ million grams

Open-Ended Response

8. How does the process by which sedimentary rock forms allow scientists to determine the relative ages of fossils?

If You Have Trouble With . . .

Question	1	2	3	4	5	6	7	8
See Lesson	19.1	19.2	19.3	19.1	19.1	19.1	19.1	19.1

ASSESSMENT

Answers

1. C
2. A
3. A
4. B
5. C
6. B
7. A
8. Sedimentary rock usually forms when particles of sand, silt, clay, or lime settle in layers at the bottom of a body of water. These layers cover the bodies of dead organisms. Other layers with other organisms build up over the lower layers. Unless the layers of rock are disturbed, scientists can infer that fossil specimens in lower layers are older than specimens buried in more recent layers that were deposited on top.

Test-Taking Tip

REVIEW ANSWERS

Tell students to use any time remaining after they have answered all of the questions on a test to review their answers. Point out that they should change only those responses they are sure are incorrect. If the answer booklet is separate from the test question booklet, students should make sure the question numbers correctly correspond with their responses in the answer booklet.

UNIT 5

Plan Ahead

Have students preview the Unit 5 Project a few days before writing to give them time to think through what they need to include in their scripts. If possible, provide students with an example of a script for a documentary. You may find one online or in a library. Point out that a script includes both text for a narrator to speak and descriptions of the images shown throughout the documentary. It might also include interviews with experts.

Monitor the Project

Suggest students begin by making a basic outline of how the documentary will proceed. As students write their scripts, circulate through the class, asking individual students how the script addresses the five misconceptions about evolution.

Ask What example are you including that demonstrates the process of natural selection?

Ask What are you including that addresses the misconception that gaps in the fossil record disprove evolution?

Project Assessment

Make sure students use the rubric and reflection questions to assess their work. Then, use the rubric to assign a final score. Note that it is important to value the creativity of students' work as well as the content when you score their projects. If desired, talk with students about any differences between their self-assessment scores and your assigned score.

Unit Project

Evolution Documentary

Have you ever flipped through the channels and stopped on a documentary that caught your eye? And before you knew it an hour had passed? Documentaries can be a great way to learn about fascinating topics. Imagine you are a TV producer and have been hired to produce a documentary on evolution for a public television station. Your target audience is the general public.

Your Task Write a script for a 5–10 minute segment of an evolution documentary and present it to your class.

Be sure to

- discuss evidence for evolution by bringing in specific examples.
- present the information clearly and in an engaging manner.
- explain why the misconceptions listed below are *not* true:
  1) Evolution causes organisms to improve—life has gotten better over time.
  2) Evolution is not observable or testable.
  3) Gaps in the fossil record disprove evolution.
  4) Natural selection involves organisms "trying" to adapt.
  5) Natural selection is the only way that populations can change over time.

Reflection Questions

1. **Score your documentary using the rubric below. What score did you give yourself?**
2. **What did you do well in this project?**
3. **What needs improvement?**
4. **What do you think a member of the general public would learn from your documentary?**

Assessment Rubric

Score	Scientific Content	Quality of Documentary Script
4	Documentary provides accurate evidence for evolution and clearly corrects several misconceptions.	Information is presented in a clear, organized, and engaging manner.
3	Documentary provides some accurate evidence for evolution and attempts to correct misconceptions.	Information is presented in a clear and organized manner, but it could be more engaging.
2	Documentary provides little evidence for evolution and does not correct misconceptions well.	Information could be presented in a clearer manner. The script needs editing.
1	Documentary does not provide evidence for evolution and does not attempt to correct misconceptions.	Information is presented in a disorganized and confusing manner. The script needs a lot of editing.

21st Century Skills

To be successful in the 21st century, students need skills and learning experiences that extend beyond subject area mastery. The Unit 5 Project helps students build the following 21st Century Skills: *Information and Media Literacy; Communication Skills; Creativity and Intellectual Curiosity; Self-Direction;* and *Accountability and Adaptability.*

FOCUS ON PROBLEM IDENTIFICATION, FORMULATION, AND SOLUTION Extend this Unit Project by having students talk with other students, relatives, friends, and neighbors about their understanding of evolution. Then, have students discuss any misunderstandings of evolution they have encountered. Suggest they think of ways a documentary could address these misconceptions.

For more practice building 21st Century Skills, see The Chapter Mystery pages in **Study Workbook A.**

IN INDIANA ACADEMIC STANDARDS

B.8.1 History of life on Earth, **B.8.4** Evidence for evolutionary relationships, **B.8.5** Survival and reproduction

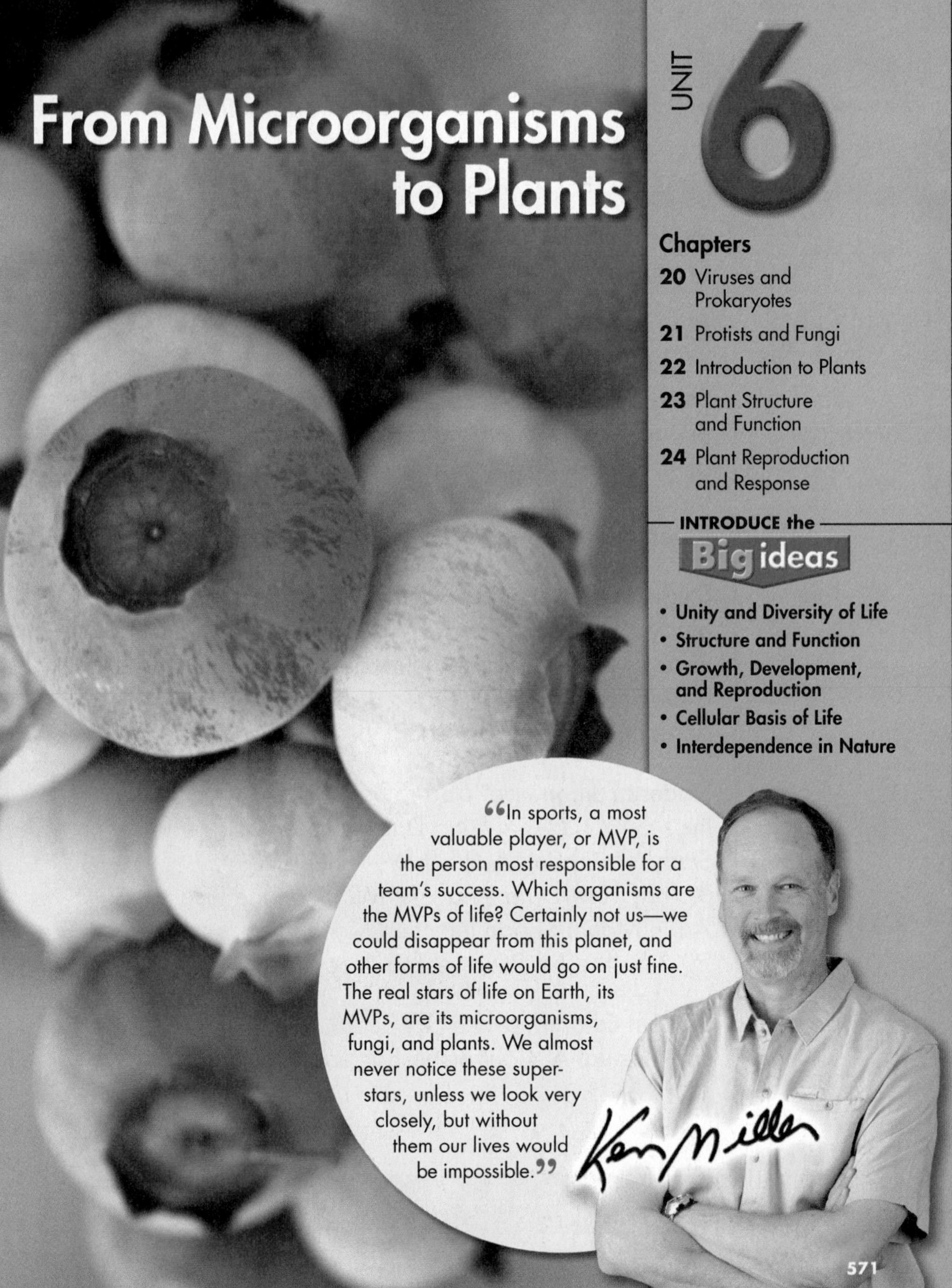

From Microorganisms to Plants
UNIT 6
Chapters
20 Viruses and Prokaryotes
21 Protists and Fungi
22 Introduction to Plants
23 Plant Structure and Function
24 Plant Reproduction and Response
INTRODUCE the Big ideas
• Unity and Diversity of Life
• Structure and Function
• Growth, Development, and Reproduction
• Cellular Basis of Life
• Interdependence in Nature
“In sports, a most valuable player, or MVP, is the person most responsible for a team's success. Which organisms are the MVPs of life? Certainly not us—we could disappear from this planet, and other forms of life would go on just fine. The real stars of life on Earth, its MVPs, are its microorganisms, fungi, and plants. We almost never notice these superstars, unless we look very closely, but without them our lives would be impossible.”
Ken Miller
571

UNIT 6

Dear Colleague,

It's only natural. Because we're animals ourselves, we tend to be more interested in the lives of other animals. We tend to think of evolution largely in terms of the origins of major groups of animals, and we often consider the well-being of ecosystems in terms of the animals that may or may not be present and part of the food chain. But, if we force ourselves to think in purely biological terms, we animals make up only a tiny part of the range and diversity of life on Earth. The real players, the ones that have changed this planet in fundamental ways, are microorganisms and plants. Students don't always appreciate this, and it's a special challenge to open their eyes to these remarkable forms of life.

Every time I take a walk through the woods near my house, I'm struck by the obvious ways in which plants dominate the landscape, and by the not-so-obvious ways in which decomposers such as bacteria, fungi, and slime molds shape the living world. Even more amazing are the protists, whose various members exemplify nearly every conceivable way of making a living on this little planet. Indeed, the cellular and biochemical diversity of these organisms is so great that, compared to them, all animals are pretty much the same. If that's a shock to your students, point out to them that biologists now suspect that huge numbers of bacteria live deep beneath the surface, thriving in darkness, often under some of the most extreme conditions imaginable. In fact, the abundance of underground bacteria is so great that their mass might dwarf all life found on Earth's surface.

Students may know that microorganisms and plants are essential to our lives, but many have a difficult time believing that these organisms are just as alive as you or I. Nonetheless, as teachers, one of the greatest gifts we can give our students is to extend their vision beyond the obvious—and I can think of no better way to do exactly that than to spend some time investigating these extraordinary organisms.

Ken Miller

Viruses and Prokaryotes

Chapter Contents	IN	Time	Core Resources
Chapter Preview			**Student Edition,** pp. 572–573 **Chapter Mystery,** p. 573
20.1 Viruses The Discovery of Viruses • Viral Infections	NoS.6	1 period 1/2 block	**Student Edition,** pp. 574–579 Inquiry 20.1 Quick Lab, p. 575 L2 **Study Workbook A** 20.1 Worksheets L2 **Biology.com** *Visual Analogy:* How a Lytic Virus Is Like an Outlaw • *InterActive Art:* Two Types of Virus Reproduction **Assessment Resources Book** Visual Quiz L2
20.2 Prokaryotes Classifying Prokaryotes • Structure and Function • The Importance of Prokaryotes	B.4.4, B.8.2, B.8.4	1 period 1/2 block	**Student Edition,** pp. 580–585 **Study Workbook A** 20.2 Worksheets L2 **Biology.com** *Art Review:* Prokaryote Structure and Classification **Assessment Resources Book** Visual Quiz L2
20.3 Diseases Caused by Bacteria and Viruses Bacterial Diseases • Viral Diseases • Emerging Diseases • *Biology & Society: Should More Vaccinations Be Required?*	NoS.3	1/2 period 1/4 block	**Student Edition,** pp. 586–593 Inquiry 20.3 Analyzing Data, p. 591 L2 **Study Workbook A** 20.3 Worksheets L2 **Biology.com** *Data Analysis:* MRSA on the Rise • *Art in Motion:* Prion Infection Mechanism • 20.3 Self-Test • 20.3 Lesson Assessment
Chapter Pre-Lab	NoS.1	1 period 1/2 block	**Student Edition,** p. 594 L2 **Lab Manual A** *Controlling Bacterial Growth* L2

Differentiated Instruction Tools

Study Workbook B includes worksheets with lesson-level differentiated instruction support and explanations of differentiated instruction teaching strategies.

Lab Manual B includes skills labs, simplified chapter labs, and hands-on activities.

ELL Handbook explains ways to make *Biology* more accessible to ELL students.

Spanish Study Workbook is a Spanish translation of Study Workbook A.

Multilingual Glossary is the glossary translated into ten languages.

Differentiated Instruction Key

- L1 Special Needs or Struggling Students
- ELL English Language Learners
- LPR Less Proficient Readers
- L2 On-Level Students
- L3 Advanced Students

Additional Resources

Biology.com Untamed Science Video • Vocabulary Flash Cards

Study Workbook B 20.1 Worksheets L1 ELL LPR
Spanish Study Workbook 20.1 Worksheets ELL
Biology.com 20.1 Lesson Overview • 20.1 Lesson Notes • 20.1 Self-Test • 20.1 Lesson Assessment

Study Workbook B 20.2 Worksheets L1 ELL LPR
Spanish Study Workbook 20.2 Worksheets ELL
Biology.com 20.2 Lesson Overview • 20.2 Lesson Notes • 20.2 Self-Test • 20.2 Lesson Assessment

Study Workbook B 20.3 Worksheets L1 ELL LPR
Spanish Study Workbook 20.3 Worksheets ELL
Biology.com 20.3 Lesson Overview • 20.3 Lesson Notes

Lab Manual B *Controlling Bacterial Growth* • Data Analysis: *MRSA on the Rise* • Hands-On Activity: *How Do Viruses Differ?* L1 ELL LPR

Chapter Review

Student Edition Study Guide, p. 595 L2
Study Workbook A Chapter 20 Vocabulary Review L2 • Chapter 20 Chapter Mystery/21st Century Skills Activity L2 L3
Transparencies, pp. 240–248 L1 ELL LPR L2
Biology.com Untamed Science Video • Editable Worksheets of Study Workbooks A and B and Lab Manuals A and B • Chapter 20 Flash Cards and Crossword Puzzle

Untamed Science DVD • Classroom Resources CD (includes lesson presentations and editable worksheets)

Chapter Assessment

Student Edition Assessment, pp. 596–599 L2
Study Workbook B Chapter 20 Chapter Review L1 ELL LPR • Chapter 20 Taking a Standardized Test L1 ELL LPR
Assessment Resources Book Chapter 20 Test A L2 • Chapter 20 Test B L1 ELL LPR
Biology.com Chapter 20 Assessment • Editable Worksheets of Chapter 20 Visual Quizzes and Chapter 20 Tests A and B

Exam*View Assessment Suite* • Classroom Resources CD (includes lesson presentations and editable worksheets)

Time: 1 period, 1/2 block

Pressed for Time?

Preview the Chapter Introduce the vocabulary for Lesson 20.1. Preview the images on pp. 1040–1043 in the Diversity of Life guide and discuss the variations that exist among different bacteria.

Cover the Chapter Quickly In 20.1, have students read the definition of a virus, the Structure and Composition section of *The Discovery of Viruses,* and *Viral Infections.* Discuss Figure 20–3. Assign students to read all of Lesson 20.2 and discuss Figures 20–7 and 20–13.

Assess Assign questions 1 and 2 in the 20.1 Assessment, the 20.2 Assessment, and questions 1–23 and 37–42 of the Chapter 20 Assessment.

Connect to the Big Idea

Use the photograph of colonies of bacteria to introduce the topic of microbes. Point out that bacteria are not the only type of microbe. Ask students if they can identify other microbes. *(Sample answer: viruses)* Ask students to identify some diseases microbes cause in people. *(Sample answer: Microbes cause colds and the flu.)* Also, explain that not all bacteria cause illness. Ask students to anticipate the answer to the question, **Are all microbes that make us sick made of living cells?**

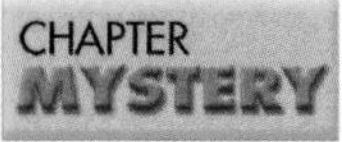

Have students read over the Chapter Mystery. Have a class discussion about possible causes of BSE. After students have completed Chapter 20, have them speculate how the solution to the Chapter Mystery might be used to help answer the chapter Essential Question.

BIOLOGY.com Have students preview the chapter vocabulary terms using the **Flash Cards.**

IN INDIANA ACADEMIC STANDARDS

For the full text of all standards, see the Course Overview in the front matter of this book.

Key standards: Chapter 20 covers key ideas from Standard 8: Evolution, including **B.8.2** Classification.

20 Viruses and Prokaryotes

Big idea **Cellular Basis of Life**

Q: Are all microbes that make us sick made of living cells?

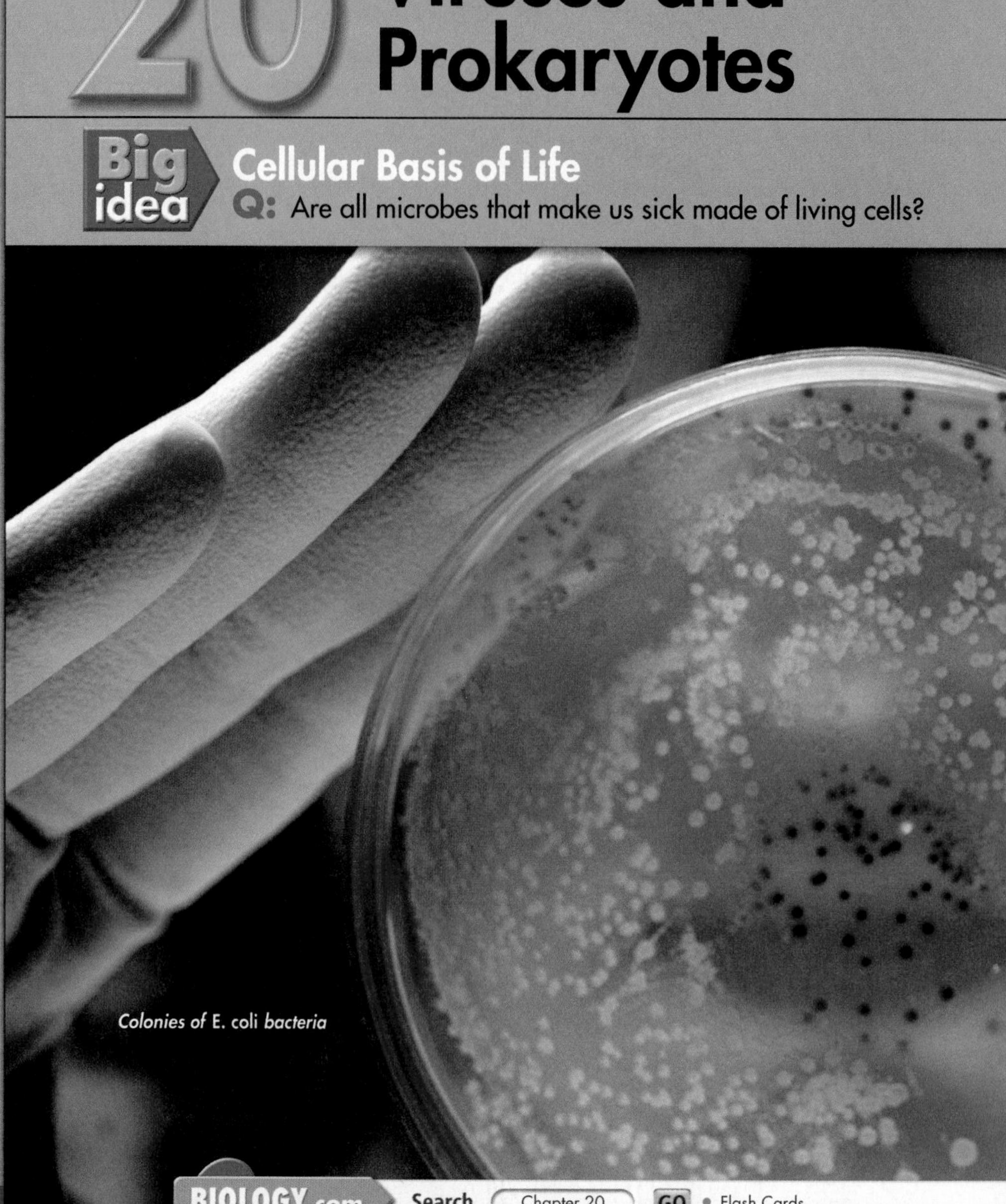

Colonies of E. coli bacteria

UbD Understanding by Design

Chapter 20 describes prokaryotes, viruses, and the diseases they cause. The graphic organizer at the right shows how these topics are connected to the chapter's Big Idea, Essential Question, and Guiding Questions. Together, these ideas and questions help students build toward the Unit 6 Enduring Understanding that *from microorganisms to plants, organisms vary widely in the way they carry out basic life processes.*

PERFORMANCE GOALS

In Chapter 20, there are many chances to assess your students' understanding of viruses and prokaryotes. For example, students will write a comic-strip illustrating a lytic or lysogenic infection, analyze data on trends in bacterial infection, and prepare an informational flier to help curb the unnecessary use of antibiotics.

INDIANA ACADEMIC STANDARDS FOR SCIENCE

Nature of Science NoS.1, NoS.3, NoS.6, NoS.11; **Interdependence** B.4.4; **Evolution** B.8.2, B.8.4. See lessons for details.

• Untamed Science Video • Chapter Mystery

CHAPTER MYSTERY

THE MAD COWS

In 1986, something strange began to happen to cattle in Great Britain. Without warning, the animals began acting strangely, losing control of their movements, staggering and stumbling, and eventually dying. Farmers watched helplessly as the disease they called "mad cow" spread through their cattle. The disease affected more than 30,000 cattle in 1991.

Studies of the brains of cattle killed by mad cow disease showed that large areas of the animals' brains had been destroyed. Under the microscope, the holes in the tissue made the brain resemble a sponge. Because of this, the disease was given the name bovine spongiform encephalopathy, or BSE. But the cause of the disease was a mystery. As you read this chapter, look for clues that explain the culprit behind this disease. Then, solve the mystery.

Never Stop Exploring Your World. Finding what caused this disease is only the beginning. Take a video field trip with the ecogeeks of Untamed Science to explore the other side of the story—you'll see that not all microbes are "bad."

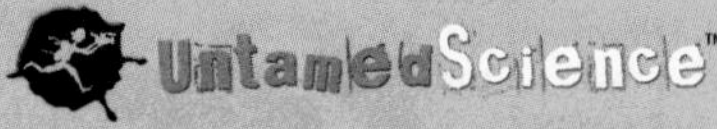

Viruses and Prokaryotes **573**

Chapter 20
Big Idea: Cellular Basis of Life

Chapter 20 EQ: Are all microbes that make us sick made of living cells?

20.1 GQ: What is a virus?

20.2 GQ: What are prokaryotes, and why are they important?

20.3 GQ: How can we prevent bacterial and viral diseases from spreading?

What's Online

BIOLOGY.com Extend your reach by using these and other digital assets offered at Biology.com.

CHAPTER MYSTERY
What was the cause of the cows' symptoms? Students use clues to gather information about the cause of "mad cow" disease, or bovine spongiform encephalopathy.

UNTAMED SCIENCE VIDEO
Have students take a video field trip to learn more about beneficial bacteria.

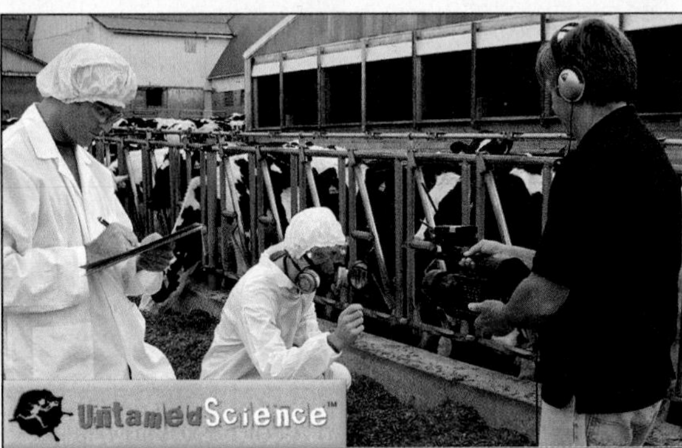

VISUAL ANALOGY
How is a virus like an outlaw? Students can go online to find out.

INTERACTIVE ART
By working with a dynamic diagram, students will understand more about virus reproduction.

ART REVIEW
Activities help students compare archaea and bacteria, learn the structure of a typical prokaryotic cell, and match pictures of bacteria to the names of their shapes.

DATA ANALYSIS
Students analyze data about MRSA to identify factors contributing to its increasing prevalence.

ART IN MOTION
Encourage students to see what prions are like and how these tiny particles set off a chain reaction in the brain.

LESSON 20.1

Getting Started

Objectives

20.1.1 Explain how viruses reproduce.

20.1.2 Explain how viruses cause infection.

Student Resources

Study Workbooks A and B, 20.1 Worksheets

Spanish Study Workbook, 20.1 Worksheets

Lab Manual A, 20.1 Quick Lab Worksheet

Lab Manual B, 20.1 Hands-On Activity Worksheet

Lesson Overview • Lesson Notes

- Activities: Visual Analogy, InterActive Art
- Assessment: Self-Test, Lesson Assessment

For corresponding lesson in the **Foundation Edition,** see pages 480–484.

Activate Prior Knowledge

Have students raise their hands if they have ever missed out on some important event, such as a football game, because they had a cold. Explain that a cold is an example of an illness caused by a virus. Tell students Lesson 20.1 describes the structure of viruses and what happens when a virus infects a cell.

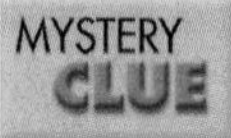

Students should infer that a substance in the meat and bone meal protein added to the cattle's feed caused the spread of BSE. Students can go online to **Biology.com** to gather their evidence.

IN INDIANA ACADEMIC STANDARDS

For the full text of all standards, see the Course Overview in the front matter of this book.

NoS.6 Use analogies and models (mathematical and physical) to simplify and represent systems that are difficult to understand or directly experience due to their size, time scale, or complexity, and recognize the limitations of analogies and models.

20.1 Viruses

IN NoS.6 Using models and analogies.

Key Questions

How do viruses reproduce?

What happens after a virus infects a cell?

Vocabulary

virus
capsid
bacteriophage
lytic infection
lysogenic infection
prophage
retrovirus

Taking Notes

Venn Diagram Make a Venn diagram in which to record the similarities and differences between viruses and cells. Fill it in as you read the lesson.

THINK ABOUT IT Imagine that you have been presented with a great puzzle. Farmers have begun to lose their valuable tobacco crop to a plant disease that first appears as a yellowing of the leaves. Eventually the leaves wither and fall, killing the plant. To determine what is causing the disease, you take leaves from a diseased plant and crush them to produce a liquid extract. You place a few drops of that liquid on the leaves of healthy plants. A few days later, the leaves turn yellow where you put the drops.

You use a light microscope to look for a germ that might cause the disease, but none can be seen. In fact, when even the tiniest of cells are filtered out of the liquid, the liquid still causes the disease. You hypothesize that the liquid must contain disease-causing agents so small that they are not visible under the microscope and can pass right through the filter. Although you cannot see the tiny disease-causing particles, you're sure they are there. What would you do next? How would you deal with the invisible?

MYSTERY CLUE

British scientists carefully investigated the veterinary histories of 169 cattle with BSE. All 169 had been given feed enriched with meat and bone meal protein from slaughtered cattle. How could this practice spread a disease?

The Discovery of Viruses

How do viruses reproduce?

If you think you could have carried out the investigation described above, congratulations! You're walking in the footsteps of a 28-year-old Russian biologist, Dmitri Ivanovski. In 1892, Ivanovski demonstrated that the cause of this particular plant disease—called tobacco mosaic disease—was found in the liquid extracted from infected plants. But he could not pin down the culprit.

Discovery of Viruses In 1897, Dutch scientist Martinus Beijerinck suggested that tiny particles in the juice caused the disease, and he named these particles *viruses,* after the Latin word for "poison." Then, in 1935, the American biochemist Wendell Stanley isolated crystals of tobacco mosaic virus. Living organisms do not crystallize, so Stanley inferred that viruses were not truly alive. This is a conclusion that biologists still recognize as being valid today. A **virus** is a nonliving particle made of proteins, nucleic acids, and sometimes lipids. **Viruses can reproduce only by infecting living cells.**

UbD Teach for Understanding

ENDURING UNDERSTANDING From microorganisms to plants, organisms vary widely in the way they carry out basic life processes.

GUIDING QUESTION What is a virus?

EVIDENCE OF UNDERSTANDING *After completing the lesson, give students the following assessment to show their understanding of the characteristics of viruses.* Have students work in pairs to make comic strips depicting either a lytic or a lysogenic infection. Explain that a comic strip uses a series of illustrations and text to depict action. Provide several appropriate comic strips as models. Tell students that their comic strips should be creative and scientifically accurate.

Structure and Composition Viruses differ widely in terms of size and structure, as you can see in **Figure 20–1.** Most viruses are so small they can be seen only with the aid of a powerful electron microscope. The protein coat surrounding a virus is called a **capsid.** In addition, some viruses, such as the influenza virus, have an additional membrane that surrounds the capsid. The simplest viruses contain only a few genes, whereas the most complex may have hundreds of genes.

To enter a host cell, most viruses have proteins on their surface membrane or capsid that bind to receptor proteins on the cell. In either case, the proteins "trick" the cell to take in the virus, or in some cases just its genetic material. Once inside the cell, the viral genes are eventually expressed and may destroy the cell.

Because viruses must bind precisely to proteins on the host cell surface and then use the host's genetic system, most viruses infect only a very specific kind of cell. Plant viruses infect plant cells; most animal viruses infect only certain related species of animals; bacterial viruses infect only certain types of bacteria. Viruses that infect bacteria are called **bacteriophages,** which literally means "bacteria eaters."

T4 Bacteriophage

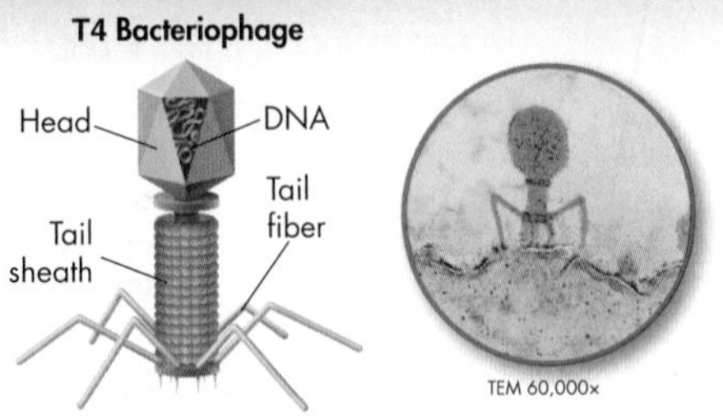

Tobacco Mosaic Virus

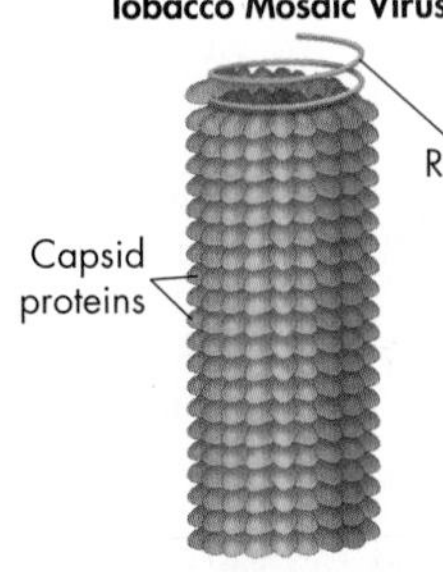

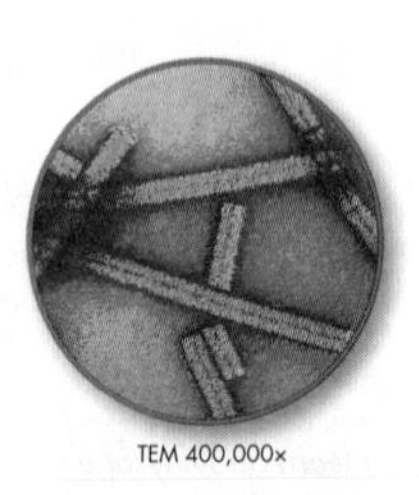

Influenza Virus

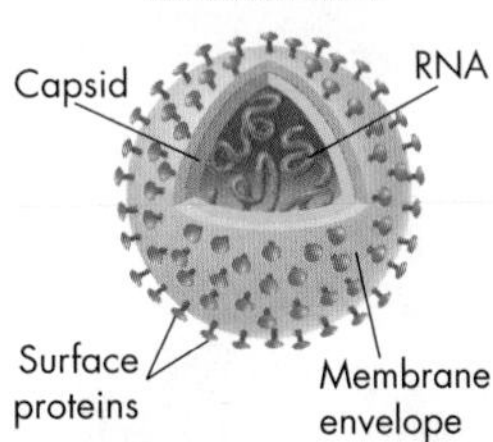

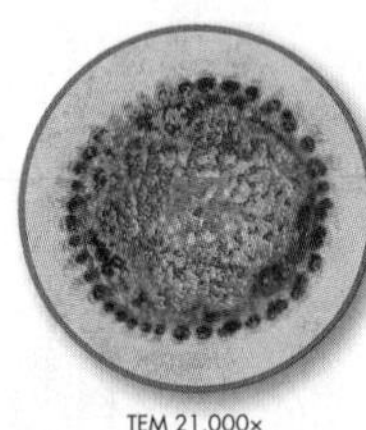

FIGURE 20–1 Diversity of Viral Forms Viruses come in a wide variety of sizes and shapes. Three types of viruses are shown here. **Interpret Diagrams** ***What kind of nucleic acid does each virus type have?***

Quick Lab
GUIDED INQUIRY

IN NoS.6

How Do Viruses Differ in Structure?

1. Make models of two of the viruses shown in **Figure 20–1.**
2. Label the parts of each of your virus models.
3. Measure and record the length of each of your virus models in centimeters. Convert the length of each model into nanometers by using the following formula: 1 cm = 10 million nm. MATH
4. Measure the length of each virus you modeled. Divide the length of each model by the length of the actual virus to determine how much larger each model is than the virus it represents. MATH

Analyze and Conclude

1. **Use Models** Which parts of your models are found in all viruses?
2. **Draw Conclusions** Which parts of one or both of your models are found in only some viruses?
3. **Calculate** How many times larger are your models than the viruses they represent? MATH

LESSON 20.1

Teach

Build Science Skills

Have students examine the structure and composition of the three viruses shown in **Figure 20–1.** Then, have students use the information in the figure and the text on this page to write a paragraph comparing and contrasting the viruses. Remind students that comparing and contrasting involves identifying both similarities and differences. Ask volunteers to share their paragraphs with the class.

DIFFERENTIATED INSTRUCTION

LPR **Less Proficient Readers** Students who might have difficulty reading the text on this page can base their compare/contrast paragraph exclusively on the information in **Figure 20–1.** Explain that their paragraphs should include ways the viruses are similar and ways they are different.

ELL Focus on ELL: Access Content

ALL SPEAKERS Have students use the **Lesson Preview** strategy to enhance their comprehension of the content of Lesson 20.1. Have students locate and read the boldface heads in the lesson and preview each of the figures and captions. Then, have students form small groups. Within the groups, have them discuss the lesson topics and figures. Ask each group to produce a written summary of its discussion. Beginning and intermediate speakers should be paired with advanced and advanced high speakers to complete the written summary.

Student Wkbks A/B, Appendix S8, Lesson Preview.

PURPOSE Students will make models of two different viruses and conclude that viruses differ in structure.

MATERIALS metric ruler, scissors, tape, craft materials

PLANNING Write the following steps on the board to help students find the length of the actual virus. They will need these results to answer Question 3.

- Measure the image of the viruses in **Figure 20–1.** (For the tobacco mosaic virus, have them measure the vertical rod at the center of the field of view.)
- Divide this length by the magnification. The resulting number is the length of the actual virus.

ANALYZE AND CONCLUDE

1. a capsid and either DNA or RNA
2. Sample answers: tail fiber, tail sheath, head, membrane envelope
3. Answers will vary. Call on volunteers to share their answers and explain their calculations.

Answers

FIGURE 20–1 The T4 bacteriophage has DNA; the tobacco mosaic virus and influenza virus have RNA.

Teach continued

Lead a Discussion

Discuss viral infections with students.

Ask In a lytic infection, how does the virus make more copies of itself? *(by inserting its genetic information into a cell, which directs the cell to make and assemble new viral parts)*

Ask Why can a lytic virus remain in a particular host cell only for a limited time? *(It eventually destroys the host cell by causing it to burst.)*

DIFFERENTIATED INSTRUCTION

L1 Struggling Students Use these basic questions to help students understand the sequence of events in a lytic infection.

Ask What is the first step in a lytic infection? *(The virus enters a cell.)*

Ask What happens after the virus gets into the cell? *(The cell makes copies of the virus.)*

Ask What happens after many copies of the virus have been made? *(The cell lyses, and hundreds of virus particles are released.)*

VISUAL ANALOGY

Have students use **Figure 20–2 to** compare a lytic virus to an outlaw.

Ask In this analogy, what represents the host cell? *(the town)*

Ask Think about how viruses enter host cells. Extend the analogy to describe the outlaw's entrance into town. *(Answers should describe the outlaw being sneaky or using trickery to gain entrance to the town.)*

Ask Think about how viruses exit host cells. Extend the analogy to describe the condition of the town after the outlaw leaves. *(Answers will vary, but should describe the outlaw destroying the town or leaving it in disarray as he leaves.)*

BIOLOGY.com Have students go online for further exploration of the **Visual Analogy: How a Lytic Virus Is Like an Outlaw.**

Answers

FIGURE 20–2 A correct response will include an analogy for the prophage being a part of the bacterium for an extended period of time. Sample answer: The outlaw pretends to be looking for work, takes a job at a nearby ranch, and hides out there for a time.

Viral Infections

What happens after a virus infects a cell?

After a virus has entered a host cell, what happens? **Inside living cells, viruses use their genetic information to make multiple copies of themselves. Some viruses replicate immediately, while others initially persist in an inactive state within the host.** These two patterns of infection are called lytic infection and lysogenic infection.

Lytic Infections In a **lytic infection,** a virus enters a bacterial cell, makes copies of itself, and causes the cell to burst, or lyse (LYS). Bacteriophage *T4* is an example of a bacteriophage that causes such an infection. Bacteriophage *T4* has a DNA core inside a protein capsid that binds to the surface of a host cell. The virus injects its DNA into the cell, and the cell then begins to make messenger RNA (mRNA) from the viral genes. The viral mRNA is translated into viral proteins that act like a molecular wrecking crew, chopping up the cell's DNA.

Under the control of viral genes, the host cell's metabolic system now makes thousands of copies of viral nucleic acid and capsid proteins. The viral DNA is assembled into new virus particles. Before long, the infected cell lyses, releasing hundreds of virus particles that may go on to infect other cells. In its own way, a lytic virus is similar to an outlaw in the Wild West of the American frontier, as illustrated in **Figure 20–2.**

VISUAL ANALOGY

FIGURE 20–2 How a Lytic Virus Is Like an Outlaw A lytic virus is similar to the Wild West of the American frontier in the demands the virus makes on its host. **Use Analogies** ***After you learn about lysogenic infections on the next page, modify this story to make it analogous to a lysogenic cycle.***

First, the outlaw eliminates the town's existing authority.
Lytic Infection The host cell's DNA is chopped up.

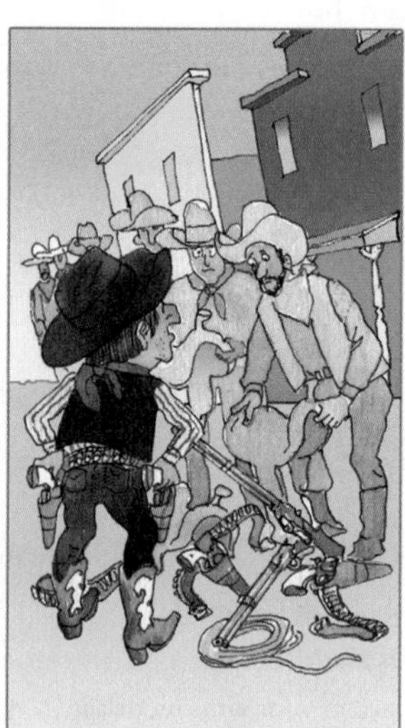

Next, the outlaw demands to be outfitted with new equipment from the local townspeople.
Lytic Infection Viruses use the host cell to make viral DNA and viral proteins.

Finally, the outlaw forms a gang that leaves the town to attack new communities.
Lytic Infection The host cell bursts, releasing hundreds of virus particles.

 BIOLOGY.com Search Lesson 20.1 GO • Visual Analogy

Quick Facts

CLASSIFYING VIRUSES

Viruses are nonliving particles; therefore, they are not classified into the domains, kingdoms, and other groupings used by scientists to classify living organisms. Instead, viruses are classified by their chemical and physical properties. The major division focuses on the type of genetic material a virus contains; thus there are DNA viruses and RNA viruses. Viruses are then further classified by their sizes and the shapes of their protein coats. Another method of classifying viruses is by the type of host a virus infects; using this strategy, viruses are classified as animal viruses, plant viruses, and bacterial viruses, or bacteriophages.

Lysogenic Infection Some bacterial viruses, including the bacteriophage *lambda*, cause a **lysogenic infection,** in which a host cell is not immediately taken over. Instead, the viral nucleic acid is inserted into the host cell's DNA, where it is copied along with the host DNA without damaging the host. Viral DNA multiplies as the host cells multiply. In this way, each generation of daughter cells derived from the original host cell is infected.

Bacteriophage DNA that becomes embedded in the bacterial host's DNA is called a **prophage.** The prophage may remain part of the DNA of the host cell for many generations. Influences from the environment—including radiation, heat, and certain chemicals—trigger the prophage to become active. It then removes itself from the host cell DNA and directs the synthesis of new virus particles. The lysogenic infection now becomes an active lytic infection, as shown in **Figure 20–3.**

The details of viral infection in eukaryotic cells differ in many ways from viral infection of bacteria by bacteriophages. But for the most part, the basic patterns of infection in animals and other eukaryotes are similar to the lytic and lysogenic infections of bacteria.

BUILD Vocabulary

WORD ORIGINS The adjective *lytic,* the verb *lyse,* and the prefix *lyso-* all come from the Greek word *lyein,* meaning "to loosen or break up."

In Your Notebook *Describe how a lysogenic infection can change into a lytic infection.*

FIGURE 20–3 Comparing Two Types of Bacteriophage Infection Viruses that infect bacteria, called bacteriophages, may infect cells in one of two ways: lytic infection or lysogenic infection.

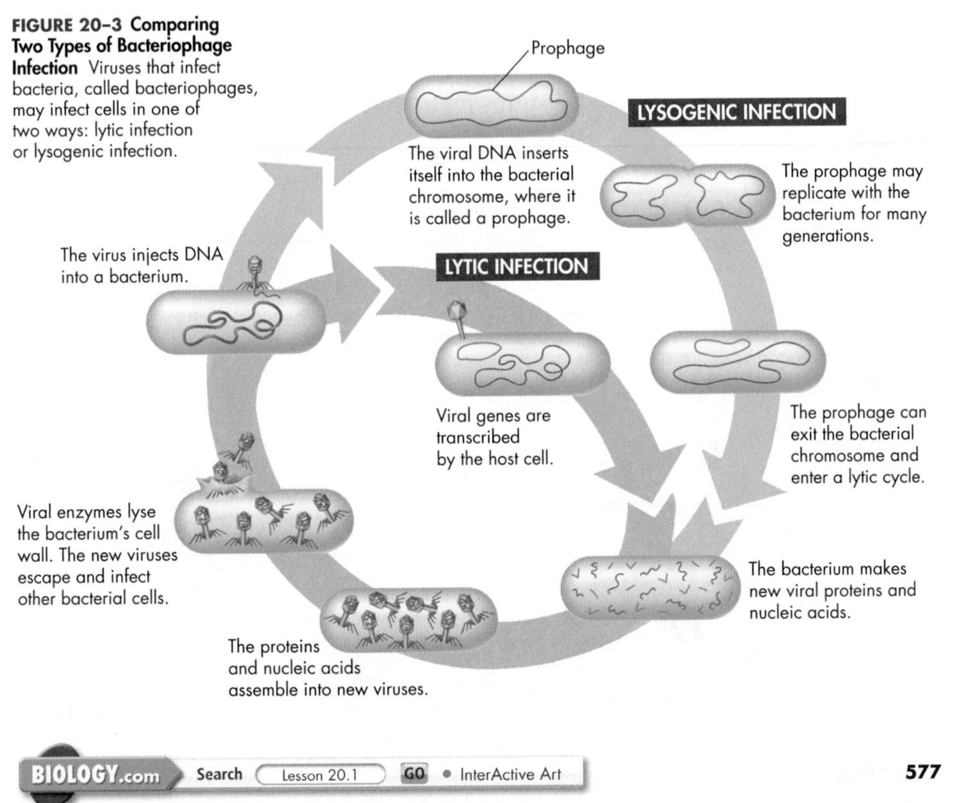

Prophage
LYSOGENIC INFECTION
The viral DNA inserts itself into the bacterial chromosome, where it is called a prophage.
The prophage may replicate with the bacterium for many generations.
The virus injects DNA into a bacterium.
LYTIC INFECTION
Viral genes are transcribed by the host cell.
The prophage can exit the bacterial chromosome and enter a lytic cycle.
Viral enzymes lyse the bacterium's cell wall. The new viruses escape and infect other bacterial cells.
The bacterium makes new viral proteins and nucleic acids.
The proteins and nucleic acids assemble into new viruses.

BIOLOGY.com Search Lesson 20.1 GO • InterActive Art

577

Use Visuals

Have students use **Figure 20–3** to compare lysogenic and lytic infections. Distribute a blank **T-Chart** to each student. Have students label the left side Similarities and the right side Differences. Have them complete their T-Charts by entering ways in which lytic and lysogenic infections are similar in the left column and ways they are different in the right column. Then, have students form small groups, review their T-Charts, and make any necessary revisions.

Study Wkbks A/B, Appendix S30, T-Chart. **Transparencies,** GO15.

DIFFERENTIATED INSTRUCTION

L1 Special Needs Have students work with a partner in order to complete the **T-Chart.** When students have completed their work, draw a T-Chart on the board, and label the columns Similarities and Differences. Ask students to volunteer information from their charts, and record their responses on the board. After the chart on the board is complete, discuss each point to clarify similarities of and differences between lytic and lysogenic infections.

L3 Advanced Students Have students learn more about applications of bacteriophages in genetic engineering and medicine. Ask each student to write a one-page paper summarizing his or her findings.

BIOLOGY.com Students can learn more about virus reproduction from the **InterActive Art: Two Types of Virus Reproduction.**

LESSON 20.1

UbD Check for Understanding

ONE-MINUTE RESPONSE

Write the following prompt on the board, and give students about a minute to write a quick response summarizing their understanding.

- What happens when a cell is infected by a lytic virus? *(Responses should describe the virus injecting its genetic material into a cell, making copies of itself, and causing the cell to burst, releasing many copies of the virus.)*

ADJUST INSTRUCTION

If responses are incorrect or incomplete, have students review **Figure 20–3.** Ask them to locate the part of the figure describing a lytic infection. (*Hint:* Follow the steps described along the path of blue arrows.) Have a volunteer read aloud the description of the sequence of events in a lytic infection.

Answers

IN YOUR NOTEBOOK Students should describe a prophage exiting the bacterial chromosome and entering a lytic cycle.

Teach continued

Expand Vocabulary

After students have read the information about the viruses that cause the common cold and AIDS, tell them the word part *retro-* means "backward."

Ask Why is the word *retrovirus* used to describe HIV? *(The genetic information of a retrovirus like HIV is copied from RNA to DNA instead of from DNA to RNA.)*

Ask If the virus that causes the common cold is also an RNA virus, why is it not called a retrovirus? *(In a cell infected with the common cold virus, RNA is not copied to make DNA. Instead, the viral RNA is translated by the cell's ribosomes to produce viral proteins.)*

DIFFERENTIATED INSTRUCTION

ELL **English Language Learners** Write the word *retrovirus* on the board. Separate the word into its parts, and explain that the word part *retro-* means "backward." Introduce other words containing the word part *retro-*, such as *retroactive, retrofit,* and *retrospective.* Then, ask students to describe in an oral or written sentence why the word *retrovirus* is used to describe some viruses.

LPR **Less Proficient Readers** Have students who struggle with reading work in pairs to master the information on this page. Have one student in each pair read the information and examine the figure describing the common cold virus. Ask the other student in each pair to read the information and examine the figure describing HIV. Then, have each pair of students work together to develop an explanation of why HIV is classified as a retrovirus, but the virus that causes the common cold is not. Call on students to share their explanations with the class.

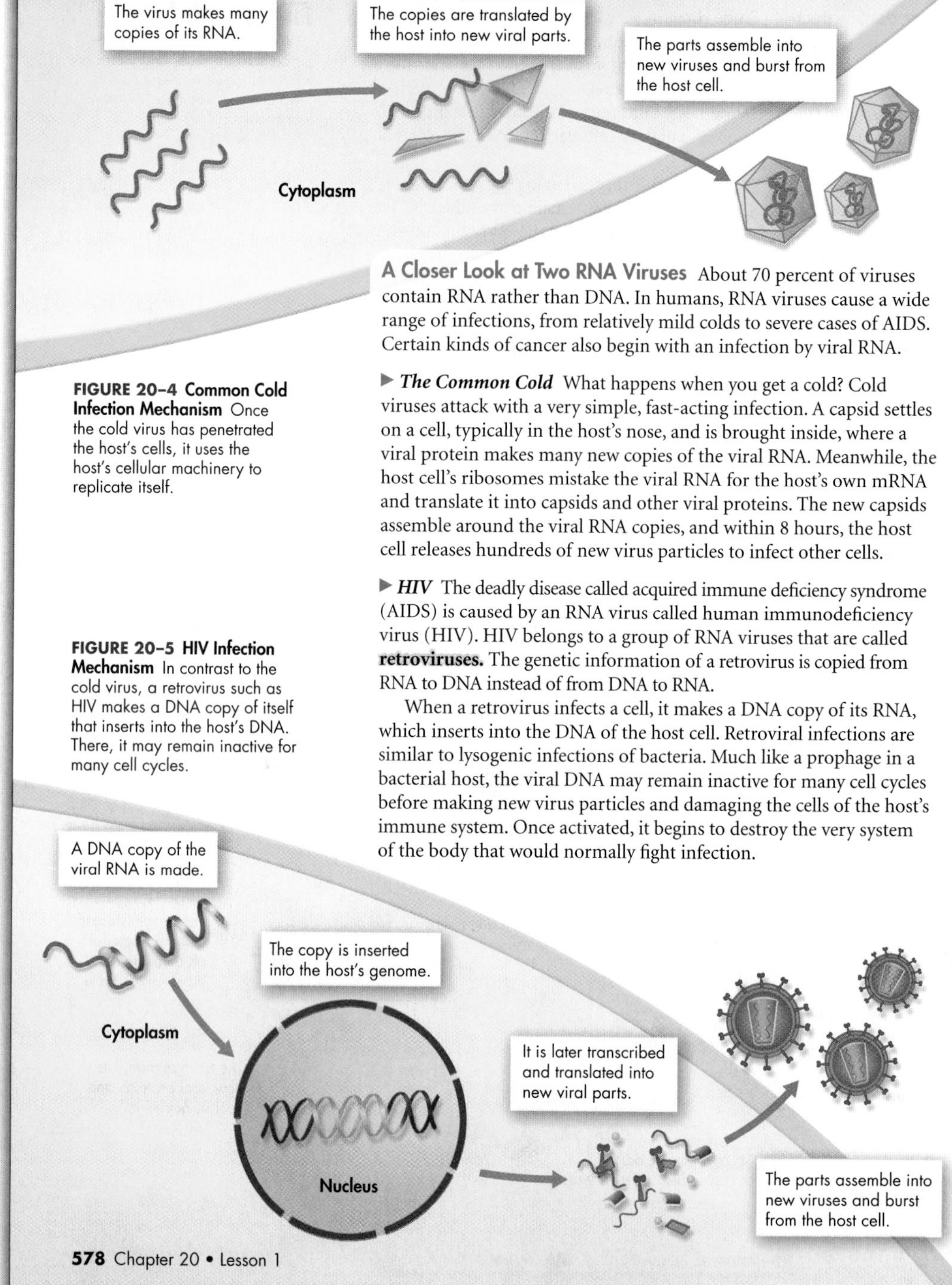

The virus makes many copies of its RNA.
The copies are translated by the host into new viral parts.
The parts assemble into new viruses and burst from the host cell.
Cytoplasm
A DNA copy of the viral RNA is made.
The copy is inserted into the host's genome.
Cytoplasm
It is later transcribed and translated into new viral parts.
Nucleus
The parts assemble into new viruses and burst from the host cell.

A Closer Look at Two RNA Viruses About 70 percent of viruses contain RNA rather than DNA. In humans, RNA viruses cause a wide range of infections, from relatively mild colds to severe cases of AIDS. Certain kinds of cancer also begin with an infection by viral RNA.

FIGURE 20–4 Common Cold Infection Mechanism Once the cold virus has penetrated the host's cells, it uses the host's cellular machinery to replicate itself.

▶ ***The Common Cold*** What happens when you get a cold? Cold viruses attack with a very simple, fast-acting infection. A capsid settles on a cell, typically in the host's nose, and is brought inside, where a viral protein makes many new copies of the viral RNA. Meanwhile, the host cell's ribosomes mistake the viral RNA for the host's own mRNA and translate it into capsids and other viral proteins. The new capsids assemble around the viral RNA copies, and within 8 hours, the host cell releases hundreds of new virus particles to infect other cells.

FIGURE 20–5 HIV Infection Mechanism In contrast to the cold virus, a retrovirus such as HIV makes a DNA copy of itself that inserts into the host's DNA. There, it may remain inactive for many cell cycles.

▶ ***HIV*** The deadly disease called acquired immune deficiency syndrome (AIDS) is caused by an RNA virus called human immunodeficiency virus (HIV). HIV belongs to a group of RNA viruses that are called **retroviruses.** The genetic information of a retrovirus is copied from RNA to DNA instead of from DNA to RNA.

When a retrovirus infects a cell, it makes a DNA copy of its RNA, which inserts into the DNA of the host cell. Retroviral infections are similar to lysogenic infections of bacteria. Much like a prophage in a bacterial host, the viral DNA may remain inactive for many cell cycles before making new virus particles and damaging the cells of the host's immune system. Once activated, it begins to destroy the very system of the body that would normally fight infection.

578 Chapter 20 • Lesson 1

UbD Check for Understanding

QUESTION BOARD

Establish a section of a bulletin board or white board in the classroom to be used by students to post questions about concepts or processes they do not understand. Have students post any questions they might have about viruses on the board. Assure students they do not need to leave their names with their questions.

ADJUST INSTRUCTION

Read over students' questions to identify common questions or areas of confusion. Use each as a topic of discussion to address students' questions or correct their misconceptions.

Characteristic	Virus	Cell
Structure	DNA or RNA in capsid, some with envelope	Cell membrane, cytoplasm; eukaryotes also contain nucleus and many organelles
Reproduction	Only within a host cell	Independent cell division, either asexually or sexually
Genetic Code	DNA or RNA	DNA
Growth and Development	No	Yes; in multicellular organisms, cells increase in number and differentiate
Obtain and Use Energy	No	Yes
Response to Environment	No	Yes
Change Over Time	Yes	Yes

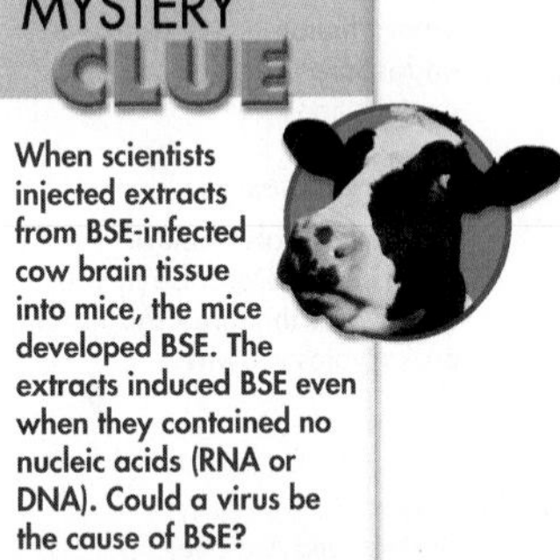

FIGURE 20–6 Comparing Viruses and Cells The differences between viruses and cells are listed in this chart. Form an Opinion ***Based on this information, would you classify viruses as living or nonliving? Explain.***

Viruses and Cells Viruses must infect living cells in order to grow and reproduce, taking advantage of the nutrients and cellular machinery of their hosts. This means that all viruses are parasites. Parasites depend entirely upon other living organisms for their existence, harming these organisms in the process.

Despite the fact that they are not alive, viruses have many of the characteristics of living things. After infecting living cells, viruses can reproduce, regulate gene expression, and even evolve. Some of the main differences between cells and viruses are summarized in **Figure 20–6.**

Although viruses are smaller and simpler than the smallest cells, it is unlikely that they were the first organisms. Because viruses are dependent upon living organisms, it seems more likely that viruses developed after living cells. In fact, the first viruses may have evolved from the genetic material of living cells. Viruses have continued to evolve, along with the cells they infect, for billions of years.

MYSTERY CLUE

When scientists injected extracts from BSE-infected cow brain tissue into mice, the mice developed BSE. The extracts induced BSE even when they contained no nucleic acids (RNA or DNA). Could a virus be the cause of BSE?

20.1 Assessment

Review Key Concepts

1. a. Review What do viruses depend on for their reproduction?
   b. Compare and Contrast How is viral reproduction different from that of cell-based organisms?
2. a. Review Describe each of the two paths viruses may follow once they have entered a cell.
   b. Compare and Contrast How are lytic and lysogenic infections similar? How are they different?

Apply the Big idea

Structure and Function

3. Compare the structure of a virus to the structure of both a prokaryotic cell and a eukaryotic cell. Use a graphic organizer of your choice to organize the information. You may wish to refer to Chapter 7, which discusses the structures of cells in detail.

BIOLOGY.com Search Lesson 20.1 GO • Self-Test • Lesson Assessment

Assessment Answers

1a. Viruses depend on living cells for reproduction.

1b. Viruses cannot reproduce independently; cell-based organisms can reproduce independently.

2a. In a lytic infection, viral genes are quickly transcribed and new viruses are made by the host cell. In a lysogenic infection, the host cell is not immediately taken over; viral nucleic acid is inserted into the host cell's DNA and becomes a prophage, which may be inactive for a long time.

2b. In both lytic and lysogenic infection, viruses gain entry to a host cell. In lytic infections, the virus replicates immediately; in lysogenic infections, the virus initially persists in an inactive state within the host.

3.  Students' graphic organizers should include information about structures found in viruses, prokaryotic cells, and eukaryotic cells.

Use Visuals

Have students use **Figure 20–6** to compare viruses and cells. Have students use the information to write a paragraph explaining why scientists do not consider viruses to be living organisms.

DIFFERENTIATED INSTRUCTION

L1 Special Needs Work with students who would struggle to complete the paragraph described above to complete several **Cloze Prompt** sentences such as:

Viruses reproduce inside a host ______. *(cell)*

Cells ______ by cell division. *(reproduce)*

______ do not grow and develop, but ______ do. *(Viruses; cells)*

Study Wkbks A/B, Appendix S2, Cloze Prompts.

 The information in this clue should lead students to infer that the infectious agent that causes BSE is not a virus, since viruses are only infective when their DNA or RNA is intact. Students can go online to Biology.com to gather their evidence.

Assess and Remediate

EVALUATE UNDERSTANDING

Have students work in pairs to make a list of words and phrases that accurately describe viruses. Call on students to share words and phrases from their lists. Then, have students complete the 20.1 Assessment.

REMEDIATION SUGGESTION

L1 Struggling Students If your students have trouble with **Questions 2a** and **2b,** have them draw a simpler version of **Figure 20–3.** Then, have them use their drawings to help answer the questions.

BIOLOGY.com Students can check their understanding of lesson concepts with the **Self-Test** assessment. They can then take an online version of the **Lesson Assessment.**

Answers

FIGURE 20–6 Answers will vary, but should be supported by information in the table. Sample answer: I would classify viruses as nonliving, because they cannot grow, develop, or obtain energy, and because they cannot reproduce independently.

LESSON 20.2

Getting Started

Objectives

20.2.1 Explain how the two groups of prokaryotes differ.

20.2.2 Describe how prokaryotes vary in structure and function.

20.2.3 Explain the role of bacteria in the living world.

Student Resources

Study Workbooks A and B, 20.2 Worksheets

Spanish Study Workbook 20.2 Worksheets

Lesson Overview • Lesson Notes
- Activity: Art Review
- Assessment: Self-Test, Lesson Assessment

For corresponding lesson in the **Foundation Edition,** see pages 485-488.

Activate Prior Knowledge

Ask students to recall from Chapter 18 the names of the three domains into which all living things are classified. *(Eukarya, Bacteria, Archaea)* Explain that prokaryotes, the topic of this lesson, make up the domains Bacteria and Archaea. All other living things are classified into the third domain, Eukarya.

IN INDIANA ACADEMIC STANDARDS

For the full text of all standards, see the Course Overview in the front matter of this book.

B.4.4 Describe how climate, the pattern of matter and energy flow, the birth and death of new organisms, and the interaction between those organisms contribute to the long term stability of an ecosystem.

B.8.2 Explain how organisms are classified and named based on their evolutionary relationships into taxonomic categories.

20.2 Prokaryotes

IN **B.4.4** Stability of an ecosystem; **B.8.2** Classification. Also covered: **B.8.4.**

Key Questions

How are prokaryotes classified?

How do prokaryotes vary in their structure and function?

What roles do prokaryotes play in the living world?

Vocabulary

prokaryote
bacillus
coccus
spirillum
binary fission
endospore
conjugation

Taking Notes

Preview Visuals Look at **Figure 20–9.** Describe in your own words the three shapes of prokaryotes shown.

For more on the diversity of Bacteria and Archaea, go to the Visual Guide. **DOL•6–DOL•9.**

THINK ABOUT IT Imagine living all your life as a member of what you believe is the only family on your street. Then, one morning, you open the front door and discover houses all around you. You see neighbors tending their gardens and children walking to school. Where did all the people come from? What if the answer turned out to be that they had always been there—you just hadn't seen them? How would your view of the world change? The sudden appearance of the new neighbors would be quite a shock.

When the microscope was first invented, we humans had just such a shock. Suddenly, the street was very crowded! Far from being alone, we share every corner of our world with microorganisms. Even something that seems clean, like a toothbrush, may be covered with a film of bacteria.

Classifying Prokaryotes

How are prokaryotes classified?

Microscopic life covers nearly every square centimeter of Earth. The smallest and most abundant of these microorganisms are **prokaryotes** (pro KAR ee ohts)—unicellular organisms that lack a nucleus. Prokaryotes have DNA, like all other cells, but their DNA is not found in a membrane-bound nuclear envelope as it is in eukaryotes. Prokaryote DNA is located in the cytoplasm. For many years, most prokaryotes were simply called "bacteria." We now know, however, that the classification of prokaryotes is more complex.

Until recently, all prokaryotes were placed in a single kingdom. More recently, however, biologists have divided prokaryotes into two very distinct groups: Bacteria and Archaea. These groups are as different from each other as both are from eukaryotes. Therefore, biologists now consider each group of prokaryotes as a separate domain. **Prokaryotes are classified as Bacteria or Archaea—two of the three domains of life.** Eukarya is the third domain. The domain Bacteria corresponds to the kingdom Eubacteria. The domain Archaea corresponds to the kingdom Archaebacteria.

UbD Teach for Understanding

ENDURING UNDERSTANDING From microorganisms to plants, organisms vary widely in the way they carry out basic life processes.

GUIDING QUESTION What are prokaryotes, and why are they important?

EVIDENCE OF UNDERSTANDING *After completing the lesson, give students the following assessment to show their understanding of the nature of prokaryotes.* Have students work in small groups to make a **Two-Column Table** describing the four modes of nutrition used by prokaryotes. Students should write the modes of nutrition (heterotroph, photoheterotroph, etc.) on the left side of the table. On the right side, students should describe each mode of nutrition.

Study Wkbks A/B, Appendix S31, Two-Column Table. **Transparencies,** GO16.

FIGURE 20–7 Typical Bacterial Structure A bacterium such as *E. coli* has the basic structure typical of most prokaryotes. *E. coli* also has an outer membrane composed of lipids. This outer membrane is not present in all bacteria. The micrograph shows *E. coli* undergoing binary fission, with pili visible.

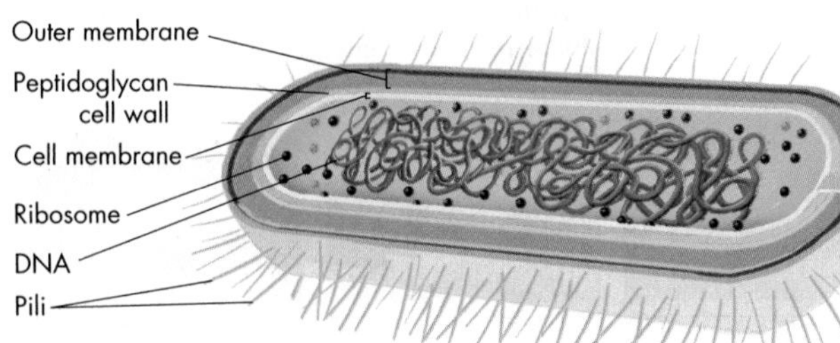

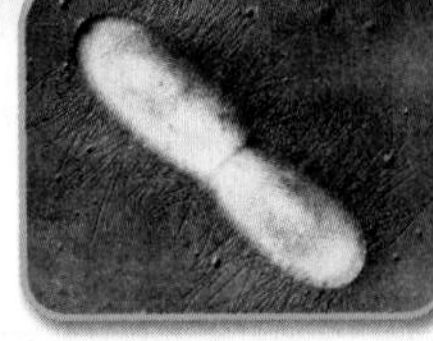

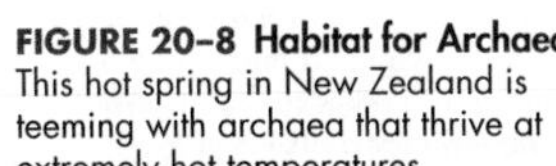

Bacteria The larger of the two domains of prokaryotes is the Bacteria. Bacteria include a wide range of organisms with lifestyles so different that biologists do not agree exactly how many phyla are needed to classify this group. Bacteria live almost everywhere. They live in fresh water, in salt water, on land, and on and within the bodies of humans and other eukaryotes. **Figure 20–7** shows a diagram of *Escherichia coli,* a typical bacterium that lives in human intestines.

Bacteria are usually surrounded by a cell wall that protects the cell from injury and determines its shape. The cell walls of bacteria contain peptidoglycan—a polymer of sugars and amino acids that surrounds the cell membrane. Some bacteria, such as *E. coli,* have a second membrane outside the peptidoglycan wall that makes the cell especially resistant to damage. In addition, some prokaryotes have flagella that they use for movement, or pili (PY ly; singular: pilus), which in *E. coli* serve mainly to anchor the bacterium to a surface or to other bacteria.

Archaea Under a microscope, archaea look very similar to bacteria. Both are equally small, lack nuclei, and have cell walls, but there are important differences. For instance, the walls of archaea lack peptidoglycan, and their membranes contain different lipids. Also, the DNA sequences of key archaea genes are more like those of eukaryotes than those of bacteria. Based on these and other observations, scientists have concluded that archaea and eukaryotes are related more closely to each other than to bacteria.

Many archaea live in extremely harsh environments. One group of archaea produce methane gas and live in environments with little or no oxygen, such as thick mud and the digestive tracts of animals. Other archaea live in extremely salty environments, such as Utah's Great Salt Lake, or in hot springs where temperatures approach the boiling point of water.

FIGURE 20–8 Habitat for Archaea This hot spring in New Zealand is teeming with archaea that thrive at extremely hot temperatures.

In Your Notebook *Create a Venn diagram in which you compare and contrast the characteristics of bacteria and archaea.*

Teach

Lead a Discussion

Have students examine **Figure 20–7** and then read the descriptions of bacteria and archaea.

Ask How would a diagram of an archaean be similar to **Figure 20–7?** *(Like the bacterium, the archaean would lack a nucleus. It would also have a cell wall.)*

Ask How would a diagram of an archaean be different from **Figure 20–7?** *(The cell wall would be labeled differently, because archaea do not have peptidoglycan in their cell walls.)*

DIFFERENTIATED INSTRUCTION

LPR **Less Proficient Readers** Point out to students the blue heads used to identify the topics discussed on this page. Have students work in pairs to find the information in the text explaining how archaea are similar to and different from bacteria. Suggest they take notes on that information. Then, have students use their notes to complete the Venn diagram for the In Your Notebook. Finally, students can use their Venn diagram to answer the questions above.

L3 **Advanced Students** The questions suggested for discusison above focus on comparing bacteria and archaea. Have students extend their comparisons to include eukaryotic cells. Remind students that Chapter 7 includes information about eukaryotic cells. Have students summarize their comparisons in a paragraph and share their completed paragraphs with the class.

BIOLOGY.com **Art Review: Prokaryote Structure and Classification** will enable students to reinforce their understanding of prokaryote structure.

Biology In-Depth

COW GUT ARCHAEA AND THE ATMOSPHERE

Some species of archaea are found in the digestive tracts of grazing animals such as cows. There, the symbiotic gut microbes help digest cellulose into a form usable by the animal. These archaea, called methanogens, are chemoautotrophs that use hydrogren and carbon to produce methane (CH_4). When a cow burps, methane is released into the air. In the atmosphere, the methane reacts with oxygen to produce CO_2, a greenhouse gas. Methane itself is also a significant greenhouse agent, being over 20 times more effective at trapping heat than carbon dioxide. According to the U.S. Environmental Protection Agency, over 80 million metric tons of methane are produced from ruminant livestock annually—about 28% of global methane emissions from human-related activities.

Answers

IN YOUR NOTEBOOK Similarities include lack of a nucleus and presence of cell walls. Differences include the fact that cell walls of archaea lack peptidoglycan, and that archaea have DNA that is more similar to eukaryotic DNA than to bacterial DNA.

Teach continued

Build Study Skills

Point out to students the Key Question and Key Concept printed in bold near the top of the page. Tell students that a **Main Ideas and Details Chart** can be used to develop an organized summary of the information about variations in the structure and function of prokaryotes. Have students list ways prokaryotes vary *(size and shape, movement, method of obtaining energy, method of releasing energy)* in the Main Ideas column of the chart. Have students add details in the right column for each main idea.

Study Wkbks A and B, Appendix S28, Main Ideas and Details Chart. **Transparencies,** GO13.

DIFFERENTIATED INSTRUCTION

L1 Struggling Students Have students work with a small group or partner to complete the **Main Ideas and Details Chart.** Help students locate the required information in the text, and check their work frequently to ensure they are progressing.

ELL Focus on ELL: Extend Language

INTERMEDIATE, ADVANCED, AND ADVANCED HIGH SPEAKERS Help students differentiate among the methods of energy capture used by prokaryotes by reviewing the word parts that make up the terms used to describe these organisms. On the board, write the following:

- *auto* = "self"
- *chemo* = "chemical"
- *photo* = "light"
- *hetero* = "other"
- *troph* = "nourishment"

Have students use this information to develop definitions for the terms used in **Figure 20–10.** Intermediate and advanced speakers should use phrases or sentences in their definitions. Encourage advanced high speakers to identify and define other English words that use these word parts—for example, *autobiography, chemistry, photography, heterozygous, atrophy.*

Answers

FIGURE 20–10 A photoautotroph uses only light as its energy source.

Structure and Function

How do prokaryotes vary in their structure and function?

Because prokaryotes are so small, it may seem hard to tell them apart. **Prokaryotes vary in their size and shape, in the way they move, and in the way they obtain and release energy.**

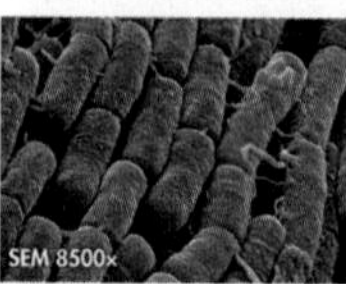

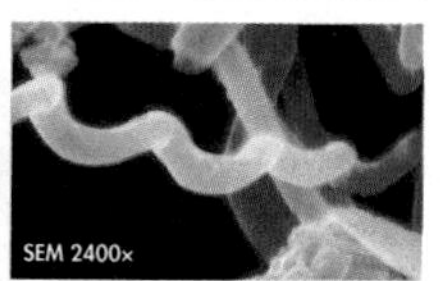

FIGURE 20–9 Prokaryotic Shapes Prokaryotes usually have one of three basic shapes: bacilli (left), cocci (middle), or spirilla (right).

Size, Shape, and Movement Prokaryotes range in size from 1 to 5 micrometers, making them much smaller than most eukaryotic cells. Prokaryotes come in a variety of shapes, as shown in **Figure 20–9.** Rod-shaped prokaryotes are called **bacilli** (buh SIL eye; singular: bacillus). Spherical prokaryotes are called **cocci** (KAHK sy; singular: coccus). Spiral and corkscrew-shaped prokaryotes are called **spirilla** (spy RIL uh; singular: spirillum). You can also distinguish prokaryotes by whether they move and how they move. Some prokaryotes do not move at all. Others are propelled by flagella. Some glide slowly along a layer of slimelike material they secrete.

Nutrition and Metabolism Like all organisms, prokaryotes need a supply of chemical energy, which they store in the form of fuel molecules such as sugars. Energy is released from these fuel molecules during cellular respiration, fermentation, or both. The diverse ways prokaryotes obtain and release energy are summarized in **Figure 20–10.** Notice that some species are able to change their method of energy capture or release depending on the conditions of their environment.

FIGURE 20–10 Energy Capture and Release by Prokaryotes Prokaryotes vary in the ways they obtain energy and the ways they release it. **Interpret Tables** ***What is the term for a prokaryote that uses only light as its energy source?***

Energy Capture by Prokaryotes

Mode of Nutrition	How Energy Is Captured	Habitat	Example
Heterotroph "other feeder"	Take in organic molecules from environment or other organisms to use as both energy and carbon supply	Wide range of environments	*Clostridium*
Photoheterotroph "light and other feeder"	Like basic heterotrophs, but also use light energy	Where light is plentiful	*Rhodobacter, Chloroflexus*
Photoautotroph "light self-feeder"	Use light energy to convert CO_2 into carbon compounds	Where light is plentiful	*Anabaena*
Chemoautotroph "chemical self-feeder"	Use energy released by chemical reactions involving ammonia, hydrogen sulfide, etc.	In chemically harsh and/or dark environments: deep in the ocean, in thick mud, in digestive tracts of animals, in boiling hot springs	*Nitrosomonas* ▼ SEM 3000×

UbD Check for Understanding

HAND SIGNALS

Present students with the following questions, and ask them to show a thumbs-up sign if they can answer, a thumbs-down sign if they are confused, or a waving-hand sign if they can partially answer.

- What are three shapes of prokaryotes?
- What are some different methods by which prokaryotes move?
- What are some ways prokaryotes capture energy?

ADJUST INSTRUCTION

Write on the board any question that received a thumbs-down signal from many students. Have each student choose one of the questions from the board and locate the answer in the text. Then, ask a volunteer to read the answer.

LESSON 20.2

Growth, Reproduction, and Recombination When a prokaryote has grown so that it has nearly doubled in size, it replicates its DNA and divides in half, producing two identical cells. This type of reproduction is known as **binary fission.** Because binary fission does not involve the exchange or recombination of genetic information, it is a form of asexual reproduction. When conditions are favorable, prokaryotes can grow and divide at astonishing rates. Some divide as often as once every 20 minutes!

When growth conditions become unfavorable, many prokaryotic cells form an **endospore**—a thick internal wall that encloses the DNA and a portion of the cytoplasm. Endospores can remain dormant for months or even years. The ability to form endospores makes it possible for some prokaryotes to survive very harsh conditions. The bacterium *Bacillus anthracis,* which causes the disease anthrax, is one such bacterium.

As in any organism, adaptations that increase the survival and reproduction of a particular prokaryote are favored. Recall that in organisms that reproduce sexually, genes are shuffled and recombined during meiosis. But prokaryotes reproduce asexually. So, how do their populations evolve?

▶ ***Mutation*** Mutations are one of the main ways prokaryotes evolve. Recall from Chapter 13 that mutations are random changes in DNA that occur in all organisms. In prokaryotes, mutations are inherited by daughter cells produced by binary fission.

▶ ***Conjugation*** Many prokaryotes exchange genetic information by a process called conjugation. During **conjugation,** a hollow bridge forms between two bacterial cells, and genetic material, usually in the form of a plasmid, moves from one cell to the other. Many plasmids carry genes that enable bacteria to survive in new environments or to resist antibiotics that might otherwise prove fatal. This transfer of genetic information increases genetic diversity in populations of prokaryotes.

FIGURE 20–11
Endospore Formation

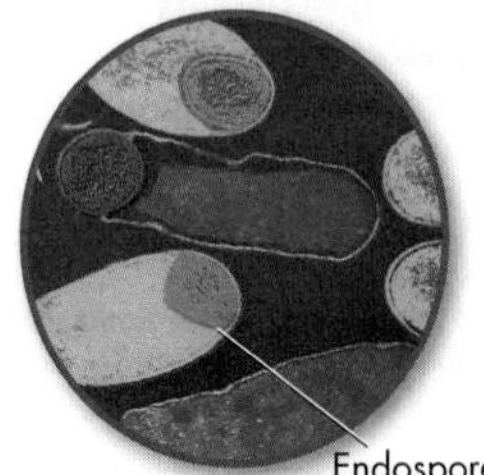

FIGURE 20–12
Conjugation

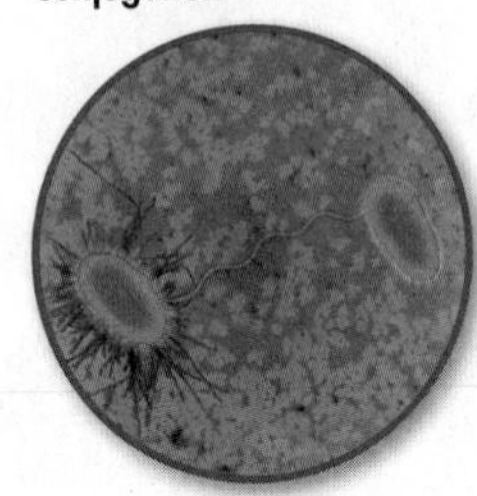

Energy Release by Prokaryotes

Mode of Metabolism	How Energy Is Released	Habitat	Example
Obligate aerobe "requiring oxygen"	Cellular respiration; must have ready supply of O_2 to release fuel energy	Oxygen-rich environments, such as near water surface or in animal lungs	*Mycobacterium tuberculosis*: Sometimes found in human lungs
Obligate anaerobe "requiring a lack of oxygen"	Fermentation; die in presence of oxygen	◀ Environments lacking O_2, such as deep soil, animal intestines, or airtight containers	*Clostridium botulinum*: Sometimes found in improperly sterilized canned food, causing food poisoning
Facultative anaerobe "surviving without oxygen when necessary"	Can use either cellular respiration or fermentation as necessary	Oxygen-rich or oxygen-poor environments	*E. coli*: Lives aerobically in sewage and anaerobically in human large intestine

Lead a Discussion

Use the following questions to help students understand the methods of reproduction and recombination used by prokaryotes.

Ask What process do prokaryotes undergo that results in the formation of two identical cells? *(binary fission)*

Ask What do the processes of mutation and conjugation result in? *(genetic changes in prokaryotes)*

Ask Are mutation and conjugation forms of reproduction? Why or why not? *(No, these processes are not forms of reproduction; they do not result in the formation of daughter cells.)*

DIFFERENTIATED INSTRUCTION

L1 Special Needs Help students master the concepts on this page by writing the following sentences summarizing the results of binary fission, mutation, and conjugation on the board.

- A population of prokaryotes *grows* because of binary fission.
- The genetic makeup of a population of prokaryotes *changes* because of mutation and conjugation.

Read the sentences aloud to students. Focus on the results of the processes of binary fission, mutation, and conjugation, rather than detailed descriptions of the processes themselves.

ELL English Language Learners Point out the word part *bi-* in the term *binary fission*. Use familiar examples of words containing the word part *bi-*, such as *bicycle* and *binoculars*, to help students remember that *bi-* means "two," and binary fission results in two identical cells.

Biology In-Depth

ANTHRAX

Anthrax was brought to national attention in 2001, when *Bacillus anthracis* was used as a weapon of bioterrorism. Anthrax is caused by the bacterium *Bacillus anthracis*. Anthrax typically occurs in animal species such as cattle and sheep. *Bacillus anthracis* can cause three forms of diseases in humans: cutaneous anthrax, which occurs when *Bacillus anthracis* comes in contact with cuts or sores on the skin; gastrointestinal anthrax, which occurs when a person eats meat from an animal infected with *Bacillus anthracis*; and inhalation anthrax, which occurs when airborne *Bacillus anthracis* spores are inhaled.

Teach continued

Connect to Ecology

Have students recall from Chapter 3 the importance of producers and decomposers in food webs and ecosystems.

Ask What type of organism is vital to recycling matter in an ecosystem? *(decomposer)*

Ask What type of organism is found at the base of every food web? *(producer)*

DIFFERENTIATED INSTRUCTION

L3 Advanced Students Have students review Chapter 3 and do additional research to learn about the role of bacteria in the carbon and nitrogen cycles. Ask students to prepare an oral report to share with the class.

ZOOMING IN

Have students work in small groups to examine the photos of the prokaryotes in **Figure 20–13.** Then, ask students to categorize each type of bacterium as a producer, decomposer, or nitrogen fixer. Finally, have students in each group write a short summary explaining why each of these types of bacteria is vital to the homeostasis of the pond and forest shown. Call on several groups to share their summaries with the class.

Answers

FIGURE 20–13 The ecological relationship between *Rhizobium* bacteria and legume plants is called a symbiosis. The specific form of symbiosis is mutualism, because both the bacteria and the plants benefit.

The Importance of Prokaryotes

What roles do prokaryotes play in the living world?

You may remember the star actors in the last movie you saw, but have you ever stopped to consider whether there would be any film at all without the hundreds of workers who never appear on screen? Prokaryotes are just like those unseen workers. **Prokaryotes are essential in maintaining every aspect of the ecological balance of the living world. In addition, some species have specific uses in human industry.** Three roles played by prokaryotes in the environment are shown in **Figure 20–13.**

Decomposers Every living thing depends on a supply of raw materials for its survival. If these materials were not recovered when organisms died, life could not continue. By assisting in breaking down, or decomposing, dead organisms, prokaryotes supply raw materials and thus help to maintain equilibrium in the environment. Bacterial decomposers are also essential to industrial sewage treatment, helping to produce purified water and chemicals that can be used as fertilizers.

Producers Photosynthetic prokaryotes are among the most important producers on the planet. The tiny cyanobacterium *Prochlorococcus* is probably the most abundant photosynthetic organism in the world. This species alone may account for more than half of the primary production in the open ocean. Food chains everywhere are dependent upon prokaryotes as producers of food and biomass.

ZOOMING IN

FIGURE 20–13 Ecological Roles Played by Prokaryotes Prokaryotes play important roles in the environment as decomposers, producers, and nitrogen fixers. **Apply Concepts** ***What is the name of the type of ecological relationship found between Rhizobium bacteria and legume plants?***

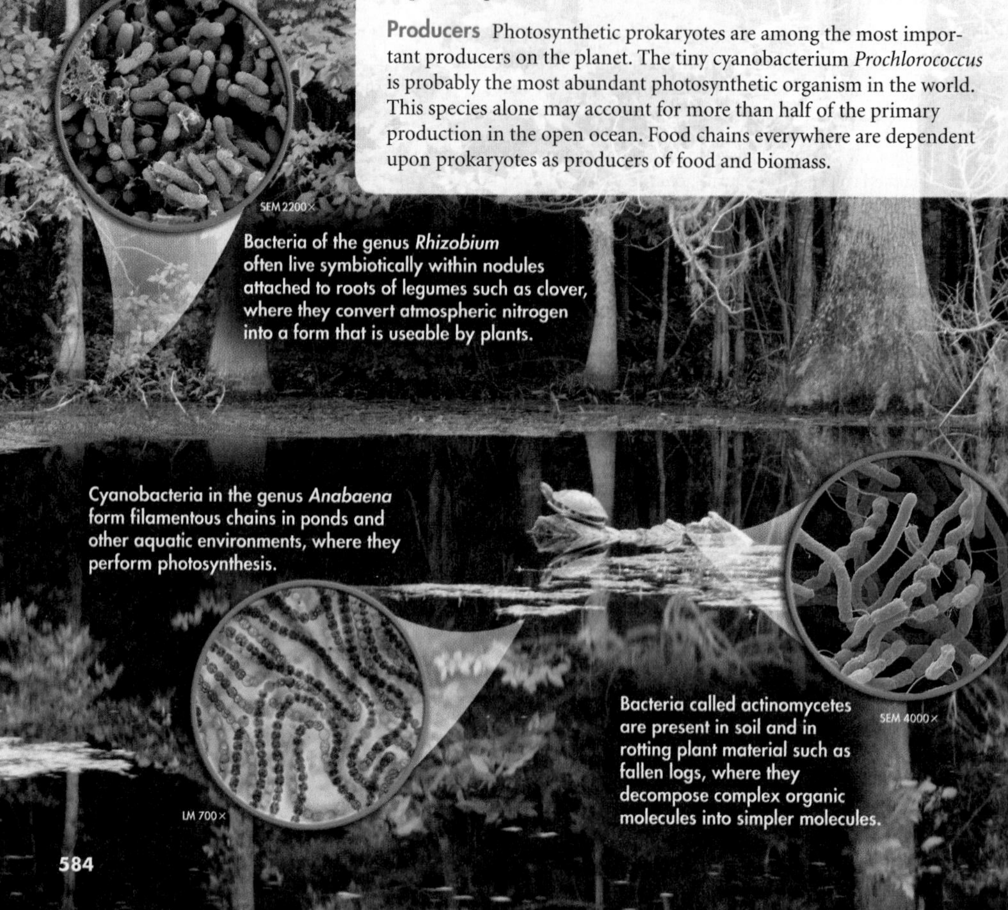

SEM 2200×
Bacteria of the genus *Rhizobium* often live symbiotically within nodules attached to roots of legumes such as clover, where they convert atmospheric nitrogen into a form that is useable by plants.
Cyanobacteria in the genus *Anabaena* form filamentous chains in ponds and other aquatic environments, where they perform photosynthesis.
LM 700×
SEM 4000×
Bacteria called actinomycetes are present in soil and in rotting plant material such as fallen logs, where they decompose complex organic molecules into simpler molecules.

584

UbD Check for Understanding

ORAL QUESTIONING

Use the following prompts to gauge students' understanding of lesson concepts.

- What is an example of a role prokaryotes play in ecosystems?
- What might happen if all of the bacteria in an ecosystem died?

ADJUST INSTRUCTION

If responses are incorrect or incomplete, remind students that producers, decomposers, and nitrogen fixers are vital to the flow of energy and cycles of matter in ecosystems. Refer students to Chapter 3 to review this information, if necessary.

Nitrogen Fixers All organisms need nitrogen to make proteins and other molecules. But while nitrogen gas (N_2) makes up 80 percent of Earth's atmosphere, only a few kinds of organisms—all of them prokaryotes—can convert N_2 into useful forms. The process of nitrogen fixation converts nitrogen gas into ammonia (NH_3). Ammonia can then be converted to nitrates that plants use, or attached to amino acids that all organisms use. Nitrogen-fixing bacteria and archaea provide 90 percent of the nitrogen used by other organisms. The rest is provided by nitrogen-containing compounds from weathering rocks. Some even comes when lightning combines oxygen and nitrogen in the atmosphere.

Some plants even have symbiotic relationships with nitrogen-fixing prokaryotes. The bacterium *Rhizobium* grows in nodules, or knobs, on the roots of legume plants such as clover and soybean. The *Rhizobium* bacteria within these nodules convert nitrogen in the air into the nitrogen compounds essential for plant growth. In effect, these plants have fertilizer factories in their roots!

FIGURE 20–14 ***Rhizobium*** These soybean root nodules contain *Rhizobium* bacteria.

In Your Notebook *Outline three important functions of prokaryotes in the environment. Fill in supporting details for each of these functions.*

Human Uses of Prokaryotes Prokaryotes, especially bacteria, are used in the production of a wide variety of foods and other commercial products. For example, yogurt is produced by the bacterium *Lactobacillus*. Some bacteria can even digest petroleum and remove human-made waste products and poisons from water. Others are used to synthesize drugs and chemicals through the techniques of genetic engineering.

Biologists continue to discover new uses for prokaryotes. For example, bacteria and archaea adapted to extreme environments may be a rich source of heat-stable enzymes that can be used in medicine, food production, and industrial chemistry.

20.2 Assessment

IN B.4.4, B.8.2

Review Key Concepts

1. a. **Review** Which two domains of life contain only prokaryotes?
   b. **Interpret Diagrams** Review **Figure 20–7.** Which feature of the cell wall is characteristic of bacteria but not of archaea?
2. a. **Review** In what ways do prokaryotes differ from one another?
   b. **Evaluate** Review **Figure 20–10.** Which category of prokaryote is the most flexible in the energy sources it can use? Explain.
3. a. **Review** List three ecological roles played by prokaryotes.
   b. **Explain** Why are nitrogen-fixing bacteria so important?
   c. **Apply Concepts** Many farmers practice "crop rotation" by planting a field with corn one year and soybeans the next. Why might they do this?

WRITE ABOUT SCIENCE

Description

4. Suppose a new bacterial species is discovered that is spherical in shape, survives drought by forming a thick outer wall, and cannot survive without oxygen. Using vocabulary terms from this lesson, describe this species to a scientific audience.

BIOLOGY.com Search  Lesson 20.2 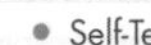 GO • Self-Test • Lesson Assessment

Assessment Answers

1a. Bacteria, Archaea

1b. peptidoglycan

2a. They differ in their size and shape, in the way they move, and in the way they obtain and release energy.

2b. Photoheterotrophs are most flexible in the energy source they use; they can use organic molecules from the environment or other organisms as well as light energy.

3a. decomposers, producers, nitrogen fixers

3b. Nitrogen-fixing bacteria and archaea produce 90 percent of the nitrogen used by other organisms.

3c. Nitrogen-fixing bacteria are found in nodules on the roots of soybeans, but not on the roots of corn. Rotating crops keeps nitrogen from being depleted from the soil.

WRITE ABOUT SCIENCE

4. Students' descriptions should use the following terms: *coccus*, *endospore*, and *obligate aerobe*.

Lead a Discussion

Help students understand the importance of the process of nitrogen fixation.

Ask How do humans and other animals get the nitrogen they need to make proteins? *(They eat plants or animals that have eaten plants. Plants get nitrogen from nitrogen-fixing bacteria.)*

DIFFERENTIATED INSTRUCTION

ELL English Language Learners The term *nitrogen fixation* may lead students to the conclusion prokaryotes somehow repair nitrogen, or that nitrogen is "broken" before nitrogen fixation occurs. Explain that the term *nitrogen fixation* describes the chemical process in which N_2 is converted to NH_3.

Assess and Remediate

EVALUATE UNDERSTANDING

Have students work in small groups to develop three quiz questions about the structures or functions of prokaryotes. Have each group use its questions to quiz the class. Then, have students complete the 20.2 Assessment.

REMEDIATION SUGGESTION

LPR Less Proficient Readers Help students locate information in the text about the cell walls of archaea, if they are struggling to answer **Question 1b.**

BIOLOGY.com Students can check their understanding of lesson concepts with the **Self-Test** assessment. They can then take an online version of the **Lesson Assessment.**

Answers

IN YOUR NOTEBOOK Students' responses should identify the functions of prokaryotes as decomposers, producers, and nitrogen fixers and provide details about each of these functions.

LESSON 20.3

Getting Started

Objectives

20.3.1 Explain how bacteria cause disease.

20.3.2 Explain how viruses cause disease.

20.3.3 Define emerging disease and explain why emerging diseases are a threat to human health.

Student Resources

Study Workbooks A and B, 20.3 Worksheets

Spanish Study Workbook, 20.3 Worksheets

Lab Manual B, 20.3 Data Analysis Worksheet

Lesson Overview • Lesson Notes • Activities: Data Analysis, Art in Motion • Assessment: Self-Test, Lesson Assessment

For corresponding lesson in the **Foundation Edition,** see pages 489-493.

Build Background

Ask students to identify some diseases and disorders affecting humans. List their responses on the board. Explain that bacteria and viruses are two causes of disease, but many other causes exist, such as fungal, genetic, and environmental hazards.

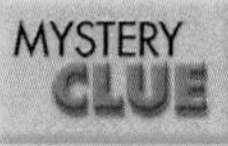

Explain to students that most bacteria cannot survive sterilization at high temperatures. This should lead them to conclude bacteria are unlikely to be the cause of BSE. Students can go online to Biology.com to gather their evidence.

IN INDIANA ACADEMIC STANDARDS

For the full text of all standards, see the Course Overview in the front matter of this book.

NoS.3 Clearly communicate their ideas and results of investigations verbally and in written form using tables, graphs, diagrams, and photographs.

Diseases Caused by Bacteria and Viruses

Key Questions

How do bacteria cause disease?

How do viruses cause disease?

Why are emerging diseases particularly threatening to human health?

Vocabulary

pathogen • vaccine • antibiotic • emerging disease • prion

Taking Notes

Outline Use the green and blue heads in this lesson to create an outline. Fill in details as you read the lesson.

The meat and bone meal substances added to cattle feed in Britain were sterilized at high temperatures (in excess of 100°C) during processing. What does this suggest about the possibility that bacteria are the cause of BSE?

THINK ABOUT IT We share this planet with prokaryotes and viruses, and most of the time we are never aware of our relationships with them. Often, these relationships are highly beneficial, but in a few cases, sharing simply doesn't work—and disease is the result.

Bacterial Diseases

How do bacteria cause disease?

Microorganisms—viruses and prokaryotes—that cause disease are called **pathogens.** All currently known prokaryotic pathogens are bacteria. This is why the discussion here is restricted to pathogenic bacteria, and it excludes archaea. However, in the future scientists may well discover that some archaea are associated with disease.

The French chemist Louis Pasteur was the first person to show convincingly that bacteria cause disease. Pasteur helped to establish what has become known as the *germ theory of disease* when he showed that bacteria were responsible for a number of human and animal diseases.

Disease Mechanisms Bacteria produce disease in one of two general ways. **Bacteria cause disease by destroying living cells or by releasing chemicals that upset homeostasis.** Some bacteria destroy living cells and tissues of the infected organism directly, while some cause tissue damage when they provoke a response from the immune system. Other bacteria release toxins (poisons) that interfere with the normal activity of the host. **Figure 20–15** lists some common human diseases caused by bacteria.

▶ ***Damaging Host Tissue*** One example of a bacterial pathogen that damages host tissue is the bacterium that causes tuberculosis. This pathogen is inhaled into the lungs, where its growth triggers an immune response that can destroy large areas of tissue. The bacterium also may enter a blood vessel and travel to other sites in the body, causing similar damage.

▶ ***Releasing Toxins*** Bacteria that produce toxins include the species that causes diphtheria, and the species responsible for a deadly form of food poisoning known as botulism. Diphtheria has largely been eliminated in developed countries by vaccination, but outbreaks of botulism still claim many lives.

Search Lesson 20.3

• Lesson Overview • Lesson Notes

UbD Teach for Understanding

ENDURING UNDERSTANDING From microorganisms to plants, organisms vary widely in the way they carry out basic life processes.

GUIDING QUESTION How can we prevent bacterial and viral diseases from spreading?

EVIDENCE OF UNDERSTANDING *After completing the lesson, give students the following assessment to show their understanding of diseases caused by bacteria and viruses.* Have students write a letter from the point of view of a specific bacterium or virus, explaining how it causes disease in humans.

Some Human Bacterial Diseases

Disease	Effect on Body	Transmission
Lyme disease	"Bull's-eye" rash at site of tick bite, fever, fatigue, headache	Ticks transmit the bacterium *Borrelia burgdorferi.* ▶
Tetanus	Lockjaw, stiffness in neck and abdomen, difficulty swallowing, fever, elevated blood pressure, severe muscle spasms	Bacteria enter the body through a break in the skin.
Tuberculosis	Fatigue, weight loss, fever, night sweats, chills, appetite loss, bloody sputum from lungs	Bacteria particles are inhaled.
Bacterial meningitis	High fever, headache, stiff neck, nausea, fatigue	Bacteria are spread in respiratory droplets caused by coughing and sneezing; close or prolonged contact with someone infected with meningitis
Strep throat	Fever, sore throat, headache, fatigue, nausea	Direct contact with mucus from an infected person or direct contact with infected wounds or breaks in the skin

SEM 7300×

FIGURE 20–15 Common Human Bacterial Diseases Some common bacterial diseases are shown in the table above. **Infer** ***Why do bacterial meningitis outbreaks sometimes occur in college dormitories?***

BUILD Vocabulary

WORD ORIGINS Pathogen comes from the Greek words *pathos,* meaning "suffering," and *genes,* meaning "produced."

Controlling Bacteria Although most bacteria are harmless, and many are beneficial, the everyday risks of any person acquiring a bacterial infection are great enough to warrant efforts to control bacterial growth. Various control methods are used.

▶ ***Physical Removal*** Washing hands or other surfaces with soap under running water doesn't kill pathogens, but it helps dislodge both bacteria and viruses.

▶ ***Disinfectants*** Chemical solutions that kill bacteria can be used to clean bathrooms, kitchens, hospital rooms, and other places where bacteria may flourish.

▶ ***Food Storage*** Low temperatures, like those inside a refrigerator, will slow the growth of bacteria and keep most foods fresher for a longer period of time than possible at room temperature.

▶ ***Food Processing*** Boiling, frying, or steaming can sterilize many kinds of food by raising the temperature of the food to a point where bacteria are killed.

▶ ***Sterilization by Heat*** Sterilization of objects such as medical instruments at temperatures well above 100° Celsius can prevent the growth of potentially dangerous bacteria. Most bacteria cannot survive such temperatures.

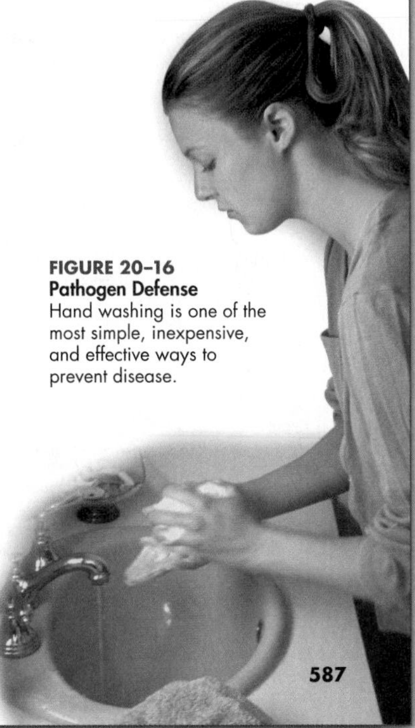

FIGURE 20–16 Pathogen Defense Hand washing is one of the most simple, inexpensive, and effective ways to prevent disease.

In Your Notebook *Relate the methods for controlling bacteria listed above to your everyday life. Which methods have you used this week? Give specific details.*

Teach

Build Study Skills

Use a **Gallery Walk** to enhance students' understanding of how bacteria produce disease, what diseases are caused by bacteria, and how bacteria can be controlled. Divide the class into four groups. Have the groups rotate around the following posted questions:

- How do bacteria cause disease?
- What are some specific diseases caused by bacteria?
- What are some ways bacteria can be controlled?
- How can bacterial diseases be prevented or treated?

Groups should write responses to each question on a paper they carry with them. When students return to their original positions, have them summarize information about that topic for the rest of the class.

Study Wkbks A and B, Appendix S6, Gallery Walk.

DIFFERENTIATED INSTRUCTION

L1 Special Needs Within each group participating in the **Gallery Walk,** pair special needs students with students who have strong reading and study skills. At each question station, have these students work together to find the information required and answer the question.

Quick Facts

BACTERIAL TOXINS

The release of toxins is one mechanism by which bacteria cause disease. Bacterial toxins are usually divided into two groups: exotoxins and endotoxins. Exotoxins are produced and released as part of the normal metabolism of certain bacteria. Endotoxins are typically lipopolysaccharides that were originally part of the bacterium's cell wall and are released by the lysis of the bacterium. In general, exotoxins are much more potent than endotoxins. Diseases caused by exotoxins include botulism, cholera, diphtheria, tetanus, and scarlet fever.

Answers

FIGURE 20–15 Bacterial meningitis spreads among students in college dormitories because the students are in continued close contact.

IN YOUR NOTEBOOK Students' responses should include a specific, detailed description of how they have used one or more of the listed methods to control the growth of bacteria, for example, washing their hands, storing food in the fridge, or cooking their food thoroughly.

LESSON 20.3

Teach continued

Build Science Skills

Have students use a **Venn Diagram** to compare and contrast bacterial diseases and viral diseases. Circulate among students as they work, to help them locate pertinent information in the text.

Study Wkbks A and B, Appendix S33, Venn Diagram. **Transparencies,** GO18.

DIFFERENTIATED INSTRUCTION

LPR Less Proficient Readers Pair struggling readers with strong readers to find the information necessary to complete their **Venn Diagrams.** Remind students to use the green and blue headings in the text to help locate information.

ELL Focus on ELL: Build Background

INTERMEDIATE, ADVANCED, AND ADVANCED HIGH SPEAKERS Write the following questions on the board:

- How do viruses cause disease?
- How can viral diseases be prevented?
- How can viral diseases be treated?

Read the questions aloud to students, and ask them to respond, based on what they already know about viruses. After students have read the information about viruses in the text, ask them these questions again. Encourage advanced and advanced high speakers to use complete sentences when answering. Point out differences in students' responses before and after reading. Ask advanced high speakers to use these differences to write brief summaries of what they learned about viruses.

Preventing Bacterial Diseases Many bacterial diseases can be prevented by stimulating the body's immune system with vaccines. A **vaccine** is a preparation of weakened or killed pathogens or inactivated toxins. When injected into the body, a vaccine prompts the body to produce immunity to a specific disease. Immunity is the body's ability to destroy pathogens or inactivated toxins.

Treating Bacterial Diseases A number of drugs can be used to attack a bacterial infection. These drugs include **antibiotics,** such as penicillin and tetracycline, that block the growth and reproduction of bacteria. Antibiotics disrupt proteins or cell processes that are specific to bacterial cells. In this way, they do not harm the host's cells.

Viral Diseases

How do viruses cause disease?

Like bacteria, viruses produce disease by disrupting the body's normal homeostasis. **Figure 20–17** lists some common human diseases caused by viruses. Viruses produce serious animal and plant diseases as well.

Disease Mechanisms In many viral infections, viruses attack and destroy certain cells in the body, causing the symptoms of the associated disease. Poliovirus, for example, destroys cells in the nervous system, producing paralysis. Other viruses cause infected cells to change their patterns of growth and development, sometimes leading to cancer. **Viruses cause disease by directly destroying living cells or by affecting cellular processes in ways that upset homeostasis.**

FIGURE 20–17 Common Human Viral Diseases Some common viral diseases are shown in the table below. Interpret Tables ***Which virus can cause cancer?***

Some Human Viral Diseases

Disease	Effect on Body	Transmission
Common cold	Sneezing, sore throat, fever, headache, muscle aches	Contact with contaminated objects; droplet inhalation
Influenza	Body aches, fever, sore throat, headache, dry cough, fatigue, nasal congestion	Flu viruses spread in respiratory droplets caused by coughing and sneezing.
AIDS (HIV)	Helper T cells, which are needed for normal immune-system function, are destroyed.	Sexual contact; contact with contaminated blood or body fluids; can be passed to babies during delivery or during breastfeeding.
Chicken pox	Skin rash of blisterlike lesions	Virus particles are spread in respiratory droplets caused by coughing and sneezing; highly contagious
Hepatitis B	Jaundice, fatigue, abdominal pain, nausea, vomiting, joint pain	Contact with contaminated blood or bodily fluids
West Nile Virus	Fever, headache, body ache	Bite from an infected mosquito ▶
Human papillomavirus (HPV)	Genital or anal warts, also cancer of the cervix, penis, and anus	Sexual contact

UbD Check for Understanding

INDEX CARD SUMMARIES/QUESTIONS

Give students each an index card. Ask them to write one concept about bacterial or viral diseases they understand on the front of the card. Then, have students identify something about bacterial or viral diseases they do not understand, and write it on the back in the form of a question.

ADJUST INSTRUCTION

Read over students' cards to get a sense of which concepts they understand well and what they are struggling with. Choose several representative questions from students' responses. Write the questions on the board. Have each student become an "expert" on one of the questions on the board. Call on several "experts" to share a response to each question.

Answers

FIGURE 20–17 human papillomavirus

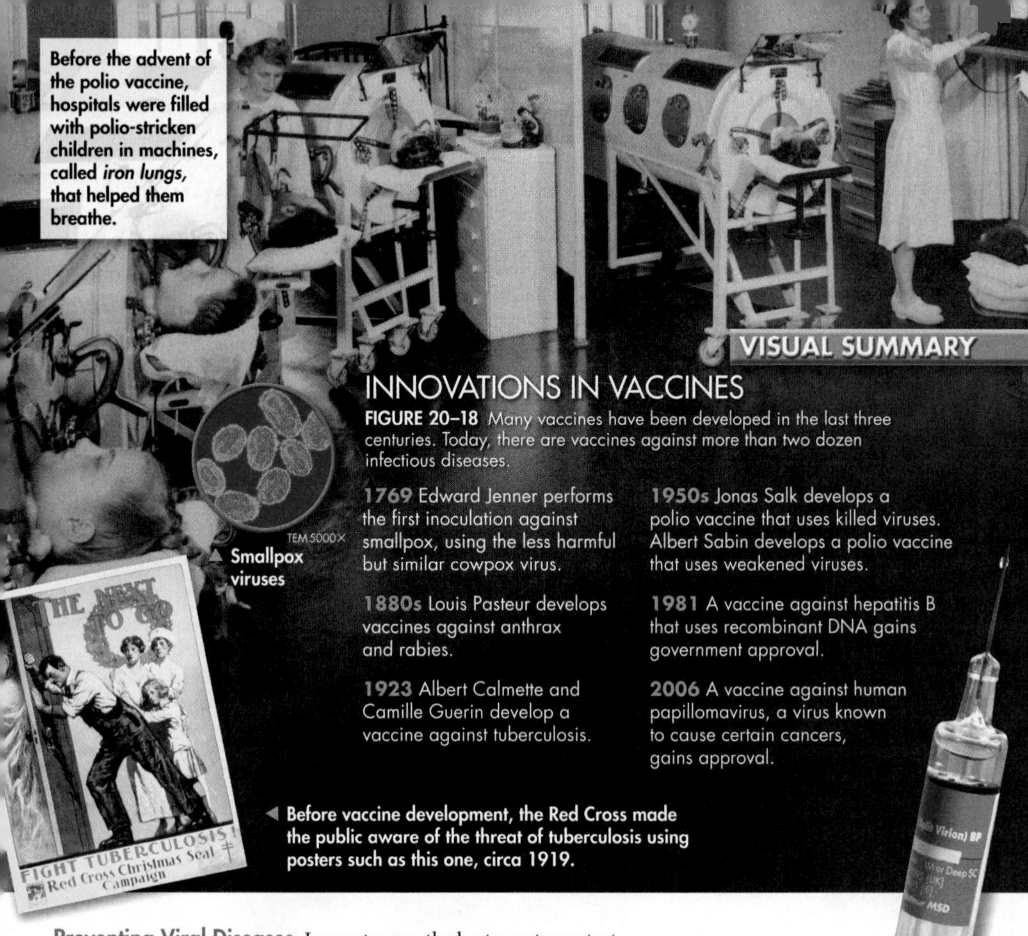
THE NEXT TO GO
FIGHT TUBERCULOSIS
Red Cross Christmas Seal Campaign

Before the advent of the polio vaccine, hospitals were filled with polio-stricken children in machines, called *iron lungs*, that helped them breathe.

Smallpox viruses TEM 5000×

VISUAL SUMMARY

INNOVATIONS IN VACCINES

FIGURE 20–18 Many vaccines have been developed in the last three centuries. Today, there are vaccines against more than two dozen infectious diseases.

1769 Edward Jenner performs the first inoculation against smallpox, using the less harmful but similar cowpox virus.

1880s Louis Pasteur develops vaccines against anthrax and rabies.

1923 Albert Calmette and Camille Guerin develop a vaccine against tuberculosis.

1950s Jonas Salk develops a polio vaccine that uses killed viruses. Albert Sabin develops a polio vaccine that uses weakened viruses.

1981 A vaccine against hepatitis B that uses recombinant DNA gains government approval.

2006 A vaccine against human papillomavirus, a virus known to cause certain cancers, gains approval.

Before vaccine development, the Red Cross made the public aware of the threat of tuberculosis using posters such as this one, circa 1919.

Preventing Viral Diseases In most cases, the best way to protect against most viral diseases lies in prevention, often by the use of vaccines. Some historical milestones in vaccine development are shown in **Figure 20–18.** Personal hygiene matters, too. Recent studies show that cold and flu viruses are often transmitted by hand-to-mouth contact. Effective ways to help prevent infection include washing your hands frequently, avoiding contact with sick individuals, and coughing or sneezing into a tissue or your sleeve, not into your hands.

Treating Viral Diseases Unlike bacterial diseases, viral diseases cannot be treated with antibiotics. In recent years, however, limited progress has been made in developing a handful of antiviral drugs that attack specific viral enzymes that host cells do not have. These treatments include an antiviral medication that can help speed recovery from the flu virus, and others that have helped prolong the lives of people infected with HIV.

Biology In-Depth

THE HISTORY OF SMALLPOX

In 1980, the World Health Organization announced that the smallpox virus had been eradicated. Smallpox was the cause of many epidemics throughout history, and as recently as 1967, it caused 2 million deaths worldwide. Smallpox has been eliminated in the human population, but the virus does still exist in culture in two laboratories—the Centers for Disease Control and Prevention and a laboratory in Russia. Due to the length of time since smallpox was eliminated, routine vaccination for smallpox is no longer carried out. In the event that the smallpox virus is reintroduced into the population of the United States, enough vaccine exists for all who would need it.

VISUAL SUMMARY

Have students use **Figure 20–18** to learn more about vaccines.

Ask Why are you unlikely to know anyone in your age group who has suffered from polio? *(The vaccine for this disease has been in existence for many years.)*

Ask What do you expect will happen to the incidence of cancers caused by human papillomavirus over the next 50 years? Explain. *(The incidence will likely decrease, due to the recent development of the vaccine for this virus.)*

Ask What advantage do vaccines have over antibiotic and antiviral drugs? *(Vaccines actually prevent the occurrence of a disease; antibiotics and antiviral drugs treat an existing disease.)*

DIFFERENTIATED INSTRUCTION

L3 Advanced Students Have students research the ongoing effort to develop a vaccine to prevent HIV. Have students share what they learn with the class in an informal discussion session.

Address Misconceptions

Vaccines The Centers for Disease Control and Prevention have identified six common misconceptions about vaccines. One of these misconceptions is that vaccines have serious, harmful side effects including illness and death. Although some vaccines are associated with mild side effects, such as soreness at the injection site and low fever, severe side effects are exceedingly rare. Students may find Web sites that use information from the Vaccine Adverse Event Reporting System to misrepresent the safety record of vaccines. Explain that events reported through this system do not necessarily have a causal link to a vaccine. Anyone can report adverse events through this Web site, and it takes further study to conclude if a vaccine caused the effects.

LESSON 20.3

Teach continued

Lead a Discussion

Have students examine the map to learn about emerging diseases. When you discuss the diseases indicated on the map, point out that *E. coli* O157:H7 is a strain of the common bacterium *Escherichia coli.* While most strains of *E. coli* are relatively harmless, the O157:H7 strain can cause severe intestinal illness.

Ask What continent is SARS associated with? *(Asia)*

Call students' attention to the fact that some emerging diseases are found in several locations, while some are found primarily in only one location.

Ask Why have emerging diseases become more of a threat recently than they were many years ago? *(High-speed travel and worldwide shipment of goods means an infected individual or contaminated shipment can rapidly spread a disease to distant locations.)*

DIFFERENTIATED INSTRUCTION

L1 Struggling Students Some students might think emerging diseases have a different cause than other diseases described in this lesson, because they are discussed separately in the text. Address this misconception using the following questions.

Ask How are emerging diseases similar to the other diseases described in this lesson? *(They are caused by bacteria or viruses.)*

Ask How do emerging diseases differ from other diseases described in this lesson? *(They have recently emerged or reemerged.)*

Emerging Diseases

Why are emerging diseases particularly threatening to human health?

If pathogenic viruses and bacteria were unable to change over time—that is, if they could not evolve—they would pose far less of a threat than they actually do. Unfortunately, the short time between successive generations of these pathogens allows them to evolve rapidly, especially in response to human efforts to control them. An unknown disease that appears in a population for the first time or a well-known disease that suddenly becomes harder to control is called an **emerging disease.**

Figure 20–19 shows locations worldwide where specific emerging diseases have broken out in recent years. Changes in lifestyle and commerce have made emerging diseases even more of a threat. High-speed travel means that a person can move halfway around the world in a day. Huge quantities of food and consumer goods are now shipped between regions of the world that previously had little contact with each other. This brings human populations that were once isolated by oceans and mountain ranges into close contact with more developed parts of the world. The possibility of the rapid spread of new diseases is a risk of every trip a person takes and every shipment of food or goods.

The pathogens that cause emerging diseases are particularly threatening to human health because human populations have little or no resistance to them, and because methods of control have yet to be developed. Because of their sudden appearance and resistance to existing control methods, emerging diseases are of particular concern. Deeper understanding of the functions of the molecular structures and genetics of bacteria and viruses will be one key to defending against them.

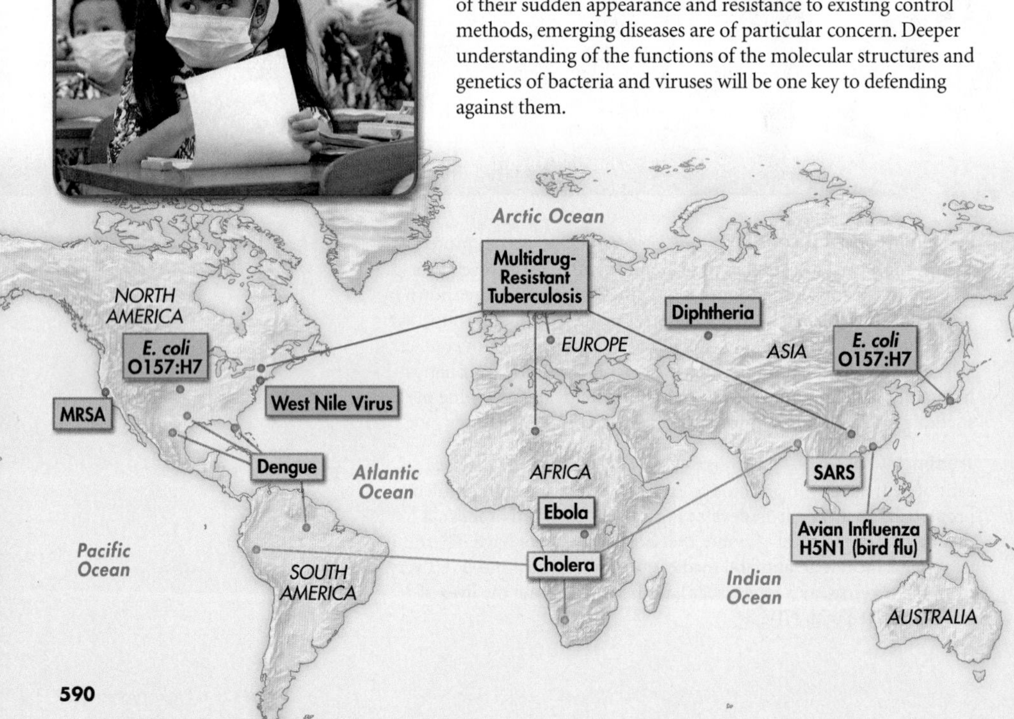

FIGURE 20–19 Emerging Diseases In recent years, new diseases, such as severe acute respiratory syndrome (SARS) in Asia, have appeared. At the same time, some diseases thought to be under control have come back. Both examples are classified as emerging diseases. Interpret Graphics *Which emerging diseases are found in Africa?*

590

UbD Check for Understanding

FOLLOW-UP PROBES

Ask Why are the pathogens that cause emerging diseases particularly threatening to human health? *(Emerging diseases are particularly threatening to human health because humans have little or no resistance to them and because methods to control them have yet to be developed.)*

ADJUST INSTRUCTION

If responses indicate a lack of understanding, have students list ways people can prevent or treat bacterial and viral diseases. *(vaccines, antibiotics, antivirals)* Then, explain that vaccines and medications take years to develop and test. Help students understand that an emerging disease could cause widespread illness or death before an effective treatment could be developed.

Answers

FIGURE 20–19 Ebola, cholera, and multidrug-resistant tuberculosis are emerging diseases found in Africa.

Analyzing Data

NoS.3

MRSA on the Rise

Infection by methicillin-resistant *Staphylococcus aureus* (MRSA) can spread very quickly in hospitals and nursing homes. The table at right shows the incidence of MRSA infections in U.S. hospitals during a 13-year period.

1. Graph Prepare a line graph showing the number of MRSA infections in U.S. hospitals over time. Describe the trend shown.

2. Calculate By what percentage did MRSA infections in U.S. hospitals increase between 1995 and 2005? MATH

3. Draw Conclusions A 2007 study reported that the average hospital stay in the United States lasted 4.6 days, while that of the average MRSA-infected patient was 10.0 days. If the trend shown by the data above continues, what effect will MRSA infections have on future hospital costs?

Incidence of MRSA

Year	Hospital Cases Reported
1993	1900
1995	38,100
1997	69,800
1999	108,600
2001	175,000
2003	248,300
2005	368,600

"Superbugs" When first introduced in the 1940s, penicillin, an antibiotic derived from fungi, was a miracle drug. Patients suffering from life-threatening infections were cured almost immediately by this powerful new drug. Conquest of bacterial diseases seemed to be in sight. Within a few decades, however, penicillin lost much of its effectiveness, as have other, more current antibiotics. The culprit is evolution.

The widespread use of antibiotics has led to a process of natural selection that favors the emergence of resistance to these powerful drugs. Physicians now must fight "superbugs" that are resistant to whole groups of antibiotics and that transfer drug-resistant genes from one bacterium to another through conjugation.

An especially dangerous form of multiple drug resistance has recently appeared in a common bacterium. Methicillin-resistant *Staphylococcus aureus*, known as MRSA (pronounced MURS uh), can cause infections that are especially difficult to control. MRSA skin infections can be spread by close contact, including the sharing of personal items such as towels and athletic gear, and can often spread in hospitals, where MRSA bacteria can infect surgical wounds and spread from patient to patient.

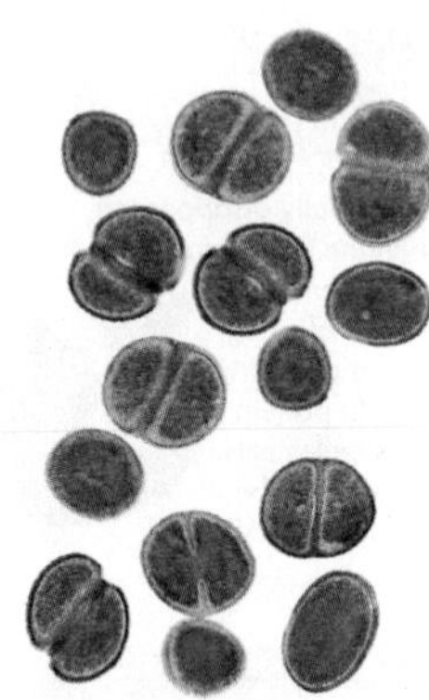

FIGURE 20–20 MRSA Methicillin-resistant *S. aureus* is a bacterium that is resistant to methicillin and other common antibiotics.

New Viruses Because viruses replicate so quickly, their genetic makeup can change rapidly, sometimes allowing a virus to jump from one host species to another. Researchers have evidence that this is how the virus that causes AIDS originated, moving from nonhuman primates into humans.

Public health officials are especially worried about the flu virus. Gene shuffling among different flu viruses infecting wild and domesticated bird populations has led to the emergence of a "bird flu" that is similar in many ways to the most deadly human versions of flu. In a few isolated cases, bird flu has indeed infected humans, and health officials warn that a major "jump" into the human population remains possible in the future.

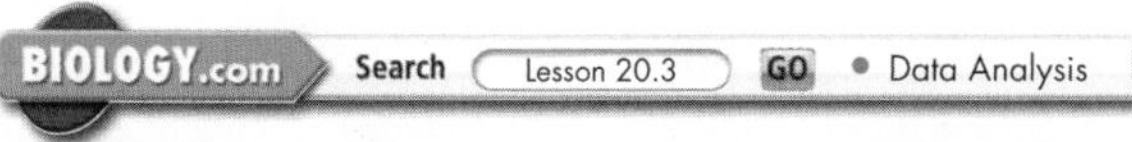

Analyzing Data

PURPOSE Students will examine and interpret data to identify trends in the incidence of MRSA infections.

PLANNING Remind students that line graphs can be used to show how a variable changes over time. Provide graph paper to students for Question 1. Write the formula for calculating percentage increase (for Question 2) on the board:

$$\frac{(2005 \text{ rate} - 1995 \text{ rate})}{1995 \text{ rate}} \times 100 = \% \text{ increase}$$

ANSWERS

1. MRSA infections have increased over time.
2. 867% increase
3. Future hospital costs will increase.

Connect to Health

MRSA is an infection spread by close contact and shared use of equipment. MRSA spreads in schools, particularly among students who share athletic mats or other equipment. Have students work in small groups to find out more about preventing the spread of MRSA in a school setting, either by interviewing a school nurse or healthcare professional or by using reliable Internet sources. Then, have each small group prepare a pamphlet that can be used to inform other students about steps they can take to keep MRSA from spreading at school.

DIFFERENTIATED INSTRUCTION

L1 Special Needs Instead of making a pamphlet, have visually impaired students prepare a public-service announcement conveying information about preventing the spread of MRSA in a school setting that can be read with the school announcements or shared with the class.

ELL English Language Learners Point out the terms *MRSA* and *AIDS* on this page. Explain that these terms are both examples of acronyms, which are abbreviations pronounced as words. Contrast these terms to abbreviations, such as *HIV*, in which each individual letter is pronounced. Have students brainstorm a list of other acronyms and abbreviations they have encountered in this book. *(acronym: SARS; abbreviations: DNA, ATP)*

BIOLOGY.com Have students use **Data Analysis: MRSA on the Rise** to examine the increased incidence of MRSA.

Teach continued

MYSTERY CLUE Have students read over **Figure 20–21** and discuss how the prion infection mechanism might help explain the incidence of mad cow disease in Great Britain. Students should infer that prions could be a cause of BSE. Students can go online to **Biology.com** to gather their evidence.

BIOLOGY.com Encourage students to check **Art in Motion: Prion Infection Mechanism** to reinforce their understanding of how misfolded proteins interact with normal ones.

Assess and Remediate

EVALUATE UNDERSTANDING

Have each student write a sentence describing how bacteria cause disease and a sentence describing how viruses cause disease. Call on several students to share their sentences with the class. Then, have students complete the 20.3 Assessment.

REMEDIATION SUGGESTION

L1 **Struggling Students** If students have difficulty answering **Question 1b,** review with the class the vocabulary term *vaccine*.

BIOLOGY.com Students can check their understanding of lesson concepts with the **Self-Test** assessment. They can then take an online version of the **Lesson Assessment.**

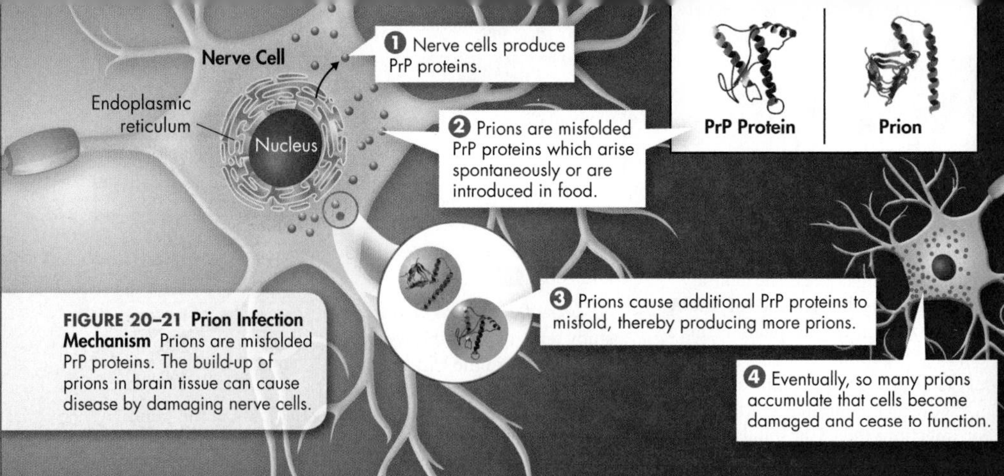

Nerve Cell
Endoplasmic reticulum
Nucleus
1 Nerve cells produce PrP proteins.
2 Prions are misfolded PrP proteins which arise spontaneously or are introduced in food.
PrP Protein
Prion
3 Prions cause additional PrP proteins to misfold, thereby producing more prions.
4 Eventually, so many prions accumulate that cells become damaged and cease to function.

FIGURE 20–21 Prion Infection Mechanism Prions are misfolded PrP proteins. The build-up of prions in brain tissue can cause disease by damaging nerve cells.

MYSTERY CLUE

BSE virtually disappeared when the British government banned the practice of using ground-up cattle tissue in protein feed supplements. Could prions be the cause of BSE?

Prions In 1972, American scientist Stanley Prusiner became interested in scrapie, an infectious disease in sheep, the exact cause of which was unknown. At first, he suspected a viral cause, but experiments revealed clumps of tiny protein particles in the brains of infected sheep. Prusiner called these particles **prions,** short for "protein infectious particles." Although prions were first discovered in sheep, many animals, including humans, can become infected with prions. Prions are formed when a protein known as PrP is improperly folded. Prions themselves can cause PrP proteins to misfold, producing even more prions. An accumulation of prions can damage nerve cells, as shown in **Figure 20–21.**

20.3 Assessment

Review Key Concepts

1. a. Review Describe how bacteria cause disease.
b. Relate Cause and Effect Are vaccines effective before or after infection? Explain.

2. a. Review How do viruses cause disease?
b. Compare and Contrast How does the treatment of viral diseases contrast with the treatment of bacterial diseases?

3. a. Review Why are emerging diseases of particular concern?
b. Explain Why are "superbugs" difficult to control?
c. Propose a Solution What actions could your school take to help combat the evolution of "superbugs"? Explain how these actions could make an impact.

BUILD VOCABULARY

4. Research the word origins for the term *vaccine*. Which word in which language does it come from and why?

BIOLOGY.com Search Lesson 20.3 GO • Self-Test • Lesson Assessment • Art in Motion

592 Chapter 20 • Lesson 3

Assessment Answers

1a. Bacteria cause disease by destroying living cells or by releasing chemicals that upset homeostasis.

1b. Vaccines are typically effective before infection. Vaccines prompt the body to produce immunity to a certain disease, preventing infection from occurring.

2a. Viruses cause disease by directly destroying living cells or by affecting cellular processes in ways that upset homeostasis.

2b. Only bacterial diseases can be treated using antibiotics. Recently, a few antiviral drugs have been developed that can help patients suffering from viral diseases.

3a. Emerging diseases are particularly threatening to human health, because humans have little or no resistance to them and because methods to control them have yet to be developed.

3b. "Superbugs" are difficult to control, because they are resistant to whole groups of antibiotics.

3c. Sample answer: Frequent hand washing with a soap that is not "antibacterial" to slow evolution of resistant strains.

BUILD VOCABULARY

4. The word *vaccine* comes from the Latin words for "cow" *(vacca)*, or "of or from cows" *(vaccinus)*, because the first vaccine was made using cowpox virus.

Biology & Society

NoS.11 Scientific knowledge: environmental and social issues.

Should More Vaccinations Be Required?

In the 1800s, diphtheria was the scourge of American children. Each winter, tens of thousands of children fell ill with fever and sore throats caused by this airborne bacterium, and thousands died from it. But you may not have heard of it, and you certainly haven't had to worry about it. Only five cases of diphtheria have been recorded in the United States since 2000. The reason is vaccination. In 1920, a vaccine for the disease was introduced and is now mandatory for American schoolchildren. As a result, diphtheria is one of several diseases, including polio, that have all but vanished from our society.

Medical guidelines call for vaccinations against at least 14 childhood diseases. New vaccines have been introduced against diseases that are not usually fatal, such as chicken pox. Some authorities have even suggested that everyone should also be vaccinated against bacteria and viruses that might be used for germ warfare, including anthrax and smallpox. Should all of these vaccinations be required for everyone entering school?

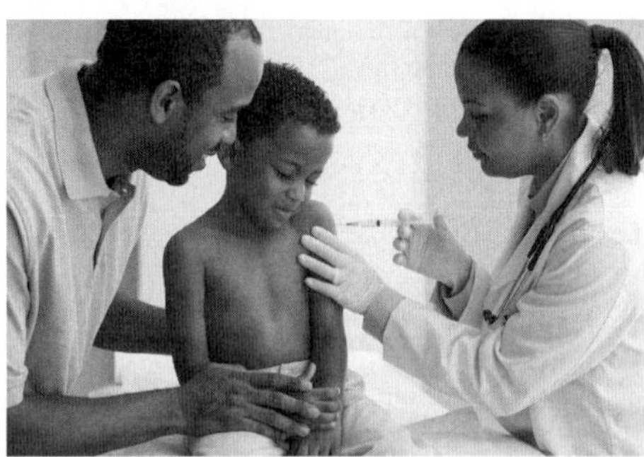

This boy is receiving a vaccination that is required before he starts school.

The Viewpoints

Expand Mandatory Vaccinations Infectious diseases are spread from person to person. When they work properly, vaccinations stimulate the immune system in a way that not only protects the vaccinated individual, but also indirectly protects others who may not have been immunized. This helps to improve public health, whether the specific disease in question is life-threatening or not. In addition, vaccination against germ warfare agents renders these potential terrorist weapons useless.

Limit Mandatory Vaccinations There is no question that a limited number of vaccinations against deadly and crippling diseases such as diphtheria and polio makes good sense. However, every vaccination carries with it the risk that the child being vaccinated will experience adverse reactions. Some reactions to vaccinations can be severe.

More young people now suffer from complications of polio vaccination than develop the disease itself, and smallpox vaccination was discontinued in the early 1970s due to deaths from the vaccine. Students should not be forced to be vaccinated for diseases that are not life-threatening nor for hypothetical threats like germ warfare.

Research and Decide

1. Analyze the Viewpoints Investigate the diseases for which vaccination is now required to enter school in your state. What would be the risks and benefits of expanding the number of required vaccines? Similarly, what would be the effects of limiting the number of required vaccines to just a handful?

2. Form an Opinion Compare the results of your research with statements published by U.S. government agencies. Prepare a list of the vaccines that you would make mandatory for all students in your school, and be prepared to defend your decisions.

Teach

Lead a Discussion

Use the following questions to initiate a class discussion of vaccine requirements. As you discuss, be sure to be sensitive to students who may not have been vaccinated for religious or other reasons.

Ask What is the advantage of having a set policy regarding required vaccines for all students entering school? *(Sample answer: The advantage is that all students will have immunity to certain diseases.)*

Ask How do laws and regulations requiring vaccines impact both public health and the health of the individual? *(Sample answer: Mandatory vaccines increase public health by decreasing the number of cases of infectious disease. Mandatory vaccines also protect the health of individuals by increasing the immunity of each individual vaccinated.)*

Biology In-Depth

PERTUSSIS

Pertussis, or whooping cough, is a highly contagious bacterial disease that causes a dangerous cough. In the past several decades, the incidence of pertussis has increased. Many of the cases reported are in adolescents. Public health officials attribute the rise in cases of pertussis to fading effects of the vaccine administered to infants. In 2005, recommendations were officially made for adolescents and adults to receive a booster of pertussis vaccine in combination with tetanus and diphtheria vaccines.

Answers

RESEARCH AND DECIDE

1. Suggest that a representative student contact the nurse's office in a local elementary school to learn what immunizations your state requires as a condition for entering school. Students' responses should include a well-researched evaluation of the risks and benefits of expanding or limiting the number of required vaccines.

2. Students should make a list of vaccines they would require for students in their area and include a well-reasoned defense for each entry on their list.

IN INDIANA ACADEMIC STANDARDS

For the full text of all standards, see the Course Overview in the front matter of this book.

CHAPTER LAB

Pre-Lab

Introduce students to the concepts they will explore in the chapter lab by assigning the Pre-Lab questions.

Lab

Tell students they will perform the chapter lab *Controlling Bacterial Growth* described in **Lab Manual A.**

 **Struggling Students** A simpler version of the chapter lab is provided in **Lab Manual B.**

SAFETY

Students should wear safety goggles and gloves while performing this lab. Be aware of students who may be allergic to penicillin or tetracycline. Remind students to follow your direction about disposal of lab materials. Have students wash their hands with soap and water when they complete the lab.

Look online for **Editable Lab Worksheets.**

For corresponding pre-lab in the **Foundation Edition,** see page 494.

IN INDIANA ACADEMIC STANDARDS

For the full text of all standards, see the Course Overview in the front matter of this book.

GUIDED INQUIRY

IN NoS.1 Develop explanations.

Pre-Lab: Controlling Bacterial Growth

Problem How can you determine the effectiveness of an antibiotic?

Materials agar plates, marker, bacterial cultures, sterile glass beads, sterile pipettes, forceps, antibiotic disks, masking tape, metric ruler

Lab Manual Chapter 20 Lab

Skills Focus Observe, Measure, Draw Conclusions

Connect to the 

Bacteria can be found on and within the human body. Most of these bacteria are harmless and some are even beneficial to humans. But others can cause diseases. These pathogens need to be controlled. Physical removal of bacteria through hand washing is one of the most effective control methods. Proper food storage and preparation is also important, as are the vaccines that have been developed to help the body build up immunity to specific bacterial diseases.

What happens if a person does develop a bacterial infection? Then doctors use drugs, such as antibiotics, to fight the infection. These drugs are designed to kill bacteria but not human cells. In this lab, you will compare the ability of two antibiotics to control the growth of two different types of bacteria.

Background Questions

a. **Review** What happens to a bacteria cell after it has grown to nearly double its size? What is this process called?

b. **Explain** How is genetic diversity increased in populations of bacteria?

c. **Review** What are the two general ways that bacteria can cause disease?

Pre-Lab Questions

Preview the procedure in the lab manual.

1. **Relate Cause and Effect** How will you know whether an antibiotic is able to control the growth of bacteria?

2. **Design an Experiment** Why is it important to leave space between the disks on the agar plates?

3. **Control Variables** Why must you avoid direct contact between your hands and the antibiotic disks?

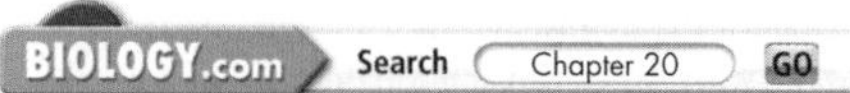

Visit Chapter 20 online to test yourself on chapter content and to find activities to help you learn.

Untamed Science Video Join the Untamed Science crew as they fire up the microscopes for a look at bacteria and all the ways they are good for us.

Art in Motion View a short animation of prion infection and see how misfolded proteins interact with normal proteins.

Art Review Review your understanding of the structure and classification of prokaryotes.

InterActive Art Build your understanding of lytic and lysogenic cycles.

Data Analysis Analyze data on MRSA and identify whether the increase in prevalence is due to increased spread, virulence, or simply increased accuracy of diagnoses.

Visual Analogy Compare an old west outlaw taking over a town to a lytic infection.

Pre-Lab Answers

BACKGROUND QUESTIONS

a. DNA within the cell is replicated and the cell divides in half, producing two identical cells. The process is called binary fission.

b. Genetic diversity is increased either through mutations or through conjugation, a process in which genetic material moves from one cell to another across a hollow bridge.

c. Bacteria can destroy living cells or release toxins that interfere with normal cell actvitiy.

PRE-LAB QUESTIONS

1. There will be a clear space on the agar plate around the antibiotic disk.

2. Sample answer: If the disks are too close together, it will be difficult to determine which antibiotic was responsible for the results.

3. Sample answer: If my hands were to touch the disks, I might transfer bacteria from my hands, which could add an unwanted variable to the experiment.

20 Study Guide

Big idea Cellular Basis of Life

Viruses are nonliving particles that reproduce by infecting cells. Building immunity to infection by preventive vaccines is key to defending against viral diseases. Bacteria and archaea are prokaryotes that play many important ecosystem roles. Bacterial infections are treated with medicines that disrupt prokaryotic cellular structure or function.

20.1 Viruses

Viruses can reproduce only by infecting living cells.

Inside living cells, viruses use their genetic information to make multiple copies of themselves. Some viruses replicate immediately, while others initially persist in an inactive state within the host.

virus (574)
capsid (575)
bacteriophage (575)
lytic infection (576)
lysogenic infection (577)
prophage (577)
retrovirus (578)

20.2 Prokaryotes

Prokaryotes are classified as Bacteria or Archaea—two of the three domains of life.

Prokaryotes vary in their size and shape, in the way they move, and in the way they obtain and release energy.

Prokaryotes are essential in maintaining every aspect of the ecological balance of the living world. In addition, some species have specific uses in human industry.

prokaryote (580)
bacillus (582)
coccus (582)
spirillum (582)
binary fission (583)
endospore (583)
conjugation (583)

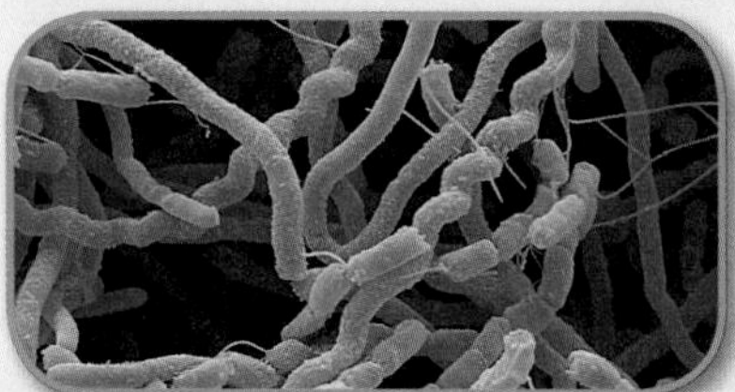

20.3 Diseases Caused by Bacteria and Viruses

Bacteria cause disease by destroying living cells or by releasing chemicals that upset homeostasis.

Viruses cause disease by destroying living cells or by affecting cellular processes in ways that upset homeostasis.

The pathogens that cause emerging diseases are particularly threatening to human health because human populations have little or no resistance to them, and because methods of control have yet to be developed.

pathogen (586)
vaccine (588)
antibiotic (588)
emerging disease (590)
prion (592)

THE NEXT TO GO
FIGHT TUBERCULOSIS!
Red Cross Christmas Seal
Campaign

Think Visually

A flipbook consists of pages of sequential drawings that, when flipped, appear to move. Create a flipbook movie of the steps in a lytic infection. Be sure to show what happens to the bacteriophage at each step. Exchange your flipbook with another student. Look at the other student's movie, and write a review of it.

BIOLOGY.com Search Chapter 20 GO • Crossword • Chapter Assessment

UbD Performance Tasks

SUMMATIVE TASK Tell students that *War of the Worlds*, a science-fiction novel by H. G. Wells, tells the story of an alien invasion of Earth. Earth is saved when the invaders die of diseases they contract. Have students write a story about people from Earth voyaging to another planet. The story should include a detailed description of precautions humans could take to protect themselves from new diseases.

TRANSFER TASK Tell students a common problem encountered by medical professionals is the misconception among their patients that antibiotics are useful for combating viral illnesses. Medical professionals who seek to avoid unnecessarily prescribing antibiotics often encounter resistance among their patients. Have students prepare an informational flier directed at patients that could be used by medical professionals to help combat this problem. Explain that the fliers should include a summary of the differences between viruses and bacteria, identification of diseases caused by each, and an explanation of the dangers of overuse of antibiotics.

Study Online

REVIEW AND ASSESSMENT RESOURCES

Editable Worksheets Pages of Study Workbooks A and B, Lab Manuals A and B, and the Assessment Resources Book are available online. These documents can be easily edited using a word-processing program.

Lesson Overview Have students reread the Lesson Overviews to help them study chapter concepts.

Vocabulary Review The *Flash Cards* and *Crossword* provide an interactive way to review chapter vocabulary.

Chapter Assessment Have students take an online version of the Chapter 20 Assessment.

Standardized Test Prep Students can take an online version of the Standardized Test Prep. You will receive their scores along with ideas for remediation.

Diagnostic and Benchmark Tests Use these tests to monitor your students' progress and supply remediation.

Answers

THINK VISUALLY

Students' flipbooks should include the steps of a lytic infection, including the virus injecting DNA into a bacterium, transcription of viral genes by the host cell, generation of viral proteins and nucleic acids by the infected bacterium, assembly of new viruses within the infected bacterium, lysis of the infected cell, and the release of new viruses.

Lesson 20.1

UNDERSTAND KEY CONCEPTS

1. d **2.** c **3.** b

4. A characteristic of all viruses is that they can reproduce only by infecting living cells. (Alternatively, students might note that all viruses have nucleic acids and a protein capsid.)

5. Capsid proteins bind to receptor proteins on the host cell to trick the cell into taking in the virus or its genetic material.

6. In a lytic infection, a virus enters a cell, makes copies of itself, and causes the cell to burst, releasing many copies of the virus.

7. A prophage is bacteriophage DNA that is embedded in the bacterial host's DNA.

THINK CRITICALLY

8. A cold virus differs from HIV in that the cold virus begins producing new viruses as soon as it penetrates a cell. HIV inserts its DNA into the DNA of the host cell and may remain inactive for many cell cycles.

9. Sample answer: A mutation in a bacterial cell that results in a change to the receptor proteins could lead to bacteriophages not being able to penetrate the cell.

10. The virus, which is a part of the host cell's chromosome, spreads when the bacterial cell undergoes binary fission.

Lesson 20.2

UNDERSTAND KEY CONCEPTS

11. a **12.** c **13.** b **14.** a

15. d

16. Prokaryotes are unicellular and lack a nucleus.

17. The three most common shapes of prokaryotes are the rod-shaped bacilli, spherical-shaped cocci, and spiral-shaped spirilli.

18. Some prokaryotes are propelled by flagella; some glide slowly along a layer of slimelike material they secrete.

THINK CRITICALLY

19. If bacteria lost the ability to fix nitrogen, most of the nitrogen used by other organisms would be unavailable. Without usable nitrogen, these other organisms could not make proteins and other molecules needed for life processes.

20. Sample answer: Bacteria, like all living things, need water. The relative dryness of uncooked rice and raisins inhibits bacterial growth.

20 Assessment

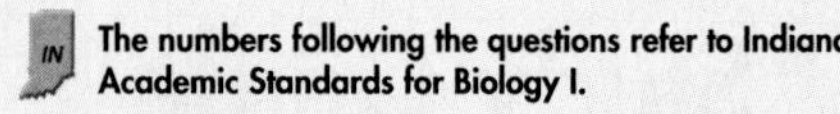

IN
The numbers following the questions refer to Indiana's Academic Standards for Biology I.

20.1 Viruses

Understand Key Concepts

1. Particles made up of proteins, nucleic acids, and sometimes lipids that can reproduce only by infecting living cells are called
- **a.** bacteria.
- **b.** capsids.
- **c.** prophages.
- **d.** viruses.

2. The structure labeled "A" in the diagram of the virus below is called the
- **a.** viral genome.
- **b.** RNA envelope.
- **c.** capsid.
- **d.** nuclear membrane.

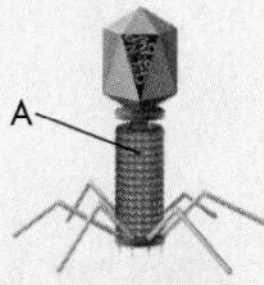

3. One group of viruses that contain RNA as their genetic information is the
- **a.** bacteriophages.
- **b.** retroviruses.
- **c.** capsids.
- **d.** prophages.

4. What characteristics do all viruses have in common?

5. How are capsid proteins important to the way a virus functions?

6. Describe the sequence of events that occurs during a lytic infection.

7. Explain what a prophage is.

Think Critically

8. **Compare and Contrast** In terms of their mechanism of infection, how does a cold virus differ from the HIV virus?

9. **Predict** Explain how a mutation in a bacterial cell could help it become resistant to infection by a bacteriophage.

10. **Apply Concepts** Explain how a virus can spread in a bacterial population during the lysogenic phase of infection.

20.2 Prokaryotes

Understand Key Concepts

11. Prokaryotes are unlike all other organisms in that their cells B.8.2
- **a.** lack nuclei.
- **b.** have organelles.
- **c.** have cell walls.
- **d.** lack nucleic acids.

12. Prokaryotes that thrive in oxygen-free environments are called
- **a.** aerobes.
- **b.** retroviruses.
- **c.** anaerobes.
- **d.** heterotrophs.

13. Which micrograph shows bacillus bacteria?

a. 

c. 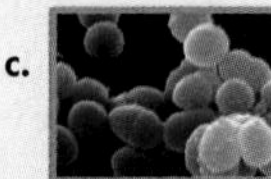

b. 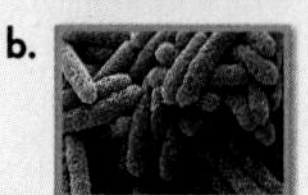

d. 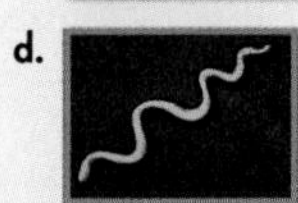

14. Prokaryotes reproduce asexually by
- **a.** binary fission.
- **b.** endospores.
- **c.** conjugation.
- **d.** mutation.

15. The process of converting nitrogen into a form plants can use is known as nitrogen
- **a.** formation.
- **b.** ammonification.
- **c.** decomposition.
- **d.** fixation.

16. What are the two distinguishing characteristics of prokaryotes? B.8.2

17. Describe the three main cell shapes of prokaryotes. B.8.2

18. Describe two methods by which prokaryotes move. B.8.2

Think Critically

19. **Predict** Suppose certain bacteria lost the ability to fix nitrogen. How would this affect other organisms in their ecosystem? B.4.4

20. **Apply Concepts** Why don't foods such as uncooked rice and raisins spoil?

21. People who do not regularly brush their teeth have more cavities than those who do brush regularly, because bacterial growth is promoted by food particles on teeth.

22. The organism probably belongs to the domain Bacteria, because it is unicellular, has a cell wall containing peptidoglycan, and lacks a nucleus.

23. Binary fission produces two cells from one, whereas endospore formation and conjugation do not increase the number of cells.

21. **Form a Hypothesis** Bacteria that live on teeth produce an acid that causes decay. Why do people who do not brush their teeth regularly have more cavities than those who do?

22. **Classify** A scientist finds a new organism but is unsure to which domain it belongs. The organism is unicellular, has a cell wall containing peptidoglycan, has a circular DNA molecule, and lacks a nucleus. Based on those characteristics, to which domain does it belong? B.8.2

23. **Compare and Contrast** Explain how the outcome of binary fission differs from that of both endospore formation and conjugation.

20.3 Diseases Caused by Bacteria and Viruses

Understand Key Concepts

24. Disease-causing organisms are known as
   a. cocci.
   b. bacteria.
   c. pathogens.
   d. archaea.

25. Which of the following scientists is responsible for developing the germ theory of disease?
   a. Ivanovski
   b. Beijerinck
   c. Pasteur
   d. Darwin

26. Viruses typically cause disease by
   a. releasing toxins.
   b. infecting and then destroying cells.
   c. causing mutations in the host cell DNA.
   d. destroying red blood cells.

27. Which of the following can be helpful in treating bacterial diseases but NOT viral diseases?
   a. vaccines.
   b. antibiotics.
   c. antiviral drugs.
   d. aspirin.

28. What is the best way for people to protect themselves against most viral diseases?

29. List three different ways bacterial growth can be controlled.

30. What is meant by the term *emerging disease*? Give three examples of emerging diseases in North America.

31. How do misfolded prions cause disease?

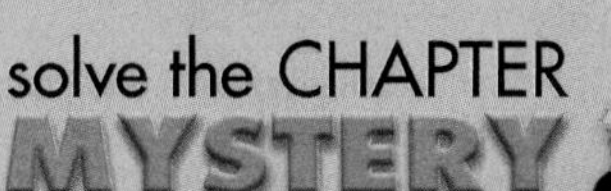

solve the CHAPTER MYSTERY

THE MAD COWS

The "mad cow" disease that appeared in 1986 in Britain spread quickly among cattle herds. Humans were afflicted by a similar disease, known as nvCJD (new variant Creutzfeld-Jacob Disease), and scores of people died. The disease virtually disappeared when the government banned the practice of using ground-up cattle tissue in protein feed supplements.

It now seems clear that "mad cow" and nvCJD were caused by prions in the meat and brain tissue of infected cattle. When these prions entered the food supply, the infection was able to spread to other cattle, and to humans eating meat from infected animals. Officials in Europe and the United States have instituted new controls on meat production to try to prevent further outbreaks of this prion-based disease.

1. **Infer** The rapid rise of BSE between 1986 and 1991 ended when British authorities banned the use of meat and bone meal in feed supplements for cattle. How does this support the hypothesis that BSE is caused by prions?

2. **Apply Concepts** Why did most scientists conclude that BSE was not caused by either viruses or bacteria?

3. **Connect to the Big idea** Prions are proteins, not organisms unto themselves. However, they have some lifelike qualities. What characteristics do prions share with cell-based life? Explain.

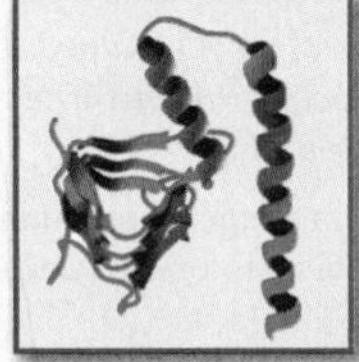

◀ Misfolded prion protein

BIOLOGY.com Search Chapter 20 GO • Untamed Science Video • Chapter Mystery

597

CHAPTER MYSTERY After students have read through the Chapter Mystery, discuss the cause of BSE and ways it can be prevented.

Ask Why was changing the food supply the best way to stop the outbreak of BSE in cattle? *(The prions that cause BSE were found in the feed supplements.)*

Ask How is the spread of a disease caused by prions different from the spread of a disease caused by viruses? *(Diseases caused by prions are spread by consumption of animal tissue that contains prions; viral diseases can be spread by contact.)*

CHAPTER MYSTERY ANSWERS

1. Prions are present in the proteins in meat and bone tissue of infected cattle. If cattle feed is partly composed of these tissues, the feed will contain prions. The hypothesis is supported by the fact that the disease disappeared when meat and bone meal were removed from the feed.

2. Sterilization kills bacteria, but cattle contracted BSE despite sterilization of their food. In addition, viruses infect via their genetic material, but BSE was induced in mice via injection of material that contained no genetic material.

3. **Big idea** Prions are similar to cell-based life in that they make more of themselves. Prions do this by causing normal proteins to misfold; cellular organisms do this by reproducing.

For a look at some beneficial bacteria, suggest students watch **Bacteria, at Your Service.**

Lesson 20.3

UNDERSTAND KEY CONCEPTS

24. c **25.** c **26.** b **27.** b

28. Prevention, with vaccines and personal hygiene, is the best way to protect against viral disease.

29. Any three of the following: physical removal, disinfectants, proper food storage, food processing, sterilization by heat

30. An emerging disease is an unknown disease that appears in a population for the first time or a well-known disease that suddenly becomes harder to control. Accept any three examples of emerging diseases in North America: multidrug-resistant tuberculosis, West Nile virus, MRSA, *E. coli* O157:H7, dengue.

31. Prions cause disease by accumulating in cells and causing damage to the point at which the cells can no longer function.

ASSESSMENT

THINK CRITICALLY

32. Use of disinfectants can lead to the development of resistant strains; physical removal does not.

33. No, bird flu is a viral disease, and antibiotics do not kill viruses.

34. a. Antibiotics B and C were least effective, because neither retarded bacterial growth.
b. Antibiotic A was most effective at retarding bacterial growth; it would probably be the most effective treatment for an infection caused by this strain of bacteria.

Connecting Concepts

USE SCIENCE GRAPHICS

35. The circles represent areas where the *E. coli* cells were infected and destroyed by a lytic bacteriophage, leaving the area clear.

36. Bacteriophage particles would be transferred and would infect cells on the second dish, creating clear areas wherever the glass rod had touched.

WRITE ABOUT SCIENCE

37. Answers will vary. Students' articles should describe bacteria as nitrogen fixers, decomposers, and producers.

38. Big idea Answers will vary. Students' responses should mention similarities in viral and prokaryotic reproduction; for example, both involve copying genetic material. Students should also mention differences in viral and prokaryotic reproduction; for example, viruses cannot reproduce independently, but prokaryotes can.

Think Critically

32. Apply Concepts What advantages does the physical removal of infectious microbes by hand washing have over the use of disinfectants? Explain.

33. Predict Would antibiotics be effective in treating an outbreak of bird flu? Explain.

34. Biologists conducted an experiment to determine the effectiveness of several antibiotics against a certain strain of bacteria. Four disks, each soaked in a different antibiotic, were placed in a petri dish where the bacteria were growing. The results are summarized below.

Effects of Antibiotics

Antibiotic	Observation After One Week
A	Growth retarded for 6 mm diameter
B	Growth not retarded
C	Growth not retarded
D	Growth retarded for 2 mm diameter

a. Analyze Data Which antibiotics were the least effective at retarding the growth of the bacteria? Explain your answer using data from the experiment.

b. Infer Which antibiotic might be the most effective treatment for an infection caused by this strain of bacteria? Explain your answer using data from the experiment.

Connecting Concepts

Use Science Graphics NoS.3

E. coli bacteria can be grown on agar in a petri dish, clouding over the entire surface and forming a bacterial "lawn." The photograph shows a lawn over which a solution containing bacteriophage particles has been poured.

35. Interpret Visuals What is the most reasonable explanation for the small, circular, clear areas on the bacterial lawn?

36. Form a Hypothesis Suppose you touched the tip of a glass rod to one of the clear areas and then touched it again to the surface of a petri dish with a fresh lawn of *E. coli*. What would happen to the new lawn of bacteria after several days?

Write About Science NoS.3

37. Explanation Write a science article titled "Bacteria in the Biosphere" for the local newspaper. Explain the environmental roles bacteria play. B.4.4

38. Assess the Big idea Compare and contrast the reproduction of viruses with that of prokaryotes.

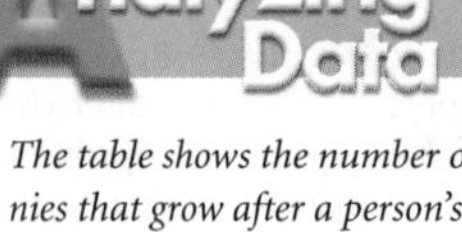

NoS.3

The table shows the number of bacteria colonies that grow after a person's treated hand is swabbed with a sterile cotton ball and the cotton ball is rubbed on the surface of a petri dish containing bacterial growth medium. The table compares bacterial growth after treating the hand in five different ways.

Hand Treatment	Trial 1: Number of Colonies	Trial 2: Number of Colonies
Unwashed	247	210
Rinsed in warm water	190	220
Washed with soap and warm water	21	15
Rinsed in alcohol and air-dried	3	0

39. Calculate Determine the average number of bacteria colonies for each treatment. MATH

40. Graph Make a bar graph to show the results of the experiment. Graph the averages you just calculated.

41. Analyze Data According to the data, what is the most effective method of preventing transfer of bacteria by hand contact?

42. Draw Conclusions What is the most logical explanation of how alcohol works?

598 Chapter 20 • Assessment

PURPOSE Students will analyze data to understand the effect of different hand treatments on bacterial growth.

PLANNING Review with students how to calculate an average value. Discuss the use of bar graphs to display data.

ANSWERS

39. Unwashed: 228.5; Rinsed in warm water: 205; Washed with soap and warm water: 18; Rinsed in alcohol and air-dried: 1.5

40. Students' graphs should include a bar of the appropriate height for each of the four hand treatments.

41. rinsing in alcohol and air drying

42. The most logical explanation is that alcohol kills bacteria.

Standardized Test Practice for Indiana

Multiple Choice

1. A type of virus that infects bacterial cells is called a
   A capsid.
   B prion.
   C bacteriophage.
   D retrovirus.

2. Prokaryotic cells that have a spherical shape are called
   A cocci.
   B methanogens.
   C spirilli.
   D bacilli. B.8.2

3. What is a capsid?
   A viral DNA that inserts into a host's DNA
   B a protein coat surrounding a virus
   C a type of plant virus
   D a rod-shaped bacterium

4. Which of the following is NOT used to identify specific prokaryotes?
   A type of nucleic acid
   B shape
   C movement
   D energy source B.8.2

5. Which method is NOT used to protect food against microorganisms?
   A heating
   B freezing
   C sterilization
   D vaccination

6. Which illness is caused by a bacterium?
   A AIDS C diphtheria
   B polio D common cold

7. Which process is used for the exchange of genetic information between two bacterial cells?
   A endospore formation
   B lysogenic cycle
   C conjugation
   D binary fission

8. All bacteria are classified as
   A eukaryotes. C archaea.
   B protists. D prokaryotes. B.8.2

Questions 9–10

Use the graph below to answer the questions.

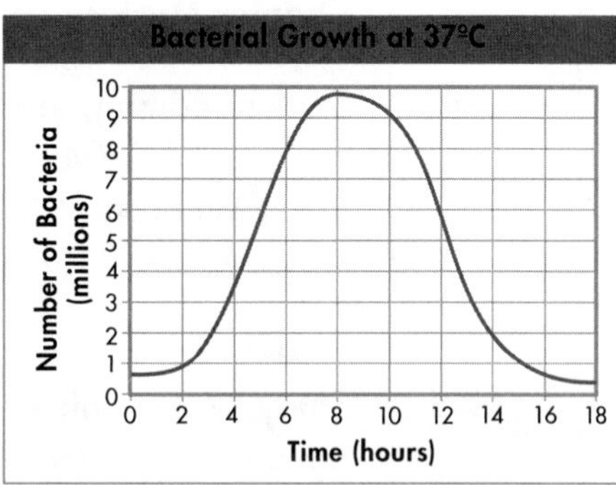

9. At which interval in the graph does the number of living bacteria increase at the greatest rate?
   A between hours 2 and 4
   B between hours 4 and 6
   C between hours 6 and 8
   D between hours 10 and 12

10. Which is the most likely reason for the decrease in bacteria shown?
   A The temperature of the bacterial culture was too high after 8 hours.
   B The bacteria stopped reproducing after 8 hours.
   C More nutrients were added to the culture at regular intervals.
   D Waste products from the bacteria accumulated in the nutrient solution.

Open-Ended Response

11. Explain why antibiotics can be useful in treating bacterial diseases but not in treating viral diseases.

If You Have Trouble With . . .

Question	1	2	3	4	5	6	7	8	9	10	11
See Lesson	20.1	20.2	20.1	20.2	20.3	20.3	20.2	20.2	20.2	20.2	20.3

Answers

1. C
2. A
3. B
4. A
5. D
6. C
7. C
8. D
9. B
10. D
11. Antibiotics disrupt proteins or cell processes that are specific to bacteria; they do not affect viruses.

Test-Taking Tip

WATCH FOR QUALIFIERS

Tell students to watch for questions containing the word *NOT* as a qualifier. For these questions, suggest students begin by reading all the distractors (answer choices). They should eliminate any choice that is a characteristic of the question stem or is true of the question stem. Finally, students should check to see that their answer is correct by confirming that it does not fit the characteristic in question.

Protists and Fungi

Chapter Contents	IN	Time	Core Resources
Chapter Preview			**Student Edition,** pp. 600–601 **Chapter Mystery,** p. 601
21.1 Protist Classification—The Saga Continues The First Eukaryotes • Protists—Ancestors and Descendants	B.8.1, B.8.2, B.8.4	1/2 period 1/4 block	**Student Edition,** pp. 602–605 Inquiry 21.1 Quick Lab, p. 603 L2 **Study Workbook A** 21.1 Worksheets L2 Biology.com 21.1 Self-Test • 21.1 Lesson Assessment
21.2 Protist Structure and Function How Protists Move • Protist Reproduction	NoS.6, B.2.5	1/2 period 1/4 block	**Student Edition,** pp. 606–609 **Study Workbook A** 21.2 Worksheets L2 Biology.com *InterActive Art:* Amoeba and Paramecium • *Visual Analogy:* How Cells Move Like Boats • 21.2 Self-Test • 21.2 Lesson Assessment
21.3 The Ecology of Protists Autotrophic Protists • Heterotrophic Protists • Symbiotic Protists—Mutualists and Parasites • *Technology & Biology: Low-Tech Weapons Against a High-Tech Parasite*	B.4.4	1 period 1/2 block	**Student Edition,** pp. 610–617 Inquiry 21.3 Quick Lab, p. 612 L2 **Study Workbook A** 21.3 Worksheets L2 Biology.com *Data Analysis:* Tiny Fossils and Ancient Oceans • *Art in Motion: Plasmodium* Life Cycle **Assessment Resources Book** Visual Quiz L2
21.4 Fungi What Are Fungi? • The Ecology of Fungi	NoS.3, B.4.4, B.8.2	1 period 1/2 block	**Student Edition,** pp. 618–625 Inquiry 21.4 Quick Lab, p. 620 L2 • 21.4 Analyzing Data, p. 624 L2 **Study Workbook A** 21.4 Worksheets L2 Biology.com *Art Review:* Structure of a Mushroom **Assessment Resources Book** Visual Quiz L2
Chapter Pre-Lab		1 period 1/2 block	**Student Edition,** p. 626 L2 **Lab Manual A** *Mushroom Farming* L2

Differentiated Instruction Tools

Study Workbook B includes worksheets with lesson-level differentiated instruction support and explanations of differentiated instruction teaching strategies.

Lab Manual B includes skills labs, simplified chapter labs, and hands-on activities.

ELL Handbook explains ways to make *Biology* more accessible to ELL students.

Spanish Study Workbook is a Spanish translation of Study Workbook A.

Multilingual Glossary is the glossary translated into ten languages.

Differentiated Instruction Key

- L1 Special Needs or Struggling Students
- ELL English Language Learners
- LPR Less Proficient Readers
- L2 On-Level Students
- L3 Advanced Students

Additional Resources

Biology.com Untamed Science Video • Vocabulary Flash Cards

Study Workbook B 21.1 Worksheets L1 ELL LPR
Spanish Study Workbook 21.1 Worksheets ELL
Biology.com 21.1 Lesson Overview • 21.1 Lesson Notes

Study Workbook B 21.2 Worksheets L1 ELL LPR
Spanish Study Workbook 21.2 Worksheets ELL
Biology.com 21.2 Lesson Overview • 21.2 Lesson Notes

Study Workbook B 21.3 Worksheets L1 ELL LPR
Spanish Study Workbook 21.3 Worksheets ELL
Biology.com 21.3 Lesson Overview • 21.3 Lesson Notes • 21.3 Self-Test • 21.3 Lesson Assessment

Study Workbook B 21.4 Worksheets L1 ELL LPR
Spanish Study Workbook 21.4 Worksheets ELL
Biology.com 21.4 Lesson Overview • 21.4 Lesson Notes • 21.4 Self-Test • 21.4 Lesson Assessment

Lab Manual B *Mushroom Farming* • Data Analysis: *Mycorrhizae and Tree Height* L1 ELL LPR

Chapter Review

Student Edition Study Guide, p. 627 L2
Study Workbook A Chapter 21 Vocabulary Review L2 • Chapter 21 Chapter Mystery/21st Century Skills Activity L2 L3
Transparencies, pp. 249–258 L1 ELL LPR L2
Biology.com Untamed Science Video • Editable Worksheets of Study Workbooks A and B and Lab Manuals A and B • Chapter 21 Flash Cards and Crossword Puzzle

Untamed Science DVD • Classroom Resources CD (includes lesson presentations and editable worksheets)

Chapter Assessment

Student Edition Assessment, pp. 628–631 L2
Study Workbook B Chapter 21 Chapter Review L1 ELL LPR • Chapter 21 Taking a Standardized Test L1 ELL LPR
Assessment Resources Book Chapter 21 Test A L2 • Chapter 21 Test B L1 ELL LPR
Biology.com Chapter 21 Assessment • Editable Worksheets of Chapter 21 Visual Quizzes and Chapter 21 Tests A and B

Exam*View* *Assessment Suite* • Classroom Resources CD (includes lesson presentations and editable worksheets)

Time: 1 period, 1/2 block

Pressed for Time?

Preview the Chapter Preview the images of protists and fungi in the Diversity of Life guide (pp. 1044–1053).

Cover the Chapter Quickly Assign the first two paragraphs of *The First Eukaryotes* in Lesson 21.1. In Lesson 21.2, discuss Figures 21–4 and 21–5 along with their associated vocabulary terms, and have students read the introduction to *Protist Reproduction*. Assign students to read all of Lesson 21.3. Assign the introduction to *What Are Fungi?* and all of *The Ecology of Fungi* in Lesson 21.4.

Assess Assign question 1a in the 21.1 Assessment, questions 1 and 2a in the 21.2 Assessment, the 21.3 Assessment, and questions 1a and 2 in the 21.4 Assessment. In the Chapter 21 Assessment, assign questions 1, 2, 9, 11, 13, 15–26, 28–33, 35, and 36.

CHAPTER 21

Connect to the Big Idea

Big idea Ask students to identify how many organisms they see in the photograph. *(four)* Explain that the tree and the frog are separate organisms. The lichen growing on the tree's branch is actually made up of two different organisms—a fungus and a photosynthetic organism—that are mutualistic symbionts. Have students give a definition of *interdependence* and examples they have studied. *(Sample answer: Interdependence is when organisms depend on each other for survival; examples include mutualism and nutrient cycles.)* Have them connect the photo to the Big Idea of Interdependence in Nature by brainstorming how the camouflage of the tree frog, as shown in the picture, is an example of interdependence. *(Sample answer: The lichens are protecting the tree frog from predators.)* Then, have them anticipate the answer to the question, **How do protists and fungi affect the homeostasis of other organisms and ecosystems?**

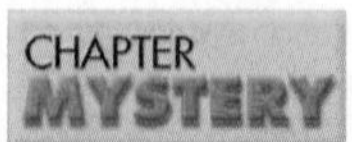

Have students read over the Chapter Mystery and make predictions about the cause of the potato blight. Use their predictions to help them start connecting the Chapter Mystery to the Big Idea of Interdependence in Nature.

BIOLOGY.com Have students preview the chapter vocabulary terms using the **Flash Cards.**

IN INDIANA ACADEMIC STANDARDS

For the full text of all standards, see the Course Overview in the front matter of this book.

Key standards: Chapter 21 covers key ideas from Standard 2: Cellular Structure, Standard 4: Interdependence, and Standard 8: Evolution, including **B.2.5** Protein structures, **B.4.4** Stability of an ecosystem, and **B.8.2** Classification.

21 Protists and Fungi

Big idea Interdependence in Nature

Q: How do protists and fungi affect the homeostasis of other organisms and ecosystems?

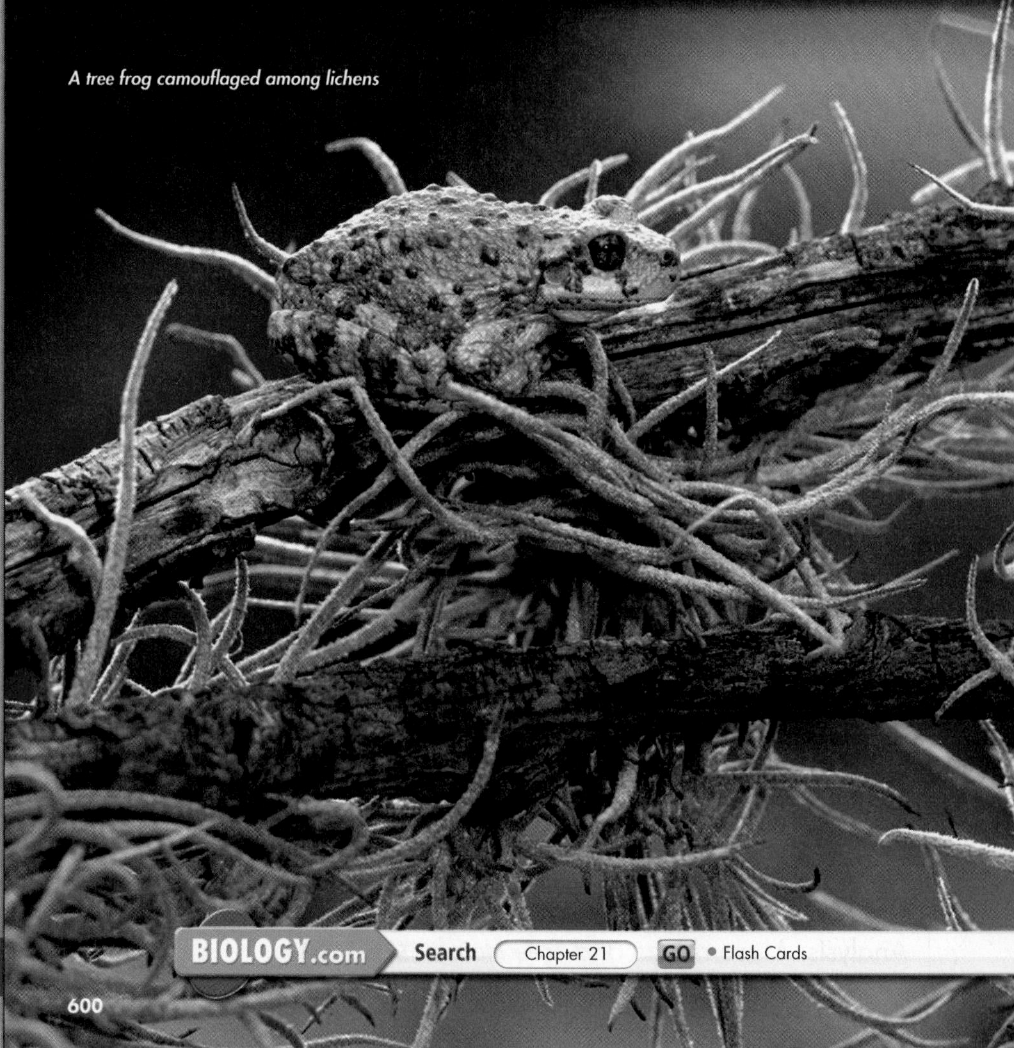

A tree frog camouflaged among lichens

BIOLOGY.com Search Chapter 21 GO • Flash Cards

600

UbD Understanding by Design

In Unit 6, students are building toward the Enduring Understanding that *from microorganisms to plants, organisms vary widely in the way they carry out basic life processes.* Students discover in Chapter 21 how protists and fungi affect the homeostasis of other organisms and ecosystems. As shown in the graphic organizer at the right, a Big Idea, Essential Question, and lesson-level Guiding Questions help frame their exploration of how chapter content informs this Enduring Understanding.

PERFORMANCE GOALS

In Chapter 21, lesson assessments require students to use critical thinking and creative writing skills to create novel classification systems, flip books, "Wanted" posters, and fictional accounts. After they have completed the chapter, students will integrate chapter content to produce a mural and apply chapter material to solve a problem.

INDIANA ACADEMIC STANDARDS FOR SCIENCE

Nature of Science NoS.3, NoS.6; **Cellular Structure** B.2.5; **Interdependence** B.4.4; **Evolution** B.8.1, B.8.2, B.8.4. See lessons for details.

• Untamed Science Video • Chapter Mystery

CHAPTER MYSTERY

"A BLIGHT OF UNUSUAL CHARACTER"

Within the first few decades of the nineteenth century, Ireland became heavily dependent on potato farming. Potatoes are nutritious and easy to grow, and they thrived in the damp soil and wet climate of the Emerald Isle. Tenant farmers began to grow potatoes as the primary source of food for themselves and their families.

Then, during the summer of 1845, something strange began to happen. A magazine called *The Gardener's Chronicle* reported that "a blight of unusual character" was attacking potatoes. Everywhere in Ireland, potatoes began to rot and turn black. By the beginning of the twentieth century, starvation and emigration would cut the population of Ireland in half, while the island's principal food crop rotted in the fields. As you read this chapter, look for clues to help you identify what caused the potato blight.

Never Stop Exploring Your World. Finding the solution to this mystery is just the beginning. Take a video field trip with the ecogeeks of Untamed Science to see where this mystery leads.

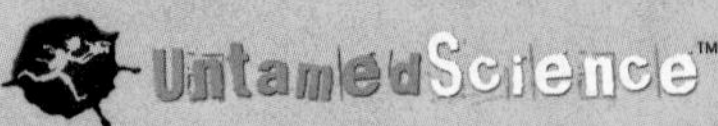

Chapter 21 Big Idea: Interdependence in Nature

Chapter 21 EQ: How do protists and fungi affect the homeostasis of other organisms and ecosystems?

21.1 GQ: Why are "protists" difficult to classify?

21.2 GQ: How do protists move and reproduce?

21.3 GQ: What roles do protists play in the environment?

21.4 GQ: What are fungi, and what roles do they play in the environment?

What's Online

BIOLOGY.com Extend your reach by using these and other digital assets offered at Biology.com.

CHAPTER MYSTERY
As they study the chapter, students collect clues and synthesize information to figure out the cause of a plant disease that changed Ireland's history.

UNTAMED SCIENCE VIDEO
The Untamed Science crew unearths some interesting facts about the structure and function of mushrooms.

VISUAL ANALOGY
Students compare the motions of cilia and flagella to the motions of many paired oars and a single oar.

INTERACTIVE ART
Students can interact with the art of an amoeba and a paramecium.

DATA ANALYSIS
Students find out how protist microfossils are used to learn about conditions and changes in ancient oceans.

ART IN MOTION
Students can watch an animated version of the *Plasmodium* life cycle.

ART REVIEW
Students can drag and drop structures to construct the features of a mushroom.

LESSON 21.1

Getting Started

Objectives

21.1.1 Explain what a protist is.

21.1.2 Describe how protists are related to other eukaryotes.

Student Resources

Study Workbooks A and B, 21.1 Worksheets

Spanish Study Workbook, 21.1 Worksheets

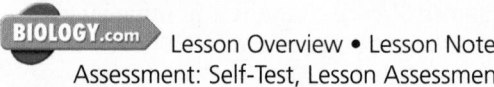

Lesson Overview • Lesson Notes • Assessment: Self-Test, Lesson Assessment

For corresponding lesson in the **Foundation Edition,** see pages 502–504.

Activate Prior Knowledge

Write these words on the board: eukaryotic, unicellular, multicellular, photosynthetic, heterotrophic, motile, immotile. Ask students to identify what kingdoms include organisms with each of these characteristics. *(Students will probably assign each characteristic to an animal, a plant, or a fungus.)* Then, explain that these characteristics can apply to different members of a group called protists.

Answers

IN YOUR NOTEBOOK Students' answers should reflect an understanding of the diverse nature of protists. Sample answer: Protists do not fit the definition of an animal, a plant, or a fungus.

IN INDIANA ACADEMIC STANDARDS

For the full text of all standards, see the Course Overview in the front matter of this book.

B.8.1 Explain how anatomical and molecular similarities among organisms that suggest life on earth began as simple, one-celled organisms about 4 billion years ago and multicellular organisms evolved later.

B.8.2 Explain how organisms are classified and named based on their evolutionary relationships into taxonomic categories.

21.1 Protist Classification—The Saga Continues

IN B.8.1 History of life on Earth; **B.8.2** Classification. Also covered: **B.8.4.**

Key Questions

What are protists?

How are protists related to other eukaryotes?

Taking Notes

Preview Visuals Look at the names of the organisms in **Figure 21–2.** Are any of the organisms familiar to you? Formulate two questions you have about this diagram.

THINK ABOUT IT Some of the organisms we call "protists" live quietly on the bottom of shallow ponds, soaking up the energy of sunlight. Others swim vigorously in search of tiny prey. Some sparkle like diamonds in coastal waters, and others drift in the human bloodstream, destroying blood cells and killing nearly a million people a year, most of them children. What kind of life is this, capable of such beauty and such destruction?

The First Eukaryotes

What are protists?

More than a billion years ago, a new form of organism appeared on Earth. Subtle clues in the microscopic fossils of these single cells mark them as the very first eukaryotes. Single-celled eukaryotes are still with us today and are often called "protists"—a name that means "first." Traditionally, protists are classified as members of the kingdom Protista. **Protists are eukaryotes that are not members of the plant, animal, or fungi kingdoms.**

Although most protists are unicellular, quite a few are not. The largest protists—brown algae called kelp—contain millions of cells arranged in differentiated tissues. They are considered protists because they are related more closely to certain unicellular protists than to members of any other kingdom. Kelp and several other protists are shown in **Figure 21–1.**

In Your Notebook *Think about the things that define a group. What do you think defines protists as a group?*

FIGURE 21–1 Extreme Diversity of Protists Protists vary greatly in size, form, and function. Here are several examples.

◀ Otters wrap themselves in giant kelp, a multicellular protist species, to keep from drifting out to sea while they sleep.

UbD Teach for Understanding

ENDURING UNDERSTANDING From microorganisms to plants, organisms vary widely in the way they carry out basic life processes.

GUIDING QUESTION Why are "protists" difficult to classify?

EVIDENCE OF UNDERSTANDING *After completing the lesson, give students the following assessment to show their understanding of the difficulty in classifying protists.* Have students identify the characteristics of protists mentioned in the lesson, for example, "swim in search of tiny prey," "photosynthetic," and "funguslike," as you write these characteristics on the board. Then, have students work in small groups to brainstorm different ways protists might be classified. Ask each group to present a brief presentation describing its classification system, as well as the advantages and limitations of each.

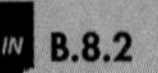

Quick Lab
GUIDED INQUIRY

B.8.2

What Are Protists?

1. Place a drop of water containing a variety of microorganisms on a microscope slide. Add a drop of methyl cellulose and a coverslip. Observe the slide under the microscope at low and high magnifications.
2. Record your observations by drawing and labeling each type of organism.
3. Make a chart listing each type of organism you observed and its characteristics.

Analyze and Conclude

1. **Observe** For any of the organisms that move, describe their motion and any structures involved in producing the motion.
2. **Draw Conclusions** Do you observe any structures that you think relate to food-gathering or reproduction? Explain why you think so.
3. **Classify** Are any of these organisms bacteria, plants, or animals? Explain your answer.

The "Protist" Dilemma In recent years, biologists have studied these eukaryotes closely, eager to learn what the organisms reveal about the history of life. They have discovered that the "protists" display a far greater degree of diversity than any other eukaryotic kingdom. Furthermore, they found that many of these organisms are far more closely related to members of other eukaryotic kingdoms than they are to other "protists."

This finding has created a dilemma. By definition, the members of a living kingdom, such as plants or animals, should be more like one another than like members of other kingdoms. This is not true of protists, which means that reclassification is necessary. Biologists continue to debate the best way to do this.

In the past, scientists sorted protists into three groups: plantlike protists, animal-like protists, and funguslike protists. This simple solution began to fail as biologists learned that many protists do not fit into any of these groups. To make matters worse, they discovered that many of the animal-like and funguslike protists are so similar that they belong in a single group, not split into two. Clearly, a new way of thinking about the "protists" is now needed.

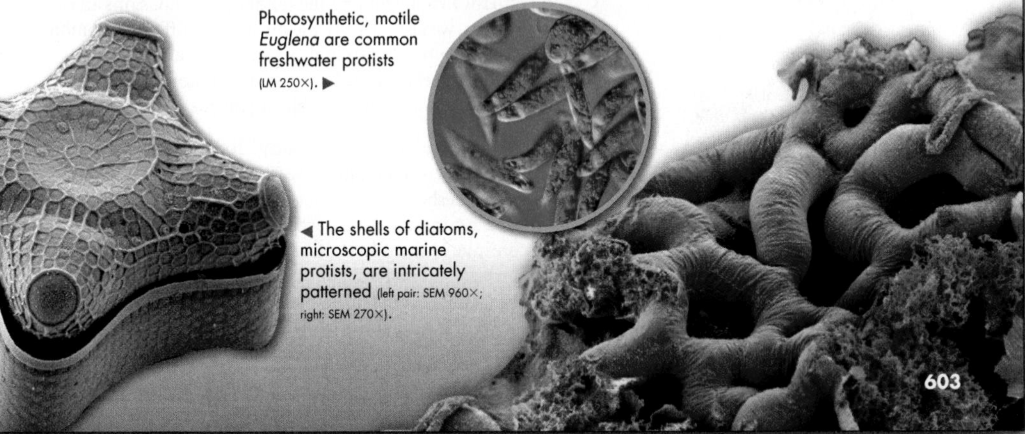

At a certain stage of their life cycle, protists called slime molds aggregate into colonies like this one (SEM 15×). ▼

Photosynthetic, motile *Euglena* are common freshwater protists (LM 250×). ▶

◀ The shells of diatoms, microscopic marine protists, are intricately patterned (left pair: SEM 960×; right: SEM 270×).

603

PURPOSE Students will observe protists and draw conclusions about their structures and classification.

MATERIALS mixed protist culture, dropper, microscope slide, methyl cellulose, coverslip, compound microscope

SAFETY Remind students to be careful when handling glass and to wash their hands after the activity.

PLANNING Prepare a mixed culture containing various protists, such as amoebas, paramecia, euglenas, and multicellular algae.

ANALYZE AND CONCLUDE

1. Answers will vary.
2. Answers will vary, but might include descriptions of vacuoles or pseudopods.
3. Students should recognize that the organisms are not bacteria, because they have nuclei. Some students might assume incorrectly that motile organisms are animals and nonmotile organisms are plants.

Teach

Lead a Discussion

Remind students that a dilemma is a choice between undesirable alternatives.

Ask What is the "dilemma" described in the lesson? *(There is no clear set of characteristics that can be used to classify an organism as a protist.)*

Ask Why does placing all protists into one kingdom present a dilemma? *(Many protists are more closely related to members of other kingdoms than they are to other protists.)*

Ask Why don't biologists place protists into other kingdoms? *(Many protists do not fit into other kingdoms.)*

DIFFERENTIATED INSTRUCTION

LPR Less Proficient Readers On the board, write the following sentence: "Protists" are eukaryotes that are NOT plants, animals, or fungi. Tell students that this is one of the Key Concepts in the lesson. Have pairs of students work together to discuss why defining a group of organisms by what they are not, rather than by what they are, might create problems. Then, have pairs read through the lesson and find details that support and add to what they have discussed.

ELL Focus on ELL: Build Background

BEGINNING AND INTERMEDIATE SPEAKERS Have students preview the images in the lesson and, with a partner, decide whether each organism shown is more like a plant, an animal, or a fungus (such as a mushroom), or whether it should be classified in a category of its own. Have each pair of students make a list of words or phrases that describe the organism. Have students share their classifications and descriptions with the class. Encourage beginning speakers to use words and intermediate speakers to use phrases or short sentences.

Address Misconceptions

Complexity of Protists Some students might think protists are simple organisms, more like prokaryotes than eukaryotes, because most are single-celled. Make sure students understand that protists are more complex than prokaryotes.

Teach continued

Use Visuals

Use **Figure 21–2** to explain the most recent classification system for protists decided upon by biologists. Read aloud the six major clades, or groups, and have students describe characteristics of the three clades pictured. Help them recognize how diverse these protists are. Point out that biologists used to group protists into one kingdom.

Ask From looking at the symbols, what might you infer about why Choanozoa are most similar to animals? *(Choanozoa have a structure that allows them to move.)*

Ask Why might Excavates, which also have a structure for movement, be grouped differently from Choanozoa? *(Sample answer: They may have other characteristics that make them too different to be grouped with Choanozoa.)*

DIFFERENTIATED INSTRUCTION

L1 Struggling Students Review with students that **Figure 21–2** represents a cladogram, which shows evolutionary relationships among a group of organisms. Point out that Choanozoa and Animals come off of a single branch, because they share characteristics that indicate they are more closely related to each other than to any other clades. Yet, they are on different sub-branches because they do have several differences from each other. Explain that the number of shared branching points in a cladogram can show how closely related two groups are. Have students count the number of branching points shared by Animals and Choanozoas and by Animals and Excavates to compare the relationships. *(Animals and Choanozoas share five, while Animals and Excavates share only one.)*

Euglena is classified as an excavate.

Brown algae and diatoms are examples of chromalveolates.

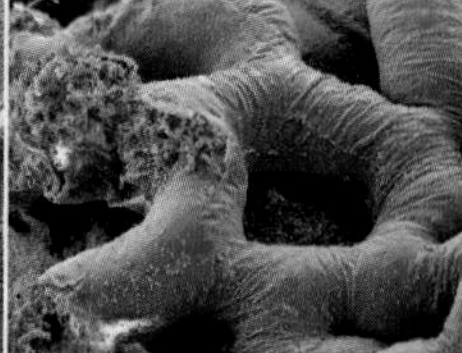

Slime molds are classified with the Amoebozoa.

Six Major Groups

- Excavata
- Chromalveolata
- Cercozoa, Foraminifera, and Radiolaria
- Rhodophyta (red algae)
- Amoebozoa
- Choanozoa

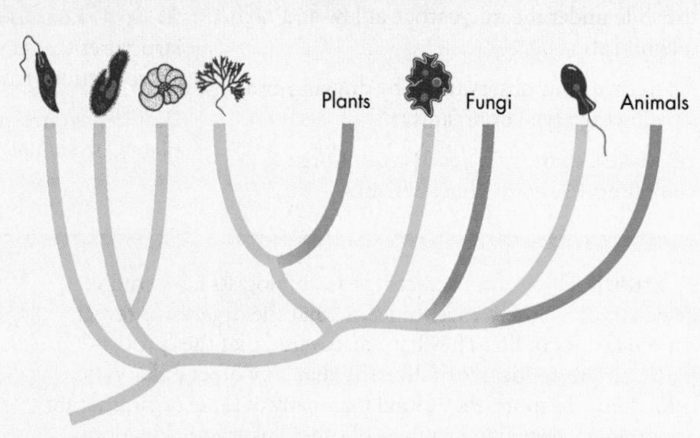

FIGURE 21–2 Protist Classification—A Work in Progress This cladogram represents an understanding of protist relationships supported by current research.
Interpret Diagrams ***Which group of "protists" is most closely related to plants? Which group is most closely related to animals? To fungi?***

For more on the diversity of protists, go to the Visual Guide. DOL•10–DOL•15

Multiple Kingdoms? The most recent studies of protists divide them into six major clades, shown in **Figure 21–2,** each of which could be considered a kingdom in its own right. Where would that leave the plant, animal, and fungi kingdoms? Surprisingly, they fit right into these six clades, and two of them, animals and fungi, actually emerge from the same protist ancestors.

In a way, this should have been expected. Protists were the first eukaryotes, and evolution has had far more time to develop differences among protists than among more recently evolved eukaryotes like plants and animals. In other words, by finding the fundamental divisions among protists, we also identify the most basic differences among all eukaryotes. You should expect protist classification to change yet again as biologists learn more about the genomes of these remarkable organisms.

What "Protist" Means Today Today biologists assembling what is often called the Tree of Life favor the classification shown above. But the word "protist" remains in such common usage, even among scientists, that we continue to use it here. Bear in mind, however, that the "protists" are not a single kingdom but a collection of organisms that includes several distinct clades. This is why the term is sometimes surrounded by quotation marks.

UbD Check for Understanding

ANALOGY PROMPT

Review with students what they might have learned about people belonging to a political party, such as Republican, Democratic, or Libertarian. Explain that independents do not belong to any political party, and might vote for different parties in different elections. Then, give students the following analogy prompt.

- Independents are like "protists," because . . . *(Sample answer: they are defined less by what they are and more by what they are not.)*

ADJUST INSTRUCTION

If students are confused, extend the analogy by drawing parallels between classifying organisms into kingdoms and classifying people into political parties.

Answers

FIGURE 21–2 Rhodophyta are most closely related to plants; Choanozoa are most closely related to animals; and Amoebozoa are most closely related to fungi.

Protists—Ancestors and Descendants

How are protists related to other eukaryotes?

Protists were the first eukaryotes. How are they related to other eukaryotic organisms today? As tempting as it might be to look among living protists to find the ancestors to the first plants or the earliest fungi, it would be a scientific mistake to do so. The reason, of course, is that protists living today have been through a process of evolution just as extensive as the one that produced every other living organism.

Microscopic fossils of eukaryotic cells, like the one shown in **Figure 21–3,** have been found in rocks as old as 1.5 billion years. Genetic and fossil evidence indicates that eukaryotes evolved from prokaryotes and are more closely related to present-day Archaea than to Bacteria. The actual split between Archaea and Eukarya may have come as early as 2.5 billion years ago. Since that time, protists have diversified into as many as 300,000 species found in every corner of the planet.

Most of the major protist groups have remained unicellular, but two have produced organisms that developed true multicellularity. It is from the ancestors of these groups that plants, animals, and fungi arose.

Today's protists include groups whose ancestors were among the very last to split from the organisms that gave rise to plants, animals, and fungi. The roots of all eukaryotic diversity, from plants to animals to fungi, are found among the ancestors of the organisms that we call protists.

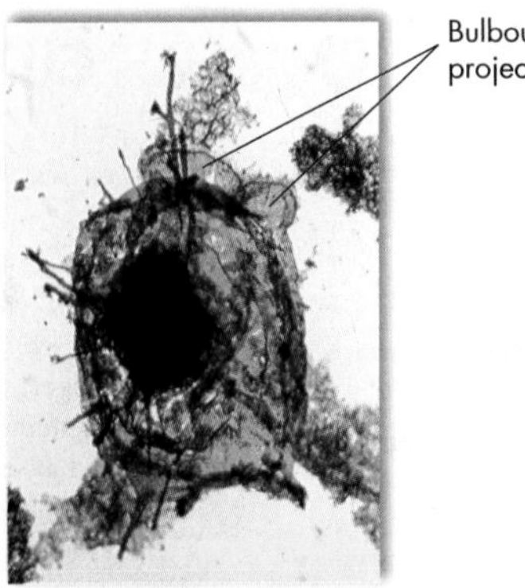

FIGURE 21–3 Fossil of an Early Eukaryote This 1.5-billion-year-old fossil of *Tappania plana* indicated to scientists that ancient eukaryotes already had the cytoskeletal structures characteristic of protists today. The bulbous projections on the cell are hypothesized to have functioned in asexual reproduction. (LM 285×)

21.1 Assessment

IN B.8.2

Review Key Concepts

1. a. **Review** What is a protist?
   b. **Compare and Contrast** Compare the updated classification of protists with the older one.
2. a. **Review** Which kingdoms arose from protist ancestors?
   b. **Apply Concepts** Why is it misguided to try to find our earliest eukaryotic ancestor among modern-day protists?

VISUAL THINKING

3. Compare **Figure 21–2** with the Tree of Life presented in Chapter 18. What simplification does **Figure 21–2** make? How could this simplification be misinterpreted? Explain your answer using your knowledge from Chapter 18 of how cladograms are constructed.

BIOLOGY.com Search Lesson 21.1 GO • Self-Test • Lesson Assessment

Lead a Discussion

Explain that all eukaryotes evolved from prokaryotes. Make sure students understand that animals, plants, and fungi evolved independently from the ancestors of today's protists.

Ask What part of **Figure 21–2** represents the common ancestor of all eukaryotes? *(the lowest branching point in the diagram)*

Ask If the diagram were to show prokaryote ancestors, from where would they branch off? *(from a point below the common ancestor shown)*

DIFFERENTIATED INSTRUCTION

L3 Advanced Students Challenge students to construct a diagram that combines information from **Figure 21–2** with the text of the section, **Protists—Ancestors and Descendants.**

Assess and Remediate

EVALUATE UNDERSTANDING

Have students write a brief paragraph that explains why "protists" are a group of exclusion. Then, have them complete the 21.1 Assessment.

REMEDIATION SUGGESTION

L1 Struggling Students If students have trouble answering **Question 1b,** have them reread The "Protist" Dilemma on the second page of this lesson.

BIOLOGY.com Students can check their understanding of lesson concepts with the **Self-Test** assessment. They can then take an online version of the **Lesson Assessment.**

Assessment Answers

1a. A protist is a eukaryote that is not a member of the animal, plant, or fungi kingdom.

1b. The old system classified all protists into one kingdom. The updated classification divides protists into six major clades, each of which could be considered a kingdom.

2a. The six protist kingdoms and the animal, plant, and fungi kingdoms all arose from protist ancestors.

2b. Other modern-day eukaryotes did not evolve from modern-day protists but from an ancestor common to both. This common ancestor no longer exists. Modern-day protists have gone through extensive evolution, just as modern-day animals, plants, and fungi have.

VISUAL THINKING

3. Figure 21–2 shows the plant, fungi, and animal groups each as one branch; there are no sub-branches. Sample misinterpretation: Since **Figure 21–2** shows only one branch each for plants, fungi, and animals, some people might think that these large groups cannot be subdivided into smaller clades.

LESSON 21.2

Getting Started

Objectives

21.2.1 Describe the various methods of protist locomotion.

21.2.2 Describe how protists reproduce.

Student Resources

Study Workbooks A and B, 21.2 Worksheets

Spanish Study Workbook, 21.2 Worksheets

Lesson Overview • Lesson Notes • Activities: Visual Analogy, InterActive Art • Assessment: Self-Test, Lesson Assessment

For corresponding lesson in the **Foundation Edition,** see pages 505–508.

Build Background

Ask students to recall from Chapter 20 the ways prokaryotes move and reproduce. *(They move in different ways, such as using flagella and gliding. Some do not move. They reproduce in different ways, such as simple cell division, conjugation, and spore formation.)* Tell students protists move and reproduce in many of the same ways as prokaryotes, and like them, protists are diverse in how they carry out these functions.

IN INDIANA ACADEMIC STANDARDS

For the full text of all standards, see the Course Overview in the front matter of this book.

B.2.5 Explain that cells use proteins to form structures, including cilia, flagella, which allow them to carry out specific functions, including movement, adhesion, and absorption.

21.2 Protist Structure and Function

IN B.2.5 Protein structures. Also covered: NoS.6.

Key Questions

How do protists move in the environment?

How do protists reproduce?

Vocabulary

pseudopod • cilium • flagellum • spore • conjugation • alternation of generations • sporangium

Taking Notes

Compare/Contrast Table As you read, make a table that compares and contrasts the different ways protists move.

BUILD Vocabulary

GREEK ROOTS The word **pseudopod** comes from the Greek roots *pseudo,* meaning "false," and *pod,* meaning "foot."

THINK ABOUT IT Our bodies are packed with specialized systems of every sort. Organ systems help us move, sense the environment, digest our food, and even reproduce. But protists have no such systems—they do it all within the confines of a single cell. Imagine what such cells would have to be like to succeed in the never-ending struggle for life on Earth. The protists we see today are winners in that struggle.

How Protists Move

How do protists move in the environment?

Before they gave rise to multicellular eukaryotes, protists evolved just about every form of cellular movement known to exist. **Some protists move by changing their cell shape, and some move by means of specialized organelles. Other protists do not move actively but are carried by wind, water, or other organisms.**

Amoeboid Movement Many unicellular protists move by changing their shape, a process that makes use of cytoplasmic projections known as **pseudopods** (SOO doh pahdz). The best-known protists with this form of movement are the amoebas. In **Figure 21–4,** you can see how the cytoplasm of the amoeba streams into the pseudopod and the rest of the cell follows. This type of locomotion is called amoeboid movement and is found in many protists. It is powered by a cytoskeletal protein called actin. Actin is also found in the muscle cells of animals, where it plays an important role in muscle contraction.

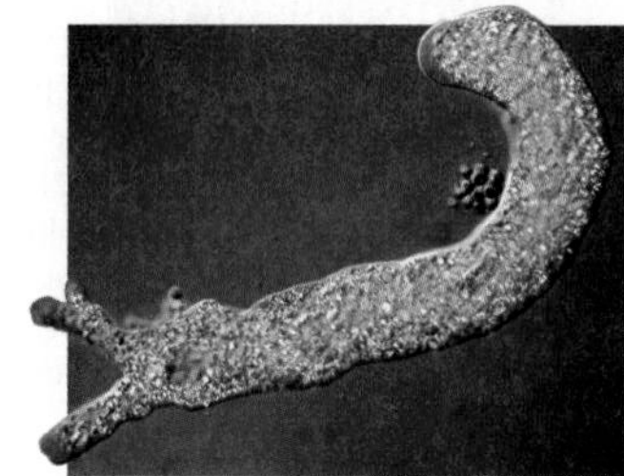
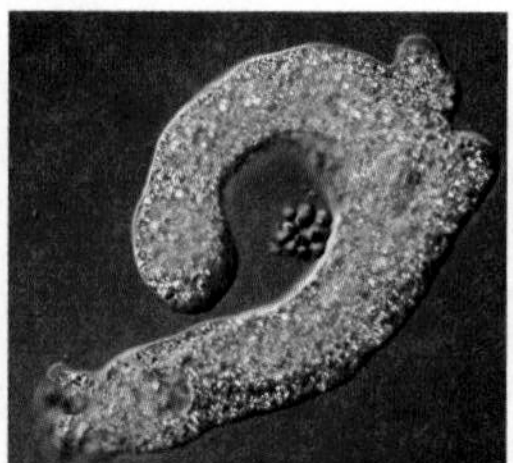
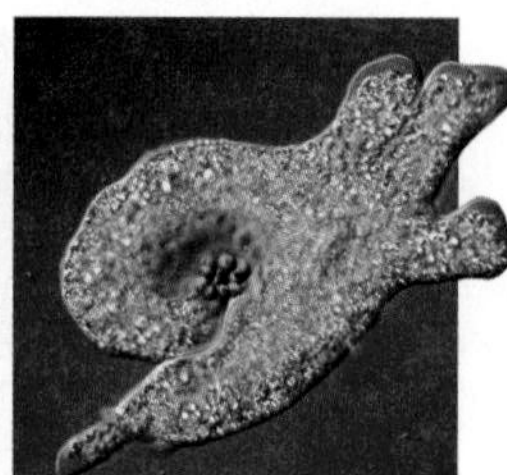

FIGURE 21–4 Amoeboid Movement An amoeba moves by first extending a pseudopod away from its body. The organism's cytoplasm then streams into the pseudopod. Amoebas also use pseudopods to surround and ingest prey. Here, the prey is a cluster of green algal cells. (LM 220×)

UbD Teach for Understanding

ENDURING UNDERSTANDING From microorganisms to plants, organisms vary widely in the way they carry out basic life processes.

GUIDING QUESTION How do protists move and reproduce?

EVIDENCE OF UNDERSTANDING *After completing the lesson, give students the following assessment to show their understanding of the different ways protists move.* Have students work in pairs to make a flip book for younger students that shows one way protists move. Provide flip books as models. Tell students to start the first page near the outer vertical edge of the paper so the figure can be easily seen when the pages are flipped. Suggest they plan the first and last drawings before they start, and trace each drawing on a blank page on top of the previous drawing. Have students include a cover, a title, and a simple written explanation of the movement.

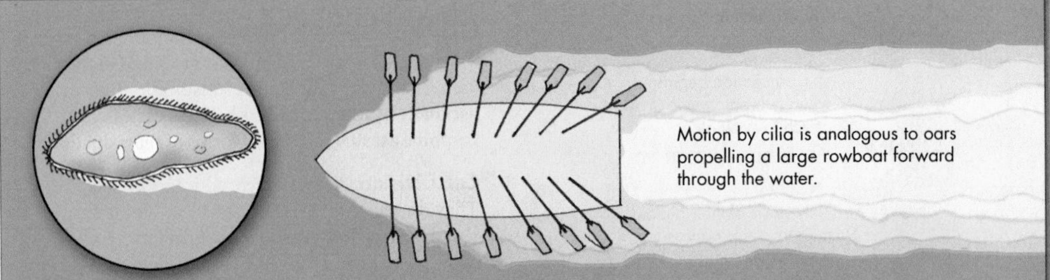

Motion by cilia is analogous to oars propelling a large rowboat forward through the water.

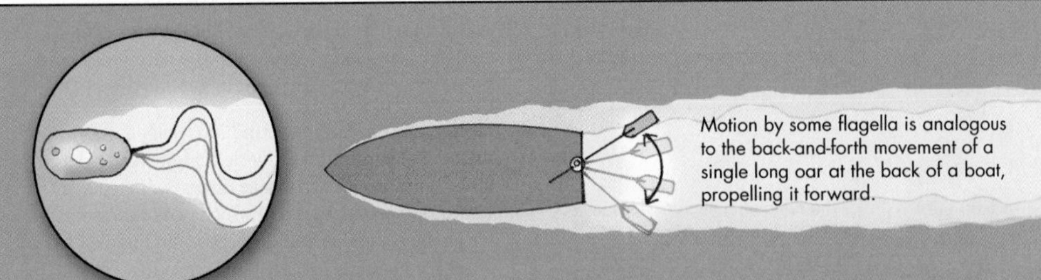

Motion by some flagella is analogous to the back-and-forth movement of a single long oar at the back of a boat, propelling it forward.

VISUAL ANALOGY

HOW CELLS MOVE LIKE BOATS

FIGURE 21–5 The forward motion provided by cilia or some flagella is similar to two ways by which oars propel a boat.

Cilia and Flagella Many protists move by means of cilia (SIL ee uh) and flagella (fluh JEL uh), structures supported by microtubules. Cilia and flagella have nearly identical internal structures, but they produce cellular motion differently. **Cilia** (singular: cilium) are short and numerous, and they move somewhat like oars on a boat. **Flagella** (singular: flagellum) are relatively long and usually number only one or two per cell. Some flagella spin like tiny propellers, but most produce a wavelike motion from base to tip. Compare these two types of motion in **Figure 21–5.** Protists that move using cilia are known as *ciliates,* and those that move with flagella are called *flagellates.*

Passive Movement It may surprise you to learn that some of the most important protists are nonmotile—they depend on air or water currents and other organisms to carry them around. These protists form reproductive cells called **spores** that can enter the cells of other organisms and live as parasites. Spore-forming protists include *Plasmodium,* which is carried by mosquitoes and causes malaria, and *Cryptosporidium,* which spreads through contaminated drinking water and causes severe intestinal disease.

In Your Notebook *Look up the word roots for cilia and flagella, and write an explanation of how each term relates to its root.*

MYSTERY CLUE

The Irish potato crop was propagated by cutting out the small buds on the potatoes—the eyes—and saving them for the next year's crop. This resulted in whole fields of genetically identical potatoes. How do you think this practice might have contributed to the spread of the blight?

 Search Lesson 21.2  • Visual Analogy

How Science Works

MORE ABOUT CILIA AND FLAGELLA

Biologists originally discriminated between cilia and flagella, because in the days of the light microscope, they thought cilia and flagella might be structurally different. The more modern and more powerful electron microscope showed the structure and biochemistry of both organelles to be identical in protists. Each cilium and flagellum is composed of a circle of nine fused pairs of microtubules—filamentous intracellular structures—surrounding a central pair of single microtubules (called a "9 + 2 configuration"). The microtubules use energy from ATP to slide against one another. Each stroke of a cilium or flagellum involves thousands of chemical reactions.

Teach

VISUAL ANALOGY

Walk students through the motions of protists with cilia and flagella shown in **Figure 21–5,** and explain that this analogy works well because motile protists require a moist or wet environment in which to move. Point out that cilia are evenly spaced and beat in a regular, efficient pattern. A flagellum whips back and forth or spins in a pattern that propels the organism through water. Ask students to recall their observations of protists with cilia or flagella in the Lesson 21.1 Quick Lab.

DIFFERENTIATED INSTRUCTION

ELL **English Language Learners** Help students pronounce the terms *cilia* and *flagella.* Point out the difference between the singular and plural forms. Ask students to think of another term they have learned that forms the plural in the same way. *(Sample answers: bacteria/bacterium, grana/granum)* Then, have them practice using the singular and plural forms by making up sentences that contain the terms *cilium, cilia, flagellum, and flagella.*

 Ask students how variation within a population affects evolution by natural selection. *(Natural selection depends on the existence of differences between individuals. Wide variation within a population means that there is a greater chance that some individuals will have characteristics that allow them to survive selective changes in their environment.)* Guide them to conclude that populations of genetically identical organisms are limited in their ability to survive changes in environmental conditions. Students can go online to Biology.com to gather their evidence.

 Students can compare the motions of cilia and flagella to the motions of many paired oars and a single oar in the **Visual Analogy: How Cells Move Like Boats.** They can further explore how protists move by watching **Interactive Art: Amoeba and Paramecium.**

Answers

IN YOUR NOTEBOOK *Cilia* is from *cilium,* meaning "eyelid," having to do with eyelashes. *Flagella* is from *flagrum,* meaning "whip." Sample answer: Cilia are like eyelashes, because both are short and numerous. Flagella are like whips, because both move back and forth.

Teach continued

Use Visuals

Help students compare conjugation and subsequent mitotic reproduction with sexual reproduction by comparing **Figure 21–6** and **Figure 21–7.**

Ask How is conjugation similar to mitosis? *(A cell that has the same number of chromosomes as the parent cell results—in this case a diploid cell.)*

Ask How is conjugation similar to meiosis and fertilization? *(The end result is a diploid cell with recombined genes.)*

Ask What is the advantage of conjugation for a paramecium species? *(Conjugation provides new combinations of genes.)*

Then, direct students' attention to the key in **Figure 21–7.** Review the terms *haploid* and *diploid.*

Ask What are the haploid forms of the water mold? *(The egg cells and male nuclei within the male reproductive structures are haploid.)*

Ask Which form of reproduction results in a greater variety of offspring? *(sexual reproduction)*

DIFFERENTIATED INSTRUCTION

L1 Special Needs Help students compare **Figure 21–6** and **Figure 21–7** by sketching both figures on the board. Have volunteers label each structure in the different stages of both diagrams as being haploid (N) or diploid (2N).

ELL Focus on ELL: Extend Language

BEGINNING AND INTERMEDIATE SPEAKERS

Have students use an **ELL Frayer Model** for each of the lesson vocabulary terms. In the center of each model, have them write the vocabulary term. In the four corners of the model, have students write the definition of the term, draw an illustration of the term, give an example, and, if possible, translate a definition of the term into their native language. Beginning speakers can work with a partner and use phrases in their examples and definitions. Ask intermediate speakers to write simple sentences.

Study Wkbks A/B, Appendix S26, ELL Frayer Model. **Transparencies,** GO10.

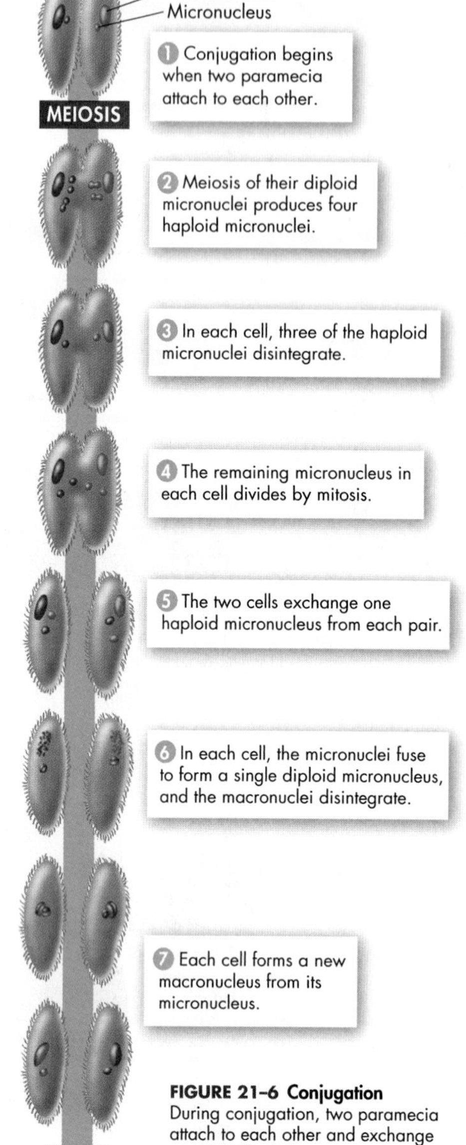

Macronucleus
Micronucleus
MEIOSIS
1 Conjugation begins when two paramecia attach to each other.
2 Meiosis of their diploid micronuclei produces four haploid micronuclei.
3 In each cell, three of the haploid micronuclei disintegrate.
4 The remaining micronucleus in each cell divides by mitosis.
5 The two cells exchange one haploid micronucleus from each pair.
6 In each cell, the micronuclei fuse to form a single diploid micronucleus, and the macronuclei disintegrate.
7 Each cell forms a new macronucleus from its micronucleus.

FIGURE 21–6 Conjugation
During conjugation, two paramecia attach to each other and exchange genetic information.
Interpret Diagrams ***What do paramecia exchange during conjugation?***

Protist Reproduction

How do protists reproduce?

The incredible variety of protists is reflected in their varied life cycles. **Some protists reproduce asexually by mitosis. Others have life cycles that combine asexual and sexual forms of reproduction.**

Cell Division Amoebas reproduce by mitosis: They duplicate their genetic material and then simply divide into two genetically identical cells. Most other protists have phases in their life cycle in which they also produce new individuals by mitosis. Mitosis enables protists to reproduce rapidly, especially under ideal conditions, but it produces cells that are genetically identical to the parent cell, and thus limits the development of genetic diversity.

Conjugation Paramecia and most ciliates reproduce asexually by mitotic cell division. However, under stress, paramecia can remake themselves through **conjugation**—a process in which two organisms exchange genetic material, as shown in **Figure 21–6.** After conjugating, the cells then reproduce by mitosis.

Paramecium has two types of nuclei: a macronucleus and one or more smaller micronuclei. The micronucleus is a bit like a reference library where books don't circulate—it holds a "reserve copy" of every gene in the cell. The macronucleus is more like a lending library—it has multiple copies of the genes the cell uses in its day-to-day activities.

Conjugation is not a type of reproduction because no new individuals are formed. It is, however, a sexual process, using meiosis to produce new combinations of genetic information. In a large population, conjugation helps produce and maintain genetic diversity, the raw material for evolution.

Sexual Reproduction Many protists have complex sexual life cycles in which they alternate between a diploid and a haploid phase, a process known as **alternation of generations.** An example is the life cycle of a type of protist known as a water mold. Water molds, or oomycetes (oh oh MY seets), thrive on dead and decaying organic matter in water or as parasites of plants on land.

UbD Check for Understanding

USE VOCABULARY

Ask each student to choose one of the lesson vocabulary terms and write it on an index card. On the back of the card, ask students to write two or three words or short phrases related to the term. Then, collect and shuffle the cards. Call out the first word or phrase on a card, and randomly call on a student to identify the term. If the student does not answer correctly, call out another word or phrase from the card, and give the student another chance to answer. Continue until you have used all the cards and given every student a chance to answer.

ADJUST INSTRUCTION

Note which vocabulary terms students have trouble with, and have them reread the text where those terms are explained. Ask students to write a definition of each term in their own words.

Answers

FIGURE 21–6 haploid micronuclei

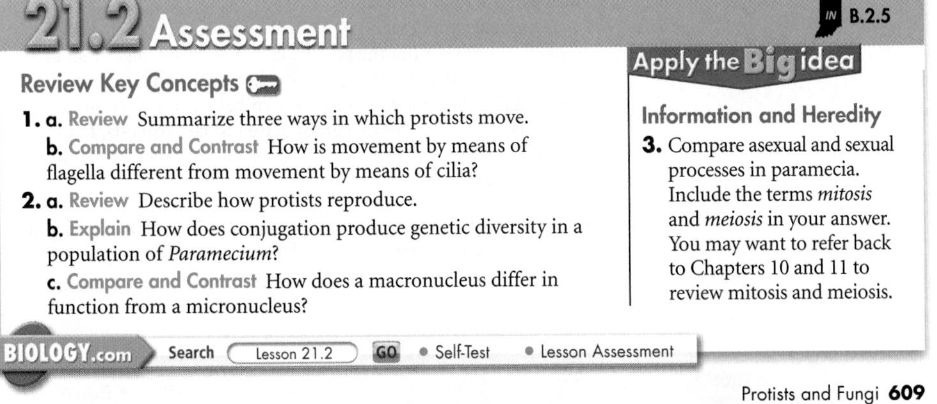

FIGURE 21–7 Water Mold Life Cycle Water molds reproduce both asexually and sexually.

The life cycle of a water mold is shown in **Figure 21–7.** Water molds grow into long branching filaments consisting of many cells formed by mitotic cell division. Water molds—and many other protists—reproduce asexually by producing spores in a structure called a **sporangium** (spoh RAN jee um). In water molds the spores are flagellated. Water molds also reproduce sexually by undergoing meiosis and forming male and female structures. These structures produce haploid nuclei that fuse during fertilization, forming a zygote that begins a new life cycle.

21.2 Assessment

IN B.2.5

Review Key Concepts

1. a. Review Summarize three ways in which protists move.
   b. Compare and Contrast How is movement by means of flagella different from movement by means of cilia?
2. a. Review Describe how protists reproduce.
   b. Explain How does conjugation produce genetic diversity in a population of *Paramecium*?
   c. Compare and Contrast How does a macronucleus differ in function from a micronucleus?

Apply the Big idea

Information and Heredity

3. Compare asexual and sexual processes in paramecia. Include the terms *mitosis* and *meiosis* in your answer. You may want to refer back to Chapters 10 and 11 to review mitosis and meiosis.

BIOLOGY.com Search Lesson 21.2 GO • Self-Test • Lesson Assessment

Assess and Remediate

EVALUATE UNDERSTANDING

Have students write and illustrate two short paragraphs summarizing how protists move and how they reproduce. Then, have them complete the 21.2 Assessment.

REMEDIATION SUGGESTION

L1 **Struggling Students** If students have trouble with **Question 2b,** have them make their own drawing of **Figure 21–6** and write each step in their own words. Suggest they use N and 2N to describe the micronuclei in each step and assume each paramecium has 60 chromosomes.

BIOLOGY.com Students can check their understanding of lesson concepts with the **Self-Test** assessment. They can then take an online version of the **Lesson Assessment.**

Assessment Answers

1a. Answers should include descriptions of amoeboid movement and locomotion with cilia and flagella.

1b. Movement by a flagellum is a back-and-forth movement like a single, long oar at the back of a boat. Movement by cilia is like many oars on both sides of a boat.

2a. Protists reproduce asexually by mitosis and spore production and sexually by egg and sperm fusing during fertilization.

2b. Conjugation results in new combinations of genes, which help create and maintain genetic diversity.

2c. A macronucleus contains multiple copies of the genes a cell needs for its day-to-day activities. A micronucleus contains a "reserve" copy of every gene in the cell.

3. Big idea Students should define the terms *mitosis* and *meiosis.* Explanations should include that, under most conditions, paramecia reproduce by mitotic cell division. Under certain conditions, they engage in conjugation, which is not a form of reproduction but is a sexual process because it involves meiosis.

LESSON 21.3

Getting Started

Objectives

21.3.1 Describe the ecological significance of photosynthetic protists.

21.3.2 Describe how heterotrophic protists obtain food.

21.3.3 Identify the symbiotic relationships that involve protists.

Student Resources

Study Workbooks A and B, 21.3 Worksheets

Spanish Study Workbook, 21.3 Worksheets

BIOLOGY.com Lesson Overview • Lesson Notes • Activities: Data Analysis, Art in Motion • Assessment: Self-Test, Lesson Assessment

For corresponding lesson in the **Foundation Edition,** see pages 509–513.

BIOLOGY.com Students see how protist microfossils are used to learn about ancient oceans in **Data Analysis: Tiny Fossils and Ancient Oceans.**

Answers

IN YOUR NOTEBOOK Tables should include the four column headings (Feeding Fish and Whales, Supporting Coral Reefs, Providing Shelter, Recycling Wastes) as well as the main ideas and details of each paragraph.

IN INDIANA ACADEMIC STANDARDS

For the full text of all standards, see the Course Overview in the front matter of this book.

B.4.4 Describe how climate, the pattern of matter and energy flow, the birth and death of new organisms, and the interaction between those organisms contribute to the long term stability of an ecosystem.

21.3 The Ecology of Protists

IN **B.4.4** Stability of an ecosystem.

Key Questions

What is the ecological significance of photosynthetic protists?

How do heterotrophic protists obtain food?

What types of symbiotic relationships involve protists?

Vocabulary

algal bloom
food vacuole
gullet
plasmodium

Taking Notes

Outline Preview the heads of this lesson to construct an outline of different types of ways that protists obtain energy. Fill in your outline with specific examples as you read.

THINK ABOUT IT After a few days of rain, you notice a small spot of yellow slime at the base of a stand of tall grass. Is it some sort of rot? You mark its position with paint. A few days later, you come back, and it has grown and moved away from the mark. Is it an animal? A fungus? A strange plant? The correct answer is none of the above. It's a protist called a slime mold.

Autotrophic Protists

What is the ecological significance of photosynthetic protists?

If you've seen greenish scum growing along the banks of a pond or maybe even at the edges of a poorly maintained swimming pool, you might have called it "algae" without thinking. What you may not have realized at the time is that many of the organisms in that scum were, in fact, protists.

Diversity Biologists long ago realized that the organisms commonly called "algae" actually belong to many different groups. Some (the cyanobacteria) are prokaryotes, some (the green algae) belong to the plant kingdom, and some are protists. Photosynthetic protists include many phytoplankton species and the red and brown algae, as well as euglenas and dinoflagellates. These organisms share an autotrophic lifestyle, marked by the ability to use the energy from light to make a carbohydrate food source.

You might think that all photosynthetic protists are closely related to plants, but this is not the case. In fact, it is the red algae that are most closely related to plants. Many other photosynthetic protists are more closely related to nonphotosynthetic protists. In some cases certain species within a group have lost chloroplasts. In other cases endosymbiosis added a chloroplast to some species but not to their relatives.

In Your Notebook *Preview the next page. Then, make a four-column table using the headings listed. Use the table to record your notes as you read.*

UbD Teach for Understanding

ENDURING UNDERSTANDING From microorganisms to plants, organisms vary widely in the way they carry out basic life processes.

GUIDING QUESTION What roles do protists play in the environment?

EVIDENCE OF UNDERSTANDING *After completing the lesson, give students the following assessment to show their understanding of the significance of protists to their environments.* Have each student choose a protist from the lesson that is harmful or beneficial to the environment and create a "Missing" or "Wanted" poster, like those of the Old West. The poster should include a picture of the protist and/or its environment and explain how the protist harms or helps the environment. The poster should also list identifying characteristics of the protist.

Ecological Roles Photosynthetic protists play major ecological roles on Earth. **The position of photosynthetic protists at the base of the food chain makes much of the diversity of aquatic life possible.** Some examples of ecological roles played by photosynthetic protists are shown in **Figure 21–8.**

▶ ***Feeding Fish and Whales*** Photosynthetic protists make up a large portion of phytoplankton, the small, free-floating photosynthetic organisms found near the surface of oceans and lakes. About half of the photosynthesis that takes place on Earth is carried out by phytoplankton, which provide a direct source of nourishment for organisms as diverse as shrimp and baleen whales. And they are an indirect source of nourishment for humans. When you eat tuna fish, you are eating fish that fed on smaller fish that fed on still smaller animals that fed on photosynthetic protists.

▶ ***Supporting Coral Reefs*** Coral reefs, which are found in warm ocean waters throughout the world, provide food and shelter to large numbers of fish and other organisms. Protist algae known as zooxanthellae provide most of the coral's energy needs by photosynthesis. By nourishing coral animals, these algae help maintain the equilibrium of the coral ecosystem. Coralline red algae also help to provide calcium carbonate to stabilize growing coral reefs.

▶ ***Providing Shelter*** The largest known protist is giant kelp, a brown alga that can grow to more than 60 meters in length. Kelp forests provide shelter for many marine species, and the kelp itself is a source of food for sea urchins. Another brown alga, called *Sargassum,* forms huge floating mats many kilometers long in an area of the Atlantic Ocean near Bermuda known as the Sargasso Sea.

▶ ***Recycling Wastes*** Many protists grow rapidly in regions where sewage is discharged, where they play a vital role in recycling waste materials. When the amount of waste is excessive, however, populations of protists like *Euglena* can grow to enormous numbers and create an **algal bloom.** Algal blooms can disrupt ecosystem homeostasis. For example, an algal bloom in a pond or lake depletes nutrients from the water, and the decomposition of the dead protists can rob water of its oxygen, causing fish and invertebrates to die. In another example, blooms of marine protists called dinoflagellates create what is known as a red tide. The buildup of toxins produced by these protists can poison fish and shellfish.

FIGURE 21–8 Ecological Roles of Protists
Photosynthetic protists play many roles in the environment. Apply Concepts ***Which example is disruptive to ecosystem homeostasis?***

Build Reading Skills

Help students focus attention on the Key Concept and guide them to interact with ideas in the text by using the **Anticipation/Reaction Guide** strategy. Discuss the term *homeostasis* as it applies to ecosystems. Then, have students use a sheet of paper to cover the text on the left side of this page so that they see only **Figure 21–8.** Write the Lesson 21.3 Guiding Question on the board, and ask students to use the figure and their prior knowledge to write one statement about each photo in response to the question. After students have read the text, have them return to their statements and make corrections or additions. Then, discuss what students learned.

Study Wkbks A/B, Appendix S1, Anticipation/Reaction Guide.

DIFFERENTIATED INSTRUCTION

LPR **Less Proficient Readers** Help students answer the Guiding Question for each photo in **Figure 21–8** by asking them to scan the text on the left side of the page to find statements in each subheading that describe ecological roles. Point out that sometimes this information is obvious because of key-word clues alerting the reader that explanatory text will follow. For example, the text for **Supporting Coral Reefs** uses the key word *role* when it states, "Red algae play two key roles in the formation of coral reefs." Ask students to find another statement in another subheading that uses a key-word clue. *(Many protists grow rapidly in regions where sewage is discharged, where they play a vital role in recycling waste materials.)* Then, have them find the answers to the Guiding Question in the remaining subheadings.

ELL Focus on ELL: Access Content

BEGINNING AND INTERMEDIATE SPEAKERS Give students a scaffolded outline of the lesson with some main ideas and details already filled in. Have them complete the outline as they progress through the lesson. Beginning speakers might use words or simple phrases, while intermediate speakers can use sentences. Encourage students to use their completed outlines as study aids.

Biology In-Depth

CHLOROPHYLL AND ACCESSORY PIGMENTS IN ALGAE

As sunlight passes through water, much of the light's energy is absorbed by the water. Seawater absorbs large amounts of the red and violet wavelengths. Dim, blue light can penetrate deeper waters. In adapting to conditions of limited light, various groups of algae have evolved different forms of chlorophyll. Each absorbs different wavelengths of light. Many algae also have accessory pigments. These are compounds that absorb and reflect light at different wavelengths than chlorophyll, giving algae a wide range of colors. Red algae contain accessory pigments called phycobilins, which enable red algae to absorb the wavelengths of light that can reach great depths. Brown algae contain the accessory pigment fucoxanthin, which along with chlorophyll, gives the algae its brown color.

Answers

FIGURE 21–8 Red tides result in buildups of toxins that can poison fish and shellfish.

LESSON 21.3

Teach continued

Use Visuals

Have students compare the feeding structures of amoebas and paramecia by examining **Figure 21–4** and **Figure 21–9.** Direct students' attention to **Figure 21–4.** Point out that amoebas use their pseudopods to move and to capture food.

Ask How do you know amoebas are heterotrophs? *(They capture food rather than using energy from sunlight to make food.)*

Ask What structure does the amoeba's pseudopod become once food is taken in? *(a food vacuole)*

Ask What is the function of a food vacuole? *(It temporarily stores food and releases indigestible waste materials outside the amoeba.)*

Next, direct students' attention to **Figure 21–9.** Explain how food and waste materials travel through a paramecium.

Ask How are cilia related to feeding? *(Cilia outside the paramecium sweep food particles into the gullet. Cilia lining the gullet move food to the organism's interior.)* Point out the difference between the contractile vacuole and the food vacuole. Tell students the contractile vacuoles collect and remove excess water, thereby helping the ciliate maintain homeostasis.

DIFFERENTIATED INSTRUCTION

L1 Special Needs Have students make their own labeled drawing of the paramecium shown in **Figure 21–9** and write a brief description of the function of each of the labeled structures. Suggest they use **Figures 21–5** and **21–6** as a reference for the descriptions of macronucleus, micronucleus, and cilia.

BUILD Vocabulary

MULTIPLE MEANINGS The name *Amoeba* refers to a particular genus of protists, but it is also used generically (in lowercase and without italicization) to mean "any protists that move using pseudopods," including the unicellular form of slime molds.

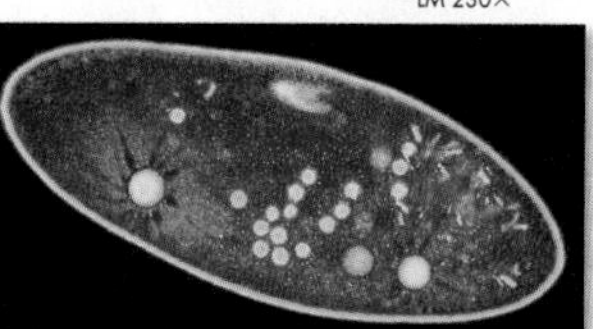

Heterotrophic Protists

How do heterotrophic protists obtain food?

Many protists are heterotrophs: They obtain food from other living organisms. **Some heterotrophic protists engulf and digest their food, while others live by absorbing molecules from the environment.**

Amoebas Amoebas can capture and digest their food, surrounding a cell or particle and then taking it inside themselves to form a food vacuole. A **food vacuole** is a small cavity in the cytoplasm that temporarily stores food. Once inside the cell, the material is digested rapidly, and the nutrients are passed along to the rest of the cell. Indigestible waste materials remain inside the vacuole until the vacuole releases them outside the cell.

Ciliates *Paramecium* and other ciliates use their cilia to sweep food particles into the **gullet,** an indentation in one side of the organism, as shown in **Figure 21–9.** The particles are trapped in the gullet and forced into food vacuoles that form at its base. The food vacuoles pinch off into the cytoplasm and eventually fuse with lysosomes, which contain digestive enzymes. Waste materials are emptied into the environment when the food vacuole fuses with a region of the cell membrane called the anal pore.

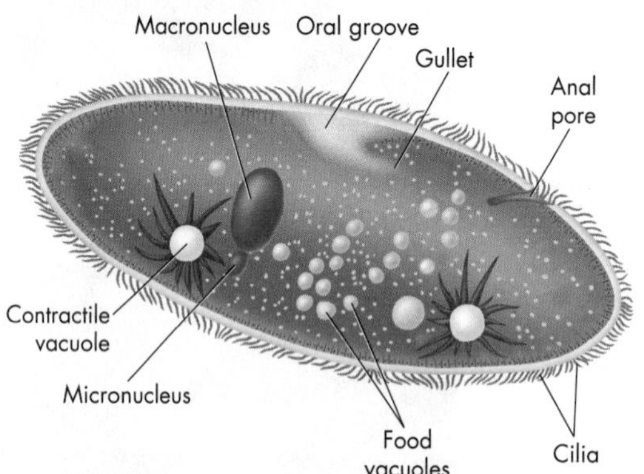

FIGURE 21–9 Feeding Structures of *Paramecium* Cilia lining the gullet move food to the organism's interior. There, the food particles are engulfed, forming food vacuoles.

Quick Lab GUIDED INQUIRY

How Does a Paramecium Eat?

1. Use separate dropper pipettes to place a drop of paramecium culture and a drop of *Chlorella* culture next to each other on a microscope slide.
2. Use a toothpick to transfer a few granules of carmine dye to the drops on the slide. Add a coverslip so that the two drops mix.
3. Place the slide on the microscope stage and use the low-power objective to locate several paramecia.
4. Use the high-power objective to observe the contents and behavior of the paramecia.

Analyze and Conclude

1. **Observe** Where did the *Chlorella* cells and carmine dye granules accumulate?
2. **Infer** How do you think this accumulation of cells and dye granules occurs?
3. **Form a Hypothesis** What process in the paramecia do you think resulted in this change?

Quick Lab

PURPOSE Students will observe paramecia and form a hypothesis about how paramecia eat.

MATERIALS 2 dropper pipettes, *Paramecium* culture, *Chlorella* culture, microscope slide, toothpick, carmine dye, coverslip, compound microscope

SAFETY Make sure students wear a lab apron to protect skin and clothing from the dye. Remind them to use care when handling glass slides and coverslips and to wash their hands after the activity.

PLANNING Order cultures of *Paramecium* and *Chlorella* and carmine dye from a biological supply house.

ANALYZE AND CONCLUDE

1. They accumulated inside the paramecia.
2. The paramecia trapped the *Chlorella* cells and dye granules in the gullet and then forced the particles into food vacuoles.
3. Sample answer: The paramecia took in the *Chlorella* cells and the dye granules by the process of endocytosis.

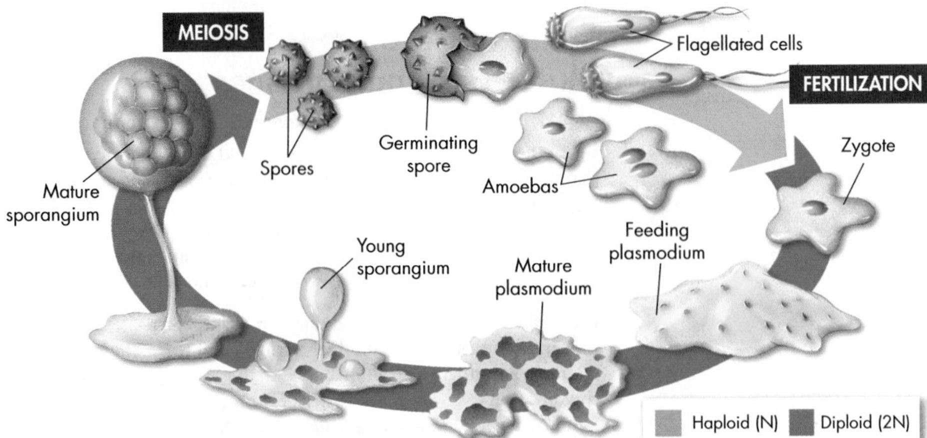

FIGURE 21–10 Slime Mold Life Cycle The feeding-plasmodium stage in the slime mold life cycle is a collection of many amoebalike organisms—in some species, these organisms are contained within a single cell membrane. The plasmodium eventually produces sporangia, which in turn undergo meiosis and produce haploid spores. The spores grow into amoebalike or flagellated cells. The flagellated cells then fuse to produce diploid zygotes that repeat the cycle.

Slime Molds Another type of heterotrophic protist is a slime mold, which thrives on decaying organic matter. Slime molds are found in places that are damp and rich in organic matter—on the floor of a forest or a backyard compost pile, for example. Slime molds play key roles in recycling nutrients in an ecosystem.

At one stage in their life cycle, shown in **Figure 21–10,** slime molds exist as a collection of individual amoebalike cells. Eventually these aggregate to form a large structure known as a **plasmodium,** which may continue to move. The plasmodium eventually develops sporangia, in which meiosis produces haploid spores to continue the cycle.

MYSTERY CLUE

Nutrients from decomposing potatoes infected by potato blight enter the blight organism by diffusing through its cell walls. Which organism described on these pages feeds in a similar way?

Protists That Absorb Some protists survive by absorbing molecules that other organisms have released to the environment. Water molds like the one shown in **Figure 21–11,** for example, grow on dead or decaying plants and animals, absorbing food molecules through their cellulose cell walls and cell membranes. If you've seen white fuzz growing on the surface of a dead fish in the water, you've seen water molds in action.

FIGURE 21–11 Water Mold This dead goldfish is covered with the common water mold *Saprolegnia.* Compare and Contrast ***Contrast how a water mold and a paramecium obtain food.***

BIOLOGY.com Search Lesson 21.3 GO • Art in Motion

613

Use Visuals

Use **Figure 21–10** to explain the different kinds of movement that occur during the life cycle of a slime mold. Have students describe two ways that slime molds can move during certain life stages. *(Slime molds can move using flagella and through pseudopods in different stages.)*

Ask Which stage(s) include cells that have flagella? *(the haploid flagellated cells)*

Ask Which stage(s) include cells that use pseudopods for movement? *(the haploid amoebas and the large group of amoeba-like organisms that make up a plasmodium)*

Ask Which stage(s) include cells that cannot move on their own? *(spores)*

DIFFERENTIATED INSTRUCTION

L1 Struggling Students Have students use **Figure 21–10** to rewrite the steps in the life cycle of a slime mold in a **Cycle Diagram.** Make sure students understand that many amoebas fuse to form one plasmodium and that only two haploid cells join to form the zygote.

Study Wkbks A/B, Appendix S23, Cycle Diagram. **Transparencies,** GO6.

If students need help answering the question, have them identify the processes by which amoebas, ciliates, slime molds, and water molds obtain food. Then, lead them to conclude that, like water molds, the potato blight organism feeds through absorption of food molecules through cell walls. Students can go online to Biology.com to gather their evidence.

Quick Facts

ECOLOGY OF SLIME MOLDS

Slime molds are important as recyclers of organic material. They help break down the tissues of dead animals and plants. The dark, rich topsoil that provides plants with nutrients results from this decomposition. The plasmodia are often found on rotting logs, in leaf litter, and on lawn grasses. One particular species, *Fuligo septica,* is known as the "dog vomit" or "scrambled egg" slime mold because of its frothy, yellow appearance. It commonly shows up on bark mulch in landscape beds. Though unsightly, this species and many others are harmless to humans, other animals, and plants. Some slime molds are plant pests, but most contribute to nutrient recycling through their role as decomposers.

Answers

FIGURE 21–11 A water mold absorbs molecules; a paramecium sweeps food into its gullet using cilia.

Teach continued

ZOOMING IN

Have students recall the definition of *symbiosis* and give examples they have studied in previous chapters. Then, review the types of symbiosis: mutualism (both species benefit), commensalism (one species benefits and the other is neither harmed nor helped), and parasitism (one species is helped by harming the other). Use **Figure 21–12** to discuss the mutualistic relationship of termites and *Trichonympha.* Ask students to explain why the relationship is a good example of mutualism. *(Termites benefit because* Trichonympha *breaks down the cellulose in wood, which allows termites to gain nutrients from it.* Trichonympha *gets a safe home inside the termite and a steady supply of wood to eat.)* Tell students this genus of protists also is found in wood-eating cockroaches. Point out that the first three photos in **Figure 21–8** also show mutualistic relationships. Then, discuss the type of symbiosis portrayed in **Figure 21–13.** *(parasitism)*

DIFFERENTIATED INSTRUCTION

ELL English Language Learners Make sure students understand the difference between mutualists and parasites. Explain that mutualists are helpful to a host, while parasites are harmful to a host. Write these sentences on the board: *Trichonympha* is mutualistic, because _____. *(it helps a termite digest wood)* Trypanosomes are parasitic, because _____. *(they destroy blood cells and infect other tissues of the body)* Pair beginning speakers with intermediate or advanced speakers, and have partners use the text to complete each statement.

Symbiotic Protists—Mutualists and Parasites

What types of symbiotic relationships involve protists?

Given the great diversity of protists, it should come as no surprise that many of them are involved in symbiotic relationships with other organisms. As you know, symbiosis is a relationship in which two species live closely together. Many of these relationships are mutualistic: Both organisms benefit. However, some are parasitic relationships, in which the protist benefits at the expense of its host.

Mutualists Earlier you learned that photosynthetic protists called zooxanthellae are essential to the health of coral reefs. These protists maintain a mutualistic relationship with the animals of the reef, which could not survive without their help. **Many protists are involved in mutualistic symbioses, in which they and their hosts both benefit.**

Another striking example of a mutualistic protist is *Trichonympha,* shown in **Figure 21–12.** *Trichonympha* is a flagellated protist that lives within the digestive system of various species of termites and makes it possible for the insects to digest wood. Termites themselves do not have enzymes to break down the cellulose in wood. How, then, does a termite digest cellulose? In a sense, it doesn't. *Trichonympha* does.

Trichonympha and other organisms in the termite's gut manufacture an enzyme called cellulase that breaks the chemical bonds in cellulose, making it possible for termites to digest wood. With the help of their protist partners, then, termites can munch away, digesting all the wood they can eat.

ZOOMING IN

A PROTIST MUTUALIST

FIGURE 21–12 *Trichonympha* is a wood-digesting protist that lives in the digestive system of termites. Digestive enzymes produced by the protist break down the particles of wood, which you can see inside the protist's body. **Predict** ***What would happen to a termite if its Trichonympha colony died?***

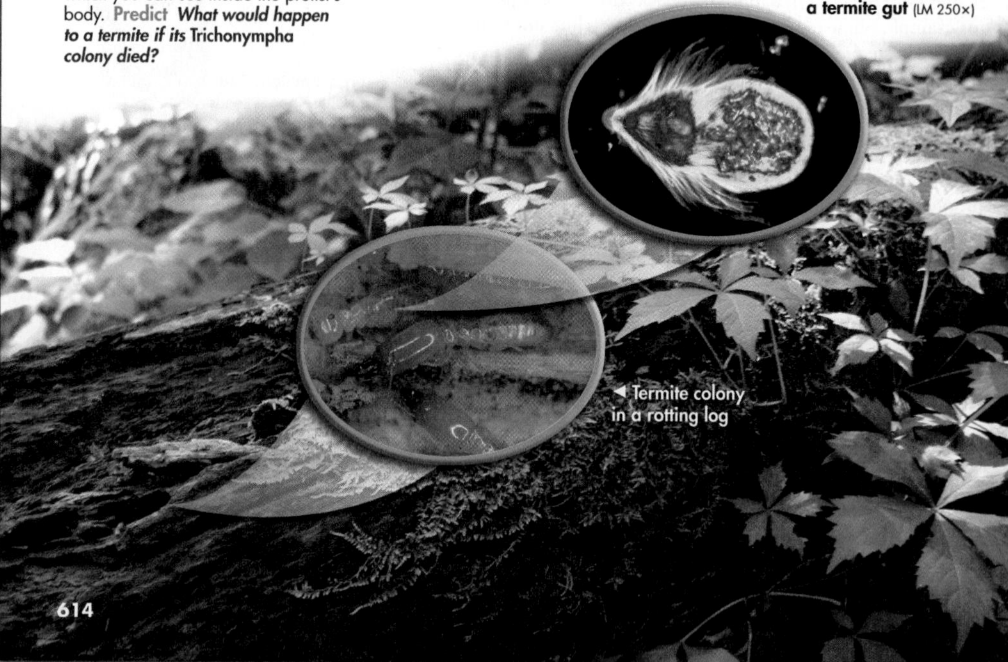

UbD Check for Understanding

INDEX CARD SUMMARIES

Give students each an index card, and ask them to summarize on one side of the card a big idea they understand about relationships involving symbiotic protists. Then, have them write on the other side a statement or statements about the relationships they do not understand.

ADJUST INSTRUCTION

Collect the cards, and write the statements from the back of the cards on the board in the form of questions. Pair students, and have them discuss and answer the questions. Encourage them to refer to the text to clarify and justify their responses. Then, have them write an answer to each question. Call on students at random to share their answers.

Answers

FIGURE 21–12 The termite would also die because of its inability to break down cellulose for food.

FIGURE 21–13 Water-Borne Protist Parasites Water supplies contaminated by animal or human feces can spread protist parasites, causing serious and sometimes deadly outbreaks of intestinal disease.

▲ *Entamoeba* causes a disease known as amebic dysentery. The amoebas live in the intestines, where they absorb food from the host. They also attack the wall of the intestine itself, shown above, destroying parts of it and causing severe bleeding. (SEM 2500×)

▶ The flagellated protist *Giardia* causes severe diarrhea and digestive-system problems. Even crystal-clear streams may be contaminated with *Giardia*, which produces tough cysts that can be killed only by boiling water thoroughly or by adding iodine to the water. (SEM 1500×)

▲ *Cryptosporidium* is resistant to the chlorine compounds often used to sanitize drinking water and therefore poses a special threat to public water systems. In 2008, an outbreak in Utah sickened more than 2000 people. (SEM 16,000×)

Parasites and Disease Unfortunately for humans and some other organisms, protists cause a number of very serious diseases. **Parasitic protists are responsible for some of the world's most deadly diseases, including several kinds of debilitating intestinal diseases, African sleeping sickness, and malaria.**

▶ ***Intestinal Diseases*** Water-borne protists are found in streams, lakes, and oceans. Most cause little harm to humans, but some of these organisms—like those shown in **Figure 21–13**—are parasites that cause serious problems.

▶ ***African Sleeping Sickness*** Flagellated protists of the genus *Trypanosoma* cause African sleeping sickness. Trypanosomes are spread from person to person by the bite of the tsetse fly. They destroy blood cells and infect other tissues in the body, including nerve cells. Severe damage to the nervous system causes some individuals to lose consciousness and lapse into a deep and sometimes fatal sleep, from which the disease gets its name. Control of the tsetse fly and the protist pathogens that it spreads is a major goal of health workers in Africa.

In Your Notebook *How do parasitic protists use passive movement to spread disease? Give examples.*

Lead a Discussion

Ask students to look at the photos of protists in **Figure 21–13** as you read the annotations. Tell them these protists are intestinal pathogens, and are passed out of the body in feces. In places where sanitation is poor, the protists may contaminate water supplies and food. Students might be surprised to learn that *Giardia* and *Cryptosporidium* are commonly reported in the United States. They are primarily spread via recreational waters, such as lakes, swimming pools, and water parks. Many cases of *Giardia* are also transmitted directly from person to person.

Ask How could the water-borne spread of parasitic protists be prevented? *(Sample answer: treatment of water supplies and asking people who have intestinal illnesses not to use recreational waters)*

Ask What might be some obstacles to the methods of prevention mentioned in the figure? *(Sample answer:* Cryptosporidium *is often resistant to chlorine treatment, and boiling water or using iodine can be difficult or expensive.)*

DIFFERENTIATED INSTRUCTION

L3 Advanced Students Have students access the Web site of the Centers for Disease Control and Prevention to find facts about a disease caused by a protist. Ask them to make a brochure stating the sources, transmission, symptoms, diagnosis, treatment, prevention, and number of cases reported annually in the United States.

Quick Facts

TRYPANOSOMES IN DISGUISE

Without treatment, African sleeping sickness is almost always fatal. Current treatments can cause severe side effects, and resistance to treatment by the trypanosomes is common. Though the immune system produces antibodies against trypanosomes, the surface proteins on the organisms constantly change, so antibodies do not recognize them. However, a drug called rapamycin, which is used in transplant patients, looks promising. In laboratory cell cultures, the drug causes trypanosomes to develop multiple nuclei, become malformed, and eventually die.

Answers

IN YOUR NOTEBOOK *Giardia, Cryptosporidium,* and *Entamoeba* are carried along in the digestive tracts of organisms they infect and then by water, if feces contaminate water supplies. Trypanosomes are carried by tsetse flies and in humans.

Teach continued

BIOLOGY.com Students can watch an animated version of **Art in Motion: *Plasmodium* Life Cycle.**

Assess and Remediate

EVALUATE UNDERSTANDING

Have each student write a question and answer on an index card related to the ecological role of protists. Collect the cards, and then read the answers and challenge students to state the questions. Then, have students complete the 21.3 Assessment.

REMEDIATION SUGGESTION

L1 **Struggling Students** If students have trouble with **Question 1b,** have them work with a partner to diagram an ocean food chain. Ask them what ocean animals would eat if photosynthetic protists disappeared.

BIOLOGY.com Students can check their understanding of lesson concepts with the **Self-Test** assessment. They can then take an online version of the **Lesson Assessment.**

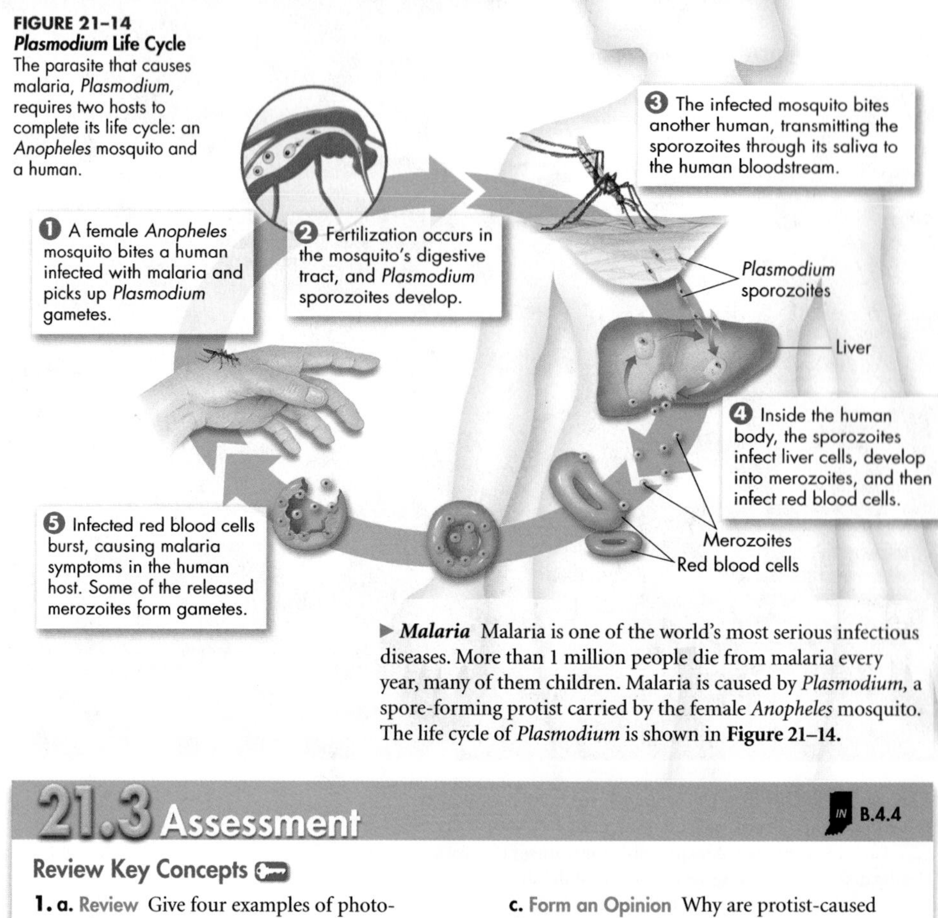

1 A female *Anopheles* mosquito bites a human infected with malaria and picks up *Plasmodium* gametes.
2 Fertilization occurs in the mosquito's digestive tract, and *Plasmodium* sporozoites develop.
3 The infected mosquito bites another human, transmitting the sporozoites through its saliva to the human bloodstream.
Plasmodium sporozoites
Liver
4 Inside the human body, the sporozoites infect liver cells, develop into merozoites, and then infect red blood cells.
Merozoites
Red blood cells
5 Infected red blood cells burst, causing malaria symptoms in the human host. Some of the released merozoites form gametes.

FIGURE 21–14 ***Plasmodium* Life Cycle** The parasite that causes malaria, *Plasmodium*, requires two hosts to complete its life cycle: an *Anopheles* mosquito and a human.

▶ ***Malaria*** Malaria is one of the world's most serious infectious diseases. More than 1 million people die from malaria every year, many of them children. Malaria is caused by *Plasmodium*, a spore-forming protist carried by the female *Anopheles* mosquito. The life cycle of *Plasmodium* is shown in **Figure 21–14.**

21.3 Assessment

IN B.4.4

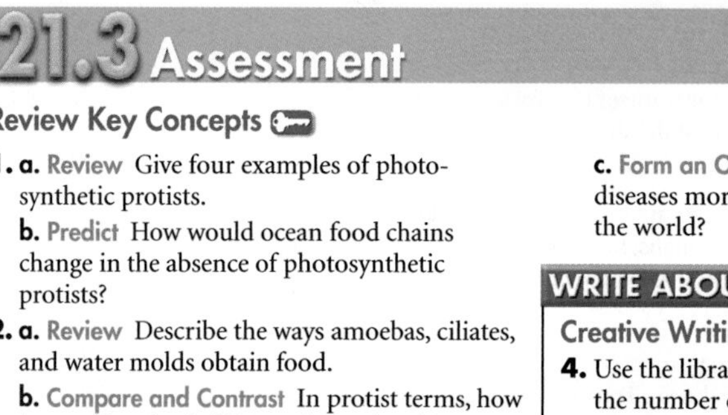

Review Key Concepts

1. a. Review Give four examples of photosynthetic protists.
   b. Predict How would ocean food chains change in the absence of photosynthetic protists?
   c. Form an Opinion Why are protist-caused diseases more widespread in tropical areas of the world?
2. a. Review Describe the ways amoebas, ciliates, and water molds obtain food.
   b. Compare and Contrast In protist terms, how is engulfing food different from absorbing it?
3. a. Review Give two examples each of mutualism and parasitism involving protists.
   b. Explain By what two methods do parasitic protists primarily spread disease?

WRITE ABOUT SCIENCE

Creative Writing

4. Use the library or the Internet to investigate the number of algal blooms off the California coast over the last ten years. Be sure to note the causes, the types of protists identified, and the effects on wildlife and people. Present your findings to the class as an unbiased investigative report.

BIOLOGY.com Search Lesson 21.3 GO • Self-Test • Lesson Assessment

Assessment Answers

1a. Answers may include four of the following: phytoplankton, red algae, brown algae (kelp), euglenas, and dinoflagellates.

1b. Many aquatic species would not survive.

2a. Amoebas use their pseudopods to capture food and form food vacuoles. Most ciliates use their cilia to sweep food particles into their gullet (though some ciliates are photosynthetic). Water molds absorb food molecules through their cellulose cell walls and cell membranes.

2b. Protists that engulf their food can capture whole organisms. Protists that absorb their food take in molecules that other organisms have released to the environment.

3a. Sample answer: Examples of mutualism occur between red algae and coral reefs and between *Trichonympha* and termites; examples of parasitism occur between *Giardia* and humans and between *Cryptosporidium* and humans.

3b. Parasitic protists spread disease primarily through contaminated water and through animals, such as mosquitoes.

3c. Sample answer: The climate is hot and humid year round, which supports the life cycle of insects that are often hosts of parasitic protists.

WRITE ABOUT SCIENCE

4. Student reports should include information on the number of algal blooms off the California coast, where the blooms occurred, the protist species involved, and the bloom's effects on other marine wildlife, such as shellfish.

Low-Tech Weapons Against a High-Tech Parasite

Malaria is one of the most serious infectious diseases in the world, claiming the life of a child every 30 seconds, day and night. The disease is caused by a spore-forming protist, *Plasmodium falciparum*, carried by the *Anopheles* mosquito. Efforts to produce vaccines against the disease have shown some promise, but even the best vaccines to date provide only marginal protection. To make matters worse, drugs that once kept the disease in check, including chloroquine, are almost useless today. In most regions of the world, the parasite has evolved resistance to these drugs.

Research on the disease continues, and scientists have now worked out the complete genome of both the parasite and the mosquito that carries it. The hope is that a better understanding of the genetics of the disease will allow scientists to fashion high-tech weapons against this killer. Surprisingly, however, one of the most promising approaches involves a very low-tech weapon—mosquito netting.

Most malaria infections are the result of mosquito bites that occur when people are sleeping. Studies have shown that when most of a village's residents sleep under insecticide-treated nets, mosquitoes begin to die off, and the likelihood of malaria infection goes down. The cost of the nets, about ten dollars, is remarkably small when measured against the human cost in lives and lost productivity. But it is estimated that as many as 250 million of the nets will be needed to protect populations at risk of this disease. Many charities are now featuring the nets in their fundraising appeals.

▼ A young woman folds insecticide-treated nets inside an African factory.

WRITING Visit several Web sites run by organizations with an antimalaria mission. Then, describe how mosquito netting, a low-tech approach, might be combined effectively with antimalarial vaccines and drugs and other high-tech approaches.

Quick Facts

CHILLING CYCLES

The signs and symptoms of malaria include recurring cycles chills, shaking, fever, and sweating, which are associated with the rupture of red blood cells (RBC) and the release of huge numbers of merozoites into the bloodstream. Not all RBCs become infected. Yet, if only 1 percent of them contain the protist cells, trillions of parasite cells would be circulating in the bloodstream at the same time. The rupture of RBCs occurs simultaneously and at regular intervals—usually a multiple of 24 hours (often every 48 hours). Different species of *Plasmodium* have different replication times, so they can cause fevers at different intervals. *P. falciparum*, which causes the mostly deadly form of malaria, has a growth cycle of 48 hours. Between periods of rupture, the infected person feels normal. With each cycle of replication, however, the parasite load increases significantly.

Teach

Lead a Discussion

Tell students malaria is common in regions where temperatures, humidity, and rainfall are high—ideal factors for the *Anopheles* mosquito to thrive and reproduce. Malaria is prevalent in Southeast Asia, Central and South America, and sub-Saharan Africa, which has the highest transmission rate. Ask students to use information from the feature and what they know about sub-Saharan Africa to infer why malaria is so difficult to bring under control today. *(Sample answer: Some drugs to treat malaria are useless, because the parasite has developed resistance to them.)*

Then, have students discuss the low-tech approach to fighting malaria. Explain that malaria is not the only disease in which a low-tech solution can help fight or prevent its incidence. Suggest pairs think of other low-tech solutions for the prevention of disease. *(Sample answers: regular exercise and a balanced diet may help prevent obesity; sunscreen can reduce the risk of developing skin cancer)* Suggest pairs talk about why it is just as important for people to consider low-tech solutions to disease as well as high-tech.

DIFFERENTIATED INSTRUCTION

L1 Special Needs Help students understand that controlling malaria requires a combination of approaches. Draw a linked chain in a circle to represent a cycle of infection. Have students sketch a mosquito net, a person receiving a vaccine, and a person being treated for malaria. Point out that any one of these measures can break the chain of infection, but all three together will accomplish the goal more quickly and efficiently.

Answers

WRITING Advise students to access reliable Web sites, such as those of the Centers for Disease Control and Prevention, World Health Organization, UNICEF, and the President's Malaria Initiative. Students may include the following ideas in their answers: mosquito nets are less expensive than vaccines and anti-malarial drugs, one net can cover several people at once, and it's best to combine vaccines with other methods.

LESSON 21.4

Getting Started

Objectives

21.4.1 Identify the defining characteristics of fungi.

21.4.2 Describe how fungi affect homeostasis.

Student Resources

Study Workbooks A and B, 21.4 Worksheets

Spanish Study Workbook, 21.4 Worksheets

Lab Manual B, 21.4 Data Analysis Worksheet

Lesson Overview • Lesson Notes • Activity: Art Review • Assessment: Self-Test, Lesson Assessment

For corresponding lesson in the **Foundation Edition,** see pages 514–519.

Activate Prior Knowledge

Ask students to name all the different kinds of fungi they can think of. *(Sample answers: molds, yeasts, morels, mushrooms, mildew)* Ask them how fungi affect their lives. *(Sample answers: A fungus causes athlete's foot. Yeast and mushrooms are used in foods.)* Then, ask them what role fungi play in the environment. *(Sample answer: Mushrooms and other fungi are decomposers.)*

21.4 Fungi

B.4.4 Stability of an ecosystem; B.8.2 Classification. Also covered: NoS.3.

Key Questions

What are the basic characteristics of fungi?

How do fungi affect homeostasis in other organisms and the environment?

Vocabulary

chitin • hypha • fruiting body • mycelium • lichen • mycorrhiza

Taking Notes

Concept Map As you read, develop a concept map showing the relationships of fungi to other organisms in their environment.

THINK ABOUT IT What is the largest organism in this photo? At first glance you might pick the tree, but in fact the largest organism is a fungus. The only trace of it is the ring of mushrooms that has popped up in the grass after a brief rainstorm.

The mushrooms are just the reproductive structures of a much larger organism. Most of the mass of the fungus is underground, spanning at least the width of the ring of mushrooms, and extending more than 2 meters into the ground! Hundreds of years ago, some cultures believed these rings of mushrooms marked spots where fairies danced in circles on warm summer nights. Today people still call them fairy rings.

What Are Fungi?

What are the basic characteristics of fungi?

Like the ring of mushrooms above, many fungi grow from the ground. This once led scientists to classify them as nonphotosynthetic plants. But they aren't plants at all. Instead of carrying out photosynthesis, fungi produce powerful enzymes that digest food outside their bodies. Then they absorb the small molecules released by the enzymes. Many fungi feed by absorbing nutrients from decaying matter in the soil. Others live as parasites, absorbing nutrients from the bodies of their hosts.

Another defining characteristic of fungi is the composition of their cell walls, which contain chitin (KY tun). **Chitin** is a polymer made of modified sugars that is also found in the external skeletons of insects. The presence of chitin is one of several features that show fungi are more closely related to animals than to plants. **Fungi are heterotrophic eukaryotes with cell walls that contain chitin.**

FIGURE 21–15
Scarlet Cup Fungus

IN INDIANA ACADEMIC STANDARDS

For the full text of all standards, see the Course Overview in the front matter of this book.

B.4.4 Describe how climate, the pattern of matter and energy flow, the birth and death of new organisms, and the interaction between those organisms contribute to the long term stability of an ecosystem.

B.8.2 Explain how organisms are classified and named based on their evolutionary relationships into taxonomic categories.

UbD Teach for Understanding

ENDURING UNDERSTANDING From microorganisms to plants, organisms vary widely in the way they carry out basic life processes.

GUIDING QUESTION What are fungi, and what roles do they play in the environment?

EVIDENCE OF UNDERSTANDING *After completing the lesson, give students the following assessment to show their understanding of how fungi affect the environment.* Ask students to write a three-paragraph fictional account of what might happen if all the fungi in the world suddenly disappeared. Each paragraph should address one role of fungi as decomposers, parasites, or partners in mutualistic associations. Encourage students to be creative and descriptive but to make their accounts plausible and based on scientific knowledge.

Structure and Function There are two general growth patterns among fungi. Yeasts are tiny fungi that live most of their lives as single cells. Mushrooms and other fungi grow much larger, their bodies made up of cells that form long, slender branching filaments called **hyphae** (HY fee; singular: hypha), as shown in **Figure 21–16.** In most fungi, cross walls divide the hyphae into compartments resembling cells, each containing one or two nuclei. In the cross walls, there are openings through which cytoplasm and organelles such as mitochondria can move.

What you recognize as a mushroom is actually the **fruiting body,** the reproductive structure of the fungus. The fruiting body grows from the **mycelium** (my SEE lee um; plural: mycelia), the mass of branching hyphae below the soil. Clusters of mushrooms are often part of the same mycelium, which means that they are actually part of the same organism.

Some mycelia live for many years and grow very large. The mycelium of the soil fungus in a fairy ring has grown so large that it has used up all of the nutrients near its center. It grows and produces fruiting bodies—the mushrooms—only at its edges, where it comes in contact with fresh soil and abundant nutrients.

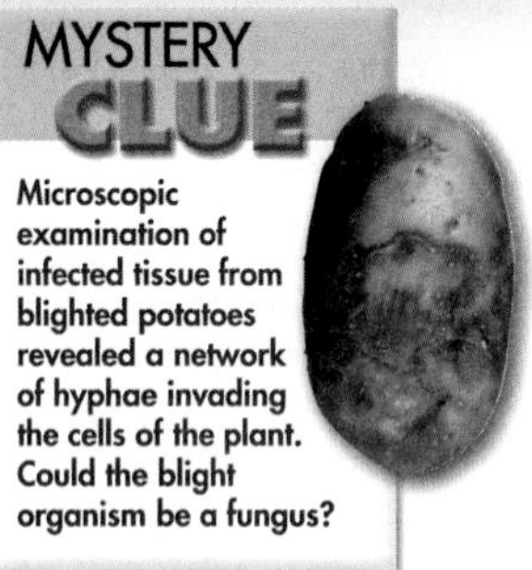

MYSTERY CLUE

Microscopic examination of infected tissue from blighted potatoes revealed a network of hyphae invading the cells of the plant. Could the blight organism be a fungus?

In Your Notebook *How do fungi differ from other multicellular organisms?*

FIGURE 21–16 Structure of a Mushroom The body of a mushroom is actually its reproductive structure, also called a fruiting body. The major portion of the organism is the mycelium, which grows underground.

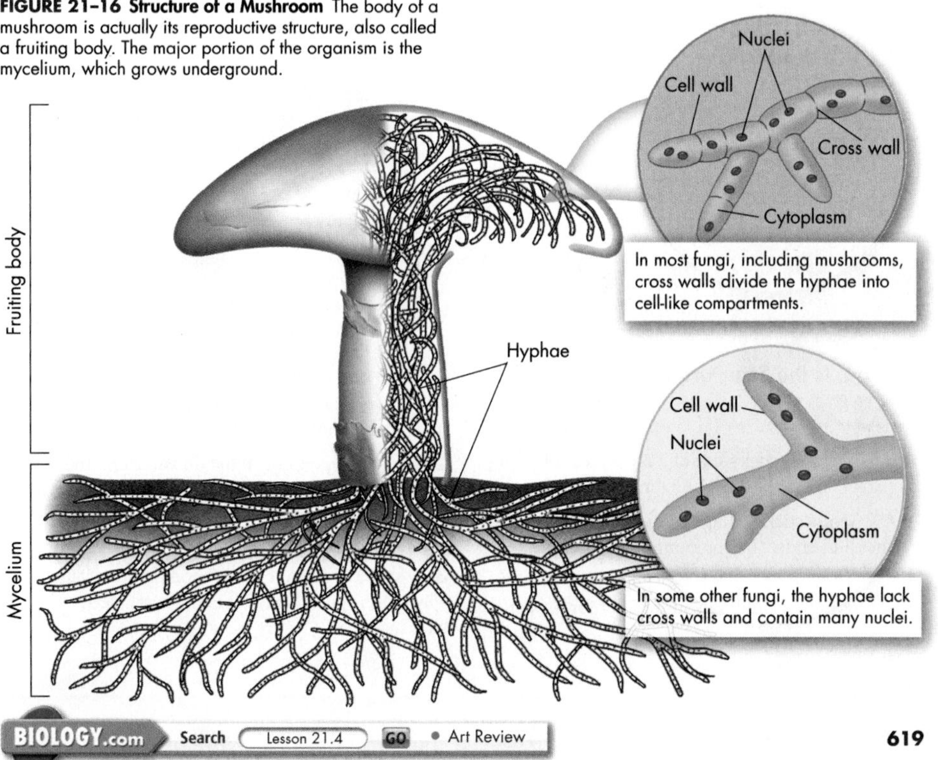
Fruiting body
Mycelium
Hyphae
Nuclei
Cell wall
Cross wall
Cytoplasm
In most fungi, including mushrooms, cross walls divide the hyphae into cell-like compartments.
Cell wall
Nuclei
Cytoplasm
In some other fungi, the hyphae lack cross walls and contain many nuclei.

BIOLOGY.com Search Lesson 21.4 GO • Art Review

Teach

Use Visuals

Point out that fungi have a great variety of shapes and sizes, and the fungus in **Figure 21–16** is only a representative that is helpful as an introduction to fungus structure. Have students examine the figure and read the caption and annotations, paying particular attention to mention of hyphae.

Ask Which part of the mushroom can be seen above the ground? *(the fruiting body, or reproductive structure)*

Ask What structures make up both the fruiting body and the mycelium? *(hyphae)* Tell students that the term *hypha* comes from the Greek word for web.

Ask How are hyphae like a web? *(Sample answer: They are long and thin and tangled together like the threads of a spider web.)*

DIFFERENTIATED INSTRUCTION

L1 Special Needs Give small groups of students a mushroom, such as the button mushrooms sold in markets. Have students compare what they observe with the fungus in **Figure 21–16.** Ask them to twist off the mushroom cap and break open the stalk from end to end to try to find hyphae.

L3 Advanced Students Have students recall that for spherical cells, as cell volume increases, the ratio of surface area to volume decreases, and with a smaller ratio, the flow of materials in and out of the cell becomes more difficult. Ask them to use this concept to explain how the structure of the mycelium is related to its function. *(The structure provides a large ratio of surface area to volume for the organism's cells, or hyphae. This large ratio correlates with the structure's function—to absorb nutrients from decaying matter.)*

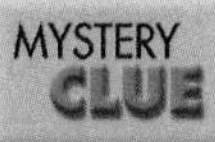

Have students discuss the significance of hyphae in the tissue of the potatoes. They can go online to Biology.com to gather their evidence.

BIOLOGY.com Students can drag and drop labels to explore the structures of a fungus in **Art Review: Structure of a Mushroom.**

Answers

IN YOUR NOTEBOOK Cells of multicellular organisms are entirely separated from one another by cell walls or cell membranes. Fungi have either cells with cross walls that allow organelles and substances through, or cells with no cross walls but many nuclei.

Quick Facts

THE HUMONGOUS FUNGUS

The largest living thing on Earth (by area) just might be a fungus. Discovered in 2000 in Oregon's Malheur National Forest, the giant *Armillaria ostoyae* covers more than 2200 acres. Researchers estimate this fungus to be thousands of years old. The main body of the fungus is located mostly underground. The only clues to its existence are mushrooms that grow at the bases of living and dead trees. *Armillaria* causes a root disease, "root rot," that can kill even healthy trees.

LESSON 21.4

Teach continued

Use Visuals

Point out that most fungi reproduce both asexually and sexually, as shown in the bread mold life cycle in **Figure 21–17.** Have students compare this life cycle with that of the water mold shown in **Figure 21–7.**

Ask How do the asexual phases of the life cycle of each organism differ? *(The water mold undergoes mitosis with diploid cells, while the bread mold undergoes mitosis with haploid cells.)*

DIFFERENTIATED INSTRUCTION

LPR Less Proficient Readers Call on students at random to describe what is occurring at each step in **Figure 21–17.** If a student has trouble, read aloud the sentences from the text that provide insight into that step. Then, have the student explain the text in his or her own words.

ELL Focus on ELL: Extend Language

ALL SPEAKERS Begin a **Word Wall** by posting the lesson vocabulary terms. As you teach the lesson, add other important terms in addition to the vocabulary terms, such as the terms for structures in **Figure 21–17.** Make transparencies of **Figures 21–16** and **21–17** with the labels blanked out but the taglines intact. Point to different structures on the transparencies, and have students use the word wall to name them and describe their functions. Encourage beginning and intermediate speakers to use a word or short phrase. Encourage advanced and advanced high speakers to use complete sentences.

Study Wkbks A/B, Appendix S17, Word Wall.

FIGURE 21–17 Bread Mold Life Cycle During sexual reproduction in the black bread mold *Rhizopus stolonifer*, hyphae from two different mating types form gametangia. The gametangia fuse, and zygotes form within a zygospore. The zygospore develops a thick wall and can remain dormant for long periods. The zygospore eventually germinates, and a sporangium emerges. The sporangium reproduces asexually, releasing haploid spores produced by meiosis.

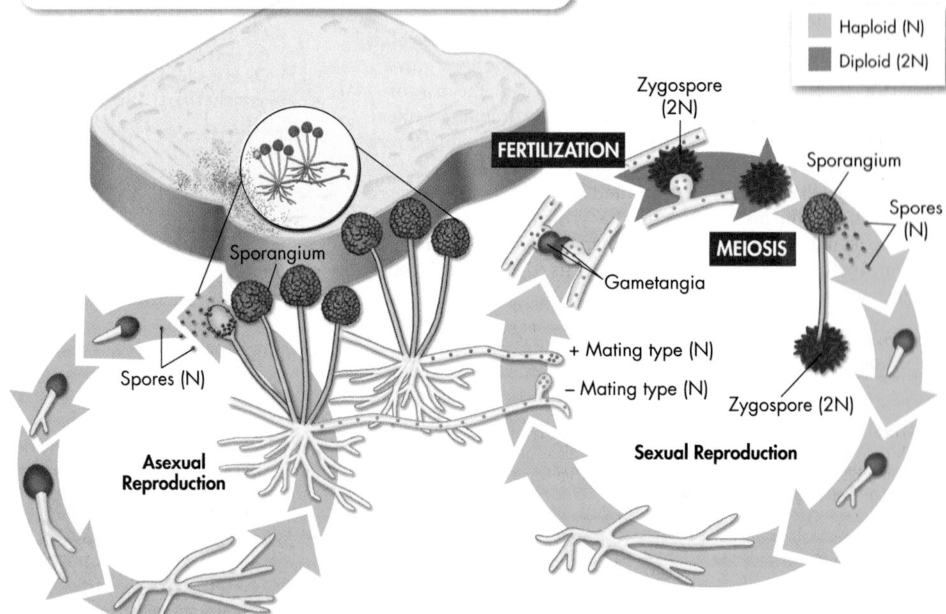

Quick Lab GUIDED INQUIRY

What Is the Structure of Bread Mold?

1. Touch the sticky side of a 2-cm piece of transparent tape to the black fuzzy area of a bread mold.
2. Gently stick the tape to a glass slide. Observe the slide under the compound microscope. Make a sketch of your observations.
3. Return all slides to your teacher for proper disposal, and wash your hands before leaving the laboratory.

Analyze and Conclude

1. **Observe** Describe the structures you observed in the bread mold.
2. **Form a Hypothesis** What do you think the function of the round structures is? Why might it be advantageous for a single mass of bread mold to produce so many of the round structures?
3. **Infer** How do your observations help explain why molds appear on foods even in very clean kitchens?

Quick Lab

PURPOSE Students will observe the major structures of a mold and hypothesize why bread mold produces so many sporangia.

MATERIALS transparent tape, moldy bread, microscope slide, compound microscope

SAFETY Remind students to be careful when handling glass slides and to wash their hands after the activity. Students who have allergies to molds should avoid exposure to the bread mold. They can answer the questions by looking at classmates' sketches.

PLANNING Prepare moldy bread by moistening slices of bread and placing them in a warm, dark place several days in advance of the activity. Use bread that has no preservatives, such as home-baked bread.

ANALYZE AND CONCLUDE

1. The tangled filaments are hyphae. The round structures are sporangia.
2. Sporangia produce and release spores. The production of such a large number of sporangia increases the number of spores released, thus increasing the chances of the mold's reproduction.
3. Molds produce large numbers of very tiny spores that are easily spread by wind and animals. Keeping all spores out of a kitchen is nearly impossible.

Reproduction Fungi can reproduce asexually, primarily by releasing spores that are adapted to travel through air and water. Simply breaking off a hypha or budding off a cell can also serve as asexual reproduction.

Most fungi also can reproduce sexually. **Figure 21–17** shows the life cycle of a type of bread mold, a fungus called *Rhizopus stolonifer.* Sexual reproduction in fungi often involves two different mating types. In *Rhizopus,* as in most fungi, gametes of both mating types are about the same size and are not usually called male and female. Instead, one mating type is called "+" (plus) and the other "–" (minus). When hyphae of opposite mating types meet, they start the process of sexual reproduction by fusing, bringing + and – nuclei together in the same cell. The + and – nuclei form pairs that divide in unison as the mycelium grows. Many of the paired nuclei fuse to form diploid zygote nuclei, which go through meiosis to make haploid spores. Each spore has a different combination of parental genes, and each can make a new mycelium.

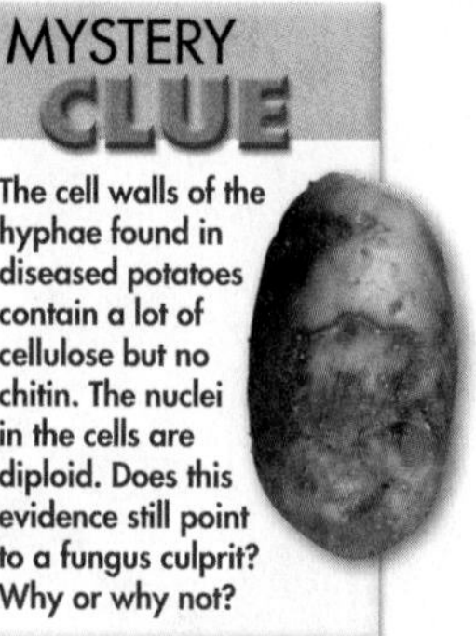

The cell walls of the hyphae found in diseased potatoes contain a lot of cellulose but no chitin. The nuclei in the cells are diploid. Does this evidence still point to a fungus culprit? Why or why not?

Diversity of Fungi More than 100,000 species of fungi are known. Of course, they all share the characteristics that define them as fungi, but they differ from one another in important ways. Biologists have used these similarities and differences, along with DNA comparisons, to place the fungi into several distinct groups. The major groups of fungi differ from one another in their reproductive structures, as summarized in **Figure 21–18.**

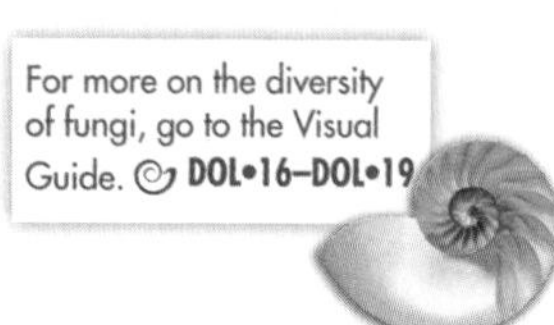
For more on the diversity of fungi, go to the Visual Guide. DOL•16–DOL•19

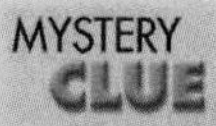

FIGURE 21–18 The Major Phyla of Fungi The table summarizes the main differences among the four major phyla of fungi. **Infer** ***Would you expect to find chytrids in aquatic or terrestrial habitats? Explain your answer.***

The Major Phyla of Fungi

Phylum	Distinguishing Features	Examples
Basidiomycota (club fungi)	Sexual spores found in club-shaped cell called a basidium	Mushrooms, puffballs, earthstars, shelf fungi, jelly fungi, rusts
Ascomycota (sac fungi)	Sexual spores found in saclike structure called an ascus	Morels, truffles, *Penicillium* species, yeasts
Zygomycota (common molds)	Tough zygospore produced during sexual reproduction that can stay dormant for long periods	*Rhizopus stolonifer* (black bread mold), molds found on rotting strawberries and other soft fruits, mycorrhizae associated with plant roots
Chytridomycota (chytrids)	Only fungi with flagellated spores	Many species are decomposers found in lakes and moist soil.

UbD Check for Understanding

ONE-MINUTE RESPONSE

Give students about one minute to write a brief essay summarizing their understanding of this Key Question:

- What are the basic characteristics of fungi? *(Students should describe how fungi obtain energy, how they reproduce, the composition of their cell walls, and their structure and function.)*

ADJUST INSTRUCTION

If students do not include significant characteristics or get bogged down in details, help them sort out the main ideas by modeling the beginning of an outline for the section of the text with the green heading, **What Are Fungi?** Have them complete the outline, and then discuss the main characteristics of fungi as a class.

Build Science Skills

Help students build classification skills by having them answer the following questions about the chart in **Figure 21–18.**

Ask What is the main characteristic used to classify fungi into major phyla? *(how their reproductive spores differ)*

Ask What distinguishes Chytridomycota from the other three phyla? *(Its spores have flagella.)*

Ask Which phylum might you infer appeared before the other ones? Explain. *(Chytridomycota; it shares the characteristic of flagella with some protists, which are thought to have a common ancestor with fungi.)*

DIFFERENTIATED INSTRUCTION

L1 Special Needs Help students observe the location and appearance of spores from club fungi. Have them place a fresh mushroom cap, gill-side down, on a sheet of white paper and cover it with a plastic container. After one or two days, students will observe that spores have fallen to the paper. Have them examine the spores under a microscope. Also, help them look on the gills for basidia. Ask them to use their observations and **Figure 21–18** to form a definition for *basidium. (a club-shaped cell that contains sexual spores)*

MYSTERY CLUE Have students discuss the kinds of organisms in this chapter that have cellulose and chitin. Then, have them infer whether the cause of the potato blight could be a fungus. Lead them to conclude that, because the cells do not contain chitin, they must not be from a fungus, which would have chitin in its cell walls. Students can go online to **Biology.com** to gather their evidence.

Address Misconceptions

Toadstools Some students think any mushroom is safe to eat and only toadstools are poisonous. Explain that *toadstool* is not a scientific term but a folk term for a poisonous mushroom. Some mushrooms are edible, but about 200 or more known species are poisonous.

Answers

FIGURE 21–18 You would expect to find them in aquatic habitats, because they are found in lakes and moist soil and the spores are flagellated to enable them to move through water.

Teach continued

Lead a Discussion

Explain that fungi play three major roles in the environment: decomposers, parasites, and mutalists. Emphasize the essential role of fungi in maintaining equilibrium in an ecosystem through the recycling of nutrients. Draw students' attention to the decomposing fungi shown in **Figure 21–19.**

Ask How does this kind of fungi maintain homeostasis of other organisms? *(The fungi break down materials in dead organisms, making them available to other organisms.)*

Then, draw students' attention to the parasitic fungi shown in **Figure 21–20.**

Ask How does this kind of fungi disrupt homeostasis of other organisms? *(The fungi may damage plants or animals to the point where the plants or animals cannot regain homeostasis, and they eventually die.)*

DIFFERENTIATED INSTRUCTION

L1 Struggling Students Help students understand how fungi help make recycled nutrients available to other organisms. Explain that the major part of soil is made of rock and mineral fragments. Soil also contains a significant amount of organic matter, called humus, the result of the breakdown of wastes and dead organisms by decomposers such as fungi, protists, and bacteria. It is this part of the soil that contains the recycled nutrients that plants take up. Show students a pile of sand and a pile of potting soil. Have them examine and compare the two. Ask which one best supports plant life and why. *(the potting soil, because it contains humus)*

ELL English Language Learners Pair beginning and intermediate speakers with advanced or advanced high speakers, or with native speakers. Have them read the bolded Key Concepts on this page. Then, write these two simplified versions on the board beside each other: Decomposers help ecosystems maintain homeostasis. Parasitic fungi disrupt homeostasis. Discuss the meanings of the words *maintain* and *disrupt*. Ask students to look for evidence to support each statement and provide it orally. Write their responses on the board under the appropriate statement.

FIGURE 21–19 Champions of Decomposition The mycelia of these mushrooms have released enzymes that are breaking down the wood tissues of the decaying tree trunk.

The Ecology of Fungi

How do fungi affect homeostasis in other organisms and the environment?

Fungi play an essential role in maintaining equilibrium in nearly every ecosystem. But there are some species that cause disease in plants and animals.

Decomposition Many fungi feed by releasing digestive enzymes that break down leaves, fruit, and other organic material into simple molecules. These molecules then diffuse into the fungus. The mycelia of fungi produce digestive enzymes that speed the breakdown of wastes and dead organisms. Many organisms, especially plants, remove important trace elements and nutrients from the soil. If these materials were not returned, the soil would quickly be depleted, and Earth would become barren and lifeless. **Fungi are champions of decomposition. Many species help ecosystems maintain homeostasis by breaking down dead organisms and recycling essential elements and nutrients.**

Parasitism As useful as many fungi are, others can infect plants and animals. **Parasitic fungi can cause serious diseases in plants and animals by disrupting homeostasis.**

▶ ***Plant Diseases*** A number of parasitic fungi cause diseases that threaten food crops. Corn smut, for example, destroys corn kernels and wheat rust affects one of the most important crops grown in North America. Some mildews, which infect a wide variety of plants, are also fungi. Fungal diseases are responsible for the loss of approximately 15 percent of the crops grown in temperate regions of the world and even more of the crops grown in tropical areas.

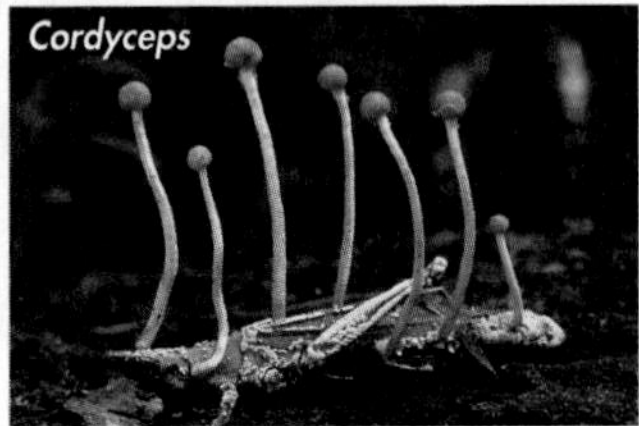

FIGURE 21–20 Parasitic Fungi Corn smut infests the kernels of a corn plant, reducing the farmer's crop yield (left). A grasshopper falls victim to the *Cordyceps* fungus (right).

▶ ***Animal Diseases*** Fungal diseases also affect insects, frogs, and mammals. One deadly example is caused by a fungus in the genus *Cordyceps.* This fungus infects grasshoppers in rain forests in Costa Rica. Microscopic spores become lodged in the grasshopper, where they germinate and produce enzymes that slowly penetrate the insect's tough external skeleton. The spores multiply in the insect's body, digesting all its cells and tissues until the insect dies. To complete the process of digestion, hyphae develop, cloaking the decaying exoskeleton in a web of fungal material. Reproductive structures, which will produce more spores and spread the infection, then emerge from the grasshopper's remains.

Biology In-Depth

WHEAT RUST

Wheat rust is caused by a type of basidiomycete that needs two different plants to complete its life cycle. Spores produced by rust in barberry plants are carried by wind into wheat fields. There, the spores germinate and infect wheat plants. The patches of rust produce a second type of spore that infects other wheat plants. This spore allows the disease to spread through the field like wildfire. Later in the growing season, the rust produces a new variety of spore. These spores easily survive through the winter. In spring, they go through a sexual phase and produce spores that infect barberry plants. On the barberry leaves, the rust produces the spores that infect wheat plants, and the cycle continues. Once scientists understood the life cycle of the rust, they were able to slow its spread in wheat crops by destroying nearby barberry plants.

Parasitic fungi can also infect humans. The fungus that causes athlete's foot forms a mycelium in the outer layers of the skin, which produces a red, inflamed sore from which the spores can easily spread from person to person. The yeast *Candida albicans* can also disrupt the equilibrium in the human body. It is often responsible for vaginal yeast infections and for infections of the mouth called thrush. *Candida* is usually kept in check by competition from bacteria and by the body's immune system. This balance can be upset by the use of antibiotics, which kill bacteria, or by damage to the immune system.

Lichens The close relationships fungi form with members of other species are not always parasitic in nature. **Some fungi form mutualistic associations with photosynthetic organisms in which both partners benefit.** For example, a **lichen** (LY-kun) is a symbiotic association between a fungus and a photosynthetic organism. The photosynthetic organism is either a green alga or a cyanobacterium, or both. **Figure 21–21** shows the structure of a lichen.

Lichens are extremely resistant to drought and cold. Therefore, they can grow in places where few other organisms can survive—on dry bare rock in deserts and on the tops of mountains. Lichens are able to survive in these harsh environments because of the relationship between the two partner organisms. The green algae or cyanobacteria carry out photosynthesis, providing the fungus with a source of energy. The fungus, in turn, provides the green algae or cyanobacteria with water and minerals. Furthermore, the densely packed hyphae protect the delicate green cells from intense sunlight.

Lichens are often the first organisms to enter barren environments, gradually breaking down the rocks on which they grow. In this way, lichens help in the early stages of soil formation. Lichens are also remarkably sensitive to air pollution: They are among the first organisms to be affected when air quality deteriorates.

In Your Notebook *Summarize three roles of fungi in the environment. Compare these roles to those of protists.*

FIGURE 21–21 Inside a Lichen The protective upper surface of a lichen is made up of densely packed fungal hyphae. Below this are layers of green algae or cyanobacteria and loosely woven hyphae. The bottom layer contains small projections that attach the lichen to a rock or tree. **Infer** ***How do lichens assist in soil formation?***

623

Connect to Earth Science

After students read about how lichens are a mutualistic association between two organisms, explain the significance of lichens in ecological succession. Emphasize that they are often the most important part of the pioneer community on bare rock. They break down rocks through both mechanical and chemical weathering, making some of their minerals available to other organisms. Remind students that mechanical weathering includes physical processes that break rock into smaller pieces and chemical weathering that changes the chemical makeup of rocks. The fungus part of a lichen mechanically weathers rock by sending its hyphae into cracks in a rock, eventually wedging the rock apart. The fungus chemically weathers rock by producing acids that seep into rock and break it apart. In addition to these weathering processes, lichens that grow on bare rock trap soil particles. As soil builds up, plants are able to grow.

DIFFERENTIATED INSTRUCTION

L1 Struggling Students Help students understand the role lichens play in the environment by having them examine **Figure 21–21.** Ask which structures break down rock. *(hyphae)* Ask students to make an inference about which layer of hyphae grows into the tree or rock. *(the bottom layer)* Then, ask them to explain how lichens can survive on bare rock. *(The fungus gets its energy from the algae or cyanobacteria, which in turn get water and minerals from the fungus.)*

UbD Check for Understanding

VISUAL REPRESENTATION

Ask students to construct a **Cluster Diagram** to show how fungi affect homeostasis in other organisms and the environment. To get them started, tell them to write "Fungi Affect Homeostasis" in the main circle. *(Diagrams should have three smaller circles attached to the center circle to represent the three main ecological roles of fungi. Smaller circles should provide details and examples.)*

ADJUST INSTRUCTION

If students have difficulty completing this task, draw a circle with surrounding circles on the board. Ask volunteers to identify a key role as you write it in the center circle. Then, ask for ideas on what is appropriate to go in the smaller circles, and encourage students to discuss what should and should not be included in the circles.

Answers

FIGURE 21–21 They gradually break down the rocks on which they grow.

IN YOUR NOTEBOOK Fungi can be decomposers, which break down dead organisms, or parasites, which disrupt the homeostasis of their hosts, or lichens, which live in mutualistic relationships with a photosynthetic organism. These roles are similar to protists, because protists can also do these things.

Teach continued

Expand Vocabulary

Tell students that another example of a mutualistic association between fungi and other organisms is mycorrhizae. Break the word into two parts, and explain that *myco* means "fungus," and *rhizae* means "roots." Have students read the Build Vocabulary feature on this page. Discuss the terms *symbiosis* and *symbiotic*. Then, ask students to make up questions and answers using the terms *symbiosis, symbiotic, symbiont,* and *mycorrhizae.*

DIFFERENTIATED INSTRUCTION

L3 Advanced Students Give students the following problem: Suppose you repot orchids by washing off the old soil and placing the roots into a sterilized soil mix. The plants soon wither and die.

Have students define the problem and describe an experiment to find out if the sterile soil is causing the problem. Tell them to devise controls that might determine whether the mechanical stress of repotting, rather than the soil mixture, is causing the problem. Their experimental designs should include a hypothesis, a control, a variable, and a means to collect the data to evaluate the results. *(A typical experiment might include retaining some of the old soil attached to the roots when repotting a plant.)*

BUILD Vocabulary

RELATED WORD FORMS *Symbiosis* is a noun for the condition of two unlike organisms living together in very close association. *Symbiotic* is an adjective referring to a symbiosis. *Symbiont* is a noun naming an organism in a symbiotic relationship, especially the smaller member of the pair.

Mycorrhizae Fungi also form mutualistic relationships with plant roots. Almost half of the tissues of trees are hidden beneath the ground in masses of tangled roots. These roots are woven into a partnership with an even larger web of fungal mycelia. These symbiotic associations of plant roots and fungi are called **mycorrhizae** (my koh RY zee; singular: mycorrhiza).

Scientists have known about this partnership for years, but recent research shows that it is more common and more important than was previously thought. Researchers now estimate that 80 to 90 percent of all plant species form mycorrhizae with fungi. The hyphae of the fungi form a network associated with the roots of the plants and extending into the soil. The hyphae collect water and minerals and bring them to the roots, greatly increasing the effective surface area of the root system. In addition, the fungi release enzymes that free nutrients in the soil. The plants, in turn, provide the fungi with the products of photosynthesis.

The presence of mycorrhizae is essential for the growth of many plants. The seeds of orchids, for example, cannot germinate in the absence of mycorrhizal fungi. Many trees are unable to survive without fungal symbionts. Interestingly, the partnership between plant and fungus does not end with a single plant. The roots of each plant are plugged into mycorrhizal networks that connect many plants. What's more astounding is that these networks appear to connect plants of different species.

In Your Notebook *Make a graphic organizer that illustrates the flow of materials between a fungus and a plant in a mycorrhizal symbiosis.*

Analyzing Data

IN NoS.3

Mycorrhizae and Tree Height

The graph below illustrates the growth rates of three species of trees—two individuals of each species. One tree of each species grew with mycorrhizae, and one grew without mycorrhizae.

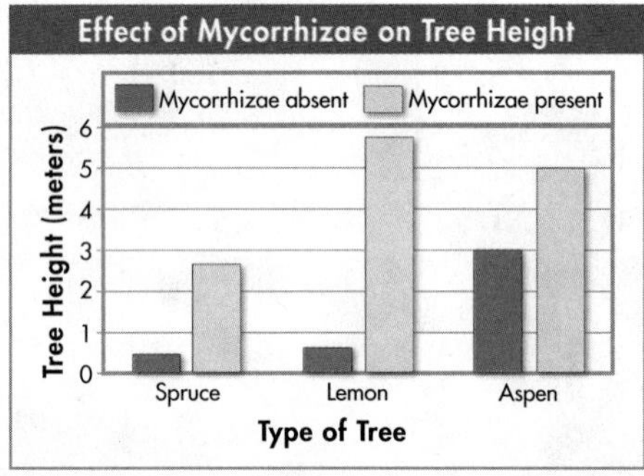

1. **Calculate** By what percentage is the height of the lemon tree grown with mycorrhizae greater than the height of the lemon tree grown without mycorrhizae? MATH
2. **Draw Conclusions** Make a generalization about the growth rate of plants with mycorrhizae.
3. **Form a Hypothesis** A citrus grower recently began using sterilized soil for repotting lemon trees with the goal of reducing disease. But many of the trees are dying in the new soil. Form a hypothesis to explain this observation.

Analyzing Data

PURPOSE Students will interpret a graph to draw conclusions and form a hypothesis about mycorrhizae and tree height.

PLANNING Remind students that bar graphs are often used to make comparisons. Review the color key.

ANSWERS

1. about 1000% (5.5 – 0.5 = 5; 5 ÷ 0.5 = 10); the lemon tree grew about 10 times higher with mycorrhizae than without them
2. Plants with mycorrhizae grow to a greater height than those without mycorrhizae.
3. Sample answer: If mycorrhizae are removed from the soil, lemon trees will not grow as well.

Answers

IN YOUR NOTEBOOK Students' graphic organizers should show that a fungus provides plants with water, minerals, and other nutrients in the soil and that a plant provides a fungus with food.

FIGURE 21–22 Mycorrhizal Research Suzanne Simard of the University of British Columbia studies the effects of mycorrhizae on birch and other tree species. Apply Concepts ***What type of symbiotic relationship is illustrated by mycorrhizae?***

▲ Dr. Simard's apparatus for measuring movement of carbon between tree species

A recent experiment showed that carbon atoms from one tree often end up in another tree nearby. In an experiment using isotopes to trace the movement of carbon, ecologist Suzanne Simard, shown in **Figure 21–22,** found that mycorrhizal fungi transferred carbon from paper birch trees growing in the sun to Douglas fir trees growing in the shade. As a result, the sun-starved fir trees thrived, basically by being "fed" carbon from the birches. Simard's findings suggest that plants—and their associated fungi—may be evolving as part of an ecological partnership.

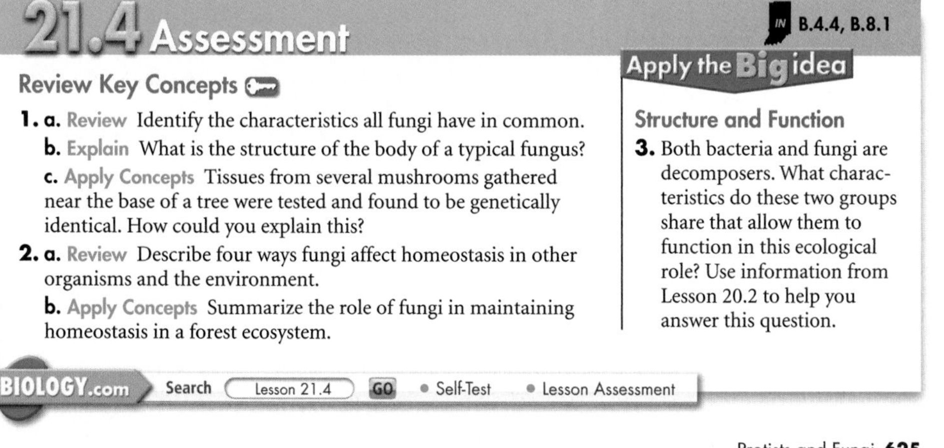

21.4 Assessment

IN B.4.4, B.8.1

Review Key Concepts

1. a. Review Identify the characteristics all fungi have in common.

b. Explain What is the structure of the body of a typical fungus?

c. Apply Concepts Tissues from several mushrooms gathered near the base of a tree were tested and found to be genetically identical. How could you explain this?

2. a. Review Describe four ways fungi affect homeostasis in other organisms and the environment.

b. Apply Concepts Summarize the role of fungi in maintaining homeostasis in a forest ecosystem.

Apply the Big idea

Structure and Function

3. Both bacteria and fungi are decomposers. What characteristics do these two groups share that allow them to function in this ecological role? Use information from Lesson 20.2 to help you answer this question.

BIOLOGY.com Search Lesson 21.4 GO • Self-Test • Lesson Assessment

Assess and Remediate

EVALUATE UNDERSTANDING

Call on students at random to compare and contrast the relationship between *Cordyceps* and grasshoppers and the relationship between a mycorrhizal fungus and a Douglas fir. *(They should contrast a parasitic relationship with a mutualistic relationship.)* Then, have them complete the 21.4 Assessment.

REMEDIATION SUGGESTION

L1 **Struggling Students** If students have trouble answering **Question 1c,** have them review **Figure 21–16.** Point out that most of the body of a fungus is underground. The fruiting bodies may grow above ground at intervals along the mycelium of the organism. Make a sketch of a tree and mushrooms as described in the question. Draw a horizontal line to denote Earth's surface and a network of hyphae under the surface connecting the mushrooms.

BIOLOGY.com Students can check their understanding of lesson concepts with the **Self-Test** assessment. They can then take an online version of the **Lesson Assessment.**

Answers

Figure 21–22 mutualism

Assessment Answers

1a. Fungi are eukaryotic heterotrophs that have cell walls containing chitin. They digest food outside their bodies and then absorb the molecules. All can reproduce asexually.

1b. The bodies of multicellular fungi are composed of many hyphae tangled together into a thick mass called a mycelium. The visible portion of the mycelium is the reproductive structure, or fruiting body.

1c. The genetically identical mushrooms were part of the same mycelium, which means they were part of the same organism.

2a. Fungi recycle nutrient material by breaking down organic matter, cause plant and animal diseases, break down rocks to form soil (lichens), and are essential for the growth of many plants (mycorrhizae).

2b. Answers will vary. Students should recognize the role of fungi as decomposers and as mycorrhizae that are essential in helping forest plants obtain nutrients.

3. Big idea Both feed by releasing digestive enzymes that break down organic matter into simple molecules. Thus, they share the characteristics of digesting food outside their bodies and of recycling nutrients, which are released into the soil and taken up by the roots of plants.

CHAPTER LAB

Pre-Lab

Introduce students to the concepts they will explore in the chapter lab by assigning the Pre-Lab questions.

Lab

Tell students they will perform the chapter lab *Mushroom Farming* described in **Lab Manual A.**

 **Struggling Students** A simpler version of the chapter lab is provided in **Lab Manual B.**

SAFETY

Inform students that organic media sometimes contain harmful microorganisms. They should wash their hands thoroughly after completing the lab. Check for possible allergies to mushrooms.

BIOLOGY.com Look online for **Editable Lab Worksheets.**

For corresponding pre-lab in the **Foundation Edition,** see page 520.

Design Your Own Lab

GUIDED INQUIRY

Pre-Lab: Mushroom Farming

Problem How does the amount of available light affect mushroom growth?

Materials mushroom growing kits, spray bottle with water, metric ruler

Lab Manual Chapter 21 Lab

Skills Focus Form a Hypothesis, Design an Experiment, Organize Data

Connect to the Big idea Fungi play an essential role in maintaining homeostasis in ecosystems. Many fungi speed up the decay of dead organisms and help recycle nutrients. Some fungi form symbiotic relationships with plants. These fungi deliver water and minerals to the plant roots. In turn, the plants supply the fungi with sugars. Do fungi grow better in some environments than in others? In this lab, you will investigate how the amount of light affects the growth and reproduction of a species of club fungi.

Background Questions

a. **Review** What are fungi?

b. **Review** Describe the general structure of a mushroom.

c. **Explain** How do fungi that are not in a symbiotic relationship obtain nutrients?

Pre-Lab Questions

Preview the procedure in the lab manual.

1. **Infer** Where will the mushrooms get the nutrients that they need to grow and reproduce?
2. **Relate Cause and Effect** Why will you have to wait about ten days to observe the mushrooms?
3. **Apply Concepts** The mushrooms you will grow are of a variety that is sold in food stores. Why do the instructions warn you not to eat the mushrooms?

BIOLOGY.com Search 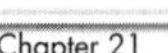

Visit Chapter 21 online to test yourself on chapter content and to find activities to help you learn.

Untamed Science Video Have a look at the fascinating world of mushrooms through the lenses of the Untamed Science crew.

Art in Motion View a short animation that shows the plasmodium life cycle and how malaria is transmitted by the *Anopheles* mosquito.

Art Review Review your understanding of the different structures of a mushroom.

InterActive Art Investigate the structures of an amoeba and paramecium.

Data Analysis Learn how microfossils can be used to learn about conditions and changes in ancient oceans.

Visual Analogy Compare the way boats move to the motion of flagella and cilia in a cell.

Pre-Lab Answers

BACKGROUND QUESTIONS

a. Fungi are heterotrophic eukaryotes with cell walls that contain chitin.

b. Sample answer: The mycelium, which is a mass of filaments called hyphae, is underground. The part of the mushroom that is above the ground is the fruiting body, or reproductive structure, of the mushroom.

c. Sample answer: Fungi release enzymes that digest waste and dead organisms. The released nutrients are absorbed through the hyphae.

PRE-LAB QUESTIONS

1. The growing medium contains food that the mushrooms can digest.
2. The mushroom spores must germinate and the mycelium form before the fruiting body will appear.
3. Sample answer: As a general rule, food should never be consumed in the lab. Plus, a lab is not an appropriate environment for growing food.

21 Study Guide

Big idea Interdependence in Nature

Some species of protists and fungi—especially in their role as photosynthesizers and decomposers—are critical to maintaining equilibrium in ecosystems. But certain species disrupt homeostasis in organisms by causing disease in various plants and animals, including humans.

21.1 Protist Classification—The Saga Continues

Protists are eukaryotes that are not members of the plant, animal, or fungi kingdoms.

Today's protists include groups whose ancestors were among the very last to split from the organisms that gave rise to plants, animals, and fungi.

21.2 Protist Structure and Function

Some protists move by changing their cell shape, and some move by means of specialized organelles. Other protists do not move actively but are carried by wind, water, or other organisms.

Some protists reproduce asexually by mitosis. Others have life cycles that combine asexual and sexual forms of reproduction.

pseudopod (606)
cilium (607)
flagellum (607)
spore (607)
conjugation (608)
alternation of generations (608)
sporangium (609)

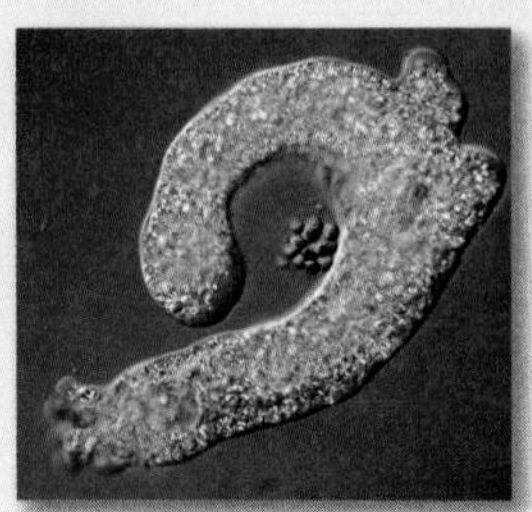

21.3 The Ecology of Protists

The position of photosynthetic protists at the base of the food chain makes much of the diversity of aquatic life possible.

Some heterotrophic protists engulf and digest their food, while others live by absorbing molecules from the environment.

Many protists are involved in mutualistic symbioses, in which they and their hosts both benefit.

Parasitic protists are responsible for some of the world's most deadly diseases, including several kinds of debilitating intestinal diseases, African sleeping sickness, and malaria.

algal bloom (611)
food vacuole (612)
gullet (612)
plasmodium (613)

21.4 Fungi

Fungi are heterotrophic eukaryotes with cell walls that contain chitin.

Fungi are champions of decomposition. Many species help ecosystems maintain homeostasis by breaking down dead organisms and recycling essential elements and nutrients.

Parasitic fungi can cause serious diseases in plants and animals by disrupting homeostasis.

Some fungi form mutualistic associations with photosynthetic organisms in which both partners benefit.

chitin (618)
hypha (619)
fruiting body (619)
mycelium (619)
lichen (623)
mycorrhiza (624)

Think Visually

Make a concept map that illustrates the various ways that protists move, reproduce, and obtain food.

UbD Performance Tasks

SUMMATIVE TASK Have students work in small groups to design a mural that shows the three main ecological roles of protists and fungi using three different protists and three different fungi—one from each group for each role. Students can draw their own illustrations or print out visuals of the organisms from the Internet. They should add annotations explaining the roles.

TRANSFER TASK Tell students to imagine their neighbors have told them about a yellow, slimy growth in a pile of leaves at the edge of their yard, and they want to kill it. Have students prepare answers to these questions:

- What kind of organism are your neighbors most likely describing? Explain.
- What might you want your neighbors to know about this kind of organism?
- How would you persuade them to identify the organism before killing it?

Study Online

REVIEW AND ASSESSMENT RESOURCES

Editable Worksheets Pages of Study Workbooks A and B, Lab Manuals A and B, and the Assessment Resources Book are available online. These documents can be easily edited using a word-processing program.

Lesson Overview Have students reread the Lesson Overviews to help them study chapter concepts.

Vocabulary Review The *Flash Cards* and *Crossword* provide an interactive way to review chapter vocabulary.

Chapter Assessment Have students take an online version of the Chapter 21 Assessment.

Standardized Test Prep Students can take an online version of the Standardized Test Prep. You will receive their scores along with ideas for remediation.

Diagnostic and Benchmark Tests Use these tests to monitor your students' progress and supply remediation.

Answers

THINK VISUALLY

Students' concept maps should include active movement by pseudopods, cilia, and flagella and passive movement; sexual and asexual reproduction; and obtaining food through photosynthesis, capturing prey, and absorption.

ASSESSMENT

Lesson 21.1

UNDERSTAND KEY CONCEPTS

1. c **2.** b **3.** c

4. Many protists do not fit within these groups.

5. Protists appear in the fossil record before any members of the plant, animal, or fungus kingdoms, and genome analysis is beginning to identify likely ancestral lines among the protists.

THINK CRITICALLY

6. Many of the animal-like and funguslike protists are so similar that they belong in a single group.

7. Like items in a junk drawer, protists do not share a set of common features with one another and are grouped together because they don't belong in any of the other groups of organisms that do share common features. Scientists would like to change this because, ideally, classification systems are based on similarities, not differences, among organisms.

Lesson 21.2

UNDERSTAND KEY CONCEPTS

8. c **9.** d **10.** d

11. Cilia and flagella are the organs of movement in the ciliates and flagellates. The structures are nearly identical, but produce motion differently. In general, cilia are comparatively shorter than flagella. Cilia move somewhat like side oars on a boat. Flagella are located at an end of an organism and move back and forth.

12. Conjugation allows ciliates to exchange genetic material. Two paramecia join. After meiosis of their diploid micronuclei, each organism is left with four haploid micronuclei. Three nuclei disintegrate, leaving one nucleus in each organism to divide by mitosis. This results in a pair of identical nuclei. The two paramecia then exchange one nucleus from their pairs. Conjugation is not a form of reproduction, because no new offspring are formed, but it is a sexual process.

THINK CRITICALLY

13. These organisms survive by being carried by air or water currents, or in the bloodstreams or digestive systems of their hosts.

14. Protists can reproduce rapidly through asexual reproduction in a favorable environment. If conditions become unfavorable, protists reproduce sexually, which results in new traits that may help the population survive.

21 Assessment

The numbers following the questions refer to Indiana's Academic Standards for Biology I.

21.1 Protist Classification

Understand Key Concepts

1. Which of the following descriptions applies to most protists? B.8.2
- **a.** unicellular prokaryotes
- **b.** multicellular prokaryotes
- **c.** unicellular eukaryotes
- **d.** multicellular eukaryotes

2. The fossil record shows that the first eukaryotes may have appeared on Earth B.8.1
- **a.** more than 4 billion years ago.
- **b.** more than 1 billion years ago.
- **c.** about 500 million years ago.
- **d.** about 100 million years ago.

3. Which of the following statements is most accurate? B.8.2
- **a.** Protists are more closely related to one another than to other organisms in other kingdoms.
- **b.** Protists are the direct descendants of bacteria.
- **c.** The classification of protists is a work in progress.
- **d.** Scientists are debating between two classification schemes for protists.

4. What is the problem with the traditional classification of protists into plantlike, animal-like, and funguslike groups? B.8.2

5. Why do scientists think that all modern plants, animals, and fungi can be traced to protist ancestors? B.8.2, B.8.4

Think Critically

6. **Apply Concepts** At one time, living things were classified as animals if they moved or ingested food and classified as plants if they did not move or ingest food. Why is it difficult to classify the protists by these criteria? B.8.2

7. **Use Analogies** You might have a drawer in your kitchen that is a "junk drawer": a drawer filled with keys, rubber bands, pens, string, rulers, and other items that aren't easy to categorize. How is the protist kingdom like a "junk drawer," and why do you think scientists would like to change that situation? NoS.6

21.2 Protist Structure and Function

Understand Key Concepts

8. Which is NOT true of amoebas?
- **a.** They reproduce by mitosis.
- **b.** They move using pseudopods.
- **c.** They have a rigid cell membrane.
- **d.** The protein actin powers their movement.

9. Which of the following protists moves by means of cilia? B.2.5

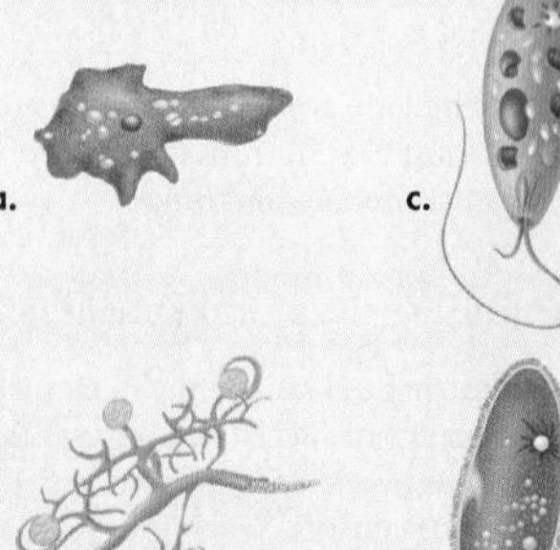

10. Alternation of generations is the process of alternating between
- **a.** mitosis and meiosis.
- **b.** asexual and sexual reproduction.
- **c.** male and female reproductive structures.
- **d.** diploid and haploid phases.

11. What function do the cilia and flagella in protists carry out? How do they differ in structure? B.2.5

12. Summarize the process of conjugation. Is conjugation a form of reproduction? Explain.

Think Critically

13. **Apply Concepts** Some protists cannot move on their own. What generalization can you make about how these organisms survive?

14. **Infer** How do you think the ability to switch between asexual and sexual reproduction has aided the evolution of water molds and many other protists?

Lesson 21.3

UNDERSTAND KEY CONCEPTS

15. c **16.** b **17.** a

18. *Trichonympha* is a protist that makes an enzyme that digests the cellulose in wood. Termites cannot digest cellulose and would starve on their wood diet without the protists. *Trichonymphas* get plenty of food and a safe, protected place to live inside the termites' guts.

19. Mosquitoes bite a human infected with malaria and pick up the parasite. Then, the mosquitoes transmit the protists through their saliva to another human when they bite again.

THINK CRITICALLY

20. Sample answer: The antibiotic destroys structures within the protist's cytoplasm, and these structures are related to the protist's ability to break down cellulose. When a termite is fed the antibiotic, these structures disappear. The termite is no longer able to obtain nutrition from its food, so it dies.

21.3 The Ecology of Protists

Understand Key Concepts

15. Which of the following statements about photosynthetic protists is most accurate?
a. Most photosynthetic protists are heterotrophs.
b. All photosynthetic protists are closely related to plants.
c. Small photosynthetic organisms near the ocean's surface are called phytoplankton.
d. Giant kelp play an important role in the formation of coral reefs.

16. Slime molds are found primarily in
a. oceans.
b. decaying organic matter.
c. fast-moving streams.
d. deserts.

17. African sleeping sickness is caused by
a. *Trypanosoma*.
b. *Plasmodium*.
c. *Trichonympha*.
d. *Amoeba*.

18. Describe the nature of the relationship between a termite and the protists that live in its gut.

19. How do insects transmit malaria?

Think Critically

20. Form a Hypothesis A scientist observes that termites that are fed a certain antibiotic die of starvation after a few days. The scientist also notices that the antibiotic affects certain protists that live inside the termite's gut in a peculiar way: Although the protists continue to thrive, a certain kind of structure disappears from their cytoplasm. Develop a hypothesis to explain these observations.

21. Infer Slime molds produce sporangia and spores only when food is scarce. Why do you think this is so? What advantages do slime molds gain from this?

22. Predict Holes in Earth's ozone layer may increase the amount of radiation that reaches the surface of the ocean. If this radiation affects the growth of phytoplankton, what do you think the long-term consequences would be for Earth's atmosphere? Explain your answer. B.4.2

23. Infer Examine the life cycle of *Plasmodium* shown in **Figure 21–14.** Based on the illustration, do you think malaria could be transmitted through a blood transfusion? Why or why not?

solve the CHAPTER MYSTERY

"A BLIGHT OF UNUSUAL CHARACTER"

In Ireland in the 1840s, conditions were just right for the rapid and devastating spread of potato blight. The potato had become a staple crop—the main source of food for the Irish population. The disease persisted from year to year because the new crop was grown from potato eyes saved from the previous year's crop. Genetically identical crops offered no new resistance to the blight.

What clues throughout the chapter point to the culprit's identity? Some of its features—notably, the presence of hyphae and the fact that it obtains food by absorption through its cell walls—are traits shared by both water molds and fungi. The final clue, however, is telling—the culprit's cells lack chitin and the hyphae are diploid. These traits eliminate the fungus option. The organism that causes the blight is a water mold—the protist *Phytophthora*— which literally means "plant eater."

Phytophthora hyphae invading a potato (SEM 100×)

1. Relate Cause and Effect Observers in Ireland noted that the weather leading up to the summer of 1845 was unusually wet and cool. How might the weather conditions in 1845 have favored this organism's life cycle?

2. Infer Scientists now believe that *Phytophthora* came with some batches of potatoes from South America. Why hadn't the same organism caused such widespread destruction there?

3. Connect to the Big idea In the 1840s, one observer remarked that potatoes were grown so widely in Ireland that they formed "a continuous canopy of leaves." In the United States, the same disease appeared several years earlier, but did not cause widespread famine. Why not?

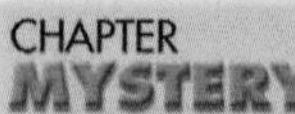

CHAPTER MYSTERY Have students read **"A Blight of Unusual Character"** and discuss the clues that led them to identify the cause of the potato blight. Ask what the Irish famine reinforces about genetic variability in crops. *(It is important not to rely on one strain of any crop. Genetic variability helps populations of organisms survive adverse environmental conditions, such as disease.)*

Then, have students look back at **Figure 21–7** and tell how the label describes the spores produced during the life cycle of a water mold. *(They are flagellated.)* Ask how this characteristic is associated with disease that spreads under wet conditions. (*Water is necessary for the spores to swim and therefore spread the disease from plant to plant.)* Have students identify another characteristic of spores that contributes to maintenance of disease in a population of organisms and apply that concept to the Irish famine. *(Spores are very tough and can survive cold conditions. Even if Ireland had cold winters, the spores might have lived through the winters.)*

CHAPTER MYSTERY ANSWERS

1. Wet and cool weather is ideal for the growth and reproduction of *Phytophthora.*
2. The climate in that part of South America was warmer and drier than the climate in Ireland and did not support the growth and reproduction of *Phytophthora.*
3. **Big idea** In the United States, the potatoes were spread farther apart, making it harder for the disease to spread from one group to the next. Also, because the U.S. had other plants that supplied food, people were less dependent on a single crop to supply the majority of their food.

Suggest students watch **Fungus Among Us** to find out more about the fascinating world of mushrooms.

21. Slime molds produce sporangia and spores when food is scarce for greater mobility and increased genetic diversity. Greater spore mobility increases the organism's chances of finding another source of food. Greater diversity helps it adapt to changes in environmental conditions.

22. If the radiation slows the growth of phytoplankton or kills them, the amount of oxygen in the air might decrease and the amount of carbon dioxide might increase. If the radiation speeds up the growth of phytoplankton, the amount of oxygen in the air might increase and the amount of carbon dioxide might decrease.

23. Yes, if red blood cells are infected, they could be passed along by a transfusion.

ASSESSMENT

Lesson 21.4

UNDERSTAND KEY CONCEPTS

24. a **25.** c

26. Both contain chitin.

27. A hypha is a tiny filament that is only one cell thick, whereas a mycelium is a thick mass composed of many hyphae tangled together.

28. Mycorrhizal associations may have been critical in the evolution of land plants from aquatic ancestors.

THINK CRITICALLY

29. Fungi obtain food by absorbing nutrients from decaying matter or from the bodies of their hosts. Humans obtain food by ingesting plants, animals, and some fungi.

30. Sample answer: As decomposers, many bacteria and fungi compete for the same food sources. Natural selection favored fungi that developed a mechanism for killing these bacteria competitors.

Connecting Concepts

USE SCIENCE GRAPHICS

31. The tree on the right shows more robust growth.

32. The tree on the right was grown with a fungal symbiont to form mycorrhizae. The fungi allowed the tree to absorb more nutrients.

WRITE ABOUT SCIENCE

33. Students' paragraphs will vary, but should include explanations of fungi as decomposers, as parasites, and in mutualistic associations. Paragraphs should also give examples of fungi that maintain or disrupt an ecosystem.

34. Big idea Students' explanations will vary, but should show an understanding of how populations of different organisms interact and influence each other, and specifically, how the protists affect homeostasis of other organisms or the equilibrium of the environment.

21.4 Fungi

Understand Key Concepts

24. Which of the following statements about fungi is false? B.8.2
- **a.** All fungi are unicellular.
- **b.** All fungi have cell walls.
- **c.** All fungi are eukaryotic.
- **d.** All fungi are heterotrophs.

25. A symbiotic relationship between a fungus and a green alga or a cyanobacterium is a
- **a.** mycorrhiza.
- **b.** fruiting body.
- **c.** lichen.
- **d.** mushroom.

26. How are the cell walls of fungi similar to the exoskeleton of insects?

27. Distinguish between the terms *hypha* and *mycelium*.

28. What is the evolutionary significance of mycorrhizae?

Think Critically

29. **Compare and Contrast** Both fungi and humans are heterotrophs. Compare the way fungi obtain food with the way humans do.

30. **Form a Hypothesis** The antibiotic penicillin is a natural secretion of a certain kind of fungus—a green mold called *Penicillium*. Penicillin kills bacteria. Why do you think a mold species has evolved a way to kill bacteria?

Connecting Concepts

Use Science Graphics NoS.3

This photograph shows a comparison of lemon tree seedlings grown without mycorrhizae (left) to seedlings of the same age that were grown with mycorrhizae. Use the photograph to answer questions 31–32.

31. **Compare and Contrast** Which lemon tree shows more robust growth?

32. **Relate Cause and Effect** What is the most likely explanation for the treatment results shown?

Write About Science NoS.3

33. **Explanation** Write a paragraph explaining how fungi either maintain or disrupt the equilibrium of an ecosystem. Use examples of fungi described in this chapter. (*Hint:* Create a table to help organize your ideas before you begin writing.) B.4.2

34. **Assess the Big idea** Choose one of the protists discussed in this chapter, and explain how the presence and the activity of that organism influence other species.

Analyzing Data

IN NoS.3

Use the graph below to answer the questions.

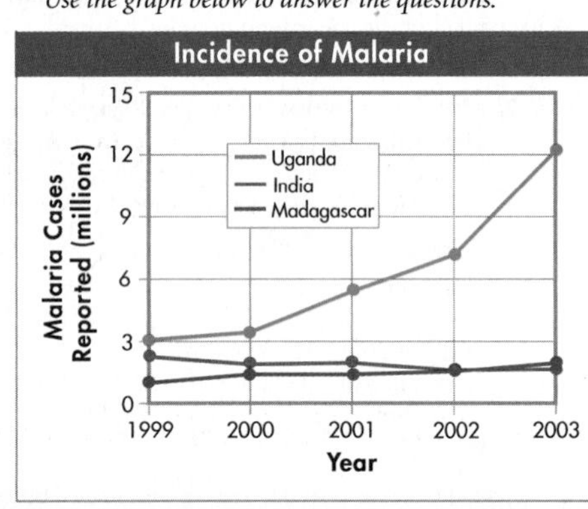

35. **Interpret Graphs** Which statement best describes the trend shown in the graph?
- **a.** Globally, malaria cases are on the rise.
- **b.** Malaria cases declined in India during the five-year period shown.
- **c.** In 2003, Uganda had four times as many malaria cases as did Madagascar.
- **d.** Annual changes in rainfall explain the patterns seen in the data.

36. **Calculate** By about what percentage did the number of malaria cases increase in Uganda between 1999 and 2003? MATH
- **a.** 50 percent
- **b.** 100 percent
- **c.** 300 percent
- **d.** 1000 percent

PURPOSE Students will interpret a graph to draw conclusions and make calculations about malaria cases.

PLANNING Remind students that a line graph is often used to show changes over time. Review the meaning of the color key and what is represented by the *y*- and *x*-axes.

ANSWERS

35. b

36. c

Standardized Test Practice for Indiana

Multiple Choice

1. All of the following are characteristics of some protists EXCEPT
   A peptidoglycan in the cell walls.
   B a membrane-bound nucleus.
   C flagella.
   D cilia. B.8.1

2. The structures in *Amoeba* that help the organism move and feed are the
   A flagella.
   B cilia.
   C food vacuoles.
   D pseudopods. B.2.5

3. In protists, the process of conjugation
   A is linked to photosynthesis.
   B results in an exchange of some genetic material.
   C produces offspring that are genetically identical to the parent.
   D decreases the genetic diversity of a population.

4. Which of the following statements about slime molds is false?
   A Slime molds are eukaryotes.
   B Slime molds play an important part in recycling nutrients.
   C Slime molds are multicellular at some time during their life cycle.
   D Slime molds are photosynthetic protists. B.8.2

5. Algal blooms can be caused by
   A paramecia.
   B lichens.
   C dinoflagellates.
   D *Trichonympha.*

6. Alternation of generations BEST describes sexual reproduction in
   A *Paramecium.*
   B water molds.
   C *Amoeba.*
   D yeast.

7. The primary carbohydrate found in the cell walls of fungi is
   A chitin.
   B actin.
   C cellulose.
   D starch.

Questions 8–10

Ripe grapes are covered with a grayish film, or bloom, that contains yeasts and sometimes other microorganisms. A group of students prepared three test tubes of fresh mashed grapes. They heated two of the test tubes to boiling and then cooled them. They inoculated one of those test tubes with live yeast, incubated all three test tubes at 30°C for 48 hours, and then examined the test tubes for signs of fermentation—an alcohol odor and bubbles. Their data are summarized in the table below.

Evidence of Fermentation

Test-Tube Contents	Alcohol Odor (yes or no)	Bubbles (yes or no)
Unheated grape mash	yes	yes
Boiled grape mash	no	no
Boiled grape mash inoculated with yeast	yes	yes

8. What is the independent variable in the students' investigation?
   A the presence of live yeast
   B an odor of alcohol
   C bubbles
   D time

9. What is the dependent variable in the students' investigation?
   A time
   B boiling
   C an odor of alcohol and the presence of bubbles
   D the presence of live yeast

10. What can you conclude based on the students' results?
    A Uninoculated, boiled grape mash does not seem to ferment over a 48-hour period.
    B Boiled grape mash that contains live yeast undergoes fermentation.
    C Grape mash does not ferment unless live yeast is added.
    D Both A and B are correct.

Open-Ended Response

11. How does each of the partners in the lichen symbiosis benefit from the relationship?

If You Have Trouble With . . .

Question	1	2	3	4	5	6	7	8	9	10	11
See Lesson	21.2	21.2	21.2	21.3	21.3	21.2	21.4	21.4	21.4	21.4	21.4

Answers

1. A
2. D
3. B
4. D
5. C
6. B
7. A
8. A
9. C
10. D
11. The photosynthetic partner supplies food to the fungus. The fungus provides water and minerals it absorbs from the surroundings and can protect the alga or cyanobacteria from too much sunlight.

ASSESSMENT

Test-Taking Tip

USE TIME WISELY

Tell students that before they begin answering questions, they should determine the total number of questions on the test and how much time, on average, they have to answer each question. Then, they can try to allocate their time accordingly.

CHAPTER PLANNER 22 Introduction to Plants

Chapter Contents	IN	Time	Core Resources
Chapter Preview			**Student Edition,** pp. 632–633 **Chapter Mystery,** p. 633
22.1 What Is a Plant? Characteristics of Plants • The History and Evolution of Plants • The Plant Life Cycle	B.8.1, B.8.2	1 period 1/2 block	**Student Edition,** pp. 634–638 Inquiry 22.1 Quick Lab, p. 635 L2 **Study Workbook A** 22.1 Worksheets L2 **Assessment Resources Book** Visual Quiz L2
22.2 Seedless Plants Green Algae • Mosses and Other Bryophytes • Vascular Plants	NoS.3, B.8.2	1 period 1/2 block	**Student Edition,** pp. 639–645 Inquiry 22.2 Analyzing Data, p. 644 L2 **Study Workbook A** 22.2 Worksheets L2 **Biology.com** *Data Analysis:* Bracken: Invasive and Deadly? • *InterActive Art:* Plant Life Cycles • 22.2 Self-Test • 22.2 Lesson Assessment
22.3 Seed Plants The Importance of Seeds • The Life Cycle of a Gymnosperm	B.8.1, B.8.2	1 period 1/2 block	**Student Edition,** pp. 646–649 **Study Workbook A** 22.3 Worksheets L2 **Biology.com** *Art in Motion:* Gymnosperm Fertilization **Assessment Resources Book** Visual Quiz L2
22.4 Flowering Plants Flowers and Fruits • Angiosperm Diversity • *Careers & Biology: Farmer, Plant Pathologist, Botanical Illustrator*	B.8.1, B.8.2	1 period 1/2 block	**Student Edition,** pp. 650–655 Inquiry 22.4 Quick Lab, p. 651 L2 **Study Workbook A** 22.4 Worksheets L2 **Biology.com** *Tutor Tube:* Males, Females, and Sexual Reproduction in Plants—An Animal Perspective • *Art Review:* Comparing Monocots and Dicots • 22.4 Self-Test • 22.4 Lesson Assessment
Chapter Pre-Lab	NoS.4, B.8.2	1 period 1/2 block	**Student Edition,** p. 656 L2 **Lab Manual A** *Exploring Plant Diversity* L2 • *Using Pollen to Solve Crimes* L2

Differentiated Instruction Tools

Study Workbook B includes worksheets with lesson-level differentiated instruction support and explanations of differentiated instruction teaching strategies.

Lab Manual B includes skills labs, simplified chapter labs, and hands-on activities.

ELL Handbook explains ways to make *Biology* more accessible to ELL students.

Spanish Study Workbook is a Spanish translation of Study Workbook A.

Multilingual Glossary is the glossary translated into ten languages.

Differentiated Instruction Key

- L1 Special Needs or Struggling Students
- ELL English Language Learners
- LPR Less Proficient Readers
- L2 On-Level Students
- L3 Advanced Students

Additional Resources

Biology.com Untamed Science Video • Vocabulary Flash Cards

Study Workbook B 22.1 Worksheets L1 ELL LPR
Spanish Study Workbook 22.1 Worksheets ELL
Biology.com 22.1 Lesson Overview • 22.1 Lesson Notes • 22.1 Self-Test • 22.1 Lesson Assessment

Study Workbook B 22.2 Worksheets L1 ELL LPR
Spanish Study Workbook 22.2 Worksheets ELL
Biology.com 22.2 Lesson Overview • 22.2 Lesson Notes

Study Workbook B 22.3 Worksheets L1 ELL LPR
Spanish Study Workbook 22.3 Worksheets ELL
Biology.com 22.3 Lesson Overview • 22.3 Lesson Notes • 22.3 Self-Test • 22.3 Lesson Assessment

Study Workbook B 22.4 Worksheets L1 ELL LPR
Spanish Study Workbook 22.4 Worksheets ELL
Biology.com 22.4 Lesson Overview • 22.4 Lesson Notes

Lab Manual B *Exploring Plant Diversity* • Data Analysis: *Keeping Ferns in Check* • Hands-On Activity: *Are All Plants the Same?* L1 ELL LPR

Chapter Review

Student Edition Study Guide, p. 657 L2
Study Workbook A Chapter 22 Vocabulary Review L2 • Chapter 22 Chapter Mystery/21st Century Skills Activity L2 L3
Transparencies, pp. 259–267 L1 ELL LPR L2
Biology.com Untamed Science Video • Editable Worksheets of Study Workbooks A and B and Lab Manuals A and B • Chapter 22 Flash Cards and Crossword Puzzle

Untamed Science DVD • Classroom Resources CD (includes lesson presentations and editable worksheets)

Chapter Assessment

Student Edition Assessment, pp. 658–661 L2
Study Workbook B Chapter 22 Chapter Review L1 ELL LPR • Chapter 22 Taking a Standardized Test L1 ELL LPR
Assessment Resources Book Chapter 22 Test A L2 • Chapter 22 Test B L1 ELL LPR
Biology.com Chapter 22 Assessment • Editable Worksheets of Chapter 22 Visual Quizzes and Chapter 22 Tests A and B

Exam*View* *Assessment Suite* • Classroom Resources CD (includes lesson presentations and editable worksheets)

Time: 1 period, 1/2 block

Pressed for Time?

Preview the Chapter Introduce students to Figures 22–2, 22–4, and 22–15.

Cover the Chapter Quickly Assign *Characteristics of Plants* in Lesson 22.1. In Lesson 22.2, have students read the key concept in *Green Algae,* the introduction and Why Bryophytes Are Small in *Mosses and Other Bryophytes,* and all of *Vascular Plants.* Assign *The Importance of Seeds* in Lesson 22.3, and *Flowers and Fruit* in Lesson 22.4.

Assess Assign question 1 in the 22.1 Assessment, questions 1a, 2a, and 3 in the 22.2 Assessment, questions 1 and 3 in the 22.3 Assessment, and question 1 in the 22.4 Assessment. In the Chapter 22 Assessment, assign questions 1, 3, 11, 14, 18, 21, 24, 27, 35, 44, and 45.

Connect to the Big Idea

Have students study the photo of the meadow. Ask them to describe the plants they see. Then, have them think about how this picture might change if it showed a desert scene. How might the plants in that environment look different? Point out that different kinds of plants thrive in different conditions. Ask students what makes this possible. *(Sample answer: Plants have adaptations that allow them to survive in particular environmental conditions.)* Then, tell them that the information they will learn in this chapter will help them answer the question, **What are the five main groups of plants, and how have four of these groups adapted to life on land?**

CHAPTER MYSTERY Have students read over the Chapter Mystery and use the clues in the second paragraph to make inferences about how Iceman lived. Then, have students predict other information that might provide clues about how he lived. Use their ideas to help them start connecting the Chapter Mystery to the Big Idea of Unity and Diversity of Life.

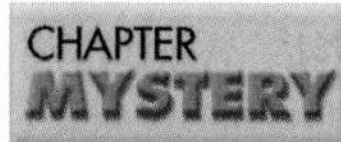
Have students preview the chapter vocabulary terms using the **Flash Cards.**

22 Introduction to Plants

Big idea **Unity and Diversity of Life**

Q: What are the five main groups of plants, and how have four of these groups adapted to life on land?

An alpine meadow provides forage for deer and other herbivores.

BIOLOGY.com Search Chapter 22 GO • Flash Cards

632

IN INDIANA ACADEMIC STANDARDS

For the full text of all standards, see the Course Overview in the front matter of this book.

Key standards: Chapter 22 covers key ideas from Standard 8: Evolution, including **B.8.2** Classification.

UbD Understanding by Design

From microorganisms to plants, organisms vary widely in the way they carry out basic life processes. This Enduring Understanding guides students' investigation of plants and how they meet their needs. As shown in the graphic organizer at the right, a Big Idea, Essential Question, and lesson-level Guiding Questions also help frame their exploration of this Enduring Understanding.

PERFORMANCE GOALS

As students progress through Chapter 22, they will be able to exhibit an understanding of the characteristics that all plants share, as well as those that distinguish the main plant groups. Lesson performance tasks require students to apply their knowledge through creative writing, active discussion, and a poster. Students integrate what they have learned from all the lessons to devise a game and to create a field guide for identifying the five main groups of plants.

INDIANA ACADEMIC STANDARDS FOR SCIENCE

Nature of Science NoS.3, NoS.4; **Evolution** B.8.1, B.8.2.
See lessons for details.

• Untamed Science Video • Chapter Mystery

CHAPTER MYSTERY

STONE AGE STORYTELLERS

Some 5300 years ago, a man died on a remote mountain pass in the Alps. In 1991, the glacier that had kept him frozen for so long melted, revealing his well-preserved corpse. The body of this "Iceman," along with his clothes, tools, and other artifacts, has provided an amazing amount of information about his society, daily life, and the circumstances of his death.

Some of the most interesting evidence found with Iceman comes from plant material. He had a storage container made from birch bark and a wooden bow and quiver of arrows. Scientists also found several species of tree pollen inside Iceman's digestive tract, which he most likely ingested by accident after the airborne pollen settled on his food. What might these and other botanical clues reveal about Iceman? As you read the chapter, look for clues to help you solve the mystery of Iceman.

Never Stop Exploring Your World.
Iceman used plants in ways that made sense for the time he lived in. Take a video field trip with the ecogeeks of Untamed Science to see how far humans have come in realizing what plants have to offer.

Chapter 22
Big Idea: Unity and Diversity of Life

Chapter 22 EQ: What are the five main groups of plants, and how have four of these groups adapted to life on land?

22.1 GQ: What are the characteristics of plants?

22.2 GQ: What are the characteristics of seedless plants?

22.3 GQ: What are the characteristics of seed plants?

22.4 GQ: What are the characteristics of flowering plants?

What's Online

Extend your reach by using these and other digital assets offered at Biology.com.

CHAPTER MYSTERY
Let botanical clues be students' guide as they explore a day in the life—and death—of Iceman, a 5,300-year-old corpse discovered in 1991.

UNTAMED SCIENCE VIDEO
In this short video, students learn about some of the many chemicals plants make that humans use as medicines.

INTERACTIVE ART
Students examine reproduction in plants by accessing these interactive life cycle diagrams.

DATA ANALYSIS
Students will analyze data to learn more about bracken, a type of fern.

ART IN MOTION
Students watch the fertilization and the development of a pine embryo.

TUTOR TUBE
This short, online tutorial helps students better understand plant life cycles by comparing sexual reproduction in plants and animals.

ART REVIEW
Students can drag and drop labels as they compare monocots and dicots.

LESSON 22.1

Getting Started

Objectives

22.1.1 Describe what plants need to survive.

22.1.2 Describe how the first plants evolved.

22.1.3 Explain the process of alternation of generations.

Student Resources

Study Workbooks A and B, 22.1 Worksheets

Spanish Study Workbook, 22.1 Worksheets

Lesson Overview • Lesson Notes • Assessment: Self-Test, Lesson Assessment

For corresponding lesson in the **Foundation Edition,** see pages 528–531.

Activate Prior Knowledge

Have students brainstorm a list of plants that are common to your area as you write them on the board. Ask volunteers to name some plant characteristics that could be used to classify them into a few large groups. For example, students might divide plants into needle-leaved and broad-leaved plants. Some students might also place mosses and ferns in separate groups.

IN INDIANA ACADEMIC STANDARDS

For the full text of all standards, see the Course Overview in the front matter of this book.

B.8.2 Explain how organisms are classified and named based on their evolutionary relationships into taxonomic categories.

22.1 What Is a Plant?

IN B.8.2 Classification. Also covered: B.8.1.

Key Questions

What do plants need to survive?

How did plants adapt to life on land?

What feature defines most plant life cycles?

Vocabulary

alternation of generations • sporophyte • gametophyte

Taking Notes

Preview Visuals Preview **Figure 22–4** and list five main groups of plants. For each group, list any characteristics or specific examples that you already know.

THINK ABOUT IT What color is life? Living things can be just about any color, of course. But imagine yourself in a place so abundant with life that living things actually blot out the sun. Now what color do you see? If you've imagined a thick forest or a teeming jungle, then just one color will fill the landscape of your mind: green—the color of plants. Plants have adapted so well to so many environments that they dominate much of the surface of our planet.

Characteristics of Plants

What do plants need to survive?

What are plants? You are already familiar with many examples, such as trees, shrubs, and grasses. But did you know that mosses and ferns are also types of plants? In the last several years, biologists have reclassified green algae as plants, too. (Green algae used to be considered protists.) What characteristics do all these organisms share?

The Plant Kingdom Traditionally, plants are classified as members of the kingdom Plantae. Plants are eukaryotes that have cell walls containing cellulose and carry out photosynthesis using chlorophyll *a* and *b*. While most plants are autotrophs, a few are parasites or saprobes.

FIGURE 22–1 Diagram of a Plant Cell Plant leaves appear green due to the photosynthetic pigments chlorophyll *a* and *b*, which are located in chloroplasts.

UbD Teach for Understanding

ENDURING UNDERSTANDING From microorganisms to plants, organisms vary widely in the way they carry out basic life processes.

GUIDING QUESTION What are the characteristics of plants?

EVIDENCE OF UNDERSTANDING *After completing the lesson, give students the following assessment to show they understand what plants need to carry out basic life processes.* Have students write a "recipe" with "ingredients" of what plants need to survive and why they need them. For example, students might write "6–8 hours of sunlight every day so the plant can carry out photosynthesis." Provide a cooking recipe that students can use as a model. Let students know it is fine if they do not list specific quantities for some of their ingredients.

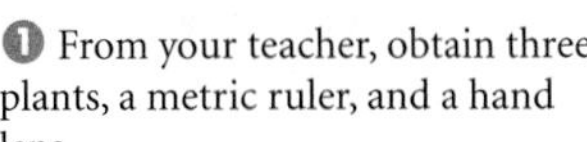

IN B.8.2

Are All Plants the Same?

1. From your teacher, obtain three plants, a metric ruler, and a hand lens.
2. Identify the major parts of each plant. Measure the heights of the plants and the sizes of their parts.
3. Use the hand lens to examine the plants. Record your observations.

Analyze and Conclude

1. **Compare and Contrast** What patterns and symmetries do you observe among the three plants? How are the three plants alike? How do they differ?
2. **Infer** What do the shapes of plant structures suggest about their functions?
3. **Classify** Use your observations to classify the three plants into two groups by outward characteristics alone. Explain your reasons for classifying them in these groups.

What Plants Need Surviving as stationary organisms on land is a difficult task that most plants face. Plants have developed a number of adaptations that enable them to succeed. **The lives of plants center on the need for sunlight, gas exchange, water, and minerals.** These basic needs are illustrated in **Figure 22–2.**

▶ ***Sunlight*** Plants use the energy from sunlight to carry out photosynthesis. As a result, every plant displays adaptations shaped by the need to gather sunlight. Photosynthetic organs such as leaves are typically broad and flat and are arranged on the stem so as to maximize light absorption.

▶ ***Gas Exchange*** Plants require oxygen to support cellular respiration as well as carbon dioxide to carry out photosynthesis. They also need to release excess oxygen made during photosynthesis. Plants must exchange these gases with the atmosphere and the soil without losing excessive amounts of water through evaporation.

▶ ***Water and Minerals*** On a hot sunny day, plants can lose a great deal of water to the air, just as we sweat when we are hot. Also, water is one of the raw materials of photosynthesis, so it is consumed when the sun is shining. Thus, land plants have evolved structures that limit water loss and speed the uptake of water from the ground.

As they absorb water, plants also absorb minerals. Minerals are nutrients in the soil needed for plant growth. Many plants have specialized tissues that carry water and nutrients upward from the soil and distribute the products of photosynthesis throughout the plant body. Simpler types of plants carry out these functions by diffusion.

In Your Notebook *Outline the basic needs of plants. Under each head, add supporting details.*

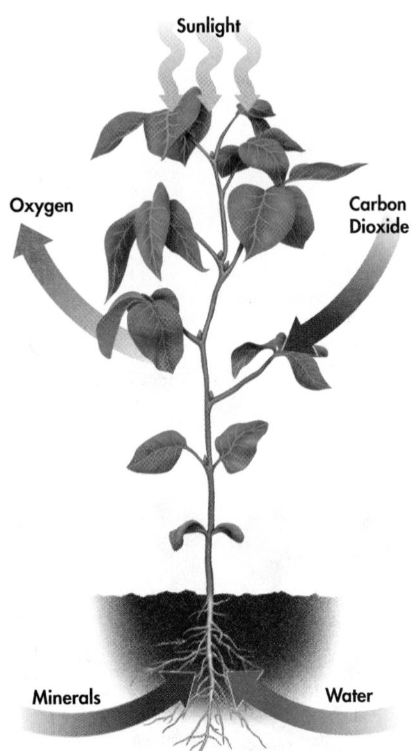

FIGURE 22–2 Basic Needs of a Plant All plants have the same basic needs: sunlight, a way to exchange gases with the surrounding air, water, and minerals. **Observe** *Where do water and minerals enter the plant?*

Teach

Use Visuals

Use **Figure 22–2** to help students understand the basic needs of plants. Point out that some of the inputs labeled are involved in photosynthesis.

Ask How are sunlight and carbon dioxide used by the plant? *(to carry out photosynthesis)*

Ask What is the purpose of photosynthesis? *(Plants use the process to make their own food.)*

DIFFERENTIATED INSTRUCTION

LPR Less Proficient Readers Have students use **Figure 22–2** to write questions and answers about what the arrows indicate and why plants need or produce the substances labeled on the figure. Then, have students team with a partner to ask each other their questions.

Address Misconceptions

Plants Without Chlorophyll Students might think all plants carry out photosynthesis. Explain that a few plant species—less than 1 percent—lack chlorophyll and must get energy from another organism. One example is *Rafflesia,* which lacks leaves, roots, and stems and attaches to a host plant for water and nutrients.

Answers

FIGURE 22–2 through the roots

IN YOUR NOTEBOOK Heads should be Sunlight, Gas Exchange, Water, and Minerals. Details should include how meeting each need helps plants to survive.

PURPOSE Students will be able to compare and contrast the structures of three plants.

MATERIALS three different types of plants, such as mosses, mature ferns with sori, and flowering plants; metric ruler; hand lens

SAFETY Avoid using plants that might cause skin irritations, such as poison ivy. Make sure students wash their hands after this activity.

PLANNING Obtain moss plants in damp, shady areas or through a biological supply house. Obtain mature ferns and potted plants from a garden store or florist.

ANALYZE AND CONCLUDE

1. Answers will vary, depending on the plants. Accept all reasonable responses.
2. Students should be able to infer the functions of roots, stems, leaves, and reproductive structures. Sample answer: The stem is shaped like a tube, so it probably carries fluid within the plant.
3. Accept all reasonable answers. Students should justify their classifications based on aspects of plant structure they observed.

LESSON 22.1

Teach continued

Build Science Skills

Talk about the evidence for all modern plants being descendants of water-dwelling organisms. Emphasize that the appearance of plants on land was a major event in evolution. Ask students to predict how the different adaptations shown on the cladogram in **Figure 22–4** may have helped plants survive on land.

DIFFERENTIATED INSTRUCTION

L1 Struggling Students Refer students who have difficulty understanding how modern land plants evolved from water organisms to the cladogram in **Figure 22–4.** Explain that it shows how plants diversified, with significant evolutionary developments represented by the green dots. Each group has all the characteristics indicated by the green dots to the left of it. Make sure students understand that one group is not the ancestor of another group; all the groups exist today and share a common ancestor. Then, ask questions that require students to read and infer information from the cladogram.

Ask What do mosses lack that other land plants have? *(water-conducting tissue and seeds)*

Answers

FIGURE 22–4 cone-bearing plants

FIGURE 22–3 A Fossilized Plant One of the earliest fossil vascular plants was *Cooksonia*. This fossil shows the branched stalks that bore reproductive structures at their tips.

The History and Evolution of Plants

How did plants adapt to life on land?

For most of Earth's history, land plants simply did not exist. Life was concentrated in oceans, lakes, and streams. Although photosynthetic prokaryotes added oxygen to our planet's atmosphere and provided food for animals and microorganisms, true plants had not yet appeared on the planet.

Origins in the Water The fossil record indicates that the ancestors of today's land plants were water-dwelling organisms similar to today's green algae. Most of these photosynthetic eukaryotes were unicellular, although a few were composed of multiple cells. At first, many biologists wondered if green algae should actually be included in a kingdom that includes organisms as large and complex as oak trees and orchids. But now it is clear that green algae have cell walls and photosynthetic pigments that are identical to those of plants. They also have reproductive cycles similar to those of plants. Finally, studies of their genomes suggest that they are so closely related to other plants that they should be considered part of the plant kingdom.

The First Land Plants Fossil spores of land plants occur in rocks 475 million years old, but the plants themselves from this time period left no fossils. The oldest fossils of land plants themselves are found roughly 50 million years later in the fossil record. Lacking leaves and roots, these plants were only a few centimeters tall. The greatest challenge that early land plants faced was obtaining water, which they achieved by growing close to the ground in damp locations. Fossils also suggest that the first true land plants were still dependent on water to complete their life cycles. **Over time, the demands of life on land favored the evolution of plants more resistant to the drying rays of the sun, more capable of conserving water, and more capable of reproducing without water.**

For more on the diversity of plants, go to the Visual Guide. DOL•20–DOL•26

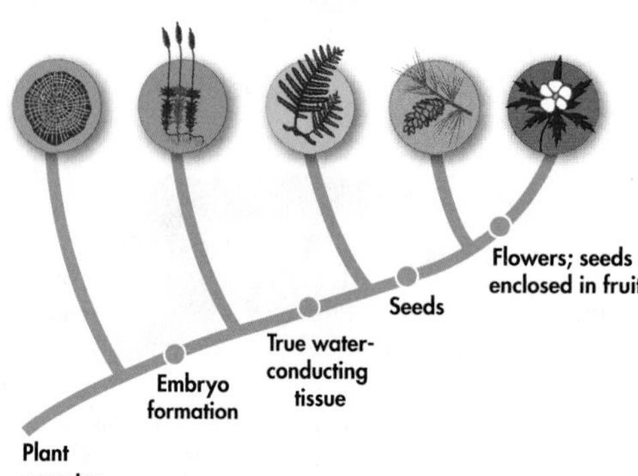

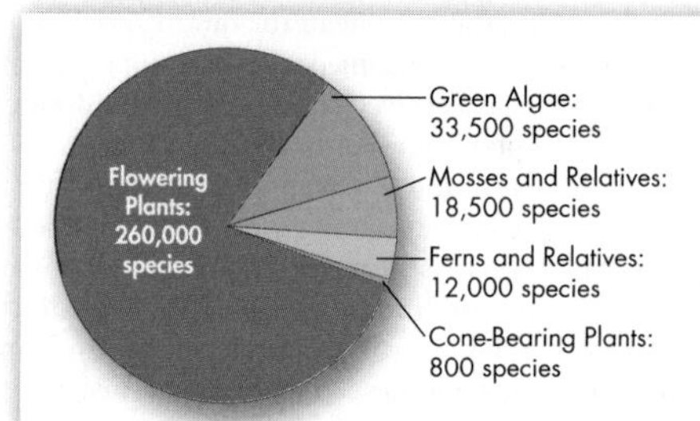

FIGURE 22–4 Major Groups of Plants There are five main groups of plants in existence today. **Interpret Diagrams** ***In the ancestor to which plant groups did seeds first evolve?***

Quick Facts

WATER PLANTS THAT EVOLVED FROM LAND PLANTS

About 60 species of flowering plants live totally under water. Collectively called seagrasses, these plants evolved from flowering land plants about 100 million years ago. They have roots, stems, and leaves, and they produce flowers. Seagrasses grow along seacoasts, coral reefs, and river estuaries all over the world except in the coldest areas. They play a critical role in many marine ecosystems, providing habitat and food for animals and sheltering coasts from storms. Some seagrass meadows are visible from space, stretching for miles along coastlines.

The appearance of plants on land changed the rest of life on Earth. As these new organisms colonized the land, they changed the environment in ways that enabled new species to evolve. New ecosystems emerged, and organic matter began to form soil.

Several groups of plants evolved from the first pioneering land plants. One group developed into mosses. Another lineage gave rise to ferns, cone-bearing plants, and flowering plants. All of these groups of plants are now successful in living on land, but they have evolved very different adaptations for a wide range of terrestrial environments.

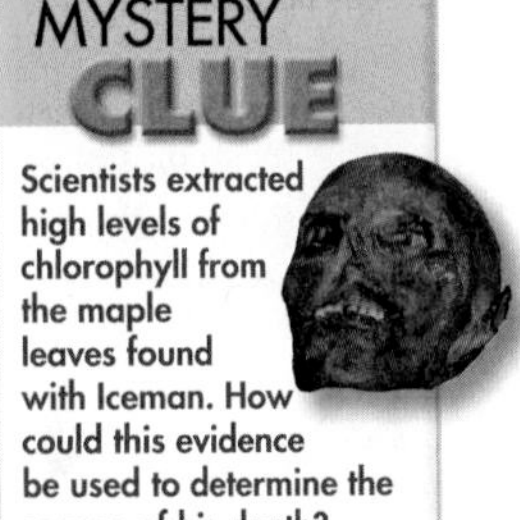

MYSTERY
CLUE
Scientists extracted high levels of chlorophyll from the maple leaves found with Iceman. How could this evidence be used to determine the season of his death?

An Overview of the Plant Kingdom Botanists divide the plant kingdom into five major groups based on four important features: embryo formation, specialized water-conducting tissues, seeds, and flowers. The relationship of these groups to one another is shown in **Figure 22–4.** Plants that form embryos are often referred to as "land plants," even though some of them now live in watery environments. Plant scientists classify plants into finer groups within these major branches by comparing the DNA sequences of various species.

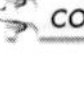

In Your Notebook *Determine the key feature that a fern has in common with a flowering plant using information in* ***Figure 22–4.***

The Plant Life Cycle

What feature defines most plant life cycles?

Land plants have a distinctive sexual life cycle that sets them apart from most other living organisms. **The life cycle of land plants has two alternating phases, a diploid (2N) phase and a haploid (N) phase.** This shift between haploid and diploid is known as the **alternation of generations.**

The multicellular diploid (2N) phase is known as the **sporophyte** (SPOH ruh fyt), or spore-producing plant. The multicellular haploid (N) phase is known as the **gametophyte** (guh MEET uh fyt), or gamete-producing plant. Recall from Chapter 11 that haploid (N) organisms carry a single set of chromosomes in their cell nuclei, while diploid (2N) organisms have two sets of chromosomes.

You can follow the basic steps of the life cycle in **Figure 22–5,** starting from the top. A sporophyte produces haploid spores through meiosis. These spores grow into multicellular structures called gametophytes. Each gametophyte produces reproductive cells called gametes—sperm and egg cells. During fertilization, a sperm and egg fuse with each other, producing a diploid zygote. The zygote develops into a new sporophyte, and the cycle begins again.

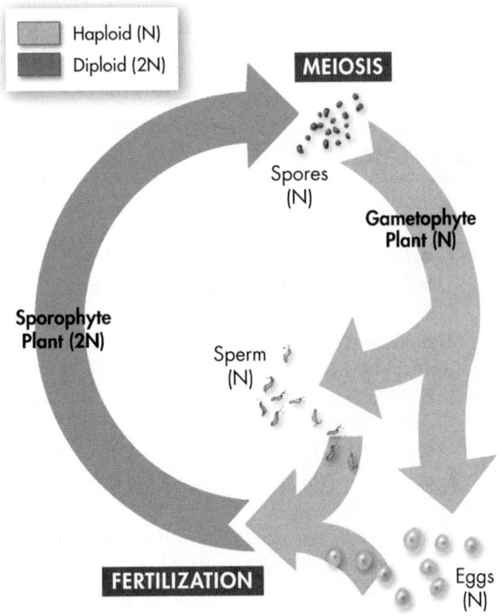

FIGURE 22–5 The Plant Life Cycle Most plants have a life cycle with alternation of generations, in which the haploid gametophyte phase alternates with the diploid sporophyte phase.

Use Visuals

Have students study **Figure 22–5** as they read **The Plant Life Cycle.** Review the difference between cells with a diploid number of chromosomes and cells with a haploid number.

Ask Which generation of a plant is diploid, and which is haploid? *(The sporophyte generation is diploid, and the gametophyte generation is haploid.)*

Ask Why does it make sense that the sporophyte generation is diploid? *(because sporophytes form when two haploid gametes fuse)*

Ask What does the sporophyte produce? *(spores)*

Ask What process produces spores? *(meiosis)*

Ask Are the spores diploid or haploid? *(haploid)*

DIFFERENTIATED INSTRUCTION

L1 Special Needs Have students model alternation of generations in the plant life cycle using pipe cleaners to represent chromosomes. Give students six pieces of pipe cleaner, two each of three different colors. Have students draw and label their own life cycle diagram, and move the pipe cleaner chromosomes through it. They should show all six pipe cleaners during the diploid stage and three pipe cleaners, one of each color, for the haploid stages.

ELL English Language Learners Explain to students that the suffix *-phyte* means "plant." Thus, *sporophyte* means "spore plant," or plant that produces spores. Ask what *gametophyte* means using this strategy. *("gamete plant," or plant that produces gametes)*

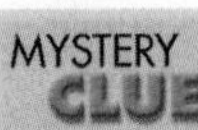

Discuss with students the role of chlorophyll in plants. Then, ask them to predict the time of year when chlorophyll levels would be highest, given what they have observed about when the leaves on trees in the neighborhood or at school are darkest green. *(summer)* Students can go online to **Biology.com** to gather their evidence.

UbD Check for Understanding

ONE-MINUTE RESPONSE

Give students one minute to write a brief essay in response to this statement: Describe the process of reproduction that is characteristic of most plant life cycles. *(Students should summarize the main steps involved in alternation of generations. Essays should include the terms* alternation of generations, sporophyte, gametophyte, diploid, *and* haploid.*)*

ADJUST INSTRUCTION

If students are unable to describe alternation of generations completely or correctly, review the difference between sexual and asexual reproduction and the difference between cells with a diploid number of chromosomes and cells with a haploid number. Then, have students draw and caption their own version of the cycle in **Figure 22–5.**

Answers

IN YOUR NOTEBOOK true water-conducting tissue

Assess and Remediate

EVALUATE UNDERSTANDING

Call on students at random to name the characteristics all plants share and the adaptations that were important in the evolution of land plants. Then, have them complete the 22.1 Assessment.

REMEDIATION SUGGESTION

L1 Struggling Students If your students have trouble with **Question 2b,** tell them to imagine people living on a boat on a river. They could simply use pails to get water. In contrast, people living some distance from the river have water piped into their homes. Without pipes, they could not live far from the river. Help students connect this analogy with the differences between the availability of water for water plants versus land plants.

BIOLOGY.com Students can check their understanding of lesson concepts with the **Self-Test** assessment. They can then take an online version of the **Lesson Assessment.**

Answers

FIGURE 22–6 Mosses have a relatively large gametophyte (N) while seed plants have the smallest gametophyte (N) of all plant groups. Mosses have smaller sporophytes (2N) than seed plants.

FIGURE 22–6 Trends in Plant Evolution An important trend in plant evolution is the reduction in size of the gametophyte and the increasing size of the sporophyte. **Interpret Visuals** ***How does the relative size of the haploid and diploid stages differ between mosses and seed plants?***

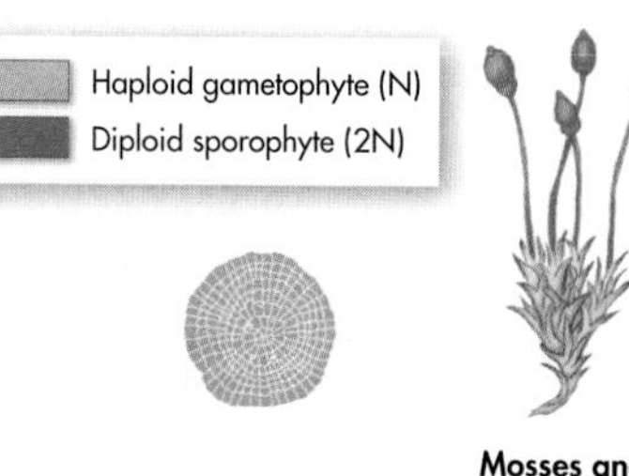

Figure 22–6 shows an important trend in plant evolution—the reduction in size of the gametophyte and the increasing size of the sporophyte. Although many green algae do have a diploid sporophyte phase, some do not; their only multicellular bodies are gametophytes. Mosses and their relatives consist of a relatively large gametophyte and smaller sporophytes. Ferns and their relatives have a small gametophyte and a larger sporophyte. Seed plants have an even smaller gametophyte, which is contained within sporophyte tissues.

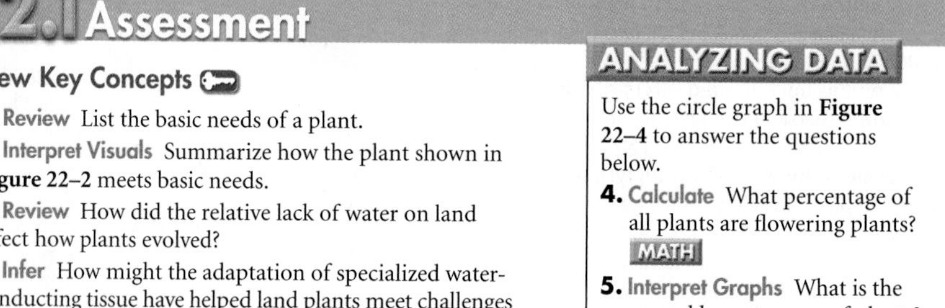

22.1 Assessment

Review Key Concepts

1. a. **Review** List the basic needs of a plant.
   b. **Interpret Visuals** Summarize how the plant shown in **Figure 22–2** meets basic needs.
2. a. **Review** How did the relative lack of water on land affect how plants evolved?
   b. **Infer** How might the adaptation of specialized water-conducting tissue have helped land plants meet challenges to life on land? Explain.
3. a. **Review** Which phrase is used to describe a plant's life cycle?
   b. **Compare and Contrast** Compare the gametophyte and sporophyte stages of plant life cycles. Which stage is haploid? Which is diploid?

ANALYZING DATA

Use the circle graph in **Figure 22–4** to answer the questions below.

4. **Calculate** What percentage of all plants are flowering plants? MATH
5. **Interpret Graphs** What is the second largest group of plants?
6. **Pose Questions** What question about plant evolution would you ask based on the data in this graph?

BIOLOGY.com Search Lesson 22.1 GO • Lesson Assessment • Self-Test

Assessment Answers

1a. sunlight, gas exchange, water, minerals

1b. The plant absorbs water and minerals through its roots. The plant's leaves capture the energy in sunlight and allow for gas exchange.

2a. Land plants evolved adaptations that made them more resistant to drying out, more capable of conserving water, and more capable of reproducing without water.

2b. Sample answer: Plants that evolved water-conducting tissue were able to better survive on land because they could pull up water from the soil and carry it to other parts of the plant.

3a. alternation of generations

3b. The sporophyte stage is diploid, while the gametophyte stage is haploid. Sporophytes are formed when gametes fuse and produce spores by meiosis. Gametophytes grow from spores and produce gametes through mitosis.

ANALYZING DATA

4. 80%

5. green algae

6. Sample answer: If green algae are the simplest plants, why are there more species in this group than in groups that are more complex?

22.2 Seedless Plants

IN B.8.2 Classification. Also covered: NoS.3.

THINK ABOUT IT We generally think of plants as growing from seeds. But there are plenty of plants, such as mosses, ferns, and green algae, that don't produce seeds at all. How do they manage to reproduce and grow without them?

Green Algae

What are the characteristics of green algae?

What do you think of when you hear the word *algae*? You might think of seaweed, given that algae make up the most common forms of seaweed, and the singular form of the word, *alga*, actually means "seaweed" in Latin. As we use the word today, the algae are not a single group of organisms. Biologists apply the name to any photosynthetic eukaryote other than a land plant. As a result, some algae are classified as protists and others are classified as plants. Those algae that are grouped with plants are called *green algae.* DOL•21

The First Plants Fossil evidence suggests that the green algae were the first plants, appearing on Earth before plants first emerged on land. In fact, fossil formations from the Cambrian Period, more than 550 million years ago, show evidence of large mats of green algae.

The green algae share many characteristics—including their photosynthetic pigments and cell wall composition—with larger, more complex plants. **Green algae are mostly aquatic. They are found in fresh and salt water, and in some moist areas on land.** Because most green algae are single cells or branching filaments, they make direct contact with the water in which they grow. They are able to absorb moisture and nutrients directly from their surroundings. Therefore, most green algae do not contain the specialized tissues found in other plants.

FIGURE 22–7 Early Plants and Animals Primitive green algae shared the ocean floor with corals and sponges in the Middle Cambrian Period, about 500 million years ago.

Key Questions

What are the characteristics of green algae?

What factor limits the size of bryophytes?

How is vascular tissue important?

Vocabulary

bryophyte • vascular tissue • archegonium • antheridium • sporangium • tracheophyte • tracheid • xylem • phloem

Taking Notes

Venn Diagram Construct a Venn diagram in which to record similarities and differences among the three major groups of seedless plants. Fill it in as you read the lesson.

Getting Started

Objectives

22.2.1 Identify the characteristics of green algae.

22.2.2 Describe the adaptations of bryophytes.

22.2.3 Explain the importance of vascular tissue.

Student Resources

Study Workbooks A and B, 22.2 Worksheets

Spanish Study Workbook, 22.2 Worksheets

Lab Manual B, 22.2 Data Analysis Worksheet

BIOLOGY.com Lesson Overview • Lesson Notes • Activities: InterActive Art, Data Analysis • Assessment: Self-Test, Lesson Assessment

For corresponding lesson in the **Foundation Edition,** see pages 532–535.

Activate Prior Knowledge

Have the class make a **Cluster Diagram** on the board. Draw a circle on the board, and write *Mosses and Ferns* in the center. Ask volunteers to come up to the board and add any facts or information they know about these plants. Leave the cluster diagram on the board and refer back to it as students work through the lesson.

Study Wkbks A/B, Appendix S19, Cluster Diagram. **Transparencies,** GO2.

IN INDIANA ACADEMIC STANDARDS

For the full text of all standards, see the Course Overview in the front matter of this book.

B.8.2 Explain how organisms are classified and named based on their evolutionary relationships into taxonomic categories.

UbD Teach for Understanding

ENDURING UNDERSTANDING From microorganisms to plants, organisms vary widely in the way they carry out basic life processes.

GUIDING QUESTION What are the characteristics of seedless plants?

EVIDENCE OF UNDERSTANDING *After completing the lesson, give students the following informal assessment to show they understand how seedless plants carry out basic life processes.* Ask students to work in groups of three to role-play a conversation between green algae, a moss, and a fern. Each group member should play the role of one of these types of plants. Have them discuss their life cycles and how they survive in their environments.

Teach

Use Visuals

Have students study **Figure 22–8** as you explain that *Chlamydomonas* switches back and forth between asexual and sexual reproduction. Emphasize that this occurs in response to environmental conditions; it does not happen automatically with every generation. Discuss the conditions under which each type of reproduction occurs. Reinforce that the production of a zygote is a survival mechanism during adverse conditions. Then, have volunteers tell what is happening in each stage of the two types of life cycle (asexual and sexual).

DIFFERENTIATED INSTRUCTION

L1 Struggling Students Students who have difficulty following the steps in the life cycle of *Chlamydomonas* might benefit from viewing them in another way. Pair students, and have them draw the diagram as two **Flowcharts**—one showing asexual reproduction and another showing sexual reproduction. Make sure students understand that the life cycle is not a continuous flow between the stages.

Study Wkbks A/B, Appendix S25, Flowchart. **Transparencies,** GO8.

ELL Focus on ELL: Access Content

BEGINNING AND INTERMEDIATE SPEAKERS Provide students with a scaffolded outline of the lesson. For example, in this section the organizing head would be I. Green Algae. The secondary heads would be A. The First Plants, B. Life Cycle, and C. Multicellularity. Model how to fill in the main points for the information on The First Plants. Then, have pairs of students fill in the main points under the next two secondary heads. Have beginning speakers write short phrases. Intermediate speakers should write longer phrases or sentences.

Answers

FIGURE 22–8 sexual reproduction

IN YOUR NOTEBOOK Sample answer: Under favorable conditions, asexual reproduction allows an organism to multiply quickly. But, the offspring of asexual reproduction are genetically identical, so they are equally vulnerable to harsh environmental conditions. New genetic combinations introduced by meiosis during sexual reproduction increase the chances that some variations will survive.

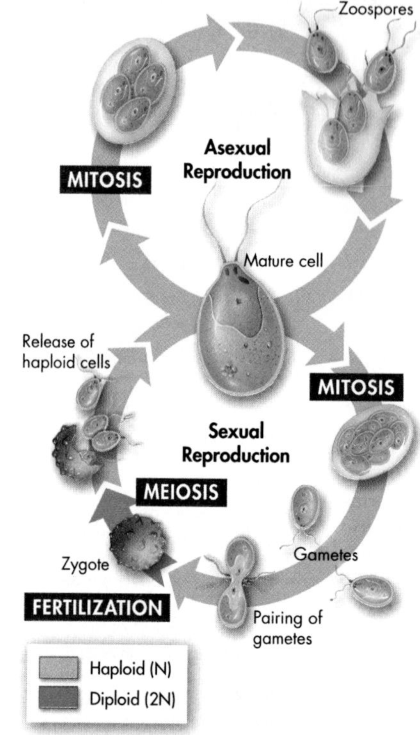

FIGURE 22–8 Life Cycle of *Chlamydomonas* The green alga *Chlamydomonas* can switch from asexual reproduction to sexual reproduction as environmental conditions change.
Interpret Visuals ***Which form of reproduction includes a diploid organism that can survive harsh conditions?***

Life Cycle Like land plants, many green algae have life cycles that switch back and forth between haploid and diploid phases. Some green algae may not alternate between haploid and diploid with each and every generation, however. Consider the single-celled green alga *Chlamydomonas.* It can stay in the haploid stage for multiple generations. As long as living conditions are suitable, the haploid cell reproduces asexually by mitosis, as shown in the top half of **Figure 22–8.**

If environmental conditions become unfavorable, *Chlamydomonas* can switch to a stage that reproduces sexually. The cell releases gametes that fuse into a diploid zygote—a sporophyte. The zygote has a thick protective wall, permitting survival in freezing or drying conditions that would ordinarily kill it. When conditions once again become favorable, the zygote begins to grow. It divides by meiosis to produce four flagellated haploid cells. These haploid cells then swim away, mature, and reproduce asexually.

In Your Notebook *Describe a more general advantage to an organism that can change its mode of reproduction under different environmental conditions.*

Multicellularity Many of the green algae form colonies, providing a hint as to how the first multicellular plants may have evolved. Two examples of colonial algae are shown in **Figure 22–9.** On the left is the freshwater alga *Spirogyra,* which forms long, threadlike colonies called filaments. The cells of a colony are stacked almost like soda cans placed end to end. The *Volvox* colonies shown on the right are more complex than those of *Spirogyra,* consisting of as few as 500 to as many as 50,000 cells arranged to form hollow spheres.

The cells in a *Volvox* colony are connected to one another by strands of cytoplasm, enabling them to communicate. When the colony moves, cells on one side of the colony "pull" with their flagella, and the cells on the other side of the colony "push." Although most cells in a *Volvox* colony are identical, a few gamete-producing cells are specialized for reproduction. Because it shows some cell specialization, *Volvox* straddles the fence between colonial and multicellular life.

Spirogyra (LM 140×)

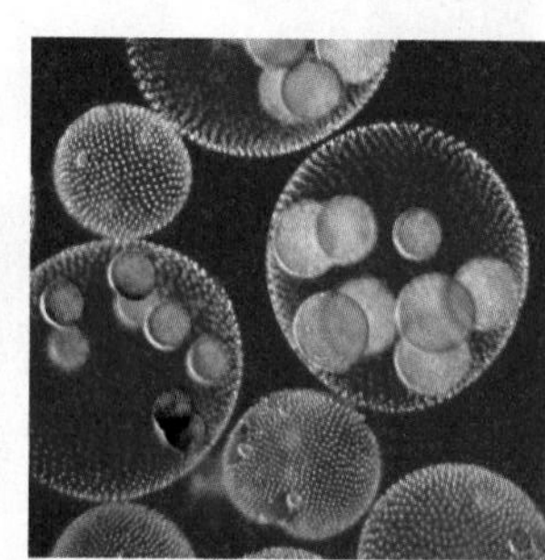

Volvox (LM 50×)

FIGURE 22–9 Multicellular Green Algae

Quick Facts

ULVA—A TRUE MULTICELLULAR ALGA

Ulva, or "sea lettuce," is a bright green marine alga that is commonly found along rocky seacoasts. *Ulva* is a true multicellular organism, containing several specialized cell types. Although the body of *Ulva* is only two cells thick, it is tough enough to survive the pounding of waves on the shores where it lives. A group of cells at its base forms a holdfast that attaches *Ulva* to a rock. The life cycle of *Ulva* involves an alternation of generations in which both the diploid and haploid phases are large, multicellular organisms. The characteristics of *Ulva*—its life cycle pattern, true multicellularity, and specialized structures—demonstrate an evolutionary link between simpler green algae and more complex land plants.

Mosses and Other Bryophytes

What factor limits the size of bryophytes?

In the cool forests of the northern United States, the moist ground is covered with green. When you walk, the ground almost feels like a soft, spongy carpet. Look closely, however, and you will see that this forest carpet is made of short, soft plants known as mosses. Mosses have a thin waxy coating that makes it possible for them to resist drying, and thin filaments known as rhizoids (RY zoydz) that anchor them to the soil. Rhizoids also absorb water and minerals from the surrounding soil. **Figure 22–10** shows the structure of a typical moss.

Mosses belong to a group of plants that is known as **bryophytes** (BRY oh fyts). Unlike algae, the bryophytes have specialized reproductive organs enclosed by other, nonreproductive cells. The bryophytes show a higher degree of cell specialization than do the green algae and were among the very first plants to become established on land. In addition to mosses, the bryophytes include two other groups, known as hornworts and liverworts. Each of the three groups is generally considered to be a separate phylum. DOL•22

BUILD Vocabulary

SUFFIXES The suffixes *-phyta* and *-phyte* come from the Greek word *phyton*, meaning "plant."

Why Bryophytes Are Small Bryophytes are generally found in damp places where there is plenty of available water, and there are good reasons for this. Most other land plants carry water in a specialized tissue called **vascular tissue,** which contains tubes hardened with a substance called lignin. Bryophytes, however, do not make lignin and do not contain true vascular tissue. **Bryophytes are small because they lack vascular tissue.** They can draw up water no higher than a meter above the ground. Without strong cell walls hardened by lignin, bryophytes also cannot support a tall plant body against the pull of gravity. These factors limit the height of bryophytes and confine them to damp environments.

Life Cycle Like all land plants, bryophytes display alternation of generations. In bryophytes, the gametophyte is the dominant, recognizable stage of the life cycle. The gametophyte is also the stage that carries out most of the plant's photosynthesis. The sporophyte is dependent on the gametophyte for its supply of water and nutrients.

Bryophytes produce sperm cells that swim using flagella. For fertilization to occur successfully, these sperm must be released where there is enough water for them to swim to an egg cell. Because of this, bryophytes live only in damp habitats where there is standing water for at least part of the year.

FIGURE 22–10 Structure of Moss In bryophytes, the gametophyte is the dominant, more familiar stage of the life cycle and is the form that carries out photosynthesis.

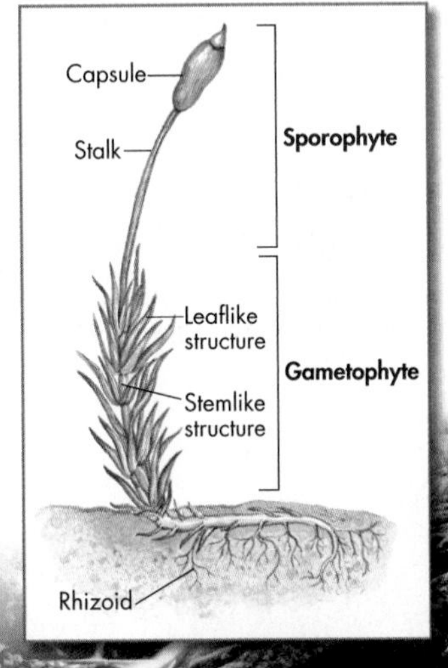

Lead a Discussion

Explain that mosses are adapted to living on land through structural adaptations such as a water resistant coating and rhizoids. Ask students to look at the photograph at the bottom of the page and recall where they have seen mosses. Point out that mosses need damp places to live. Make sure students understand how the lack of vascular tissue affects where bryophytes generally live and the size of bryophytes.

DIFFERENTIATED INSTRUCTION

LPR Less Proficient Readers Break the text on this page into smaller, more manageable chunks. Have students read through the first two paragraphs. Then, have each student list two new things he or she learned from the text. Have them share their lists with a partner. Then, have them repeat the activity two more times, once for the section on **Why Bryophytes Are Small** and again for the section on **Life Cycle.**

L3 Advanced Students After discussing bryophyte structure, have students examine living or preserved specimens of mosses with a hand lens and under a microscope at low power. Ask them to diagram what they see. Then, have students relate the structures to their functions.

Quick Facts

MOSSES IN SURPRISING PLACES

As the text emphasizes, mosses need abundant water to grow and reproduce. Yet, many mosses have adapted to survive in areas with seasonal droughts. Even more surprising, some mosses live in tundras and other frigid climates, where liquid water may be unavailable for months at a time. Mosses survive such habitats by entering a state similar to suspended animation. Their tissues almost completely dehydrate, sometimes for years, when water is not available. During this time they neither grow nor reproduce, but contact with water can rehydrate them in seconds. Mosses may not grow and thrive without water, but they have adapted to periods without it.

LESSON 22.2

Teach continued

Use Visuals

Have students examine the life cycle of a moss in **Figure 22–11.** As you discuss the steps, ask them to note adaptations in the life cycle that enable mosses to live on land. For example, point out that the structures of archegonia and antheridia protect gametes from drying out; additionally the archegonium protects the growing embryo from drying out. Also draw attention to the young gametophyte and the rhizoids that develop as the gametophyte matures. Have students recall the function of rhizoids. *(anchor gametophyte to soil and absorb water and minerals)* Then, ask them questions to check their understanding of mosses.

Ask Is the gametophyte haploid or diploid? *(haploid)*

Ask Where does the sporophyte develop? *(within the gametophyte)*

Ask Is the sporophyte haploid or diploid? *(diploid)*

Ask What does the sporophyte produce? *(spores)*

Ask When a spore germinates, what does it produce? *(a young gametophyte)*

DIFFERENTIATED INSTRUCTION

L1 Struggling Students Some students may be overwhelmed by the complex life cycle pictured in **Figure 22–11.** Take the time to work through each pictured step. Have volunteers describe what is occurring at each step in their own words. You might also suggest they redraw each step of the life cycle as you discuss it. Students can then refer to their own diagrams as they review the lesson.

BIOLOGY.com Students can more fully examine the life cycle of mosses and other plants by accessing the **InterActive Art: Plant Life Cycles** activity.

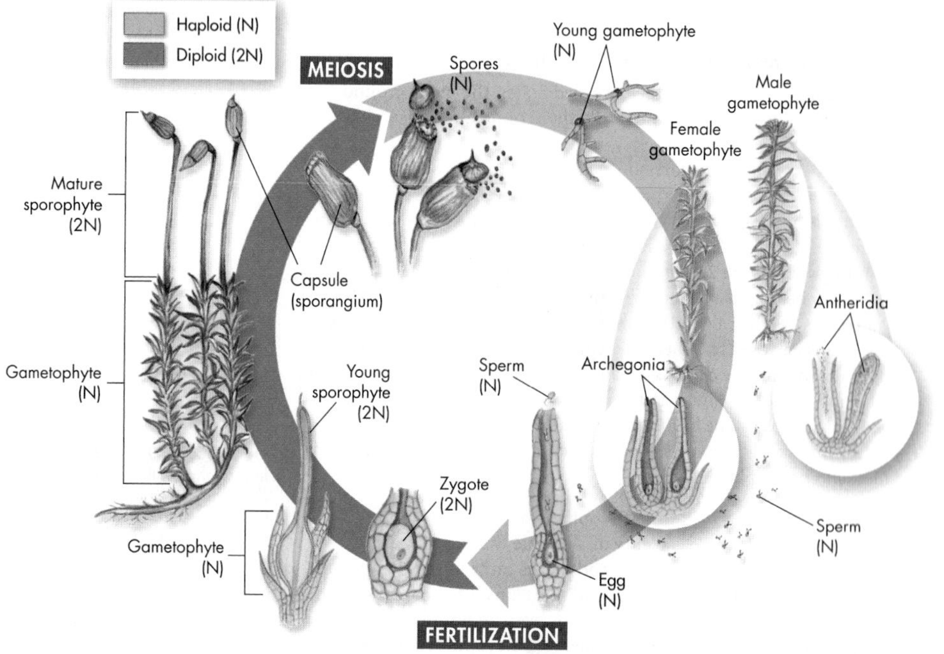

FIGURE 22–11 Moss Life Cycle This life cycle shows the dominance of the gametophyte stage that is typical of mosses and other bryophytes. **Interpret Visuals** ***In which structure are eggs found?***

▶ ***Gametophyte*** When a moss spore lands in a moist place, it sprouts and grows into a tangled mass of green filaments. **Figure 22–11** shows the life cycle of a typical moss. As this young gametophyte grows, it forms rhizoids that grow into the ground and shoots that grow into the air. These shoots grow into the familiar green moss plants.

Gametes are formed in reproductive structures at the tips of the gametophytes. Some bryophyte species produce both sperm and eggs on the same plant, whereas other species produce sperm and eggs on separate plants. Eggs are produced in **archegonia** (ahr kuh GOH nee uh; singular: archegonium). Sperm are produced in **antheridia** (an thur ID ee uh; singular: antheridium). Sperm and egg cells fuse to produce a diploid zygote.

▶ ***Sporophyte*** The zygote marks the beginning of the sporophyte stage of the life cycle. It develops into a multicellular embryo, growing within the body of the gametophyte and depending on it for water and nutrients. Eventually, the sporophyte grows out of the gametophyte, and develops a long stalk ending in a capsule that looks a bit like a salt shaker. The spore capsule is called a **sporangium** (spoh RAN jee um; plural: sporangia). Inside the capsule, haploid spores are produced by meiosis. When the capsule ripens, it opens, and haploid spores are scattered to the wind to start the cycle again.

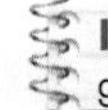

In Your Notebook *Classify each of these moss structures as gametophyte or sporophyte: sporangium, spore, archegonium, zygote.*

UbD Check for Understanding

USE VOCABULARY

Have students compose a short rap song that includes the vocabulary terms they have learned in this lesson so far. Tell them the lyrics should indicate understanding of lesson concepts. Provide an example: "Mosses lack *vascular tissue*, so standing up tall is an issue." Students may team up to bounce ideas off one another.

ADJUST INSTRUCTION

Review or listen to the rap songs, and identify any vocabulary terms or concepts with which students are having difficulty. Discuss the terms with students, and recite several rap lines in which the terms were used correctly. Then, have students write a definition of the terms in their own words.

Answers

FIGURE 22–11 archegonium

IN YOUR NOTEBOOK Gametophyte (N): spore, archegonium; Sporophyte (2N): sporangium, zygote

Vascular Plants

How is vascular tissue important?

For millions of years, early plants grew no taller than a meter high because they lacked vascular tissue. Then, about 420 million years ago, something remarkable happened. The small, mosslike plants on land were suddenly joined by taller plants, some of which were as large as small trees. What happened? Fossil evidence shows that these new plants were the first to have a transport system with true vascular tissue. Vascular tissue carries water and nutrients much more efficiently than does any tissue found in bryophytes. With the evolution of vascular tissue, plants were able to grow high above the ground.

Evolution of a Transport System Vascular plants are also known as **tracheophytes** (TRAY kee uh fyts), after a specialized type of water-conducting cell they contain. These cells, called **tracheids** (TRAY kee idz), are hollow tubelike cells with thick cell walls strengthened by lignin, as shown in **Figure 22–12.** Tracheids were one of the great evolutionary innovations of the plant kingdom.

Tracheids are found in **xylem** (ZY lum), a tissue that carries water upward from the roots to every part of a plant. Tracheids are connected end to end like a series of tin cans. Openings between tracheids known as pits allow water to move through a plant more efficiently than by diffusion alone.

Vascular plants also have a second transport tissue called phloem. **Phloem** (FLOH um) transports solutions of nutrients and carbohydrates produced by photosynthesis. Like xylem, the main cells of phloem are long and specialized to move fluids throughout the plant body. **Vascular tissues—xylem and phloem—make it possible for vascular plants to move fluids through their bodies against the force of gravity.**

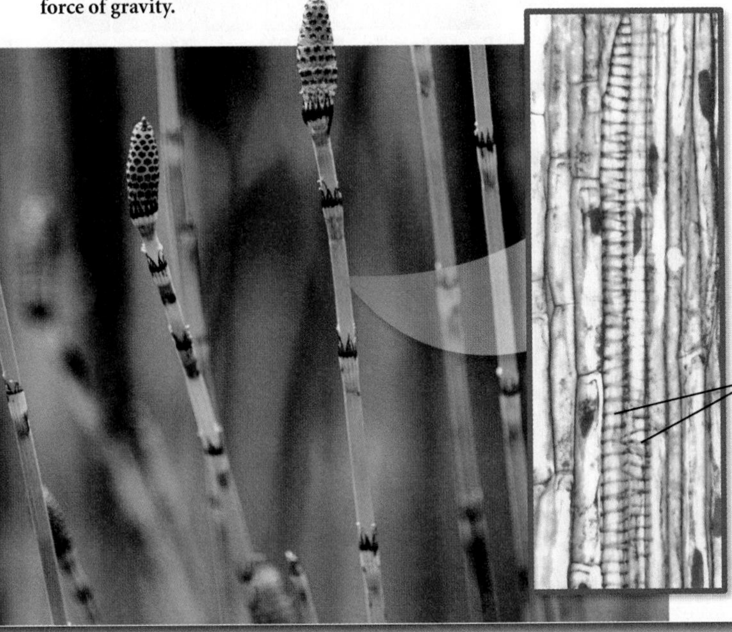

ZOOMING IN

VASCULAR TISSUE

FIGURE 22–12 Horsetails are among the most primitive plant species to have specialized vascular tissue. The micrograph at right shows a much-magnified view of the tracheids. You can see the rings of reinforcing lignin surrounding the tracheids.

Expand Vocabulary

Tell students that *xylem* and *phloem* are major terms they will encounter in future lessons and chapters. Encourage them to develop a mnemonic device to help them remember the difference. One example is that *xy-* rhymes with "sky," and the sky is upwards; xylem moves water up. *Phlo-* sounds like "flow," which helps students remember that carbohydrates and nutrients flow throughout a plant.

DIFFERENTIATED INSTRUCTION

ELL English Language Learners Have students use a **Venn Diagram** to compare and contrast the functions of xylem and phloem. In the area where the two circles overlap, write "transport fluids" and say these words aloud. Under Xylem, write and say "transports water." Under Phloem, write and say "transports nutrients." Have students repeat the words and phrases as you point to them.

Study Wkbks A/B, Appendix S33, Venn Diagram. **Transparencies,** GO18.

ZOOMING IN

Have students examine the horsetail and the magnified view of tracheids. Point out how the long, narrow, hollow structure of the tracheids enables the plant to conduct water. The lignin surrounding the tracheids makes them strong enough to support the plant. Help students make the connection between the evolution of vascular tissue and the ability of land plants to live in a variety of environments.

Biology In-Depth

MORE ABOUT HORSETAILS

Horsetails are an ancient plant. Reaching a height of 18 m and a diameter of 30 cm, they dominated the landscape about 300 million years ago. Today, only one genus, Equisetum, remains. Modern horsetails are much smaller and range in height from a few centimeters to about 10 meters. They have true leaves, stems, and roots; photosynthesis generally takes place in the stem. The scale-like leaves are arranged in distinctive whorls at joints along the stem. Horsetails, or scouring rush, got their name because their stems look similar to horses' tails and contain crystals of abrasive silica. During colonial times, horsetails were commonly used to scour pots and pans.

Teach continued

Use Visuals

Walk students through the steps in the life cycle of a fern in **Figure 22–14,** having them note similarities and differences between the fern and the moss life cycle. For example, archegonia and antheridia are present in both life cycles, but in the fern life cycle, the sporophyte is the dominant stage and the one that is visible aboveground.

Ask How are gametophytes produced? *(The sporophyte makes spores that grow into gametophytes.)*

Ask Is the gametophyte diploid or haploid? *(haploid)* the sporophyte? *(diploid)*

DIFFERENTIATED INSTRUCTION

L1 Struggling Students As students work through **Figure 22–14,** suggest they refer to the text on the moss life cycle for a review of terms, such as *archegonia*. Then, pair students and have them take turns describing in their own words what is happening in each step of the figure.

L3 Advanced Students Provide students with fronds from a fern plant or several fern species, along with metric rulers, slides, and microscopes. Ask students to observe and write descriptions of characteristics such as size and structure of the fronds. Have students make sketches of what they see, both with the unaided eye and with the microscope under low power. Ask them to compare the location and density of any sporangia on their specimen(s) with those shown in the life cycle in **Figure 22–14.**

BIOLOGY.com Have students access **Data Analysis: Bracken: Invasive and Deadly?** to analyze the distribution, utilization, and carcinogenic potential of bracken, a type of fern.

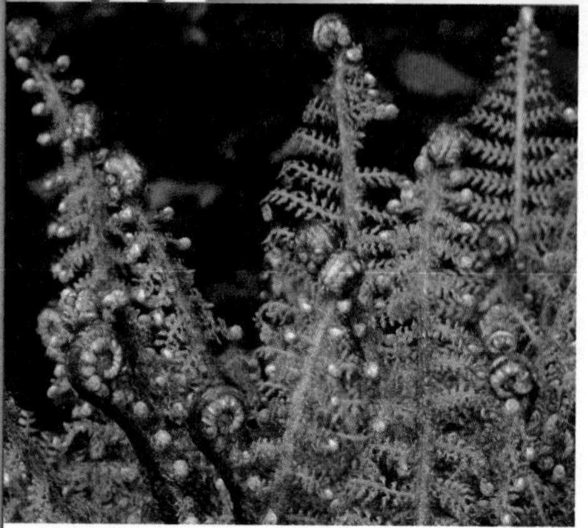

FIGURE 22–13 Structure of a Fern Ferns are easily recognized because of their delicate leaves, called fronds. Before a frond unfurls, it is called a fiddlehead.

Seedless Vascular Plants Although the tracheophytes include all seed-bearing plants, vascular tissue is also found in many groups of plants that do not produce seeds. Among the seedless vascular plants alive today are three phyla commonly known as club mosses, horsetails, and ferns. DOL•23

The most numerous seedless plants are the ferns. More than 11,000 species of ferns are living today. Ferns have true vascular tissues, strong roots, creeping or underground stems called rhizomes (RY zohmz), and large leaves called fronds, shown in **Figure 22–13.** Ferns can thrive in areas with little light. They are most abundant in wet, or at least seasonally wet, habitats.

Life Cycle The large plants we recognize as ferns are actually diploid sporophytes. The fern life cycle is shown in **Figure 22–14.** Ferns and other vascular plants have a life cycle in which the diploid sporophyte is the dominant stage.

In the fern life cycle, spores grow into thin, heart-shaped haploid gametophytes. Although it is tiny, the gametophyte grows independently of the sporophyte. As in bryophytes, sperm and eggs are produced on these gametophytes in antheridia and archegonia, respectively.

Fertilization requires at least a thin film of water, so that the sperm can swim to the eggs. The diploid zygote produced by fertilization immediately begins to develop into a new sporophyte plant. As the sporophyte matures, haploid spores develop on the undersides of the fronds in sporangia, and the cycle begins again.

Analyzing Data

IN NoS.3

Keeping Ferns in Check

Dennstaedtia punctilobula is a fern that grows on the forest floor and often crowds out tree seedlings, blocking efforts to regrow trees after logging or other work in a forest. To understand the fern better, scientists measured the number of viable fern spores per square centimeter of soil at various distances from a plot of existing fern plants. They counted spores in the soil in July, as the ferns were just beginning to grow; and in November, after they had released their spores.

1. Graph Place the data from the table on a line graph showing the number of spores per square centimeter versus their distance from the plot. Use different colors for the before and after dispersal data points.

Number of Spores in Soil

Distance From Plot of Ferns (meters)	Before Dispersal (July)	After Dispersal (November)
0	14	54
2	16	18
4	5	9
10	10	17
50	2	7

2. Calculate What percentage of the spores after dispersal are found within 4 meters of the parent plants? MATH

3. Interpret Graphs Are spore numbers higher before dispersal or after dispersal? Explain.

4. Draw Conclusions Would cutting down nearby clusters of ferns prevent ferns from invading patches of the forest that have just been cut for timber? Explain your reasoning on the basis of the data.

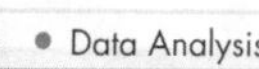

BIOLOGY.com Search Lesson 22.2 GO • Data Analysis • InterActive Art

Analyzing Data

PURPOSE Students will graph data to analyze patterns of spore dispersal.

PLANNING Remind students that line graphs show the change in a variable over time.

ANSWERS

1. Remind students that the *x* axis represents the independent variable (distance from plot of ferns) and the *y* axis represents the dependent variable (number of spores).
2. 77%
3. The spore numbers are higher after dispersal for each distance measured and much higher for the area around the fern. You would expect the spore numbers to be higher after dispersal because new spores have been released from the fern.
4. Sample answer: Cutting down nearby plants might reduce the number of new ferns but would not eliminate them; many viable spores from the previous season are dispersed several meters from the parent plant.

FIGURE 22–14 Fern Life Cycle In the life cycle of a fern, the dominant and recognizable stage is the diploid sporophyte.
Interpret Visuals ***Are the spores haploid or diploid?***

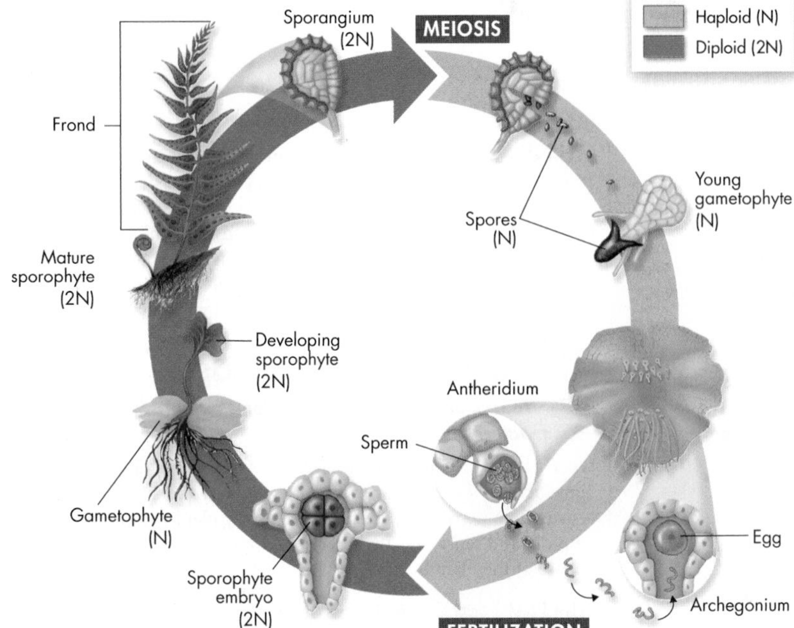

22.2 Assessment

IN B.8.2

Review Key Concepts

1. a. Review In what kind of environments are green algae found?

b. Compare and Contrast How are green algae similar to and different from other plants?

2. a. Review Why are bryophytes small?

b. Apply Concepts How is water essential to the life cycle of a bryophyte?

3. a. Review What function do vascular tissues allow?

b. Infer The size of plants increased dramatically with the evolution of vascular tissue. How might these two events be related?

BUILD VOCABULARY

4. Find all the word roots for the terms in this lesson that end in *-phyte.* (Recall that the suffix *-phyte* means "plant.") Now, look up the meaning of each word root paired with *-phyte.* Write down the root-suffix translation of each of these words. Which translations help you remember what each word means? Explain.

BIOLOGY.com Search Lesson 22.2 GO • Lesson Assessment • Self-Test

Assess and Remediate

EVALUATE UNDERSTANDING

Have students use their completed Venn diagrams and/or cluster diagrams they started at the beginning of this lesson to take turns posing questions to the class, for example, "Which group has vascular tissue?" Call on students to answer the questions. Then, have students complete the 22.2 Assessment.

REMEDIATION SUGGESTION

L1 **Struggling Students** If your students have trouble with **Question 1b,** have them fill out a **Compare/Contrast Table** to help them organize the similarities and differences between green algae and the other plant types discussed in this lesson.

Study Wkbks A/B, Appendix S20, Compare/Contrast Table. **Transparencies,** GO3.

BIOLOGY.com Students can check their understanding of lesson concepts with the **Self-Test** assessment. They can then take an online version of the **Lesson Assessment.**

Answers

FIGURE 22–14 haploid

Assessment Answers

1a. in fresh and salt water and some moist areas on land

1b. Similar: photosynthetic, have a cell wall; Different: don't have specialized tissues

2a. They lack vascular tissue, which transports fluids and supports a tall plant body.

2b. Bryophytes produce sperm that must swim through water to the eggs.

3a. Vascular tissues make it possible for plants to move fluids through their bodies against the force of gravity.

3b. Plants without vascular tissue are small because they can draw up water no more than a meter above the ground. Plants with vascular tissue are able to grow taller because the vascular tissue carries water and nutrients to greater heights against the force of gravity. In addition, cell walls hardened by lignin help support a tall plant.

BUILD VOCABULARY

4. Sporo-phyte translates: "sowing" or "seed" plant; bryo-phyte: "moss" plant; tracheo-phyte: "artery" plant. Accept all logical explanations of how the translations help students remember the meanings.

LESSON 22.3

Getting Started

Objectives

22.3.1 Describe the reproductive adaptations of seed plants.

22.3.2 Identify the reproductive structures of gymnosperms.

Student Resources

Study Workbooks A and B, 22.3 Worksheets

Spanish Study Workbook, 22.3 Worksheets

Lesson Overview • Lesson Notes • Activity: Art in Motion • Assessment: Self-Test, Lesson Assessment

For corresponding lesson in the **Foundation Edition,** see pages 536–539.

Build Background

Display a pine cone and an apple. (Make sure you are using a cone with seeds still present. Many older cones will have lost all their seeds.) Cut the apple in half to expose the seeds, and shake or pull some of the seeds off the scales of the cone. Ask students what the pine cone and the apple have in common. *(Both contain seeds.)* Explain that cone-bearing plants such as pine trees and fruit-bearing plants such as apple trees produce seeds in different ways. Notably, the pine cone's seeds are exposed on the scale surfaces, while the apple's seeds are found within the fruit.

IN INDIANA ACADEMIC STANDARDS

For the full text of all standards, see the Course Overview in the front matter of this book.

B.8.1 Explain how anatomical and molecular similarities among organisms suggests that life on earth began as simple, one-celled organisms about 4 billion years ago and multicellular organisms evolved later.

B.8.2 Explain how organisms are classified and named based on their evolutionary relationships into taxonomic categories.

Seed Plants

IN B.8.1 History of life on Earth; B.8.2 Classification.

Key Questions

What adaptations allow seed plants to reproduce without standing water?

How does fertilization take place in gymnosperms in the absence of water?

Vocabulary

seed • gymnosperm • angiosperm • pollen grain • pollination • seed coat • ovule • pollen tube

Taking Notes

Preview Visuals Preview **Figure 22–17** and record your first impressions about how the pine life cycle differs from the fern life cycle.

THINK ABOUT IT Whether they are acorns, pine nuts, dandelion seeds, or beans, seeds can be found everywhere. What are seeds? Are they gametes? Reproductive structures? Do they contain sperm or eggs? The truth is that they are none of the above. Each and every seed contains a living plant ready to sprout as soon as it encounters the proper conditions for growth. The production of seeds has been one key to the ability of plants to colonize even the driest environments on land.

The Importance of Seeds

What adaptations allow seed plants to reproduce without open water?

A characteristic shared by all seed plants is, as you might guess, the production of seeds. A **seed** is a plant embryo and a food supply, encased in a protective covering. The living plant within a seed is diploid and represents the early developmental stage of the sporophyte phase of the plant life cycle.

The First Seed Plants Fossils of seed-bearing plants exist from almost 360 million years ago. These fossils document several evolutionary stages in the development of the seed. Similarities in DNA sequences from modern plants provide evidence that today's seed plants are all descended from common ancestors.

The fossil record indicates that ancestors of seed plants evolved new adaptations that enabled them to survive in many environments on dry land. Unlike mosses and ferns, the gametes of seed plants do not need standing water for fertilization. **Adaptations that allow seed plants to reproduce without standing water include a reproductive process that takes place in cones or flowers, the transfer of sperm by pollination, and the protection of embryos in seeds.**

Cones and Flowers In seed plants, the male gametophytes and the female gametophytes grow and mature directly within the sporophyte. The gametophytes usually develop in reproductive structures known as cones or flowers. In fact, seed plants are divided into two groups on the basis of which of these structures they have. Nearly all **gymnosperms** (JIM noh spurmz) bear their seeds directly on the scales of cones. In contrast, flowering plants, or **angiosperms** (AN jee oh spurmz), bear their seeds in flowers inside a layer of tissue that protects the seed. **Figure 22–15** compares the reproductive structures of gymnosperms and angiosperms.

BUILD Vocabulary

WORD ORIGINS The prefix *gymno-* comes from the Greek word *gymnos*, meaning "naked." The prefix *angio-* comes from the Greek word *angeion*, meaning "vessel." The suffix *-sperm* means "seed."

UbD Teach for Understanding

ENDURING UNDERSTANDING From microorganisms to plants, organisms vary widely in the way they carry out basic life processes.

GUIDING QUESTION What are the characteristics of seed plants?

EVIDENCE OF UNDERSTANDING *At the end of the lesson, have students complete this assessment to show understanding of gymnosperm characteristics and how gymnosperms carry out basic life processes.* Have students write a short biography of a pine tree. The biography should start with a seed and describe the important events in its life cycle, including its formation, transportation away from the parent plant, germination, and the growth into a mature plant.

VISUAL SUMMARY
GYMNOSPERMS
ANGIOSPERMS
Cones
Male cones produce male gametophytes (pollen grains).
Female cones produce female gametophytes.
Pollen
Wind carries pollen to seed cones.
Seeds
Female cones bear seeds directly on the inside surfaces of scales.
Flowers
Most flowers produce both male gametophytes (pollen grains) and female gametophytes in each flower. Some species have separate male and female flowers.
Pollen
Wind distributes the pollen of some species. But, in many species, animals carry pollen directly to other flowers.
Seeds
Seeds are enclosed in a layer of ovary tissue.

REPRODUCTION IN SEED PLANTS

FIGURE 22–15 The two major groups of seed plants can be distinguished by their reproductive structures. Interpret Visuals ***How is the location of developing seeds different in the two groups?***

Pollen In seed plants, the entire male gametophyte is contained in a tiny structure called a **pollen grain.** Sperm produced by this gametophyte do not swim through water to fertilize the eggs. Instead, pollen grains are carried to the female reproductive structure by wind or animals such as insects. The transfer of pollen from the male reproductive structure to the female reproductive structure is called **pollination.**

Seeds After fertilization, the zygote contained within a seed grows into a tiny plant—the sporophyte embryo. The embryo often stops growing while it is still small and contained within the seed. The embryo can remain in this condition for weeks, months, or even years. A tough **seed coat** surrounds and protects the embryo and keeps the contents of the seed from drying out. Seeds can survive long periods of bitter cold, extreme heat, or drought. The embryo begins to grow when conditions are once again right; it does this by using nutrients from the stored food supply until it can carry out photosynthesis on its own.

MYSTERY CLUE

Samples of material taken from Iceman's digestive tract contained pollen from plant species that grow at different elevations. How could this evidence be used to reconstruct Iceman's movements on his last day alive?

In Your Notebook *Make a Venn diagram that records the shared and distinct characteristics of gymnosperms and angiosperms.*

How Science Works

PROVING THE SURVIVABILITY OF SEEDS

In 1879, a botany professor at Michigan Agricultural College (now Michigan State University) designed a long-term experiment to investigate the survivability of common weed seeds. Dr. W. J. Beal gathered 50 seeds from each of 23 different types of plants, including common mallow and common mullein. He then prepared 20 sets of seeds, mixed each set with moist sand, and filled 20 pint bottles with the mixture. He buried those bottles with the tops left uncovered and the bottles slanting down so they would not fill with water. Since then, one of Beal's bottles has been dug up every five or ten years to see if any of the seeds in it would germinate. Some of the seeds in the 15th bottle, dug up in 2000—after 120 years, still germinated when placed in good growing conditions.

Teach

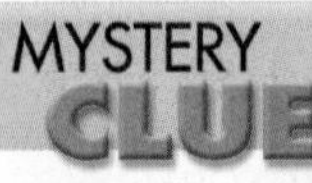

VISUAL SUMMARY

Use **Figure 22–15** to help students compare and contrast reproduction in gymnosperms and angiosperms. Have them note similarities and differences in the location of gametophyte production, mechanisms of pollination, and seeds. Point out that the two trees in the figure do not require open water to survive, and make sure students understand how the evolution of seeds allowed plants to live in places where mosses and ferns could not live.

DIFFERENTIATED INSTRUCTION

L1 Struggling Students For students who have a difficult time understanding **Figure 22–15,** work through it as a class. Explain that all the information to the right of the label Gymnosperms relates to the reproduction of this type of plant. Talk about the pictures and information associated with gymnosperms. Then, focus on angiosperms.

ELL Focus on ELL: Extend Language

ALL SPEAKERS Have students use an **ELL Frayer Model** to reinforce the lesson vocabulary terms. Students should write a vocabulary term in the center box, and then do the following in each of the four sections: write the definition of the term, draw an illustration of the term, write a sentence using the term, and write a translation of the term in their primary language. Beginning speakers can work with a partner and use single words rather than sentences. Intermediate speakers might write words and phrases rather than sentences.

Study Wkbks A/B, Appendix S26, ELL Frayer Model. **Transparencies,** GO10.

MYSTERY CLUE

Have students recall from the introduction on page 633 how Iceman might have taken in pollen. Then, guide them to speculate that Iceman was likely at different elevations during his last day alive. Students can go online to **Biology.com** to gather their evidence.

Answers

FIGURE 22–15 In gymnosperms, seeds are on cone scales; in angiosperms, seeds are in ovary tissue.

IN YOUR NOTEBOOK Venn diagrams should indicate characteristics that differ, such as cones/flowers and shared characteristics, such as reproduction without open water.

Teach continued

Use Visuals

Help students connect the text on this page with **Figure 22–17.** Read through **The Life Cycle of a Gymnosperm** as a class. As you read through the section, point out the corresponding stage on the figure. For example, as you read about pollen cones, point to the diagram of the pollen cone producing pollen grains in the figure.

DIFFERENTIATED INSTRUCTION

L1 Struggling Students In **Figure 22–17,** make sure students understand which drawings are enlargements of the previous drawing. For example, explain that the single cone scale is just one of many cone scales on the seed cone in the previous drawing. The drawing of the diploid cell in the cone scale is an enlargement of the previous drawing. The same holds true for the male pollen cone and its pollen grains.

L3 Advanced Students Have students make a survey of gymnosperms in a specific area near the school or their home. They should use a field guide to help them identify specific trees and shrubs. Their product should be a table that lists observed gymnosperms, locations, descriptions of habitat, and characteristics. Encourage students to locate and print online photos or illustrations to accompany their table.

Have students infer how quickly (as from an accident) or slowly (as from disease) Iceman died given that his bow was unfinished and he was physically fit enough to walk great distances. Have students brainstorm ways Iceman could have died a quick death. Students can go online to **Biology.com** to gather their evidence.

The Life Cycle of a Gymnosperm

How does fertilization take place in gymnosperms in the absence of water?

The word *gymnosperm* actually means "naked seed." The name reflects the fact that gymnosperms produce seeds that are exposed on the scales within cones. Gymnosperms alive today include relatively rare plants such as cycads and ginkgoes and the much more abundant plants known as conifers, which include pines and firs. DOL•24–DOL•25

FIGURE 22–16 Pollen Cone This pollen cone on a pine tree is shedding pollen, which will be carried by wind to seed cones.

Pollen Cones and Seed Cones Reproduction in conifers takes place in cones, which are produced by the mature sporophyte plant. Conifers produce two types of cones: pollen cones and seed cones. Pollen cones, also called male cones, produce the pollen grains. As tiny as it is, a pollen grain makes up the entire male gametophyte stage of the gymnosperm life cycle. One of the haploid nuclei in the pollen grain will divide later to produce two sperm nuclei.

The more familiar seed cones, or female cones, produce female gametophytes. Seed cones are generally much larger than pollen cones. Near the base of each scale of the seed cones are two **ovules** (AHV yoolz), the structures in which the female gametophytes develop. Within the ovules, meiosis produces haploid cells that grow and divide to produce female gametophytes. These gametophytes may contain hundreds or thousands of cells. When mature, each gametophyte contains a few large egg cells, each ready for fertilization by sperm nuclei.

Pollination and Fertilization The conifer life cycle typically takes two years to complete. The life cycle of a pine is shown in **Figure 22–17.** The cycle begins in the spring as male cones release enormous numbers of pollen grains that are carried away by the wind. Some of these pollen grains reach female cones. There, pollen grains are caught in a sticky secretion on the scales of the female cone and pulled inside toward the ovule. **In gymnosperms, the direct transfer of pollen to the female cone allows fertilization to take place without the need for gametes to swim through standing water.**

Development Inside Seeds If a pollen grain lands near an ovule, the grain splits open and begins to grow a structure called a **pollen tube,** which contains two haploid sperm nuclei. Once the pollen tube reaches the newly developed female gametophyte, one sperm nucleus disintegrates; the other fertilizes the egg contained within the female gametophyte. Fertilization produces a diploid zygote, which grows into an embryo—the new sporophyte plant. The embryo is then encased to form a seed. The seed is ready to be scattered by the wind and grow into a new plant.

MYSTERY CLUE

An unfinished bow made from conifer wood was found with Iceman. No other weapons for hunting or self-defense were found with him. How might he have died?

In Your Notebook *Make a flowchart that records the events leading up to fertilization in a gymnosperm.*

Check for Understanding

QUESTION BOARD

Establish an area on a bulletin board where students may post questions anonymously about seed plants, and more specifically, gymnosperms. Encourage all students to post at least one question. Read all questions and discuss topics of general confusion as a class.

ADJUST INSTRUCTION

Type up a list of the questions and pass them out to small groups of students. Have groups try to answer all of the questions on the list. Then, have groups combine and discuss their answers.

Answers

IN YOUR NOTEBOOK Steps should include the production of male and female gametophytes, release of pollen grains from the male cone, dispersal by wind, landing near an ovule, growing a pollen tube, and a sperm nucleus fertilizing an egg.

FIGURE 22–17 Pine Life Cycle In the life cycle of pine trees and other gymnosperms, the mature sporophyte trees produce male and female cones containing the gametophytes.
Sequence ***Which sporophyte stage develops immediately after fertilization?***

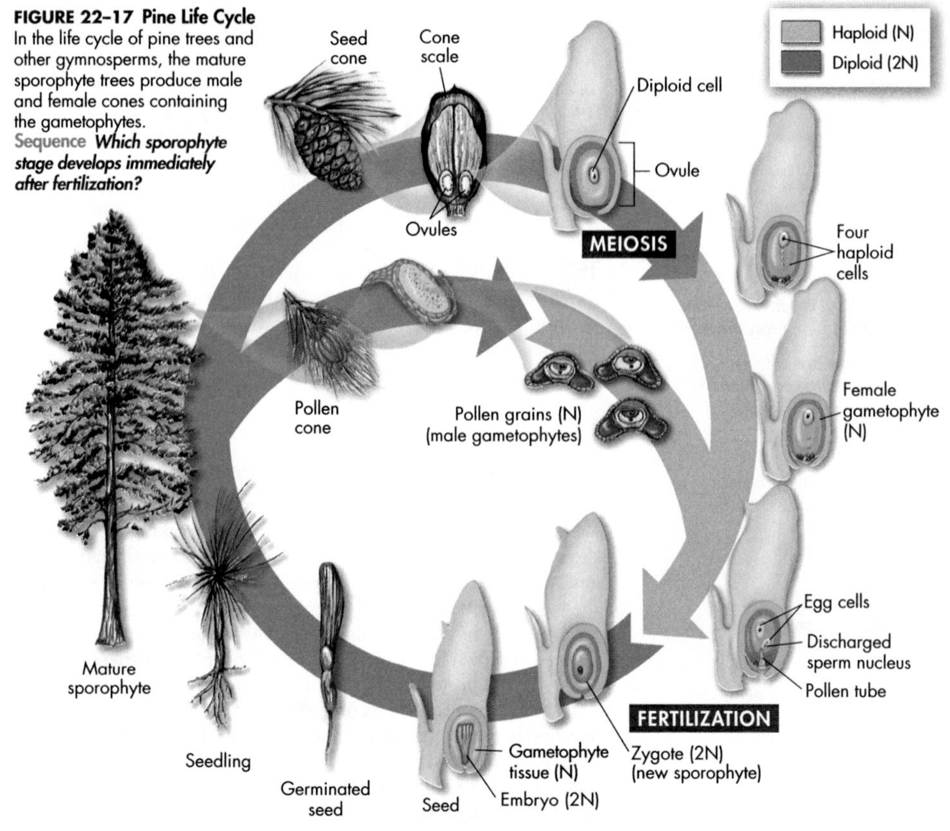

Haploid (N)
Diploid (2N)
Seed cone
Cone scale
Diploid cell
Ovule
Ovules
MEIOSIS
Four haploid cells
Female gametophyte (N)
Pollen cone
Pollen grains (N) (male gametophytes)
Egg cells
Discharged sperm nucleus
Pollen tube
Mature sporophyte
FERTILIZATION
Seedling
Germinated seed
Seed
Gametophyte tissue (N)
Embryo (2N)
Zygote (2N) (new sporophyte)

22.3 Assessment

Review Key Concepts

1. a. Review List three adaptations of seed plants that allow them to reproduce without open water.

b. Apply Concepts Pollination is a process that occurs only in seed plants. What process in seedless plants is analogous to pollination?

2. a. Review Describe how fertilization takes place in a gymnosperm.

b. Classify Make a table with two columns—labeled haploid and diploid—and assign each of the following structures from the pine life cycle to the appropriate column: pollen tube, seed cone, embryo, ovule, seedling.

WRITE ABOUT SCIENCE

Creative Writing

3. Design and write an advertisement promoting seeds. Your target audience, or customers, are seedless plants. Include information on how seeds will make their lives easier.

BIOLOGY.com Search Lesson 22.3  GO  • Lesson Assessment • Self-Test • Art in Motion

BIOLOGY.com Students can watch the fertilization and development of a pine embryo in **Art in Motion: Gymnosperm Fertilization.**

Assess and Remediate

EVALUATE UNDERSTANDING

Have students write a short paragraph or bulleted list that includes why seeds were a significant development in the evolution of plants. Then, have them complete the 22.3 Assessment.

REMEDIATION SUGGESTION

ELL **English Language Learners** If your students have trouble creating a descriptive advertisement for **Question 3,** suggest they make a poster that includes one or more drawings. Accept short captions that detail the advantages of seeds.

BIOLOGY.com Students can check their understanding of lesson concepts with the **Self-Test** assessment. They can then take an online version of the **Lesson Assessment.**

Answers

FIGURE 22–17 the zygote

Assessment Answers

1a. a reproductive process that takes place in cones or flowers, the transfer of sperm by pollination, and the protection of embryos in seeds

1b. the swimming of the male gametes to the female gametes

2a. The pollen grains containing male gametophytes are transferred by wind to the female cone. A pollen tube containing two sperm nuclei grows from the pollen grain. When the pollen tube reaches the egg, one nucleus disintegrates while the other sperm nucleus fertilizes the egg.

2b. Haploid: pollen tube; Diploid: ovule, seed cone, embryo, seedling

WRITE ABOUT SCIENCE

3. Students' advertisements should include that the embryo may be able to remain dormant for long periods under adverse conditions, the seed coat protects the embryo and keeps the seed from drying out, and the food supply is contained in the seed.

LESSON 22.4

Getting Started

Objectives

22.4.1 Identify the reproductive structures of angiosperms.

22.4.2 Identify some of the ways angiosperms can be categorized.

Student Resources

Study Workbooks A and B, 22.4 Worksheets

Spanish Study Workbook, 22.4 Worksheets

Lab Manual B, 22.4 Hands-On Activity Worksheet

Lesson Overview • Lesson Notes
- Activities: Tutor Tube, Art Review
- Assessment: Self-Test, Lesson Assessment

For corresponding lesson in the **Foundation Edition,** see pages 540–543.

Activate Prior Knowledge

Have a class discussion about gardening experiences. Have students think about times they have planted seeds or bought plants at a garden store. Probe for recall of the terms *annual, perennial,* and *biennial,* and have students brainstorm plants they know that fall into these categories. As a class or in small groups, have students come up with operational definitions for these terms based on their real-life experiences. Then, tell students they will be learning more about these terms later in the chapter.

IN INDIANA ACADEMIC STANDARDS

For the full text of all standards, see the Course Overview in the front matter of this book.

B.8.1 Explain how anatomical and molecular similarities among organisms suggests that life on earth began as simple, one-celled organisms about 4 billion years ago and multicellular organisms evolved later.

B.8.2 Explain how organisms are classified and named based on their evolutionary relationships into taxonomic categories.

22.4 Flowering Plants

IN **B.8.1** History of life on Earth; **B.8.2** Classification.

Key Questions

What are the key features of angiosperm reproduction?

How are different angiosperms conveniently categorized?

Vocabulary

ovary • fruit • cotyledon • monocot • dicot • woody plant • herbaceous plant

Taking Notes

Compare/Contrast Table As you read, use a table to contrast three methods commonly used to categorize angiosperms.

THINK ABOUT IT Flowering plants are everywhere. They dominate the surface of the earth and are by far the most abundant organisms in the plant kingdom. And yet they evolved much more recently than did other seed plants. What features of these plants enabled them to take Earth by storm? What are the secrets of their success?

Flowers and Fruits

What are the key features of angiosperm reproduction?

Flowering plants, or angiosperms, first appeared during the Cretaceous Period, about 135 million years ago, making their origin the most recent of all plant phyla. Flowering plants originated on land and soon came to dominate Earth's plant life. Angiosperms make up the vast majority of plant species.

Angiosperms develop unique reproductive organs known as flowers, as shown in **Figure 22–18.** Flowers contain **ovaries,** which surround and protect the seeds. The presence of an ovary gives angiosperms their name: *Angiosperm* means "enclosed seed." **Angiosperms reproduce sexually by means of flowers. After fertilization, ovaries within flowers develop into fruits that surround, protect, and help disperse the seeds.** In Chapter 24, you will explore angiosperm reproduction in more detail.

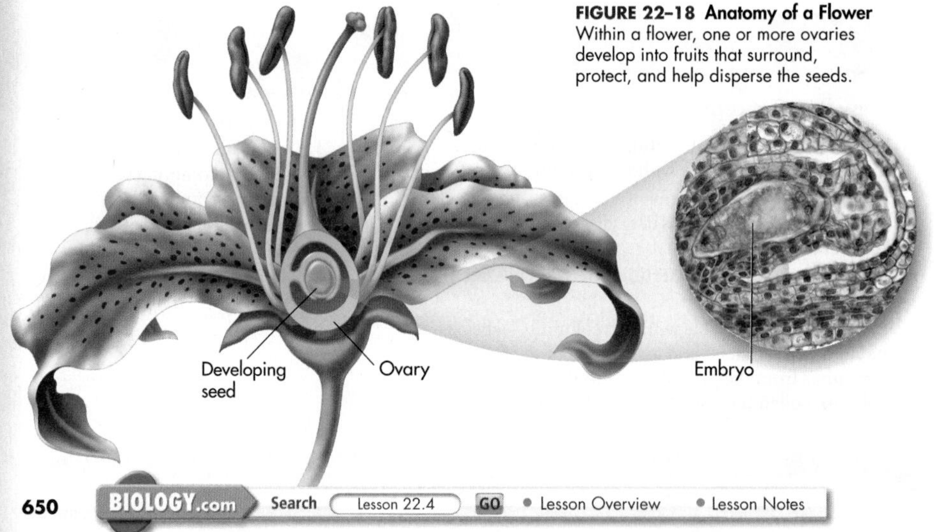

FIGURE 22–18 Anatomy of a Flower Within a flower, one or more ovaries develop into fruits that surround, protect, and help disperse the seeds.

 BIOLOGY.com Search Lesson 22.4 GO • Lesson Overview • Lesson Notes

UbD Teach for Understanding

ENDURING UNDERSTANDING From microorganisms to plants, organisms vary widely in the way they carry out basic life processes.

GUIDING QUESTION What are the characteristics of flowering plants?

EVIDENCE OF UNDERSTANDING *After completing the lesson, give students this assessment to show they understand the characteristics of flowering plants.* Provide students with pictures of plants, such as from nature and gardening magazines and catalogues. Ask students to choose one of the classification systems discussed in **Angiosperm Diversity.** Have them find pictures of plants they can classify according to characteristics shown either in the pictures or described in the text. Students should arrange the pictures on a poster with labels to indicate the category to which each belongs.

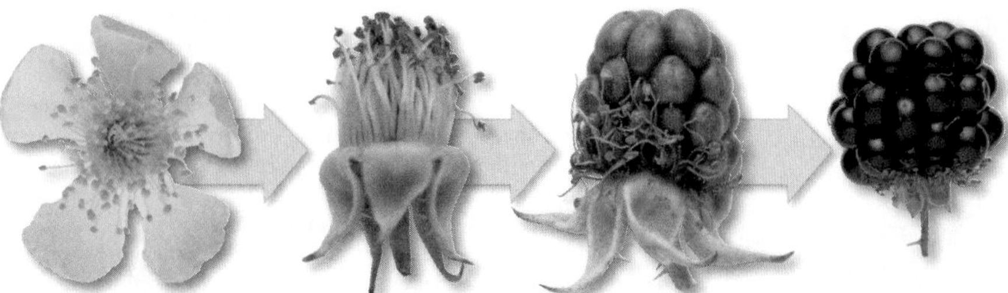

Advantages of Flowers In general, flowers are an evolutionary advantage to plants because they attract animals such as bees, moths, or hummingbirds. These animals—drawn by the color, scent, or even the shape of the flower—carry pollen with them as they leave. Because these animals go directly from flower to flower, they can carry pollen to the next flower they visit. This means of pollination is much more efficient than the wind pollination of most gymnosperms.

FIGURE 22–19 From Flower to Fruit Following pollination and fertilization, a blackberry flower's multiple ovaries develop into a cluster of many individual fruits.

Advantages of Fruits After pollination, the ovary develops into a fruit. In **Figure 22–19,** you can see the progression of development of a blackberry flower into a fruit. The angiosperm **fruit** is a structure containing one or more matured ovaries. The wall of the fruit helps disperse the seeds inside it, carrying them away from the parent plant.

Consider what happens when an animal eats a fleshy fruit, such as a berry. Seeds from the fruit generally enter the animal's digestive system. By the time these seeds leave the digestive system—ready to sprout—the animal may have traveled many kilometers. By using fruit, flowering plants increase the ranges they inhabit, spreading seeds over hundreds of square kilometers. The fruit—a unique feature of angiosperms—is yet another reason for their success.

In Your Notebook *Summarize the function of flowers and fruits in the reproduction of angiosperms.*

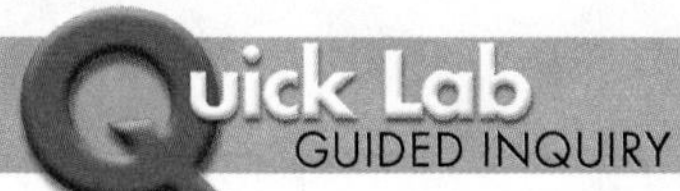

Quick Lab
GUIDED INQUIRY

What Forms Do Fruits Take?

1. Use a hand lens to examine a variety of fruits. Write down or draw your observations.
2. Place each fruit in a petri dish and use a scalpel to dissect it. **CAUTION:** *Use care with sharp instruments.*
3. Locate the seeds within each fruit.

Analyze and Conclude

1. **Compare and Contrast** How do the fruits vary in structure?
2. **Infer** For each fruit, infer how its structure affects its function—that is, how might it aid seed dispersal? Explain your answers.

Teach

Build Reading Skills

Help students develop their reading skills and thinking processes by completing a **Directed Reading-Thinking Activity (DR-TA).** Write the steps on the board as you model them using the first two pages of this lesson.

1. **Preview** Have students look at the title, headings, and illustrations, and then read the introductory paragraph and boldfaced questions.
2. **Predict** Ask students to predict what they will learn and formulate questions that a teacher might ask. An example is "How did flowers give angiosperms an evolutionary advantage?" List students' questions on the board.
3. **Read/Evaluate/Refine** Have students read a paragraph and then pause to discuss any answers they learned to their questions. Ask students to formulate refined predictions and questions based on the new information.

Have students work in pairs to repeat the process for the remaining lesson pages.

Study Wkbks A/B, Appendix S5, DR-TA.

DIFFERENTIATED INSTRUCTION

ELL English Language Learners Have beginning speakers preview the visuals, and allow them to ask simple questions orally, such as "How did the flower turn into a fruit?" Write down their questions. Then, read aloud each paragraph that is relevant to the question. Help students find text clues to identify any answers that might be found in that paragraph. When possible, direct students' attention to visuals that contain information that will help them answer the questions.

BIOLOGY.com Have students access **Tutor Tube: Males, Females, and Sexual Reproduction in Plants—An Animal Perspective** to learn more about the anatomy of sexual reproduction in angiosperms by comparing male and female reproductive structures in flowers and vertebrates.

Quick Lab

PURPOSE Students will observe structures in fruits and infer how the structures are involved in reproduction.

MATERIALS hand lens, variety of fruits, petri dishes, scalpel

SAFETY Remind students to keep the sharp edge of the scalpel away from themselves. Check for allergies to any of the fruits before allowing students to handle them.

PLANNING Provide a variety of fruits you can easily obtain at a grocery store. Make sure fruits such as grapes are not the seedless varieties. Try to include some more unusual and inedible fruits, too, such as maple whirligigs, horse chestnuts, and burs.

ANALYZE AND CONCLUDE

1. Students might note the texture and thickness of the skin, whether the fruit is edible, and how many seeds there are.
2. Sample answer: Grapes have thin skin, making them easy to eat.

Answers

IN YOUR NOTEBOOK Students' summaries should include that flowers attract animals to carry pollen from flower to flower and that fruits protect and help disperse seeds.

Teach continued

Build Science Skills

Guide students to recognize that systems of classification change as new evidence is discovered. Remind them that biologists group organisms based on their evolutionary history, not just physical similarities.

Ask How does the newest system of classification differ from the former one? *(Angiosperms were previously divided into two main groups, monocot and dicot. The most recent system divides angiosperms into five main groups.)*

Ask What kind of evidence did scientists use to change the classification system of angiosperms? *(They used recent studies of plant genomes and new fossil discoveries.)*

DIFFERENTIATED INSTRUCTION

L3 Advanced Students Have interested students find out more about the discovery of *Archaefructus*. For example, they might research how and when it was found as well as the reaction of the scientific community to the discovery. Have them present their findings to the class.

ELL Focus on ELL: Build Background

BEGINNING SPEAKERS Provide English language learners with **Cloze Prompts** to help them better understand the content of the page, as well as give them practice using words that occur often in scientific writing. Write the following words on the board: classify, evidence, fossil, genome, ancient, monocots, dicots, and cotyledons. Then, write several cloze sentences that use these words. For example:

- Scientists used to divide angiosperms into two classes, ______ and ______. *(monocots; dicots)*
- When scientists ______ organisms, they group them according to their evolutionary relationships. *(classify)*

Study Wkbks A/B, Appendix S2, Cloze Prompts.

FIGURE 22–20 *Archaefructus*

BUILD Vocabulary

PREFIXES The prefix *mono-* means "one," while the prefix *di-* means "two." A **monocot** embryo has one cotyledon, while a **dicot** has two cotyledons.

Angiosperm Classification The great diversity of angiosperms has made them especially difficult to classify in the scientific sense. For many years, flowering plants were classified according to the number of seed leaves, or **cotyledons** (kaht uh LEED uns), in their embryos. Those with one seed leaf were called **monocots.** Those with two seed leaves were called **dicots.** At one time, these two groups were considered classes within the angiosperm phylum, and all angiosperms were placed in one class or the other.

More recent studies of plant genomes and new fossil discoveries have shown that things are actually a little more complicated than that. For example, in 2002, an extraordinary plant fossil was discovered in northeastern China. Given the name *Archaefructus,* which means "ancient fruit," this organism is the oldest known plant with reproductive organs like those found in modern flowers. It is more ancient than modern-day monocots and dicots and can't be classified as either.

Other recent evidence suggests that *Amborella,* a plant found only on the Pacific island of New Caledonia, belongs to still another ancient lineage of plants. Information gained from the *Amborella* discovery led scientists to place other plants, such as the water lilies, near the base of angiosperm evolution.

Figure 22–21 summarizes one modern view of angiosperm classification. Scientific classification now places the monocots into a single group but places the dicots in a variety of distinct and different categories. This means, of course, that the term *dicot* is no longer used for classification. However, it can still be used to describe many of the characteristics of plant structure, and that is how it is used in this book. DOL•30–DOL•33

FIGURE 22–21 Angiosperm Clades Five of the major clades of angiosperms are represented here. Scientists are still working out the relationships among these groups.

Amborella Clade Only one species still exists in this oldest branch of angiosperms. Its floral parts have a spiral arrangement.

Water Lily Clade The water lilies are another very old group. Early water lily flowers may have been no more than 1 cm across, in contrast to the large and showy water lilies of today.

Magnoliids This clade contains a wide range of floral diversity, from species with rather small, plain flowers to the dinner-plate sized *Magnolia* flower shown here.

Monocots This clade contains about 20 percent of all angiosperms. Monocots include several important crop species, such as rice, corn, and wheat, as well as orchids, lilies, and irises.

Eudicots About 75 percent of angiosperms are eudicots. This clade is nearly as old as the angiosperms themselves. Eudicots diversified tremendously several times in their history.

UbD Check for Understanding

FOLLOW-UP PROBES

Have students write short responses to gauge their understanding.

- How might pollination in angiosperms be more efficient than pollination in gymnosperms? *(Gymnosperm pollen travels by wind, so reaching a female cone is random. In angiosperms, animals often carry pollen from flower to flower, so the transfer is more efficient.)*
- How has angiosperm classification recently changed? *(The two classes, monocot and dicot, are no longer used.)*

ADJUST INSTRUCTION

If students have a difficult time answering the questions, suggest they make an outline of the lesson up to this point. Have them discuss their outlines with a partner.

Angiosperm Diversity

How are different angiosperms conveniently categorized?

While scientific classification best reflects the evolutionary relationships among flowering plants, many people who work with plants—for example, farmers, gardeners, and foresters—tend to categorize angiosperms using more convenient methods. **Angiosperms are often grouped according to the number of their seed leaves, the strength and composition of their stems, and the number of growing seasons they live.** Naturally, these categories can overlap. An iris, for example, is a nonwoody plant, it has a single seed leaf, and it may live for many years.

MYSTERY CLUE

Fragments of cultivated wheat were found in Iceman's digestive tract. How did scientists confirm it was a monocot? How do you think they knew it was a cultivated form instead of wild?

Monocots and Dicots As **Figure 22–22** shows, angiosperms may be termed monocots or dicots based on the number of seed leaves, or cotyledons, they produce. Although we no longer classify both as scientific groups, the term is still useful. Monocots and dicots differ in characteristics such as the distribution of vascular tissue in stems, roots, and leaves, and the number of petals per flower. Monocots include plants such as corn, wheat, lilies, orchids, and palms. Monocot grasses—especially wheat, corn, and rice—have the important distinction of being the first plants to be cultivated in mass quantities for food. Dicots include roses, clover, tomatoes, oaks, and daisies.

Characteristics of Monocots and Dicots

	Seeds	Leaves	Flowers	Stems	Roots
Monocots	Single cotyledon	Parallel veins	Floral parts often in multiples of 3	Vascular bundles scattered throughout stem	Fibrous roots
Dicots	Two cotyledons	Branched veins	Floral parts often in multiples of 4 or 5	Vascular bundles arranged in a ring	Taproot

FIGURE 22–22 Comparing Monocots and Dicots This table compares the characteristics of monocots and dicots. Interpret Tables ***How do the flowers of monocots and dicots typically differ?***

Woody and Herbaceous Plants The flowering plants can also be subdivided into groups according to the characteristics of their stems. One of the most important and noticeable stem characteristics is woodiness. **Woody plants** are made primarily of cells with thick cell walls that support the plant body. Woody plants include trees, shrubs, and vines. Shrubs are typically smaller than trees, and vines have stems that are long and flexible.

Plant stems that are smooth and nonwoody are characteristic of **herbaceous plants** (hur BAY shus). Herbaceous plants do not produce wood as they grow. Examples of herbaceous plants include dandelions, zinnias, petunias, and sunflowers.

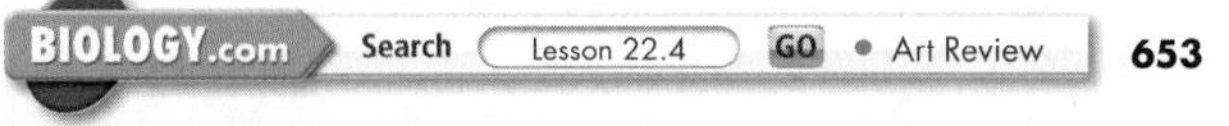

Use Visuals

Use **Figure 22–22** to help students compare and contrast monocots and dicots.

Ask Which type of plant has two cotyledons? *(dicots)*

Ask If the veins in the leaves of an unknown plant are parallel, what do you know about that plant? *(It is a monocot.)*

Ask What is the difference in stem structure between monocots and dicots? *(Monocots have vascular bundles scattered throughout the stem. Dicots have vascular bundles arranged in a ring.)*

DIFFERENTIATED INSTRUCTION

L1 Struggling Students To reinforce the characteristics shown in **Figure 22–22,** suggest students sketch their own pictures of the characteristics of monocots and dicots. Ask them to share their pictures with the class and explain the features of each plant that classify it as a monocot or a dicot.

Ask students to review **Figure 22–22** and speculate on which monocot characteristics might still be identifiable from partially digested wheat fragments. Then, ask students to brainstorm how scientists knew the wheat was cultivated. Students can go online to Biology.com to gather their evidence.

BIOLOGY.com Students can drag and drop labels to compare monocots and dicots in **Art Review: Comparing Monocots and Dicots.**

Quick Facts

ALL ABOUT ANGIOSPERMS

There are at least 260,000 known species of angiosperms. Given their numbers, it is not surprising that there is great variability among angiosperm species. They can be found almost everywhere on Earth, and display tremendous diversity in size, shape, longevity, reproductive morphology, and other characteristics. For example, pollen tubes show great variation. In corn, the pollen tube may be as long as 50 cm, while the tubes of many other species have a much shorter distance to grow. In addition, a pollen tube may complete its growth in less than 24 hours, while in some plants it takes over a year. The size of flowers varies greatly, too. The smallest flowers are those of the genus *Wolffia* of the duckweed family. Its flowers are less than 2 mm long. The largest flowers are those of the *Rafflesia* plant, found in the rainforests of Southeast Asia. Its huge blooms can grow to 1 m in diameter and attain a mass of 7 kg.

Answers

FIGURE 22–22 Monocot flowers have floral parts often in multiples of 3. Dicots have floral parts often in multiples of 4 or 5.

LESSON 22.4

Assess and Remediate

EVALUATE UNDERSTANDING

Ask students to work in groups of four. Ask each group member to review one of the four ways to classify angiosperms discussed in this chapter. Then, have them each discuss the advantages of classifying angiosperms in the way they focused on. Then, have them complete the 22.4 Assessment.

REMEDIATION SUGGESTION

L1 Struggling Students If your students have trouble with **Question 2c,** have them discuss with a partner the advantages and disadvantages of each method of classifying. Then, ask students to state their opinion and give at least one reason for their choice.

BIOLOGY.com Students can check their understanding of lesson concepts with the **Self-Test** assessment. They can then take an online version of the **Lesson Assessment.**

Comparing Plants by Life Span

Category	Life Span				Characteristics	Examples
Annuals	Year 1	Year 2	Year 3	Year 4	• Grow from seed to maturity, flower, produce seeds, and die in just one growing season	Marigolds, petunias, pansies, zinnias, tomatoes, wheat, cucumbers
Biennials					• Year 1: Sprout and grow very short stems and sometimes leaves • Year 2: Grow new stems and leaves, flower, produce seeds, then die	Parsley, celery, evening primroses, foxgloves
Perennials					• Most have woody stems. • Some have herbaceous stems that die each winter and are replaced in the spring.	Peonies, many grasses, palm trees, maple trees, honeysuckle, asparagus

FIGURE 22–23 Comparing Plants by Life Span Categories of plant life spans include annuals, biennials, and perennials. **Interpret Tables** ***Which flowering plant completes its life cycle in one year?***

Annuals, Biennials, and Perennials If you've ever planted a garden, you know that many flowering plants grow, flower, and die in a single year. Other types of plants continue to grow from year to year. The life span of plants is determined by a combination of genetic and environmental factors. Many long-lived plants continue growing despite yearly environmental fluctuations. However, harsh environmental conditions can shorten the life span of other plants. The characteristics of the three categories of plant life spans—annual, biennial, and perennial—are summarized in **Figure 22–23.**

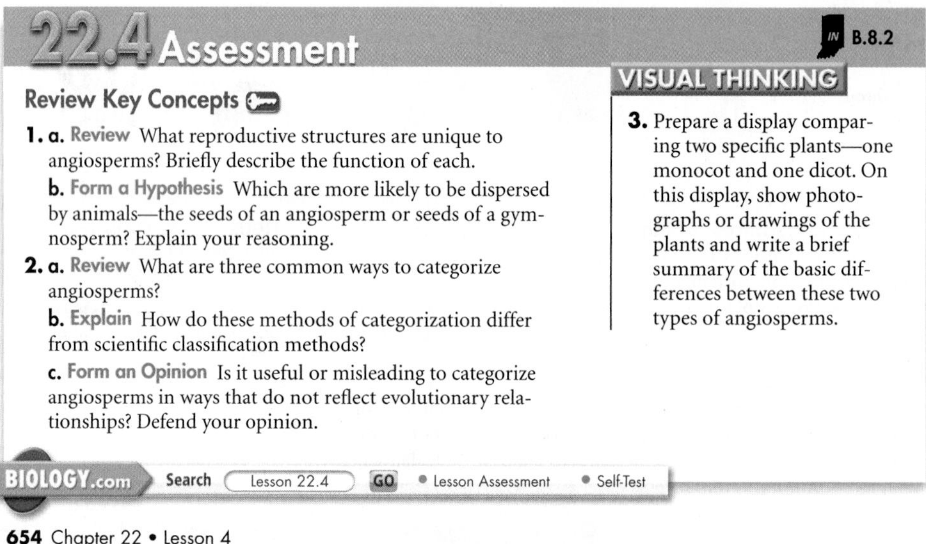

22.4 Assessment

IN B.8.2

Review Key Concepts

1. a. Review What reproductive structures are unique to angiosperms? Briefly describe the function of each.

b. Form a Hypothesis Which are more likely to be dispersed by animals—the seeds of an angiosperm or seeds of a gymnosperm? Explain your reasoning.

2. a. Review What are three common ways to categorize angiosperms?

b. Explain How do these methods of categorization differ from scientific classification methods?

c. Form an Opinion Is it useful or misleading to categorize angiosperms in ways that do not reflect evolutionary relationships? Defend your opinion.

VISUAL THINKING

3. Prepare a display comparing two specific plants—one monocot and one dicot. On this display, show photographs or drawings of the plants and write a brief summary of the basic differences between these two types of angiosperms.

BIOLOGY.com Search Lesson 22.4 GO • Lesson Assessment • Self-Test

Answers

FIGURE 22–23 annuals

Assessment Answers

1a. flowers and fruits; Flowers attract pollinators. Fruits protect the seed and aid in its dispersal.

1b. The seeds of angiosperms are more likely to be dispersed by animals because they are enclosed in a fruit that may be eaten.

2a. the number of seed leaves, the strength and composition of the stems, and the number of growing seasons lived

2b. Scientific classification methods reflect the evolutionary relationships among flowering plants. The common ways to categorize angiosperms are based on observations of the plants' structures and life spans.

2c. Students should defend their positions using what they have learned in this lesson. Sample answer: It is useful because anyone can categorize plants based on characteristics they can easily see instead of needing an advanced knowledge of biology.

VISUAL THINKING

3. Student displays should show how the plants they selected have the characteristics of monocots or dicots. Encourage students to use reference sources such as encyclopedias, field guides, gardening magazines, seed catalogues, and reliable online sources to research specific plants.

In addition to providing oxygen, plants are a source of food, fiber, and beauty. If you'd like to work with plants, you might want to consider one of the careers below.

FARMER

Farmers grow and harvest food. In the United States, nearly 20 percent of all land is used to grow crops such as corn, soybeans, wheat, and barley. Crop farmers must prepare their land for farming and make decisions about fertilizer use, crop rotation, and pest resistance.

PLANT PATHOLOGIST

Just as animals need doctors, so do plants. Plant pathologists are specialists in plant health. Plant diseases can have a huge economic impact. For example, from 1990 to 2000, one fungal disease destroyed $2.6 billion of wheat in the United States. Using microbiology, soil science, cell biology, genetics, and biochemistry, plant pathologists diagnose and treat plant diseases.

BOTANICAL ILLUSTRATOR

Botanical illustrators provide visuals that help people understand and appreciate biology. Working in a museum, outdoors, in a botanical garden, or at home, botanical illustrators create images of both plants and organisms related to plants. Illustrations may be used in various locations, such as guidebooks, textbooks, or museum displays.

CAREER CLOSE-UP:

Marya C. Roddis, Botanical Illustrator and Educator

Marya Roddis uses her talents as a botanical illustrator to inspire enthusiasm for the natural world. The granddaughter of an ethnobotanist—that is, someone who studies how people use plants—Ms. Roddis was taught to see the value and importance of all living things. Through workshops and after-school activities with local children, Ms. Roddis encourages her students to observe their environment and communicate what they learn. Whether through these educational efforts or her professional guidebook illustrations, Ms. Roddis's goal is to use art as a tool to help students who do not learn well in traditional settings.

"Illustration is a natural part of biology study. The detailed work required to create drawings can lead to success in all areas of scientific work."

WRITING Choose a topic that you have studied so far in biology (such as ecology, cells, or evolution) and explain how illustrations helped you understand the material.

Teach

Lead a Discussion

Have students read **Career Close-Up.** Point out that botanical illustrators combine artistic skills with detailed knowledge of botany. Have students talk about how detailed drawings might help a person learn about plants. Then, ask students to identify the skills a botanical illustrator might need. *(Sample answers: ability to observe nature, artistic talent, knowledge of biology, and attention to detail)* Explain that botanical illustrators also need a two- or four-year college degree in an art school or other school noted for its art and design department.

DIFFERENTIATED INSTRUCTION

ELL **English Language Learners** Explain the meanings of the terms *pathologist* and *illustrator.* Divide the words into parts and have students pronounce each word. Point out that a pathologist is one who studies diseases, and explain that an illustrator is one who draws illustrations (pictures) by hand or using a computer. Ask students what a botanical illustrator and a plant pathologist would do.

Quick Facts

MORE ABOUT FARMING

Farmers work mainly on family-owned farms. Most farmers get their work experience through being raised on a farm. While post-secondary education is not required to farm, it is recommended. College courses include dairy science, horticulture, and plant diseases. Farmers also need economic and business skills to run a business, and computer skills to keep records. Specialty farming is growing in importance. Horticultural specialty farmers produce fruits, flowers, and plants used in landscaping. Aquaculture farmers raise fish and shellfish. Farming is hard work and involves long hours. However, farmers generally enjoy living in a rural area, working outdoors, and being self-employed.

Answers

WRITING Students' explanations should include a specific concept, such as the parts of an animal cell, and a description of how the illustration made that particular content clearer.

CHAPTER LAB

Pre-Lab

Introduce students to the concepts they will explore in the chapter lab by assigning the Pre-Lab questions.

Lab

Tell students they will perform the chapter lab *Exploring Plant Diversity* described in **Lab Manual A.**

 **Struggling Students** A simpler version of the chapter lab is provided in **Lab Manual B.**

SAFETY

Students should wear gloves and use care when handling microscope slides and scalpel. Remind students to handle plants only as directed in the activity. Check for students who might be allergic to the plants.

BIOLOGY.com Look online for **Editable Lab Worksheets.**

For corresponding pre-lab in the **Foundation Edition,** see page 544.

IN INDIANA ACADEMIC STANDARDS

For the full text of all standards, see the Course Overview in the front matter of this book.

Real-World Lab

OPEN-ENDED INQUIRY

IN B.8.2 Classification. Also covered: NoS.4.

Pre-Lab: Exploring Plant Diversity

Problem How many different kinds of plants are in a small ecosystem?

Materials notebook, protective work gloves, measuring tape, tweezers, scissors, small plastic bags, labels, hand lens, field guides for plants, camera (optional)

Lab Manual Chapter 22 Lab

Skills Focus Observe, Measure, Classify, Infer

Connect to the Big idea There are more than 290,000 known species of plants that exist on Earth—from tiny green algae to large-leaved ferns to imposing redwood trees. What do these species have in common? They all need light, carbon dioxide, oxygen, water, and minerals to survive. But plant species vary in the way they obtain and retain resources.

Plants have adaptations that allow them to succeed in different habitats. Thus, you will not find 290,000 species of plants in your community. But you should be able to find a variety of plants. In this lab, you will survey a small ecosystem and identify as many plant species as possible.

Background Questions

a. Review What are the features that botanists use to divide the plant kingdom into five major groups?

b. Compare and Contrast Compare abiotic and biotic factors in an ecosystem.

c. Applying Concepts Suppose an ecosystem includes a stream or pond. Would you include that part of the ecosystem in your plant survey? Explain your answer.

Pre-Lab Questions

Preview the procedure in the lab manual.

1. Design an Experiment What are some ways that you can make sure that you survey all the plants in your ecosystem?
2. Classify What should you do if you are not sure that an organism is a plant?
3. Infer Why might you want to use a regional field guide rather than a national field guide when identifying plants?

BIOLOGY.com Search  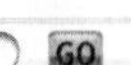

Visit Chapter 22 online to test yourself on chapter content and to find activities to help you learn.

Untamed Science Video The Untamed Science biologists interview plant experts to learn about healing chemicals manufactured by plants.

Data Analysis Investigate bracken (a type of fern) to see if there is a connection between bracken and stomach cancer.

Tutor Tube Is this plant a girl? Compare animals and plants to understand plant reproduction.

Art Review See how well you can distinguish monocots and dicots.

InterActive Art Review and compare life cycles of vascular and nonvascular plants.

Art in Motion Follow the process of pollination and fertilization in a pine to see how a plant embryo is formed.

Pre-Lab Answers

BACKGROUND QUESTIONS

a. The features used to divide plants into five major groups are embryo formation, specialized water-conducting tissues, seeds, and flowers.

b. Biotic factors are all the living organisms in an ecosystem. Abiotic factors are the physical or nonliving parts of an ecosystem.

c. Sample answer: Yes, because some plants are aquatic. For example, microscopic green algae and other plants, such as water lilies and duckweed, are aquatic.

PRE-LAB QUESTIONS

1. Answers will vary, but students might suggest dividing the area into smaller sections and investigating one section at a time. Or they may suggest doing the survey by type of plants, trees, shrubs, and so on.
2. Sample answer: I would record my observations of the organism and use reference materials later to decide whether the organism is a plant.
3. Sample answer: The national field guide will include many plants that don't grow in my region. It also may exclude some plants that do grow in my region.

22 Study Guide

Big idea **Unity and Diversity of Life**

The five main groups of plants are the green algae, bryophytes, seedless vascular plants, gymnosperms, and angiosperms. Over time, plants accumulated adaptations that allowed for success on dry land.

22.1 What Is a Plant?

The lives of plants center on the need for sunlight, gas exchange, water, and minerals.

Over time, the demands of life on land favored the evolution of plants more resistant to the drying rays of the sun, more capable of conserving water, and more capable of reproducing without water.

The life cycle of land plants has two alternating phases, a diploid (2N) phase and a haploid (N) phase. The shift between haploid and diploid is known as the alternation of generations.

alternation of generations (637)
sporophyte (637)
gametophyte (637)

22.2 Seedless Plants

Green algae are mostly aquatic. They are found in fresh and salt water, and in some moist areas on land.

Bryophytes are small because they lack vascular tissue.

Vascular tissues—xylem and phloem—make it possible for vascular plants to move fluids through their bodies against the force of gravity.

bryophyte (641)
vascular tissue (641)
archegonium (642)
antheridium (642)
sporangium (642)
tracheophyte (643)
tracheid (643)
xylem (643)
phloem (643)

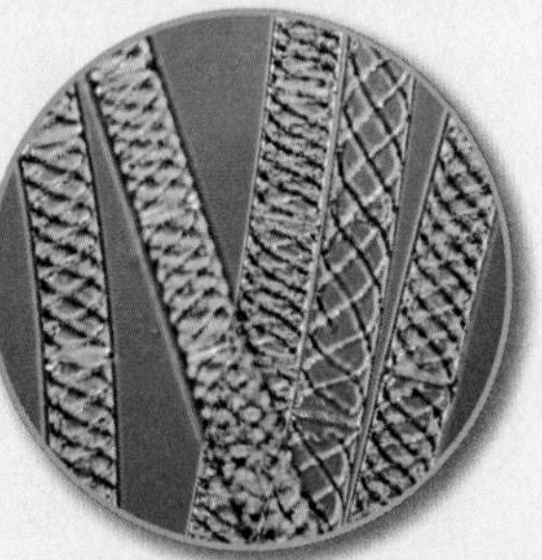
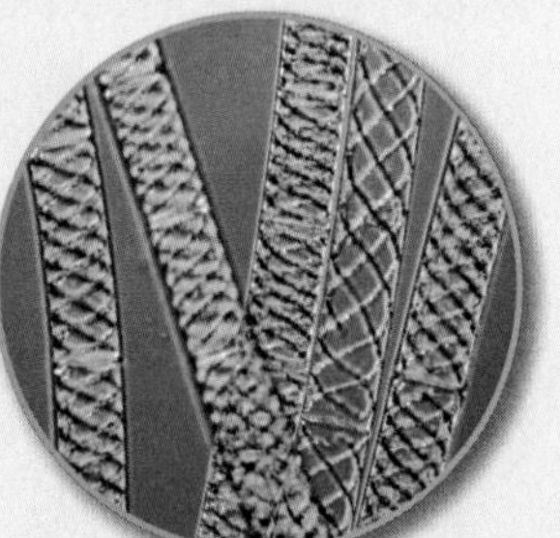

22.3 Seed Plants

Adaptations that allow seed plants to reproduce without standing water include a reproductive process that takes place in cones or flowers, the transfer of sperm by pollination, and the protection of embryos in seeds.

In gymnosperms, the direct transfer of pollen to the female cone allows fertilization to take place without the need for gametes to swim through standing water.

seed (646)
gymnosperm (646)
angiosperm (646)
pollen grain (647)
pollination (647)
seed coat (647)
ovule (648)
pollen tube (648)

22.4 Flowering Plants

Angiosperms reproduce sexually by means of flowers. After fertilization, ovaries within flowers develop into fruits that surround, protect, and help disperse the seeds.

Angiosperms are often grouped according to the number of their seed leaves, the strength and composition of their stems, and the number of growing seasons they live.

ovary (650)
fruit (651)
cotyledon (652)
monocot (652)
dicot (652)
woody plant (653)
herbaceous plant (653)

Think Visually Copy and fill in the table below using information from this chapter. Fill in "yes" or "no" for each blank box.

Comparison of Major Plant Groups

	Vascular Tissue?	Dominant Sporophyte?	Seeds?
Green Algae	no	1. ______	2. ______
Bryophytes	3. ______	no	4. ______
Seedless Vascular Plants	5. ______	6. ______	no
Gymnosperms	7. ______	8. ______	9. ______
Angiosperms	yes	10. ______	yes

Study Online

REVIEW AND ASSESSMENT RESOURCES

Editable Worksheets Student pages of Study Workbooks A and B, Lab Manuals A and B, and the Assessment Resources Book are available online. These documents can be easily edited using a word-processing program.

Lesson Overview Have students reread the Lesson Overviews to help them study chapter concepts.

Vocabulary Review The *Flash Cards* and *Crossword* provide an interactive way to review chapter vocabulary.

Chapter Assessment Have students take an online version of the Chapter 22 Assessment.

Standardized Test Prep Students can take an online version of the Standardized Test Prep. You will receive their scores along with ideas for remediation.

Diagnostic and Benchmark Tests Use these tests to monitor your students' progress and supply remediation.

Answers

THINK VISUALLY

1. no **2.** no **3.** no **4.** no
5. yes **6.** yes **7.** yes **8.** yes
9. yes **10.** yes

UbD Performance Tasks

SUMMATIVE TASK Divide the class into small groups, and have students work together to write 10–15 questions for a game of "Who Am I?" The questions should be based on characteristics of each of the five groups of plants discussed in this chapter; green algae, bryophytes, seedless vascular plants, gymnosperms, and angiosperms. If one characteristic is common to more than one group, the question should include a second clue that narrows the answer to just one group. Provide index cards so students can write the question on one side and the answer on the other side. Collect the cards, and call out the questions, with groups taking turns answering questions they did not write. Place a time limit on answering, and keep score, with each correct answer receiving one point.

TRANSFER TASK Have students work in small groups to develop a field guide for the five main groups of plants. The guide should be a booklet that a high school student who has not studied the chapter could use to identify plants in each group. The field guide should include an introduction about what all plants have in common and the distinguishing characteristics of each group.

ASSESSMENT

Lesson 22.1

UNDERSTAND KEY CONCEPTS

1. b **2.** b **3.** c **4.** a

5. The term is *alternation of generations,* which refers to the two alternating phases of a plant's life cycle: the gametophyte, or haploid phase, and the sporophyte, or diploid phase.

6. embryo formation, vascular tissue, seeds, and flowers

THINK CRITICALLY

7. In a very dry environment, leaves would provide too much surface area for water loss, and a cactus must conserve water. The barrel shape allows the plant to store water whenever it is available.

8. The plant is probably a green alga.

Lesson 22.2

UNDERSTAND KEY CONCEPTS

9. c **10.** d **11.** d **12.** b

13. *Spirogyra* forms long, threadlike colonies. The cells of a colony are stacked like soda cans placed end to end. The cells in a *Volvox* colony form hollow spheres and are connected to one another by strands of cytoplasm.

14. Without lignin, cell walls are not hardened, so a tall plant body cannot be supported. Also, there is no means for supporting the "tubes" that comprise vascular tissue.

15. Bryophytes depend upon the presence of water to complete their life cycle, because the only way the sperm can reach the egg is to swim through water.

16. A sporangium is a spore capsule within which haploid spores are produced by meiosis.

17. Tracheids are hollow cells with thick cell walls that make up xylem. Their function is to transport water through a plant.

18. The evolution of lignin made the cell walls of plants rigid. This enabled plants to grow upright and reach great heights.

19. Rhizomes are creeping or underground stems. Rhizoids are thin filaments that anchor bryophytes to the soil and absorb water and minerals. Roots are underground organs that absorb water and minerals from the soil.

20. A fern gametophyte is thin, heart-shaped, and tiny.

22 Assessment

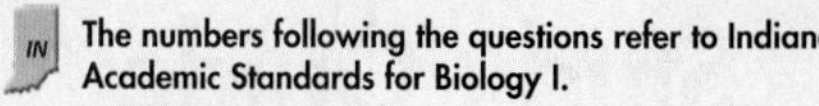
The numbers following the questions refer to Indiana's Academic Standards for Biology I.

22.1 What Is a Plant?

Understand Key Concepts

1. Which of the following is NOT a characteristic of plants?
a. eukaryotic cells
b. cell walls containing chitin
c. multicellular structure
d. chlorophyll

2. The first land plants likely evolved from B.8.1
a. protists. **c.** mosses.
b. green algae. **d.** red algae.

3. Two gases that plants must exchange are
a. oxygen and nitrogen.
b. carbon dioxide and nitrogen.
c. oxygen and carbon dioxide.
d. carbon dioxide and carbon monoxide.

4. Recent changes in the classification of the plant kingdom are based on B.8.2
a. studies comparing DNA sequences.
b. comparison of physical structures.
c. differences and similarities in life cycles.
d. whether or not a plant uses seeds to reproduce.

5. Give the term for the process shown below. Then describe what this term means.

6. List the features biologists use to distinguish among the major plant groups. B.8.2

Think Critically

7. Infer As its name indicates, the barrel cactus is shaped like a barrel and has no leaves. Given the basic needs of plants, explain why this shape is an advantage for a plant that survives where very little water is available.

8. Draw Conclusions If all you know about a particular plant is that it lives virtually all of its life as a multicellular haploid organism, what can you conclude about the kind of plant it is?

22.2 Seedless Plants

Understand Key Concepts

9. Under unfavorable conditions, the green alga *Chlamydomonas* reproduces by forming a
a. haploid zygote.
b. multicellular sporophyte.
c. diploid zygote.
d. multicellular gametophyte.

10. The dominant stage of a moss is the
a. sporophyte. **c.** archegonium.
b. protonema. **d.** gametophyte.

11. Water is carried upward from the roots to every part of a vascular plant by
a. cell walls. **c.** cuticle.
b. phloem. **d.** xylem.

12. The leaves of ferns are called
a. sori. **c.** rhizomes.
b. fronds. **d.** spores.

13. Give two examples of colonial green algae and briefly describe their structure.

14. Describe two ways that a lack of lignin limits the height of bryophytes.

15. In the life cycle of a moss, what environmental conditions are necessary for fertilization?

16. What is a sporangium?

17. What are tracheids? What is their function in a vascular plant?

18. How was the ability to produce lignin significant to the evolution of plants?

19. Compare the structure and function of rhizomes, rhizoids, and roots.

20. Describe a fern gametophyte.

Think Critically

21. Compare and Contrast Moss plants are small, but ferns can grow as tall as small trees. Explain why this is so.

22. Apply Concepts A friend of yours lives in one of the desert areas of New Mexico and wants to grow a garden of bryophytes. What environmental conditions would your friend need to provide the garden for it to be successful?

THINK CRITICALLY

21. Vascular tissue supports a tall plant and carries water and nutrients from the soil to the plant's upper regions. Thus, ferns, which have vascular tissue, can grow tall, whereas mosses, which lack vascular tissue, cannot grow tall.

22. The friend needs to provide constant moisture for the bryophytes and protection from the drying effects of too much sun.

Lesson 22.3

UNDERSTAND KEY CONCEPTS

23. d **24.** c **25.** d **26.** a

27. A seed coat surrounds and protects the embryo and keeps the contents of the seed from drying out.

28. Gymnosperm seeds are uncovered and lie directly on the scales of cones where they are produced. Angiosperm seeds are embedded within a protective layer of tissue.

Understand Key Concepts

23. All of the following are characteristics of gymnosperms EXCEPT B.8.2
a. vascular tissue.
b. seeds.
c. cones.
d. flowers.

24. The male reproductive structures of seed plants are called
a. sperm.
b. ovules.
c. pollen grains.
d. sporophytes.

25. The structures on a pine tree that contain the gametophytes are
a. flowers.
b. sporangia.
c. sori.
d. cones.

26. The green structure in the diagram is called
a. an embryo.
b. a seed coat.
c. a spore.
d. stored food.

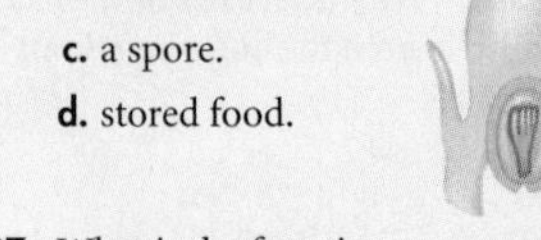

27. What is the function of a seed coat?

28. How do gymnosperm seeds differ from angiosperm seeds? B.8.2

29. What reproductive adaptations allow conifers to live in dry habitats?

Think Critically

30. Compare and Contrast Describe the primary similarities and differences between gymnosperms and angiosperms. B.8.2

31. Infer During the age of the dinosaurs, the vast majority of land plants were ferns and mosses. Today, the vast majority are seed plants. Provide an explanation for this change based on the basic requirements of plants.

32. Apply Concepts Explain the structure and function of a seed cone and pollen cone. Explain their respective roles in reproduction.

solve the CHAPTER MYSTERY

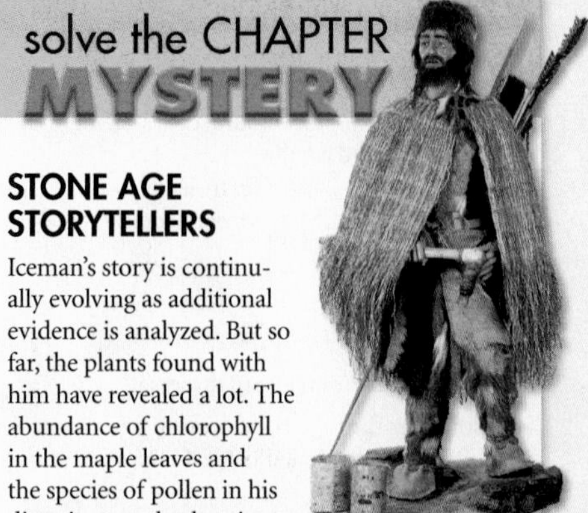

STONE AGE STORYTELLERS

Iceman's story is continually evolving as additional evidence is analyzed. But so far, the plants found with him have revealed a lot. The abundance of chlorophyll in the maple leaves and the species of pollen in his digestive tract both point to a death in late spring. Distinct layers of pollen in his digestive tract suggest that Iceman changed his elevation quite dramatically several times on his final day.

The unfinished bow suggests that Iceman's journey into the mountains was unplanned. Perhaps he was fleeing an enemy? In fact, several years after the bow was found a CT scan of Iceman revealed a stone arrowhead lodged beneath his left shoulder blade and the large gash that the arrowhead left in a major artery.

And what of his society? The primitive wheat in his digestive tract and other intact grains found on his clothes suggest that Iceman's society practiced an early form of agriculture.

1. Apply Concepts A clump of moss was also found with Iceman's possessions. Some scientists hypothesize that Iceman used the moss like we use tissues or paper towels today. What property of moss would allow this function? Why is this adaptation necessary for mosses? *Hint*: What kind of tissue do they lack that other land plants have?

2. Communicate Write a letter to a friend summarizing the information provided by plant evidence found with Iceman.

3. Connect to the Big idea Pollen and seeds are the most reliable plant-related evidence at archeological sites and at modern-day crime scenes because they are long-lasting. Relate this quality to their structure and function in living plants.

BIOLOGY.com Search Chapter 22 GO  • Untamed Science Video • Chapter Mystery

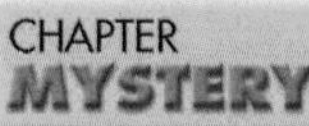

After students solve the Chapter Mystery, discuss how they arrived at their inferences.

Ask How might the presence of large amounts of chlorophyll in the maple leaves and the species of pollen in his digestive tract point to a death in late spring? *(Students might infer that particular plant species release their pollen at particular times of the year. They might also conclude that the amount of chlorophyll indicates that photosynthesis, which requires chlorophyll, was in high gear. This would most likely occur in late spring or summer as the hours of daylight increase.)*

Point out that the plant evidence found on Iceman not only reveals clues about his life, but also provides information about the plants that he was surrounded by.

Ask Iceman's whereabouts on his last day alive could be partially inferred from the layers of pollen deposited in his digestive tract. Why would different elevations support different populations? *(Students might list some of the environmental factors that vary with elevation, such as temperature and moisture.)*

Ask What type of information might a plant scientist studying Iceman try to obtain? *(Answers will vary, but should center on identifying characteristics about the types of plant life that surrounded Iceman. For example, was there plant matter from a species that no longer exists? Was there a surprising amount of a certain type of pollen in his digestive tract?)*

CHAPTER MYSTERY ANSWERS

1. Since mosses lack vascular tissue, they are well adapted to absorb water through their cell walls.

2. Student letters should include all the information provided by all the Mystery Clues in this chapter.

3. Big idea Pollen has to be able to withstand a certain amount of harsh conditions so the male gametophyte is protected as it travels. Seeds have a tough outer coat to protect the embryo inside. The seeds may need to last a long time to survive harsh conditions until the environment is favorable for growth.

29. protective seed coats, dispersal of pollen by wind

THINK CRITICALLY

30. Similarities: reproduce without requiring open water, produce seeds; Differences: Gymnosperms produce seeds in cones, the seeds are not encased in fruit, and wind carries pollen. Angiosperms produce seeds in flowers, the seeds are protected within a fruit, and animals play a large role in pollination.

31. Seed plants are probably more common today since they do not require water for reproduction like ferns and mosses do. Therefore, seed plants can survive in a broader range of habitats than ferns and mosses.

32. A seed cone is larger than a pollen cone and produces female gametophytes, which develop in ovules near the base of each scale. A pollen cone is small and produces pollen grains that make up the entire male gametophyte stage of the gymnosperm life cycle. The pollen cones release pollen grains that are carried by the wind. Some of the pollen grains reach female cones.

Have students take a video field trip to explore the many drugs humans derive from plants by watching **Paging Dr. Greenthumb.**

Lesson 22.4

UNDERSTAND KEY CONCEPTS

33. c **34.** c

35. Some fruits attract and are eaten by animals that spread the seeds enclosed in the fruits after the seeds pass through their digestive tracts. This increases the ranges the angiosperms inhabit.

36. Drawings should show that monocots have leaves with parallel veins. Dicots have leaves with branched veins.

37. Sample answer: Woody—maple tree; Herbaceous—sunflower

38. Annuals complete a life cycle within one growing season. Perennials live for many years.

THINK CRITICALLY

39. Students' answers should be consistent with the information in the chapter on the reproduction and development in green algae, bryophytes, ferns, gymnosperms, and angiosperms.

40. In bryophytes, the gametophytes are large and support the stalk-like sporophytes. In ferns, the gametophytes are smaller and less obvious, but they can be seen as flat structures near the base of a young sporophyte. In seed plants, the gametophytes are housed within the sporophytes (within flowers or cones). This means that the gametophytes of seed plants are much less obvious than those of bryophytes and ferns.

Connecting Concepts

USE SCIENCE GRAPHICS

41. The plant is a dicot, because its floral parts are in multiples of five.

WRITE ABOUT SCIENCE

42. Student paragraphs should include comparisons between how sperm and eggs are produced, how sperm reach eggs, what occurs during fertilization, and embryo development.

43. Big idea Sample answer: Like animals, plants are multicellular eukaryotes. Both grow, reproduce, and obtain energy through cellular respiration. The distinguishing features of an oak tree are cell walls made of cellulose and the ability to carry out photosynthesis using chlorophylls *a* and *b*.

22.4 Flowering Plants

Understand Key Concepts

33. In angiosperms, the mature seed is surrounded by a structure called a

a. cone. **c.** fruit.
b. flower. **d.** cotyledon.

34. A plant that has a two-year life cycle is a

a. dicot. **c.** biennial.
b. monocot. **d.** perennial.

35. How do fruits aid in seed dispersal?

36. How does the pattern of veins in a monocot leaf differ from that in a dicot leaf? Draw an example of each. B.8.2

37. Give one example each of a woody plant and an herbaceous plant.

38. How does the life span of an annual differ from that of a perennial?

Think Critically

39. **Compare and Contrast** Describe the methods of reproduction and development in the five major plant groups. Include information about the size of the mature plants.

40. **Compare and Contrast** Compare the size and function of gametophytes in bryophytes, ferns, and seed plants.

Connecting Concepts

Use Science Graphics NoS.3

41. **Classify** Study the photograph of the flower below. Is this plant a monocot or dicot? Explain your answer. B.8.2

Write About Science NoS.3

42. **Explanation** Choose a particular group of seedless vascular plants and a particular group of seed plants. Then, write a paragraph that compares reproduction in these two groups.

43. **Assess the Big idea** At first glance, an oak tree and a zebra hardly seem similar in any way. Describe the characteristics that they do share in common. What are the characteristics of the oak tree that distinguish it from the other kingdoms of living things? B.8.2

Analyzing Data

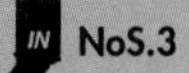

NoS.3

A homeowner has noticed moss growing in the backyard lawn and wants to understand the conditions that cause moss to grow where grass had grown before. Half the homeowner's property is in shade all year, and the other half gets direct sun. The table shown summarizes his observations.

Growth of Moss in Sun and Shade

	Year					
	2003	2004	2005	2006	2007	2008
Area of Moss in Sun (m^2)	0	0	1	2	1	1
Area of Moss in Shade (m^2)	0	2	5	7	6	9

44. **Interpret Tables** It is clear from the table that moss grows best in areas shaded from the sun. If one of the years in the table had below average rainfall, what would be your guess as to which year that was, based on the data given?

45. **Form a Hypothesis** What hypothesis about the difference between the shaded and the sunny areas would explain the observed growth of moss?

PURPOSE Students will analyze data to form a hypothesis about the conditions in which mosses grow.

PLANNING Have students review the information from the chapter about the kind of environment in which mosses grow best.

ANSWERS

44. 2007, because the area of moss decreased from 2006.

45. Mosses grow better in shaded areas than in sunny areas because sunny areas tend to be drier.

Standardized Test Practice for Indiana

Multiple Choice

1. Which of the following is a basic requirement of plants?
   A sunlight
   B carbon dioxide
   C water
   D all of the above

2. What stage in the alternation of generations is represented by fern fronds?
   A sporophyte
   B female gametophyte
   C male gametophyte
   D zygote

3. Which of the following is NOT a characteristic of dicots?
   A branched veins
   B taproot
   C parallel veins
   D two cotyledons B.8.2

4. Which of the following is a structure associated with gymnosperms?
   A flower
   B cone
   C fruit
   D enclosed seed B.8.2

5. The mature plant ovary is also referred to as the
   A gymnosperm.
   B pollen grain.
   C fruit.
   D cotyledon.

6. Plants cultivated for food are mostly
   A gymnosperms.
   B woody plants.
   C angiosperms.
   D bryophytes.

Questions 7–9

A group of students placed a sprig of a conifer in a beaker of water. They measured the amount of oxygen given off during a set period of time to determine the rate of photosynthesis. They changed the temperature of the water in the beaker using an ice bucket and a hot plate. Their data are summarized in the graph below.

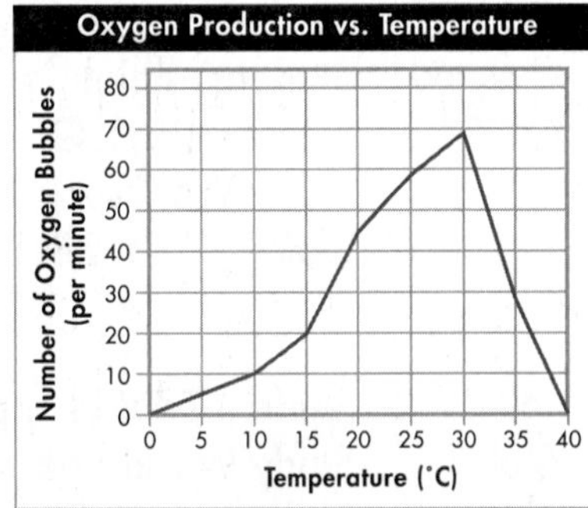

7. What is the independent variable?
   A light intensity
   B temperature
   C oxygen bubbles
   D photosynthesis rate

8. Which variable(s) should the students have held constant?
   A plant type
   B temperature
   C light intensity
   D plant type and light intensity

9. What can you conclude based on the data?
   A The higher the temperature, the more oxygen bubbles are released.
   B There is an optimum temperature for photosynthesis in this species of conifer.
   C All plants are most efficient at 30°C.
   D The lower the temperature, the more oxygen bubbles are released. NoS.3

Open-Ended Response

10. Explain why seeds were an important adaptation for the success of plants on Earth.

If You Have Trouble With . . .

Question	1	2	3	4	5	6	7	8	9	10
See Lesson	22.1	22.2	22.4	22.3	22.4	22.4	22.3	22.3	22.3	22.3

Answers

1. D
2. A
3. C
4. B
5. C
6. C
7. B
8. D
9. B
10. Seeds make it possible for plants to reproduce without being dependent on water. Seeds also enable plants to disperse their offspring over long distances and protect the embryos from harsh environmental conditions.

Test-Taking Tip

USE TIME WISELY

Explain to students that if they find a particular question difficult, they should put a light pencil mark beside the question and keep working. Tell them to not spend a lot of time trying to figure out the answer, because they might run out of time to finish the test. As students answer later questions, they may find information that helps them answer the difficult question.

Plant Structure and Function

Chapter Contents	IN	Time	Core Resources
Chapter Preview			**Student Edition,** pp. 662–663 **Chapter Mystery,** p. 663
23.1 Specialized Tissues in Plants Seed Plant Structure • Plant Tissue Systems • Plant Growth and Meristems	B.2.6	1/2 period 1/4 block	**Student Edition,** pp. 664–668 **Inquiry** 23.1 Quick Lab, p. 665 L2 **Study Workbook A** 23.1 Worksheets L2 **Biology.com** 23.1 Self-Test • 23.1 Lesson Assessment
23.2 Roots Root Structure and Growth • Root Functions		1 period 1/2 block	**Student Edition,** pp. 669–673 **Study Workbook A** 23.2 Worksheets L2 **Biology.com** *Art in Motion:* Water Passage Into a Root **Assessment Resources Book** Visual Quiz L2
23.3 Stems Stem Structure and Function • Growth of Stems	NoS.3	1 period 1/2 block	**Student Edition,** pp. 674–679 **Inquiry** 23.3 Analyzing Data, p. 678 L2 **Study Workbook A** 23.3 Worksheets L2 **Biology.com** *InterActive Art:* Primary and Secondary Growth • *Tutor Tube:* Understanding Plant Growth **Assessment Resources Book** Visual Quiz L2
23.4 Leaves Leaf Structure and Function • Gas Exchange and Homeostasis	B.2.6	1 period 1/2 block	**Student Edition,** pp. 680–684 **Inquiry** 23.4 Quick Lab, p. 683 L2 **Study Workbook A** 23.4 Worksheets L2 **Biology.com** *Art Review:* Anatomy of a Leaf • *Data Analysis:* Effects of Humidity and CO_2 on Plant Stomata • 23.4 Self-Test • 23.4 Lesson Assessment
23.5 Transport in Plants Water Transport • Nutrient Transport	NoS.6	1/2 period 1/4 block	**Student Edition,** pp. 685–687 **Inquiry** 23.4 Quick Lab, p. 686 L2 **Study Workbook A** 23.5 Worksheets L2 **Biology.com** *Visual Analogy:* Transpirational Pull • 23.4 Self-Test • 23.4 Lesson Assessment
Chapter Pre-Lab	NoS.1, NoS.5	1 period 1/2 block	**Student Edition,** p. 688 L2 **Lab Manual A** *Identifying Growth Zones in Roots* L2

Additional Resources

Biology.com Untamed Science Video • Vocabulary Flash Cards

Study Workbook B 23.1 Worksheets L1 ELL LPR
Spanish Study Workbook 23.1 Worksheets ELL
Biology.com 23.1 Lesson Overview • 23.1 Lesson Notes

Study Workbook B 23.2 Worksheets L1 ELL LPR
Spanish Study Workbook 23.2 Worksheets ELL
Biology.com 23.2 Lesson Overview • 23.2 Lesson Notes • 23.2 Self-Test • 23.2 Lesson Assessment

Study Workbook B 23.3 Worksheets L1 ELL LPR
Spanish Study Workbook 23.3 Worksheets ELL
Biology.com 23.3 Lesson Overview • 23.3 Lesson Notes • 23.3 Self-Test • 23.3 Lesson Assessment

Study Workbook B 23.4 Worksheets L1 ELL LPR
Spanish Study Workbook 23.4 Worksheets ELL
Biology.com 23.4 Lesson Overview • 23.4 Lesson Notes

Study Workbook B 23.5 Worksheets L1 ELL LPR
Spanish Study Workbook 23.5 Worksheets ELL
Biology.com 23.5 Lesson Overview • 23.5 Lesson Notes

Lab Manual B *Identifying Growth Zones in Roots* • Data Analysis: *Reading a Tree's History* L1 ELL LPR

Chapter Review

Student Edition Study Guide, p. 689 L2
Study Workbook A Chapter 23 Vocabulary Review L2 • Chapter 23 Chapter Mystery/21st Century Skills Activity L2 L3
Transparencies, pp. 268–279 L1 ELL LPR L2
Biology.com Untamed Science Video • Editable Worksheets of Study Workbooks A and B and Lab Manuals A and B • Chapter 23 Flash Cards and Match It

Untamed Science DVD • Classroom Resources CD (includes lesson presentations and editable worksheets)

Chapter Assessment

Student Edition Assessment, pp. 690–693 L2
Study Workbook B Chapter 23 Chapter Review L1 ELL LPR • Chapter 23 Taking a Standardized Test L1 ELL LPR
Assessment Resources Book Chapter 23 Test A L2 • Chapter 23 Test B L1 ELL LPR
Biology.com Chapter 23 Assessment • Editable Worksheets of Chapter 23 Visual Quizzes and Chapter 23 Tests A and B

Exam*View* *Assessment Suite* • Classroom Resources CD (includes lesson presentations and editable worksheets)

Time: 1 period, 1/2 block

Pressed for Time?

Preview the Chapter Preview Figures 23–1, 23–6, 23–12, and 23–15.

Cover the Chapter Quickly Have students read *Seed Plant Structure* and *Plant Tissue Systems* in Lesson 23.1, focusing on Figure 23–2. In Lesson 23.2, assign *Root Structure and Growth,* go over Figure 23–6, and read the key concept in *Root Functions.* Assign *Stem Structure and Function* in Lesson 23.3, *Leaf Structure and Function* in Lesson 23.4, and go over Figure 23–15. Assign *Water Transport* in Lesson 23.5.

Assess Assign questions 1, 2, and 4 in the 23.1 Assessment, question 1 in the 23.2 Assessment, question 1 in the 23.3 Assessment, questions 1 and 3 in the 23.4 Assessment, and question 1 in the 23.5 Assessment. In the Chapter 23 Assessment, assign questions 1, 3–7, 9, 10, 21, 22, 25, 27, 31, and 33.

CHAPTER 23

Connect to the Big Idea

Ask students to describe what they see in the photograph. Lead them to answer that the insect has been caught by the plant. (Some students may at first think the insect is a pollinator.) Explain that carnivorous plants live in environments where little or no nitrogen is present in the soil. The plants get nitrogen from live prey rather than from the soil, as most plants do. Ask students to infer how the structure of the leaves help sundew plants obtain nitrogen. As a hint, point out the structures on the leaves of the sundew plant in the photograph—sticky, tentacle-like projections that *trap* insects. Tell students that in this chapter, they will study the relationships between the structure and function of plant parts. Then, read the question, **How are cells, tissues, and organs organized into systems that carry out the basic functions of a seed plant?** Have students predict some of the basic functions of a seed plant and how a plant might carry them out. Then, tell students that, by the end of the chapter, they will be able to answer this question more fully.

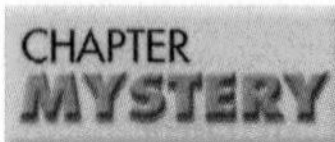
Have students read the Chapter Mystery and brainstorm reasons that the interior of the tree might be hollow. Then have students predict how the tree can have such an unusual structure and still carry out the basic functions of a seed plant.

Have students preview the chapter vocabulary terms using the **Flash Cards.**

23 Plant Structure and Function

Big idea Structure and Function

Q: How are cells, tissues, and organs organized into systems that carry out the basic functions of a seed plant?

BIOLOGY.com Search Chapter 23 GO • Flash Cards

662

IN INDIANA ACADEMIC STANDARDS

For the full text of all standards, see the Course Overview in the front matter of this book.

Key standards: Chapter 23 covers key ideas from The Nature of Science, including **NoS.3** Communicate ideas and **NoS.6** Use analogies and models.

UbD Understanding by Design

In Chapter 23, students learn how the cells, tissues, and organs of plants enable them to survive. This knowledge will directly inform the Unit 6 Enduring Understanding of how *from microorganisms to plants, organisms vary widely in the way they carry out basic life processes.* The Big Idea, Essential Question, and lesson Guiding Questions shown in the graphic organizer to the right help frame students' exploration of how plants carry out life processes.

PERFORMANCE GOALS

As students learn about the structures and functions of plants in Chapter 23, they will be able to demonstrate their understanding of these relationships through drawings, creative writing, and oral presentations. The culminating project for the chapter requires students to combine their knowledge of plant structures, functions, and processes to create a narrative that describes a plant in the context of a tour of a manufacturing facility. Students will also solve problems posed to a horticultural columnist.

INDIANA ACADEMIC STANDARDS FOR SCIENCE

Nature of Science NoS.1, NoS.3, NoS.5, NoS.6; **Cellular Structure** B.2.6. See lessons for details.

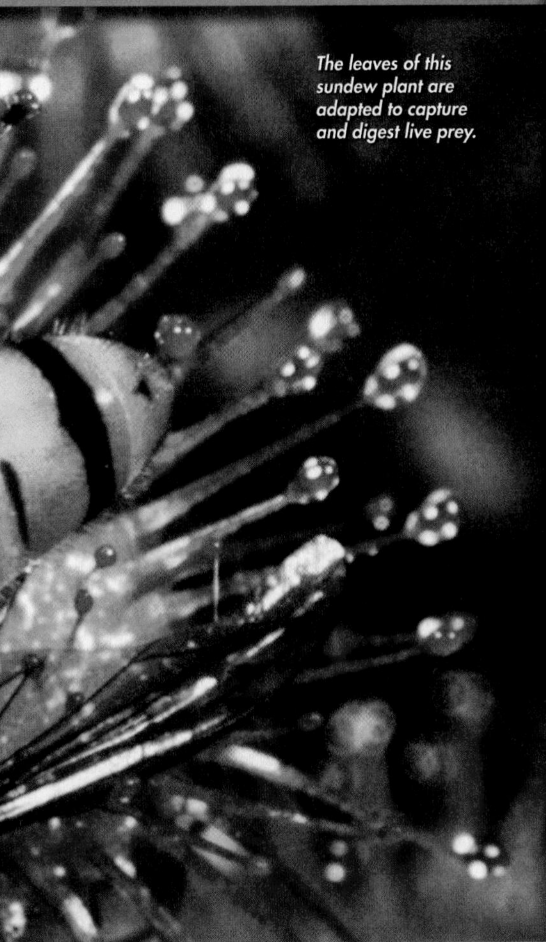

The leaves of this sundew plant are adapted to capture and digest live prey.

CHAPTER
MYSTERY

THE HOLLOW TREE

As you hike through a Central American rain forest on a steamy afternoon on the last day of your tropical vacation, you see many unusual plants and animals. A monkey calls from a distant tree, and a dense fog covers the landscape. Then you stumble on a root and look up. A massive tree stands before you. Its trunk seems to be made up of many intertwined woody branches. Edging closer, you nervously slip your head through one of the larger gaps and look straight up. Inside, you find that the tree is completely hollow.

This tree, a species of fig, is indeed unusual. What happened to the interior of the tree? And how did the tree grow to such a great height if it has no center? As you read this chapter, look for clues that explain the structure of this strange plant. Then, solve the mystery.

Never Stop Exploring Your World. Finding the solution to The Hollow Tree mystery is only the beginning. Take a video field trip with the ecogeeks of Untamed Science to see where the mystery leads.

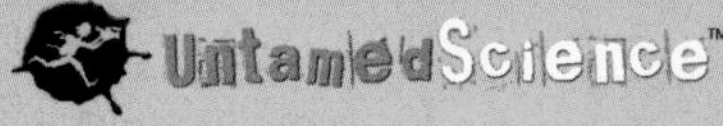

• Untamed Science Video • Chapter Mystery

What's Online

BIOLOGY.com Extend your reach by using these and other digital assets offered at Biology.com.

CHAPTER MYSTERY
Investigate the strange structure of a type of fig tree to find out how it's possible for a tree to be "hollow."

UNTAMED SCIENCE VIDEO
Take a field trip around the world to see the amazing ways plants have adapted to their environments.

ART IN MOTION
Students watch water passing through the dermal tissue of a root and into xylem cells.

INTERACTIVE ART
A short animation shows primary and secondary growth in plants.

TUTOR TUBE
Short, online tutorial addresses misconceptions about how and where plant growth occurs in most plants.

ART REVIEW
Students can drag and drop labels to review the structure of a leaf.

DATA ANALYSIS
This virtual data set shows how the activity of plant stomata changes in response to different atmospheric carbon dioxide levels.

VISUAL ANALOGY
Transpirational pull is modeled by the animated movements of a chain of circus clowns.

Chapter 23 Big Idea: Structure and Function

Chapter 23 EQ: How are cells, tissues, and organs organized into systems that carry out the basic functions of a seed plant?

- **23.1 GQ:** How are plant tissues organized?
- **23.2 GQ:** How do the structure and function of roots help a plant carry out life processes?
- **23.3 GQ:** How do the structure and function of stems help a plant carry out life processes?
- **23.4 GQ:** How do the structure and function of leaves help a plant carry out life processes?
- **23.5 GQ:** How do plants move materials through their bodies?

Getting Started

Objectives

23.1.1 Identify the principal organs of seed plants.

23.1.2 Explain the primary functions of the main tissue systems of seed plants.

23.1.3 Contrast meristems with other plant tissues.

Student Resources

Study Workbooks A and B, 23.1 Worksheets

Spanish Study Workbook, 23.1 Worksheets

Lesson Overview • Lesson Notes • Assessment: Self-Test, Lesson Assessment

For corresponding lesson in the **Foundation Edition**, see pages 552–555.

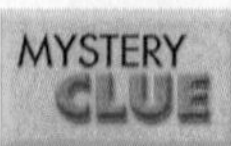

Ask students to review the functions of roots and leaves and infer which structure makes up the fig tree "branches." Students can go online to **Biology.com** to gather their evidence.

Answers

IN YOUR NOTEBOOK Answers should explain how roots, stems, and leaves absorb sunlight, take in water and minerals, and exchange gases.

IN INDIANA ACADEMIC STANDARDS

For the full text of all standards, see the Course Overview in the front matter of this book.

B.2.6 Investigate a variety of different cell types and relate the proportion of different organelles within these cells to their functions.

23.1 Specialized Tissues in Plants

IN B.2.6 Variation in cell structure and function.

Key Questions

What are the three principal organs of seed plants?

What are the primary functions of the main tissue systems of seed plants?

How do meristems differ from other plant tissues?

Vocabulary

epidermis • lignin • vessel element • sieve tube element • companion cell • parenchyma • collenchyma • sclerenchyma • meristem • apical meristem

Taking Notes

Concept Map As you read, make a concept map to organize the information in this lesson.

THINK ABOUT IT Have you ever wondered if plants were really alive? Compared to animals, plants don't seem to do much. If you look deep inside a living plant, this first impression of inactivity disappears. Instead, you will find a busy and complex organism. Plants move materials, grow, repair themselves, and constantly respond to the environment. They may act at a pace that seems slow to us, but their cells and tissues work together in remarkably effective ways.

Seed Plant Structure

What are the three principal organs of seed plants?

The cells of a seed plant are organized into different tissues, organs, and systems. **The three principal organs of seed plants are roots, stems, and leaves.** The organs are linked together by systems that run the length of the plant. These systems produce, store, and transport nutrients, and provide physical support and protection.

Roots Roots anchor plants in the ground, holding soil in place and preventing erosion. Root systems often work with soil bacteria and fungi in mutualistic relationships that help the roots absorb water and dissolved nutrients. Roots transport these materials to the rest of the plant, store food, and hold plants upright against forces such as wind and rain.

Stems Plant stems provide a support system for the plant body, a transport system that carries nutrients, and a defensive system that protects the plant against predators and disease. Stems also produce leaves and reproductive organs such as flowers. Whatever the size of a stem, its support system must be strong enough to hold up leaves and branches. The stem's transport system contains tissues that lift water from the roots up to the leaves and carry the products of photosynthesis from the leaves back down to the roots.

MYSTERY CLUE

The tangled fig "branches" are not actually stems. What are they?

Leaves Leaves are the plant's main photosynthetic organs. The broad, flat surfaces of many leaves increase the amount of sunlight plants absorb. Leaves also expose a great deal of tissue to the dryness of the air and, therefore, have adaptations that protect against water loss. Adjustable pores in leaves help conserve water while letting oxygen and carbon dioxide enter and exit the leaf.

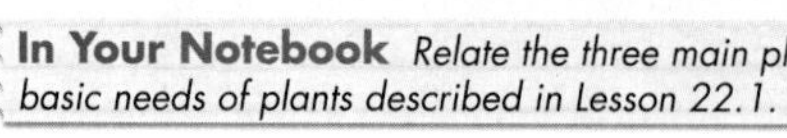

In Your Notebook *Relate the three main plant organs back to the basic needs of plants described in Lesson 22.1.*

BIOLOGY.com Search Lesson 23.1 GO • Lesson Overview • Lesson Notes

UbD Teach for Understanding

ENDURING UNDERSTANDING From microorganisms to plants, organisms vary widely in the way they carry out basic life processes.

GUIDING QUESTION How are plant tissues organized?

EVIDENCE OF UNDERSTANDING *After students have finished the lesson, this assessment should show their understanding of how plant tissues are organized to carry out the functions of plants.* Have students work in groups of three to develop a narrative from the point of view of a leaf, a stem, and a root. Each "organ" will describe how the structure and arrangement of each main tissue system relates to its function; for example, "I'm a leaf, and my ground tissue is broad and flat to increase the amount of sunlight I can absorb." Ask groups to present their narratives to the class.

Quick Lab
GUIDED INQUIRY

What Parts of Plants Do We Eat?

❶ Examine an onion, a potato, and an artichoke. Record your observations as notes and labeled sketches. **CAUTION:** *Do not eat the vegetables.*

❷ Use your observations to classify each vegetable as a root, stem, leaf, or other plant part.

Analyze and Conclude

1. **Classify** How did you classify the onion? Explain what characteristics you used to make this decision.
2. **Infer** How did you classify the potato? How is its structure related to its function?
3. **Infer** How did you classify the artichoke? What does its inner structure tell you about its function?

Plant Tissue Systems

What are the primary functions of the main tissue systems of seed plants?

Within the roots, stems, and leaves of plants are specialized tissue systems, shown in **Figure 23–1.** Plants have three main tissue systems: dermal, vascular, and ground. Dermal tissue covers a plant almost like skin covers you. Vascular tissue forms a system of pipelike cells that help support the plant and serve as its "bloodstream," transporting water and nutrients. Ground tissue produces and stores food. Next, you will see how the cells in these systems compare to one another.

Dermal Tissue Dermal tissue in young plants consists of a single layer of cells called the **epidermis** (ep uh DUR mis). The outer surfaces of epidermal cells are often covered with a thick waxy layer called the cuticle, which protects against water loss. Some epidermal cells have tiny projections known as trichomes (TRY kohmz). Trichomes help protect the leaf and may give the leaf a fuzzy appearance. **Dermal tissue is the protective outer covering of a plant.**

In older plants, dermal tissue may be many cell layers deep and may be covered with bark. In roots, dermal tissue includes root hair cells that help absorb water.

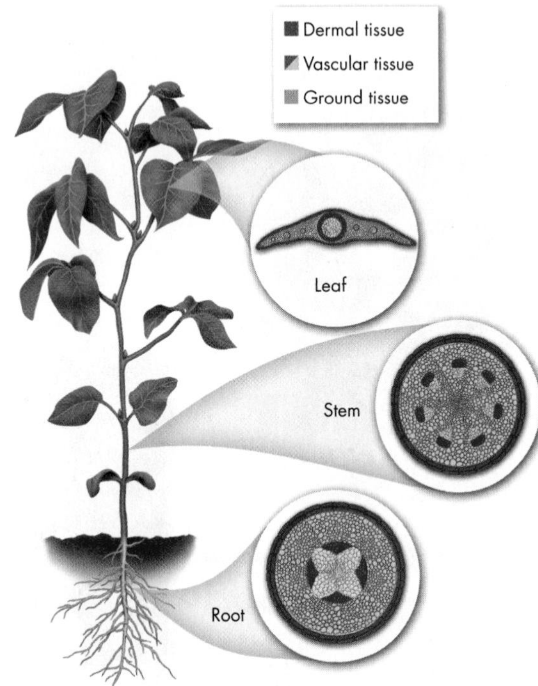

FIGURE 23–1 Principal Organs of Plants These cross sections of the principal organs of seed plants show that all three organs contain dermal tissue, vascular tissue, and ground tissue. **Interpret Visuals** *Which tissue type is found in the center of a root?*

LESSON 23.1

Teach

Use Visuals

Use **Figure 23–1** to help students understand the hierarchy of plant structure. Have volunteers name the three principal plant organs and the three types of tissue found in each organ. Point out that organs are made up of tissues working together and tissues are made up of cells working together.

Ask What is the function of vascular tissue in stems and leaves? *(It helps support the plant, and it transports nutrients and water throughout the plant.)*

Reinforce that each tissue type (dermal, vascular, and ground) has the same basic function in each of the three principal plant organs.

DIFFERENTIATED INSTRUCTION

LPR Less Proficient Readers Suggest students start a lesson outline to help them organize the information on plant organs and tissue systems. As they read through the text, have them continue to add to their outlines. Eventually, their outlines should include the three plant organs, the three types of plant tissue, and the specialized cells of each type of plant tissue.

ELL Focus on ELL: Extend Language

BEGINNING AND INTERMEDIATE SPEAKERS To familiarize students with the vocabulary in this lesson, start by pronouncing each term. If needed, divide multi-syllabic words into parts, and slowly pronounce each part. Then, have students repeat the words so that they become more comfortable using the new vocabulary. As the lesson progresses, point out where each term appears. Have students read the paragraph the word is in and try to determine a meaning for the word from its context.

Quick Lab

PURPOSE Students will start to think about what parts of plants they eat.

MATERIALS onion, potato, artichoke

PLANNING Trim the stems of the artichoke to avoid having students confuse the leaf bud with the stem. You can also substitute Brussels sprouts for artichokes. Obtain onions that have visible roots, such as green onions.

ANALYZE AND CONCLUDE

1. The onion is a small stem surrounded by leaves, which are thin and flat and are attached to the stem at the base.
2. The potato is a stem, and the "eyes" are buds that grow into branches.
3. The artichoke is a floral bud surrounded by modified leaves, which contain chloroplasts. The leaves are active in photosynthesis.

Answers

FIGURE 23–1 Vascular tissue is found in the center of a root.

Teach continued

Build Science Skills

Provide prepared microscope slides of xylem and phloem tissues for students to observe. If possible, provide samples from roots, stems, and leaves of dicots and monocots. Have students compare and contrast the structures of xylem and phloem. Then, ask them to diagram the tissues and label the tracheids, vessel elements, companion cells, and sieve tube elements.

DIFFERENTIATED INSTRUCTION

L1 Special Needs Set up two distinct microscope stations. Set up one that clearly shows xylem tissue, and another that shows phloem. Have students identify which station shows xylem and which shows phloem. Have them discuss their conclusions with a partner.

L3 Advanced Students Challenge students to compare the distribution of vascular tissue in the stems of monocots and dicots. Have them create simple diagrams to illustrate their comparisons.

Vascular Tissue The two kinds of vascular tissue are xylem, a water-conducting tissue, and phloem, a tissue that carries dissolved food. As you can see in **Figure 23–2,** both xylem and phloem consist of long, slender cells that connect almost like sections of pipe. **Vascular tissue supports the plant body and transports water and nutrients throughout the plant.**

▶ ***Xylem: Tracheids*** All seed plants have xylem cells called tracheids. Recall from Chapter 22 that tracheids are long and narrow, with tough cell walls that help to support the plant. As they mature, tracheids die, leaving only their cell walls. These cell walls contain **lignin,** a complex molecule that resists water and gives wood much of its strength. Openings in the walls connect neighboring cells and allow water to flow from cell to cell. Thinner regions of the wall, known as pits, allow water to diffuse from tracheids into surrounding ground tissue. These adaptations allow tracheids to carry water throughout the plant and distribute it to tissues where it is needed.

▶ ***Xylem: Vessel Elements*** In addition to tracheids, angiosperms possess a second form of xylem tissue known as a **vessel element.** Vessel elements are wider than tracheids and are arranged end to end on top of one another like a stack of tin cans. After they mature and die, cell walls at both ends are left with slitlike openings through which water can move freely. In some vessel elements, the end walls disappear altogether, producing a continuous tube.

▶ ***Phloem: Sieve Tube Elements*** Unlike xylem cells, phloem cells are alive at maturity. The main phloem cells are **sieve tube elements,** which are arranged end to end, forming sieve tubes. The end walls of sieve tube elements have many small holes through which nutrients move from cell to cell in a watery stream. As sieve tube elements mature, they lose their nuclei and most other organelles. The remaining organelles hug the inside of the cell wall and are kept alive by companion cells.

▶ ***Phloem: Companion Cells*** The cells that surround sieve tube elements are called **companion cells.** Companion cells keep their nuclei and other organelles through their lifetime. Companion cells support the phloem cells and aid in the movement of substances in and out of the phloem.

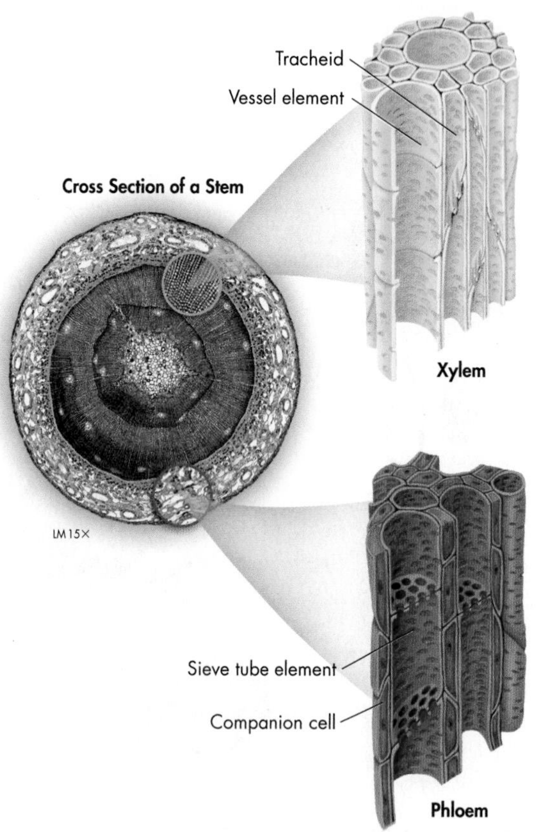

FIGURE 23–2 Vascular Tissue Xylem and phloem form the vascular transport system that moves water and nutrients throughout a plant. Compare and Contrast ***How are tracheids and sieve tube elements similar? How are they different?***

UbD Check for Understanding

ANALOGY PROMPT

Have students complete the following analogy prompts in small groups.

- Sieve tube elements are like *(Sample answer: strainers)* because *(Sample answer: they have many small holes).*
- A companion cell is like *(Sample answer: a good friend)* because *(Sample answer: it supports the phloem and helps it do its job).*

ADJUST INSTRUCTION

If student responses are incomplete or incorrect, have them work in small groups to draw a **T-Chart** and list each type of cell and tissue. Ask students to locate and record descriptions of the structure and function of each part in their chart. Then, have each group use its chart to generate analogies.

Answers

FIGURE 23–2 Tracheids and sieve tube elements both have openings in the walls that allow materials to move from cell to cell. Tracheids carry water and die as they mature. Sieve tube elements carry nutrients and are alive at maturity.

Ground Tissue Plant tissue called ground tissue is neither dermal nor vascular. **Ground tissue produces and stores sugars, and contributes to physical support of the plant.** Ground tissue is an important part of food at the dinner table, too. The edible portions of plants like potatoes, squash, and asparagus are mostly ground tissue. Most ground tissue consists of **parenchyma** (puh RENG kih muh). Parenchyma cells have a thin cell wall and a large central vacuole surrounded by a thin layer of cytoplasm. In leaves, these cells contain many chloroplasts and are the site of most of a plant's photosynthesis.

Parenchyma Thin cell walls

Collenchyma Thicker cell walls

Sclerenchyma Thickest cell walls

FIGURE 23–3 Ground Tissue These micrographs show how three types of ground tissue found in a sunflower stem vary in thickness (LM 250×).

Ground tissue may also contain two types of cells with thicker cell walls. **Collenchyma** (kuh LENG kih muh) cells have strong, flexible cell walls that help support plant organs. Chains of such cells make up the familiar "strings" of a stalk of celery. **Sclerenchyma** (sklih RENG kih muh) cells have extremely thick, rigid cell walls that make ground tissue such as seed coats tough and strong. Sclerenchyma fibers are used to make rope from hemp, and when you last used a nutcracker to open a walnut, you broke through some really tough sclerenchyma!

In Your Notebook *Make a three-column chart in which to summarize information about the three main tissue systems of plants.*

Plant Growth and Meristems

How do meristems differ from other plant tissues?

When most animals reach adulthood, they stop growing. Not so with most plants. Even the oldest trees produce new leaves and new reproductive organs every year, almost as if they remained "forever young." How do they do it? The secrets of plant growth are found in **meristems,** tissues that, in a sense, really do stay young. **Meristems are regions of unspecialized cells in which mitosis produces new cells that are ready for differentiation.** Meristems are found in places where plants grow rapidly, such as the tips of stems and roots. The undifferentiated cells they produce are very much like the stem cells of animals.

MYSTERY CLUE

The seeds of this fig species sprout high up in the branches of other forest trees, called hosts. The roots grow downward, through the air.

Lead a Discussion

Talk about how the thickness of the cell walls of different types of ground tissue allows it to function in different ways.

Ask How do the thin cell walls of parenchyma in leaves relate to the function of leaves? *(Thin cell walls allow for gas exchange and penetration of sunlight.)*

Ask Why might you find parenchyma in roots? *(Sample answer: The thin walls of parenchyma allow materials to pass through, allowing roots to absorb materials.)*

Ask How do the thicknesses of collenchyma cells and sclerenchyma cells relate to their functions? *(These cells provide support and protection.)*

DIFFERENTIATED INSTRUCTION

ELL English Language Learners Use **Figure 23–3** as visual reinforcement for your discussion on cell wall thickness and ground tissue function. As you talk about the different cell types, trace the cell walls with your finger or a pointer so that students can connect the names of the cell types with a visual.

Discuss with students why the roots are growing downward. Suggest they look at **Figure 23–1** and read the **Roots** paragraph on the first page of the lesson. Students can go online to **Biology.com** to gather their evidence.

Quick Facts

CHARACTERISTICS OF PARENCHYMA CELLS

Parenchyma cells are found in all the major parts of plants. Although these cells are usually spherical when first produced, their thin walls are easily flattened as they are packed against one another. Most parenchyma cells end up having a shape with 14 sides. The main function of parenchyma cells with chloroplasts is photosynthesis; those without chloroplasts store water or food.

Answers

IN YOUR NOTEBOOK Students' charts should include the types of cells that make up each type of tissue (dermal, vascular, and ground) as well as the functions of each tissue.

LESSON 23.1

Teach continued

Use Visuals

Have students use **Figure 23–4** to compare and contrast root and stem meristems.

Ask How are both meristems similar? *(Both contain new cells that form by mitosis and then differentiate into each type of plant tissue.)*

Ask How are they different? *(They produce different types of cells.)*

DIFFERENTIATED INSTRUCTION

LPR Less Proficient Readers Make sure students understand that meristems are not located just in stems, even though the word *meristem* contains the word part *-stem*. Explain that the word *meristem* comes from the Greek word *meristos*, meaning "divided."

Assess and Remediate

EVALUATE UNDERSTANDING

Play a word-association game in which you name a type of plant cell, tissue, or organ and a volunteer then names its function. Then, have students complete the 23.1 Assessment.

REMEDIATION SUGGESTION

L1 Struggling Students If your students have trouble with **Question 3b,** discuss the meanings of *unspecialized, specialized,* and *differentiated.* Have students work in pairs to sequence the process described in the **Apical Meristems** section of the lesson and then apply this knowledge by summarizing how a new plant can form from a cutting.

BIOLOGY.com Students can check their understanding of lesson concepts with the **Self-Test** assessment. They can then take an online version of the **Lesson Assessment.**

BUILD Vocabulary

RELATED WORD FORMS *Apex* and *apical* are related word forms. *Apex* is a noun meaning the narrowed or pointed end, or tip, and *apical* is an adjective describing something related to or located at the apex.

Apical Meristems Because the tip of a stem or root is known as its apex, meristems in these rapidly growing regions are called **apical meristems.** Unspecialized cells produced in apical meristems divide rapidly as stems and roots increase in length. **Figure 23–4** shows examples of stem and root apical meristems.

At first, the new cells that are pushed out of meristems look very much alike: They are unspecialized and have thin cell walls. Gradually, they develop into mature cells with specialized structures and functions. This process is called differentiation. As the cells differentiate, they produce each of the tissue systems of the plant, including dermal, vascular, and ground tissue.

Meristems and Flower Development The highly specialized cells found in cones and flowers (which are the reproductive organs of seed plants), are also produced in meristems. Flower or cone development begins when the pattern of gene expression changes in a stem's apical meristem. These changes transform the apical meristem of a flowering plant into a floral meristem. Floral meristems produce the tissues of flowers, which include the plant's reproductive organs as well as the colorful petals that surround them.

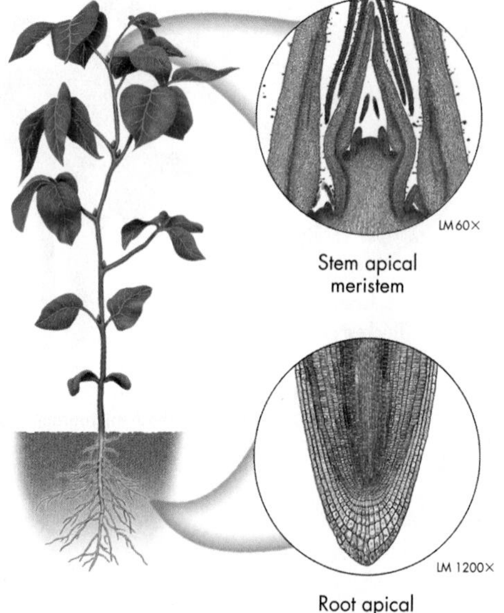

FIGURE 23–4 Apical Meristems Apical meristems are found in the growing tips of stems and roots. Within these meristems, unspecialized cells are produced by mitosis.

23.1 Assessment

Review Key Concepts

1. a. **Review** What are the three main organs of seed plants?
   b. **Interpret Diagrams** Review **Figure 23–1.** How are the three main organs of seed plants similar in structure?
2. a. **Review** What are the three main tissue systems of plants?
   b. **Compare and Contrast** How do the main functions of a plant's tissue systems differ?
3. a. **Review** What is the function of meristems?
   b. **Form a Hypothesis** How might the presence of meristems explain the ability of plants to regenerate from cuttings?

Apply the Big idea

Structure and Function

4. You probably have some knowledge of the human circulatory system. Based on this knowledge, write a paragraph comparing and contrasting the structure and function of the vascular system of a plant to the human circulatory system. *Hint:* Show how the systems are alike and different.

BIOLOGY.com Search Lesson 23.1 GO • Lesson Assessment • Self-Test

Assessment Answers

1a. roots, stems, and leaves

1b. All contain dermal tissue, vascular tissue, and ground tissue.

2a. dermal, vascular, and ground

2b. Dermal tissue protects a plant. Vascular tissue transports water and nutrients through the plant. Ground tissue produces and stores sugars and helps support the plant.

3a. to produce new cells by mitosis

3b. Because meristems can differentiate into each of the tissue systems of a plant, a cutting that contains meristems can form a new plant.

4. Big idea Students' paragraphs should explain that the systems are alike in that they contain tubes that transport materials through the body of the organism. Students might state the systems are different in that the human circulatory system has a heart that pumps materials through the tubes; plants do not have this organ.

23.2 Roots

THINK ABOUT IT Can you guess how large a typical plant's root system is? Get ready for a surprise if you think that roots are small and insignificant. In a 1937 study of a single rye plant, botanist Howard Dittmer showed that the length of all the branches in the rye plant's root system was an astonishing 623 kilometers (387 miles). The surface area of these roots was more than 600 square meters—130 times greater than the combined areas of its stems and leaves!

Key Questions

 ***What are the main tissues in a mature root?***

What are the different functions of roots?

Vocabulary

root hair • cortex • endodermis • vascular cylinder • root cap • Casparian strip

Taking Notes

Outline Before you read, use the headings of the lesson to make an outline about plant roots. As you read, fill in phrases after each heading that provide key information.

Root Structure and Growth

What are the main tissues in a mature root?

As soon as a seed begins to sprout, it puts out its first root to draw water and nutrients from the soil. Other roots soon branch out from this first root, adding length and surface area to the root system. Rapid cell growth pushes the tips of the growing roots into the soil. The new roots provide raw materials for the developing stems and leaves before they emerge from the soil.

Types of Root Systems The two main types of root systems are taproot systems and fibrous root systems, shown in **Figure 23–5.** Taproot systems are found mainly in dicots. Fibrous root systems are found mainly in monocots. Recall from Chapter 22 that monocots and dicots are two categories of flowering plants.

▶ ***Taproot System*** In some plants, the primary root grows long and thick and gives rise to smaller branch roots. The large primary root is called a taproot. Taproots of oak and hickory trees grow so long that they can reach water several meters down. Carrots, dandelions, and beets have short, thick taproots that store sugars and starches.

▶ ***Fibrous Root System*** In other plants, such as grasses, the system begins with one primary root. But it is soon replaced by many equally sized branch roots that grow separately from the base of the stem. These fibrous roots branch to such an extent that no single root grows larger than the rest. The extensive fibrous root systems produced by many plants help prevent topsoil from being washed away by heavy rain.

FIGURE 23–5 A Comparison of Two Root Systems Dandelions have a taproot system (left), while grasses have a fibrous root system (right).

UbD Teach for Understanding

ENDURING UNDERSTANDING From microorganisms to plants, organisms vary widely in the way they carry out basic life processes.

GUIDING QUESTION How do the structure and function of roots help a plant carry out life processes?

EVIDENCE OF UNDERSTANDING *After students finish the lesson, this assessment should show their understanding of how the structures of a root enable a plant to take in water and other nutrients.* Ask students to work in pairs to make a diagram of a longitudinal cross section of a root with the structures labeled and numbered in the sequence in which materials move into and through a root. Have them draw an arrow that indicates the path of materials and use the numbered structures to write a summary of the movement.

LESSON 23.2

Getting Started

Objectives

23.2.1 Describe the main tissues in a mature root.

23.2.2 Describe the different functions of roots.

Student Resources

Study Workbooks A and B, 23.2 Worksheets

Spanish Study Workbook, 23.2 Worksheets

BIOLOGY.com Lesson Overview • Lesson Notes • Activity: Art in Motion • Assessment: Self-Test, Lesson Assessment

For corresponding lesson in the **Foundation Edition**, see pages 556–559.

Activate Prior Knowledge

Show students a potted plant or a picture of one. Ask them where they pour water when they water a plant. *(around the base of the plant)* Then, ask why they do this rather than watering the leaves, for example. *(Some students might know that roots, which are beneath the soil surface, take in water for the plant.)* Tell students that this is one function of roots, and in this section, they will learn more about the structure and function of roots.

LESSON 23.2

Teach

ZOOMING IN

Use the diagram to reinforce the three types of plant tissue systems. Ask students to identify the location of dermal tissue, vascular tissue, and ground tissue. Help them identify the different cell types within each tissue (such as xylem and phloem in the vascular tissue and parenchyma in the cortex). Discuss where new growth originates. Then, provide prepared slides of longitudinal segments and cross sections of plant roots. Have students draw diagrams of their observations and use **Figure 23–6** to help label their diagrams.

DIFFERENTIATED INSTRUCTION

L1 **Struggling Students** Help students organize the information in the diagram by using the text and the diagram to construct a **Two-Column Table.** Column heads should include Tissue Type and Description. Rows should list the structures labeled in the diagram.

Study Wkbks A/B, Appendix S31, Two-Column Table. **Transparencies,** GO16.

ELL Focus on ELL: Build Background

BEGINNING AND INTERMEDIATE SPEAKERS Bring a variety of plants to class, such as grass, dandelions, and other weeds with intact roots. Provide hand lenses, and allow students time to observe, feel, and sketch the roots. Ask students to orally describe their observations, using their textbook as a reference. Then, have intermediate speakers write phrases describing their observations.

ZOOMING IN

ANATOMY OF A ROOT

FIGURE 23–6 A root consists of a central vascular cylinder surrounded by ground tissue and the epidermis.

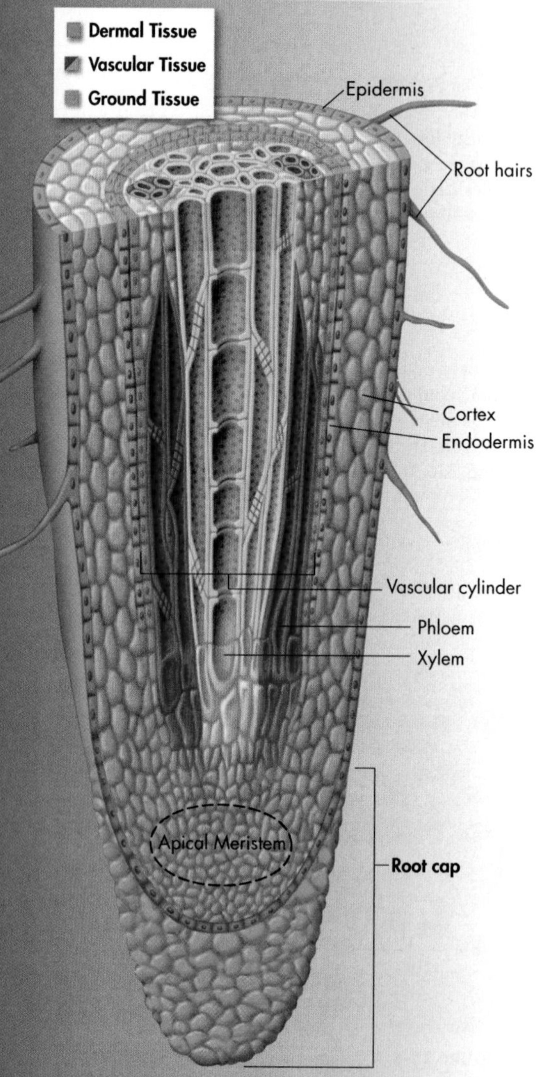

Anatomy of a Root Roots contain cells from the three tissue systems—dermal, vascular, and ground tissue, as shown in **Figure 23–6.** **A mature root has an outside layer, called the epidermis, and also contains vascular tissue and a large area of ground tissue.** The root system plays a key role in water and mineral transport. The cells and tissues of a root are specialized to carry out these functions.

▶ ***Dermal Tissue: Epidermis*** The root's epidermis performs the dual functions of protection and absorption. Its surface is covered with thin cellular projections called **root hairs.** These hairs penetrate the spaces between soil particles and produce a large surface area that allows water and minerals to enter.

▶ ***Ground Tissue*** Just inside the epidermis is a region of ground tissue called the **cortex.** Water and minerals move through the cortex from the epidermis toward the center of the root. The cortex also stores the products of photosynthesis, such as starch.

A layer of ground tissue known as the **endodermis** completely encloses the vascular cylinder. The endodermis, as you will see, plays an essential role in the movement of water and minerals into the center of the root.

▶ ***Vascular Tissue*** At the center of the root, the xylem and phloem together make up a region called the **vascular cylinder.** Dicot roots like the one shown at left have a central column of xylem cells.

▶ ***Apical Meristem*** Roots grow in length when apical meristems produce new cells near the root tips. The root tip is covered by a tough **root cap** that protects the fragile meristem as the root tip forces its way through the soil. As the root grows, the root cap secretes a slippery substance that eases the progress of the root through the soil. Cells at the very tip of the root cap are constantly being scraped away, and new root cap cells are continually added by the meristem.

In Your Notebook *Relate the role of the root cap to that of your outer skin layer, which loses dead cells at a rate of billions of cells per day.*

How Science Works

GREEN CLEANING

Phytoremediation is the use of plants to clean up hazardous wastes. One mechanism of this technology is absorption of contaminants through roots, where contaminants are stored or transported to other plant parts to be stored, destroyed, or changed to less toxic forms. For example, sunflowers concentrate uranium in their roots. These plants were used to help clean up radioactive waste in 1986 at Chernobyl in the Ukraine after a nuclear reactor exploded. Other ways people use phytoremediation is to clean up heavy metals in soil and pesticides and explosive wastes in water.

Answers

IN YOUR NOTEBOOK Students' responses should indicate an understanding of the similarity of the two processes: Cells at the root cap and cells in the outer skin layer are constantly being sloughed off, and new cells are constantly being added.

Root Functions

What are the different functions of roots?

How does a root go about the job of absorbing water and minerals from the soil? Although it might seem to, water does not just "soak" into the root from soil. It takes energy on the part of the plant to absorb water. **Roots support a plant, anchor it in the ground, store food, and absorb water and dissolved nutrients from the soil.**

MYSTERY CLUE

Until its roots reach the soil below, how might the fig seedling get nutrients?

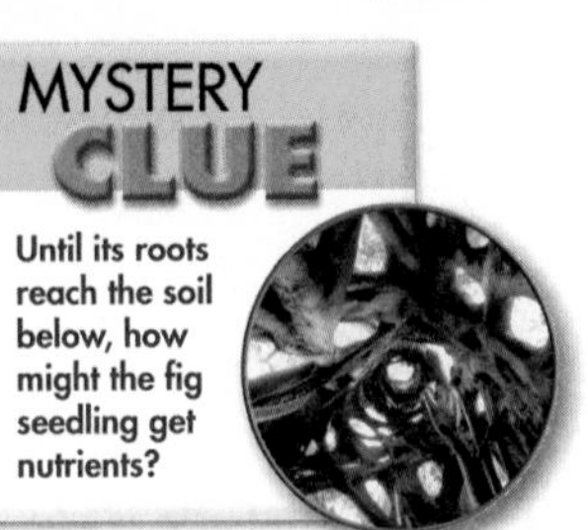

Uptake of Plant Nutrients An understanding of soil helps explain how plant roots function. Soil is a complex mixture of sand, silt, clay, air, and bits of decaying animal and plant tissue. Soil in different places contains varying amounts of these ingredients. Sandy soil, for example, is made of large particles that retain few nutrients, whereas the finely textured silt and clay soils of the Midwest and southeastern United States are high in nutrients. The ingredients define the soil and determine, to a large extent, the kinds of plants that can grow in it.

To grow, flower, and produce seeds, plants require a variety of inorganic nutrients in addition to carbon dioxide and water. The nutrients needed in largest amounts are nitrogen, phosphorus, potassium, magnesium, sulfur, and calcium. The functions of these essential nutrients within a plant are described in **Figure 23–7.**

In addition to large amounts of these nutrients, small amounts of other nutrients, called trace elements, are just as important. These trace elements include iron, zinc, molybdenum, boron, copper, manganese, and chlorine. As important as they are, excessive amounts of any of these nutrients in soil can also be poisonous to plants.

Essential Plant Nutrients

Nutrient (Chemical Symbol)	Some Roles in Plant	Result of Deficiency
Nitrogen (N)	• Proper leaf growth and color • Synthesis of amino acids, proteins, nucleic acids, and chlorophyll	• Stunted plant growth • Pale yellow leaves ▶
Phosphorus (P)	• Synthesis of DNA • Development of roots, stems, flowers, and seeds	• Poor flowering • Stunted growth
Potassium (K)	• Synthesis of proteins and carbohydrates • Development of roots, stems, and flowers • Resistance to cold and disease	• Weak stems • Stunted roots • Edges of leaves turn brown ▶
Magnesium (Mg)	• Synthesis of chlorophyll	• Thin stems • Mottled, pale leaves
Calcium (Ca)	• Cell growth and division • Cell wall structure • Cellular transport • Enzyme action	• Stunted growth • Curled leaves ▶

FIGURE 23–7 Important Plant Nutrients
Soil contains several nutrients that are essential for plant growth. **Interpret Tables** ***If you notice that a plant is becoming paler and more yellow, what nutrient might it be lacking?***

Use Visuals

Use **Figure 23–7** to discuss the major nutrients plants need. Have students examine the chart and identify the roles of each nutrient in the health of plants. Make sure students understand that these nutrients are not a source of energy or food, but are necessary for plants to carry out photosynthesis and other life processes. Point out that commercial fertilizers often are added to nutrient-deficient soil. Reinforce that commercial fertilizers are not food for the plant. A plant's food comes primarily from the high-energy sugars it produces by photosynthesis.

DIFFERENTIATED INSTRUCTION

L1 Struggling Students Show the association between plant nutrients and commercial fertilizers. Display different types of plant fertilizers, and ask students to locate the nutrients listed in the analysis that correspond to those listed in the table. Ask questions about the functions of these nutrients in plants, based on **Figure 23–7,** and have students respond orally.

MYSTERY CLUE Have students review the roles of plant nutrients in the table, and then brainstorm how and where water and nutrients might collect on a fig seedling or its host. Students can go online to **Biology.com** to gather their evidence.

UbD Check for Understanding

FOLLOW-UP PROBES

Ask Would you generally expect to observe chlorophyll in the parenchyma cells of a root? Explain. *(No, most roots do not carry out photosynthesis, and have no need for chlorophyll.)*

ADJUST INSTRUCTION

If students cannot answer the question correctly, have them review the functions of a root on this page and the information on parenchyma in leaves in Lesson 23.1. Then, ask student volunteers to name the functions of a root as you list them on the board.

Answers

FIGURE 23–7 The plant might be lacking nitrogen.

Teach continued

Use Visuals

Have students study **Figure 23–8** to learn how water and minerals move through the epidermis, through the cortex, and into the vascular cylinder. Point out that water moves through the cortex cell membranes on its way to the vascular cylinder. Some water also travels through the cell walls and spaces between cells. Make sure students understand that the Casparian strip in the endodermal walls prevents water and nutrients from entering the vascular cylinder without passing through any cell membranes.

Ask What stops dissolved minerals from moving back through the endodermis cells into the cortex? *(Active transport moves minerals just one way—into the vascular cylinder.)*

Ask What stops water from diffusing backward through endodermis cells? *(If water moved backward, it would have to move from an area of low water concentration to one of high water concentration.)*

DIFFERENTIATED INSTRUCTION

LPR Less Proficient Readers Provide students with a copy of this page. Have them highlight key phrases and sentences that explain the sequence of movement of nutrients into a root. Students should use their highlighted text and **Figure 23–8** to construct a **Flowchart** that describes in their own words the movement of nutrients through a root.

Study Wkbks A/B, Appendix S25, Flowchart. **Transparencies,** GO8.

BIOLOGY.com Students can watch water passing through roots and into vascular tissue in **Art in Motion: Water Passage Into a Root.**

Active Transport of Dissolved Nutrients The cell membranes of root hairs and other cells in the root epidermis contain active transport proteins. As you know, active transport is a process that uses the energy of ATP to move ions and other materials across membranes. Active transport brings the mineral ions of dissolved nutrients from the soil into the plant. The high concentration of mineral ions in the plant cells causes water molecules to move into the plant by osmosis.

BUILD Vocabulary

ACADEMIC WORDS The term **accumulate** means to increase gradually in quantity or number.

Water Movement by Osmosis You may recall that osmosis is the movement of water across a membrane toward an area where the concentration of dissolved material is higher. By using active transport to accumulate mineral ions from the soil, cells of the root epidermis create conditions under which osmosis causes water to "follow" those ions and flow into the root. Note that the root does not actually pump water. But by pumping mineral ions into its own cells, the end result is almost the same—the water moves from the epidermis through the cortex into the vascular cylinder, as shown in **Figure 23–8.**

Movement Into the Vascular Cylinder Next, the water and dissolved minerals pass the inner boundary of the cortex and move toward the vascular cylinder. The cylinder itself is enclosed by a layer of cortex cells known as the endodermis. The cells of the endodermis are each shaped a bit like a brick. Where these cells meet, their cell walls form a special waterproof zone called a **Casparian strip.** Most of the time, water can diffuse through cell walls, but not here. The strip is almost like a layer of waterproof cement between the bricks in a wall. Imagine many of these bricks placed edge to edge to build a cylinder, with this waterproof cement surrounding each of the bricks. The only way that water and dissolved nutrients could enter that cylinder would be through the bricks themselves.

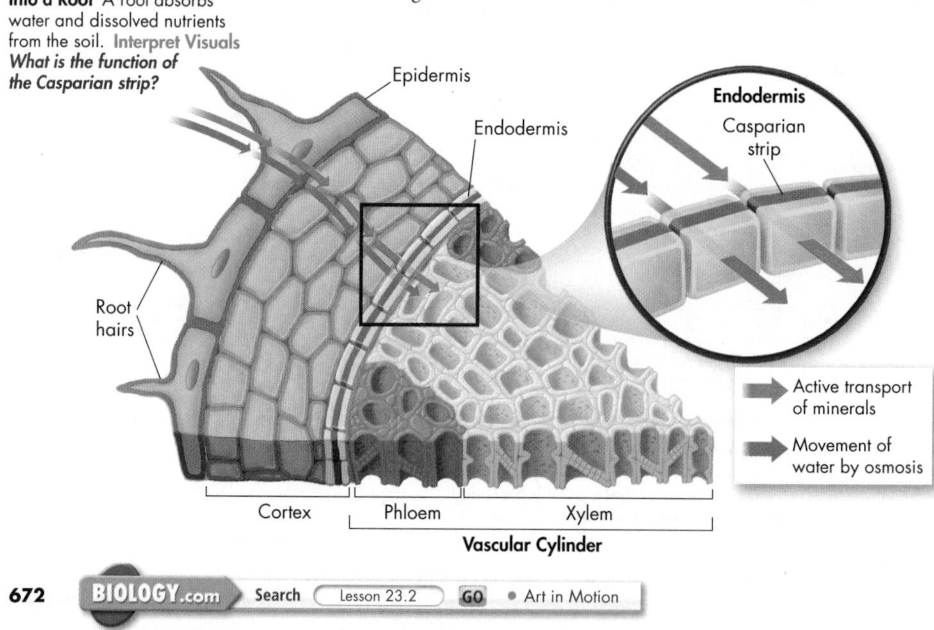

FIGURE 23–8 Water Passage Into a Root A root absorbs water and dissolved nutrients from the soil. **Interpret Visuals** *What is the function of the Casparian strip?*

Biology In-Depth

NUTRIENTS AND ACTIVE TRANSPORT

Active transport is required to move nutrients into roots because nutrient ions are present in soil water in lower concentrations than they are in epidermal cells. These ions would tend to move out of root hairs by diffusion if active transport did not actively move them inside. Active transport requires ATP and oxygen. Thus, roots need a constant supply of oxygen. Roots normally obtain oxygen from the air in soil spaces. If the soil spaces are filled with water, the roots of most land plants cannot obtain the oxygen they need. This is why overwatering houseplants can kill them. However, if the concentration of water in soil spaces is too low, water may move out of root hairs and back into the soil. This is called root burn.

Answers

FIGURE 23–8 The Casparian strip forces water and minerals to move through the cell membranes of endodermal cells.

The waxy Casparian strip forces water and minerals to move through the cell membranes of endodermis cells rather than in between the cells. This enables the endodermis to filter and control the water and dissolved nutrients that enter the vascular cylinder. More importantly, the Casparian strip ensures that valuable nutrients will not leak back out. As a result, there is a one-way passage of water and nutrients into the vascular cylinder.

Root Pressure Why do plants "need" a system that ensures the one-way movement of water and minerals? That system is how the plant generates enough pressure to move water out of the soil and up into the body of the plant. As minerals are pumped into the vascular cylinder, more and more water follows by osmosis, producing a strong pressure. If the pressure were not contained, roots would expand as they filled with water.

Instead, contained within the Casparian strip, the water has just one place to go—up. Root pressure, produced within the cylinder by active transport, forces water through the vascular cylinder and into the xylem. As more water moves from the cortex into the vascular cylinder, more water in the xylem is forced upward through the root into the stem. In **Figure 23–9,** you can see a demonstration of root pressure in a carrot root.

Root pressure is the starting point for the movement of water through the vascular system of the entire plant. But it is just the beginning. Once you have learned about stems and leaves, you will see how water and other materials are transported within an entire plant.

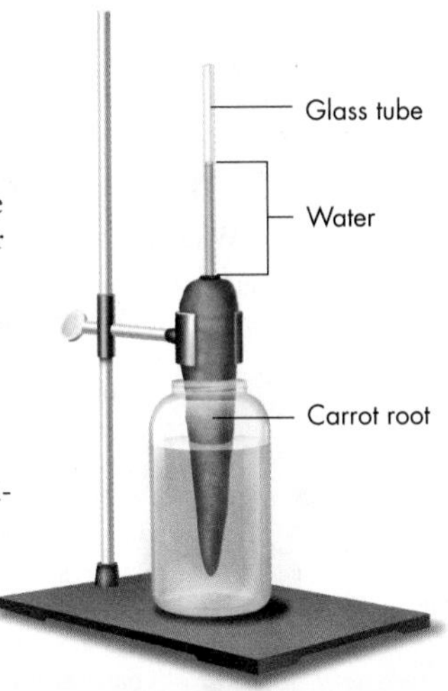

FIGURE 23–9 Root Pressure Demonstration In this setup, a glass tube takes the place of the carrot plant's stem and leaves. As the root absorbs water, root pressure forces water upward into the tube.

23.2 Assessment

Review Key Concepts

1. a. **Review** How are tissues distributed in a plant root?
   b. **Compare and Contrast** How is the structure of cells in a root's transport system different from the structure of cells making up the epidermis?
2. a. **Review** Describe the main functions of roots.
   b. **Explain** How is osmosis involved in the absorption of water and nutrients?
   c. **Apply Concepts** Why is it important that the root endodermis permits only a one-way passage of materials?

VISUAL THINKING

3. Draw a diagram to show how roots absorb water and nutrients. Label the diagram and write brief descriptions of the processes shown.

BIOLOGY.com Search Lesson 23.2 GO • Lesson Assessment • Self-Test

LESSON 23.2

Assess and Remediate

EVALUATE UNDERSTANDING

Make up word cards that include all vocabulary terms from the lesson and some of the Key Concepts. Then, play a game in which students must draw on the board or overhead projector a picture of the word they have on a card for other students to guess. While drawing, students may not speak or use body language to give clues. Then, have them complete the 23.2 Assessment.

REMEDIATION SUGGESTION

L1 **Struggling Students** If your students have trouble with **Question 2b,** have them review the information under the heading, **Water Movement by Osmosis.** Ask students to rewrite the information in the form of cause-and-effect statements. Suggest they construct a **Cause-and-Effect Diagram.**

Study Wkbks A/B, Appendix S18, Cause-and-Effect Diagram. **Transparencies,** GO1.

BIOLOGY.com Students can check their understanding of lesson concepts with the **Self-Test** assessment. They can then take an online version of the **Lesson Assessment.**

Assessment Answers

1a. Roots have an outside layer of epidermal cells and a central cylinder of vascular tissue; between these lies ground tissue.

1b. The root's transport system (vascular cylinder) cells contain a Casparian strip, which allows the one-way absorption of water and nutrients into the transport system. The root's epidermal cells do not have this structure.

2a. The main functions of roots are to support a plant, anchor it in the ground, store food, and absorb water and dissolved nutrients from the soil.

2b. Active transport through the root epidermis results in a high concentration of mineral ions in the root cells, which causes water molecules to move into the root by osmosis.

2c. A one-way passage is necessary to make sure water and nutrients do not leak back out.

VISUAL THINKING

3. Students' drawings should include labels from **Figure 23–8.** Descriptions should include the processes of active transport and osmosis.

LESSON 23.3

Getting Started

Objectives

23.3.1 Describe the main functions of stems.

23.3.2 Contrast the processes of primary growth and secondary growth in stems.

Student Resources

Study Workbooks A and B, 23.3 Worksheets

Spanish Study Workbook, 23.3 Worksheets

Lab Manual B, 23.3 Data Analysis Worksheet

Lesson Overview • Lesson Notes
- Activities: InterActive Art, Tutor Tube
- Assessment: Self-Test, Lesson Assessment

For corresponding lesson in the **Foundation Edition**, see pages 560–563.

Activate Prior Knowledge

Show students various stems, such as woody tree branches and various weed or garden plant stems that are easily obtainable. Include some more unusual stems, such as potatoes and daffodil bulbs. Ask students to identify which ones are stems. *(all)* Have a student volunteer recall the functions of stems. *(Stems provide a support system for the plant body, a transport system that carries nutrients, and a defensive system that protects the plant against predators and disease.)*

IN INDIANA ACADEMIC STANDARDS

For the full text of all standards, see the Course Overview in the front matter of this book.

NoS.3 Clearly communicate their ideas and results of investigations verbally and in written form using tables, graphs, diagrams, and photographs.

23.3 Stems

IN NoS.3 Communicate ideas.

Key Questions

What are three main functions of stems?

How do primary growth and secondary growth occur in stems?

Vocabulary

node • bud • vascular bundle • pith • primary growth • secondary growth • vascular cambium • cork cambium • heartwood • sapwood • bark

Taking Notes

Preview Visuals Before you read, preview the art in **Figure 23–14.** Define any familiar terms in your own words, and list any unfamiliar ones. Revise and add to your definitions as you read.

THINK ABOUT IT While visiting the salad bar for lunch, you notice an intriguing range of offerings. After making your basic salad, you decide to add some sliced water chestnuts and bamboo shoots on top. Then you serve yourself some asparagus and potato salad on the side. These good things are all from plants, of course, but can you think of something else that ties them together? They all come from the same part of the plant. Do you have any idea which part?

Stem Structure and Function

What are three main functions of stems?

What do water chestnuts, bamboo shoots, asparagus, and potatoes all have in common? They are all types of stems. Stems vary in size, shape, and method of development. Some grow entirely underground; others reach high into the air. **Aboveground stems have several important functions: Stems produce leaves, branches, and flowers; stems hold leaves up to the sun; and stems transport substances throughout the plant.**

Stems make up an essential part of the water and mineral transport systems of the plant. Xylem and phloem form continuous tubes from the roots through the stems to the leaves. These vascular tissues link all parts of the plant, allowing water, nutrients, and other compounds to be carried throughout the plant. In many plants, stems also function in storage and aid in the process of photosynthesis.

FIGURE 23–10 Cactus Stems Desert cacti have thick green stems that carry out photosynthesis and are adapted to store water.

 BIOLOGY.com Search Lesson 23.3 GO • Lesson Overview • Lesson Notes • Tutor Tube

UbD Teach for Understanding

ENDURING UNDERSTANDING From microorganisms to plants, organisms vary widely in the way they carry out basic life processes.

GUIDING QUESTION How do the structure and function of stems help a plant carry out life processes?

EVIDENCE OF UNDERSTANDING *After students have finished the lesson, this assessment should show their understanding of the structure and function of a stem.* Have students work in small groups to prepare a short story with simple illustrations for an elementary audience that tells about the functions of a stem and the structures that help carry out those functions. Students should incorporate appropriate vocabulary terms and make the story easy to understand, such as by comparing the tubes in a plant to drinking straws.

Anatomy of a Stem Stems contain the plant's three tissue systems: dermal, vascular, and ground tissue. Stems are surrounded by a layer of epidermal cells that have thick cell walls and a waxy protective coating. Growing stems contain distinct **nodes,** where leaves are attached, as shown in **Figure 23–11.** Small buds are found where leaves attach to the nodes. **Buds** contain apical meristems that can produce new stems and leaves. In larger plants, stems develop woody tissue that helps support leaves and flowers.

FIGURE 23–11 Anatomy of a Stem Stems produce leaves from their nodes and new branches from buds. They hold leaves up to the sunlight, where they carry out photosynthesis.

Vascular Bundle Patterns The arrangement of tissues in a stem differs among seed plants. In monocots, clusters of xylem and phloem tissue, called **vascular bundles,** are scattered throughout the stem. In most dicots and gymnosperms, vascular bundles are arranged in a cylinder, or ring. For a comparison of monocot and dicot stems, look at **Figure 23–12.**

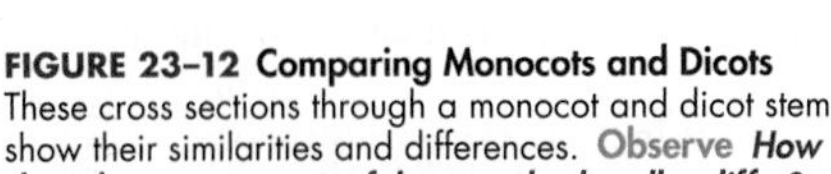

FIGURE 23–12 Comparing Monocots and Dicots These cross sections through a monocot and dicot stem show their similarities and differences. **Observe** ***How does the arrangement of the vascular bundles differ?***

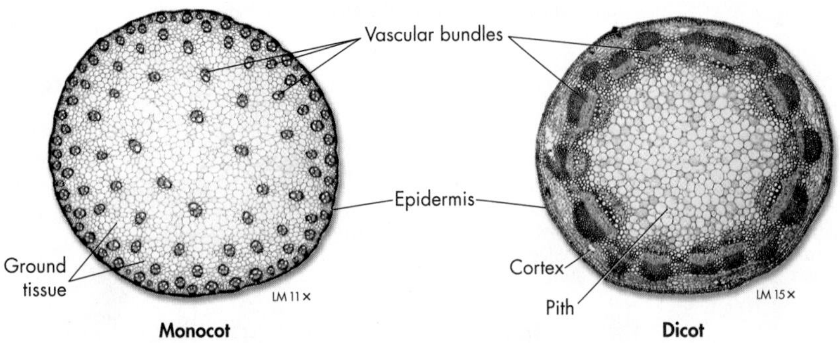

▶ ***Monocot Stems*** The cross section of a young monocot stem shows all three tissue systems clearly. The stem has a distinct epidermis, which encloses ground tissue and a series of vascular bundles. In monocots, vascular bundles are scattered throughout the ground tissue. The ground tissue is fairly uniform, consisting mainly of parenchyma cells.

▶ ***Dicot Stems*** Young dicot stems have vascular bundles, too, but they are generally arranged in an organized, ringlike pattern. The parenchyma cells inside the ring of vascular tissue are known as **pith,** while those outside form the cortex of the stem. These relatively simple tissue patterns become more complex as the plant grows larger and the stem increases in diameter.

In Your Notebook *Create a Venn diagram in which to record similarities and differences in the stem structure of monocots and dicots.*

Quick Facts

STEMS THAT STORE FOOD

Many kinds of plants have modified stems that store food. The stems remain dormant during cold or dry periods until favorable conditions for growth return. Tubers, such as potatoes, are stems that usually grow underground. The stem of the ginger plant is a rhizome, which is a horizontal, underground stem. A bulb, such as an amaryllis bulb, is made up of a central stem surrounded by short, thick leaves. The leaves wrap around and protect the stem and also store food. A corm forms in plants such as gladiolus and crocus. A corm looks similar to a bulb, but is a thickened stem that stores food. It has an outer covering that consists of layers of papery leaves.

Teach

Use Visuals

Use the stem cross sections in **Figure 23–12** to compare and contrast stem structure in monocots and dicots. Discuss characteristics of the stem structures that are different and similar. Make sure students can correctly identify all the tissues in the stem.

DIFFERENTIATED INSTRUCTION

L1 Struggling Students If students cannot visualize what the circles of the cross sections in the figure represent, cut a flower stem in two crosswise. Pass the pieces around, and have students view the ends so they can relate the circular shape of the cross section in their hands to the micrographs shown in **Figure 23–12.** Then, have students review the functions of the three tissue systems and draw and label their own cross sections of a monocot and a dicot.

ELL Focus on ELL: Access Content

ADVANCED HIGH SPEAKERS Have English learners complete a **QAR** using the text under **Vascular Bundle Patterns.** Through QAR, students learn how to answer questions by recognizing different question types. Start with questions whose answers can be found "In the Book." Ask students a "Right There" question, such as "What tissues are found in a stem?" Then, ask "Think and Search" questions, for example, "How is a monocot stem similar to a dicot stem? How is it different?" Next, move to a question whose answer can be found "In My Head." Ask an "Author and Me" question, such as "What is the main point the author is trying to make with the text and photographs?" Finally, ask an "On My Own" question, such as "What analogy can you use to describe the vascular bundle pattern seen in monocots and dicots?" *(Sample answer for monocots: blueberry muffin or a starry sky; for dicots: beaded necklace, football huddle)*

Study Wkbks A/B, Appendix S10, QAR.

Answers

FIGURE 23–12 In a monocot, vascular bundles are scattered throughout the stem. In a dicot, vascular bundles are arranged in a ring.

IN YOUR NOTEBOOK Venn diagrams should show the following characteristics: for both monocot and dicots: epidermis; for monocots only: vascular bundles scattered, ground tissue uniform; for dicots only: vascular bundles in ring, ground tissue divided into pith and cortex.

Teach continued

VISUAL SUMMARY

As students study the text, use **Figure 23–13** to reinforce how stems grow. Make sure they know the close-up illustrations represent a cross section of the stem.

Ask Where does the vascular cambium appear when secondary growth begins? *(between the xylem and phloem of the vascular bundles)*

Ask What causes the stem to become thicker? *(Divisions of vascular cambium give rise to new layers of xylem and phloem, thickening the stem.)*

Ask Where do new phloem and xylem cells form? *(Phloem cells form toward the outside of the stem. Xylem cells form toward the center of the stem.)*

DIFFERENTIATED INSTRUCTION

L1 Struggling Students Make sure students understand that the close-up cross sections are progressively larger from year to year to indicate the growing thickness of the plant. Students may have difficulty understanding that a tree does not grow only at the outer layer. Point out the layers of secondary phloem and secondary xylem in the close-up of Year 2, and ask students to describe how they have changed by Year 3.

ELL English Language Learners Refer students to **Figure 23–13,** and point out the parts of the stem as you read the labels. Distribute copies of the figure with the labels and caption blanked out. Have students work together to fill in the labels and captions, using their books.

L3 Advanced Students Challenge students to design an experiment to determine whether two different tree species have the same rate of primary growth. Students should decide how they will measure primary growth and what plants they will study after doing some research on appropriate species. They should write a complete procedure and estimate the time it will take to complete the study. They should describe all variables that need to be controlled (light, temperature, water level, soil type, etc.).

MYSTERY CLUE Discuss with students how they think the fig, in wrapping itself around the host, might affect the secondary growth of the host. Refer students to the visuals on this page for clues. Students can go online to Biology.com to gather their evidence.

Answers

FIGURE 23–13 xylem and phloem

MYSTERY CLUE

As the fig grows, its aboveground roots grow in both length and thickness, and they completely wrap themselves around the host's trunk. How might this affect the host?

Growth of Stems

How do primary growth and secondary growth occur in stems?

Plants grow in ways that are very different from how animals grow. Cows have four legs, ants have six, and spiders have eight, but roses and tomatoes don't have a set number of leaves or branches. Unlike animals, the growth of most plants isn't precisely determined. However, plant growth is still carefully controlled and regulated. Depending upon the species, plant growth follows general patterns that produce the characteristic size and shape of the adult plant.

Primary Growth The growth of new cells produced by the apical meristems of roots and stems adds length to the plant. This pattern of growth, occurring at the ends of a plant, is called **primary growth.** The increase in length in a plant due to primary growth from year to year is shown in **Figure 23–13.** **Primary growth of stems is the result of elongation of cells produced in the apical meristem. It takes place in all seed plants.**

Secondary Growth As a plant grows larger, the older stems and roots have more mass to support and more fluid to move through their vascular tissues. As a result, they must increase in thickness as well as in length. This increase in the thickness of stems and roots is known as **secondary growth.** Secondary growth is very common among dicots and nonflowering seed plants such as pines, but it is rare in monocots. This limits the girth of most monocots.

VISUAL SUMMARY

PRIMARY AND SECONDARY GROWTH

FIGURE 23–13 New cells produced by the apical meristem cause stems to grow in length (primary growth). Meanwhile, the vascular cambium increases the stem's width (secondary growth). **Interpret Diagrams** ***What kinds of tissues are formed by the vascular cambium?***

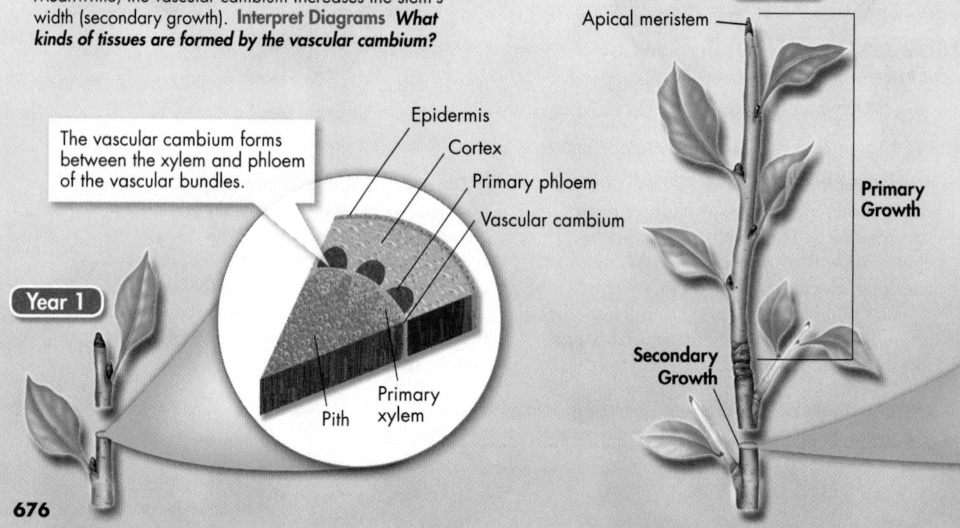

676

UbD Check for Understanding

DEPTH OF UNDERSTANDING

Ask Where do the materials for new tissue come from when a stem grows?

- A student who does not relate photosynthesis to growth might suggest the materials are water and other nutrients, which come from the soil.
- A student who understands the process of photosynthesis would respond that plants use the energy from light to make carbohydrates using carbon dioxide from the air and water from the roots.

ADJUST INSTRUCTION

Point out that just as we use carbohydrates for growth, so do plants. Write the chemical equation for photosynthesis on the board, and review the sources of carbon dioxide and water. Review that in this process, molecules are rearranged to form carbohydrates.

Unlike monocots, most dicots have meristems within their stems and roots that can produce true secondary growth. This enables many dicots to grow to great heights because the increase in width supports the extra weight. In addition to showing primary growth, **Figure 23–13** illustrates the pattern of secondary growth in a dicot stem.

In conifers and dicots, secondary growth takes place in meristems called the vascular cambium and cork cambium. The **vascular cambium** produces vascular tissues and increases the thickness of stems over time. The **cork cambium** produces the outer covering of stems. Similar types of cambium tissue enable roots to grow. The addition of new tissue in these cambium layers increases the thickness of stems and roots.

Growth From the Vascular Cambium In a young dicot stem, bundles of xylem and phloem are arranged in a ring. Once secondary growth begins, the vascular cambium appears as a thin, cylindrical layer of cells between clusters of vascular tissue. This new meristem forms between the xylem and phloem of each vascular bundle. Divisions in the vascular cambium give rise to new layers of xylem and phloem. As a result, the stem becomes wider. Each year, the cambium continues to produce new layers of vascular tissue, causing the stem to become thicker and thicker.

In Your Notebook *List in sequence all the tissues found in a mature woody stem. Start from the center and move outward.*

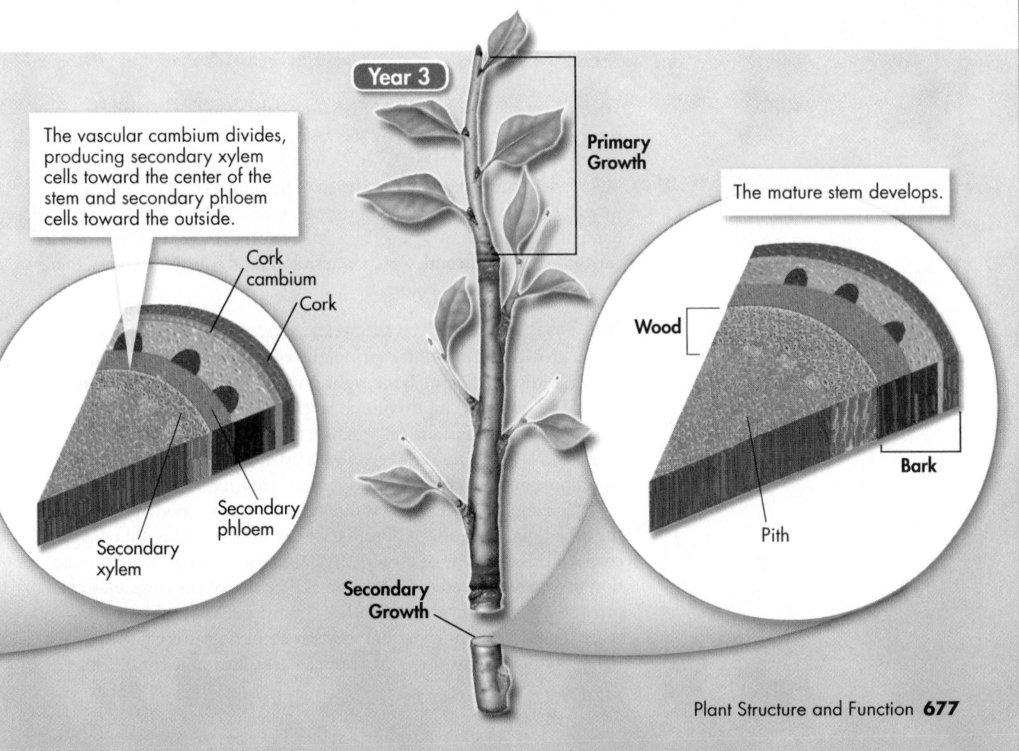
Year 3
The vascular cambium divides, producing secondary xylem cells toward the center of the stem and secondary phloem cells toward the outside.
Cork cambium
Cork
Secondary phloem
Secondary xylem
Primary Growth
Secondary Growth
The mature stem develops.
Wood
Bark
Pith

Lead a Discussion

Talk about the process of secondary growth in a dicot stem. Review the structure of the monocot stem and the dicot stem. Challenge students to infer why secondary growth does not commonly occur in monocots.

Ask How does the structure of the monocot stem differ from that of the dicot stem? *(In a monocot stem, the vascular bundles are scattered throughout. In dicots, they are arranged in a ring.)*

Ask Could secondary growth occur in a monocot stem? *(No, there is no specific location for the lateral meristematic tissue to form.)*

Ask Is secondary growth necessary in monocots? *(No, monocots are generally shorter plants and do not require the extra support of a wider stem.)*

DIFFERENTIATED INSTRUCTION

LPR Less Proficient Readers Write the following questions on the board. Ask students to ask themselves these questions and answer them as they read:

- What is the main idea?
- What new information did I learn?
- Where in the text can I find information related to the Visual Summary?

BIOLOGY.com Suggest students use **InterActive Art: Primary and Secondary Growth** to see how plants grow. For more help, students can watch **Tutor Tube: Understanding Plant Growth** to uncover misconceptions about how and where plant growth occurs.

Quick Facts

TREE WORLD RECORDS

The largest tree in the world is the General Sherman, a giant sequoia in California's Sequoia National Park. "Largest" means the volume of the trunk, which measures 31.1 m in circumference at the base and extends 83.8 m above the ground. The wood in the trunk would fill a room 30 by 20 m and 2.4 m high. Scientists estimate that the tree is about 2150 years old, but age isn't the reason sequoias are so large—they grow quickly. Sequoias live longer and grow faster than any other conifer. The tallest tree in the world is a redwood, a distant cousin to the giant sequoia, called Hyperion. Standing at 115.6 m in California's Redwood National Park, this tree is taller than the Statue of Liberty!

Answers

IN YOUR NOTEBOOK Students should write in order: pith, primary xylem, secondary xylem, vascular cambium, secondary phloem, primary phloem, cortex, cork cambium, and cork.

LESSON 23.3

Teach continued

Lead a Discussion

Have students read about the formation of wood, tree rings, and the formation of bark. Then, suggest they study the layers of wood and bark in **Figure 23–14.**

Ask Where is new growth of vascular tissues occurring? *(in the vascular cambium)*

Ask Where is new growth of dermal tissues occurring? *(in the cork cambium)*

Ask Which layer of xylem is the newest? *(the layer that is farthest away from the center)*

Ask How are the functions of sapwood and heartwood similar and different? *(Both help support the tree. Only sapwood transports water and nutrients.)*

DIFFERENTIATED INSTRUCTION

L1 Special Needs Have students work in pairs to roll up several sheets of newsprint and place them inside an empty paper-toweling roll. Tell students this represents the heartwood of a mature tree. Next, have students label five additional sheets of paper "sapwood," "vascular cambium," "phloem," "cork cambium," and "cork." Direct them to wrap these sheets around their model in the correct order. Finally, have partners take turns unwrapping the model, naming and explaining the function of each layer.

L3 Advanced Students Explain to students that when European settlers were struggling to clear heavily wooded land in North America for farming, they often "girdled" large trees by removing a strip of bark all the way around the base of the tree. Ask students to form a hypothesis to explain why the practice of girdling would cause a tree to die. *(Sample answer: Girdling removes the phloem from the entire circumference of the tree, preventing the tree from transporting sugars from the leaves to the roots. Without these sugars, active transport cannot occur, and the roots will not take up nutrients and water, causing the tree to die.)*

Analyzing Data

IN NoS.3

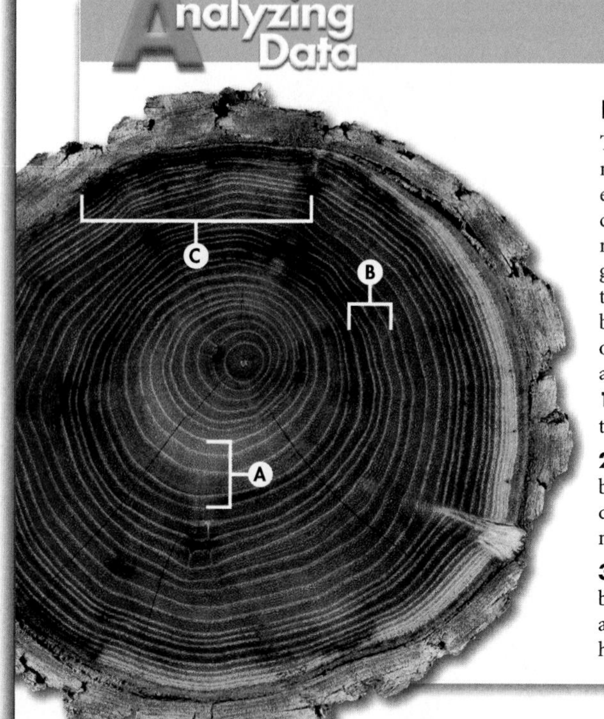

Reading a Tree's History

The analysis of tree rings can help determine information about a tree and the environment in which it grew. A tree's age can be measured by counting its growth rings—each ring is produced by a year of growth. The specific environmental conditions for each year of growth can be inferred by examining the relative width and color of each ring. Use the photograph at left to answer the questions.

1. Calculate Approximately how old was this tree when it was cut down? MATH

2. Infer Areas A and B were both produced by four years of growth, yet they are different widths. What climatic conditions might account for this difference?

3. Interpret Visuals The area at C is blackened from a fire that apparently affected only one side of the tree. Describe how the tree grew after this fire.

Formation of Wood Most of what we call "wood" is actually layers of secondary xylem produced by the vascular cambium. These cells build up year after year, layer on layer. As woody stems grow thicker, the older xylem near the center of the stem no longer conducts water and instead becomes what is known as **heartwood.** Heartwood usually darkens with age because it accumulates colored deposits. Heartwood is surrounded by **sapwood,** which is active in fluid transport and is, therefore, usually lighter in color.

Tree Rings In most of the temperate zone, tree growth is seasonal. When growth begins in the spring, the vascular cambium begins to grow rapidly, producing large, light-colored xylem cells with thin cell walls. The result is a light-colored layer of early wood. As the growing season continues, the cells grow less and have thicker cell walls, forming a layer of darker late wood. This alternation of dark and light wood produces what we commonly call tree rings.

Each ring has light wood at one edge and dark wood at the other, making a sharp boundary between rings. Usually, a ring corresponds to a year of growth. By counting the rings in a cross section of a tree, you can estimate its age. The size of the rings may even provide information about weather conditions, such as wet or dry years. Thick rings indicate that weather conditions were favorable for tree growth, whereas thin rings indicate less-favorable conditions.

PURPOSE Students will examine and interpret data to identify a tree's age and the environmental conditions for each year of growth.

PLANNING Students should read the text on this page before doing the activity. Remind students that a ring usually corresponds to a year of growth and that the size of the rings provides information about weather conditions. Thick growth rings indicate the growing season had adequate moisture. Narrow growth rings form during dry years.

ANSWERS

1. about 25 years old

2. Rainfall and temperature; the years that Area A grew had adequate rainfall and temperatures that were better suited for optimal growth.

3. The tree laid down more new wood on the side away from the fire than on the side of the fire.

FIGURE 23–14 Formation of Wood and Bark This diagram shows the layers of wood and bark in a mature tree that has undergone several years of secondary growth. **Classify** ***Which two tissues are meristems?***

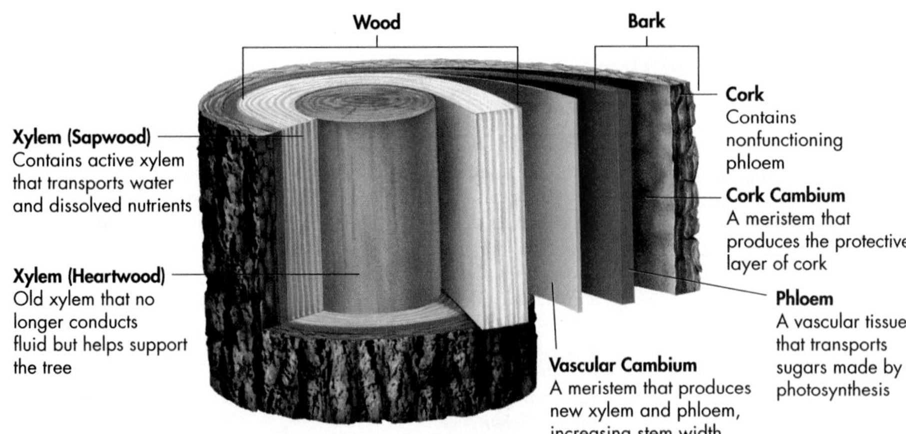
Wood
Bark
Xylem (Sapwood)
Contains active xylem that transports water and dissolved nutrients
Xylem (Heartwood)
Old xylem that no longer conducts fluid but helps support the tree
Vascular Cambium
A meristem that produces new xylem and phloem, increasing stem width
Cork
Contains nonfunctioning phloem
Cork Cambium
A meristem that produces the protective layer of cork
Phloem
A vascular tissue that transports sugars made by photosynthesis

Formation of Bark In a mature stem, all of the tissues found outside the vascular cambium make up the **bark,** as shown in **Figure 23–14.** These tissues include phloem, the cork cambium, and cork. As a tree expands in width, the phloem layer must grow as well. This expansion may cause the oldest tissues to split and fragment as the expanding stem stretches them. The cork cambium surrounds the cortex and produces a thick, protective layer of waterproof cork that prevents the loss of water from the stem. As the stem increases in size, outer layers of dead bark often crack and flake off the tree.

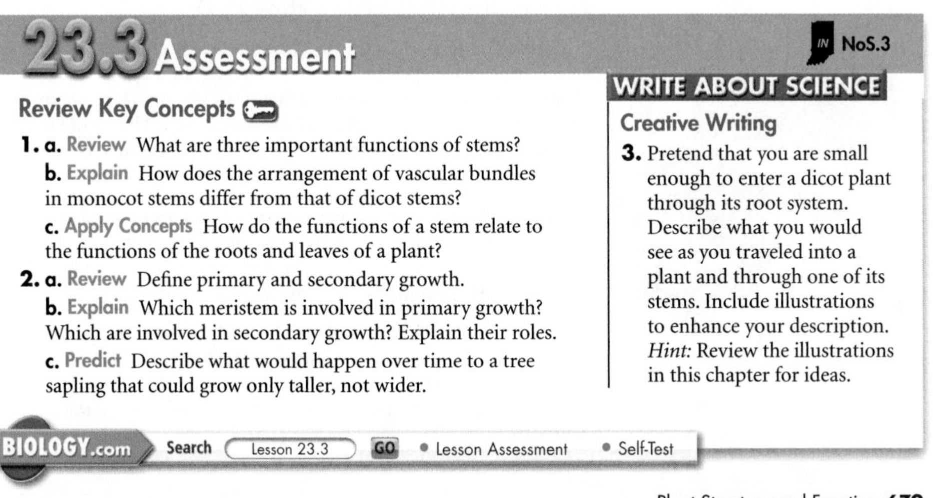

23.3 Assessment

NoS.3

Review Key Concepts

1. a. Review What are three important functions of stems?

b. Explain How does the arrangement of vascular bundles in monocot stems differ from that of dicot stems?

c. Apply Concepts How do the functions of a stem relate to the functions of the roots and leaves of a plant?

2. a. Review Define primary and secondary growth.

b. Explain Which meristem is involved in primary growth? Which are involved in secondary growth? Explain their roles.

c. Predict Describe what would happen over time to a tree sapling that could grow only taller, not wider.

WRITE ABOUT SCIENCE

Creative Writing

3. Pretend that you are small enough to enter a dicot plant through its root system. Describe what you would see as you traveled into a plant and through one of its stems. Include illustrations to enhance your description. *Hint:* Review the illustrations in this chapter for ideas.

BIOLOGY.com Search Lesson 23.3 GO • Lesson Assessment • Self-Test

Assess and Remediate

EVALUATE UNDERSTANDING

Have students write three review questions for the lesson. Invite them to take turns asking one question of the class. Continue until everyone has had a turn or until all unique questions have been answered. Then, have students complete the 23.3 Assessment.

REMEDIATION SUGGESTION

L1 Struggling Students If your students have trouble with **Question 2c,** tell them to visualize a scrap metal junkyard in which cars are being piled on top of one another to make a tall stack. Ask them what will eventually happen to the cars on the bottom. Then, have them read the first paragraph under **Secondary Growth** and relate the stacked car analogy to the growth of stems.

BIOLOGY.com Students can check their understanding of lesson concepts with the **Self-Test** assessment. They can then take the online version of the **Lesson Assessment.**

Answers

FIGURE 23–14 vascular cambium and cork cambium

Assessment Answers

1a. to produce leaves, branches, and flowers; hold leaves up to the sun; transport substances throughout the plant

1b. monocots: vascular bundles scattered throughout stem; dicots: vascular bundles arranged in a cylinder, or ring

1c. Stems enable leaves to carry out photosynthesis by transporting water from the roots to leaves and by holding the leaves up to the sunlight. Stems carry sugars from the leaves to the roots so that root cells can carry out the active (energy-requiring) process of absorbing nutrients.

2a. Primary growth occurs at the ends of plants, adding length. Secondary growth increases a plant stem's thickness.

2b. The apical meristems of roots and shoots are involved in primary growth. They add new cells to the ends. The vascular cambium and the cork cambium are involved in secondary growth. They add new cells within a stem, increasing its width.

2c. It would collapse before it grew very tall, because the stem has to grow in thickness to support its mass.

WRITE ABOUT SCIENCE

3. Students' descriptions and illustrations should trace the path of water and nutrients into a plant's roots from the soil and up into the stem. Students should include the process of absorbing materials from the soil and transporting them up through the plant's stem.

LESSON 23.4

Getting Started

Objectives

23.4.1 Describe how the structure of a leaf enables it to carry out photosynthesis.

23.4.2 Explain how gas exchange in leaves relates to homeostasis.

Student Resources

Study Workbooks A and B, 23.4 Worksheets

Spanish Study Workbook, 23.4 Worksheets

Lesson Overview • Lesson Notes
- Activities: Art Review, Data Analysis
- Assessment: Self-Test, Lesson Assessment

For corresponding lesson in the **Foundation Edition**, see pages 564–566.

Activate Prior Knowledge

Write the following words on the board: *epidermis, xylem, phloem, parenchyma, chloroplast,* and *photosynthesis.* Give student pairs a few minutes to write a question that each word answers. The question should relate to leaves, and students cannot use their text. Then, say each word aloud and call on students to provide a question that the word answers.

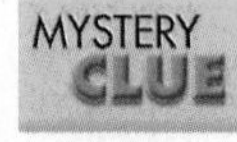
Have students predict how the lack of sunlight will affect photosynthesis in the host. Students can go online to **Biology.com** to gather their evidence.

IN INDIANA ACADEMIC STANDARDS

For the full text of all standards, see the Course Overview in the front matter of this book.

B.2.6 Investigate a variety of different cell types and relate the proportion of different organelles within these cells to their functions.

23.4 Leaves

B.2.6 Variation in cell structure and function.

Key Questions

How is the structure of a leaf adapted to make photosynthesis more efficient?

What role do stomata play in maintaining homeostasis?

Vocabulary

blade • petiole • mesophyll • palisade mesophyll • spongy mesophyll • stoma • transpiration • guard cell

Taking Notes

Preview Visuals Before you read the lesson, look at **Figure 23–15.** Locate the three main tissue systems and infer which tissue system makes up the leaf veins.

MYSTERY CLUE

The mature fig's stems and leaves block sunlight from the host. How might this affect photosynthesis in the host?

THINK ABOUT IT We hear a lot these days about "green industry," such as biofuels and material recycling, but did you know that the most important manufacturing sites on Earth are already green? They are the leaves of plants. In a sense, plant leaves are the world's most important manufacturers. Using the energy captured in their leaves, plants make the sugars, starches, and oils that feed virtually all land animals, including us.

Leaf Structure and Function

How is the structure of a leaf adapted to make photosynthesis more efficient?

Recall from Chapter 8 that photosynthesis uses carbon dioxide and water to produce sugars and oxygen. Leaves, therefore, must have a way of obtaining carbon dioxide and water as well as distributing end products. **The structure of a leaf is optimized to absorb light and carry out photosynthesis.**

Anatomy of a Leaf To collect sunlight, most leaves have a thin, flattened part called a **blade.** The flat shape of a leaf blade maximizes the amount of light it can absorb. The blade is attached to the stem by a thin stalk called a **petiole** (PET ee ohl). Like roots and stems, leaves have an outer covering of dermal tissue and inner regions of ground and vascular tissues, as shown in **Figure 23–15.**

▶ ***Dermal Tissue*** Leaves are covered on their top and bottom surfaces by epidermis. Leaf epidermis is made of a layer of tough, irregularly shaped cells with thick outer walls that resist tearing. The epidermis of nearly all leaves is also covered by a waxy cuticle. The cuticle is a waterproof barrier that protects tissues and limits the loss of water through evaporation.

▶ ***Vascular Tissue*** The vascular tissues of leaves are connected directly to the vascular tissues of stems, making them part of the plant's fluid transport system. Xylem and phloem tissues are bundled in leaf veins that run from the stem throughout the leaf.

▶ ***Ground Tissue*** The area between leaf veins is filled with a specialized ground tissue known as **mesophyll** (MES uh fil), where photosynthesis occurs. The sugars produced in mesophyll move to leaf veins, where they enter phloem sieve tubes for transport to the rest of the plant.

Search Lesson 23.4

• Lesson Overview • Lesson Notes

UbD Teach for Understanding

ENDURING UNDERSTANDING From microorganisms to plants, organisms vary widely in the way they carry out basic life processes.

GUIDING QUESTION How do the structure and function of leaves help a plant carry out life processes?

EVIDENCE OF UNDERSTANDING *After students finish the lesson, this assessment should show their understanding of how leaf structures help a plant carry out photosynthesis.* Have students work in small groups to list the ways the structures of a leaf are adapted to make photosynthesis more efficient. Then, ask groups to create a "reverse" list that describes how each structure and characteristic could be modified to slow down or stop photosynthesis, for example, "Make the cuticle permeable, causing excessive loss of water." Have groups read their lists to the class, and call on volunteers to give the correct instruction to facilitate photosynthesis.

ZOOMING IN

ANATOMY OF A LEAF

FIGURE 23–15 Leaves absorb light and carry out most of the photosynthesis in a plant. **Compare and Contrast** ***Compare the structure of the two types of mesophyll cells in a leaf.***

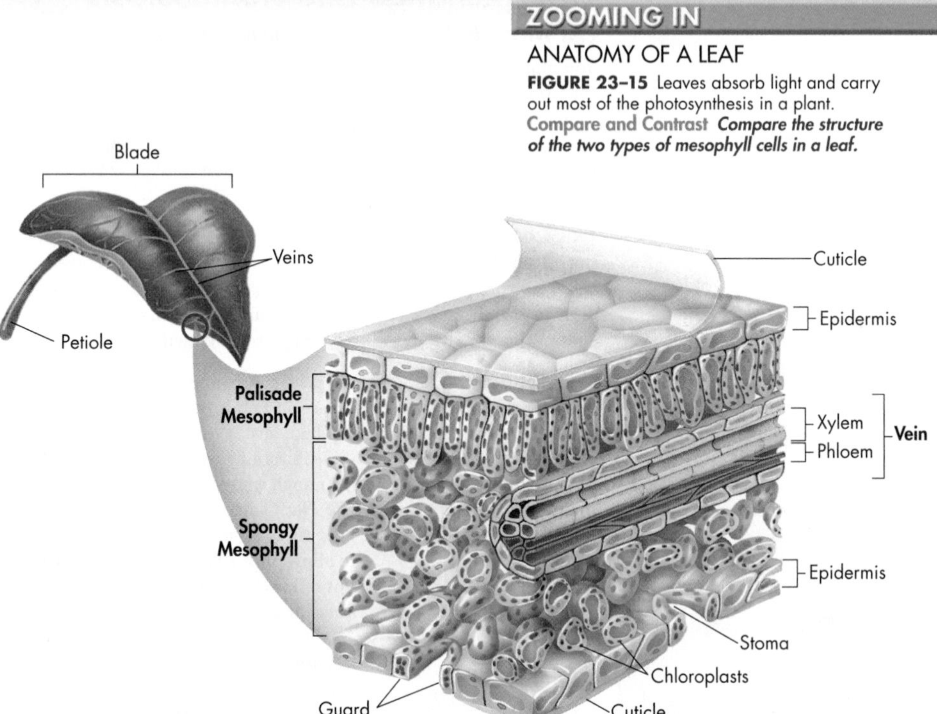

Photosynthesis The mesophyll tissue in most leaves is highly specialized for photosynthesis. Beneath the upper epidermis is a layer of cells called the **palisade mesophyll,** containing closely packed cells that absorb light that enters the leaf. Beneath the palisade layer is a loose tissue called the **spongy mesophyll,** which has many air spaces between its cells. These air spaces connect with the exterior through **stomata** (singular: stoma). Stomata are small openings in the epidermis that allow carbon dioxide, water, and oxygen to diffuse into and out of the leaf.

Transpiration The walls of mesophyll cells are kept moist so that gases can enter and leave the cells easily. The trade-off to this feature is that water evaporates from these surfaces and is lost to the atmosphere. **Transpiration** is the loss of water through leaves. This lost water may be replaced by water drawn into the leaf through xylem vessels in the vascular tissue. Transpiration helps to cool leaves on hot days, but it may also threaten the leaf's survival if water is scarce.

BUILD Vocabulary

WORD ORIGINS **Mesophyll** comes from two Greek words: *meso,* meaning "middle," and *phyllon,* meaning "leaf." **Stomata** comes from the Greek word meaning "mouths."

In Your Notebook *Make a two-column table in which you list structures found in a leaf cross section and describe their functions.*

BIOLOGY.com Search Lesson 23.4 GO • Art Review

ZOOMING IN

Review the structure of a leaf as diagrammed in **Figure 23–15.** Discuss the function of each labeled leaf structure. For each part, have students describe how it helps the leaf carry out photosynthesis.

Ask How does the cuticle make photosynthesis more efficient? *(It is transparent to allow light to easily pass into the leaf and it is a waterproof barrier that limits the loss of water through evaporation.)*

Ask How do air spaces in the spongy mesophyll make photosynthesis more efficient? *(The air spaces allow gases to move freely throughout the leaf.)*

DIFFERENTIATED INSTRUCTION

LPR Less Proficient Readers Help students make connections between the names of the parts of a leaf and everyday objects. For example, show a picture of a palisade fence, which is tall. Show a sponge and point out that the sponge has air spaces.

ELL Focus on ELL: Extend Language

BEGINNING AND INTERMEDIATE SPEAKERS Begin a **Word Wall** by posting lesson vocabulary terms. As you teach the lesson, add other important words, such as the labels in **Figure 23–15.** Refer to the Word Wall often, and use the words to teach concepts. For example, make a transparency of **Figure 23–15** with the labels blanked out and have students use the Word Wall to name the structures and to say a word or phrase that describes their function. For example, they might say, "cuticle protects." Intermediate speakers can use a complex phrase or simple sentence that describes the functions.

Study Wkbks A/B, Appendix S17, Word Wall.

BIOLOGY.com Students can drag and drop labels to explore the structures of a leaf in **Art Review: Anatomy of a Leaf.**

UbD Check for Understanding

HAND SIGNALS

Present students with the following questions and ask them to show a thumbs-up sign if they understand, a thumbs-down sign if they are confused, or a waving-hand sign if they partially understand.

- What is the function of leaf veins?
- Why is it important that stomata allow gases into and out of the leaf?
- Why is transpiration important?

ADJUST INSTRUCTION

If students showed a thumbs-down or waving-hand sign for any questions, pair students and have them reread the text, study **Figure 23–15,** and discuss the answers. Then, have volunteers share their answers with the class.

Answers

FIGURE 23–15 The cells in palisade mesophyll are closely packed in one layer. Spongy mesophyll is loose tissue with many air spaces between its cells.

IN YOUR NOTEBOOK Students' tables should include all the structures shown in **Figure 23–15,** with a description of the function of each structure.

Teach continued

Use Models

Give student pairs two elongated balloons and tape to model open and closed stomata. They should start by putting a strip of tape lengthwise along the center of each balloon. To show a closed stoma, students can blow air into the balloons until they are partially inflated and place them together, similar to the bottom picture in **Figure 23–16.** To show open stomata, students can fully inflate the balloons, which will move the edges of the balloons away from each other. (The strips of tapes will emphasize the curve of the balloon's shape.)

Ask Which model shows how stomata function when a plant is taking in carbon dioxide? *(balloons fully inflated)*

Ask How does the model of a closed stoma show how a plant maintains homeostasis? *(Plants need the right balance of water to function. The model shows that if a plant is losing too much water, the stoma closes to conserve water.)*

DIFFERENTIATED INSTRUCTION

L3 Advanced Students Ask advanced students to develop another model that represents stomata function. Students should write a detailed description of how the model works and present their model to the class.

BIOLOGY.com Students will look at how different levels of CO_2 affect the activity of plant stomata in **Data Analysis: Effects of Humidity and CO_2 on Plant Stomata.**

Address Misconceptions

Oxygen Use by Plants When focusing only on the process of photosynthesis, students might think plants have no need for oxygen. Make sure they understand plants use the carbohydrates they manufacture for growth, repair, and the active transport required to take up nutrients and water through roots. To carry out these functions, plants need oxygen for the process of cellular respiration.

Answers

FIGURE 23–16 Guard cells have thin outer walls that are forced into a curved shape when water pressure increases. This pulls the thick inner walls apart, opening the stoma.

Gas Exchange and Homeostasis

What role do stomata play in maintaining homeostasis?

You might not think of plants as "breathing" the same way that animals do, but plants need to exchange gases with the atmosphere, too. Plants, in fact, can even be suffocated by lack of oxygen, something that often happens during extensive flooding. A plant's control of gas exchange is actually one of the most important elements of homeostasis for these remarkable organisms.

Gas Exchange Leaves take in carbon dioxide and give off oxygen during photosynthesis. When plant cells use the food they make, the cells respire, taking in oxygen and giving off carbon dioxide (just as animals do). Plant leaves allow gas exchange between air spaces in the spongy mesophyll and the exterior by opening their stomata.

Homeostasis It might seem that stomata should be open all the time, allowing gas exchange to take place and photosynthesis to occur at top speed. However, this is not what happens! If stomata were kept open all the time, water loss due to transpiration would be so great that few plants would be able to take in enough water to survive. So, plants maintain a kind of balance. **Plants maintain homeostasis by keeping their stomata open just enough to allow photosynthesis to take place but not so much that they lose an excessive amount of water.**

Guard cells in the epidermis of each leaf are the key to this balancing act. **Guard cells** are highly specialized cells that surround the stomata and control their opening and closing. Guard cells regulate the movement of gases, especially water vapor and carbon dioxide, into and out of leaf tissues.

The stomata open and close in response to changes in water pressure within the guard cells, as shown in **Figure 23–16.** When water is abundant, it flows into the leaf, raising water pressure in the guard cells, which then open the stomata. The thin outer walls of the cells are forced into a curved shape, which pulls the thick inner walls of the guard cells away from one another, opening the stoma. Carbon dioxide can then enter through the stoma, and water is lost by transpiration.

When water is scarce, the opposite occurs. Water pressure within the guard cells decreases, the inner walls pull together, and the stoma closes. This reduces further water loss by limiting transpiration.

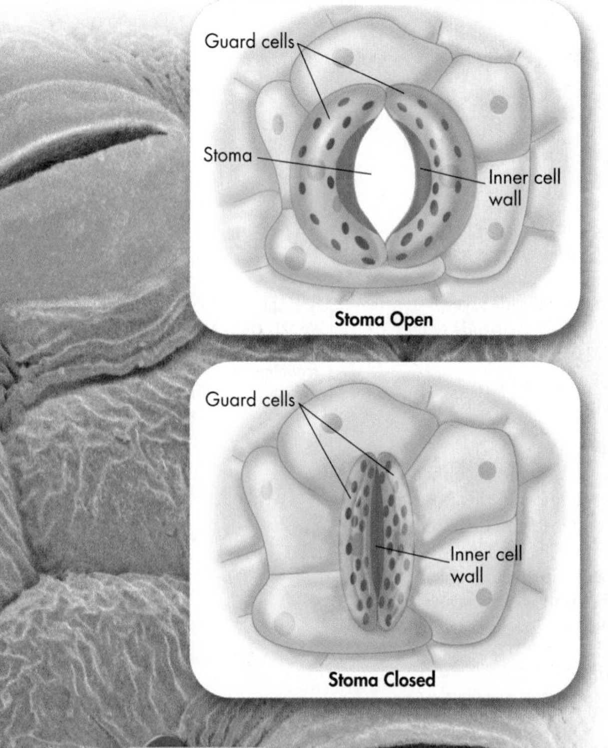

FIGURE 23–16 How Guard Cells Function Plants regulate the opening and closing of their stomata to balance water loss with rates of photosynthesis. The photo shows two partly open stomata on the underside of a camellia leaf (SEM 1500×). **Observe** ***How is the structure of guard cells related to their function?***

682 BIOLOGY.com Search Lesson 23.4 GO • Data Analysis

Quick Facts

STOMATA IN AQUATIC PLANTS

The arrangement and number of stomata differ between terrestrial and aquatic plants. The stomata in leaves that float, such as those of water lilies, are arranged opposite from the stomata of terrestrial plants. Most of the stomata are present on the upper epidermis, which is the side out of water and facing the air. Water loss is not a problem for the underside of leaves, nor for the leaves of submerged plants, such as *Elodea*. Submerged plants have no stomata because they are surrounded by water.

Quick Lab GUIDED INQUIRY

Examining Stomata

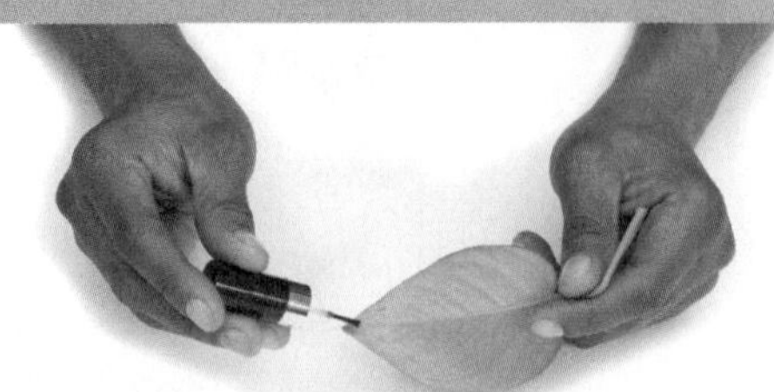

1. Obtain different kinds of leaves from your teacher.
2. Spread a thick coating of clear nail polish on the underside of each leaf.
3. Wait about 10 minutes for the polish to dry completely.
4. Attach a strip of clear tape to the polish and gently peel off the tape, lifting the dried polish.
5. Tape the polish to a clean microscope slide and examine under a 400× lens.
6. For each leaf, move the microscope stage so you can count stomata from three distinct fields of view.

Analyze and Conclude

1. **Calculate** What is the average number of stomata per square cm for each leaf? MATH
2. **Graph** Make a graph that compares these averages.
3. **Form a Hypothesis** What could account for differences in stoma density among plants? Write a hypothesis.

In general, stomata are open during the daytime, when photosynthesis is active, and closed at night, when open stomata would only lead to water loss. However, stomata may be closed even in bright sunlight under hot, dry conditions in which water conservation is a matter of life and death. Guard cells respond to conditions in the environment, such as wind and temperature, helping to maintain homeostasis within a leaf.

Transpiration and Wilting Osmotic pressure keeps a plant's leaves and stems rigid, or stiff. High transpiration rates can lead to wilting. Wilting results from the loss of water—and therefore pressure—in a plant's cells. Without this internal pressure to support them, the plant's cell walls bend inward, and the plant's leaves and stems wilt. When a leaf wilts, its stomata close. As a result, transpiration slows down significantly. Thus, wilting helps a plant to conserve water.

FIGURE 23–17 Wilting A plant may wilt when water is scarce.

In Your Notebook *Make a list of molecules that are exchanged through the stomata. Which ones primarily enter the leaf? Which ones primarily exit the leaf?*

Build Science Skills

Place two of the same type of plant in a well-lighted area. Water one plant normally, and let the other plant begin to wilt. Have students compare the rigidity of the stems and leaves in the two plants. Then, cover each plant with a plastic bag. After a few days, have students observe and describe any changes.

Ask What differences do you observe in the amount of water that collected on the inside surface of the bags? *(The watered plant released more water.)*

Ask Why was transpiration slower in the wilted plant? *(The stomata closed to conserve water.)*

Ask Under what conditions would transpiration slow down in the watered plant? *(in darkness)*

DIFFERENTIATED INSTRUCTION

L1 Struggling Students Students may be confused about how the combination of different environmental factors affect the function of guard cells. Help students make a 2 × 2 table in which they label the columns Day and Night, and the rows Water Abundant and Water Scarce. Then, have them fill in the table with the responses of guard cells to these factors and the effects on stomata. Finally, ask students to explain in their own words how the combination of factors affects the plant's survival. For example, in the space for Day and Water Scarce, the student might say that the guard cells close the stomata, conserving water.

Answers

IN YOUR NOTEBOOK Enter the leaf: carbon dioxide, oxygen; Exit the leaf: carbon dioxide, oxygen, water

Quick Lab

PURPOSE Students will observe, calculate, and compare stomata of different leaves.

MATERIALS different kinds of leaves, clear nail polish, transparent tape, microscope slide, compound microscope

SAFETY Remind students to use care when handling microscope slides. Use toluene-free nail polish, and tell students to keep the cap on when not in use.

PLANNING Before students start the activity, use a millimeter ruler to model how to determine the field of view of a microscope at low power. Then, show students how to convert this number to arrive at the area of the field of view at 400× magnification.

ANALYZE AND CONCLUDE

1. Answers will vary, but should include units (number of stomata per square centimeter).
2. Students should construct a bar graph to show the comparisons.
3. Student responses should indicate an understanding of the role of stomata in water conservation. Sample answer: Stomata density is greatest in the leaf of a plant that lives in environments that receive the most abundant rainfall.

Assess and Remediate

EVALUATE UNDERSTANDING

Have students draw and label a diagram that shows the structures of a leaf involved in photosynthesis. Ask them to write a caption beside each label that briefly describes the function of each structure. Then, have them complete the 23.4 Assessment.

REMEDIATION SUGGESTION

L1 Struggling Students If your students have trouble with **Question 1a,** help them list the sequence of the main steps in photosynthesis. Then, have them use the text under **Leaf Structure and Function** and **Figure 23–15** to relate each structure to the appropriate step.

BIOLOGY.com Students can check their understanding of lesson concepts with the **Self-Test** assessment. They can then take an online version of the **Lesson Assessment.**

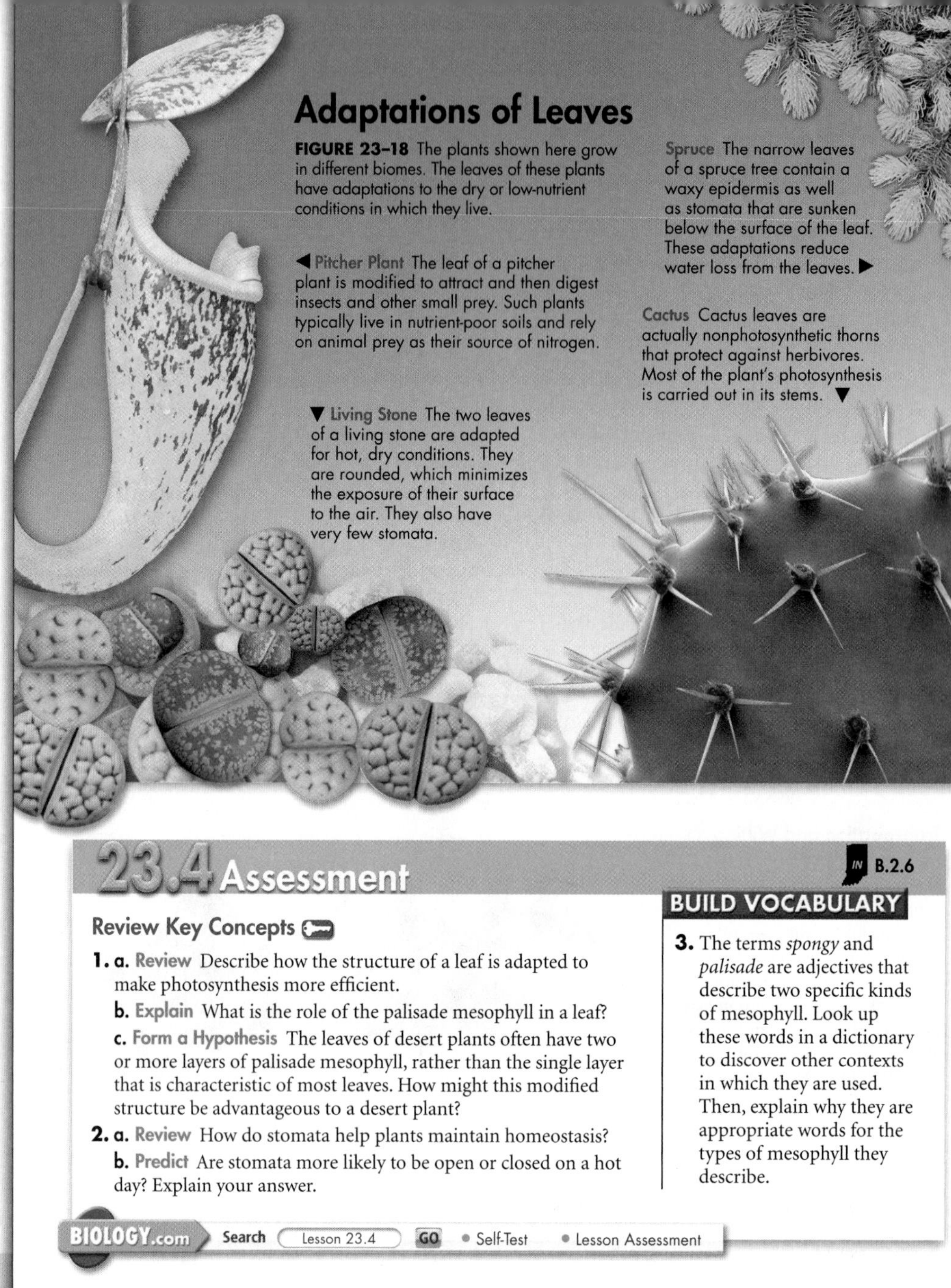

Adaptations of Leaves

FIGURE 23–18 The plants shown here grow in different biomes. The leaves of these plants have adaptations to the dry or low-nutrient conditions in which they live.

◀ **Pitcher Plant** The leaf of a pitcher plant is modified to attract and then digest insects and other small prey. Such plants typically live in nutrient-poor soils and rely on animal prey as their source of nitrogen.

▼ **Living Stone** The two leaves of a living stone are adapted for hot, dry conditions. They are rounded, which minimizes the exposure of their surface to the air. They also have very few stomata.

Spruce The narrow leaves of a spruce tree contain a waxy epidermis as well as stomata that are sunken below the surface of the leaf. These adaptations reduce water loss from the leaves. ▶

Cactus Cactus leaves are actually nonphotosynthetic thorns that protect against herbivores. Most of the plant's photosynthesis is carried out in its stems. ▼

23.4 Assessment

IN B.2.6

Review Key Concepts

1. a. Review Describe how the structure of a leaf is adapted to make photosynthesis more efficient.

b. Explain What is the role of the palisade mesophyll in a leaf?

c. Form a Hypothesis The leaves of desert plants often have two or more layers of palisade mesophyll, rather than the single layer that is characteristic of most leaves. How might this modified structure be advantageous to a desert plant?

2. a. Review How do stomata help plants maintain homeostasis?

b. Predict Are stomata more likely to be open or closed on a hot day? Explain your answer.

BUILD VOCABULARY

3. The terms *spongy* and *palisade* are adjectives that describe two specific kinds of mesophyll. Look up these words in a dictionary to discover other contexts in which they are used. Then, explain why they are appropriate words for the types of mesophyll they describe.

BIOLOGY.com Search Lesson 23.4 GO • Self-Test • Lesson Assessment

684 Chapter 23 • Lesson 4

Assessment Answers

1a. The leaf is flat to maximize its surface area for light absorption. In addition, the leaf contains large amounts of mesophyll, a tissue specialized for photosynthesis.

1b. to absorb light that enters the leaf

1c. Sample answer: It helps reduce the loss of water from the plant.

2a. Stomata keep a balance by opening just enough to allow photosynthesis to take place; they keep the walls of mesophyll cells moist so that gases can enter and leave the cells easily; if a plant starts losing too much water, stomata close to prevent evaporation.

2b. They are more likely to be closed to prevent the loss of too much water (due to evaporation) from the plant.

BUILD VOCABULARY

3. Students' responses should indicate an understanding that *palisade* refers to a closely packed row of fence pickets (or similar) with no breaks in it; similarly the cells of palisade mesophyll are lined up in a row and are closely packed. *Spongy* refers to something (like a kitchen sponge) that is full of air holes; spongy mesophyll has many air spaces between its cells.

23.5 Transport in Plants

 NoS.6 Using analogies and models.

THINK ABOUT IT Look at a tall tree. Maybe there's one outside your school that's 15 meters high or even taller. Think about how much work it would be to haul water up to the top of that tree. Now think of a giant redwood, a hundred meters high. How does water get to the top?

Water Transport

What are the major forces that transport water in a plant?

Recall that active transport and root pressure cause water to move from soil into plant roots. The pressure created by water entering the tissues of a root can push water upward in a plant stem. However, this pressure does not exert nearly enough force to lift water up into trees. Other forces are much more important.

Transpiration The major force in water transport is provided by the evaporation of water from leaves during transpiration. As water evaporates through open stomata, the cell walls within the leaf begin to dry out. Cell walls contain cellulose, the same material used in paper. As you know, dry paper towels strongly attract water. Similarly, the dry cell walls draw water from cells deeper inside the leaf. The pull extends into vascular tissue so that water is pulled up through xylem.

How important is transpirational pull? On a hot day, even a small tree may lose as much as 100 liters of water to transpiration. The hotter and drier the air, and the windier the day, the greater the amount of water lost. As a result of this water loss, the plant draws up even more water from the roots. **Figure 23–19** shows an analogy for transpirational pull.

Key Questions

What are the major forces that transport water in a plant?

What drives the movement of fluid through phloem tissue in a plant?

Vocabulary

adhesion • capillary action • pressure-flow hypothesis

Taking Notes

Compare/Contrast Table As you read, create a table in which to compare and contrast the functions of xylem and phloem.

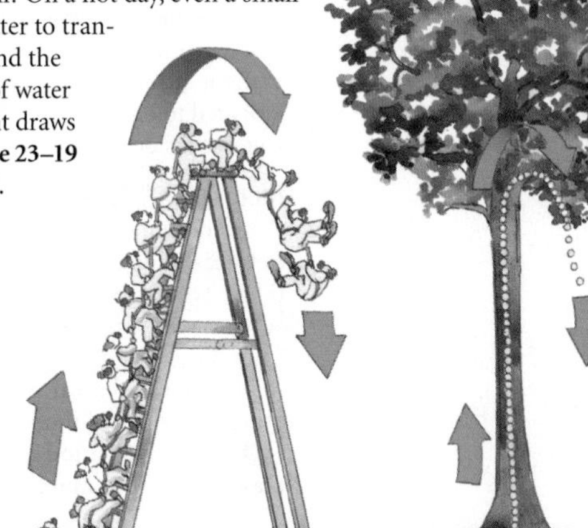

TRANSPIRATIONAL PULL

FIGURE 23–19 Imagine a chain of circus clowns who are tied together and climbing a tall ladder. When the first clown reaches the top, he falls off, pulling the clowns behind him up and over the top. Similarly, the chain of water molecules in a plant extends from the leaves down to the roots. As molecules exit leaves through transpiration, they pull up the molecules behind them.

Teach for Understanding

ENDURING UNDERSTANDING From microorganisms to plants, organisms vary widely in the way they carry out basic life processes.

GUIDING QUESTION How do plants move materials through their bodies?

EVIDENCE OF UNDERSTANDING *After students have finished the lesson, this assessment should show their understanding of the processes that cause materials to move through a plant.* Have students work in groups of four to develop a script describing how materials move through xylem and phloem. Students should write the script as if they were sportscasters announcing "play-by-play" action. Assign each student one component: capillary action, transpiration, active transport, or osmosis. Ask groups to present their scripts to the class.

LESSON 23.5

Getting Started

Objectives

23.5.1 Explain the process of water movement in a plant.

23.5.2 Describe how the products of photosynthesis are transported throughout a plant.

Student Resources

Study Workbooks A and B, 23.5 Worksheets

Spanish Study Workbook, 23.5 Worksheets

 Lesson Overview • Lesson Notes • Activity: Visual Analogy • Assessment: Self-Test, Lesson Assessment

 For corresponding lesson in the **Foundation Edition**, see pages 567–569.

Teach

VISUAL ANALOGY

Explore the comparison of a chain of circus clowns to transpirational pull by asking what the individual clowns represent *(a water molecule)*, what the ladder represents *(the path from the roots to the leaves)*, and what the clowns falling off the ladder represent *(transpiration)*.

 Students can further explore the circus clown analogy in **Visual Analogy: Transpirational Pull.**

IN INDIANA ACADEMIC STANDARDS

For the full text of all standards, see the Course Overview in the front matter of this book.

NoS.6 Use analogies and models (mathematical and physical) to simplify and represent systems that are difficult to understand or directly experience due to their size, time scale, or complexity, and recognize the limitations of analogies and models.

Teach continued

Build Science Skills

Demonstrate capillary action by placing empty glass tubes of various sizes in a dish of colored water, as shown in **Figure 23–20.** Have students observe the water moving. Then, have them draw conclusions about why it moves.

Ask What causes the water to move up the tubes? *(Water molecules are attracted to the walls of the tube—adhesion—and to one another—cohesion.)*

Ask In which tube do you expect water to move highest? *(the thinnest one)*

Ask Why doesn't gravity pull down the water? *(It does. However, the combined forces of adhesion and cohesion are greater than gravity.)*

DIFFERENTIATED INSTRUCTION

L1 Struggling Students Help students make the connection between the demonstration and plants by having them review a diagram of xylem shown in **Figure 23–2.** Ask them to compare the appearance of tracheids and vessel elements with the appearance of the glass tubes in **Figure 23–20.**

ELL English Language Learners Before performing the demonstration of capillary action, write these terms on the board: *cohesion, adhesion, water molecule, capillary action.* As students observe the demonstration, have them use the terms to write their observations in complex phrases or simple sentences. Then, repeat the demonstration, and ask questions to check comprehension, such as: What causes the water molecules to rise in the tube? Tell students to use their notes and edit them if they think their original notes were incorrect or unclear.

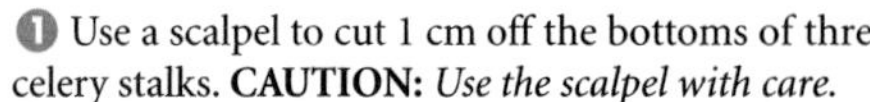

What Is the Role of Leaves in Transpiration?

1. Use a scalpel to cut 1 cm off the bottoms of three celery stalks. **CAUTION:** *Use the scalpel with care.*
2. Remove the leaves from one stalk. Use a cotton swab to apply petroleum jelly to both sides of all the leaves on another stalk. Place all three stalks into a plastic container holding about 200 mL of water and several drops of food coloring.
3. Place the plastic container in a sunny location. Observe the celery at the end of the class and the next day. Record your observations each day.

Analyze and Conclude

1. Observe In which stalk did the colored water rise the most? The least?

2. Infer What effect did the petroleum jelly have on transpiration? What part of the leaf did the petroleum jelly affect?

3. Draw Conclusions How are leaves involved in transpiration?

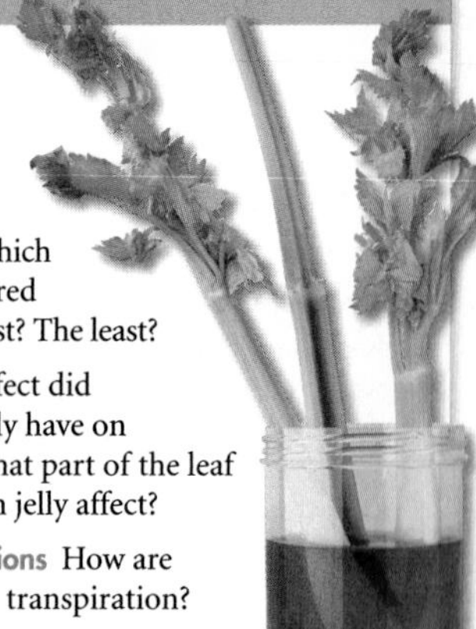

BUILD Vocabulary

WORD ORIGINS The word *capillary* comes from the Latin word for "hair." Hairs are long and thin, like the narrow spaces in which **capillary action** takes place.

How Cell Walls Pull Water Upward To pull water upward, plants take advantage of some of water's most interesting physical properties. Water molecules are attracted to one another by a force called cohesion. Recall from Chapter 2 that cohesion is the attraction of molecules of the same substance to each other. Water cohesion is especially strong because of the tendency of water molecules to form hydrogen bonds with each other. Water molecules can also form hydrogen bonds with other substances. This results from a force called **adhesion,** which is attraction between unlike molecules.

If you were to place empty glass tubes of various diameters into a dish of water, you would see both cohesion and adhesion at work. The tendency of water to rise in a thin tube is called **capillary action.** Water is attracted to the walls of the tube, and water molecules are attracted to one another. The thinner the tube, the higher the water will rise inside it, as shown in **Figure 23–20.**

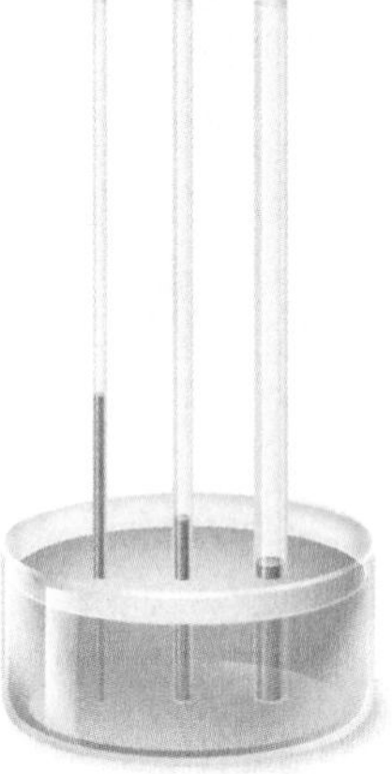

FIGURE 23–20 Capillary Action Capillary action causes water to move much higher in a narrow tube than in a wide tube.

Putting It All Together What does capillary action have to do with water movement through xylem? Recall that xylem tissue is composed of tracheids and vessel elements that form many hollow, connected tubes. These tubes are lined with cellulose cell walls, to which water adheres very strongly. So, when transpiration removes some water from the exposed walls, strong adhesion forces pull in water from the wet interior of the leaf. That pull is so powerful that it extends even down to the tips of roots and, through them, to the water in the soil. **The combination of transpiration and capillary action are the major forces that move water through the xylem tissues of a plant.**

In Your Notebook *Distinguish between the terms* cohesion *and* adhesion *by writing two sentences that use the terms.*

PURPOSE Students will be able to observe the role of leaves in transpiration.

MATERIALS scalpel, cutting board, metric ruler, 3 stalks of celery with leaves, cotton swab, petroleum jelly, plastic container, water, food coloring

SAFETY Remind students to be careful when using the scalpel. Have them wash their hands after the activity.

PLANNING Separate the individual stalks before distributing.

ANALYZE AND CONCLUDE

1. the leafy stalk not coated with petroleum jelly; the stalk without leaves
2. It reduced transpiration by plugging the stomata.
3. Transpiration occurs through leaf stomata.

Answers

IN YOUR NOTEBOOK Sample answer: Water molecules that form hydrogen bonds with one another are an example of cohesion. When water molecules are attracted to the molecules in glass, adhesion occurs.

Nutrient Transport

What drives the movement of fluid through phloem tissue in a plant?

How do sugars move in the phloem? The leading explanation of phloem transport is known as the **pressure-flow hypothesis,** shown in **Figure 23–21.** As you know, unlike the cells that form xylem, the sieve tube cells in phloem remain alive. ❶ Active transport moves sugars into the sieve tube from surrounding tissues. ❷ Water then follows by osmosis, creating pressure in the tube at the source of the sugars. ❸ If another region of the plant has a need for sugars, they are actively pumped out of the tube and into the surrounding tissues. Osmosis then causes water to leave the tube, reducing pressure in the tube at such places. The result is a pressure-driven flow of nutrient-rich fluid from the sources of sugars (source cells) to the places in the plants where sugars are used or stored (sink cells). **Changes in nutrient concentration drive the movement of fluid through phloem tissue in directions that meet the nutritional needs of the plant.**

The pressure-flow system gives plants enormous flexibility in responding to changing seasons. During the growing season, sugars from the leaves are directed into ripening fruits or into roots for storage. As the growing season ends, the plant drops its fruits and stores nutrients in the roots. As spring approaches, chemical signals stimulate phloem cells in the roots to pump sugars back into phloem sap. Then the pressure-flow system raises these sugars into stems and leaves to support rapid growth.

FIGURE 23–21 Pressure-Flow Hypothesis The diagram shows the movement of sugars as explained by the pressure-flow hypothesis. Relate Cause and Effect ***How does the movement of sugars affect the movement of water?***

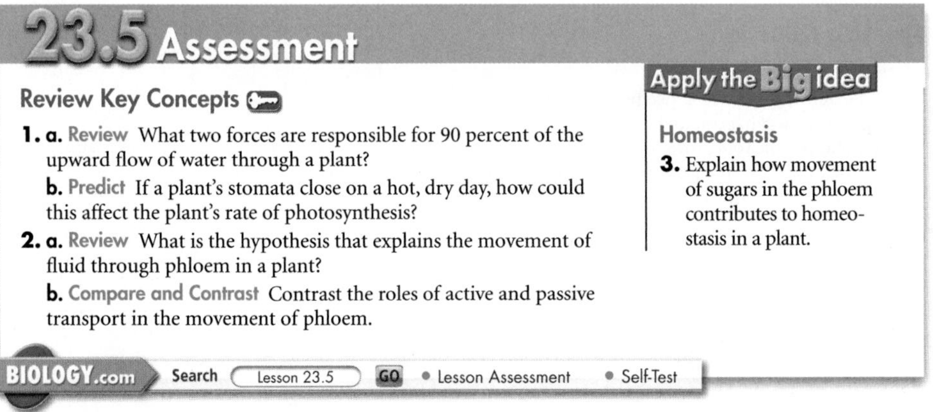

23.5 Assessment

Review Key Concepts

1. a. Review What two forces are responsible for 90 percent of the upward flow of water through a plant?
   b. Predict If a plant's stomata close on a hot, dry day, how could this affect the plant's rate of photosynthesis?
2. a. Review What is the hypothesis that explains the movement of fluid through phloem in a plant?
   b. Compare and Contrast Contrast the roles of active and passive transport in the movement of phloem.

Apply the Big idea

Homeostasis

3. Explain how movement of sugars in the phloem contributes to homeostasis in a plant.

BIOLOGY.com Search Lesson 23.5 GO • Lesson Assessment • Self-Test

Assessment Answers

1a. transpiration and capillary action

1b. The rate would decrease because leaves would not be able to take in carbon dioxide.

2a. The pressure-flow hypothesis explains that when sugars are pumped into or removed from the phloem tissue, the change in concentration causes a movement of fluid in the same direction as the sugars.

2b. Active transport pumps sugars into or out of sieve tubes. Through passive transport, water follows.

3. Big idea Students' responses should indicate their understanding that the pressure-flow system enables sugars to move through the plant as needed, thereby meeting the plant's energy needs and contributing to homeostasis.

Use Visuals

Use **Figure 23–21** to make sure students understand the pressure-flow hypothesis.

Ask Where is the pressure in the phloem the highest? Why? *(At the source; the concentration of nutrients is highest there.)*

Ask In which direction do sugars flow? *(to the sink)*

DIFFERENTIATED INSTRUCTION

LPR Less Proficient Readers Have students focus on the sentence preceded by the number 3 on this page. Point out that the "If-then" (implied) construction of the sentence gives a clue about cause and effect. Guide students to recognize that sugars move to a region of the plant because of a lower concentration of the sugars there. Then ask students to fill out a **Cause-and-Effect Diagram** to show how sugars move through phloem.

Study Wkbks A/B, Appendix S18, Cause-and-Effect Diagram. **Transparencies,** GO1.

Assess and Remediate

EVALUATE UNDERSTANDING

Have students create a **Cluster Diagram** to show the ways in which water and nutrients are transported through a plant. Then, have them complete the 23.5 Assessment.

Study Wkbks A/B, Appendix S19, Cluster Diagram **Transparencies,** GO2.

REMEDIATION SUGGESTION

L1 Struggling Students If students have trouble with **Question 2b,** place drops of food coloring in a beaker of water or on a porous substance such as a piece of bread. Have students describe their observations in terms of concentration (color diffuses away from areas of high concentration to areas of low concentration). Point out that the opposite movement, from low to high concentration, requires energy. Help students relate this to active and passive transport in phloem.

BIOLOGY.com Students can check their understanding of lesson concepts with the **Self-Test** assessment. They can then take an online version of the **Lesson Assessment.**

Answers

FIGURE 23–21 When sugars move into a particular area, the change in concentration causes water to move in the same direction as the sugars.

CHAPTER LAB

Pre-Lab

Introduce students to the concepts they will explore in the chapter lab by assigning the Pre-Lab questions.

Lab

Tell students they will perform the chapter lab *Identifying Growth Zones in Roots* described in **Lab Manual A.**

L1 Struggling Students A simpler version of the chapter lab is provided in **Lab Manual B.**

SAFETY

Students should handle the glassware and plant material with care. Remind them to wash their hands before they leave the lab.

Look online for **Editable Lab Worksheets.**

For corresponding pre-lab in the **Foundation Edition**, see page 570.

IN INDIANA ACADEMIC STANDARDS

For the full text of all standards, see the Course Overview in the front matter of this book.

Design Your Own Lab

GUIDED INQUIRY

NoS.1 Develop explanations. Also covered: NoS.5.

Pre-Lab: Identifying Growth Zones in Roots

Problem Where does growth occur in plant roots?

Materials 150-mL beaker, paper towels, large bean seeds, petri dish, masking tape, metric ruler, fine-tip permanent marker

Lab Manual Chapter 23 Lab

Skills Focus Design an Experiment, Measure, Organize Data, Analyze Data

Connect to the Big idea A plant's root system absorbs nutrients, stores food, and provides support for the rest of the plant. As a plant grows, the root system must be able to absorb more nutrients, store more food, and provide more support. Thus, growth in the root system must keep pace with growth in the other parts of a plant. Where in a root does the growth occur that increases the root's length? In this lab, you will design an experiment to answer this question.

Background Questions

a. Review What are the three principal organs of seed plants?

b. Compare and Contrast What are the main functions of dermal tissue, vascular tissue, and ground tissue?

c. Review What are meristems?

Pre-Lab Questions

Preview the procedure in the lab manual.

1. Predict A root is marked at two points along its length. What will happen to the distance between these marks if the root grows longer only near the tip? What will happen if growth occurs evenly along the entire length of the root?

2. Design an Experiment The procedure in Part A asks you to use four seeds. Why not use two seeds instead?

3. Design an Experiment How will you keep track of which seedling is which?

Visit Chapter 23 online to test yourself on chapter content and to find activities to help you learn.

Untamed Science Video The Untamed Science crew takes you to several exotic locations to see unique plant structures and adaptations.

Data Analysis Find out how plants "breathe" through stomata as conditions change.

Tutor Tube Tune in to Tutor Tube to see how new tissue growth makes plants taller.

Art Review Test your knowledge of leaf structures.

Art in Motion See how plant roots absorb nutrients and water molecules.

Visual Analogy Compare the motion of clowns climbing a ladder with water molecules being pulled up a tree.

Pre-Lab Answers

BACKGROUND QUESTIONS

a. roots, stems, and leaves

b. Dermal tissue provides a protective outer layer for plants. Vascular tissue supports the plant body and transports water and nutrients. Ground tissue produces and stores sugars and helps support the plant.

c. Meristems are regions of unspecialized cells in which mitosis produces new cells that are ready for differentiation.

PRE-LAB QUESTIONS

1. The marks will stay the same distance apart if growth only occurs near the tip. If growth occurs evenly all along the root, then the distance between the marks will increase.

2. Sample answer: One seed might not germinate or one seedling might die before the experiment is done. Also, having a larger sample makes it more likely that the gathered data is typical (not the result of abnormal growth).

3. Sample answer: Use a small piece of tape on the outside of the beaker to label the location of each seedling. Remove only one seedling at a time from the beaker when taking measurements.

23 Study Guide

Big idea Structure and Function

The main organs of a plant—the roots, stems, and leaves—contain dermal, vascular, and ground tissue systems that carry out the basic functions of the plant. These functions include protection, transport, and photosynthesis.

23.1 Specialized Tissues in Plants

The three principal organs of seed plants are roots, stems, and leaves.

Dermal tissue is the protective outer covering of a plant. Vascular tissue supports the plant body and transports water and nutrients throughout the plant. Ground tissue produces and stores sugars and contributes to the physical support of the plant.

Meristems are regions of unspecialized cells in which mitosis produces new cells that are ready for differentiation.

epidermis (665)	parenchyma (667)
lignin (666)	collenchyma (667)
vessel element (666)	sclerenchyma (667)
sieve tube element (666)	meristem (667)
companion cell (666)	apical meristem (668)

23.2 Roots

A mature root has an outside layer, called the epidermis, and also contains vascular tissue and a large area of ground tissue.

Roots support a plant, anchor it in the ground, store food, and absorb water and dissolved nutrients from the soil.

root hair (670)	vascular cylinder (670)
cortex (670)	root cap (670)
endodermis (670)	Casparian strip (672)

23.3 Stems

Aboveground stems have several important functions: Stems produce leaves, branches, and flowers; stems hold leaves up to the sun; and stems transport substances throughout the plant.

Primary growth of stems is the result of elongation of cells produced in the apical meristem. It takes place in all seed plants.

In conifers and dicots, secondary growth takes place in meristems called the vascular cambium and cork cambium.

node (675)	vascular cambium (677)
bud (675)	cork cambium (677)
vascular bundle (675)	heartwood (678)
pith (675)	sapwood (678)
primary growth (676)	bark (679)
secondary growth (676)	

23.4 Leaves

The structure of a leaf is optimized to absorb light and carry out photosynthesis.

Plants maintain homeostasis by keeping their stomata open just enough to allow photosynthesis to take place but not so much that they lose an excessive amount of water.

blade (680)	spongy mesophyll (681)
petiole (680)	stoma (681)
mesophyll (680)	transpiration (681)
palisade mesophyll (681)	guard cell (682)

23.5 Transport in Plants

The combination of transpiration and capillary action are the major forces that move water through the xylem tissues of a plant.

Changes in nutrient concentration drive the movement of fluid through phloem tissue in directions that meet the nutritional needs of the plant.

adhesion (686)
capillary action (686)
pressure-flow hypothesis (687)

Think Visually Make a flowchart of the tissues through which water passes, from where it enters a plant at the root until it exits the plant through the leaves. Use the following terms in your flowchart: *epidermis, cortex, endodermis, xylem, stomata.*

Study Online

REVIEW AND ASSESSMENT RESOURCES

Editable Worksheets Pages of Study Workbooks A and B, Lab Manuals A and B, and the Assessment Resources Book are available online. These documents can be easily edited using a word-processing program.

Lesson Overview Have students reread the Lesson Overviews to help them study chapter concepts.

Vocabulary Review The *Flash Cards* and *Match It* provide an interactive way to review chapter vocabulary.

Chapter Assessment Have students take an online version of the Chapter 23 Assessment.

Standardized Test Prep Students can take an online version of the Standardized Test Prep. You will receive their scores along with ideas for remediation.

Diagnostic and Benchmark Tests Use these tests to monitor your students' progress and supply remediation.

Answers

THINK VISUALLY

Students' flowcharts should begin with water entering through root hairs and end with water passing out of stomata, using the names of as many different tissues as possible.

UbD Performance Tasks

SUMMATIVE TASK Have each student describe a living plant as a factory. Students should assume the role of a reporter touring the factory. They should include as many vocabulary terms as possible. Write the following prompts on the board to guide students.

- Who are the workers?
- What does the factory make?
- How is the product used?
- What materials do the workers need?
- How do materials get to the workers?

TRANSFER TASK Tell students to imagine they are horticulturists who write a newspaper column for gardening enthusiasts. Ask them to answer the following letters with detailed explanations that someone who had taken biology in high school would understand.

- Dear Green Thumb, I read that most water taken in by plants is not used for photosynthesis. Why do my plants need so much water? Signed, Waterlogged *(Answer might mention the huge amount of water lost to transpiration.)*
- Dear Green Thumb, I just returned from a tropical rainforest, and I noticed large tree stumps with no annual rings. I'm confused—how did that happen? Signed, Going in Circles *(Answer might mention the absence of a dormant or slow-growth season in tropical climates.)*
- Dear Green Thumb, The water lily leaves in my pond are green on top but red underneath. Why aren't they green on both sides? Signed, Color Challenged *(Answer might mention that photosynthesis takes place only in the top half of the leaves, which are exposed to air.)*

Lesson 23.1

UNDERSTAND KEY CONCEPTS

1. b **2.** a **3.** c **4.** c

5. Mature xylem cells have died, leaving behind only their cell walls. Mature phloem cells contain living cells.

6. The three main functions of leaves are to absorb sunlight, carry out photosynthesis, and let oxygen and carbon dioxide enter and exit the leaf.

THINK CRITICALLY

7. Dermal tissue in roots and leaves both consists of a single layer of epidermal cells. Leaf epidermis may have hair-like projections that protect them from predators, whereas the projections from root epidermis (called root hairs) increase the surface area available for absorption of water and nutrients. Leaf epidermal cells may also have a waxy cuticle to prevent water loss.

8. A tall building grows from the top as each new floor is added and becomes "specialized" as all the details are added. This is much like plants that grow from the tip of the stem. Plants, however, also grow in diameter as they get taller, unlike a building.

Lesson 23.2

UNDERSTAND KEY CONCEPTS

9. d **10.** a **11.** c **12.** c

13. The cell membranes of root hairs contain active transport proteins, which pump mineral ions from the soil into the plant, a process that leads to the movement of water into the plant by osmosis. By increasing the surface area of the root system, root hairs also help maximize a plant's ability to absorb water from the soil.

14. water and inorganic nutrients (including trace elements)

15. Water moves by osmosis into the vascular tissue of the roots. Osmosis occurs because minerals have accumulated in the vessels by active transport. The function is to generate enough pressure to move water out of the soil and up into the body of the plant.

THINK CRITICALLY

16. Without the Casparian strip, water could flow out of the xylem and back into the cortex of the root. The Casparian strip seals and waterproofs the cells of the endodermis around their edges so that water can move through them in only one direction.

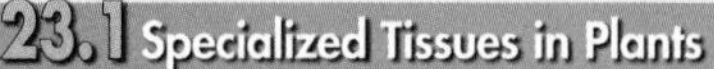

23 Assessment

IN The numbers following the questions refer to Indiana's Academic Standards for Biology I.

23.1 Specialized Tissues in Plants

Understand Key Concepts

1. The plant organ that supports the plant body and carries nutrients between different parts of the plant is the
a. root. **c.** leaf.
b. stem. **d.** flower.

2. Which type of plant tissue would be found ONLY in the circled areas of the plant shown?
a. meristem tissue
b. vascular tissue
c. dermal tissue
d. ground tissue

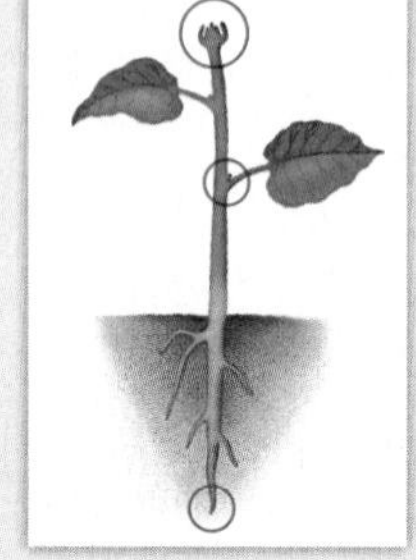

3. Tracheids and vessel elements make up
a. phloem. **c.** xylem.
b. trichomes. **d.** meristem.

4. Phloem functions primarily in
a. transport of water.
b. growth of the root.
c. transport of products of photosynthesis.
d. increasing stem width.

5. What is the principal difference between mature xylem and mature phloem cells?

6. What are the three main functions of leaves?

Think Critically

7. Compare and Contrast What are similarities and differences in the dermal tissues of roots and of leaves?

8. Use Analogies How accurate is the following analogy for describing plant growth?
Apical meristems cause plants to grow the way a high-rise office building grows during construction.

23.2 Roots

Understand Key Concepts

9. Which of the following are found in roots?
a. vascular tissue only
b. ground tissue only
c. dermal and vascular tissue only
d. dermal, vascular, and ground tissue

10. As a growing root pushes through the soil, the delicate apical meristem is protected by
a. a root cap. **c.** bark.
b. xylem. **d.** root hairs.

11. Which of the following is a trace element absorbed by roots?
a. nitrogen **c.** zinc
b. phosphorus **d.** potassium

12. The waterproof strip that is found in the cell walls of the endodermis is the
a. vascular cambium. **c.** Casparian strip.
b. vascular cylinder. **d.** cortex.

13. How are root hairs important to plants?

14. What are the primary kinds of material that plants obtain from the soil through roots?

15. What causes root pressure, and what is the function of root pressure for the plant?

Think Critically

16. Predict How would the function of a plant root be affected if it lacked a Casparian strip?

17. Form a Hypothesis While transplanting a houseplant to a larger pot, you notice that the roots had been very crowded in the old pot. Over the next few weeks, the plant's growth and overall appearance improve greatly. Develop a hypothesis that explains this observation.

23.3 Stems

Understand Key Concepts

18. Increases in the thickness of stems result from the production of new tissue by the
a. vascular cambium. **c.** apical meristem.
b. mesophyll. **d.** ground tissue.

17. With more volume in the new pot, roots could increase their ability to absorb nutrients by increasing their surface area, and thus support the growth of more stems and leaves.

Lesson 23.3

UNDERSTAND KEY CONCEPTS

18. a **19.** d

20. from the cork cambium

21. Monocot stems have scattered vascular bundles throughout the stem. In dicots, the vascular bundles are located in organized rings.

THINK CRITICALLY

22. A dicot root has a vascular cylinder at its center, surrounded by cortex (ground tissue). A dicot stem has ground tissue in the center, surrounded by a ring of vascular tissue bundles.

690 Chapter 23 • Assessment

19. Most water transport in stems takes place in
a. heartwood.
b. pith.
c. phloem.
d. sapwood.

20. From what type of tissue does bark develop?

21. What is the primary difference between monocot and dicot stems?

Think Critically

22. **Infer** If your classmate gave you a slide showing a cross section of a dicot, how would you know whether it was from a root or a stem?

23. **Design an Experiment** What relationship would you expect between a plant's life span and its ability to undergo secondary growth? What data could you collect? Describe an experiment to collect the data.

24. **Apply Concepts** In the art of bonsai, gardeners keep trees small by cutting the roots and tips of the branches. The trunk of the tree, however, continues to increase in width. How do you explain the ever-increasing width of the trunk?

23.4 Leaves

Understand Key Concepts

25. Most of the photosynthetic activity of a leaf takes place in the
a. vascular bundles.
b. waxy cuticle and epidermis.
c. palisade and spongy mesophyll.
d. guard cells and stomata.

26. Stomata open and close in response to water pressure within
a. root cells.
b. cell walls.
c. guard cells.
d. xylem.

27. What is the function of the epidermis and cuticle layers in a leaf?

28. What needs of the plant are met by controlling the opening and closing of stomata?

Think Critically

29. **Compare and Contrast** Compare the ways in which a cactus and a conifer are adapted to their respective biomes.

30. **Relate Cause and Effect** A plant's stomata are open early on a summer day when the air is cool and moist. By afternoon, when the air is hot and dry, the stomata are closed. Explain this observation.

solve the CHAPTER MYSTERY

THE HOLLOW TREE

The life of a strangler fig starts with a sticky seed deposited on a high tree branch by an animal such as a bird, bat, or monkey. At first, growth is slow because the roots have access only to the few dissolved nutrients found in the rainwater and leaf litter that collect in the crevices of the host's branches. But, after the first roots grow down the host's trunk and enter the ground, the fig's growth rate increases rapidly. The fig sends down many more roots. These roots become tangled and grafted together, crushing the host's bark and constricting the circulation of nutrients inside the phloem.

In addition, the fig's stems and leaves eventually grow taller than the host, shading it from the sun. This makes photosynthesis by the host less efficient. Below ground, the fig's roots compete with the host's roots for limited nutrients in the soil.

This triple punch—strangulation, competition for light, and competition for nutrients—usually kills the host. Left behind is an impressive "hollow" fig tree.

1. **Use Analogies** One scientist has described the strangler fig as a "vegetable octopus." Explain how this analogy relates to the habits of the strangler fig. NoS.6

2. **Predict** Plants that sprout and grow on top of other plants are called epiphytes. In what biome do you think epiphytes are most common? Explain your prediction.

3. **Connect to the** 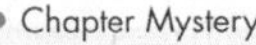 How is the structure of the strangler fig different from that of the "typical plant" you studied in this chapter? Compare the advantages and disadvantages of a rain-forest plant that sprouts in the soil versus one that sprouts high off the ground.

After students have read through the Chapter Mystery, discuss the functions of the three principal organs of plants.

Ask What is different about the growth of strangler fig roots from the growth of most other tree roots? *(The roots of the strangler fig start their growth high above the ground and grow down through the air into the ground. The roots of most trees begin their growth and continue their growth underground.)*

Ask How do the organs of the strangler fig compete with those of the host? *(The leaves and stems of the fig compete with the leaves of the host tree for sunlight. The roots of the fig compete with the roots of the host tree for water and other nutrients.)*

CHAPTER MYSTERY ANSWERS

1. An octopus has tentacles that it uses to grasp prey. In the same way, the strangler fig has many branching roots that wrap around the host.

2. Epiphytes are most common in tropical rainforests because the plant growth is so dense. Epiphytes grow on top of other plants to get more sunlight. Epiphytes get water from the air or from rainwater that collects on their host, and nutrients from their host.

3.  Part 1: Students' answers should include a comparison of the structure of stems and roots in strangler figs with the structure of these organs in most other trees. Part 2: Sample answer: An advantage of a rain forest plant that sprouts in the soil is that more water and other nutrients are available to the roots. A disadvantage is that less sunlight is available for the leaves.

Follow the Untamed Science crew in the video, **Plants Inside and Out,** and watch as they examine the unique plants that have found a way to survive and thrive in exotic locations.

23. Students' experimental designs should include a reasonable hypothesis and controls.

24. The person training the miniature tree trims off the apical meristems at the tips of shoots and roots. This keeps the tree short. However, the person does not touch the vascular cambium and cork cambium in the stem, so the stem continues to increase in thickness.

Lesson 23.4

UNDERSTAND KEY CONCEPTS

25. c 26. c

27. The epidermis and cuticle layers of dermal tissue, which form the outer covering of a leaf, protect tissues and limit water loss.

28. Regulation of stomata allows gas exchange between the plant and the environment without excessive water loss.

THINK CRITICALLY

29. A cactus has spinelike leaves that are nonphotosynthetic and protect the plant from herbivores; the stem carries out most of the photosynthesis and stores water. A conifer has narrow leaves with a waxy epidermis and sunken stomata that reduce water loss.

30. Stomata open when the air is cool and moist because the transpiration rate is low. In hot, dry air, stomata close to prevent excessive water loss from higher rates of transpiration.

ASSESSMENT

Lesson 23.5

UNDERSTAND KEY CONCEPTS

31. d **32.** b **33.** a

34. to transport sugars throughout the plant

35. Source cells are located where sugars are made, and sink cells are located in areas with a low concentration of sugars. Nutrient-rich fluid moves from source cells to sink cells.

THINK CRITICALLY

36. Transpirational pull would be stronger on a hot, dry day because water loss from stomata would be greater (until stomata started to close in response). Water loss is the cause of transpirational pull.

37. Springtime is when the maple trees are removing stored sugars from their roots and transporting sugar-rich sap to their stems and leaves to fuel growth.

Connecting Concepts

USE SCIENCE GRAPHICS

38. between about 12:30 and 3:30 PM

39. about 35 grams of water in 2 hours

40. As transpiration increases or decreases, water intake also increases or decreases, with changes in water intake lagging behind transpiration changes by a few hours.

WRITE ABOUT SCIENCE

41. Students should describe how the cell structures of tracheids, vessel elements, sieve tube elements, and companion cells are specialized for their functions. They should also describe the location of vascular tissue within roots. They might also mention the endodermis and the function of the Casparian strip.

42. Big idea A leaf is flat and thin to maximize its surface area for light absorption. The tough, waxy dermal layer prevents physical damage and water loss. The mesophyll performs photosynthesis to make sugars for the plant's food. The vascular tissue transports water to the leaf and sugars away from the leaf.

23.5 Transport in Plants

Understand Key Concepts

31. The rise of water in a tall plant depends on capillary action and
a. osmosis.
b. evaporation.
c. nutrient transport.
d. transpirational pull.

32. The pressure-flow hypothesis explains
a. water movement in xylem.
b. water and nutrient movement in phloem.
c. water and nutrient movement in xylem.
d. water movement in phloem.

33. Attraction between water molecules and other substances is
a. adhesion.
b. capillary action.
c. transpiration.
d. cohesion.

34. What is the main function of phloem?

35. What are source cells and sink cells?

Think Critically

36. Relate Cause and Effect Would transpirational pull be stronger on a hot, humid day or on a hot, dry day? Explain.

37. Apply Concepts Why are maple trees tapped for their sugar in the early spring rather than in the summer or autumn?

Connecting Concepts

Use Science Graphics NoS.3

Use the graph to answer questions 38–40.

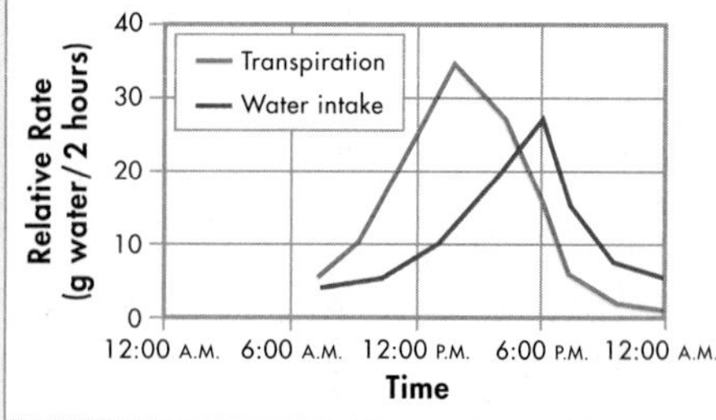

38. Analyze Data During which span of time is the greatest amount of water lost through transpiration?

39. Analyze Data About how many grams of water are lost every two hours when the transpiration curve is at its highest peak?

40. Draw Conclusions What is the relationship between transpiration and water intake?

Write About Science NoS.3

41. Explanation Explain how the cells in the vascular tissue of a root are specialized for transport of water and minerals. B.2.6

42. Assess the Big idea Describe how several different tissue types in a leaf work together to support a functioning plant organ.

Analyzing Data

NoS.3

A scientist selects a single three-year-old birch tree to study growth patterns. She inserts a nail into the trunk 1.0 m above ground level. At intervals over the next 15 years, she measures the total height of the tree and the circumference of the tree at the point where the nail is sticking out. She records the results, which are shown here.

Tree Age (yr)	Height of Tree (m)	Height of Nail (m)	Tree Circumference (cm)
3	2.1	1.0	9.0
8	4.5	1.0	15.0
13	8.0	1.0	26.0
18	9.0	1.0	29.5

43. Interpret Tables In which time interval was tree growth the greatest?
a. 0 to 3 years **c.** 8 to 13 years
b. 3 to 8 years **d.** 13 to 18 years

44. Calculate What was the average growth in the height of the tree from sprouting to age 18?
a. 0.2 meters per year
b. 0.5 meters per year
c. 1.0 meters per year
d. 2.0 meters per year

PURPOSE Students will analyze data to understand the location of primary and secondary growth in a tree and interpret a data table.

PLANNING Have students review the information from the chapter about how primary and secondary growth occurs. Some students may have difficulty with **Question 44** because there is no row for the sprouting plant. Lead students to understand that they need to look at only one number to answer the question (height at 18 years divided by 18).

ANSWERS

43. c

44. b

Standardized Test Practice for Indiana

Multiple Choice

1. Which of the following cell types is NOT found in a plant's vascular tissue?
 A tracheid
 B vessel element
 C guard cell
 D companion cell

2. Where in a plant does mitosis produce new cells?
 A meristems
 B chloroplasts
 C mesophyll
 D heartwood

3. Which tissues make up tree bark?
 A phloem
 B cork
 C cork cambium
 D all of the above

4. Which is NOT a factor in the movement of water through a plant's vascular tissues?
 A transpiration
 B capillary action
 C osmotic pressure
 D meristems

5. All of the following conduct fluids in a plant EXCEPT
 A heartwood.
 B sapwood.
 C phloem.
 D xylem.

6. Where does most of the photosynthesis occur in a plant?
 A stomata
 B guard cells
 C vascular cambium
 D mesophyll tissue

7. Which of the following structures prevents the backflow of water into the root cortex?
 A palisade mesophyll
 B root cap
 C cambium
 D Casparian strip

8. Which of the following plants has a fibrous root system?
 A dandelion
 B beet
 C radish
 D grass

Questions 9–10

A student compared the average number of stomata on the top side and the underside of the leaves of different plants. Her data are summarized in the table below.

Average Number of Stomata (per square mm)		
Plant	Top Surfaces of Leaves	Bottom Surfaces of Leaves
Pumpkin	29	275
Tomato	12	122
Bean	40	288

9. What generalization can be made based on the data? NoS.3
 A All plants have more stomata on the top side of their leaves than on the bottom side.
 B Plants have fewer stomata on the top side of their leaves than on the bottom side.
 C Some plants have more stomata on the top side of their leaves than on the bottom side.
 D The number of stomata is the same from plant to plant.

10. Pumpkins, tomatoes, and beans all grow in direct sunlight. Assuming the plants receive plenty of water, stomata on the lower surface of their leaves
 A are always closed.
 B are usually clogged with dust.
 C are unlikely to close at night.
 D stay open during daylight hours.

Open-Ended Response

11. Contrast the functions of xylem and phloem.

If You Have Trouble With . . .

Question	1	2	3	4	5	6	7	8	9	10	11
See Lesson	23.1	23.1	23.3	23.5	23.3	23.4	23.2	23.2	23.4	23.4	23.5

ASSESSMENT

Answers

1. C
2. A
3. D
4. D
5. A
6. D
7. D
8. D
9. B
10. D
11. Xylem is dead tissue that conducts water and minerals from roots to leaves. It conducts in only one direction. Phloem is living tissue that conducts the products of photosynthesis from leaves to roots or in the reverse direction, depending on where sugars are needed in the plant.

Test-Taking Tip

REVIEW ANSWERS

Tell students if they finish a test early, they should use the time to go back and review the questions and answers. If they are unsure about an answer, tell them not to change it without a good reason; a test-taker's first instinct for an answer choice is often correct. However, if students realize their first answer was incorrect, they should change it. For example, on reviewing their answers, they might discover they misinterpreted a question or did not read through all the answers.

CHAPTER PLANNER 24 Plant Reproduction and Response

Chapter Contents	IN	Time	Core Resources
Chapter Preview			**Student Edition,** pp. 694–695 **Chapter Mystery,** p. 695
24.1 Reproduction in Flowering Plants The Structure of Flowers • The Angiosperm Life Cycle • Vegetative Reproduction		1½ periods ¾ block	**Student Edition,** pp. 696–703 Inquiry 24.1 Quick Lab, p. 698 L2 **Study Workbook A** 24.1 Worksheets L2 Biology.com *Art Review:* The Parts of a Flower • *Art in Motion:* The Development of Gametophytes **Assessment Resources Book** Visual Quiz L2
24.2 Fruits and Seeds Seed and Fruit Development • Seed Dispersal • Seed Dormancy and Germination	NoS.3	½ period ¼ block	**Student Edition,** pp. 704–707 Inquiry 24.2 Analyzing Data, p. 706 L2 **Study Workbook A** 24.2 Worksheets L2 Biology.com *Tutor Tube:* Flowers and Fruits • *Real-World Inquiry:* Fugitive Seeds? • 24.2 Self-Test • 24.2 Lesson Assessment
24.3 Plant Hormones Hormones • Tropisms and Rapid Movements • Response to Seasons	NoS.3, B.1.2	1½ periods ¾ block	**Student Edition,** pp. 708–714 Inquiry 24.3 Analyzing Data, p. 710 L2 **Study Workbook A** 24.3 Worksheets L2 Biology.com *InterActive Art:* Photoperiodism **Assessment Resources Book** Visual Quiz L2
24.4 Plants and Humans Agriculture • Fiber, Wood, and Medicine • *Biology & History: The Evolution of Agriculture*	B.4.2	½ period ¼ block	**Student Edition,** pp. 715–719 **Study Workbook A** 24.4 Worksheets L2 Biology.com *Data Analysis:* Plant Energy • 24.4 Self-Test • 24.4 Lesson Assessment
Chapter Pre-Lab	NoS.1	1 period ½ block	**Student Edition,** p. 720 L2 **Lab Manual A** *Plant Hormones and Leaves* L2 • *Using Pollen to Solve Crimes* L2

Differentiated Instruction Tools

Study Workbook B includes worksheets with lesson-level differentiated instruction support and explanations of differentiated instruction teaching strategies.

Lab Manual B includes skills labs, simplified chapter labs, and hands-on activities.

ELL Handbook explains ways to make *Biology* more accessible to ELL students.

Spanish Study Workbook is a Spanish translation of Study Workbook A.

Multilingual Glossary is the glossary translated into ten languages.

Differentiated Instruction Key

- L1 Special Needs or Struggling Students
- ELL English Language Learners
- LPR Less Proficient Readers
- L2 On-Level Students
- L3 Advanced Students

Additional Resources

Biology.com Untamed Science Video • Vocabulary Flash Cards

Study Workbook B 24.1 Worksheets L1 ELL LPR
Spanish Study Workbook 24.1 Worksheets ELL
Biology.com 24.1 Lesson Overview • 24.1 Lesson Notes • 24.1 Self-Test • 24.1 Lesson Assessment

Study Workbook B 24.2 Worksheets L1 ELL LPR
Spanish Study Workbook 24.2 Worksheets ELL
Biology.com 24.2 Lesson Overview • 24.2 Lesson Notes

Study Workbook B 24.3 Worksheets L1 ELL LPR
Spanish Study Workbook 24.3 Worksheets ELL
Biology.com 24.3 Lesson Overview • 24.3 Lesson Notes • 24.3 Self-Test • 24.3 Lesson Assessment

Study Workbook B 24.4 Worksheets L1 ELL LPR
Spanish Study Workbook 24.4 Worksheets ELL
Biology.com 24.4 Lesson Overview • 24.4 Lesson Notes

Lab Manual B *Plant Hormones and Leaves* • Data Analysis: *Temperature and Seed Germination, Increasing Crop Yields* • Hands-On Activity: *A-Mazing Plants* L1 ELL LPR

Chapter Review

Student Edition Study Guide, p. 721 L2 • Unit Project, p. 726 L2
Study Workbook A Chapter 24 Vocabulary Review L2 • Chapter 24 Chapter Mystery/21st Century Skills Activity L2 L3
Transparencies, pp. 280–289 L1 ELL LPR L2
Biology.com Untamed Science Video • You're the Director • Editable Worksheets of Study Workbooks A and B and Lab Manuals A and B • Chapter 24 Flash Cards and Crossword Puzzle

Untamed Science DVD • Classroom Resources CD (includes lesson presentations and editable worksheets)

Chapter Assessment

Student Edition Assessment, pp. 722–725 L2
Study Workbook B Chapter 24 Chapter Review L1 ELL LPR • Chapter 24 Taking a Standardized Test L1 ELL LPR
Assessment Resources Book Chapter 24 Test A L2 • Chapter 24 Test B L1 ELL LPR • Unit 6 Test A L2 • Unit 6 Test B L1 ELL LPR
Biology.com Chapter 24 Assessment • Editable Worksheets of Chapter 24 Visual Quizzes, Chapter 24 Tests A and B, and Unit 6 Tests A and B

Exam*View* *Assessment Suite* • Classroom Resources CD (includes lesson presentations and editable worksheets)

Time: 1 period, 1/2 block

Pressed for Time?

Preview the Chapter Introduce the first two Key Questions for Lessons 24.1 and 24.2, and preview Figures 24–6 and 24–9.

Cover the Chapter Quickly In Lesson 24.1, have students read *The Structure of Flowers* and go over Figure 24–6. Assign *Seed and Fruit Development* and *Seed Dispersal* in Lesson 24.2. Have students read the introduction and the How Hormones Act section of *Hormones,* all of *Tropisms and Rapid Movements,* and the Photoperiod and Flowering section of *Response to Seasons* in Lesson 24.3.

Assess Assign question 1 in the 24.1 Assessment, questions 1 and 2 in the 24.2 Assessment, and questions 1a, 2a, 3b, and 3c in the 24.3 Assessment. In the Chapter 24 Assessment, assign questions 1, 4, 7, 8, 10, 12, 15, 17, 19, 20, 22, 23, 36, and 37.

Connect to the Big Idea

Ask students to look at the photo of pollen grains and read the caption. Point out how pollen grains relate to the Big Idea by reviewing the role of pollen grains in reproduction. *(Pollen grains contain the male gametophyte, which produces sperm.)*

Then, ask students who have allergies to ragweed, or "hay fever," to comment on the time of year when their allergies seem to kick in. *(late summer through autumn)* Explain that ragweed is a flowering plant that begins to bloom in August. It releases pollen during warm, dry, windy conditions. It does not release pollen if it is raining or the humidity is more than 80 percent. Ask students to infer why this is so. *(During windy, dry conditions, the pollen will be dispersed farther. Rain would wash the pollen to the ground.)* Tell students that in this chapter, they will learn about many other effects of environmental conditions on the reproduction, development, and growth of plants. Have students anticipate the answer to the question, **How do changes in the environment affect the reproduction, development, and growth of plants?**

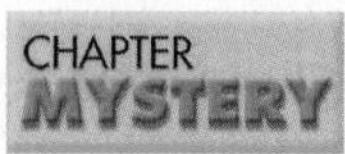

Have students read over the Chapter Mystery and suggest possible factors that could cause the lemons to remain unripe. By pointing out that lemons are fruits, and that fruits are involved in plant reproduction, you can start connecting the Chapter Mystery to the Big Idea of Growth, Development, and Reproduction.

Have students preview the chapter vocabulary terms using the **Flash Cards.**

INDIANA ACADEMIC STANDARDS

For the full text of all standards, see the Course Overview in the front matter of this book.

Key standards: Chapter 24 covers key ideas from Standard 1: Cellular Chemistry and Standard 4: Interdependence, including **B.1.2** Molecules and cellular processes and **B.4.2** Effects of human activities and natural phenomena.

24 Plant Reproduction and Response

Big idea: Growth, Development, and Reproduction

Q: How do changes in the environment affect the reproduction, development, and growth of plants?

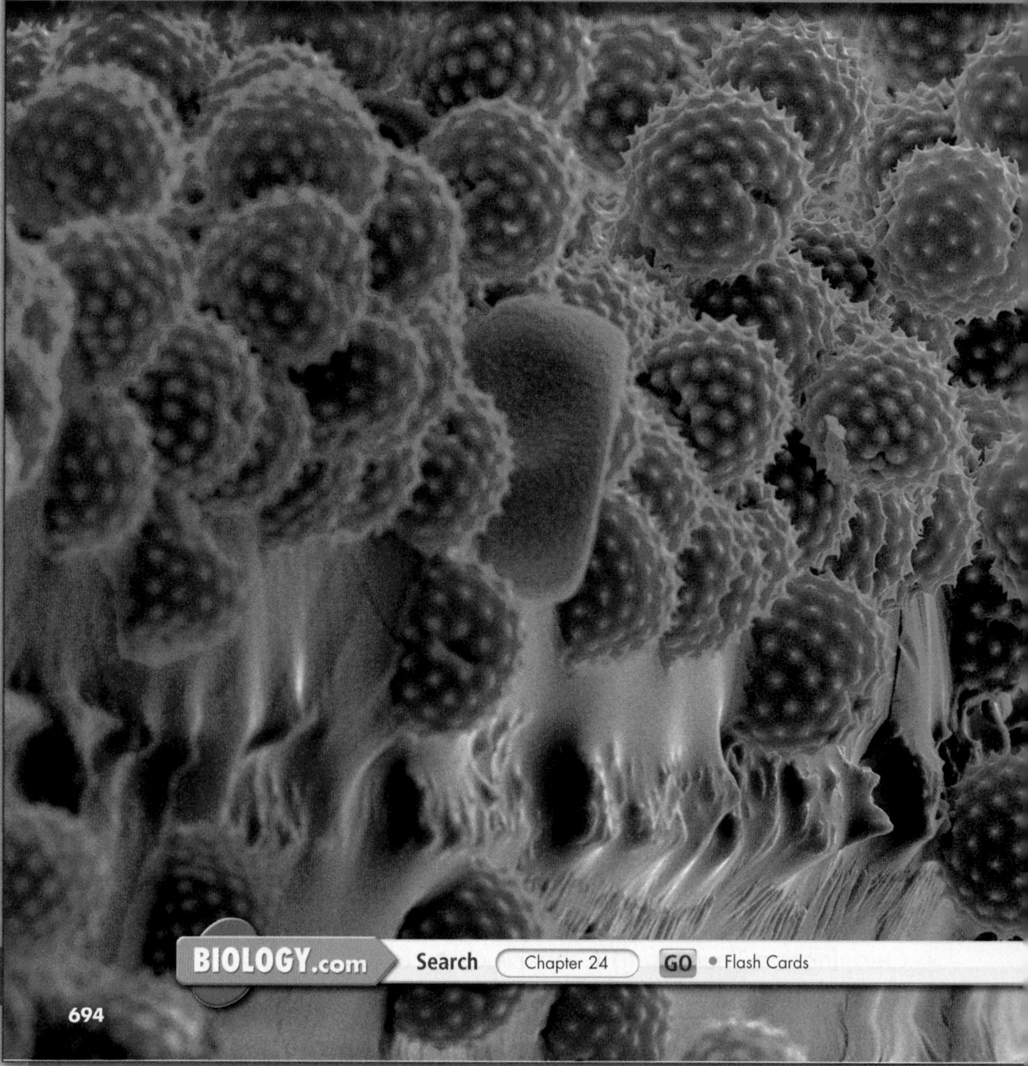

BIOLOGY.com Search Chapter 24 GO • Flash Cards

694

UbD Understanding by Design

Chapter 24 helps students move toward the Enduring Understanding for Unit 6: *From microorganisms to plants, organisms vary widely in the way they carry out basic life processes.* Students discover in Chapter 24 how plants grow, develop, and reproduce, and how the environment plays a role in these processes. As shown in the graphic organizer at the right, a Big Idea, Essential Question, and lesson-level Guiding Questions help frame students' exploration of this Enduring Understanding.

PERFORMANCE GOALS

Chapter 24 will lead students to understand how plants grow, develop, and reproduce, and how these life processes are connected with changes in the environment. Intermediate performance tasks require students to show their understandings through written tasks, visual presentation of concepts, and an infomercial. After completing the chapter, students will synthesize chapter concepts by designing a garden.

INDIANA ACADEMIC STANDARDS FOR SCIENCE

Nature of Science NoS.1, NoS.3; **Cellular Chemistry** B.1.2; **Interdependence** B.4.2. See lessons for details.

Pollen grains from the common ragweed (SEM 1375×)

• Untamed Science Video • Chapter Mystery

CHAPTER MYSTERY

THE GREEN LEMONS

For years, a California warehouse had stored freshly picked green lemons before they were shipped to market. The warehouse managers knew that the lemons would be a ripe yellow and ready to ship to market about five days after they arrived. Or so they thought. One year, for safety reasons, they decided to replace the warehouse's kerosene heaters with modern electric ones. Then, to their astonishment, when they began to pack their first shipment of five-day-old lemons, they had to call a halt. The fruit they expected to ship were still a bright, and very unripe, green. What had happened? As you read the chapter, look for clues that provide information about the case of the green lemons. Solve the mystery.

Never Stop Exploring Your World. Finding the solution to The Green Lemons mystery is only the beginning. Take a video field trip with the ecogeeks of Untamed Science to see where this mystery leads.

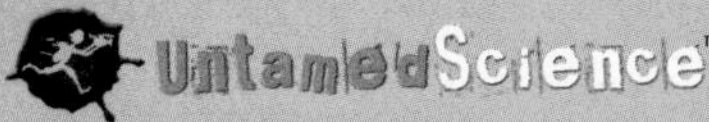

Chapter 24 Big Idea: Growth, Development, and Reproduction

Chapter 24 EQ: How do changes in the environment affect the reproduction, development, and growth of plants?

24.1 GQ: How do flowering plants reproduce?

24.2 GQ: How are fruits and seeds important adaptations for plants?

24.3 GQ: How do plants respond to their environments?

24.4 GQ: In what ways do humans depend on plants?

What's Online

Extend your reach by using these and other digital assets offered at **Biology.com.**

CHAPTER MYSTERY
Students use their knowledge of plant processes to solve the mysterious case of the green lemons.

UNTAMED SCIENCE VIDEO
Plants move in mysterious ways . . . or so it seems. Follow the Untamed Science crew as they get to the root of the problem: how do plants move in response to their environment?

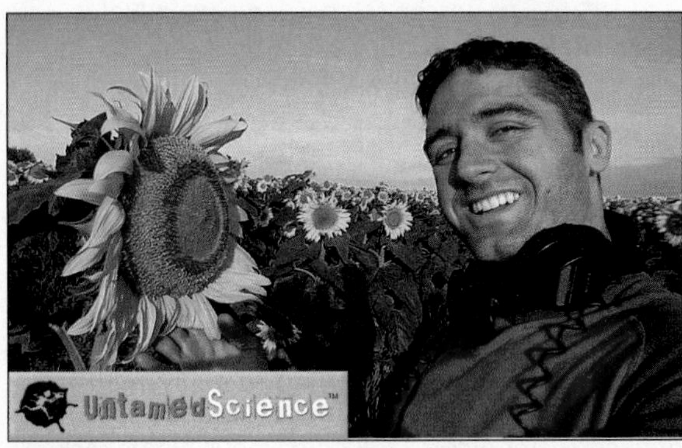

ART REVIEW
Students can drag and drop labels onto a diagram of a flower.

ART IN MOTION
This animation shows the processes of meiosis and mitosis in the production of ova and pollen in an angiosperm.

INTERACTIVE ART
This activity allows students to examine the effects of changing day length on plants.

DATA ANALYSIS
This activity allows students to analyze potential fuel energy that can be obtained from plants.

LESSON 24.1

Getting Started

Objectives

24.1.1 Identify the functions of various structures in a flower.

24.1.2 Explain how fertilization differs between angiosperms and other plants.

24.1.3 Describe vegetative reproduction.

Student Resources

Study Workbooks A and B, 24.1 Worksheets

Spanish Study Workbook, 24.1 Worksheets

Lesson Overview • Lesson Notes

- Activities: Art Review, Art in Motion
- Assessment: Self-Test, Lesson Assessment

For corresponding lesson in the **Foundation Edition**, see pages 578–584.

Activate Prior Knowledge

Display pictures of a wide variety of angiosperms, including flowering trees, shrubs, ground covers, grasses, water plants, and herbaceous plants. Ask students to identify which ones are angiosperms. *(Some students might identify only plants that are showing flowers, such as herbaceous plants.)* Tell students all the pictures show angiosperms. Then ask them to recall the defining characteristic of angiosperms. *(Angiosperms produce flowers and seeds in fruits.)* Explain that some angiosperms, such as grasses and many types of trees, have flowers at some point in their life cycle, but the flowers are small and easy to miss.

24.1 Reproduction in Flowering Plants

Key Questions

What are flowers?

How does fertilization in angiosperms differ from fertilization in other plants?

What is vegetative reproduction?

Vocabulary

stamen • anther • carpel • stigma • pistil • embryo sac • double fertilization • endosperm • vegetative reproduction • grafting

Taking Notes

Two-Column Table Construct a two-column table with the headings, *Male Gametophyte* and *Female Gametophyte.* As you read, take notes on the characteristics of each type of gametophyte.

THINK ABOUT IT What makes a flower beautiful? The symmetry of its petals, its rich colors, and, sometimes, its fragrance. But, at the heart of it, what's behind all this beauty? The answer is, simply, angiosperm sexual reproduction. To a plant, the whole point of a flower is to bring gametes together for reproduction and to protect the resulting zygote and embryo.

The Structure of Flowers

What are flowers?

You may think of flowers as decorative objects that brighten our world, and so they are. However, the presence of so many flowers in the world is visible evidence of something else—the stunning evolutionary success of the angiosperms, or flowering plants. The structure of a typical angiosperm flower is shown in **Figure 24–1. Flowers are reproductive organs that are composed of four different kinds of specialized leaves: sepals, petals, stamens, and carpels.**

Sepals and Petals The outermost circle of floral parts contains the sepals (SEE pulz). In many plants, the sepals are green and closely resemble ordinary leaves. Sepals enclose the bud before it opens, and they protect the flower while it is developing. Petals, which are often brightly colored, are found just inside the sepals. The colors, number, and shapes of such petals attract insects and other pollinators to the flower.

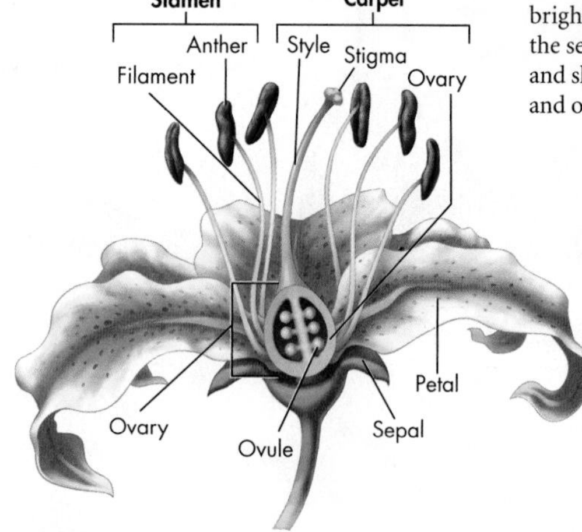

FIGURE 24–1 The Parts of a Flower This diagram shows the parts of a typical flower. The flowers of some angiosperm species, however, do not have all the parts shown here.

UbD Teach for Understanding

ENDURING UNDERSTANDING From microorganisms to plants, organisms vary widely in the way they carry out basic life processes.

GUIDING QUESTION How do flowering plants reproduce?

EVIDENCE OF UNDERSTANDING *After completing the lesson, give students the following assessment to show they understand the major steps in the reproduction of angiosperms.* Give a copy of **Figure 24–6** without labels to each student. Have students write labels and captions in their own words to summarize the life cycle. Tell them to include specific references to pollination, double fertilization, and the endosperm.

Stamens Within the ring of petals are the structures that produce male and female gametophytes. The **stamens** are the male parts of the flower. Each stamen consists of a stalk called a filament with an anther at its tip. **Anthers** are the structures in which pollen grains—the male gametophytes—are produced. In most angiosperm species, the flowers have several stamens. If you rub your hand on the anthers of a flower, a yellow-orange dust may stick to your skin. This dust is made up of thousands of individual pollen grains.

Carpels The innermost floral parts are the carpels. **Carpels** produce and shelter the female gametophytes and, later, seeds. Each carpel has a broad base forming an ovary, which contains one or more ovules where female gametophytes are produced. The diameter of the carpel narrows into a stalk called the style. At the top of the style is a sticky or feathery portion known as the **stigma,** which is specialized to capture pollen. Botanists sometimes call a single carpel or several fused carpels a **pistil.**

In Your Notebook *Make a two-column table labeled Male and Female. Then list and define the structures that make up a flower in the appropriate column.*

Variety in Flowers Flowers vary greatly in shape, color, and size, as shown in **Figure 24–2.** A typical flowering plant produces both male and female gametophytes. In some species, however, male and female gametophytes are produced on different plants. In some species, many flowers grow close together to form a composite structure that looks like a single flower, as seen in the Queen Anne's lace at right.

FIGURE 24–2 Variety Among Flowers Flowers vary greatly in structure. **Form a Hypothesis** ***How might it be an advantage for a plant to have many flowers clustered in a single structure?***

◀ **Iris** The drooping petal-like structures are in fact modified sepals. The fuzzy yellow stripe running down the center guides bees and other pollinators to the male and female parts at the interior of the flower.

Queen Anne's Lace Some flowerlike structures are actually clusters of many individual flowers. ▶

Passion Flower Some flowers have stamens and pistils you can easily count. In this dramatic flower, five stamens lie beneath three pistils. ▼

Wild Rose This flower has many stamens surrounding a tight cluster of carpels at the center. ▶

697

Quick Facts

FLOWER TYPES

A species that has male and female flowers on separate plants is called dioecious. Male flowers lack carpels, and female flowers lack stamens. Examples of dioecious plants are holly and willow. Monoecious plants, such as pecan trees, birches, and corn, have male and female flowers on the same plant. Monoecious plants and perfect flowers (those with stamens and carpels in each flower) can self-pollinate. This confers a survival advantage to a plant that is too far away from others of the same species to be cross-pollinated. However, plants that result from cross-pollination are usually more successful because of the combination of different genetic material.

Teach

Use Visuals

Refer students to **Figure 24–1.** Emphasize that the reproductive organs of flowers are specialized leaves. Ask students to locate and study each kind of specialized leaf as a student volunteer reads the sentences in the text that describe them. Call on students to describe the roles of the different structures of a flower.

DIFFERENTIATED INSTRUCTION

L1 Special Needs Have students refer to **Figure 24–1** to construct a model of a flower. Provide various materials, or ask students to bring in materials from home. For example, students might use construction paper (sepals and petals), toothpicks (filaments), cornmeal (pollen), drinking straws (styles), dry peas (ovules), modeling clay, or other art supplies. Invite students to explain their models to the class.

ELL Focus on ELL: Access Content

BEGINNING AND INTERMEDIATE SPEAKERS Have students use a **T-Chart** to organize information on flower structure. On the left side of the chart, have them list the main parts of a flower: *sepal, petal, stamen, carpel.* On the right side, they can draw and describe each part. Beginning speakers can use phrases with less than precise vocabulary to describe the main parts of a flower, or use their native language. Intermediate speakers should use simple sentences.

Study Wkbks A/B, Appendix S30, T-Chart. **Transparencies,** GO15.

BIOLOGY.com Have students use the **Art Review: The Parts of a Flower** to review the parts of an angiosperm flower.

Answers

FIGURE 24–2 Sample answer: Having many flowers clustered together might improve each flower's chance of being pollinated by a pollen-carrying insect that touches the flower.

IN YOUR NOTEBOOK The Male column should include the stamen, consisting of the filament and anther. The Female column should include the carpel, which consists of the ovary, style, and stigma.

Teach continued

Build Reading Skills

Point out that reading comprehension sometimes involves an understanding of the order, or sequence, in which events occur. Help students understand the sequence of steps in the development of male gametophytes. Have students read the first paragraph on this page. Then, have students read the next paragraph, thinking about what takes place first, second, third, and so on. Refer students to **Figure 24–3** to help them visualize the steps. Call on students to name each step in the development of male gametophytes in sequence.

DIFFERENTIATED INSTRUCTION

LPR Less Proficient Readers Point out that the text does not always use order words, such as *first, next, then,* and *finally.* However, illustrations may offer clues to the sequence of events. Call students' attention to the arrows in **Figure 24–3.** Point out the words, *meiosis* and *mitosis,* that appear above the arrows.

Ask In the formation of male gametes, which happens first, mitosis or meiosis? *(meiosis)* How can you tell? *(Because, in the illustration, the arrow labeled* meiosis *appears before—i.e., to the left of—the arrow labeled* mitosis.*)*

Answers

IN YOUR NOTEBOOK Sample flowchart: The first step is the production of four haploid pollen spores by meiosis. The second step is the division of the nucleus of each pollen spore by mitoisis. The third step is the formation of the male gametophyte when the pair of nuclei are surrounded by a cell wall.

Quick Lab GUIDED INQUIRY

What Is the Structure of a Flower?

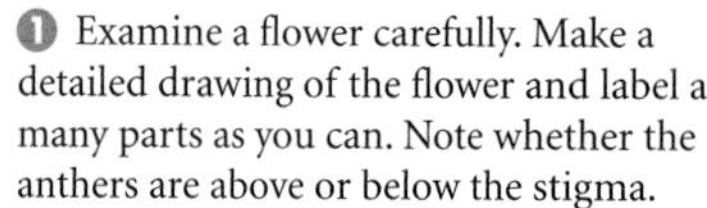

1. Examine a flower carefully. Make a detailed drawing of the flower and label as many parts as you can. Note whether the anthers are above or below the stigma.
2. Remove an anther and place it on a slide. While holding the anther with forceps, use the scalpel to cut one or more thin slices across the anther. **CAUTION:** *Be careful with sharp tools. Place the slide on a flat surface before you start cutting.*
3. Lay the slices flat on the microscope slide and add a drop of water and a coverslip. Observe the slices with the microscope at low power. Make a labeled drawing of your observations.
4. Repeat steps 2 and 3 with the ovary.

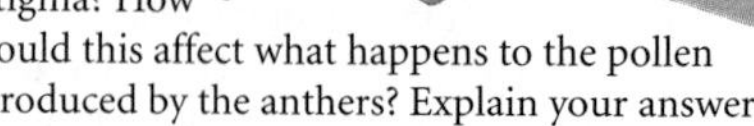

Analyze and Conclude

1. **Observe** Are the anthers in this flower located above or below the stigma? How could this affect what happens to the pollen produced by the anthers? Explain your answer.
2. **Apply Concepts** What structures did you identify in the anther? What is the function of these structures?
3. **Apply Concepts** What structures did you identify in the ovary? What is the function of these structures?
4. **Draw Conclusions** Which parts of the flower will become the seeds? Which parts will become the fruit?

The Angiosperm Life Cycle

How does fertilization in angiosperms differ from fertilization in other plants?

Like other plants, angiosperms have a life cycle that shows an alternation of generations between a diploid sporophyte phase and a haploid gametophyte stage. Recall that in vascular plants, including ferns and gymnosperms, the sporophyte plant is much larger than the gametophyte. This trend continues in angiosperms, where male and female gametophytes live within the tissues of the sporophyte.

Development of Male Gametophytes The male gametophytes—the pollen grains—develop inside anthers. This process is shown in the top half of **Figure 24–3.** First, meiosis produces four haploid spore cells. Each spore undergoes one mitotic division to produce the two haploid nuclei of a single pollen grain. The two nuclei are surrounded by a thick wall that protects the male gametophyte from dryness and damage when it is released. The pollen grains stop growing until they are released from the anther and land on a stigma.

In Your Notebook *Make a flowchart that records the stages of development of an angiosperm's male gametophyte.*

Quick Lab

PURPOSE Students will observe the structures of a flower and conclude which become seeds and which become the fruit.

MATERIALS flower, microscope slide, forceps, scalpel, water, dropper pipette, coverslips, microscope

SAFETY Remind students to be careful when using the scalpel. Have students handle glassware with care.

PLANNING Before students cut their flower, make sure they have noted whether the anthers are above or below the stigma.

ANALYZE AND CONCLUDE

1. Answers will vary. If the anthers are higher than the stigma, pollen could fall directly from the anthers onto the stigma; the flower could self-pollinate. If the anthers are below the stigma, the flower would be more likely to be cross-pollinated.
2. Students may be able to observe pollen. Pollen grains form male gametophytes that can fertilize female gametophytes.
3. Students may be able to observe ovules. The ovules produce female gametophytes containing eggs that can be fertilized by male gametophytes.
4. The ovules will become the seeds. Generally, the ovary becomes the fruit.

Development of Female Gametophytes While the male gametophytes are forming, female gametophytes develop inside each carpel of a flower. The ovules—the future seeds—are enveloped in a protective ovary—the future fruit.

How do the female gametophytes form? As shown in the bottom half of **Figure 24–3,** a single diploid cell goes through meiosis to produce four haploid cells, three of which disintegrate. The remaining cell undergoes mitosis, producing eight nuclei. These eight nuclei and the surrounding membrane are called the **embryo sac.** The embryo sac, contained within the ovule, makes up the female gametophyte of a flowering plant.

Next, cell walls form around six of the eight nuclei. One of the eight nuclei, near the base of the gametophyte, is the nucleus of the egg—the female gamete. If fertilization takes place, this egg cell will fuse with the male gamete to become the zygote that grows into a new sporophyte plant.

ZOOMING IN

THE DEVELOPMENT OF GAMETOPHYTES

FIGURE 24–3 The diagrams show the development of the male gametophyte inside an anther and the development of the female gametophyte inside a single ovule. Interpret Visuals ***In each case—male and female—which cellular process produces the first haploid cell?***

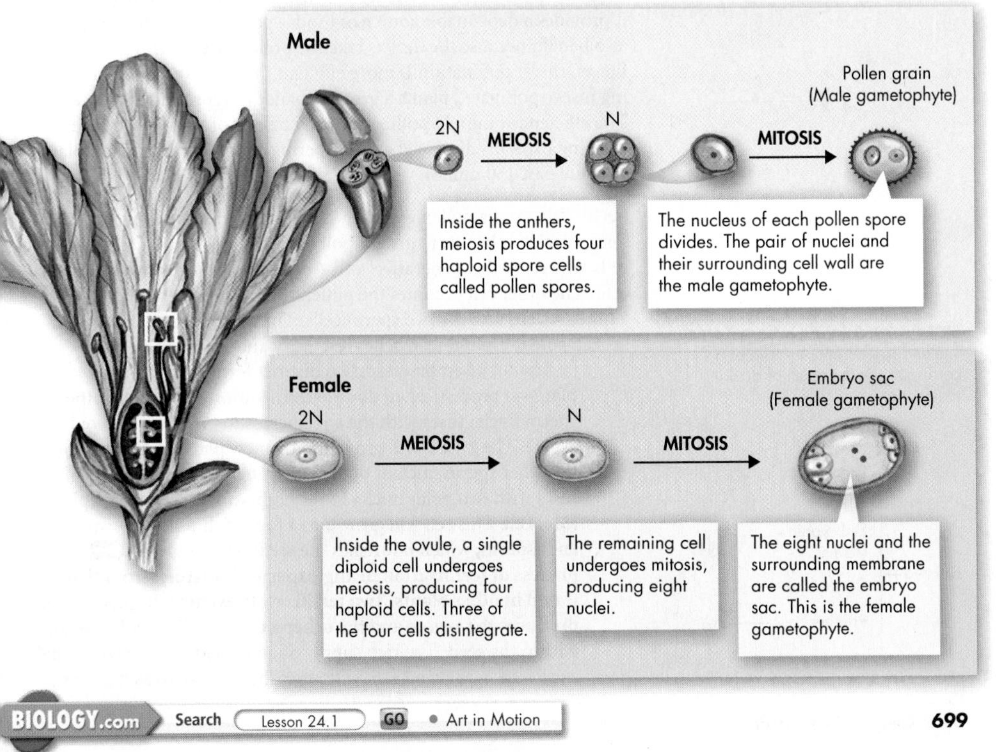

Male
Pollen grain
(Male gametophyte)
2N
MEIOSIS
N
MITOSIS
Inside the anthers, meiosis produces four haploid spore cells called pollen spores.
The nucleus of each pollen spore divides. The pair of nuclei and their surrounding cell wall are the male gametophyte.
Female
Embryo sac
(Female gametophyte)
2N
MEIOSIS
N
MITOSIS
Inside the ovule, a single diploid cell undergoes meiosis, producing four haploid cells. Three of the four cells disintegrate.
The remaining cell undergoes mitosis, producing eight nuclei.
The eight nuclei and the surrounding membrane are called the embryo sac. This is the female gametophyte.

Check for Understanding

INDEX CARD SUMMARIES

Give each student an index card. Ask them to summarize a major concept they understand about the angiosperm life cycle on one side. Then, have them write something about the life cycle they don't understand on the back of the card in the form of a question.

ADJUST INSTRUCTION

If more than one student is having difficulty understanding a concept, have the class work together to rephrase the part of the text where the concept is discussed or to present the concept visually in a different way than the text; all students may benefit from reinforcement. If only one student is having difficulty, work with the student one-on-one, or assign a peer buddy to help.

ZOOMING IN

Direct students' attention to **Figure 24–3,** and have them read the captions and labels. Ask students to compare and contrast development of male and female gametophytes. Reinforce that meiosis results in four haploid cells for both male and female (three of which disintegrate in the case of the female gametophyte), while mitosis results in two nuclei for each pollen grain and eight nuclei for the embryo sac.

DIFFERENTIATED INSTRUCTION

L1 Special Needs Students may benefit from drawing the steps in development of gametophytes or working with manipulatives, such as buttons, to make models of the process. Pair special-needs students with more proficient students so they can work together to produce the model.

ELL English Language Learners Pair beginning speakers with advanced speakers whose native language is the same as that of the beginners. The advanced speaker should discuss **Figure 24–3** with the beginner, helping the beginner to take notes. The beginner can use his or her native language or a combination of English and the native language.

BIOLOGY.com Have students access the **Art in Motion: The Development of Gametophytes** to examine the production of ova and pollen in an angiosperm.

Address Misconceptions

Gamete versus Gametophyte Students may think that pollen is the male gamete. Make sure they understand that pollen is the male gametophyte, which contains male gametes. Reinforce that in angiosperms, the male gametes are the two sperm nuclei inside the pollen grain.

Answers

FIGURE 24–3 Meiosis produces the first haploid cell in both male and female gametophyte development.

Teach continued

Lead a Discussion

Explain to students that insects, like humans, have cone cells in their retinas that perceive certain wavelengths of light. However, the color vision of insects is shifted toward the shorter wavelengths: yellow-green to ultraviolet. Many flowers pollinated by insects have patterns that can be seen only by animals whose vision centers in the ultraviolet range.

To humans, for example, a blue flower may look blue all over, but bees see a large dark area in the middle of the blue petals. Patterns such as this are called nectar guides. They help the bee find the flower's center, where the nectar is located.

Emphasize that sensing particular colors and scents are adaptations that have developed in animals that enable them to find sources of food. These adaptations are also key to the reproduction of angiosperms. Review the concept of coevolution, and have students discuss how this has contributed to angiosperms' dominance among land plants.

DIFFERENTIATED INSTRUCTION

L3 Advanced Students Have students hypothesize from an evolutionary and ecological viewpoint why it might be an advantage for different pollinators to "specialize" in certain flower colors or types. In addition, students should hypothesize how this benefits plants. *(Sample answer: The pollinators share the same habitat and same resources, so utilizing different food sources avoids direct competition. This benefits plants because the more diverse and numerous the pollinators, the better the chances that plants will reproduce.)* Encourage students to use state wildlife resources to find out the pollinators of ten herbaceous plants common to your state, and to look for correlations between the two groups (for example, is the abundance of certain pollinators correlated with the blooming season of certain plants?). Have them present their findings and conclusions to the class.

FIGURE 24–4 Pollination The appearance of a flower often indicates how it is pollinated. The flowers of an oak tree (left) are typical of wind-pollinated flowers in that they are small and not very showy but produce vast amounts of pollen. In contrast, many animal-pollinated flowers are large and brightly colored (right).

BUILD Vocabulary

RELATED WORD FORMS Several word forms are derived from the word *pollen*. *Pollination* is the transfer of pollen from one flower to another. A *pollinator* is an animal that moves pollen.

Pollination Pollination is the transfer of pollen to the female portions of the flower. Some angiosperms are wind pollinated, but most are pollinated by animals. These animals, mainly insects, birds, and bats, carry pollen from one flower to another. Because wind pollination is less efficient than animal pollination, wind-pollinated plants, such as the oak tree in **Figure 24–4,** rely on favorable weather and sheer numbers of pollen grains to get pollen from one plant to another. Animal-pollinated plants have a variety of adaptations, such as bright colors and sweet nectar, to attract and reward animals. Animals have evolved body shapes that enable them to reach nectar deep within certain flowers. For example, hummingbirds have long, thin beaks that can probe deep into flowers to reach the nectar supply.

Insect pollination is beneficial to insects and other animals because it provides a dependable source of food—pollen and nectar. Plants also benefit because the insects take the pollen directly from flower to flower. Insect pollination is more efficient than wind pollination, giving insect-pollinated plants a greater chance of reproductive success. The efficiency of insect pollination may be one of the main reasons why angiosperms displaced gymnosperms as the dominant land plants over the past 130 million years.

Fertilization If a pollen grain lands on the stigma of a flower of the same species, it begins to grow a pollen tube. Of the pollen grain's two cells, one cell—the "generative" cell—divides and forms two sperm cells. The other cell becomes the pollen tube. The pollen tube contains a tube nucleus and the two sperm cells. The pollen tube grows into the style, where it eventually reaches the ovary and enters an ovule.

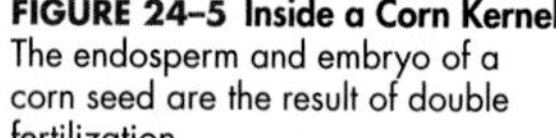

FIGURE 24–5 Inside a Corn Kernel The endosperm and embryo of a corn seed are the result of double fertilization.

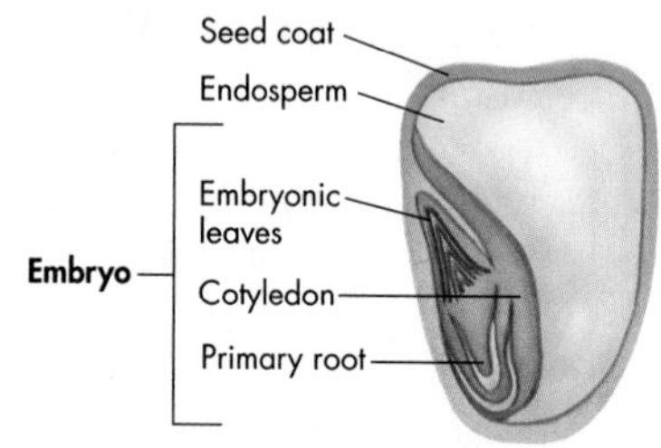

Inside the embryo sac, two distinct fertilizations take place—a process called **double fertilization.** First, one of the sperm nuclei fuses with the egg nucleus to produce a diploid zygote. The zygote will grow into the new plant embryo. Second, the other sperm nucleus does something truly remarkable—it fuses with two polar nuclei in the embryo sac to form a triploid (3N) cell. This cell will grow into a food-rich tissue known as **endosperm,** which nourishes the seedling as it grows. **The process of fertilization in angiosperms is distinct from that found in other plants. Two fertilization events take place—one produces the zygote and the other a tissue, called endosperm, within the seed.** The rich supply of endosperm, as shown in the corn seed in **Figure 24–5,** will nourish the embryo as it grows.

Biology In-Depth

ALLERGIES TO POLLEN

Many people are allergic to the pollen of certain angiosperms. Most pollen allergies are caused by wind-pollinated species. Many trees, grasses, and weeds produce huge quantities of pollen that are carried for hundreds of miles and can end up inside the lining of nasal passages. In people who are allergic to pollen, the immune system treats the pollen as an invader and releases chemicals, such as histamine, which cause the symptoms of allergy. The body reacts to proteins in the coat of the pollen grain. People may be allergic to certain pollens but not to other pollens, because each type of pollen has a different protein coat. Allergies to the pollen of insect-pollinated flowers are uncommon and usually limited to people who have had prolonged contact with these types of flowers, such as florists.

VISUAL SUMMARY

ANGIOSPERM LIFE CYCLE

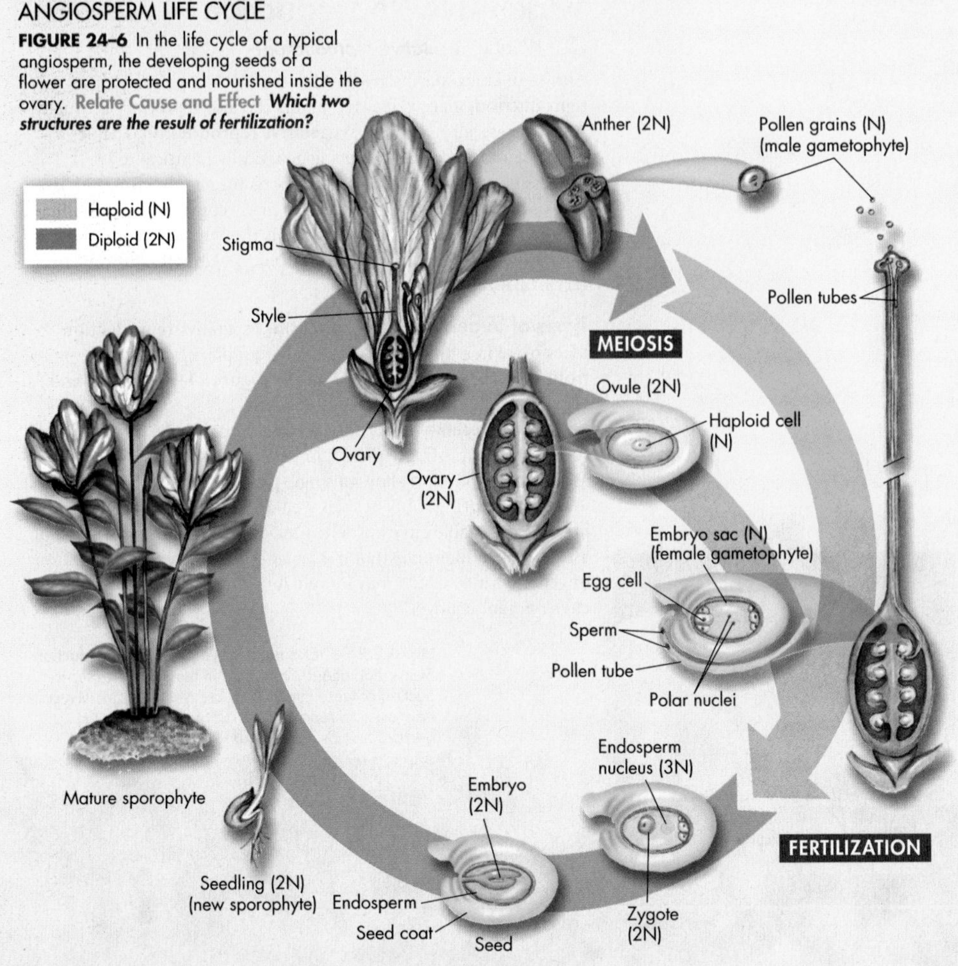

FIGURE 24–6 In the life cycle of a typical angiosperm, the developing seeds of a flower are protected and nourished inside the ovary. Relate Cause and Effect ***Which two structures are the result of fertilization?***

Double fertilization may be another reason why the angiosperms have been so successful. By using endosperm to store food, the flowering plant spends very little energy on producing seeds from ovules until double fertilization has actually taken place. The energy saved can be used to make many more seeds. **Figure 24–6** summarizes the life cycle of a typical angiosperm.

In Your Notebook *Make an outline detailing the key features of angiosperm reproduction.*

VISUAL SUMMARY

Use **Figure 24–6** to discuss double fertilization, the endosperm, and the entire angiosperm life cycle. Emphasize that double fertilization in angiosperms is unique among plants. Make sure students recognize the alternation of generations in the angiosperm life cycle by having them compare this figure to the general plant life cycle in **Figure 22–5.**

Ask Where does fertilization take place? *(inside an ovule in the ovary)*

Ask How do sperm cells reach the ovary? *(through a pollen tube that grows down through the style)*

Ask Which parts of the seed are haploid? *(none)* Diploid? *(embryo)* Triploid? *(endosperm)*

Ask How does the endosperm form? *(A sperm nucleus fuses with two polar nuclei in the embryo sac.)*

DIFFERENTIATED INSTRUCTION

L1 Struggling Students Make sure students are not confused by the two paths in the life cycle at the points where haploid cells are produced. Explain that the path on top shows how the male gametophyte is formed, and the path under it shows the formation of the female gametophyte. If necessary, have students review **Figure 24–3** and the text describing the development of male and female gametophytes. To help students understand the color coding differentiating between haploid and diploid stages, work with them so that they understand **Figure 22–5,** which shows a generalized life cycle.

ELL English Language Learners On the board, write the boldface sentence of the Key Concept under the subhead **Fertilization.** Point to the structures in **Figure 24–6** involved in the formation of the zygote and the endosperm as you orally describe how both events occur. Ask intermediate and advanced speakers to write descriptions of these events on the board; rephrase or correct their descriptions if necessary.

UbD Check for Understanding

ONE-MINUTE RESPONSE

Give students one minute to write a brief summary of the process of double fertilization. *(Students should summarize the fusion of one sperm nucleus with the egg to produce a zygote and the fusion of the other sperm nucleus with two polar nuclei to form an endosperm nucleus.)*

ADJUST INSTRUCTION

If students are unable to describe double fertilization completely or correctly, use the appropriate parts of **Figure 24–6** as a guide to draw the process on the board. It may be helpful to use an overhead projector and different color markers for the male and female gametes.

Answers

FIGURE 24–6 The zygote and the endosperm nucleus result from fertilization.

IN YOUR NOTEBOOK Student outlines should include development of male and female gametophytes, pollination, and double fertilization with the formation of a zygote and endosperm.

Teach continued

Use Visuals

Remind students they have been learning about sexual reproduction in angiosperms. Explain that many flowering plants can also reproduce asexually. Use **Figure 24–7** to discuss some of the ways angiosperms reproduce vegetatively. Have students read the caption and recall the kind of tissue present at the tips of stems. *(apical meristem)* Remind them that this tissue is originally undifferentiated, but it can differentiate into each of the three tissue systems of a plant. Emphasize that vegetative reproduction involves only mitosis, not meiosis, and that gametes, flowers, or fertilization are not required. Have students discuss the advantages and disadvantages of vegetative reproduction.

DIFFERENTIATED INSTRUCTION

ELL English Language Learners Point out that the word *vegetative* in the term *vegetative reproduction* means "growing as or like a plant" and not "having to do with vegetables," as students might assume. Explain that the term *vegetative reproduction* refers to any type of reproduction in plants that involves vegetating, or growing, tissues instead of reproductive tissues and seeds.

LPR Less Proficient Readers For students having trouble reading or understanding the captions in **Figure 24–7,** ask them to first describe what they see. Give them clues such as pointing out the potato and asking what they see happening to it. Ask them to write their own captions based on what they see. Then, have them reread the captions on the book page, which should now make more sense.

Answers

FIGURE 24–7 Plants that reproduce asexually can grow quickly because they do not follow the steps in the life cycle of pollination, fertilization, and development from seeds.

Vegetative Reproduction

What is vegetative reproduction?

Although angiosperms are best known by their patterns of sexual reproduction, many flowering plants can also reproduce asexually. This process, also known as **vegetative reproduction,** enables a single plant to produce offspring genetically identical to itself. This process takes place naturally in many plants, and horticulturalists also use it as a technique to produce many copies of an individual plant. **Vegetative reproduction is the formation of new individuals by mitosis. It does not require gametes, flowers, or fertilization.**

Types of Vegetative Reproduction Vegetative reproduction takes place in a number of ways. For example, new plants may grow from roots, leaves, stems, or plantlets. **Figure 24–7** shows several ways plant species reproduce vegetatively.

Because vegetative reproduction does not involve pollination or seed formation, a single plant can reproduce quickly. In addition, asexual reproduction allows a single plant to produce genetically identical offspring. This enables well-adapted individuals to rapidly fill a favorable environment. One of the obvious drawbacks of asexual reproduction is that it does not produce new combinations of genetic traits, which may be valuable if conditions in the physical environment change.

FIGURE 24–7 Examples of Vegetative Reproduction Stem adaptations play a role in the vegetative reproduction of these three plants. Apply Concepts ***Describe how asexual reproduction might allow a plant to become rapidly established in a new area.***

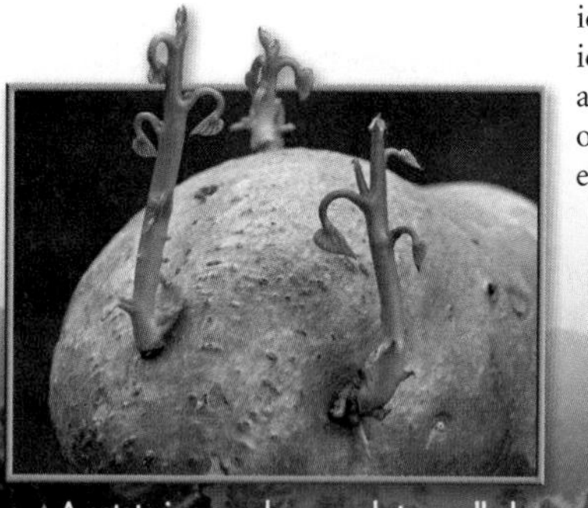

▲ A potato is an underground stem called a tuber that can grow whole new plants from buds called *eyes*.

▲ Strawberry plants send out long, trailing stems called stolons. Nodes that rest on the ground produce roots and upright stems and leaves.

Cholla and many other cactus species can reproduce by dropping sections of their stems. The small individuals growing at the base of the larger adults are, in fact, clones.

702 Chapter 24 • Lesson 1

How Science Works

VEGETATIVE PROPAGATION OF ENDANGERED PLANTS

Vegetative propagation can sometimes be used to help save plant species that are in danger of becoming extinct. When researchers find individual plants growing in the wild, they can carefully remove cuttings from the plants and take the cuttings to a laboratory. There, the researchers try to use vegetative propagation techniques to produce additional plants from the cuttings. For example, botanists in Tasmania have begun to use vegetative propagation in an attempt to save the shrub *Philotheca freyciana,* whose common name is the Freycinet wax flower. Only about 100 plants of this species survive in the wild. The botanists have taken cuttings from some of the surviving plants and successfully propagated them, producing 70 new plants growing in pots.

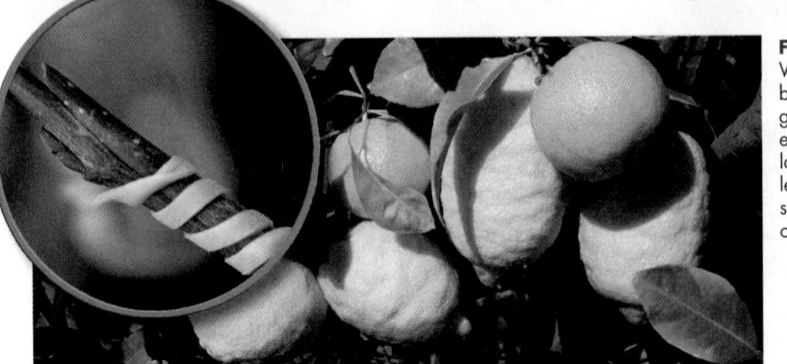

FIGURE 24–8 Grafting When just starting to bud, a branch from a lemon tree is grafted onto the branch of an established orange tree. Months later, the mature branch bears lemon fruit. Grafting leads to a single plant bearing more than one species of fruit.

Plant Propagation Horticulturists often take advantage of vegetative reproduction. To propagate plants with desirable characteristics, horticulturists use cuttings or grafting to make many identical copies of a plant or to produce offspring from seedless plants.

One of the simplest ways to reproduce plants vegetatively is by cuttings. A grower cuts from the plant a length of stem that includes a number of buds containing meristem tissue. That stem is then partially buried in soil or in a special mixture of nutrients that encourages root formation.

Grafting is a method of propagation used to reproduce seedless plants and varieties of woody plants that cannot be propagated from cuttings. To graft, a piece of stem or a lateral bud is cut from the parent plant and attached to another plant, as shown in **Figure 24–8.** Grafting works only when the two plants are closely related, such as when a bud from a lemon tree is grafted onto an orange tree. Grafting usually works best when plants are dormant, which allows the wounds created by the cut to heal before new growth starts.

MYSTERY CLUE

Whether the lemons grew on a grafted branch or not did not affect the ripening schedule. Rather, a certain variable that changed after the lemons were harvested contributed to the failure of the lemons to ripen. What might it have been?

24.1 Assessment

Review Key Concepts

1. a. **Review** Name and describe four kinds of specialized leaves that make up a flower.
   b. **Classify** Which of the structures of a flower are the male sexual organs? Which are the female organs?
2. a. **Review** Describe the features of fertilization that are characteristic of angiosperms.
   b. **Explain** How is fertilization in angiosperms different from fertilization in other types of plants?
   c. **Apply Concepts** Relate the characteristics of angiosperm reproduction to angiosperm success.
3. a. **Review** Define vegetative reproduction.
   b. **Compare and Contrast** Compare the advantages and disadvantages of sexual reproduction versus asexual reproduction in flowering plants.

VISUAL THINKING

4. Review the life cycle of the green alga *Chlamydomonas* in Lesson 22.2. Make a compare/contrast table comparing alternation of generations in flowering plants and in *Chlamydomonas.* Include which stage (haploid or diploid) of each organism's life cycle is dominant and when meiosis occurs.

BIOLOGY.com Search Lesson 24.1  • Lesson Assessment • Self-Test

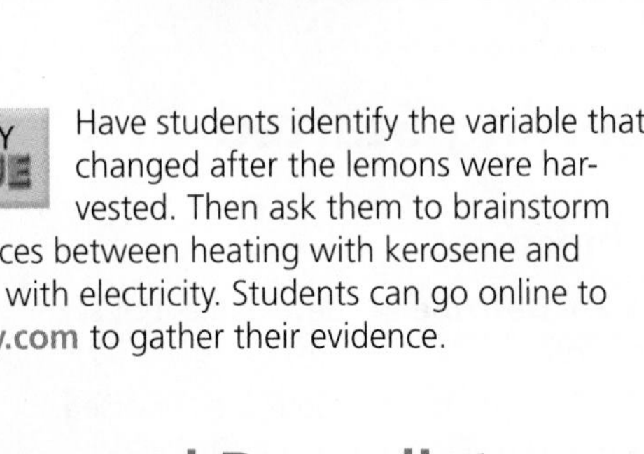

MYSTERY CLUE Have students identify the variable that changed after the lemons were harvested. Then ask them to brainstorm differences between heating with kerosene and heating with electricity. Students can go online to Biology.com to gather their evidence.

Assess and Remediate

EVALUATE UNDERSTANDING

Start a progressive series of statements related to the Key Concepts of the lesson. For example, you might start by saying, "Flowers have four different kinds of specialized leaves." Call on students to take turns providing statements that logically follow the previous statements. A student might follow your statement with "Petals are one kind of specialized leaf, and they attract pollinators." Continue until everyone has had a turn. Then, have students complete the 24.1 Assessment.

REMEDIATION SUGGESTION

L1 Struggling Students If your students have trouble with **Question 2,** review how fertilization takes place in seedless plants and gymnosperms. Then ask them to reread the last paragraphs under **Pollination** and **Fertilization.** Have students summarize in two or three sentences how pollination and fertilization are distinct in angiosperms and how these features have helped them to become successful.

BIOLOGY.com Students can check their understanding of lesson concepts with the **Self-Test** assessment. They can then take the online version of the **Lesson Assessment.**

Assessment Answers

1a. sepals: green and resemble ordinary leaves; petals: often brightly colored and found just inside the sepals; stamen: a filament and an anther; carpel: a style, a stigma, and an ovary

1b. male: stamens; female: carpels

2a. Answers should include development of male and female gametophytes, pollination, and double fertilization.

2b. Fertilization in other plants involves one event. In angiosperms, two events take place—one produces the zygote and the other an endosperm.

2c. Angiosperms tend to be successful because many have flowers that attract pollinators, and they use the endosperm to store food.

3a. Vegetative reproduction is a process in which a single plant produces offspring genetically identical to itself.

3b. Sexual: new combinations of genetic traits are produced that help plants survive changing environmental conditions, but it takes time and resources to produce offspring. Asexual: plants grow rapidly in a favorable environment, but it does not result in new combinations of traits that may aid survival.

VISUAL THINKING

4. Tables should include that the dominant stage in flowering plants is diploid and meiosis occurs inside anthers. In *Chlamydomonas,* the dominant stage is haploid, and meiosis occurs in the zygote.

Getting Started

Objectives

24.2.1 Describe the development of seeds and fruits.

24.2.2 Explain how seeds are dispersed.

24.2.3 List the factors that influence the dormancy and germination of seeds.

Student Resources

Study Workbooks A and B, 24.2 Worksheets

Spanish Study Workbook, 24.2 Worksheets

Lab Manual B, 24.2 Data Analysis Worksheet

Lesson Overview • Lesson Notes • Assessment: Self-Test, Lesson Assessment

For corresponding lesson in the **Foundation Edition**, see pages 585–587.

Activate Prior Knowledge

Display an apple, a tomato, and a green bean. Point out that each specimen is an enlarged and ripened ovary, or fruit. Then open each fruit to reveal the seeds inside.

Answers

FIGURE 24–9 the peanut shell

IN YOUR NOTEBOOK Students should not have checked roots (such as carrots), stems (such as celery), and leaves (such as spinach).

IN INDIANA ACADEMIC STANDARDS

For the full text of all standards, see the Course Overview in the front matter of this book.

NoS.3 Clearly communicate their ideas and results of investigations verbally and in written form using tables, graphs, diagrams, and photographs.

24.2 Fruits and Seeds

IN NoS.3 Communicate ideas.

Key Questions

How do fruits form?

How are seeds dispersed?

What factors influence the dormancy and germination of seeds?

Vocabulary

dormancy
germination

Taking Notes

Flowchart Make a flowchart that shows the process of germination and the factors that influence it. Indicate the differences between monocots and dicots.

THINK ABOUT IT What are fruits, and what purpose do they serve for the plants that produce them? Would it surprise you to learn that if you ate a meal of corn on the cob and baked beans, from the point of view of a biologist, you were actually eating fruit? And have you ever wondered why plants go to the "trouble" of surrounding their seeds with tasty, fleshy fruits like those produced by apples, oranges, and grapes? Here's a hint: You, and all the animals that enjoy those fruits, are being used. Plants may be smarter than you think.

Seed and Fruit Development

How do fruits form?

The development of the seed, which protects and nourishes the plant embryo, contributed greatly to the success of plants on land. The *angiosperm* seed, encased inside a fruit, was an even better adaptation. As you will see, by helping a seed get into the best possible location to start its new life, fruits were immediately favored by natural selection.

Once fertilization of an angiosperm is complete, nutrients flow into the flower tissue and support the development of the growing embryo within the seed. **As angiosperm seeds mature, ovary walls thicken to form a fruit that encloses the developing seeds.** A fruit is simply a matured angiosperm ovary, usually containing seeds. An exception is found in commercially grown fruits that are selectively bred to be seedless, such as some varieties of grapes. Examples of fruits are shown in **Figure 24–9.**

The term *fruit* applies to the sweet things we usually think of as fruits, such as apples, grapes, and strawberries. However, foods such as peas, corn, beans, rice, cucumbers, and tomatoes, which we commonly call vegetables, are also fruits.

The ovary wall surrounding a simple fruit may be fleshy, as it is in grapes and tomatoes, or tough and dry, like the shell that surrounds peanuts. (The peanuts themselves are the seeds.)

Strawberries ▼

Rose Hips ▼

Peanut Shell ▼

FIGURE 24–9 Variety Among Fruits Like the flowers from which they develop, fruits vary in structure. **Observe** *Which example is a dry fruit?*

In Your Notebook *Make a list of the first ten "vegetables" that come to mind and place a check mark next to ones you think are fruits. Explain why.*

UbD Teach for Understanding

ENDURING UNDERSTANDING From microorganisms to plants, organisms vary widely in the way they carry out basic life processes.

GUIDING QUESTION How are fruits and seeds important adaptations for plants?

EVIDENCE OF UNDERSTANDING *After completing the lesson, give students the following assessment to show they understand how fruits are an adaptation to promote seed dispersal.* Ask students to work in pairs or small groups to create a one-minute infomercial to "sell" a fruit to a potential "buyer"—an animal that will disperse the seeds. Students should include how the fruit forms, why it might appeal to the animal, and how it benefits the animal.

Seed Dispersal

How are seeds dispersed?

What are fleshy fruits for, and why have they been favored by natural selection? They are not there to nourish the seedling—the endosperm does that. So why should these plants have seeds that are wrapped in an additional layer of nutrient-packed tissue? It seems pointless, but in evolutionary terms, it makes all the sense in the world.

Think of the blackberries that grow wild in the forests of North America. Each seed is enclosed in a sweet, juicy fruit, making it a tasty treat for all kinds of animals. What good is such sweetness if all it does is get the seed eaten? Well, believe it or not, that's exactly the point.

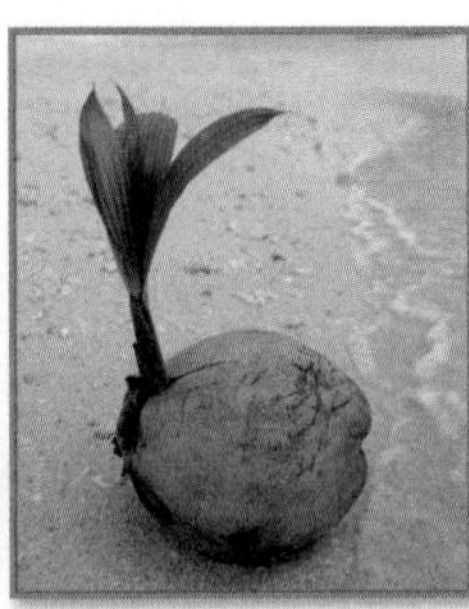

FIGURE 24–10 Mechanisms of Seed Dispersal A Bohemian waxwing feasts on mountain ash berries (left) and will later disperse the seeds in its feces. Parachute-like dandelion fruits catch the wind, carrying the tiny attached seeds far and wide (middle). The buoyant coconut fruit can disperse its seed over great distances of water (right).

Dispersal by Animals The seeds of many plants, especially those encased in sweet, fleshy fruits, are often eaten by animals. The seeds are covered with tough coatings, allowing them to pass through an animal's digestive system unharmed. The seeds then sprout in the feces eliminated from the animal. These fruits provide nutrition for the animal and also help the plant disperse its seeds—often to areas where there is less competition with the parent plants. **Seeds contained in fleshy, nutritious fruits are usually dispersed by animals.** Three mechanisms of seed dispersal are shown in **Figure 24–10.**

Animals also disperse many dry fruits, but not necessarily by eating them. Dry fruits sometimes have burs or hooks that catch in an animal's fur, enabling them to be carried many miles from the parent plant.

Dispersal by Wind and Water Animals are not the only means by which plants can scatter their seeds. Seeds are also adapted for dispersal by wind and water. **Seeds dispersed by wind or water are typically contained in lightweight fruits that allow them to be carried in the air or in buoyant fruits that allow them to float on the surface of the water.** A dandelion seed, for example, is attached to a dry fruit that has a parachute-like structure. This adaptation allows the seed to glide considerable distances away from the parent plant. Some seeds, like the coconut, are dispersed by water. Coconut fruits are buoyant enough to float in seawater for many weeks, enabling the seeds to reach and colonize even remote islands.

Teach

Lead a Discussion

Start a discussion by asking students to identify ways in which seeds are spread. Point out that animals, wind, and water allow seed dispersal into new habitats, which is important because plants are rooted in one place. Have students note that the structural adaptations of seeds and their fruits determine the mechanisms of dispersal.

DIFFERENTIATED INSTRUCTION

L1 Special Needs Provide students with a large selection of various fruits, such as berries, apples, walnuts, winged dandelion seeds, and burdock burs. Have students observe the fruits, noting distinguishing characteristics. Then, ask students to infer from those characteristics the mechanism by which each seed is dispersed.

ELL Focus on ELL: Build Background

BEGINNING SPEAKERS After students have seen the photos of seed dispersal on this page, brainstorm with students to answer the question "What are some other ways in which seeds are dispersed, or spread?" Help beginning speakers use words or phrases, for example, "stick to dog fur," or "squirrel buries acorn." Provide additional help by showing students photos of seed dispersal similar to those on this page. List the responses on the board. Then help students organize their responses in a **T-Chart**—one column listing ways seeds are spread by animals, and the other column listing ways seeds are spread by wind and water. Encourage students to add new information to their lists as they read.

Study Wkbks A/B, Appendix S30, T-Chart. **Transparencies,** GO15.

UbD Check for Understanding

VISUAL REPRESENTATION

Ask students to construct a **Two-Column Table** that describes the details of the two major ways in which seeds are dispersed. Information in one column should describe the characteristics of fruits adapted to disperse their seeds by animal means; the other column should describe the same for fruits adapted for wind or water dispersal.

ADJUST INSTRUCTION

If students do not fully understand seed dispersal, focus their attention on the information in **Figure 24–10.** Discuss each photo, and have students describe, in detail, the characteristics of the seeds and their fruit that facilitate dispersal by animals, wind, or water.

Study Wkbks A/B, Appendix S31, Two-Column Table. **Transparencies,** GO16.

Teach continued

Use Visuals

Use **Figure 24–11** to explain the steps in germination. Point out that seeds must have water to begin the process. Emphasize that a seed germinates only when environmental factors are favorable. Make sure students understand that the cotyledons provide food to the growing embryo. Have them note the differences between monocots and dicots in the way the young shoots grow.

DIFFERENTIATED INSTRUCTION

L1 Struggling Students You can help students understand the process shown in **Figure 24–11** by having students observe it firsthand. Have them place corn and bean seeds between two wet paper towels on a plate and place plastic wrap over the plate. Place the plates in a warm place, and after a few days, remove the plastic and the paper towels. Have students observe the roots and shoots under low-power magnification and draw what they see. Work with students to help them understand how their observations of seed germination correlate with the stages shown in **Figure 24–11.**

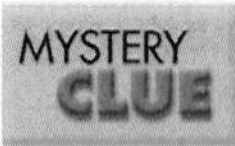

Have students visualize conditions in a storage warehouse. Then have students discuss how those conditions could have changed with the switch to electric heating. Students may suggest that the kerosene heaters emitted a substance that the electric heaters did not, or that the electric current somehow interfered with ripening. Students can go online to Biology.com to gather their evidence.

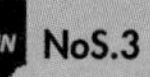

NoS.3

Temperature and Seed Germination

Arisaema dracontium—"green dragon"—is a plant that grows from the southern United States to Canada. The graph shows germination rates of *Arisaema* seeds gathered from two locations and stored at two different temperatures.

1. Interpret Graphs What effect does chilling have on germination of seeds from Ontario? How does it affect the seeds from Louisiana?

2. Form a Hypothesis Describe how the different rates of seed germination might be explained in terms of adaptation to the local climate.

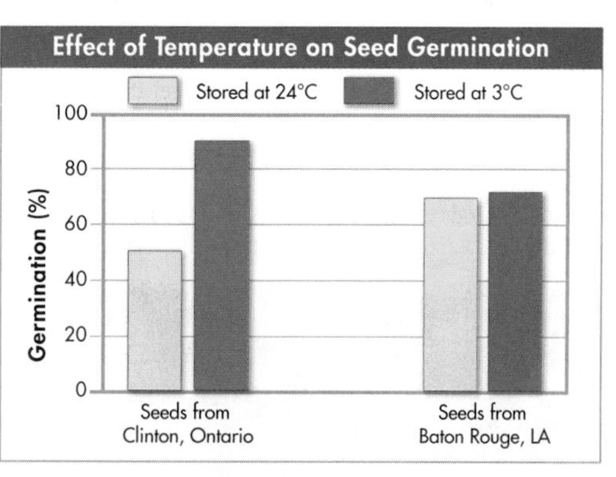

BUILD Vocabulary

WORD ORIGINS The word **dormancy** comes from the Latin word *dormire*, meaning "to sleep."

What variables in the lemons' environment could have changed with the switch to electric heating? Start a list of variables that affect seed development and fruit ripening. Add to your list as you continue reading the chapter.

Seed Dormancy and Germination

What factors influence the dormancy and germination of seeds?

Some seeds sprout so rapidly that they are practically instant plants. Bean seeds are a good example. With proper amounts of water and warmth, a mature bean seed rapidly sprouts and develops into a green plant. But many seeds will not grow when they first mature. Instead, these seeds enter a period of **dormancy,** during which the embryo is alive but not growing. The length of dormancy varies in different species. **Germination** is the resumption of growth of the plant embryo. **Environmental factors such as temperature and moisture can cause a seed to end dormancy and germinate.**

How Seeds Germinate Before germinating, seeds absorb water. The absorbed water causes food-storing tissues to swell, cracking open the seed coat. Through the cracked seed coat, the young root emerges and begins to grow. The shoot—the part of the plant that will grow above ground—emerges next.

The Role of Cotyledons Cotyledons are a flowering plant's first leaves. Their job is to store nutrients and then transfer them to the growing embryo as the seed germinates. **Figure 24–11** compares germination in a monocot and a dicot. Monocots have a single cotyledon, which usually remains underground while it passes nutrients to the young plant. The growing monocot shoot emerges from the soil protected by a sheath. In dicots, which have two cotyledons, there is no sheath to protect the tip of the young plant. Instead, the upper end of the shoot bends to form a hook that forces its way through the soil. This protects the delicate tip of the plant, which straightens as it emerges into the sunlight. In some species, the cotyledons appear above ground as the plant emerges, while in others, such as the garden pea, the cotyledons remain underground.

PURPOSE Students will interpret data to analyze germination rates of seeds stored at different temperatures.

PLANNING Remind students that bar graphs are commonly used to show comparisons.

ANSWERS

1. Chilling greatly increases the percentage of seeds from Ontario that germinate. The difference is very slight for seeds from Louisiana.
2. Sample answer: As a result of natural selection, the plants in Ontario produce seeds with adaptations that enable them to germinate better in the very low temperatures that characterize early spring in Ontario. Chilling does not enhance germination of Louisiana seeds because cold-temperature germination is not a survival-enhancing characteristic in the warmer Louisiana environment.

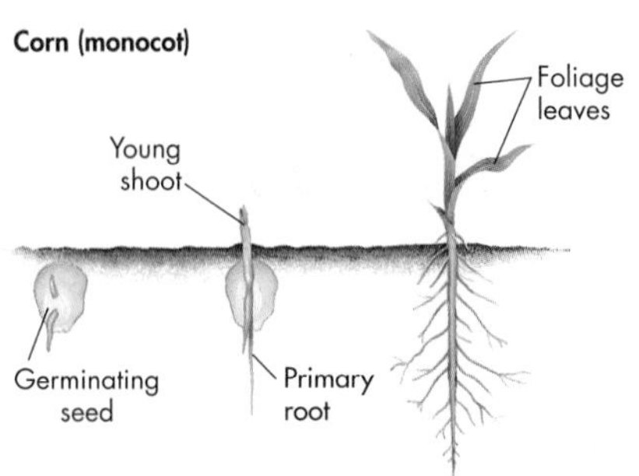

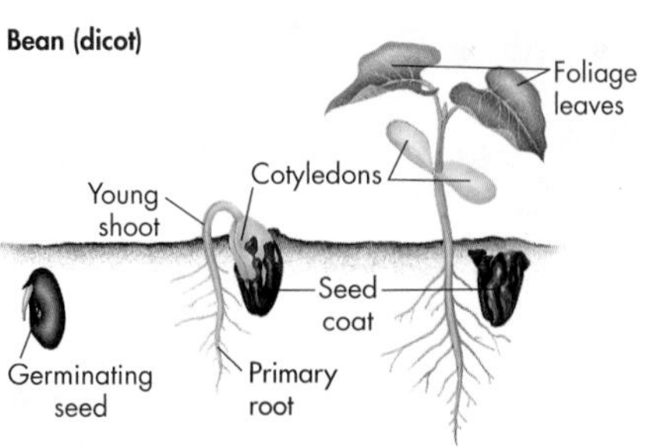

FIGURE 24–11 Germination: A Comparison The monocot corn seedling (left) grows directly upward, protected by a sheath of tissue that surrounds the developing leaves. In contrast, the garden bean (right) forms a hook in its stem that gently pulls the new plant tissues through the soil. Predict *What might happen to a germinating seedling that lacked such adaptations?*

Advantages of Dormancy Seed dormancy can be adaptive in several ways. For one, it can allow for long-distance dispersal. And it also allows seeds to germinate under ideal growth conditions. The seeds of most temperate plants, for example, germinate in the spring, when conditions are best for growth. For some species, a period of cold temperatures during which the seeds are dormant is required before growth can begin. Seeds can easily survive winter cold, but many young green plants cannot. The period of cold that is required is long enough that seeds will not germinate until the dangerous winter season has passed.

Sometimes, only extreme environmental conditions can end seed dormancy. Some pine trees, for example, produce seeds in cones that remain sealed until the high temperatures generated by forest fires cause the cones to open. The high temperature both activates and releases the seeds, allowing the plants to reclaim the forest quickly after a fire.

24.2 Assessment

NoS.3

Review Key Concepts

1. a. Review Describe how fruits form.
   b. Infer Is a pumpkin a fruit? Describe any evidence you use in making your inference.
2. a. Review Describe two methods of seed dispersal.
   b. Pose Questions A new angiosperm species is discovered. What questions would you ask before predicting how its seeds are dispersed? Explain the rationale for asking each question.
3. a. Review Summarize the environmental factors that affect seed germination.
   b. Explain Why is it adaptive for some seeds to remain dormant before they germinate?
   c. Apply Concepts The seeds of a bishop pine germinate only after exposure to the extreme heat of a forest fire. Evaluate the significance of this structural adaptation.

WRITE ABOUT SCIENCE

Creative Writing

4. Imagine that you are writing a children's book about seeds and that you are working on the chapter on dispersal. Write from one to three paragraphs on seed dispersal by wind. *Hint:* Try to include details that you would have found appealing when you were about eight years old.

BIOLOGY.com Search Lesson 24.2  • Lesson Assessment • Self-Test

Assess and Remediate

EVALUATE UNDERSTANDING

Read the boldface sentences and the sentences defining the vocabulary terms. In each case, leave blank the most significant term or terms in the sentence. Call on students to fill in the blanks without referring to their texts. Then, have students complete the 24.2 Assessment.

REMEDIATION SUGGESTION

L1 **Struggling Students** If your students have trouble with inferring in **Question 1b,** help them think of the question in another way, for example, "How do you know that a plant part is a fruit?" Students should recall that a fruit is a matured ovary that usually contains seeds.

Ask Does a pumpkin have seeds inside? (*yes*)

BIOLOGY.com Students can check their understanding of lesson concepts with the **Self-Test** assessment. They can then take an online version of the **Lesson Assessment.**

Answers

FIGURE 24–11 The delicate, growing tips would not be protected, and if damaged, the plant might not be able to continue growing.

Assessment Answers

1a. As angiosperm seeds mature, ovary walls thicken around the seed; the mature ovary is the fruit.

1b. A pumpkin is a fruit. Sample answer: A pumpkin forms from the ovary of a flower, and it has seeds inside.

2a. Students should describe any two methods by animals, wind, or water.

2b. Answers will vary. Sample answer: Is the fruit fleshy? If yes, then it will probably be eaten by animals. Are the fruits dry, lightweight, or buoyant? If so, they may be dispersed by wind or water.

3a. Temperature and moisture affect seed germination.

3b. Dormancy enables a seed to survive until environmental conditions become favorable. Dormancy may also allow long-distance dispersal.

3c. Sample answer: Since most of the trees in the forest will have been destroyed by fire, this adaptation decreases competition for resources, thus creating a favorable environment. Also, it helps ensure that the species will survive fires.

WRITE ABOUT SCIENCE

4. Students' paragraphs should contain accurate details about the physical characteristics of seeds that allow them to be dispersed by wind, e.g., seeds are lightweight and may have a structure that enables them to glide on wind currents.

LESSON 24.3

Getting Started

Objectives

24.3.1 Describe the effects of hormones on plant growth and development.

24.3.2 Identify three tropisms exhibited in plants.

24.3.3 Describe how plants respond to seasonal change.

Student Resources

Study Workbooks A and B, 24.3 Worksheets

Spanish Study Workbook, 24.3 Worksheets

Lab Manual B, 24.3 Hands-On Activity

Lesson Overview • Lesson Notes • Activity: InterActive Art • Assessment: Self-Test, Lesson Assessment

For corresponding lesson in the **Foundation Edition**, see pages 588–592.

Build Background

Call students' attention to the vocabulary terms *phototropism, gravitropism,* and *thigmotropism.* Explain that the root word *tropism* is from a Greek word meaning "turning." Challenge students to infer the meaning of the three terms. *(phototropism—turning due to light, gravitropism—turning due to gravity, thigmotropism—turning due to touch)* Note that the prefixes *photo* and *gravi* may be ones they can infer, but you will most likely need to supply the meaning of *thigmo (touch).*

IN INDIANA ACADEMIC STANDARDS

For the full text of all standards, see the Course Overview in the front matter of this book.

B.1.2 Understand that the shape of a molecule determines its role in the many different types of cellular processes including metabolism, homeostasis, growth and development, and heredity, and understand that the majority of these processes involve proteins that act as enzymes.

24.3 Plant Hormones

IN B.1.2 Molecules and cellular processes. Also covered: NoS.3.

Key Questions

What roles do plant hormones play?

What are some examples of environmental stimuli to which plants respond?

How do plants respond to seasonal changes?

Vocabulary

hormone • target cell • receptor • auxin • apical dominance • cytokinin • gibberellin • abscisic acid • ethylene • tropism • phototropism • gravitropism • thigmotropism • photoperiodism

Taking Notes

Concept Map As you read, build a concept map summarizing the effects of different hormones on plant growth.

THINK ABOUT IT Plants, like all organisms, are collections of cells. Plants grow in response to factors such as light, moisture, temperature, and gravity. But how do roots "know" to grow down, and how do stems "know" to grow up? How do the tissues of a plant determine the right time of year to produce flowers? In short, how do the collections of cells in a plant manage to act together as a single organism? Is something carrying messages from cell to cell?

Hormones

What roles do plant hormones play?

Hormones are chemical signals produced by living organisms that affect the growth, activity, and development of cells and tissues. In plants, hormones may act on the same cells in which they are made, or they may travel to different cells and tissues. This is in contrast to *animal* hormones, which typically act at a location some distance away from the cells that produce them.

Plant hormones serve as signals that control development of cells, tissues, and organs. They also coordinate responses to the environment. The two functions fit together well, because plants respond to the environment mainly by changing their development.

The steps in one mechanism of hormone action in plants is shown in **Figure 24–12.** In this case, the hormone moves through the plant from the place where it is produced to the place where it triggers its response.

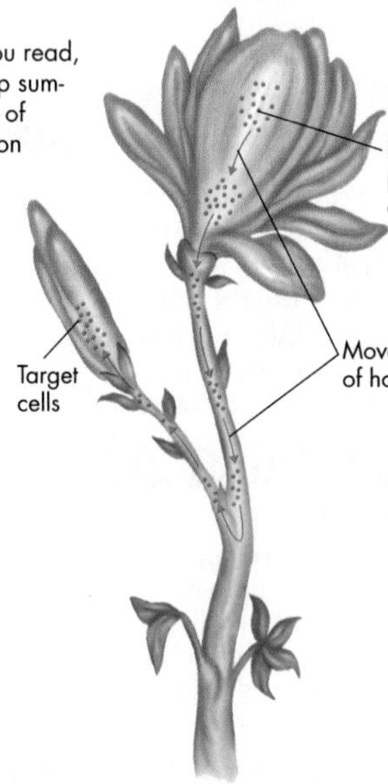

Hormone-producing cells

Target cells

Movement of hormone

FIGURE 24–12 Hormones and Flower Development In some species, hormone-producing cells in a mature flower release hormones that travel into flower buds and inhibit development. Once the mature flower is done blooming, production of the inhibiting hormone will decline, and the flower bud can then begin its bloom.

UbD Teach for Understanding

ENDURING UNDERSTANDING From microorganisms to plants, organisms vary widely in the way they carry out basic life processes.

GUIDING QUESTION How do plants respond to their environments?

EVIDENCE OF UNDERSTANDING *After completing the lesson, give students the following assessment to show whether they understand how and why plants respond to light, temperature, moisture, and gravity.* Ask students to draw lines that divide a sheet of paper into fourths. In each section, they should write "Light," "Temperature," "Moisture," and "Gravity." Have students describe one plant response to each stimulus. Then have them connect to the Big Idea by writing a brief paragraph summarizing how each response is important to the reproduction, development, and/or growth of the plant.

How Hormones Act Cells in an organism affected by a particular hormone are called **target cells.** To respond to a hormone, a cell must contain hormone **receptors**—usually proteins—to which hormone molecules bind. The response that results will depend on what kinds of receptors are present in the target cell. One kind of receptor might alter metabolism; a second might speed growth; a third might inhibit cell division. Thus, depending on the receptors present, a given hormone may affect roots differently from stems or flowers—and the effects may change as the developing organs add or remove receptors. Cells that do not contain receptors are generally unaffected by hormones.

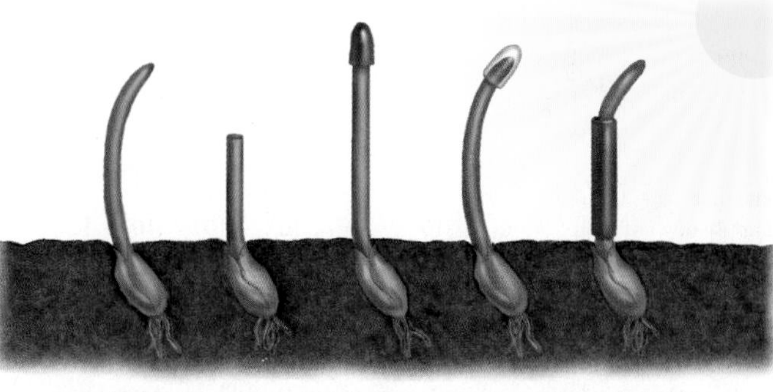

FIGURE 24–13 How Plants Detect Light The Darwins conducted controlled experiments to determine which region of the plant senses light. When they removed the seedling tip or placed an opaque cap over the tip, they observed no bending toward light. But when they placed a clear cap on the tip or an opaque shield around the base, they observed bending similar to that seen in the control. Control Variables ***What variable did the Darwins control for by comparing the results of seedlings treated with a clear cap versus no cap?***

Auxins The first step in the discovery of plant hormones came over a century ago, and was made by a scientist already familiar to you. In 1880, Charles Darwin and his son Francis published the results of a series of experiments exploring the mechanism behind a grass seedling's tendency to bend toward light as it grows.

The results of their experiments, shown in **Figure 24–13,** suggested that the tip of the seedling somehow senses light. The Darwins hypothesized that the tip produces a substance that regulates cell growth. More than forty years later, the regulatory substances produced by the tips of growing plants were identified and named *auxins.* **Auxins** stimulate cell elongation and the growth of new roots, among other roles that they play. They are produced in the shoot apical meristem and transported to the rest of the plant.

▶ ***Auxins and Cell Elongation*** One of the effects of auxins is to stimulate cell elongation, as shown in **Figure 24–14.** In the Darwins' experiment, when light hits one side of the shoot, auxins collect in the shaded part of the shoot. This change in concentration stimulates cells on the dark side to lengthen. As a result, the shoot bends away from the shaded side and toward the light.

FIGURE 24–14 Auxins and Cell Elongation Cells elongate more on the shaded side of the shoot, where there is a higher concentration of auxins.

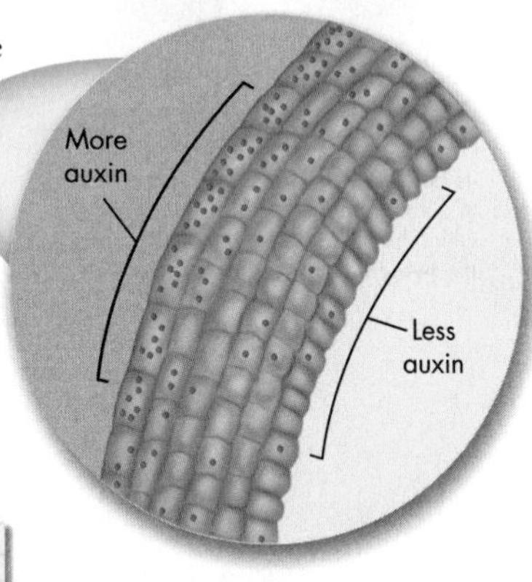

In Your Notebook *Review **Figure 24–13.** Describe how the results led the Darwins to conclude that the tip of the seedling senses light.*

Teach

Use Visuals

Have students examine **Figure 24–12** and read the caption. Explain that plant hormones control growth and development as well as responses to the environment. Tell students that hormones are produced in apical meristems, in young leaves, in roots, and in growing flowers and fruits. Then, direct students' attention to **Figure 24–13** and have them follow along as you describe the Darwins' experiment. Make sure students understand in **Figure 24–14** that high concentrations of auxin cause cells on the side of the shoot away from the light source to lengthen.

DIFFERENTIATED INSTRUCTION

L3 Advanced Students Students might enjoy trying to duplicate the Darwins' experiment. They can use oat seedlings, which grow quickly. Challenge them to think of materials they could use. (*Hint:* Aluminum foil will work for the opaque caps and bands, and clear plastic wrap for the clear caps.) Have students share their methods and results with the class.

ELL Focus on ELL: Extend Language

ADVANCED HIGH SPEAKERS Have students write a detailed description of **Figure 24–13,** including a description of what each part of the illustration shows. Where appropriate, their descriptions should include the words *auxin, stimulate,* and *elongation.* Have students read their descriptions aloud in small groups. Each group should then use the detailed description as the starting point for a discussion about how plants detect light.

How Science Works

SYNTHETIC AUXINS

Growers of apples and citrus fruits used to lose considerable amounts of their crops when fruits fell from trees before harvest time. Now, orchards often are sprayed with synthetic auxins, such as 2,4-D (2,4-dichlorophenoxyacetic acid), to induce fruits to remain on trees longer. The auxins apparently retard the formation of the fruit abscission layer. (When this layer of cells forms at the base of a fruit stalk, the stalk breaks free and the fruit falls to the ground.)

Synthetic auxins are also used for a different purpose. Because high concentrations of auxins inhibit growth, high concentrations of synthetic auxins can be used as selective herbicides, which kill certain plants but not others. For example, 2,4-D acts on broad-leaved plants but not grasses with narrow, bladelike leaves.

Answers

FIGURE 24–13 They controlled for whether the presence of a cap by itself would affect a plant's response to light.

IN YOUR NOTEBOOK Changes that still allowed the tip of the stem to be exposed to light had no effect on bending; removing the tip and preventing the tip from exposure to light resulted in an absence of bending.

Teach continued

Connect to the Real World

Help students recall that primary growth in stems occurs at the tip. The stem also produces lateral buds, which are meristematic areas on the side of a stem that give rise to side branches. These do not start growing right away because auxins from the tip inhibit their growth. Discuss apical dominance, and tell students that gardeners help give landscape plants a more compact, filled-in look by snipping off the tips of stems. Have students look at **Figure 24–15** and relate the shapes of the plants to the presence or absence of auxins in the lateral branches of the plants.

Ask How will the plant on the left look if it is not cut back? Explain. *(It will continue to grow taller. It will have few lateral branches, because auxins in the apical meristem will continue to inhibit the growth of lateral buds.)*

Then, discuss how the effects of cytokinins are opposite those of auxins.

Ask What can you infer about the effect of cytokinins on lateral buds when the apical meristem is cut off? *(The cytokinins would help lateral buds to grow because they stimulate cell division, and the action of cytokinins would not be opposed by auxins.)*

DIFFERENTIATED INSTRUCTION

L1 Struggling Students If students have difficulty understanding the opposite ways in which auxins and cytokinins act, have them make a simple sketch of a plant. With a partner, have students use differently colored pencils for auxin and cytokinin to show the site of production and target sites for each hormone. Students should draw an arrow showing the movement of each hormone through the plant, then write a short summary of each hormone's action.

Answers

FIGURE 24–15 The plant on the left is taller but not as full. The plant on the right is shorter and bushier.

IN YOUR NOTEBOOK In shoots, auxins stimulate cell elongation and inhibit lateral buds; auxins stimulate the growth of new roots. Cytokinins stimulate cell division in shoots and inhibit the growth of new roots.

Analyzing Data

NoS.3

Auxins and Plant Growth

This graph shows the results of experiments in which carrot cells were grown in the presence of varying concentrations of auxins. The blue line shows the effects on root growth. The red line shows the effects on stem growth.

1. **Interpret Graphs** At what auxin concentration are the stems stimulated to grow the most?
2. **Interpret Graphs** How is the growth of the roots affected by the auxin concentration at which stems grow the most?
3. **Infer** If you were a carrot farmer, what concentration of auxin should you apply to your fields to produce the largest carrot roots?

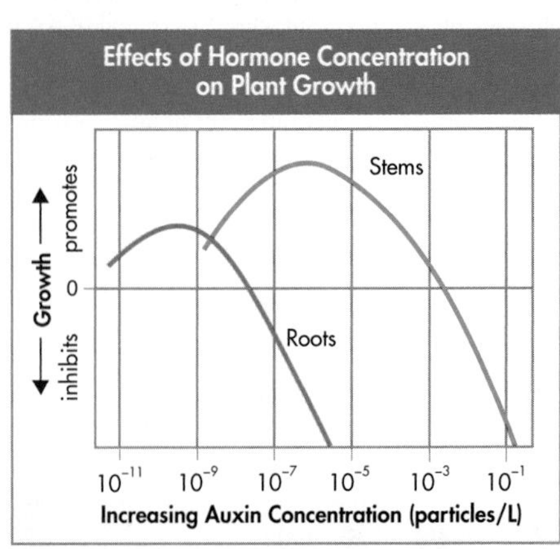

FIGURE 24–15 Apical Dominance The basil plant on the right has had its apical meristem pinched off, in contrast to the plant on the left, which hasn't. **Observe** *How are the two plants different?*

▶ ***Auxins and Branching*** Auxins also regulate cell division in meristems. As a stem grows in length, it produces lateral buds. As you may have observed, the buds near the apex grow more slowly than those near the base of a plant. The reason for this delay is that growth at the lateral buds is inhibited by auxins. Because auxins move out from the apical meristem, the closer a bud is to the stem's tip, the more it is inhibited. This phenomenon is called **apical dominance.** If you snip off the tip of a plant, these lateral buds begin to grow more quickly. The plant becomes bushier. This is because the apical meristem—the source of the growth-inhibiting auxins—has been eliminated.

Cytokinins **Cytokinins** are plant hormones that are produced in growing roots and in developing fruits and seeds. Cytokinins stimulate cell division, they interact with auxins to help to balance root and shoot growth, and stimulate regeneration of tissues damaged by injury. Cytokinins also delay the aging of leaves and play important roles in the early stages of plant growth.

Cytokinins often produce effects opposite to those of auxins. For example, root tips make cytokinins and send them to shoots; shoot tips make auxins and send them to roots. This exchange of signals can restore lost organs and keep root and shoot growth in balance. Auxins stimulate the initiation of new roots, and they inhibit the initiation and growth of new shoot tips. Cytokinins do just the opposite. So if a tree is cut down, the stump will often make new shoots because auxins have been removed and cytokinins accumulate near the cut.

In Your Notebook *Make a 2×2 table labeled* Shoot *and* Root *across the top and* Auxins *and* Cytokinins *down the side. Then, fill in the effects of these hormones.*

Analyzing Data

PURPOSE Students will analyze data to make an inference about the concentration of auxin that should be applied to maximize carrot yield.

PLANNING Review with students how data are shown on the graph: Increasing auxin concentration is shown on the *x*-axis and plant growth is shown on the *y*-axis. The effects on stems and roots are shown using red and blue lines, respectively. Explain the significance of the negative exponents, e.g., why a concentration of 10^{-11} is lower than a concentration of 10^{-9}.

ANSWERS

1. Maximum stem growth occurs at about 10^{-6} particles/L.
2. That concentration produces the greatest inhibition of root growth.
3. Carrots are roots; a concentration of approximately 10^{-10} particles/L would produce the largest-sized carrots.

Gibberellins For years, farmers in Japan knew of a disease that weakened rice plants by causing them to grow unusually tall. The plants would flop over and fail to produce a high yield of rice grain. Farmers called the disease the "foolish seedling" disease. In 1926, Japanese biologist Eiichi Kurosawa discovered that a fungus, *Gibberella fujikuroi*, caused this extraordinary growth. His experiments showed that the fungus produced a growth-promoting substance.

In fact, the chemical produced by the fungus mimicked hormones produced naturally by plants. These hormones, called **gibberellins,** stimulate growth and may cause dramatic increases in size, particularly in stems and fruits.

MYSTERY CLUE

Kerosene lamps emit carbon dioxide and ethylene as they burn, while electric heaters do not. Could this fact help explain the delayed ripening of the lemons?

Abscisic Acid Gibberellins also interact with another hormone, abscisic acid, to control seed dormancy. **Abscisic acid** inhibits cell division, thereby halting growth.

Recall that seed dormancy allows the embryo to rest until conditions are good for growth. When seed development is complete, abscisic acid stops the seed's growth and shifts the embryo into a dormant state. The embryo rests until environmental events shift the balance of hormones. Such events may include a strong spring rain that washes abscisic acid away. (Gibberellins do not wash away as easily.) Without the opposing effect of abscisic acid, the gibberellins can signal germination.

Abscisic acid and gibberellins have opposite effects, much like the auxins and cytokinins. **The opposing effects of plant hormones contribute to the balance necessary for homeostasis.**

Ethylene One of the most interesting plant hormones, ethylene, is actually a gas. Fruit tissues release small amounts of the hormone **ethylene,** stimulating fruits to ripen. Ethylene also plays a role in causing plants to seal off and drop organs that are no longer needed. For example, petals drop after flowers have been pollinated, leaves drop in autumn, and fruits drop after they ripen. In each case, ethylene signals cells at the base of the structure to seal off from the rest of the plant by depositing waterproof materials in their walls.

A Summary of Plant Hormones

Hormone	Some of the Effects	Where Found
Auxins	Promote cell elongation and apical dominance; stimulate growth of new roots	Produced in shoot apical meristem and transported elsewhere
Cytokinins	Stimulate cell division; affect root growth and differentiation; may work in opposition to auxins	Growing roots
Gibberellins	Stimulate growth; influence various developmental processes; promote germination	Meristems of shoot, root, and seed embryo
Abscisic acid	Inhibits cell division; promotes seed dormancy	Terminal buds; seeds
Ethylene	Stimulates fruits to ripen; causes plants to seal off and drop unnecessary organs, such as leaves in autumn	Fruit tissues; aging leaves and flowers

FIGURE 24–16
A Summary of Plant Hormones This table lists some of the effects of the major plant hormones and where the hormones can be found in the plant body. **Interpret Tables** ***Name two pairs of hormones that work in opposition to each other.***

How Science Works

TRICKING THE TREATS

Commercial fruit producers sometimes use ethylene to control the ripening process. Many crops, including lemons and tomatoes, are picked before they ripen so they can be handled without damaging the fruit. Just before they are delivered to market, the fruits are treated with synthetic ethylene to quickly produce a ripe color. However, this trick does not always produce a ripe flavor, which is one reason that naturally ripened fruits often taste much better.

Lead a Discussion

Explain that, like auxins and cytokinins, another pair of hormones, gibberellins and abscisic acid, interact in opposite ways. While abscisic acid effects a state of dormancy in seeds, gibberellins can induce germination. Have students recall the first step in germination. *(The seed absorbs water.)* Point out that when enough water is present, it often washes away the abscisic acid, so the gibberellins are left and can stimulate seed growth. Emphasize that when hormones act together in opposite ways, they usually help to maintain balance, or homeostasis, in an organism. Then discuss the effects of ethylene.

Ask What could you do to hasten ripening of store-bought pears that are not quite ripe enough to eat? *(Store them in a sealed or closed bag.)*

Ask Why would this speed up the ripening process? *(because the bag would trap ethylene, a gas)*

DIFFERENTIATED INSTRUCTION

L1 Special Needs Encourage students who struggle with memorizing and taking notes to draw pictures to help them remember information. For example, suggest they draw a flower and then a taller flower to represent the effect of gibberellins. Then, encourage them to add descriptive words or phrases that will help them make the connection between the visual and the concept.

Have students use the information under the subhead **Ethylene** to help them answer the question. Students can go online to **Biology.com** to gather their evidence.

Answers

FIGURE 24–16 The two pairs are auxins and cytokinins, and gibberellins and abscisic acid.

LESSON 24.3

Teach continued

Use Visuals

Use **Figure 24–17** to discuss plant responses to stimuli. Point out that animals often respond to stimuli by moving. Plants respond by moving, too, but the movement is achieved by growing either toward or away from the stimulus. After explaining the meanings of the tropisms in the figure, ask students to explain how these responses are important in the growth and development of plants.

DIFFERENTIATED INSTRUCTION

ELL English Language Learners Provide photos or other illustrations that show the three tropisms featured in **Figure 24–17.** Ask students to say in their own words what they see in the visuals. For beginning speakers, accept less than precise vocabulary, and give them time to come up with vocabulary. Also have them work in one-to-one peer tutoring for this exercise. Intermediate and advanced speakers should be able to give a simple but precise definition of the tropisms shown.

L3 Advanced Students Challenge interested students to hypothesize what a plant would look like if it were grown in very low gravity conditions, such as on a space station. Have them draw pictures and write a defense of their hypothesis. Then, ask them to find out about studies that have been performed on plants in space and analyze whether their hypothesis is supported by actual studies.

Tropisms and Rapid Movements

What are some examples of environmental stimuli to which plants respond?

Like all living things, plants need the power of movement to cope with the environment. Many plant movements are slow, but some are so fast that even animals cannot keep up with them.

BUILD Vocabulary

WORD ORIGINS The word **tropism** comes from a Greek word that means "turning."

Tropisms Plant sensors that detect environmental stimuli signal elongating organs to reorient their growth. These growth responses are called **tropisms. Plants respond to environmental stimuli such as light, gravity, and touch.**

FIGURE 24–17
Three Tropisms

▶ ***Light*** The tendency of a plant to grow toward a light source is called **phototropism.** This response can be so quick that young seedlings reorient themselves in a matter of hours. Recall that changes in auxin concentration are responsible for phototropism. Experiments have shown that auxins migrate toward shaded tissue, possibly due to changes in membrane permeability in response to light.

▶ ***Gravity*** Auxins also affect **gravitropism,** the response of a plant to gravity. For reasons still not understood, auxins migrate to the lower sides of horizontal roots and stems. In horizontal stems, the migration causes the stem to bend upright. In horizontal roots, however, the migration causes roots to bend downward.

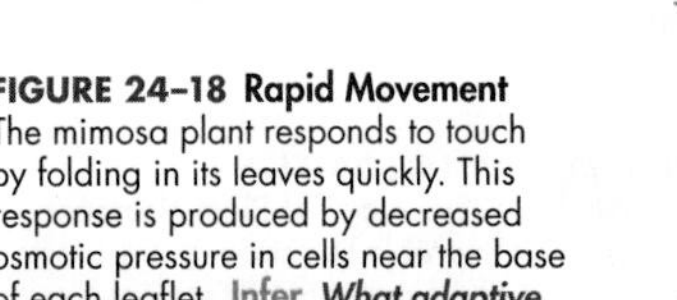

▶ ***Touch*** Some plants even respond to touch, a process called **thigmotropism.** Vines and climbing plants exhibit thigmotropism when they encounter an object and wrap around it. Other plants, such as grape vines, have extra growths called tendrils that emerge near the base of the leaf and wrap tightly around any object they encounter.

FIGURE 24–18 Rapid Movement The mimosa plant responds to touch by folding in its leaves quickly. This response is produced by decreased osmotic pressure in cells near the base of each leaflet. Infer ***What adaptive value might this response have?***

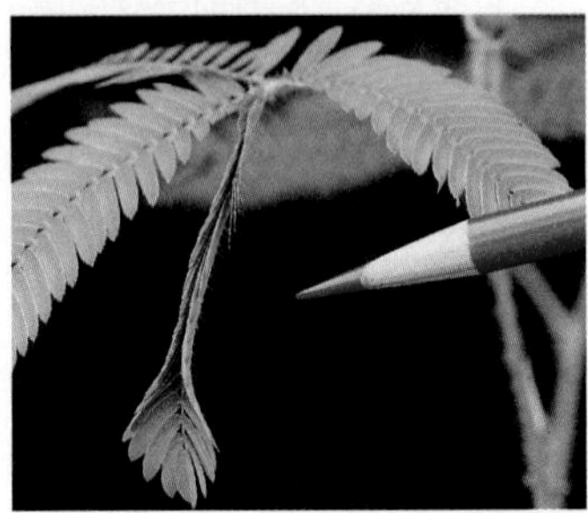

Rapid Movements Some plant responses are so rapid that it would be a mistake to call them tropisms. **Figure 24–18** shows what happens if you touch a leaf of *Mimosa pudica*, appropriately called the "sensitive plant." Within only two or three seconds, its two leaflets fold together completely. The carnivorous Venus' flytrap also demonstrates a rapid response. When an insect lands on a flytrap's leaf, it triggers sensory cells on the inside of the leaf, sending electrical signals from cell to cell. A combination of changes in osmotic pressure and cell wall expansion causes the leaf to snap shut, trapping the insect inside.

 BIOLOGY.com Search Lesson 24.3 GO • InterActive Art

Biology In-Depth

THIGMOTROPISM IN VINES

Climbing plants use structures such as other plants or fences for support. The stems of vines and climbing plants do not grow straight up. Rather, the growing tip of each stem points sideways and twists in circles as the shoot grows. When the tip encounters an object, it quickly wraps around it. This adaptation allows a plant to forgo the energy-costly investment other plants must make to produce tall, sturdy stems. In addition, vines that grow upward on the trunks of tall trees in areas of dense forests, such as tropical rain forests, have the added advantage of receiving more sunlight the farther they climb from the forest floor.

Answers

FIGURE 24–18 Sample answer: The leaves are less prone to damage by insects and other animals when they are folded closed. The rapid movement may also cause the insect or other herbivore to be scared off the plant.

Response to Seasons

How do plants respond to seasonal changes?

"To every thing there is a season." Nowhere is this more evident than in the regular cycles of plant growth. Year after year, some plants flower in the spring, others in summer, and still others in the fall. Plants such as chrysanthemums and poinsettias flower when days are short and are therefore called short-day plants. Plants such as spinach and irises flower when days are long and are therefore known as long-day plants.

Photoperiod and Flowering How do all these plants manage to time their flowering so precisely? In the early 1920s, scientists discovered that tobacco plants flower according to their photoperiod, the number of hours of light and darkness they receive. Additional research showed that many other plants also respond to changing photoperiods, a response called **photoperiodism.** This type of response is summarized in **Figure 24–19.** **Photoperiodism is a major factor in the timing of seasonal activities such as flowering and growth.**

It was later discovered that a plant pigment called phytochrome (FYT oh krohm) is responsible for plant responses to photoperiod. Phytochrome absorbs red light and activates a number of signaling pathways within plant cells. By mechanisms that are still not understood completely, plants respond to regular changes in these pathways. These changes determine the patterns of a variety of plant responses.

FIGURE 24–19 Effects of Photoperiod Changes in the photoperiod can affect the seasonal timing of flowering. **Form an Opinion** ***Are "short-day plant" and "long-day plant" the best names for categorizing these plants, or would it be better to name plants after their responses to night length? Explain your reasoning.***

Build Science Skills

Ask volunteers to relate their observations on the time of year in which different flowers bloom. Point out that plants bloom in different seasons largely in response to photoperiod. Tell students they will interpret the chart on this page to learn more about this. Explain that the columns in **Figure 24–19** represent three different photoperiods, or relative lengths of day and night. The rows show how short-day plants and long-day plants respond to each photoperiod. Ask questions students can answer by interpreting the chart.

Ask Which plant needs long, uninterrupted darkness to flower? *(the short-day plant)*

Ask Which plant is more likely to flower in the summer, when nights are short? *(the long-day plant)*

Ask How do short-day plants respond to interrupted night? Explain. *(The plants do not flower because a long period of darkness is broken up into two shorter periods. These plants need a long period of continuous darkness to flower.)*

DIFFERENTIATED INSTRUCTION

L1 Struggling Students Some students might have difficulty relating the chart to seasonal patterns of flowering. Construct another way to present the information by first drawing a line on the board. Write Spring underneath the line near the left end. Write Summer in the middle and Autumn near the right end. Next, ask students which seasons have short days versus long days. *(Spring and autumn have short days; summer has long days.)* Write "short day" or "long day" under the appropriate season. Then, help students determine where to write "short-day plant" and "long-day plant." *(short under spring and autumn; long under summer)*

BIOLOGY.com The **InterActive Art: Photoperiodism** will help students explore the effect of changing day length on plants.

UbD Check for Understanding

VISUAL REPRESENTATION

Have students identify the relationship between the stimulus and the response in short-day and long-day plants. Ask them to construct four **Cause-and-Effect Diagrams** to represent each one. *(Students should indicate relative length of light and darkness as the cause and the presence or absence of flowers as the effect.)*

Study Wkbks A/B, Appendix S18, Cause-and-Effect Diagram. **Transparencies,** GO1.

ADJUST INSTRUCTION

Some students may have difficulty with framing the task in terms of stimulus and response. Explain that a stimulus is a signal or event to which an organism responds. The response is the activity of the organism because of the stimulus.

Answers

FIGURE 24–19 Accept all logical answers. Answers should reflect an understanding of the effects of photoperiod on flowering.

LESSON 24.3

Teach continued

Lead a Discussion

Have students read the boldface statement. Explain that shorter days and lower temperatures gradually reduce the efficiency of photosynthesis. Under these conditions, plants would gain little by keeping their leaves alive. Then, discuss the effects of hormone changes related to winter dormancy.

DIFFERENTIATED INSTRUCTION

LPR **Less Proficient Readers** Have students complete a **Cause-and-Effect Diagram** to show the effects of changing hormone levels in autumn.

Study Wkbks A/B, Appendix S18, Cause-and-Effect Diagram. **Transparencies,** GO1.

Assess and Remediate

EVALUATE UNDERSTANDING

Have students review the vocabulary terms with a partner. Then, have them complete the 24.3 Assessment.

REMEDIATION SUGGESTION

L1 **Struggling Students** If your students have trouble with **Question 3c,** have them review **Figure 24–19.**

BIOLOGY.com Students can check their understanding of lesson concepts with the **Self-Test** assessment. They can then take an online version of the **Lesson Assessment.**

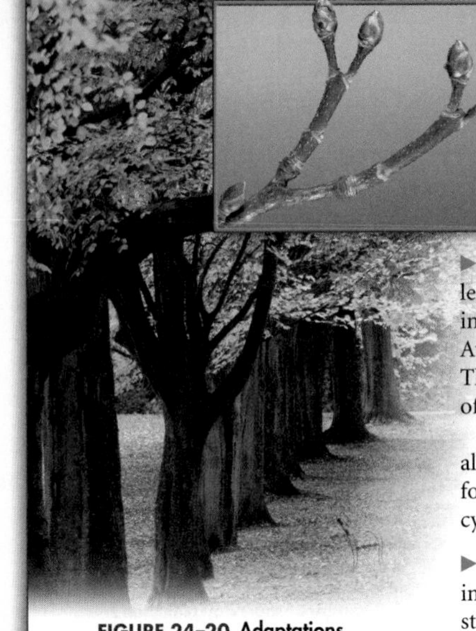

FIGURE 24–20 Adaptations for Winter In autumn, leaves shut down photosynthesis and fall from deciduous trees. Meanwhile, meristems at the tips of the branches produce thick, waxy scales that cover and protect new stem and leaf buds through the harsh winter.

Winter Dormancy Phytochrome also regulates the changes in activity that prepare many plants for dormancy as winter approaches. Recall that dormancy is the period during which an organism's growth and activity decrease or stop. **As cold weather approaches, deciduous plants turn off photosynthetic pathways, transport materials from leaves to roots, and seal off leaves from the rest of the plant.**

▶ ***Leaf Loss*** In temperate regions, many flowering plants lose their leaves during the colder months. At summer's end, the phytochrome in leaves absorbs less light as days shorten and nights become longer. Auxin production drops, but the production of ethylene increases. The change in the relative amounts of these two hormones starts a series of events that gradually shut down the leaf.

As chlorophyll breaks down, other pigments that have been present all along—including yellow and orange carotenoids—become visible for the first time. The brilliant reds come from freshly made anthocyanin pigments.

▶ ***Changes to Meristems*** Hormones also produce important changes in apical meristems. Instead of continuing to produce leaves, meristems produce thick, waxy scales that form a protective layer around new leaf buds. Enclosed in its coat of scales, a terminal bud can survive the coldest winter days. At the onset of winter, xylem and phloem tissues pump themselves full of ions and organic compounds. The resulting solution acts like antifreeze in a car, preventing the tree's sap from freezing. This is one of several mechanisms plants use to survive the bitter cold.

24.3 Assessment

Review Key Concepts

1. a. Review Describe how plant hormones contribute to homeostasis.
   b. Infer Why should a person who trims trees for a living know about the effect of apical dominance on the shape of trees? Explain.
2. a. Review Give three examples of plant responses to external stimuli.
   b. Apply Concepts Using a houseplant, a marker, and a sunny windowsill, describe how you might measure the plant's response to light.
3. a. Review Summarize plant responses to seasonal changes.
   b. Explain Which type of plant—short-day or long-day—is likely to bloom in the summer? Explain your answer.
   c. Design an Experiment How could a garden-store owner determine what light conditions are needed for a particular flowering plant to bloom? Design a controlled experiment to find out.

Apply the Big idea

Evolution

4. Review what you learned about evolution by natural selection in Chapter 16. Then, using what you know about natural selection, describe how plant adaptations for dormancy may have developed over time.

BIOLOGY.com Search Lesson 24.3 GO • Lesson Assessment • Self-Test

Assessment Answers

1a. The opposing effects of auxins and cytokinins keep root and shoot growth in balance. Similarly, gibberellins and abscisic acid have opposite effects, ensuring conditions are favorable before a seed germinates. Without this balance, a seed might germinate too soon or not germinate when it should.

1b. A tree trimmer should know about apical dominance because when a stem's tip is cut, lateral buds grow more quickly. If the tips of the branches on one side are cut more than the other, the plant will grow lopsided.

2a. gravitropism: response to gravity; phototropism: response to light; thigmotropism: response to touch

2b. Sample answer: Draw two circles around a stem, one in the middle of the stem and the other close to the tip. Measure the distance between the two circles. Then, after several days, measure the distance between the marks on the side exposed to sun as well as the shaded side.

3a. Short-day plants flower when nights are long. Long-day plants flower when nights are short. During winter, deciduous plants go into dormancy.

3b. A long-day plant is likely to bloom in the summer in the Northern Hemisphere because the nights are shortest then.

3c. Students' experiments should involve exposing plants to different photoperiods. Students should describe controls in their experimental design, such as equivalent water and nutrients.

4. Big idea Check that students' proposed mechanisms agree with the process of natural selection as described in Chapter 16.

24.4 Plants and Humans

B.4.2 Effects of human activities and natural phenomena.

THINK ABOUT IT A stroll through the produce section of a grocery store will convince you that plants are important. Even a medium-sized food store will contain products made from hundreds of different plant species. But which ones are the most important? Are there certain plants that we simply couldn't live without?

Agriculture

Which crops are the major food supply for humans?

The importance of agriculture—the systematic cultivation of plants—should be obvious, even to those of us who live in urban areas and seldom visit a farm. Modern farming is the foundation on which human society is built. North America has some of the richest, most productive cropland in the world. As a result, farmers in the United States and Canada produce so much food that they are able to feed millions of people around the world as well as their own citizens.

Worldwide Patterns Many scholars now trace the beginnings of human civilization to the cultivation of crop plants. Evidence suggests that agriculture developed separately in many parts of the world about 10,000 to 12,000 years ago. Once people discovered how to grow plants for food, the planting and harvesting of crops tended to keep them in one place for much of the year, leading directly to the establishment of social institutions. Even today, agriculture is the principal occupation of more human beings than any other activity.

Thousands of different plants—nearly all of which are angiosperms—are raised for food in various parts of the world. Yet, despite this diversity, much of human society depends upon just a few of these plants. **Worldwide, most people depend on a few crop plants, such as rice, wheat, soybeans, and corn, for the bulk of their food supply.** The same crops are also used to feed livestock.

Key Questions

Which crops are the major food supply for humans?

What are some examples of benefits besides food that humans derive from plants?

Vocabulary

green revolution

Taking Notes

Preview Visuals Preview **Figure 24–24.** Identify what plants provided the raw materials for the products shown in the photos. Then list any other products you can think of that come from plants.

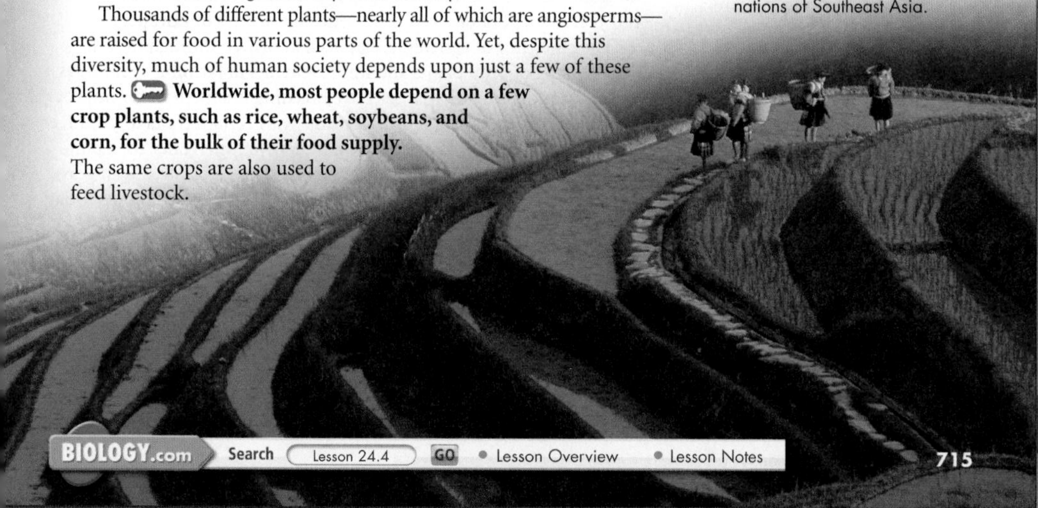

FIGURE 24–21 Plants and Agriculture Rice is a staple crop in China and many nations of Southeast Asia.

BIOLOGY.com Search Lesson 24.4 GO • Lesson Overview • Lesson Notes

LESSON 24.4

Getting Started

Objectives

24.4.1 Identify the major food-supply crops for humans.

24.4.2 Describe how humans benefit from plants.

Student Resources

Study Workbooks A and B, 24.4 Worksheets

Spanish Study Workbook, 24.4 Worksheets

Lab Manual B, 24.4 Data Analysis Worksheet

Lesson Overview • Lesson Notes • Activity: Data Analysis • Assessment: Self-Test, Lesson Assessment

For corresponding lesson in the **Foundation Edition**, see pages 593–595.

Activate Prior Knowledge

Give students a moment to list some of the foods they eat. Have them note which foods are plants and which foods are made from plants. For example, tomatoes, peppers, onions, bread/wheat, tortilla/corn, pizza/wheat. Have students recall that plants are the base of food chains and that humans could not live without plants.

IN INDIANA ACADEMIC STANDARDS

For the full text of all standards, see the Course Overview in the front matter of this book.

B.4.2 Describe how human activities and natural phenomena can change the flow of matter and energy in an ecosystem and how those changes impact other species.

UbD Teach for Understanding

ENDURING UNDERSTANDING From microorganisms to plants, organisms vary widely in the way they carry out basic life processes.

GUIDING QUESTION In what ways do humans depend on plants?

EVIDENCE OF UNDERSTANDING *After completing the lesson, give students the following assessment to determine whether they understand the many ways humans depend on plants.* Challenge students to come up with as many slogans as they can that highlight the ways humans depend on plants. Before they begin, have the class brainstorm advertising slogans or jingles to use as models if needed, and write them on the board. As students share their slogans with the class, they should briefly tell why each slogan makes sense and how it connects to lesson concepts.

Teach

Lead a Discussion

Ask students to identify the four crops grown on 80 percent of cropland in the United States. *(wheat, corn, soybeans, and hay)* Use **Figure 24–22** to talk about the importance of selective breeding in agriculture. Draw attention to the close-up of teosinte, and have students compare it to modern corn, especially the relative sizes of the kernels. You may want to emphasize the point by having students measure the length of the "ear" of teosinte relative to a quarter and compare it to the length of the ear of corn relative to a quarter.

DIFFERENTIATED INSTRUCTION

ELL **English Language Learners** Have the class work in small groups, making sure that beginning speakers are placed with more proficient English speakers. Ask students to have a dialogue about the plant-derived foods they eat using the lists they wrote in the lesson opener. Encourage students to talk about common food plants in their native countries that may be uncommon in the United States. Ask students to identify other plant foods that people eat today that have resulted from selective breeding. (*Sample answer: sugar beets, cabbage, broccoli, Brussels sprouts*)

ELL Focus on ELL: Build Background

BEGINNING AND INTERMEDIATE SPEAKERS Help students construct a **Concept Map** with the word "Agriculture" in the center circle. As students study the lesson, tell them to write important information around the circle. Model an example, such as "Seeds are what we eat from most crop plants." Pair beginning speakers with more proficient speakers to construct complete sentences. Intermediate speakers might choose to work alone.

Study Wkbks A/B, Appendix S21, Concept Map. **Transparencies,** GO4.

This detail of a mural painted by Mexican artist Desiderio Hernandez Xochitiotzin shows Tiaxcala Indians farming maize.

FIGURE 24–22 From Wild Grass to Staple Crop The selective breeding of a wild grass called teosinte about 8000 years ago led to the development of maize and modern corn.

You may not have thought of it this way, but the food we eat from most crop plants is taken from their seeds. For nutrition, most of humanity worldwide depends on the endosperm of only a few carefully cultivated species of grass. The pattern in the United States follows this trend. Roughly 80 percent of all U.S. cropland is used to grow just four crops: wheat, corn, soybeans, and hay. Of these crops, three—wheat, corn, and hay—are derived from grasses.

New Plants The discovery and introduction of new crop plants has frequently changed human history. Before they were discovered in the Americas, many important crops—including corn, peanuts, and potatoes—were unknown in Europe. The introduction of these plants changed European agriculture rapidly. We think of boiled potatoes, for example, as a traditional staple of German and Irish cooking, but 400 years ago, potatoes were new items in the diets of Europeans.

The efficiency of agriculture has been improved through the selective breeding of crop plants and improvements in farming techniques. Recall from Chapter 15 that selective breeding is a method for improving a species by allowing only organisms with certain traits to produce the next generation. The corn grown by Native Americans, for example, was developed more than 8000 years ago from teosinte, a wild grass found in Mexico. Further selective breeding has produced modern-day corn. The changes caused by selective breeding can be very dramatic, as shown in **Figure 24–22.**

In more recent times, other familiar crops have been the product of selective breeding. Sugar beets, the source of most refined sugar from the United States, were produced from the ordinary garden beet using selective breeding. Plants as different as cabbage, broccoli, and Brussels sprouts have been developed from a single species of wild mustard.

UbD Check for Understanding

ORAL QUESTIONING

Ask How is knowledge about the growth and development of plants important to human survival? (*Sample answer: This knowledge is crucial to growing the kinds of plants that provide food and other important products to people.*)

ADJUST INSTRUCTION

If students cannot make the connection between plant growth and development and the benefits to humans, direct their attention to the passages under **New Plants** and **Changes in Agriculture.** Discuss specifically what people need to know about plant growth to develop and apply new techniques and improvements in agriculture. For example, farmers must know the environmental conditions under which crops thrive.

Since 1980, the amount of corn grown in the United States has increased dramatically.

Modern Corn

Modern corn has greatly exaggerated kernels compared to its ancestor, teosinte. Note how much larger corn is than teosinte when compared to the size of a quarter.

Annual Corn Yield in the United States

Bushels per Acre: 50, 75, 100, 125, 150, 175, 200

Year: 1980, 1990, 2000, 2010

Changes in Agriculture Between 1950 and 1970, a worldwide effort to combat hunger and malnutrition led to dramatic improvements in farming techniques and crop yields. This effort came to be called the **green revolution** because it greatly increased the world's food supply. Green revolution technologies enabled many countries to end chronic food shortages and, in some cases, become exporters of surplus food.

At the heart of the green revolution was the use of high-yield varieties of seed and fertilizer. For thousands of years, farmers have added essential nutrients in the form of natural fertilizers such as animal manure. While some farmers today still use these traditional methods, many farmers use artificial fertilizers.

Fertilizers are labeled with three numbers that reflect the percentage by weight of three elements: nitrogen (N), phosphorus (P), and potassium (K). A bag of garden fertilizer labeled "20-10-5" is 20 percent nitrogen, 10 percent phosphorus, and 5 percent potassium by weight.

Fertilizers and pesticides must be used with great care. Overfertilizing can kill crop plants by putting too high a concentration of salts into the soil. The intensive use of fertilizers can also affect the groundwater. When large amounts of nitrogen- and phosphate-containing fertilizer are used near wetlands and streams, runoff from the fields may contaminate the water. Pesticides can also pose a health risk. Chemical pesticides are poisons, and they have the potential to harm wildlife and leave dangerous chemical residues in food.

In Your Notebook *Write a paragraph summarizing the risks and benefits of modern agricultural practices.*

FIGURE 24–23 Reading a Fertilizer Label Three numbers typically appear on a fertilizer label. Apply Concepts ***Describe what the numbers on this label mean.***

Use Visuals

Have students examine the graph in **Figure 24–22,** and point out that crop yields continue to increase as farmers make improvements in agriculture. Emphasize that pesticides and fertilizers have made it possible for farmers to grow more food. Discuss the advantages and disadvantages of pesticides and natural versus artificial fertilizers.

DIFFERENTIATED INSTRUCTION

L1 Struggling Students Some students may be confused by the fact that the line on the graph is not smooth, but rather has ups and downs. Discuss the shape of the graph line and what this shape means. (*The increase in corn yield was not steady; it went up in some years and down in others.*) Help students see that, despite the fluctuation from year to year, the overall trend shows an increase in corn production.

Ask What might account for the ups and downs? *(variations in weather or market forces from year to year)*

Ask How many bushels per acre were produced in 1980? (*about 90*) How many bushels per acre were produced in 2005? (*about 145*) What is the overall trend shown by the data on the graph? (*Corn yield has increased significantly since 1980.*)

Quick Facts

THE SCOOP ON MANURE

Using raw animal manure as a fertilizer is a food safety concern. Pathogens such as *Salmonella, Campylobacter,* and *E. coli* are found in animal feces and can contaminate water and food. This contamination is of particular concern with foods that are not cooked, such as fresh produce. Many outbreaks of disease linked to produce have been caused by contamination with animal manure. Crops can be contaminated by direct application of improperly treated manure or by run-off water from grazing lands, feed lots, or dairies that flows onto nearby fields. Animal manure can be treated to destroy pathogens with technologies such as composting, anaerobic storage, and aeration.

Answers

FIGURE 24–23 The numbers mean that the fertilizer contains 3 percent nitrogen, 8 percent phosphorus, and 8 percent potassium by weight.

IN YOUR NOTEBOOK Risks might include contamination of water with chemicals in commercial fertilizers, and health risks from pesticides. Benefits might include growing more food with the use of fertilizers and losing less food to insects with the use of pesticides.

Teach continued

Connect to the Real World

Use **Figure 24–24** to start a discussion on the ways people use plants other than for food. Have volunteers read the captions. Then, challenge students to identify as many items as they can in the classroom, including their clothes and possessions, that are made from plants.

DIFFERENTIATED INSTRUCTION

L3 Advanced Students Have interested students research natural and synthetic medicines that are derived from plants or mimic plant compounds, such as aspirin and digoxin. Ask students to share their findings with the class.

In the **Data Analysis: Plant Energy** students can analyze the potential fuel energy of different plants.

Assess and Remediate

EVALUATE UNDERSTANDING

Ask students to write a paragraph summarizing the techniques that enabled the green revolution to take place and what its effects have been. Then, have them complete the 24.4 Assessment.

REMEDIATION SUGGESTION

L1 Struggling Students If your students have trouble with **Question 2b,** point out that medicines are one kind of therapeutic drug. Have them focus on the word *development* and explain that the question refers to medicines that have not yet been discovered.

BIOLOGY.com Students can check their understanding of lesson concepts with the **Self-Test** assessment. They can then take an online version of the **Lesson Assessment.**

FIGURE 24–24
Products From Plants
Plants provide the raw materials for many useful products.

The succulent plant *Aloe vera* contains many chemicals that soothe and moisturize the skin. Extracts of this plant are used in many skin lotions as well as in burn and wound ointments.

The acoustical properties of Sitka spruce wood make it ideal for use in pianos, guitars, violins, and other musical instruments.

Cotton is used in countless products including thread, fabrics, bandages, carpeting, and insulation. Cotton fibers are outgrowths of the seed coat epidermis.

Fiber, Wood, and Medicine

What are some examples of other benefits besides food that humans derive from plants?

Some of the most important uses of plants have nothing to do with food. **Plants produce the raw materials for our homes and clothes, and some of our most powerful and effective medicines.** Some examples of plant products are shown in **Figure 24–24.** If you're reading this page out of the printed book in your classroom, you are turning paper pages made from the conifer forests of North America, possibly sitting on a chair made from oak tree xylem, and probably wearing at least one piece of clothing made from the fibers of the cotton plant.

24.4 Assessment

Review Key Concepts

1. a. Review Name four crops that make up the base of the world's food supply.
b. Relate Cause and Effect Describe how selective breeding was used to develop corn from an ancestral grass that looked very different.

2. a. Review Besides food, what other important products are developed from plants?
b. Infer What effect could plant species extinction have on therapeutic drug development?

ANALYZING DATA

Use the line graph from **Figure 24–22** to answer the questions below.

3. Calculate By about how much did the amount of corn produced per acre of farmland increase between 1985 and 2005? MATH

4. Interpret Graphs How would you describe the overall trend in the data?

5. Predict What factors do you think might influence corn production in the next decade?

BIOLOGY.com Search Lesson 24.4 GO • Self-Test • Lesson Assessment • Data Analysis

Assessment Answers

1a. rice, wheat, soybeans, and corn

1b. Selective breeding led to the development of corn from a wild grass found in Mexico called teosinte, and further selective breeding has led to modern-day corn.

2a. Sample answer: materials for clothes and buildings, and medicines

2b. Sample answer: Scientists might never know about a particular drug if a plant species that could provide that drug becomes extinct before its medicinal value is discovered.

ANALYZING DATA

3. about 25 bushels per acre

4. The annual corn yield in bushels per acre has increased overall.

5. Sample answer: average temperatures and rainfall, and supply and demand

The Evolution of Agriculture More than 10,000 years ago, humans began a gradual transition from hunter-gatherer societies to civilizations that were reliant on crops—many of which are still grown today.

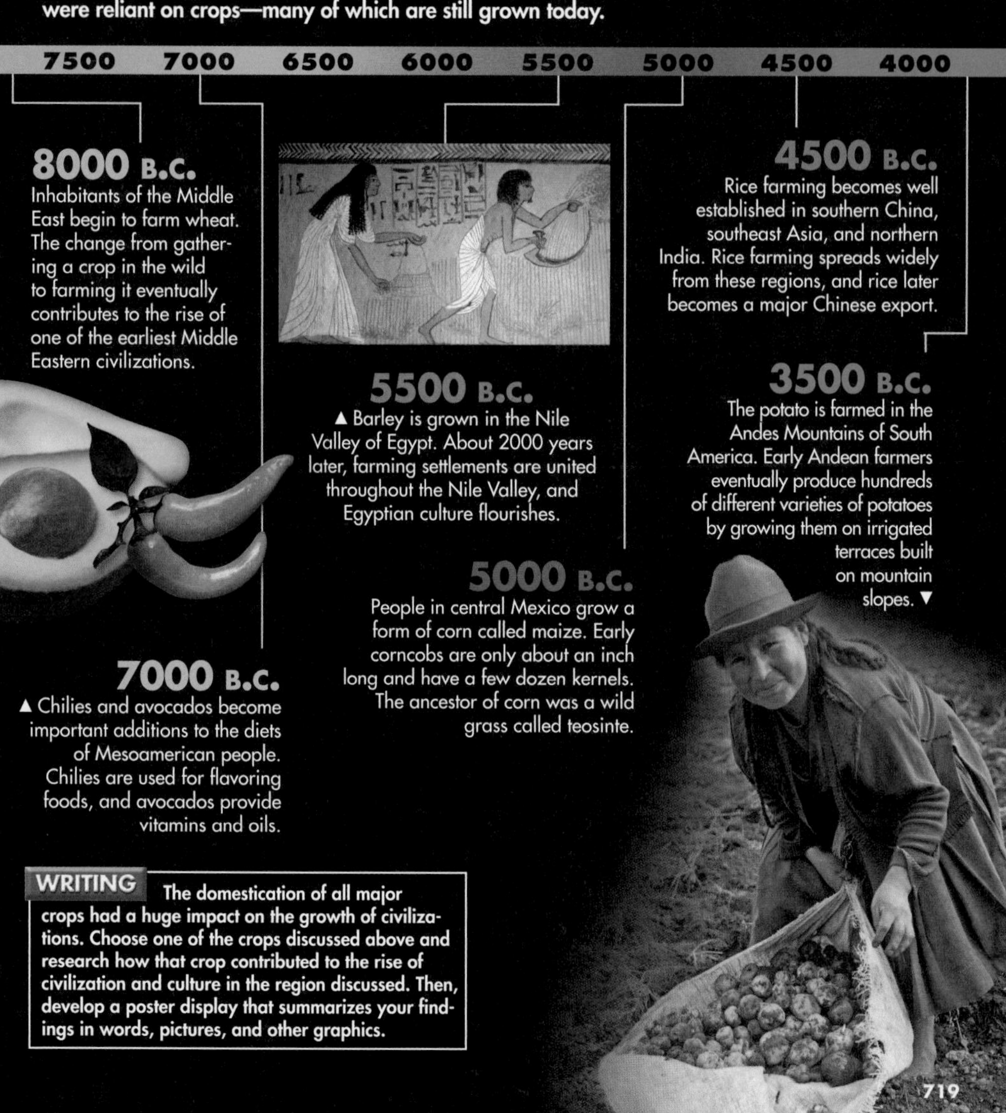

8000 B.C. Inhabitants of the Middle East begin to farm wheat. The change from gathering a crop in the wild to farming it eventually contributes to the rise of one of the earliest Middle Eastern civilizations.

7000 B.C. ▲ Chilies and avocados become important additions to the diets of Mesoamerican people. Chilies are used for flavoring foods, and avocados provide vitamins and oils.

5500 B.C. ▲ Barley is grown in the Nile Valley of Egypt. About 2000 years later, farming settlements are united throughout the Nile Valley, and Egyptian culture flourishes.

5000 B.C. People in central Mexico grow a form of corn called maize. Early corncobs are only about an inch long and have a few dozen kernels. The ancestor of corn was a wild grass called teosinte.

4500 B.C. Rice farming becomes well established in southern China, southeast Asia, and northern India. Rice farming spreads widely from these regions, and rice later becomes a major Chinese export.

3500 B.C. The potato is farmed in the Andes Mountains of South America. Early Andean farmers eventually produce hundreds of different varieties of potatoes by growing them on irrigated terraces built on mountain slopes. ▼

WRITING The domestication of all major crops had a huge impact on the growth of civilizations. Choose one of the crops discussed above and research how that crop contributed to the rise of civilization and culture in the region discussed. Then, develop a poster display that summarizes your findings in words, pictures, and other graphics.

719

How Science Works

FROM STICKS TO SATELLITES

Technology has been important to the evolution of agriculture. Thousands of years ago, farmers used plows made of sticks hitched to oxen. Several civilizations improved upon the plow over the course of many centuries. For example, a solid, cast iron plow was developed in America in the eighteenth century. The invention of the internal combustion engine led to a plow on wheels—the tractor. Today, some farmers use GPS (global positioning satellites) to automatically steer tractors in straight rows, and to analyze soil data to help pinpoint problems such as where fertilizers are needed.

Teach

Lead a Discussion

Ask volunteers to read the captions on the timeline. Help students make the connection between the crops featured here and the crops mentioned in **Lesson 24.4.** *(Most of the plants on the timeline are still major crop plants today.)* Ask students to explain whether they agree with the statement that agriculture is the single most important factor in the rise of civilizations. *(Students will probably say that they agree, because the development of agriculture enabled people to settle in one place; people did not have to keep moving to find food.)* Discuss reasons, such as climate, that different crops were predominant in different areas of the world. Have students infer whether it was coincidence that civilizations sprang up in river valleys. *(No, people had to have a reliable water supply to grow crops.)*

DIFFERENTIATED INSTRUCTION

L1 Struggling Students Students may have difficulty interpreting the placement of events. Make sure they know that the colors of the dates match the colors on the timeline. Have students trace the white lines from the year to the caption. Remind students that years progress from higher to lower when they are B.C.E.

Answers

WRITING Arrange to have students share their research so they can compare the effects of climate and other factors on the type of crop that was important in each region. Students should give specific examples of ways in which the cultivation of crops in the region they selected affected the human population and its culture.

CHAPTER LAB

Pre-Lab

Introduce students to the concepts they will explore in the chapter lab by assigning the Pre-Lab questions.

Lab

Tell students they will perform the chapter lab *Plant Hormones and Leaves* described in **Lab Manual A.**

L1 **Struggling Students** A simpler version of the chapter lab is provided in **Lab Manual B.**

SAFETY

Students should wear gloves and use care when handling scissors. Check for students who might be allergic to the plants.

 Look online for **Editable Lab Worksheets.**

For corresponding pre-lab in the **Foundation Edition**, see page 596.

GUIDED INQUIRY

IN NoS.1 Develop explanations.

Pre-Lab: Plant Hormones and Leaves

Problem How does a plant hormone affect leaf loss?

Materials leafy plant, masking tape, permanent marker, scissors, string, toothpick, auxin paste, plastic container or tray

Lab Manual Chapter 24 Lab

Skills Focus Observe, Draw Conclusions, Apply Concepts

Connect to the  A plant may flower in response to a change in the hours of daylight, or a plant may stop growing in response to colder temperatures. These responses to changes in the environment are coordinated by plant hormones, which regulate plant development. A hormone may stimulate roots to grow, seeds to germinate, or fruits to ripen. A hormone may inhibit cell division or promote dormancy of seeds or plants. In this lab, you will investigate the effect of a plant hormone on leaf loss.

Background Questions

a. Explain Do all plant cells respond to every plant hormone? Why or why not?

b. Explain What is photoperiod? What is dormancy? How are they related?

c. Review In the fall, what happens to the production of auxin and ethylene in the leaves of flowering plants?

Pre-Lab Questions

Preview the procedure in the lab manual.

1. Use Visuals Draw a simple leaf. Label the blade and the petiole.

2. Control Variables What is the control in this experiment?

3. Infer How will auxins move from the paste to the base of the petiole?

 Search Chapter 24 

Visit Chapter 24 online to test yourself on chapter content and to find activities to help you learn.

Untamed Science Video Using time-lapse videography, the Untamed Science crew reveals how plants move in response to various stimuli.

Art in Motion Watch how meiosis and mitosis produce ova and pollen in an angiosperm.

Art Review Review the structures of a flower.

InterActive Art Change the length of day and see how it affects both short- and long-day plants.

Data Analysis Analyze potential fuel energy that comes from different plants and different plant parts.

IN INDIANA ACADEMIC STANDARDS

For the full text of all standards, see the Course Overview in the front matter of this book.

Pre-Lab Answers

BACKGROUND QUESTIONS

a. No. To respond to a hormone, a cell must contain receptors to which a given hormone can bind.

b. Sample answer: Photoperiod is the relative length of daylight and darkness. Dormancy is the period during which an organism's growth and activity slow down or stop. Photoperiod is a stimulus for plants that respond to seasonal changes. Dormancy is one possible response to this stimulus.

c. The production of auxin decreases; the production of ethylene increases.

PRE-LAB QUESTIONS

1. Students should identify the flat area as the blade and the thin stalk as the petiole.

2. The control is the petiole that is not treated with auxin paste.

3. Sample answer: Auxins will move through the layer of vascular tissue (specifically phloem) in the petiole.

24 Study Guide

Big idea Growth, Development, and Reproduction

Plants reproduce, develop, and grow in response to cues from the environment such as light, temperature, and moisture. Hormones manufactured by the plant regulate the plant's responses to change.

24.1 Reproduction in Flowering Plants

Flowers are reproductive organs that are composed of four different kinds of specialized leaves: sepals, petals, stamens, and carpels.

The process of fertilization in angiosperms is distinct from that found in other plants. Two fertilization events take place—one produces the zygote and the other a tissue, called endosperm, within the seed.

Vegetative reproduction is the formation of new individuals by mitosis. It does not require gametes, flowers, or fertilization.

stamen (697)
anther (697)
carpel (697)
stigma (697)
pistil (697)
embryo sac (699)
double fertilization (700)
endosperm (700)
vegetative reproduction (702)
grafting (703)

24.2 Fruits and Seeds

As angiosperm seeds mature, ovary walls thicken to form a fruit that encloses the developing seeds.

Seeds contained in fleshy, nutritious fruits are usually dispersed by animals.

Seeds dispersed by wind or water are typically contained in lightweight fruits that allow them to be carried in the air or in buoyant fruits that allow them to float on the surface of the water.

Environmental factors such as temperature and moisture can cause a seed to end dormancy and germinate.

dormancy (706)
germination (706)

24.3 Plant Hormones

Plant hormones serve as signals that control development of cells, tissues, and organs. They also coordinate responses to the environment.

The opposing effects of plant hormones contribute to the balance necessary for homeostasis.

Plants respond to environmental stimuli such as light, gravity, and touch.

Photoperiodism is a major factor in the timing of seasonal activities such as flowering and growth.

As cold weather approaches, deciduous plants turn off photosynthetic pathways, transport materials from leaves to roots, and seal off leaves.

hormone (708)
target cell (709)
receptor (709)
auxin (709)
apical dominance (710)
cytokinin (710)
gibberellin (711)
abscisic acid (711)
ethylene (711)
tropism (712)
phototropism (712)
gravitropism (712)
thigmotropism (712)
photoperiodism (713)

24.4 Plants and Humans

Worldwide, most people depend on a few crop plants for the bulk of their food supply.

Plants produce the raw materials for our homes and clothes, and some of our most powerful and effective medicines.

green revolution (717)

Think Visually Make a concept map that includes the major concepts for the four lessons of this chapter. A sample map for Lesson 24.1 is shown here.

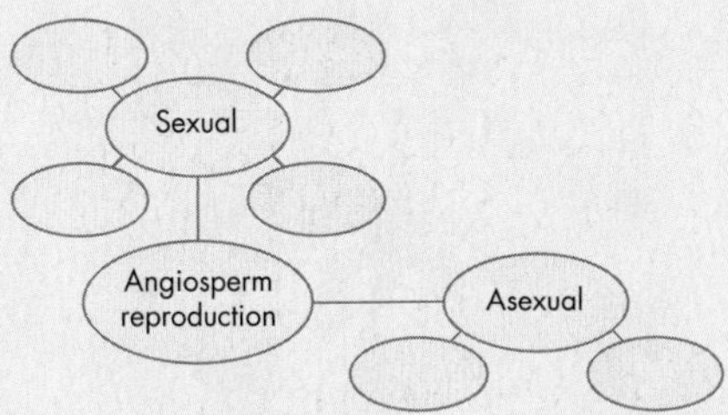

Study Online

REVIEW AND ASSESSMENT RESOURCES

Editable Worksheets Pages of Study Workbooks A and B, Lab Manuals A and B, and the Assessment Resources Book are available online. These documents can be easily edited using a word-processing program.

Lesson Overview Have students reread the Lesson Overviews to help them study chapter concepts.

Vocabulary Review The *Flash Cards* and *Crossword* provide an interactive way to review chapter vocabulary.

Chapter Assessment Have students take an online version of the Chapter 24 Assessment.

Standardized Test Prep Students can take an online version of the Standardized Test Prep. You will receive their scores along with ideas for remediation.

Diagnostic and Benchmark Tests Use these tests to monitor your students' progress and supply remediation.

Answers

THINK VISUALLY

Check students' concept maps for accuracy. Suggest they use vocabulary terms, headings, and subheadings as a guide for important concepts.

UbD Performance Tasks

SUMMATIVE TASK Tell students to make a list of every vocabulary term in the chapter. Then, students should use their list to write a summary of the reproduction, development, and growth of a plant from pollination to winter dormancy. They should use each vocabulary term at least once, but terms do not have to be used in the order of their appearance in the chapter.

TRANSFER TASK Tell students to imagine they are horticulturists who are planning a garden for a client. The only stipulation the client has made is that the garden must have some flowers blooming continuously from late spring until late fall. Have students work in small groups to write a design proposal that informs the client about environmental factors in their area that must be considered when choosing plants. Students might include factors such as photoperiods and those that influence pollination, germination, and dormancy. For example, if year-round temperatures in their area are mild, a seed that requires a long period of cold temperatures before germinating might not survive.

ASSESSMENT

Lesson 24.1

UNDERSTAND KEY CONCEPTS

1. a **2.** b **3.** d

4. The carpel is a specialized leaf that produces and shelters the female gametophytes and, later, seeds. It is located in the innermost part of the flower.

5. Pollen may be transferred from plant to plant by wind or by animals such as insects, birds, and bats.

6. The zygote forms from the fusion of a sperm nucleus with the egg nucleus and grows into the new plant embryo. The endosperm is a food-rich tissue that forms from the fusion of a sperm nucleus with the two polar nuclei in the embryo sac. The endosperm nourishes the seedling.

THINK CRITICALLY

7. a. inside C; the anther **b.** the style; connects the stigma to the ovary **c.** in the ovary, labeled F **d.** sepal

Lesson 24.2

UNDERSTAND KEY CONCEPTS

8 a **9.** c

10. Sample answers: Animal: some dry fruits have burs that catch in an animal's fur. Wind: a dandelion seed is attached to a dry fruit that has a parachute-like structure that is carried by wind. Water: coconut fruits float in seawater and are carried to other islands.

11. Dormancy enables a seed to survive until environmental conditions become favorable. Dormancy may also allow long-distance dispersal.

THINK CRITICALLY

12. No, fruit forms from the ovary, which is part of the carpel.

13. For much of the year, the arctic is extremely cold and dark. Lupine seeds might have to wait many years until a suitable combination of soil, moisture, light, and temperature would allow for successful germination.

14. Sample answer: Choose seeds with large cotyledons and remove them before planting the seeds. Leave the cotyledons on some seeds as a control.

24 Assessment

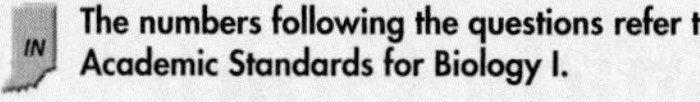
The numbers following the questions refer to Indiana's Academic Standards for Biology I.

24.1 Reproduction in Flowering Plants

Understand Key Concepts

1. In angiosperms, the structures that produce the male gametophyte are called the
a. anthers. **c.** pollen tubes.
b. sepals. **d.** stigmas.

2. Pollination occurs when pollen lands on
a. the style. **c.** the filament.
b. the stigma. **d.** the anther.

3. The process in which a single plant produces many offspring genetically identical to itself is
a. sexual reproduction.
b. agriculture.
c. dormancy.
d. vegetative reproduction.

4. What is a carpel? Where is it located in a typical flower?

5. Describe at least two ways in which pollen is transferred from one plant to another.

6. What are the products of double fertilization? Describe them.

Think Critically

7. Interpret Visuals The diagram below shows the parts of a typical flower.
a. Inside which structure is pollen produced?
b. What structure is represented by A? What is its function?
c. In which structure do seeds develop?
d. What is the name of structure G?

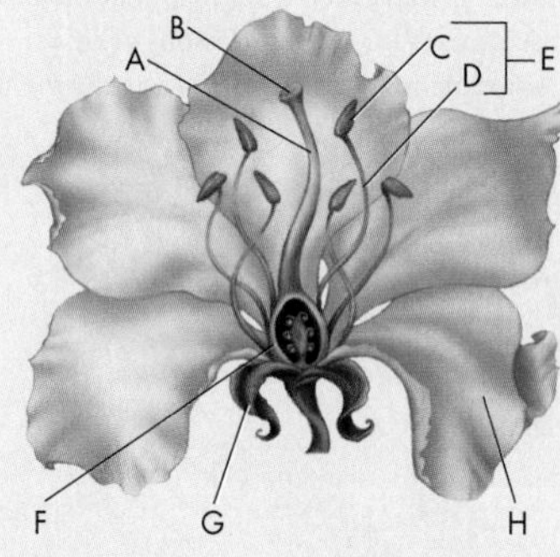

24.2 Fruits and Seeds

Understand Key Concepts

8. The thickened ovary wall of a plant may join with other parts of the flower to become the
a. fruit. **c.** endosperm.
b. seed. **d.** cotyledon.

9. The period during which the embryo is alive but not growing is called
a. fertilization. **c.** dormancy.
b. vegetative growth. **d.** germination.

10. Give examples of seed dispersal by animal, wind, and water.

11. What is the function of dormancy?

Think Critically

12. Predict Some plants form flowers that produce stamens but no carpels. Could fruit form on one of these flowers? Explain your answer.

13. Infer The seeds of lupines, an arctic plant, can remain dormant for thousands of years. Why might this trait be important to a plant in an arctic environment?

14. Design an Experiment A friend suggests that seeds do not need cotyledons to grow. You argue that cotyledons are important to seeds. Design a controlled experiment that shows the effect on seed growth of removing cotyledons.

24.3 Plant Hormones

Understand Key Concepts

15. Chemical signals in plants affecting the growth, activity, and development of cells and tissues are called B.1.2
a. hormones. **c.** auxins.
b. enzymes. **d.** phytochromes.

16. Substances that stimulate cell division and cause dormant seeds to sprout are B.1.2
a. gibberellins. **c.** cytokinins.
b. auxins. **d.** phytochromes.

Lesson 24.3

UNDERSTAND KEY CONCEPTS

15. a **16.** a **17.** b

18. Auxins stimulate the initiation of new roots and inhibit the growth of new shoot tips. Cytokinins stimulate the initiation of new shoots and inhibit the growth of new roots.

19. A tropism is a growth response to a stimulus. Stems show phototropism when they grow toward light. Roots show gravitropism when they grow downward.

20. Short-day plants flower when the number of hours of darkness is high. Long-day plants flower when the number of hours of darkness is low.

21. A plant's growth and activity decrease or stop. Changing levels of hormones cause photosynthesis to stop, protective layers to form around new leaf buds, and a winterizing solution to fill xylem and phloem, which protects plant sap from freezing.

17. Photoperiod is a measurement of
a. water level. **c.** gravity.
b. day length. **d.** nutrients.

18. Explain how auxins act in opposition to cytokinins.

19. What is a tropism? Give one example of a tropism that affects plant stems and another example of a tropism that affects roots.

20. Describe two different ways in which a plant may respond to changes in photoperiod.

21. Describe what happens to deciduous plants during winter dormancy.

Think Critically

22. **Form a Hypothesis** Describe a particular plant thigmotropism and hypothesize how it benefits the plant.

23. **Infer** Spinach is a long-day plant that grows best with a night length of 10 hours or less. Why is spinach not usually grown in regions near the equator?

24.4 Plants and Humans

Understand Key Concepts

24. The first indications of human agriculture occurred about B.4.2
a. 1000 years ago. **c.** 100,000 years ago.
b. 10,000 years ago. **d.** 1,000,000 years ago.

25. The majority of human plant food comes from plants that are
a. gymnosperms. **c.** angiosperms.
b. perennials. **d.** conifers.

26. Give an example of a plant you have eaten in the last 24 hours that you think is a product of selective breeding. Explain why you think so.

Think Critically

27. **Infer** The bulk of human plant foods comes from seeds, which constitute only a small part of the plant body. Explain how this is possible.

28. **Compare and Contrast** Compare and contrast the benefits and the dangers of using pesticides and fertilizers to grow food crops. B.4.2

29. **Form a Hypothesis** Form a hypothesis to explain why plants are a good source of medicines.

solve the CHAPTER MYSTERY

THE GREEN LEMONS

To solve the mystery of why the lemons remained unripe, growers remembered a story from the nineteenth century. In those days, gas streetlights were commonly used in large cities. A few years after such streetlights were installed, city dwellers noticed that trees growing near the streetlamps had developed short, thick stems, and dropped their leaves much earlier than they should have. It was as if hormone levels in the trees had been affected. And, in fact, the levels had changed. One of the components of the gas used in the lights was ethylene.

Recall from Lesson 24.3 that one effect of ethylene is to stimulate the ripening of fruit. Whether the ethylene is manufactured by the plant or externally, as in the case of a kerosene heater, doesn't matter. Because ethylene is a gas, it can diffuse through the air, cell walls, and membranes of a plant and its fruit. When that source of ethylene was taken away from the picked lemons (when the electric heaters replaced the kerosene ones)—the ripening stimulus was removed, and the lemons stayed green.

1. **Relate Cause and Effect** Tomatoes put in a paper bag with apples ripen much more quickly than those placed in the open air. What would this suggest about the effects of ripe apples on unripe tomatoes?

2. **Propose a Solution** How could farmers, shippers, and produce marketers use the effects of ethylene to their advantage?

3. **Connect to the Big idea** Recent studies have shown that gaseous hormones are involved in a plant's systemwide response to an attack by herbivores such as caterpillars. What might be the benefits of a gaseous hormone in such a situation?

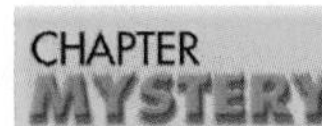

Have students read through the Chapter Mystery. Ask them to recall functions of ethylene that might explain its effects on trees growing near gas streetlights. *(Ethylene causes leaves to drop.)* Point out that, in effect, the trees responded as if winter were arriving. Then, pass around a fruit you bought from a grocery that is colorful but hard, such as a tomato or peach. Encourage students to note the color and to feel it for ripeness. Have them share their experiences with fruit that looked good enough to eat but wasn't ready to eat. Discuss the advantages and disadvantages of food producers using ethylene to accelerate ripening.

CHAPTER MYSTERY ANSWERS

1. The ripe apples produce ethylene, which is trapped in the paper bag and causes the tomatoes to ripen faster.

2. They could use ethylene to time the ripening of produce to better fit their schedules. For example, farmers could pick produce before it is ripe and then shippers could apply ethylene just before the fruit is shipped. In this way, produce wouldn't ripen and rot before it can be picked or shipped.

3. Big idea Sample answer: Gaseous hormones that deter herbivores could diffuse out of the plant—the animals would detect them and leave before they damage the plant. Or, the gaseous hormone could be detected by nearby plants of the same species and stimulate a defensive response, such as the production of poisonous chemicals in the leaves.

Students can further their understanding of plant tropisms by watching the short video **Did That Plant Just Move?**

THINK CRITICALLY

22. Sample answer: A vine shows thigmotropism when it comes in contact with an object such as a fence or another tree and wraps around it. This benefits the vine because the vine does not have to expend energy producing a strong trunk.

23. Days and nights near the equator are each about 12 hours long. So, the nights are not short enough to allow spinach to flower and grow properly.

Lesson 24.4

UNDERSTAND KEY CONCEPTS

24. b **25.** c

26. Sample answer: Broccoli is a product of selective breeding; it has been developed from a single species of wild mustard.

THINK CRITICALLY

27. The endosperm is adapted to be a rich food supply for the germinating seed. Humans have capitalized on this source of energy by selectively breeding to enhance this rich endosperm "energy" feature (as in the case of corn).

28. Benefits: Pesticides kill insects so that less food is lost. Fertilizers help to increase crop yields per acre. Dangers: Pesticides can pose health risks to people and wildlife. Fertilizers can contaminate water or kill crops if overused.

29. Plants are good sources of medicines because those with beneficial properties have been selected for over time.

Connecting Concepts

USE SCIENCE GRAPHICS

30. In the first setup, the plant was upright and grew upward. In the second setup, the plant was positioned on its side; the stem bent 90° and grew upward. In the third setup, the plant was positioned upside down; its stem bent 180° and grew upward.

31. Even when a plant is placed in a horizontal or inverted position, the plant stem will grow upward due to negative gravitropism.

32. No. The fact that light sources were suspended above the plants means that these results could be due to phototropism, not gravitropism.

33. Sample answer: Set up the experiment so that light is coming from multiple directions, including from above the plant, from beneath the plant, and from all sides.

WRITE ABOUT SCIENCE

34. Students' paragraphs should explain phototropism and explain that window light comes from only one direction. A plant growing in a window will exhibit phototropism by growing toward the light. Turning the plant exposes a new part of the stem to light, so the stem will continue to grow straight.

35. Big idea Students' answers should include the attraction of pollinators to flowers; the development of fruits that protect the seeds and enhance their chances for dispersal; and double fertilization, in which an endosperm is produced that provides food for the embryo and young seedling.

Connecting Concepts

Use Science Graphics NoS.3

Recall that growth responses of plants to external stimuli are called *tropisms.* A tropism is positive if the affected plant part grows toward the stimulus. The response is negative if the plant part grows away from the stimulus. The experiment shown below was intended to test the effect of gravitropism on plant growth. The conclusion drawn from the experiment was that the plant stems grow upward due to negative gravitropism. Use the diagram to answer questions 30–33.

30. Interpret Visuals Describe the three experimental setups and the result of each.

31. Form a Hypothesis What was the probable hypothesis for this experiment?

32. Interpret Visuals From the experimental setups shown, was the hypothesis successfully tested? Explain.

33. Evaluate and Revise Indicate what kinds of changes you would make to improve this experimental design.

Write About Science NoS.3

34. Explanation Sometimes, people grow houseplants on a windowsill. Books on houseplants often advise giving the plants a one-quarter turn every other week. Write a paragraph explaining why turning the plant is a good idea. (*Hint:* Be sure to include an explanation of tropisms in your answer.)

35. Assess the Big idea Explain why flowers are the key to the evolutionary success of the angiosperms.

Analyzing Data

IN NoS.3

In a laboratory experiment, fruits from five different kinds of trees were dropped from a height of 4 meters, and the time it took them to reach the ground was measured. Assume that for every second a fruit falls, it is carried 1.5 meters away from the parent tree.

Fruit Type Versus Dispersal Time

Type of Tree	Average Time (s) for Seed to Fall 4 m
Norway maple	5.2
Silver maple	4.9
White ash	3.1
Shagbark hickory	0.9
Red oak	0.9

36. Draw Conclusions Based on the data and the illustrations of the fruit structures, which of the following is the most reasonable conclusion?

a. Winged seeds carry more nutrition for the growing embryo than do seeds without wings.
b. Wind is not very effective in carrying seeds away from the parent plant.
c. Acorns are more likely to germinate if they fall close to the parent plant.
d. Red oak and hickory depend on factors other than wind to achieve dispersal.

37. Analyze Data Given the same wind, which fruit type is most likely to be carried farthest from the parent tree?

a. Red oak
b. Silver maple
c. Norway maple
d. White ash

724 Chapter 24 • Assessment

PURPOSE Students will analyze data to draw conclusions about characteristics of fruits that affect seed dispersal.

PLANNING Have students review the information from the chapter about seed dispersal, in particular noting how the structure of a fruit helps determine the mode of dispersal for its seeds.

ANSWERS

36. d

37. c

Standardized Test Practice for Indiana

Multiple Choice

1. Where in a flower are pollen grains produced?
   A sepals
   B carpels
   C anthers
   D ovary

2. Which part of the flower develops into a fruit?
   A pollen tube
   B sepals
   C stigma
   D ovary

3. Which flower structure includes all the others?
   A style
   B carpel
   C stigma
   D ovary

4. The trumpet honeysuckle has long, red, narrow tubular flowers. What is the most likely means of pollination?
   A wind
   B water
   C bee
   D hummingbird

5. All of the following are fruits EXCEPT
   A tomato.
   B corn.
   C potato.
   D cucumber.

6. Seeds that are contained in large, fleshy fruits are usually dispersed by
   A animals.
   B water.
   C wind.
   D rotting.

7. Which of the following causes fruit to ripen?
   A auxin
   B cytokinin
   C ethylene
   D gibberellin

8. Which is an example of thigmotropism?
   A change in leaf color
   B climbing vines
   C blooming
   D photoperiod

Questions 9–10

The results of an experiment are summarized in the art below.

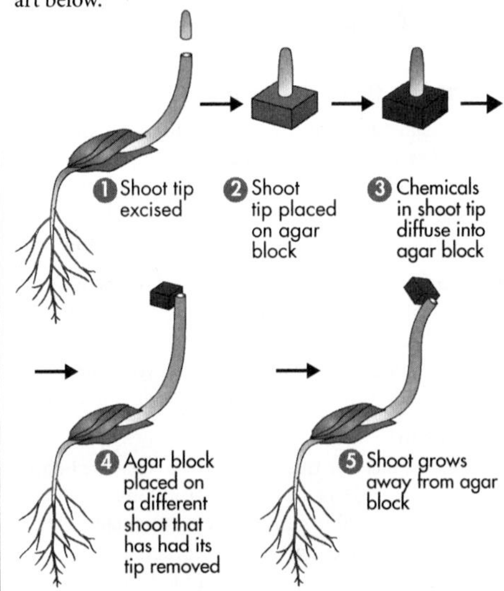
1 Shoot tip excised
2 Shoot tip placed on agar block
3 Chemicals in shoot tip diffuse into agar block
4 Agar block placed on a different shoot that has had its tip removed
5 Shoot grows away from agar block

9. Which of the following can be concluded from the results of this experiment alone?
   A Hormones are produced in the growing tips of plant roots.
   B Plants grow toward the sun due to compounds produced in their stems.
   C Agar blocks contain a variety of plant compounds.
   D Compounds produced in shoot tips can cause stems to bend.

10. Applying your knowledge of specific plant hormones, explain the results.

Open-Ended Response

11. Describe why seed dormancy is a valuable adaptation that has helped explain the evolutionary success of seed plants.

If You Have Trouble With . . .

Question	1	2	3	4	5	6	7	8	9	10	11
See Lesson	24.1	24.2	24.1	24.1	24.2	24.2	24.3	24.3	24.3	24.3	24.2

Test-Taking Tip

INTERPRET EXPERIMENTAL DATA

Tell students that when answering questions pertaining to experimental situations, they should read all of the questions and multiple-choice answers first. Then, they should read the passage carefully and/or examine any accompanying data, looking for the specific information required to answer the questions.

Answers

1. C
2. D
3. B
4. D
5. C
6. A
7. C
8. B
9. D
10. Auxins produced in the first shoot tip diffused from the agar block into the second shoot, and caused the cells in contact with the agar to increase in length. Cells on the side of the stem opposite the agar did not increase in length, and the shoot bent accordingly.
11. Dormancy allows seeds to survive winter or long periods of dry climate so that they do not germinate in unfavorable conditions. Seeds are much more likely to survive, germinate, and grow if they "wait" for the right conditions via dormancy.

UNIT 6

Plan Ahead

Have students read through the description of the Unit 6 Project a few days before they begin designing their board game to get their creative ideas flowing. Tell them you will provide some materials for them to use, but they may want to bring other materials from home. Display a few popular board games in the classroom to give students ideas about how they might create a good game.

Materials posterboard, colored markers or pens, notecards, small objects used for board tokens, number cubes

Monitor the Project

Emphasize to students that the game they create should be one in which the winner is largely determined by who has the most knowledge, not the most luck. Moving to the finish line should not just depend on a throw of number cubes or some other chance action. Suggest a good way to start is by writing some basic rules of the game, to get a sense of how the game will proceed and how it will be won. After writing basic rules, students can design the game board and write questions to be used during the game. Suggest students "tweak" their rules after a trial run through the game.

Project Assessment

Make sure students use the rubric and reflection questions to assess their work. Then, use the rubric to assign a final score. Note that it is important to value the creativity of students' work as well as the content when you score their projects. If desired, talk with students about any differences between their self-assessment scores and your assigned score.

Unit Project

Create a Board Game

Did you have any favorite board games as a kid? Remember how much fun they were to play? Now you get to relive that fun as an employee of an educational toy company! You have been asked to design a board game about the diversity of living things.

Your Task Create a board game based on the groups of living things discussed in this unit—bacteria, archaea, "protists," fungi, and plants. You will exchange games with classmates to test your knowledge and to evaluate the quality of their games.

Be sure to

- include a clever title and colorful, creative board.
- write clear "How to Play" instructions.
- write answerable game questions related to the groups of organisms you've learned about.
- design the game so that winning depends on mastery of the material in this unit.

Reflection Questions

1. **Score your game using the rubric below. What score did you give yourself?**
2. **What did you do well in this project?**
3. **What needs improvement?**
4. **What aspects of another group's game did you like? Why?**
5. **After playing the game, what topics did you do well with? What topics do you need to study more?**

Assessment Rubric

Score	Scientific Content	Quality of Game
4	Game includes challenging, but answerable, questions about all of the groups discussed in the unit. Winning the game depends on how well a player knows the material.	Game is very well designed and creative. "How to Play" instructions are clear and easy to follow.
3	Game includes answerable questions on all of the groups discussed in the unit. Winning the game depends on how well a player knows the material.	Game is designed effectively. "How to Play" instructions can be followed.
2	Game includes some answerable questions, but others are unclear or impossible to answer. Winning the game does not necessarily depend on how well a player knows the material.	Game design could use improvement. "How to Play" instructions are difficult to follow.
1	Many questions are vague and/or unanswerable. Winning the game does not depend on how well a player knows the material.	Game design shows little evidence of planning. "How to Play" instructions are impossible to follow.

IN INDIANA ACADEMIC STANDARDS

B.8.2 Classification, **B.8.3** Evolutionary relationships

21st Century Skills

To be successful in the 21st century, students need skills and learning experiences that extend beyond subject area mastery. The Unit 6 Project helps students build the following 21st Century Skills: *Creativity and Intellectual Curiosity; Interpersonal and Collaborative Skills; Self-Direction;* and *Accountability and Adaptability.*

FOCUS ON ACCOUNTABILITY AND ADAPTABILITY Extend this Unit Project by having small groups of students adapt elements of different students' games to a game that could be used by any biology student taking a more comprehensive biology test. Ask students to consider how material they have learned in other units could be incorporated into the game questions and how the board game could be both fun and instructive.

For more practice building 21st Century Skills, see The Chapter Mystery pages in **Study Workbook A.**

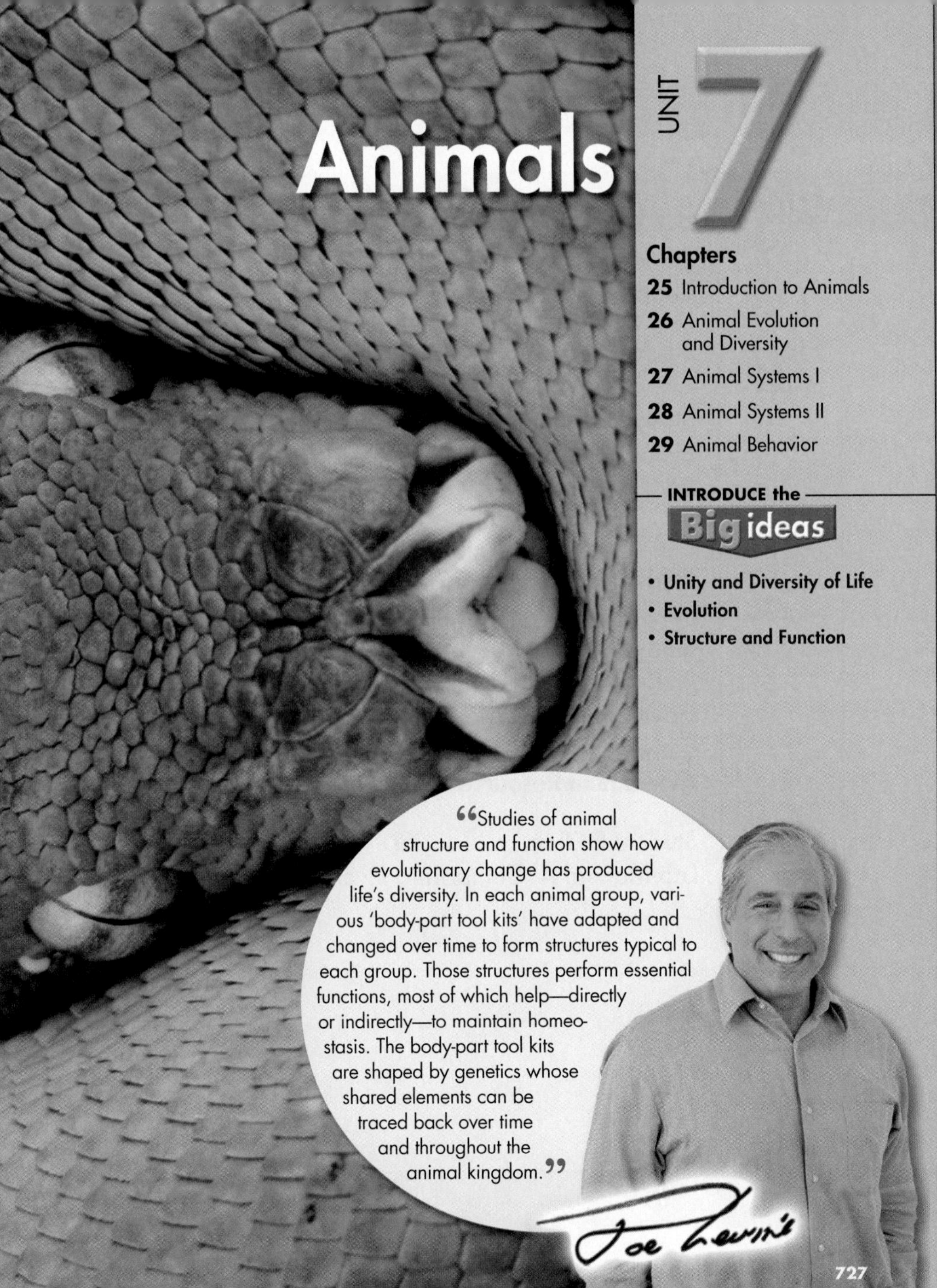

Animals
UNIT 7
Chapters
25 Introduction to Animals
26 Animal Evolution and Diversity
27 Animal Systems I
28 Animal Systems II
29 Animal Behavior
INTRODUCE the
Big ideas
• Unity and Diversity of Life
• Evolution
• Structure and Function
"Studies of animal structure and function show how evolutionary change has produced life's diversity. In each animal group, various 'body-part tool kits' have adapted and changed over time to form structures typical to each group. Those structures perform essential functions, most of which help—directly or indirectly—to maintain homeostasis. The body-part tool kits are shaped by genetics whose shared elements can be traced back over time and throughout the animal kingdom."
727

Dear Colleague,

Most biologists have a particular group of critters they are especially fond of, and I'm no exception. When I was a kid, I desperately wanted a pet, but I lived in an apartment building that prohibited dogs, cats, and birds. Then, I won a goldfish at a county fair. I named him Oscar. It was love at first sight, and the infatuation stuck. Years later, when professors steered me away from medical school to a marine biological station, fishes were on my mind.

Much of my graduate training focused on vertebrates, but an interest in rainforests and coral reefs also kept me informed about invertebrates—which was good, because of a sobering reality. If we think about "success" in terms of total numbers of species and individuals, invertebrates win hands down over the piddling few of us with backbones. Their diversity of body forms and ways of making a living are fascinating. A number of inverts, in fact, have life cycles bizarre enough to inspire sci-fi/horror films. (Compare the life cycle of the beast in "Alien" to those of certain solitary hymenopterans.) And, the more I learn about these beasts, the more I see the inspiration for Jonathan Swift, who wrote:

"So naturalists observe, a flea
Has smaller fleas that on him prey;
And these have smaller still to bite 'em;
And so proceed ad infinitum."

As fascinating as animals are though, I suspect that many of you look at this unit with mixed feelings. How could you cover all this stuff? The answer depends on your likes and dislikes (and state standards), but here's my take. We've rewritten and reorganized this material to focus on the evolutionary history of major animal groups and on the structures and functions that enable animals to carry out basic life processes and maintain homeostasis. The "march through the phyla" has been moved into our biodiversity appendix, which emphasizes taxonomic groups and their names. Hope you like the new conceptual organization of this unit!

CHAPTER PLANNER 25 Introduction to Animals

Chapter Contents	IN	Time	Core Resources
Chapter Preview			**Student Edition,** pp. 728–729 **Chapter Mystery,** p. 729
25.1 What Is an Animal? Characteristics of Animals • Types of Animals • What Animals Do to Survive • *Careers & Biology: Zoo Curator, Beekeeper, Invertebrate Biologist*	B.8.2	1 period 1/2 block	**Student Edition,** pp. 730–736 Inquiry 25.1 Quick Lab, p. 732 L2 **Study Workbook A** 25.1 Worksheets L2 **Biology.com** *InterActive Art:* Structure of a Sponge • 25.1 Self-Test • 25.1 Lesson Assessment
25.2 Animal Body Plans and Evolution Features of Body Plans • The Cladogram of Animals	NoS.3, B.6.3, B.8.2	1 1/2 periods 3/4 block	**Student Edition,** pp. 737–743 Inquiry 25.2 Analyzing Data, p. 740 L2 **Study Workbook A** 25.2 Worksheets L2 **Biology.com** *Art Review:* Body Symmetry and Cavities • *Art in Motion:* Protostome and Deuterostome Early Development **Assessment Resources Book** Visual Quiz L2
Chapter Pre-Lab	B.8.3	1 period 1/2 block	**Student Edition,** p. 744 L2 **Lab Manual A** *Comparing Invertebrate Body Plans* L2

Differentiated Instruction Tools

Study Workbook B includes worksheets with lesson-level differentiated instruction support and explanations of differentiated instruction teaching strategies.

Lab Manual B includes skills labs, simplified chapter labs, and hands-on activities.

ELL Handbook explains ways to make *Biology* more accessible to ELL students.

Spanish Study Workbook is a Spanish translation of Study Workbook A.

Multilingual Glossary is the glossary translated into ten languages.

Differentiated Instruction Key

- L1 Special Needs or Struggling Students
- ELL English Language Learners
- LPR Less Proficient Readers
- L2 On-Level Students
- L3 Advanced Students

Additional Resources

Biology.com Untamed Science Video • Vocabulary Flash Cards

Study Workbook B 25.1 Worksheets L1 ELL LPR
Spanish Study Workbook 25.1 Worksheets ELL
Biology.com 25.1 Lesson Overview • 25.1 Lesson Notes

Study Workbook B 25.2 Worksheets L1 ELL LPR
Spanish Study Workbook 25.2 Worksheets ELL
Biology.com *Data Analysis: The Simplest Animal?* • 25.2 Lesson Overview • 25.2 Lesson Notes • 25.2 Self-Test • 25.2 Lesson Assessment

Lab Manual B *Comparing Invertebrate Body Plans* • Data Analysis: *Differences in Differentiation* L1 ELL LPR

Chapter Review

Student Edition Study Guide, p. 745 L2
Study Workbook A Chapter 25 Vocabulary Review L2 • Chapter 25 Chapter Mystery/21st Century Skills Activity L2 L3
Transparencies, pp. 290–296 L1 ELL LPR L2
Biology.com Untamed Science Video • Editable Worksheets of Study Workbooks A and B and Lab Manuals A and B • Chapter 25 Flash Cards and Match It

Untamed Science DVD • Classroom Resources CD (includes lesson presentations and editable worksheets)

Chapter Assessment

Student Edition Assessment, pp. 746–749 L2
Study Workbook B Chapter 25 Chapter Review L1 ELL LPR • Chapter 25 Taking a Standardized Test L1 ELL LPR
Assessment Resources Book Chapter 25 Test A L2 • Chapter 25 Test B L1 ELL LPR
Biology.com Chapter 25 Assessment • Editable Worksheets of Chapter 25 Visual Quiz and Chapter 25 Tests A and B

Exam*View* *Assessment Suite* • Classroom Resources CD (includes lesson presentations and editable worksheets)

Time: 1 period, 1/2 block

Pressed for Time?

Preview the Chapter Introduce the Key Questions for each lesson and preview Figure 25–10.

Cover the Chapter Quickly Have students read *Characteristics of Animals* and *Types of Animals* in Lesson 25.1. To cover Lesson 25.2, have students read the introduction to *Features of Body Plans*, go over Figures 25–7 through 25–9, and assign the Segmentation: Repeating Parts and Cephalization: Getting a Head sections.

Assess Assign questions 1 and 2 in the 25.1 Assessment, and question 1 in the 25.2 Assessment. In the Chapter 25 Assessment, assign questions 1, 2, 4, 7, 9, 11, 15–19, 22, 23, 27, 28, 30, and 35–38.

CHAPTER 25

Connect to the Big Idea

Big idea Use the photograph of organisms in a coral reef to introduce students to the Big Idea of Unity and Diversity of Life. Activate prior knowledge by having students volunteer what they already know about coral reefs and identify organisms they recognize in the photograph. *(different kinds of coral, anemones, tropical fish, sharks)* Ask them what all of the different organisms pictured in the reef have in common. *(They are all animals.)* Some students may not know that corals and anemones are classified as animals. If necessary, state that they are. Then, have students suggest what sets animals apart from other organisms. *(Accept all well-reasoned replies.)* Ask them to anticipate the answer to the question, **What characteristics and traits define animals?**

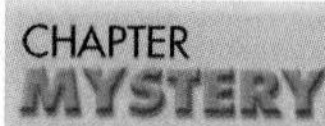

Have students read over the Chapter Mystery. Ask them to brainstorm what the pulsating gooey blobs might be. *(Some students may suggest jellyfish.)* After they have completed Chapter 25, have students explain how the solution to the Chapter Mystery is related to the chapter Essential Question.

BIOLOGY.com Have students preview the chapter vocabulary using the **Flash Cards.**

IN INDIANA ACADEMIC STANDARDS

For the full text of all standards, see the Course Overview in the front matter of this book.

Key standards: Chapter 25 covers key ideas from Standard 6: Cellular reproduction and gene expression and Standard 8: Evolution, including **B.6.3** Specialization and organization in multicellular organisms and **B.8.2** Classification.

Introduction to Animals

Big idea Unity and Diversity of Life

Q: What characteristics and traits define animals?

BIOLOGY.com Search Chapter 25 GO • Flash Cards

728

UbD Understanding by Design

In Chapter 25, students explore animal characteristics and the evolution and diversity of their body plans. The graphic organizer at the right shows how these concepts help students build toward the Unit 7 Enduring Understanding of how *animals have evolved diverse ways to carry out basic life processes and maintain homeostasis.*

PERFORMANCE GOALS

In Chapter 25, students learn about characteristics that set animals apart from other organisms and what animals do to survive. The Chapter Mystery challenges students to look at features of animals to identify an unfamiliar organism. The Performance Tasks enable students to pull together what they have learned about animals by making a scrapbook and writing a scientific journal article.

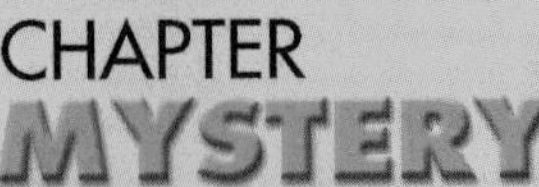

CHAPTER MYSTERY

SLIME DAY AT THE BEACH

It was a warm October day in Massachusetts when phone calls started streaming in to beach offices, aquariums, and even 9-1-1 lines. Beaches near Boston were coated with a thick, glistening layer of jellylike ooze. Beachgoers were mystified and worried. Some thought there had been an oil spill, but police and fire personnel verified that it was not oil.

More slimy masses kept washing up onto the seashores. People noticed that some of the gooey blobs appeared to be pulsating with life. When they looked closely, investigators saw that the slime was made up of small, individual critters—each transparent and the size of a fingernail. But what were they? As you read this chapter, look for clues to help you determine what the slime was.

Never Stop Exploring Your World. Discovering what the slime was is only the beginning. Take a video field trip with the ecogeeks of Untamed Science to see where the mystery leads.

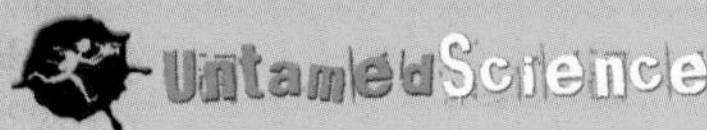

INDIANA ACADEMIC STANDARDS FOR SCIENCE

Nature of Science NoS.3; **Cellular Reproduction and Gene Expression** B.6.3; **Evolution** B.8.2, B.8.3. See lessons for details.

Though they look very different, the hundreds of animal species that make up and live near a coral reef share characteristics common to all animals.

• Untamed Science Video • Chapter Mystery

Chapter 25
Big Idea: Unity and Diversity of Life

Chapter 25 EQ: What characteristics and traits define animals?

25.1 GQ: What is an animal?

25.2 GQ: How have different animal body plans evolved?

What's Online

BIOLOGY.com Extend your reach by using these and other digital assets offered at Biology.com.

CHAPTER MYSTERY

Students investigate the mass arrival of an unfamiliar organism on beaches near Boston and apply what they learn about animal characteristics to identify the organism.

UNTAMED SCIENCE VIDEO

Travel to Coconut Island with the Untamed Science crew to find out just what, exactly, an animal is.

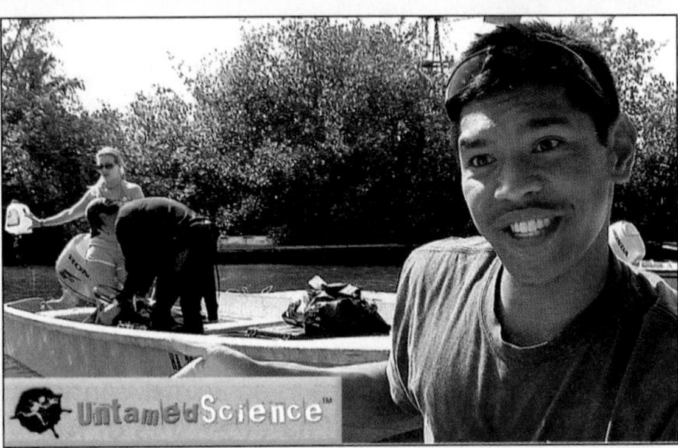

INTERACTIVE ART
Students can observe the structures and functions of a sponge.

ART REVIEW
Use this drag-and-drop labeling activity to help students review body symmetry and cavities.

ART IN MOTION
This short animation shows the differences between early development of protostomes and deuterostomes.

DATA ANALYSIS
Students analyze classification data to determine where *Trichoplax* belongs on the tree of life.

LESSON 25.1

Getting Started

Objectives

25.1.1 List the characteristics that all animals share.

25.1.2 Differentiate between invertebrates and chordates.

25.1.3 List and discuss the essential functions that animals perform in order to survive.

Student Resources

Study Workbooks A and B, 25.1 Worksheets

Spanish Study Workbook, 25.1 Worksheets

Lesson Overview • Lesson Notes • Activity: InterActive Art • Assessment: Self-Test, Lesson Assessment

For corresponding lesson in the **Foundation Edition**, see pages 606–610.

Build Background

Have students offer examples of animals and explain why they would classify each as an animal. *(Answers will vary.)* As students read **Characteristics of Animals,** draw a **Cluster Diagram** on the board, with four circles branching separately from a center circle. Write the word *Animals* in the center circle, and then ask students to supply the four characteristics of animals to complete the diagram *(heterotrophic, multicellular, eukaryotic, cells lack cell walls).*

Study Wkbks A/B, Appendix S19, Cluster Diagram. **Transparencies,** GO2.

IN INDIANA ACADEMIC STANDARDS

For the full text of all standards, see the Course Overview in the front matter of this book.

B.8.2 Explain how organisms are classified and named based on their evolutionary relationships into taxonomic categories.

25.1 What Is an Animal?

B.8.2 Classification.

Key Questions

- What characteristics do all animals share?
- What characteristics distinguish invertebrates and chordates?
- What essential functions must animals perform to survive?

Vocabulary

invertebrate
chordate
notochord
pharyngeal pouch
vertebrate
feedback inhibition

Taking Notes

Outline As you read, make an outline about the features of animals.

For more on the diversity of animals, go to the Visual Guide. DOL•30–DOL•64

THINK ABOUT IT An osprey circles a salt marsh searching for prey. Suddenly, it dives, extending razor-sharp talons. With a triumphant whistle, it carries a struggling fish back to its young. On the bottom of the bay, worms burrow beneath rocks carpeted with orange sponges. In the air above, mosquitoes swarm, searching for a blood meal. All these different inhabitants of the Atlantic coast are animals.

Characteristics of Animals

What characteristics do all animals share?

All members of the animal kingdom share certain characteristics. Animals are all heterotrophs; they obtain nutrients and energy by eating other organisms. Animals are also multicellular; their bodies are composed of many cells. The cells that make up animal bodies are eukaryotic, containing a nucleus and membrane-bound organelles. Unlike the cells of algae, fungi, and plants, animal cells lack cell walls. **Animals, which are members of the kingdom Animalia, are multicellular, heterotrophic, eukaryotic organisms whose cells lack cell walls.**

Types of Animals

What characteristics distinguish invertebrates and chordates?

Animal diversity is so vast and differences among animals so great that we need to divide these organisms into groups to even begin talking about them. Animals are often classified into two broad categories: invertebrates and chordates.

Invertebrates More than 95 percent of animal species are informally called **invertebrates. Invertebrates include all animals that lack a backbone, or vertebral column.** Because this category lumps together organisms that *lack* a characteristic, rather than those that *share* a characteristic, "invertebrates" do not form a clade or any other kind of true category in the system of biological classification. Invertebrates include at least 33 phyla, which are the largest taxonomic groups of animals. Invertebrates include sea stars, worms, jellyfishes, and in sects. They range in size from dust mites to colossal squid more than 14 meters long. DOL•31–DOL•45.

UbD Teach for Understanding

ENDURING UNDERSTANDING Animals have evolved diverse ways to carry out basic life processes and maintain homeostasis.

GUIDING QUESTION What is an animal?

EVIDENCE OF UNDERSTANDING *After completing the lesson, assign the following assessment to determine if students understand the characteristics of an animal.* Divide the class into pairs, and assign an organism to each pair. (Include unfamiliar organisms, some of which are not animals.) Tell students their task is to decide whether their assigned organism is an animal and to justify their conclusion based on the four main characteristics of animals and the essential functions animals must carry out to survive. Give students time to research their assigned organism. Then, have pairs present their results to the class.

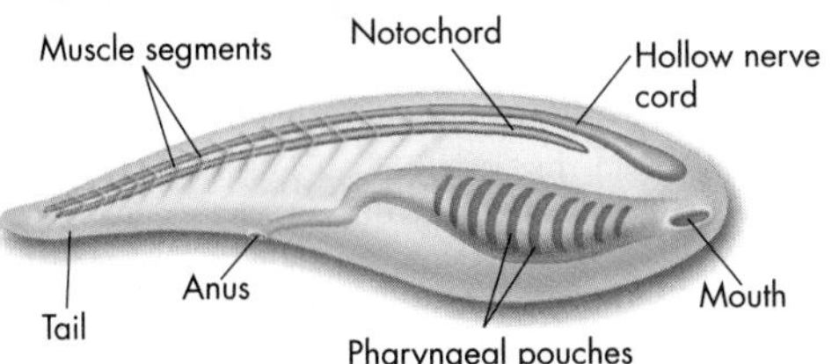

FIGURE 25–1 Characteristics of Chordates All chordates have a dorsal, hollow, nerve cord; a notochord; pharyngeal pouches; and a tail that extends beyond the anus. Some chordates possess all these traits as adults; others possess them only as embryos.

MYSTERY CLUE

Scientists verified that the organisms were young animals that had a stiff rod running along the tail. What does this suggest about the slimy critters?

Chordates Fewer than 5 percent of animal species are **chordates,** members of the clade commonly known as Phylum Chordata. **All chordates exhibit four characteristics during at least one stage of life: a dorsal, hollow nerve cord; a notochord; a tail that extends beyond the anus; and pharyngeal** (fuh RIN jee ul) **pouches.** As you see in **Figure 25–1,** the hollow nerve cord runs along the dorsal (back) part of the body. Nerves branch from this cord at intervals. The **notochord** is a long supporting rod that runs through the body just below the nerve cord. Most chordates have a notochord only when they are embryos. At some point in their lives, all chordates have a tail that extends beyond the anus. **Pharyngeal pouches** are paired structures in the throat region, which is also called the pharynx. In some chordates, such as fishes, slits develop that connect pharyngeal pouches to the outside of the body. Pharyngeal pouches may develop into gills used for gas exchange.

Phylum Chordata includes some odd aquatic animals known as nonvertebrate chordates, which lack vertebrae. Most chordates, however, develop a backbone, or vertebral column, constructed of bones called vertebrae (singular: vertebra). Chordates with backbones are called **vertebrates.** Vertebrates include fishes, amphibians, reptiles, birds, and mammals. DOL•46–DOL•64

FIGURE 25–2 Invertebrates and Chordates Both of these animals have fuzzy bodies with wings and both can fly, but the similarities end there. Butterflies are insects, which are invertebrates, and bats are mammals, which are chordates. Classify ***Bats have backbones. In which of the two major groups of chordates would you classify bats?***

Quick Facts

SO MANY ANIMALS

Animals are tremendously diverse and are found in almost all habitats, although most animal phyla inhabit Earth's seas. There are about 35 animal phyla, encompassing about 1.8 million named species—almost a million of which are insects! In contrast, only about 300,000 plant species have been formally described. Scientists think that there could be between 10–30 million unclassified species, most living in the rain forest. In general, animals tend to be very mobile—they move about in an interesting variety of ways and expend energy to acquire the foods they need to live. The great variety of animals is, in part, a consequence of the adaptations made to the variety of foods they eat and the variety of habitats they live in—from deep ocean vents to the skies above us! The diversity of animals and of their habitats, however, is easily dwarfed by those of the single-celled organisms. Earth is, and will probably always be, in "the age of bacteria."

Teach

Lead a Discussion

Have students read **Types of Animals.** Ask how they would distinguish invertebrates from chordates. Then, use **Figure 25–1** to call attention to the four characteristics shared by chordates: a dorsal, hollow nerve cord; a notochord; a tail that extends beyond the anus; and pharyngeal pouches.

DIFFERENTIATED INSTRUCTION

LPR **Less Proficient Readers** Students might have difficulty with the large number of unfamiliar terms on the page. Have pairs of students work together to complete a **Vocabulary Word Map** for each new term, with characteristics and examples or attributes in the boxes under the term.

Study Wkbks A/B, Appendix S32, Vocabulary Word Map. **Transparencies,** GO17.

ELL Focus on ELL: Access Content

ALL SPEAKERS Pair beginning and intermediate speakers with advanced and advanced high speakers. Have each pair use a **Main Idea and Details Chart** to learn the descriptions of the four characteristics of chordates. Help students with vocabulary terms as needed.

Study Wkbks A/B, Appendix S28, Main Idea and Details Chart. **Transparencies,** GO13.

MYSTERY CLUE From the clue about the organisms having a stiff rod running along the tail (a notochord), students should suspect that the organism is a chordate. Students can go online to Biology.com to gather their evidence.

BIOLOGY.com Students can use **InterActive Art: Structure of a Sponge** to observe the basic anatomy and functions of a sponge.

Answers

FIGURE 25–2 Bats are vertebrates.

Teach continued

Lead a Discussion

Write the term *homeostasis* on the board, and ask students to define it in their own words. *(Sample answer: Homeostasis refers to all of the ways or systems an organism has evolved for maintaining its internal environment as its external environment changes.)* Discuss why feedback inhibition is an important adaptation for animals. Explain that animals often cope with changing external conditions through feedback processes.

Ask How does your body respond when you feel cold? *(Sample answer: It shivers.)*

Ask What does a dog do when it gets hot? *(It pants with its tongue hanging out.)*

Explain that these are ways that feedback helps maintain body systems at a temperature range in which they work most efficiently.

DIFFERENTIATED INSTRUCTION

L1 Struggling Students Have students use a **Cycle Diagram** to help them think about what takes place when feedback inhibition restores homeostasis. Provide small groups with a blank cycle diagram they can use to show how feedback inhibition works when a person's body temperature rises.

Study Wkbks A/B, Appendix S23, Cycle Diagram. **Transparencies,** GO6.

ELL English Language Learners Have students skim the first paragraph of **What Animals Do to Survive.** Ask them to list words in the paragraph they do not understand. *(Sample answers: survive, bewildering, diversity, feedback inhibition)* Then, have them work with fluent English speakers to define these words and quiz one another on their meanings.

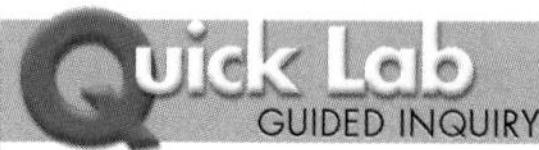

How Hydra Feed

❶ Your teacher will provide you with hydra and *Daphnia,* small aquatic invertebrates. Using a dropper pipette, gently place one hydra onto a well slide.

❷ Let the hydra adjust to its surroundings for 5 to 10 minutes.

❸ Using your dropper, add one *Daphnia* to the slide.

❹ Observe the hydra under a microscope.

Analyze and Conclude

1. **Observe** What happens when the *Daphnia* is added to the same slide as the hydra?
2. **Draw Conclusions** How do the hydra's tentacles help it to maintain homeostasis?

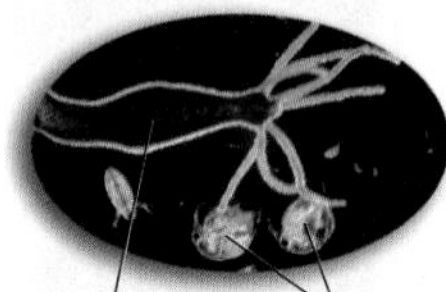

3. **Pose Questions** Formulate two questions about how the hydra survives in its environment.

What Animals Do to Survive

What essential functions must animals perform to survive?

Animals display a bewildering variety of body shapes, sizes, and colors. The best way to study and understand this diversity is not to memorize all the body parts of these animals, but to understand how the structures function and why. No matter their appearance, all animals must perform similar functions to stay alive. **Like all organisms, animals must maintain homeostasis by gathering and responding to information, obtaining and distributing oxygen and nutrients, and collecting and eliminating carbon dioxide and other wastes. They also reproduce.** The body systems that perform these functions are closely linked to one another. Over time, members of different animal phyla have evolved very different body structures that perform these essential functions. You will study these structures in more detail in Chapters 27 and 28.

Maintaining Homeostasis Recall that all organisms must keep their internal environment relatively stable, a process known as maintaining homeostasis. In animals, maintaining homeostasis is the most important function of all body systems. For example, most reptiles, birds, and mammals cannot excrete excess salt very well. Those that hunt or feed in salt water, such as the marine iguana in **Figure 25–3,** have adaptations that allow them to remove salt from their bodies.

Often, homeostasis is maintained by feedback inhibition. **Feedback inhibition,** or negative feedback, is a system in which the product or result of a process limits the process itself. If your house gets too cold, for example, the thermostat turns on the heat. As heat warms the house, the thermostat turns the heater off. Your body's thermostat works the same way. If you get too cold, you shiver, using muscle activity to generate heat. If you get too hot, you sweat, which helps you lose heat.

In this unit, you will learn about body systems in various animal groups. You will see how different groups have evolved different ways of ensuring their body systems stay in balance.

FIGURE 25–3 Homeostasis Marine iguanas are reptiles that feed in salt water. Reptile excretory systems are not adapted to process salt water. So these reptiles maintain homeostasis by sneezing a combination of salt and nasal mucus you might call "snalt." Snalt sometimes coats their bumpy heads and spiny necks, as you can see in this photo.

PURPOSE Students will observe how hydra are adapted to obtain nutrients.

MATERIALS live hydra and *Daphnia* cultures, microscope, dropper pipette, depression slides

SAFETY Tell students to treat the animals with care to avoid injury to them. Caution students to handle breakable materials, such as glass slides, carefully and not to touch broken glass.

PLANNING Provide a container into which used hydra and remaining *Daphnia* can be collected.

ANALYZE AND CONCLUDE

1. The hydra extend their tentacles to capture the *Daphnia.*
2. Hydra tentacles help maintain homeostasis by capturing food and delivering it to the hydra's mouth.
3. Sample answer: What adaptations help hydra survive? How do tentacles help hydra feed?

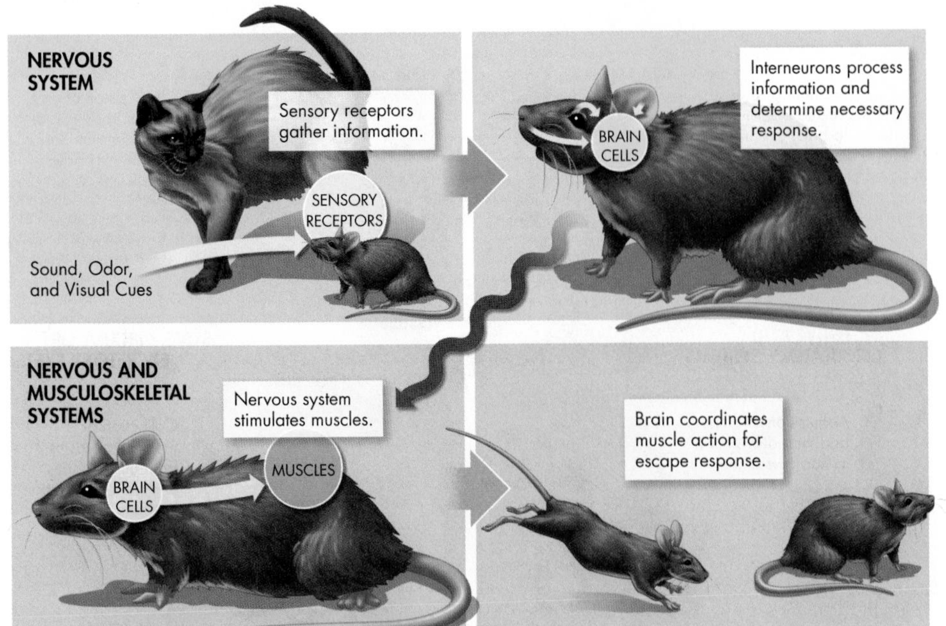
NERVOUS SYSTEM
Sensory receptors gather information.
SENSORY RECEPTORS
Sound, Odor, and Visual Cues
Interneurons process information and determine necessary response.
BRAIN CELLS
NERVOUS AND MUSCULOSKELETAL SYSTEMS
Nervous system stimulates muscles.
MUSCLES
BRAIN CELLS
Brain coordinates muscle action for escape response.

FIGURE 25–4 Gathering and Responding to Information The nervous and muscular systems work together to produce a response. Predict ***Would an animal with a malfunctioning nervous system be likely to produce an appropriate muscular response to a predator? Explain.***

Gathering and Responding to Information Complex animals, such as mammals, use several linked body systems to respond to events in their environment, as shown in **Figure 25–4.** The nervous system gathers information using cells called receptors that respond to sound, light, chemicals, and other stimuli. Other nerve cells collect and process that information and determine how to respond. Some invertebrates have only a loose network of nerve cells, with no real center. Other invertebrates and most chordates have large numbers of nerve cells concentrated into a brain.

Animals often respond to the information processed in their nervous system by moving around. Muscle tissue generates force by becoming shorter when stimulated by the nervous system. Muscles work together with some kind of supporting structure called a skeleton to make up the musculoskeletal system. Skeletons vary widely from phylum to phylum. Some invertebrates, such as earthworms, have skeletons that are flexible and function through the use of fluid pressure. Insects and some other invertebrates have external skeletons. The bones of vertebrates form an internal skeleton. For example, the hard shell of a lobster is an external skeleton, while your bones are part of your internal skeleton.

In Your Notebook *Construct a flowchart showing the events in **Figure 25–4** in chronological order.*

Use Visuals

Have students examine **Figure 25–4.** Then, ask them to describe the events from the rat's point of view.

Ask Where are the sensory receptors located that come into play when the rat first notices the cat? *(in the rat's eyes, nose, and ears)*

Ask What do you think is going on in the interaction between the rat's nervous system and its musculoskeletal system? *(Sample answer: Nerve cells cause muscles to contract, and movement occurs.)*

DIFFERENTIATED INSTRUCTION

L1 **Struggling Students** If some students have trouble understanding **Figure 25–4,** cover the bottom of the figure and ask students to describe what the rat senses.

Ask How did the rat gather information? *(Its senses detected the cat.)*

Then, cover the top of the figure, and ask what message the brain is sending to the muscles.

Ask How did the rat respond to this information? *(Its muscles contracted, and it escaped.)*

Biology In-Depth

BODY TALK

To maintain homeostasis, the body must have internal communication. Both the endocrine and nervous systems fulfill this role in humans and in many other animals. Endocrine communication depends on the release of chemicals that travel though the body in blood. Hours, or even days, may elapse (as in the case of the menstrual cycle) between the release of a chemical by an endocrine gland and the response by the specific cells (target tissue) that are sensitive to the chemical. Nervous system communication, in contrast, is very rapid and depends on the transmission of impulses along nerve pathways. Depending on the type and size of nerve fiber, nerve impulses can relay information from an event in one part of the body to the brain or another organ (in the case of a reflex) at speeds from 1 m/s to over 100 m/s.

Answers

FIGURE 25–4 Sample answer: I predict that an organism with a malfunctioning nervous system would be in danger of producing an inappropriate response to a predator for several reasons. If the organism has faulty sensory receptors, it might not be aware of the predator and its nervous system would not signal its muscles that it needs to run away. If its brain cells are faulty, the nervous system might misinterpret information about the predator.

IN YOUR NOTEBOOK Check that students' flowcharts reflect stimulus-response activities in the sequence shown in **Figure 25–4.**

LESSON 25.1

Teach continued

VISUAL SUMMARY

Have students examine **Figure 25–5** to understand how body systems function and are connected via the circulatory system. Have students work in small groups to write three questions—one for each section of the diagram—which, when answered, will help them understand how each set of systems specifically helps maintain homeostasis. Use the groups' questions to check student understanding.

DIFFERENTIATED INSTRUCTION

L1 Special Needs If **Figure 25–5** confuses some students, cover all but one part of the figure. Then, working in small groups, have students discuss each part. For example, for the top part, students might discuss how the respiratory and circulatory systems work together to take in oxygen and deliver it to body cells. Then, repeat the exercise with another part of the diagram.

L3 Advanced Students Challenge students to write a paragraph comparing a circulatory system to a city's highway system. Ask them how traffic flow would be affected if there were an accident on the highway at rush hour. How would the city be affected? Have students describe this in terms of a breakdown in homeostasis.

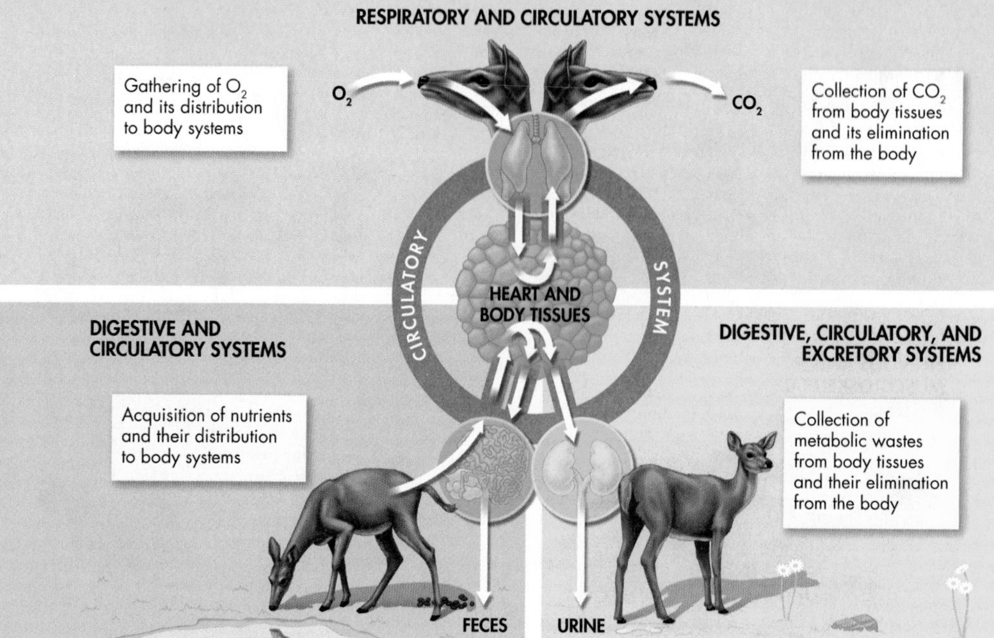

VISUAL SUMMARY

MOVING MATERIALS IN, AROUND, AND OUT OF THE BODY

FIGURE 25–5 The structures of an animal's respiratory, digestive, and excretory systems must work together with those of its circulatory system.

Obtaining and Distributing Oxygen and Nutrients All animals must breathe to obtain oxygen. Small animals that live in water or in wet places can "breathe" by allowing oxygen to diffuse across their skin. Larger animals use a respiratory system based on one of many different kinds of gills, lungs, or air passages. In addition, all animals must eat to obtain nutrients. Most animals have a digestive system that acquires food and breaks it down into forms cells can use.

After acquiring oxygen and nutrients, animals must transport them to cells throughout their bodies. For many animals, this task of transporting oxygen and nutrients requires some kind of circulatory system. Therefore, the structures and functions of respiratory and digestive systems must work together with circulatory systems, as shown in **Figure 25–5.** Among vertebrates, including humans, the circulatory system is especially important in supplying oxygen and nutrients. In humans, for example, brain tissue begins to die within moments if its blood supply is interrupted by a stroke.

Collecting and Eliminating CO_2 and Other Wastes Animals' metabolic processes generate carbon dioxide and other waste products. Some of those waste products contain nitrogen, often in the form of ammonia. Both carbon dioxide and ammonia are toxic in high concentrations. So these wastes must be excreted, or eliminated from the body.

UbD Check for Understanding

ONE-MINUTE RESPONSE

Give students about a minute to write a response to the following prompt.

- Describe the importance of the circulatory system to other systems in maintaining homeostasis. *(Answers should include that the circulatory system supplies nutrients from the digestive system and oxygen from the lungs to the cells of the body. It also transports wastes from cells to the excretory system and carbon dioxide from the cells to the lungs, helping the body maintain homeostasis.)*

ADJUST INSTRUCTION

If responses are incorrect or incomplete, have students review the Visual Summary and edit their original responses. Then, have each student share his or her edited response with a partner.

Many animals eliminate carbon dioxide by simply using their respiratory systems. However, most complex animals have a specialized organ system—the excretory system—for eliminating other wastes, such as ammonia. The excretory system concentrates or processes these wastes and either expels them immediately or stores them before eliminating them.

Before waste products can be discharged from the body, they must first be collected from cells throughout body tissues and then delivered to the respiratory or excretory system. Some sort of circulatory system is often necessary to perform these functions. So the collection and elimination of wastes requires close interactions between the structures and functions of three body systems, as shown in **Figure 25–5** on the previous page.

Reproducing Most animals reproduce sexually by producing haploid gametes. Sexual reproduction helps create and maintain genetic diversity, which increases a species' ability to evolve and adapt as the environment changes. Many invertebrates and a few vertebrates can also reproduce asexually. Asexual reproduction usually produces offspring that are genetically identical to the parent. It allows animals to increase their numbers rapidly but does not generate genetic diversity.

FIGURE 25–6 Reproduction Like many vertebrates, this pygmy marsupial frog is caring for her young while they develop. Unlike most animals, she is carrying her eggs on her back!

25.1 Assessment

Review Key Concepts

1. a. Review Which characteristics do all animals share?

b. Classify A classmate is looking at a unicellular organism under a microscope. She asks you if it is an animal. What would you say, and why?

2. a. Review What is the defining characteristic of invertebrates? What are four characteristics of chordates?

b. Explain Why would you be unlikely to find a notochord in an adult chordate?

c. Compare and Contrast How do vertebrates differ from other chordates?

3. a. Review Describe the essential functions performed by all animals.

b. Explain Why must waste products produced by metabolic processes be eliminated from an animal's body?

c. Sequence Which body system delivers waste products to the respiratory and excretory systems?

VISUAL THINKING

4. Make a two-column chart that lists the ways that animals gather and respond to information. In the first column, list each function. In the second column, include a drawing, photograph, or clipping of a structure that performs that function.

BIOLOGY.com Search Lesson 25.1  • InterActive Art • Self-Test • Lesson Assessment

Assess and Remediate

EVALUATE UNDERSTANDING

Ask a student to name an essential function animals perform to survive. Then, have a second student describe how that function contributes to homeostasis. Continue until all essential functions have been discussed. Then, have students complete the 25.1 Assessment.

REMEDIATION SUGGESTIONS

LPR Less Proficient Readers If students have trouble answering **Question 3b,** rephrase the question in simpler terms. For example, you could ask them why eliminating waste is an important animal function. Have pairs discuss the simplified question and write a response.

BIOLOGY.com Students can check their understanding of lesson concepts with the **Self-Test** assessment. They can then take an online version of the **Lesson Assessment.**

Assessment Answers

1a. All are heterotrophs, are multicellular, and have eukaryotic cells without cell walls.

1b. Sample answer: It is not an animal, because one of the characteristics shared by all animals is that they are multicellular.

2a. Invertebrates lack a notochord and backbone. Chordates have a hollow nerve cord, a notochord, a tail that extends beyond the anus, and pharyngeal pouches at some point in their development.

2b. Most chordates have a notochord only when they are embryos.

2c. Vertebrates are chordates that have a backbone made up of vertebrae. A few aquatic chordates lack vertebrae.

3a. maintaining homeostasis, gathering and responding to information, obtaining and distributing oxygen and nutrients, collecting and eliminating CO_2 and other wastes, reproducing

3b. Metabolic wastes, such as CO_2 and ammonia, are toxic in high concentrations and must be eliminated.

3c. the circulatory system

VISUAL THINKING

4. Answers will vary. Column one might list:
- Hearing sounds
- Detecting chemicals
- Seeing movement, light, or color

Accept all entries that students have correctly illustrated.

Teach

Lead a Discussion

Ask students what they think Dr. Henderson means in her statement, "Stop and take a look at the world around you. Biology is exciting! There are many unanswered questions . . . and many waiting to be asked."

DIFFERENTIATED INSTRUCTION

L1 Struggling Students For students who have difficulty appreciating the great variety of organisms an invertebrate biologist might study, collect photographs of different types of invertebrates and display them around the classroom. You may also display field guides of invertebrates. Have students select one organism and explain why it is an invertebrate and why an invertebrate biologist might find it interesting.

Are you interested in a career with animals? If so, you might be interested in one of the careers below.

ZOO CURATOR

When you think of a zoo worker, you likely picture a keeper feeding animals, right? Zookeepers are not the only people working in zoos, however! Zoo curators are responsible for overseeing a specific part of a zoo's work. There are many different kinds of curators, including research curators, animal curators, and conservation curators. Each contributes to the zoo's mission of wildlife protection and preservation.

BEEKEEPER

More than one quarter of the American diet comes from food plants that are pollinated by bees. Beekeepers maintain beehives and are therefore a vital part of the agriculture business. Bees are rented to farmers for pollination of crops such as almonds, apples, peaches, soybeans, and many types of berries. Beekeepers may also use their hives to produce beeswax and honey.

INVERTEBRATE BIOLOGIST

More than 95 percent of animals lack a backbone. From corals to spiders, earthworms to sea stars, the variety is amazing! Biologists may study invertebrate behavior, evolution, ecology, or anatomy. With so many species to choose from, the research is as varied as the animals themselves.

CAREER CLOSE-UP:

Dr. Scottie Yvette Henderson, Invertebrate Biologist

The strange and diverse creatures of the ocean inspire Dr. Scottie Henderson, an instructor of biology at the University of Puget Sound in Tacoma, Washington. Her current research focuses on tiny, potentially parasitic crabs that infest a clam called *Nuttallia obscurata*. Dr. Henderson and her colleagues are looking at the interactions of the clam and crab to better understand the nature of their symbiotic relationship. Some evidence points to parasitism, but the relationship may be commensal. Nothing, however, is as important to Dr. Henderson as getting her students interested in and excited about science.

"Stop and take a look at the world around you. Biology is exciting! There are many unanswered questions . . . and many questions waiting to be asked."

WRITING Suppose you were one of Dr. Henderson's students. What question would you most like to ask her about her research? Explain why that aspect interests you.

Answers

WRITING

Sample answers: How can one animal infest another animal? How did you learn about these animals to begin with? Does all of your research take place outside? Each question should be accompanied by the student's reason for asking the question.

Quick Facts

WORKING WITH INVERTEBRATES

A biological curator cares for a specific collection of preserved or living organisms at a zoo or museum. Curators also help select items to add to the collection. Large zoos may have separate curators for insects, birds, large animals, and other special interests. Curators generally have at least a bachelor's degree in their area of interest.

A beekeeper should have a thorough understanding of types of bees, their care, and uses. Training can be through a beekeepers' association or a county extension service.

Becoming an invertebrate zoologist like Dr. Henderson requires at least a bachelor's degree in biology. It usually also requires graduate study and research in a specialized area of zoology, such as invertebrate ecology, behavior, or physiology.

25.2 Animal Body Plans and Evolution

B.6.3 Specialization and organization in multicellular organisms; B.8.2 Classification. Also covered: NoS.3.

THINK ABOUT IT Animals alive today have typically been produced by two processes: the development of a multicellular individual from a single fertilized egg cell, and the evolution of a modern species from its ancestors over many millions of years. The history of the evolutionary changes to animal body structures has been known for years. Today, exciting research is revealing how changes in the genes that control embryological development are connected to the evolution of body structures. This research field, often referred to as "evo-devo," is one of the hottest areas in biology today.

Features of Body Plans

What are some features of animal body plans?

Our survey of the animal kingdom focuses on how animal body structures and systems perform life's essential functions. Each animal phylum has a unique organization of particular body structures that is often referred to as a body plan. **Features of animal body plans include levels of organization, body symmetry, differentiation of germ layers, formation of body cavities, patterns of embryological development, segmentation, cephalization, and limb formation.**

Levels of Organization As the first cells of most animals develop, they differentiate into specialized cells that are organized into tissues. Recall that a tissue is a group of cells that perform a similar function. Animals typically have several types of tissues, including epithelial, muscle, connective, and nervous tissues. Epithelial tissues cover body surfaces, inside and out. The epithelial cells that line lung surfaces, for example, have thin, flat structures through which gases can diffuse easily.

Tissues combine during growth and development to form organs. Organs work together to make up organ systems that carry out complex functions. Your digestive system, for example, includes tissues and organs such as your lips, mouth, stomach, intestines, and anus.

Key Questions

 ***What are some features of animal body plans?***

How are animal phyla defined?

Vocabulary

radial symmetry • bilateral symmetry • endoderm • mesoderm • ectoderm • coelom • pseudocoelom • zygote • blastula • protostome • deuterostome • cephalization

Taking Notes

Concept Map Draw a concept map showing the different features of animal body plans and the different types of each feature.

UbD Teach for Understanding

ENDURING UNDERSTANDING Animals have evolved diverse ways to carry out basic life processes and maintain homeostasis.

GUIDING QUESTION How have different animal body plans evolved?

EVIDENCE OF UNDERSTANDING *After completing the lesson, assign students the following assessment to show their understanding of the importance of animal body plans.* Divide the class into pairs. Write the following prompt on the board, and ask each pair to spend about five minutes developing a response.

- Animals are classified into separate phyla based on their body plans and how they develop as embryos.

Have pairs present their responses for a class discussion.

Getting Started

Objectives

25.2.1 Discuss some trends in animal evolution.

25.2.2 Explain the differences among the animal phyla.

Student Resources

Study Workbooks A and B, 25.2 Worksheets

Spanish Study Workbook, 25.2 Worksheets

Lab Manual B, 25.2 Data Analysis Worksheet

BIOLOGY.com Lesson Overview • Lesson Notes • Activities: Art Review, Art in Motion, Data Analysis • Assessment: Self-Test, Lesson Assessment

For corresponding lesson in the **Foundation Edition**, see pages 611–616.

Build Background

Begin a discussion by having students brainstorm what they recall about the four levels of body organization. Then, introduce the four main types of tissues in the body: epithelial, muscle, connective, and nerve. Draw examples on the board or show photographs, and explain where each type of tissue is found.

IN INDIANA ACADEMIC STANDARDS

For the full text of all standards, see the Course Overview in the front matter of this book.

B.6.3 Explain that in multicellular organisms the zygote produced during fertilization undergoes a series of cell divisions that lead to clusters of cells that go on to specialize and become the organism's tissues and organs.

B.8.2 Explain how organisms are classified and named based on their evolutionary relationships into taxonomic categories.

Teach

Use Visuals

Use **Figure 25–8** to introduce germ layers. Call on students to describe the differences among acoelomate, pseudocoelomate, and coelomate body plans. *(Acoelomate—no cavity between the body wall and digestive cavity; pseudocoelomate—cavity partially lined with tissue from the mesoderm; coelomate—body cavity completely lined with tissue from the mesoderm.)*

Ask Which cell layer develops into the lining of the digestive tract? *(endoderm)*

DIFFERENTIATED INSTRUCTION

L1 Struggling Students Use **Figure 25–7** to introduce the concept and vocabulary of body symmetry. Give students practice with the terms *ventral, dorsal, anterior,* and *posterior* by writing the following **Cloze Prompts** on the board and having them complete the sentences aloud.

- The head is at the ______ end of a cat. *(anterior)*
- The belly is the ______ surface of the fish. *(ventral)*
- The tail of a lizard is at its ______ end. *(posterior)*
- The back of a wasp is its ______ surface. *(dorsal)*

Study Wkbks A/B, Appendix S2, Cloze Prompts.

ELL Focus on ELL: Extend Language

ALL SPEAKERS Have students use **Cornell Notes** to help them learn the vocabulary and concepts described in **Features of Body Plans.** Pair beginning and intermediate speakers with advanced and advanced high speakers. Have pairs read the information under each blue heading, and then complete their notes on the body plan feature discussed in that subsection. Partners should use their notes to ask each other questions before continuing on to the next subsection.

Study Wkbks A/B, Appendix S22, Cornell Notes. **Transparencies,** GO5.

BIOLOGY.com Students can review body symmetry and body cavities with **Art Review: Body Symmetry and Cavities.**

FIGURE 25–7 Body Symmetry Animals with radial symmetry have body parts that extend from a central point. Animals with bilateral symmetry have distinct anterior and posterior ends and right and left sides.

Radial Symmetry

Planes of symmetry

Bilateral Symmetry

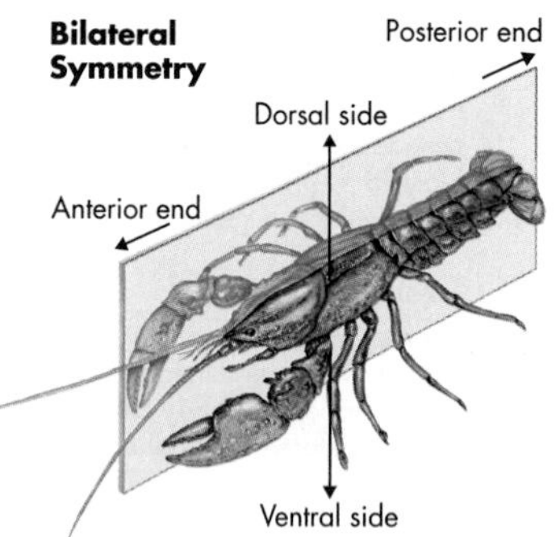

Body Symmetry The bodies of most animals exhibit some type of symmetry. Some animals, such as the sea anemone in **Figure 25–7,** have body parts that extend outward from the center, like the spokes of a bicycle wheel. These animals exhibit **radial symmetry,** in which any number of imaginary planes drawn through the center of the body could divide it into equal halves. The most successful animal groups exhibit **bilateral symmetry,** in which a single imaginary plane divides the body into left and right sides that are mirror images of one another. Animals with bilateral symmetry have a definite front, or anterior, end and a back, or posterior, end. Bilaterally symmetrical animals also have an upper, or dorsal, side and a lower, or ventral, side. When you ride a horse, you are riding on its dorsal side.

Differentiation of Germ Layers During embryological development, the cells of most animal embryos differentiate into three layers called germ layers. Cells of the **endoderm,** or innermost germ layer, develop into the linings of the digestive tract and much of the respiratory system. Cells of the **mesoderm,** or middle layer, give rise to muscles and much of the circulatory, reproductive, and excretory organ systems. The **ectoderm,** or outermost layer, produces sense organs, nerves, and the outer layer of the skin.

Formation of a Body Cavity Most animals have some kind of body cavity—a fluid-filled space between the digestive tract and body wall. A body cavity provides a space in which internal organs can be suspended, and room for those organs to grow. For example, your stomach and other digestive organs are suspended in your body cavity. Most complex animal phyla have a true **coelom** (SEE lum), a body cavity that develops within the mesoderm and is completely lined with tissue derived from mesoderm. Some invertebrates have only a primitive jellylike layer between the ectoderm and endoderm. Other invertebrates lack a body cavity altogether, and are called acoelomates. Still other invertebrate groups have a **pseudocoelom,** which is only partially lined with mesoderm. **Figure 25–8** summarizes the tissue structures of animals with and without coeloms.

FIGURE 25–8 Body Cavities Acoelomates lack a coelom between their body wall and digestive cavity. Pseudocoelomates have body cavities that are partially lined with tissues from the mesoderm.

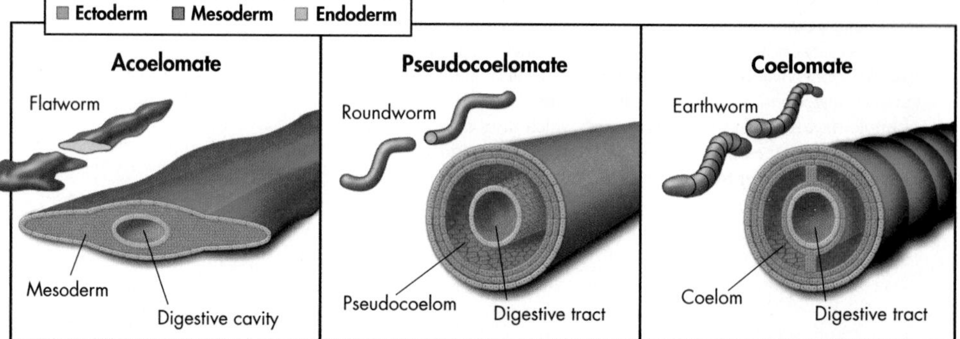

Quick Facts

ADVANTAGES OF A COELOM

A coelom is a fluid-filled cavity between the digestive cavity and the outer body wall, resulting in a tube-within-a-tube body construction. The coelom has a number of functions. It serves as a buffer between the outer wall and the inner organs, cushioning them against harm. It allows for the growth of internal organs without distorting the body's outer wall. For invertebrates that have an open circulatory system, the coelom is the place where circulation occurs. The fluid in the cavity further serves as a hydrostatic skeleton for animals such as roundworms. Scientists in various disciplines have competing theories about when and how often the coelom evolved.

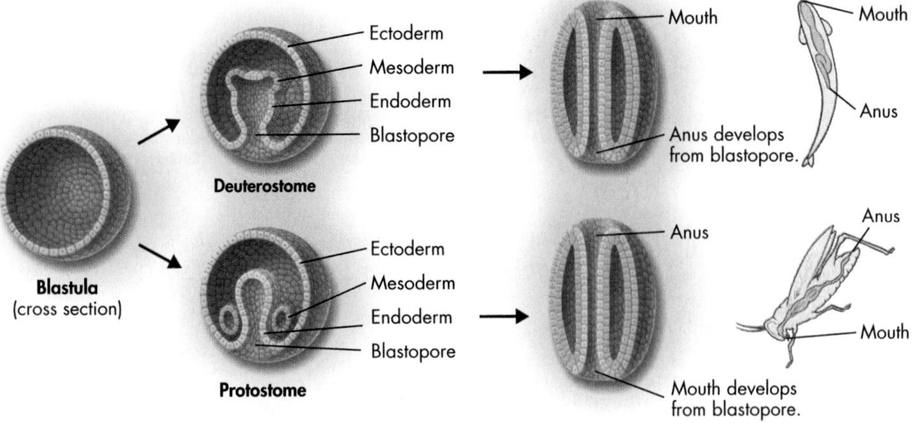

FIGURE 25–9 Blastula and Blastopore Formation During the early development of an animal embryo, a hollow ball of cells called a blastula forms. An opening called a blastopore forms in this ball. In deuterostomes, such as fishes, the blastopore forms an anus. In protostomes, such as grasshoppers, the blastopore develops into the mouth.

Patterns of Embryological Development Every animal that reproduces sexually begins life as a **zygote,** or fertilized egg. As the zygote begins to develop, it forms a **blastula** (BLAS tyoo luh), a hollow ball of cells like an inflated balloon. As the blastula develops, it folds in on itself, as if you were holding the balloon and pushing your thumbs toward the center. This folding changes a ball of cells into an elongated structure with a tube that runs from one end to the other. This tube becomes the digestive tract, as shown in **Figure 25–9.**

At first, this digestive tract has only a single opening to the outside, called a blastopore. An efficient digestive tract, however, needs two openings: a mouth through which food enters and an anus through which wastes leave. In phyla that are **protostomes** (PROH tuh stohms), the blastopore becomes the mouth. In protostomes, including most invertebrates, the anus develops at the opposite end of the tube. In phyla that are **deuterostomes** (DOO tur uh stohms), the blastopore becomes the anus, and the mouth is formed from the second opening that develops. Chordates and echinoderms are deuterostomes. This similarity in development is one of several characteristics that indicate that echinoderms are closely related to chordates.

Segmentation: Repeating Parts As many bilaterally symmetrical animals develop, their bodies become divided into numerous repeated parts, or segments. These animals are said to exhibit segmentation. Segmented animals, such as worms, insects, and vertebrates, typically have at least some internal and external body parts that repeat on each side of the body. Bilateral symmetry and segmentation are found together in many of the most successful animal groups.

Segmentation has been important in animal evolution because of the way genes control the production and growth of body segments. If an organism has segmentation, simple mutations can cause changes in the number of body segments. Different segments can also become specialized, such as having a head or specialized limbs.

Use Visuals

Have students examine **Figure 25–9** to help them understand what a blastopore is and how it becomes either an organism's mouth or anus. Reinforce that all animal embryos form a blastula.

Ask If you were given an animal and told that the anus had arisen from the blastopore, what might you infer about the classification of the organism? *(It would be a chordate or an echinoderm.)*

Ask Are humans protostomes or deuterostomes? *(deuterostomes)*

DIFFERENTIATED INSTRUCTION

ELL English Language Learners Write the terms *protostome* and *deuterostome* on the board. Ask students to tell you what the two terms have in common. *(The suffix -stome)* Explain that *-stome* means "a mouth" or "mouthlike opening." Have students locate the definitions of the terms in the text, and discuss why the meaning of the suffix makes sense with the definition of the term.

BIOLOGY.com Students can review differences in early development of protostomes and deuterostomes with **Art in Motion: Protostome and Deuterostome Early Development.**

How Science Works

FOLLOWING THE PATH OF STAINED CELLS

Early in animal development, the cells in a blastula are rearranged and become an embryo called the gastrula, usually with three tissue layers. The cells move from the surface of a blastula to interior locations in a process called gastrulation. How do biologists know what happens during this process? In the 1920s, German embryologist, W. Vogt, carried out classic studies of frog blastulas that revealed where cells ended up in developed frogs. His method involved staining blastula cells with different colors of non-toxic dyes. After allowing the process to proceed for different amounts of time, he would dissect the stained embryos to see where the stained cells had moved. Through this method, he charted "fate maps" for the various cells in the blastula and, thus, mapped out gastrulation. Today, similar studies are done using fluorescent substances to mark cells.

Teach continued

Lead a Discussion

After students have read about cephalization, discuss sense organs in different animals. First, ask students to identify the senses. *(hearing, odor detection, vision, taste, touch)* List the senses across the board, and then ask students to identify the sense organ associated with each sense. *(ears, nose, eyes, tongue/taste buds, skin)*

Ask Where are the sense organs (other than skin) found in most animals? *(in the anterior end, or head)*

DIFFERENTIATED INSTRUCTION

L1 Special Needs Arrange students into small groups. Provide animal photographs from old magazines that show the head ends of animals. Assign a sense organ to each group, and challenge students to put together a collage of photographs that illustrates that sense organ in at least five different kinds of animals. Have students present their collages to the class.

Answers

IN YOUR NOTEBOOK Sample answer: Sense organs tend to be located in the head region, so when animals move "head-first," they can sense their surroundings as they move forward.

NoS.3, B.6.3

Differences in Differentiation

The table shows the length of time it takes various animals to reach important stages in their early development. Study the data table and answer the questions.

Time Variations in Developmental Stages of Various Animals

Stage	Chicken	Hamster	Rabbit	Rhesus Monkey
2 cells	3 hours	16 hours	8 hours	24 hours
4 cells	3.25 hours	40 hours	11 hours	36 hours
Three germ layers begin to form	1.5 days	6.5–7 days	6.5 days	19 days
Three germ layers differentiate	3 days	8 days	9 days	25 days
Formation of tail bud	3.25 days	8.5 days	9.5 days	26 days
Birth/Hatching	22 days	16 days	32 days	164 days

1. Compare and Contrast Which animal takes the most time to reach the differentiation stage? Which takes the least time?

2. Calculate How much longer does it take a rhesus monkey zygote to reach the 4-cell stage than it does a chicken zygote? MATH

3. Infer In all these animals, which developmental stage would you expect to occur first—formation of the coelom or formation of the blastula?

BUILD Vocabulary

SUFFIXES The word **cephalization** has two suffixes: *-ize*, meaning "to make of," and *-ation*, meaning "the process of." When these suffixes are added to the root word *cephal-*, meaning "head," the new word means "the process of making a head."

Cephalization: Getting a Head Animals with bilateral symmetry typically exhibit **cephalization** (sef uh lih ZAY shun), the concentration of sense organs and nerve cells at their anterior end. This anterior end is often different enough from the rest of the body that it is called a head. The most successful animal groups, including arthropods and vertebrates, exhibit pronounced cephalization.

Close examination of insect and vertebrate embryos shows that their heads are formed by the fusion and specialization of several body segments during development. As those segments fuse, their internal and external parts combine in ways that concentrate sense organs, such as eyes, in the head. Nerve cells that process information and "decide" what the animal should do also become concentrated in the head. Not surprisingly, animals with heads usually move in a "head-first" direction. This is so that the concentration of sense organs and nerve cells comes in contact with new parts of the environment first.

Limb Formation: Legs, Flippers, and Wings Segmented, bilaterally symmetrical animals typically have external appendages on both sides of the body. These appendages vary from simple groups of bristles in some worms, to jointed legs in spiders, wings in dragonflies, and a wide range of limbs, including bird wings, dolphin flippers, and monkey arms. These very different kinds of appendages have evolved several times, and have been lost several times, in various animal groups.

In Your Notebook *Explain in your own words why animals with heads tend to move in a "head-first" direction.*

Analyzing Data

PURPOSE Students will analyze and interpret data about the length of time it takes different species of animals to reach certain stages in early development.

PLANNING Review the use of rows and columns in tables. Have students look at the table and ask questions about anything they do not understand. For instance, point out that the times given do not add up to the total time from fertilization to birth or hatching because the times given are for the early stages of development only.

ANSWERS

1. most time: rhesus monkey; least time: chicken
2. It takes the rhesus monkey zygote 32.75 hours more to reach the 4-cell stage than it takes the chicken zygote. (36 – 3.25 = 32.75 hours)
3. blastula

VISUAL SUMMARY

BODY PLANS

FIGURE 25–10 The body plans of modern invertebrates and chordates suggest evolution from a common ancestor.

Ectoderm / Mesoderm / Endoderm	Sponges	Cnidarians	Arthropods	Roundworms	Flatworms
Levels of Organization	Specialized cells	Specialized cells, tissues	Specialized cells, tissues, organs	Specialized cells, tissues, organs	Specialized cells, tissues, organs
Body Symmetry	Absent	Radial	Bilateral	Bilateral	Bilateral
Germ Layers	Absent	Two	Three	Three	Three
Body Cavity	–	Acoelom	True coelom	Pseudocoelom	Acoelom
Embryological Development	–	–	Protostome	Protostome	Protostome
Segmentation	Absent	Absent	Present	Absent	Absent
Cephalization	Absent	Absent	Present	Present	Present

Ectoderm / Mesoderm / Endoderm	Annelids	Mollusks	Echinoderms	Chordates
Levels of Organization	Specialized cells, tissues, organs	Specialized cells, tissues, organs	Specialized cells, tissues, organs	Specialized cells, tissues, organs
Body Symmetry	Bilateral	Bilateral	Radial (as adults)	Bilateral
Germ Layers	Three	Three	Three	Three
Body Cavity	True coelom	True coelom	True coelom	True coelom
Embryological Development	Protostome	Protostome	Deuterostome	Deuterostome
Segmentation	Present	Absent	Absent	Present
Cephalization	Present	Present	Absent (as adults)	Present

Check for Understanding

ORAL QUESTIONING

Use the following prompts to gauge students' understanding of lesson concepts.

- What type of symmetry do snails exhibit? *(bilateral symmetry)*
- What germ layer do muscles develop from? *(mesoderm)*
- In protostomes, the blastopore becomes what structure? *(mouth)*

ADJUST INSTRUCTION

If students have difficulty answering the questions, have them outline the information under **Features of Body Plans.** Then, have pairs use their outlines and **Figure 25–10** to quiz each other on animal body plans.

VISUAL SUMMARY

Ask the following questions about trends in animal body plans as shown in **Figure 25–10.** Note that the different shades of green only serve to help students quickly identify differences across groups for any trait.

Ask What two general statements could you make about the levels of organization in animal groups? *(Sample answer: All have specialized cells; most have tissues and organs.)*

Ask What type of body cavity do most groups have? *(true coelom)*

Ask What is the most common means of embryological development? *(Most groups are protostomes.)*

Ask In what ways are echinoderms unusual? *(Sample answer: As adults, they break the trends in body symmetry, segmentation, and cephalization; they are also the only invertebrates that are deuterostomes.)*

Call attention to the germ layer color key showing ectoderm, mesoderm, and endoderm.

DIFFERENTIATED INSTRUCTION

L1 Struggling Students Some students might become overwhelmed by the amount of information in the table. Reinforce the main idea of the table, that is, that the body plans of modern animals suggest evolution from a common ancestor. Then, take the time to point out a few body plan characteristics that clearly show this concept. For example, walk students through the **Body Cavity** row and point out how it suggests the evolution of a true coelom.

Teach continued

Use Visuals

Use the cladogram in **Figure 25–11** to review the concepts covered in the chapter.

Ask Upon what three things is the evolutionary history presented in a cladogram based? *(characteristics of living species, fossil evidence, and comparative genomic studies)*

Ask What characteristic do all of the animal groups have in common? *(multicellularity)*

Explain that all groups to the right of echinoderms (represented by a sea star) are members of the same phyla—chordata. Then, have students work in small groups to write two questions based on the cladogram. Use these questions as a basis for a class discussion.

DIFFERENTIATED INSTRUCTION

LPR Less Proficient Readers Write this question on the board: How are animal phyla defined? Then, have students work in pairs to read the text under **The Cladogram of Animals,** find the answer, and write an answer to the question in their own words. *(Sample answer: Animal phyla are usually defined by what their adult bodies look like. They are also defined by how they develop as embryos.)*

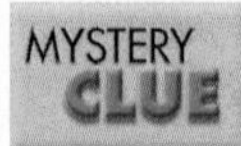

To help students arrive at the answer, have them use the cladogram to determine that the organisms likely belong to the group positioned to the right of the echinoderms. Explain that these organisms are called tunicates. To learn more, suggest they look up nonvertebrate chordates in **The Diversity of Life** guide on pages 46–47.

BIOLOGY.com Students learn what types of data are analyzed to classify *Trichoplax* in **Data Analysis: The Simplest Animal?**

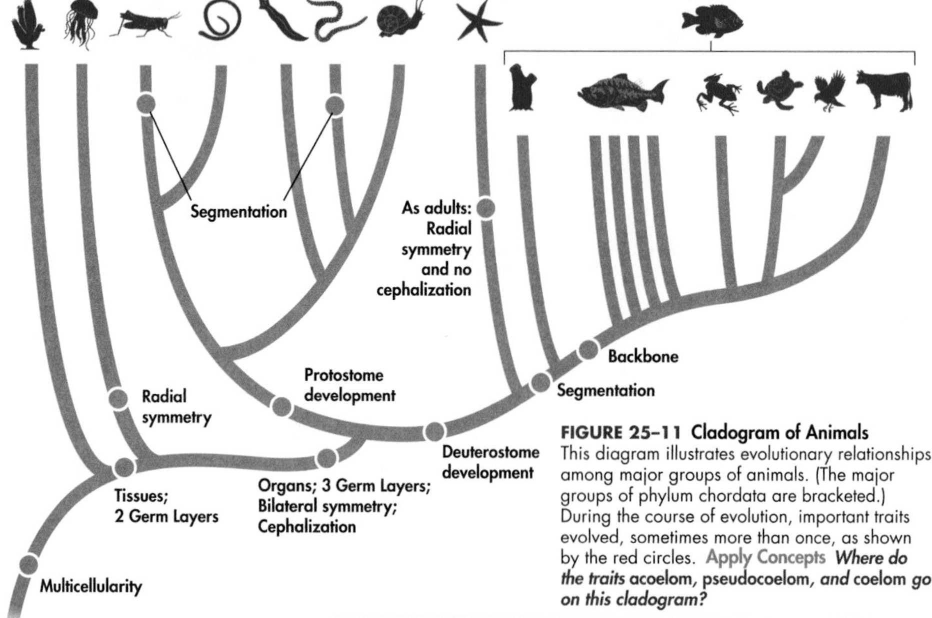

FIGURE 25–11 Cladogram of Animals This diagram illustrates evolutionary relationships among major groups of animals. (The major groups of phylum chordata are bracketed.) During the course of evolution, important traits evolved, sometimes more than once, as shown by the red circles. **Apply Concepts** ***Where do the traits acoelom, pseudocoelom, and coelom go on this cladogram?***

The Cladogram of Animals

🔑 ***How are animal phyla defined?***

The features of animal body plans you have just learned about provide information for building the cladogram, or phylogenetic tree, of animals. Recall that the evolutionary history presented in a cladogram represents a set of evolutionary hypotheses based on characteristics of living species, evidence from the fossil record, and comparative genomic studies. The cladogram in **Figure 25–11** presents our current understanding of relationships among animal phyla. 🔑 **Animal phyla are typically defined according to adult body plans and patterns of embryological development.** For example, the phylum Arthropoda is defined by a body plan that includes bilateral symmetry, segmentation, cephalization, an external skeleton, and jointed legs.

Differences Between Phyla The cladogram of animals indicates the sequence in which important body plan features evolved. Every phylum has a unique combination of ancient traits inherited from its ancestors and new traits found only in that particular phylum. It may be tempting to think of a cladogram as a story about "improvements" from one phylum to the next over time. But that isn't the case. The complicated body systems of vertebrates aren't necessarily better than the "simpler" systems of invertebrates. Any system found in living animals functions well enough to enable those animals to survive and reproduce. For example, most chordate brains are more complex than the brains of flatworms. But flatworm brains obviously work well enough to enable flatworms, as a group, to survive.

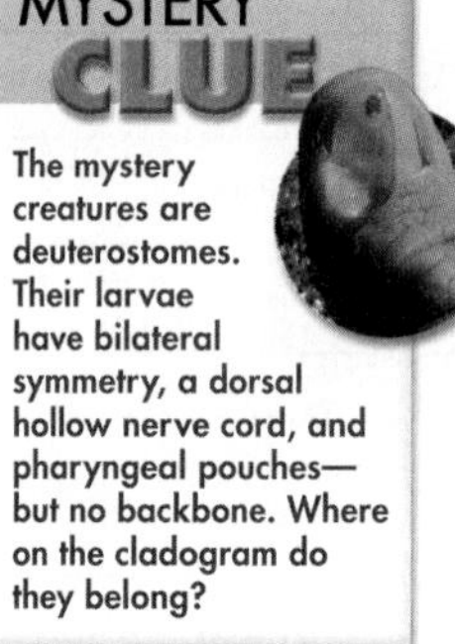

MYSTERY
CLUE
The mystery creatures are deuterostomes. Their larvae have bilateral symmetry, a dorsal hollow nerve cord, and pharyngeal pouches—but no backbone. Where on the cladogram do they belong?

UbD Check for Understanding

FOLLOW-UP PROBES

Ask Do you agree or disagree that the cladogram of animals can change? Explain your answer. *(The cladogram of animals could change if research were to reveal new information about the evolutionary relationships between groups of animals.)*

ADJUST INSTRUCTION

If students struggle to answer the question, have them reread the first paragraph under **The Cladogram of Animals.** Point out that a cladogram represents "our current understanding of relationships among animal phyla." Using the information in the first paragraph, begin a class discussion about why the current cladogram is likely to change.

Answers

FIGURE 25–11

acoelom: along the base before the cnidarian branch and along the flatworm branch

pseudocoelom: on the roundworm branch

coelom: on the base after the cnidarian branch

Changes Within Phyla: Themes and Variations Within each phylum, different groups represent different variations on the basic body plan themes that have evolved over time. Land vertebrates, for example, typically have four limbs. Many, such as frogs, walk (or hop) on four limbs that we call "legs." Among birds, the front limbs have evolved into wings. In many primates, the front limbs have evolved into what we call "arms." Both wings and arms evolved through changes in the standard vertebrate forelimb.

Evolutionary Experiments In a sense, you can think of each phylum's body plan as an evolutionary "experiment," in which a particular set of body structures performs essential functions. An organism's first appearance represents the beginning of this "experiment." The very first versions of most major animal body plans were established hundreds of millions of years ago, as you'll learn in the next chapter. Ever since that time, each phylum's evolutionary history has shown variations in body plan as species have adapted to changing conditions. If the changes have enabled members of a phylum to survive and reproduce, the phylum still exists. If the body plan hasn't functioned well enough over time, members of the phylum, or particular groups within the phylum, have become extinct.

FIGURE 25–12 Limb Variations Birds have evolved front limbs specialized as wings, whereas frogs have evolved four "legs."

25.2 Assessment

IN B.8.2

Review Key Concepts 

1. a. **Review** List eight features of animal body plans.
   b. **Infer** How is the embryology of echinoderms similar to that of vertebrates? What might this similarity indicate about their evolutionary relationship?
2. a. **Review** What two features define animal phyla?
   b. **Relate Cause and Effect** What happens to a phylum over time if its body plan doesn't enable its members to survive and reproduce?

WRITE ABOUT SCIENCE

Description

3. Explain the description of a body plan as an evolutionary "experiment." In your explanation, describe the difference between successful and unsuccessful body plans in terms of the different outcomes.

BIOLOGY.com Search Lesson 25.2 GO • Self-Test • Lesson Assessment

Lead a Discussion

Have students brainstorm variations on basic phylum body plans, such as the limbs of land chordates (tetrapods). Ask students to explain the meaning of the term *evolutionary experiment.* (Try to elicit responses that reflect the randomness in which body plans arise.) Then, ask students to explain how a phylum's body plan would become a successful "experiment." *(Answers should include mention of adaptation to a changing environment that enables members with that body plan to survive and reproduce.)*

DIFFERENTIATED INSTRUCTION

LPR **Less Proficient Readers** Ask students why some phyla still exist while others have become extinct. If they cannot answer the question, have them reread each sentence, one-by-one, in the section, **Evolutionary Experiments,** to find the answer.

Assess and Remediate

EVALUATE UNDERSTANDING

Have students write a paragraph explaining what a cladogram shows about animal body plan features. Then, have them complete the 25.2 Assessment.

REMEDIATION SUGGESTION

L1 **Struggling Students** If students have trouble answering **Question 2b,** have them work in small groups to brainstorm a reasonable example that would show how a particular body plan characteristic might lead a phylum to extinction.

BIOLOGY.com Students can check their understanding of lesson concepts with the **Self-Test** assessment. They can then take an online version of the **Lesson Assessment.**

Assessment Answers

1a. level of organization, body symmetry, differentiation of germ layers, formation of a body cavity, patterns of embryological development, segmentation, cephalization, limb formation

1b. Both are deuterostomes, which indicates that echinoderms are closely related to chordates.

2a. adult body plans and patterns of embryological development

2b. The phylum becomes extinct.

WRITE ABOUT SCIENCE

3. Sample answer: A phylum's body plan is an evolutionary "experiment," because it is a set of body structures that may be either successful or unsuccessful. A successful body plan performs the functions essential for keeping the group alive, so members survive and reproduce over time. An unsuccessful body plan is not well adapted to changing conditions, so its members go extinct.

CHAPTER LAB

Pre-Lab

Introduce students to the concepts they will explore in the chapter lab by assigning the Pre-Lab questions.

Lab

Tell students they will perform the chapter lab *Comparing Invertebrate Body Plans* described in **Lab Manual A.**

 **Struggling Students** A simpler version of the chapter lab is provided in **Lab Manual B.**

SAFETY

Caution students to keep water away from electrical equipment. Check for tangled cords, and disconnect microscopes when not in use. Tell students to be careful with sharp edges on microscope slides and to report any broken glass to you.

Look online for **Editable Lab Worksheets.**

For corresponding pre-lab in the **Foundation Edition**, see page 617.

GUIDED INQUIRY

Pre-Lab: Comparing Invertebrate Body Plans

Problem What characteristics can be used to classify invertebrates?

Materials compound microscope; prepared slides of cnidarian, roundworm, and earthworm cross sections; red, blue, and yellow colored pencils

Lab Manual Chapter 25 Lab

Skills Focus Observe, Classify, Compare and Contrast

Connect to the Big idea All members of Kingdom Animalia share a set of characteristics that define them as animals. However, the diversity within the kingdom is vast. For example, some animals have a backbone, but many do not. Some animals have radial symmetry, but many do not. In this lab, you will use preserved cross sections to compare the body plans of three invertebrates. You will pay particular attention to germ layers and body cavities.

Background Questions

a. Review Describe three characteristics that all animals share.

b. Review What are the three germ layers, and what structures do they give rise to?

c. Explain What is the function of a body cavity?

Pre-Lab Questions

Preview the procedure in the lab manual.

1. Compare and Contrast Which two features of animal body plans will you be comparing in this lab?
2. Apply Concepts Where will you look for tissue that formed from the ectoderm layer?
3. Infer Is a hydra smaller than, larger than, or about the same size as an earthworm? Base your answer on the procedure in this lab.

BIOLOGY.com Search Chapter 25 GO

Visit Chapter 25 online to test yourself on chapter content and to find activities to help you learn.

Untamed Science Video Learn how scientists determine that an organism is an animal as the Untamed Science crew visits a research facility on Coconut Island.

InterActive Art Learn how a sponge performs its life processes while staying still.

Art in Motion View an animation that shows the differences in early development in protostomes and deuterostomes.

Art Review Review your understanding of body symmetry with this drag-and-drop activity.

Data Analysis Compare *Trichoplax* to other animals to get an appreciation of the difficulty of classifying animals.

IN INDIANA ACADEMIC STANDARDS

For the full text of all standards, see the Course Overview in the front matter of this book.

Pre-Lab Answers

BACKGROUND QUESTIONS

a. Sample answer: Animals are multicellular, obtain nutrients and energy by eating other organisms, and have eukaryotic cells.

b. The endoderm gives rise to linings of the digestive tract and the respiratory system. The mesoderm gives rise to muscles plus much of the circulatory, reproductive, and excretory systems. The ectoderm gives rise to the sense organs, nerves, and outer layer of skin.

c. A body cavity provides a space in which organs can be suspended and room for those organs to grow.

PRE-LAB QUESTIONS

1. type of body cavity and number of germ layers
2. the outermost layer of each organism
3. Sample answer: I think a hydra is smaller than an earthworm because I will be able to view the earthworm under low power, but I will need to use high power to view the hydra.

25 Study Guide

Big idea Unity and Diversity of Life

Animals are multicellular, heterotrophic, eukaryotic organisms whose cells lack cell walls.

25.1 What Is an Animal?

Animals, members of the kingdom Animalia, are multicellular, heterotrophic, eukaryotic organisms whose cells lack cell walls.

Invertebrates include all animals that lack a backbone, or vertebral column.

All chordates exhibit four characteristics during at least one stage of life: a dorsal, hollow nerve cord; a notochord; a tail that extends beyond the anus; and pharyngeal pouches.

Like all organisms, animals must maintain homeostasis by gathering and responding to information, obtaining and distributing oxygen and nutrients, and collecting and eliminating carbon dioxide and other wastes. They also reproduce.

invertebrate (730)
chordate (731)
notochord (731)
pharyngeal pouch (731)
vertebrate (731)
feedback inhibition (732)

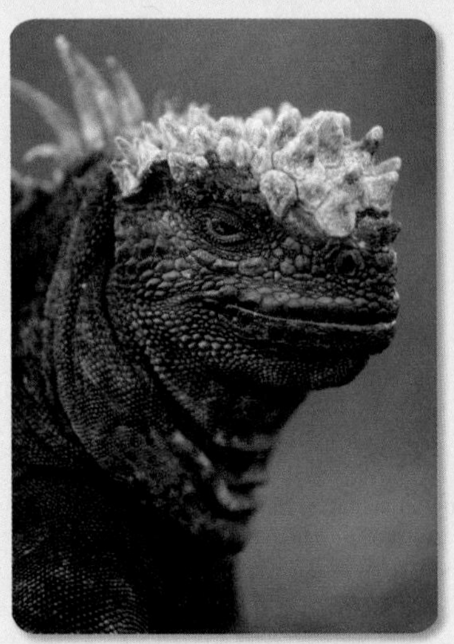

25.2 Animal Body Plans and Evolution

Features of animal body plans include levels of organization, body symmetry, differentiation of germ layers, formation of body cavities, patterns of embryological development, segmentation, cephalization, and limb formation.

Animal phyla are typically defined according to adult body plans and patterns of embryological development.

radial symmetry (738)
bilateral symmetry (738)
endoderm (738)
mesoderm (738)
ectoderm (738)
coelom (738)
pseudocoelom (738)
zygote (739)
blastula (739)
protostome (739)
deuterostome (739)
cephalization (740)

Think Visually

Using information from this chapter, complete the following concept map.

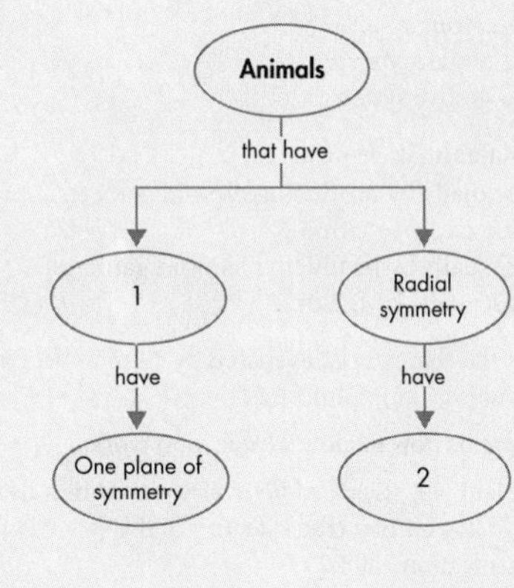

Study Online

REVIEW AND ASSESSMENT RESOURCES

Editable Worksheets Pages of Study Workbooks A and B, Lab Manuals A and B, and the Assessment Resources Book are available online. These documents can easily be edited using a word-processing program.

Lesson Overview Have students reread the Lesson Overviews to help them study chapter concepts.

Vocabulary Review The *Flash Cards* and *Match It* provide an interactive way to review chapter vocabulary.

Chapter Assessment Have students take an online version of the Chapter 25 Assessment.

Standardized Test Prep Students can take an online version of the Standardized Test Prep. You will receive their scores along with ideas for remediation.

Diagnostic and Benchmark Tests Use these tests to monitor your students' progress and supply remediation.

UbD Performance Tasks

SUMMATIVE TASK Have students use what they have learned about the essential functions of animals and their body plan features to assemble a class scrapbook. Divide the class into pairs, and assign each pair an essential function or a body plan feature described in the chapter. Each pair should prepare a two-page spread on the assigned topic. Students should use labeled drawings and/or photographs. Each spread in the scrapbook should have a title and a summary of the importance of the essential function or body plan feature.

TRANSFER TASK Ask students to imagine they have discovered a new animal. Then, divide the class into small groups, and ask each group to write an article for a science journal announcing its discovery. In their article, students should describe what the animal is like, explain how it meets the four criteria of an animal, and how it carries out essential functions. Finally, describe where it should be placed in the animal cladogram based on its body plan.

Answers

THINK VISUALLY

1. bilateral symmetry

2. any number of planes of symmetry

ASSESSMENT

Lesson 25.1

UNDERSTAND KEY CONCEPTS

1. c **2.** a **3.** c **4.** d

5. c **6.** c

7. All members of the animal kingdom are multicellular, eukaryotic heterotrophs whose cells lack cell walls.

8. Feedback inhibition, or negative feedback, is a system in which the product or result of a process limits the process itself. Descriptions will vary. For example, when a person becomes too hot, he or she sweats to help lose heat. When the person is sufficiently cool, he or she will stop sweating.

9. The term *invertebrate* is used to describe all animals that are not chordates. It is a negative definition. Normally, a clade or category of true biological classification is defined by the presence of characteristics, rather than their absence.

10. The raccoon's nervous system collects and processes information such as the smell of a food source. The nervous and musculoskeletal systems move the raccoon to the food.

THINK CRITICALLY

11. Vertebrates develop a backbone made up of individual bones called vertebrae; nonvertebrate chordates do not.

12. The circulatory system picks up nutrients from the digestive system and oxygen from the respiratory system and takes these essential materials to all cells in the body. It also removes carbon dioxide from cells and carries it to the respiratory system for elimination.

13. Carbon dioxide exits the body through the respiratory system. Ammonia is removed by the excretory system.

14. Sensory receptors in the rabbit's nervous system gather visual, auditory, and chemical clues. This information is processed in the nervous system, which stimulates the muscles to contract, causing the rabbit to move away from the predator.

Lesson 25.2

UNDERSTAND KEY CONCEPTS

15. b **16.** c **17.** c

18. b **19.** d **20.** a **21.** b

22. An acoelomate is an animal that lacks a body cavity or coelom.

23. In protostomes, the blastopore becomes the mouth, and the anus forms from a second opening at the opposite end of a tube that connects the two openings. In deuterostomes, the blastopore becomes the anus, and the mouth is formed from a second opening.

24. a hollow ball of cells

25. ectoderm, mesoderm, endoderm

26. Sample answer: bilateral symmetry and segmentation

27. With cephalization, animals respond efficiently, because sense organs and nerve cells generally encounter the environment first.

THINK CRITICALLY

28. Animals with bilateral symmetry usually have specialized anterior, posterior, dorsal, and ventral regions. Sense organs are clustered at the head end, encounter the environment first, and give the animal an advantage in orientation, navigation, feeding, and defense.

29. multicellularity, tissues, protostome development, deuterostome development

IN The numbers following the questions refer to Indiana's Academic Standards for Biology I.

25.1 What Is an Animal?

Understand Key Concepts

1. A multicellular, eukaryotic heterotroph whose cells lack cell walls is a(n)
a. protist. **c.** animal.
b. virus. **d.** plant.

2. Which of the following is characteristic of all chordates but not found in invertebrates? B.8.2
a. a notochord **c.** a circulatory system
b. four legs **d.** an exoskeleton

3. The process by which animals take in oxygen and give off carbon dioxide is known as
a. responding. **c.** breathing.
b. reproducing. **d.** excreting.

4. Animals that have a backbone, also called a vertebral column, are known as B.8.2
a. invertebrates. **c.** homeostasis.
b. prokaryotes. **d.** vertebrates.

5. The job of collecting waste materials from a complex animal's body cells and delivering them to organs that will release them from the body is carried out by the
a. excretory system.
b. nervous system.
c. circulatory system.
d. digestive system.

6. Most animals reproduce
a. sexually by producing diploid gametes.
b. asexually by cloning.
c. sexually by producing haploid gametes.
d. asexually by fission.

7. List the characteristics shared by all members of the animal kingdom. B.8.2

8. Describe how feedback inhibition works.

9. Explain why the word *invertebrate* may be a useful word but is not a true category in the system of classification. B.8.2

10. Which body systems are most involved when a raccoon discovers that a full trash can is a food source, and it knocks over the can to find the food?

Think Critically

11. Classify What characteristic distinguishes vertebrates from nonvertebrate chordates? B.8.2

12. Apply Concepts In what ways do the digestive and respiratory systems depend on the circulatory system to carry out the functions of obtaining nutrients and eliminating wastes?

13. Compare and Contrast How does the way animals dispose of carbon dioxide differ from the way they dispose of ammonia?

14. Relate Cause and Effect Describe generally how the nervous and musculoskeletal systems of a rabbit react when it sees a predator such as a coyote.

25.2 Animal Body Plans and Evolution

Understand Key Concepts

15. Many animals have body symmetry with distinct front and back ends. This type of symmetry is
a. radial. **c.** circular.
b. bilateral. **d.** dorsal.

16. The developing embryo shown below is a __?__, a group that includes __?__. B.8.2

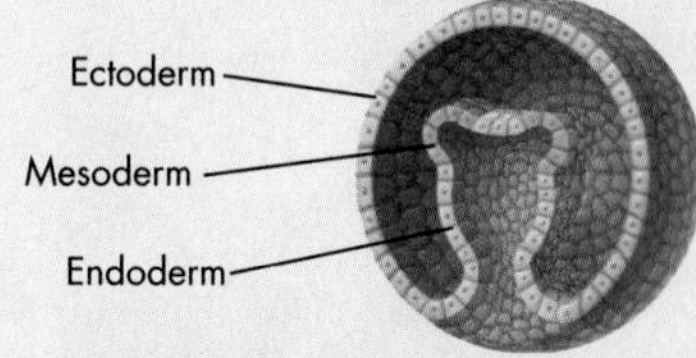

a. protostome; invertebrates other than echinoderms
b. protostome; vertebrates
c. deuterostome; echinoderms and chordates
d. deuterostome; invertebrates

17. An animal whose mouth is formed from the blastopore is a(n) B.8.2
a. deuterostome. **c.** protostome.
b. endoderm. **d.** mesoderm.

18. A concentration of sense organs and nerve cells in the anterior end of the body is known as B.6.3
   a. fertilization. c. symmetry.
   b. cephalization. d. multicellularity.

19. Which of the following animals shows radial symmetry?
   a. earthworm c. insect
   b. fish d. sea anemone

20. Which germ layer produces the nerves and sense organs of animals? B.6.3
   a. ectoderm c. mesoderm
   b. endoderm d. periderm

21. Most chordates that live on land have B.8.2
   a. two limbs. c. six limbs.
   b. four limbs. d. eight limbs.

22. What is an acoelomate?

23. Describe the major developmental difference that distinguishes protostomes from deuterostomes. B.8.2

24. What is a blastula? B.6.3

25. List the three germ layers. B.6.3

26. Name two body plan characteristics shared by all arthropods and vertebrates. B.8.2

27. What is one major advantage of cephalization?

Think Critically

28. **Apply Concepts** Why is bilateral symmetry an important development in the evolution of animals? B.8.2

29. **Sequence** Rank the following developments in the order of their appearance during evolution: tissues, deuterostome development, multicellularity, protostome development. B.8.2

30. **Form a Hypothesis** Animals with radial symmetry, such as sea anemones, lack cephalization, while animals with bilateral symmetry have it. State a hypothesis that would explain this observation.

31. **Infer** Why is it inaccurate to state that the cladogram of animals shows the improvements in body plans that have occurred over time?

 B.8.2

solve the CHAPTER MYSTERY

SLIME DAY AT THE BEACH

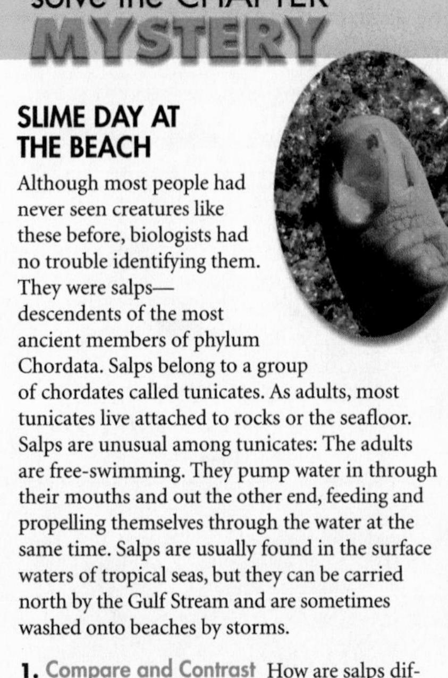

Although most people had never seen creatures like these before, biologists had no trouble identifying them. They were salps—descendents of the most ancient members of phylum Chordata. Salps belong to a group of chordates called tunicates. As adults, most tunicates live attached to rocks or the seafloor. Salps are unusual among tunicates: The adults are free-swimming. They pump water in through their mouths and out the other end, feeding and propelling themselves through the water at the same time. Salps are usually found in the surface waters of tropical seas, but they can be carried north by the Gulf Stream and are sometimes washed onto beaches by storms.

1. **Compare and Contrast** How are salps different from jellyfish?
2. **Connect to the Big idea** Use the Internet to research salps and other tunicates. Explain why these peculiar-looking animals are classified in the phylum Chordata.

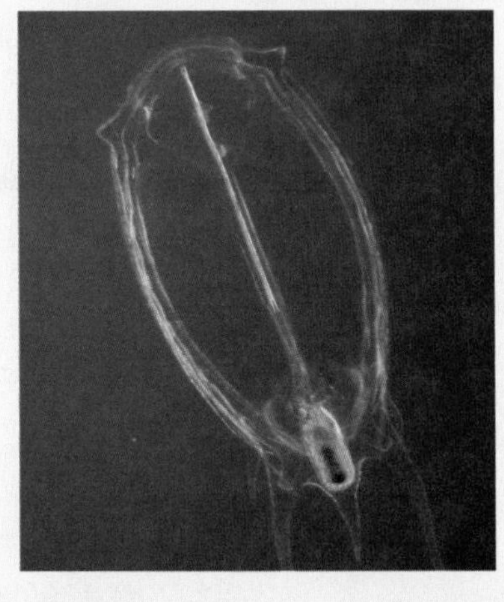

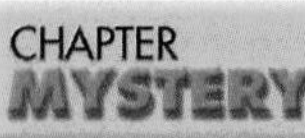

After students have read through the Chapter Mystery, discuss the characteristics of salps to confirm where they fit into the animal kingdom.

Ask What two functions does the mouth of a salp serve? *(By taking water into the mouth and pumping it out the other end, a salp is propelled through the water. At the same time, it feeds on matter in the incoming water.)*

Ask What characteristics distinguish salps from other tunicates? *(In contrast to other tunicates, salps are free-swimming.)*

Ask If salps show bilateral symmetry and propel themselves through the water, what might you infer about their nervous system? Explain. *(You could infer that they have some cephalization, with nerve cells at the anterior end.)*

CHAPTER MYSTERY ANSWERS

1. Salps are chordates: they are deuterostomes with bilateral symmetry and two body openings. Jellyfish are invertebrates: they are protostomes with radial symmetry and one body opening.
2. Big idea The characteristics that define chordates are a notochord; a dorsal, hollow nerve cord; pharyngeal pouches; and a postanal tail. Tunicates are classified as chordates, because at least while they are larvae, they show these characteristics. By the time they metamorphose to adulthood, however, most tunicates have lost all of these characteristics except the pharyngeal pouches.

Follow the crew of Untamed Science in the short movie, **What Is an Animal?,** as they find out how scientists decide if an organism is an animal.

ASSESSMENT

30. Sample answer: Animals with radial symmetry have no cephalization, because they have no anterior end, while animals with bilateral symmetry have an anterior end and may exhibit cephalization.

31. While body plans in some groups may appear to be more "complex," it is inaccurate to say they are "improved." The fact that groups with less complex bodies continue to survive indicates that they are well adapted to their environments.

Connecting Concepts

USE SCIENCE GRAPHICS

32. Body temperature appears closest to the environment around 3 P.M.

33. There is virtually no relationship between body temperature and the temperature of the environment. Body temperature is largely independent of environmental temperature.

34. There is a minuscule increase in body temperature at the highest environmental reading. Basically, body temperature stays relatively constant throughout the day, no matter what the temperature of the environment is. Body temperature is controlled homeostatically through feedback inhibition.

WRITE ABOUT SCIENCE

35. Sample answer: Cephalization concentrates sense organs and nervous tissue in the part of the body that encounters the environment first. Such concentration allows specialization of senses and responses to specific environmental conditions experienced by the animal. Segmentation allows modification of similar structures in different segments to adapt the animal to its environment.

36. Big idea Sample answer: I would look for evidence of multicellularity (if it were large enough to see without a microscope, it would be multicellular). I would then examine its cells for the presence of nuclei and the absence of cell walls. I would also look for evidence of heterotrophism, perhaps by seeing if it eats smaller organisms near it.

Connecting Concepts

Use Science Graphics NoS.3

Use the graph to answer questions 32–34.

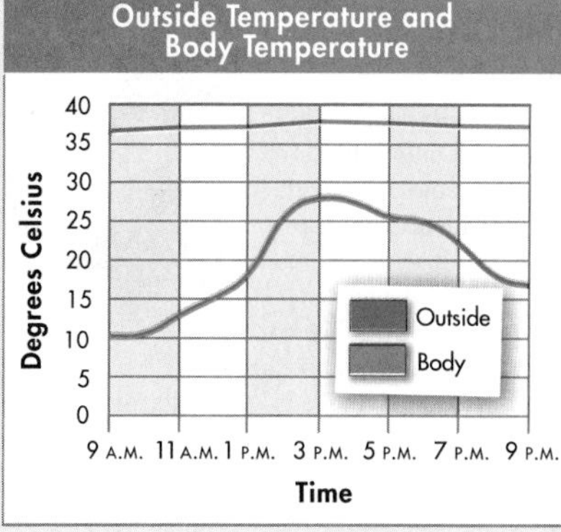

32. Interpret Graphs At what time of day is the body temperature closest to that of the outside environment?

33. Draw Conclusions What is the relationship between body temperature and the temperature of the environment?

34. Infer How do you explain the shape of the graph for body temperature?

Write About Science NoS.3

35. Explanation Discuss how cephalization and segmentation have helped animals achieve such great diversity.

36. 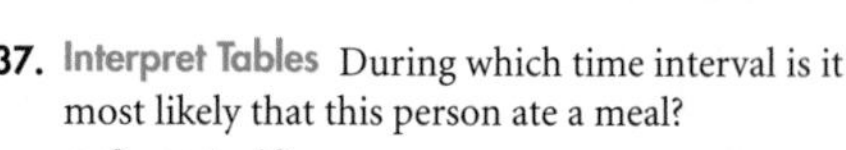

If you were presented with a small, living organism, how would you try to determine whether it was an animal? B.8.2

Analyzing Data

IN NoS.3

The human digestive system converts food into glucose, a sugar that the body can use for energy. The following data were collected by taking a sample of blood from a person at various times during the day and measuring the relative volume of glucose in the blood.

Time of Day	Amount of Glucose (mg/100 mL)
9 A.M.	102
10 A.M.	98
11 A.M.	130
12 noon	115
1 P.M.	103
2 P.M.	100
3 P.M.	102

37. Interpret Tables During which time interval is it most likely that this person ate a meal?
a. 9 A.M. to 10 A.M.
b. 10 A.M. to 11 A.M.
c. 1 P.M. to 2 P.M.
d. 2 P.M. to 3 P.M.

38. Infer Which value in the table would you expect to be closest to the homeostatic value for the amount of glucose in the blood?

39. Apply Concepts Explain how feedback inhibition might be involved in the changing levels of glucose in the blood.

748 Chapter 25 • Assessment

PURPOSE Students will analyze data to understand the effect of time on blood glucose levels.

PLANNING Explain to students that after eating, food is broken down to glucose in the digestive system. A healthy pancreas produces insulin, which acts as a gatekeeper, allowing glucose to enter cells where it can be broken down to release energy.

ANSWERS

37. b

38. About 102 mg/100 mL

39. Sample answer: The body likely has a way to sense changing glucose levels in the blood and regulate it with feedback inhibition. If glucose levels are high (such as after a meal), the body will decrease blood glucose levels. If glucose levels get too low, the body will respond by increasing blood glucose levels.

Standardized Test Practice for Indiana

Multiple Choice

1. Which of the following is a type of tissue that arises in most animals during development?
   A endoderm
   B mesoderm
   C ectoderm
   D all of the above B.6.3

2. Which of the following is NOT a characteristic of animals?
   A the ability to make their own food
   B the ability to move
   C eukaryotic cells
   D cells that lack cell walls B.8.2

3. A hollow ball of cells formed after the zygote undergoes division is called a
   A coelom.
   B protostome.
   C deuterostome.
   D blastula. B.6.3

4. Which trend did NOT occur during invertebrate evolution?
   A specialization of cells
   B development of a notochord
   C bilateral symmetry
   D cephalization B.8.2

5. What is a function of the excretory system?
   A to supply cells with oxygen and nutrients
   B to rid the body of metabolic wastes
   C to gather information from the environment
   D to break down food

6. Animals often respond to information processed by their nervous system by moving around, using their
   A circulatory system.
   B excretory system.
   C musculoskeletal system.
   D digestive system.

7. The concentration of nerve tissue and organs in one end of the body is called
   A cephalization.
   B segmentation.
   C body symmetry.
   D nerve nets. B.6.3

Questions 8 and 9

A biology student has two samples of earthworms in soil, as shown below. The student knows that, because the worms' body temperature changes with the environment, the worms in Sample A have a higher body temperature than those in Sample B. The student uses a stereomicroscope to count the number of heartbeats per minute for three worms from each sample.

Sample A: At temperature of worms' soil environment

Sample B: In ice water

8. Look at the student's two samples. What can you conclude?
   A Sample A is the control.
   B Sample B is the control.
   C Either sample can serve as a control.
   D This is not a controlled experiment.

9. The student finds that the worms from Sample A have a faster heart rate than the worms from Sample B. What hypothesis might you form based on this observation?
   A The worms in Sample A are healthier than the worms in Sample B.
   B A decrease in body temperature corresponds to an increase in heart rate.
   C There is no relationship between body temperature and heart rate.
   D A decrease in body temperature corresponds to a decrease in heart rate.

Open-Ended Response

10. What characteristics distinguish invertebrates from nonvertebrate chordates? B.8.2

If You Have Trouble With . . .

Question	1	2	3	4	5	6	7	8	9	10
See Lesson	25.2	25.1	25.2	25.2	25.1	25.1	25.2	25.1	25.1	25.1

Answers

1. D
2. A
3. D
4. B
5. B
6. C
7. A
8. A
9. A
10. Nonvertebrate chordates are animals that have a dorsal nerve cord, pharyngeal pouches, a tail that extends beyond the anus, and a notochord at some time during development. Invertebrates do not have all of the above characteristics.

Test-Taking Tip

READ ALL THE ANSWER CHOICES

Caution students that when evaluating multiple-choice answers, they should read all of the answer choices before making a selection. Even if the first choice seems correct, students should make certain the one they choose is the best answer.

CHAPTER PLANNER 26 Animal Evolution and Diversity

Chapter Contents	IN	Time	Core Resources
Chapter Preview			**Student Edition,** pp. 750–751 **Chapter Mystery,** p. 751
26.1 Invertebrate Evolution and Diversity Origins of the Invertebrates • Cladogram of Invertebrates	NoS.6, B.8.1, B.8.2	1/2 period 1/4 block	**Student Edition,** pp. 752–756 **Study Workbook A** 26.1 Worksheets L2 **Biology.com** *InterActive Art:* Cladogram of Invertebrates **Assessment Resources Book** Visual Quiz L2
26.2 Chordate Evolution and Diversity Origins of the Chordates • Cladogram of Chordates	NoS.3, NoS.6, B.8.1, B.8.2	1 period 1/2 block	**Student Edition,** pp. 757–764 **Inquiry** 26.2 Analyzing Data, p. 763 L2 **Study Workbook A** 26.2 Worksheets L2 **Biology.com** *Art in Motion:* From Fins to Feet • 26.2 Self-Test • 26.2 Lesson Assessment
26.3 Primate Evolution What Is a Primate? • Evolution of Primates • Hominine Evolution • The Road to Modern Humans • *Biology & History: Human-Fossil Seekers*	NoS.6, B.8.1, B.8.2	1 period 1/2 block	**Student Edition,** pp. 765–773 **Inquiry** 26.3 Quick Lab, p. 766 L2 **Study Workbook A** 26.3 Worksheets L2 **Biology.com** *Art Review:* Comparison of Hominoids • *Data Analysis:* Who Is *H. floresiensis*? **Assessment Resources Book** Visual Quiz L2
Chapter Pre-Lab	NoS.2, NoS.5, B.8.2, B.8.3	1 period 1/2 block	**Student Edition,** p. 774 L2 **Lab Manual A** *Investigating Hominoid Fossils* L2

Differentiated Instruction Tools

Study Workbook B includes worksheets with lesson-level differentiated instruction support and explanations of differentiated instruction teaching strategies.

Lab Manual B includes skills labs, simplified chapter labs, and hands-on activities.

ELL Handbook explains ways to make *Biology* more accessible to ELL students.

Spanish Study Workbook is a Spanish translation of Study Workbook A.

Multilingual Glossary is the glossary translated into ten languages.

Differentiated Instruction Key

- L1 Special Needs or Struggling Students
- ELL English Language Learners
- LPR Less Proficient Readers
- L2 On-Level Students
- L3 Advanced Students

Additional Resources

Biology.com Untamed Science Video • Vocabulary Flash Cards

Study Workbook B 26.1 Worksheets L1 ELL LPR
Spanish Study Workbook 26.1 Worksheets ELL
Biology.com 26.1 Lesson Overview • 26.1 Lesson Notes • 26.1 Self-Test • 26.1 Lesson Assessment

Study Workbook B 26.2 Worksheets L1 ELL LPR
Spanish Study Workbook 26.2 Worksheets ELL
Biology.com 26.2 Lesson Overview • 26.2 Lesson Notes

Study Workbook B 26.3 Worksheets L1 ELL LPR
Spanish Study Workbook 26.3 Worksheets ELL
Biology.com 26.3 Lesson Overview • 26.3 Lesson Notes • 26.3 Self-Test • 26.3 Lesson Assessment

Lab Manual B *Investigating Hominoid Fossils* • Data Analysis: *Feather Evolution* • Hands-On Activity: *Binocular Vision* L1 ELL LPR

Chapter Review

Student Edition Study Guide, p. *775* L2
Study Workbook A Chapter 26 Vocabulary Review L2 • Chapter 26 Chapter Mystery/21st Century Skills Activity L2 L3
Transparencies, pp. 297–305 L1 ELL LPR L2
Biology.com Untamed Science Video • Editable Worksheets of Study Workbooks A and B and Lab Manuals A and B • Chapter 26 Flash Cards and Crossword Puzzle

Untamed Science DVD • Classroom Resources CD (includes lesson presentations and editable worksheets)

Chapter Assessment

Student Edition Assessment, pp. *776–779* L2
Study Workbook B Chapter 26 Chapter Review L1 ELL LPR • Chapter 26 Taking a Standardized Test L1 ELL LPR
Assessment Resources Book Chapter 26 Test A L2 • Chapter 26 Test B L1 ELL LPR
Biology.com Chapter 26 Assessment • Editable Worksheets of Chapter Visual Quizzes and Chapter 26 Tests A and B

Exam*View* *Assessment Suite* • Classroom Resources CD (includes lesson presentations and editable worksheets)

Time: 1 period, 1/2 block

Pressed for Time?

Preview the Chapter Preview the images of invertebrates on pp. 754–756 and briefly discuss the diversity of invertebrates. Read the Key Questions for Lessons 26.2 and 26.3.

Cover the Chapter Quickly Have students read *Origins of the Invertebrates* in Lesson 26.1 and go over Figure 26–3. In Lesson 26.2, assign the introduction to *Origins of the Chordates* and go over Figure 26–5. Have students read *What Is a Primate?*, the introduction to *Hominine Evolution*, and *The Road to Modern Humans* in Lesson 26.3.

Assess Assign questions 1 and 2b in the 26.1 Assessment, questions 1a, 2a, and 2c in the 26.2 Assessment, and questions 1, 3, and 4 in the 26.3 Assessment. In the Chapter 26 Assessment, assign questions 1, 9, 11, 20, 21, 23, 25–30, and 35–38.

Connect to the Big Idea

Direct students' attention to the photograph of the gopher snake skeleton, and explain that gopher snakes are relatively common in North America, especially in the western United States. Then, ask what structure is most prominent in this skeleton. *(the backbone)* Have students name other animal groups that have backbones. *(mammals, amphibians, birds, and fish)* Remind students that many animals lack backbones, such as insects, worms, and jellyfish. Ask which group of animals they think appeared first on Earth, vertebrates or invertebrates. *(invertebrates)* Through a discussion of which group appeared first, have students anticipate the answer to the question, **How have animals descended from earlier forms through the process of evolution?**

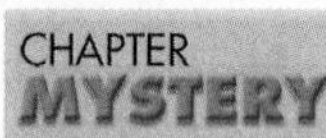

Have students read over the Chapter Mystery and predict when the first animals appeared on Earth and when the earliest birds evolved. Then, have students predict where they could go to find fossils of the first animals and the earliest birds. Use their predictions to help them start connecting the Chapter Mystery to the Big Idea of Evolution.

BIOLOGY.com Have students preview the chapter vocabulary using the **Flash Cards.**

26 Animal Evolution and Diversity

Big idea **Evolution**

Q: How have animals descended from earlier forms through the process of evolution?

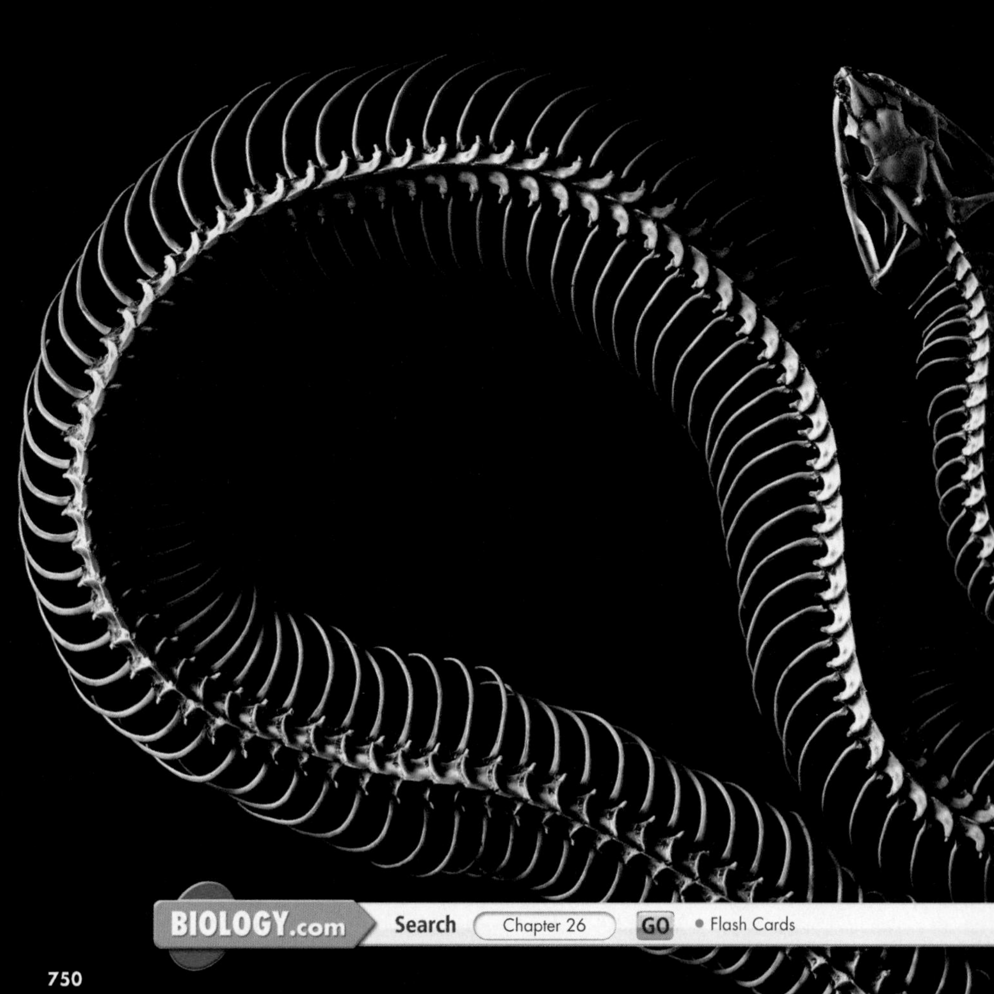

BIOLOGY.com Search Chapter 26 GO • Flash Cards

750

IN INDIANA ACADEMIC STANDARDS

For the full text of all standards, see the Course Overview in the front matter of this book.

Key standards: Chapter 26 covers key ideas from Standard 8: Evolution, including **B.8.1** History of life on Earth.

UbD Understanding by Design

In Unit 7, students have been developing the Enduring Understanding that *animals have evolved diverse ways to carry out basic life processes and maintain homeostasis.* Students explore this Enduring Understanding in Chapter 26 by studying the evolution and diversity of invertebrates and chordates, including an in-depth examination of the evolution of primates. As shown in the graphic organizer to the right, the Big Idea, Essential Question, and Guiding Questions help direct their exploration.

PERFORMANCE GOALS

In Chapter 26, students will learn about the evolution and diversity of animals. They will accomplish this through activities such as examining cladograms, analyzing data about feather evolution, and testing the usefulness of binocular vision. At the end of the chapter, students will create a pamphlet to inform the public about animal evolution. They will also classify and describe the evolution of a living animal.

CHAPTER 26

What's Online

Extend your reach by using these and other digital assets offered at **Biology.com.**

CHAPTER MYSTERY
Students can learn about the places to find fossils of the very first animals and of the ancestors of birds.

UNTAMED SCIENCE VIDEO
Why does there always seem to be a new type of bug crawling out of the woodwork? Join the Untamed Science crew as they investigate why there are so many different types of insects.

INTERACTIVE ART
In this drag-and-drop activity, students will become more familiar with the cladogram of invertebrates.

ART REVIEW
This activity helps students review the differences between human skeletons and gorilla skeletons.

DATA ANALYSIS
Students investigate if fossils are of a species separate from *H. sapiens* or from a population of *H. sapiens*.

INDIANA ACADEMIC STANDARDS FOR SCIENCE

Nature of Science NoS.2, NoS.3, NoS.5, NoS.6; **Evolution** B.8.1, B.8.2, B.8.3. See lessons for details.

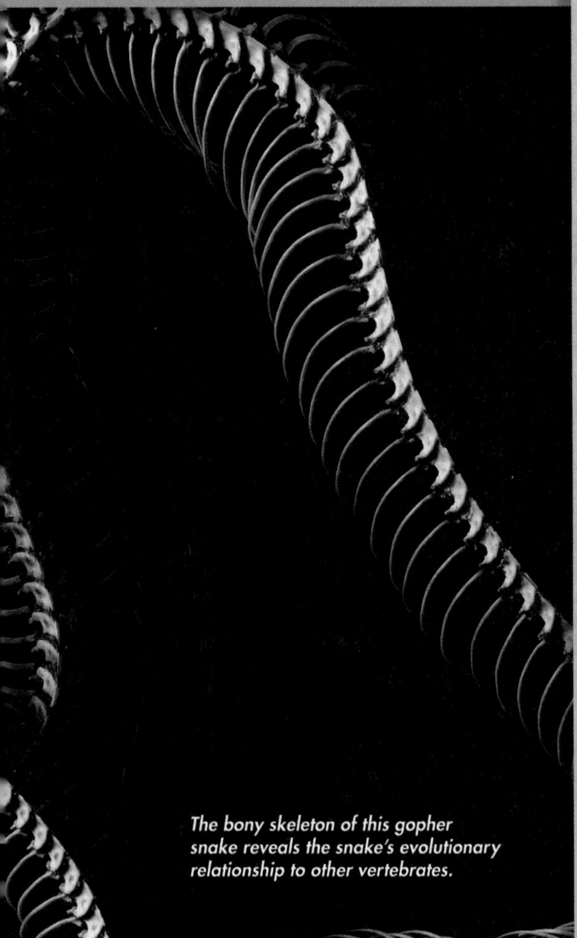

The bony skeleton of this gopher snake reveals the snake's evolutionary relationship to other vertebrates.

• Untamed Science Video • Chapter Mystery

CHAPTER MYSTERY

FOSSIL QUEST

To Josh and Pedro, it sounded like a great summer trip: fossil hunting. They would be outside, and the trip would look awesome on college applications. But where should they go? And who would lead them? Their parents were okay with the idea—if they stayed within the United States. Both boys liked dinosaurs and extinct mammals, but for this trip, Josh wanted to search for the very *first* animals. Pedro, on the other hand, loved his pet parakeet so he wanted to look for the ancestors of birds. But where could they find these fossils . . . and were any good sites close enough to satisfy their parents?

They realized that they needed to figure out in which periods their target animals lived. Then, they needed to figure out where they could find rocks of the appropriate ages. As you read this chapter, look for clues to the geologic time periods Josh and Pedro's target animals might have lived in and where the two boys might expect to find their fossils. Then, solve the mystery.

Never Stop Exploring Your World. Discovering where Josh and Pedro's "Fossil Quest" will take them is only the beginning. Take a video field trip with the ecogeeks of Untamed Science to see where the mystery leads.

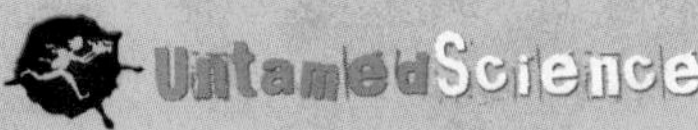

Animal Evolution and Diversity 751

Chapter 26 Big Idea: Evolution

Chapter 26 EQ: How have animals descended from earlier forms through the process of evolution?

- **26.1 GQ:** How did invertebrates evolve?
- **26.2 GQ:** How did chordates evolve?
- **26.3 GQ:** How did primates evolve?

LESSON 26.1

Getting Started

Objectives

26.1.1 Explain what fossil evidence indicates about the timing of the evolution of the first animals.

26.1.2 Interpret the cladogram of invertebrates.

Student Resources

Study Workbooks A and B, 26.1 Worksheets

Spanish Study Workbook, 26.1 Worksheets

Lesson Overview • Lesson Notes • Activity: InterActive Art • Assessment: Self-Test, Lesson Assessment

For corresponding lesson in the **Foundation Edition**, see pages 624–627.

Activate Prior Knowledge

Ask students to brainstorm a list of animals that are invertebrates—animals with no backbone. As students name kinds of animals, write the list on the board. After brainstorming, have students look at the list of invertebrates they generated and identify two or three of the invertebrates that may be closely related. Ask students on what basis they made these judgments. *(Sample answer: physical similarities)* Explain that modern scientists often use DNA analysis to determine relationships among groups of animals, and this sometimes results in surprising relationships.

IN INDIANA ACADEMIC STANDARDS

For the full text of all standards, see the Course Overview in the front matter of this book.

B.8.1 Explain how anatomical and molecular similarities among organisms that suggest life on earth began as simple, one-celled organisms about 4 billion years ago and multicellular organisms evolved later.

26.1 Invertebrate Evolution and Diversity

B.8.1 History of life on Earth. Also covered: **NoS.6, B.8.2.**

Key Questions

When did the first animals evolve?

What does the cladogram of invertebrates illustrate?

Vocabulary

appendage
larva
trochophore

Taking Notes

Preview Visuals Before you read, preview the cladogram of invertebrates in **Figure 26–3.** Take note of any questions you have about it and try to answer them as you read.

For more on the diversity of animals, go to the Visual Guide. DOL•30–DOL•64

THINK ABOUT IT The origins of the first animals are shrouded in mystery. Since Darwin, paleontologists have known, on the basis of fossil evidence, that many modern multicellular phyla first appeared during a geologically brief period called the "Cambrian Explosion," between 530 and 515 million years ago. How did so many kinds of animals evolve so quickly? What simpler forms could they have evolved from? Until recently, few fossils predating the Cambrian Period had been found, so there was no way to answer these questions. Then, over the last few decades, a series of discoveries revolutionized our understanding of early animal evolution.

Origins of the Invertebrates

When did the first animals evolve?

For roughly 3 billion years after the first prokaryotic cells evolved, all prokaryotes and eukaryotes were single-celled. We don't know when the first multicellular animals evolved from single-celled eukaryotes. Several kinds of data support the hypothesis that animals evolved from ancestors they shared with organisms called choanoflagellates (koh AN uh FLAJ uh layts). These are usually single-celled eukaryotes, but they sometimes grow in colonies. They share several characteristics with sponges, the simplest multicellular animals.

Traces of Early Animals Our oldest evidence of multicellular life comes from recently discovered microscopic fossils that are roughly 600 million years old. The first animals were tiny and soft-bodied, so few fossilized bodies exist. Still, recent studies have uncovered incredibly well preserved fossils of eggs and embryos, such as the embryo in **Figure 26–1.** Other fossils from this time period have been identified as parts of sponges and animals similar to jellyfish. Paleontologists have also identified what are called "trace fossils" from this time period. Trace fossils are tracks and burrows made by animals whose body parts weren't fossilized. **Such fossil evidence indicates that the first animals began evolving long before the Cambrian Explosion.**

FIGURE 26–1 Fossil Evidence Fossils such as the 565-million-year-old embryo at left are among the rarest and most valuable treasures that the backbreaking work of hunting for microfossils can yield. (SEM 100×)

 BIOLOGY.com Search Lesson 26.1 GO • Lesson Overview • Lesson Notes

UbD Teach for Understanding

ENDURING UNDERSTANDING Animals have evolved diverse ways to carry out basic life processes and maintain homeostasis.

GUIDING QUESTION How did invertebrates evolve?

EVIDENCE OF UNDERSTANDING *This assessment should show student understanding of one invertebrate group, how invertebrates evolved, and some of the important traits of invertebrates.* After students have finished the lesson, ask each student to choose a modern invertebrate group and write a paragraph explaining what the invertebrate's earliest ancestors were like, which phylum it is in, the important traits it possesses, and which other invertebrate groups it is closely related to.

The Ediacaran Fauna Some of the most exciting and important discoveries about animal life before the Cambrian Period come from fossils in the Ediacara Hills of Australia. These strange fossils, which date from roughly 565 to about 544 million years ago, have intrigued paleontologists for years. The body plans they show are different from those of anything alive today. They show little evidence of cell, tissue, or organ specialization, and no organization into a front and back end. Some may have had photosynthetic algae living within their bodies. Some were segmented and had bilateral symmetry. Some seem to be related to invertebrates such as jellyfishes and worms. Many of the organisms were flat and lived on the bottom of shallow seas.

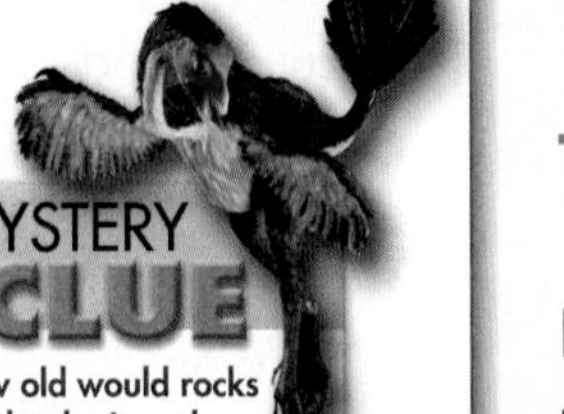

MYSTERY CLUE

How old would rocks need to be in order to contain fossils of the earliest known animals?

The Cambrian Explosion Fossils from the Cambrian Period, which began about 542 million years ago, paint a fascinating picture of invertebrate life. Two major Cambrian fossil sites are in Chengjiang, China, and in the Burgess Shale of Canada. Cambrian fossils show that over a period of 10–15 million years, animals evolved complex body plans, including specialized cells, tissues, and organs. Many had body symmetry; segmentation; a front and back end; and **appendages,** structures such as legs or antennae protruding from the body. Some Cambrian animals had also evolved shells, skeletons, and other hard body parts. Hard body parts tend to persist longer after an organism dies, so they are more likely to become fossilized.

A number of Cambrian fossils have been identified as ancient members of modern invertebrate phyla, such as the arthropod *Marrella* in **Figure 26–2.** However, some early Cambrian fossils represent extinct groups so peculiar that no one knows what to make of them! Other Cambrian animals appear to be early chordates. By the end of the Cambrian Period, all the basic body plans of modern phyla had been established. Later evolutionary changes, which produced the more familiar body structures of modern animals, involved significant variations on these basic body plans.

Modern Invertebrate Diversity Today, invertebrates are the most abundant animals on Earth. They live in nearly every ecosystem, participate in nearly every food web, and vastly outnumber so-called "higher animals," such as reptiles and mammals.

FIGURE 26–2 Cambrian Animals This Cambrian Period fossil of *Marrella splendens* was found in the Burgess Shale in Canada. The illustration shows what *Marrella* and other Burgess Shale animals may have looked like. **Infer** ***Why do scientists have more detailed data on Cambrian animals than they do on pre-Cambrian animals?***

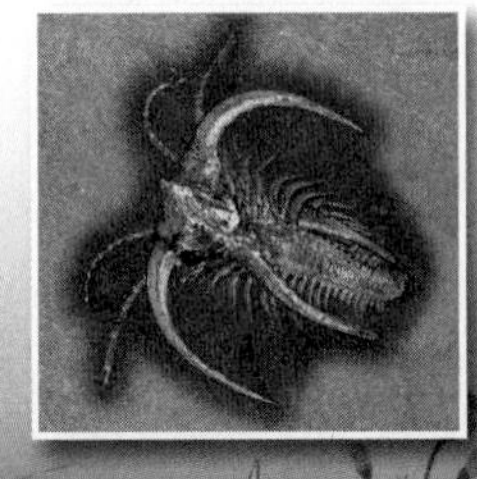

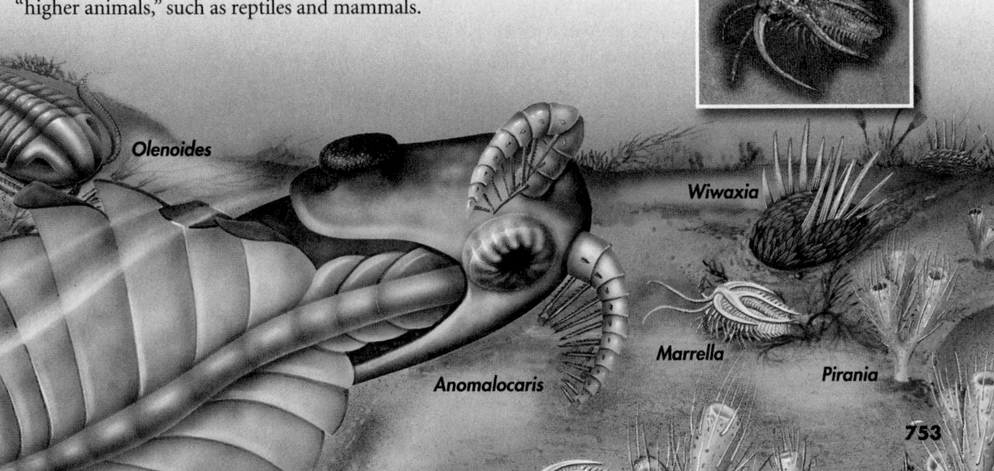

Teach

Lead a Discussion

Discuss with students the Ediacaran fauna and the fossils from the Cambrian Period, including the ages of the fossils. Ask students about some of the peculiarities of the Ediacaran fauna. *(The body plans are different from those of any of today's animals.)* Ask about the body plans evident in Cambrian Period fossils. *(Over a period of 10 to 15 million years, animals evolved complex body plans, including basic versions of the body plans of all modern phyla.)*

DIFFERENTIATED INSTRUCTION

LPR Less Proficient Readers Make a **Venn Diagram** on the board, with one circle for the Ediacaran fauna and the other circle for the Burgess Shale animals. Ask students to help you fill in the characteristics the fossils show for each group. Then have students copy this diagram and work on their own to fill in the characteristics shared by both groups. These characteristics should include that the animals were invertebrates and some animals of both groups were segmented and had bilateral symmetry.

Study Wkbks A/B, Appendix S33, Venn Diagram. **Transparencies,** GO18.

L3 Advanced Students Ask interested students to read parts of *Wonderful Life: The Burgess Shale and the Nature of History* (New York: Norton, 1989) by Stephen Jay Gould. This noted author provides background for understanding the fossils of the Burgess Shale and describes many of the animals. Ask students to make a brief presentation to the class.

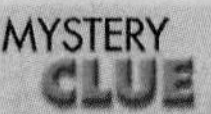

MYSTERY CLUE Help students infer that since the oldest animal fossil is about 600 million years old, the rocks containing these fossils would be the same age. Students can go online to Biology.com to gather their evidence.

Biology In-Depth

BASIC BODY PLANS

An important distinction needs to be made clear to students about basic body plans. Although it's true that all the basic body plans of modern phyla had been established by the end of the Cambrian Period, this does not mean that any of those ancient organisms looked like modern insects, fishes, or birds. Actually, Cambrian organisms that are classified as members of existing phyla bear little obvious resemblance to animals alive today. Over hundreds of millions of years, many structures that make up animal bodies and their organ systems have changed in major ways. It is only the *basic* body plans that were established in the Cambrian Period.

Answers

FIGURE 26–2 The animals from the Cambrian Period had evolved shells, skeletons, and other hard body parts, which were more likely to become fossilized than the soft bodies of earlier animals.

Teach continued

Use Visuals

Use the cladogram in **Figure 26–3** to begin a discussion of both the major groups of animals and the evolutionary relationships among those groups. Point out that each group included on the cladogram with a representative drawing—except for the chordates—have their own section in the table that makes up the rest of Lesson 26.1.

Ask What traits does the cladogram show that arthropods have but that cnidarians do not have? *(three germ layers, bilateral symmetry, and protostome development)*

Ask Which invertebrate group has the closest evolutionary relationship to chordates? *(echinoderms)*

DIFFERENTIATED INSTRUCTION

L1 Struggling Students Have students work in small groups to use the information in **Figure 26–3** to make a **Compare/Contrast Table** of invertebrates. Each group's table should have eight columns. Groups of invertebrates should be listed in the first column, with the heading Invertebrate Groups. The headings for the next seven columns should be important traits included in the cladogram: Multicellularity, Tissues, Radial Symmetry, Three Germ Layers, Bilateral Symmetry, Protostome Development, and Deuterostome Development. Group members can then work together to write a "Yes" or a "No" in each cell below a heading, depending on whether a group has that trait or not.

Study Wkbks A/B, Appendix S20, Compare/Contrast Table. **Transparencies,** GO3.

BIOLOGY.com In this **InterActive Art: Cladogram of Invertebrates,** students will review the characteristics of the groups in **Figure 26–3.**

Address Misconceptions

Evolution Means Progress Many students have the misconception that the evolution of animals from one form to another is an indication of progress. Point out that as animals evolve, they don't necessarily "get better." Animals evolve as they adapt to their environments. A sponge, which is so simple an animal that it doesn't have many of the traits included in the cladogram, is suited so well to its environment that it has not evolved significant new traits for millions of years.

Nonchordate Invertebrates

What does the cladogram of nonchordate invertebrates illustrate?

The groups of living invertebrates are shown in **Figure 26–3.** **The cladogram of nonchordate invertebrates presents current hypotheses about evolutionary relationships among major groups of modern invertebrates. It also indicates the sequence in which some important features evolved.** These features include body symmetry, cephalization, segmentation, and formation of a coelom. Many of these features evolved in Cambrian animals.

FIGURE 26–3 Cladogram of Nonchordate Invertebrates This diagram shows current hypotheses of evolutionary relationships among major groups of animals. During the course of evolution that produced these different groups, important traits evolved. These are shown by the red circles (nodes). Note that the invertebrate chordates, which you will learn about in the next lesson, are not shown. Also, note that nonchordate invertebrates do not form a clade.

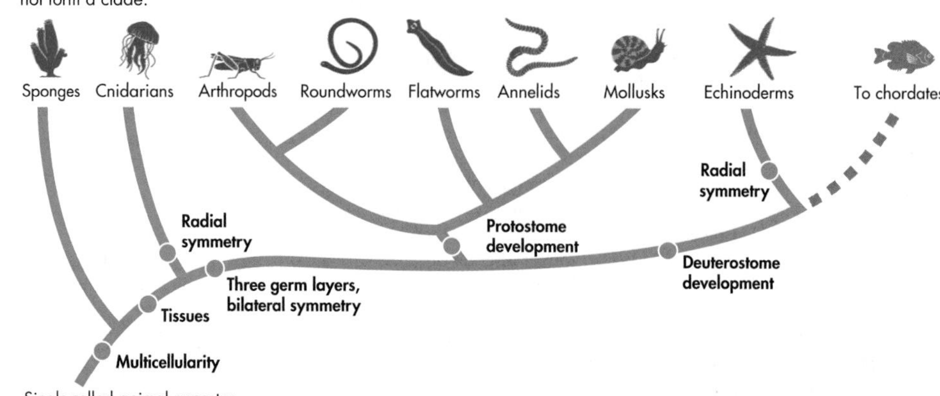

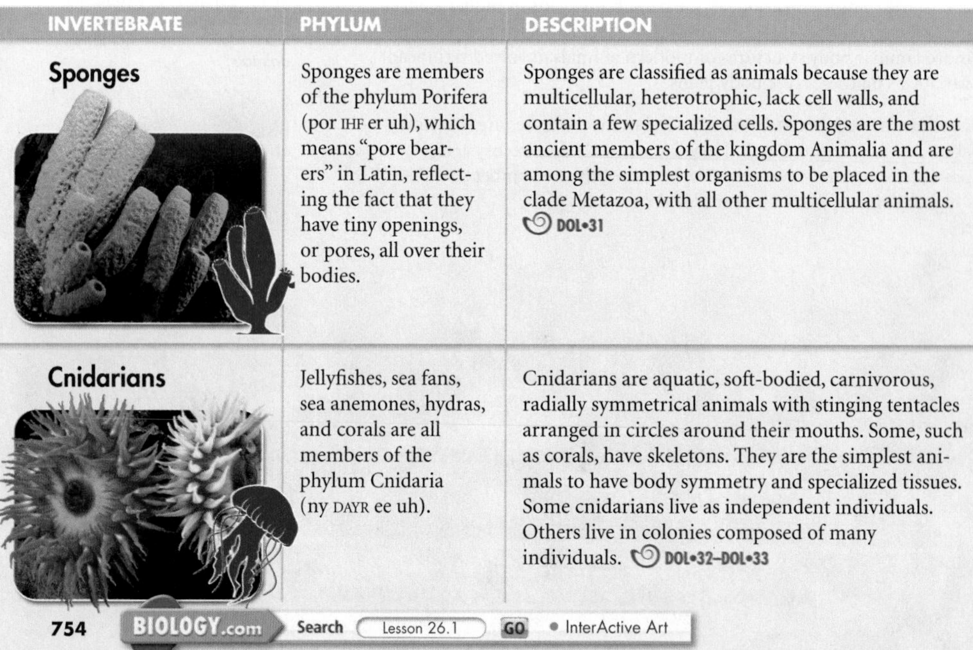

INVERTEBRATE	PHYLUM	DESCRIPTION
Sponges	Sponges are members of the phylum Porifera (por IHF er uh), which means "pore bearers" in Latin, reflecting the fact that they have tiny openings, or pores, all over their bodies.	Sponges are classified as animals because they are multicellular, heterotrophic, lack cell walls, and contain a few specialized cells. Sponges are the most ancient members of the kingdom Animalia and are among the simplest organisms to be placed in the clade Metazoa, with all other multicellular animals. DOL•31
Cnidarians	Jellyfishes, sea fans, sea anemones, hydras, and corals are all members of the phylum Cnidaria (ny DAYR ee uh).	Cnidarians are aquatic, soft-bodied, carnivorous, radially symmetrical animals with stinging tentacles arranged in circles around their mouths. Some, such as corals, have skeletons. They are the simplest animals to have body symmetry and specialized tissues. Some cnidarians live as independent individuals. Others live in colonies composed of many individuals. DOL•32–DOL•33

Biology In-Depth

CLASSIFICATION OF NEMATODES

The roundworms, also called nematodes, make up the phylum Nematoda. Traditionally, these invertebrates were grouped together with other wormlike animals because they had a pseudocoelom. The "pseudocoelomate" grouping is no longer recognized as valid. Modern analysis has shown that the nematodes are closely related to the arthropods, including insects and crustaceans. The large group that includes both nematodes and arthropods is called Ecdysozoa, a name derived from the term used for the molting process, ecdysis. Insects, nematodes, and other ecdysozoans have the ability to molt, or shed their skin. Because there are so many arthropods and roundworms, Ecdysozoa is the largest group in the animal kingdom.

INVERTEBRATE	PHYLUM	DESCRIPTION
Arthropods 	Members of the phylum Arthropoda (ahr THRAHP oh duh) include spiders; centipedes; insects; and crustaceans, such as crabs. *Arthron* means "joint" in Greek, and *podos* means "foot."	Arthropods have bodies divided into segments, a tough external skeleton called an exoskeleton, cephalization, and jointed appendages. Arthropods appeared in the sea about 600 million years ago and have since colonized freshwater habitats, the land, and the air. At least a million species have been identified—more than three times the number of all other animal species combined! DOL•34–DOL•37
Nematodes (Roundworms) 	Members of the phylum Nematoda range in size from microscopic to 1 meter in length.	Nematodes, or roundworms, are unsegmented worms with pseudocoeloms, specialized tissues and organ systems, and digestive tracts with two openings—a mouth and an anus. Some are free-living and inhabit soil or various aquatic habitats. Others are parasites that infect a wide range of plants and animals, including humans. Nematodes were once thought to be closely related to flatworms, annelids, and mollusks but have been found to be more closely related to arthropods. DOL•38
Flatworms 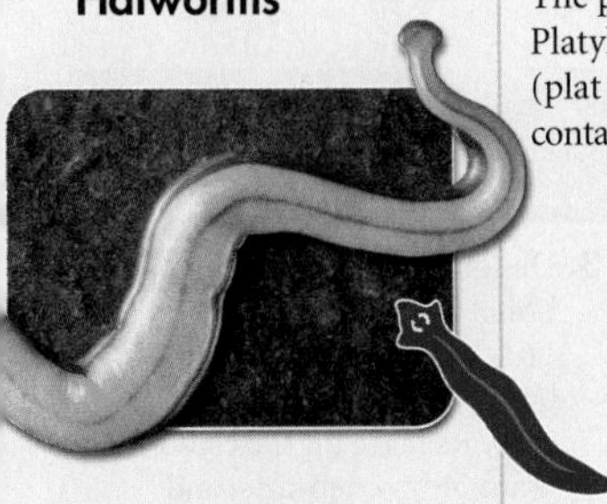	The phylum Platyhelminthes (plat ih hel MIN theez) contains the flatworms.	Flatworms are soft, unsegmented, flattened worms that have tissues and internal organ systems. They are the simplest animals to have three embryonic germ layers, bilateral symmetry, and cephalization. Most flatworms are no more than a few millimeters thick. Flatworms do not have coeloms. DOL•39
Annelids 	The phylum Annelida (un NEL ih duh) includes earthworms, some exotic-looking marine worms, and parasitic, bloodsucking leeches.	Annelids are worms with segmented bodies and a true coelom lined with tissue derived from mesoderm. The name Annelida is derived from the Latin *annellus*, which means "little ring." The name refers to the ringlike appearance of the body segments of annelids. DOL•40–DOL•41

UbD Check for Understanding

HAND SIGNALS

Ask students the following questions, and have them show a thumbs-up sign if they can answer the question correctly, a thumbs-down sign if they can't, or a waving-hand sign if they're not sure.

- What are characteristics of the earliest animals?
- What is the significance of the Cambrian Explosion?
- Which evolved first in invertebrates—bilateral symmetry or tissues?
- Into which phylum are insects classified?

ADJUST INSTRUCTION

For any question that received a thumbs-down or waving-hand sign, have students find the information in the text and write a correct answer.

Build Science Skills

Display pictures of as many different kinds of invertebrates as possible around the classroom. The only label each picture should have is a number. Try to include pictures of organisms from each group, including organisms mentioned in the textbook as well as a variety of others. Explain that *classifying* is an important skill in science. Then, have pairs of students use what they've learned in this lesson to identify each picture as an invertebrate belonging to one of the major groups. Each pair should make a numbered list of their classifications. In class discussion, call on pairs to label a picture and give reasons for their classification. Correct erroneous classifications, making the point that classifications based on appearance alone are often invalid.

DIFFERENTIATED INSTRUCTION

LPR Less Proficient Readers Have struggling readers make a bulleted list for each group of invertebrates, using simplified phrases derived from the sentences in the Description column. Making these bulleted lists will provide students with information they need to more fully participate in the classifying of invertebrates.

ELL Focus on ELL: Build Background

BEGINNING AND INTERMEDIATE SPEAKERS

To supplement the photographs on these pages, display photographs or illustrations of additional organisms in each group. Write the English words for these groups as part of the display. Point to the word for each group, say it aloud, and use nonverbal cues to indicate which animals pictured belong to which specific groups. Then, students should copy the names of the groups in their notebook. If possible, encourage students to write the names of animals that belong in each group in their native language.

Teach continued

Build Study Skills

Divide the class into eight groups, and assign each group one of the major groups of invertebrates on which to become "specialists." Encourage students to use online and other resources to gather more information. Ask each group to make a class presentation.

DIFFERENTIATED INSTRUCTION

ELL English Language Learners Pair each beginning English language learner with a partner who has the same native language as the beginning ELL but is a more proficient English speaker. Ask partners to help each other determine the correct pronunciation of names and terms and understand concepts related to their assigned invertebrate group.

Assess and Remediate

EVALUATE UNDERSTANDING

Name an invertebrate group, and then call on students at random to identify examples or characteristics of the group. Continue in the same manner with the remaining invertebrate groups. Then, have students complete the 26.1 Assessment.

REMEDIATION SUGGESTION

L1 Struggling Students If your students have trouble answering **Question 2c,** use **Figure 26–3** to review with them how a cladogram shows the sequence in which features evolved.

BIOLOGY.com Students can check their understanding of lesson concepts with the **Self-Test** assessment. They can then take an online version of the **Lesson Assessment.**

INVERTEBRATE	PHYLUM	DESCRIPTION
Mollusks 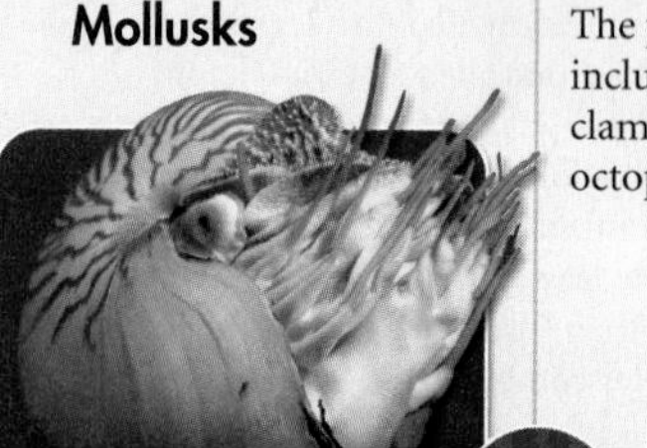	The phylum Mollusca includes snails, slugs, clams, squids, and octopi.	Mollusks are soft-bodied animals that typically have an internal or external shell. Like annelids, mollusks have true coeloms surrounded by mesoderm. They also have complex organ systems. Why are animals as different-looking as snails, clams, and squid in the same phylum? One answer lies in the behavior of their **larvae** (singular: larva), or immature stages. Many mollusks have a free-swimming larval stage called a **trochophore** (TRAHK oh fawr). The trochophore is also characteristic of many annelids, indicating that annelids and mollusks are closely related. DOL•42–DOL•43
Echinoderms 	The phylum Echinodermata (ee KY noh durm aht uh) includes sea stars, sea urchins, and sand dollars, all of which live only in the sea. *Echino-* means "spiny" in Greek, and *dermis* means "skin" in Latin.	Echinoderms have spiny skin and an internal skeleton. They also have a water vascular system—a network of water-filled tubes that include suction-cuplike structures called tube feet, which are used for walking and for gripping prey. Most adult echinoderms exhibit five-part radial symmetry. The skin of an echinoderm is stretched over an internal skeleton of calcium carbonate plates. Although radial symmetry is characteristic of simpler animals such as cnidarians, echinoderms are more closely related to humans and other chordates because they are deuterostomes. DOL•44–DOL•45

26.1 Assessment

IN NoS.3, B.8.1, B.8.2

Review Key Concepts

1. a. Review What was the Cambrian Explosion?
   b. Explain When does fossil evidence indicate that the first animals evolved?
   c. Relate Cause and Effect What two characteristics of early animals explain the scarcity of animal fossils older than the Cambrian Period?
2. a. Review What is a cladogram?
   b. Explain What does the cladogram of invertebrates show?
   c. Sequence Which body plan feature evolved first—radial symmetry or deuterostome development?

VISUAL THINKING

3. Design a "new" invertebrate. Create an illustration on which you point out its body plan features. Then, show its place on the cladogram of invertebrates, and write a caption explaining how its features helped you decide where it belongs.

BIOLOGY.com Search Lesson 26.1  • Lesson Assessment • Self-Test

Assessment Answers

1a. a period between 530 and 515 million years ago when many modern multicellular phyla first appeared

1b. roughly 600 million years ago

1c. The first animals were tiny and soft-bodied.

2a. a diagram that shows the evolutionary relationships among groups of organisms

2b. current hypotheses about evolutionary relationships among major groups of modern invertebrates; the sequence in which some important features evolved

2c. radial symmetry

VISUAL THINKING

3. Answers will vary. A "new" invertebrate might incorporate any of the body plans and traits of modern invertebrates. The place on the invertebrate cladogram should correctly indicate which traits have been incorporated in the new organism.

Chordate Evolution and Diversity

 B.8.1 History of life on Earth. Also covered: NoS.3, NoS.6, B.8.2.

THINK ABOUT IT At first glance, fishes, amphibians, reptiles, birds, and mammals appear to be very different. Some have feathers, others have fins. Some fly, others swim or crawl. Yet, all are members of the phylum in which we ourselves are classified—phylum Chordata.

Origins of the Chordates

What are the most ancient chordates?

Chordates are the animals we know best because they are generally large (as animals go), often conspicuous, and strike us as beautiful, impressive, cute, or frightening. Some we keep as pets, others many of us eat as sources of protein. How did all these diverse forms arise?

The Earliest Chordates What were the earliest chordates like? **Embryological studies suggest that the most ancient chordates were related to the ancestors of echinoderms.** The rich Cambrian fossil deposits that record invertebrate history also include some early chordate fossils, such as *Pikaia* (pih KAY uh), which is shown in **Figure 26–4.** When *Pikaia* was first discovered, it was thought to be a worm. Then scientists determined that it had a notochord and paired muscles arranged in a series, like those of simple modern chordates. In 1999, fossil beds from later in the Cambrian Period yielded specimens of *Myllokunmingia* (MY loh kuhn min jee uh), the earliest known vertebrate. These fossils show muscles arranged in a series, traces of fins, sets of feathery gills, a head with paired sense organs, and a skull and skeletal structures likely made of cartilage. **Cartilage** is a strong connective tissue that is softer and more flexible than bone. It supports all or part of a vertebrate's body. In humans, cartilage supports the nose and external ears.

Modern Chordate Diversity Modern chordates are very diverse, consisting of six groups: the nonvertebrate chordates and the five groups of vertebrates—fishes, amphibians, reptiles, birds, and mammals. About 96 percent of all modern chordate species are vertebrates. Among vertebrates, fishes are the largest group by far. Yet, today's chordate species are only a small fraction of the total number of chordates that have existed over time.

DOL•46–DOL•64

Key Questions

What are the most ancient chordates?

What can we learn by studying the cladogram of chordates?

Vocabulary

cartilage
tetrapod

Taking Notes

Venn Diagram Construct a Venn diagram comparing and contrasting nonvertebrate chordates and vertebrates.

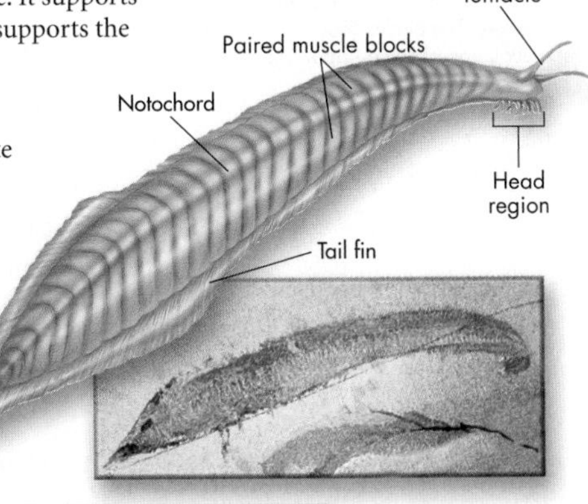

FIGURE 26–4 *Pikaia*, an Early Chordate *Pikaia* is the earliest chordate known from the fossil record. **Classify** ***Which chordate characteristics did Pikaia possess?***

 Search Lesson 26.2 GO • Lesson Overview • Lesson Notes

UbD Teach for Understanding

ENDURING UNDERSTANDING Animals have evolved diverse ways to carry out basic life processes and maintain homeostasis.

GUIDING QUESTION How did chordates evolve?

EVIDENCE OF UNDERSTANDING *After students have completed the lesson, this assessment should show their understanding of how chordates evolved, what some important chordate adaptations are, and how chordate groups are related.* Have students work in pairs. Each pair should choose a chordate group and prepare a brief presentation that includes important chordate adaptations in the group, other chordate groups that are closely related, and examples of living animals that are members of that group.

Getting Started

Objectives

26.2.1 Describe the most ancient chordates.

26.2.2 Interpret the cladogram of chordates.

Student Resources

Study Workbooks A and B, 26.2 Worksheets

Spanish Study Workbook, 26.2 Worksheets

Lab Manual B, 26.2 Data Analysis Worksheet

 Lesson Overview • Lesson Notes • Activity: Art in Motion • Assessment: Self-Test, Lesson Assessment

For corresponding lesson in the **Foundation Edition**, see pages 628–633.

Build Background

Direct students to **Figure 26–4.** Ask what type of animal the *Pikaia* reminds them of. *(Sample answers: a worm; a fish)* Explain that worms are invertebrates and fish are vertebrates; *Pikaia* is neither. It is a nonvertebrate chordate. Scientists who discovered it weren't sure how to classify it, until they saw it had a notochord and paired muscle blocks, much like a modern group of nonvertebrate chordates, the lancelets.

Answers

FIGURE 26–4 a notochord and paired muscles arranged in a series

IN INDIANA ACADEMIC STANDARDS

For the full text of all standards, see the Course Overview in the front matter of this book.

B.8.1 Explain how anatomical and molecular similarities among organisms that suggest life on earth began as simple, one-celled organisms about 4 billion years ago and multicellular organisms evolved later.

Teach

LESSON 26.2

Use Visuals

Use **Figure 26–5** to familiarize students with the relationships among the major groups of chordates and introduce the evolution of important chordate adaptations. Emphasize that adaptive radiation was the result of the evolution of one or more important chordate adaptations.

DIFFERENTIATED INSTRUCTION

L1 Struggling Students Have small groups use the information in **Figure 26–5** to make a **Compare/Contrast Table** of chordates, similar to the table they made of invertebrates. Each group's table should have nine columns. Groups of chordates should be listed in the first column, with the heading Chordate Groups. The headings for the next eight columns should be important chordate adaptations included in the cladogram: Vertebrae, Jaws, Paired Appendages, True Bone, Lungs, Four Limbs, Amniotic Egg, and Endothermy. Group members can then work together to write a "Yes" or a "No" in each cell below a heading, depending on whether a group has that trait or not.

Study Wkbks A/B, Appendix S20, Compare/Contrast Table. **Transparencies,** GO3.

L3 Advanced Students Have students who show a good understanding of chordate classification work together to make a poster that lists the names of the chordate subphyla and classes from the text. Encourage students to include common names and illustrations, as well. Place the finished poster on a classroom wall.

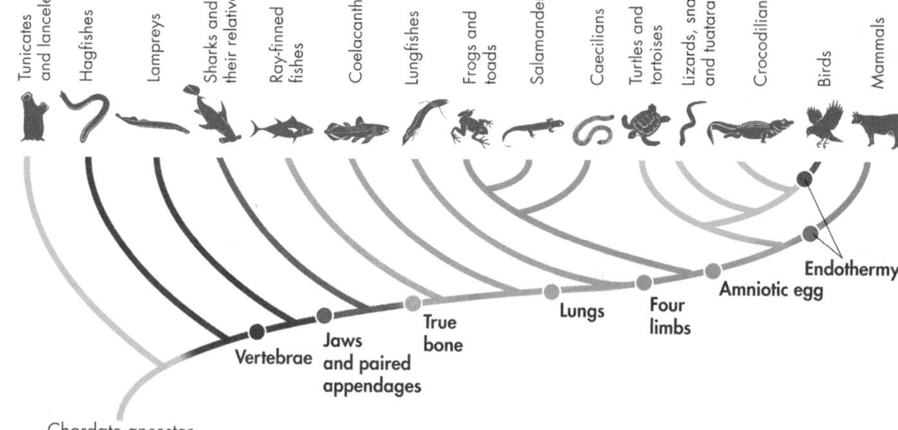

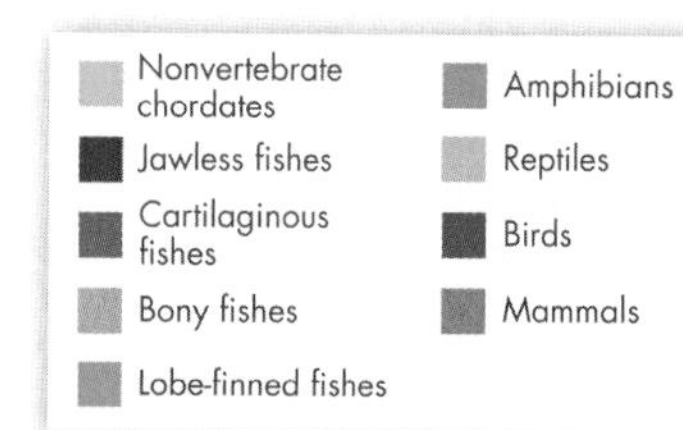

FIGURE 26–5 Cladogram of Chordates The phylum Chordata includes both vertebrates and nonvertebrate chordates. All groups (clades) share a common invertebrate ancestor. This cladogram shows current hypotheses about the evolutionary relationships among living chordate groups. The different colored lines represent the traditional groupings of these animals, as listed in the key. The circles (nodes) indicate the evolution of some important chordate adaptations.

Cladogram of Chordates

What can we learn by studying the cladogram of chordates?

The hard body structures of many chordates fossilize well, so there is an excellent fossil record of chordate evolutionary history. **The cladogram of chordates presents current hypotheses about relationships among chordate groups. It also shows at which points important vertebrate features, such as jaws and limbs, evolved.** The cladogram of chordates is shown in **Figure 26–5.**

The circles (nodes) in the cladogram represent the appearance of certain adaptive features during chordate evolution. Each time a new adaptation evolved in chordate ancestors, a major adaptive radiation occurred. One notable adaptation, for example, was the development of jaws, which jump-started the adaptive radiation of jawed fishes—now the most diverse chordate group. Other important adaptations include the development of true bone and paired appendages. Refer to the geologic time scale in Chapter 19 as you read about the evolutionary history of chordates.

Nonvertebrate Chordates Two chordate groups lack backbones. These nonvertebrate chordates are tunicates and lancelets. Fossil evidence from the Cambrian Period suggests that the ancestors of living nonvertebrate chordates diverged from the ancestors of vertebrates more than 550 million years ago.

Adult tunicates (subphylum Urochordata) look more like sponges than us. They have neither a notochord nor a tail. But their larval forms have all the key chordate characteristics. The small, fishlike lancelets (subphylum Cephalochordata) live on the sandy ocean bottom. DOL•46–DOL•47

Quick Facts

NONVERTEBRATE CHORDATES

The living nonvertebrate chordates include the interesting but little known tunicates and lancelets. Tunicates are stationary filter feeders that live attached to rocks or shells. They are often called sea squirts. A tunicate larva has bilateral symmetry, a notochord, and a tail, and it swims for a few days before attaching to a hard surface. It then loses its notochord and tail and becomes an adult that, in most species, looks very different from the larva. Lancelets, also called amphioxus, are eel-like sea animals that live in shallow water. Adult lancelets have typical chordate features, including a notochord, gill slits, and a tail.

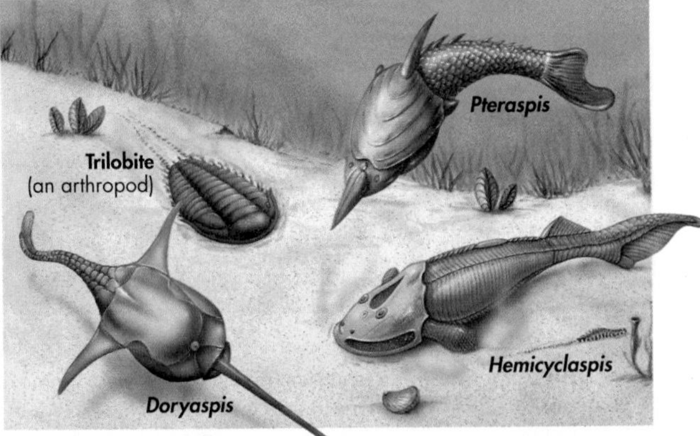

FIGURE 26–6 Ancient Jawless Fishes Ancient jawless fishes, some of which were armored, such as those shown here, lived during the early Devonian Period. Since they lacked jaws, they were limited in their ability to feed and defend themselves. Paired fins, however, gave these fishes control over their movement, and the lineage led to today's hagfishes and lampreys.

Jawless Fishes The earliest fishes appeared in the fossil record during the late Cambrian Period, about 510 million years ago. These odd-looking creatures had no true jaws or teeth, and their skeletons were made of cartilage. During the Ordovician and Silurian periods fishes had a major adaptive radiation. The products of this radiation ruled the seas during the Devonian Period, also called the Age of Fishes. Some armored jawless fishes, such as those in **Figure 26–6,** became extinct at the end of the Devonian, about 360 million years ago. Two other ancient clades of jawless fishes gave rise to the two clades, sometimes called classes, of modern jawless fishes: lampreys and hagfishes. DOL•48–DOL•51

Lampreys and hagfishes both lack vertebrae and have notochords as adults. (They do have parts of what could be called a skull, which is one of the reasons they are still classified as vertebrates.) Lampreys are filter feeders as larvae and parasites as adults. Hagfishes have pinkish gray, wormlike bodies, secrete incredible amounts of slime, and tie themselves into knots!

Sharks and Their Relatives Other ancient fishes evolved a revolutionary feeding adaptation: jaws. Jaws hold teeth and muscles, which make it possible to bite and chew plants and other animals.

Early fishes also evolved paired pectoral (anterior) and pelvic (posterior) fins. These fins were attached to limb girdles, which are supporting structures made of cartilage or bone. Paired fins offered more control of body movement, while tail fins and powerful muscles gave greater thrust.

These adaptations launched the adaptive radiation of the class Chondrichthyes (kahn DRIK theez): the sharks, rays, and skates. The Greek word *chondros* means "cartilage," the tissue that makes up the skeletons of these "cartilaginous" fishes. There are hundreds of species of modern sharks, skates, and rays, ranging from predatory carnivores, such as the great white shark in **Figure 26–7,** to shy plankton feeders.

FIGURE 26–7 Jaws Though about 360 million years separate *Dunkleosteus* (fossil, top) and today's great white shark (bottom), you can easily see the important adaptation they have in common—jaws. But *Dunkleosteus* could have bitten "Jaws" the shark in half! **Pose Questions** ***What question would you ask a researcher about*** **Dunkleosteus?**

In Your Notebook *How did the evolution of paired fins help early fishes succeed in their environments?*

Check for Understanding

INDEX CARD SUMMARIES

Give students each an index card, and ask them to write on the front of the card one idea they understand about the cladogram in **Figure 26–5.** Then, have them write one idea they don't understand about it on the back of the card in the form of a question.

ADJUST INSTRUCTION

Read over students' cards to get a sense of what they do—and do not—understand about the information presented in the cladogram, including the evolution of important chordate adaptations and how chordate groups are related. Review the cladogram with the whole class by reading aloud some of the questions students wrote and then answering them by referring to the cladogram.

Lead a Discussion

Have students discuss the differences in the three groups of fishes—jawless fishes, cartilaginous fishes, and bony fishes.

Ask What adaptations launched the adaptive radiation of the cartilaginous fishes—the sharks, rays, and skates? *(the development of jaws and paired fins)*

Ask What is the major difference between fishes of the class Chondrichthyes and fishes of the class Osteichthyes? *(Fishes of the class Chondrichthyes have skeletons made of cartilage, while fishes of the class Osteichthyes have skeletons made of true bone.)*

DIFFERENTIATED INSTRUCTION

LPR **Less Proficient Readers** Have students work in small groups to organize the information on the three groups of fishes into a **Cluster Diagram.** The circle in the center should contain the heading Fishes. Three circles radiating from the center should contain the three types of fishes: Jawless Fishes, Sharks and Their Relatives, and Bony Fishes. Connected to these circles should be information from the text, including important adaptations, examples of each group, and other descriptive information.

Study Wkbks A/B, Appendix S19, Cluster Diagram. **Transparencies,** GO2.

ELL Focus on ELL: Access Content

ALL SPEAKERS Have students make a **T-Chart** and write the following titles on the left side of the chart: Nonvertebrate Chordates, Jawless Fishes, Sharks and Their Relatives, Bony Fishes, Amphibians, Reptiles, Birds, and Mammals. Pair advanced or advanced high speakers with beginning and intermediate speakers. Have advanced speakers help the less proficient speakers read the text. As they read, students should collaboratively fill in the right side of the chart. They can record translations into their native language and sketches to help them remember terms and concepts. Beginning speakers may rely on sketches more than intermediate speakers.

Study Wkbks A/B, Appendix S30, T-Chart. **Transparencies,** GO15.

Answers

FIGURE 26–7 Sample answer: If *Dunkleosteus* was so powerful, why did it become extinct?

IN YOUR NOTEBOOK Paired fins gave fishes more control over their movement.

Teach continued

Use Visuals

Use **Figure 26–8** to start a discussion of bony fishes and the adaptations that led to their adaptive radiation.

Ask What is a main difference between the fish shown here and a shark? *(This fish had a skeleton made of true bone, while a shark has a skeleton made of cartilage.)*

Ask If you could see the left side of this fish, would you expect to see a pectoral fin? Explain your reasoning. *(Yes; I would see a pectoral fin because the fish has one on the right side, and bony fish have paired fins.)*

DIFFERENTIATED INSTRUCTION

L1 Special Needs Making and/or being able to touch a model of a fish skeleton will benefit many special-needs students. Have small groups of students use clay and cardboard to make a model of a bony fish skeleton, using the skeleton in **Figure 26–8** as an example.

L3 Advanced Students Explain that the modern bony fish whose skeleton is shown in **Figure 26–8** is a ray-finned fish. Point out that the other group of bony fishes, the lobe-finned fishes, includes lungfishes and coelacanths. Explain that scientists thought coelacanths were extinct for millions of years until one was caught off the coast of South Africa in 1938. Have students use online resources to find an image and description of a coelacanth. Ask them to present what they find to the class.

BIOLOGY.com The **Art in Motion: From Fins to Feet** is a series of short animations of the fish in **Figure 26–9** and their likely motions.

FIGURE 26–8 Bony Fishes Bony fishes, such as the perch this skeleton once belonged to, have skeletons made of true bone.
Compare and Contrast *List two ways that bony fishes differ from the fishes in Figure 26–6.*

Bony Fishes Another group of ancient fishes evolved skeletons made of hard, calcified tissue called true bone. This launched the radiation of the class Osteichthyes (ahs tee IK theez), the bony fishes. You can see the skeleton of a modern bony fish in **Figure 26–8.** Most modern bony fishes belong to a huge group called ray-finned fishes.

▶ ***Ray-Finned Fishes*** Ray-finned fishes are aquatic vertebrates with skeletons of true bone; most have paired fins, scales, and gills. The name “ray-finned” refers to bony rays connected by a layer of skin to form fins. The fin rays support the skin much as the thin rods in a handheld folding fan support the webbing of the fan. Most fishes you are familiar with, such as eels, goldfish, and catfish, are ray-finned fishes.

▶ ***Lobe-Finned Fishes*** Lobe-finned fishes are a different group of bony fishes that evolved fleshy fins supported by larger, more substantial bones. The few modern fishes that are descendants of ancient lobe-finned fishes include lungfishes and coelacanths (SEE luh kanths). Another group of ancient lobe-finned fishes evolved into the ancestors of four-limbed vertebrates, or **tetrapods.**

VISUAL SUMMARY

FROM FINS TO FEET

FIGURE 26–9 The cladogram shows a few of the animal groups in the evolution of the feet of tetrapods from the fins of ancient bony fish. All of the illustrated animal groups are extinct.

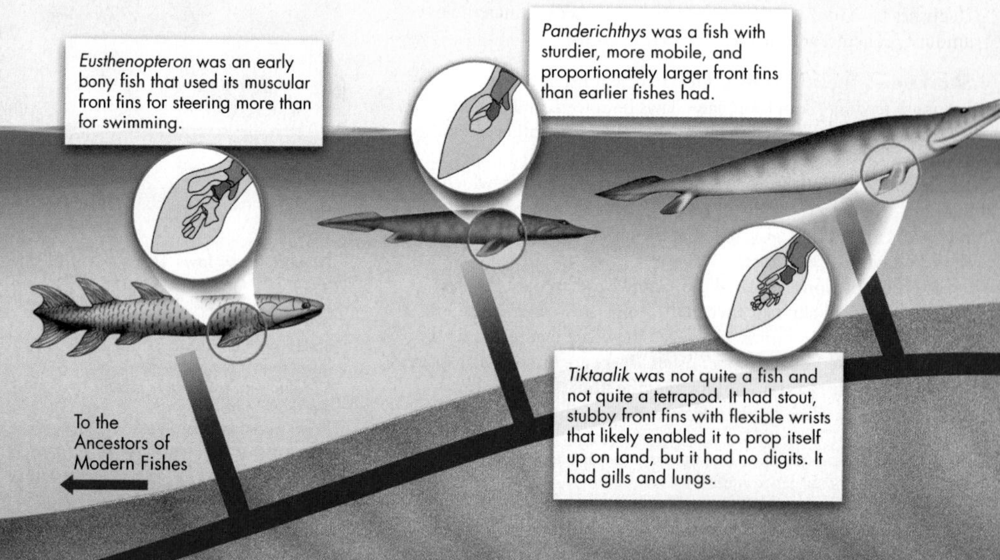

Eusthenopteron was an early bony fish that used its muscular front fins for steering more than for swimming.
Panderichthys was a fish with sturdier, more mobile, and proportionately larger front fins than earlier fishes had.
Tiktaalik was not quite a fish and not quite a tetrapod. It had stout, stubby front fins with flexible wrists that likely enabled it to prop itself up on land, but it had no digits. It had gills and lungs.
To the Ancestors of Modern Fishes

UbD Check for Understanding

QUESTION BOX

Set up a question box where students can drop in questions they have about the evolution of limbs from fins.

ADJUST INSTRUCTION

Read over the students' questions and look for common themes of confusion. Address these common themes with the whole class or have students work in groups to come up with answers.

Answers

FIGURE 26–8 Bony fishes have jaws and a skeleton made of true bone, neither of which are present in the jawless fishes in **Figure 26–6.**

LESSON 26.2

Amphibians The word *amphibian* means "double life," referring to the fact that these animals live in water as larvae but on land as adults. Amphibians are vertebrates that also, with some exceptions, require water for reproduction, breathe with lungs as adults, have moist skin with mucous glands, and lack scales and claws. DOL•52–DOL•53

▶ ***The Unique "Fishapod"*** The general story of early amphibian evolution has been known for years. Several fossils indicate that various lines of lobe-finned fishes evolved sturdier and sturdier appendages, which resembled the limbs of tetrapods. But in recent years, a series of spectacular transitional fossils have been discovered that document in detail the skeletal transformation from lobe-fins to limbs, as shown in **Figure 26–9.** One of the most interesting of these finds is *Tiktaalik*, a fossil of which is shown in **Figure 26–10.** It is an animal with such a mix of fish and tetrapod features that its discoverers informally referred to it as a "fishapod"—part fish, part tetrapod.

▶ ***Terrestrial Adaptations*** Of course, life on land requires more than just legs to crawl around on. Early amphibians also evolved ways to breathe air and protect themselves from drying out, as you will read in Chapters 27 and 28. These adaptations fueled another adaptive radiation. Amphibians became the dominant vertebrates of the warm, swampy Carboniferous Period, about 359 to 300 million years ago. But this success didn't last. Climate changes caused many low, swampy habitats to disappear. Most amphibian groups became extinct by the end of the Permian Period, about 250 million years ago. Only three orders of amphibians survive today—frogs and toads, salamanders, and caecilians (see SIL ee unz).

In Your Notebook *Explain how the climate changes of the Permian Period could have caused the decline of amphibians.*

BUILD Vocabulary

WORD ORIGINS The word **tetrapod** comes from the Greek words "tetra," meaning *four*, and "pod," meaning *foot.*

FIGURE 26–10 *Tiktaalik*, the Fishapod The 375-million-year-old *Tiktaalik* fossil was discovered in Canada in 2004. It is considered a transitional fossil because it shows features of both tetrapods and the fish they evolved from—fins *with* wrist bones; gills *and* lungs. *Tiktaalik* could swim and breathe underwater like a fish OR crawl and breathe out of water like a tetrapod, so its discoverers called it a "fishapod."

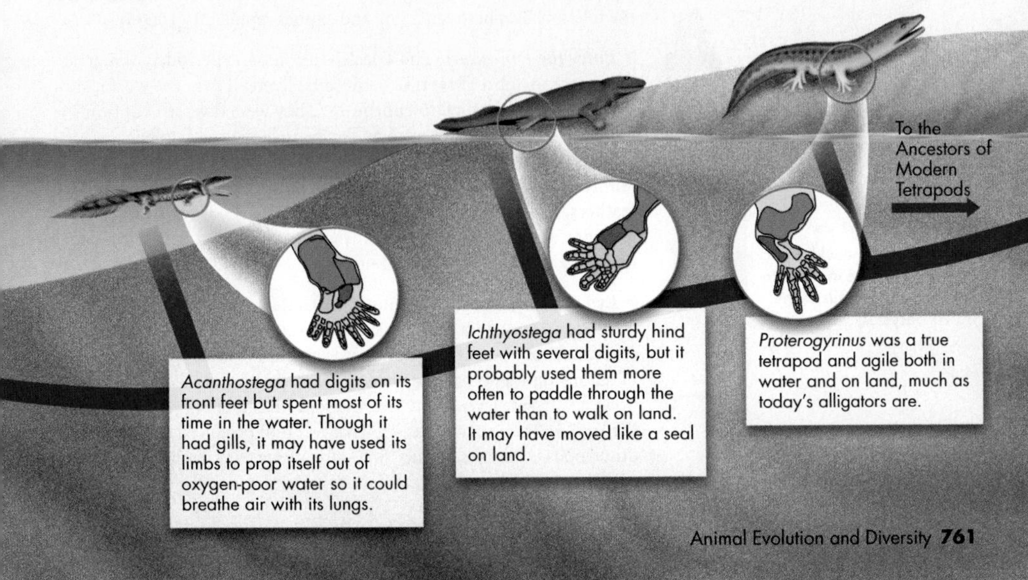

To the Ancestors of Modern Tetrapods
Acanthostega had digits on its front feet but spent most of its time in the water. Though it had gills, it may have used its limbs to prop itself out of oxygen-poor water so it could breathe air with its lungs.
Ichthyostega had sturdy hind feet with several digits, but it probably used them more often to paddle through the water than to walk on land. It may have moved like a seal on land.
Proterogyrinus was a true tetrapod and agile both in water and on land, much as today's alligators are.

VISUAL SUMMARY

Use **Figure 26–9** to introduce students to the transition of chordates from water to land. Point out that the inset for each organism shows adaptations that show the transition of lobe-fins to limbs. Ask questions that engage students in studying the details of the illustrations. For example:

Ask How is the body shape of *Tiktaalik* different from that of most tetrapods today? *(It is more streamlined.)*

Ask How are the limb bones of *Proterogyrinus* different from those of *Ichthyostega? (The digits are longer and more fingerlike.)*

DIFFERENTIATED INSTRUCTION

LPR Less Proficient Readers Some students may have trouble identifying the adaptation(s) of each illustrated organism that show(s) the gradual transition from bony fish to true tetrapod. Write the following list of adaptations on the board, summarizing the changes.

- *Eusthenopteron*—muscular front fins for steering
- *Panderichthys*—sturdier, more movable, and larger front fins
- *Tiktaalik*—stubby front fins with flexible wrists
- *Acanthostega*—digits (fingers and toes) on front feet
- *Ichthyostega*—sturdy hind feet with several digits
- *Proterogyrinus*—true tetrapod

Call on volunteers to read each annotation, helping them pronounce the names of the animals. For each annotation, point to the adaptation listed on the board to emphasize the evolution of chordate adaptations that resulted in tetrapods walking on land.

L3 Advanced Students Ask students to write a story in the first person from the perspective of *Tiktaalik* the "fishapod." Challenge them to use their imagination in seeing life from the perspective of an organism that was one of the first to crawl on land.

Biology In-Depth

TAKE A STAND

The relative positions of vertebrate limbs are adaptations to terrestrial life. Two trends can be seen in the evolution from amphibians to reptiles and mammals. First, the position of the limbs relative to the body shifted toward the center. Second, the movement of the vertebral column when the animal ran became up-and-down rather than side-to-side. The positions of the pectoral and pelvic girdles and the limb bones differ among vertebrates, depending on how early they evolved. Amphibians, such as salamanders, have limbs that stick out from the sides of the body. The limbs of reptiles allow the body to be lifted higher off the ground. In many mammals, the limbs are positioned directly beneath the body.

Answers

IN YOUR NOTEBOOK The climate changes caused many of the low, swampy habitats of amphibians to disappear.

LESSON 26.2

Teach continued

Build Science Skills

Explain that scientists look for reasons why changes occur in organisms. Point out that the skill of *identifying cause and effect* is necessary for a scientist to have in order to understand why a change has taken place. Have students meet in small groups to discuss the reasons why adaptations such as dry, scaly skin and shelled eggs improved the survivability of reptiles. Then, in full class discussion, ask groups to identify how these characteristics enabled animals to survive and reproduce in their environments. *(During the beginning of the Permian Period, Earth's environment became cooler and less humid, and many lakes and swamps dried up. These climate changes favored organisms with characteristics that enabled them to conserve water.)*

DIFFERENTIATED INSTRUCTION

L1 Struggling Students Struggling students may have difficulty identifying the causal relationship between reptile characteristics and improved survivability. Remind them that evolution occurs when changes in the environment favor some characteristics over others. Have students look in the text for a description of a change in the environment. *(The environment became drier.)*

Ask What characteristics might help an animal survive in a drier environment? *(Characteristics that help animals conserve water.)* Help students see that shelled eggs and dry skin are both adaptations that conserve water.

L3 Advanced Students Point out to students that the text identifies the cause of the extinction of dinosaurs at the end of the Cretaceous Period—a series of natural disasters that included volcanic eruptions, a fall in sea level, and the impact of an asteroid. Explain that these disasters likely didn't kill all the dinosaurs outright. Ask students to write a paragraph explaining what effect these disasters had on the environment that made the survival of dinosaurs impossible.

MYSTERY CLUE To find the answer to the question, suggest students identify the first bird fossil found and to what period that fossil was dated. *(Jurassic, about 150 million years ago)* Students can go online to **Biology.com** to gather their evidence.

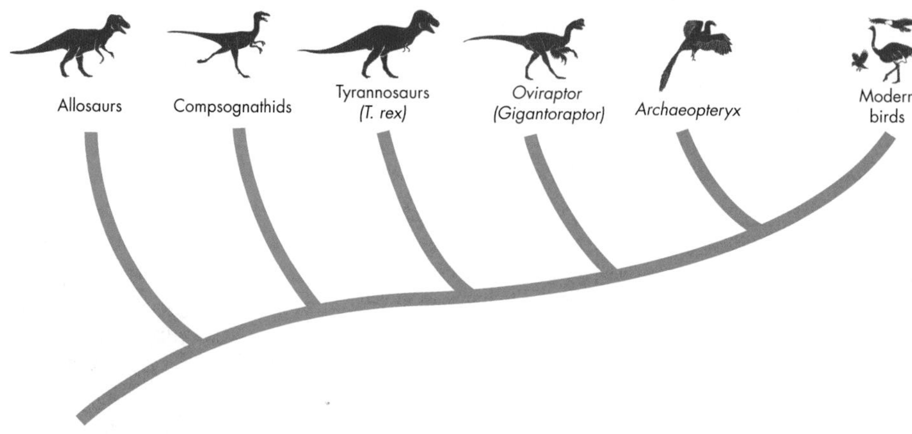

FIGURE 26–11 Evolution of Reptiles and Birds The diagram shows current hypotheses about the evolutionary relationships between living and extinct reptiles. None of the groups shown are direct ancestors of modern reptiles or modern birds.

Reptiles Reptiles, which evolved from ancient amphibians, were the first vertebrates to evolve adaptations to drier conditions. A reptile is a vertebrate with dry, scaly skin, well-developed lungs, strong limbs, and shelled eggs that do not develop in water. Living reptiles are represented by four groups: lizards and snakes, crocodilians, turtles and tortoises, and the tuatara (too uh TAH ruh).

The first known reptile fossil dates back to the Carboniferous Period, 350 million years ago. As the Carboniferous Period ended and the Permian Period began, Earth's climate became cooler and less humid. Many lakes and swamps dried up. Under these drier conditions, the first great adaptive radiation of reptiles began. By the end of the Permian Period, about 250 million years ago, a great variety of reptiles roamed Earth. The cladogram in **Figure 26–11** shows current hypotheses about the relationships between living and extinct reptiles. DOL•54–DOL•55

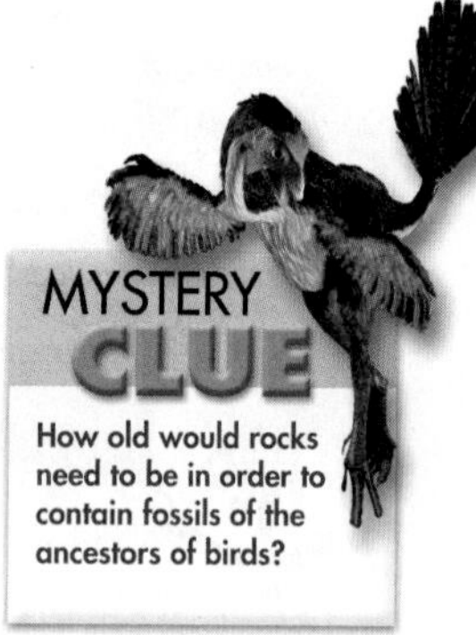

MYSTERY CLUE

How old would rocks need to be in order to contain fossils of the ancestors of birds?

▶ ***Enter the Dinosaurs*** The Triassic and Jurassic periods saw a great adaptive radiation of reptiles. Dinosaurs lived all over the world, and they ranged from small to enormous. They were diverse in appearance and in habit: Some, such as *Plateosaurus,* ate leafy plants; others, such as *Coelophysis,* were carnivorous. Duckbilled *Maiasaura* lived in family groups and cared for eggs and young. Some dinosaurs even had feathers, which may have first evolved as a means of regulating body temperature. The evolutionary lineage that led to modern birds came from one group of feathered dinosaurs.

▶ ***Exit the Dinosaurs*** At the end of the Cretaceous Period, about 66 million years ago, a worldwide mass extinction occurred. According to current hypotheses, this extinction was probably caused by a combination of natural disasters, including massive and widespread volcanic eruptions, a fall in sea level, and a huge asteroid smashing into what is now the Yucatán Peninsula in Mexico. That collision produced forest fires and dust clouds. After these events, dinosaurs, along with many other animal and plant groups, became extinct both on land and in the sea.

762 Chapter 26 • Lesson 2

UbD Check for Understanding

ORAL QUESTIONING

Use the following questions to gauge student understanding of concepts related to the evolution of chordates.

- In what ways are bony fishes different from jawless fishes?
- What adaptations enabled vertebrates to make the transition to land?
- What caused the mass extinction at the end of the Cretaceous Period?

ADJUST INSTRUCTION

If students have difficulty answering the questions, have them review the evolution of fishes, amphibians, reptiles. Then, repeat the questions in class discussion, and call on students at random for answers.

Birds Today's birds are extremely diverse. Birds are reptiles that regulate their internal body temperature. They have an outer covering of feathers; strong yet lightweight bones; two legs covered with scales that are used for walking or perching; and front limbs modified into wings. DOL•56–DOL•59

▶ ***Bird Roots*** If you've ever wished that dinosaurs were still around, you're in luck! Recent fossil discoveries strongly support the hypothesis that birds evolved from a group of dinosaurs. The first birdlike fossil discovered was *Archaeopteryx* (ahr kee AHP tur iks), from the late Jurassic Period, about 150 million years ago. *Archaeopteryx* looked so much like a small, running dinosaur that it would be classified as a dinosaur except for its highly evolved feathers. You can see a fossil and an artist's conception of *Archaeopteryx* in **Figure 26–12.** A whole series of recent discoveries of well-preserved ancient birds and feathered dinosaurs has done a lot to "connect the dots" between modern birds and their dinosaur ancestors.

▶ ***Bird Classification*** As you recall, a clade is a branch of a cladogram that includes a single common ancestor and all the descendants of that ancestor. If you look back at **Figure 26–11,** you will see that recognizing birds as descendants of dinosaurs should cause a change in their classification. Modern birds by themselves, the traditional class Aves, form a clade within the clade containing dinosaurs. And because the clade containing dinosaurs is part of a larger clade of reptiles, modern birds are also reptiles. The traditional class Reptilia, which includes living reptiles and dinosaurs but *not* birds, however, is not a clade.

FIGURE 26–12 *Archaeopteryx*, an Early Bird *Archaeopteryx*, shown both in the fossil and artist's conception, was a bird that showed both dinosaur characteristics (teeth, bony tail) and bird characteristics (flight feathers). Because of the weight of its teeth and bony tail and its small breastbone, it might not have been able to fly very well.

Analyzing Data

IN NoS.3, B.8.1

Feather Evolution

The information in the table shows the evolution of feathers in some groups of dinosaurs that preceded modern birds.

Group (listed alphabetically)	Feather Status
Allosaurs	None
Archaeopteryx	Flight feathers
Compsognathids	Hairlike feathers
Oviraptors	True feathers
Tyrannosaurs	Branched feathers

1. Organize Data Recalling what you learned about drawing cladograms in Chapter 18, use the information to place these traits correctly on **Figure 26–11.** (Redraw the cladogram in your notebook.)

2. Draw Conclusions Which type of feathers would you expect modern birds to possess?

LESSON 26.2

Use Visuals

Use **Figure 26–12** to discuss the evolution of birds from one group of feathered dinosaurs. Then, ask students to write a paragraph summarizing how *Archaeopteryx* was like a bird and how it was like a dinosaur.

DIFFERENTIATED INSTRUCTION

L1 Special Needs Point out that the *Archaeopteryx* fossil, shown in **Figure 26–12** does not prominently show the teeth of the animal. However, students can observe the dinosaur-like shape, bony tail, and the feathered wings.

LPR Less Proficient Readers Some students may have trouble picking out important content on this page. Point out that the last sentence in the caption to **Figure 26–12** gives two main reasons why *Archaeopteryx* may not have been able to fly very well. Have students search for those reasons. *(weight of teeth and bony tail, small breastbone)* Explain that a small breastbone may not be able to hold the strong muscles needed for an animal to fly.

PURPOSE Students will analyze data in a table of dinosaurs that preceded modern birds and then draw a cladogram showing feather status as an adapted derived characteristic.

PLANNING Review with students what a cladogram shows and how a cladogram can be drawn using derived characteristics to show evolutionary relationships among groups.

ANSWERS

1. Students should redraw **Figure 26–11** and add the characters as follows:
   - Hairlike feathers—between Allosaurus and Compsognathids
   - Branched feathers—between Compsognathids and Tyrannosaurs
   - True feathers—between Tyrannosaurs and Oviraptor
   - Flight feathers—between Oviraptor and Archaeopteryx
2. flight feathers

Teach continued

Lead a Discussion

List on the board the five characteristics of mammals given in the first paragraph. Then, discuss how environmental conditions changed after the Cretaceous Period that allowed mammals to diversify, increase in size, and occupy many niches.

ELL English Language Learners Construct a time line that summarizes the main events described following the heading, **The First Mammals.** To help students understand the relevant geologic periods and eras, refer them to the explanation of the geologic time scale in Chapter 19.

Assess and Remediate

EVALUATE UNDERSTANDING

Call on students at random to identify the major groups of chordates and the important chordate adaptations that each group possesses. Then, have students complete the 26.2 Assessment.

REMEDIATION SUGGESTION

L1 Struggling Students If students have difficulty answering **Question 2c,** review how a cladogram indicates the sequence in which important adaptations evolved and how those adaptations are connected to major adaptive radiations. After reviewing the concept, have students examine the cladogram in **Figure 26–5** to find the answer.

BIOLOGY.com Students can check their understanding of lesson concepts with the **Self-Test** assessment. They can then take an online version of the **Lesson Assessment.**

FIGURE 26–13 Early Mammal Look-Alike The first mammals appeared on Earth about 220 million years ago. They may have resembled this modern tree shrew and probably, like this tree shrew, ate insects.

Mammals Members of the traditional class Mammalia include about 5000 species that range in size from mice to whales. Characteristics unique to mammals include mammary glands in females, which produce milk to nourish young, and hair. Mammals also breathe air, have four-chambered hearts, and regulate their internal body temperature. DOL•60–DOL•64

▶ ***The First Mammals*** True mammals first appeared during the late Triassic Period, about 220 million years ago. They were very small and resembled modern tree shrews, like the one in **Figure 26–13.** While dinosaurs ruled, mammals remained generally small and were probably active mostly at night. New fossils and DNA analyses suggest, however, that the first members of modern mammalian groups, including primates, rodents, and hoofed mammals, evolved during this period. After the great dinosaur extinction at the end of the Cretaceous Period, about 65 million years ago, mammals underwent a long adaptive radiation. Over millions of years, mammals diversified, increased in size, and occupied many niches. The Cenozoic Era, which began at the end of the Cretaceous Period, is usually called the Age of Mammals.

▶ ***Modern Mammals*** By the beginning of the Cenozoic Era, three major groups of mammals had evolved—monotremes (MAHN oh treemz), marsupials (mahr SOO pee ulz), and placentals. These three groups differ in their means of reproduction and development.

Only five species of the egg-laying monotremes, including the duckbill platypus, exist today, all in Australia and New Guinea. Marsupials, which include kangaroos, koalas, and wombats, bear live young that usually complete their development in an external pouch. Placental mammals—which include most of the mammals you are familiar with—have embryos that develop further while still inside the mother. After birth, most placental mammals care for their young and nurse them to provide nourishment.

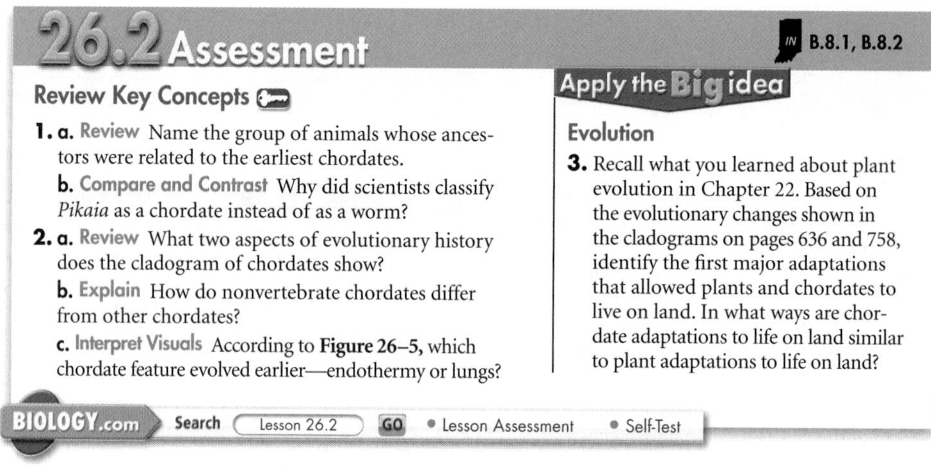

26.2 Assessment

IN B.8.1, B.8.2

Review Key Concepts

1. a. **Review** Name the group of animals whose ancestors were related to the earliest chordates.
   b. **Compare and Contrast** Why did scientists classify *Pikaia* as a chordate instead of as a worm?
2. a. **Review** What two aspects of evolutionary history does the cladogram of chordates show?
   b. **Explain** How do nonvertebrate chordates differ from other chordates?
   c. **Interpret Visuals** According to **Figure 26–5,** which chordate feature evolved earlier—endothermy or lungs?

Apply the Big idea

Evolution

3. Recall what you learned about plant evolution in Chapter 22. Based on the evolutionary changes shown in the cladograms on pages 636 and 758, identify the first major adaptations that allowed plants and chordates to live on land. In what ways are chordate adaptations to life on land similar to plant adaptations to life on land?

BIOLOGY.com Search Lesson 26.2 GO • Lesson Assessment • Self-Test

Assessment Answers

1a. echinoderms

1b. It had a notochord and paired muscles arranged in series.

2a. It shows current hypotheses about relationships among chordate groups and at which points important vertebrate features evolved.

2b. Nonvertebrate chordates lack backbones.

2c. lungs

3. Big idea Plants: embryo formation; chordates: amniotic egg. The adaptations of both plants and chordates to life on land centered on conserving water and reproduction outside of water.

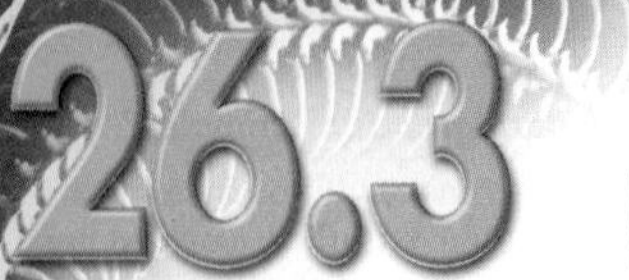

26.3 Primate Evolution

 B.8.1 History of life on Earth. Also covered: NoS.6, B.8.2.

THINK ABOUT IT Carolus Linnaeus placed our species, *Homo sapiens*, in an order he named Primates, which means "first" in Latin. But what are primates "first" in? When primates appeared, there was little to distinguish them from other mammals, aside from an increased ability to use their eyes and front limbs together. As primates evolved, however, several other characteristics became distinctive.

What Is a Primate?

What characteristics do all primates share?

Primates, including lemurs, monkeys, and apes, share several adaptations for a life spent in trees. **In general, a primate is a mammal that has relatively long fingers and toes with nails instead of claws, arms that can rotate around shoulder joints, a strong clavicle, binocular vision, and a well-developed cerebrum.** The lemur in **Figure 26–14** shows many of these characteristics. DOL•64

Fingers, Toes, and Shoulders Primates typically have five flexible fingers and toes on each hand or foot that can curl to grip objects firmly and precisely. This enables many primates to run along tree limbs and swing from branch to branch with ease. In addition, most primates have thumbs and big toes that can move against the other digits. This allows many primates to hold objects firmly in their hands or feet. Primates' arms are well suited for climbing because they can rotate in broad circles around a strong shoulder joint attached to a strong clavicle, or collar bone.

Binocular Vision Many primates have a broad face, so both eyes face forward with overlapping fields of view. This facial structure gives primates excellent binocular vision. **Binocular vision** is the ability to combine visual images from both eyes, providing depth perception and a three-dimensional view of the world. This comes in handy for judging the locations of tree branches, from which many primates swing.

Well-Developed Cerebrum In primates, the "thinking" part of the brain—the cerebrum—is large and intricate. This well-developed cerebrum enables more-complex behaviors than are found in many other mammals. For example, many primate species create elaborate social systems that include extended families, adoption of orphans, and even warfare between rival troops.

Key Questions

What characteristics do all primates share?

What are the major evolutionary groups of primates?

What adaptations enabled later hominine species to walk upright?

What is the current scientific thinking about the genus Homo?

Vocabulary

binocular vision • anthropoid • prehensile tail • hominoid • hominine • bipedal • opposable thumb

Taking Notes

Outline Before you read, outline this lesson. As you read, add details to your outline.

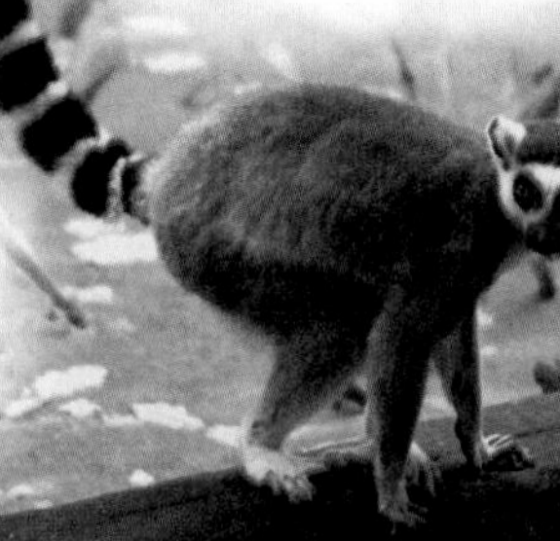

FIGURE 26–14 Primate This lemur displays several primate characteristics—it has flexible fingers and toes, arms that can rotate in broad circles around the shoulder joint, and forward-facing eyes that allow for binocular vision.

 Search Lesson 26.3 GO • Lesson Overview • Lesson Notes 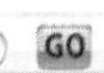

Teach for Understanding

ENDURING UNDERSTANDING Animals have evolved diverse ways to carry out basic life processes and maintain homeostasis.

GUIDING QUESTION How did primates evolve?

EVIDENCE OF UNDERSTANDING *The following assessment, to be given after the lesson is finished, should show student understanding of the characteristics of primates and how hominines evolved.* Have students work in small groups to make a poster that includes a labeled drawing showing the characteristics all primates share and a time line of hominine evolution that includes when important hominine species lived.

Getting Started

Objectives

26.3.1 Identify the characteristics that all primates share.

26.3.2 Describe the major evolutionary groups of primates.

26.3.3 Describe the adaptations that enabled later hominine species to walk upright.

26.3.4 Describe the current scientific thinking about the genus *Homo*.

Student Resources

Study Workbooks A and B, 26.3 Worksheets

Spanish Study Workbook, 26.3 Worksheets

Lab Manual B, 26.3 Hands-On Activity

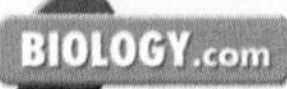 Lesson Overview • Lesson Notes • Activities: Art Review, Data Analysis • Assessment: Self-Test, Lesson Assessment

 For corresponding lesson in the **Foundation Edition**, see pages 634–637.

Build Background

Show students several pictures of living primates, such as gorillas, gibbons, spider monkeys, and baboons. Then, have students work in small groups to make a list of characteristics all primates share and discuss it with the class. After students have finished this lesson, have them look at their lists again and correct any errors.

IN INDIANA ACADEMIC STANDARDS

For the full text of all standards, see the Course Overview in the front matter of this book.

B.8.1 Explain how anatomical and molecular similarities among organisms that suggest life on earth began as simple, one-celled organisms about 4 billion years ago and multicellular organisms evolved later.

Teach

Use Visuals

Use the cladogram in **Figure 26–15** to introduce students to the major groups of modern primates.

Ask If you were to draw a bracket similar to the Hominoids bracket that would include all the anthropoids, where would the bracket begin and end? *(It would begin with the New World monkeys and end with humans.)*

Ask Which primate group does this cladogram show is most closely related to humans? *(chimpanzees)*

DIFFERENTIATED INSTRUCTION

LPR **Less Proficient Readers** Some students may have difficulty differentiating the relationships among the different primate groups. Work with students to draw a **Concept Map** on the board that shows the relationships among these groups. (Primates is written at the top, with the linking word *include* beneath it; two subgroups directly beneath Primates include Lemurs, Lorises and Bush Babies; Tarsiers and Anthropoids; beneath Anthropoids are the three groups New World Monkeys, Old World Monkeys, and Hominoids; beneath Hominoids are Gibbons, etc.)

Study Wkbks A/B, Appendix S21, Concept Map. **Transparencies,** GO4.

ELL Focus on ELL: Extend Language

BEGINNING AND INTERMEDIATE SPEAKERS
Before reading, have students make a **T-Chart**, and place the following terms on the left side of the chart: primate, anthropoid, hominoid, and hominine. As students read, have them fill in the right side of the chart with important information about the terms, including definitions and examples. Students can draw illustrations or write phrases in their native language to help remember the meanings of the terms.

Study Wkbks A/B, Appendix S30, T-Chart. **Transparencies,** GO15.

Binocular Vision

1. Throw a paper ball to your partner, who should try to catch the ball with one hand. Record whether your partner caught the ball.
2. Now have your partner close one eye. Repeat Step 1.

Analyze and Conclude

1. **Use Tables and Graphs** Exchange results with other groups. Make a bar graph for the class data comparing the results with both eyes open and one eye shut.
2. **Draw Conclusions** How is binocular vision useful to primates?

Evolution of Primates

What are the major evolutionary groups of primates?

Humans and other primates evolved from a common ancestor that lived more than 65 million years ago. One recently discovered fossil, *Carpolestes,* which lived 56 million years ago in Wyoming, has been proposed as an example of the first primate. Early in their history, primates split into two groups. **Primates in one of these groups look very little like typical monkeys. This group contains the lemurs and lorises. The other group includes tarsiers and the anthropoids, the group that includes monkeys, great apes, and humans.** Refer to **Figure 26–15** as you read about the evolutionary relationships between these groups.

Lemurs and Lorises With few exceptions, lemurs and lorises are small, nocturnal primates with large eyes adapted to seeing in the dark. Many have long snouts. Living members include the bush babies of Africa, the lemurs of Madagascar, and the lorises of Asia.

Tarsiers and Anthropoids Primates more closely related to humans than to lemurs belong to a different group, members of which have broader faces and widely separated nostrils. This group includes the tarsiers of Asia and the anthropoids. **Anthropoids** (AN thruh poydz), or humanlike primates, include monkeys, great apes, and humans. Anthropoids split into two groups around 45 million years ago, as the continents on which they lived moved apart.

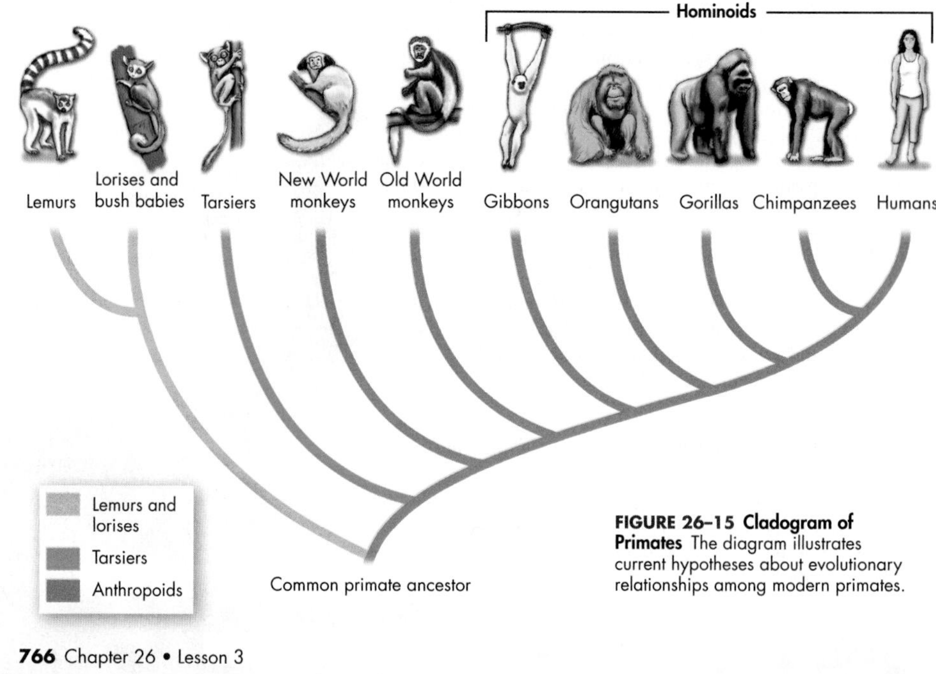

FIGURE 26–15 Cladogram of Primates The diagram illustrates current hypotheses about evolutionary relationships among modern primates.

PURPOSE Students investigate the usefulness of binocular vision.

MATERIALS sheet of notebook paper, graph paper

SAFETY Warn students not to throw the ball hard or aim the ball at their partner's face.

PLANNING Have students read the procedure and discuss any questions they have about what to do.

ANALYZE AND CONCLUDE

1. Graphs should show that more students were able to catch the ball with both eyes open than with one eye closed.
2. Many primates move by swinging through trees. The ability to judge distances accurately enables them to grasp branches quickly and securely.

▶ ***New World Monkeys*** Members of one anthropoid branch, the New World monkeys, are found in Central and South America. (Europeans used the term *New World* to refer to North and South America.) Members of this group, which includes squirrel monkeys and spider monkeys, live almost entirely in trees. They have long, flexible arms that enable them to swing from branch to branch. New World monkeys also have a long, **prehensile tail** that can coil tightly enough around a branch to serve as a "fifth hand."

▶ ***Old World Monkeys and Great Apes*** The other anthropoid branch, which evolved in Africa and Asia, includes the Old World monkeys and great apes. Old World monkeys, such as langurs and macaques (muh KAHKS), spend time in trees but lack prehensile tails. Great apes, also called **hominoids,** include gibbons, orangutans, gorillas, chimpanzees, and humans. Recent DNA analyses confirm that, among the great apes, chimpanzees are humans' closest relatives.

Hominine Evolution

What adaptations enabled later hominine species to walk upright?

Between 6 and 7 million years ago, the lineage that led to humans split from the lineage that led to chimpanzees. The hominoids in the lineage that led to humans are called **hominines.** Hominines include modern humans and all other species more closely related to us than to chimpanzees. Hominines evolved the ability to walk upright, grasping thumbs, and large brains. **Figure 26–16** shows some ways in which the skeletons of modern humans differ from those of hominoids such as gorillas. **The skull, neck, spinal column, hip bones, and leg bones of early hominine species changed shape in ways that enabled later species to walk upright.** The evolution of this **bipedal,** or two-footed, locomotion was very important, because it freed both hands to use tools. Meanwhile, the hominine hand evolved an **opposable thumb** that could touch the tips of the fingers, enabling the grasping of objects and the use of tools.

Hominines also evolved much larger brains. The brains of chimpanzees, our closest living relatives, typically range in volume from 280 to 450 cubic centimeters. The brains of *Homo sapiens,* on the other hand, range in size from 1200 to 1600 cubic centimeters! Most of the difference in brain size results from a radically expanded cerebrum.

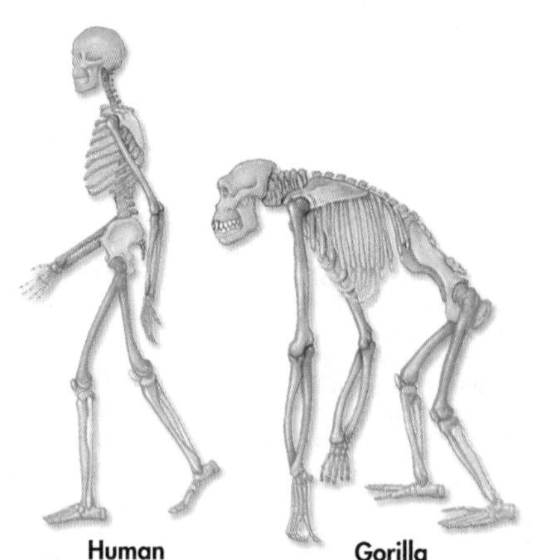

Comparing Human and Gorilla Skeletons

Feature	Human	Gorilla
Skull	Atop S-shaped spine	Atop C-shaped spine
Spinal cord	Exits at bottom of skull	Exits near back of skull
Arms and hands	Arms shorter than legs; hands don't touch ground when walking	Arms longer than legs; hands touch ground when walking
Pelvis	Bowl-shaped	Long and narrow
Thigh bones	Angled inward, directly below body	Angled away from pelvis

FIGURE 26–16 Comparison of Hominoids Modern hominines walk upright on two legs; gorillas use all four limbs. The diagrams show many of the skeletal characteristics that allow hominines to walk upright. Compare and Contrast ***According to the chart and illustrations, what are the other skeletal differences between humans and gorillas?***

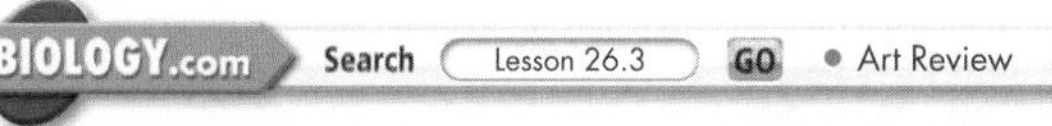

LESSON 26.3

Lead a Discussion

As students begin to learn about hominine evolution, talk about differences between hominines and other hominoids. Use **Figure 26–16** in part of the discussion, but don't limit the discussion to skeletal differences. Point out that as larger brains evolved in hominines, behavior changed as well as anatomy.

DIFFERENTIATED INSTRUCTION

L1 Special Needs Some students may have difficulty understanding the anatomical differences between hominoids and hominines. Derive from **Figure 26–16** a list of structures that changed shape in early hominine species, and write the list on the board. Then, use the illustrations and chart in the figure to discuss how each bone in the list changed from bones in other hominoids. For example, point to the word *skull* on the board, and direct students to the first row in the chart. Read aloud what the chart says about human and gorilla skulls, and have students confirm what they have read and heard by examining the illustrations.

BIOLOGY.com Students do a drag-and-drop activity to compare human and gorilla skeletons in **Art Review: Comparison of Hominoids.**

How Science Works

NEW TERMINOLOGY

In recent years, researchers have developed many new names for groups of all sizes across all domains of organisms, including the names for groups of primates. The new terminology is a reflection of the new techniques being used to group organisms. There have been many instances where old Linnaean groups do not line up with true clades as determined by new analyses. For example, among primates the tarsiers used to be grouped with the lemurs, lorises, and bush babies under the name *prosimians.* New evidence, though, does not support that grouping, and *prosimian* is no longer a valid taxonomic term. Similarly, instead of hominid, we now use the term hominine for hominoids in the lineage that led to humans.

Answers

FIGURE 26–16 Humans have an S-shaped spine; gorillas have a C-shaped spine. The human spinal cord exits at the bottom of the skull; the gorilla spinal cord exits near the back of the skull. Human arms are shorter than the legs; gorilla arms are longer than the legs. The human pelvis is bowl-shaped; the gorilla pelvis is long and narrow. Human thigh bones are angled inward, directly below the body; gorilla thigh bones are angled away from the pelvis.

Teach continued

Build Reading Skills

Explain that it is normal if the long list of hominine fossil names and dates is confusing. One way to organize the information is to make a **Compare/Contrast Table** to organize names, dates, and characteristics. Make a three-column table on the board, with these column headings: Hominine, Approximate Age, and Description/Characteristics. Then, begin to fill in the table by pointing out the oldest probable hominine described in the text. Write *Sahelanthropus* in the first column, "7 million years ago" in the second column, and fill in the third column with characteristics of this hominine. Have students copy this information into their own table and continue to fill it in as they read.

Study Wkbks A/B, Appendix S20, Compare/Contrast Table. **Transparencies,** GO3.

DIFFERENTIATED INSTRUCTION

L3 **Advanced Students** Ask interested students to find or make a current map of Africa that can be posted on a bulletin board or the classroom wall. Also, ask them to use online resources to find out where important hominine fossils have been discovered in Africa. Then, have students make labels to affix to the map to show those locations.

FIGURE 26–17 Laetoli Footprints Between 3.8 and 3.6 million years ago, members of a species of *Australopithecus* made these footprints at Laetoli in Tanzania. The footprints show that hominines walked upright millions of years ago.

New Findings and New Questions The study of human ancestors is exciting and constantly changing. Since the 1990s, new discoveries in Africa have doubled the number of known hominine species. Those discoveries also doubled the length of the known hominine fossil record—from 3.5 million years to 7 million years, a time that corresponds closely to the time at which DNA studies suggest that the lineage that led to humans split from the lineage that led to chimpanzees. These new data have enhanced the picture of our species' past. Questions still remain as to how fossil hominines are related to one another—and to humans. In fact, the field is changing so rapidly that all we can present here is a sampling of current hypotheses.

Relatives Versus Ancestors Most paleontologists agree that the hominine fossil record includes seven genera—*Sahelanthropus, Orrorin, Ardipithecus, Australopithecus, Paranthropus, Kenyanthropus,* and *Homo*—and at least 20 species. These diverse hominine fossils stretch back in time roughly 7 million years. All these species are *relatives* of modern humans, but not all of them are human *ancestors.* To understand that distinction, think of your family. Your relatives may include aunts, uncles, cousins, parents, grandparents, and great-grandparents. All of these folks are your relatives, but only your parents, grandparents, and great-grandparents are your ancestors. Distinguishing relatives from ancestors in the hominine family is an ongoing challenge.

The Oldest Hominine? In 2002, paleontologists working in north-central Africa discovered a fossil skull roughly 7 million years old. This fossil, called *Sahelanthropus,* is a million years older than any known hominine. *Sahelanthropus* had a brain about the size of that of a modern chimp, but its short, broad face was more like that of a human. Scientists are still debating whether this fossil represents a hominine.

Australopithecus Some early hominine fossil species seem to belong to the lineage that led to modern humans, while others formed separate branches off the main hominine line. One early group of hominines, of the genus *Australopithecus,* lived from about 4 million to about 1.5 million years ago. These hominines were bipedal apes, but their skeletons suggest that they probably spent at least some time in trees. The structure of their teeth suggests a diet rich in fruit.

The best-known of these species is *Australopithecus afarensis,* which lived from roughly 4 million to 2.5 million years ago. The humanlike footprints in **Figure 26–17,** about 3.6 million years old, were probably made by members of this species. *A. afarensis* fossils indicate the species had small brains, so the footprints show that hominines walked bipedally long before large brains evolved. Other fossils of this genus indicate that males were much larger than females. You can see artists' conceptions of young female and adult female *A. afarensis* in **Figure 26–18.**

In Your Notebook *How long ago does DNA evidence suggest that the human lineage split from the chimpanzee lineage?*

768

Biology In-Depth

CHANGING AFRICAN CLIMATE AND PRIMATE EVOLUTION

Modern studies of primate evolution involve more than just primate fossils. Researchers also study fossils of other organisms and the history of climate over the last 10 million years. Several hypotheses link primate evolution to climate change and changes in ancient ecosystems in Africa. In general, many areas became drier, and forests gave way to grasslands. Some primates remained in forests, while others adapted to open grasslands. Savannah species gradually added meat to their diets, and began walking upright on two feet. Data show that climate in some parts of Africa switched back and forth several times between wet and dry. These changes in climate caused rapid shifts in plant and animal communities. New hypotheses link these repeated changes in climate and ecology to the evolution of body form, brain size, and behavior of hominines—including early members of the genus *Homo.*

Answers

IN YOUR NOTEBOOK about 7 million years ago

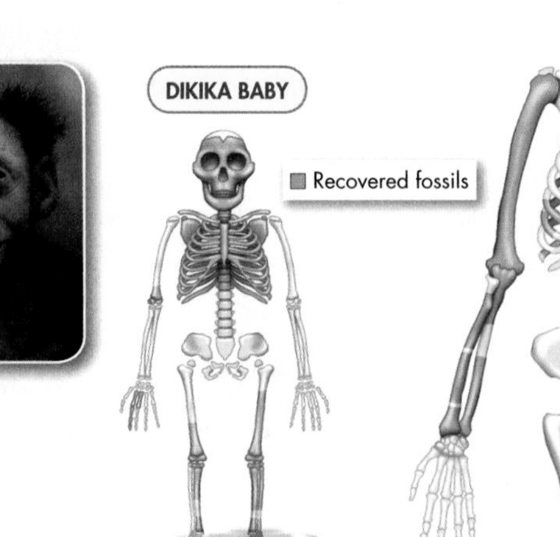

▶ ***Lucy*** The best-known *A. afarensis* specimen is a remarkably complete skeleton of a female discovered in 1974, nicknamed "Lucy." Lucy stood about 1 meter tall and lived about 3.2 million years ago.

▶ ***The Dikika Baby*** In 2006, an Ethiopian researcher announced the discovery of some incredibly well preserved 3.3 million-year-old fossils of a very young female hominine. The skeleton included a nearly complete skull and jaws, torso, spinal column, limbs, and left foot. This fossil was assigned to *A. afarensis*, the same species as Lucy, and nicknamed "the Dikika Baby," after the region in Africa where it was discovered. Leg bones confirmed that the Dikika Baby walked bipedally, while her arm and shoulder bones suggest that she would have been a better climber than modern humans. Researchers will be extracting information from these bones for years.

Paranthropus Three more-recent species, which grew to the size of well-fed football linebackers, have been placed in their own genus, *Paranthropus*. These *Paranthropus* species had huge, grinding back teeth. Their diets probably included coarse and fibrous plant foods like those eaten by modern gorillas. Paleontologists now place *Paranthropus* on a separate, dead-end branch of our family tree.

Hominine Relationships Researchers once thought that human evolution took place in relatively simple steps in which hominine species, over time, became gradually more humanlike. But it is now clear that a series of hominine adaptive radiations produced a number of species whose relationships are difficult to determine. As a result, what once looked like a simple hominine "family tree" with a single main trunk now looks more like a shrub with multiple trunks.

FIGURE 26–18 Lucy and the Dikika Baby "Lucy" and "the Dikika Baby" are nicknames of two very important fossils of the hominine *A. afarensis*. Lucy is a partial skeleton of an adult female. The Dikika Baby is the most-complete fossil yet found of this species. These two fossils were discovered just 6 miles apart in Ethiopia. **Interpret Visuals** ***Given the fossils recovered, which face shape would you expect scientists to be more confident about—the Dikika Baby's or Lucy's?***

Use Visuals

Use **Figure 26–18** to compare and contrast two fossils of *Australopithecus afarensis.*

Ask In which species do scientists classify both Lucy and the Dikika Baby? *(Australopithecus afarensis)*

Ask Where and when did these hominines live? *(They both lived in Africa in what is present-day Ethiopia. Lucy lived about 3.2 million years ago, and the Dikika Baby lived about 3.3 million years ago.)*

Ask What kind of food did Lucy probably eat? *(fruit, because the teeth of* Australopithecus *suggest a diet rich in fruit.)*

DIFFERENTIATED INSTRUCTION

L1 Struggling Students Make sure students understand that the illustrations in **Figure 26–18** are both reconstructions. The darker bones in the drawings represent the fossils that were discovered. Scientists inferred what the lighter bones likely looked like based on characteristics of the recovered fossils. Explain that the faces are artists' renditions of what these individuals might have looked like, given what the face bones suggest.

L3 Advanced Students Ask interested students to do further research about the technique of forensic facial reconstruction as it is used both in fossil reconstruction and in police work. In an oral presentation to the class, students might show examples of forensic reconstructions and explain why the technique is controversial.

Quick Facts

LUCY

The discovery of the fossil nicknamed Lucy was a sensational find at the time. Here are a few facts about Lucy.

- She was a fully grown woman, probably in her 30s.
- She probably weighed 60–65 pounds.
- She lived in an area that was wooded, though by the time her skeleton was found the area was arid.
- The fossil was discovered by paleontologist Donald Johanson. As Johanson and his colleagues were celebrating the discovery, they listened to the Beatles song, "Lucy in the Sky With Diamonds."

Answers

FIGURE 26–18 the Dikika Baby, because many more fossils of her skull were recovered

LESSON 26.3

Teach continued

VISUAL SUMMARY

After students have studied **Figure 26–19,** ask them to find species included in the time line that they have already learned about in the text. Explain that they may have learned the genus name, but not the species name. (e.g. *Sahelanthropus* and *Paranthropus*) Then, discuss why the fossil record is not complete. Explain that fossil formation happens only under special conditions; most bones deteriorate naturally after the death of the animal.

DIFFERENTIATED INSTRUCTION

L1 Special Needs Call on students to choose a species listed on the time line, read its name, and tell when it lived. *(Sample answer:* Homo ergaster *is shown to have lived from about 2 million years ago to about 1.4 million years ago.)* After several examples have been read aloud, emphasize that the fossil record of hominine evolution does not show a straight-line of descent to modern humans. Much is yet to be discovered about the details of human evolution.

BIOLOGY.com In **Data Analysis: Who Is *H. floresiensis?*** students look at data on the *H. floresiensis* fossils. Students can then use this data to weigh in on the debate of whether these fossils represent a separate species or a population of *H. sapiens.*

Address Misconceptions

Humans Descended From Monkeys Some students will persist in the misconception, heard often, that the evolution of *Homo sapiens* essentially means humans descended from monkeys. As students begin to read about the road to modern humans, have them turn back to **Figure 26–15.** Point out that the cladogram shows humans and monkeys share a common primate ancestor, *not* that humans evolved from monkeys.

Answers

FIGURE 26–19 *Homo habilis, H. ergaster,* and *H. erectus* lived at the same time. *H. erectus, H. cepranensis,* and *H. antecessor* lived at the same time. *H. erectus* and *H. heidelbergensis* also lived at the same time. *H. sapiens, H. neanderthalensis, H. erectus,* and *H. floresiensis* lived at the same time.

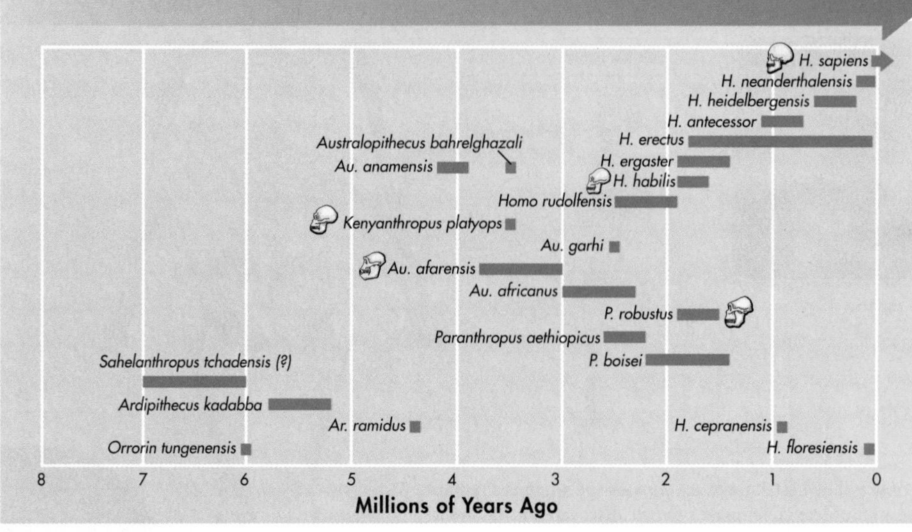

VISUAL SUMMARY

HOMININE TIME LINE

FIGURE 26–19 The diagram shows hominine species known from fossils and the time ranges during which each species probably existed. These time ranges may change as paleontologists gather new data. At this writing, several competing hypotheses present different ideas about how these species are related to one another and to *Homo sapiens.* So far, there is no single, universally accepted hypothesis, so we present these data as a time line, rather than as a cladogram. The fossil record shows that hominine evolution did not proceed along a simple, straight-line transformation of one species into another. Rather, a series of adaptive radiations produced a number of species, several of which display a confusing mix of primitive and modern traits. **Interpret Graphs** ***According to this time line, which species in the genus* Homo *lived at the same time?***

The Road to Modern Humans

***What is the current scientific thinking about the genus* Homo?**

The hominines discussed so far lived millions of years before modern humans. **Many species in our genus existed before our species, *Homo sapiens,* appeared. Furthermore, at least three other *Homo* species existed at the same time as early humans.** Paleontologists still do not completely understand the relationships among species in our own genus.

The Genus *Homo* About 2 million years ago, a new group of hominine species appeared. Several of these fossils resemble modern human bones enough that they have been classified in the genus *Homo.* One set of fossils from this time period was found with tools made of stone and bone, so it was named *Homo habilis* (HAB uh luhs), which means "handy man" in Latin. The earliest fossils that most researchers agree can be definitely assigned to the genus *Homo* have been called *Homo ergaster. H. ergaster* was larger than *H. habilis* and had a bigger brain and downward-facing nostrils that resemble those of modern humans. *Homo rudolfensis* appeared before *H. ergaster,* but some researchers choose to classify it in the genus *Australopithecus* instead of *Homo.*

Out of Africa—But When and Who? Researchers agree that our genus originated in Africa and migrated from there to populate the world. But many questions remain. When did hominines first leave Africa? Did more than one species make the trip? Which of those species were human ancestors and which were merely relatives? You can see some of the current hypotheses in **Figure 26–20.**

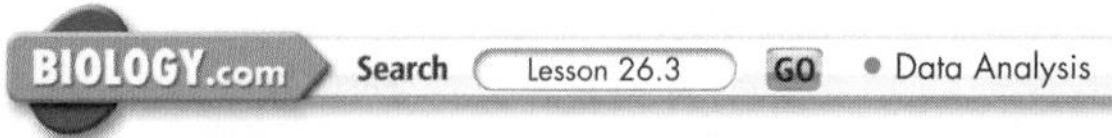

How Science Works

THE STUDY OF HUMAN ANCESTORS

There is almost no scientific field that is as crowded, as contentious, and as constantly changing as the study of human ancestry. The information provided in this lesson is a best effort to present current consensus hypotheses. The noted professor and author Steven Jay Gould once said that every year when he prepared to lecture on this topic, he would throw his previous year's notes into the trash and start from scratch. So, if you and your students research the literature for more information, do not be surprised when you find genuine disagreements about the identification, age, and relationships of hominine fossils. These debates provide an excellent demonstration of how science works.

▶ ***The First to Leave*** Fossil and molecular evidence suggest that some hominines left Africa long before *Homo sapiens* evolved. It also appears that more than one *Homo* species made the trip in waves. Again, researchers differ as to the identity of various fossils, but agree that hominines began migrating out of Africa at least 1.8 million years ago. Hominine remains from that period were found in the Republic of Georgia, which is north of Turkey and far from Africa. Some researchers who have examined those remains argue that they might belong to a smaller-brained *Homo* species, *Homo habilis*.

▶ **Homo erectus *in Asia*** According to some researchers, groups of *Homo erectus* left Africa and traveled all the way across India and through China to Southeast Asia. In fact, some of the oldest known specimens of *H. erectus* were uncovered on the Indonesian island of Java. This suggests that these ancient wanderers spread very rapidly once they left Africa. These *H. erectus* populations continued to survive and evolve across Asia for as long as 1.5 million years.

▶ ***The First* Homo sapiens** Paleontologists have long debated where and when *Homo sapiens* arose. One hypothesis, called the multiregional model, suggests that, in several parts of the world, modern humans evolved independently from widely separated populations of *H. erectus.* Another hypothesis, the "out-of-Africa" model, proposes that modern humans evolved in Africa about 200,000 years ago, migrated out of Africa through the Middle East, and replaced the descendants of earlier hominine species.

Recently, molecular biologists analyzed mitochondrial DNA from living humans around the world to determine when they last shared a common ancestor. The estimated date for that African common ancestor is between 200,000 and 150,000 years ago. More recent DNA data suggest that a small subset of those African ancestors left northeastern Africa between 65,000 and 50,000 years ago to colonize the world. These data strongly support the out-of-Africa model.

BUILD Vocabulary

MULTIPLE MEANINGS The word *sapient* means "wise." It is also used as an adjective referring to *Homo sapiens.*

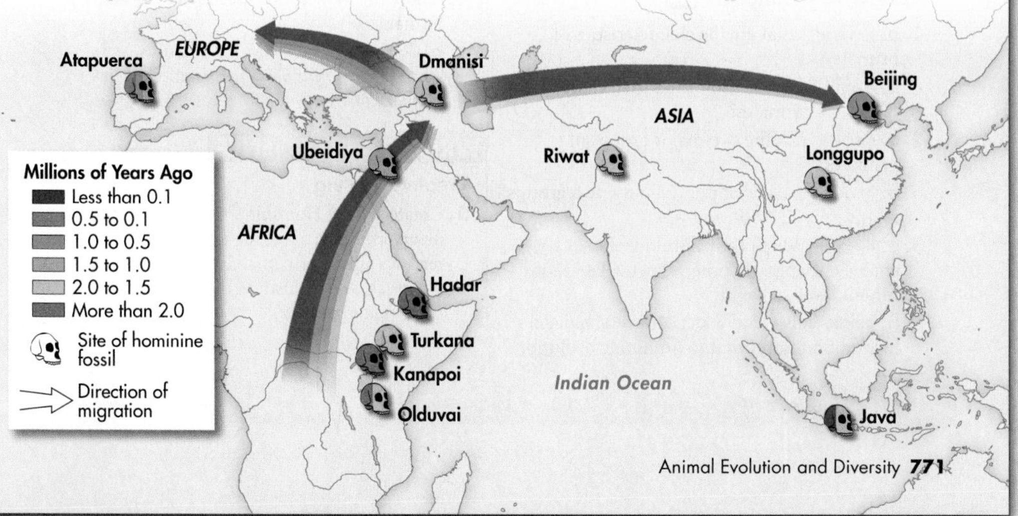

FIGURE 26–20 Out of Africa Data show that relatives and ancestors of modern humans left Africa in waves. But when—and how far did they travel? By comparing the mitochondrial DNA of living humans and by continuing to study the fossil record, scientists hope to improve our understanding of the complex history of *Homo sapiens.* (Note: Skulls on the map do not indicate that skulls were found at each location.)

UbD Check for Understanding

ONE-MINUTE RESPONSE

Write the following question on the board, and give students about a minute to write a quick response.

- What is the difference between the multiregional hypothesis and the "out-of-Africa" hypothesis?

ADJUST INSTRUCTION

If students' responses are incorrect or incomplete, lead a short class discussion on the two hypotheses for the spread of *Homo sapiens* around the world. Make sure students understand that both hypotheses have advocates among scientific experts.

Use Visuals

Have students examine **Figure 26–20,** and then call on volunteers to explain what it shows. Point out that all the hominine fossils students have learned about thus far, including *Australopithecus* and *Paranthropus,* were discovered in Africa, and the skulls placed on the map of Africa represent some of those discoveries.

Ask Where does the map show that hominines first spread when they left Africa? *(to the Middle East)*

Point out that today the Middle East includes such countries as Syria, Lebanon, Israel, and Iraq.

DIFFERENTIATED INSTRUCTION

L1 Struggling Students Some students may have trouble understanding **Figure 26–20.** Work with them so they understand what the colors in the key show, what the arrows mean, and what the skull icons indicate. Explain how to interpret each arrow.

L3 Advanced Students Ask students who are interested in this topic to research any recent hominine discoveries. Have them search for information using online search engines and online or hard-copy indexes of *National Geographic* and the academic journal, *Nature*. Ask them to report back to the class on what they find.

LESSON 26.3

Assess and Remediate

EVALUATE UNDERSTANDING

Call on students to define each of the lesson's vocabulary terms. Then, have them complete the 26.3 Assessment.

REMEDIATION SUGGESTION

L1 Struggling Students If students have trouble with **Question 3a,** have them find the highlighted sentence in their text that answers this Key Question: What adaptations enabled later hominine species to walk upright?

Students can check their understanding of lesson concepts with the **Self-Test** assessment. They can then take an online version of the **Lesson Assessment.**

Answers

FIGURE 26–21 Answers will vary. Sample answer: The animals in the paintings may be the animals that were hunted by Cro-Magnons.

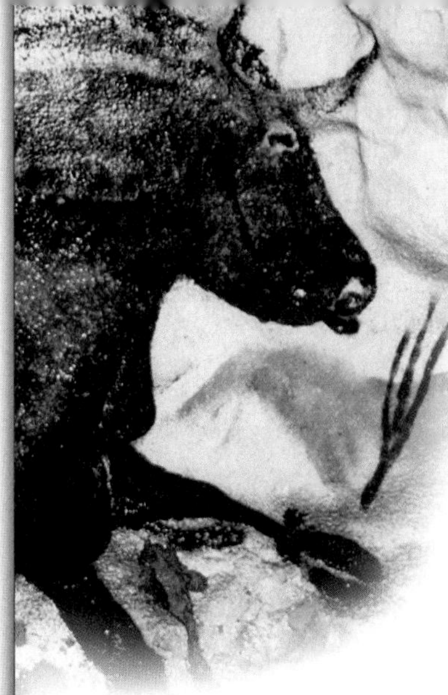

FIGURE 26–21 Cro-Magnon Art This ancient cave painting from France shows the remarkable artistic abilities of Cro-Magnons. **Infer** ***How might these painted images be related to the way in which these early humans lived?***

Modern Humans The story of modern humans over the past 200,000 years involves two main species in the genus *Homo*.

▶ **Homo neanderthalensis** Neanderthals flourished in Europe and western Asia beginning about 200,000 years ago. Evidence suggests that they made stone tools, lived in complex social groups, had controlled use of fire, and were excellent hunters. They buried their dead with simple rituals. Neanderthals survived in parts of Europe until about 28,000 to 24,000 years ago.

▶ ***Modern* Homo sapiens** Anatomically modern *Homo sapiens,* whose skeletons look like those of today's humans, arrived in the Middle East from Africa about 100,000 years ago. By about 50,000 years ago, *H. sapiens* populations were using new technology to make more sophisticated stone blades. They also began to make elaborately worked tools from bones and antlers. They produced spectacular cave paintings and buried their dead with elaborate rituals. In other words, these people, including the group known as Cro-Magnons, began to behave like modern humans.

When *H. sapiens* arrived in the Middle East, they found Neanderthals already living there. Neanderthals and *H. sapiens* lived side by side in the Middle East for about 50,000 years. Groups of modern humans moved into Europe between 40,000 and 32,000 years ago. There, too, *H. sapiens* coexisted alongside Neanderthals for several thousand years. For the last 24,000 years, however, our species has been Earth's only hominine. Why did Neanderthals disappear? Did they interbreed with *H. sapiens*? No one knows for sure. What we do know is that our species, *Homo sapiens,* is the only surviving member of the once large and diverse hominine clade.

26.3 Assessment

IN B.8.1, B.8.2

Review Key Concepts

1. a. **Review** What are the characteristics of primates?
   b. **Apply Concepts** How does each characteristic benefit primates?
2. a. **Review** List the two major groups of primates.
   b. **Sequence** At what point did the two groups of anthropoids split, and why?
3. a. **Review** Which early hominine bones changed shape over time, allowing later hominines to walk upright?
   b. **Relate Cause and Effect** How was bipedal locomotion important to hominine evolution?
4. a. **Review** Which two species are considered humans?
   b. **Compare and Contrast** List two ways in which *Homo neanderthalensis* differed from *Homo sapiens.*

WRITE ABOUT SCIENCE

Creative Writing

5. Create a "Lost Hominine" poster for *Homo neanderthalensis.* Include its known characteristics and approximately when and where it was last seen. Illustrate the poster with a drawing or clipping.

BIOLOGY.com Search Lesson 26.3 GO • Lesson Assessment • Self-Test

Assessment Answers

1a. In general, a primate is a mammal that has relatively long fingers and toes with nails instead of claws, arms that can rotate around shoulder joints, a strong clavicle, binocular vision, and a well-developed cerebrum.

1b. The fingers and toes allow primates to swing in trees and grasp objects. The strong shoulders and clavicles are well suited for climbing. Binocular vision provides depth perception. The well-developed cerebrum enables complex behaviors.

2a. Lemurs and lorises make up one group, and tarsiers and anthropoids make up a second group.

2b. The two groups split apart around 45 million years ago as continents moved apart.

3a. the skull, neck, spinal column, hip bones, and leg bones

3b. Bipedal locomotion freed both hands to use tools.

4a. *Homo neanderthalensis* and *Homo sapiens*

4b. Sample answer: *H. neanderthalensis* flourished in areas out of Africa 100,000 years before *H. sapiens. H. neanderthalensis* did not develop the elaborate tools that *H. sapiens* developed.

WRITE ABOUT SCIENCE

5. Have students do library or online research to find out about the known characteristics and to find images of Neanderthals.

Biology & HISTORY

Human-Fossil Seekers **The study of human origins is an exciting search for our past. Piecing together this complicated story requires the skills of many scientists.**

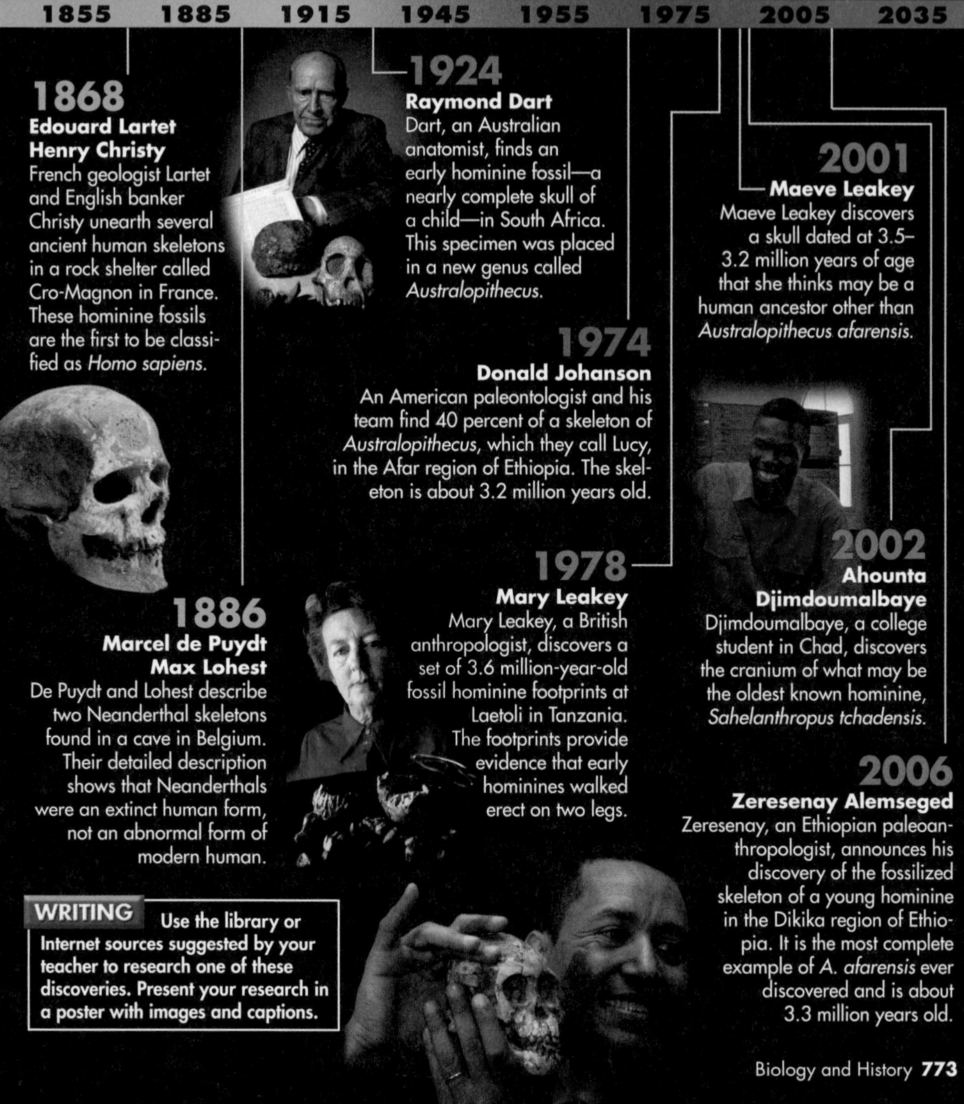

1855 | 1885 | 1915 | 1945 | 1955 | 1975 | 2005 | 2035

1868
Edouard Lartet
Henry Christy
French geologist Lartet and English banker Christy unearth several ancient human skeletons in a rock shelter called Cro-Magnon in France. These hominine fossils are the first to be classified as *Homo sapiens*.

1886
Marcel de Puydt
Max Lohest
De Puydt and Lohest describe two Neanderthal skeletons found in a cave in Belgium. Their detailed description shows that Neanderthals were an extinct human form, not an abnormal form of modern human.

1924
Raymond Dart
Dart, an Australian anatomist, finds an early hominine fossil—a nearly complete skull of a child—in South Africa. This specimen was placed in a new genus called *Australopithecus*.

1974
Donald Johanson
An American paleontologist and his team find 40 percent of a skeleton of *Australopithecus*, which they call Lucy, in the Afar region of Ethiopia. The skeleton is about 3.2 million years old.

1978
Mary Leakey
Mary Leakey, a British anthropologist, discovers a set of 3.6 million-year-old fossil hominine footprints at Laetoli in Tanzania. The footprints provide evidence that early hominines walked erect on two legs.

2001
Maeve Leakey
Maeve Leakey discovers a skull dated at 3.5–3.2 million years of age that she thinks may be a human ancestor other than *Australopithecus afarensis*.

2002
Ahounta Djimdoumalbaye
Djimdoumalbaye, a college student in Chad, discovers the cranium of what may be the oldest known hominine, *Sahelanthropus tchadensis*.

2006
Zeresenay Alemseged
Zeresenay, an Ethiopian paleoanthropologist, announces his discovery of the fossilized skeleton of a young hominine in the Dikika region of Ethiopia. It is the most complete example of *A. afarensis* ever discovered and is about 3.3 million years old.

WRITING **Use the library or Internet sources suggested by your teacher to research one of these discoveries. Present your research in a poster with images and captions.**

Quick Facts

THE LEAKEY FAMILY

The Leakey family has been in the forefront of the study of human origins since the 1920s. These are the most prominent members of the family.

- Louis Leakey (1903–1972), married to Mary Leakey, was influential in convincing anthropologists to look in Africa for fossils of human ancestors.
- Mary Leakey (1913–1996), married to Louis Leakey, made many discoveries, including the Laetoli footprints and *Australopithecus* fossils.
- Richard Leakey (b. 1944), son of Louis and Mary, discovered many fossils of human ancestors in Kenya.
- Maeve Leakey (b. 1942), married to Richard, was first hired by Louis Leakey to study monkeys and apes. She later made important fossil finds.

Teach

Lead a Discussion

Discuss with students how theories about human ancestors have changed over time and how each discovery included here helped change those theories.

Ask What method are scientists increasingly using today to determine relationships among hominoids? *(DNA analysis)*

Point out that analysis of mitochondrial DNA has been used in determining when human ancestors left Africa.

DIFFERENTIATED INSTRUCTION

L3 Advanced Students Mary Leakey and Donald Johanson have both written books about their experiences as fossil hunters and the implications of their discoveries on hypotheses about human evolution. Students might read one of these books and then present significant information from the book to the class. Some ways that students might present this information include the following: reading a passage from the book followed by leading a class discussion or making a poster showing important events described in the book.

Answers

WRITING Have students work in small groups. Make sure not all groups decide to research the same discovery. For students' sources, suggest Web sites with reliable scientific information. Ask students to provide detailed information about the sources they use.

CHAPTER LAB

Pre-Lab

Introduce students to the concepts they will explore in the chapter lab by assigning the Pre-Lab questions.

Lab

Tell students they will perform the chapter lab *Investigating Hominoid Fossils* described in **Lab Manual A.**

L1 **Struggling Students** A simpler version of the chapter lab is provided in **Lab Manual B.**

Look online for **Editable Lab Worksheets.**

For corresponding pre-lab in the **Foundation Edition**, see page 638.

INDIANA ACADEMIC STANDARDS

For the full text of all standards, see the Course Overview in the front matter of this book.

Forensics Lab

GUIDED INQUIRY

IN B.8.2 Classification. Also covered: NoS.2, NoS.5, B.8.3.

Pre-Lab: Investigating Hominoid Fossils

Problem What can a comparison of skulls and hands reveal about the evolution of humans?

Materials metric ruler, protractor

Lab Manual Chapter 26 Lab

Skills Focus Measure, Analyze Data, Compare and Contrast

Connect to the Big idea To learn about the evolution of humans, scientists study both close relatives and possible ancestors. Fossils of possible ancestors are rare, and complete skeletons are even rarer. Yet, scientists have gained valuable information from those fossils that have been found. In this lab, you will make measurements that a paleontologist might make after finding a fossil. Then, you will use your data to make inferences about human evolution.

Background Questions

a. **Review** What are hominoids, and what are hominines?

b. **Explain** Use the examples of chimpanzees and humans to explain the difference between evolutionary relatives and ancestors.

c. **Compare and Contrast** What is the difference between the locomotion of humans and the locomotion of chimpanzees?

Pre-Lab Questions

Preview the procedure in the lab manual.

1. **Use Models** What will you use instead of actual skulls and hands to make your measurements?
2. **Interpret Visuals** The bony cavities in a skull that protect the eyes are called orbits, or eye sockets. On the skulls, what does line AC measure? What does line BC measure?
3. **Use Analogies** Shoe sizes such as 9A and 11E (or 9 narrow and 11 extra-wide) are an example of an index. What two measurements are being compared in a shoe index?

BIOLOGY.com Search Chapter 26 GO

Visit Chapter 26 online to test yourself on chapter content and to find activities to help you learn.

Untamed Science Video Join the Untamed Science crew as they talk with insect experts to better understand why there are more than a million insects.

Art Review Review your understanding of different hominoids.

InterActive Art Build a cladogram of invertebrates.

Data Analysis Compare data on the *H. floresiensis* fossil and modern *H. sapiens* and determine if they are separate species.

Pre-Lab Answers

BACKGROUND QUESTIONS

a. Hominoids are the anthropoid branch that includes gibbons, orangutans, gorillas, chimpanzees, and humans. Hominines are hominoids in the lineage that led to humans (or modern humans and all species more closely related to humans than chimpanzees).

b. Sample answer: Chimpanzees and humans are relatives who are descended from a common primate ancestor. Species that are not in the direct line of descent are not ancestors.

c. Chimpanzees walk on all four limbs while humans are bipedal, meaning that they walk upright on two limbs.

PRE-LAB QUESTIONS

1. I will be using images of skulls and hands.
2. Line AC measures the distance from the bottom of the eye socket to the top of the skull. Line BC measures the distance from the top of the eye socket to the top of the skull.
3. Sample answer: In a shoe size, the width of the shoe is being compared to the length of the shoe.

26 Study Guide

Big idea Evolution

Invertebrates and chordates share common structures that emphasize that all animals descended, with modifications, from common ancestors.

26.1 Invertebrate Evolution and Diversity

Fossil evidence indicates that the first animals began evolving long before the Cambrian Explosion.

The cladogram of invertebrates presents current hypotheses about evolutionary relationships among major groups of modern invertebrates. It also indicates the sequence in which some important features evolved.

appendage (753) trochophore (756)
larva (756)

26.2 Chordate Evolution and Diversity

Embryological studies suggest that the most ancient chordates were related to the ancestors of echinoderms.

The cladogram of chordates presents current hypotheses about relationships among chordate groups. It also shows at which points important vertebrate features, such as jaws and limbs, evolved.

cartilage (757) tetrapod (760)

26.3 Primate Evolution

A primate is a mammal that has relatively long fingers and toes with nails instead of claws, arms that can rotate around shoulder joints, a strong clavicle, binocular vision, and a well-developed cerebrum.

Primates in one group look very little like typical monkeys and include lemurs and lorises. The other group includes tarsiers and the anthropoids, the group that includes monkeys and humans.

The skull, neck, spinal column, hip bones, and leg bones of early hominine species changed shape in ways that enabled later species to walk upright.

Many species in our genus existed before our species, *Homo sapiens*, appeared. Furthermore, at least three other *Homo* species existed at the same time as early humans.

binocular vision (765) hominine (767)
anthropoid (766) bipedal (767)
prehensile tail (767) opposable thumb (767)
hominoid (767)

Think Visually Using information from this chapter, complete the following concept map.

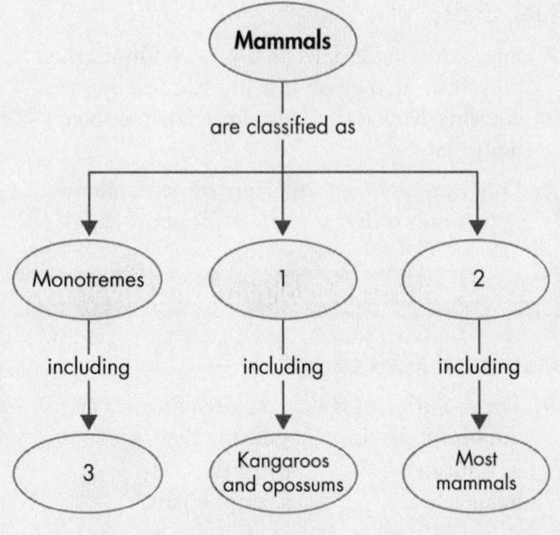

Study Online

REVIEW AND ASSESSMENT RESOURCES

Editable Worksheets Pages of Study Workbooks A and B, Lab Manuals A and B, and the Assessment Resources Book are available online. These documents can be easily edited using a word-processing program.

Lesson Overview Have students reread the Lesson Overviews to help them study chapter concepts.

Vocabulary Review The *Flash Cards* and *Crossword* provide an interactive way to review chapter vocabulary.

Chapter Assessment Have students take an online version of the Chapter 26 Assessment.

Standardized Test Prep Students can take an online version of the Standardized Test Prep. You will receive their scores along with ideas for remediation.

Diagnostic and Benchmark Tests Use these tests to monitor your students' progress and supply remediation.

Answers

THINK VISUALLY

1. Marsupials

2. Placental mammals

3. Duckbill platypus

UbD Performance Tasks

SUMMATIVE TASK Have students work in small groups to produce an illustrated pamphlet that explains the basics of the evolution of invertebrates, chordates, and primates to someone with no biology background. Tell students that a reader should be able to answer such questions as these after reading the pamphlet:

- What are the main groups of invertebrates, and what are their proposed evolutionary relationships?
- What are the main groups of chordates, and what are their proposed evolutionary relationships?
- What are characteristics that all primates share, and what are their proposed evolutionary relationships?
- When did humans appear, and how might they have spread around the world?

TRANSFER TASK Have students choose a living animal they are familiar with. Then, ask students to write a report about the animal that includes such information as the group in which this animal is classified, the major adaptations it possesses, other groups it is closely related to, and how it has evolved from ancestors.

Lesson 26.1

UNDERSTAND KEY CONCEPTS

1. b **2.** c **3.** c **4.** a

5. specialized cells, tissues, and organs; body symmetry; segmentation; a front and a back end; appendages; shells, skeletons, and other hard parts

6. Both have true coeloms surrounded by mesoderm, and trochophore larvae.

THINK CRITICALLY

7. Sample answer: Cnidarians are very simple organisms. They do not have body structures that allow them to swim toward their prey.

8. Unlike arthropods, echinoderms have spiny skin, radial symmetry, an internal skeleton, and a water-vascular system that includes a network of water-filled tubes and suction-cuplike structures called tube feet. Echinoderms are deuterostomes. In contrast, arthropods are bilaterally symmetrical, exhibit cephalization, possess many appendages, and have an exoskeleton. Anthropods are protostomes.

Lesson 26.2

UNDERSTAND KEY CONCEPTS

9. c **10.** c **11.** c **12.** a

13. b **14.** b

15. class Chondrichthyes, or the cartilaginous fishes; and class Osteichthyes, or the bony fishes

16. Birds regulate their internal body temperature.

17. All young mammals receive nourishment from milk produced by their mothers' bodies.

THINK CRITICALLY

18. Either as adults or as larvae, nonvertebrate chordates have the key chordate characteristics, such as a notochord, a nerve cord, pharyngeal pouches, and a tail that extends beyond the anus.

26 Assessment

The numbers following the questions refer to Indiana's Academic Standards for Biology I.

26.1 Invertebrate Evolution and Diversity

Understand Key Concepts

1. The ancestors of many modern animal phyla first appeared during the B.8.1
- **a.** Burgess Period.
- **b.** Cambrian Period.
- **c.** Precambrian Era.
- **d.** Ediacaran Period.

2. Animals in the phylum Porifera include
- **a.** chordates.
- **b.** sea stars.
- **c.** sponges.
- **d.** sea anemones.

3. Most adult echinoderms show
- **a.** bilateral symmetry.
- **b.** top and bottom symmetry.
- **c.** radial symmetry.
- **d.** no symmetry.

4. Of the following groups, which has the largest number of species by far?
- **a.** arthropods
- **b.** annelids
- **c.** mollusks
- **d.** echinoderms

5. What body plan features did Cambrian animals evolve over 10 to 15 million years? B.8.1

6. What evidence exists to indicate that annelids and mollusks are closely related? B.8.1

Think Critically

7. **Infer** Most cnidarians do not swim toward their prey. Instead, they capture prey carried by water currents. How is this behavior related to their body plan?

8. **Compare and Contrast** How are echinoderms structurally different from arthropods? B.8.1

26.2 Chordate Evolution and Diversity

Understand Key Concepts

9. The evolution of jaws and paired fins was an important development during the rise of
- **a.** tunicates.
- **b.** lancelets.
- **c.** fishes.
- **d.** amphibians.

10. Examine the diagrams below. Which of these is a jawed cartilaginous fish?

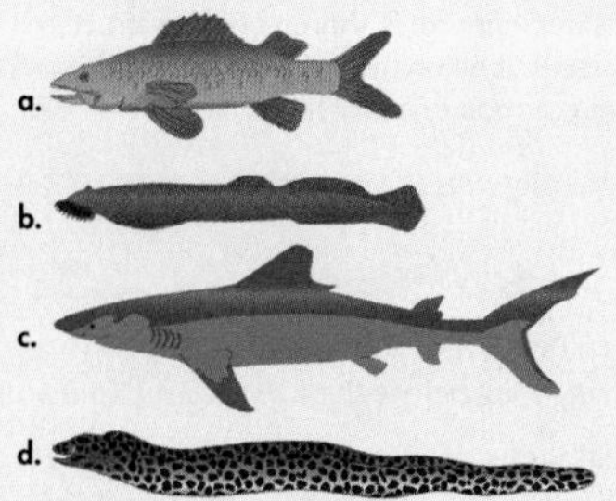

11. Which adaptation is NOT characteristic of reptiles? B.8.1
- **a.** scaly skin
- **b.** shelled egg
- **c.** gills
- **d.** lungs

12. Dinosaurs became extinct at the end of the
- **a.** Cretaceous Period.
- **b.** Triassic Period.
- **c.** Carboniferous Period.
- **d.** Permian Period.

13. The single most important characteristic that separates birds from other living animals is the presence of B.8.1
- **a.** hollow bones.
- **b.** feathers.
- **c.** two legs.
- **d.** wings.

14. Which of the following is a placental mammal?
- **a.** duckbill platypus
- **b.** whale
- **c.** kangaroo
- **d.** koala

15. Which two major groups of fishes evolved from the early jawed fishes and still survive today? B.8.2

16. What adaptation enables birds to live in environments that are colder than those in which most reptiles live?

17. Describe how the young of monotremes, marsupials, and placental mammals obtain nourishment.

Think Critically

18. **Apply Concepts** Which anatomical characteristics of nonvertebrate chordates suggest that, in terms of evolutionary relationships, these animals are more closely related to vertebrates than to other groups of animals? B.8.2

26.3 Primate Evolution

Understand Key Concepts

19. Anthropoids include monkeys and
a. lemurs. c. tarsiers.
b. lorises. d. humans.

20. Which of the following is a characteristic specific to primates? B.8.2
a. body hair
b. rotation at the shoulder joint
c. notochord
d. ability to control body temperature

21. How many hominine species exist today?
a. one c. nine
b. two d. twelve

22. The first hominines appear in the fossil record about B.8.1
a. 30,000 years ago.
b. 100,000 years ago.
c. 6 to 7 million years ago.
d. 120 million years ago.

23. What anatomical characteristic allows for the binocular vision that occurs in primates?

24. Describe the adaptations that make some primates successful tree dwellers.

25. List the unique characteristics of hominines. Give an example of a hominine. B.8.2

Think Critically

26. **Interpret Photos** List three primate characteristics shown by the monkey in the photo. B.8.2

solve the CHAPTER MYSTERY

FOSSIL QUEST

Josh was working against great odds. "His" fossils would be about 600 million years old. He learned that there are few places where rocks that old haven't been destroyed by geological activity. Most known sites are in China and Australia—none are in the United States. Pedro found better news. Reptiles related to bird ancestors lived around the same time as his favorite dinosaurs, during the Cretaceous Period. There are a number of places where fossils of that age have been found—including the Green River area in Utah. Because both boys like dinosaurs, they joined an Earthwatch teen expedition to the Green River to search for bird ancestors!

1. **Infer** Why is it so much harder to find fossils from the Proterozoic Eon, when the earliest known animals lived, than it is to find fossils from the Cretaceous Period, when the ancestors of birds lived? (*Hint:* See the graph below.)

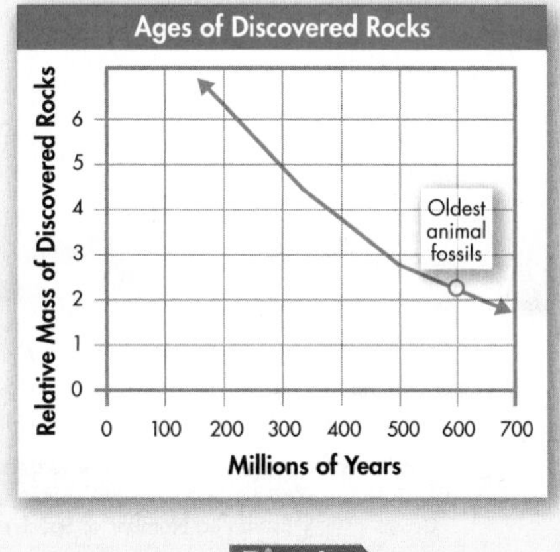

2. **Connect to the Big idea** Starting at the Earthwatch Web site, do an Internet search for fossil hunting expeditions you could join.

CHAPTER MYSTERY After students have read through the Chapter Mystery, discuss the topic of fossil hunting and how fossils provide evidence for the evolution of organisms over time.

Ask Why are there so few of the fossils Josh is interested in finding? *(Sample answer: The earliest animals were soft-bodied organisms, and fossils usually form from an organism's hard parts.)*

Ask Why can't fossils be found everywhere in all kinds of rock? *(Sample answer: Fossils can form in only some kinds of materials. Fossils are mostly found in sedimentary rocks.)*

Ask How do fossils provide evidence for the evolution of organisms? *(Sample answer: Fossils provide researchers with evidence of the structure of ancient organisms. By comparing different fossils, scientists can determine how species have changed over time.)*

CHAPTER MYSTERY ANSWERS

1. Sample answer: There are more than three times the mass of discovered rocks from the Cretaceous Period than there are from the Proterozoic Eon.
2. Big idea Answers will vary. Students should be able to find the Earthwatch Web site by searching for Earthwatch with an online search engine. Once students reach the Earthwatch home page, they should be able to find various fossil hunting expeditions around the world. Ask students to describe two expeditions they might be interested in joining.

To help students understand why insects are such a diverse group, suggest they watch **Untamed Science: Insects Rule!**

ASSESSMENT

Lesson 26.3

UNDERSTAND KEY CONCEPTS

19. d **20.** b **21.** a **22.** c

23. Both eyes face forward, with overlapping fields of vision.

24. Primates have flexible fingers and toes that can curl and grip objects. Their arms can rotate around strong shoulder joints, which are attached to strong clavicles. Primates have binocular vision, which provides good depth perception.

25. Hominines have the ability to walk upright, opposable thumbs, and large brains. Sample hominine: *Homo sapiens*

THINK CRITICALLY

26. forward-facing eyes, long fingers, arms that can rotate

ASSESSMENT

Connecting Concepts

USE SCIENCE GRAPHICS

27. It is similar to a cladogram because it shows the ancestry and relationship between the groups. This type of diagram also shows the relative number of species contained in each group.

28. Bony fishes

29. Separating out birds makes it clear that birds experienced adaptive radiation while the rest of the archosaurs largely died out.

30. The number of bony fish species increased gradually during the Mesozoic, then grew explosively beginning in the Paleogene. The number of archosaur species increased during the Cretaceous then declined suddenly, quite drastically. Birds evolved at the end of the Jurassic and their number increased greatly during the Paleogene. The mammal species increased steadily over time. Archosaurs were affected by the mass extinction at the end of the Mesozoic, while birds experienced major adaptive radiations.

WRITE ABOUT SCIENCE

31. Paragraphs should include a topic sentence and the following characteristics of the first animals: they were small and had soft bodies; many had body plans that were different than anything living today; many were flat and lived on the bottom of shallow seas; they showed little evidence of cell, tissue, or organ specialization; some may have had photosynthetic algae living within their bodies; some had bilateral symmetry.

32. Students should explain that at the end of the Cretaceous Period, about 66 million years ago, a worldwide extinction occurred that scientists think was caused by a series of natural disasters: a string of volcanic eruptions, a fall in sea level, and a huge asteroid smashing into what is now the Yucatán Peninsula in Mexico.

33. By estimating the fossil's age, paleontologists can infer when it was alive relative to other hominine species. Structural characteristics help them infer possible evolutionary relationships.

34. Big idea Sample answer: Major adaptations included the ability to breathe air; strong limbs on which to move around; dry, scaly skin to protect the body from drying out; and the ability to reproduce in a way that does not require water.

Connecting Concepts

Use Science Graphics NoS.3

The chart below shows the relative numbers of species in four groups of vertebrates over time. The thickness of each band shows the relative number of species in that group. Use the chart to answer questions 27–30.

Era	Period	Number of Species
Cenozoic	Recent	
	Paleogene	
Mesozoic	Cretaceous	
	Jurassic	
	Triassic	
Paleozoic	Permian	
	Carbonif-erous	
	Devonian	
	Silurian	
	Ordovician	

27. Compare and Contrast How is this kind of diagram similar to a traditional cladogram? What additional information can be learned from it?

28. Interpret Visuals Which of the groups shown has the greatest number of species today?

29. Infer Archosaurs are a group of reptiles that includes the dinosaurs, pterosaurs, modern crocodiles, and birds. Why do you think that birds are shown separately from the other archosaurs in the diagram? B.8.2

30. Apply Concepts Describe the trend for each group shown from the beginning of the Mesozoic to today. Which groups were affected by the mass extinction at the end of the Mesozoic? Which groups have experienced adaptive radiations?

Write About Science NoS.3

31. Explanation Write a paragraph in which you describe, in your own words, what the first animals were like.

32. Description In a paragraph, describe in your own words when the dinosaurs went extinct and what events contributed to the extinction.

33. Explanation Why is it important to estimate the age of a hominine fossil as well as to analyze its structural characteristics? B.8.2

34. Assess the Big idea Life on Earth began in water. What were some of the major adaptations that animals evolved that allowed them to survive out of water?

IN NoS.3

Living members of the reptile clade include more than 8000 species of reptiles and about 10,000 species of birds. Review the data in the table and respond to the following.

Reptile Clade Diversity

Group	Estimated Number of Species
Lizards and snakes	8400
Turtles and tortoises	310
Crocodilians	23
Tuataras	2
Birds	10,000

35. Graph Construct a circle graph that presents the data in the table.

36. Evaluate What was your biggest challenge in representing these data in a circle graph?

37. Analyze Data Consider other methods of graphing data. Which type of graph might represent these data in a more helpful way?

38. Graph Graph these data using a method you would consider more helpful to a reader or explain why none would be.

PURPOSE Students will analyze data related to different groups within the reptile clade. Students will recognize that bird species make up over half of the number of species in the reptile clade, with lizard and snake species making up about 45 percent of the total. They will also learn that representing numbers with great difference in a graph is challenging.

PLANNING Review with students how different kinds of graphs show portions of a total.

ANSWERS

35. Circle graphs should show the following approximate percentages: birds, 53%; lizards and snakes, 45%; turtles and tortoises, 2%; tuataras and crocodilians, less than 1% each. Sections should be labeled.

36. Sample answer: The biggest challenge was representing the smallest group, tuataras, when the largest group, birds, have 5,000 times more species than the smallest.

Standardized Test Practice for Indiana

Multiple Choice

1. Which of the following is NOT a mollusk?
   A leech C clam
   B squid D snail

2. Which of the following invertebrates have segmented bodies?
   A flatworms C cnidarians
   B roundworms D annelids B.8.2

3. All animals have some form of body symmetry EXCEPT
   A sponges. C worms.
   B jellyfishes. D arthropods.

4. Which of the following groups can be classified as nonvertebrate chordates?
   A sponges
   B tunicates
   C fishes
   D all of the above B.8.2

5. Many scientists think that birds evolved from
   A mammal-like reptiles.
   B amphibians.
   C mammals.
   D dinosaurs. B.8.1

6. Which of the following is NOT a characteristic of reptiles?
   A scaly skin C lungs
   B eggs with shells D mammary glands B.8.2

7. Which of the following are hominoids?
   A all mammals C humans only
   B all primates D all great apes

8. When did the first true mammals appear?
   A Cretaceous Period
   B Triassic Period
   C Cenozoic Era
   D Carboniferous Period B.8.1

Questions 9–11 Refer to the following cladogram.

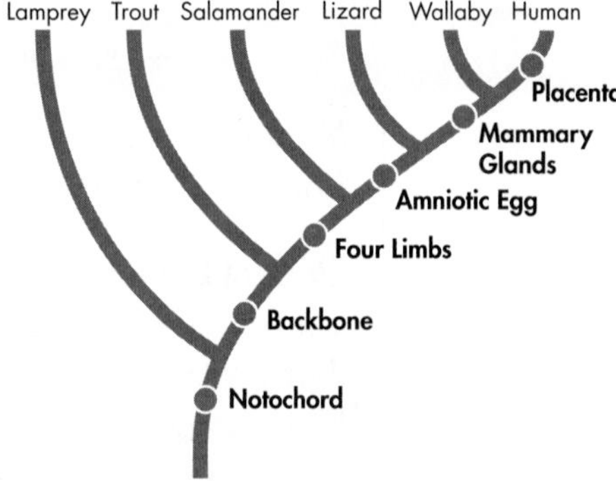

9. Which characteristic is shared by humans, wallabies, and trout?
   A placenta C four limbs
   B notochord D mammary glands B.8.2

10. Which animals have the closest evolutionary relationship, as shown by the cladogram?
    A humans and wallabies
    B humans and lizards
    C humans and lampreys
    D humans and trout B.8.2

11. A valid conclusion from this cladogram is that
    A salamanders, trout, and lampreys all have a backbone.
    B four limbs appeared in vertebrate evolution before the notochord appeared.
    C humans and lampreys share a common ancestor.
    D mammary glands appeared in vertebrate evolution after the placenta appeared. NoS.6

Open-Ended Response

12. What is the difference between a hominoid and a hominine? B.8.2

If You Have Trouble With . . .												
Question	1	2	3	4	5	6	7	8	9	10	11	12
See Lesson	26.1	26.1	26.1	26.2	26.2	26.2	26.3	26.2	26.2	26.2	26.2	26.3

ASSESSMENT

Answers

1. A
2. D
3. A
4. B
5. D
6. D
7. D
8. B
9. B
10. A
11. C
12. Hominoids include all the great apes, including gibbons, orangutans, gorillas, chimpanzees, and humans. The hominoids in the lineage that led to humans are called hominines, which include modern humans and all other species more closely related to humans than to chimpanzees. Unlike other hominoids, hominines evolved opposable thumbs, the ability to walk upright, and large brains.

37. Answers may vary. Most students will likely say a bar graph would be a better choice.
38. Check students' graphs for accuracy. (If students say no other graph besides a circle graph will work well, evaluate their reasons.)

Test-Taking Tip

INTERPRET VISUALS

Suggest students first study a diagram carefully before attempting to answer questions about it to see the basic kind of information that is contained in the diagram. In interpreting the diagram, students should look for any relationships or trends shown. After thoroughly examining the diagram and interpreting the information it contains, students should read the questions that relate to the diagram. They should recheck all answers by reexamining the diagram.

Animal Systems I

Chapter Contents	IN	Time	Core Resources
Chapter Preview			**Student Edition,** pp. 780–781 **Chapter Mystery,** p. 781
27.1 Feeding and Digestion Obtaining Food • Processing Food • Specializations for Different Diets	NoS.3, NoS.6	1 period 1/2 block	**Student Edition,** pp. 782–786 Inquiry 27.1 Analyzing Data, p. 784 L2 **Study Workbook A** 27.1 Worksheets L2 Biology.com *Visual Analogy:* Specialized Teeth **Assessment Resources Book** Visual Quiz L2
27.2 Respiration Gas Exchange • Respiratory Surfaces of Aquatic Animals • Respiratory Surfaces of Terrestrial Animals		1 period 1/2 block	**Student Edition,** pp. 787–790 Inquiry 27.2 Quick Lab, p. 788 L2 **Study Workbook A** 27.2 Worksheets L2 Biology.com *Art Review:* Respiratory Systems • *Data Analysis:* Giant Insects of the Paleozoic • 27.2 Self-Test • 27.2 Lesson Assessment
27.3 Circulation Open and Closed Circulatory Systems • Single- and Double-Loop Circulation		1/2 period 1/4 block	**Student Edition,** pp. 791–793 **Study Workbook A** 27.3 Worksheets L2 Biology.com *InterActive Art:* Vertebrate Circulatory Systems **Assessment Resources Book** Visual Quiz L2
27.4 Excretion The Ammonia Problem • Excretion in Aquatic Animals • Excretion in Terrestrial Animals • *Technology & Biology: Bioartificial Kidneys*	NoS.6	1 period 1/2 block	**Student Edition,** pp. 791–799 Inquiry 27.4 Quick Lab, p. 797 L2 **Study Workbook A** 27.4 Worksheets L2 Biology.com *Art in Motion:* Excretion in Aquatic Animals • 27.4 Self-Test • 27.4 Lesson Assessment
Chapter Pre-Lab		1 period 1/2 block	**Student Edition,** p. 800 L2 **Lab Manual A** *Anatomy of Squid* L2 • *The Effect of Chemicals on the Heart Rate* L2

Differentiated Instruction Tools

Study Workbook B includes worksheets with lesson-level differentiated instruction support and explanations of differentiated instruction teaching strategies.

Lab Manual B includes skills labs, simplified chapter labs, and hands-on activities.

ELL Handbook explains ways to make *Biology* more accessible to ELL students.

Spanish Study Workbook is a Spanish translation of Study Workbook A.

Multilingual Glossary is the glossary translated into ten languages.

Differentiated Instruction Key

- L1 Special Needs or Struggling Students
- ELL English Language Learners
- LPR Less Proficient Readers
- L2 On-Level Students
- L3 Advanced Students

Additional Resources

Biology.com Untamed Science Video • Vocabulary Flash Cards

Study Workbook B 27.1 Worksheets L1 ELL LPR
Spanish Study Workbook 27.1 Worksheets ELL
Biology.com 27.1 Lesson Overview • 27.1 Lesson Notes • 27.1 Self-Test • 27.1 Lesson Assessment

Study Workbook B 27.2 Worksheets L1 ELL LPR
Spanish Study Workbook 27.2 Worksheets ELL
Biology.com 27.2 Lesson Overview • 27.2 Lesson Notes

Study Workbook B 27.3 Worksheets L1 ELL LPR
Spanish Study Workbook 27.3 Worksheets ELL
Biology.com 27.3 Lesson Overview • 27.3 Lesson Notes • 27.3 Self-Test • 27.3 Lesson Assessment

Study Workbook B 27.4 Worksheets L1 ELL LPR
Spanish Study Workbook 27.4 Worksheets ELL
Biology.com 27.4 Lesson Overview • 27.4 Lesson Notes

Lab Manual B *Anatomy of a Squid* • Data Analysis: *Protein Digestion* • Hands-On Activity: *How a Bird "Chews"* L1 ELL LPR

Chapter Review

Student Edition Study Guide, p. 801 L2
Study Workbook A Chapter 27 Vocabulary Review L2 • Chapter 27 Chapter Mystery/21st Century Skills Activity L2 L3
Transparencies, pp. 306–315 L1 ELL LPR L2
Biology.com Untamed Science Video • Editable Worksheets of Study Workbooks A and B and Lab Manuals A and B • Chapter 27 Flash Cards and Match It

Untamed Science DVD • Classroom Resources CD (includes lesson presentations and editable worksheets)

Chapter Assessment

Student Edition Assessment, pp. 802–805 L2
Study Workbook B Chapter 27 Chapter Review L1 ELL LPR • Chapter 27 Taking a Standardized Test L1 ELL LPR
Assessment Resources Book Chapter 27 Test A L2 • Chapter 27 Test B L1 ELL LPR
Biology.com Chapter 27 Assessment • Editable Worksheets of Chapter 27 Visual Quizzes and Chapter 27 Tests A and B

Exam*View Assessment Suite* • Classroom Resources CD (includes lesson presentations and editable worksheets)

Time: 1 period, 1/2 block

Pressed for Time?

Preview the Chapter Have students read the first Key Question for each lesson and preview Figures 27–2, 27–8, 27–9, and 27–16.

Cover the Chapter Quickly In Lesson 27.1, have students read *Processing Food* and discuss Figure 27–2. Assign *Gas Exchange* in Lesson 27.2 and *Open and Closed Circulatory Systems* in Lesson 27.3. Have students read *The Ammonia Problem* in Lesson 27.4 and discuss Figure 27–16.

Assess Assign question 2 in the 27.1 Assessment, question 1 in the 27.2 Assessment, question 1 in the 27.3 Assessment, and question 1 in the 27.4 Assessment. In the Chapter 27 Assessment, assign questions 1, 4, 7, 10, 15, 16–18, 25–27, 31, 32, and 34.

Connect to the Big Idea

Big idea Have students look at the photograph and read the caption about the red-billed oxpecker. Call on a volunteer to tell what a carnivore is and why this bird can be classified as one. Then, ask if students would classify all birds as carnivores. *(Sample answer: No, because I've seen birds eating seeds at birdfeeders.)* Ask if there's anything they can see in the bird's physical characteristics that could be considered an adaptation that helps the bird eat food. *(Sample answer: The large bill is adapted to picking ticks and insects off the zebra's skin.)* Then, have students anticipate an answer to the question, **How do the structures of animals allow them to obtain essential materials and eliminate wastes?**

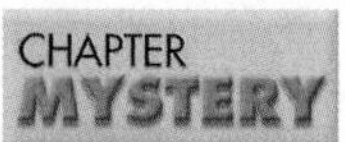

Have students read over the Chapter Mystery and consider why one survivalist became ill. Then, have students predict whether drinking the coconut "milk" will prevent the other group members from becoming ill.

BIOLOGY.com Have students preview the chapter vocabulary terms using the **Flash Cards.**

27 Animal Systems I

Big idea Structure and Function

Q: How do the structures of animals allow them to obtain essential materials and eliminate wastes?

BIOLOGY.com Search Chapter 27 GO • Flash Cards

780

IN INDIANA ACADEMIC STANDARDS

For the full text of all standards, see the Course Overview in the front matter of this book.

Key standards: Chapter 27 covers key ideas from The Nature of Science, including **NoS.3** Communicate ideas and **NoS.6** Use analogies and models.

UbD Understanding by Design

Students have been building toward the Unit 7 Enduring Understanding of how *animals have evolved diverse ways to carry out basic life processes and maintain homeostasis.* In Chapter 27, students investigate feeding and digestion, respiration, circulation, and excretion in animals. The graphic organizer at the right shows how chapter content informs this Enduring Understanding.

PERFORMANCE GOALS

In Chapter 27, students will learn about body systems that carry out essential functions, including feeding and digestion, respiration, circulation, and excretion. Students will gain understanding by interpreting and using information in the many labeled figures found in the chapter. At the end of the chapter, students will transfer their knowledge by describing a fictitious animal that has all the types of systems they learned about in the chapter.

INDIANA ACADEMIC STANDARDS FOR SCIENCE

Nature of Science NoS.3, NoS.6, NoS.10. See lessons for details.

Red-billed oxpeckers are carnivores that have a mutualistic relationship with zebras. These birds eat ticks and insects that feed on the zebras, freeing them of these parasites.

• Untamed Science Video • Chapter Mystery

CHAPTER MYSTERY

(NEAR) DEATH BY SALT WATER

It started as an adventure. Some college buddies tried their own version of a "survivor" experience. During summer vacation, they were dropped off on an uninhabited tropical island, with minimal supplies. They would be picked up in a few days.

The island was hot and dry, and they discovered that there was no fresh water. They knew that coconuts could provide fluids in the form of coconut "milk." But one group member hated coconuts. He figured he'd get his fluids by drinking salt water. At first, he was fine—although he was thirstier than his friends. Then, he became nauseated and weak. His condition worsened quickly. Soon he was seriously ill—with dizziness, headaches, and an inability to concentrate. His friends began to panic. What was happening? As you read the chapter, look for clues to help you explain the reason for the survivalist's illness. Then, solve the mystery.

Never Stop Exploring Your World. Finding out what happened to the survivalist is only the beginning. Take a video field trip with the ecogeeks of Untamed Science to see where the mystery leads.

Animal Systems I **781**

Chapter 27 Big Idea: Structure and Function

Chapter 27 EQ: How do the structures of animals allow them to obtain essential materials and eliminate wastes?

27.1 GQ: How do different animals obtain and digest food?

27.2 GQ: How do animals in different environments breathe?

27.3 GQ: How have animals evolved complex, efficient ways to move materials through their bodies?

27.4 GQ: How do animals in different environments excrete metabolic wastes?

What's Online

Extend your reach by using these and other digital assets offered at Biology.com.

CHAPTER MYSTERY
Students will discover why a "survivor" on a tropical island who drinks seawater almost *didn't* survive.

UNTAMED SCIENCE VIDEO
Follow the ecogeeks of Untamed Science as they explore the amazing adaptations of bears in **Bearly Asleep.**

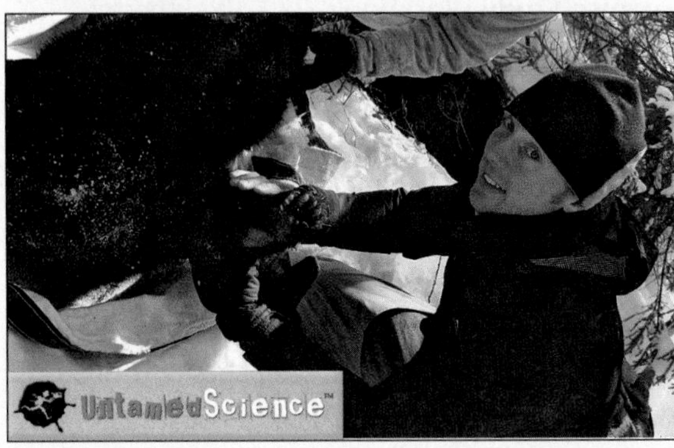

VISUAL ANALOGY
This short animation compares the structure and function of teeth.

ART REVIEW
This drag-and-drop activity helps students distinguish the different types of respiratory systems.

DATA ANALYSIS
Students explore why insects were larger in the Paleozoic than they are today.

INTERACTIVE ART
Students can watch this animation to help them compare single- and double-loop circulatory systems in vertebrates.

ART IN MOTION
The challenges of maintaining water balance in freshwater and saltwater animals are the focus of this animation.

LESSON 27.1

Getting Started

Objectives

27.1.1 Describe the different ways animals get food.

27.1.2 Explain how digestion occurs in different animals.

27.1.3 Describe how mouthparts are adapted for an animal's diet.

Student Resources

Study Workbooks A and B, 27.1 Worksheets

Spanish Study Workbook, 27.1 Worksheets

Lab Manual B, 20.1 Data Analysis Worksheet, 20.1 Hands-On Activity Worksheet

Lesson Overview • Lesson Notes • Activity: Visual Analogy, Assessment: Self-Test, Lesson Assessment

For corresponding lesson in the **Foundation Edition**, see pages 646–649.

Activate Prior Knowledge

Show students pictures of a wolf, a cow, and a fiddler crab, or write the names of these animals on the board. Ask students to try to classify each animal according to how it obtains food. Have students describe the differences in feeding among these animals using terms they learned in Chapter 3. *(wolf, carnivore; cow, herbivore; crab, detritivore)*

IN INDIANA ACADEMIC STANDARDS

For the full text of all standards, see the Course Overview in the front matter of this book.

NoS.3 Clearly communicate their ideas and results of investigations verbally and in written form using tables, graphs, diagrams, and photographs.

27.1 Feeding and Digestion

IN NoS.3 Communicate ideas. Also covered: NoS.6.

Key Questions

How do animals obtain food?

How does digestion occur in animals?

How are mouthparts adapted for different diets?

Vocabulary

intracellular digestion
extracellular digestion
gastrovascular cavity
digestive tract
rumen

Taking Notes

Outline Before you read, use the headings in this lesson to outline the ways animals obtain and digest food. As you read, add details to your outline.

THINK ABOUT IT From tiny insects that dine on our blood, to bison that feed on prairie grasses, to giant blue whales that feed on plankton, all animals are heterotrophs that obtain nutrients and energy from food. In fact, adaptations for different styles of feeding are a large part of what makes animals so interesting.

Obtaining Food

How do animals obtain food?

As the old saying goes, you are what you eat. For animals, we can rephrase that as "how you look and act depends on what and how you eat." The converse is also true: What and how you eat depends on how you look and act. To learn why that's true, we'll compare the various ways animals, such as those in **Figure 27–1,** obtain their food.

Filter Feeders Filter feeders strain their food from water. **Most filter feeders catch algae and small animals by using modified gills or other structures as nets that filter food items out of water.** Many invertebrate filter feeders are small or colonial organisms, like worms and sponges, that spend their adult lives in a single spot. Many vertebrate filter feeders such as whale sharks and blue whales, on the other hand, are huge, and feed while swimming.

Detritivores Detritus is made up of decaying bits of plant and animal material. **Detritivores feed on detritus, often obtaining extra nutrients from the bacteria, algae, and other microorganisms that grow on and around it.** From earthworms on land to a wide range of worms and crustaceans in aquatic habitats, detritivores are essential components of many ecosystems.

Carnivores **Carnivores eat other animals.** Mammalian carnivores, such as wolves, use teeth, claws, and speed or stealthy hunting tactics to bring down prey. You probably don't often think about carnivorous invertebrates, but many would be terrifying if they were larger. Some cnidarians paralyze prey with poison-tipped darts, while some spiders immobilize their victims with venomous fangs.

UbD Teach for Understanding

ENDURING UNDERSTANDING Animals have evolved diverse ways to carry out basic life processes and maintain homeostasis.

GUIDING QUESTION How do different animals obtain and digest food?

EVIDENCE OF UNDERSTANDING *After completing the lesson, assign the following assessment to show students understand the differences in how animals obtain food and digest food.* Ask each student to choose two different animals and sketch or attach a clipping of it to a piece of paper. Then, for each animal, students should make a list that identifies how the animal obtains food, how it processes food, and whether it has any specialized mouthparts for its diet. Call on volunteers to share their work with the class.

Herbivores 🔑 **Herbivores eat plants or parts of plants in terrestrial and aquatic habitats.** Some herbivores, such as locusts and cattle, eat leaves, which is not an easy way to make a living! Leaves don't have much nutritional content, are difficult to digest, and can contain poisons or hard particles that wear down teeth. Other herbivores, including birds and many mammals, specialize in eating seeds or fruits, which, in contrast to leaves, are often filled with energy-rich compounds.

Nutritional Symbionts Recall that a symbiosis is the dependency of one species on another. Symbionts are the organisms involved in a symbiosis. 🔑 **Many animals rely upon symbiosis for their nutritional needs.**

▶ ***Parasitic Symbionts*** Parasites live within or on a host organism, where they feed on tissues or on blood and other body fluids. Some parasites are just nuisances, but many cause serious diseases in humans, livestock, and crop plants. Parasitic flatworms and roundworms afflict millions of people, particularly in the tropics.

▶ ***Mutualistic Symbionts*** In mutualistic relationships, both participants benefit. Reef-building corals depend on symbiotic algae that live within their tissues for most of their energy. Those algae capture solar energy, recycle nutrients, and help corals lay down their calcium carbonate skeletons. The algae, in turn, gain nutrition from the corals' wastes and protection from algae eaters. Also, animals that eat wood or plant leaves rely on microbial symbionts in their guts to digest cellulose.

BUILD Vocabulary

WORD ORIGINS The word part *-vore* comes from the Latin verb *vorare,* which means "to devour."

FIGURE 27–1 Obtaining Food The orca, sea slug, barnacles, and cleaner shrimp obtain their food in different ways.

Quick Facts

WHALES AS FILTER FEEDERS

Biologists classify whales into two major groups, toothed whales and baleen whales. Baleen whales are filter feeders, and they get their name from the hundreds of thin plates, or baleen, that hang from their upper jaw. These plates, also called whalebone, are made of the same material as fingernails. Baleen whales include blue whales, which are the largest animals that have ever lived on Earth. They can grow to more than 30 meters long and can weigh close to 200 metric tons. Blue whales eat mostly krill, which are tiny, shrimplike animals that make up part of the ocean's plankton. To feed, a blue whale gulps in a huge amount of water and krill. Then, it closes its mouth and forces the water back out through the filter of hundreds of baleen. The baleen trap the krill inside the whale's mouth.

Teach

Build Study Skills

Explain that a good way to organize information such as the classification of animals by feeding style is to make a **Compare/Contrast Table.** Have pairs of students work together to make a table entitled Different Styles of Feeding. They can use these column heads: Feeding Style, Description, and Examples. Tell students they should record examples from the text, as well as examples mentioned in class discussion.

Study Wkbks A/B, Appendix S20, Compare/Contrast Table. **Transparencies,** GO3.

DIFFERENTIATED INSTRUCTION

ELL English Language Learners Pair English language learners with native speakers to work together on the table described above. In addition, have pairs work on the pronunciation of terms such as *herbivore, parasitic symbionts,* and *mutualistic symbionts.* Ask English language learners to add an extra column to their table for pronunciation guides and drawings to help them remember these terms.

L3 Advanced Students Ask students to use online sources to make lists and print images of animals that can be classified as filter feeders, detritivores, carnivores, herbivores, and nutritional symbionts. Then, have students make a poster about how these animals obtain food. Display the posters in the classroom.

Teach continued

Lead a Discussion

Use **Figure 27–2** and the section, **Processing Food,** to differentiate between intracellular and extracellular digestion and between a gastrovascular cavity and a digestive tract. Point out that the visual includes three parts: diagrams of a sponge, cnidarian, and bird. Have pairs of students make a **Concept Map** that categorizes the organisms and structures in the figure. Students should use these terms in the map: *intracellular digestion, extracellular digestion, sponge, cnidarian, bird, gastrovascular cavity, digestive tract.* Then, discuss the figure as a class.

Ask In a cnidarian, how is food digested? *(Some cells secrete enzymes and absorb digested food. Other cells surround food particles and digest them in vacuoles.)*

Ask In a bird's digestive tract, what are the two openings called? *(mouth and anus)*

Study Wkbks A/B, Appendix S21, Concept Map. **Transparencies,** GO4.

DIFFERENTIATED INSTRUCTION

L1 Special Needs Use a simple model to help students understand the difference between a gastrovascular cavity and a digestive tract. First, have students feel a large sock, and explain that this is like a gastrovascular cavity with only one opening. Then, cut the toe off the sock and turn it halfway inside out. Have students again feel the sock. Explain that the sock's inner layer represents the digestive tract and the sock's outer layer represents the animal's outside body wall. Point out that the inside tube has two openings.

ELL English Language Learners Before students read, introduce them to the terms: *intracellular digestion, extracellular digestion,* and *gastrovascular cavity.* Explain that *intra-* means "within," *extra-* means "outside," and *gastro-* means "belly or stomach." Help students arrive at the meaning of each term by saying and discussing its prefix and then putting the whole term together. Encourage students to write definitions in their own words to help them remember the meanings.

IN NoS.3

Protein Digestion

A scientist performed an experiment to determine the amount of time needed for a certain carnivorous animal to digest animal protein. He placed pieces of hard-boiled egg white (an animal protein) in a test tube containing hydrochloric acid, water, and the enzyme pepsin, which digests protein. The graph shows the rate at which the egg white was "digested" over a 24-hour period.

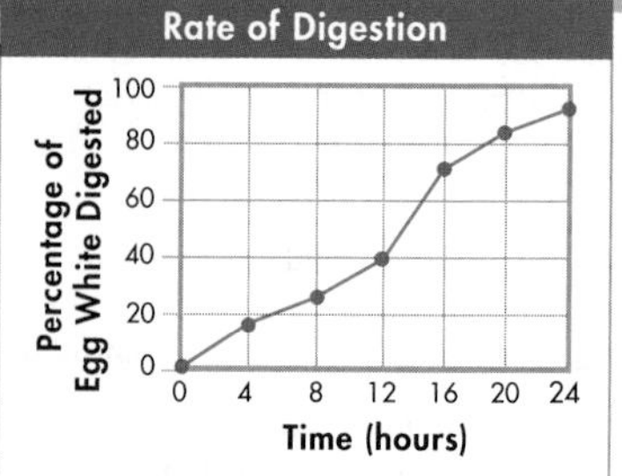

1. Interpret Graphs Describe the trend in the amount of protein digested over time.

2. Analyze Data About how many hours did it take for half of the protein to be digested?

3. Draw Conclusions How would you expect the rate of meat digestion to differ in an animal whose digestive tract had less of the enzyme pepsin?

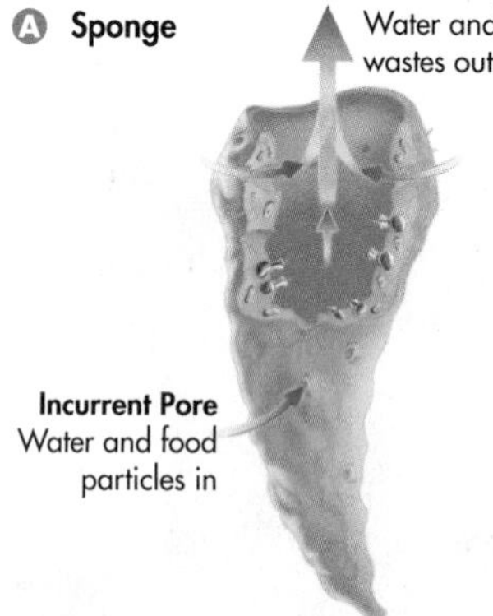

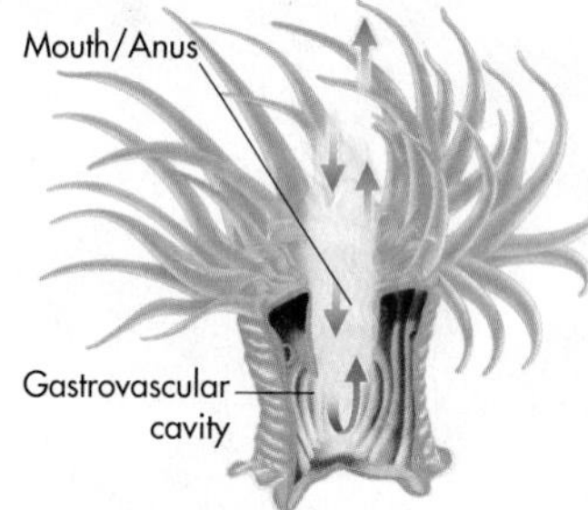

Processing Food

How does digestion occur in animals?

Obtaining food is just the first step. Food must then be broken down, or digested, and absorbed to make energy and nutrients available to body tissues. **Some invertebrates break down food primarily by intracellular digestion, but many animals use extracellular digestion to break down food.** A variety of digestive systems are shown in **Figure 27–2.**

Intracellular Digestion Animals have evolved many ways of digesting and absorbing food. The simplest animals, such as sponges, digest food inside specialized cells that pass nutrients to other cells by diffusion. This digestive process is known as **intracellular digestion.**

Extracellular Digestion Most more-complex animals rely on extracellular digestion. **Extracellular digestion** is the process in which food is broken down outside cells in a digestive system and then absorbed.

▶ ***Gastrovascular Cavities*** Some animals have an interior body space whose tissues carry out digestive and circulatory functions. Some invertebrates, such as cnidarians, have a **gastrovascular cavity** with a single opening through which they both ingest food and expel wastes. Some cells lining the cavity secrete enzymes and absorb digested food. Other cells surround food particles and digest them in vacuoles. Nutrients are then transported to cells throughout the body.

▶ ***Digestive Tracts*** Many invertebrates and all vertebrates, such as birds, digest food in a tube called a **digestive tract,** which has two openings. Food moves in one direction, entering the body through the mouth. Wastes leave through the anus.

Analyzing Data

PURPOSE Students will interpret a graph about protein digestion and draw a conclusion that the enzyme pepsin aids in the digestion of protein.

PLANNING Have students review the type of food carnivores eat. Remind them to read the introductory paragraph carefully to help them find the information they need to draw a conclusion from the graph.

ANSWERS

1. Sample answer: Protein was digested at a rate of a little over 3 percent per hour for the first 12 hours. In the next 4 hours, the rate increased, and then dropped back down during the remaining 8 hours.
2. about 14 hours
3. Sample answer: Because pepsin digests protein and meat contains relatively high amounts of protein, the rate of meat digestion would be slower in an animal whose digestive tract had less of the enzyme pepsin.

One-way digestive tracts often have specialized structures, such as a stomach and intestines, that perform different tasks as food passes through them. You can think of a digestive tract as a kind of "disassembly line" that breaks down food one step at a time. In some animals, the mouth secretes digestive enzymes that start the chemical digestion of food. Then, mechanical digestion may occur as specialized mouthparts or a muscular organ called a gizzard breaks food into small pieces. Then, chemical digestion begins or continues in a stomach that secretes digestive enzymes. Chemical breakdown continues in the intestines, sometimes aided by secretions from other organs such as a liver or pancreas. Intestines also absorb the nutrients released by digestion.

▶ ***Solid Waste Disposal*** No matter how efficiently an animal breaks down food and extracts nutrients, some indigestible material will always be left. These solid wastes, or feces, are expelled either through the single digestive opening or through the anus.

C Bird

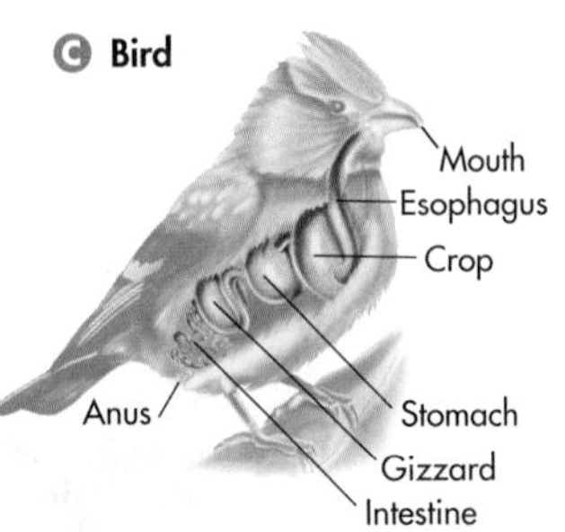

FIGURE 27–2 Digesting Food Animals have different digestive structures with different functions. **A** The sponge (previous page) has one digestive opening and uses intracellular digestion to process its food. **B** The cnidarian (previous page) processes its food by extracellular digestion in a gastrovascular cavity. **C** The bird has a one-way digestive tract with two openings.

Specializations for Different Diets

How are mouthparts adapted for different diets?

The mouthparts and digestive systems of animals have evolved many adaptations to the physical and chemical characteristics of different foods, as shown in **Figure 27–3.** As a window into these specializations, we'll examine adaptations to two food types that are very different physically and chemically: meat and plant leaves.

Specialized Mouthparts Carnivores and leaf-eating herbivores usually have very different mouthparts. These differences are typically related to the different physical characteristics of meat and plant leaves.

VISUAL ANALOGY

SPECIALIZED TEETH

FIGURE 27–3 Mouthparts The specialized jaws and teeth of animals are well adapted to their diets.

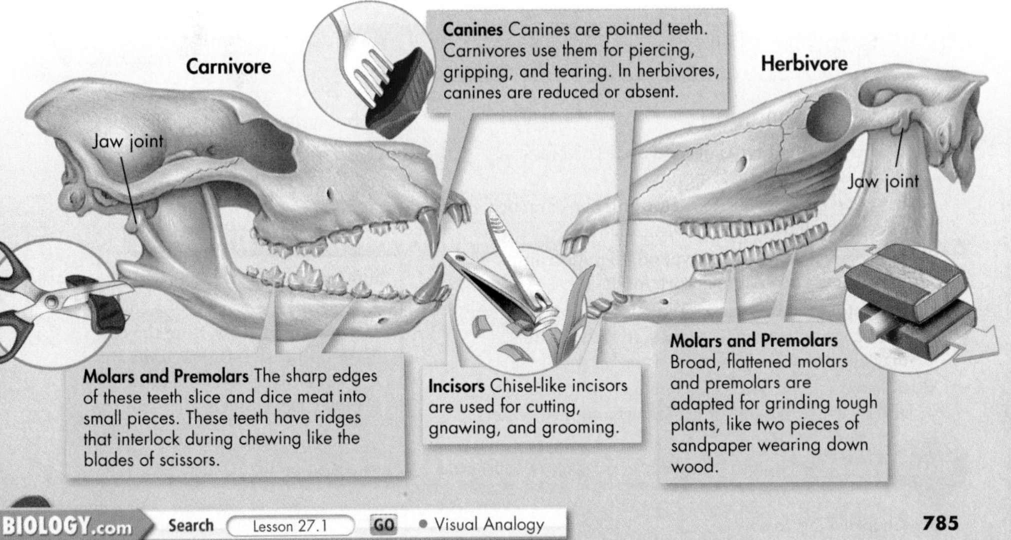

Carnivore
Herbivore
Jaw joint
Jaw joint
Canines Canines are pointed teeth. Carnivores use them for piercing, gripping, and tearing. In herbivores, canines are reduced or absent.
Molars and Premolars The sharp edges of these teeth slice and dice meat into small pieces. These teeth have ridges that interlock during chewing like the blades of scissors.
Incisors Chisel-like incisors are used for cutting, gnawing, and grooming.
Molars and Premolars Broad, flattened molars and premolars are adapted for grinding tough plants, like two pieces of sandpaper wearing down wood.

BIOLOGY.com Search Lesson 27.1 GO • Visual Analogy

UbD Check for Understanding

USE VOCABULARY

List the lesson's vocabulary terms on the board. Ask students to create a **Concept Map** that includes each vocabulary term and identifies the relationships between the terms. *(Students' concept maps should show the following relationships: intracellular digestion and extracellular digestion are the two types of digestive processes in animals. To carry out extracellular digestion, animals have either a gastrovascular cavity or a digestive tract. A rumen is a structure in the digestive tract of some animals.)*

ADJUST INSTRUCTION

If students have trouble identifying the relationships among the terms, have them review the definitions in their text and re-examine the digestive systems shown in **Figure 27–2.**

VISUAL ANALOGY

As a class, discuss the different kinds of teeth animals have (premolars, molars, canines, incisors) and how these specialized mouthparts are adapted to an animal's diet. If you have any animals in the classroom—a snake, a lizard, gerbils, a terrarium with earthworms—have students observe their eating habits and make observations and drawings of the animals' mouthparts. Discuss how each animal is adapted for its special diet.

DIFFERENTIATED INSTRUCTION

L1 Special Needs To help students visualize how their teeth are adapted to eating plant foods, suggest that the next time they eat a fruit or vegetable they need to bite into, such as an apple or stalk of celery, they use a mirror to observe which teeth are used to bite and tear and which teeth are used to grind the food into a form that can be swallowed.

L1 Struggling Students Have students create a **Two-Column Table** that organizes the information in **Figure 27–3.** The left column should be labeled Carnivore Teeth, and the right column should be labeled Herbivore Teeth. In each column, students should include all the tooth types shown in the figure. Have students add definitions and sketches to their table that help them remember the shape and function of each kind of tooth.

Study Wkbks A/B, Appendix S31, Two-Column Table. **Transparencies,** GO16.

ELL Focus on ELL: Build Background

BEGINNING AND INTERMEDIATE SPEAKERS Have students collect images (drawings, Internet printouts, clippings) of the teeth of carnivores and herbivores and sort the animals into those two groups. Then, instruct students to label whichever teeth they can in English, using **Figure 27–3** as a model, while explaining their decisions either orally or in captions in their native language.

BIOLOGY.com Students can compare the structure and function of teeth in the **Visual Analogy: Specialized Teeth.**

LESSON 27.1

Teach continued

Assess and Remediate

EVALUATE UNDERSTANDING

Read aloud each of the boldface Key Concepts in the lesson. For each, call on a volunteer to provide a supporting detail. Then, ask others in the class for additional supporting details. After students have provided support for a Key Concept, ask a volunteer to explain the importance of it in understanding feeding and digestion in animals. After reviewing all Key Concepts, have students complete the 27.1 Assessment.

REMEDIATION SUGGESTION

L1 **Struggling Students** If your students have trouble answering **Question 1a,** have them reread the subsection, **Nutritional Symbionts,** and use the Key Concept in the section to help them write a definition of the term in their own words.

BIOLOGY.com Students can check their understanding of lesson concepts with the **Self-Test** assessment. They can then take an online version of the **Lesson Assessment.**

▶ ***Eating Meat*** **Carnivores typically have sharp mouthparts or other structures that can capture food, hold it, and "slice and dice" it into small pieces.** Carnivorous mammals, such as wolves, have sharp teeth that grab, tear, and slice food like knives and scissors would. The jaw bones and muscles of carnivores are adapted for up and down movements that chop meat into small pieces.

▶ ***Eating Plant Leaves*** **Herbivores typically have mouthparts adapted to rasping or grinding.** To digest leaf tissues, herbivores usually need to tear plant cell walls and expose their contents. To do this, many herbivorous invertebrates, from mollusks to insects, have mouthparts that grind and pulverize leaf tissues. Herbivorous mammals, such as the horse in **Figure 27–4,** have front teeth and muscular lips adapted to grabbing and pulling leaves, and flattened molars that grind leaves to a pulp. The jaw bones and muscles of mammalian herbivores are also adapted for side-to-side "grinding" movements.

FIGURE 27–4 Eating Plant Leaves The teeth and jaws of herbivores, such as horses, are adapted for pulling, rasping, and grinding plant leaves.

Specialized Digestive Tracts Carnivorous invertebrates and vertebrates typically have short digestive tracts that produce fast-acting, meat-digesting enzymes. These enzymes can digest most cell types found in animal tissues.

No animal produces digestive enzymes that can break down the cellulose in plant tissue, however. Some herbivores have very long intestines or specialized pouches in their digestive tracts that harbor microbial symbionts that digest cellulose. Cattle, for example, have a pouchlike extension of their esophagus called a **rumen** (plural: rumina), in which symbiotic bacteria digest cellulose. Animals with rumina, or ruminants, regurgitate food that has been partially digested in the rumen, chew it again, and reswallow it. This process is called "chewing the cud."

27.1 Assessment

IN NoS.3, NoS.6

Review Key Concepts

1. a. Review What types of food do herbivores eat? What are nutritional symbionts?
   b. Relate Cause and Effect How might a coral be affected if all its symbiotic algae died?
2. a. Review What are two types of digestion animals use to break down and absorb food?
   b. Compare and Contrast What is a major structural difference between gastrovascular cavities and digestive tracts?
3. a. Review Describe the adaptations of the mouthparts and digestive systems of leaf-eaters and meat-eaters.
   b. Use Analogies Describe the relationship between a ruminant and its microbial symbionts in terms of "teamwork."

WRITE ABOUT SCIENCE

Summary

4. Describe the process of a cow's digestion of grass, from the cow's uprooting of the grass to its reswallowing of it. Use the terms *molar, rumen, symbiont,* and *cud.*

BIOLOGY.com Search Lesson 27.1 GO • Self-Test • Lesson Assessment

Assessment Answers

1a. Herbivores eat plants or parts of plants. Nutritional symbionts are organisms that rely upon other animals for their nutritional needs.

1b. The coral would die.

2a. intracellular and extracellular

2b. A gastrovascular cavity has only one opening, while a digestive tract has two openings.

3a. Leaf-eaters typically have mouthparts adapted to pulling and rasping or grinding. Some leaf-eaters have very long intestines or rumina in their digestive tracts that harbor microbial symbionts that digest cellulose. Meat-eaters typically have sharp mouthparts to "slice and dice" food into small pieces. Meat-eaters typically have short digestive tracts that produce fast-acting, meat-digesting enzymes.

3b. Sample answer: The herbivore and the symbionts work together in digestion. The herbivore takes in the food, and the symbionts digest the cellulose. The herbivore provides the symbionts with a place to live, and the symbionts help the herbivore digest plant parts.

WRITE ABOUT SCIENCE

4. Answers will vary. All answers should describe the grinding of food by the molars, symbiont digestion of cellulose in a pouchlike extension of the stomach called the rumen, and "chewing the cud," a process that involves regurgitation, re-chewing, and swallowing again.

27.2 Respiration

THINK ABOUT IT All animal tissues require oxygen for respiration and produce carbon dioxide as a waste product. For that reason, all animals must obtain oxygen from their environment and release carbon dioxide. In other words, all animals need to "breathe." Humans can drown because our lungs can't extract the oxygen we need from water. Most fishes have the opposite problem; out of water, their gills don't work. How are these different respiratory systems adapted to their different functions?

Key Questions

What characteristics do the respiratory structures of all animals share?

How do aquatic animals breathe?

What respiratory structures enable land animals to breathe?

Vocabulary
gill • lung • alveolus

Taking Notes
Concept Map Draw a concept map showing the characteristics of the lung structures of vertebrates.

Gas Exchange

What characteristics do the respiratory structures of all animals share?

Despite all the amazing things living cells can do, none can actively pump oxygen or carbon dioxide across membranes. Yet, in order to breathe, all animals must exchange oxygen and carbon dioxide with their surroundings. How do they do it? Animals have evolved respiratory structures that promote the movement of these gases in the required directions by passive diffusion.

Gas Diffusion and Membranes As you may recall, substances diffuse from an area of higher concentration to an area of lower concentration. Gases diffuse most efficiently across a thin, moist membrane that is permeable to those gases. The larger the surface area of that membrane, the more diffusion can take place, just as a bumpy paper towel absorbs more liquid than a smooth one does. These physical principles create a set of requirements that respiratory systems must meet, one way or another.

Requirements for Respiration Because of the behavior of gases, all respiratory systems share certain basic characteristics. **Respiratory structures provide a large surface area of moist, selectively permeable membrane. Respiratory structures maintain a difference in the relative concentrations of oxygen and carbon dioxide on either side of the respiratory membrane, promoting diffusion.**

FIGURE 27–5 Requirements for Respiration Respiratory surfaces are moist, so exhaled air contains a lot of moisture. That exhaled moisture condenses into visible "fog" if outside air is cold.

Getting Started

Objectives

27.2.1 Describe the characteristics of respiratory structures that all animals share.

27.2.2 Explain how aquatic animals breathe.

27.2.3 Identify the respiratory structures that enable land animals to breathe.

Student Resources

Study Workbooks A and B, 27.2 Worksheets

Spanish Study Workbook, 27.2 Worksheets

BIOLOGY.com Lesson Overview • Lesson Notes • Activities: Art Review, Data Analysis • Assessment: Self-Test, Lesson Assessment

For corresponding lesson in the **Foundation Edition**, see pages 650–652.

Build Background

Explain that breathing involves taking needed gases from air or water into the body and expelling waste gases from the body. Ask students if they know what gas the body needs to take in and what gas it has to expel. *(The body needs oxygen and needs to expel carbon dioxide.)* Point out that to enter or leave a body, gases diffuse across a membrane. Ask students which way gas will move across a membrane if the gas is more concentrated on one side of a membrane than on the other. *(from the more concentrated side to the less concentrated side)*

UbD Teach for Understanding

ENDURING UNDERSTANDING Animals have evolved diverse ways to carry out basic life processes and maintain homeostasis.

GUIDING QUESTION How do animals in different environments breathe?

EVIDENCE OF UNDERSTANDING *After completing the lesson, assign the following assessment to show students understand how animals in different environments breathe.* Have students work in small groups to create a series of labeled drawings or clippings, similar to a flowchart, that shows how one animal carries out the process of respiration. The drawings should show how and where gases are exchanged and the structures involved. Have groups share their completed graphics with the class.

Teach

Use Visuals

Refer to **Figure 27–6** to show how many aquatic animals breathe with gills. Explain that gill filaments are selectively permeable membranes. Point out that the gill filaments are shown in red, and make sure students understand that water is pumped *across* or *over* the gill filaments, not *through* them.

Ask What structures are inside the gill filaments that connect the gills with the rest of the body? *(capillaries)*

DIFFERENTIATED INSTRUCTION

L1 Special Needs Have students observe fishes. Tell them to look for the gills on either side of a fish's head and the movement of the operculum, or gill cover, as water that has moved across the gills is pumped out.

ELL Focus on ELL: Access Content

BEGINNING AND INTERMEDIATE SPEAKERS
Before students read, have them make a **KWL Chart.** Have them write what they know about respiration in the K column and what they want to learn about it in the W column. Students can write sentences, make lists, or make sketches. After reading each section of the lesson, they can fill in the L column.

Study Wkbks A/B, Appendix S27, KWL Chart. **Transparencies,** GO11.

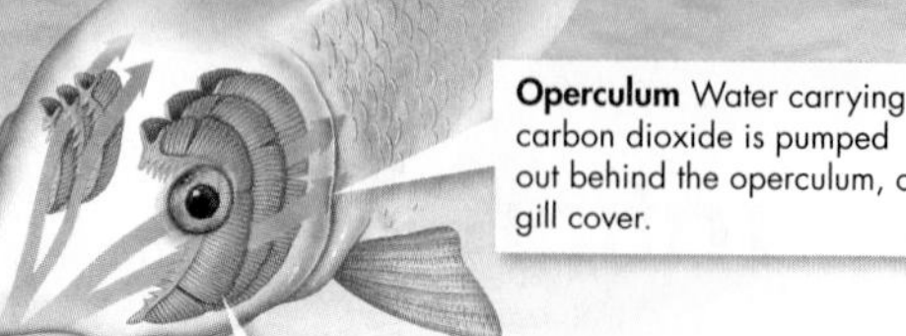

Operculum Water carrying carbon dioxide is pumped out behind the operculum, or gill cover.

Gill Filaments Water is pumped past thousands of threadlike gill filaments, which are rich with capillaries. Filaments absorb oxygen from water and release carbon dioxide.

Mouth A muscular pump pulls water in through the mouth and pushes it back across the gills.

FIGURE 27–6 Respiration With Gills Many aquatic animals, such as fishes, respire with gills, which are thin, selectively permeable membranes. As water passes over the gills, gas exchange is completed within the gill capillaries.

Respiratory Surfaces of Aquatic Animals

How do aquatic animals breathe?

Some aquatic invertebrates, such as cnidarians and some flatworms, are relatively small and have thin-walled bodies whose outer surfaces are always wet. These animals rely on diffusion of oxygen and carbon dioxide through their outer body covering. A few aquatic chordates, including lancelets, some amphibians, and even some sea snakes, rely to varying extents on gas exchange by diffusion across body surfaces.

For large, active animals, however, skin respiration alone is insufficient. **Many aquatic invertebrates and most aquatic chordates other than reptiles and mammals exchange gases through gills.** As shown in **Figure 27–6, gills** are feathery structures that expose a large surface area of thin, selectively permeable membrane to water. Inside gill membranes is a network of tiny, thin-walled blood vessels called capillaries. Many animals, including aquatic mollusks and fishes, actively pump water over their gills as blood flows through inside. This helps maintain differences in oxygen and carbon dioxide concentration that promote diffusion. **Aquatic reptiles and aquatic mammals, such as whales, breathe with lungs and must hold their breath underwater. Lungs** are organs that exchange oxygen and carbon dioxide between blood and air. You will learn more about lungs shortly.

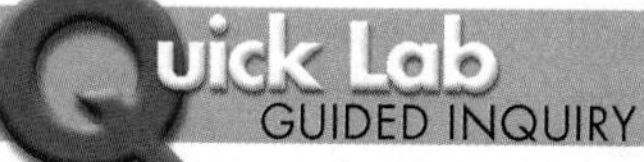

GUIDED INQUIRY

Breathing in Clams and Crayfishes

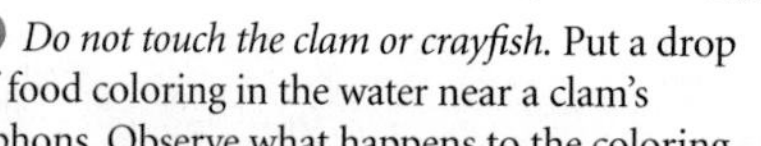

1. *Do not touch the clam or crayfish.* Put a drop of food coloring in the water near a clam's siphons. Observe what happens to the coloring.
2. Put a drop of food coloring in the water near the middle of a crayfish. **CAUTION:** *Keep your fingers away from the crayfish's pincers.* Observe what happens to the coloring.

Analyze and Conclude

1. **Observe** Describe what happened to the coloring in step 1. How does water move through a clam's gills?
2. **Infer** What is the clam's main defense? How is the location of the clam's siphons related to this defense?
3. **Compare and Contrast** What happened in step 2? Compare the flow of water through the gills of clams and crayfishes.
4. **Infer** Unlike many other arthropods, crayfishes have gills. Why do crayfishes need gills?

788 Chapter 27 • Lesson 2

PURPOSE Students will be able to relate differences in the mechanisms of gas exchange to the overall adaptations in a clam and a crayfish.

MATERIALS live clam, food coloring, dropper, live crayfish, 2 small containers of water

SAFETY Make sure students do not touch the organisms, and have them wash their hands in warm, soapy water when finished.

PLANNING You can keep marine clams alive for a few days in a 4% solution of sodium chloride.

ANALYZE AND CONCLUDE

1. The coloring entered one siphon and left through the other. Inside the clam, the coloring flowed over the gills.
2. Sample answer: Its main defense is its shell. The location of the siphons allows the clam to pump water over its gills without opening its shell very wide.
3. Sample answer: The coloring flowed into the crayfish's gills and then flowed back out. Both clams and crayfishes draw water into the body, pass it over the gills, and then release it. A clam must open its shell to do this, while a crayfish has openings through which water passes in and out.
4. Crayfishes need gills, because they are aquatic arthropods that use gills for the exchange of gases.

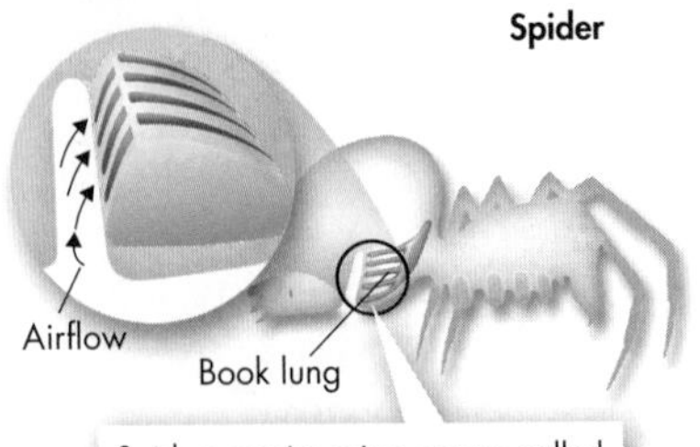

Spiders respire using organs called book lungs, which are made of parallel, sheetlike layers of thin tissues that contain blood vessels.

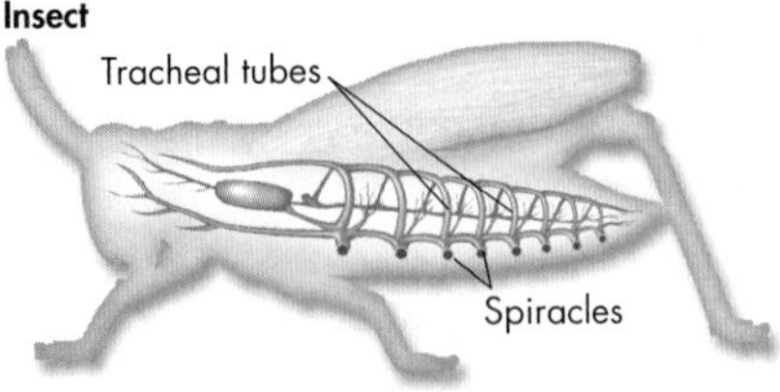

In most insects, a system of tracheal tubes extends throughout the body. Air enters and leaves the system through openings in the body surface called spiracles. In some insects, oxygen and carbon dioxide diffuse through the tracheal system, and in and out of body fluids. In other insects, body movements help pump air in and out of the tracheal system.

FIGURE 27–7 Respiratory Structures of Terrestrial Invertebrates Terrestrial invertebrates have a wide variety of respiratory structures, including skin, mantle cavities, book lungs, and tracheal tubes. These structures must stay moist even in the driest of conditions in order to function properly.

Respiratory Surfaces of Terrestrial Animals

What respiratory structures enable land animals to breathe?

Terrestrial animals, as you might have guessed, face a challenge that aquatic animals don't. Terrestrial animals must keep their respiratory membranes moist in dry environments.

Respiratory Surfaces in Land Invertebrates The wide range of body plans among terrestrial invertebrates reveals very different strategies for respiration. **Respiratory structures in terrestrial invertebrates include skin, mantle cavities, book lungs, and tracheal tubes.** Some land invertebrates, such as earthworms, that live in moist environments can respire across their skin, as long as it stays moist. In other invertebrates, such as land snails, respiration is accomplished by the mantle cavity, which is lined with moist tissue and blood vessels. Insects and spiders have more complex respiratory systems, as you can see in **Figure 27–7.**

Lung Structure in Vertebrates Terrestrial vertebrates display a wide range of breathing adaptations. **But all terrestrial vertebrates—reptiles, birds, mammals, and the land stages of most amphibians—breathe with lungs.** Although lung structure in these animals varies, the processes of inhaling and exhaling are similar. Inhaling brings oxygen-rich air through the trachea (TRAY kee uh), or airway, into the lungs. Inside the lungs, oxygen diffuses into the blood through lung capillaries. At the same time, carbon dioxide diffuses out of capillaries into the lungs. Oxygen-poor air is then exhaled.

In Your Notebook *Would you expect dolphins to breathe with gills or lungs? Explain your answer.*

BUILD Vocabulary

MULTIPLE MEANINGS The biological term *respiration* has different, though related, meanings. In animals, it can refer to gas exchange, the intake of oxygen and release of waste gases, or to *cellular respiration*, the cell process that releases energy by breaking down food molecules in the presence of oxygen. Because cellular respiration requires oxygen, the two processes are related.

Use Models

Have students examine the respiratory structures of a spider and an insect in **Figure 27–7,** and point out that both structures are adaptations that provide a large surface area in which gas exchange can occur. To drive home this concept, have students measure the front and back of a closed book. Then, have them divide the book into ten sections, holding the sections together with rubber bands. Ask students to calculate the total surface area of the divided book. They will determine that this surface area is more than ten times that of the closed book.

Ask What invertebrate respiratory structure is like a book with sections exposed to the air? *(a spider's book lungs)*

DIFFERENTIATED INSTRUCTION

L1 Struggling Students Show students a three-ring binder with several pieces of paper clipped inside. Trace the binder cover on the board near the top of the board. Below this, retrace the binder cover, and then take out each sheet of paper and tape them edge to edge to the side of the second tracing. Explain how the binder, with the sheets of paper inside, models the book lungs of a spider. Have them compare the surface area available for respiration of the binder "book lungs" to the set of lungs represented just by the cover tracing. Make sure they understand the advantage of the book lung structure.

Address Misconceptions

Respiration and Circulation Some students may have the misconception that air is inhaled into the lungs and then simply exhaled without any connection to the heart and the rest of the circulatory system. Emphasize that the gas exchange that occurs in the lungs is necessary because of the process of cellular respiration carried out by all cells. Have students re-examine the overall equation for cellular respiration in Chapter 9, with a special focus on oxygen as a reactant and carbon dioxide as a product. Then, discuss how the respiratory and circulatory systems work together.

BIOLOGY.com Students distinguish different types of respiratory systems in **Art Review: Respiratory Systems.** In **Data Analysis: Giant Insects of the Paleozoic,** students examine why insects were larger during the Paleozoic than they are today.

Answers

IN YOUR NOTEBOOK Dolphins breathe with lungs, because they are mammals.

UbD Check for Understanding

INDEX CARD SUMMARIES

Give each student an index card, and ask students to write one idea about respiration in animals that they understand on the front of the card. Then, have them write a question about respiration they have on the back of the card.

ADJUST INSTRUCTION

Read over the cards to get a sense of concepts students understand and concepts they are having trouble with. Read some of the questions aloud to the class, without identifying the students who wrote the questions, and call on volunteers to provide an answer. This will allow students to hear concepts expressed in various ways by their peers and give you a chance to address any misunderstandings.

LESSON 27.2

Assess and Remediate

EVALUATE UNDERSTANDING

Call on students at random to explain or show how gas exchange occurs over gills, through spiracles and book lungs, or inside vertebrate lungs. Then, have students complete the 27.2 Assessment.

REMEDIATION SUGGESTION

L1 Struggling Students If your students have trouble answering **Question 3a,** have them review **Figures 27–7** and **27–8.** Have them write summaries of the information in the annotations and captions of the two figures.

BIOLOGY.com Students can check their understanding of lesson concepts with the **Self-Test** assessment. They can then take an online version of the **Lesson Assessment.**

Answers

FIGURE 27–8 The large surface area enables mammals to process the large amount of oxygen required by their high metabolic rates.

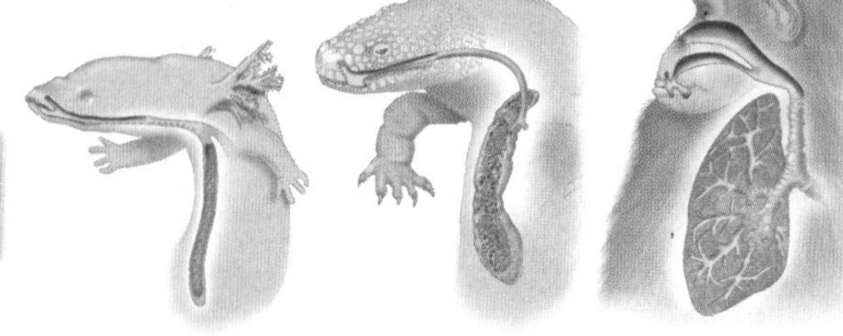

FIGURE 27–8 Lungs Terrestrial vertebrates breathe with lungs. Lungs with a larger surface area can take in more oxygen and release more carbon dioxide. Mammals have the greatest lung surface area among animals. Infer ***Why do mammals require a large surface area with which to process oxygen?***

▶ ***Amphibian, Reptilian, and Mammalian Lungs*** The internal surface area of lungs increases from amphibians to reptiles to mammals, as shown in **Figure 27–8.** A typical amphibian lung is little more than a sac with ridges. Reptilian lungs are often divided into chambers that increase the surface area for gas exchange. Mammalian lungs branch extensively, and their entire volume is filled with bubblelike structures called **alveoli** (al VEE uh ly; singular: alveolus). Alveoli provide an enormous surface area for gas exchange. The structure of mammalian lungs enables mammals to take in the large amounts of oxygen required by their high metabolic rates. However, in the lungs of mammals and most other vertebrates, air moves in and out through the same tracheal passageway. For this reason, some stale, oxygen-poor air is trapped in the lungs. In humans, this stale air is typically equivalent to about one third of the air inhaled in a normal breath.

▶ ***Bird Lungs*** In birds, the lungs are structured so that air flows mostly in only one direction. No stale air gets trapped in the system. A unique system of tubes and air sacs in birds' respiratory systems enables this one-way airflow. Thus, gas exchange surfaces are continuously in contact with fresh air. This highly efficient gas exchange helps birds obtain the oxygen they need to power their flight muscles at high altitudes for long periods of time.

27.2 Assessment

Review Key Concepts

1. a. Review In what ways are the respiratory structures of all animals similar?

b. Apply Concepts Explain why it is important that respiratory surfaces are moist and selectively permeable.

2. a. Review Which groups of aquatic animals breathe with gills? With lungs?

b. Relate Cause and Effect Why do some animals actively pump water over their gills?

3. a. Review How do terrestrial invertebrates and terrestrial vertebrates breathe?

b. Interpret Visuals Contrast the structures of amphibian, reptilian, and mammalian lungs, as shown in **Figure 27–8.**

WRITE ABOUT SCIENCE

Description

4. Describe the events that occur when a mammal respires, including the path of air through its lungs.

BIOLOGY.com Search Lesson 27.2 GO • Self-Test • Lesson Assessment

Assessment Answers

1a. Animals all have respiratory structures that promote the movement of oxygen and carbon dioxide across moist, selectively permeable membranes by passive diffusion.

1b. Gases diffuse most efficiently across moist membranes. Surfaces must be selectively permeable so that not all substances can pass through.

2a. Many aquatic invertebrates and most aquatic chordates, other than reptiles and mammals, breathe with gills. Aquatic reptiles and aquatic mammals breathe with lungs.

2b. This helps maintain differences in oxygen and carbon dioxide concentration that promote diffusion.

3a. Some terrestrial invertebrates exchange gases through the skin. Other invertebrates breathe through respiratory structures, including mantle cavities, book lungs, and tracheal tubes. Terrestrial vertebrates breathe with lungs.

3b. All terrestrial vertebrates have lungs. The internal surface area of lungs increases from amphibians to reptiles to mammals. A typical amphibian lung is little more than a sac with ridges. A reptilian lung is often divided into chambers. A mammalian lung branches extensively and contains bubblelike structures called alveoli.

WRITE ABOUT SCIENCE

4. Sample answer: Air moves in through the tracheal passageway. On its way in, air moves through branches and into alveoli, where gas exchange takes place. Air moves out the same way it moved in.

27.3 Circulation

THINK ABOUT IT Your mouth takes food into your body, and your digestive tract breaks it down. But how do the energy and nutrients get to your body cells? How does oxygen from your lungs get to your brain and the rest of your body? How do carbon dioxide and wastes generated within your body get eliminated? While some aquatic animals with bodies only a few cells thick rely solely on diffusion to transport materials, most animals rely on a circulatory system.

Key Questions

How do open and closed circulatory systems compare?

How do the patterns of circulation in vertebrates compare?

Vocabulary

heart
open circulatory system
closed circulatory system
atrium
ventricle

Taking Notes

Cycle Diagram As you read, draw a cycle diagram showing a five-step sequence in which blood pumps through a closed, two-loop circulatory system.

Open and Closed Circulatory Systems

How do open and closed circulatory systems compare?

Many animals move blood through their bodies using one or more hearts. A **heart** is a hollow, muscular organ that pumps blood around the body. A heart can be part of either an open or a closed circulatory system.

Open Circulatory Systems Arthropods and most mollusks have **open circulatory systems,** such as the one in **Figure 27–9.** **In an open circulatory system, blood is only partially contained within a system of blood vessels as it travels through the body.** One or more hearts or heartlike organs pump blood through vessels that empty into a system of sinuses, or spongy cavities. There, blood comes into direct contact with body tissues. Blood then collects in another set of sinuses and eventually makes its way back to the heart.

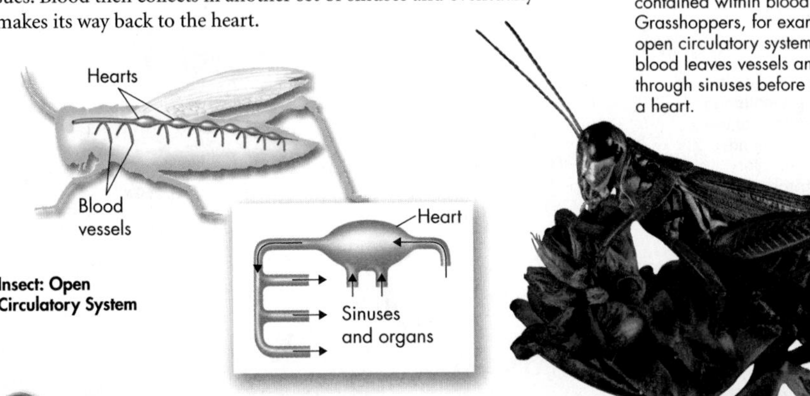

FIGURE 27–9 Open Circulatory System In an open circulatory system, blood is not entirely contained within blood vessels. Grasshoppers, for example, have open circulatory systems in which blood leaves vessels and moves through sinuses before returning to a heart.

LESSON 27.3

Getting Started

Objectives

27.3.1 Compare open and closed circulatory systems.

27.3.2 Compare patterns of circulation in vertebrates.

Student Resources

Study Workbooks A and B, 27.3 Worksheets

Spanish Study Workbook, 27.3 Worksheets

BIOLOGY.com Lesson Overview • Lesson Notes • Activity: InterActive Art • Assessment: Self-Test, Lesson Assessment

For corresponding lesson in the **Foundation Edition**, see pages 653–655.

Build Background

Explain that many animals, including insects, have an open circulatory system instead of the closed system of blood vessels that humans have. Have students observe an open system in **Figure 27–9.** Point out that, in an open circulatory system, the blood comes in direct contact with tissues and cells. As students read through the lesson, suggest they think about why an open circulatory system might work well for a grasshopper, but perhaps not as well for a human.

UbD Teach for Understanding

ENDURING UNDERSTANDING Animals have evolved diverse ways to carry out basic life processes and maintain homeostasis.

GUIDING QUESTION How have animals evolved complex, efficient ways to move materials through their bodies?

EVIDENCE OF UNDERSTANDING *After completing the lesson, assign the following assessment to show students understand the two types of circulatory systems found in animals.* Divide the class in half, and assign one half to be advocates of an open circulatory system and the other half to be advocates of a closed circulatory system. Have students meet in small groups to discuss how to advocate for one system or the other. Then, have all groups advocating the same system meet to agree on arguments for that system. Finally, stage a debate about the two systems.

LESSON 27.3

Teach

Use Visuals

Have small groups of students compare and contrast single- and double-loop circulation by discussing the two systems shown in **Figure 27–11.** After groups have had time for an exchange of ideas, discuss the two patterns of circulation as a class. Call on groups to report important differences they observed in the two systems. Encourage students from other groups to build on what earlier groups have reported.

DIFFERENTIATED INSTRUCTION

L1 Struggling Students For students who don't seem to grasp the main differences in the two systems shown in **Figure 27–11,** have them trace each system with a finger, following the arrows, and then identify how the two systems are different.

L3 Advanced Students If school policy permits, have students dissect a mammalian heart to gain a better understanding of a four-chambered heart. Obtain cow, pig, or sheep hearts from a local butcher, and provide students with dissecting tools and a dissecting tray. Remind students to handle the sharp dissecting tools with care, and make sure they wear goggles, a lab apron, and disposable plastic gloves during the dissection. Ask students to diagram what they observe and add labels for parts they can identify. Be sure students wash their hands thoroughly in warm, soapy water afterward.

BIOLOGY.com Students compare single- and double-loop circulation in **InterActive Art: Vertebrate Circulatory Systems.**

FIGURE 27–10 Closed Circulatory System Annelids, such as earthworms, and many more-complex animals have closed circulatory systems. Blood stays within the vessels of a closed circulatory system.

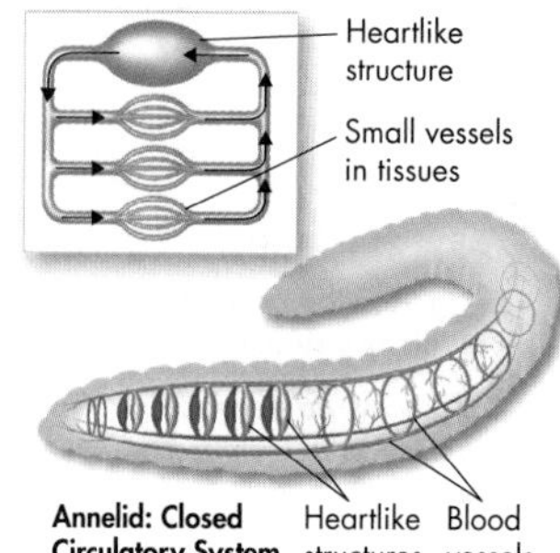

Closed Circulatory Systems Many larger, more active invertebrates, including annelids and some mollusks, and all vertebrates have **closed circulatory systems,** such as the one shown in **Figure 27–10.** **In a closed circulatory system, blood circulates entirely within blood vessels that extend throughout the body.** A heart or heartlike organ forces blood through these vessels. Nutrients and oxygen reach body tissues by diffusing across thin walls of capillaries, the smallest blood vessels. Blood that is completely contained within blood vessels can be pumped under higher pressure, and thus can be circulated more efficiently, than can blood in an open system.

Single- and Double-Loop Circulation

How do the patterns of circulation in vertebrates compare?

As chordates evolved, they developed more-complex organ systems and more-efficient channels for internal transport. You can see two main types of circulatory systems of vertebrates in **Figure 27–11.**

Single-Loop Circulation **Most vertebrates with gills have a single-loop circulatory system with a single pump that forces blood around the body in one direction.** In fishes, for example, the heart consists of two chambers: an atrium and a ventricle. The **atrium** (plural: atria) receives blood from the body. The **ventricle** then pumps blood out of the heart and to the gills. Oxygen-rich blood then travels from the gills to the rest of the body and returns, oxygen-poor, to the atrium.

BUILD Vocabulary

MULTIPLE MEANINGS The word **atrium** has different but parallel meanings in everyday usage and in biology. In everyday usage, it means a large entrance hall. In biology, it means a heart chamber through which blood from the body enters the heart.

Double-Loop Circulation As terrestrial vertebrates evolved into larger and more active forms, their capillary networks became larger. Using a single pump to force blood through the entire system would have been increasingly difficult. This issue was avoided as the lineage of vertebrates that led to reptiles, birds, and mammals evolved. **Most vertebrates that use lungs for respiration have a double-loop, two-pump circulatory system.**

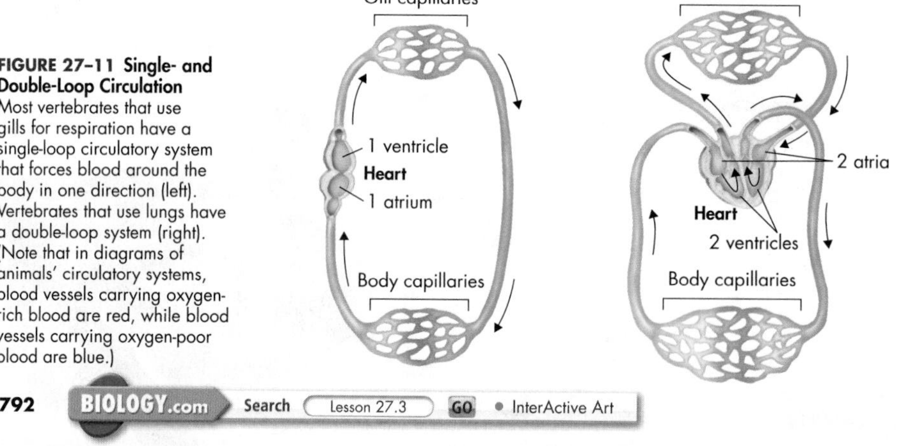

FIGURE 27–11 Single- and Double-Loop Circulation Most vertebrates that use gills for respiration have a single-loop circulatory system that forces blood around the body in one direction (left). Vertebrates that use lungs have a double-loop system (right). (Note that in diagrams of animals' circulatory systems, blood vessels carrying oxygen-rich blood are red, while blood vessels carrying oxygen-poor blood are blue.)

 BIOLOGY.com Search Lesson 27.3 GO • InterActive Art

UbD Check for Understanding

ONE-MINUTE RESPONSE

Give students one minute to write a response to the following:

- In double-loop circulation, how does the heart work like two pumps operating together? *(Responses should mention that one side of the heart pumps blood from the heart to the lungs. When oxygen-rich blood returns from the lungs, the other side of the heart pumps it to the rest of the body.)*

ADJUST INSTRUCTION

If responses show that students do not understand the role of the heart in double-loop circulation, provide pairs of students with an unlabeled drawing of double-loop circulation similar to **Figure 27–11.** Ask partners to label the drawing and add arrows showing the path of blood through the heart as well as the rest of the system.

The first loop, powered by one side of the heart, forces oxygen-poor blood from the heart to the lungs. After the blood picks up oxygen (and drops off carbon dioxide) in the lungs, it returns to the heart. Then, the other side of the heart pumps this oxygen-rich blood through the second circulatory loop to the rest of the body. Oxygen-poor blood from the body returns to the heart, and the cycle begins again.

Mammalian Heart-Chamber Evolution Four-chambered hearts like those in modern mammals are actually two separate pumps working next to one another. But where did the second pump come from? During chordate evolution, partitions evolved that divided the original two chambers into four. Those partitions transformed one pump into two parallel pumps. The partitions also separated oxygen-rich blood from oxygen-poor blood. We can get an idea of how the partitions evolved by looking at other modern vertebrates.

Amphibian hearts usually have three chambers: two atria and one ventricle. The left atrium receives oxygen-rich blood from the lungs. The right atrium receives oxygen-poor blood from the body. Both atria empty into the ventricle. Some mixing of oxygen-rich and oxygen-poor blood in the ventricle occurs. However, the internal structure of the ventricle directs blood flow so that most oxygen-poor blood goes to the lungs, and most oxygen-rich blood goes to the rest of the body.

Reptilian hearts typically have three chambers. However, most reptiles have a partial partition in their ventricle. Because of this partition, there is even less mixing of oxygen-rich and oxygen-poor blood than there is in amphibian hearts.

MYSTERY CLUE

Human blood is only about a third as salty as seawater. It needs to circulate through very small capillaries. What might happen if the water content of a person's blood were to drop too low?

FIGURE 27–12 Reptilian Heart Under the armor-like hide of this crocodile lies a heart with two atria and one ventricle.

27.3 Assessment

Review Key Concepts 

1. a. Review Describe an open circulatory system. Describe a closed circulatory system.
   b. Explain Which groups of animals tend to have each type of circulatory system?
   c. Relate Cause and Effect How does having a closed circulatory system benefit a large, active animal?
2. a. Review What are two different patterns of circulation found in vertebrates?
   b. Compare and Contrast What is the major structural difference between vertebrates that have single-loop circulatory systems and those that have double-loop systems?

Apply the Big idea

Structure and Function

3. Do you think large, active vertebrates would have been likely to succeed if closed circulatory systems had not evolved? Explain your reasoning.

BIOLOGY.com Search Lesson 27.3 GO • Self-Test • Lesson Assessment

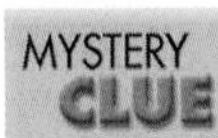

MYSTERY CLUE Point out to students that blood is made up of many different molecules and cells suspended in fluid. Have them speculate on what might happen to blood if there were less fluid but the same amount of materials suspended in it. Lead them to conclude that the blood might get thicker. Then, have students infer what could happen inside vessels and a four-chambered heart if the water content of blood dropped below normal. Students can go online to Biology.com to gather their evidence.

Assess and Remediate

EVALUATE UNDERSTANDING

List the lesson's five vocabulary terms on the board. Then, call on a student at random to explain what one of the terms means. After the student gives a definition, call on other students to contribute details related to circulation in animals that the term brings to mind. Continue until all terms have been defined and discussed. Then, have students complete the 27.3 Assessment.

REMEDIATION SUGGESTION

L1 **Struggling Students** If students have trouble answering **Question 2b,** have them re-examine **Figure 27–11.**

BIOLOGY.com Students can check their understanding of lesson concepts with the **Self-Test** assessment. They can then take an online version of the **Lesson Assessment.**

Assessment Answers

1a. In an open circulatory system, one or more hearts or heartlike organs pump blood through vessels that empty into a system of sinuses, or spongy cavities. There, blood comes into contact with tissues. Blood then collects in another set of sinuses and eventually makes its way back to the heart. In a closed circulatory system, blood circulates entirely within blood vessels. A heart or heartlike organ forces blood through the vessels. Nutrients and oxygen reach body tissues by diffusing across thin walls of capillaries.

1b. Arthropods and most mollusks have open circulatory systems. Many larger, more active invertebrates and all vertebrates have closed circulatory systems.

1c. Blood is pumped under higher pressure, and thus, can be circulated more efficiently, thereby providing the oxygen needed for a higher metabolism.

2a. single-loop circulation and double-loop circulation

2b. The heart in a single-loop system has one atrium and one ventricle; the heart in a double-loop system has two atria and one or two ventricles.

3. Big idea Answers will vary. Students should back up their opinions with reasoning that shows an understanding of the structures and functions of both open and closed circulatory systems.

LESSON 27.4

Getting Started

Objectives

27.4.1 Describe the methods animals use to manage nitrogenous wastes.

27.4.2 Explain how aquatic animals eliminate wastes.

27.4.3 Explain how land animals eliminate wastes.

Student Resources

Study Workbooks A and B, 27.4 Worksheets

Spanish Study Workbook, 27.4 Worksheets

Lesson Overview • Lesson Notes • Activity: Art in Motion • Assessment: Self-Test, Lesson Assessment

For corresponding lesson in the **Foundation Edition**, see pages 656–659.

Build Background

MATERIALS beaker, household ammonia

As students observe, pour some household ammonia from a commercial bottle into a clear glass beaker. Read the warning labels on the bottle, including cautions about swallowing and avoiding contact with eyes. Explain that although the commercial form is not pure ammonia, it can still be harmful to the body. Then, explain that natural processes within cells, especially the breakdown of proteins, produce ammonia. All animals must have some process for releasing or converting ammonia.

INDIANA ACADEMIC STANDARDS

For the full text of all standards, see the Course Overview in the front matter of this book.

NoS.6 Use analogies and models (mathematical and physical) to simplify and represent systems that are difficult to understand or directly experience due to their size, time scale, or complexity, and recognize the limitations of analogies and models.

Excretion

Key Questions

How do animals manage toxic nitrogenous waste?

How do aquatic animals eliminate wastes?

How do land animals remove wastes while conserving water?

Vocabulary

excretion • kidney • nephridium • Malpighian tubule

Taking Notes

Preview Visuals Note three questions you have about **Figure 27–15**. As you read, try to answer your questions.

THINK ABOUT IT If you think about the first three lessons in this chapter, you'll realize that they are missing something. We've discussed how respiratory systems obtain oxygen and get rid of carbon dioxide. We've also discussed how animals obtain and digest food and get rid of indigestible material. But cellular respiration generates other kinds of wastes that are released into body fluids and that must be eliminated from the body. What are these wastes and how do animals get rid of them?

The Ammonia Problem

How do animals manage toxic nitrogenous waste?

The breakdown of proteins by cells releases a nitrogen-containing, or nitrogenous, waste: ammonia. This creates a problem, because ammonia is poisonous! Even moderate concentrations of ammonia can kill most cells. Animal systems address this difficulty in one of two ways. **Animals either eliminate ammonia from the body quickly or convert it into other nitrogenous compounds that are less toxic.** The elimination of metabolic wastes, such as ammonia, is called **excretion.** Some small animals that live in wet environments rid their bodies of ammonia by allowing it to diffuse out of their body fluids across their skin. Most larger animals, and even some smaller ones that live in dry environments, have excretory systems that process ammonia and eliminate it from the body.

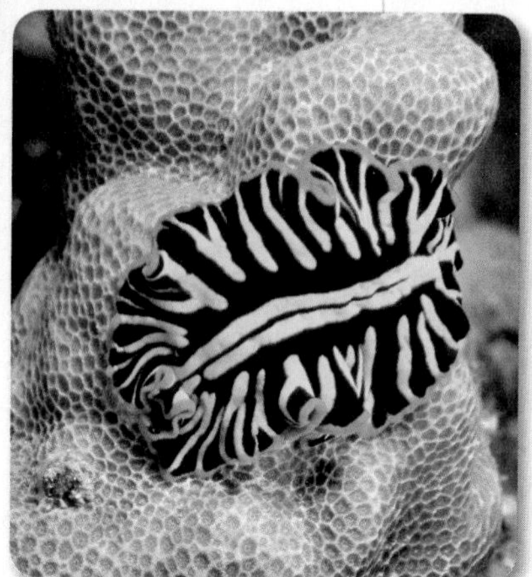

FIGURE 27–13 Ammonia Some aquatic animals, such as this zebra flatworm, release ammonia as soon as they produce it.

Storing Nitrogenous Wastes Animals that cannot dispose of ammonia continuously, as it is produced, have evolved ways to hold, or "store," nitrogenous wastes until they can be eliminated. In most cases, ammonia itself cannot be stored in body fluids, because it is too toxic. Insects, reptiles, and birds typically solve this problem by converting ammonia into a sticky white compound called uric acid, which you can see in **Figure 27–14.** Uric acid is much less toxic than ammonia and is also less soluble in water. Mammals and some amphibians, on the other hand, convert ammonia to a different nitrogenous compound—urea. Like uric acid, urea is less toxic than ammonia, but unlike uric acid, urea is highly soluble in water.

Teach for Understanding

ENDURING UNDERSTANDING Animals have evolved diverse ways to carry out basic life processes and maintain homeostasis.

GUIDING QUESTION How do animals in different environments excrete metabolic wastes?

EVIDENCE OF UNDERSTANDING *After completing the lesson, assign the following assessment to show students understand why animals must remove ammonia from their bodies and how animals excrete nitrogenous wastes.* Have students work in small groups to prepare a brief poster presentation that explains why all animals carry out excretion and how the excretory system of one type of animal functions. Have each group present its poster to the class, and encourage other students to ask questions.

Maintaining Water Balance Getting rid of any type of nitrogenous waste involves water. For that reason, excretory systems are extremely important in maintaining the proper balance of water in blood and body tissues. In some cases, excretory systems eliminate excess water along with nitrogenous wastes. In other cases, excretory systems must eliminate nitrogenous wastes while conserving water. Many animals use **kidneys** to separate wastes and excess water from blood. This waste and water forms a fluid called urine.

Kidneys perform these functions despite a serious limitation: No living cell can actively pump water across a membrane. Yet kidneys need to separate water from waste products. You may recall that cells can pump ions across their membranes. Kidney cells pump ions from salt to create osmotic gradients. Water then "follows" those ions passively by osmosis. This process works well but leaves kidneys with one weakness: They usually cannot excrete excess salt.

In Your Notebook *Explain how kidneys remove excess water from the blood.*

FIGURE 27–14 Other Nitrogenous Compounds Large and/or terrestrial animals either convert ammonia to uric acid and excrete it as sticky white guano, as have these gulls, or they convert ammonia into urea and release it, diluted, as urine.

Humans, like most land-dwelling mammals, have evolved kidneys that are designed to conserve salt, not to get rid of it. How could this have posed a problem for the sick "survivor"?

Excretion in Aquatic Animals

How do aquatic animals eliminate wastes?

Aquatic animals have an advantage in getting rid of nitrogenous wastes because they are surrounded by water. **In general, aquatic animals can allow ammonia to diffuse out of their bodies into surrounding water, which dilutes the ammonia and carries it away.** But aquatic animals still face excretory challenges. Many need to either eliminate water from their bodies or to conserve it, depending on whether they live in fresh or salt water. The excretion issues of aquatic animals are summarized in **Figure 27–15** on the next page.

Quick Facts

DEALING WITH AMMONIA

Protein is an essential part of animals' diets, and the digestion of protein produces amino acids. Animals use some of these amino acids to produce the proteins and other compounds they need. The amino acids that proteins are made of also provide energy for cellular respiration, and this process produces ammonia as a byproduct. Because ammonia is highly poisonous, it must be eliminated from the body. Invertebrates that allow ammonia to diffuse out of their bodies are limited to aquatic environments, because water is necessary to dilute the ammonia. Therefore, the ability to produce the relatively harmless uric acid is an important reason why invertebrates, particularly insects, have been so successful on land. Also, because uric acid is excreted in a solid or semisolid form, these land animals are able to conserve precious water.

Teach

Lead a Discussion

Discuss with students the importance of keeping the proper water balance in a body. Explain that methods of maintaining water balance differ among animals, but in order to maintain homeostasis, each type of animal must maintain the appropriate balance of water in its body.

Ask What animals might need to eliminate excess water to maintain a water balance in their bodies? *(animals that live in water, such as fishes and aquatic invertebrates)*

Ask What animals might need to conserve water to maintain water balance? *(terrestrial animals, especially those that live in very dry environments)*

DIFFERENTIATED INSTRUCTION

LPR Less Proficient Readers Some students may have trouble following the explanation of how kidney cells separate water from waste products. To help students understand the process of creating osmotic gradients, write the following steps and concepts on the board. Then, make sure students understand each before moving on to the next.

- Kidney cells pump ions from salt across membranes.
- This results in different concentrations of ions on the two sides of the membranes.
- There is a lower concentration of water on the side with more ions than on the other side.
- Water always diffuses across a membrane from the side of higher concentration to the side of lower concentration.
- So, water will diffuse across the membrane to the side where there are more ions (and less water).

Have students review why kidneys cannot excrete excess salt. Then, ask them to think about the damage a buildup of salt could cause to the kidneys in terms of water balance in the cells. Students can go online to Biology.com to gather their evidence.

Answers

IN YOUR NOTEBOOK Kidney cells pump ions from salt to create osmotic gradients. Water then "follows" those ions passively by osmosis.

Teach continued

VISUAL ANALOGY

Use **Figure 27–15** to discuss the differences in how freshwater and saltwater animals maintain water balance in their bodies.

Ask Why don't freshwater fishes drink water? *(Water moves into their bodies by osmosis. Therefore, to maintain proper water balance in their bodies they need to get rid of water, not take in more.)*

Ask Why do saltwater fishes lose water through osmosis? *(Their bodies contain a lower concentration of salt than the water they live in. As a result, water diffuses out of their bodies.)*

DIFFERENTIATED INSTRUCTION

ELL English Language Learners Call on volunteers to read aloud the annotation for a panel. Then, call on another student to describe what the cartoon in that panel shows. Ask volunteers to summarize what the panel explains.

LPR Less Proficient Readers Suggest students work in pairs to check comprehension of **Figure 27–15.** Have one student ask a question about a panel and the other student answer with a response derived from reading the annotation and looking at the cartoon. Tell students to make sure both partners understand a panel before moving on.

BIOLOGY.com Have students review the differences in how freshwater and saltwater animals maintain water balance in their bodies with **Art in Motion: Excretion in Aquatic Animals.**

Fresh Water

More water
Less salt
More salt
Less water

The bodies of freshwater animals, such as fishes, contain a higher concentration of salt than the water they live in.

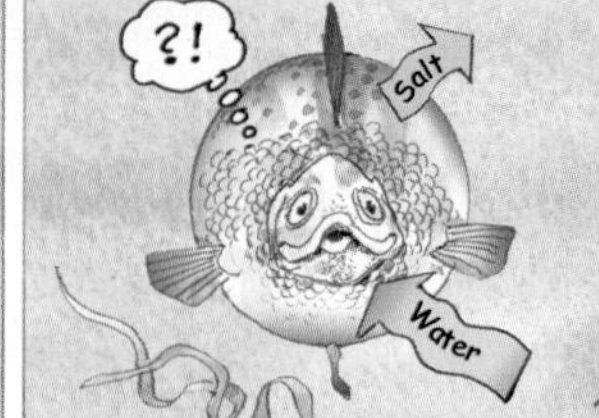

So water moves into their bodies by osmosis, mostly across the gills. Salt diffuses out. If they didn't excrete water, they'd look like water balloons with eyes!

So they excrete water through kidneys that produce lots of watery urine. They don't drink, and they actively pump salt in across their gills.

The bodies of saltwater animals, such as fishes, contain a lower concentration of salt than the water they live in.

So they lose water through osmosis, and salt diffuses in. If they didn't conserve water and eliminate salt, they'd shrivel up like dead leaves.

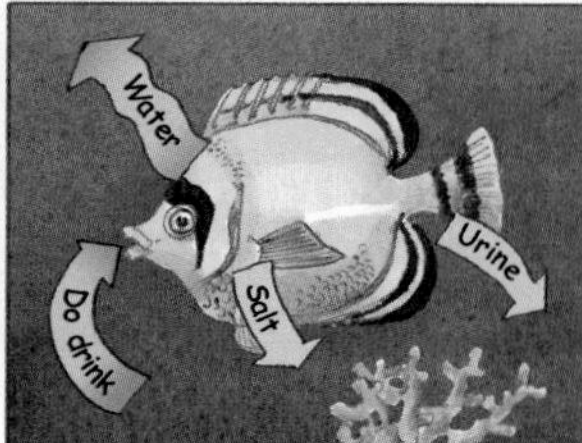

So they conserve water by producing very little concentrated urine. They drink, and they actively pump salt out across their gills.

VISUAL ANALOGY

EXCRETION IN AQUATIC ANIMALS

FIGURE 27–15 All animals must rid their bodies of ammonia while maintaining appropriate water balance. Freshwater and saltwater animals face very different challenges in this respect. Interpret Visuals ***What are two ways freshwater fishes avoid looking like "water balloons with eyes"?***

Freshwater Animals Many freshwater invertebrates lose ammonia to their environment by simple diffusion across their skin. Many freshwater fishes and amphibians eliminate ammonia by diffusion across the same gill membranes they use for respiration.

The situation is more complex for some freshwater invertebrates and most freshwater fishes. The concentration of water in their freshwater environments is higher than the concentration of water in their body fluids. So water moves passively into their bodies by osmosis, and salt leaves by diffusion. To help maintain water balance, flatworms have specialized cells called flame cells that remove excess water from body fluids. That water travels through excretory tubules and leaves through pores in the skin. Amphibians and freshwater fishes typically excrete excess water in very dilute urine. Freshwater fishes also pump salt actively inward across their gills.

Saltwater Animals Marine invertebrates and vertebrates typically release ammonia by diffusion across their body surfaces or gill membranes. Many marine invertebrates have body fluids with water concentrations similar to that of the seawater around them. For that reason, these animals have less of a problem with water balance than do freshwater invertebrates. Marine fishes, however, tend to lose water to their surroundings because their bodies are less salty than the water they live in. These animals actively excrete salt across their gills. Their kidneys also produce small quantities of very concentrated urine to conserve water.

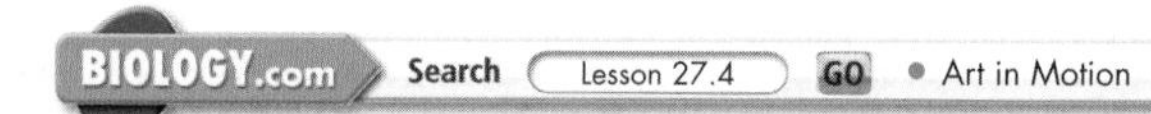

UbD Check for Understanding

HAND SIGNALS

Ask students the following questions, and have them show a thumbs-up sign if they think they can answer the question correctly, a thumbs-down sign if they definitely can't, or a waving-hand sign if they're not sure.

- What is the purpose of excretion?
- What can most aquatic animals do to eliminate ammonia from their bodies?
- How do mammals and reptiles differ in the way they excrete nitrogenous wastes?

ADJUST INSTRUCTION

For any question that received a thumbs-down or waving-hand sign, ask students to find where the topic is discussed in the text and write a one- or two-sentence answer to the question. Ask volunteers to read their answers to the class.

Answers

FIGURE 27–15 Their kidneys produce lots of watery urine, and they don't drink.

Excretion in Terrestrial Animals

How do land animals remove wastes while conserving water?

Land animals also face challenges. In dry environments, they can lose large amounts of water from respiratory membranes that must be kept moist. In addition, they must eliminate nitrogenous wastes in ways that require disposing of water—even though they may not be able to drink water. **Figure 27–16** shows the excretory systems of some terrestrial animals.

Terrestrial Invertebrates **Some terrestrial invertebrates, including annelids and mollusks, produce urine in nephridia.** **Nephridia** (singular: nephridium) are tubelike excretory structures that filter body fluid. Typically, body fluid enters the nephridia through openings called nephrostomes and becomes more concentrated as it moves along the tubes. Urine leaves the body through excretory pores. **Other terrestrial invertebrates, such as insects and arachnids, convert ammonia into uric acid.** Nitrogenous wastes, such as uric acid, are absorbed from body fluids by structures called **Malpighian tubules,** which concentrate the wastes and add them to digestive wastes traveling through the gut. As water is absorbed from these wastes, they form crystals that form a thick paste, which leaves the body through the anus. This paste contains little water, so this process minimizes water loss.

Terrestrial Vertebrates In terrestrial vertebrates, excretion is carried out mostly by the kidneys. **Mammals and land amphibians convert ammonia into urea, which is excreted in urine. In most reptiles and birds, ammonia is converted into uric acid.** Reptiles and birds pass uric acid through ducts into a cavity that also receives digestive wastes from the gut. The walls of this cavity absorb most of the water from the wastes, causing the uric acid to separate out as white crystals. The result is a thick, milky-white paste that you would recognize as "bird droppings."

Quick Lab GUIDED INQUIRY

Water and Nitrogen Excretion

1. Label one test tube Urea and the other Uric Acid. Place 2 grams of urea in the one labeled Urea. Place 2 grams of uric acid in the one labeled Uric Acid.
2. Add 15 mL of water to each test tube. Stopper and shake the test tubes for 3 minutes.
3. Observe each test tube. Record your observations.

Analyze and Conclude

1. **Observe** Which substance—urea or uric acid—is less soluble in water? Explain.
2. **Infer** Reptiles excrete nitrogenous wastes in the form of uric acid. How does this adaptation help reptiles survive on land?

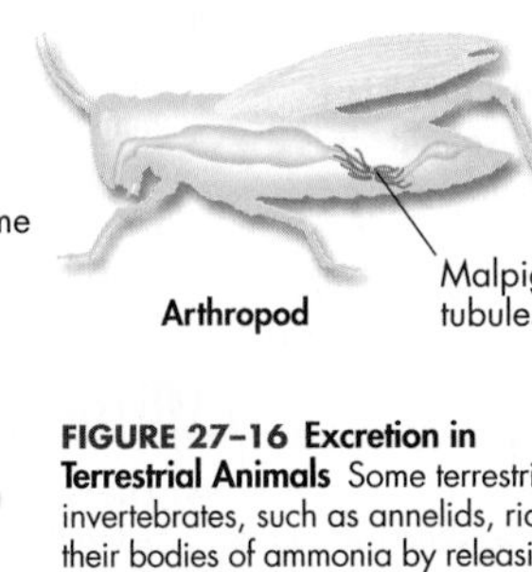

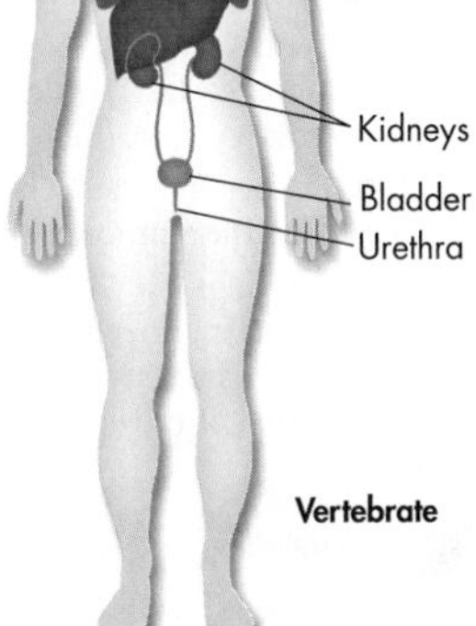

FIGURE 27–16 Excretion in Terrestrial Animals Some terrestrial invertebrates, such as annelids, rid their bodies of ammonia by releasing urine created in their nephridia (left). Some insects and arachnids have Malpighian tubules, which absorb uric acid from body fluids and combine it with digestive wastes (above). In vertebrates, such as humans, excretion is carried out mostly by the kidneys (right).

Lead a Discussion

Use **Figure 27–16** to discuss excretion in terrestrial animals. Point out that the three systems shown in the figure are representative examples, and that other land invertebrates and vertebrates have similar, if not identical, systems. In discussing each example, call on students to read aloud related material in the text.

DIFFERENTIATED INSTRUCTION

ELL English Language Learners Have English language learners work with native English speakers to practice the pronunciation and develop understanding of challenging terms related to excretion, including *nephridia, nitrogenous wastes,* and *Malpighian tubules.*

ELL Focus on ELL: Extend Language

INTERMEDIATE, ADVANCED, AND ADVANCED HIGH SPEAKERS Have students fill in a **Vocabulary Word Map** for the term *excretion.* First, ask them to write *excretion* in the top rectangle. As they read the lesson, have them think of words and concepts that relate to excretion and write them in the rectangles below. Accept short phrases from intermediate speakers. Encourage advanced speakers to write complete sentences. Require advanced high speakers to use complex sentences that show they fully understand the lesson concepts. Then, lead a discussion about students' maps and how they relate to the lesson material.

Study Wkbks A/B, Appendix S32, Vocabulary Word Map. **Transparencies,** GO17.

PURPOSE Students will be able to infer how a nitrogenous waste's solubility affects excretion.

MATERIALS 2 test tubes, 2 stoppers, test-tube rack, graduated cylinder, balance, urea, uric acid, glass-marking pencil

SAFETY Read safety information for urea and uric acid before doing the lab. Make sure students wear goggles, a lab apron, and heat-resistant gloves. Caution them to handle glassware carefully and not to touch any broken glass. Have students wash their hands when finished.

PLANNING Before the lab, discuss why terrestrial animals must conserve water. Review solubility with students, and explain that some substances dissolve easily in water, while others do not.

ANALYZE AND CONCLUDE

1. Uric acid is less soluble. The solution of urea appears to be clear, whereas the uric acid produced solid crystals in the water.
2. Sample answer: To live successfully on land, reptiles must conserve water. Because uric acid crystallizes as a solid precipitate in water, it does not carry water with it when it is excreted from the body.

Assess and Remediate

EVALUATE UNDERSTANDING

Play a game in which you give students the answers to questions about animal excretion and students respond with the right questions. Students can play the game in teams or as individuals. Then, have students complete the 27.4 Assessment.

REMEDIATION SUGGESTION

L1 **Struggling Students** If your students have trouble answering **Question 3b,** ask them to think about which of the two compounds are soluble in water. Point out that the insoluble compound uric acid does not take water with it when it is eliminated from the body. Therefore, excreting uric acid rather than urea conserves water.

BIOLOGY.com Students can check their understanding of lesson concepts with the **Self-Test** assessment. They can then take an online version of the **Lesson Assessment.**

Adaptations to Extreme Environments The kidneys of most terrestrial vertebrates are remarkable organs, but the way they operate results in some limitations. Most vertebrate kidneys, for example, cannot excrete concentrated salt. That's why most vertebrates cannot survive by drinking seawater. All that extra salt would overwhelm the kidneys, and the animal would die of dehydration. Some marine reptiles and birds, such as the petrel in **Figure 27–17,** have evolved specialized glands in their heads that excrete very concentrated salt solutions. Another remarkable excretory adaptation is found in the kangaroo rats of the American southwest. The kidneys of these desert rodents produce urine that is 25 times more concentrated than their blood! In addition, their intestines are so good at absorbing water that their feces are almost dry.

FIGURE 27–17 Excretion Adaptations Some terrestrial animals that spend a large amount of time in salt water, such as this petrel, have special adaptations to rid themselves of excess salt. This bird, which hunts for fish in the ocean, has special glands in its nostrils that separate salt from the water it swallows and excrete the salt as a thick, sticky fluid.

27.4 Assessment

Review Key Concepts 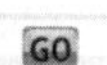

1. a. Review Why does the metabolic waste ammonia pose a problem for all animals?

b. Explain How do insects, reptiles, and birds eliminate ammonia? How do mammals and some amphibians eliminate it?

c. Apply Concepts How do kidneys help maintain homeostasis while processing nitrogenous wastes?

2. a. Review In general, how do aquatic animals address the ammonia problem?

b. Compare and Contrast How do the differing water balance needs of freshwater animals and saltwater animals explain the difference in their excretion of nitrogenous wastes?

3. a. Review In what form do (a) annelids and mollusks, (b) insects and arachnids, (c) mammals and land amphibians, and (d) reptiles and birds excrete nitrogenous wastes?

b. Relate Cause and Effect Explain how differing water balance needs relate to an animal's conversion of ammonia to either urea or uric acid.

BUILD VOCABULARY

4. The Greek word *ouron,* meaning "urine," has led to the root *uro-*, of *urea* and *uric* (acid). Why is it appropriate that these two words are each formed from a root word meaning "urine"?

BIOLOGY.com Search Lesson 27.4 GO • Self-Test • Lesson Assessment

Assessment Answers

1a. Ammonia is poisonous.

1b. Insects convert ammonia into uric acid. Some insects have Malpighian tubules, which absorb uric acid from body fluids and combine it with digestive wastes. In most reptiles and birds, ammonia is converted to uric acid, which is separated out from other wastes as white crystals. Mammals and land amphibians convert ammonia into urea, which is excreted as urine.

1c. Kidneys separate nitrogenous wastes and excess water from blood. This helps maintain the proper balance of water in blood and body tissues.

2a. In general, aquatic animals can allow ammonia to diffuse out of their bodies into surrounding water, which dilutes the ammonia and carries it away.

2b. For freshwater animals, the concentration of water in their environments is higher than the concentration in their body fluids. As a result, they excrete water through kidneys that produce lots of watery urine. The bodies of saltwater animals contain a lower concentration of salt than the water they live in. So, they conserve water by producing very little concentrated urine.

3a. (a) urine, (b) in crystals that form a thick paste, (c) urine, (d) thick, milky white paste

3b. Sample answer: Animals that need to conserve water convert ammonia into uric acid, which is less soluble in water. Animals that do not have as great a need to conserve water convert ammonia into urea, which is highly soluble in water.

BUILD VOCABULARY

4. Sample answer: Both urea and uric acid are nitrogenous compounds that animals excrete. Urea is one component of urine.

Technology & BIOLOGY

IN **NoS.10** Scientific discoveries and technologies.

Bioartificial Kidneys

Hundreds of thousands of people suffer from kidney failure. Kidneys eliminate wastes from blood while retaining vital compounds, so if your kidneys fail, you can die, poisoned by your own nitrogenous wastes. Because kidney function is so important, researchers are always working on better replacements for it.

Today's techniques save lives but are far from ideal. Techniques such as artificial kidney dialysis pass a patient's blood through a system of extremely fine tubes that retain blood cells and vital proteins while filtering out wastes, which are discarded. But important compounds are also filtered out, and they must be given back to the patient intravenously.

A technique invented by Dr. H. David Humes at the University of Michigan could eliminate this drawback. It combines the technique above with the latest in biotechnology to produce what is called a renal tubule assist device, or RAD. Tiny tubes (blue in the figure to the right) are lined with a matrix (shown in yellow) on which living cells can grow. The matrix-covered tubes are then "seeded" with cells from kidneys that were donated for transplant but could not be used. When properly cared for, these kidney cells grow one layer thick (shown in pink) to cover the matrix.

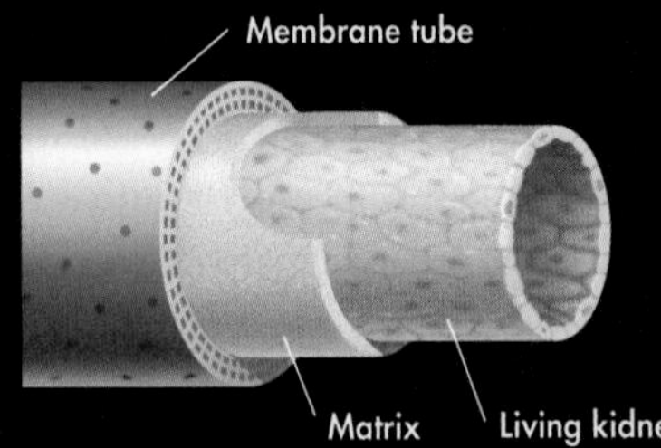

During treatment, the fluid that would normally be discarded is passed through the inside of these tubes, while the patient's blood passes by on the other side. The living kidney cells then act on the waste fluid, returning valuable compounds like glucose to the blood, and adding the important compounds made in healthy kidneys. Researchers hope that this technique can someday improve the lives of the many people whose kidneys fail.

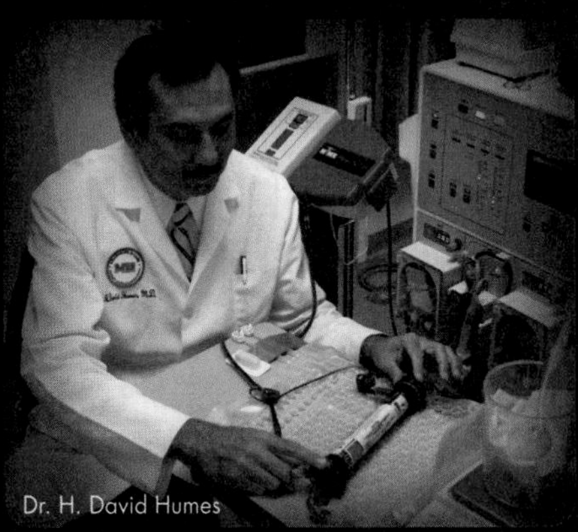

Dr. H. David Humes

WRITING If possible, interview someone who has undergone kidney dialysis, asking about five questions you have about the experience. Transcribe your interview, and include a short introduction to the topic. Alternately, read about the experience of kidney dialysis, and write a one-page summary.

Teach

Lead a Discussion

Make sure students understand the advantage that bioartificial kidneys have over artificial kidney dialysis.

Ask How does artificial kidney dialysis help a person who has kidney failure? *(Sample answer: by performing the functions the person's kidneys would by filtering out harmful wastes from the person's blood)*

Direct students' attention to the illustration of the renal tubule assist device.

Ask Where do the living kidney cells in the RAD come from? *(from kidneys that were donated for transplants but couldn't be used)*

Ask What do those cells do that an artificial dialysis machine can't do? *(Sample answer: The cells filter the waste fluid from kidney dialysis and separate the valuable compounds from wastes that need to be discarded. The cells return the valuable compounds back to the person's blood.)*

DIFFERENTIATED INSTRUCTION

L3 **Advanced Students** Ask students to use online or library resources to find out more about kidney disease. Have them investigate causes of kidney disease as well as more about what treatments are available, including kidney transplants and different kinds of kidney dialysis. Students should prepare a written report of what they find, with reliable sources cited for all facts included.

Quick Facts

KIDNEY DISEASE AND TREATMENT

Kidney disease is a serious problem for millions of Americans. Here are some facts about kidney disease and treatment.

- According to the Centers for Disease Control and Prevention (CDC), an estimated 26 million adult Americans have chronic kidney disease, whether they know it or not.
- The main causes of kidney disease are diabetes, hypertension, and heredity.
- There are two main forms of kidney dialysis. In hemodialysis, a patient's blood is drawn from the body and filtered through a dialysis machine. In peritoneal dialysis, a fluid is put into the abdomen that captures waste products; after a few hours the fluid and wastes are drained away.

Answers

WRITING Tell students that not all people want to talk about their illnesses, but they might have a relative or family friend who will. Alternatively, students might contact a treatment facility in the area and set up an interview with one of the nurses or technicians who help carry out artificial kidney dialysis. Make sure students prepare interview questions in advance. Review the questions before students ask them.

IN INDIANA ACADEMIC STANDARDS

For the full text of all standards, see the Course Overview in the front matter of this book.

CHAPTER LAB

Pre-Lab

Introduce students to the concepts they will explore in the chapter lab by assigning the Pre-Lab questions.

Lab

Tell students they will perform the chapter lab *Anatomy of a Squid* described in **Lab Manual A.**

 **Struggling Students** A simpler version of the chapter lab is provided in **Lab Manual B.**

SAFETY

Students should wear goggles, a lab apron, and disposable plastic gloves when dissecting the animals. Caution students to handle the scalpel, dissecting scissors, and dissecting pins with care. Make sure they wash their hands at the end of the lab.

BIOLOGY.com Look online for **Editable Lab Worksheets.**

For corresponding pre-lab in the **Foundation Edition**, see page 660.

Skills Lab

GUIDED INQUIRY

Pre-Lab: Anatomy of a Squid

Problem What structures does a squid use to obtain nutrients and eliminate wastes?

Materials squid, dissecting tray, hand lens, forceps, dissecting scissors, dissecting pins, dissecting probe

Lab Manual Chapter 27 Lab

Skills Focus Observe, Infer, Sequence, Draw Conclusions

Connect to the Big idea All animals obtain their food by eating other organisms. All animals need a way to digest the food, and most animals need a way to circulate the absorbed nutrients to all the cells in the body. Animals also need to absorb oxygen from their environment for cellular respiration. Finally, animals need to rid their bodies of wastes.

The ways that animals meet these needs vary greatly. Often, different habitats require different structures. For example, an animal that must obtain its oxygen from air will not have the same respiratory structures as an animal that must obtain its oxygen from water. In this lab, you will dissect a squid and observe parts of several body systems.

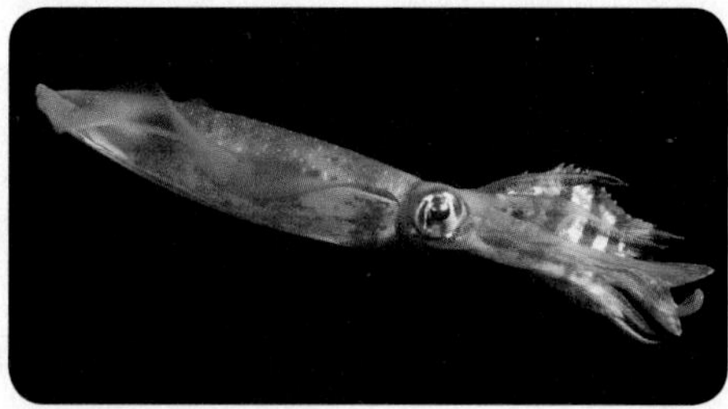

Background Questions

a. Compare and Contrast How are a gastrovascular cavity and a digestive tract different?

b. Review What process takes place in all respiratory structures?

c. Compare and Contrast What is the difference between an open and a closed circulatory system?

Pre-Lab Questions

Preview the procedure in the lab manual.

1. Interpret Visuals What structure can you use to distinguish the ventral side of a squid from the dorsal side?

2. Infer Why is it important to lift the mantle while cutting it?

3. Predict What do you expect the gills to look like, and why?

BIOLOGY.com Search Chapter 27 

Visit Chapter 27 online to test yourself on chapter content and to find activities to help you learn.

Untamed Science Video Trek carefully with the Untamed Science crew as they get up close and personal with bears to learn about their adaptations.

Art in Motion What happens when fresh and salt-water fishes excrete water or salt? Find out by watching this animation.

Art Review Review your knowledge of the different types of respiratory systems with this activity.

InterActive Art See how single- and double-loop circulation systems compare.

Data Analysis Investigate the relationship between body size, tracheal structure and the amount of atmospheric oxygen to understand why insects were larger in the Paleozoic than they are today.

Visual Analogy Compare the structure and function of the types of teeth with common objects.

Pre-Lab Answers

BACKGROUND QUESTIONS

a. A gastrovascular cavity has a single opening through which food is ingested and wastes are expelled. A digestive tract has two openings, one for ingesting food and one for expelling wastes.

b. Sample answer: In all respiratory structures gases diffuse across a selectively permeable membrane.

c. In an open circulatory system, blood is only partially contained within a system of blood vessels as it travels through the body. In a closed circulatory system, blood circulates entirely within blood vessels.

PRE-LAB QUESTIONS

1. The siphon is located on the ventral side.

2. Sample answer: If the mantle is not lifted, the scissors may cut through the organs that lie beneath the mantle.

3. Sample answer: Because gas exchange takes place in the gills, I expect the gills to have a large surface area.

27 Study Guide

Big idea Structure and Function

The circulatory system transports nutrients from the digestive system and oxygen from the respiratory system to body cells. It then transports cellular waste to the excretory system and carbon dioxide to the respiratory system.

27.1 Feeding and Digestion

Most filter feeders catch algae and small animals by using modified gills or other structures as nets that filter food items out of water. Detritivores feed on detritus. Carnivores eat other animals. Herbivores eat plants or parts of plants. Nutritional symbionts rely upon symbiosis.

Some invertebrates break down food primarily through intracellular digestion, but many animals use extracellular digestion.

Carnivores typically have sharp mouthparts or other structures that capture food, hold it, and cut it into small pieces. Herbivores typically have mouthparts adapted to rasping or grinding.

intracellular digestion (784) digestive tract (784)
extracellular digestion (784) rumen (786)
gastrovascular cavity (784)

27.2 Respiration

Respiratory structures provide a large surface area of moist, selectively permeable membrane and maintain a difference in the concentrations of oxygen and carbon dioxide on either side of the respiratory membrane, promoting diffusion.

Many aquatic invertebrates and most aquatic chordates other than reptiles and mammals exchange gases through gills. Aquatic reptiles and aquatic mammals, such as whales, breathe with lungs and must hold their breath underwater.

Respiratory structures in terrestrial invertebrates include skin, mantle cavities, book lungs and tracheal tubes. Terrestrial vertebrates breathe with lungs.

gill (788) lung (788) alveolus (790)

27.3 Circulation

In an open circulatory system, blood is only partially contained within blood vessels. In a closed circulatory system, blood circulates entirely within blood vessels.

Most vertebrates with gills have a single-loop circulatory system with a single pump that forces blood around the body in one direction. Most vertebrates that use lungs for respiration have a double-loop, two-pump circulatory system.

heart (791) atrium (792)
open circulatory system (791) ventricle (792)
closed circulatory system (792)

27.4 Excretion

Animals either eliminate ammonia from the body quickly or convert it into other nitrogenous compounds that are less toxic.

Aquatic animals allow ammonia to diffuse out of their bodies into surrounding water.

Some terrestrial invertebrates, including annelids and mollusks, produce urine in nephridia. Other terrestrial invertebrates, such as insects and arachnids, convert ammonia into uric acid. Mammals and land amphibians convert ammonia into urea. Most reptiles and birds convert ammonia into uric acid.

excretion (794) nephridium (797)
kidney (795) Malpighian tubule (797)

Think Visually

Fill in the table below showing different types of animals and their differing respiratory structures.

Animal Type	Aquatic Invertebrates	2	Land Invertebrates	4
Respiratory Structures	1	Reptiles and mammals—lungs; Others—gills	3	Lungs

Study Online

REVIEW AND ASSESSMENT RESOURCES

Editable Worksheets Pages of Study Workbooks A and B, Lab Manuals A and B, and the Assessment Resources Book are available online. These documents can be easily edited using a word-processing program.

Lesson Overview Have students reread the Lesson Overviews to help them study chapter concepts.

Vocabulary Review The *Flash Cards* and *Match It* provide an interactive way to review chapter vocabulary.

Chapter Assessment Have students take an online version of the Chapter 27 Assessment.

Standardized Test Prep Students can take an online version of the Standardized Test Prep. You will recieve their scores along with ideas for remediation.

Diagnostic and Benchmark Tests Use these tests to monitor your students' progress and supply remediation.

UbD Performance Tasks

SUMMATIVE TASK Have students work in pairs to prepare an illustrated pamphlet about one kind of animal. Students can focus on any invertebrate or vertebrate. The pamphlet should describe what structures and processes the animal uses to obtain essential materials and eliminate wastes. It should also include information about how the animal obtains food, how food is digested, what kind of respiratory and circulatory systems the animal has, and how it manages nitrogenous wastes.

TRANSFER TASK Have students work in small groups to create an animal that doesn't exist but might have existed if animals had evolved differently. Remind students that their animal should be well adapted to its environment. Each group should prepare a "field report" about its animal, with descriptions and sketches, as if members of the group were researchers who had just discovered a new organism. The report should include information on its methods of feeding, digestion, respiration, circulation, and excretion.

Answers

THINK VISUALLY

1. Body covering; gills
2. Aquatic Vertebrates
3. Skin; mantle cavities; book lungs; tracheal tubes
4. Land Vertebrates

Lesson 27.1

UNDERSTAND KEY CONCEPTS

1. a **2.** c **3.** b

4. In intracellular digestion, food is digested inside specialized cells that pass nutrients to other cells by diffusion. In extracellular digestion, food is broken down outside cells in a digestive system and then absorbed into cells.

5. Canine teeth, prominent in carnivorous mammals, are pointed teeth used for piercing, gripping, and tearing. In herbivorous mammals, canines are reduced or absent. Molars in herbivorous mammals are broad, flattened teeth adapted for grinding. Molars in carnivorous mammals have sharp edges for slicing and dicing meat.

6. Many vertebrate filter feeders feed while swimming.

THINK CRITICALLY

7. It practices extracellular digestion, because a digestive tract breaks down food into nutrients that cells can absorb.

8. Sample answer: Do birds that require more energy eat more foods with higher energy content than birds that require less energy do?

Lesson 27.2

UNDERSTAND KEY CONCEPTS

9. b **10.** d **11.** a

12. Sample answer: Spiders respire using organs called book lungs, which are made of parallel, sheetlike layers of thin tissues that contain blood vessels. Most insects have a system of tracheal tubes that extend throughout the body. Air enters and leaves the system through openings in the body surface called spiracles.

13. lungs

14. They breathe with lungs. Lungs cannot exchange gases in water, so these animals must hold their breath underwater.

THINK CRITICALLY

15. Earthworms can respire across their skins as long as the skin stays moist. If they remained above ground, the skin would dry out and the earthworms could not respire.

16. The mucus keeps the surface of the cavity moist; probably so that gases may diffuse more efficiently across the membrane.

27 Assessment

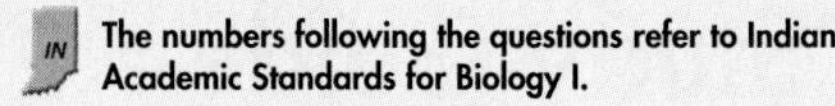

IN
The numbers following the questions refer to Indiana's Academic Standards for Biology I.

27.1 Feeding and Digestion

Understand Key Concepts

1. An animal that relies primarily on intracellular digestion is the
a. sponge. **c.** dragonfly.
b. clam. **d.** earthworm.

2. Animals that obtain food by ingesting decaying bits of plant and animal material are called
a. herbivores. **c.** detritivores.
b. carnivores. **d.** filter feeders.

3. Algae that live in the bodies of reef-building corals are
a. parasitic symbionts.
b. mutualistic symbionts.
c. occupants that have no effect on the coral animals.
d. consumed as food by the coral animals.

4. Compare the processes of intracellular and extracellular digestion.

5. Describe the differences between the canine and molar teeth of herbivorous and carnivorous mammals.

6. How do vertebrate filter feeders obtain food?

Think Critically

7. **Classify** You are observing an animal that has a digestive tract. Does this animal practice intracellular digestion or extracellular digestion? Explain your answer.

8. **Pose Questions** Hummingbirds eat high-energy foods, such as nectar. Many ducks eat foods that contain less energy, such as plant leaves. What are some research questions you could investigate to discover more about the diet of a bird species and its energy needs?

27.2 Respiration

Understand Key Concepts

9. Most terrestrial insects breathe using a network of structures called
a. gills. **c.** book gills.
b. tracheal tubes. **d.** book lungs.

10. In order for the exchange of oxygen and carbon dioxide to take place, an animal's respiratory surfaces must be kept
a. cold. **c.** hot.
b. dry. **d.** moist.

11. Most fishes exchange gases by pumping water from their mouths
a. over their gills.
b. through the lungs.
c. over their atria.
d. through their esophagus.

12. Describe two types of respiratory structures found in terrestrial invertebrates.

13. What respiratory structures do all terrestrial vertebrates possess?

14. With what respiratory structures do aquatic reptiles and aquatic mammals breathe? What inconvenience does this cause when they are underwater?

Think Critically

15. **Predict** During heavy rains, earthworms often emerge from their burrows. What might happen to an earthworm if it did not return to its burrow when the ground dried out?

16. **Infer** Land snails have a respiratory structure called a mantle cavity, which is covered with mucus. What might the purpose of the mucus be?

27.3 Circulation

Understand Key Concepts

17. Most arthropods have
a. no circulatory system.
b. an open circulatory system.
c. a closed circulatory system.
d. skin gills.

18. In a closed circulatory system, blood
a. comes in direct contact with tissues.
b. remains within blood vessels.
c. empties into sinuses.
d. does not transport oxygen.

Lesson 27.3

UNDERSTAND KEY CONCEPTS

17. b **18.** b **19.** c

20. Sample answer: The gills are where gas exchange takes place, which is the function of the respiratory system. Inside the gill membranes is a network of tiny, thin-walled blood vessels called capillaries, which are part of the circulatory system. Blood that flows through the capillaries brings carbon dioxide to the gills and carries oxygen from the gills to the body's cells. This process supplies the body with the oxygen it needs and removes the carbon dioxide.

21. A mammal has a closed circulatory system that has double-loop circulation and a four-chambered heart.

22. In single-loop circulation, a single pump forces blood around the body in one direction. In double-loop circulation, a pump powered by one side of the heart forces oxygen-poor blood from the heart to the lungs. After the blood picks up oxygen, it returns to the heart, and the other side of the heart pumps the blood through the second circulatory loop to the rest of the body.

19. Most chordates that have gills for respiration have a(n)
   a. double-loop circulatory system.
   b. accessory lung.
   c. single-loop circulatory system.
   d. four-chambered heart.

20. In the gills of aquatic animals, how do the respiratory and circulatory systems interact?

21. Describe the circulatory system of a mammal as open or closed, and state the number of loops and the number of heart chambers.

22. Compare single-loop circulation and double-loop circulation.

Think Critically

23. **Interpret Graphics** The diagrams below represent two kinds of circulatory systems.

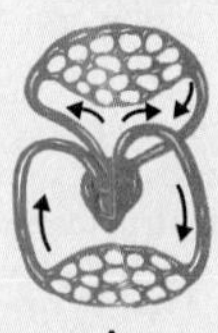
A

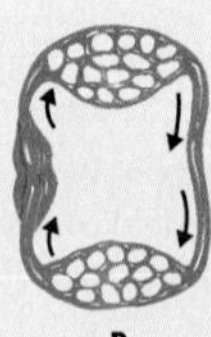
B

   a. Which diagram illustrates a heart with blood containing carbon dioxide but little oxygen?
   b. Which diagram shows a circulatory system with a four-chambered heart?

24. **Apply Concepts** How do a fish's respiratory and circulatory systems work together to maintain homeostasis in the body as a whole?

27.4 Excretion

Understand Key Concepts

25. The composition of and levels of body fluids in mammals are controlled by the
   a. lungs. c. intestine.
   b. kidneys. d. heart.

26. The elimination of metabolic wastes from the body is called
   a. excretion. c. respiration.
   b. circulation. d. digestion.

27. Why do most animals convert ammonia into urea or uric acid?

solve the CHAPTER MYSTERY

(NEAR) DEATH BY SALT WATER

Luckily, the pick-up the group arranged arrived earlier than planned. They rushed the sick man to a hospital, where he was diagnosed with severe dehydration and given water and intravenous fluids. If he had gone much longer without treatment, doctors told his friends, he would have died. What had happened? Why didn't his friends suffer the same problems?

As sailors have known for centuries, humans can't drink seawater for any length of time. But why *can't* we drink seawater?

Because seawater is saltier than human blood and body fluids, drinking it loads the body with excess salt. Human kidneys cannot produce urine with salt concentrations high enough to get rid of that salt efficiently. So the kidneys are forced to excrete more water in urine than the amount of salt water consumed. This lowers body water content to the point that blood literally becomes thicker and harder to push through fine capillary networks. Cells and tissues begin to dehydrate, and fatal kidney failure can result.

1. **Compare and Contrast** While the group member who drank seawater became seriously ill, the other group members experienced some water stress as well. What was going on in their circulatory and excretory systems, and why was it not as serious?
2. **Propose a Solution** If you were marooned on an island that had no fresh water, what would be your plan for getting some?
3. **Connect to the Big idea** Although humans can't drink salt water, and can't exist without fresh water, many marine birds and reptiles can do either or both. Using the Web, research the different strategies other animals use to regulate salt content and water balance.

THINK CRITICALLY

23. a. B, **b.** A

24. The fish's respiratory system takes in oxygen from the water that passes over the gills. The oxygen diffuses into the blood through capillaries in the gills, and the circulatory system carries the oxygen to body cells. The waste product, carbon dioxide, is removed from the body as the circulatory system carries the gas to the gills, where it passes from the body. By bringing in oxygen and getting rid of carbon dioxide, the two systems help maintain a fish's homeostasis.

ASSESSMENT

CHAPTER MYSTERY After students have read through the Chapter Mystery, discuss the importance to terrestrial vertebrates of having an adequate supply of fresh water for drinking.

Ask How does water cross kidney membranes? *(Kidneys pump ions from salt across their membranes to create osmotic gradients. Water then follows those ions passively.)*

Point out that if the kidneys pumped too many ions from salt across their membranes, too much water would follow, depriving the body of the water it needs to function well. That is a reason why kidneys cannot excrete excess salt.

Ask How do saltwater fishes solve the problems of losing water to their salty environment and gaining salt from it? *(They produce very small amounts of concentrated urine, and they actively pump salt out across their gills.)*

Emphasize that humans are adapted to land, not to seawater, and do not have the adaptations to conserve water and pump out salt that saltwater fishes have.

CHAPTER MYSTERY ANSWERS

1. Sample answer: Although the other group members took in some water by drinking the coconut "milk," they probably didn't get enough water to keep their circulatory and excretory systems functioning normally. The lack of fresh water caused some water stress in these group members.
2. Sample answer: You could collect condensation underneath smooth surfaces at night, collect rainwater if it were available, and eat juicy plants.
3. Big idea Have students use Internet search engines to find out about the strategies marine reptiles and marine birds use to regulate water balance. They should find, for example, that some reptiles get their water mostly or solely from food. Students should also learn that some marine birds and reptiles have salt glands that secrete a salty solution from their body. These and other adaptations allow birds and reptiles to live in extreme environments where there is little fresh water or mostly salt water available.

To explore how bears have adapted to survive in extreme environments, have students watch the short video **Bearly Asleep.**

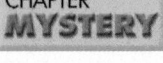

ASSESSMENT

Lesson 27.4

UNDERSTAND KEY CONCEPTS

25. b **26.** a

27. Ammonia is poisonous, and urea and uric acid are nitrogenous compounds that are less toxic than ammonia.

28. In freshwater fishes, the kidneys produce lots of watery urine, because their bodies contain a higher concentration of salt than the water they live in, and they take in excess water by osmosis. In saltwater fishes, the kidneys produce very little concentrated urine, because their bodies contain a lower concentration of salt than the water they live in, and they take in excess salt and lose water by osmosis.

THINK CRITICALLY

29. Small aquatic animals are able to rid their bodies of ammonia quickly, allowing it to diffuse into the water.

30. Terrestrial animals must remove wastes while conserving water.

Connecting Concepts

USE SCIENCE GRAPHICS

31. Caffeine causes a rise in the heart rate.

32. Sample answer: The heart rate may further increase, but after rising sharply with the third drop, the rate seems to be leveling off. Therefore, the rate would probably not increase much more with five or more drops.

WRITE ABOUT SCIENCE

33. Sample answer: Fishes have a single-loop circulation system with a two-chambered heart. The one atrium receives blood from the body, and the one ventricle pumps blood out of the heart to the gills and then to the rest of the body. Mammals have a double-loop circulation system with a four-chambered heart. One side of the heart forces oxygen-poor blood from the heart to the lungs. After the blood picks up oxygen and returns to the heart, the other side of the heart forces the blood through the second circulatory loop to the rest of the body.

34. Big idea Sample answer: A digestive tract allows animals to take in food whenever it is available and, at the same time, continue digesting a previous meal. An animal with a gastrovascular cavity, which has only one opening, must digest food and expel wastes before more food can be taken in.

28. What is the difference in kidney function of freshwater fishes and saltwater fishes?

Think Critically

29. Infer The excretory systems of terrestrial invertebrates, such as earthworms, convert ammonia to less toxic substances. Explain why this change is unnecessary in small aquatic invertebrates, such as planarians.

30. Apply Concepts Of all the nitrogenous wastes eliminated by animals, uric acid requires the least water to excrete. Why is the production of uric acid an advantage to animals that live on land?

Connecting Concepts

Use Science Graphics NoS.3

A student conducts an experiment to measure the effect of caffeine on the heart rate of a small pond-water crustacean called Daphnia. The heart of this animal is visible through its transparent shell. With the help of a dissecting microscope, the student counts the heartbeats per minute before and after adding increasing amounts of coffee to the water surrounding the animal. Each data point in the graph at the top right represents the mean of five trials. Use the graph to answer questions 31 and 32.

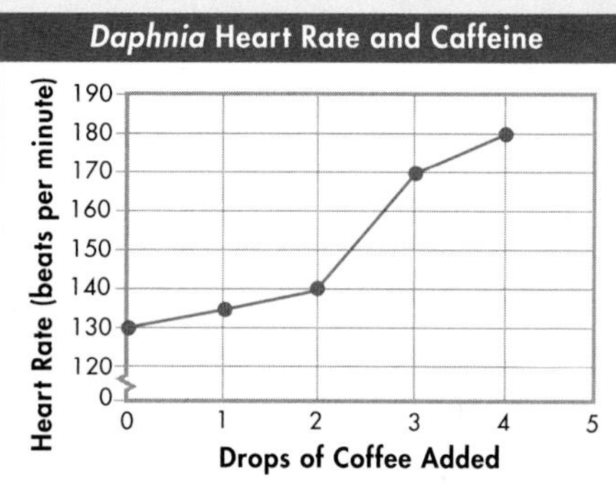

31. Interpret Graphs Describe the effect of caffeine on the heart rate of *Daphnia*.

32. Predict What would be your prediction of the effect of five or more drops of coffee on the heart rate of *Daphnia*?

Write About Science NoS.3

33. Explanation Write a paragraph in which you compare and contrast the structures and functions of the heart of a fish and the heart of a mammal.

34. Assess the Big idea Explain why a digestive tract is a more efficient structure for taking in and processing the food eaten by a large animal than a gastrovascular cavity would be.

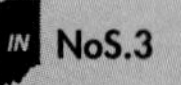

NoS.3

A researcher conducted an experiment to see how air temperature affects the speed at which a snake can hunt for food. The experimenter placed the snake a fixed distance away from a piece of food and recorded the air temperature. Then, she recorded the time it took for the snake to reach the food. She repeated the experiment four times. Each time, the experimenter changed the air temperature. The data are shown to the right.

35. Interpret Tables At what temperature did the snake reach the food the fastest?

36. Analyze Data How did the time to reach the food change as the temperature increased?

37. Draw Conclusions What conclusion about snake hunting and temperature can you draw from the data?

The Effect of Temperature on Snake Hunting Speed

Temperature (°C)	Time (seconds)
4	51
10	50
15	43
21	37
27	35

PURPOSE Students will analyze data to understand how air temperature affects a snake's ability to hunt for food.

PLANNING Discuss body temperature regulation in reptiles with your students. Point out the difference between ectotherms and endotherms.

ANSWERS

35. 27°C

36. The time decreased as the temperature increased.

37. Sample answer: Snake hunting is affected by temperature—the higher the temperature, the faster a snake can move.

Standardized Test Practice for Indiana

Multiple Choice

1. Animals that live on an animal and feed on its body tissues are called
   A parasites.
   B carnivores.
   C herbivores.
   D detritivores.

2. Examining the teeth of an animal can give information about whether it
   A practices intracellular or extracellular digestion.
   B is a filter feeder or a detritivore.
   C is a nutritional symbiont.
   D is a herbivore or a carnivore.

3. Movement of oxygen and carbon dioxide across a respiratory surface requires
   A that the respiratory surface be moist.
   B active transport by the cells of the respiratory surface.
   C alveoli.
   D an equal concentration of both gases on both sides of the membrane.

4. In an open circulatory system, blood
   A is confined to blood vessels at all times.
   B circulates around body tissues.
   C exchanges gases with lung alveoli.
   D is not required for exchanging gases with body cells.

5. In chordates with four-chambered hearts, there is
   A only one loop in the circulatory system.
   B mixing of oxygen-rich and oxygen-poor blood.
   C partial partition of the ventricle.
   D no mixing of oxygen-rich and oxygen-poor blood.

6. Most reptiles excrete wastes in the form of
   A urea.
   B ammonia.
   C uric acid.
   D toxins.

7. What is a function of the excretory system?
   A to supply cells with oxygen and nutrients
   B to rid the body of metabolic wastes
   C to exchange oxygen and carbon dioxide with the environment
   D to break down food

Questions 8–9

A biology student is investigating the relationship between cricket chirping and air temperature. She catches a cricket and places it in a jar. She leaves the jar outside, and each day she counts the number of chirps during a 15-second period. At the same time, she records the outside temperature near the cricket. Her data for a 5-day period are shown below.

Temperature and Cricket Chirping

Day	Number of Chirps in 15 Seconds	Outside Temperature (°C)
Monday	31	23
Tuesday	20	16
Wednesday	12	11
Thursday	29	21
Friday	25	19

8. At which of the following temperatures would a cricket be most likely to chirp 9 times in 15 seconds?
   A 10°C
   B 18°C
   C 0°C
   D 25°C
   NoS.3

9. What can the student conclude from this experiment?
   A Crickets cannot chirp more than 31 times in 15 seconds.
   B The number of times a cricket chirps decreases when the temperature decreases.
   C The number of times a cricket chirps increases when the temperature decreases.
   D There is no relationship between the number of times a cricket chirps and temperature.
   NoS.3

Open-Ended Response

10. Which types of vertebrates have double-loop circulation and which types have single-loop circulation?

If You Have Trouble With . . .

Question	1	2	3	4	5	6	7	8	9	10
See Lesson	27.1	27.1	27.2	27.3	27.3	27.4	27.4	27.3	27.3	27.3

Answers

1. A
2. D
3. A
4. B
5. D
6. C
7. B
8. A
9. B
10. Most vertebrates that use lungs for respiration have double-loop circulation. These include mammals, reptiles, birds, and adult amphibians. Most vertebrates with gills have single-loop circulation. This includes fishes.

Test-Taking Tip

USE TIME WISELY

Tell students that when they are taking a long time to answer a question on a test, they should consider moving on to the next question and coming back to the harder question later. When answering other questions, they may remember the information needed to answer the skipped question.

CHAPTER PLANNER 28 Animal Systems II

Chapter Contents	IN	Time	Core Resources
Chapter Preview			**Student Edition,** pp. 806–807 **Chapter Mystery,** p. 807
28.1 Response How Animals Respond • Trends in Nervous System Evolution • Sensory Systems		1 period ½ block	**Student Edition,** pp. 808–813 **Inquiry** 28.1 Quick Lab, p. 810 L2 **Study Workbook A** 28.1 Worksheets L2 **Biology.com** *Art Review:* Vertebrate Brains **Assessment Resources Book** Visual Quiz L2
28.2 Movement and Support Types of Skeletons • Muscles and Movement		1 period ½ block	**Student Edition,** pp. 814–818 **Inquiry** 28.2 Quick Lab, p. 816 L2 **Study Workbook A** 28.2 Worksheets L2 **Biology.com** *InterActive Art:* Sea Star Water Vascular System • *Art in Motion:* Muscles and Joints • 28.2 Self-Test • 28.2 Lesson Assessment
28.3 Reproduction Asexual and Sexual Reproduction • Internal and External Fertilization • Development and Growth • Reproductive Diversity in Chordates	B.6.4	1½ periods ¾ block	**Student Edition,** pp. 819–826 **Study Workbook A** 28.3 Worksheets L2 **Assessment Resources Book** Visual Quiz L2
28.4 Homeostasis Interrelationship of Body Systems • Body Temperature Control • *Biology & Society: Head for the Hills?*	NoS.3	½ period ¼ block	**Student Edition,** pp. 827–831 **Inquiry** 28.4 Analyzing Data, p. 828 L2 **Study Workbook A** 28.4 Worksheets L2 **Biology.com** *Data Analysis:* Winter Survival • 28.4 Self-Test • 28.4 Lesson Assessment
Chapter Pre-Lab	NoS.5	1 period ½ block	**Student Edition,** p. 832 L2 **Lab Manual A** *Comparing Bird and Mammal Bones* L2 • *Observing Hydra* L2

Differentiated Instruction Tools

Study Workbook B includes worksheets with lesson-level differentiated instruction support and explanations of differentiated instruction teaching strategies.

Lab Manual B includes skills labs, simplified chapter labs, and hands-on activities.

ELL Handbook explains ways to make *Biology* more accessible to ELL students.

Spanish Study Workbook is a Spanish translation of Study Workbook A.

Multilingual Glossary is the glossary translated into ten languages.

Differentiated Instruction Key

- L1 Special Needs or Struggling Students
- ELL English Language Learners
- LPR Less Proficient Readers
- L2 On-Level Students
- L3 Advanced Students

Additional Resources

Biology.com Untamed Science Video • Vocabulary Flash Cards

Study Workbook B 28.1 Worksheets L1 ELL LPR
Spanish Study Workbook 28.1 Worksheets ELL
Biology.com 28.1 Lesson Overview • 28.1 Lesson Notes • 28.1 Self-Test • 28.1 Lesson Assessment

Study Workbook B 28.2 Worksheets L1 ELL LPR
Spanish Study Workbook 28.2 Worksheets ELL
Biology.com 28.2 Lesson Overview • 28.2 Lesson Notes

Study Workbook B 28.3 Worksheets L1 ELL LPR
Spanish Study Workbook 28.3 Worksheets ELL
Biology.com 28.3 Lesson Overview • 28.3 Lesson Notes • 28.3 Self-Test • 28.3 Lesson Assessment

Study Workbook B 28.4 Worksheets L1 ELL LPR
Spanish Study Workbook 28.4 Worksheets ELL
Biology.com 28.4 Lesson Overview • 28.4 Lesson Notes

Lab Manual B *Comparing Bird and Mammal Bones* • Data Analysis: *Soaking Up Sun* L1 ELL LPR

Chapter Review

Student Edition Study Guide, p. 833 L2
Study Workbook A Chapter 28 Vocabulary Review L2 • Chapter 28 Chapter Mystery/21st Century Skills Activity L2 L3
Transparencies, pp. 316–325 L1 ELL LPR L2
Biology.com Untamed Science Video • Editable Worksheets of Study Workbooks A and B and Lab Manuals A and B • Chapter 28 Flash Cards and Match It

Untamed Science DVD • Classroom Resources CD (includes lesson presentations and editable worksheets)

Chapter Assessment

Student Edition Assessment, pp. 834–837 L2
Study Workbook B Chapter 28 Chapter Review L1 ELL LPR • Chapter 28 Taking a Standardized Test L1 ELL LPR
Assessment Resources Book Chapter 28 Test A L2 • Chapter 28 Test B L1 ELL LPR
Biology.com Chapter 28 Assessment • Editable Worksheets of Chapter 28 Visual Quizzes and Chapter 28 Tests A and B

Exam*View Assessment Suite* • Classroom Resources CD (includes lesson presentations and editable worksheets)

Time: 1 period, 1/2 block

Pressed for Time?

Preview the Chapter Introduce students to the first two Key Questions for Lessons 28.1 and 28.3. Discuss how each animal system in this chapter (Response, Movement and Support, Reproduction, and Homeostasis) might be at work in the picture on pp. 806–807.

Cover the Chapter Quickly Have students read *How Animals Respond* in Lesson 28.1 and go over Figure 28–3. Read the Key Concepts in Lesson 28.2 and use Figure 28–12 to discuss animal movement and support. In Lesson 28.3, have students read *Asexual and Sexual Reproduction, Internal and External Fertilization,* and *Reproductive Diversity in Chordates.* Assign *Body Temperature Control* in Lesson 28.4.

Assess Assign question 1 in the 28.1 Assessment, questions 1, 2, and 4 in the 28.3 Assessment, and questions 2 and 3 in the 28.4 Assessment. In the Chapter 28 Assessment, assign questions 1, 8, 17, 19–25, 27, 28, 31, 32, 34, and 39–41.

CHAPTER 28

Connect to the Big Idea

Have students look at the photograph of the penguin chicks and read the caption about how they stay warm. Point out that many penguins live on or near the coast of Antarctica, where temperatures are often quite cold, and they spend most of their lives in cold ocean water. Ask students how the feathers on a penguin help it stay warm. *(The feathers insulate the body, keeping the body heat from escaping into the environment.)* Explain that the feathers are like a coat that holds the body's heat inside. Then, ask what else they know about penguins, including what sense organs these birds have, how they move, and how they reproduce. Through a discussion of penguins, have students anticipate answers to the question, **How do the body systems of animals allow them to collect information about their environments and respond appropriately?**

Have students read over the Chapter Mystery and think about how a bonnethead shark could have become pregnant when there were no male bonnetheads in the tank with it.

BIOLOGY.com Have students preview the chapter vocabulary terms using the **Flash Cards.**

IN INDIANA ACADEMIC STANDARDS

For the full text of all standards, see the Course Overview in the front matter of this book.

Key standards: Chapter 28 covers key ideas from Standard 6: Cellular Reproduction and Gene Expression, including **B.6.4** Meiosis.

28 Animal Systems II

Big idea **Structure and Function**

Q: How do the body systems of animals allow them to collect information about their environments and respond appropriately?

BIOLOGY.com Search Chapter 28 GO • Flash Cards

806

UbD Understanding by Design

In Unit 7, students have been building toward the Enduring Understanding that *animals have evolved diverse ways to carry out basic life processes and maintain homeostasis.* In Chapter 28, students study response, movement and support, reproduction, and homeostasis in animals. The graphic organizer at the right shows how chapter content informs this Enduring Understanding.

PERFORMANCE GOALS

In Chapter 28, students will learn about animal nervous systems, movement and support, reproduction, and how body systems work together so that animals can maintain homeostasis. Students will observe an invertebrate's reaction to light and the skeletal structures in the neck of a vertebrate. At the end of the chapter, students will transfer their knowledge and apply it to the design and creation of an advertisement for the "sale" of a familiar animal.

INDIANA ACADEMIC STANDARDS FOR SCIENCE

Nature of Science NoS.3, NoS.5; **Cellular Reproduction** B.6.4. See lessons for details.

The dense down feathers and shared body heat of these huddled young penguins help them stay warm.

• Untamed Science Video • Chapter Mystery

CHAPTER MYSTERY

SHE'S JUST LIKE HER MOTHER!

It was December 2001, and the employees of the shark exhibits at the Henry Doorly Zoo in Omaha, Nebraska, had just discovered that one of their bonnethead sharks had given birth to a female baby bonnethead. They were shocked. For three years, there had been only three bonnethead sharks in the tank in which the baby shark was born. They were all female.

Some female sharks, including bonnetheads, which are related to hammerheads, are known to store sperm for later fertilization. Did this explain how the shark got pregnant? As you read this chapter, look for clues that help explain how the baby bonnethead's mother got pregnant. Also, think about how sharks typically reproduce and the effect of that process on the offspring's genetic material. Then, solve the mystery.

Never Stop Exploring Your World. Finding the solution to what happened in the shark tank is just the beginning. Take a video field trip with the ecogeeks of Untamed Science to see where the mystery leads.

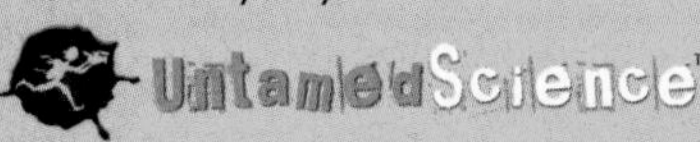

Chapter 28
Big Idea: Structure and Function

Chapter 28 EQ: How do the body systems of animals allow them to collect information about their environments and respond appropriately?

- **28.1 GQ:** How do animals sense and respond to the environment?
- **28.2 GQ:** How are different animals adapted to move through their environments?
- **28.3 GQ:** What are the different strategies animals have evolved to help them produce offspring?
- **28.4 GQ:** How do animals maintain homeostasis?

What's Online

Extend your reach by using these and other digital assets offered at **Biology.com**.

CHAPTER MYSTERY
Students determine how a female bonnethead shark can produce offspring without genetic material from a male bonnethead shark.

UNTAMED SCIENCE VIDEO
Join the Untamed Science crew as they interview experts to learn more about how the gender of offspring is determined in some animals in **Boy? . . . Or Girl?**

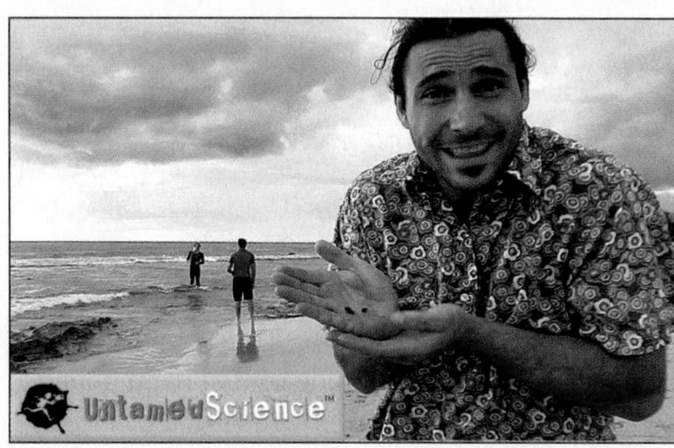

ART REVIEW
This drag-and-drop activity allows students to compare vertebrate brains.

INTERACTIVE ART
Students can use this activity to learn more about the sea star water vascular system.

ART IN MOTION
This activity animates the motion of joints, so students can compare joint function in exoskeletons and endoskeletons.

DATA ANALYSIS
Students use data to learn more about strategies that mammals use to survive cold weather.

Getting Started

LESSON 28.1

Objectives

28.1.1 Describe how animals respond to stimuli.

28.1.2 Summarize the trends in the evolution of nervous systems in animals.

28.1.3 Describe some of the different sensory systems in animals.

Student Resources

Study Workbooks A and B, 28.1 Worksheets

Spanish Study Workbook, 28.1 Worksheets

Lesson Overview • Lesson Notes • Activity: Art Review • Assessment: Self-Test, Lesson Assessment

For corresponding lesson in the **Foundation Edition,** see pages 668–673.

Activate Prior Knowledge

Switch on a classroom light, and ask students to imagine turning on an outside light at night during summer.

Ask What would the light attract? *(flying insects)*

Ask How would the insects know the light is on? *(Insects have eyes that can see the light.)*

Discuss the sense organs of various animals that students have observed.

28.1 Response

Key Questions

How do animals respond to events around them?

What are the trends in nervous system evolution?

What are some types of sensory systems in animals?

Vocabulary

neuron • stimulus • sensory neuron • interneuron • response • motor neuron • ganglion • cerebrum • cerebellum

Taking Notes

Preview Visuals Before you read, preview the diagram of neural circuits in **Figure 28–1.** Take note of any questions you have about it and try to answer them as you read.

THINK ABOUT IT Imagine that you are at a favorite place—a beach or the basketball court. Think about how the sun and wind feel on your face or how good it feels to make the perfect layup. Now, think about the way you experience that place. You gather information about your surroundings through senses such as vision and hearing. Your nervous system collects that information. Your brain decides how to respond to it. The same is true for all animals—though the structures that perform these functions vary from phylum to phylum.

How Animals Respond

How do animals respond to events around them?

Animals must often respond to events or environmental conditions within seconds, or even tiny fractions of a second. Sometimes they need to catch food. Other times, they need to escape predators. Most animals have evolved specialized nervous systems that enable them to respond to events around them. Nervous systems are composed of specialized nerve cells, or **neurons.** The structure of neurons enables them to receive and pass on information. Working together, neurons acquire information from their surroundings, interpret that information, and then "decide" what to do about it.

Detecting Stimuli Information in the environment that causes an organism to react is called a **stimulus** (plural: stimuli). Chemicals in air or water can stimulate the nervous system. Light or heat can also serve as a stimulus. The sound of your phone ringing on a Friday night is a stimulus to which you might respond by running to answer it!

Animals' ability to detect stimuli depends on specialized cells called **sensory neurons.** Each type of sensory neuron responds to a particular stimulus such as light, heat, or chemicals. Humans share many types of sensory cells with other animals. For that reason, many animals react to stimuli that humans notice, including light, taste, odor, temperature, sound, water, gravity, and pressure. But many animals have types of sensory cells that humans lack. That's one reason why some animals respond to stimuli that humans cannot detect, such as very weak electric currents or Earth's magnetic field.

UbD Teach for Understanding

ENDURING UNDERSTANDING Animals have evolved diverse ways to carry out basic life processes and maintain homeostasis.

GUIDING QUESTION How do animals sense and respond to the environment?

EVIDENCE OF UNDERSTANDING *After completing the lesson, assign students the following assessment to show their understanding of how animals respond to stimuli in their environment.* Ask each student to choose an animal and create a cartoon strip showing how it responds to a stimulus in its environment. Tell students their cartoons can be humorous but should include accurate information about the animal's nervous system and the neurons involved in the response. Post finished cartoon strips on the classroom wall.

Processing Information When sensory neurons detect a stimulus, they pass information about it to other nerve cells. Those neurons, which typically pass information to still other neurons, are called **interneurons,** as shown in **Figure 28–1.** Interneurons process information and determine how an animal responds to stimuli.

Does a particular odor mean food . . . or danger? Is the immediate environment too hot, too cold, or just right? The number of interneurons an animal has, and the ways those interneurons process information, determine how flexible and complex an animal's behavior can be.

Some invertebrates, such as cnidarians and worms, have very few interneurons. These animals are capable of only simple responses to stimuli. They may swim toward light or toward a chemical stimulus that signals food. Vertebrates have more highly developed nervous systems with larger numbers of interneurons. The brain is made up of many of these interneurons. That's why the behaviors of vertebrates can be more complex than those of most invertebrates.

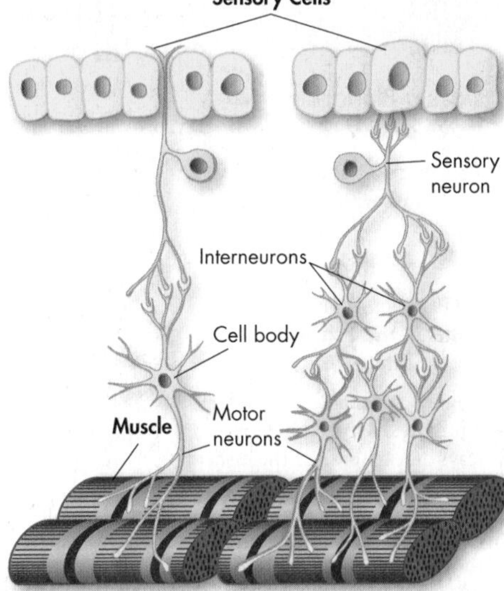

FIGURE 28–1 Neural Circuits In some neural circuits, sensory neurons connect to motor neurons in ways that enable fast but simple responses (left). In others, specialized sensory cells connect to sensory neurons, which connect to interneurons, which connect to motor neurons (right). The more complex a circuit is, the more complex an animal's responses to stimuli can be.

Responding A specific reaction to a stimulus is called a **response.** For example, waking up when you hear the alarm is a response. **When an animal responds to a stimulus, body systems—including the nervous system and the muscular system—work together to generate a response.** Responses to many stimuli are directed by the nervous system. However, those responses are usually carried out by cells or tissues that are not nerve cells. A lion's decision to lunge at prey, as in **Figure 28–2,** is carried out by muscle cells that produce movement. In that case, nerve cells called **motor neurons** carry "directions" from interneurons to muscles. Other responses to environmental conditions may be carried out by other body systems, such as respiratory or circulatory systems.

FIGURE 28–2 Response Mammals, like the lion and wart hog shown here, have complex sensory organs and many interneurons. These animals can therefore process and respond to information in complex ways. Lions stalk and pursue their prey, and wart hogs try to evade their attackers.

809

Teach

Use Visuals

Use **Figure 28–1** to discuss how the different types of neurons work together in an animal's response. Explain that students will learn more about neurons in Chapter 31, including parts of neurons. Point out that the largest part of a neuron is called the cell body, one of which is labeled in the figure. Then, describe a common stimulus—an object too hot to touch. Call on volunteers to identify which neurons detect the stimulus *(sensory neurons)* and which pass information from the sensory neurons to other neurons *(interneurons).*

Ask If sensory neurons in an animal's paw were to detect the stimulus of a hot rock, which muscles might motor neurons direct to respond? *(the muscles in the animal's leg)*

DIFFERENTIATED INSTRUCTION

LPR **Less Proficient Readers** List the main ideas about neural circuits on the board in simplified language. For example, write these sentences:

- Sensory neurons detect a stimulus.
- Interneurons pass information to motor neurons.
- Motor neurons give directions to muscles.
- Muscles carry out a response.

Suggest students keep these concepts in mind as they read the text and study **Figure 28–1.**

ELL Focus on ELL: Build Background

ALL SPEAKERS Give each student a **T-Chart** to help them organize terms and concepts referring to the nervous system. Ask them to write terms they have previous knowledge of as well as the vocabulary terms in the left-hand column and add translations, definitions, and drawings in the right-hand column.

Study Wkbks A/B, Appendix S30, T-Chart.
Transparencies, GO15.

Quick Facts

FOR ARTHROPODS, EVERY DECISION IS A NO-BRAINER

One of the most important differences between animals such as arthropods and "higher" animals is that the responses of arthropods depend only on the various stimuli received by their nerves. Although arthropods have a well-developed nervous system and a simple brain, it is a mistake to attribute "thought" to these animals. Arthropods do not depend on "decision making"; most of their behaviors are genetically programmed. Their reactions in a particular situation are almost totally predictable. Aristotle, a great observer of natural phenomena, was the first to document the fact that wasps remain at almost normal activity levels for a while after their heads have been removed.

LESSON 28.1

Teach continued

Build Reading Skills

Before students read **Trends in Nervous System Evolution,** suggest they start an outline of the section. Explain that the blue headings, **Invertebrates** and **Chordates,** can be used for the first level of the outline. The run-in heads, such as **Nerve Nets, Nerve Cords, and Ganglia,** can be used for the second level. Then, under each second-level head, students can add important details for the third level. Tell students that making an outline helps them understand the content more fully and that the outline will also be useful for later review.

DIFFERENTIATED INSTRUCTION

ELL English Language Learners Pair English language learners with native English speakers for composition of the outline described above. Suggest English language learners add drawings to their outlines to help them remember basic concepts.

L3 Advanced Students Enrich students' understanding of invertebrate nervous systems by having them do further research on one of the phyla represented in **Figure 28–3.** Ask students to present what they learned to the class.

GUIDED INQUIRY

Does a Planarian Have a Head?

1. Cover half of the outside of a petri dish with black paper.
2. Place a white sheet of paper under the other half.
3. Place a planarian in the center of the dish, and add spring water to keep it moist.
4. Observe the planarian for 2 minutes. Record how long it stays on each side of the dish.

Analyze and Conclude

1. **Form a Hypothesis** When the planarian moved, did one end always lead the way? Form a hypothesis that explains your observation.

Trends in Nervous System Evolution

What are the trends in nervous system evolution?

Nervous systems vary greatly in organization and complexity across the animal kingdom. **Animal nervous systems exhibit different degrees of cephalization and specialization.**

Invertebrates Invertebrate nervous systems range from simple collections of nerve cells to complex organizations that include many interneurons. You can see some examples in **Figure 28–3.**

▶ ***Nerve Nets, Nerve Cords, and Ganglia*** Cnidarians, such as jellyfishes, have simple nervous systems called nerve nets. As the name implies, nerve nets consist of neurons connected into a netlike arrangement with few specializations. In other radially symmetric invertebrates, echinoderms such as sea stars, for example, some interneurons are grouped together into nerves, or nerve cords, that form a ring around the animals' mouths and stretch out along their arms. In still other invertebrates, a number of interneurons are grouped together into small structures called **ganglia** (singular: ganglion), in which interneurons connect with one another.

▶ ***"Heads"*** As you learned in Chapter 25, bilaterally symmetric animals often exhibit cephalization, the concentration of sensory neurons and interneurons in a "head." Certain flatworms and roundworms show some cephalization. Some cephalopod mollusks and many arthropods show higher degrees of cephalization. In these animals, interneurons form ganglia in several places. Typically, the largest ganglia are located in the head region and are called cerebral ganglia.

▶ ***Brains*** In some species, cerebral ganglia are further organized into a structure called a brain. The brains of some cephalopods, such as octopi, enable complex behavior, including several kinds of learning.

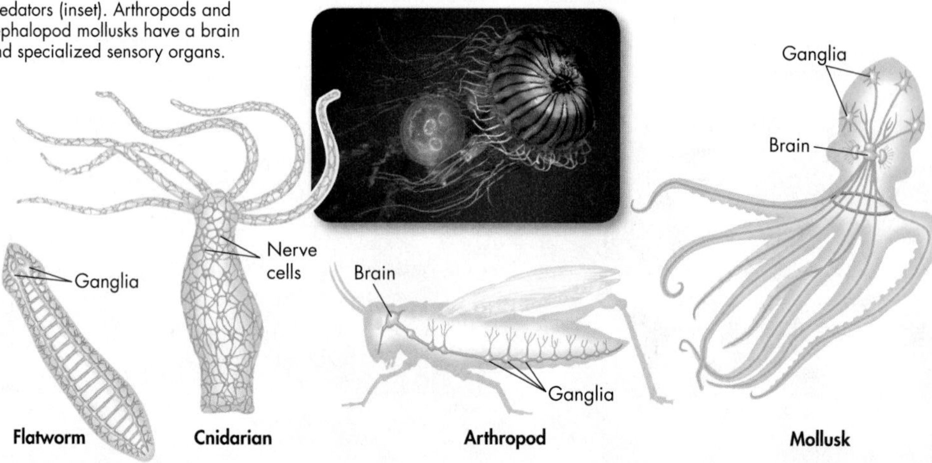

FIGURE 28–3 Invertebrate Nervous Systems Invertebrate nervous systems have different degrees of cephalization and specialization. Flatworms have centralized nervous systems with small ganglia in their heads. Cnidarians have a nerve net which, despite its simplicity, enables them to be successful predators (inset). Arthropods and cephalopod mollusks have a brain and specialized sensory organs.

PURPOSE Students investigate the responses to stimuli in planaria.

MATERIALS planarian, petri dish, black paper, white paper, spring water, clock or watch

SAFETY Tell students to treat the planarians with care to avoid injuring them. Have students wear disposable plastic gloves during the lab and wash their hands afterward.

PLANNING Have students read the procedure and discuss any questions they have about what to do. You may want to place the planarians in the petri dishes for the students.

ANALYZE AND CONCLUDE

1. Sample answer: Yes, the head end always led the way. A planarian's head end leads the way because its eyespots sense light.

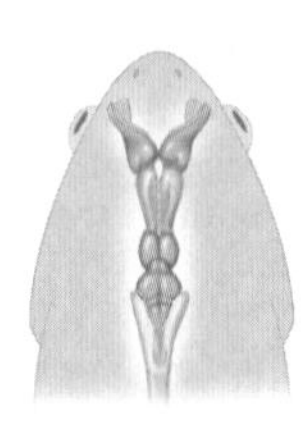
Bony Fish

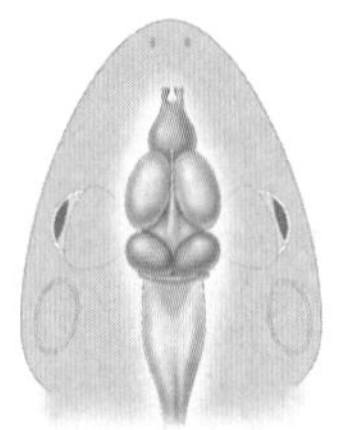
Amphibian

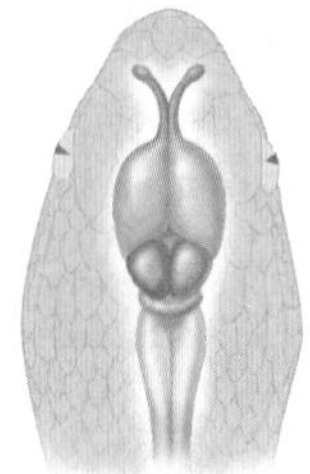
Reptile

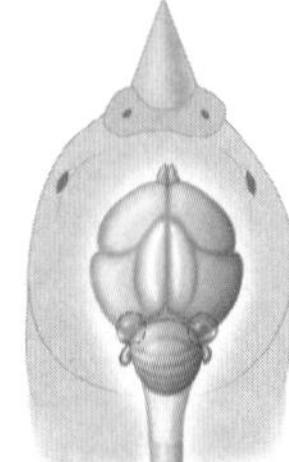
Bird

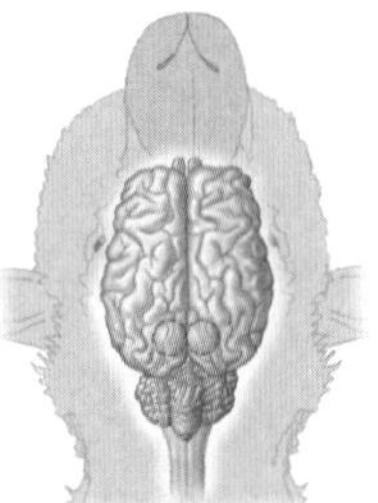
Mammal

Olfactory bulb	Cerebellum
Cerebrum	Medulla oblongata
Optic lobe	Spinal cord

FIGURE 28–4 Vertebrate Brains The cerebrum and cerebellum increase in size from fishes to mammals. In fishes, amphibians, and reptiles, the cerebrum, or "thinking" region, is relatively small. In birds and mammals, and especially in primates, the cerebrum is much larger and may contain folds that increase its surface area. The cerebellum is also most highly developed in birds and mammals.

Chordates Nonvertebrate chordates, which have no vertebrate-type "head" as adults, still have a cerebral ganglion. Vertebrates, on the other hand, show a high degree of cephalization and have highly developed nervous systems. Vertebrate brains are formed from many interneurons within the skull. These interneurons are connected with each other and with sensory neurons and motor neurons in the head and elsewhere in the body. The human brain contains more than 100 billion nerve cells, each of which sends signals to as many as 1000 other nerve cells and receives signals from up to 10,000 more.

▶ ***Parts of the Vertebrate Brain*** Regions of the vertebrate brain include the cerebrum, cerebellum, medulla oblongata, optic lobes, and olfactory bulbs. The **cerebrum** is the "thinking" region of the brain. It receives and interprets sensory information and determines a response. The cerebrum is also involved in learning, memory, and conscious thought. The **cerebellum** coordinates movement and controls balance, while the medulla oblongata controls the functioning of many internal organs. Optic lobes are involved in vision, and olfactory bulbs are involved in the sense of smell. Vertebrate brains are connected to the rest of the body by a thick collection of nerves called a spinal cord, which runs through a tube in the vertebral column.

▶ ***Vertebrate Brain Evolution*** Brain evolution in vertebrates follows a general trend of increasing size and complexity from fishes, through amphibians and reptiles, to birds and mammals. **Figure 28–4** shows how the size and complexity of the cerebrum and cerebellum increase.

FIGURE 28–5 Not Such a Bird Brain The brains of some chickadee species are so sophisticated that the part responsible for remembering locations gets bigger when the bird stores food in the fall. When winter comes, the tiny bird is better able to find its hundreds of storage places. (In spring, its brain returns to normal size.) **Infer** ***Which of the six main parts of the chickadee brain would you expect to grow in the fall?***

In Your Notebook *Construct a figure of speech that explains, in terms of another object, how the folds of the mammalian cerebellum increase its surface area.*

Use Visuals

Discuss the regions of vertebrate brains using **Figure 28–4.** Begin by focusing students' attention on the key, which lists the different regions of the brain. For each region, ask a volunteer to describe its function. Then, after making sure students understand the color coding of the regions, discuss differences among vertebrates.

Ask Do amphibians or reptiles likely have a better sense of smell, and how can you tell? *(Reptiles probably have a better sense of smell, because the olfactory bulbs are relatively larger in reptiles than in amphibians.)*

Ask What indicates that a bird is probably more capable of learning than a reptile? *(The cerebrum in a bird is relatively larger and more complex than it is in a reptile.)*

DIFFERENTIATED INSTRUCTION

L1 Special Needs Provide students with a model of a brain that differentiates in a tactile way between the different regions. (Most often, this will be a model of the human brain, which can be used to represent the mammalian brain.) As students handle the brain, explain how the sizes of the different regions differ in the different groups of vertebrates.

L1 Struggling Students Provide students with unlabeled drawings of the five vertebrate brains shown in **Figure 28–4.** Have pairs of students work together to label the different regions in each brain.

BIOLOGY.com Have students find out more about the comparative anatomy of vertebrate brains by using **Art Review: Vertebrate Brains.**

Quick Facts

BIRD BRAINS

The brains of birds are suprisingly complex organs. Here are some interesting facts about bird brains.

- The cerebellum is well developed in birds; it is relatively larger in birds than in mammals. This part of the brain is involved in muscle coordination and the regulation of balance, both of which are necessary for flight.
- In most birds, the optic lobes are relatively large, while the olfactory bulbs are relatively small. Most birds can see very well but smell poorly.
- The hippocampus, the part of the cerebrum involved in memory, is relatively large in some birds, especially those that must remember where they have stored seeds. In some species, it becomes enlarged as the bird stores seeds, later shrinking back to its original size.

Answers

FIGURE 28–5 the cerebrum

IN YOUR NOTEBOOK Sample answer: The folds of the mammalian cerebrum increase its surface area like the folds of an accordion increase the surface area of its bellows.

Teach continued

Use Visuals

Begin a discussion with students of invertebrate sense organs with a focus on the invertebrate eyes shown in **Figure 28–6.** Point out that the planarian included in the figure is the same organism they observed in the **Quick Lab.**

Ask What can a planarian "see" with its eyespot? *(changes in the amount of light)*

Explain that each type of invertebrate eye detects light or forms images in a different way, and students should not assume that an invertebrate "sees" objects in the same way that humans do.

DIFFERENTIATED INSTRUCTION

LPR Less Proficient Readers Struggling readers may have difficulty understanding the subcaptions in the figure. Help them make bulleted lists of characteristics of each of the four invertebrate eyes. For example, on the board, write this bulleted list for the scallop eye:

Scallop

- 40–60 simple eyes
- Do not form images
- Detect movement well
- Enable scallop to detect predators

Call on students to help you make similar lists for the three other invertebrate eyes.

L3 Advanced Students Challenge students to write a paragraph explaining how the complex eye of the octopus might have evolved as an adaptation that gives this cephalopod an advantage in its environment. *(Answers may vary. Students should mention that an octopus is a predator, and the complex eye allows it to identify prey.)*

Sensory Systems

What are some types of sensory systems in animals?

The more complex an animal's nervous system is, the more developed its sensory systems tend to be. **Sensory systems range from individual sensory neurons to sense organs that contain both sensory neurons and other cells that help gather information.**

Invertebrate Sense Organs Many invertebrates have sense organs that detect light, sound, vibrations, movement, body orientation, and chemicals in air or water. Invertebrate sense organs vary widely in complexity. Flatworms, for example, have simple eyespots that detect only the presence and direction of light. More-cephalized invertebrates have specialized sensory tissues and well-developed sense organs. Some cephalopods and arthropods, for example, have complex eyes that detect motion and color and form images. In **Figure 28–6,** you can see a variety of invertebrate visual systems.

FIGURE 28–6 Invertebrate Eyes Invertebrate sense organs, such as the eyes shown in the photos, vary greatly in structure and complexity.

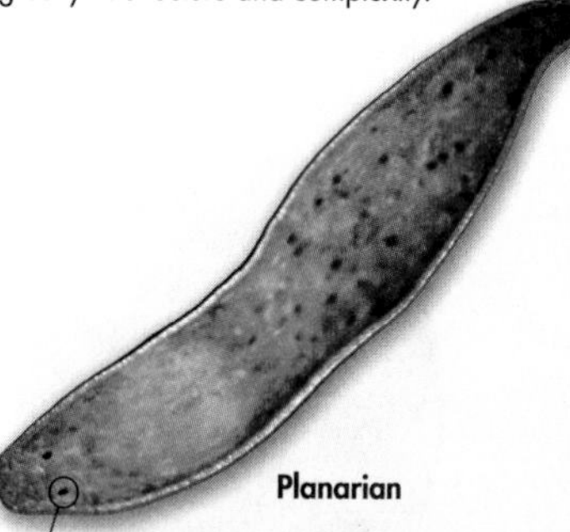

Eyespot: Some animals have eyespots, which are groups of cells that can detect changes in the amount of light (LM 50×).

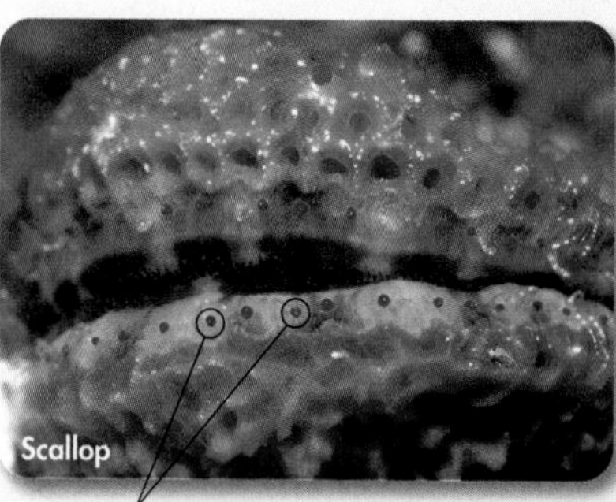

Simple Eye: The 40–60 simple eyes of a scallop do not form images. They do, however, detect movement well enough to enable the scallop to escape its predators.

Compound Eye: The compound eyes of arthropods are made up of many lenses that detect minute changes in movement and color but produce less-detailed images than human eyes do.

Complex Eye: Octopi and squid have eyes as complex as fishes and humans, though their structures differ.

812

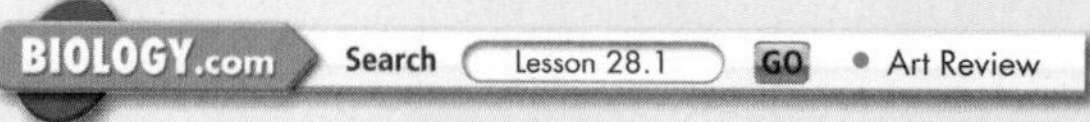

UbD Check for Understanding

INDEX CARD SUMMARIES

Give students each an index card, and ask them to write one main idea from the lesson on the front of the card. This idea could be about how animals respond, animal nervous systems, or animal sense organs. Then, ask them to write an idea that they don't understand on the back of the card.

ADJUST INSTRUCTION

Read over the cards to determine which concepts students understand and which they are having trouble with. For concepts that students don't understand, call on volunteers to explain to the class what a term means, how one structure differs from another, or how a process occurs.

Chordate Sense Organs Nonvertebrate chordates have few specialized sense organs. In tunicates, sensory cells in and on the siphons and other internal surfaces help control the amount of water passing through the pharynx. Lancelets have a cerebral ganglion with a pair of eyespots that detect light.

In contrast, most vertebrates have highly evolved sense organs. Many vertebrates have very sensitive organs of taste, smell, and hearing. Some sharks, for example, can sense 1 drop of blood in 100 liters of water! And although all mammalian ears have the same basic parts, they differ in their ability to detect sound, as you can see in **Figure 28–7.** In fact, bats and dolphins can even find objects in their environment using echoes of their own high-frequency sounds. A great many species of fishes, amphibians, reptiles, birds, and mammals have color vision that is as good as, or better than, that of humans.

Some species, including certain fishes and the duckbill platypus, can detect weak electric currents in water. Some animals, such as sharks, use this "electric sense" to navigate by detecting electric currents in seawater that are caused by Earth's magnetic field. Other "electric fishes" can create their own electric currents. These fishes use electric pulses to communicate with one another, in much the same way that other animals communicate using sound. Many species that can detect electric currents use the ability to track down prey in dark, murky water. Some birds can detect Earth's magnetic field directly, and they use that ability to navigate during long-distance migrations.

Animal	Hearing Range (Hz)
Tree frog	50–4000
Canary	250–8000
Dog	67–45,000
Bat	2000–110,000
Human	30–23,000
Elephant	16–12,000
Bottlenose dolphin	75–150,000

FIGURE 28–7 Vertebrate Hearing Human senses are not necessarily superior to those of other animals. Interpret Tables ***Would you expect to be able to hear the highest pitch a dog can hear? Explain.***

28.1 Assessment

Review Key Concepts 

1. a. Review List three body systems that work together to create a response to a stimulus.
   b. Explain What is the role of a motor neuron?
   c. Sequence What is the correct sequence of the roles played by the following in the response to a stimulus: interneuron, motor neuron, sensory neuron, muscle.
2. a. Review What are two general ways in which nervous systems differ among animal groups?
   b. Compare and Contrast Describe the degree of cephalization shown by cnidarians, flatworms, octopi, and vertebrates.
3. a. Review Give an example of an animal with a very simple sensory system and an example of one with a complex sensory system.
   b. Infer What is the general relationship between the complexity of an animal's nervous system and that of its sensory system?

WRITE ABOUT SCIENCE

Explanation

4. The compound eyes of insects detect movement better than they distinguish details. How might the ability to detect movement be more important to an insect than the ability to see fine details? (*Hint:* Consider the size of an insect in relation to that of its predators.)

BIOLOGY.com Search Lesson 28.1 GO • Self-Test • Lesson Assessment

LESSON 28.1

Assess and Remediate

EVALUATE UNDERSTANDING

Read aloud each boldface Key Concept in the lesson. For each, call on a volunteer to provide a supporting detail. Then, ask other students for additional supporting details. After students have provided support for the Key Concept, ask a volunteer to explain the importance of it in understanding response in animals. After reviewing all Key Concepts, have students complete the 28.1 Assessment.

REMEDIATION SUGGESTION

L1 **Struggling Students** If students have difficulty answering **Question 1c,** have them review the text material that defines each term and then make a **Flowchart** that begins with a stimulus and ends with a physical response by an animal.

Study Wkbks A/B, Appendix S25, Flowchart. **Transparencies,** GO8.

BIOLOGY.com Students can check their understanding of lesson concepts with the **Self-Test** assessment. They can then take an online version of the **Lesson Assessment.**

Answers

FIGURE 28–7 No; The range of a dog's hearing goes up to 45,000 Hz, while the range of human hearing goes up to only 23,000 Hz.

Assessment Answers

1a. sensory neurons, the nervous system, and muscles

1b. Motor neurons carry "directions" from interneurons to muscles.

1c. sensory neuron, interneuron, motor neuron, muscle

2a. Sample answer: whether or not the nervous system has sensory neurons and interneurons centralized in a head region (cephalization), and the degree to which sensory cells are specialized (specialization)

2b. Cnidarians have no cephalization; flatworms have some cephalization; octopi and vertebrates have high degrees of cephalization.

3a. Sample answer: Cnidarians have a very simple sensory system that consists of a nerve net and no sensory organs. Octopi have a complex sensory system, including a brain and eyes as complex as human eyes.

3b. The more complex an animal's nervous system is, the more developed its sensory systems tend to be.

WRITE ABOUT SCIENCE

4. Sample answer: An insect must be able to detect movement in order to detect the presence of predators in its area, but it has no need to see fine details of the predator in order to escape it.

LESSON 28.2

Getting Started

Objectives

28.2.1 Describe the three types of skeletons in animals.

28.2.2 Explain how muscles produce movement in animals.

Student Resources

Study Workbooks A and B, 28.2 Worksheets

Spanish Study Workbook, 28.2 Worksheets

Lesson Overview • Lesson Notes
- Activities: InterActive Art, Art in Motion
- Assessment: Self-Test, Lesson Assessment

For corresponding lesson in the **Foundation Edition,** see pages 674–677.

Build Background

Partially fill an oblong balloon with water. Explain that the balloon represents an invertebrate's gastrovascular cavity and the water represents fluids within that cavity. Then, squeeze parts of the balloon to show how the movement of the fluid changes the shape of the balloon. Point out that squeezing the balloon is similar to the way an invertebrate uses contractile cells in its body wall to move fluids around and change its shape. Explain that the water balloon is a model of a hydrostatic skeleton.

28.2 Movement and Support

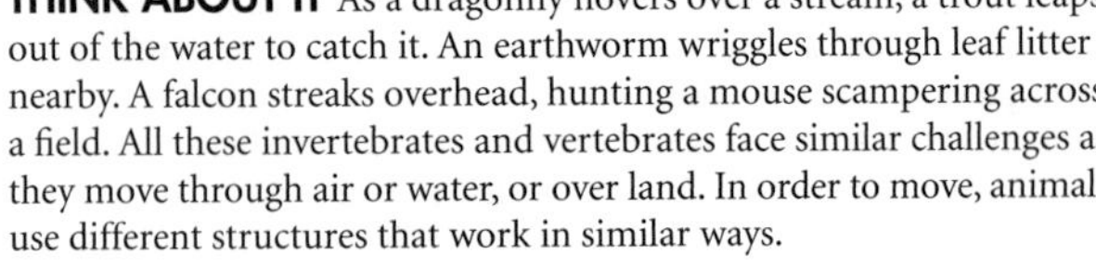

Key Questions

What are the three types of skeletons?

How do muscles enable movement?

Vocabulary

hydrostatic skeleton • exoskeleton • molting • endoskeleton • joint • ligament • tendon

Taking Notes

Compare/Contrast Table As you read, create a table comparing and contrasting the three types of skeletons.

THINK ABOUT IT As a dragonfly hovers over a stream, a trout leaps out of the water to catch it. An earthworm wriggles through leaf litter nearby. A falcon streaks overhead, hunting a mouse scampering across a field. All these invertebrates and vertebrates face similar challenges as they move through air or water, or over land. In order to move, animals use different structures that work in similar ways.

Types of Skeletons

What are the three types of skeletons?

To move efficiently, all animals must do two things. First, they must generate physical force. Then, they must somehow apply that force against air, water, or land in order to push or pull themselves around.

Skeletal Support An animal's ability to move efficiently is greatly enhanced by rigid body parts. Legs push against the ground. Bird wings push against air, and fins or flippers apply force against water. Each of these body parts is supported by some sort of skeleton. **Animals have three main kinds of skeletal systems: hydrostatic skeletons, exoskeletons, and endoskeletons.**

▶ *Hydrostatic Skeletons* Some invertebrates, such as cnidarians and annelids, have hydrostatic skeletons. The **hydrostatic skeleton** of a cnidarian such as a hydra, for example, consists of fluids held in a gastrovascular cavity that can alter the animal's body shape drastically by working with contractile cells in its body wall. When a hydra closes its mouth and the cells encircling its body wall constrict, the animal elongates and its tentacles extend, as shown in the left photo of **Figure 28–8.** Because water is not compressible, constricting the cavity elongates the animal, somewhat like a water balloon that has been squeezed. A hydra often sits in this position for hours, waiting for prey to swim by. If it is disturbed, its mouth opens, allowing water to flow out, and longitudinal cells in its body wall contract, shortening the body, as in the right photo of **Figure 28–8.**

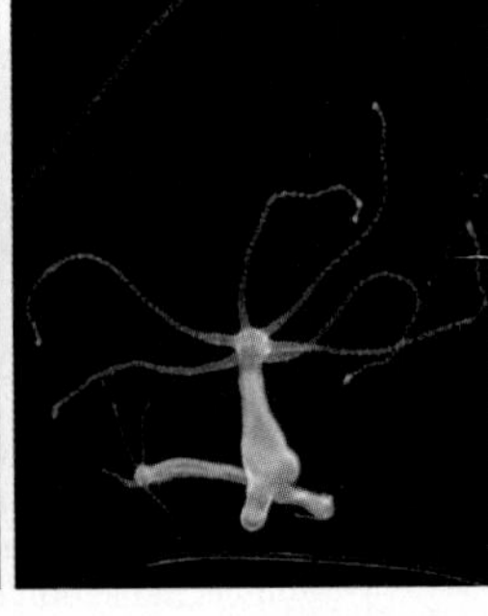

FIGURE 28–8 Hydrostatic Skeleton Some invertebrates, such as this hydra, have hydrostatic skeletons. When a hydra closes its mouth, water trapped in its body causes it to elongate (left). When it opens its mouth again, water is released, and it becomes shorter (right).

UbD Teach for Understanding

ENDURING UNDERSTANDING Animals have evolved diverse ways to carry out basic life processes and maintain homeostasis.

GUIDING QUESTION How are different animals adapted to move through their environments?

EVIDENCE OF UNDERSTANDING *After students have completed the lesson, assign the following assessment to show their understanding of different types of animal skeletons.* Ask students to work in pairs to make a labeled drawing that identifies an organism, names the type of skeleton it has, and shows how its skeleton provides support. Ask students to share their drawings with the class.

▶ ***Exoskeletons*** Many arthropods have exoskeletons, as do most mollusks, such as snails and clams. The **exoskeleton,** or external skeleton, of an arthropod is a hard body covering made of a complex carbohydrate called chitin. Most mollusks have exoskeletons, or shells, made of calcium carbonate.

Jointed exoskeletons enable various arthropods to swim, fly, burrow, walk, crawl, and leap. They can also provide watertight coverings that enable some arthropods to live in Earth's driest places. An exoskeleton can also provide physical protection from predators—as you know if you have ever tried to crack a crab or lobster shell or seen a mollusk withdraw into its shell. Mollusks with two-part shells are called bivalves. Bivalves such as clams can also close their shells to avoid drying out.

But exoskeletons have disadvantages. An external skeleton poses a problem when the animal it belongs to needs to grow. To increase in size, arthropods break out of their exoskeleton and grow a new one, in a process called **molting,** shown in **Figure 28–9.** Exoskeletons are also relatively heavy. The larger arthropods get, the heavier their skeletons become in proportion to their body weight. This is one reason that some science-fiction monsters could never exist. The legs of an elephant-size spider would collapse under the spider's weight!

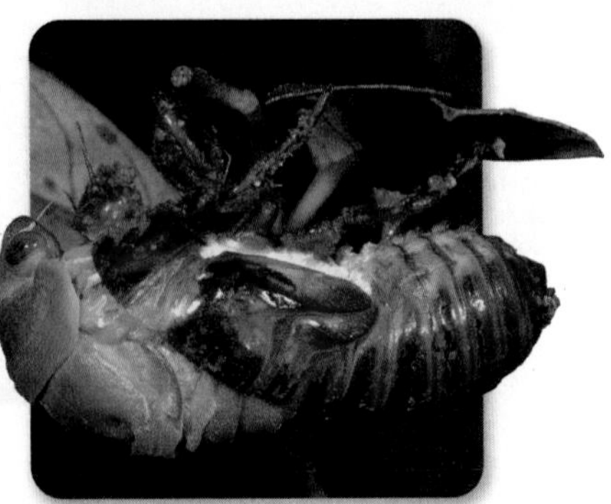

FIGURE 28–9 Exoskeleton Arthropods such as this cicada periodically "grow out" of their exoskeletons and have to break out of them in order to grow new ones. **Infer** ***How might molting be a dangerous inconvenience?***

▶ ***Endoskeletons*** Echinoderms and vertebrates have endoskeletons. An **endoskeleton** is a structural support system within the body. Sea stars and other echinoderms have an endoskeleton made of calcified plates, as you can see in **Figure 28–10.** These skeletal plates support and protect echinoderms, and also give them a bumpy texture.

Vertebrates have an endoskeleton made of cartilage or a combination of cartilage and bone. Sharks and some other fishes have skeletons made almost entirely of cartilage. In other vertebrates, most of the skeleton is bone. Four-limbed vertebrates also have structures called limb girdles that support limbs and allow the animal to move around.

FIGURE 28–10 Endoskeleton Not every endoskeleton looks like yours! Some invertebrates, including echinoderms such as this sea star, have rigid internal body supports. These supports are not, however, made of bone.

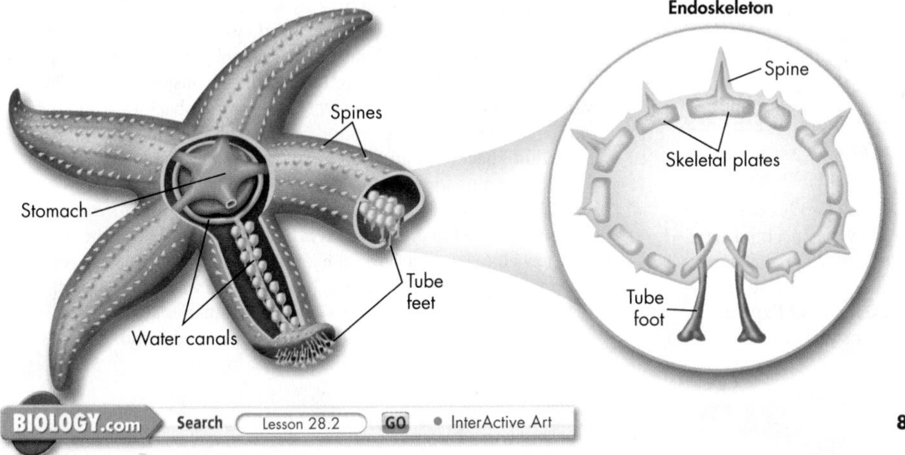

BIOLOGY.com Search Lesson 28.2 GO • InterActive Art

Quick Facts

MOLLUSK SHELLS

Mollusk shells occur in such a variety of shapes and sizes that they serve as the main means of identification for many mollusk species. The obvious advantage of a hard exterior shell is the protection it provides for the animal's soft body. Like the exoskeletons of arthropods, exterior shells have one major disadvantage: Because shells do not consist of living, dividing cells, mollusks outgrow them. Many mollusks, however, have evolved shell designs that allow them to build onto the shell to accommodate their increased body size. The shell is not continuously added to but is expanded periodically as needed. Another disadvantage of shells is that they reduce mobility. Most mollusks, such as snails, lumber along under the load of their heavy shells. Other mollusks, such as clams, are largely stationary throughout their adult lives.

Teach

Use Visuals

Use **Figures 28–9** and **28–10** to compare and contrast exoskeletons and endoskeletons.

Ask What are two advantages of an exoskeleton? *(It provides a watertight covering and protects the animal's soft body.)*

Ask Are endoskeletons always made of bone? *(No, the endoskeletons of echinoderms are not bone, and the endoskeletons of cartilaginous fishes are made of cartilage.)*

DIFFERENTIATED INSTRUCTION

ELL English Language Learners Explain that the prefix *exo-* means "outer," and the prefix *endo-* means "inside." Ask English language learners to use those meanings to write definitions of *exoskeleton* and *endoskeleton* in their notebook. Suggest students add drawings next to their definitions to help them remember.

LPR Less Proficient Readers To help students who have difficulty absorbing information they read, set up a classroom display of examples of exoskeletons for them to observe. You might display a variety of mollusk shells, such as clam, nautilus, and snail shells. Display a cicada exoskeleton that has been left behind by a molting insect. If possible, show students a live lobster, crab, or crayfish.

BIOLOGY.com The **InterActive Art: Sea Star Water Vascular System** shows how sea stars move, feed, circulate nutrients, and get rid of wastes.

Answers

FIGURE 28–9 Right after molting, the exoskeleton is soft, which makes the arthropod vulnerable to predators.

LESSON 28.2

Teach continued

Lead a Discussion

Make sure students understand the relationships between skeletons, joints, ligaments, tendons, and muscles.

Ask What connects bones to other bones at a joint? *(ligament)*

Ask What connects a muscle to a bone? *(tendon)*

DIFFERENTIATED INSTRUCTION

L1 Struggling Students Provide each student with a **T-Chart,** and suggest they write the terms *joints, ligaments,* and *tendons* in the left column. In the right column, they can add descriptions, examples, and drawings that will help them remember what these vocabulary terms mean.

Study Wkbks A/B, Appendix S30, T-Chart. **Transparencies,** GO15.

L3 Advanced Students If school policy permits, obtain a whole bony fish, and have a small group of students dissect it. Provide dissecting tools, and instruct them to wear goggles, lab apron, and disposable plastic gloves. Ask them to observe and make drawings of muscle blocks on the fish's back as well as the features of the skeleton. Have the group report to the class what they observed.

Students can use the **Art in Motion: Muscles and Joints** animation to compare exoskeletons and endoskeletons.

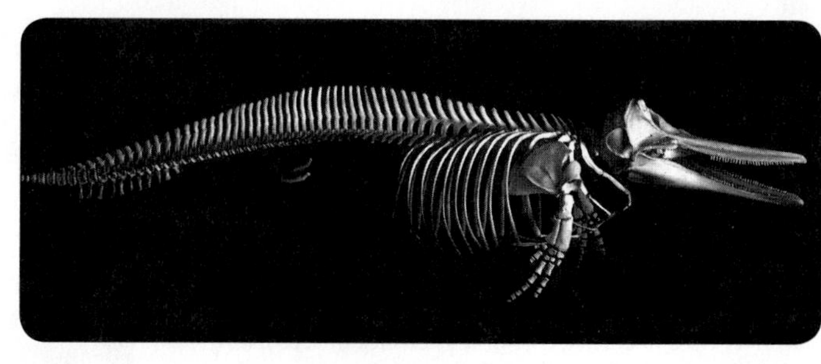

FIGURE 28–11 Vertebrate Skeleton A typical vertebrate skeleton, such as that of this dolphin, is made up mostly of bone.

Evolution has produced a wide range of variations of the vertebrate endoskeleton that enables these animals to swim, fly, burrow, walk, crawl, or leap, but they all provide strong, lightweight support. Of course, because an internal skeleton does not surround the body, it cannot protect an animal the way that an exoskeleton can. On the other hand, an internal skeleton can grow as an animal grows, so the animal does not need to molt. Because endoskeletons are lightweight in proportion to the bodies they support, even land-dwelling vertebrates can grow very large.

Joints If an animal's rigid skeleton were made of one piece, or if its parts were rigidly attached to each other, the animal couldn't move. Arthropods and vertebrates can move because their skeletons are divided into many parts that are connected by **joints.** Joints are places where parts of a skeleton are held together in ways that enable them to move with respect to one another. In vertebrates, bones are connected at joints by strong connective tissues called **ligaments.** Most joints are formed by a combination of ligaments, cartilage, and lubricating joint fluid that enables bones to move without painful friction.

Quick Lab GUIDED INQUIRY

What Are Some Adaptations of Vertebrae?

1. Obtain a chicken neck from your teacher. Bend the neck back and forth and from side to side.
2. Insert a dissecting probe into the opening at the top of the neck. What do you observe? **CAUTION:** *Use care with sharp instruments.*

Analyze and Conclude

1. **Infer** How is the structure of the chicken's neck related to its function?
2. **Predict** What would happen if the chicken's neck were just one vertebra with no central opening?
3. **Draw Conclusions** How would you expect the vertebrae in an elephant's neck to differ from those in the chicken's neck? Explain your answer.

Muscles and Movement

How do muscles enable movement?

Muscles are specialized tissues that produce physical force by contracting, or getting shorter, when they are stimulated. Muscles can relax when they aren't being stimulated, but they cannot actively get longer. That presents a problem. Think about how animals move. Fishes swim by moving their bodies back and forth, and by pushing against the water with their fins. Your legs work by swinging backward and forward, pushing against the ground as you walk. But how can animals move limbs backward and forward or push against water or land if muscles generate force in only one direction?

In many animals, muscles work together in pairs or groups that are attached to different parts of a supporting skeleton. Muscles are attached to bones around the joints by tough connective tissue called **tendons.** Tendons are attached in such a way that they pull on bones when muscles contract. Typically, muscles are arranged in groups that pull parts of the skeleton in opposite directions. Here's how muscles and parts of a skeleton work together.

 BIOLOGY.com Search Lesson 28.2 GO • Art in Motion

Quick Lab

PURPOSE Students infer how the structure of vertebrae is related to the function of vertebrae.

MATERIALS chicken neck, dissecting probe

SAFETY Warn students to handle the dissecting probe carefully. Have them wear disposable, plastic gloves as they dissect the chicken neck and then wash their hands thoroughly when finished.

PLANNING Obtain fresh chicken necks from a butcher. Soak the necks in bleach, and then rinse thoroughly. Practice before the lab so you can demonstrate inserting the dissecting probe into the hole for the spinal cord. You may want to cut away the skin from around the neck to better view the vertebrae.

ANALYZE AND CONCLUDE

1. The many bones of the neck allow for a wide range of motion. The opening in each vertebra surrounds and protects the spinal cord.
2. The chicken would have a rigid, inflexible body, and the vertebra could not support or protect its spinal cord.
3. Sample answer: They would be larger so they could support a larger skull.

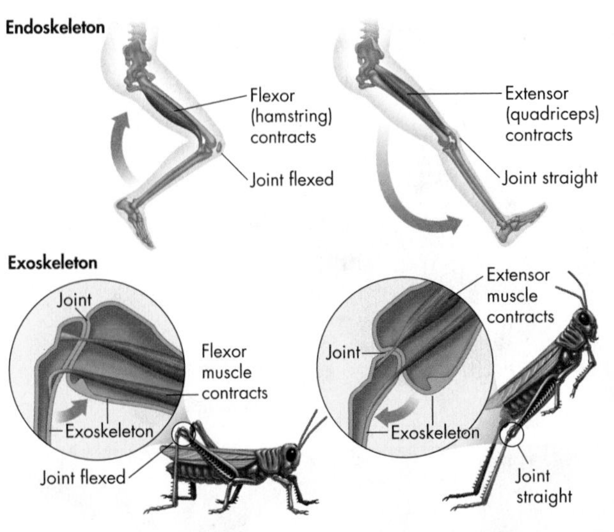

FIGURE 28–12 Muscles and Joints The diagrams show how muscles work with a vertebrate endoskeleton and an arthropod exoskeleton to bend and straighten joints. Compare and Contrast ***To what structure are arthropod muscles attached? To what structure are vertebrate muscles attached?***

Movement Arthropod muscles are attached to the inside of the exoskeleton. Vertebrate muscles are attached around the outside of bones. In both cases, different pairs or groups of muscles pull across joints in different directions. As you can see in **Figure 28–12,** when one muscle group contracts, it bends, or flexes, the joint. When the first group relaxes and the second group contracts, the joint straightens.

Vertebrate Muscular and Skeletal Systems An amazing variety of complex combinations of bones, muscle groups, and joints have evolved in vertebrates. In many fishes and snakes, muscles are arranged in blocks on opposite sides of the backbone. These muscle blocks contract in waves that travel down the body, bending it first to one side and then to the other. As these waves of movement travel down the body, they generate thrust. The limbs of many modern amphibians and reptiles stick out sideways from the body, as though the animals were doing push-ups. If you watch these animals move, you will see that many use sideways movements of their backbone to move their limbs forward and backward.

Most mammals stand with their legs straight under them, whether they walk on two legs or four. Mammalian limbs have evolved in ways that enable many different kinds of movement, as you can see in **Figure 28–13** on the next page. The shapes and relative positions of bones and muscles, and the shapes of joints, are linked very closely to the functions they perform. Limbs that are specialized for high-speed running or long-distance jumping have very differently shaped bones, muscles, and joints than limbs adapted for flying, swimming, or manipulating objects. In fact, paleontologists can reconstruct the habits of extinct animals by studying the joints of fossil bones and the places where tendons and ligaments once attached.

UbD Check for Understanding

FOLLOW-UP PROBES

Ask Why must muscles work together in pairs? *(Muscles produce physical force by contracting, or getting shorter. So, a joint bends when a muscle or a group of muscles contracts in one direction, and then the joint straightens when a second muscle or group contracts in a different direction.)*

ADJUST INSTRUCTION

If students have difficulty answering the question, have them review the information in the subsection, **Movement,** and **Figure 28–12.** Then, call on students at random to explain why muscles in both invertebrates and vertebrates work in pairs or groups.

Use Visuals

After students have read **Muscles and Movement** and reviewed **Figure 28–12,** have them discuss how muscles work with skeletons to produce movement in different kinds of animals. Explain that most animals, including invertebrates, have muscle tissues.

Ask What is the difference in how muscles are attached in animals with exoskeletons and animals with endoskeletons? *(In animals with exoskeletons, muscles are attached to the inside of the exoskeleton. In animals with endoskeletons, muscles are attached around the outside of bones.)*

Emphasize that muscles move a joint by working in opposing pairs or groups. As an example, point out that biceps and triceps are opposing muscles in the human upper arm. Ask what happens when a student contracts the biceps. *(The arm bends at the elbow joint.)* Ask what contracts to straighten the arm again. *(the triceps muscle)*

DIFFERENTIATED INSTRUCTION

L1 Struggling Students Have students work in small groups, and challenge each group to choose one type of animal and make a model that shows how it moves. Students can use any common materials, such as rubber bands, paper clips, straws, suction cups, and craft sticks. Suggest students use library or online sources to find out more about how their animal moves. After all models have been built, invite each group to present its model to the class.

ELL Focus on ELL: Access Content

ALL SPEAKERS Set up a **Gallery Walk** about animal movement and support by writing *hydrostatic skeleton, exoskeleton,* and *endoskeleton* on separate pieces of chart paper. Post the pieces of chart paper at different places on the classroom wall and have three groups rotate among them. At each poster, each group should write what they know about the type of skeleton, using a pen color different from that of the other groups. Remind students to include information about how muscles work with each skeleton. As each group rotates to a poster, its members should add to the previous group's comments and correct mistakes. When groups return to their first poster, have members summarize information about that skeleton for the class.

Study Wkbks A/B, Appendix S6, Gallery Walk.

Answers

FIGURE 28–12 the exoskeleton; bones

Assess and Remediate

EVALUATE UNDERSTANDING

Call on students at random to explain the differences among the three main kinds of animal skeletons. Then, have students complete the 28.2 Assessment.

REMEDIATION SUGGESTION

L1 **Struggling Students** If students have difficulty answering **Question 1b,** review with them the advantages and disadvantages of endoskeletons.

BIOLOGY.com Students can check their understanding of lesson concepts with the **Self-Test** assessment. They can then take an online version of the **Lesson Assessment.**

◀ Raccoon

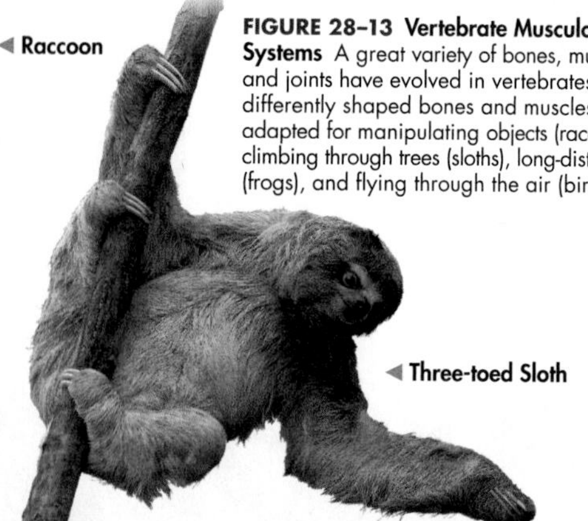
◀ Three-toed Sloth

FIGURE 28–13 Vertebrate Musculoskeletal Systems A great variety of bones, muscle groups, and joints have evolved in vertebrates. For instance, differently shaped bones and muscles form limbs adapted for manipulating objects (raccoons), climbing through trees (sloths), long-distance jumping (frogs), and flying through the air (birds).

▲ Tree Frog

▲ Harris's Hawk

28.2 Assessment

Review Key Concepts 

1. a. Review What body structures generate force? With what other body structure do these structures work to enable movement?
   b. Infer Why are the largest land animals vertebrates?
2. a. Review What characteristics are common to the skeletons of all vertebrates?
   b. Form a Hypothesis Suppose that you were to find a vertebrate fossil that showed a joint structure with muscle and tendon relationships similar to that of a squirrel. For which kinds of movement would you predict the animal had been best adapted?

Apply the Big idea

Structure and Function

3. Create a model of a vertebrate or invertebrate joint. Make sure the muscles are attached to the same skeletal structures they would be attached to in a real animal and that the muscles and skeletal structure allow the joint to bend and flex.

BIOLOGY.com Search Lesson 28.2  • Self-Test • Lesson Assessment

Assessment Answers

1a. Muscles generate force, and they work with skeletons to enable movement.

1b. Vertebrates and a few invertebrates have endoskeletons, which grow as the animal grows. Because endoskeletons are lightweight in proportion to the bodies they support, land-dwelling vertebrates can grow very large.

2a. Vertebrates have an endoskeleton made of cartilage and/or bone, and endoskeletons are lightweight in proportion to the bodies they support.

2b. Sample answer: running and climbing

3.  Models will vary. To build these models, students might use slender dowels for the bones or tongue depressors for the exoskeleton, and rubber bands for the muscles.

28.3 Reproduction

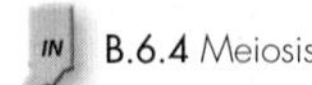

B.6.4 Meiosis.

THINK ABOUT IT Sexual reproduction can be dangerous. Just ask a male praying mantis—who may be devoured by his mate. Or a male peacock, whose success in courting a female depends on his growing and lugging around a huge tail that makes it harder for him to escape predators. Or a male emperor penguin, who incubates an egg for months on antarctic ice in temperatures far below zero. Or a female deer, who carries around the ever-increasing weight of her developing young for seven months, while she runs from predators such as coyotes and seeks food for herself and the young she carries. Yet, most animal species engage in sexual reproduction during at least part of their life cycles. Why?

Key Questions

How do asexual and sexual reproduction in animals compare?

How do internal and external fertilization differ?

Where do embryos develop?

How are terrestrial vertebrates adapted to reproduction on land?

Vocabulary

oviparous • ovoviviparous • viviparous • placenta • metamorphosis • nymph • pupa • amniotic egg • mammary gland

Taking Notes

Outline Before you read, use the headings and key concepts in this lesson to make an outline about animal reproduction. As you read, add details to your outline.

Asexual and Sexual Reproduction

How do asexual and sexual reproduction in animals compare?

Many invertebrates and a few chordates can reproduce asexually.

Asexual Reproduction Animals reproduce asexually in many ways. Some cnidarians divide in two. Some animals reproduce through budding, which produces new individuals as outgrowths of the body wall. Females of some species, such as the whiptail lizard in **Figure 28–14,** can reproduce asexually by producing eggs that develop without being fertilized. This process is called parthenogenesis (pahr thuh noh JEN uh sis). Parthenogenesis produces offspring that carry DNA inherited only from their mothers. This means of reproduction occurs in some crustaceans and insects but very rarely in vertebrates.

Asexual reproduction requires only one parent, so individuals in favorable environmental conditions can reproduce rapidly. But since offspring produced asexually carry only a single parent's DNA, they have less genetic diversity than do offspring produced sexually. Lack of genetic diversity can be a disadvantage to a population if its environment changes.

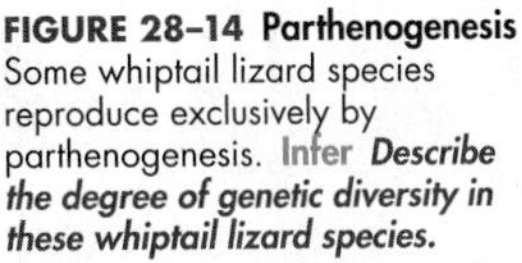

FIGURE 28–14 Parthenogenesis Some whiptail lizard species reproduce exclusively by parthenogenesis. **Infer** *Describe the degree of genetic diversity in these whiptail lizard species.*

UbD Teach for Understanding

ENDURING UNDERSTANDING Animals have evolved diverse ways to carry out basic life processes and maintain homeostasis.

GUIDING QUESTION What are the different strategies animals have evolved to help them produce offspring?

EVIDENCE OF UNDERSTANDING *After students complete the lesson, assign the following assessment to show their understanding of the difference between asexual reproduction and sexual reproduction.* Have each student write a brief article, that could appear in a general-circulation magazine, explaining the difference between sexual and asexual reproduction. Tell students the article should identify an advantage and a disadvantage of each.

Getting Started

Objectives

28.3.1 Compare asexual and sexual reproduction.

28.3.2 Contrast internal and external fertilization.

28.3.3 Describe the different patterns of embryo development in animals.

28.3.4 Explain how terrestrial vertebrates are adapted to reproduction on land.

Student Resources

Study Workbooks A and B, 28.3 Worksheets

Spanish Study Workbook, 28.3 Worksheets

BIOLOGY.com Lesson Overview • Lesson Notes • Assessment: Self-Test, Lesson Assessment

For corresponding lesson in the **Foundation Edition,** see pages 678–683.

Activate Prior Knowledge

Ask student volunteers to list ideas and concepts that they learned about sexual and asexual reproduction in previous lessons on cell division and meiosis. Write the list on the board, and explain to students that they will be applying their knowledge during this lesson on animal reproduction.

Answers

FIGURE 28–14 These whiptail lizards have little or no genetic diversity.

IN INDIANA ACADEMIC STANDARDS

For the full text of all standards, see the Course Overview in the front matter of this book.

B.6.4 Describe and model the process of meiosis and explain the relationship between the genetic make-up of the parent cell and the daughter cells (gametes).

LESSON 28.3

Teach

Lead a Discussion

After students have read the information on this page and reviewed **Figure 28–16,** discuss how some animals alternate between asexual reproduction and sexual reproduction. Ask students why they think having an alternating reproductive cycle might be advantageous for some organisms. *(Sample answer: Having an asexual stage helps the organism reproduce quickly when needed, but still allows them the genetic diversity that results from sexual reproduction.)* Then, review each step of the cycle shown in **Figure 28–16.** Begin by having students focus on the fertilization of gametes, which produces a zygote that develops into a polyp.

DIFFERENTIATED INSTRUCTION

LPR **Less Proficient Readers** If students struggle with the large amount of text on this page and in **Figure 28–16,** have them work in pairs to write a list of main ideas and create a simplified version of the visual. Then, have two pairs work together to discuss the similarities and differences between their lists of main ideas and drawings.

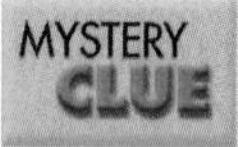

Review with students the meaning of *homozygous,* which they learned in Chapter 11. Discuss why most organisms are homozygous for some traits and heterozygous for other traits. Then, talk about why it is interesting that the baby shark was homozygous for every trait the researchers examined. Students can go online to Biology.com to gather their evidence.

MYSTERY CLUE

When investigators analyzed the baby shark's DNA, they found that it was homozygous for all the traits they examined, including two rare traits. Why was that unusual?

Sexual Reproduction Recall from Chapter 11 that sexual reproduction involves meiosis, the process that produces haploid reproductive cells, or gametes. Gametes carry half the number of chromosomes found in body cells. Typically, male animals produce small gametes, called sperm, which swim. Females produce larger gametes called eggs, which do not swim. When haploid gametes join during fertilization, they produce a zygote that contains the diploid number of chromosomes.

Sexual reproduction maintains genetic diversity in a population by creating individuals with new combinations of genes. Because genetic diversity is the raw material on which natural selection operates, sexually reproducing populations are better able to evolve and adapt to changing environmental conditions. On the other hand, sexual reproduction requires two individuals of different sexes. So, the density of a population must be high enough to allow mates to find each other.

In most animal species that reproduce sexually, each individual is either male or female. Among annelids, mollusks, and fishes, however, some species are hermaphrodites (hur MAF roh dyts), which means that some individuals can be both male and female or can convert from one sex to the other. In some species, individuals can produce eggs and sperm at the same time. Usually, these animals don't fertilize their own eggs, but exchange sperm with another individual. Some species, such as the clownfish in **Figure 28–15,** may change from one sex to the other as they mature.

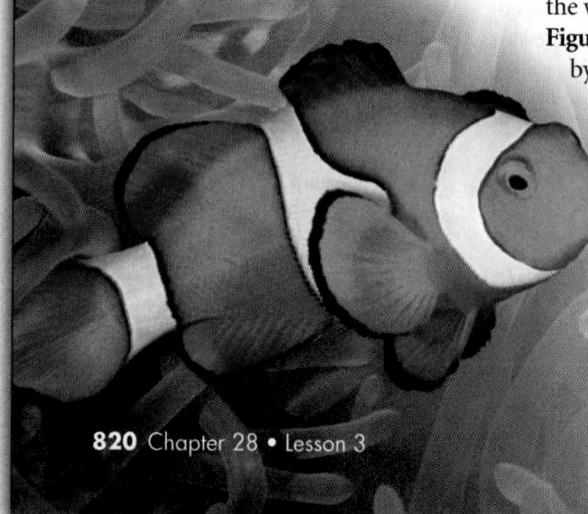

FIGURE 28–15 Hermaphrodites In this species of clownfish, *Amphiprion percula,* all individuals are born male and change to female as they grow. In some other hermaphroditic species, individuals are born female and change to male as they grow, or are both sexes at the same time.

Reproductive Cycles A number of invertebrates have life cycles that alternate between sexual and asexual reproduction. Parasitic worms and cnidarians alternate between forms that reproduce sexually and forms that reproduce asexually.

Parasitic worms such as blood flukes mature in the body of an infected person, reproduce sexually, and release embryos that pass out of the body in feces. If the embryos reach fresh water, they develop into larvae and infect snails, in which they reproduce asexually. Then the larvae are released, ready to infect another person.

Many cnidarians alternate between two body forms: polyps that grow singly or in colonies and medusas that swim freely in the water. The life cycle of a common jellyfish, *Aurelia,* is shown in **Figure 28–16.** In these jellyfish, polyps produce medusas asexually by budding. The medusas then reproduce sexually by producing eggs and sperm that are released into the water. After fertilization, the resulting zygote grows into a free-swimming larva. The larva eventually attaches to a hard surface and develops into a polyp that may continue the cycle.

In Your Notebook *Explain why a genetically diverse species can adapt more easily to disease and change.*

Biology In-Depth

INVERTEBRATE HERMAPHRODITISM

In Greek myth, Hermaphroditus, the son of Hermes and Aphrodite, caught the eye of a nymph of the spring in which he was bathing. She fell in love with him, and they melded into one being—half male and half female. Likewise, a hermaphroditic animal contains both male and female organs and thus can produce both eggs and sperm. Hermaphroditism is common in invertebrates such as worms, some gastropods, some leeches, and barnacles. Self-fertilization is possible, but usually, during sexual reproduction, two separate individuals exchange sperm. As a result, eggs in both organisms become fertilized. That result is an advantage of hermaphroditism, because two organisms, not one, are impregnated by each encounter and because genetic variation is maintained. Such an event is called mutual cross-fertilization. Other hermaphrodites practice self-fertilization. Scientists are investigating the evolutionary advantages of that approach.

Answers

IN YOUR NOTEBOOK A genetically diverse species is more likely to have members with adaptations that allow them, and therefore, the species, to survive changing environmental conditions or disease.

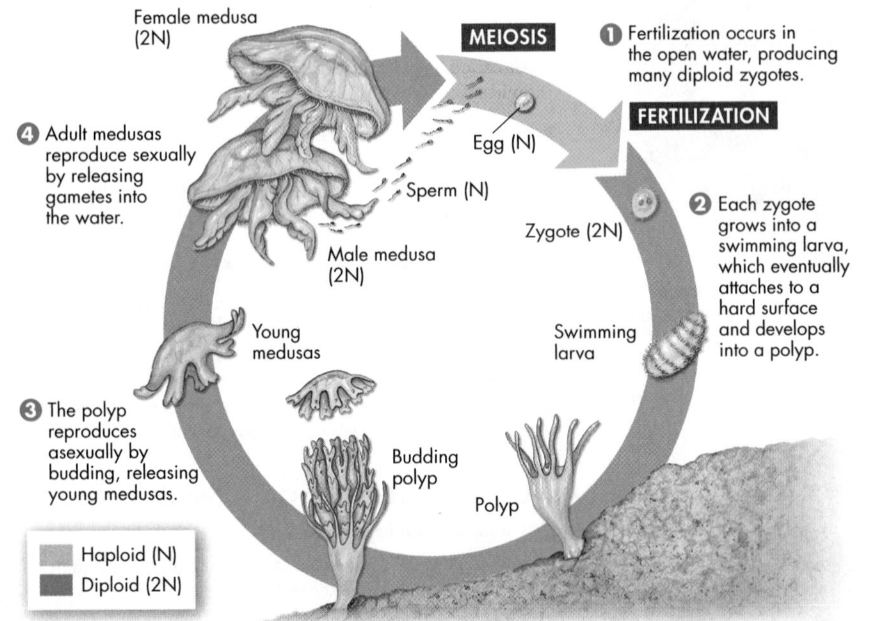

Female medusa (2N)
MEIOSIS
1 Fertilization occurs in the open water, producing many diploid zygotes.
FERTILIZATION
4 Adult medusas reproduce sexually by releasing gametes into the water.
Egg (N)
Sperm (N)
Zygote (2N)
2 Each zygote grows into a swimming larva, which eventually attaches to a hard surface and develops into a polyp.
Male medusa (2N)
Young medusas
Swimming larva
3 The polyp reproduces asexually by budding, releasing young medusas.
Budding polyp
Polyp
Haploid (N)
Diploid (2N)

FIGURE 28–16 Alternating Reproductive Cycles The reproductive cycle of *Aurelia*, a jellyfish, alternates between asexual and sexual reproduction. A zygote is produced sexually by medusas and grows into a larva. The larva develops into a polyp that buds, reproducing asexually. The polyp releases a medusa.

Internal and External Fertilization

How do internal and external fertilization differ?

In sexual reproduction, eggs and sperm meet either inside or outside the body of the egg-producing individual. These alternatives are called internal and external fertilization, respectively.

Internal Fertilization Many aquatic animals and nearly all terrestrial animals reproduce by internal fertilization. **During internal fertilization, eggs are fertilized inside the body of the egg-producing individual.**

▶ ***Invertebrates*** Invertebrates that reproduce by internal fertilization range in complexity from sponges to arachnids. The eggs of sponges and some other aquatic animals are fertilized by sperm released by others of their species and taken in from the surrounding water. In many arthropod species, males deposit sperm inside the female's body during mating.

▶ ***Chordates*** Some fishes and amphibians, and all reptiles, birds, and mammals, reproduce by internal fertilization. In some amphibian species, males deposit "sperm packets" into the surrounding environment; females then pick up these packets and take them inside their bodies. In many other chordate species, males have an external sexual organ that deposits sperm inside the female during mating.

MYSTERY CLUE

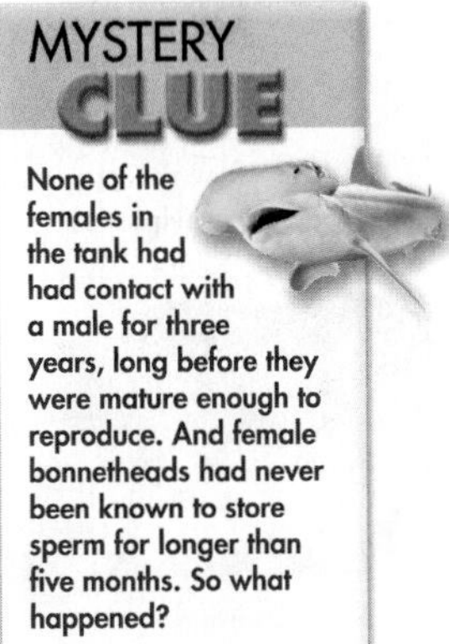

None of the females in the tank had had contact with a male for three years, long before they were mature enough to reproduce. And female bonnetheads had never been known to store sperm for longer than five months. So what happened?

Lead a Discussion

Point out that fertilization occurs only in sexual reproduction. Among animals that reproduce sexually, the egg can either be fertilized outside the body or inside the body of the egg-producing individual, which is usually identified as the female of the species.

Ask Name some invertebrates that reproduce by internal fertilization, and name some invertebrates that reproduce by external fertilization. *(Sponges, arachnids, and many other arthropod species reproduce by internal fertilization. Corals, worms, and mollusks reproduce by external fertilization.)*

DIFFERENTIATED INSTRUCTION

L1 Struggling Students Some students may have difficulty visualizing how external fertilization could occur. Direct their attention to **Figure 28–16,** which includes an example of external fertilization, or to **Figure 28–17,** which shows a fish releasing sperm. As students look at the cycle in **Figure 28–16,** explain that the male medusa releases sperm and the female medusa releases eggs into the open water, where fertilization occurs.

ELL Focus on ELL: Extend Language

INTERMEDIATE AND ADVANCED SPEAKERS
Have students fill out a **Venn Diagram** to organize information about internal and external fertilization. In the shared portion of the diagram, they should record that both are forms of sexual reproduction, both include fertilization of eggs by sperm, and both include some invertebrates and chordates. Students can record contrasting details of each after labeling one side Internal Fertilization and the other External Fertilization. Accept short phrases from intermediate speakers, but require advanced speakers to write sentences in their Venn diagrams.

Study Wkbks A/B, Appendix S33, Venn Diagram. **Transparencies,** GO18.

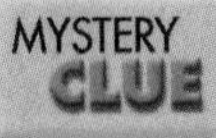

Suggest students look in this section for a way that some vertebrates can reproduce asexually. Students can go online to Biology.com to gather their evidence.

UbD Check for Understanding

ONE-MINUTE RESPONSE

Write the following prompt on the board, and give students about a minute to write a quick response.

- Compare and contrast asexual and sexual reproduction. Describe a life cycle that alternates between the two.

ADJUST INSTRUCTION

If students' responses are incorrect or incomplete, lead a short class discussion to review the basic differences between asexual and sexual reproduction. Then, have small groups of students talk about alternating reproductive cycles so students can hear the concepts discussed in different ways.

Teach continued

Build Science Skills

Tell students there are both similarities and differences among species regarding the growth and development of their embryos. Explain that the science skill of comparing and contrasting can be used to identify these similarities and differences. Ask each student to write a sentence comparing, or identifying a similarity, among the three types of development: oviparous, ovoviviparous, and viviparous. Then, have students write a sentence contrasting, or identifying differences between, embryo growth and development among the three types. Call on volunteers to share their sentences with the class.

DIFFERENTIATED INSTRUCTION

ELL English Language Learners Write these three terms on the board, dividing each into word parts: *ovi-parous, ovo-vivi-parous,* and *vivi-parous.* Explain that *ovi* and *ovo* mean "egg," *vivi* means "alive," and *parous* means "giving birth to." Work with students on the pronunciation of these terms, and use the meanings of the word parts to help explain what each term means.

LPR Less Proficient Readers Have students organize information about where embryos develop in a **Compare/Contrast Table.** Have them write these four column headings: Characteristics, Oviparous Species, Ovoviviparous Species, and Viviparous Species. The rows should include: Definition/Description, How Young Are Nourished, and Examples. After students have finished filling in the table, suggest they work in small groups to check one another's tables.

Study Wkbks A/B, Appendix S20, Compare/Contrast Table. **Transparencies,** GO3.

FIGURE 28–17 External Fertilization One type of external fertilization results from spawning. When aquatic animals spawn, females release eggs and males release sperm at the same time. Infer ***What is the cloudy substance behind this spawning male wrasse?***

External Fertilization A wide range of aquatic invertebrate and vertebrate species reproduce by external fertilization. **In external fertilization, eggs are fertilized outside the body of the egg-producing individual.**

▶ ***Invertebrates*** Invertebrates with external fertilization include corals, worms, and mollusks. These animals release large numbers of eggs and sperm into the water. Gamete release is usually synchronized with tides, phases of the moon, or seasons so that eggs and sperm are present at the same time. Fertilized eggs develop into free-swimming larvae that typically develop for a time before changing into adult form.

▶ ***Chordates*** Chordates with external fertilization include most nonvertebrate chordates and many fishes and amphibians. In some fish species, such as the wrasse in **Figure 28–17,** males and females spawn in a school, releasing large numbers of eggs and sperm into the water. Other fishes and many amphibians spawn in pairs. In these cases, the female usually releases eggs onto which the male deposits sperm.

FIGURE 28–18 Embryo Development

Robin - Oviparous

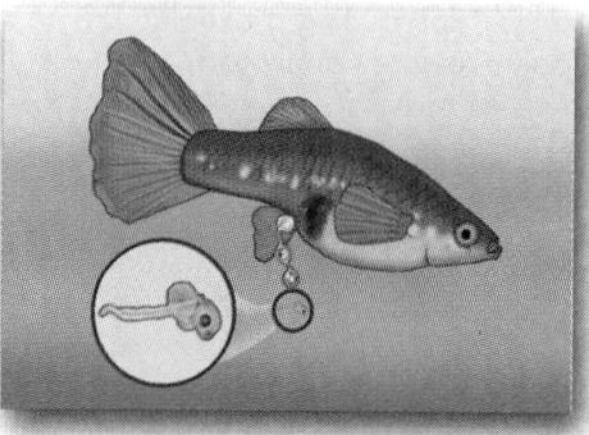

Guppy - Ovoviviparous

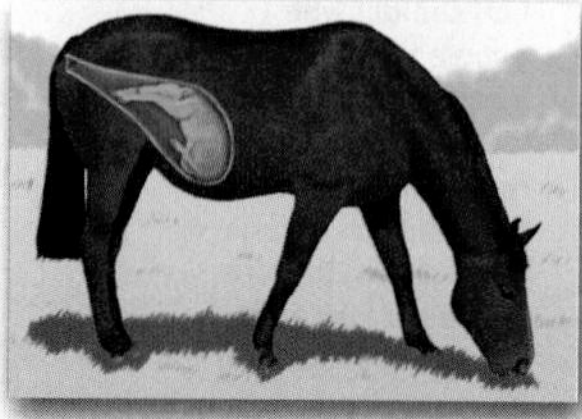

Horse - Viviparous

Development and Growth

Where do embryos develop?

After eggs are fertilized, the resulting zygote divides through mitosis and differentiates as described in Chapter 25. This development occurs under different circumstances in different species. The care and protection given to developing embryos also varies widely.

Where Embryos Develop Embryos develop either inside or outside the body of a parent in various ways. **Animals may be oviparous, ovoviviparous, or viviparous.**

▶ ***Oviparous Species*** **Oviparous** (oh VIP uh rus) species are those in which embryos develop in eggs outside the parents' bodies. Most invertebrates, many fishes and amphibians, most reptiles, all birds, and a few odd mammals are oviparous.

▶ ***Ovoviviparous Species*** In **ovoviviparous** (oh voh vy VIP uh rus) species, embryos develop within the mother's body, but they depend entirely on the yolk sac of their eggs. The young do not receive any additional nutrients from the mother. They either hatch within the mother's body or are released immediately before hatching. Young swim freely shortly after hatching. Guppies and other fishes in their family, along with some shark species, are ovoviviparous.

▶ ***Viviparous Species*** **Viviparous** (vy VIP uh rus) species are those in which embryos obtain nutrients from the mother's body during development. Viviparity occurs in most mammals and in some insects, sharks, bony fishes, amphibians, and reptiles. In viviparous insects, and in some sharks and amphibians, young are nourished by secretions produced in the mother's reproductive tract. In placental mammals, young are nourished by a **placenta**—a specialized organ that enables exchange of respiratory gases, nutrients, and wastes between the mother and her developing young.

Quick Facts

FISH PARENTS

Most oviparous fishes provide no care for their young; they simply produce hundreds, or even millions, of fertilized eggs and "let nature take its course." Most eggs do not develop into young fishes; they are eaten or damaged. Some oviparous fishes, however, do care for their young. Some fishes build nests to protect the fertilized eggs. Siamese fighting fishes build nests of bubbles, and sticklebacks use fragments of aquatic plants, twigs, and other debris. Some cichlids hold their eggs and young in the mouth. Seahorses hold fertilized eggs in a pouch until the eggs are ready to hatch. Fishes that care for their young usually do not produce as many eggs as those that simply lay the eggs and leave.

Answers

FIGURE 28–17 large numbers of sperm

How Young Develop Most newborn mammals and newly hatched birds and reptiles look a lot like miniature adults. Infant body proportions are different from those of adults, and newborns have more or less hair, fur, or feathers than adults have. But it is pretty clear that a newly hatched snake is not going to grow up to be something totally different, such as an eagle!

For many other groups of animals, however, it's not as clear. As most invertebrates, nonvertebrate chordates, fishes, and amphibians develop, they undergo metamorphosis. **Metamorphosis** is a developmental process that leads to dramatic changes in shape and form.

▶ ***Aquatic Invertebrates*** Many aquatic invertebrates have a larval stage, which looks nothing like an adult. These larvae often swim or drift in open water before undergoing metamorphosis and assuming their adult form. Members of some phyla, such as cnidarians, have a single larval stage. Other groups, such as crustaceans, may pass through several larval stages before they look like miniature adults.

▶ ***Terrestrial Invertebrates*** Insects may undergo one of two types of metamorphosis. Some insects, such as grasshoppers, undergo gradual or incomplete metamorphosis, as shown in **Figure 28–19.** Immature forms, or **nymphs** (nimfs), resemble adults, but they lack functional sexual organs and some adult structures such as wings. As they molt several times and grow, nymphs gradually acquire adult structures.

Other insects, such as butterflies, undergo complete metamorphosis. Larvae of these animals look nothing like their parents, and they feed in different ways. Larvae molt and grow, but they change little in appearance. Then they undergo a final molt and change into a **pupa** (PYOO puh; plural: pupae), the stage in which an insect larva develops into an adult. During the pupal stage, the entire body is remodeled inside and out! The adult that emerges looks like a completely different animal. Don't let your familiarity with caterpillars and butterflies dull your wonder at this change. If land vertebrates underwent this kind of metamorphosis, a larva that looks like a snake could, in fact, grow up into an eagle!

FIGURE 28–19 Insect Metamorphosis Insects usually undergo metamorphosis during their growth and development. The chinch bug (left) undergoes incomplete metamorphosis, in which the nymphs look similar to the adults. The ladybug (right) undergoes complete metamorphosis. The developing larva and the pupa look completely different from the adult.

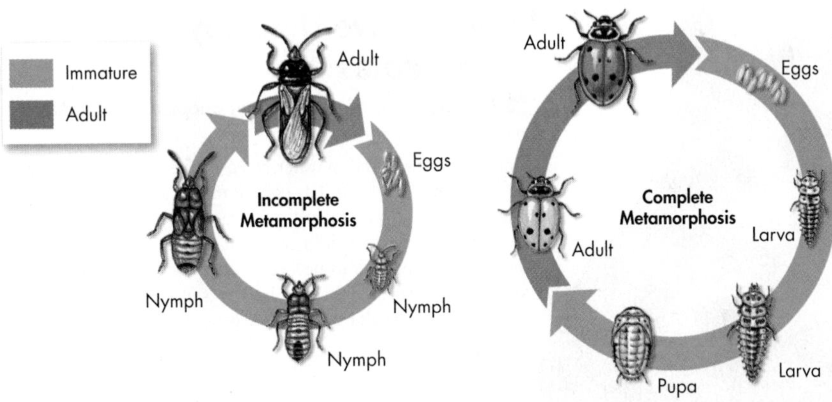

UbD Check for Understanding

HAND SIGNALS

Ask students the following questions, and have them show a thumbs-up sign if they think they can answer the question correctly, a thumbs-down sign if they definitely can't, or a waving-hand sign if they're not sure.

- How are ovoviviparous species different from viviparous species?
- What is the purpose of a placenta?
- What is the difference between complete and incomplete metamorphosis?

ADJUST INSTRUCTION

For any question that received a thumbs-down or waving-hand sign, ask students to find the answer in their text and write a one-sentence response to the question.

Use Visuals

Use **Figure 28–19** to start a discussion on insect metamorphosis. Emphasize that other kinds of animals also develop through metamorphosis.

Ask If you observed a very small grasshopper that closely resembled a larger grasshopper, would you identify it as a nymph or a pupa? *(a nymph, because grasshoppers undergo incomplete metamorphosis, which doesn't include a pupal stage)*

Ask The caterpillars of monarch butterflies form a chrysalis in which they develop into their adult form. What developmental stage is the chrysalis an example of? *(the pupal stage)*

DIFFERENTIATED INSTRUCTION

LPR Less Proficient Readers Many students would benefit from observing insect metamorphosis first hand. Place food, such as a piece of overripe banana, in an open jar, and leave it for a few days in a place where flies can have access to it. Then, wave the flies away and cover the jar with a nylon stocking or similar porous material. Within a few days, students will be able to observe maggots on the food. Explain that maggots are fly larvae. In time, they will metamorphose into pupae, and, eventually, emerge as adults.

L3 Advanced Students Ask interested students to find images and information about metamorphosis in frogs. Have them make a presentation to the class about the life cycle of frogs. Students may be able to find a video online showing how tadpoles develop into adult frogs.

Teach continued

Lead a Discussion

Ask volunteers to describe their observations of how pet cats or dogs take care of their kittens or puppies. Then, discuss other observations they've made of animals caring for their young, such as birds feeding chicks in a nest.

Ask How is it that some offspring of animals that provide little parental care survive? *(These animals produce so many offspring that some are bound to survive.)*

Ask Why do you think maternal care is an important mammalian characteristic? *(Mammals don't produce large numbers of offspring, and maternal care helps ensure that some offspring survive into adulthood.)*

DIFFERENTIATED INSTRUCTION

L1 **Struggling Students** Help students understand how some animal species can succeed without caring for their young by directing them back to **Figure 28–17.** Explain that the great numbers of eggs and sperm released by these organisms ensure that some offspring will survive.

FIGURE 28-20 Amphibian Metamorphosis Amphibians typically begin their lives in the water and metamorphose into adults that live on land. Frog tadpoles, such as the one in the photo, start out with flippers, gills, and a tail and mature into adults that have legs, lungs, and no tail.

Control of metamorphosis in arthropods is accomplished by hormones. Recall that hormones are chemicals produced in one organ of an organism that affect that organism's other tissues and organs. In insects that undergo complete metamorphosis, high levels of a juvenile hormone keep an insect in its larval form. As the insect matures, its production of juvenile hormone decreases. Eventually, the concentration of juvenile hormone drops below a certain threshold. The next time the insect molts, it becomes a pupa. When no juvenile hormone is produced, the insect undergoes a pupa-to-adult molt.

▶ ***Amphibians*** Amphibians typically undergo metamorphosis that is controlled by hormones. This metamorphosis changes amphibians from aquatic young into terrestrial adults. Tadpoles, such as the one in **Figure 28–20,** are one type of amphibian larvae.

In Your Notebook *What chemicals control metamorphosis in arthropods and amphibians?*

Care of Offspring Animals' care of their offspring varies from no care at all to years of nurturing. Most aquatic invertebrates and many fishes and amphibians release large numbers of eggs that they completely ignore. This reproductive strategy succeeds in circumstances favoring populations that disperse and grow rapidly.

But other animals care for their offspring. Some amphibians incubate young in their mouth, on their back, or even in their stomach! Birds and mammals generally care for their young. Maternal care is an important mammalian characteristic, and the bond between mother and young is often very close, as the pandas in **Figure 28–21** demonstrate. Males of many species also help care for young. Parental care helps young survive in crowded, competitive environments. Typically, species that provide intensive or long-term parental care give birth to fewer young than do species that offer no parental care.

FIGURE 28-21 Care of Offspring Long-term, intensive care of offspring is a characteristic of mammals, such as the mother panda in the photo. A wild panda cub will stay with its mother for up to 18 months while she protects it and teaches it how to be a panda.

Reproductive Diversity in Chordates

How are terrestrial vertebrates adapted to reproduction on land?

Chordates first evolved in water, so early chordate reproduction was suited to aquatic life. The eggs of most modern fishes and amphibians still need to develop in water, or at least in very moist places. As some vertebrate lineages left the water to live on land, they evolved a number of new reproductive strategies. These strategies now enable the fertilized eggs of many terrestrial chordates to develop somewhere other than in a body of water.

Quick Facts

IT TAKES A VILLAGE TO RAISE AN ELEPHANT

Elephants have complex social interactions and behaviors associated with raising their young. The gestation period for elephants is about 22 months. Females first start mating around the age of 20 years. They will continue to have calves every two to four years until they reach about 50 years of age. Calves are highly dependent on their mothers for food for the first two years. These calves are cared for not only by their mothers but also by the other females in the herd. Older females help new mothers. Younger females play with the babies. When a young elephant has been weaned, it enters a sort of adolescence. Young males leave the herd, often joining bachelor herds. Young females stay with the herd and help care for newborns, which helps prepare them to become mothers.

Answers

IN YOUR NOTEBOOK Hormones control metamorphosis in both arthropods and amphibians.

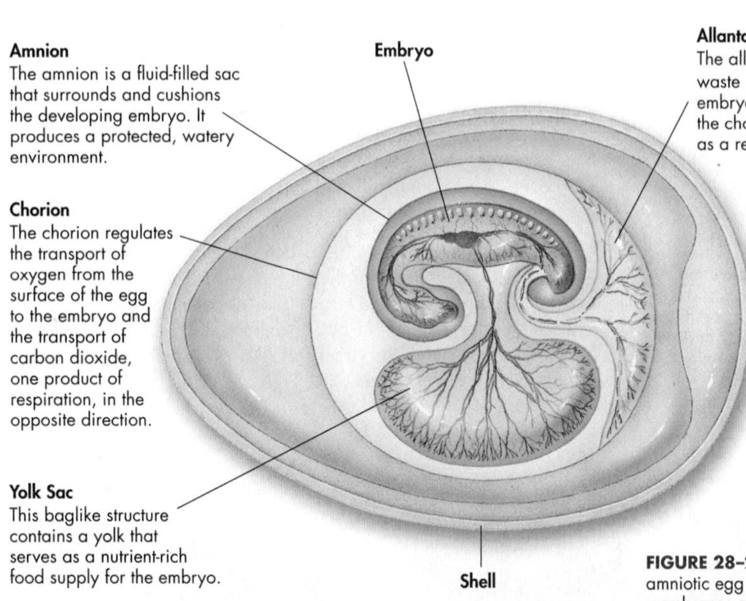

Amnion
The amnion is a fluid-filled sac that surrounds and cushions the developing embryo. It produces a protected, watery environment.
Embryo
Allantois
The allantois stores the waste produced by the embryo. It later fuses with the chorion and serves as a respiratory organ.
Chorion
The chorion regulates the transport of oxygen from the surface of the egg to the embryo and the transport of carbon dioxide, one product of respiration, in the opposite direction.
Yolk Sac
This baglike structure contains a yolk that serves as a nutrient-rich food supply for the embryo.
Shell

FIGURE 28–22 Amniotic Egg An amniotic egg contains several membranes and an external shell. Although it is waterproof, the eggshell is porous, allowing gases to pass through. The shell of a reptile egg is usually soft and leathery, while the shell of a bird egg is hard and brittle.

The Amniotic Egg **Reptiles, birds, and a few mammals have evolved amniotic eggs in which an embryo can develop outside its mother's body, and out of water, without drying out.** The **amniotic** (am nee AH tik) **egg** is named after the amnion, one of four membranes that surround the developing embryo. The amnion, yolk sac, chorion, and allantois membranes of the amniotic egg, along with its shell, provide a protected environment in which an embryo can develop out of water. You can learn about the functions of the membranes in **Figure 28–22.** The amniotic egg is one of the most important vertebrate adaptations to life on land.

Mammalian Reproductive Strategies Mammals have evolved various adaptations for reproducing and caring for their young. **The three groups of mammals—monotremes, marsupials, and placentals—differ greatly in their means of reproduction and development, but all nourish their young with mother's milk.**

▶ ***Monotremes*** Reproduction in monotremes, such as the echidna in **Figure 28–23,** combines reptilian and mammalian traits. Like a reptile, a female monotreme lays soft-shelled, amniotic eggs that are incubated outside her body. The eggs hatch in about ten days. But like other mammals, young monotremes are nourished by milk produced by the mother's **mammary glands.** Female monotremes secrete milk, not through well-developed nipples like other mammals, but through pores on the surface of the abdomen.

FIGURE 28–23 Monotremes There are only five species of monotremes, four of which are spiny echidnas similar to the one above. Monotremes lay eggs but, like all mammals, feed their young with milk produced by the mother.

Biology In-Depth

THE AMNIOTIC EGG AND LIFE ON LAND

As the climate became drier at the end of the Carboniferous Period, many amphibians were at a disadvantage because their life cycle required bodies of water for fertilization and embryonic development. Reptiles, which had evolved from an amphibian clade already living on land, began to diversify and occupy ecological niches once occupied by amphibians. Reptiles were better adapted to survival and reproduction in drier environments by their internal fertilization and amniotic egg. The amniotic egg was well adapted to drier environments because it provided gas exchange, nourishment, and a self-contained watery environment for the developing embryo.

Use Visuals

Have students look at **Figure 28–22.** Then, call on students at random to read each annotation. For each structure, discuss the function it serves for the developing embryo. Emphasize that the amniotic egg was an important adaptation that allowed animals to live on land.

DIFFERENTIATED INSTRUCTION

ELL English Language Learners Point out that the amnion is described as a sac, and the baglike structure that contains the yolk is called a yolk sac. Explain that *sac* comes from a French word meaning "bag." A *sac* is a pouch or baglike structure within an organism that often contains a fluid. Explain that the everyday word *sack,* which is spelled differently but pronounced the same, also indicates a type of bag. A *sack* is usually a rectangular paper bag. When English language learners see either *sac* or *sack,* they should think of some kind of bag.

L3 Advanced Students Provide each student with a raw egg, tweezers, and a bowl. Have them carefully break the egg into the bowl and observe both the shell and the structures inside, using tweezers to separate the parts. Ask them to identify the membranes and other parts of the egg and then make a drawing of what they observed. Students should wear disposable plastic gloves and wash their hands in warm, soapy water when they finish.

LESSON 28.3

Teach continued

Use Visuals

Discuss differences in how mammals reproduce and care for young by referring to **Figures 28–23, 28–24,** and **28–25.** For each figure, ask students to identify reproductive adaptations that distinguish each group from the other two.

DIFFERENTIATED INSTRUCTION

L1 **Struggling Students** Have volunteers describe what **Figures 28–24** and **28–25** show. Call on other students to read the captions aloud. Then, discuss the reproductive adaptations of each type of mammal.

Assess and Remediate

EVALUATE UNDERSTANDING

Call on students at random to describe the differences between sexual and asexual reproduction; internal and external fertilization; oviparous, ovoviviparous, and viviparous development; and monotremes, marsupials, and placental mammals. Then, have students complete the 28.3 Assessment.

REMEDIATION SUGGESTION

L1 **Struggling Students** If students have trouble answering **Question 1,** review meiosis and fertilization, as well as forms of asexual reproduction with them.

BIOLOGY.com Students can check their understanding of lesson concepts with the **Self-Test** assessment. They can then take an online version of the **Lesson Assessment.**

FIGURE 28–24 Marsupials Marsupial young, such as this wallaby peeking out of its mother's pouch, are born at a very early stage of development. They complete their development nursing in their mother's pouch.

▶ ***Marsupials*** Marsupials, such as the wallabies in **Figure 28–24,** bear live young that usually complete their development in an external pouch. Marsupial young are born at a very early stage of development. Little more than embryos, they crawl across their mother's fur and attach to a nipple in her pouch, or marsupium (mar soo pee um). Inside the marsupium, the young spend months attached to a nipple. They continue drinking milk and growing inside the marsupium until they can survive independently.

▶ ***Placentals*** Placental mammals, such as the harp seals shown in **Figure 28–25,** are named for the placenta, which allows nutrients, oxygen, carbon dioxide, and other wastes to be exchanged between the embryo and the mother. The placenta allows the embryo to develop for a long time inside the mother and allows it to be born at a fairly advanced stage of development.

FIGURE 28–25 Placental Mammals Placental mammals, such as harp seals, are nourished through a placenta before they are born and by their mother's milk after they are born.

28.3 Assessment

IN B.6.4

Review Key Concepts

1. a. Review Compare asexual reproduction and sexual reproduction in terms of the genetic diversity resulting from each.
   b. Infer Why might sexual reproduction, as opposed to asexual reproduction, produce a population better able to survive disease or environmental changes?
2. a. Review Define the two types of fertilization.
   b. Predict Why would you expect species that employ external fertilization to reproduce in the water?
3. a. Review Define the three ways in which embryos develop.
   b. Compare and Contrast What is the difference between a nymph and a pupa?
4. a. Review What structure enables reptiles and birds to reproduce outside of water?
   b. Interpret Visuals In your own words, describe the functions of two of the membranes shown in **Figure 28–22.**

WRITE ABOUT SCIENCE

Creative Writing

5. Write an advertisement for an amniotic egg. Draw and label the parts of the egg, including each of the membranes and the shell. Describe the purpose of each structure and how it's ideally suited for its function.

BIOLOGY.com Search Lesson 28.3 GO • Self-Test • Lesson Assessment

Assessment Answers

1a. Asexual reproduction results in less genetic diversity than sexual reproduction.

1b. Sexually reproducing populations are better able to adapt to changing environmental conditions.

2a. During internal fertilization, eggs are fertilized inside the body of the egg-producing individual. In external fertilization, eggs are fertilized outside the body of the egg-producing individual.

2b. Sample answer: In water, sperm can swim to and fertilize eggs. On land, sperm cannot swim to eggs.

3a. Oviparous: embryos develop in eggs outside the parent's body; ovoviviparous: embryos develop within the mother's body, but they depend entirely on the yolk sac of their eggs; viviparous: embryos obtain nutrients from the mother's body during development.

3b. A nymph is the stage of development of an animal that undergoes incomplete metamorphosis in which it resembles an adult but lacks functional sexual organs and some other adult structures. A pupa is the stage of development of an animal that undergoes complete metamorphosis in which a larva develops into an adult.

4a. amniotic egg

4b. Sample answer: The amnion's watery environment protects the embryo by cushioning it. The chorion regulates gas exchange between the embryo and the outside environment.

WRITE ABOUT SCIENCE

5. Drawings will vary. Students should be creative in designing the advertisement but accurate in labeling and describing the purpose of all structures labeled in **Figure 28–22.**

28.4 Homeostasis

NoS.3 Communicate ideas.

THINK ABOUT IT A herd of wildebeests plods across Africa's Serengeti Plain. The land is parched, so they are on the move toward greener pastures. They move mechanically, their steps using as little energy as possible. With no food in their guts, their bodies mobilize energy stored in fat deposits for distribution to body tissues. Between drinking holes, their bodies conserve water by producing as little urine as possible. All their body systems work together in a joint effort to survive this difficult passage.

Key Questions

Why is the interdependence of body systems essential?

How do animals control their body temperature?

Vocabulary

endocrine gland • ectotherm • endotherm

Taking Notes

Venn Diagram Draw a Venn diagram comparing and contrasting the temperature control strategies of ectotherms and endotherms.

Interrelationship of Body Systems

Why is the interdependence of body systems essential?

Homeostasis, or control of internal conditions, is essential to an organism's survival. Wildebeest brain cells, like those of humans, must be kept at a stable temperature and supplied with a steady stream of glucose for energy—even when the animal is under stress. The brain cells must be bathed in fluid with a constant concentration of water and be cleansed of metabolic waste products. These conditions must not change during droughts, floods, famines, heat, or cold. Failure of homeostasis, even for a few minutes, would lead to permanent brain injury or death.

You've learned about digestive, respiratory, circulatory, excretory, nervous, muscular, and skeletal systems separately. Yet all of these systems are interconnected. **All body systems work together to maintain homeostasis.** In most animals, respiratory and digestive systems would be useless without circulatory systems to distribute oxygen and nutrients. Similarly, the excretory system needs a circulatory system to collect carbon dioxide and nitrogenous wastes from body tissues and deliver them to the lungs and excretory organs. Muscles wouldn't work without a nervous system to direct them and a skeletal system to support them.

In addition to the organ systems that you have already learned about, you will now learn about other body systems, those that fight disease, produce and release chemical controls, and manage body temperature—all to help ensure homeostasis.

FIGURE 28–26 Interrelationship of Body Systems All body systems must work together to keep stressed animals, such as these migrating wildebeests, alive.

Teach for Understanding

ENDURING UNDERSTANDING Animals have evolved diverse ways to carry out basic life processes and maintain homeostasis.

GUIDING QUESTION How do animals maintain homeostasis?

EVIDENCE OF UNDERSTANDING *After students have studied the lesson, assign the following assessment to show their understanding of the difference between ectotherms and endotherms.* Have students meet in small groups to discuss differences between ectotherms and endotherms. Then, arbitrarily divide the class in half. Assign one half to argue for the advantages of being ectothermic, and assign the other half to argue for the advantages of being endothermic. Have the class stage a mock debate on the issue of body temperature control.

Getting Started

Objectives

28.4.1 Explain how homeostasis is maintained in animals.

28.4.2 Describe the importance of body temperature control in animals.

Student Resources

Study Workbooks A and B, 28.4 Worksheets

Spanish Study Workbook, 28.4 Worksheets

Lab Manual B, 28.4 Data Analysis Worksheet

Lesson Overview • Lesson Notes • Activity: Data Analysis • Assessment: Self-Test, Lesson Assessment

For corresponding lesson in the **Foundation Edition,** see pages 684–687.

Activate Prior Knowledge

List on the board all the animal body systems students have learned about so far in Chapters 27 and 28. Call on students to describe ways these systems interact in an animal to help it maintain homeostasis. *(Sample answer: The respiratory system has membranes in which gas exchange occurs; the circulatory system carries the products of this gas exchange—oxygen to cells and carbon dioxide back to lungs, gills, or other respiratory structures where gas exchange occurs.)*

IN INDIANA ACADEMIC STANDARDS

For the full text of all standards, see the Course Overview in the front matter of this book.

NoS.3 Clearly communicate their ideas and results of investigations verbally and in written form using tables, graphs, diagrams, and photographs.

LESSON 28.4

Teach

Lead a Discussion

Discuss with students how an immune system and chemical controls help animals maintain homeostasis. Explain that in later chapters they will learn specifically about the immune system and the endocrine system in humans.

Ask What are examples of pathogens that can enter an animal's body and cause disease? *(Sample answer: viruses and bacteria)*

Ask In what part of the process of metamorphosis in insects does a juvenile hormone play a role? *(the change from larva to pupa in complete metamorphosis)*

DIFFERENTIATED INSTRUCTION

L1 Struggling Students Help students organize the information in the subsections, **Fighting Disease** and **Chemical Controls,** by using several short sentences to summarize the content. For example, write these sentences on the board:

- Most environments contain pathogens.
- Pathogens that enter the body can cause disease.
- An animal's immune system recognizes pathogens as "others."
- The immune system attacks invading pathogens.

Ask students to help you generate short sentences that summarize information about chemical controls.

ELL English Language Learners Write the word *homeostasis* on the board, and have students repeat the word after you. Draw a box around the prefix *homeo-* and explain that it means "same." Explain that maintaining homeostasis, then, means keeping a steady state—or "sameness"—in the body. Then, pair English language learners and ask partners to work together to construct sentences that summarize how the immune system and the endocrine glands restore or maintain homeostasis in an organism's body. Call on partners to share their sentences with the class.

Fighting Disease The controlled environment within an animal's body is a comfortable place for hostile invaders as well as for its own cells. Most environments contain disease-causing microorganisms, or pathogens, that may take advantage of steady supplies of oxygen and nutrients intended for body tissues. If pathogens enter the body and grow, they may disrupt homeostasis in ways that cause disease.

Most animals have an immune system that can distinguish between "self" and "other." Once the immune system discovers "others" in the body, it attacks the invaders and works to restore homeostasis. Your body experiences this process regularly, any time you catch a cold or fight off other kinds of infections. During the process, you may develop a fever and feel other effects of the battle going on within your body.

BUILD Vocabulary

WORD ORIGINS Not all hormones are produced by endocrine glands. Erythropoietin is released by the kidneys. It prompts the body to make more red blood cells, which carry oxygen through the body. And when you look at the Greek words *erythropoietin* is made from—*erythros,* meaning "red," and *poiesis,* meaning "a making"—the hormone's function isn't much of a surprise.

Chemical Controls Vertebrates, such as the migrating wildebeest, along with arthropods and many other invertebrates, regulate many body processes using a system of chemical controls. **Endocrine glands** are part of that system. Endocrine glands regulate body activities by releasing hormones into the blood. Hormones are carried by blood or body fluids to organs. Some hormones, as you have learned, control growth, development, and metamorphosis in insects.

Mammals, like other vertebrates, have endocrine glands that are part of an endocrine system. Some hormones control the way the body stores energy or mobilizes it—as in the case of the wildebeests. Other hormones regulate the amount of water in the body and the amount of calcium in bones.

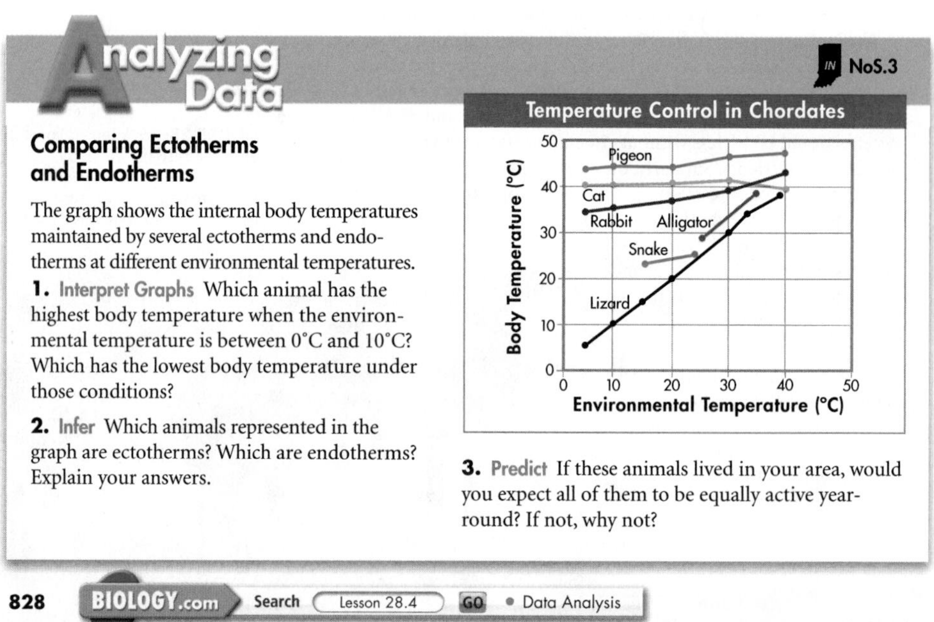

Comparing Ectotherms and Endotherms

The graph shows the internal body temperatures maintained by several ectotherms and endotherms at different environmental temperatures.

1. Interpret Graphs Which animal has the highest body temperature when the environmental temperature is between 0°C and 10°C? Which has the lowest body temperature under those conditions?

2. Infer Which animals represented in the graph are ectotherms? Which are endotherms? Explain your answers.

3. Predict If these animals lived in your area, would you expect all of them to be equally active year-round? If not, why not?

PURPOSE Students will interpret a graph to compare ectotherms and endotherms.

PLANNING Have students discuss how ectotherms and endotherms control body temperature.

ANSWERS

1. highest: pigeon; lowest: lizard
2. The lizard, snake, and alligator are ectotherms. Their body temperatures fluctuate based on the temperature of the environment. The pigeon, cat, and rabbit are endotherms. Their body temperatures are regulated mostly from within.
3. Answers will vary. In all areas, the pigeon, cat, and rabbit would be expected to be active year-round. In colder areas, the alligator, snake, and lizard would probably not be as active in the colder months of the year.

Body Temperature Control

How do animals control their body temperature?

Control of body temperature is important for maintaining homeostasis, particularly in areas where temperature varies widely with time of day and with season. Why is temperature control so important? Because many body functions are influenced by temperature. For example, muscles cannot operate if they are too cold or too hot. Cold muscles contract slowly, making an animal slow to react. If muscles get too hot, on the other hand, they may tire easily.

Body temperature control requires three components: a source of heat, a way to conserve heat when necessary, and a method of eliminating excess heat when necessary. An animal may be described as an ectotherm or endotherm based on the structures and behaviors that enable it to control its body temperature.

Ectotherms On cool, sunny mornings, lizards bask in the sun. This doesn't mean that they are lazy! A lizard is an **ectotherm**—an animal whose regulation of body temperature depends mostly on its relationship to sources of heat outside its body. **Most reptiles, invertebrates, fishes, and amphibians are ectotherms that regulate body temperature primarily by absorbing heat from, or losing heat to, their environment.**

Ectotherms have relatively low metabolic rates when resting, so their bodies don't generate much heat. When active, their muscles generate heat, just as your muscles do. However, most ectotherms lack effective body insulation, so their body heat is easily lost to the environment. That's why ectotherms warm up by basking in the sun. They also have to regulate their body temperature in hot conditions. The lizard in **Figure 28–27** is "stilting" to cool off. Ectotherms also often use underground burrows, where there are fewer temperature extremes. On hot, sunny days, they might seek shelter in a burrow that is cooler than the land surface. On chilly nights, those same burrows are warmer than the surface, enabling the animal to conserve some body heat.

In Your Notebook *Explain in your own words why the word* coldblooded *is an incorrect way to describe an ectotherm.*

Endotherms An **endotherm** is an animal whose body temperature is regulated, at least in part, using heat generated by its body. **Endotherms, such as birds and mammals, have high metabolic rates that generate heat, even when they are resting.** Birds conserve body heat primarily with insulating feathers, such as fluffy down. Mammals use combinations of body fat and hair for insulation. Some birds and most mammals can get rid of excess heat by panting, as the dingo in **Figure 28–28** is doing. Humans sweat to help reduce their body temperature. As sweat evaporates, it removes heat from the skin and the blood in capillaries just under the surface of the skin. Thus, as warm blood flows through the cooled capillaries, it loses heat.

FIGURE 28–27 Ectotherm This shovel-snouted lizard, an ectotherm, lives in the Namib Desert in Africa, one of the hottest places on Earth. It is regulating its body temperature by stilting—raising its body off the hot sand by performing a sort of push-up. **Infer** ***Do you think stilting is more likely to raise or lower body temperature? Explain.***

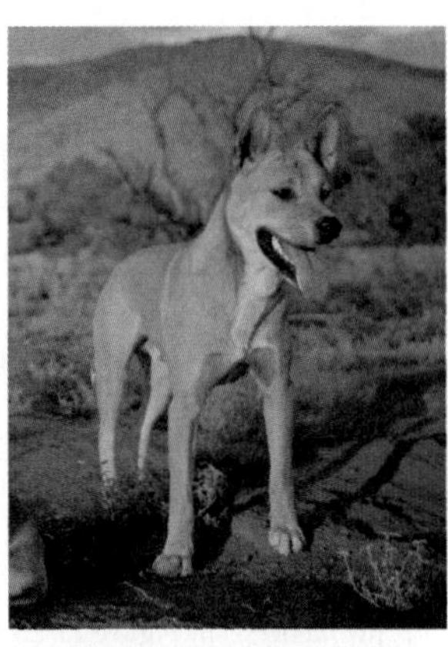

FIGURE 28–28 Endotherm Many endotherms, such as this dingo, pant when they are very warm. Panting allows air to evaporate some of the moisture in the blood-vessel rich mouth and respiratory tract, cooling the blood.

UbD Check for Understanding

ORAL QUESTIONING

Use the following questions to gauge understanding of body temperature control.

- What three components are required for body temperature control?
- What do ectotherms lack that causes their body heat to be easily lost to the environment?
- How do birds and most mammals get rid of excess heat?

ADJUST INSTRUCTION

Assess students' answers to determine what concepts they understand and what concepts they are having trouble with. Review difficult concepts in class discussion so students can hear how others explain terms and processes.

Connect to the Real World

Explain that an ectotherm is like a house with no central heating or air conditioning and no insulation. The temperature inside the house is going to be similar to the temperature outside the house. An endotherm is like a house with central heating (which is always on low), air conditioning, and insulation.

Ask Which house would you prefer in a cold climate? Why? *(the "endothermic house," because it would be easier to get warm)*

Ask Which house would you prefer in a hot climate? *(Answers may vary, but many will decide on the "ectothermic house," because there's no central heating that's on all the time.)*

DIFFERENTIATED INSTRUCTION

LPR Less Proficient Readers Help struggling readers reinforce differences between ectotherms and endotherms by having them make a bulleted list under each term. The lists should include the definition of the term, ways each group regulates body heat, and examples of animals that are ectotherms and endotherms.

BIOLOGY.com Have students access **Data Analysis: Winter Survival** to evaluate the effectiveness of strategies mammals use to survive cold temperatures.

Address Misconceptions

Coldblooded Animals Because ectotherms are often referred to as "coldblooded," some students may think the blood of fish, reptiles, and amphibians is always cold. Explain that when its environment is cold, an ectotherm's body, including its blood, may be relatively cold. This is because ectotherms have little body insulation and low metabolic rates that generate little heat, unlike birds or mammals. But when the environmental temperature is warm, such as in the direct sun, an ectotherm's body, including its blood, becomes warm. In fact, in areas with high temperatures, such as deserts, ectotherms need to keep their body—and blood—from becoming too *hot.* An ectotherm, therefore, is not always "coldblooded."

Answers

FIGURE 28–27 It is more likely to lower body temperature by exposing more of the body to the air, which is cooler than the hot sand.

IN YOUR NOTEBOOK Sample answer: The blood of an ectotherm can be quite warm when the environmental temperature is hot.

LESSON 28.4

Assess and Remediate

EVALUATE UNDERSTANDING

Ask each student to write a brief paragraph describing how an animal of their choosing maintains homeostasis. Call on students at random to share their paragraphs with the class. Then, have students complete the 28.4 Assessment.

REMEDIATION SUGGESTION

L1 **Struggling Students** If students have trouble answering **Question 2b,** review how a high metabolic rate requires more Calories.

BIOLOGY.com Students can check their understanding of lesson concepts with the **Self-Test** assessment. They can then take an online version of the **Lesson Assessment.**

FIGURE 28–29 Endotherm Insulation Like some of their dinosaur ancestors, modern birds such as this pine grosbeak use feathers to stay warm. When a bird gets cold, its dense, fluffy undercoat of down feathers stands up and creates spaces next to the bird's skin in which body heat is trapped.

Comparing Ectotherms and Endotherms Ectothermy and endothermy each have advantages and disadvantages in different situations. Endotherms move around easily during cool nights or in cold weather because they generate and conserve body heat. That's how musk oxen live in the tundra and killer whales swim through polar seas. But the high metabolic rate that generates this heat requires a lot of fuel. The amount of food needed to keep a single cow alive would be enough to feed ten cow-sized lizards!

Ectothermic animals need much less food than similarly sized endotherms. In environments where temperatures stay warm and fairly constant, ectothermy is a more energy-efficient strategy. But large ectotherms run into trouble if it gets very cold at night or stays cold for long periods. It takes a long time for a large animal to warm up in the sun after a cold night. That's one reason why most large lizards and amphibians live in tropical or subtropical areas.

Evolution of Temperature Control There is little doubt that the first land vertebrates were ectotherms. But questions remain about when and how often endothermy evolved. Although modern reptiles are ectotherms, a great deal of evidence suggests that at least some dinosaurs were endotherms. Many feathered dinosaur fossils have been discovered recently, suggesting that these animals, like modern birds such as that in **Figure 28–29,** used feathers for insulation. Current evidence suggests that endothermy has evolved at least twice among vertebrates. It evolved once along the lineage of ancient reptiles that led to birds, and once along the lineage of ancient reptiles that led to mammals.

28.4 Assessment

IN NoS.3

Review Key Concepts

1. a. Review How do the immune system and endocrine glands help to maintain homeostasis?

b. Explain Give an example of how multiple body systems function together to maintain homeostasis.

c. Apply Concepts Describe how the circulatory and endocrine systems of the migrating wildebeests in **Figure 28-26** help them maintain homeostasis.

2. a. Review Define *ectotherm.* Define *endotherm.*

b. Explain Why must an endotherm eat more food than an ectotherm of the same size?

c. Form a Hypothesis How might birds and mammals have evolved different means of insulating their bodies?

VISUAL THINKING

3. Construct a table that compares ectothermy and endothermy. Include the ways body temperature is controlled, relative rates of metabolism, relative amounts of food eaten, advantages, disadvantages, and examples of animals with each method of temperature regulation.

BIOLOGY.com Search Lesson 28.4 GO • Self-Test • Lesson Assessment

Assessment Answers

1a. The immune system can distinguish between "self" and "other"; it attacks invaders and works to restore homeostasis. Endocrine glands regulate body activities by releasing hormones into the blood.

1b. Sample answer: After gas exchange occurs in the respiratory system, the circulatory system carries oxygen to muscle cells, where cellular respiration takes place. The energy supplied by cellular respiration to the muscular system allows the body to move.

1c. The hormones produced by the endocrine system are carried throughout the body by the circulatory system. Hormones control the way the body stores energy or mobilizes it, helping to ensure homeostasis while the animal is undergoing the stresses of migration.

2a. ectotherm—an animal whose regulation of body temperature depends mostly on its relationship to sources of heat in its environment; endotherm—an animal whose body temperature is regulated, at least in part, using heat generated by its body

2b. because endotherms have a higher metabolic rate than ectotherms

2c. Sample answer: Different adaptations for body insulation evolved in different animal populations.

VISUAL THINKING

3. Tables may vary but should include accurate information from the lesson. Endothermy: body temperature controlled by heat generated by the body; high metabolic rates; relatively more food needed; ability to live in cold environments an advantage; need for fuel a disadvantage. Ectothermy: body temperature mainly controlled by sources of heat in its environment; low metabolic rates; relatively less food needed; need for less fuel an advantage; less ability to live in cold environments a disadvantage.

Biology & Society

Head for the Hills?

The Miami soccer coach was upset. The Denver team *was* tops in the league. But his players were well-trained—and several had *still* collapsed from fatigue in the second quarter. He knew that "the mile-high city" was aptly named: its air was less dense than his players were accustomed to. But he'd flown his team in three days early. Why didn't that help? He decided to do some research.

He learned that the lower air density in Denver means that every breath has 15 percent less oxygen than it has at sea level. This means that there is less oxygen for the lungs and blood to deliver to muscles. Less oxygen decreases the performance of muscles that work for long periods. The body can adapt to altitude, but it takes about a week—so his strategy of arriving three days early fell short.

High-altitude adaptation includes an increase in the lung's ability to get oxygen into blood, as well as an improvement in the ability of muscle cells to use oxygen. The body's production of active red blood cells also increases, stimulated by low oxygen availability. So people who live or train at high altitudes have an advantage over "flatlanders." This information helps explain why runners from places like Nairobi, Kenya (altitude 5450 feet), compete so well in endurance events.

High-Altitude Training Should Not Be Restricted

Several training regimes legally use the effects of altitude to maximize performance. Some coaches have their players live or train at high altitude. Other players sleep in special tents whose air contains less oxygen. So even teams that live at low altitudes can mimic the effects of high altitude in their training. These techniques cause a natural increase in the body's production of the hormone erythropoietin (EPO), which stimulates the production of red blood cells that carry oxygen.

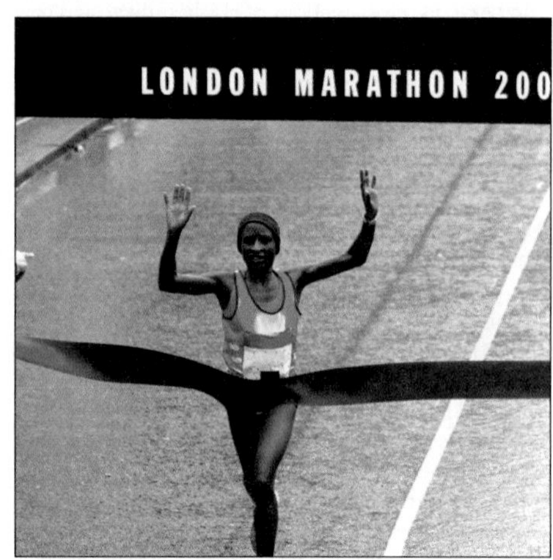

Elite marathoners, such as this Kenyan runner, often live and/or train in high-altitude areas.

High-Altitude Training Should Be Restricted

The injection of extra EPO during training—a biotech method of what is called "blood doping"—is illegal. High-altitude training regimes are just a "natural" way to accomplish exactly what blood doping does. It is unfair and possibly unsafe.

Research and Decide

Analyze the Viewpoints Using the Internet, research high-altitude training and "blood doping." Compare and contrast the effects of high-altitude training regimes with the effects of blood doping.

Form an Opinion Are current regulations fair to athletes from low-altitude states and countries?

Teach

Lead a Discussion

Define blood doping and explain the effects of anabolic steroids for students. Have students discuss the fairness of athletes using blood doping. Many students will condemn such methods as unfair, though some may accept the injection of extra EPO as a part of modern sports, just as some find the use of anabolic steroids acceptable. Then, turn the discussion to the fairness of high-altitude training.

Ask Do athletes who live and/or train at high-altitudes have an unfair advantage over athletes who live and/or train at low altitudes? *(Answers will vary. Accept any response that is backed by sound reasoning.)*

Ask Is it unfair for athletes to train at high altitudes just to get the benefits of high-altitude adaptation? *(Answers will vary. Challenge students to back their opinions with persuasive arguments.)*

Answers

RESEARCH AND DECIDE

1. Answers may vary. Students should find that the effects of blood doping and high-altitude training are similar. How similar they are depends on substances used for blood doping and techniques used in high-altitude training. Students should cite reliable online sources for their information.
2. Students' paragraphs should clearly express an opinion, backed by logical reasoning, about whether current regulations are fair.

Quick Facts

WORLD ANTI-DOPING AGENCY

In 1999, the International Olympic Committee established the World Anti-Doping Agency (WADA) to coordinate the fight against doping in sports. Various substances used in blood doping, including EPO, are on WADA's list of prohibited substances, and tests to detect blood doping were introduced at the 2000 Olympics. In 2006, WADA considered banning the use of oxygen tents but decided against it. Low-oxygen tents—also called altitude tents—simulate high-altitude conditions with lower oxygen levels in the air. By sleeping in these tents, some athletes have tried to gain the benefits of training at high altitudes without moving to high-altitude training facilities.

CHAPTER LAB

Pre-Lab

Introduce students to the concepts they will explore in the chapter lab by assigning the Pre-Lab questions.

Lab

Tell students they will perform the chapter lab *Comparing Bird and Mammal Bones* described in **Lab Manual A.**

 **Struggling Students** A simpler version of the chapter lab is provided in **Lab Manual B.**

SAFETY Students should wear gloves and aprons. Caution them to be careful when handling glassware. At the end of the lab, have students wash their hands in warm, soapy water.

BIOLOGY.com Look online for **Editable Lab Worksheets.**

For corresponding pre-lab in the **Foundation Edition,** see page 688.

IN INDIANA ACADEMIC STANDARDS

For the full text of all standards, see the Course Overview in the front matter of this book.

Real-World Lab

OPEN-ENDED INQUIRY

IN NoS.5 Standard laboratory techniques.

Pre-Lab: Comparing Bird and Mammal Bones

Problem Is the density of an animal's bones related to the way the animal moves?

Materials cross-sections of chicken, duck, and cow bones; hand lens; small chicken, duck, and cow bones; balance

Lab Manual Chapter 28 Lab

Skills Focus Form a Hypothesis, Design an Experiment, Measure

Connect to the Big idea In order to move, an animal must generate physical force and apply this force against the air, the water, or the ground. The force is generated by the contraction of muscles. In vertebrates, the muscles are attached to bones. The joints that connect bones bend or straighten when groups of muscles contract. There is a close link between the structure of an animal's skeletal and muscular systems and how the animal moves. In this lab, you will investigate whether there is a similar link between the density of bones and how an animal moves.

Background Questions

a. Review What type of skeleton do vertebrates have? List one advantage of this type of skeleton.

b. Explain Why are pairs of muscles or two different groups of muscles needed to bend and straighten a joint?

c. Apply Concepts Why do you think humans have only 4 bones in each arm and shoulder, but 27 bones in each wrist and hand? *Hint:* Compare the movement of your arm and your hand when you button a shirt?

Pre-Lab Questions

Preview the procedure in the lab manual.

1. Compare and Contrast Compare the type of data you will collect in Part A to the type of data you will collect in Part B.

2. Predict How might looking at cross-sections of bones help you form a hypothesis about the relative density of the bones?

3. Design an Experiment Will you need to use samples with the same mass in Part B? Why or why not?

 Search Chapter 28 

Visit Chapter 28 online to test yourself on chapter content and to find activities to help you learn.

Untamed Science Video Join the Untamed Science crew as they interview experts to learn more about how the sex of offspring is determined in some animals.

Art in Motion Watch an animation that shows the motion of joints in both exoskeletons and endoskeletons.

Art Review Review your understanding of vertebrate brains.

InterActive Art Look at the structure and function of the water vascular system in a sea star.

Data Analysis Investigate some of the ways mammals survive in cold temperatures.

Pre-Lab Answers

BACKGROUND QUESTIONS

a. Sample answer: Vertebrates have an endoskeleton, which can grow as the vertebrate grows.

b. Sample answer: Muscle contraction can cause a tendon to pull on a bone but it cannot cause the tendon to push the bone back to its original position. So pairs of muscles are needed to generate a full range of motion around a joint.

c. Sample answer: Many small movements are required for a hand to grasp and manipulate objects.

PRE-LAB QUESTIONS

1. Sample answer: In Part A, the data will be qualitative. In Part B, the data will be quantitative.

2. Sample answer: I will be able to observe whether the bones are solid or contain air spaces.

3. Sample answer: No, because density is ratio of mass to volume.

28 Study Guide

Big idea Structure and Function

Nervous systems collect and process information from the environment and coordinate the responses of muscular, endocrine, immune, and reproductive systems, so that animals can maintain homeostasis and reproduce.

28.1 Response

When an animal responds to a stimulus, body systems work together to generate a response.

Animal nervous systems exhibit different degrees of cephalization and specialization.

Sensory systems range from individual sensory neurons to sense organs.

neuron (808)
stimulus (808)
sensory neuron (808)
interneuron (809)
response (809)
motor neuron (809)
ganglion (810)
cerebrum (811)
cerebellum (811)

28.2 Movement and Support

Animals have three main kinds of skeletal systems: hydrostatic skeletons, exoskeletons, and endoskeletons.

In many animals, muscles work together in pairs or groups that are attached to different parts of a supporting skeleton.

hydrostatic skeleton (814)
exoskeleton (815)
molting (815)
endoskeleton (815)
joint (816)
ligament (816)
tendon (816)

28.3 Reproduction

Asexual reproduction requires only one parent, so individuals may reproduce rapidly. But offspring produced asexually have less genetic diversity than do offspring produced sexually. Sexual reproduction maintains genetic diversity in a population by creating individuals with new combinations of genes.

During internal fertilization, eggs are fertilized inside the body of the egg-producing individual. During external fertilization, eggs are fertilized outside the body.

Animals may be oviparous, ovoviviparous, or viviparous.

Reptiles, birds, and a few mammals have evolved amniotic eggs in which an embryo can develop without drying out. Mammals differ greatly in their means of reproduction and development, but all nourish their young with mother's milk.

oviparous (822)
ovoviviparous (822)
viviparous (822)
placenta (822)
metamorphosis (823)
nymph (823)
pupa (823)
amniotic egg (825)
mammary gland (825)

28.4 Homeostasis

All body systems work together to maintain homeostasis.

Most reptiles, invertebrates, fishes, and amphibians are ectotherms that regulate body temperature primarily by picking up heat from, or losing heat to, their environment. Endotherms, such as birds and mammals, have high metabolic rates that generate heat, even when they are resting.

endocrine gland (828)
ectotherm (829)
endotherm (829)

Think Visually

Fill in the following concept map.

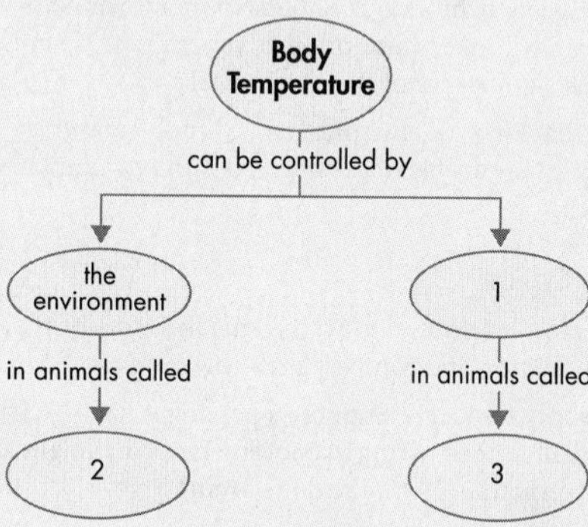

UbD Performance Tasks

SUMMATIVE TASK Have students work in small groups to design a Web site about one type of animal that includes information about the animal's nervous system, skeletal system, muscular system, as well as descriptions of the animal's reproduction, care of offspring, and maintenance of homeostasis. Make sure no two groups choose the same animal. Explain that the Web site should include written text and labeled illustrations. If possible, groups should make their pages electronically. As an alternative, groups can use a large sheet of paper to represent each page of the Web site.

TRANSFER TASK Ask students to imagine that they have transformed into another animal for a day. Ask them to choose a non-mammal, such as an insect, fish, turtle, or octopus. Have students write a friend about the physical differences between their new body and their human one. Suggest they comment on differences in the brain and sense organs, the skeleton, the muscles, and body temperature control.

Study Online

REVIEW AND ASSESSMENT RESOURCES

Editable Worksheets Pages of Study Workbooks A and B, Lab Manuals A and B, and the Assessment Resources Book are available online. These documents can be easily edited using a word-processing program.

Lesson Overview Have students reread the Lesson Overviews to help them study chapter concepts.

Vocabulary Review The *Flash Cards* and *Match It* provide an interactive way to review chapter vocabulary.

Chapter Assessment Have students take an online version of the Chapter 28 Assessment.

Standardized Test Prep Students can take an online version of the Standardized Test Prep. You will receive their scores along with ideas for remediation.

Diagnostic and Benchmark Tests Use these tests to monitor your students' progress and supply remediation.

Answers

THINK VISUALLY

1. heat generated by the body

2. ectotherms

3. endotherms

Lesson 28.1

UNDERSTAND KEY CONCEPTS

1. b **2.** c **3.** d **4.** a

5. cephalization and specialization

6. The cerebrum and cerebellum increase in size from fishes to mammals. In mammals, the cerebrum is much larger than in other vertebrates and may contain folds that increase the surface area. The significance is that the capacity for learning and memory is greater in mammals than in other vertebrates.

7. Sample answer: sounds that are lower and higher in pitch than humans can hear; electric currents in seawater; Earth's magnetic field

THINK CRITICALLY

8. Sensory neurons detect stimuli in the environment; interneurons process information and determine how an animal responds to stimuli; motor neurons carry "directions" from interneurons to muscles.

9. Sample answer: to determine whether there is a tumor in the cerebellum, which controls movement, or a fractured vertebra

Lesson 28.2

UNDERSTAND KEY CONCEPTS

10. d **11.** a **12.** b **13.** b

14. Muscles are arranged in blocks on opposite sides of the backbone. These muscles contract in waves that travel down the body, bending it first to one side and then to the other. As these waves of movement travel down the body, they move the fish forward.

THINK CRITICALLY

15. Sample answer: Exoskeleton advantages: provides a watertight covering, provides protection from predators; disadvantages: doesn't grow with animal, relatively heavy. Endoskeleton advantages: provides lightweight support, grows with the animal; disadvantages: does not provide a watertight covering, does not provide protection from predators.

16. This hydrostatic skeleton consists of fluids held in the gastrovascular cavity that can alter an animal's shape drastically by working with contractile cells in the body wall.

28 Assessment

IN The numbers following the questions refer to Indiana's Academic Standards for Biology I.

28.1 Response

Understand Key Concepts

1. Information received from the environment that causes an organism to respond is called a
a. response. **c.** reaction.
b. stimulus. **d.** trigger.

2. The simplest nervous systems are called
a. cephalopods. **c.** nerve nets.
b. motor neurons. **d.** sensory neurons.

3. In vertebrates, the part of the brain that coordinates body movements is the
a. olfactory lobe. **c.** cerebrum.
b. optic lobe. **d.** cerebellum.

4. The arrows in this diagram are pointing to which structures?

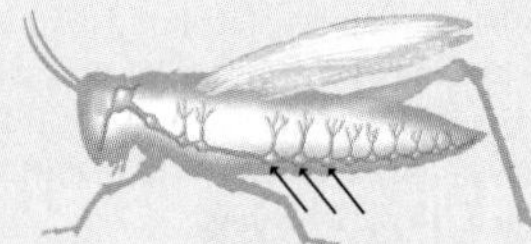

a. ganglia **c.** nerve nets
b. brains **d.** motor neurons

5. What two major trends in the evolution of the nervous system do invertebrates exhibit?

6. In general, how do the brains of mammals compare with the brains of other vertebrates? What is the significance of that difference?

7. What kinds of environmental stimuli are some animals capable of sensing that humans cannot sense?

Think Critically

8. Compare and Contrast List the three major types of neuron and compare their roles.

9. Apply Concepts Suppose a pet dog is having difficulty coordinating its movements. Why might a veterinarian X-ray the dog's brain?

28.2 Movement and Support

Understand Key Concepts

10. Which of the following animals uses a hydrostatic skeleton to move?
a. arthropod **c.** fish
b. sponge **d.** annelid

11. An arthropod's exoskeleton performs all of the following functions EXCEPT
a. production of gametes.
b. protection of internal organs.
c. support of the animal's body.
d. prevention of loss of body water.

12. Vertebrates have endoskeletons made of
a. chitin. **c.** calcium carbonate.
b. cartilage and/or bone. **d.** bone only.

13. Muscles generate force
a. only when they lengthen.
b. only when they shorten.
c. when they lengthen or shorten.
d. all the time.

14. How do a fish's muscles function when the fish swims?

Think Critically

15. Compare and Contrast List two advantages and two disadvantages of exoskeletons and endoskeletons.

16. Apply Concepts The diagrams below show a type of skeletal system found in invertebrates. What is the name for this type of skeleton? Describe how it functions.

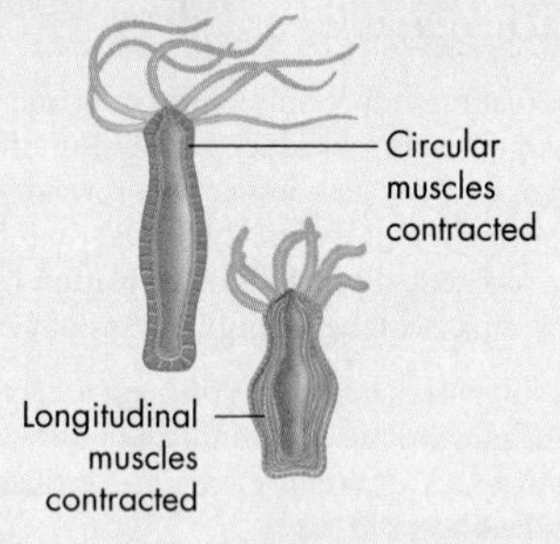

Lesson 28.3

UNDERSTAND KEY CONCEPTS

17. b **18.** a **19.** c **20.** b

21. Fertilization occurs in the open water, producing zygotes. Each zygote grows into a swimming larva, which attaches to a hard surface and develops into a polyp. The polyp reproduces asexually by budding, releasing young medusas. Adult medusas reproduce sexually by releasing gametes into the water.

22. During internal fertilization, eggs are fertilized inside the body of the egg-producing individual. In external fertilization, eggs are fertilized outside the body of the egg-producing individual.

23. The placenta supplies nutrients, which allow the embryo to develop for a long time inside the mother, and to be born at a fairly advanced stage of development.

28.3 Reproduction

Understand Key Concepts

17. Individual animals that produce both sperm and eggs are called
    a. gametes. c. fragments.
    b. hermaphrodites. d. buds.

18. A species that lays eggs that develop outside of the mother's body is
    a. oviparous.
    b. viviparous.
    c. ovoviviparous.
    d. nonviparous.

19. Which structure in female mammals produces milk to nourish young?
    a. kidney c. mammary gland
    b. pupa d. placenta

20. Which of the following are NOT placental mammals?
    a. seals c. carnivores
    b. marsupials d. primates

21. Describe the life cycle of a typical cnidarian. Be sure to include the alternation of the polyp form with the medusa form.

22. Compare and contrast internal and external fertilization.

23. What survival advantage does the placenta confer on mammals?

Think Critically

24. **Compare and Contrast** Describe the differences between a newborn placental mammal and a newborn marsupial.

25. **Infer** Many mammals care for their young for extended periods of time. This parental behavior does not help the parent survive. Why, then, might extended parental care have been naturally selected for in these species?

28.4 Homeostasis

Understand Key Concepts

26. The control of an animal's internal conditions is called
    a. homeostasis. c. endothermy.
    b. ectothermy. d. reactivity.

solve the CHAPTER MYSTERY

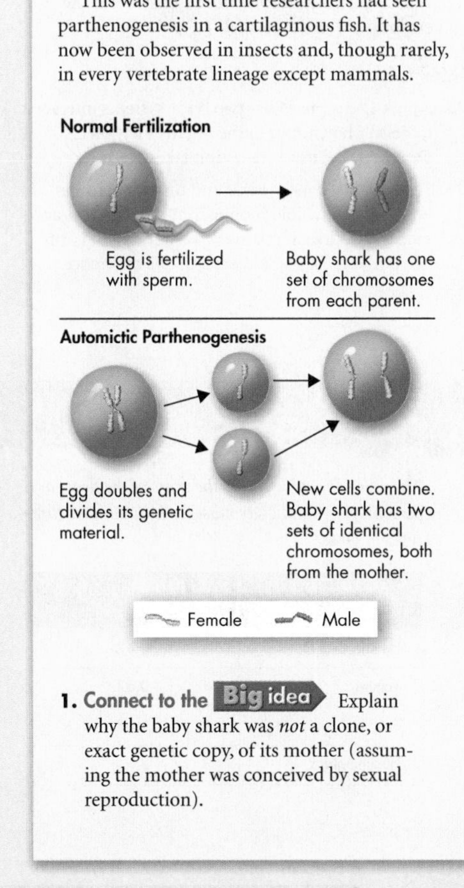

SHE'S JUST LIKE HER MOTHER!
In May 2007, the researchers published their conclusions. The baby bonnethead had been produced by a process called automictic parthenogenesis, in which the mother's unfertilized egg divides and the resulting elements fuse to make a zygote with two sets of identical chromosomes. (See below.) That is why the baby shark was homozygous for every trait; she had two identical sets of alleles.
This was the first time researchers had seen parthenogenesis in a cartilaginous fish. It has now been observed in insects and, though rarely, in every vertebrate lineage except mammals.
Normal Fertilization
Egg is fertilized with sperm.
Baby shark has one set of chromosomes from each parent.
Automictic Parthenogenesis
Egg doubles and divides its genetic material.
New cells combine. Baby shark has two sets of identical chromosomes, both from the mother.
Female
Male
1. Connect to the Big idea Explain why the baby shark was *not* a clone, or exact genetic copy, of its mother (assuming the mother was conceived by sexual reproduction).

THINK CRITICALLY

24. A newborn placental mammal is at a fairly advanced stage of development, while a newborn marsupial is at a very early stage of development, little more than an embryo.

25. Sample answer: Caring for young for extended periods ensures that more young will survive and eventually reproduce.

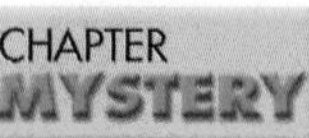

After students have read through the Chapter Mystery, use the two flowcharts to clarify the difference between normal fertilization and automictic parthenogenesis.

Ask In normal fertilization, what is the cellular process that results in eggs and sperm? *(meiosis)*

Point out that meiosis results in haploid cells that become eggs or sperm.

Ask In normal fertilization, describe the chromosome number of the cell that results when the egg is fertilized by the sperm. *(diploid)*

Ask In automictic parthenogenesis, what process produced the haploid cells in the middle of the flowchart? *(meiosis)*

Point out that the zygote of the baby shark is diploid.

Ask What is the difference in the diploid zygote of a baby shark produced by normal fertilization and a baby shark zygote produced by automictic parthenogenesis? *(The baby shark zygote produced by normal fertilization has genetic material from two parents. The baby shark zygote produced by automictic parthenogenesis has two sets of chromosomes, but both came from haploid cells produced by the mother.)*

CHAPTER MYSTERY ANSWERS

1.  Sample answer: The baby shark was not a clone, because its genetic material was not an exact copy of the mother's. In automictic parthenogenesis, the haploid genetic material in an egg doubles and divides its genetic material. The haploid egg carries only half the mother's genetic diversity, assuming she was conceived by normal fertilization. Also, in the new cell, the genetic material recombines, and in the recombining, slightly different combinations of genes can occur.

Watch the Untamed Science crew in **Boy? . . . Or Girl?** as they interview experts to learn more about how the gender of offspring is determined in some animals.

ASSESSMENT

Lesson 28.4

UNDERSTAND KEY CONCEPTS

26. a **27.** b **28.** b

29. They regulate body activities by releasing hormones into the blood.

30. to distinguish between "self" and "other" and to attack invaders

31. Sample answer: Ectothermy advantage: relatively less food needs to be eaten; disadvantage: less ability to live in cold environments. Endothermy advantage: ability to live in cold environments; disadvantage: need for relatively more food.

32. Current evidence suggests that endothermy evolved once along the lineage of ancient reptiles that led to birds and once along the lineage of ancient reptiles that led to mammals.

THINK CRITICALLY

33. The endocrine system releases hormones into the blood, and the circulatory system carries the hormones in the blood to all parts of the body.

34. Sample hypothesis: Endotherms can more easily live in cold biomes than ectotherms can, because endotherms can regulate their body temperature.

Connecting Concepts

USE SCIENCE GRAPHICS

35. to surround and cushion the developing embryo

36. Membrane B is the yolk sac. The yolk inside the yolk sac serves as a nutrient-rich food supply for the embryo.

WRITE ABOUT SCIENCE

37. Answers may vary. Students should explain that the brain in both a fish and a mammal is composed of the cerebrum, cerebellum, medulla oblongata, optic lobes, and olfactory bulbs. The mammalian brain, however, has a much larger and more complex cerebrum and cerebellum, resulting in greater abilities to think and learn and better control of more sophisticated movements.

38. Big idea Sample answer: Sensory neurons can sense the body is getting colder and transmit signals to interneurons that transmit signals to motor neurons to move to a warmer environment that can warm the body.

27. The main source of heat for an ectotherm is
a. its high rate of metabolism.
b. the environment.
c. its own body.
d. its food.

28. Endotherms
a. control body temperature through behavior.
b. control body temperature from within.
c. obtain heat from outside their bodies.
d. have relatively low rates of metabolism.

29. How do endocrine glands help regulate body activities?

30. What is the function of the immune system?

31. Explain the advantages and disadvantages of ectothermy and endothermy.

32. What does current evidence suggest about the evolution of endothermy?

Think Critically

33. Apply Concepts What two body systems interact to deliver hormones to the organs they affect? Describe how this interaction takes place.

34. Form a Hypothesis Birds and mammals live in both warm and cold biomes, but most reptiles and amphibians live in relatively warm biomes. Form a hypothesis that would explain this difference.

Connecting Concepts

Use Science Graphics NoS.3

Use the diagram to answer questions 35 and 36.

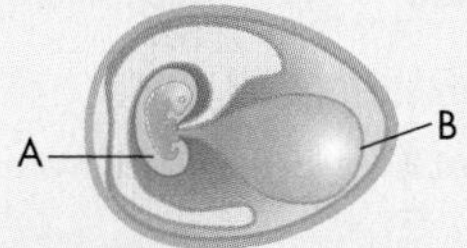

35. Interpret Visuals What is the function of the membrane labeled A?

36. Infer What is membrane B? What is the function of the structure it surrounds?

Write About Science NoS.3

37. Explanation Write a paragraph in which you compare the brain of a fish to the brain of a mammal. In your paragraph, identify the main parts of the brain and compare and contrast their structures and functions in the two animals. (*Hint:* Before you write, construct a Venn diagram that compares the two brains.)

38. Assess the Big idea Give an example of how the nervous system of an ectotherm could initiate behavior that would help the animal regulate its internal temperature.

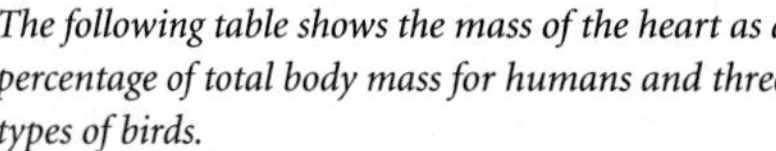

IN NoS.3

The following table shows the mass of the heart as a percentage of total body mass for humans and three types of birds.

Heart	Percentage of Total Body Mass
Human	0.42
Vulture	0.57
Sparrow	1.68
Hummingbird	2.37

39. Interpret Tables Which animal has the largest heart in proportion to its body mass?

40. Draw Conclusions Based on the data, what general conclusion can you draw about the relative heart sizes of humans and birds?

41. Form a Hypothesis Form a hypothesis that could explain your conclusion. (*Hint:* Consider the different energy needs of humans and birds.)

PURPOSE Students will interpret data to form a hypothesis about how relative heart size is connected to energy needs in an animal.

PLANNING Review with students the function the heart plays in the circulatory system and what the circulatory system provides to cells.

ANSWERS

39. the hummingbird

40. Heart size represents a greater percentage of total body mass in birds than in humans.

41. Sample hypothesis: In animals, heart size relative to body mass increases as the energy needs of an animal increase. Birds must have a relatively higher energy need than humans.

Standardized Test Prctice for Indiana

Multiple Choice

1. What part of a vertebrate's brain is the "thinking" region?
   A olfactory bulb
   B cerebellum
   C cerebrum
   D medulla oblongata

2. Neurons that receive and send information from and to other neurons are called
   A ganglia.
   B motor neurons.
   C sensory neurons.
   D interneurons.

3. The skeleton of a shark is composed primarily of
   A bone.
   B vertebrae.
   C cartilage.
   D tendons.

4. Joints between bones of the human skeleton are held together mostly by
   A tendons.
   B muscles.
   C ligaments.
   D skin.

5. In oviparous species, embryos
   A develop internally.
   B obtain nutrients directly from the mother's body.
   C obtain nutrients from the external environment.
   D develop outside of the body.

6. Most animals reproduce sexually by producing
   A buds.
   B clones.
   C haploid gametes.
   D diploid gametes.

7. Maintaining homeostasis in multicellular organisms requires
   A a properly functioning heart.
   B a nervous system.
   C hormones.
   D all body systems working together.

8. Which of the following are endothermic?
   A fish and amphibians
   B mammals and birds
   C reptiles and mammals
   D all vertebrates

Questions 9–10

Study the illustration of a reptile brain and answer questions 9 and 10.

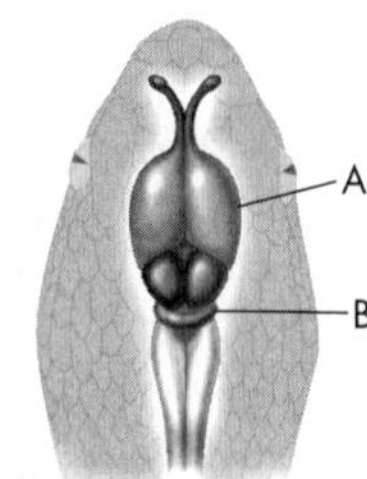

9. What is the name of the structure labeled A?
   A cerebrum
   B optic lobe
   C cerebellum
   D olfactory bulb

10. What are some functions of the structure labeled B?
   A vision
   B control of internal organ functions
   C connection of the brain to the rest of the body
   D coordination of movement and control of balance

Open-Ended Response

11. Why can't muscles function individually?

If You Have Trouble With . . .											
Question	1	2	3	4	5	6	7	8	9	10	11
See Lesson	28.1	28.1	28.2	28.2	28.3	28.3	8.4	28.4	28.1	28.1	28.2

Answers

1. C
2. D
3. C
4. C
5. D
6. C
7. D
8. B
9. A
10. D
11. Sample answer: A muscle can exert force only when it contracts. The contraction of a single muscle can move a joint in only one way. Another muscle must contract in the opposite direction as the first muscle relaxes in order for the joint to move in the opposite way.

Test-Taking Tip

REPHRASE THE QUESTION

Tell students that some questions on a standardized test may seem confusing the first time they read them. Suggest in such cases that students rephrase the question in their own words. Rephrasing a question often will allow the reader to better understand it.

CHAPTER PLANNER 29 Animal Behavior

Chapter Contents	IN	Time	Core Resources
Chapter Preview			**Student Edition,** pp. 838–839 **Chapter Mystery,** p. 839
29.1 Elements of Behavior Behavior and Evolution • Innate Behavior • Learned Behavior • Complex Behaviors • *Biology & Society: Should Marine Mammals Be Kept in Captivity?*	B.8.5	1 period 1/2 block	**Student Edition,** pp. 840–846 Inquiry 29.1 Quick Lab, p. 844 L2 **Study Workbook A** 29.1 Worksheets L2 **Biology.com** *Tutor Tube:* Sing . . . Sing a Song • 29.1 Self-Test • 29.1 Lesson Assessment
29.2 Animals in Their Environments Behavioral Cycles • Social Behavior • Communication	NoS.3, B.8.5	1/2 period 1/4 block	**Student Edition,** pp. 847–851 Inquiry 29.2 Analyzing Data, p. 850 L2 **Study Workbook A** 29.2 Worksheets L2 **Biology.com** *Data Analysis:* Tracking Shark Migrations • *Art Review:* Animal Communication **Assessment Resources Book** Visual Quiz L2
Chapter Pre-Lab	NoS.2	1 period 1/2 block	**Student Edition,** p. 852 L2 **Lab Manual A** *Termite Tracks* L2

Differentiated Instruction Tools

Study Workbook B includes worksheets with lesson-level differentiated instruction support and explanations of differentiated instruction teaching strategies.

Lab Manual B includes skills labs, simplified chapter labs, and hands-on activities.

ELL Handbook explains ways to make *Biology* more accessible to ELL students.

Spanish Study Workbook is a Spanish translation of Study Workbook A.

Multilingual Glossary is the glossary translated into ten languages.

Differentiated Instruction Key

- L1 Special Needs or Struggling Students
- ELL English Language Learners
- LPR Less Proficient Readers
- L2 On-Level Students
- L3 Advanced Students

Additional Resources

Biology.com Untamed Science Video • Vocabulary Flash Cards

Study Workbook B 29.1 Worksheets L1 ELL LPR
Spanish Study Workbook 29.1 Worksheets ELL
Biology.com 29.1 Lesson Overview • 29.1 Lesson Notes

Study Workbook B 29.2 Worksheets L1 ELL LPR
Spanish Study Workbook 29.2 Worksheets ELL
Biology.com *Art in Motion:* Social Behavior in Fiddler Crabs • 29.2 Lesson Overview • 29.2 Lesson Notes • 29.2 Self-Test • 29.2 Lesson Assessment

Lab Manual B *Termite Tracks* • Data Analysis: *Caring for Young* L1 ELL LPR

Chapter Review

Student Edition Study Guide, p. 853 L2 • Unit Project, p. 858 L2
Study Workbook A Chapter 29 Vocabulary Review L2 • Chapter 29 Chapter Mystery/21st Century Skills Activity L2 L3
Transparencies, pp. 326–330 L1 ELL LPR L2
Biology.com Untamed Science Video • You're the Director • Editable Worksheets of Study Workbooks A and B and Lab Manuals A and B • Chapter 29 Flash Cards and Crossword Puzzle

Untamed Science DVD • Classroom Resources CD (includes lesson presentations and editable worksheets)

Chapter Assessment

Student Edition Assessment, pp. 854–857 L2
Study Workbook B Chapter 29 Chapter Review L1 ELL LPR • Chapter 29 Taking a Standardized Test L1 ELL LPR
Assessment Resources Book Chapter 29 Test A L2 • Chapter 29 Test B L1 ELL LPR • Unit 7 Test A L2 • Unit 7 Test B L1 ELL LPR
Biology.com Chapter 29 Assessment • Editable Worksheets of Chapter 29 Visual Quiz, Chapter 29 Tests A and B, and Unit 7 Tests A and B

Exam*View* *Assessment Suite* • Classroom Resources CD (includes lesson presentations and editable worksheets)

Time: 1 period, 1/2 block

Pressed for Time?

Preview the Chapter Introduce the chapter with a discussion of Figure 29–9.

Cover the Chapter Quickly Have students read *Behavior and Evolution, Innate Behavior,* and the introduction to *Learned Behavior* in Lesson 29.1. In Lesson 29.2, have students read *Social Behavior.*

Assess Assign questions 1 and 2 in the 29.1 Assessment, questions 2 and 4 in the 29.2 Assessment, and questions 1, 5, 7, 14, 15, 17, 20, 21, 24, and 25 in the Chapter 29 Assessment.

CHAPTER 29

Connect to the Big Idea

Big idea Ask students to examine the photograph of timber wolves and read the caption. Then, ask students how fighting might be advantageous to a wolf, and how this behavior may have evolved in wolves. *(Wolves that were more successful fighters got the resources they needed, such as food. These wolves were able to survive and pass on their genes for aggressive behavior.)* Ask students to think of other ways they have observed animals interacting with one another. *(Sample answers: mating; rearing young; communicating vocally; feeding one another; grooming one another; migrating in groups; and defending resources, such food and nesting spaces, by chasing out intruders)* Have them consider the question, **How do animals interact with one another and their environments?** Ask what it means that an animal's actions are influenced by others and by the environment.

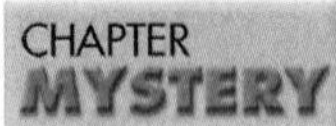

Have students read the Chapter Mystery and infer what the elephants could be responding to and what their various actions might signify. Ask students to think of the role that evolution might play in animal behavior in general, and the behavior of the elephants in particular. Use students' ideas to start connecting the Chapter Mystery to the Big Idea of Evolution.

BIOLOGY.com Have students preview the chapter vocabulary using the **Flash Cards.**

29 Animal Behavior

Big idea **Evolution**

Q: How do animals interact with one another and their environments?

Timber wolves fighting over a meal

BIOLOGY.com Search Chapter 29 GO • Flash Cards

IN INDIANA ACADEMIC STANDARDS

For the full text of all standards, see the Course Overview in the front matter of this book.

Key standards: Chapter 29 covers key ideas from Standard 8: Evolution, including **B.8.5** Survival and reproduction.

UbD Understanding by Design

In Unit 7, students work toward the Enduring Understanding of how *animals have evolved diverse ways to carry out life processes and maintain homeostasis.* In Chapter 29, students explore what animal behavior is and the factors that influence an animal's behavior. The graphic organizer at the right shows how the Big Idea, Essential Question, and lesson-level Guiding Questions help frame students' exploration of how chapter content informs this Enduring Understanding.

PERFORMANCE GOALS

In Chapter 29, students will express their knowledge of different kinds of learned and innate behaviors in writing and through the use of hands-on activities. Students will interpret data about how behavior affects reproductive success and design a lab to investigate social behavior in ants. At the end of the chapter, students will develop a game that demonstrates how various behaviors help animals survive.

INDIANA ACADEMIC STANDARDS FOR SCIENCE

Nature of Science NoS.2, NoS.3; **Molecular Basis of Heredity** B.5.6; **Evolution** B.8.5. See lessons for details.

• Untamed Science Video • Chapter Mystery

CHAPTER MYSTERY

ELEPHANT CALLER ID?

On a hot, dusty afternoon in Africa's Etosha National Park, a group of elephants approaches a watering hole. They begin to drink and splash around. Suddenly, they freeze. One places her trunk flat on the ground, the tip pointing toward her feet. Soon, the elephants clump together defensively, nudging young calves into the center of the group. Some place weight on the front of their feet—as close to standing on tiptoe as elephants get. Most keep their huge ears flattened against their heads. Soon, they shuffle nervously away from the watering hole, staying in defensive formation. Human observers nearby can't see or hear anything that might have alarmed the group. What are these elephants doing—and why? As you read this chapter, look for clues that explain the behavior of this elephant group. Then, solve the mystery.

Never Stop Exploring Your World. Finding the solution to the Elephant Caller ID mystery is only the beginning. Take a video field trip with the ecogeeks of Untamed Science to see where the mystery leads.

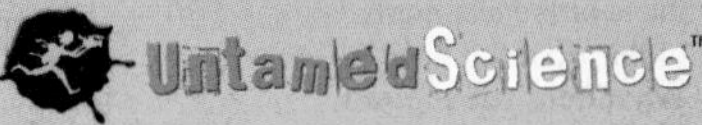

Chapter 29
Big Idea: Evolution

Chapter 29 EQ: How do animals interact with one another and their environment?

29.1 GQ: What are the elements of animal behavior?

29.2 GQ: How do the environment and other organisms affect an animal's behavior?

What's Online

Extend your reach by using these and other digital assets offered at **Biology.com.**

CHAPTER MYSTERY
Students explore elephant behavior to learn how elephants communicate.

UNTAMED SCIENCE VIDEO
This short movie will take students on a field trip in which scientists use remote sensing to study animal behavior.

TUTOR TUBE
Using actual bird songs as examples, this tutorial explains how both innate and learned behaviors are involved in complex behavior.

DATA ANALYSIS
Students will analyze different kinds of data on migrating animals. They will determine how migration data can be used to derive migration routes and rates of travel.

ART IN MOTION
Students explore various social behaviors, including courtship behavior and aggression.

ART REVIEW
Students can drag and drop labels to identify different communication strategies.

LESSON 29.1

Getting Started

Objectives

29.1.1 Identify the significance of behavior in the evolution of a species.

29.1.2 Explain what an innate behavior is.

29.1.3 Describe the major types of learning.

29.1.4 Explain what types of behaviors are usually considered complex.

Student Resources

Study Workbooks A and B, 29.1 Worksheets

Spanish Study Workbook, 29.1 Worksheets

Lesson Overview • Lesson Notes • Activity: Tutor Tube • Assessment: Self-Test, Lesson Assessment

For corresponding lesson in the **Foundation Edition**, see pages 696–700.

Activate Prior Knowledge

Have students brainstorm examples of animal behaviors. Then, ask how these behaviors help the animals survive. Write selected responses on the board.

Discuss with students how a species' fitness could be linked to not only physical adaptations, but also to its behavior. Students can go online at **Biology.com** to gather their evidence.

29.1 Elements of Behavior

IN B.5.6 Types of traits; B.8.5 Survival and reproduction.

Key Questions

What is the significance of behavior in the evolution of animal species?

What is an innate behavior?

What are the major types of learning?

How do many complex behaviors arise?

Vocabulary

behavior • innate behavior • learning • habituation • classical conditioning • operant conditioning • insight learning • imprinting

Taking Notes

Concept Map As you read, create a concept map to organize the information in this section.

THINK ABOUT IT At a table by a Caribbean seaside restaurant, a young tourist eats a hamburger, unaware that he's being watched—by an iguana. The lizard crawls closer, looking dangerous. The boy spots him and, with a cry of fear, jumps up onto his chair. But the iguana isn't interested in human toes. This lizard, a shy tree-dwelling species, is a vegetarian. He makes a beeline for the French fries that the boy, in his panic, knocked to the ground. What's so interesting about this scene? These iguanas normally don't approach humans. And they're not known for being as clever as, say, dogs or cats. But this particular male iguana has learned that getting close to humans can mean easy access to food.

Behavior and Evolution

What is the significance of behavior in the evolution of animal species?

The activity of that hungry iguana is just one example of **behavior,** which is usually defined as the way an organism reacts to stimuli in its environment. Some behaviors are as simple as a dog turning its head and pricking up its ears in response to a noise. Other behaviors can be quite complex. For example, some animals wash some of their food before eating it. Usually, behaviors are performed when an animal detects and responds to some sort of stimulus in its environment. The way an animal responds to a stimulus, however, often depends on its internal condition. If our friend the iguana hadn't been hungry, for example, it would probably have kept its distance from the boy and his French fries!

Many behaviors are essential to survival. To survive and reproduce, animals must be able to find and catch food, select habitats, avoid predators, and find mates. Behaviors that make these activities possible are therefore as vital to survival and reproduction as any physical characteristic, such as teeth or claws.

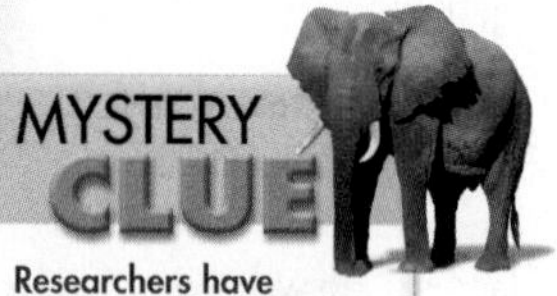

Researchers have noticed that elephants living elsewhere exhibit behaviors similar to those of the elephants at the watering hole. What does this suggest about the importance of these behaviors?

IN INDIANA ACADEMIC STANDARDS

For the full text of all standards, see the Course Overview in the front matter of this book.

B.5.6 Recognize that traits can be structural, physiological or behavioral and can include readily observable characteristics at the organismal level or less recognizable features at the molecular and cellular level.

B.8.5 Describe how due to genetic variations, environmental forces, and reproductive pressures, organisms with beneficial traits are more likely to survive, reproduce, and pass on their genetic information.

UbD Teach for Understanding

ENDURING UNDERSTANDING Animals have evolved diverse ways to carry out basic life processes and maintain homeostasis.

GUIDING QUESTION What are the elements of animal behavior?

EVIDENCE OF UNDERSTANDING *After students have completed the lesson, assign them the following assessment to evaluate their understanding of what animal behavior is and how it enables animals to carry out life processes, survive, and produce offspring.* Have students work in small groups to list the kinds of behaviors that a squirrel engages in to get food. *(Sample answers: climbing trees, gathering nuts, digging in the ground)* Ask students how these behaviors increase the squirrel's evolutionary fitness. *(By enabling the squirrel to find food, they help ensure the squirrel's survival, and ultimately, the squirrel's ability to produce offspring.)*

You've learned how physical traits are shaped by instructions coded in an organism's genome. The nervous system, which makes behaviors possible, is clearly influenced by genes. So, it shouldn't surprise you to learn that some behaviors are also influenced by genes and can therefore be inherited. That's why certain behaviors can evolve under the influence of natural selection, just as physical traits do. For example, the genes that code for the behavior of the moth in **Figure 29–1** help the moth escape predators. **If a behavior that is influenced by genes increases an individual's fitness, that behavior will tend to spread through a population. Over many generations, various kinds of adaptive behaviors can play central roles in the survival of populations and species.**

In Your Notebook *In your own words, explain how animal behavior can evolve through natural selection.*

FIGURE 29–1 Anti-Predatory Display Moths of the genus *Automeris* normally rest with their front wings over their hind wings (left). If disturbed, the moth will move its front wings to expose a striking circular pattern on its hind wings (right). This behavior may scare off predators that mistake the moth's hind-wing pattern for the eyes of a predatory owl such as the great horned owl. **Infer** ***Given that the moth displays this wing pattern and doesn't fly away when confronted by a predator, predict two characteristics of the moth's typical predator.***

Innate Behavior

What is an innate behavior?

Why do newly hatched birds beg for food within moments after hatching? How does a spider know to spin its web? These animals are exhibiting **innate behaviors,** also called instincts. **Innate behaviors appear in fully functional form the first time they are performed, even though the animal has had no previous experience with the stimuli to which it responds.** The suckling of a newborn mammal is a classic example of a simple innate behavior. Other innate behaviors, such as the weaving of a spider web or the building of hanging nests by weaver birds, can be quite complex. All innate behaviors depend on patterns of nervous system activity that develop through complex interactions between genes and the environment. Biologists do not yet fully understand just how these interactions occur, but the usefulness of innate behaviors is obvious. They enable animals to perform certain tasks essential to survival without the need for experience.

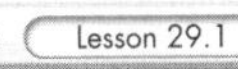

Teach

Connect to the Real World

Have a pair of students take turns gently tossing a cotton ball at each other's face. Students should wear safety goggles to protect their eyes. When students toss the cotton ball, they should watch for their partner's response. *(blinking his or her eyes)* Explain that blinking is a simple innate behavior.

Ask What is the importance of blinking behavior? *(It protects the eyes.)*

Ask How might blinking have evolved as a protective behavior? *(Organisms that blinked were able to protect their vision, which helped them do the things they needed to survive—find food, shelter, and mates. Organisms without this behavior could not protect their vision as well. They were less likely to keep their vision and therefore were less likely to survive.)*

DIFFERENTIATED INSTRUCTION

LPR Less Proficient Readers Point out that in the Connect to the Real World activity, the moving cotton ball is a stimulus and the blinking is a behavior. To help students remember the definitions of *stimulus* and *behavior,* post a card with the word *stimulus* on the left side of a bulletin board and one with the word *behavior* on the right side. Add an arrow pointing from *stimulus* to *behavior.* Use visual imagery to help students create mental pictures of these terms. Under the words, post pictures of familiar stimuli and their corresponding behaviors, such as cat food and a cat eating. Encourage students to bring in additional pictures of both concepts to post.

Biology In-Depth

ANIMAL BEHAVIOR UNDER ANALYSIS

Scientists approach the systematic study of animal behavior in different ways. Some scientists directly analyze the function of the brain and nerves. These neurophysiologists might stimulate neurons with electrodes and observe the response. Ethologists observe the behavior of animals in their natural environments. They are interested in the biological significance of behavior patterns and how these behaviors might have evolved. Related to ethology is behavioral ecology, which focuses on the ecological and evolutionary bases for behavior—why, rather than how, animals behave as they do. A behavioral ecologist may study foraging behavior or the territoriality of a particular species in its niche.

Answers

FIGURE 29–1 Sample answer: The predator responds to visual stimuli. The predator may be prey for predatory owls, such as the great horned owl.

IN YOUR NOTEBOOK A behavior that is influenced by genes and that helps an individual survive will be passed to its offspring and spread through the population over time.

Teach continued

Lead a Discussion

Ask students to name behaviors that they have learned. Examples include tying shoes, riding a bike, reading, and writing. Ask students if they can describe the process of learning these behaviors. Do they remember how long it took to learn the skill? Were there multiple steps involved? Was there an "aha" moment when the skill suddenly seemed to come naturally? Next, compare the process of learning a skill with the process of habituation.

Ask How long did it take before you didn't notice something, such as the sound of airplanes taking off from a nearby airport? Did you notice these stimuli again after returning from a vacation? How long did it take you to habituate again? *(Answers will vary.)*

Emphasize that habituation is the loss of a response to a stimulus. Summarize by telling students that learning is a process and that the length of time for different skills to develop or for habituation to occur varies.

DIFFERENTIATED INSTRUCTION

L3 Advanced Students Have students read Aesop's fable about the boy who cried wolf. Then, have them write a short report focusing on why this is an example of habituation. Encourage them to include other examples of habituation in their reports.

FIGURE 29–2 Learned Behavior This chimpanzee is using a stick as a tool to "fish" for termites in a termite nest.

Learned Behavior

What are the major types of learning?

If all behaviors were innate, animals would have a tough time adapting to unpredictable changes in their environments. (And if all behavior were innate, you wouldn't be reading this book!) Many complex animals live in unpredictable environments, where their fitness can depend on behaviors that can be altered as a result of experience. Acquiring changes in behavior during one's lifetime is called **learning.**

Many animals have the ability to learn. Organisms with simple nervous systems, such as sea stars, shrimp, and most other invertebrates, may learn only rarely. Among a few invertebrates, and many chordates, learning is common and occurs under a wide range of circumstances. In animals that care for their young, for example, offspring can learn behaviors from their parents or other caretakers. The chimpanzee in **Figure 29–2** is exhibiting a complex learned behavior—using a tool to gather food. Scientists have identified several different ways of learning. **The four major types of learning are habituation, classical conditioning, operant conditioning, and insight learning.**

Habituation The simplest type of learning is habituation. **Habituation** is a process by which an animal decreases or stops its response to a repetitive stimulus that neither rewards nor harms the animal. Often, learning to ignore a stimulus that offers neither a reward nor a threat can enable an individual to spend its time and energy more efficiently. Consider the common shore ragworm, an invertebrate shown to be capable of simple learning. This animal lives in a sandy tube that it leaves to feed. If a shadow passes overhead, the worm will instantly retreat to the safety of its burrow. Yet, if repeated shadows pass within a short time span, this response quickly subsides. When the worm has learned that the shadow is neither food nor threat, it will stop responding. At this point the worm has been habituated to the stimulus. In **Figure 29–3,** you can see birds becoming habituated to the stimulus of passing cars.

FIGURE 29–3 Habituation Birds on the side of a road take flight when a car approaches (left). After many cars have passed and not harmed them, these birds have become habituated to cars, and they no longer take flight when one approaches (right).

How Science Works

PAVLOV'S INCIDENTAL DISCOVERY

Ivan Pavlov (1849–1936) was a Russian physiologist working in St. Petersburg. He pioneered studies of the digestive system and won the Nobel Prize in Physiology or Medicine in 1904 for his work on the physiology of the circulatory, digestive, and nervous systems. In his research, he measured the saliva produced when dogs, secured in harnesses, were fed. After a while, he noticed that the dogs started to salivate even before they were fed. Fascinated by the observation, Pavlov went on to conduct his famous experiments on classical conditioning. In his studies, he learned that the dogs' conditioned response (salivation) to a stimulus (such as the sound of a metronome or the sight of bread) can be extinguished over time. For example, when a dog is teased repeatedly with the sight of food held at a distance, its saliva production will eventually decrease to zero. The lost response can be restored, however. Letting the dog eat the food will again induce the dog to salivate at the sight of food held at a distance.

Classical Conditioning One evening you sit down to eat a kind of food you've never tried before. But shortly after you start eating, you get sick from a stomach virus. You feel better the next day, but as your parents present you with leftovers of the same food, you feel sick again. From that time on, whenever you smell that particular food, you become nauseated. This is an example of classical conditioning. **Classical conditioning** is a form of learning in which a certain stimulus comes to produce a particular response, usually through association with a positive or negative experience. In this case, the stimulus is the smell of that particular food, and the response is nausea. The food didn't make you sick, but you've been conditioned to associate the smell of that food with illness.

Classical conditioning was first described around 1900 by Russian physiologist Ivan Pavlov, who was studying dogs' responses to food. Pavlov first noted that dogs salivate as an innate response to food. Then Pavlov discovered that if he always rang a bell when he offered food, a dog would salivate whenever it heard a bell, even if no food was present. Pavlov's experiment produced salivation (a response) in reaction to the bell (a stimulus) associated with food.

Operant Conditioning Conditioning is often used to train animals. **Operant conditioning** occurs when an animal learns to behave in a certain way through repeated practice, to receive a reward or avoid punishment. Operant conditioning was first described in the 1940s by the American psychologist B. F. Skinner. Skinner invented a testing procedure that used a box called a "Skinner box." A Skinner box contains a colored button or lever that delivers a food reward when pressed. After an animal is rewarded several times, it learns that it gets food whenever it presses the button or lever. At this point, the animal has learned by operant conditioning how to obtain food. In **Figure 29–4,** you can see how a dog can be trained to ring a bell to be let out of the house.

Operant conditioning is sometimes described as a form of trial-and-error learning. Trial-and-error learning begins with a random behavior that is rewarded in an event called a trial. Most trials result in errors, but occasionally a trial will lead to a reward or punishment.

Insight Learning The most complicated form of learning is insight learning, or reasoning. **Insight learning** occurs when an animal applies something it has already learned to a new situation, without a period of trial and error. For instance, if you are given a new math problem on an exam, you may apply principles you have already learned in the class to solve the problem. Insight learning is common among humans and some other primates. In one experiment, a hungry chimpanzee used insight learning to figure out how to reach a bunch of bananas hanging overhead: It stacked some boxes on top of one another and climbed to the top of the stack. In contrast, if a dog accidentally wraps its leash around a tree, the dog is usually unable to figure out how to free itself.

FIGURE 29–4 Operant Conditioning A dog randomly brushes its tail against a bell hanging on a doorknob (top). The owner responds by opening the door to let the dog outside (middle). After the "ring the bell; open the door" sequence has occurred several times, the dog has learned to ring the bell when it wants to go out (bottom).

LESSON 29.1

Lead a Discussion

Tell students that the work of Pavlov and Skinner was important to early human behavioral psychology. Pavlov and Skinner both used animal models to explain what elicits certain human behaviors, though their theories of human psychology are not universally accepted today.

Ask How are classical and operant conditioning similar, and how are they different? *(In both, the animal learns to respond to a stimulus. In classical conditioning, the stimulus is different from the one that originally caused the response. In operant conditioning, the stimulus—the button that releases food, for example—is discovered through trial and error.)*

Compare conditioning to insight learning.

Ask How is insight learning different from each of the two types of conditioning? *(The response is more complex. There is no trial and error, as in operant conditioning. There is not the simple association between stimuli, as in classical conditioning.)*

DIFFERENTIATED INSTRUCTION

ELL English Language Learners Have students work in pairs to check comprehension of the four major types of learning. Have one student name a type of learning. Have the other student write the definition. Then have students exchange roles to quiz each other. If students still have trouble with the terms, have them work together to review the material.

L3 Advanced Students Tell students to imagine that they are writing a training manual for dog owners. Students should write instructions on how classical or operant conditioning can be used to train an animal to obey a command. For example, a dog can be trained to respond to hand signals (classical conditioning) or by using a food reward to elicit a certain behavior (operant conditioning).

Address Misconceptions

Anthropomorphism While discussing animal behavior, students might attribute human feelings and motivations to animals. Explain that this tendency, called anthropomorphism, is a common mistake that biologists and behaviorists must be careful not to make. Remind students that most animals respond to stimuli in their environment without thought. As animals react to their surroundings, they may alter certain behaviors through learning.

UbD Check for Understanding

INDEX CARD SUMMARIES

Distribute four index cards to each student. On one side of a card, have students define one of the four kinds of learned behavior. Tell students to turn the card over and explain the adaptive significance of that behavior. Repeat for each of the other three behaviors. *(Habituation allows an individual to spend time and energy efficiently. Classical conditioning enables quick response to familiar stimuli. Operant conditioning enables quick response to a potential reward or punishment. Insight learning allows effective response to novel situations.)*

ADJUST INSTRUCTION

Call out examples of each of the four kinds of behavior, and ask which kind of behavior the example represents and why. Point out how each type of behavior helps an organism survive and reproduce.

Teach continued

Lead a Discussion

Show students a picture of ducklings or goslings following a person. (You might find pictures of Konrad Lorenz, who studied imprinting in geese.)

Ask Why are these birds following a human? *(The birds have imprinted on the human.)*

Discuss how this behavior might affect the birds' ability to survive in their environment. Tell students that imprinting is one of many complex behaviors that combine innate behavior with learning.

Ask What are some other complex behaviors that have innate and learned components? *(Sample answers: innate—urge to eat, learned—which foods are safe; innate—sleep, learned—when to sleep, wake; innate—ability to sing, learned—song)*

DIFFERENTIATED INSTRUCTION

L1 Struggling Students Some students may have trouble with the idea that behavior can be either innate or learned. Use the photographs on this page to help clarify the distinction. For each photo, help students first identify the behavior and then distinguish its innate and learned aspects. For example, in the photo of the young crane following its mother, the young crane follows innately, but it first must learn what to follow.

ELL Focus on ELL: Access Content

ALL SPEAKERS Make an audio recording of **Lesson 29.1.** Have students listen to the recording to help them review the lesson. Then, assign students to small groups for a **Core Concept Discussion.** Have each student write down one core concept about the lesson. Have students take turns discussing the concept he or she wrote down. Bring the class back together, and have one student from each group share with the class one of the group's core concepts.

Study Wkbks A/B, Appendix S3, Core Concept Discussion.

BIOLOGY.com Students can use the **Tutor Tube: Sing . . . Sing a Song** to explore how both innate and learned behaviors are involved in bird song.

FIGURE 29–5 Imprinting in the Wild These wild, baby sandhill cranes have imprinted on their mother and will follow her in flight.

Complex Behaviors

How do many complex behaviors arise?

Though behaviors may be learned, they often involve significant innate components. **Many complex behaviors combine innate behavior with learning.** Young white-crowned sparrows, for example, have an innate ability to recognize their own species' song and to distinguish it from the songs of other species. To sing their complete species-specific song, however, young birds must hear it sung by adults.

Another example of behavior with both innate and learned components is called imprinting. Some animals, such as birds, recognize and follow the first moving object that they see during a critical time in their early lives. This process is called **imprinting.** How does imprinting involve both innate and learned behavior? The young birds have an innate urge to follow the first moving object they see. But they are not born knowing what that object will look like, so they must learn from experience what to follow. Usually, birds such as cranes imprint on their mother, as shown in **Figure 29–5.**

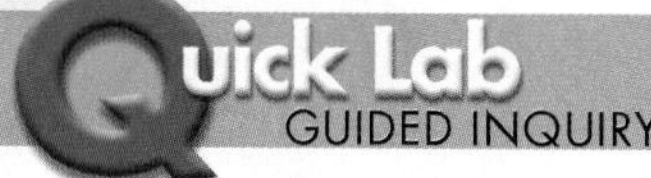

GUIDED INQUIRY

What Kind of Learning Is Practice?

1. Draw straight lines on a piece of paper to divide it into several sections of different sizes and shapes. Then, cut the paper into sections along those lines.
2. Shuffle the pieces, and then time another student as he or she tries to reassemble the pieces. Record how long it takes the student to do this task.
3. Repeat step 2 three times. Construct a graph showing how the time needed to assemble the puzzle changed with repeated practice.

Analyze and Conclude

1. Analyze Data Explain the shape of your graph. How did the time needed to reassemble the pieces change with repeated trials?

2. Draw Conclusions What kind of learning was displayed in this activity? Was it habituation, classical conditioning, operant conditioning, or some other kind of learning? Explain your answer.

PURPOSE Students will be able to draw conclusions to classify practice as a kind of learning.

MATERIALS ruler, scissors, clock with second hand, graph paper

PLANNING Students will achieve straighter cuts if they use the ruler to draw the cutting lines.

ANALYZE AND CONCLUDE

1. Graphs should show that the time required to assemble the puzzle decreased as students repeated the task.
2. Some students may think that learning by practice is different from other types of learning. Recognizing the shape of puzzle pieces requires conscious insight, an ability not involved in the other types of learning. Others may see this type of practice as operant conditioning because the first trial on the puzzle is a random effort.

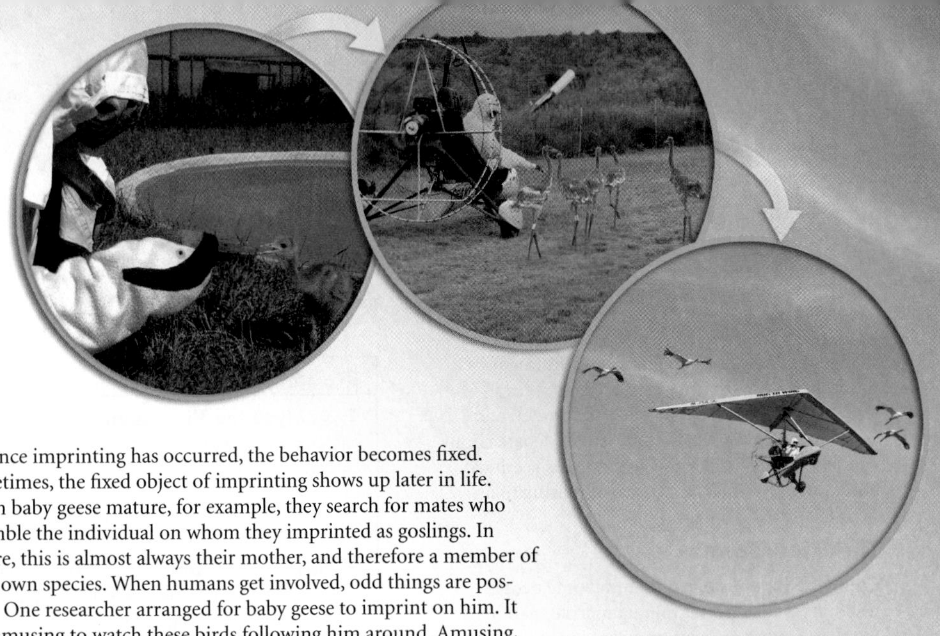

FIGURE 29–6 Imprinting in Captivity Recently hatched cranes raised in captivity imprint on a hand puppet (top left). Later, that puppet is used to help introduce these birds to the wild by guiding them along a migration route that they would normally learn by following their parents (top center and top right).

Once imprinting has occurred, the behavior becomes fixed. Sometimes, the fixed object of imprinting shows up later in life. When baby geese mature, for example, they search for mates who resemble the individual on whom they imprinted as goslings. In nature, this is almost always their mother, and therefore a member of their own species. When humans get involved, odd things are possible. One researcher arranged for baby geese to imprint on him. It was amusing to watch these birds following him around. Amusing, that is, until the birds matured—and began to court the researcher! Sometimes experiments have even caused birds to imprint on objects such as the hand puppet shown in **Figure 29–6.**

Imprinting doesn't have to involve vision. Animals can imprint on sounds, odors, or any other sensory cues. Newly hatched salmon, for example, imprint on the odor of the stream in which they hatch. Young salmon then head out to sea. Years later, when they mature, the salmon remember the odor of their home stream and return there to spawn.

29.1 Assessment

IN B.8.5

Review Key Concepts 

1. a. Review What is behavior?

b. Apply Concepts How does natural selection affect animal behavior?

2. a. Review How does a newborn animal know exactly "what to do" the moment it is born?

b. Predict What would happen if a newborn kitten did not have the suckling instinct?

3. a. Review What are the four types of learning?

b. Apply Concepts Give an example of how humans learn through classical conditioning.

4. a. Review Which aspect of imprinting is innate? Which aspect is learned?

b. Infer How might isolating a newborn animal from members of its own species affect it?

Apply the Big idea

Evolution

5. Use what you learned in this lesson to explain why behavioral responses are important to the survival of a species.

BIOLOGY.com Search Lesson 29.1 GO • Lesson Assessment • Self-Test

Assess and Remediate

EVALUATE UNDERSTANDING

Have students study each figure in the lesson and identify the type of behavior that is represented—innate, learned, or complex. Have them also explain why they think it represents that type of behavior. Then, have them complete the 29.1 Assessment.

REMEDIATION SUGGESTION

L1 Struggling Students If your students have trouble with **Question 1b,** have them review the concept of natural selection by discussing it with a partner. Then, have pairs write a response to the question.

BIOLOGY.com Students can check their understanding of lesson concepts with the **Self-Test** assessment. They can then take an online version of the **Lesson Assessment.**

Assessment Answers

1a. Behavior is the way an organism reacts to stimuli in its environment.

1b. Behaviors that can be inherited evolve under the influence of natural selection. If the behavior increases fitness, it tends to spread through a population.

2a. Its behavior is innate, or instinctive.

2b. The kitten would not be able to feed properly and could starve.

3a. habituation, classical conditioning, operant conditioning, insight learning

3b. Sample answer: Humans may become nauseated when they associate the smell of a certain food with being sick.

4a. The urge to follow the first moving object seen is innate. Animals need to learn what to follow.

4b. The animal may not learn to recognize members of its own species, which could affect its ability to survive and mate.

5. Big idea The appropriate behavioral response helps an animal find food, mates, shelter, and avoid predators in its environment and makes it possible for that animal to reproduce, sustaining its species.

Teach

Lead a Discussion

Although marine mammals are protected, they can still be captured for the reasons stated in the Marine Mammal Protection Act of 1972. (See the **Biology In-Depth** below.) Lead students in a discussion of the pros and cons of this legislation.

Ask Do you think there is any defensible reason for taking a marine mammal from the wild? *(Accept all well-supported responses.)*

Ask Do you think all captive marine mammals should be released back into the wild? *(Accept all well-supported responses.)*

Answers

RESEARCH AND DECIDE

1. Sample answers: Some research options that involve captive marine animals include learning about their diet, breeding behavior, and how they raise young. In addition to research, benefits of entertaining people with trained marine mammals and otherwise exhibiting them include educating people and thereby generating empathy for the animals. Costs include the general restrictions of captivity, plus shorter life expectancies for captive mammals due to exotic diseases, such as intestinal gangrene.
2. Sample answers: Captivity may be a good solution for injured animals that could not survive in the wild. Captivity would not be a good solution if the animal had a disease or infection that could be passed to other members of the captive population. Accept all points of view that are supported by facts and logical reasoning.

Biology & Society

Should Marine Mammals Be Kept in Captivity?

Many types of marine mammals, including dolphins, killer whales, and seals, are kept in captive display for educational, entertainment, and research purposes. Yet, there is strong debate about whether public display of such animals is ethical. Should we prohibit the capture of marine mammals for public display?

The Viewpoints

Captivity Should Be Prohibited Some people feel that capturing and training marine mammals purely for entertainment purposes is not justified. They believe that because marine mammals are naturally social, with strong family bonds, they are not suited to capture or confinement. These people are concerned that the process of capture disrupts social groups.

Those opposed to the captivity of marine mammals also argue that confinement places the animals in an unnatural situation—one that is monotonous, limited, and unhealthful. In the wild, whales and dolphins travel long distances and dive much deeper than is possible in a shallow display tank. There is also a concern that human interaction with captive marine mammals increases the risk of transmitting diseases to the animals.

Captivity Should Be Allowed Other people believe that we have an obligation to convey knowledge of the natural world to the public by displaying animals and educating ourselves about them. Information obtained by observing captive animals and interacting with them may be helpful in managing their populations in the wild. Many people argue that the adverse effects of captivity are outweighed by the benefits of conservation, an enhanced human appreciation for animals, and the advancement of scientific knowledge. There is also evidence that human interactions with captive dolphins may help people with disabilities, such as autism.

Research and Decide

1. Analyze the Viewpoints To make an informed decision, learn more about this issue by consulting library or Internet resources. Then, list the options for education, entertainment, and research involving marine mammals. What are the benefits? What are the costs?

2. Form an Opinion Should marine mammals be kept in captivity? Are there some instances when captivity is a good solution and other instances when it is not? Explain.

Biology In-Depth

PROTECTING MARINE MAMMALS

In 1972, the United States Congress passed the Marine Mammal Protection Act for the protection and preservation of marine mammals. Passage of the act was based on these findings: some species are in danger of extinction as a result of human activities; knowledge of the ecology and population dynamics of marine mammals is inadequate; marine mammals are resources of great international significance.

The National Oceanographic and Atmospheric Organization (NOAA) is responsible for administering the Marine Mammal Protection Act. The act generally prohibits taking marine mammals in U.S. waters by anyone, and in international waters by any U.S. citizen. NOAA can authorize the taking of marine mammals for the following activities: scientific research, enhancing survival or recovery of a species, capture of wild mammals for public display, incidental capture during commercial fishing operations.

29.2 Animals in Their Environments

IN B.8.5 Survival and reproduction. Also covered: NoS.3.

THINK ABOUT IT As twilight falls on a coral reef, its inhabitants act like New York commuters during evening rush hour. Daytime workers, whose "jobs" involve feeding near the reef, head for home. Some form lines and create traffic jams as they jockey for position in "apartment buildings"—cracks, crevices, and caves in the reef where they will rest until dawn. For a time, twilight predators menace any straggling daytime fishes disoriented by the gloom. Then the night shift emerges. These creatures of darkness may have huge, staring eyes—or none at all. They take over the coral metropolis at night. At dawn, the cycle reverses. Critters of the night disappear, and the workday begins.

Key Questions

How do environmental changes affect animal behavior?

How do social behaviors increase an animal's evolutionary fitness?

How do animals communicate with others in their environments?

Vocabulary

circadian rhythm • migration • courtship • territory • aggression • society • kin selection • communication • language

Taking Notes

Outline Before you read, use the headings in this lesson to make an outline about animals in their environments. As you read, add details to your outline.

Behavioral Cycles

How do environmental changes affect animal behavior?

The daily changeover on coral reefs is an example of regular cycles in nature. **Many animals respond to periodic changes in the environment with daily or seasonal cycles of behavior.** Behavioral cycles that occur daily, like those on coral reefs, are called **circadian** (sur KAY dee un) **rhythms.** You sleep at night and attend school during the day in another example of a circadian rhythm.

Other cycles are seasonal. In temperate and polar regions, for example, many species are active during spring, summer, and fall, but enter into a sleeplike state, or dormancy, during winter. In mammals, dormancy is called hibernation. Dormancy allows an animal to survive periods when food and other resources may not be available.

Another type of seasonal behavior is **migration,** the seasonal movement from one environment to another. Many species of animals migrate—often over huge distances. **Figure 29–7** shows the long migration of green sea turtles. Migration allows animals to take advantage of favorable environmental conditions. For example, many songbirds live in tropical regions where temperatures are moderate and food remains available during northern winters. When these birds fly north in the spring, they take advantage of seasonally abundant food and find space to nest and raise their young.

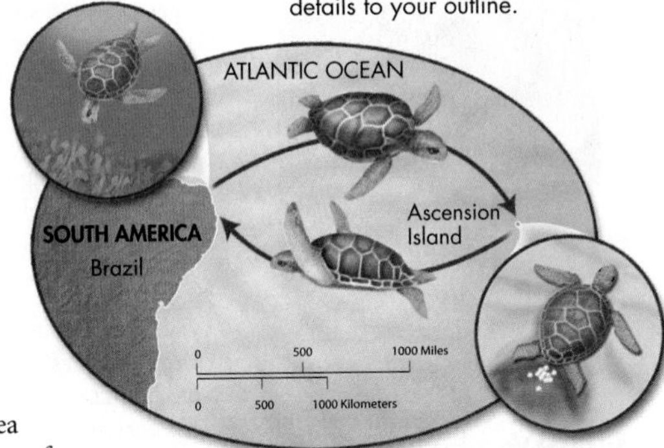

FIGURE 29–7 Seasonal Behavior of Green Sea Turtles Each year, green sea turtles migrate back and forth between their feeding grounds on Brazil's coast and their nesting grounds on Ascension Island.

BIOLOGY.com Search Lesson 29.2 GO • Lesson Overview • Lesson Notes • Data Analysis

Teach for Understanding

ENDURING UNDERSTANDING Animals have evolved diverse ways to carry out basic life processes and maintain homeostasis.

GUIDING QUESTION How do the environment and other organisms affect an animal's behavior?

EVIDENCE OF UNDERSTANDING *The following assessment, to be assigned after students have finished the lesson, should show student understanding of how animal behavior is related to survival.* Have students make a table with three columns. In the left-hand column, have them list some of the behaviors in this lesson: migration, courtship, territoriality, societal behavior, and communication. In the middle column, have them list one or two things that elicit the behavior. In the right-hand column, have them describe how the behavior enhances survival.

Getting Started

Objectives

29.2.1 Explain how environmental changes affect animal behavior.

29.2.2 Explain how social behaviors increase the evolutionary fitness of a species.

29.2.3 Summarize the ways that animals communicate.

Student Resources

Study Workbooks A and B, 29.2 Worksheets

Spanish Study Workbook, 29.2 Worksheets

Lab Manual B, 29.2 Data Analysis Worksheet

BIOLOGY.com Lesson Overview • Lesson Notes • Activities: Data Analysis, Art in Motion, Art Review • Assessment: Self-Test, Lesson Assessment

For corresponding lesson in the **Foundation Edition**, see pages 700–704.

BIOLOGY.com Students can analyze migration data with **Data Analysis: Tracking Shark Migrations.**

IN INDIANA ACADEMIC STANDARDS

For the full text of all standards, see the Course Overview in the front matter of this book.

B.8.5 Describe how due to genetic variations, environmental forces, and reproductive pressures, organisms with beneficial traits are more likely to survive, reproduce, and pass on their genetic information.

Teach

Use Visuals

Refer students to the chapter opener photograph of wolves fighting over food. Point out that this is an example of aggression. While it might not look very social, aggression when competing over limited resources is, indeed, social behavior. Animals may aggressively defend the limited resources in their territories from others in order to increase their own evolutionary fitness.

Ask What aspect of aggressive behavior is social? *(interaction with others of one's species)*

Then, point out the photograph of the courting gannets in **Figure 29–8.**

Ask How does courtship behavior increase evolutionary fitness? *(Courtship behavior helps to ensure mating and the passing of one's genes to offspring.)*

DIFFERENTIATED INSTRUCTION

LPR **Less Proficient Readers** After the class has discussed the social behaviors shown in the photos, have less proficient readers work in small groups to organize information on social behaviors in a **Compare/Contrast Table.** The table should include the types of behavior, a description of the behaviors, and how the behaviors increase evolutionary fitness.

Study Wkbks A/B, Appendix S20, Compare/Contrast Table. **Transparencies,** GO3.

ELL Focus on ELL: Extend Language

ALL SPEAKERS Write the different types of social behaviors on the board. Point to each one and say it aloud as you point to it. Have students repeat the word after you. Define each kind of social behavior and point to a photo in the lesson that shows the behavior.

Then, pair beginning and intermediate speakers with advanced and advanced high speakers. Have the advanced speakers define the behaviors for the beginning speakers, using the students' native language, if possible.

Have each beginning and intermediate speaker write the behavior and its definition. Students may draw illustrations that show what the terms mean.

BIOLOGY.com Students can examine territoriality, aggression, and courtship with **Art in Motion: Social Behavior in Fiddler Crabs.**

FIGURE 29–8 Types of Social Behavior Social behaviors such as courtship and territorial marking help define social groups.

▲ Gannets perform a courtship ritual.

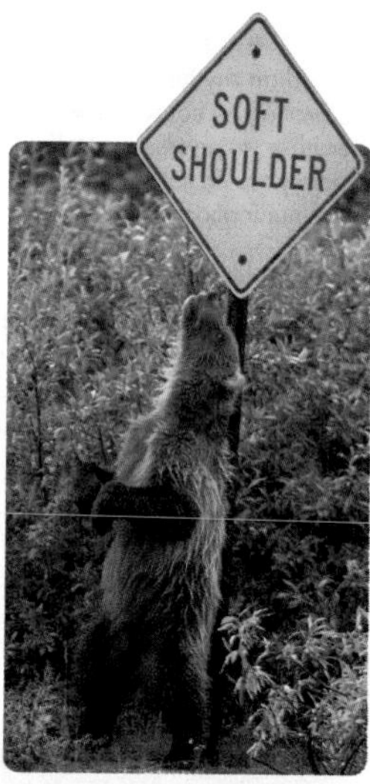

▲ A grizzly bear marks its territory with its fur and scent.

BUILD Vocabulary

WORD ORIGINS The adjective *social* is related to the Latin words *socialis,* meaning "social," and *societas,* meaning "companionship." Animals that are social spend most of their time in a group.

Social Behavior

How do social behaviors increase an animal's evolutionary fitness?

Whenever birds sing, bighorn sheep butt heads, or chimpanzees groom each other, they are engaging in social behavior. Social behaviors include courtship, territoriality, aggression, and the forming of societies. **Choosing mates, defending or claiming territories or resources, and forming social groups can increase evolutionary fitness.**

Courtship For sexually reproducing animal species, evolutionary survival requires individuals to locate and mate with another member of its species at least once. **Courtship** is behavior during which members of one sex (usually males) advertise their willingness to mate, and members of the opposite sex (usually females) choose which mate they will accept. Typically, males send out signals—sounds, visual displays, or chemicals—that attract females. The musical trill of a tree frog, for example, is a breeding call.

In some species, courtship involves an elaborate series of behaviors called rituals. A ritual is a series of behaviors performed the same way by all members of a population for the purpose of communicating. Most rituals consist of specific signals and responses that continue until mating occurs. For example, gannets bond by engaging in "beak-pointing"—intertwining their necks while pointing their beaks to the sky, a behavior you can see in **Figure 29–8.**

Territoriality and Aggression Many animals behave in ways that prevent other individuals from using limited resources. Often, these animals occupy a specific area, or **territory,** that they defend against competitors. Territories usually contain resources, such as food, water, nesting sites, shelter, and potential mates, which are necessary for survival and reproduction. If a rival enters a territory, the "owner" of the territory attacks in an effort to drive the rival away. Grizzly bears will often mark their territories with their fur and scent by scratching their backs on rough surfaces, such as trees or signposts.

While competing for resources, animals may also show **aggression,** threatening behaviors that one animal uses to exert dominance over another. Fights between male sea lions over territory and "harems" of females often leave both rivals bloodied.

Animal Societies An animal **society** is a group of animals of the same species that interact closely and often cooperate. Mammals form many types of societies, which offer a range of advantages. Zebras and other grazers, for example, are safer from predators when they are part of a group than when they are alone. Societies can also improve animals' ability to hunt, to protect their territory, to guard their young, or to fight with rivals. In wild African dog packs, for instance, adult females take turns guarding all the pups in the pack, while the other adults hunt for prey. Macaque, baboon, and other primate societies hunt together, travel in search of new territory, and interact with neighboring societies.

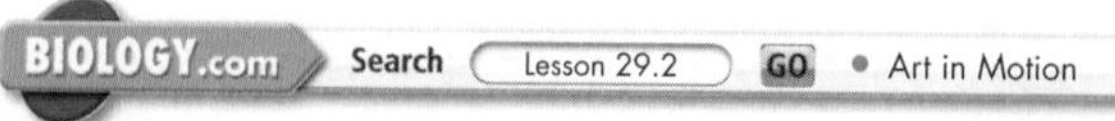

How Science Works

WILD CHIMPANZEES

Jane Goodall began her studies of east African chimpanzees in 1960. Goodall's approach was nonintrusive. She quietly observed chimpanzees from a distance until they accepted her presence. She observed that chimpanzees have more complex social interactions and behaviors similar to those of humans than scientists had expected. She learned that chimpanzees are skilled at making and using tools, that they are omnivores, and sometimes will hunt and eat other animals, and engage in warfare against one another.

In 1977, Goodall founded the Jane Goodall Institute for Wildlife Research, Education, and Conservation to provide support for research on wild chimpanzees. Today she spends much of her time lecturing and encouraging young people to become involved in environmental and social issues.

Members of a society are often related to one another. Elephant herds, for example, consist of mothers, aunts, and their offspring. (Males are kicked out when they reach puberty.) The theory of **kin selection** holds that helping relatives can improve an individual's evolutionary fitness because related individuals share a large proportion of their genes. Helping a relative survive therefore increases the chance that the genes an individual shares with that relative will be passed along to offspring.

The most extreme examples of relatedness, and the most complex animal societies (other than human societies), are found among social insects such as ants, bees, and wasps. In social insect colonies, all individuals cooperate to perform extraordinary feats, such as building complex nests. In an ant colony, such as the one in **Figure 29–9**, all workers in the colony are females who are very closely related—which means that they share a large proportion of each others' genes. Worker ants are also sterile. For this reason it is advantageous for them to cooperate to help their "mother" (the queen) reproduce and raise their "sisters" (other workers). Male ants function only to fertilize the queen.

MYSTERY CLUE

When threatened by predators, adult elephants in a herd form a defensive circle around the youngest members. What may have triggered this behavior in the elephants at the watering hole?

FIGURE 29–9 An Ant Society In a leaf-cutter ant society, only a single queen reproduces. Different groups of ants within the colony perform other tasks.

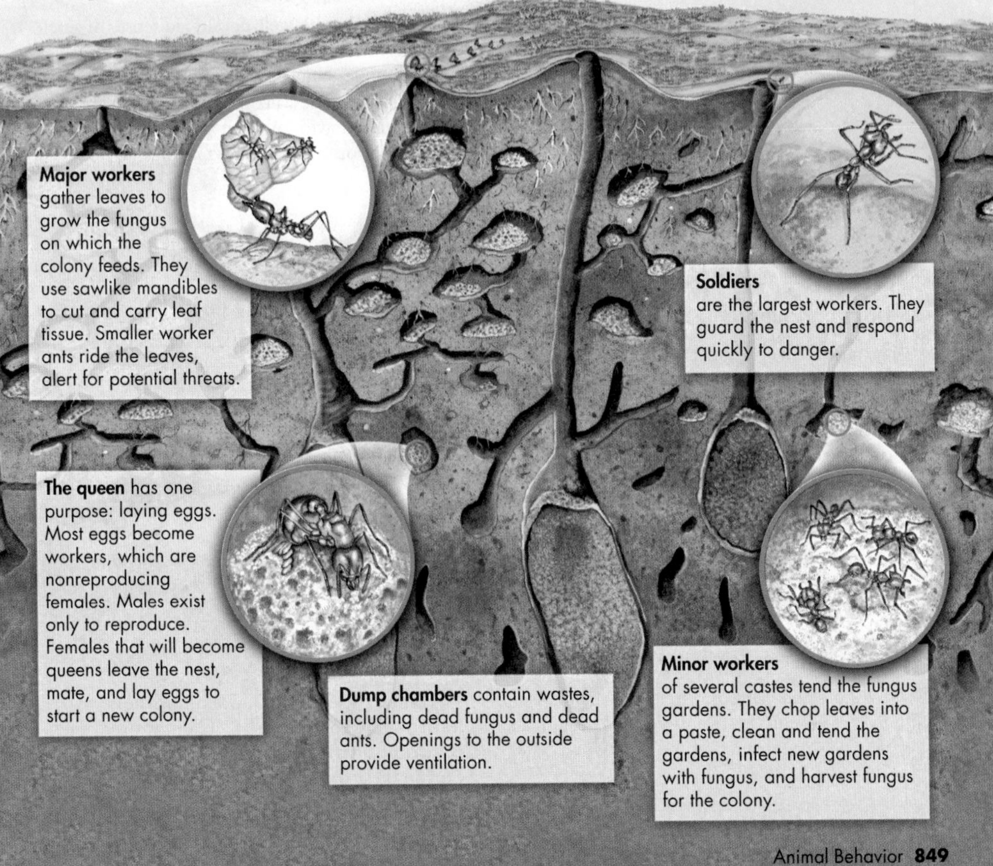

Major workers gather leaves to grow the fungus on which the colony feeds. They use sawlike mandibles to cut and carry leaf tissue. Smaller worker ants ride the leaves, alert for potential threats.

Soldiers are the largest workers. They guard the nest and respond quickly to danger.

The queen has one purpose: laying eggs. Most eggs become workers, which are nonreproducing females. Males exist only to reproduce. Females that will become queens leave the nest, mate, and lay eggs to start a new colony.

Dump chambers contain wastes, including dead fungus and dead ants. Openings to the outside provide ventilation.

Minor workers of several castes tend the fungus gardens. They chop leaves into a paste, clean and tend the gardens, infect new gardens with fungus, and harvest fungus for the colony.

Use Visuals

Have students examine **Figure 29–9.** Ask them to work in small groups to write a dramatization that includes the four roles of individuals in a leaf-cutter ant society. Their dramatizations can be written in first person and include dialogue. One student in the group can act as the narrator to explain the dump chamber, as well as how kin selection is related to the structure of the society. Have students perform their dramatizations before the class.

DIFFERENTIATED INSTRUCTION

L1 Struggling Students Allow students to observe the interactions of ants in an ant farm. You can purchase one ready-made from a hobby store or science supply company. Have students identify the role that each ant, or group of ants, has in the colony.

The elephants' behavior at the watering hole may have been triggered by the threat of a predator, perhaps communicated by other elephants. Ask students how this possibility relates to the concepts presented on this page. *(The members of the elephant herd are related; they cooperate and act collectively for the good of the entire herd.)* Students can go online at **Biology.com** to find out more about defensive behavior in elephants.

UbD Check for Understanding

HAND SIGNALS

Ask students the following questions, and have them show a thumbs-up sign if they think they can answer the question correctly, a thumbs-down sign if they definitely can't, or a waving-hand sign if they're not sure.

- What do individuals do during courtship behavior?
- What are the functions of a territory?
- What is the relationship between an animal society and kin selection?

ADJUST INSTRUCTION

For any questions that received thumbs-down or waving-hand signs, have students work in pairs to reread the relevant text and then write a one-sentence response. Then, have volunteers share their sentences with the class.

LESSON 29.2

Teach continued

Use Models

Communicate with the class without using verbal or written language. Try to get students to perform a specific task, such as preparing to take notes or opening their books to a certain page. After students successfully complete the task, have them identify the types of signals you used to communicate with them. Ask them to identify other ways animals communicate. Explain that pheromones are usually organic acids or alcohols that are highly volatile and can be detected in very small quantities.

DIFFERENTIATED INSTRUCTION

L1 Special Needs Give students magazines with photos of animals communicating, and have them cut out the photos. If possible, the modes of communication should include visual, chemical, sound, and language. Have students work in groups with more able students to make labels that identify the mode of communication. Post the photos and labels on the bulletin board.

ELL English Language Learners Give English language learners a list of the most important vocabulary terms that they must know to master the concepts of the lesson. Have them find the terms in the text and derive their meaning from context clues. Then, have students place the terms in one of the three categories: behavioral cycles, social behavior, or communication.

BIOLOGY.com Students can drag and drop labels to identify different communication strategies in **Art Review: Animal Communication.**

FIGURE 29–10 Types of Communication Different animals rely on different methods of communication to get their messages across. Fireflies, for example, flash a light generated within their bodies to attract mates.

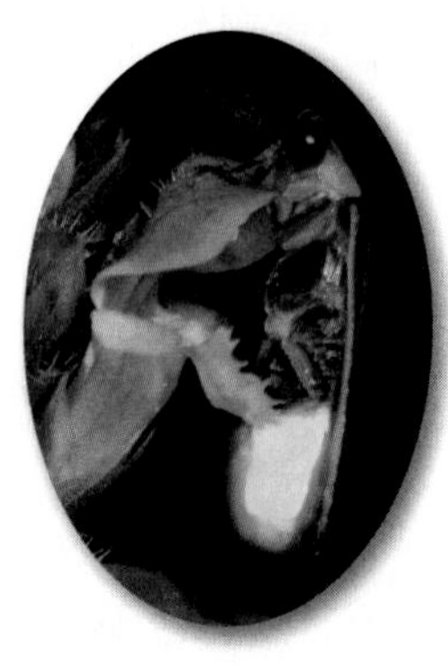

Communication

How do animals communicate with others in their environments?

Because social behavior involves more than one individual, it requires **communication**—the passing of information from one organism to another. **Animals may use a variety of signals to communicate with one another. Some animals are also capable of language.** The specific techniques that animals use depend on the types of stimuli their senses can detect.

Visual Signals Many animals have eyes that sense shapes and colors at least as well as humans do, and they often use visual signals. For example, squids, which have large eyes, change their color to broadcast a variety of signals. In many animal species, males and females have different color patterns, and males use color displays to advertise their readiness to mate. Some animals, such as fireflies, even send signals using light generated within their bodies, as you can see in **Figure 29–10.**

Chemical Signals Animals with well-developed senses of smell, including insects, fishes, and many mammals, can communicate with chemicals. For example, some animals, including lampreys, bees, and ants, release pheromones (FEHR uh mohnz), chemical messengers that affect the behavior of other individuals of the same species, to mark a territory or to signal their readiness to mate.

Analyzing Data

IN NoS.3, B.8.5

Caring for Young

Can experience help animals other than humans learn to care for their young better? The data at the right are from field studies of a seabird, the short-tailed shearwater. Each pair produces only one egg a year. If that egg breaks or if the chick dies, the egg is not replaced. The graph shows the percentage of eggs that develop into free-flying young, in relation to the breeding experience of the parents. This ratio is called reproductive success.

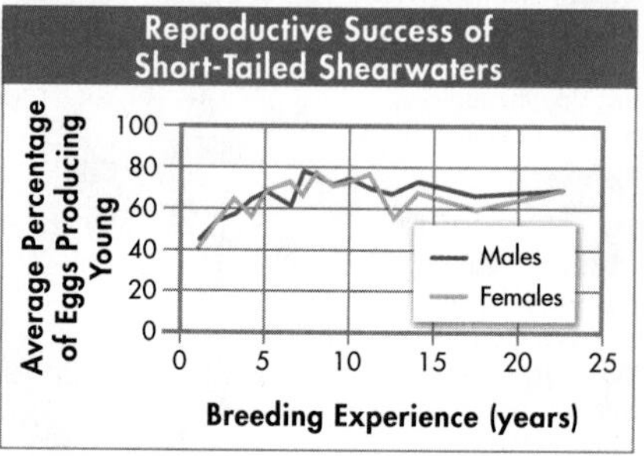

1. Interpret Tables What is the approximate success rate of a female shearwater with five years of breeding experience?
2. Compare and Contrast Are there obvious differences in reproductive success between male and female shearwaters?
3. Draw Conclusions Do older shearwaters have better reproductive success than younger birds have? Explain your answer.
4. Form a Hypothesis Do you think these birds learn to raise young more successfully over time? Is there an alternative hypothesis that could explain these data?

Analyzing Data

PURPOSE Students will be able to interpret data on the reproductive success of short-tailed shearwaters.

PLANNING Make sure students understand what is measured on the vertical axis and the horizontal axis of the graph.

ANSWERS

1. about 70%
2. no
3. In general, yes; this is indicated by the rise in the graph until about 11 years. After 11 years, there is a slight decrease in reproductive success.
4. Most will hypothesize that over time, shearwaters learn to raise young more successfully. Alternative hypothesis: The fertility of shearwaters is highest between 7 and 11 years.

Sound Signals Most animal species that have vocal abilities and a good sense of hearing communicate using sound. Some have evolved elaborate systems of communication. Dolphins communicate in the ocean using sound signals. Bottlenose dolphins each have their own unique "signature" whistle that, amazingly, functions to inform others of who is sending the communication. Elephants also make distinctive sounds, both with their vocal apparatus and with their feet, that can identify them. Elephants, and some other animals, can send messages that the recipient feels rather than hears.

Language The most complicated form of communication is language. **Language** is a system of communication that combines sounds, symbols, and gestures according to rules about sequence and meaning, such as grammar and syntax. Many animals, including elephants, primates, and dolphins such as those in **Figure 29–11,** have complex communication systems. Some even seem to have "words"—calls with specific meanings such as "lions on the prowl." Many species, including honeybees, convey complex information using various kinds of signals. However, untrained animals don't seem to use the rules of grammar and syntax we use to define human language.

FIGURE 29–11 Language Dolphins seem to have a language of their own.

In Your Notebook *Distinguish between sound signals and language.*

29.2 Assessment

IN B.8.5

Review Key Concepts

1. **a. Review** Name two ways in which animal behavior is related to environmental cycles.
   b. Apply Concepts Travelers who travel across time zones often experience what is called jet lag, which includes fatigue and disrupted sleep patterns. How can you explain this condition?
2. **a. Review** List three types of social behavior.
   b. Relate Cause and Effect How does membership in a society increase the evolutionary fitness of individuals in the society?
3. **a. Review** What are the main ways in which animals communicate with one another?
   b. Draw Conclusions Suppose you discover a new type of animal that is very different in appearance from other animals you have seen. How could observing the sense organs of this animal help you to understand if and how it communicates?

Apply the Big idea

Evolution

4. Explain two ways that an animal's social behavior can influence its evolutionary fitness.

BIOLOGY.com Search 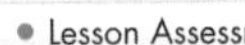 Lesson 29.2  GO • Self-Test • Lesson Assessment • Art Review

Assess and Remediate

EVALUATE UNDERSTANDING

Have students write a paragraph in which they explain how animals communicate with one another during courtship or competition. Then, have them complete the 29.2 Assessment.

REMEDIATION SUGGESTION

L1 Struggling Students If your students have trouble with identifying and relating cause and effect in **Question 2b,** discuss human societies and the benefits derived from belonging to one.

BIOLOGY.com Students can check their understanding of lesson concepts with the **Self-Test** assessment. They can then take an online version of the **Lesson Assessment.**

Answers

IN YOUR NOTEBOOK Sound signals are simpler than language, which is a system of communication that combines sounds, symbols, and gestures according to rules about sequence and meaning.

Assessment Answers

1a. migration and circadian rhythms

1b. The circadian rhythm has been disrupted by the difference in time between the starting point and destination.

2a. Accept any three: courtship, territoriality, aggression, formation of societies

2b. The evolutionary fitness of animals within a society is increased by the cooperative performance of tasks such as hunting, defense, and guarding young.

3a. by visual, sound, chemical signals, or touch

3b. Animals usually communicate in ways that can be detected with those of their sense organs that are most acute. For example, if an animal has well-developed ears, you can infer that the animal communicates with sounds.

4. Big idea Answers may vary. An animal that is injured by a predator may be unable to maintain a territory and unable to reproduce. An animal that is especially adept at vocalizing to attract a mate may be able to mate more frequently.

CHAPTER LAB

Pre-Lab

Introduce students to the concepts they will explore in the chapter lab by assigning the Pre-Lab questions.

Lab

Tell students they will perform the chapter lab *Termite Tracks* described in **Lab Manual A**.

L1 Struggling Students A simpler version of the chapter lab is provided in **Lab Manual B**.

SAFETY

Make sure students handle the termites with care.

 Look online for **Editable Lab Worksheets.**

For corresponding pre-lab in the **Foundation Edition**, see page 705.

see page 705

Design Your Own Lab

OPEN-ENDED INQUIRY

IN NoS.2 Explanations based on data.

Pre-Lab: Termite Tracks

Problem How can you determine the type of stimulus that triggers a particular response?

Materials petri dishes, paper, scissors, termites, small paintbrushes, forceps, ballpoint pens, rollerball pens, felt-tip pens

Lab Manual Chapter 29 Lab

Skills Focus Form a Hypothesis, Design an Experiment, Draw Conclusions

Connect to the Big idea Animals react to their environments as they search for food, avoid predators, and look for a mate. The survival of a species can depend on these behaviors. Some behaviors are inherited and evolve over time due to natural selection. Over many generations, behaviors that help animals survive spread through a population. Behaviors that are not adaptive become less common. In this lab, you will observe an inherited behavior of termites. Then you will design an experiment to determine the type of stimulus that triggers the behavior.

Background Questions

a. Review How is a behavior usually defined?

b. Explain How do innate behaviors, or instincts, help animals survive?

c. Infer You see an ant walk across the ground. A minute later, you see another ant walk in the same exact line. What type of communication do you think is taking place?

Pre-Lab Questions

Preview the procedure in the lab manual.

1. Control Variables Why do you think the instructions ask you to draw a figure eight rather than a straight line?

2. Draw Conclusions How will you decide whether a termite has a positive reaction, a negative reaction, or no reaction to a stimulus?

3. Predict Read pages 850–851 of your textbook. Which of the signals described could be a stimulus for the termite in this lab? Explain your answer.

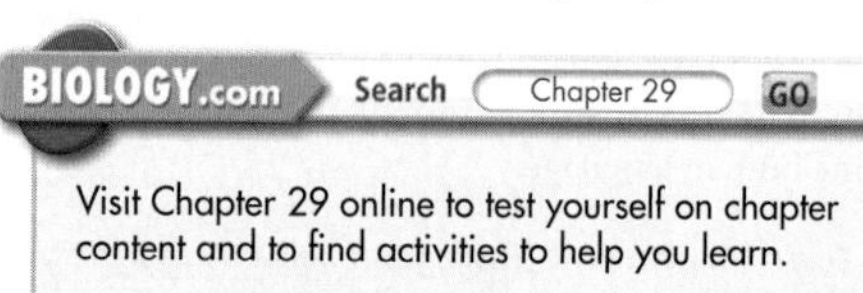

Visit Chapter 29 online to test yourself on chapter content and to find activities to help you learn.

Untamed Science Video See how the latest technologies help the explorers from Untamed Science track the movements of different animals.

Data Analysis See how researchers improve understanding of animal migration behavior by improving data collection technology.

Tutor Tube Instinct? Sorting out everyday and scientific behavior terms.

Art Review Identify animal communications strategies.

Art in Motion Watch social behavior in a population.

IN INDIANA ACADEMIC STANDARDS

For the full text of all standards, see the Course Overview in the front matter of this book.

Pre-Lab Answers

BACKGROUND QUESTIONS

a. A behavior is usually defined as the way an organism reacts to stimuli in its environment.

b. Sample answer: Innate behaviors allow animals to perform tasks that are essential for survival without having to learn the task.

c. Sample answer: The ants are using chemical signals, or pheromones, to mark the path.

PRE-LAB QUESTIONS

1. Sample answer: With the figure eight, it will be easier to tell whether the termite is responding to the drawn path.

2. Sample answer: I will classify a positive reaction as movement towards the stimulus, a negative reaction as movement away from the stimulus, and no reaction as no obvious change in movement.

3. Sample answer: The termite could respond to a visual signal or a chemical signal.

29 Study Guide

Big idea Evolution

Animal behavior may be innate, learned, or a combination of both. An animal's behavior is affected by other organisms and changes in its environment.

29.1 Elements of Behavior

If a behavior that is influenced by genes increases an individual's fitness, that behavior will tend to spread through a population. Over many generations, various kinds of adaptive behaviors can play central roles in the survival of populations and species.

Innate behaviors appear in fully functional form the first time they are performed, even though the animal has had no previous experience with the stimuli to which it responds. Innate behaviors are also called instincts.

The four major types of learning are habituation, classical conditioning, operant conditioning, and insight learning.

Many complex behaviors combine innate behavior with learning.

behavior (840)
innate behavior (841)
learning (842)
habituation (842)
classical conditioning (843)
operant conditioning (843)
insight learning (843)
imprinting (844)

29.2 Animals in Their Environments

Many animals respond to periodic changes in the environment with daily or seasonal cycles of behavior.

Choosing mates, defending or claiming territories or resources, and forming social groups can increase evolutionary fitness.

Animals may use a variety of signals to communicate with one another. Some animals are also capable of language.

circadian rhythm (847)
migration (847)
courtship (848)
territory (848)
aggression (848)
society (848)
kin selection (849)
communication (850)
language (851)

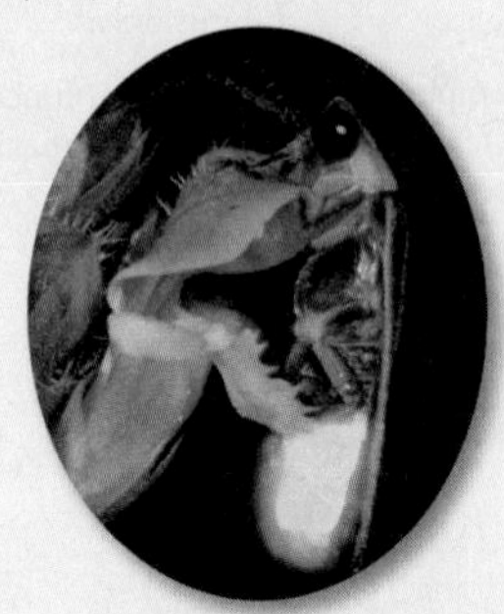

Think Visually Using information from this chapter, complete the following concept map:

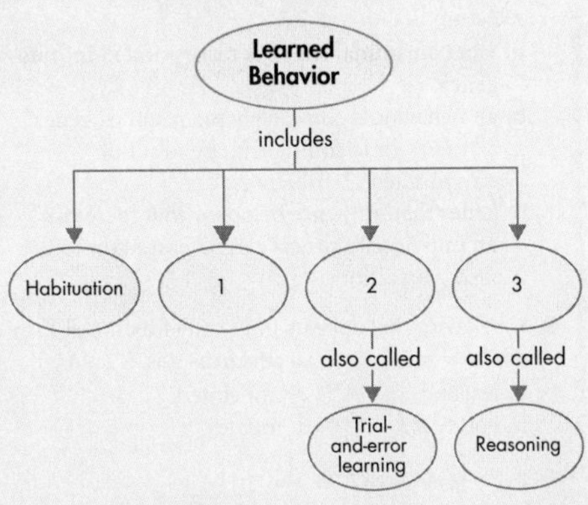

Study Online

REVIEW AND ASSESSMENT RESOURCES

Editable Worksheets Pages of Study Workbooks A and B, Lab Manuals A and B, and the Assessment Resources Book are available online. These documents can be easily edited using a word-processing program.

Lesson Overview Have students reread the Lesson Overviews to help them study chapter concepts.

Vocabulary Review The *Flash Cards* and *Crossword* provide an interactive way to review chapter vocabulary.

Chapter Assessment Have students take an online version of the Chapter 29 Assessment.

Standardized Test Prep Students can take an online version of the Standardized Test Prep. You will receive their scores along with ideas for remediation.

Diagnostic and Benchmark Tests Use these tests to monitor your students' progress and supply remediation.

Answers

THINK VISUALLY

1. Classical conditioning
2. Operant conditioning
3. Insight learning

UbD Performance Tasks

SUMMATIVE TASK Have students work in small groups to create a game demonstrating how behavior helps animals survive. The game should include several different kinds of animals and the behaviors discussed in the chapter. An animal that exhibits a behavior that enhances survival advances through the game, while an animal that fails to do so may go backward or die (be taken out of the game). Students may design game boards and game pieces that reflect different ecosystems, such as an African savannah, South American rain forest, or American prairie. Have each group demonstrate its game to the class, explaining the behaviors and their adaptive significance. Have the other students give feedback on the game. Discuss any problems or misconceptions students have about animal behaviors.

TRANSFER TASK Ask students to imagine that they are zookeepers. Insofar as possible, they want to enable zoo animals to behave as if they were in their natural environment. Each student should choose one zoo animal and write a plan for how the zoo could best accommodate the animal's natural behaviors, such as circadian rhythms, territoriality, and imprinting. Students can use library or the Internet to research the behavior of the animal they choose.

ASSESSMENT

Lesson 29.1

UNDERSTAND KEY CONCEPTS

1. a **2.** c **3.** b **4.** b

5. d **6.** d

7. Sample answer: A dog turns its head in response to a noise.

8. Senses detect a stimulus and pass the information to the brain. The brain interprets the information and directs the body's response.

9. Habituation enables animals to ignore irrelevant stimuli, thus conserving energy for real threats.

10. Pavlov rang a bell and at the same time offered food to a dog. After awhile, he rang the bell without feeding the dog, and the dog salivated in response. This is called classical conditioning.

11. Operant conditioning occurs when an animal learns to behave in a certain way through practice, to receive a reward or avoid punishment.

THINK CRITICALLY

12. Operant conditioning; smiling is reinforced by the reward of cuddling.

13. Horses are bred for desirable characteristics but can be conditioned, or trained, over time.

14. The three questions should address the animal's behavior. Observations might include interactions with other animals or responses to certain stimuli.

Lesson 29.2

UNDERSTAND KEY CONCEPTS

15. d **16.** a **17.** a **18.** b

19. No; migration is seasonal movement from one environment to another. The movement of these animals had nothing to do with changing seasons.

20. Sample answer: If a group searches for food, it is more likely to find it than if an individual searches; a large group is safer from predators than an individual is.

21. Animals exhibit aggression or threatening behaviors to establish a territory and defend it when a rival tries to claim it.

22. Pheromones are chemical messengers that are released by an animal and affect the behavior of other animals of the same species. Pheromones are used to mark territories.

23. Kin selection is a behavior in which individuals help relatives, with whom they share a large proportion of their genes. This behavior can improve the evolutionary fitness of the individual.

THINK CRITICALLY

24. a. The squirrel's body temperature fluctuates during winter months and is stable in warmer months.

b. In winter, it is in a state of dormancy.

25. Sample answer: Solitary animals have less competition for resources and are less conspicuous to predators.

29 Assessment

The numbers following the questions refer to Indiana's Academic Standards for Biology I.

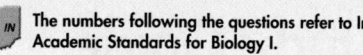

29.1 Elements of Behavior

Understand Key Concepts

1. The way an organism reacts to stimuli in its environment is called
a. behavior. **c.** conditioning.
b. learning. **d.** imprinting.

2. A decrease in response to a stimulus that neither rewards nor harms an animal is called
a. instinct.
b. operant conditioning.
c. habituation.
d. classical conditioning.

3. Insight learning is common among
a. dogs. **c.** birds and insects.
b. primates. **d.** birds only.

4. Many complex behaviors combine innate behavior with learning. Which of these behaviors is shown below?

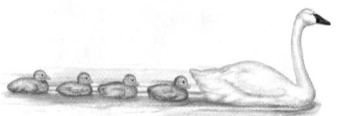

a. insight learning
b. imprinting
c. classical conditioning
d. operant conditioning

5. Animal behaviors can evolve through natural selection because B.8.5
a. what an animal learns is incorporated into its genes.
b. all behavior is completely the result of genes.
c. all behavior is completely the result of environmental influences.
d. genes that influence behavior that increases an individual's fitness can be passed on to the next generation.

6. A behavior that appears in its fully functional form the first time an animal performs it is
a. learned. **c.** imprinted.
b. habituated. **d.** innate.

7. Describe an example of a stimulus and a corresponding response in animal behavior.

8. What is the brain's role in an animal's response to a stimulus?

9. How can habituation contribute to an animal's survival? B.8.5

10. Describe Pavlov's experiment. What is this type of learning called?

11. What is operant conditioning?

Think Critically

12. Infer A baby smiles when her mother comes near. Often, the baby is picked up and cuddled as a result of smiling. Explain what type of learning the baby is showing.

13. Apply Concepts Explain how a racehorse's ability to win races is a combination of inherited and learned behaviors.

14. Pose Questions Choose a kind of animal with which you are familiar. Think of three questions about that animal's behavior that you might ask. Then describe the observations you would need to make in order to answer the questions.

29.2 Animals in Their Environments

Understand Key Concepts

15. A threatening behavior with which an animal exerts dominance over another is
a. migration. **c.** habituation.
b. courtship. **d.** aggression.

16. Each year, a bird called the American redstart travels from its winter home in South America to its nesting area in New York. This behavior is called
a. migration. **c.** imprinting.
b. competition. **d.** courtship.

17. Which of the following is NOT a type of social behavior?
a. operant conditioning
b. territoriality
c. hunting in a pack
d. courtship

854 Chapter 29 • Assessment

18. A system of communication that uses meaningful sounds, symbols, or gestures according to specific rules is called
   a. behavior.
   b. language.
   c. competition.
   d. a signature.

19. Because a highway has been constructed through a forest, many of the animals that once lived there have had to move to a different wooded area. Is their move an example of migration? Explain your answer.

20. Identify two ways in which social behavior can benefit an animal. B.8.5

21. Explain how aggression and territorial behavior are related.

22. What are pheromones? Give an example of how they are used.

23. What is kin selection?

Think Critically

24. **Interpret Graphs** When temperatures are low and food is scarce, some mammals enter into a state of dormancy. Dormancy is an energy-saving adaptation in which metabolism decreases and, therefore, body temperature declines. The graph below tracks a ground squirrel's body temperature over the course of a year.
   a. Describe the pattern that you observe.
   b. What can you infer about the squirrel's behavior at different times of the year?

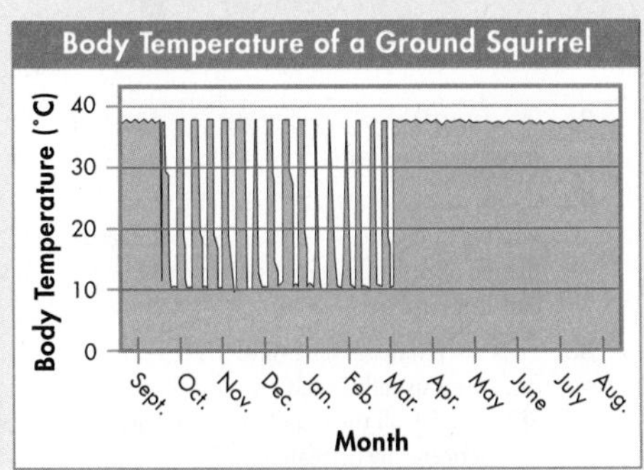

25. **Form a Hypothesis** Although the members of many animal species derive benefits from living in social groups, members of other species live alone. What might be some of the advantages of solitary living? B.8.5

solve the CHAPTER MYSTERY

ELEPHANT CALLER ID?

Elephants can communicate with loud calls. But they can also communicate with vibrations that can travel for several kilometers. They do so by drumming on the ground with their feet and by making low rumbling calls that contain very low frequency sounds called "infrasound." The air vibrations can travel up to 16 kilometers while the in-ground vibrations can travel up to 32 kilometers.

Elephants detect these vibrations with specialized pads of fat in their feet and receptor cells in their feet and trunks. By standing motionless and pressing their feet and trunks to the ground, the elephants are better able to sense the vibrations. Particular patterns of vibrations can even identify individuals—like caller ID for elephants!

The vibrations can contain greetings, locations of food, and warnings of danger. The elephants at the watering hole had detected a message from another herd of elephants far away: "Warning! Lions!"

1. **Compare and Contrast** How do vibrations in the ground compare with airborne sounds as a means of long-distance communication?
2. **Form a Hypothesis** When researchers play back sounds and vibrations from elephant groups living far from Etosha, the elephants in Etosha don't always react. Why might this be the case?
3. **Connect to the Big idea** How do elephants' responses to low-frequency vibrations in their environment affect their survival?

 B.8.5

ASSESSMENT

After students have read through the Chapter Mystery, discuss social behavior, communication, and how these aspects of animal behavior are important to evolutionary fitness.

Ask How does living in a society benefit an elephant? *(Elephants help one another survive. They help one another hunt, protect their territory and its resources, protect the young, and defend against predators.)*

Ask What is kin selection? *(Kin selection is the theory that living with and helping a group of related individuals to survive can increase one's own fitness because genes are shared among related individuals in the group.)*

Ask How is communication related to an elephant's ability to survive? *(Elephants warn each other when there is danger.)*

CHAPTER MYSTERY ANSWERS

1. Ground vibrations are more effective than air vibrations as a means of long-distance communication because ground vibrations travel about twice as far.
2. Sample answer: Since the groups are separated by a long distance, they are probably not related and have developed some different signals to use in communication.
3. Big idea Elephants' responses to low-frequency vibrations help them survive possible attack by predators by allowing them to leave an area before the predators arrive.

To learn about how scientists use remote sensing to study animal behavior, have students watch **Untamed Science Video: When Animals Go Digital.**

ASSESSMENT

Connecting Concepts

USE SCIENCE GRAPHICS

26. By trial 8, the mice have learned how to get through the maze as fast as possible with the fewest wrong turns. They take about 10 seconds, though the time varies a bit between the first and second series of trials.

27. Sample answer: Will the time it takes the mice to run the maze stay the same? Will the time improve (decrease)? Will the time be poorer (increase)?

28. After one month, the mice remember something about how to get through the maze, but they need several trials to relearn the details.

WRITE ABOUT SCIENCE

29. Student paragraphs should give an accurate example of insight learning, which occurs when a person has applied something he or she has already learned to a new situation, without a period of trial and error.

30. Big idea Students will have a variety of answers that may include courtship, competition, aggression, communication, or territoriality. Answers should focus on how the behavior helps to garner resources, procure mates, protect young, and defend against predation.

Connecting Concepts

Use Science Graphics NoS.3

Mice can learn to run through a maze to find a food reward. As they have more practice runs in the maze, they take fewer wrong turns and reach the food more quickly. Twelve mice are put in a maze once a day for 10 days. The mean of their times to reach the food is calculated and plotted as the red line below. The mice are then kept out of the maze for a month. The blue line shows the results of those later trials. Use the graph to answer questions 26–28.

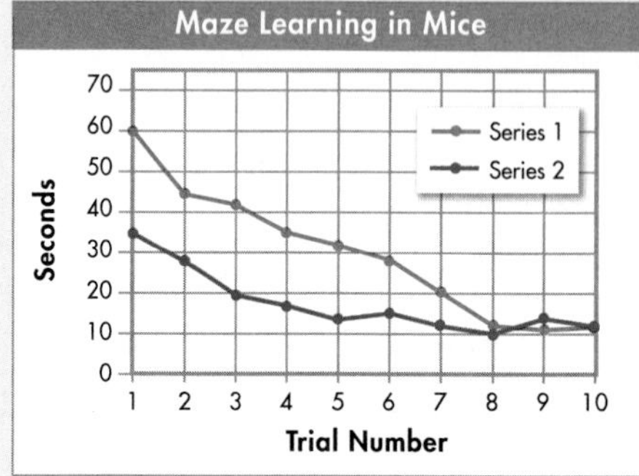

26. Interpret Graphs Explain what is happening after trial 8 on both sets of trials.

27. Pose Questions After the first set of trials, what kinds of questions might the experimenters have asked that resulted in their performing the second set of trials?

28. Draw Conclusions Explain the difference in the shapes of the graphs of the two trials.

Write About Science NoS.3

29. Description Write a paragraph describing something you have learned by insight learning. Explain how you used past knowledge and experience in learning it. (*Hint:* In your paragraph, explain what insight learning is.)

30. Assess the Big idea Choose a social behavior in an animal. Describe how the behavior represents a response to the environment that aids in the survival of the species. B.8.5

Analyzing Data

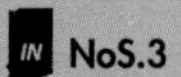 NoS.3

A researcher found that the likelihood that a duckling would imprint depended on its age. After hatching, ducklings were kept isolated for different lengths of time and then placed with an adult duck. The imprinting data appear in this table.

Age (in hours)	Percent Successful Imprints
2	0
6	0
12	15
15	50
18	20
24	0
28	0

31. Interpret Tables At what age is a duckling most likely to imprint?

32. Draw Conclusions Based on this data, what is one general conclusion that can be drawn about the ages at which ducklings can imprint?

33. Infer In a natural setting, all the eggs in a duck nest usually hatch within a few hours. Shortly after all the ducklings have hatched, and periodically thereafter, the mother duck will lead them all to a food source and then back to the nest to rest. Given this situation, which ducklings are most likely to imprint on their mother?

PURPOSE Students will analyze data to understand the critical period for imprinting.

PLANNING Have students read about imprinting under the head **Complex Behaviors.**

ANSWERS

31. 15 hours

32. Ducklings imprint from 12 to 18 hours of age.

33. Ducklings that are 10–18 hours old will be most successful at imprinting during this first walk. However, eventually all the ducklings will imprint, because the mother duck will repeatedly lead the group, and at some point within the critical time period, all the ducklings will see and follow her.

Standardized Test Practice for Indiana

Multiple Choice

1. A rat that learns to press a button to get food is exhibiting
   A insight learning. C classical conditioning.
   B operant conditioning. D habituation.

2. A dog that always salivates at the ringing of a bell is exhibiting
   A insight learning. C classical conditioning.
   B operant conditioning. D habituation.

3. A chimpanzee that stacks boxes in order to reach a banana hanging from the ceiling is showing
   A insight learning. C classical conditioning.
   B operant conditioning. D habituation.

4. A bird that stops responding to a repeated warning call when the call is not followed by an attack is showing
   A insight learning. C classical conditioning.
   B operant conditioning. D habituation.

5. Which kind of behavior does NOT involve learning?
   A habituation C imprinting
   B trial and error D instinct

6. A male three-spined stickleback fish will attack male red-bellied sticklebacks and models of fishes that have a red underside. It will not attack males or models lacking a red underside. What can you conclude from the three-spined stickleback's behavior?
   A The stimulus for an attack is a red underside.
   B The stimulus for an attack is aggression.
   C The stimulus for an attack is the presence of a fish with red fins.
   D The stimulus for an attack is the presence of a fish model.

7. Which of the following is NOT an innate behavior?
   A a dog looking for its food dish
   B a baby mammal sucking milk
   C a worm moving away from bright light
   D a spider spinning a web

Questions 8–9

A researcher observed sedge warblers during breeding season. She charted the number of different songs a male bird sang compared to the time it took him to pair with a mate. The graph shows her data.

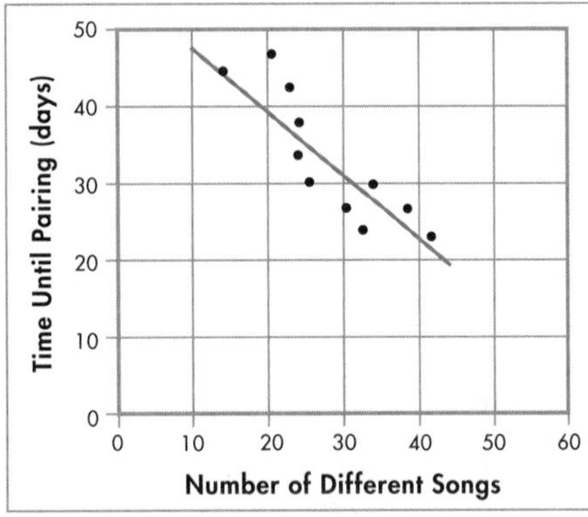

8. The researcher was trying to find out whether there is a correlation between
   A the number of a male bird's songs and the number of offspring.
   B the number of a male bird's songs and his attractiveness to females.
   C a male's age and when he mates.
   D a female's age and when she mates. NoS.3

9. What can you conclude based on the graph?
   A Males prefer females that do not sing.
   B Females prefer males that do not sing.
   C Males prefer females with a larger number of songs.
   D Females prefer males with a larger number of songs. NoS.3

Open-Ended Response

10. How does defending a specific territory benefit an animal? B.8.5

If You Have Trouble With . . .										
Question	1	2	3	4	5	6	7	8	9	10
See Lesson	29.1	29.1	29.1	29.1	29.1	29.1	29.1	29.2	29.2	29.2

Answers

1. B
2. C
3. A
4. D
5. D
6. A
7. A
8. B
9. D
10. Defending a territory reduces competition for resources within the territory, such as food, water, and shelter, and helps to ensure survival for the one defending the area and its offspring.

Test-Taking Tip

INTERPRET GRAPHS

Advise students that when they are asked to analyze a graph showing experimental data, they should look at the shape of the line first. Students should ask themselves what trend the line shows. Students should then identify the variables that are plotted on each axis. Finally, students should determine how the variables are related. To help students practice interpreting graphs, provide the class with copies of different kinds of graphs. As a group, discuss what the graphs show and how they should be interpreted.

Plan Ahead

Have students preview the Unit 7 Project a few days before they begin work on their exhibit. Suggest they "visit" zoos online, especially to see how exhibits have been designed to display a wide variety of animals. Consider having students work in small groups. Individual students can take responsibility for creating an exhibit of a particular group of animals, and then work with other group members to show similarities and differences among the animal groups.

Materials poster board, modeling clay, materials for papier-mâché, aluminum foil, cardboard, toothpicks, string, yarn, tape, glue, colored markers, additional art materials

Monitor the Project

Suggest students or groups begin their exhibit design by making lists of animal groups, specific animals, and life processes that should be included in the exhibit. As students work, ask groups or individuals questions that will help them organize and design their exhibits.

Ask What examples of animals are you including in your exhibit to represent different animal groups?

Ask How are you showing similarities and differences in the ways animals carry out basic life processes?

Project Assessment

Make sure students use the rubric and reflection questions to assess their work. Then, use the rubric to assign a final score. Note that it is important to value the creativity of students' work as well as the content when you score their projects. If desired, talk with students about any differences between their self-assessment scores and your assigned score.

Unit Project

Zoo Exhibit

Have you ever been to the zoo? Going to the zoo is a great way to see and learn about living things from around the world. Imagine you work for a zoo in your local city and have been asked to set up a new exhibit entitled *The Diversity of Animals.*

Your Task Design an exhibit that highlights the different groups of animals in the animal kingdom and their characteristics.

Be sure to

- show the differences in shapes and forms of animals.
- show the similarities/differences in the ways in which groups of animals carry out basic life processes (circulation, respiration, excretion, movement, response, feeding).
- design the exhibit so that it is clear and engaging.

Reflection Questions

1. **Score your exhibit using the rubric below. What score did you give yourself?**
2. **What did you do well in this project?**
3. **What needs improvement?**
4. **What aspects of another group's exhibit did you like? Why?**

Assessment Rubric

Score	Scientific Content	Quality of Exhibit
4	Exhibit reveals a thorough understanding of animals and the ways they carry out life processes.	Exhibit is very organized, educational, and engaging to visitors.
3	Exhibit reveals an adequate understanding of animals and the ways they carry out life processes.	Exhibit is organized and clear, but it could be more engaging to visitors.
2	Exhibit reveals a limited understanding of animals and the ways they carry out life processes.	Exhibit needs improvement in clarity and organization. It is somewhat engaging.
1	Exhibit reveals significant misunderstandings about animals and the ways they carry out life processes.	Exhibit is very unclear and disorganized. It is not engaging.

21st Century Skills

To be successful in the 21st century, students need skills and learning experiences that extend beyond subject area mastery. The Unit 7 Project helps students build the following 21st Century Skills: *Communication Skills; Critical Thinking and Systems Thinking; Creativity and Intellectual Curiosity; Self-Direction;* and *Accountability and Adaptability.*

FOCUS ON INTERPERSONAL AND COLLABORATIVE SKILLS Extend this Unit Project by having small groups of students work together to design a contemporary zoo in which the animals are kept and exhibited responsibly. Ask students to discuss how representative animals from each of the major animal groups could be responsibly kept in captivity in ways that would allow them to thrive.

For more practice building 21st Century Skills, see The Chapter Mystery pages in **Study Workbook A.**

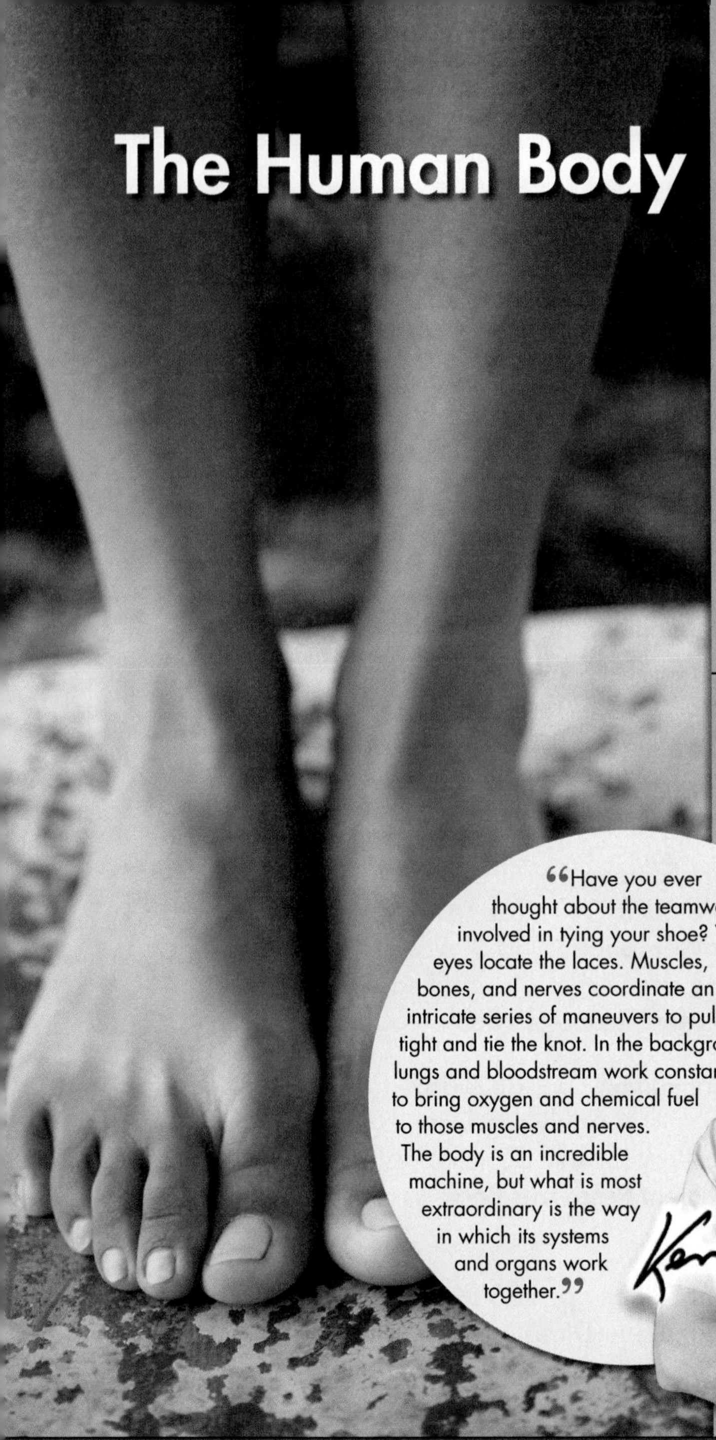

The Human Body

UNIT 8

Chapters

30 Digestive and Excretory Systems

31 Nervous System

32 Skeletal, Muscular, and Integumentary Systems

33 Circulatory and Respiratory Systems

34 Endocrine and Reproductive Systems

35 Immune System and Disease

INTRODUCE the Big ideas

- **Homeostasis**
- **Structure and Function**

"Have you ever thought about the teamwork involved in tying your shoe? Your eyes locate the laces. Muscles, bones, and nerves coordinate an intricate series of maneuvers to pull them tight and tie the knot. In the background, lungs and bloodstream work constantly to bring oxygen and chemical fuel to those muscles and nerves. The body is an incredible machine, but what is most extraordinary is the way in which its systems and organs work together."

Ken Miller

859

Dear Colleague,

I still remember how it happened. I saw one of my teammates, took a step back, and looped a perfect pass over a defender right into his arms. It was only a touch football game, but it felt great to watch the ball spiral through the air—except for one little thing. One of guys on the other team tried to block the pass, and even though he failed, his arm collided with my wrist as I followed though.

It didn't hurt much at first. That night, I had to take a couple of aspirin tablets to dull the pain. But in the morning, I couldn't even move the hand. I had broken my navicular, a small bone in the palm just below the thumb. As he wrapped a cast around my hand, the doctor warned me that the navicular heals slowly. "Say goodbye to your hand," he said. "You won't see it for four months."

Unfortunately, he was right. But, during those four months, the most amazing things happened. The pain—my nervous system's warning that something was broken—subsided. Bone cells tore up the matrix on both sides of the break, and then began to lay down a new matrix joining both parts of the bone back together. The digestive system extracted calcium from my food, while the endocrine and excretory systems made sure that the right amount of that calcium was put into the circulatory system. My skeletal system used the calcium, together with phosphate, to build a new bone matrix. In short, the body healed itself. Even my nervous and muscular systems adjusted, getting used to the extra weight from the cast on my right hand.

Homeostasis is a complex process, but at its core is a simple idea. The body takes care of itself. It adjusts to changes in the environment, manages adversity, keeps things on an even keel, and finally, as I found out when the cast came off, it can even heal itself. If we can teach these things to our students, we can help them learn to appreciate one of the most remarkable things about their lives—the wonder of the human body and the role that homeostasis plays in keeping us alive.

Ken Miller

CHAPTER PLANNER 30 Digestive and Excretory Systems

Chapter Contents	IN	Time	Core Resources
Chapter Preview			**Student Edition,** pp. 860–861 **Chapter Mystery,** p. 861
30.1 Organization of the Human Body Organization of the Human Body • Homeostasis		1 period $^1/_2$ block	**Student Edition,** pp. 862–867 Inquiry 30.1 Quick Lab, p. 866 L2 **Study Workbook A** 30.1 Worksheets L2 Biology.com *Art Review:* Human Body Systems • *Tutor Tube:* Working Together to Stay Balanced • 30.1 Self-Test • 30.1 Lesson Assessment
30.2 Food and Nutrition Food and Energy • Nutrients • Nutrition and a Balanced Diet • *Biology & Society: Who Should Solve America's Obesity Problem?*	B.1.1, B.1.2	$^1/_2$ period $^1/_4$ block	**Student Edition,** pp. 868–874 **Study Workbook A** 30.2 Worksheets L2 Biology.com *Data Analysis:* Balance Your Virtual Diet • 30.2 Self-Test • 30.2 Lesson Assessment
30.3 The Digestive System Functions of the Digestive System • The Process of Digestion • Absorption and Elimination	B.5.5	2 periods 1 block	**Student Edition,** pp. 875–881 Inquiry 30.3 Quick Lab, p. 878 L2 **Study Workbook A** 30.3 Worksheets L2 Biology.com *Art in Motion:* Peristalsis **Assessment Resources Book** Visual Quiz L2
30.4 The Excretory System Structures of the Excretory System • Excretion and the Kidneys • The Kidneys and Homeostasis	NoS.3	$1^1/_2$ periods $^3/_4$ block	**Student Edition,** pp. 882–887 Inquiry 30.4 Analyzing Data, p. 883 L2 **Study Workbook A** 30.4 Worksheets L2 **Assessment Resources Book** Visual Quiz L2
Chapter Pre-Lab		1 period $^1/_2$ block	**Student Edition,** p. 888 L2 **Lab Manual A** *Digestion of Dairy Products* L2 • *Reducing Excess Gas* L2

Differentiated Instruction Tools

Study Workbook B includes worksheets with lesson-level differentiated instruction support and explanations of differentiated instruction teaching strategies.

Lab Manual B includes skills labs, simplified chapter labs, and hands-on activities.

ELL Handbook explains ways to make *Biology* more accessible to ELL students.

Spanish Study Workbook is a Spanish translation of Study Workbook A.

Multilingual Glossary is the glossary translated into ten languages.

Differentiated Instruction Key

- L1 Special Needs or Struggling Students
- ELL English Language Learners
- LPR Less Proficient Readers
- L2 On-Level Students
- L3 Advanced Students

Additional Resources

Biology.com Untamed Science Video • Vocabulary Flash Cards

Study Workbook B 30.1 Worksheets L1 ELL LPR
Spanish Study Workbook 30.1 Worksheets ELL
Biology.com 30.1 Lesson Overview • 30.1 Lesson Notes

Study Workbook B 30.2 Worksheets L1 ELL LPR
Spanish Study Workbook 30.2 Worksheets ELL
Biology.com 30.2 Lesson Overview • 30.2 Lesson Notes

Study Workbook B 30.3 Worksheets L1 ELL LPR
Spanish Study Workbook 30.3 Worksheets ELL
Biology.com 30.3 Lesson Overview • 30.3 Lesson Notes • 30.3 Self-Test • 30.3 Lesson Assessment

Study Workbook B 30.4 Worksheets L1 ELL LPR
Spanish Study Workbook 30.4 Worksheets ELL
Biology.com 30.4 Lesson Overview • 30.4 Lesson Notes • 30.4 Self-Test • 30.4 Lesson Assessment

Lab Manual B *Digestion of Dairy Products* • Hands-On Activity: *Maintaining Temperature* • Data Analysis: *The American Diet* L1 ELL LPR

Chapter Review

Student Edition Study Guide, p. 889 L2
Study Workbook A Chapter 30 Vocabulary Review L2 • Chapter 30 Chapter Mystery/21st Century Skills Activity L2 L3
Transparencies, pp. 332–341 L1 ELL LPR L2
Biology.com Untamed Science Video • Editable Worksheets of Study Workbooks A and B and Lab Manuals A and B • Chapter 30 Flash Cards and Match It

Untamed Science DVD • Classroom Resources CD (includes lesson presentations and editable worksheets)

Chapter Assessment

Student Edition Assessment, pp. 890–893 L2
Study Workbook B Chapter 30 Chapter Review L1 ELL LPR • Chapter 30 Taking a Standardized Test L1 ELL LPR
Assessment Resources Book Chapter 30 Test A L2 • Chapter 30 Test B L1 ELL LPR
Biology.com Chapter 30 Assessment • Editable Worksheets of Chapter 30 Visual Quizzes and Chapter 30 Tests A and B

Exam*View Assessment Suite* • Classroom Resources CD (includes lesson presentations and editable worksheets)

Time: 1 period, 1/2 block

Pressed for Time?

Preview the Chapter Preview Figures 30–1 and 30–15, and have students read the first Key Question for Lesson 30.4.

Cover the Chapter Quickly Have students read *Organization of the Human Body* in Lesson 30.1, all of Lesson 30.3, and *Structures of the Excretory System* in Lesson 30.4.

Assess Assign question 1 in the 30.1 Assessment, the 30.3 Assessment, and question 1 in the 30.4 Assessment. In the Chapter 30 Assessment, assign questions 1, 3, 5, 6, 14–21, 23, 24, and 31.

Connect to the Big Idea

Big idea Use the photograph of the floating food market to help students connect to concepts they will learn in this chapter. Point out that the human diet varies greatly from one region of the world to another, but all people require the same basic nutrients—water, carbohydrates, proteins, fats, vitamins, and minerals—for energy and materials to maintain homeostasis. Ask students what the photograph indicates about the diet of people living in this part of India. *(Sample answer: They seem to eat a great variety of vegetables and fruits.)* Then, ask them to identify foods that are missing from the picture that would be found at a typical American food market. *(Sample answers: dairy products, meats, bread)* Ask students to anticipate the answer to the question, **How are the materials that enter and leave your body related to the processes that maintain homeostasis?** Have them explain why it is important that the body maintain a stable internal environment.

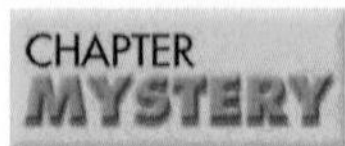

Have students read over the Chapter Mystery and predict how a urine sample could be used to learn about health and behavior. Help students connect the overlying concept of the Chapter Mystery—the relationship between materials that enter the body and those that leave the body—with the Big Idea of Homeostasis.

BIOLOGY.com Have students preview the chapter vocabulary terms using the **Flash Cards.**

INDIANA ACADEMIC STANDARDS

For the full text of all standards, see the Course Overview in the front matter of this book.

Key standards: Chapter 30 covers key ideas from Standard 1: Cellular Chemistry, including **B.1.2** Molecules and cellular processes.

30 Digestive and Excretory Systems

Big idea **Homeostasis**

Q: How are the materials that enter and leave your body related to the processes that maintain homeostasis?

Food sellers display their goods at a floating food market on Dal Lake in northern India.

BIOLOGY.com Search Chapter 30 GO • Flash Cards

860

UbD Understanding by Design

The topics covered in Chapter 30—organization of the human body, food and nutrition, the digestive system, and the excretory system—help students master the Unit 8 Enduring Understanding: *The human body is a complex system. The coordinated functions of its many structures support life processes and maintain homeostasis.* The Big Idea, Essential Question, and Guiding Questions shown in the graphic organizer at right help frame their mastery.

PERFORMANCE GOALS

In Chapter 30, students will use written responses, models, and graphic organizers to show what they have learned about human body organization, food and nutrition, and the digestive and excretory systems. At the end of the chapter, students will synthesize what they have learned to explain how the computer science phrase "garbage in, garbage out" could be applied to the human body.

IN
INDIANA ACADEMIC STANDARDS FOR SCIENCE

Nature of Science NoS.3; **Cellular Chemistry** B.1.1, B.1.2; **Molecular Basis of Heredity** B.5.5. See lessons for details.

CHAPTER MYSTERY

THE TELLTALE SAMPLE

On the first day of summer football practice, all players were required to have a physical. Each student was handed a plastic cup and directed to the restroom. "Please provide me with a sample," the physician requested. The athletes had no idea how much could be learned about their health and behavior from a small urine sample.

Immediately after handing over their samples, Philip and Seth were sent home and told to drink plenty of water before practice the next day. The next day, Andrew was told to see his family physician because he could have diabetes. Several days later, another student was dropped from the team for violating the school's well-known antidrug policy. How was all of this information gained from a urine sample? As you read this chapter, look for clues to help you discover what can be learned about the body by simply examining what leaves it. Solve the mystery.

Never Stop Exploring Your World. Finding the solution to the Telltale Sample mystery is only the beginning. Take a video field trip with the ecogeeks of Untamed Science to see where this mystery leads.

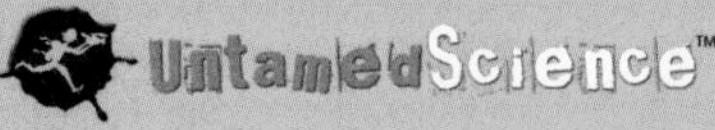

What's Online

BIOLOGY.com Extend your reach by using these and other digital assets offered at Biology.com.

CHAPTER MYSTERY
Follow the mystery to find out the immense amount of information that can be learned about a person's health and behavior from a urine sample.

UNTAMED SCIENCE
The Untamed Science crew gets to the bottom of a stinky mystery: What can we find out about animals from what they leave behind?

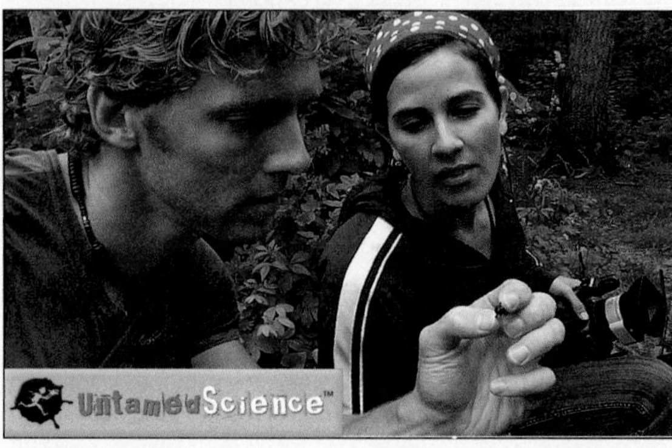

ART REVIEW
Students can drag and drop labels to help them learn about the different structures and functions of human body systems.

TUTOR TUBE
Online tutorials provide information about the nature of human body systems and homeostasis.

DATA ANALYSIS
Students analyze their own calorie and nutritional needs and plan a virtual meal that will help them meet those needs.

ART IN MOTION
Students watch an animation of peristalsis in the esophagus.

Chapter 30 Big Idea: Homeostasis

Chapter 30 EQ: How are the materials that go into your body and the materials that come from your body related to homeostasis?

- **30.1 GQ:** How is the human body organized and regulated?
- **30.2 GQ:** Why are the essential nutrients important?
- **30.3 GQ:** How does the human body convert food into useful molecules?
- **30.4 GQ:** How does the human body get rid of wastes?

LESSON 30.1

Getting Started

Objectives

30.1.1 Describe how the human body is organized.

30.1.2 Explain homeostasis.

Student Resources

Study Workbooks A and B, 30.1 Worksheets

Spanish Study Workbook, 30.1 Worksheets

Lab Manual B, 30.1 Hands-On Activity Worksheet

Lesson Overview • Lesson Notes • Activities: Art Review, Tutor Tube • Assessment: Self-Test, Lesson Assessment

For corresponding lesson in the **Foundation Edition,** see pages 714–718.

Answers

IN YOUR NOTEBOOK Students' tables should list: water, carbohydrates, fats, proteins, vitamins, and minerals; foods in which each is found; and a description of each nutrient's role in the body.

30.1 Organization of the Human Body

Key Questions

How is the human body organized?

What is homeostasis?

Vocabulary

epithelial tissue
connective tissue
nervous tissue
muscle tissue
homeostasis
feedback inhibition

Taking Notes

Preview Visuals Examine **Figure 30–2.** For each system, describe how you think it interacts with at least one other system.

THINK ABOUT IT The batter slaps a ground ball to the shortstop, who fields it cleanly and throws the ball toward your position—first base. In a single motion, you extend your glove hand, catch the ball, and extend your foot to touch the edge of the base. An easy out, a routine play. But think about how many systems of your body are involved in making this type of "routine" play. How do they all work together?

Organization of the Body

How is the human body organized?

Every cell in the human body is both an independent unit and an interdependent part of a larger community—the entire organism. To complete a winning play, a player at first base has to use her eyes to watch the ball and use her brain to figure out how to position her body. With the support of her bones, muscles move her body to first base. Meanwhile, the player's lungs absorb oxygen, which her blood carries to cells for use during cellular respiration. Her brain monitors the location of the ball and sends signals that guide her glove hand to make the catch.

How can so many individual cells and parts work together so efficiently? One way to answer this question is to study the organization of the human body. **The levels of organization in the body include cells, tissues, organs, and organ systems.** At each level of organization, these parts of the body work together to carry out the major body functions.

Cells A cell is the basic unit of structure and function in living things. As you learned in Chapter 7, individual cells in multicellular organisms tend to be specialized. Specialized cells, such as bone cells, blood cells, and muscle cells, are uniquely suited to perform a particular function.

Tissues A group of cells that perform a single function is called a tissue. There are four basic types of tissue in the human body—epithelial, connective, nervous, and muscle. **Figure 30–1** shows examples of each type of tissue.

UbD Teach for Understanding

ENDURING UNDERSTANDING The human body is a complex system. The coordinated functions of its many structures support life processes and maintain homeostasis.

GUIDING QUESTION How is the human body organized and regulated?

EVIDENCE OF UNDERSTANDING *After completing the lesson, give students this assessment to show they understand that the human body is a complex, organized system.* Have students work in small groups. Each group should write and prepare a short presentation in which an individual cell (portrayed by one student) explains how it is part of a tissue, organ, and organ system.

	Epithelial Tissue	Connective Tissue	Nervous Tissue	Muscle Tissue
FUNCTIONS	Protection, absorption, and excretion of materials	Binding of epithelial tissue to structures, support, and transport of substances	Receiving and transmitting nerve impulses	Voluntary and involuntary movements
LOCATIONS	Skin, lining of digestive system, certain glands	Under skin, surrounding organs, blood, bones	Brain, spinal cord, and nerves	Skeletal muscles, muscles surrounding digestive tract and blood vessels, the heart

LM 65× LM 280× SEM 295× LM 275×

FIGURE 30–1 Types of Tissues The four major types of tissues in the human body are epithelial tissue, connective tissue, nervous tissue, and muscle tissue. Predict ***Which organ may not contain all four types of tissue?***

▶ ***Epithelial Tissue*** The tissue that lines the interior and exterior body surfaces is called **epithelial tissue.** Your skin and the lining of your stomach are both examples of epithelial tissue.

▶ ***Connective Tissue*** A type of tissue that provides support for the body and connects its parts is **connective tissue.** This type of tissue includes fat cells, bone cells, and even blood cells. Many connective tissue cells produce collagen, a long, tough fiber-like protein that is the most common protein in the body. Collagen gives tissues strength and resiliency, helping them to keep their shape even under pressure.

▶ ***Nervous Tissue*** Nerve impulses are transmitted throughout the body by **nervous tissue.** Neurons, the cells that carry these impulses, and glial cells, which surround and protect neurons, are both examples of nervous tissue.

▶ ***Muscle Tissue*** Movements of the body are possible because of **muscle tissue.** Some muscles are responsible for the movements you control, such as the muscles that move your arms and legs. Some muscles are responsible for movements you cannot control, such as the tiny muscles that control the size of the pupil in the eye.

Organs A group of different types of tissues that work together to perform a single function or several related functions is called an organ. The eye is an organ made up of epithelial tissue, nervous tissue, muscle tissue, and connective tissue. As different as these tissues are, they all work together for a single function—sight.

Organ Systems An organ system is a group of organs that perform closely related functions. For example, the brain and spinal cord are organs of the nervous system. The organ systems interact to maintain homeostasis in the body as a whole. The organ systems, along with their structures and main functions, are shown on the next page.

Biology In-Depth

TISSUE AND ORGAN TRANSPLANTS

Most people are aware that organs, such as the heart and kidneys, can be transplanted; however, many tissues, such as heart valves, corneas, and parts of bones can also be transplanted. The Food and Drug Administration regulates and monitors tissue transplants, whereas the Health Resources and Services Administration regulates bone marrow and organ transplants.

Although a liver transplant is considered an organ transplant, many times only part of a liver is removed from a deceased or living person and transplanted into the recipient. Unlike other organs, just a section of a healthy liver can regrow into a normal-size liver in the organ recipient. When the liver tissue is taken from a living donor, the donor's liver will regrow to normal size in just weeks.

Teach

Lead a Discussion

Tell students that the words *complex* and *organized* are often used to describe the human body.

Ask What does it mean when someone describes the human body as "complex"? *(Sample answer:* Complex *means "having many interconnected parts," so when the word* complex *is used to describe the human body, it is referring to the fact that the body has many parts that are related to one another.)*

Ask Why is the human body described as "organized"? *(The many parts of the body are organized into systems based on their functions.)*

DIFFERENTIATED INSTRUCTION

L1 Struggling Students Distribute four index cards or slips of paper to each student. Have students label the cards "cells," "tissues," "organs," and "organ systems." On the back of each card, ask students to write a brief definition of the term and list one or two examples from the human body. Then have them arrange the cards in a way that shows how the human body is organized. For example, students might stack the cards in the following order: organ systems, organs, tissues, and cells to show how tissues are made up of cells, organs are made up of tissues, and organ systems are made up of organs. Have each student explain his or her arrangement to a partner. As they work through this lesson, have them continue to add information to their cards.

ELL Focus on ELL: Build Background

BEGINNING AND INTERMEDIATE SPEAKERS

Have students make a three-column chart with column heads "Background," "Questions," and "Predictions." Show students pictures, diagrams, and models of the human body. Talk about these visuals to help students begin building background knowledge on the organization of the human body. Have them take notes on this discussion in the "Background" column of their charts. Then have them record any questions they have about the organization of the body in the "Questions" column. Ask students to look at the figures and headings in this lesson. Have them predict answers to their questions and record these in the "Predictions" column.

Answers

FIGURE 30–1 Sample answer: The brain is an organ that does not contain all four types of tissue.

Teach continued

VISUAL SUMMARY

Make sure students are familiar with all of the human body systems.

Ask What are the main structures of the circulatory system? *(heart, blood vessels, blood)*

Ask What are the functions of the digestive system? *(breaks down food; absorbs nutrients; eliminates wastes)*

Have students work in small groups to review the structures and functions of each of the human body systems. Have groups identify two organ systems that interact with one another and describe how they work together. For example, the respiratory system brings oxygen into the body and the circulatory system transports this oxygen to the rest of the body. Call on each group to describe the two organ systems it selected and explain how the systems interact in the body.

DIFFERENTIATED INSTRUCTION

L1 Special Needs The large amount of information in **Figure 30–2** might overwhelm some students. For these students, go over the information, system by system. Point to each body system and make a simple statement about how that system helps the body function. For example, you might say, "The nervous system helps the body function by sending messages from one part of the body to another." If desired, have students use blank sheets of paper to cover all of the systems you are not discussing.

BIOLOGY.com Students can match organ systems with their main structures and functions by completing the **Art Review: Human Body Systems** activity.

VISUAL SUMMARY

HUMAN BODY SYSTEMS

FIGURE 30–2 Although each of the organ systems shown here has a different set of functions, they all work together, as a whole, to maintain homeostasis.

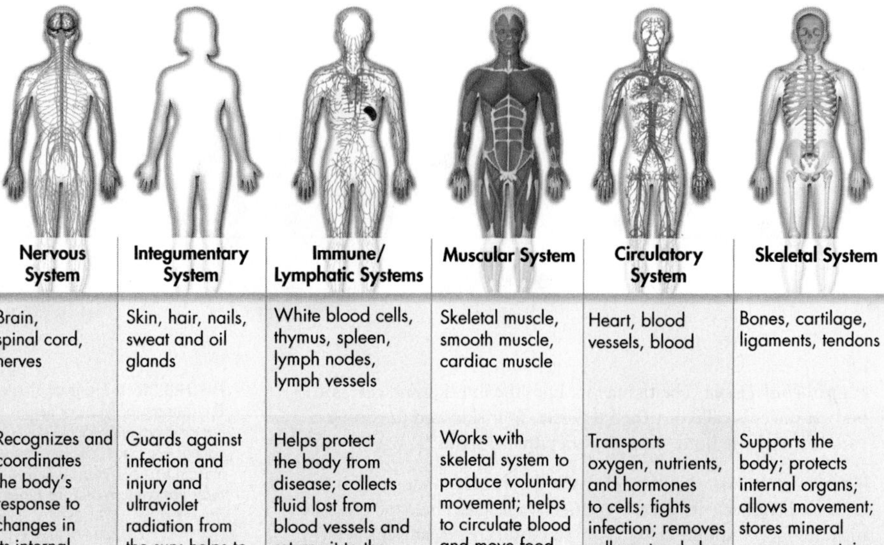

	Nervous System	Integumentary System	Immune/ Lymphatic Systems	Muscular System	Circulatory System	Skeletal System
STRUCTURES	Brain, spinal cord, nerves	Skin, hair, nails, sweat and oil glands	White blood cells, thymus, spleen, lymph nodes, lymph vessels	Skeletal muscle, smooth muscle, cardiac muscle	Heart, blood vessels, blood	Bones, cartilage, ligaments, tendons
FUNCTIONS	Recognizes and coordinates the body's response to changes in its internal and external environments	Guards against infection and injury and ultraviolet radiation from the sun; helps to regulate body temperature	Helps protect the body from disease; collects fluid lost from blood vessels and returns it to the circulatory system	Works with skeletal system to produce voluntary movement; helps to circulate blood and move food through the digestive system	Transports oxygen, nutrients, and hormones to cells; fights infection; removes cell wastes; helps to regulate body temperature	Supports the body; protects internal organs; allows movement; stores mineral reserves; contains cells that produce blood cells

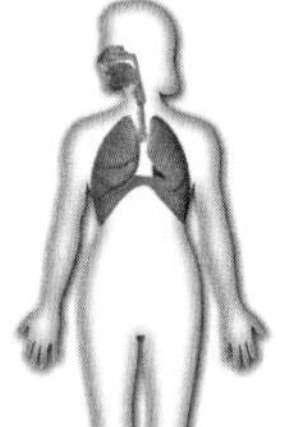
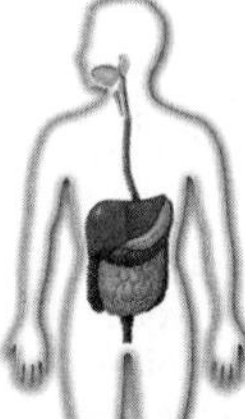
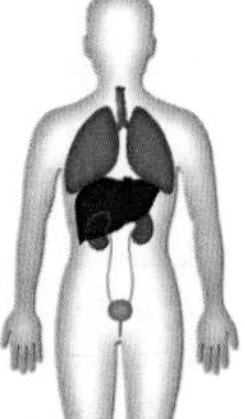
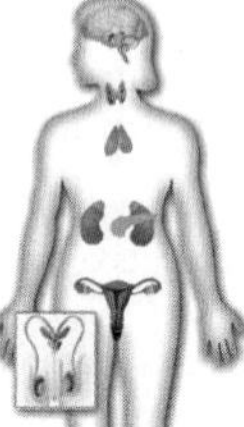
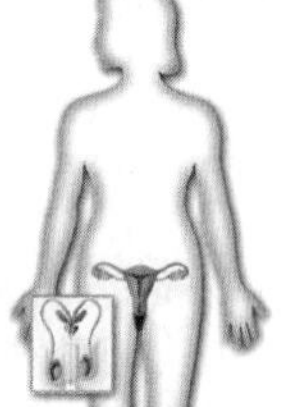

	Respiratory System	Digestive System	Excretory System	Endocrine System	Reproductive System
STRUCTURES	Nose, pharynx, larynx, trachea, bronchi, bronchioles, lungs	Mouth, pharynx, esophagus, stomach, small and large intestines, rectum	Skin, lungs, liver, kidneys, ureters, urinary bladder, urethra	Hypothalamus, pituitary, thyroid, parathyroids, adrenals, pancreas, ovaries (in females), testes (in males)	Testes, epididymis, vas deferens, urethra, and penis (in males); ovaries, Fallopian tubes, uterus, vagina (in females)
FUNCTIONS	Brings in oxygen needed for cellular respiration and removes excess carbon dioxide from the body	Breaks down food; absorbs nutrients; eliminates wastes	Eliminates waste products from the body	Controls growth, development, and metabolism; maintains homeostasis	Produces gametes; in females, nurtures and protects developing embryo

Biology In-Depth

ORGANIZATION OF ANIMAL BODY PLANS

Not all animals have the same types of organ systems. In fact, organ systems with similar functions can take very different forms in different animals. For example, tube worms found near deep-sea hydrothermal vents include species with virtually no digestive system. These worms do not consume food. Instead their digestive tracts consist of only a specialized organ that houses symbiotic chemosynthetic bacteria that produce organic nutrients that fuel the tube worms. In contrast, ruminants, such as cows, have a more complicated digestive system than humans, including a stomach with four distinct compartments. Bacteria that can break down hard-to-digest foods such as hay inhabit parts of their stomachs.

Homeostasis

What is homeostasis?

Some things are easy to observe. When you run or swim or even write the answer to a test question, you can see your body at work. But behind the scenes, your body's systems are working constantly to do something that is difficult to see and that few people appreciate—maintaining a controlled, stable internal environment. This stable environment is called **homeostasis,** which means "similar standing." **Homeostasis describes the relatively constant internal physical and chemical conditions that organisms maintain despite changes in internal and external environments.** Homeostasis may not be obvious, but for a living organism, it's literally a matter of life or death.

Feedback Inhibition If you've ever watched someone driving a car down a relatively straight road, you may have noticed how the person constantly moves the wheel left or right, adjusting direction to keep the vehicle in the middle of the lane. In a certain sense, that's how the systems of the body work, too, keeping internal conditions within a certain range, and never allowing them to go too far to one side or the other.

▶ ***A Nonliving Example*** One way to understand homeostasis is to look at a nonliving system that automatically keeps conditions within a certain range like a home heating system. In most homes, heat is supplied by a furnace that burns oil or natural gas. When the temperature within the house drops below a set point, a thermostat sensor switches the furnace on. Heat produced by the furnace warms the house. When the temperature rises above the set point, the thermostat switches the furnace off, keeping the temperature within a narrow range.

A system like this is said to be controlled by feedback inhibition. **Feedback inhibition,** or negative feedback, is the process in which a stimulus produces a response that opposes the original stimulus. **Figure 30–3** summarizes the feedback inhibition process in a home heating system. When the furnace is switched on, it produces a product (heat) that changes the environment of the house (by raising the air temperature). This environmental change then "feeds back" to "inhibit" the operation of the furnace. In other words, heat from the furnace eventually raises the temperature high enough to trigger a feedback signal that switches the furnace off. Systems controlled by feedback inhibition are generally very stable.

In Your Notebook *Describe another example of a nonliving system that requires constant adjustment.*

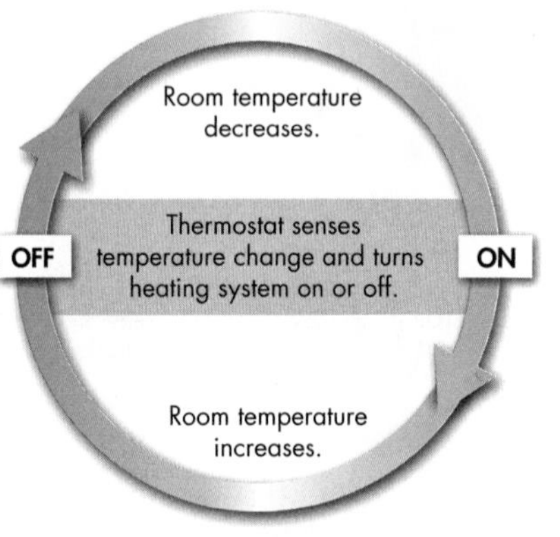
Room temperature decreases.
Thermostat senses temperature change and turns heating system on or off.
OFF
ON
Room temperature increases.

FIGURE 30–3 Feedback Inhibition A home heating system uses a feedback loop to maintain a stable, comfortable environment within a house. Interpret Diagrams ***What is the stimulus in this feedback loop?***

BUILD Vocabulary

ACADEMIC WORDS The noun **inhibition** means "the act of blocking the action of." Therefore, feedback inhibition refers to a response that blocks further actions of a stimulus.

BIOLOGY.com Search Lesson 30.1 GO • Tutor Tube

Use Models

Review the information in the text that uses a home heating system as a model for temperature control in the body.

Ask What is the overall function of a home heating system? *(to maintain a stable and comfortable temperature in the home)*

Ask How is this similar to temperature control in the human body? *(A stable temperature within a certain range must also be maintained in the human body.)*

Ask Name another condition, other than temperature, that you think needs to be stable in the human body? *(Sample answer: The amount of water in the body must be kept within a certain range.)*

DIFFERENTIATED INSTRUCTION

L3 Advanced Students The model described on this page describes feedback inhibition, or negative feedback, and its role in maintaining homeostasis. Explain that positive feedback also occurs in the human body. In positive feedback mechanisms, the response does not oppose the original stimulus, instead it reinforces the original stimulus. Two examples of positive feedback are the release of oxytocin during childbirth and chemicals released during blood clotting. Have advanced students research and find an example of positive feedback in the human body. Have students share what they learn with the class.

BIOLOGY.com Have students use the **Tutor Tube: Working Together to Stay Balanced** to explore how the body responds to environmental change and maintains homeostasis.

UbD Check for Understanding

HAND SIGNALS

Present students with the following questions, and ask them to show a thumbs-up sign if they can answer the questions, a thumbs-down sign if they definitely can't, or a waving-hand sign if they are not sure.

- What is homeostasis?
- How is feedback inhibition important in maintaining homeostasis?
- Why is a home heating system a good model for feedback inhibition in the body?

ADJUST INSTRUCTION

If students are struggling with one or more questions, ask them to review the material about homeostasis on this page. Then, have students work in pairs to discuss the questions.

Answers

FIGURE 30–3 High room temperature is the opposing stimulus to cold room temperature.

IN YOUR NOTEBOOK Sample answer: A nonliving system that requires constant adjustment is a bicycle being ridden over hilly terrain. The gearing of the bicycle must be repeatedly adjusted to maintain an optimal speed.

Teach continued

Lead a Discussion

Explain that maintaining stable temperature conditions is important for the chemical reactions that occur in the body. Point out that most of the biochemical processes that are essential for life occur in a very limited temperature range. Temperatures above or below this range can inhibit or denature enzymes, which means that chemical reactions cannot occur as needed.

DIFFERENTIATED INSTRUCTION

LPR Less Proficient Readers Have students work in small groups to make **Flowcharts** that organize the information in the text about body temperature control. Each group should make two flowcharts: one that begins with "Body temperature drops" and one that begins with "Body temperature rises." Have each group share its flowcharts with the class. During the class discussion, point out the importance of keeping the body's temperature within a certain range by briefly explaining the role of temperature in biochemical reactions.

Study Wkbks A/B, Appendix S25, Flowchart. **Transparencies,** GO8.

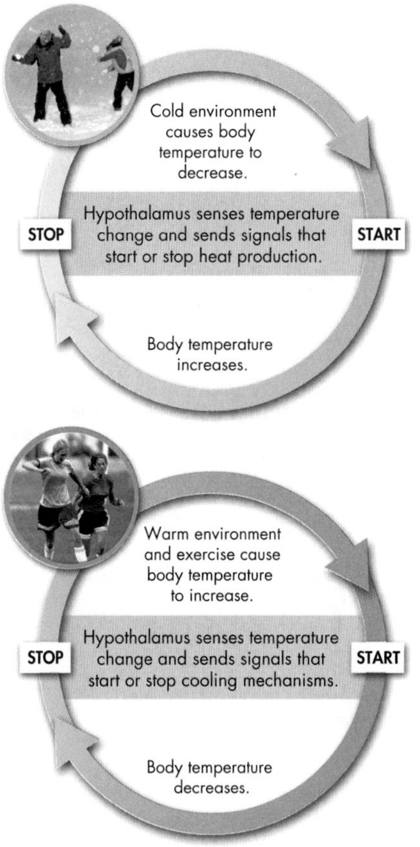

Answers

FIGURE 30–4 Moving around on a cold day will help you stay warm because when muscles work, they produce heat.

Cold environment causes body temperature to decrease.

STOP — Hypothalamus senses temperature change and sends signals that start or stop heat production. — START

Body temperature increases.

Warm environment and exercise cause body temperature to increase.

STOP — Hypothalamus senses temperature change and sends signals that start or stop cooling mechanisms. — START

Body temperature decreases.

FIGURE 30–4 Body Temperature Control In the human body, temperature is controlled through various feedback inhibition mechanisms. **Infer** ***Why do you think moving around on a cold day helps to keep you warm?***

▶ ***A Living Example*** Could biological systems achieve homeostasis through feedback inhibition? Absolutely. All that is needed is a system that regulates some aspect of the cellular environment and that can respond to feedback from its own activities by switching on or off as needed. Such mechanisms are very common, not only in the human body, but in all forms of life.

One example is the maintenance of body temperature. The body regulates temperature by a mechanism that is remarkably similar to that of a home heating system. You can follow body temperature regulation in **Figure 30–4.** A part of the brain called the hypothalamus contains nerve cells that monitor both the temperature of the skin at the surface of the body and the temperature of organs in the body's core.

If the nerve cells sense that the core temperature has dropped much below 37°C, the hypothalamus produces chemicals that signal cells throughout the body to speed up their activities. Heat produced by this increase in activity, especially cellular respiration, causes a gradual rise in body temperature, which is detected by nerve cells in the hypothalamus.

Have you ever been so cold that you began to shiver? If your body temperature drops well below its normal range, the hypothalamus releases chemicals that signal muscles just below the surface of the skin to contract involuntarily—to "shiver." These muscle contractions release heat, which helps the body temperature to rise toward the normal range.

If body temperature rises too far above 37°C, the hypothalamus slows down cellular activities to reduce heat production. This is one of the reasons you may feel tired and sluggish on a hot day. The body also responds to high temperatures by producing sweat, which helps to cool the body surface by evaporation.

OPEN-ENDED INQUIRY

Maintaining Temperature 

You will receive a thermometer and three beakers of water at the following temperatures: 25°C, 35°C, and 40°C. Develop a method to keep the temperature of the 35°C water within one degree for a period of fifteen minutes. You may use the contents of the other two beakers.

Analyze and Conclude

1. Compare and Contrast Compare this experiment to what happens in your own body during temperature regulation.

2. Interpret Visuals Make a feedback loop similar to the ones in **Figure 30–4** that shows how feedback inhibition was involved in this activity.

PURPOSE Students will maintain a beaker of water at a stable temperature to model maintenance of a stable body temperature.

MATERIALS three 250-mL beakers, water, thermometers

SAFETY Have students use caution when handling the hot water. Remind them to report any broken glassware immediately.

PLANNING Each student or group of students will receive water at 25°C, 35°C, and 40°C. Heat a sufficient quantity of water to each temperature, and then divide it among the students.

ANALYZE AND CONCLUDE

1. This experiment is similar to what happens in the body, because the water is heated or cooled in order to maintain a stable temperature.
2. Students' feedback loops should resemble those in **Figure 30–4,** but should reflect temperature control in a beaker of water rather than in the human body.

The Liver and Homeostasis The liver is technically part of the digestive system because it produces bile, which aids in the digestion of fats. However, it is also fair to say that the liver is one of the body's most important organs for homeostasis.

For example, when proteins are broken down for energy, ammonia, a toxic byproduct, is produced. The liver quickly converts ammonia to urea, which is much less toxic. The kidneys, as you will read a bit later, then remove urea from the blood. The liver also converts many dangerous substances, including some drugs, into compounds that can be removed from the body safely.

One of the liver's most important roles involves regulating the level of a substance we take almost for granted as something completely harmless—the simple sugar, glucose. Glucose is obtained from the foods we eat, and cells take glucose from the blood to serve as a source of energy for their everyday activities. Naturally, right after a meal, as the body absorbs food molecules, the level of glucose in the blood begins to rise. That's where the liver comes in. By taking glucose out of the blood, it keeps the level of glucose from rising too much. As the body uses glucose for energy, the liver releases stored glucose to keep the level of the sugar from dropping too low.

The liver's role in keeping blood glucose levels within a certain range is critical. Too little glucose, and the cells of the nervous system will slow down to the point that you may lose consciousness and pass out. On the other hand, too much glucose gradually damages cells in the eyes, kidneys, heart, and even the immune system. Abnormally high levels of glucose are associated with a disease called diabetes. In diabetes, changes occur in either the pancreas or body cells that affect the cells' ability to absorb glucose. Diabetes, one of the fastest-growing health problems in the developed world, is the unfortunate result of failure of homeostasis with respect to blood glucose levels.

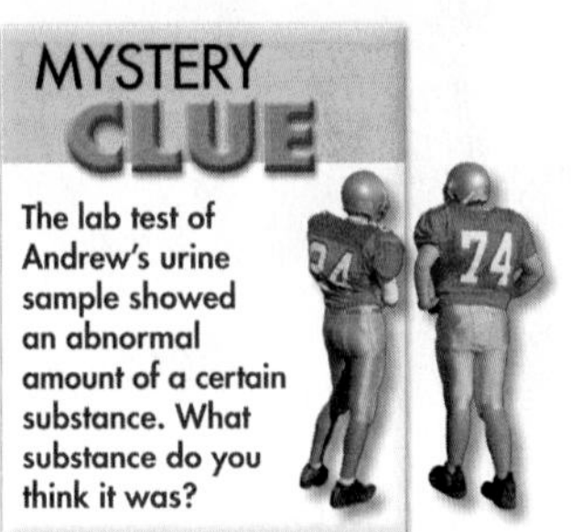

MYSTERY
CLUE
The lab test of Andrew's urine sample showed an abnormal amount of a certain substance. What substance do you think it was?
74

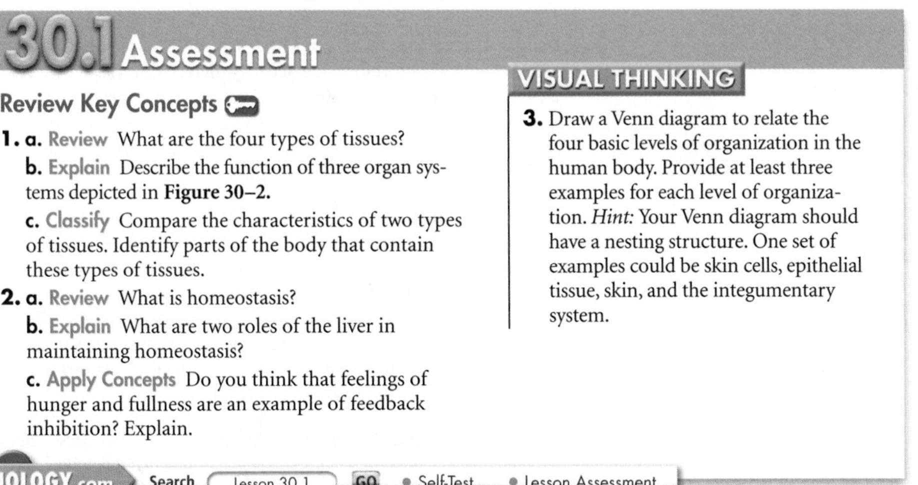

30.1 Assessment

Review Key Concepts

1. a. Review What are the four types of tissues?

b. Explain Describe the function of three organ systems depicted in **Figure 30–2.**

c. Classify Compare the characteristics of two types of tissues. Identify parts of the body that contain these types of tissues.

2. a. Review What is homeostasis?

b. Explain What are two roles of the liver in maintaining homeostasis?

c. Apply Concepts Do you think that feelings of hunger and fullness are an example of feedback inhibition? Explain.

VISUAL THINKING

3. Draw a Venn diagram to relate the four basic levels of organization in the human body. Provide at least three examples for each level of organization. *Hint:* Your Venn diagram should have a nesting structure. One set of examples could be skin cells, epithelial tissue, skin, and the integumentary system.

BIOLOGY.com Search (Lesson 30.1) GO • Self-Test • Lesson Assessment

MYSTERY CLUE Students should infer that the substance in Andrew's urine was glucose. Then, have students explain why the presence of glucose in the urine could indicate diabetes. Students can go online to **Biology.com** to gather their evidence.

Assess and Remediate

EVALUATE UNDERSTANDING

Call on volunteers to describe how the human body is organized. Have them discuss the different levels of organization. Then, have students complete the 30.1 Assessment.

REMEDIATION SUGGESTION

L1 Struggling Students If students have trouble with **Question 2c,** have them work in small groups to make a cycle diagram similar to **Figure 30–4** showing how feelings of hunger and fullness are part of a feedback loop that helps maintain homeostasis in the body.

BIOLOGY.com Students can check their understanding of lesson concepts with the **Self-Test** assessment. They can then take an online version of the Lesson Assessment.

Assessment Answers

1a. epithelial, connective, nervous, muscle

1b. Answers will vary. Students should choose three systems from **Figure 30–2** and correctly identify their functions.

1c. Sample answer: Epithelial tissue functions in protection, absorption, and excretion. Nervous tissue receives and transmits nerve impulses. Epithelial tissue is found in the skin, lining of the digestive system, and some glands; nervous tissue is found in the brain, spinal cord, and nerves.

2a. Homeostasis is the relatively stable internal conditions that organisms maintain despite changes in internal and external environments.

2b. The liver regulates blood sugar and breaks down toxic substances.

2c. Yes, because the stimuli hunger and fullness are opposing stimuli. Hunger stimulates a person to eat. Fullness then stimulates a person to stop eating, which opposes the original action.

VISUAL THINKING

3. Students' Venn diagrams should have a nesting structure, with concentric circles representing the four levels of organization, from smallest and simplest (cells) to largest and most complex (organ systems). Examples might include a neuron for "cells," nervous tissue for "tissues," brain for "organs," and nervous system for "organ systems."

LESSON 30.2

Getting Started

Objectives

30.2.1 Explain how food provides energy.

30.2.2 Identify the essential nutrients your body needs and tell how each is important to the body.

30.2.3 Explain how to plan a balanced diet.

Student Resources

Study Workbooks A and B, 30.2 Worksheets

Spanish Study Workbook, 30.2 Worksheets

Lab Manual B, 30.2 Data Analysis Worksheet

Lesson Overview • Lesson Notes • Activity: Data Analysis • Assessment: Self-Test, Lesson Assessment

For corresponding lesson in the **Foundation Edition,** see pages 719–722.

Answers

IN YOUR NOTEBOOK Students' tables should list: water, carbohydrates, fats, proteins, vitamins, and minerals; foods in which each is found; and a description of each nutrient's role in the body.

IN INDIANA ACADEMIC STANDARDS

For the full text of all standards, see the Course Overview in the front matter of this book.

B.1.2 Understand that the shape of a molecule determines its role in the many different types of cellular processes including metabolism, homeostasis, growth and development, and heredity, and understand that the majority of these processes involve proteins that act as enzymes.

30.2 Food and Nutrition

IN B.1.2 Molecules and cellular processes. Also covered: B.1.1.

Key Questions

Why do we need to eat?

What nutrients does your body need?

What is meant by the term "balanced diet"?

Vocabulary

Calorie
carbohydrate
fat
protein
vitamin
mineral

Taking Notes

Outline Before you read, make an outline of the major headings in the lesson. As you read, fill in main ideas and supporting details for each heading.

THINK ABOUT IT When you feel hungry, how would you describe the feeling? Do you feel full of energy and ready to go? Or do you feel weak and just a little bit lazy? Why? What do these sensations tell us about the purpose of food in the body?

Food and Energy

Why do we need to eat?

Have you ever wondered why you need food? The most obvious answer is energy. You need energy to climb stairs, lift books, run, and even to think. Just as a car needs gasoline, your body needs fuel, and food is that fuel. **Molecules in food contain chemical energy that cells use to produce ATP. Food also supplies raw materials your body needs to build and repair tissues.**

Energy The energy available in food can be measured in a laboratory in a surprisingly simple way—by burning it! When food is burned, most energy in the food is converted to heat, which is measured in terms of calories. A calorie is the amount of heat needed to raise the temperature of 1 gram of water by 1 degree Celsius. The "Calories" you've heard about in food are actually dietary Calories, written with a capital *C*. One dietary **Calorie** is equal to 1000 calories, or 1 kilocalorie (kcal). As you may recall, the energy stored in food molecules is released during cellular respiration and used to produce the ATP molecules that power cellular activities.

Raw Materials Chemical pathways, including cellular respiration, can extract energy from almost any type of food. So why does it matter which foods you eat? The reason is that food also supplies the raw materials used to build and repair body tissues. Some of these raw materials are needed to make enzymes, the lipids in cell membranes, and even DNA. In fact, food contains at least 45 substances that the body needs but cannot manufacture. A healthy diet ensures that your body receives all of these required substances.

In Your Notebook *Prepare a table to fill in with information about the nutrients. For each nutrient, include foods in which it is found and describe its role in the body.*

UbD Teach for Understanding

ENDURING UNDERSTANDING The human body is a complex system. The coordinated functions of its many structures support life processes and maintain homeostasis.

GUIDING QUESTION Why are the essential nutrients important?

EVIDENCE OF UNDERSTANDING *After the lesson, students should complete this assessment to show they understand why essential nutrients are important.* Have students keep a food diary for one week. For each entry, ask students to write several sentences discussing their diet in relation to the essential nutrients. Students could answer questions such as: Do they think they are consuming enough of the essential nutrients? If not, how could they change their diet to consume more essential nutrients? What tools could they use to further assess their diets?

Nutrients

What nutrients does your body need?

Nutrients are substances in food that supply the energy and raw materials your body uses for growth, repair, and maintenance. **The nutrients that the body needs include water, carbohydrates, fats, proteins, vitamins, and minerals.**

MYSTERY CLUE

Philip's and Seth's samples were both a very dark yellow. Neither boy drank water before or during practice. Why do you think they were sent home from practice?

Water The most important nutrient is water. Every cell in the human body needs water because many of the body's processes, including chemical reactions, take place in water. Water makes up the bulk of blood, extracellular fluid, and other bodily fluids. On hot days or when you take part in strenuous exercise, sweat glands remove water from your tissues and release it as sweat on the surface of your body. Water is also lost from the body in urine and with every breath you exhale.

Humans need to drink at least 1 liter of fluid each day. If enough water is not taken in to replace what is lost, dehydration can result. Dehydration leads to problems with many body systems, and under extreme conditions it can be fatal.

Carbohydrates Simple and complex **carbohydrates** are a major source of energy for the body. **Figure 30–5** shows some of the foods that contain carbohydrates. The sugars found in fruits, honey, and sugar cane are simple carbohydrates, or monosaccharides and disaccharides. The starches found in grains, potatoes, and vegetables are complex carbohydrates, or polysaccharides. Starches are broken down by the digestive system into simple sugars. These molecules are absorbed into the blood and carried to cells throughout the body. Excess blood sugar is converted into glycogen, which is stored in the liver and in skeletal muscles. Excess sugar may also be converted to and stored as body fat.

Whole-grain breads, bran, and many fruits and vegetables contain the complex carbohydrate cellulose, often called fiber. Although the human digestive system cannot break down cellulose, you need fiber in your diet. The bulk supplied by fiber helps muscles move food and wastes through your digestive system. Fiber may also have other benefits, such as reducing the risk of heart disease and Type II diabetes.

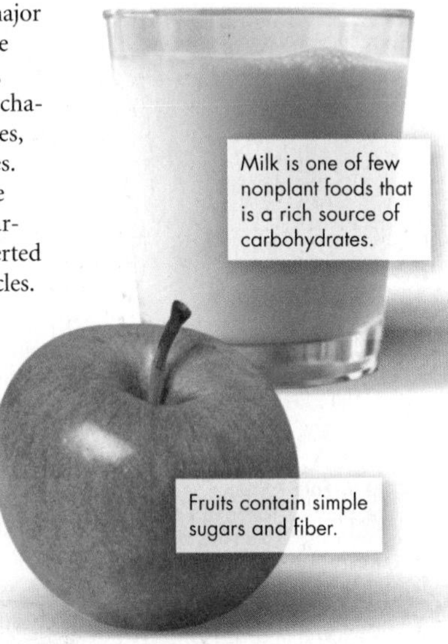

Milk is one of few nonplant foods that is a rich source of carbohydrates.
Fruits contain simple sugars and fiber.

Whole-grain products contain more fiber than processed grains.

FIGURE 30–5 Carbohydrates Pastas and cereals are also foods that are rich in carbohydrates. Simple carbohydrates do not have to be digested or broken down. Complex carbohydrates, such as those found in whole grains, must be broken down before they can be used by the body. **Infer** ***Which type of carbohydrate—simple or complex—provides the body with quick energy?***

LESSON 30.2

Teach

Build Science Skills

Explain that populations with high-fiber diets have been found to have lower rates of colon cancer than populations with low-fiber diets. Add that people who eat high-fiber diets often also have low-fat diets, which are known to lower colon cancer rates as well. Challenge students to identify the data they would use to determine if high-fiber diets, low-fat diets, or a combination of the two is responsible for the lower colon cancer rates in these populations. *(Students should say they would compare colon cancer rates of the following four populations: high-fiber, low-fat diets; high-fiber, high-fat diets; low-fiber, high-fat diets; and low-fiber, low-fat diets. These comparisons should allow students to determine whether amounts of fiber, fat, or a combination of the two affect colon cancer rates.)*

DIFFERENTIATED INSTRUCTION

L1 Struggling Students Help students build their research and inquiry skills by performing some additional background research on a particular nutrient. Point out that scientists regularly conduct background research to help them design their experiments and keep abreast of current research in their fields. Have students choose one of the vitamins or minerals described in this lesson and ask them to find out as much as they can about it. Then have them prepare a short essay or make a poster explaining the results of their research.

Have students review the importance of water as a nutrient before they respond to the question. Students should respond that the boys were sent home because they were dehydrated. Students can go online to **Biology.com** to gather their evidence.

Quick Facts

HOW SWEET IT IS

Milk does not taste sweet; therefore, many students are surprised to learn that it contains sugar. In fact, 8 ounces of milk contains 11 grams of sugar, more than half the sugar in the same amount of orange juice. Most of the sugar in milk is lactose, which is broken down into simpler sugars in the digestive tract by the enzyme lactase. Most human infants produce lactase and can digest lactose. Many human adults, on the other hand, do not produce enough lactase. When someone who is lactose-intolerant drinks milk, the lactose ferments in their intestines causing gas, cramps, and diarrhea. To get around the problem, these individuals can take lactase enzyme supplements to help them digest foods containing lactose, or they can consume foods with reduced lactose.

Answers

FIGURE 30–5 Simple carbohydrates provide the body with quick energy.

Teach continued

Lead a Discussion

Have students review the functions served by fats and proteins in the body.

Ask What might be some consequences of not consuming enough fat? *(Sample answers: You would not be able to absorb enough fat-soluble vitamins. The function of the nervous system could be impaired, because fats form parts of nerve cells.)*

Ask What might be some consequences of not consuming enough protein? *(Sample answers: The chemical reactions that occur as a part of many body functions would be impaired because enzymes are made of protein.)*

DIFFERENTIATED INSTRUCTION

LPR Less Proficient Readers Struggling readers may become overwhelmed by the amount of information presented on this page. Suggest students work in small groups to come up with a short list of summary sentences for **Fats** and **Proteins.** Suggest that they write at least three sentences for each nutrient. Then have volunteers from each group share their sentences.

BUILD Vocabulary

PREFIXES The prefix *poly-* is Greek for "many." Polyunsaturated fats contain more than one double bond. The prefix *mono-* means "single." Monounsaturated fats, such as olive oil, contain only one double bond.

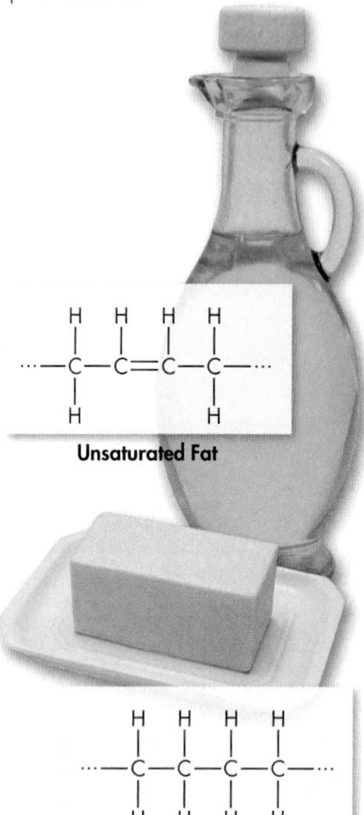

FIGURE 30–6 Fats At room temperature, most saturated fats are solid and most unsaturated fats are liquid. Saturated fats have been tied to many health problems. Consuming limited amounts of unsaturated fats, such as those found in avocados and olive oil, may have some benefits.

Fats Because our society places great emphasis on a trim appearance, the word "fat" has a bad reputation. But fats, or lipids, are an important part of a healthy diet. **Fats** help the body absorb fat-soluble vitamins and are a part of cell membranes, nerve cells, and certain hormones. Deposits of fat protect and insulate body organs and are a source of stored energy.

Fats usually form when a glycerol molecule combines with fatty acids. Some of these acids, called essential fatty acids, cannot be made in the body and are needed to perform many of fat's functions. Based on the structure of their fatty acid chains, fats are classified as saturated or unsaturated. When there are only single bonds between the carbon atoms in the fatty acids, each carbon atom has the maximum number of hydrogen atoms and the fat is said to be saturated. Most saturated fats, such as butter, are solids at room temperature.

Unsaturated fats have one or more double bonds between carbon atoms, which reduces the number of hydrogen atoms in their fatty acids. Unsaturated fats are usually liquids at room temperature. Because many vegetable oils contain more than one double bond, they are called polyunsaturated.

Food manufacturers often modify unsaturated fats in vegetable oils by adding hydrogen to them. These processed fats are called trans fats. Trans fats are solid at room temperature and have a longer shelf life than unsaturated fats. However, recent studies suggest that trans fats may be associated with serious health concerns, including heart disease.

Proteins Proteins have a wide variety of roles in the body. **Proteins** supply raw materials for growth and repair of structures such as skin and muscle. Many enzymes that control cellular chemistry by increasing the rates of chemical reactions are made of proteins. Proteins also have regulatory and transport functions. For example, the hormone insulin is a protein that regulates the level of sugar in the blood. Hemoglobin, a protein found in red blood cells, helps transport oxygen. Proteins can also be used as energy sources when other nutrients, such as carbohydrates and fats, are in short supply.

Proteins are polymers of amino acids. The body is able to synthesize only 12 of the 20 amino acids used to make proteins. The other eight are called essential amino acids. Essential amino acids must be obtained from the foods that you eat. Foods shown below, such as meat, fish, eggs, and milk, generally contain all eight essential amino acids. Foods derived from plants, such as grains and beans, do not. People who don't eat animal products must eat a combination of plant foods, such as beans and rice, to obtain all of the essential amino acids.

870 Chapter 30 • Lesson 2

UbD Check for Understanding

ORAL QUESTIONING

Use the following prompts to gauge students' understanding of lesson concepts.

- How are carbohydrates, fats, and proteins similar to one another?
- How is each used by the body?
- How do nutrients help the body maintain homeostasis?

ADJUST INSTRUCTION

If students have difficulty making the connection between nutrients and homeostasis, point out that they would not expect a car to run without gasoline and other fluids. In the same way, food supplies what the body needs to make it run efficiently and maintain homeostasis.

Vitamins Organic molecules that the body needs in very small amounts are called **vitamins.** Most vitamins are needed by the body to help perform chemical reactions. If we think of proteins, fats, and carbohydrates as the building blocks of the body, then vitamins are the tools that help to put them together. As shown in **Figure 30–7,** most vitamins must be obtained from food. However, the bacteria that live in the large intestine are able to synthesize vitamins K and B_{12}.

There are two types of vitamins: fat-soluble and water-soluble. The fat-soluble vitamins A, D, E, and K can be stored in the fatty tissues of the body. The body can build up small deposits of these vitamins for future use. The water-soluble vitamins, which include vitamin C and the B vitamins, dissolve in water and cannot be stored in the body. Therefore, they should be included in the foods you eat each day.

A diet lacking certain vitamins can have serious health consequences. Eating a variety of foods will supply the daily vitamin needs of most people. Large doses of vitamin supplements do not benefit the body. Excessive amounts of the fat-soluble vitamins A, D, and K can be toxic.

FIGURE 30–7 Vitamins This table lists the food sources and functions of 14 essential vitamins. The fat-soluble vitamins are listed in the first four rows. **Interpret Tables** ***What is the function of vitamin K?***

Vitamins

Vitamin	Sources	Function
A (retinol)	Yellow, orange, and dark-green vegetables; fortified dairy products	Important for growth of skin cells; important for night vision
D (calciferol)	Fish oils, eggs; made by skin when exposed to sunlight; added to dairy products	Promotes bone growth; increases calcium and phosphorus absorption
E (tocopherol)	Green leafy vegetables, seeds, vegetable oils	Antioxidant; prevents cellular damage
K 	Green leafy vegetables; made by bacteria that live in human intestine	Needed for normal blood clotting
B_1 (thiamine)	Whole grains, pork, legumes, milk	Metabolism of carbohydrates
B_2 (riboflavin)	Dairy products, meats, vegetables, whole grains	Growth; energy metabolism
Niacin	Liver, milk, whole grains, nuts, meats, legumes	Important in energy metabolism
B_6 (pyridoxine)	Whole grains, meats, vegetables	Important for amino acid metabolism
Pantothenic acid	Meats, dairy products, whole grains	Needed for energy metabolism
Folic acid 	Legumes, nuts, green leafy vegetables, oranges, broccoli, peas, fortified grains	Involved in nucleic acid metabolism; prevents neural-tube defects
B_{12} (cyanocobalamin)	Meats, eggs, dairy products, enriched cereals	Involved in nucleic acid metabolism; maturation of red blood cells
C (ascorbic acid) 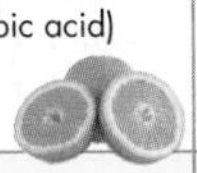	Citrus fruits, tomatoes, red or green peppers, broccoli, cabbage, strawberries	Maintains cartilage and bone; antioxidant; improves iron absorption; important for healthy gums and wound healing
Biotin	Legumes, vegetables, meat	Coenzyme in synthesis of fat; glycogen formation; amino acid metabolism
Choline	Egg yolk, liver, grains, legumes	Part of phospholipids and neurotransmitters

How Science Works

HOW VITAMINS WERE NAMED

In the 1800s, sailors in the Japanese navy developed a nervous disorder named beriberi when they were fed a diet that consisted mostly of white rice. The sailors became extremely weak and suffered uncontrollable muscle spasms. Toward the end of the 1800s, a Dutch doctor noticed that prisoners who were fed mostly white rice also developed beriberi, whereas prisoners who were fed brown rice did not. The doctor inferred that some factor in the hull of the rice, which is removed when brown rice is converted to white rice, was needed by the body to prevent beriberi. A short time later, a Polish chemist isolated the factor and called it "vital amine." The word *vital* means "necessary for life" and *amine* refers to a chemical structure. He was incorrect; the substance was not an amine, but the name stuck and gave rise to the term *vitamin*. Now it is known that beriberi is specifically caused by a lack of thiamine.

Use Visuals

Use the information in **Figure 30–7** to introduce the sources and functions of vitamins.

Ask How important are vitamins to the proper function of your body—could you do without them? *(No. Vitamins provide valuable functions to the human body, such as promoting bone growth and helping with normal blood clotting.)*

Ask Look at the different vitamin sources listed in the figure. What are some vitamin-rich foods? *(vegetables, dairy products, meat, eggs, and whole grains)*

Ask Do you think soda is vitamin-rich? What might you drink instead? *(No. I might drink milk or fruit juice instead of soda.)*

DIFFERENTIATED INSTRUCTION

L1 Struggling Students For students who become overwhelmed by the level of detail in the table, write on the board: *Vitamins help the body use fats, proteins, and carbohydrates.* Start by focusing on this general concept with students, rather than detailed information about specific vitamins. Once students have grasped the main idea, explain that the table tells them about how different vitamins function in the human body.

Address Misconceptions

Dietary Supplements Students may not understand the potential health hazards of dietary supplements, such as vitamin and mineral supplements and herb-based products. Students may think that "more is better" when it comes to vitamins and minerals. Explain that this is not the case, and that many vitamins and minerals can be harmful in excessive doses. Point out that products made with herbs can also have many harmful side-effects, including negative interactions with prescription and over-the-counter medications. Also explain to students that supplements are not regulated in the same way as medications. Just because they are sold in stores does not mean they are safe. Ask interested students to research specific examples of health hazards related to the overuse of dietary supplements. Have them share their examples with the class.

Answers

FIGURE 30–7 Vitamin K is needed for normal blood clotting.

Teach continued

Connect to Health

Ask students to bring in a variety of food labels (or alternatively, you could provide the labels). Have students analyze the serving size information found on each label. Point out that the nutrition information listed applies to a single serving of food, which might differ greatly from a typical portion. Have students work in small groups to make a display that shows a serving size of commonly consumed foods, such as breakfast cereal, pasta, or bread.

Ask Why is serving size an important piece of information for you to know as you plan your meals? *(Sample answer: It helps me figure out how many Calories I'm consuming and the nutrients I'm getting when I eat a certain amount of food.)*

DIFFERENTIATED INSTRUCTION

ELL English Language Learners Some of the language on food labels, especially the ingredients list, may be difficult for English language learners to read and understand. If possible, encourage students to bring in food labels that are in their native language. Bring in a comparable product with a label in English. Have students analyze and discuss the information on these labels. Then have them work with native English speakers to translate as much information from the native-language food label as they can into English.

BIOLOGY.com Students analyze caloric and nutritional needs tailored to their age, gender, body mass, and activity level. They then plan a virtual meal that will meet those needs in **Data Analysis: Balance Your Virtual Diet.**

Answers

FIGURE 30–8 Fluoride is not found in many foods; adding it to drinking water helps ensure that people get enough fluoride to maintain the health of their bones and teeth.

IN YOUR NOTEBOOK Sample answer: serving size, servings per container, calories per serving, total fat per serving, total carbohydrates per serving, how much calcium it contains, its ingredients

Important Minerals

Mineral	Sources	Function
Calcium	Dairy products, salmon, kale, tofu, collard greens, legumes	Bone and tooth formation; blood clotting; nerve and muscle function
Phosphorus	Dairy products, meats, poultry, grains	Bone and tooth formation; acid-base balance
Iron	Meats, eggs, legumes, whole grains, green leafy vegetables, dried fruit	Component of hemoglobin and of electron carriers used in energy metabolism
Chlorine	Table salt, processed foods	Acid-base balance; formation of gastric juice
Sodium	Table salt, processed foods	Acid-base balance; water balance; nerve and muscle function
Potassium	Meats, dairy products, fruits and vegetables, grains	Acid-base balance; water balance; nerve and muscle function
Magnesium	Whole grains, green leafy vegetables	Activation of enzymes in protein synthesis
Fluorine	Fluoridated drinking water, tea, seafood	Maintenance of bone and tooth structure
Iodine	Seafood, dairy products, iodized salt	Component of thyroid hormones
Zinc	Meats, seafood, grains	Component of certain digestive enzymes

FIGURE 30–8 Minerals A healthful diet should include small amounts of certain minerals to maintain a healthy body. Infer ***Why do you think some cities and towns add fluoride to their water supplies?***

Minerals Inorganic nutrients that the body needs, usually in small amounts, are called **minerals. Figure 30–8** lists some of the minerals needed by the body. Calcium, for example, is required to produce the calcium phosphate that makes up bones and teeth. Iron is needed to make hemoglobin, the oxygen-carrying protein in red blood cells. A constant supply of minerals in the diet is needed to replace those lost in sweat, urine, and digestive wastes.

Nutrition and a Balanced Diet

What is meant by the term "balanced diet"?

The science of nutrition—the study of food and its effects on the body—tries to determine how food helps the body meet all of its various needs. Because of the work of nutritionists, many tools have been developed to help people plan healthful diets. **A balanced diet provides nutrients in adequate amounts and enough energy for a person to maintain a healthful weight.**

Balancing Your Diet Food labels can be used to choose healthful foods. Food labels provide general information about nutrition as well as specific information about the product. They can be used to determine if you are consuming enough of some of the important vitamins and minerals.

In Your Notebook *List seven types of information you can learn about a food from its food label.*

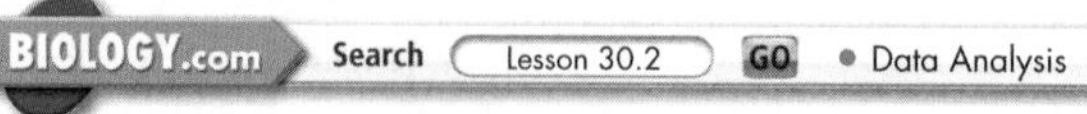

UbD Check for Understanding

ONE-MINUTE RESPONSE

Write the following prompt on the board and give students about a minute to write a quick response summarizing their understanding:

- Why is it important to consume a balanced diet? *(Responses should mention that eating a balanced diet provides the nutrients and energy required to maintain a healthy body and weight.)*

ADJUST INSTRUCTION

If responses are incorrect or incomplete, ask students to think about the role each nutrient described in the lesson plays in helping the body maintain homeostasis. Then, point out that eating a balanced diet is the way to provide the body with optimal amounts of each nutrient.

Note on the food label shown in **Figure 30–9** that fat contains about 9 Calories per gram, while carbohydrate and protein contain 4 Calories per gram. Why the difference? The carbon atoms in fats generally have more C–H (carbon to hydrogen) bonds than the carbon atoms in carbohydrates or proteins. Oxidizing these C–H bonds releases a great deal of energy. Because of this, oxidizing a gram of fat releases more energy than does oxidizing a gram of protein or carbohydrate, giving fats a greater energy value in Calories per gram.

When using food labels, it is important to remember that Percent Daily Values are based on a 2000-Calorie diet. However, nutrient needs are affected by age, gender, and lifestyle. The daily energy needs of an average-sized teenager who exercises regularly are about 2200 Calories for females and about 2800 Calories for males. People who are more active than average have greater energy needs. When a person stops growing or becomes less active, energy needs decrease.

Maintaining a Healthful Weight Inactive lifestyles and high-Calorie diet are contributing factors to the growing rate of obesity in the United States during the last several decades. Exercising about 30 minutes a day and eating a balanced diet can help maintain a healthful weight. Regular physical activity helps to maintain a healthful weight by burning excess Calories. Other benefits of physical activity include strengthening of the heart, bones, and muscles.

The American Heart Association recommends a diet with a maximum of 30 percent of Calories from fat, of which only 7 percent should be from saturated fats and 1 percent from trans fats. Controlling fat intake is important for several reasons. Foods that contain a high amount of any type of fat are high in Calories. A diet high in saturated fats and trans fats increases the risk for developing heart disease, Type II diabetes, or both.

Nutrition Facts

Serving Size	1 cup (30g)
Servings Per Container	About 10
Amount Per Serving	
Calories 110	Calories from Fat 17
	% Daily Value*
Total Fat 2g	**3%**
Saturated Fat 0g	**0%**
Trans Fat 0.5g	
Cholesterol 0mg	**0%**
Sodium 280mg	**12%**
Total Carbohydrate 22g	**7%**
Dietary Fiber 3g	**12%**
Sugars 1g	
Protein 3g	
Vitamin A 10%	• Vitamin C 20%
Calcium 4%	• Iron 45%

* Percent Daily Values are based on a 2,000 Calorie diet. Your Daily Values may be higher or lower depending on your calorie needs:

	Calories	2,000	2,500
Total Fat	Less than	65g	80g
Sat. Fat	Less than	20g	25g
Cholesterol	Less than	300mg	300mg
Sodium	Less than	2,400mg	2,400mg
Total Carbohydrate		300g	375g
Fiber		25g	30g

Calories per gram:
Fat 9 • Carbohydrate 4 • Protein 4

Ingredients: Whole grain oats, sugar, salt, milled corn, oat fiber, dried whey,

FIGURE 30–9 Food Label Reading food labels can help you track how many Calories you consume in a day and if you are meeting your requirements for important nutrients.

30.2 Assessment

Review Key Concepts

1. a. Review What are the two reasons humans need to eat?

b. Infer Foods that contain many Calories but few raw materials are said to contain empty Calories. What do you think the phrase *empty Calories* means?

2. a. Review List six nutrients that the body needs.

b. Compare and Contrast How are saturated and unsaturated fats similar? How are they different?

3. a. Review How can food labels be used to plan a balanced diet?

b. Calculate One serving of a particular food contains 16 g of carbohydrates, 2 g of protein, and 10 g of fats. Approximately how many Calories does it contain? MATH

ANALYZING DATA

Examine **Figure 30–9** and answer the questions.

4. a. Calculate If you ate 2 cups of this product, how many grams of fat would you eat? How many total Calories would you eat? MATH

b. Evaluate This product's packaging advertises that it contains 0 g of trans fat. Does that mean the product contains no trans fat? Explain.

BIOLOGY.com Search Lesson 30.2 GO • Lesson Assessment • Self-Test

Assess and Remediate

EVALUATE UNDERSTANDING

Have students write a short summary sentence for each of the six nutrients. Their sentences should explain why the nutrient is important for the proper function of the human body. Have them discuss their sentences in small groups. Then, have students complete the 30.2 Assessment.

REMEDIATION SUGGESTION

ELL English Language Learners If students have difficulty answering **Question 1b,** explain that the phrase *empty Calories* is a figure of speech. Tell students that a figure of speech should not be interpreted literally.

BIOLOGY.com Students can check their understanding of lesson concepts with the **Self-Test** assessment. They can then take an online version of the Lesson Assessment.

Assessment Answers

1a. Humans need to eat to get energy and to get the materials they need to build and repair tissue.

1b. The phrase *empty Calories* refers to foods that supply Calories without also supplying raw materials the body needs.

2a. water, carbohydrates, fats, proteins, vitamins, and minerals

2b. Saturated and unsaturated fats are similar in that they both help the body absorb fat-soluble vitamins and are part of cell membranes, nerve cells, and some hormones. They are different because saturated fats contain only single bonds between their carbon atoms while unsaturated fats have one or more double bonds between carbon atoms. Saturated fats are solid at room temperature, while unsaturated fats are liquid.

3a. Food labels display the amounts of nutrients contained in a serving of food; so food labels can be used to plan a diet that contains all of the nutrients your body needs and the right amount of Calories.

3b. 162 Calories

ANALYZING DATA

4a. 4 grams of fat, 220 Calories

4b. This product contains 0.5 g trans fats, so the statement on the packaging does not mean that it contains no trans fat.

Digestive and Excretory Systems 873

CHAPTER FEATURE

Teach

Lead a Discussion

Have students consider how food choices at school can affect students' overall diets.

Ask Do you think schools should offer only healthy food choices in vending machines and in the cafeteria? *(Accept all well-supported responses.)*

Ask What are some other ways that schools and the government can encourage healthy food choices and physical activity? *(Sample answers: Schools could encourage healthy food choices by educating students about the advantages of healthy eating. Schools could also encourage fund-raising events that do not involve selling candy or baked goods. The government could encourage physical activity by mandating that schools offer physical education.)*

Biology & Society

Who Should Solve America's Obesity Problem?

As old subway cars are replaced and new sport stadiums are built, a trend is obvious. Seats are much larger than they used to be. For example, in the old arena of the Indiana Pacers, seats were 18 inches wide. In the new arena, the *smallest* seats are 21 inches wide. Advertisers tout that the seats are more comfortable. But the reality is, larger seats are needed because Americans have become fatter.

From the late 1970s to the early 2000s, the percentage of adults in the United States who are obese increased from 15 percent to 32.9 percent. During the same time period, the percentage of adolescents (ages 12 to 19) who are overweight more than tripled, from 5 percent to 17.4 percent. The trend shows no sign of changing.

The causes for what has been called the "obesity epidemic" seem apparent—a lifestyle of high-Calorie diets and lack of exercise. But the solutions are not so obvious. Many state and local governments have tried to gain control of the epidemic by removing high-Calorie foods from schools. Some people support these efforts, but others believe the government is encroaching too closely on personal lives. Should the government play a role in fighting obesity by controlling the foods served in school?

Viewpoints

The Government Must Play a Role Obesity increases the risk of high blood pressure, Type II diabetes, stroke, arthritis, and some cancers. An increase in the rates of these diseases will strain the healthcare system and affect the economy by reducing the number of healthy adults in the workforce.

Overweight children are likely to become obese adults. Schools should play an active role in limiting students' exposure to high-Calorie foods that are not nutritious.

Many schools throughout the country have replaced vending machines that offered soda and other sugary drinks with those that offer only water, milk, or 100 percent juice.

The Government Should Not Play a Role Food choices are a personal decision. Keeping unhealthful foods out of school will not prepare students for making healthful decisions in the real world. Parents and educators should teach children how to make healthful choices, rather than simply controlling their options.

Research and Decide

1. Evaluate Discuss changes that have been proposed or made recently in your school to address the obesity epidemic. Have some foods been removed from the cafeteria? Have the offerings in vending machines changed? Explain.

2. Form an Opinion Do you think that recent changes in your school menu, if any, are positive changes? Should more be done? Or should less be done? Explain.

Answers

RESEARCH AND DECIDE

1. Answers may vary. Students' responses should accurately reflect recent changes in foods available at their school.
2. Answers may vary. Students' opinions should be supported by reasonable explanations.

Biology In-Depth

ADVERTISING IN SCHOOLS

In addition to concerns about foods available in school cafeterias and vending machines, there is concern about food advertising that occurs at school. Many food products are advertised directly to students, through posters, free gifts such as book covers, athletic scoreboards, videos, and other means. The food products being advertised are typically candy, soda, and other high-Calorie foods. In return for allowing this advertising to occur, schools may receive cash, equipment, or other incentives.

The Digestive System

B.5.5 Roles of proteins.

THINK ABOUT IT When you're hungry, your whole body needs food. But the only system in the body that food actually enters is the digestive system. So, how does food get to the rest of the body after the process of digestion?

Functions of the Digestive System

What are the functions of the digestive system?

The need for food presents every animal with at least two challenges. The first is how to obtain it. Once an animal has caught or gathered its food, its body faces a new challenge—how to convert the food into useful molecules. In humans and many other animals, this is the job of the digestive system. **The digestive system converts food into small molecules that can be used by the cells of the body. Food is processed by the digestive system in four phases—ingestion, digestion, absorption, and elimination.**

Ingestion Naturally, the first step in digestion is getting food into the system. Ingestion, as the process is called, is the process of putting food into your mouth—the opening to the digestive tract.

Digestion As food passes through the digestive system, it is broken down in two ways—by mechanical and chemical digestion. **Mechanical digestion** is the physical breakdown of large pieces of food into smaller pieces. These smaller pieces can be swallowed and accessed by digestive enzymes. During **chemical digestion,** enzymes break down food into the small molecules the body can use.

Absorption Once food has been broken into small molecules, it can be absorbed by cells in the small intestine. From the small intestine, the molecules enter the circulatory system, which transports them throughout the body.

Elimination The digestive system cannot digest and absorb all the substances in food that enter the body. Some materials, such as cellulose, travel through the large intestine and are eliminated from the body as feces.

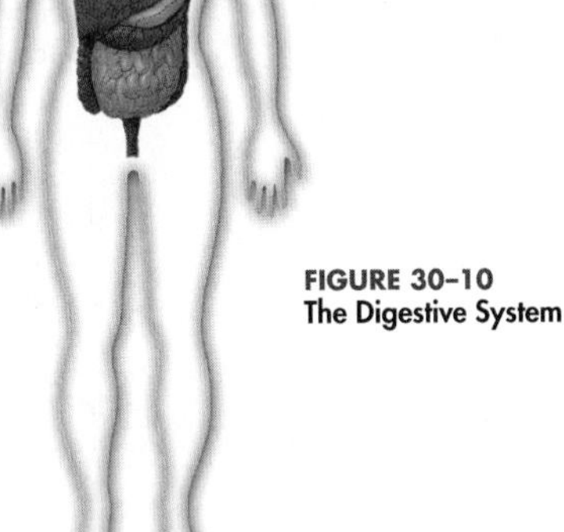

FIGURE 30–10
The Digestive System

Key Questions

What are the functions of the digestive system?

What occurs during digestion?

How are nutrients absorbed and wastes eliminated?

Vocabulary

mechanical digestion • chemical digestion • amylase • esophagus • peristalsis • stomach • pepsin • chyme • small intestine • villus • large intestine

Taking Notes

Flowchart Make a flowchart that shows the route food takes through the digestive system.

Search Lesson 30.3 GO • Lesson Overview • Lesson Notes

UbD Teach for Understanding

ENDURING UNDERSTANDING The human body is a complex system. The coordinated functions of its many structures support life processes and maintain homeostasis.

GUIDING QUESTION How does the human body convert food into useful molecules?

EVIDENCE OF UNDERSTANDING *Have students complete this assessment to show they understand how the body converts food into useful molecules.* Have students work in small groups to develop an analogy for each of the four functions of the digestive system. For example, putting food in a blender is a good analogy for mechanical digestion. Have each group share its analogies with the class.

LESSON 30.3

Getting Started

Objectives

30.3.1 Describe the organs of the digestive system and explain their functions.

30.3.2 Explain what happens during digestion.

30.3.3 Describe how nutrients are absorbed into the bloodstream and wastes are eliminated from the body.

Student Resources

Study Workbooks A and B, 30.3 Worksheets

Spanish Study Workbook, 30.3 Worksheets

Lesson Overview • Lesson Notes • Activity: Art in Motion • Assessment: Self-Test, Lesson Assessment

For corresponding lesson in the **Foundation Edition,** see pages 723–728.

Build Background

Create a class **Cluster Diagram** on the digestive system. In the center of the board, write the term *digestive system* inside a circle. Have volunteers come up to the board and add facts they know about the digestive system.

Study Wkbks A/B, Appendix S19, Cluster Diagram. **Transparencies,** GO2.

IN INDIANA ACADEMIC STANDARDS

B.5.5 Understand that proteins are responsible for the observable traits of an organism and for most of the functions within an organism.

LESSON 30.3

Teach

Use Visuals

Use **Figure 30–11** to start a discussion relating mouth structures to their function in digestion.

Ask How do your teeth help you ingest and digest food? *(Sample answer: For ingestion, teeth help me cut and tear bites of food. They then start the process of mechanical digestion as they cut, grind, and crush food into a bolus.)* Point out that a small amount of absorption also occurs in the mouth.

DIFFERENTIATED INSTRUCTION

L1 Struggling Students Have students review **Figure 30–11** to reinforce what they have learned about the mouth. Explain how the mouth ingests and starts breaking down food. Point out that humans have different types of teeth that help break down food in different ways. For example, incisors, cuspids, and bicuspids tear and cut food, while molars crush food. Ask them to think of some analogies for how teeth work.

Ask Can you think of tools that perform similar mechanical functions as human teeth? *(Sample answers: Knives and saws cut food, like incisors, cuspids, and bicuspids, and hammers or mallets crush like molars.)*

ELL Focus on ELL: Extend Language

ADVANCED SPEAKERS Have students draw a box in the middle of a piece of paper and a box in each corner of the paper. Students should connect the boxes in the corners to the box in the middle with lines. Have students write the term *digestive system* in the middle box. Ask them to write words related to the digestive system in each corner box. Then, inside each corner box, have them define each word and write a list of synonyms if possible. Discuss with students the relationships between the words in the corner boxes to the term *digestive system.*

Answers

FIGURE 30–11 Sample answer: Some types of teeth have a structure that allows them to tear into meat. Others have a structure that allows them to grind plant materials.

IN YOUR NOTEBOOK Lysozyme in saliva can kill bacteria in food. The epiglottis prevents food and liquid from entering the airway.

The Process of Digestion

What occurs during digestion?

The human digestive system, like those of other chordates, is built around an alimentary canal—a one-way tube that passes through the body. **During digestion, food travels through the mouth, esophagus, stomach, and small intestine. Mechanical digestion and chemical digestion are the two processes by which food is reduced to molecules that can be absorbed.** Both mechanical digestion and chemical digestion start in the mouth.

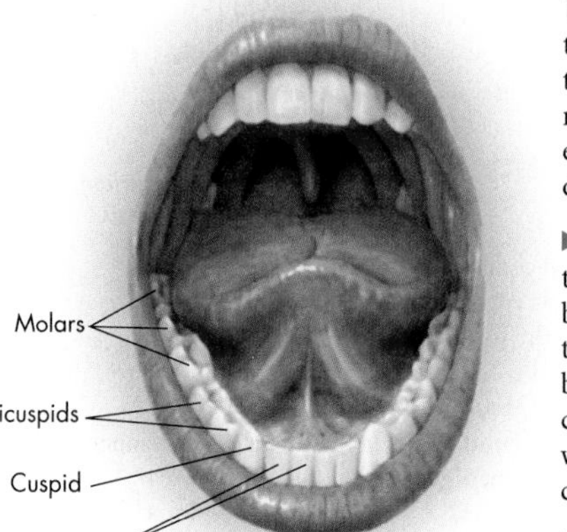

FIGURE 30–11 The Mouth Digestion begins in the mouth, where the tongue, teeth, and saliva form food into a moist lump that can be swallowed. **Infer** ***How do human teeth reflect an omnivorous diet?***

The Mouth As you take a forkful of food into your mouth, the work of the digestive system begins. Teeth and saliva start to work on your food first. Chewing begins the process of mechanical digestion. Chemical digestion begins as digestive enzymes in saliva start the breakdown of complex carbohydrates into smaller molecules.

▶ ***Teeth*** The teeth, shown in **Figure 30–11,** are anchored in the bones of the jaw. The surfaces of the teeth are protected by a coating of mineralized enamel. The teeth do much of the mechanical work of digestion. The incisors, cuspids, and bicuspids cut into and tear at food. The molars grind and crush food into a fine paste that can be swallowed. Meanwhile, your tongue moves food around so that it comes in contact with your teeth.

▶ ***Saliva*** As the teeth cut and grind the food, the salivary glands secrete saliva, which helps to moisten the food and make it easier to chew. The release of saliva is under the control of the nervous system and can be triggered by the scent of food—especially when you are hungry!

Saliva not only eases the passage of food through the digestive system but also begins the process of chemical digestion. Saliva contains an enzyme called **amylase** that begins to break the chemical bonds in starches, forming sugars. If you chew on a starchy food like a cracker long enough, it will begin to taste sweet—the result of amylase's work in breaking down starches into sugars. Saliva also contains lysozyme, an enzyme that fights infection by digesting the cell walls of many bacteria that may enter the mouth with food.

Once food is chewed, the combined actions of the tongue and throat muscles push the clump of food, called a bolus, down the throat. When you swallow, the bolus first enters the area at the back of the throat called the pharynx. As this occurs, a flap of connective tissue called the epiglottis closes over the opening to the trachea. This action prevents food from moving into the air passageways to the lungs as it passes through the pharynx and into the esophagus.

BUILD Vocabulary

WORD ORIGINS The prefix *amyl-* refers to starch and has both Greek (*amylon*) and Latin (*amylum*) origins. The suffix *-ase* is commonly used to indicate that a substance is an enzyme. **Amylase** is an enzyme that acts on starch.

In Your Notebook *Explain in your own words two protective functions of the mouth and throat.*

How Science Works

WATCHING AS THE STOMACH CHURNS

In 1822, a U.S. Army surgeon named William Beaumont was called upon to treat a gunshot wound in the stomach of a Canadian fur trapper. Although the wound healed enough for the trapper to survive, it left a permanent hole in his stomach. Beaumont saw this as a rare opportunity to study the role of the stomach in digestion. With his patient's reluctant permission, Beaumont inserted bits of food tied to strings into his stomach through the hole. Then, he withdrew them periodically to see the extent of digestion. Beaumont also siphoned off gastric secretions and had their chemical composition analyzed. He learned that digestion is primarily a chemical process and that gastric secretions consist mostly of hydrochloric acid. These and other results of Beaumont's innovative research remain valid today.

The Esophagus From the throat, the bolus passes through a tube called the **esophagus** into the stomach. You might think that gravity draws food down through the esophagus, but this is not correct. In fact, you can swallow quite well in zero gravity, as astronauts do, or even while standing on your head. The reason is that contractions of smooth muscles, known as **peristalsis** (pehr uh STAL sis), provide the force that moves food through the esophagus toward the stomach. Peristalsis in the esophagus is shown in **Figure 30–12.**

After food passes into the stomach, a thick ring of muscle called the cardiac sphincter closes the esophagus. This prevents the contents of the stomach from flowing back. Overeating or drinking excess caffeine can cause a backflow of stomach acid into the esophagus. The result is a burning sensation in the center of the chest known as heartburn. Despite its name, heartburn has nothing to do with the heart. Nonetheless, persistent heartburn can cause serious damage to the esophagus and is a reason to visit a doctor.

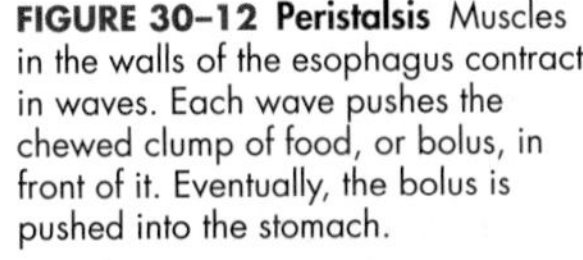

FIGURE 30–12 Peristalsis Muscles in the walls of the esophagus contract in waves. Each wave pushes the chewed clump of food, or bolus, in front of it. Eventually, the bolus is pushed into the stomach.

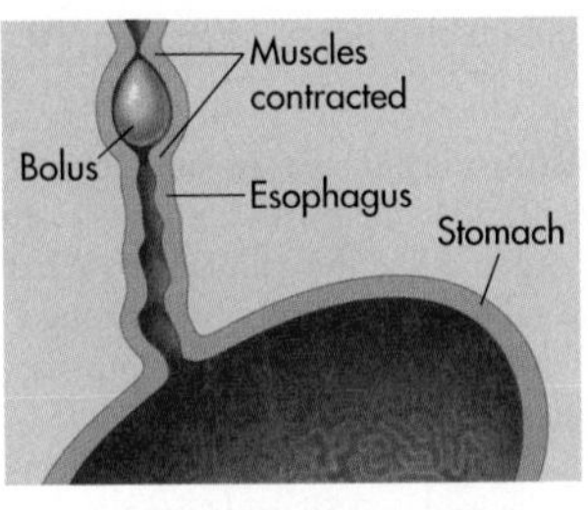

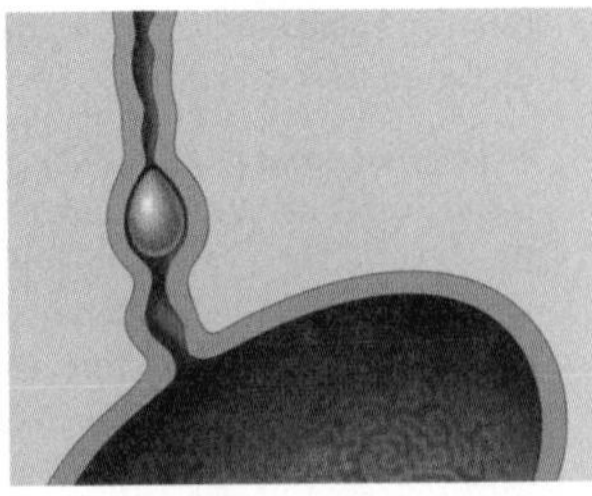

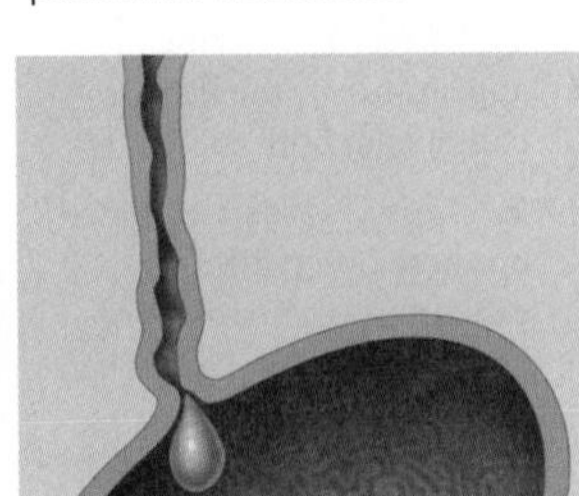

Chemical Digestion in the Stomach The **stomach** is a large muscular sac that continues the chemical and mechanical digestion of food. The lining of the stomach contains millions of microscopic gastric glands that release many substances into the stomach. Some of these glands produce hydrochloric acid. Other glands release an enzyme called pepsin that is activated in and functions best in acidic conditions. **Pepsin** breaks proteins into smaller polypeptide fragments.

Another stomach gland produces mucus, a fluid that lubricates and protects the stomach wall. If this protective layer fails, acids may erode the stomach lining and cause a sore called a peptic ulcer. For years, physicians thought that the primary cause of ulcers was too much stomach acid. They prescribed drugs that reduced symptoms but did not cure ulcers. Scientists have since discovered that most peptic ulcers are the result of infection with the bacterium *Helicobacter pylori.* Most peptic ulcers can now be cured with antibiotics that kill the bacteria.

Mechanical Digestion in the Stomach Alternating contractions of the stomach's three smooth muscle layers thoroughly churn and mix the swallowed food. The churning causes further breakdown of the chunks of swallowed food and allows enzymes greater access to the food. Gradually, a mixture with an oatmeal-like consistency called **chyme** (KYM) is produced. After an hour or two, the pyloric valve, which is located between the stomach and small intestine, opens, and chyme begins to spurt into the small intestine.

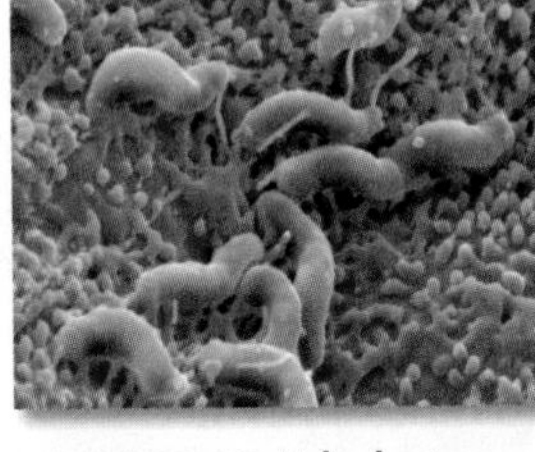

FIGURE 30–13 *Helicobacter pylori* After many years of blaming lifestyle factors for ulcers, researchers discovered that these bacteria are the cause. *H. pylori* burrow into the stomach wall and cause inflammation (SEM 6800×).

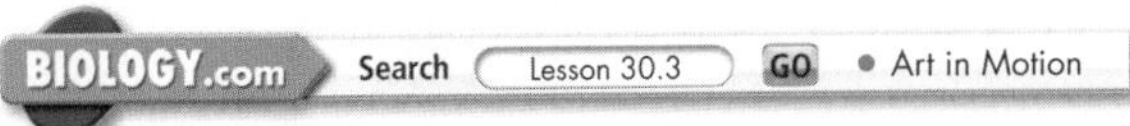

Expand Vocabulary

Write the word *esophagus* on the board. Point out that the word *esophagus* contains the root word *phage,* which means "to eat." Ask students to identify other scientific terms that contain this root word. *(Sample answers: bacteriophage—a virus that infects bacteria, phagocytosis—a form of active transport in which a cell's cytoplasm engulfs a particle and brings it into the cell)* Then, have students relate the meaning of the root word *phage* to the function of the esophagus. *(When food is eaten, the esophagus "engulfs" the food when it is swallowed.)*

DIFFERENTIATED INSTRUCTION

LPR **Less Proficient Readers** Have students preview the vocabulary on the page. Pronounce each word aloud for students and give a quick definition. Then, have them write a sentence that uses each word. Suggest they share their sentences with a partner before reading the text.

BIOLOGY.com Students can learn more about peristalsis using an animated version of **Figure 30–12** by watching **Art in Motion: Peristalsis.**

UbD Check for Understanding

INDEX CARD SUMMARIES

Give each student an index card. Ask students to write one concept about digestion that they understand on the front of the card. Then, have them identify something about digestion they do not understand and write it on the back of the card in the form of a question.

ADJUST INSTRUCTION

Read over students' cards to identify concepts that are well understood and those that are causing confusion. Choose several representative questions to discuss with the class.

Teach continued

Lead a Discussion

Point out that although the pancreas, liver, and gallbladder serve important functions in digestion, food does not pass through these organs.

Ask The enzymes produced by the pancreas break down which types of nutrients? *(proteins, fats, and carbohydrates)*

Ask Bile, which is produced by the liver and released by the gallbladder, affects digestion of which type of nutrient? *(fats)*

DIFFERENTIATED INSTRUCTION

L1 Struggling Students Point out that most chemical digestion occurs in the small intestine.

Ask Where do the substances that digest food in the small intestine come from? *(Some are made by the small intestine itself; some are produced in the pancreas and released into the small intestine; some are produced in the liver and released from the gallbladder into the small intestine.)*

Address Misconceptions

Enzymes Many students think that enzymes are made up of cells. Point out that the cell is the basic unit of life, but not all substances within the body are made up of cells. Remind students that enzymes are proteins, a kind of macromolecule. Students should review the information about the chemistry of life found in this book if they have more questions about enzymes.

Answers

FIGURE 30–14 Digestion of carbohydrates begins in the mouth.

IN YOUR NOTEBOOK The two roles of the pancreas in fat digestion are the production of lipase that breaks down fats and the production of sodium bicarbonate, a substance that allows enzymes to function by neutralizing stomach acid.

Modeling Bile Action 

❶ Add 10 mL of water and 2 drops of olive oil into two test tubes.

❷ Add 3 mL of a 5 percent liquid soap solution to one test tube.

❸ Stir the contents of both tubes. Record your observations.

Analyze and Conclude

1. Observe Describe the appearance of the liquid contents in both tubes.

2. Draw Conclusions Based on these observations, explain in your own words how bile aids fat digestion.

Digestion in the Small Intestine As chyme is pushed through the pyloric valve, it enters the duodenum (doo oh DEE num). The duodenum is the first part of the **small intestine,** and it is where almost all of the digestive enzymes enter the intestine. Most of the chemical digestion and absorption of the food you eat occurs in the small intestine. As chyme enters the duodenum from the stomach, it mixes with enzymes and digestive fluids from the pancreas, the liver, and even the lining of the duodenum itself. The pancreas and liver are shown in **Figure 30–15.**

▶ ***Pancreas*** Just behind the stomach is the pancreas, a gland that serves three important functions. One function is to produce hormones that regulate blood sugar levels. Within the digestive system, the pancreas has two other roles. It produces enzymes that break down carbohydrates, proteins, lipids, and nucleic acids. The pancreas also produces sodium bicarbonate, a base that quickly neutralizes stomach acid as chyme enters the duodenum. The enzymes produced by the pancreas, unlike those produced in the stomach, would be destroyed by strong acid, and therefore the sodium bicarbonate is necessary for digestion to proceed.

▶ ***The Liver and Gallbladder*** Assisting the pancreas in fat digestion is the liver. The liver produces bile, a fluid loaded with lipids and salts. Bile is stored in a small, pouchlike organ called the gallbladder. When fat is present in the duodenum, the gallbladder releases bile through a duct into the small intestine. Fats tend to glob together, which makes fat digestion by enzymes such as lipase difficult. Bile breaks up the globs of fat into smaller droplets that disperse in the watery environment of the small intestine. This action makes it possible for enzymes to reach the smaller fat droplets and break them down.

In Your Notebook *Summarize the two roles of the pancreas in fat digestion.*

FIGURE 30–14 Effects of Digestive Enzymes Digestive enzymes hasten the breakdown of foods and make nutrients available to the body. **Interpret Tables** ***Where in the body does the digestion of carbohydrates begin?***

Effects of Digestive Enzymes

Active Site	Enzyme	Effect on Food
Mouth	Salivary amylase	Breaks down starches into disaccharides
Stomach	Pepsin	Breaks down proteins into large peptides
Small intestine (released from pancreas)	Pancreatic amylase	Continues the breakdown of starch
	Trypsin	Continues the breakdown of protein
	Lipase	Breaks down fat
Small intestine	Maltase, sucrase, lactase	Breaks down remaining disaccharides into monosaccharides
	Peptidase	Breaks down dipeptides into amino acids

PURPOSE Students will model the role of bile in the digestion of fat.

MATERIALS large test tubes, 10-mL graduated cylinder, olive oil, 5% liquid soap solution

SAFETY Remind students to be careful handling glassware.

PLANNING Make the 5% liquid soap solution by mixing 5 mL liquid soap in 100 mL water.

ANALYZE AND CONCLUDE

1. Students should observe that the olive oil in the tube with only water forms large drops; the olive oil with water and soap forms small droplets.
2. Bile aids fat digestion by breaking the fat into smaller droplets, allowing enzymes to act on more of the fat.

THE DIGESTIVE SYSTEM

FIGURE 30–15 Food travels through many organs as it is broken down into nutrients your body can use. The time needed for each organ to perform its role varies based on the type of food consumed.

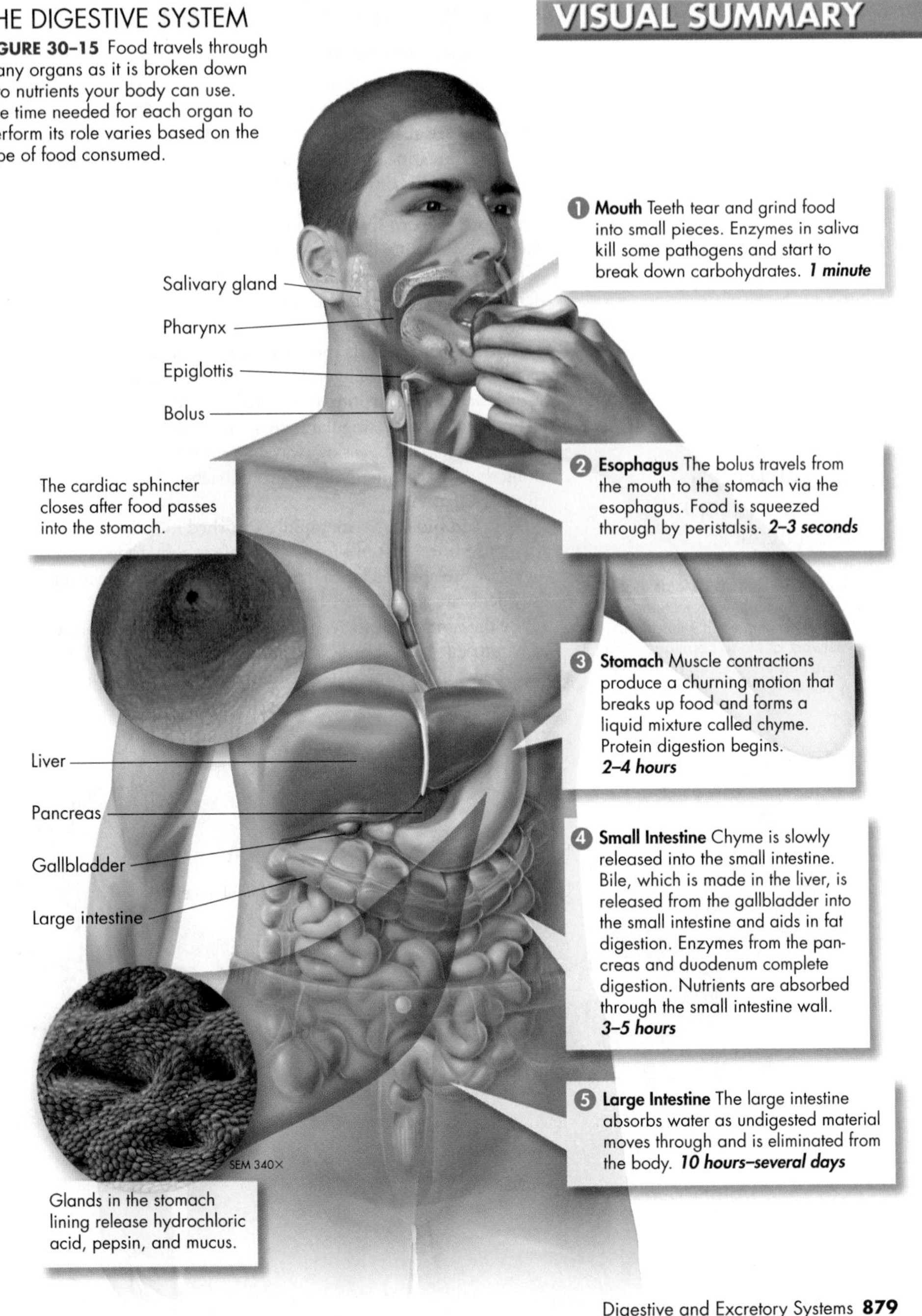

VISUAL SUMMARY
Salivary gland
Pharynx
Epiglottis
Bolus
The cardiac sphincter closes after food passes into the stomach.
Liver
Pancreas
Gallbladder
Large intestine
SEM 340×
Glands in the stomach lining release hydrochloric acid, pepsin, and mucus.
1 Mouth Teeth tear and grind food into small pieces. Enzymes in saliva kill some pathogens and start to break down carbohydrates. 1 minute
2 Esophagus The bolus travels from the mouth to the stomach via the esophagus. Food is squeezed through by peristalsis. 2–3 seconds
3 Stomach Muscle contractions produce a churning motion that breaks up food and forms a liquid mixture called chyme. Protein digestion begins. 2–4 hours
4 Small Intestine Chyme is slowly released into the small intestine. Bile, which is made in the liver, is released from the gallbladder into the small intestine and aids in fat digestion. Enzymes from the pancreas and duodenum complete digestion. Nutrients are absorbed through the small intestine wall. 3–5 hours
5 Large Intestine The large intestine absorbs water as undigested material moves through and is eliminated from the body. 10 hours–several days

How Science Works

VIEWING THE DIGESTIVE SYSTEM

In 2004, the Food and Drug Administration approved the use of a miniature camera, which is swallowed like a pill, for use in diagnosing problems with the digestive system. The camera transmits images as it moves through the digestive system, allowing doctors to visualize and diagnose conditions such as gastroesophageal reflux, unexplained abdominal pain, or polyps. Recent improvements in this technology allow doctors to manipulate the camera as it moves through the digestive system via a magnetic device held outside the body. This is particularly helpful for viewing parts of the digestive system through which the camera moves very rapidly, such as the esophagus and the upper part of the stomach.

VISUAL SUMMARY

Have students use **Figure 30–15** to trace the path of food through the digestive system. Ask them to work in pairs to talk about what happens to the food as it passes through, or by, each digestive structure. Then, suggest they review the four functions of the digestive system—ingestion, digestion, absorption, and elimination. Have them talk about how each labeled structure is involved in one or more of these functions.

DIFFERENTIATED INSTRUCTION

L1 Struggling Students Have groups of students work through the visual step by step. Ask them to carefully read and discuss the caption for each numbered step. Suggest they discuss reasons why the steps take the time that they do and that they take notes on the discussion.

ELL English Language Learners Photocopy **Figure 30–15.** Next to each structure's English name, write its name in your students' native language. For example, if your students are Spanish speakers, write the word *Boca* next to *Mouth*. Pass out the photocopy and have students use it to help them review digestive structures.

Teach continued

ZOOMING IN

Have students examine the structure of the small intestine shown in **Figure 30–16.**

Ask How is the structure of the small intestine related to its function? *(The many folds and projections of the small intestine result in an enormous surface area. Because absorption requires contact between the nutrient molecules and the cells lining the small intestine, a large surface area is critical to the function of the small intestine.)*

DIFFERENTIATED INSTRUCTION

L1 Special Needs Have students feel and examine a terrycloth towel. Ask them to note the many tiny loops of thread that make up the surface of the towel. Tell students these loops help the towel soak up water. Relate the structure and function of the bath towel to the structure and function of the small intestine.

L1 Struggling Students Make sure students understand the relationships between the different structures pictured in **Figure 30–16.** Start by pointing at the picture of the small intestine. Explain that the diagram directly to the right shows a larger version of two of the circular folds circled in the small intestine diagram. Walk through the rest of the diagram with students. Have students discuss how each labeled structure helps the small intestine absorb nutrients.

Absorption and Elimination

How are nutrients absorbed and wastes eliminated?

Once the small intestine has completed the digestive process, nutrients must be absorbed from the alimentary canal. **Most nutrients from food are absorbed through the walls of the small intestine. The large intestine absorbs water and several vitamins and prepares waste for elimination from the body.**

Absorption From the Small Intestine After leaving the duodenum, chyme moves along the rest of the small intestine. By this time, most of the chemical digestion has been completed. The chyme is now a rich mixture of small- and medium-sized nutrient molecules that are ready to be absorbed.

The small intestine is specially adapted for absorption of nutrients. Its folded surface and fingerlike projections provide an enormous surface area for absorption of nutrient molecules. The fingerlike projections, called **villi** (singular: villus), are covered with tiny projections known as microvilli. As slow, wavelike contractions move the chyme along the surface, microvilli absorb nutrients. **Figure 30–16** illustrates villi and microvilli.

Nutrient molecules are rapidly absorbed into the cells lining the small intestine. Most of the products of carbohydrate and protein digestion are absorbed into the capillaries in the villi. Most fats and fatty acids are absorbed by lymph vessels.

By the time chyme is ready to leave the small intestine, it is basically nutrient-free. Complex organic molecules have been digested and absorbed, leaving only water, cellulose, and other undigestible substances behind.

ZOOMING IN

ABSORPTION IN THE SMALL INTESTINE

FIGURE 30–16 The lining of the small intestine consists of folds that are covered with tiny projections called villi. Within each villus there is a network of blood capillaries and lymph vessels that absorb and carry away nutrients.

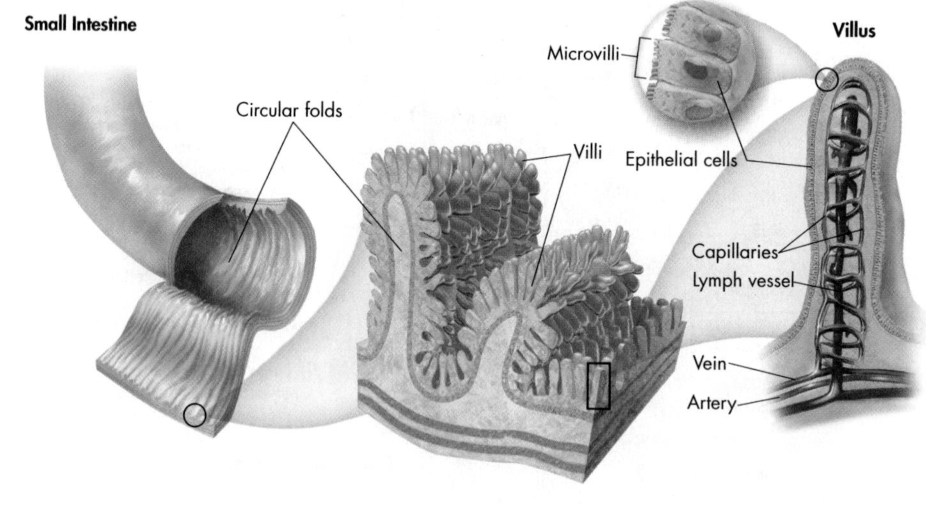

UbD Check for Understanding

DEPTH OF UNDERSTANDING

Write the following question on the board:

- Does the process of digestion release chemical energy from food and form ATP for use in cell processes? Explain.

Students with a superficial understanding of the processes of digestion and cellular respiration may answer *yes* to this question. These students may not have a clear understanding of how digestion affects food molecules (digestion breaks down food molecules into small molecules), or how these molecules are used after being transported to the body's cells.

Students with a sophisticated understanding of the processes of digestion and cellular respiration will answer *no* to this question. These students understand that the molecules that result from the process of digestion are transported to the body's cells, where they may be used to make ATP molecules through the processes of cellular respiration and fermentation (in active muscle cells).

ADJUST INSTRUCTION

If students answer *yes* to the question, have them review the functions of the digestive system, which are described in this lesson, and the process of cellular respiration, which is described in Chapter 9. Then, suggest they discuss the answer in small groups.

As material leaves the small intestine and enters the large intestine, it passes by a small saclike organ called the appendix. In some mammals, the appendix processes cellulose and other materials. The only time humans notice their appendix is when it becomes clogged and inflamed, causing appendicitis. The remedy for appendicitis is to remove the infected organ by surgery—as quickly as possible—before it can rupture or break open.

Absorption From the Large Intestine When chyme leaves the small intestine, it enters the **large intestine,** or colon. The large intestine is actually much shorter than the small intestine. The large intestine gets its name due to its diameter, which is much greater than the small intestine's diameter. The primary function of the large intestine is to remove water from the undigested material that is left. Water is absorbed quickly across the wall of the large intestine, leaving behind the undigested materials. Rich colonies of bacteria present in the large intestine produce compounds that the body is able to absorb and use, including vitamin K. When large doses of antibiotics are given to fight an infection, they can destroy these bacteria, and vitamin K deficiency can occur.

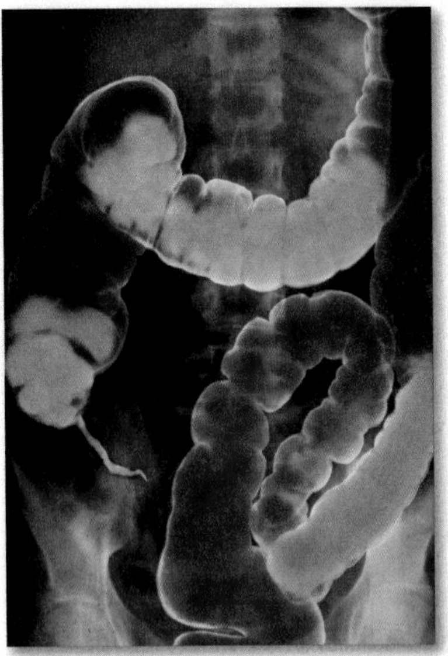

FIGURE 30–17 The Large Intestine This X-ray shows the large intestine and its contents.

Elimination The concentrated waste material—the feces—that remains after most of the water has been removed passes into the rectum and is eliminated from the body through the anus. When something happens that interferes with the removal of water by the large intestine, you usually become aware of it right away. If not enough water is absorbed, a condition known as diarrhea occurs. If too much water is absorbed from the undigested materials, a condition known as constipation occurs.

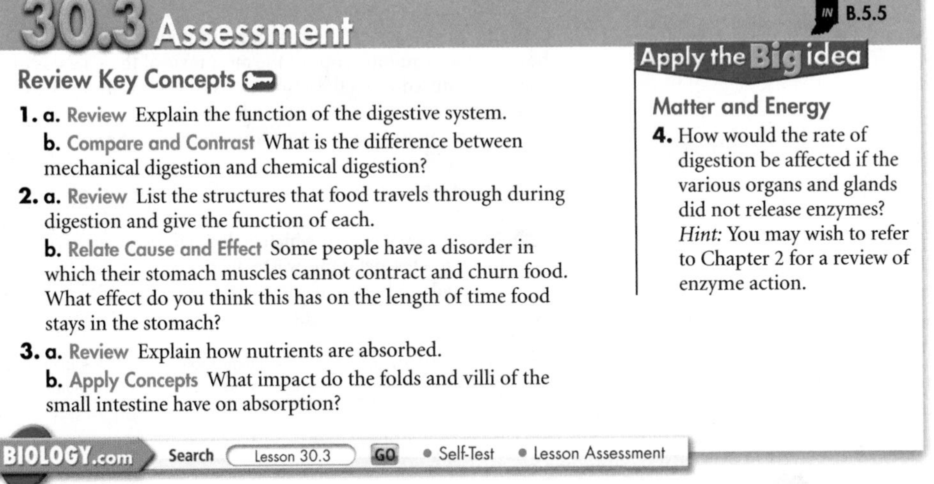

30.3 Assessment

IN B.5.5

Review Key Concepts

1. a. Review Explain the function of the digestive system.
   b. Compare and Contrast What is the difference between mechanical digestion and chemical digestion?
2. a. Review List the structures that food travels through during digestion and give the function of each.
   b. Relate Cause and Effect Some people have a disorder in which their stomach muscles cannot contract and churn food. What effect do you think this has on the length of time food stays in the stomach?
3. a. Review Explain how nutrients are absorbed.
   b. Apply Concepts What impact do the folds and villi of the small intestine have on absorption?

Apply the Big idea

Matter and Energy

4. How would the rate of digestion be affected if the various organs and glands did not release enzymes? *Hint:* You may wish to refer to Chapter 2 for a review of enzyme action.

BIOLOGY.com Search Lesson 30.3 GO • Self-Test • Lesson Assessment

Assess and Remediate

EVALUATE UNDERSTANDING

Ask students to write a short paragraph that describes the path food takes through the digestive system. Call on volunteers to share what they have written with the class. Then, have students complete the 30.3 Assessment.

REMEDIATION SUGGESTION

L1 **Struggling Students** If students have difficulty answering **Question 2b,** ask them to explain what happens when the stomach churns. *(Food is mixed with digestive enzymes.)* Then, have students consider what would happen if this mixing did not occur. *(Chemical digestion would proceed more slowly.)*

BIOLOGY.com Students can check their understanding of lesson concepts with the **Self-Test** assessment. They can then take an online version of the **Lesson Assessment.**

Assessment Answers

1a. to get food into the body and to break it down into small molecules that can be used by the body

1b. Mechanical digestion is the physical breakdown of large pieces of food into smaller pieces; chemical digestion changes large food molecules into smaller molecules.

2a. the mouth, where ingestion occurs and digestion begins; the esophagus, through which food passes on its way to the stomach; the stomach, where digestion continues; and the small intestine, where chemical digestion is completed and absorption of nutrients occurs

2b. If a person's stomach cannot contract and churn, food must stay in the stomach longer in order to be digested.

3a. Nutrients are absorbed when they come into contact with the villi in the small intestine. They are absorbed into and carried away by networks of capillaries and lymph vessels inside the villi.

3b. The folds and villi of the small intestine greatly increase its surface area, thereby increasing the amount of nutrients that can be absorbed.

4.  The rate of digestion would be decreased if various organs and glands did not release enzymes.

LESSON 30.4

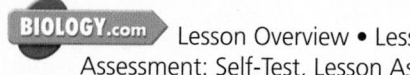

Getting Started

Objectives

30.4.1 Describe the structures of the excretory system and explain their functions.

30.4.2 Explain how the kidneys clean the blood.

30.4.3 Describe how the kidneys maintain homeostasis.

Student Resources

Study Workbooks A and B, 30.4 Worksheets

Spanish Study Workbook, 30.4 Worksheets

Lesson Overview • Lesson Notes • Assessment: Self-Test, Lesson Assessment

For corresponding lesson in the **Foundation Edition,** see pages 729–733.

Activate Prior Knowledge

Have students discuss what might happen if a city's trash removal program stopped working. *(Trash would begin to pile up in the city.)* Then ask how this might relate to what students will be learning in this lesson. *(The excretory system collects and removes wastes much like a city's trash removal system.)*

Answers

IN YOUR NOTEBOOK Students' tables should list skin, lungs, liver, kidneys, ureters, urinary bladder, and urethra, and the function of each.

INDIANA ACADEMIC STANDARDS

For the full text of all standards, see the Course Overview in the front matter of this book.

NoS.3 Clearly communicate their ideas and results of investigations verbally and in written form using tables, graphs, diagrams, and photographs.

The Excretory System

Key Questions

What is the principal role of the structures of the excretory system?

How do the kidneys clean the blood?

How do the kidneys help maintain homeostasis?

Vocabulary

excretion
ureter
urinary bladder
urethra
nephron
filtration
glomerulus
Bowman's capsule
reabsorption
loop of Henle

Taking Notes

Preview Visuals Examine **Figure 30–19.** What does this Figure reveal about the important functions of the kidneys?

THINK ABOUT IT It's a hot day, and you've been getting thirsty for hours. Finally, you get the chance to go inside, and you gulp down more than a liter of water. The water tastes great, but as you drink, you begin to wonder. Where's all that water going? Will it just dilute your blood, or is something in your body making sure that everything stays in balance?

Structures of the Excretory System

What is the principal role of the structures of the excretory system?

The chemistry of the human body is a marvelous thing. An intricate system of checks and balances controls everything from your blood pressure to your body temperature. Nutrients are absorbed, stored, and carefully released when they are needed. However, every living system, including the human body, produces chemical waste products, some of which are so toxic that they will cause death if they are not eliminated.

For example, as a normal consequence of being alive, every cell in the body produces waste compounds, including excess salts and carbon dioxide. Ammonia, one of the most toxic of these waste compounds, is produced when the amino acids from proteins are used for energy. Ammonia is converted to a less toxic compound called urea, but it, too, must be eliminated from the body. The process by which these metabolic wastes are eliminated to maintain homeostasis is called **excretion.** Excretion is one part of the many processes that maintain homeostasis.

The excretory system, which includes the skin, lungs, liver, and kidneys, excretes metabolic wastes from the body. The ureters, urinary bladder, and urethra are also involved in excretion. **Figure 30–18** shows the major organs of excretion.

In Your Notebook *Make a two-column table that lists the organs of excretion in the first column and their function in the second column.*

UbD Teach for Understanding

ENDURING UNDERSTANDING The human body is a complex system. The coordinated functions of its many structures support life processes and maintain homeostasis.

GUIDING QUESTION How does the human body get rid of wastes?

EVIDENCE OF UNDERSTANDING *At the end of the lesson, give students this assessment to show they understand how the excretory system helps the body maintain homeostasis.* Break the class into small groups. Have each group develop a pamphlet that describes the importance of the excretory system to the body. Have each group share its pamphlet with the class.

The Skin The skin excretes excess water, salts, and a small amount of urea in sweat. By releasing sweat in very small amounts, this process eliminates wastes even when you may not think you're sweating.

The Lungs The blood transports carbon dioxide, a waste product of cellular respiration, from the body cells to the lungs. When you exhale, your lungs excrete carbon dioxide and small amounts of water vapor.

The Liver The liver plays many important roles in excretion. As we have seen, one of its principal activities is the conversion of potentially dangerous nitrogen wastes, a product of protein breakdown, into less toxic urea. Urea, which is highly soluble, is then transported through the blood to the kidneys for elimination from the body.

The Kidneys The major organs of excretion are the kidneys, a pair of fist-sized organs located on either side of the spinal column near the lower back. Through a complex filtering process, the kidneys remove excess water, urea, and metabolic wastes from the blood. The kidneys produce and excrete a waste product known as urine. **Ureters** transport urine from the kidneys to the **urinary bladder,** where the urine is stored until it is released through the **urethra.**

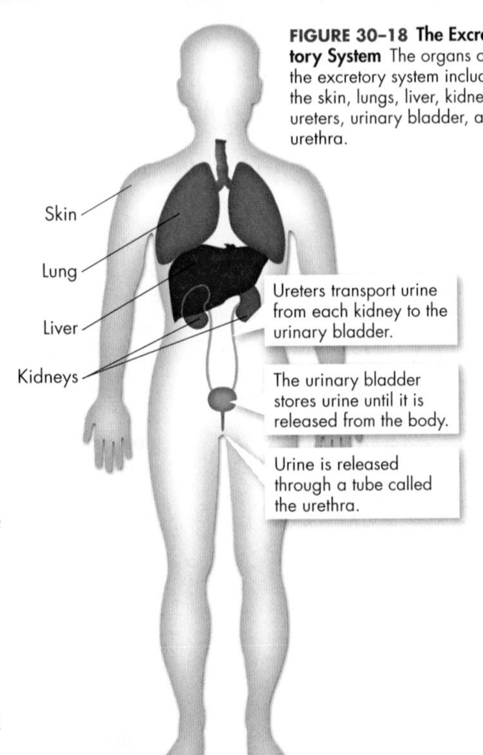
Skin
Lung
Liver
Kidneys
Ureters transport urine from each kidney to the urinary bladder.
The urinary bladder stores urine until it is released from the body.
Urine is released through a tube called the urethra.

FIGURE 30–18 The Excretory System The organs of the excretory system include the skin, lungs, liver, kidneys, ureters, urinary bladder, and urethra.

Analyzing Data

NoS.3

The Composition of Urine

The kidneys are selective filters. As blood passes through them, urea, other impurities, and excess salts are removed from the blood. But important substances such as water, protein, and glucose remain in circulation. The collected waste products are excreted in urine. The concentrations of certain substances in the blood compared to their concentration in urine reveal the important work of the kidneys.

Concentrations of Selected Substances in Blood and Urine

Substance	Average Concentration in Blood (g/mL)	Average Concentration in Urine (g/mL)
Calcium	0.01	0.02
Glucose	0.10	0.00
Potassium	0.02	0.20
Sodium	0.32	0.60
Urea	0.03	2.00

1. Interpret Data Which substances listed have the highest and lowest concentrations in the blood? Which substances have the highest and lowest concentrations in the urine?

2. Calculate Approximately how many times more concentrated is urea in urine than in the blood? MATH

3. Infer Recall that urea is a byproduct of amino acid breakdown. How might the urea concentration vary in the blood and urine as the result of high protein diets? Explain.

Teach

Use Visuals

Have students examine the structures of the excretory system, which are shown in **Figure 30–18.** Have students talk about how each of the labeled structures help the body remove wastes.

DIFFERENTIATED INSTRUCTION

LPR Less Proficient Readers Help students relate the labeled structures in **Figure 30–18** to the information in the text. Show them that each boldface paragraph head and its associated text correspond with a label on the left side of the diagram. Then, point out that each lesson vocabulary term on this page is described in a text box on the right side of the diagram. Make sure students understand that all seven labeled structures in the diagram are organs of the excretory system.

L3 Advanced Students Have advanced students make connections between the excretory system and waste removal at the cellular level. Point out that, like the human body, individual cells also need to remove wastes.

Ask What structures in your cells are involved in waste removal? Explain. *(Lysosomes break down and recycle macromolecules. The cell membrane regulates materials leaving the cell.)*

Then have them write a short paragraph describing why waste removal at the cellular level is important.

PURPOSE Students will examine and interpret data to identify substances that are removed from the blood by the kidneys and those that are not.

PLANNING Remind students to carefully read the heading of each column of the table.

ANSWERS

1. Sodium has the highest concentration in the blood; calcium has the lowest concentration in the blood. The substance that has the highest concentration in urine is urea; glucose has the lowest concentration in urine.
2. Urea is approximately 67 times more concentrated in urine than it is in blood.
3. A high-protein diet includes more amino acids than a typical diet, so the urea concentrations in both blood and urine would increase as a result.

LESSON 30.4

Teach continued

Use Models

Point out that the function of the kidneys is to filter out wastes from the blood and reabsorb useful substances. Model how the kidney works by pouring water mixed with food coloring and clean sand through a coffee filter. Invite students to examine the contents of the coffee filter and the colored water that emerges from it.

Ask What process did this model demonstrate? *(filtration)*

Ask What substances in blood are modeled by the sand in this demonstration? *(blood cells and large molecules)*

Ask In the kidney, what process follows filtration? *(reabsorbtion)*

DIFFERENTIATED INSTRUCTION

L1 Special Needs Have a classmate describe the model to visually-impaired students. As they discuss the model, remind students that the model simulates only filtration, not reabsorption.

MYSTERY CLUE Students should note that almost every substance is removed from blood during the process of filtration; then substances needed by the body are reabsorbed. Students can go online to **Biology.com** to gather their evidence.

Excretion and the Kidneys

How do the kidneys clean the blood?

What does a kidney do? **As waste-laden blood enters the kidney through the renal artery, the kidney removes urea, excess water and minerals, and other waste products.** The clean, filtered blood leaves the kidney through the renal vein and returns to circulation.

Each kidney contains nearly a million individual processing units called **nephrons.** These nephrons are where most of the work of the kidney takes place—impurities are filtered out, wastes are collected, and purified blood is returned to circulation. Blood purification in the kidneys is complex and involves two distinct processes: filtration and reabsorption.

BUILD Vocabulary

WORD ORIGINS The word **glomerulus** derives from the Latin words *glomus,* which means "ball of yarn," and *glomerare,* which means "to form into a ball." The twisted capillaries of a glomerulus resemble a ball of yarn.

Filtration Passing a liquid or gas through a filter to remove wastes is called **filtration.** The filtration of blood mainly takes place in the **glomerulus** (gloh MUR yoo lus). A glomerulus is a small but dense network of capillaries (very small blood vessels) encased in the upper end of each nephron by a hollow, cup-shaped structure called **Bowman's capsule.** A glomerulus is shown in **Figure 30–19.**

Because the blood is under pressure and the walls of the capillaries and Bowman's capsule are permeable, much of the fluid from the capillaries flows into Bowman's capsule. The material that is filtered from the blood is called the filtrate. The filtrate contains water, urea, glucose, salts, amino acids, and some vitamins. Large substances in the blood, such as proteins and blood cells, are too large to pass through the capillary walls.

Reabsorption Nearly 180 liters of filtrate pass from the blood into nephron tubules every day. That's the equivalent of 90 2-liter bottles of soft drink. Thank goodness, not all of those 180 liters are excreted. In fact, nearly all of the material that moves into Bowman's capsule makes its way back into the blood. The process by which water and dissolved substances are taken back into the blood is called **reabsorption.**

A number of materials, including salts, vitamins, amino acids, fats, and glucose, are removed from the filtrate by active transport and reabsorbed by the capillaries. Because water follows these materials by osmosis, almost 99 percent of the water that enters Bowman's capsule is actually reabsorbed into the blood. In effect, the kidney first throws away nearly everything and then takes back only what the body needs. This is how the kidney is able to remove drugs and toxic compounds from the blood—even chemicals the body has never seen before.

A section of the nephron tubule called the **loop of Henle** is responsible for conserving water and minimizing the volume of the filtrate. The waste material—now called urine—that remains in the tubule is emptied into a collecting duct.

MYSTERY CLUE

The illegal drug taken by one of the athletes contained a synthetic compound never found in nature. How did his body remove the compound from his blood and eliminate it in urine?

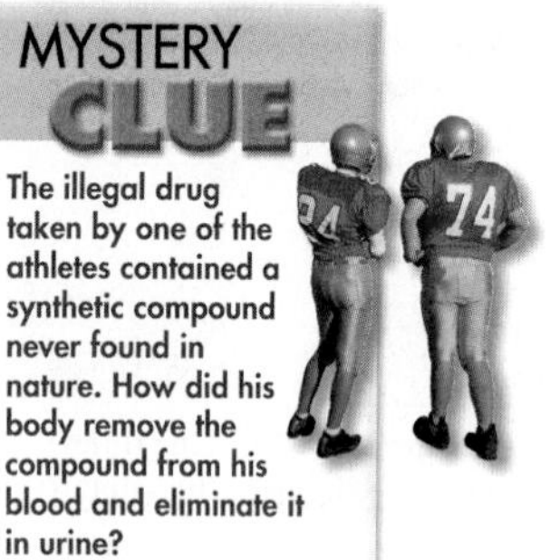

Urine Excretion From the collecting ducts, urine flows to the ureter of each kidney. The ureters carry urine to the urinary bladder for storage until the urine leaves the body through the urethra.

UbD Check for Understanding

QUESTION BOARD

Establish a section of a bulletin board or white board in the classroom that can be used by students to post questions about concepts or processes that they do not understand. After discussing excretion and the kidneys, ask students to post their questions in the designated area. Assure students that they do not need to post their names with their questions.

ADJUST INSTRUCTION

Read over students' questions to identify common topics that students are struggling to understand. Then, have students form small groups. Assign one of these topics to each group. Have each group prepare a short report on its assigned topic.

ZOOMING IN

STRUCTURE AND FUNCTION OF THE KIDNEYS

FIGURE 30–19 Kidneys are made up of nephrons. Blood enters the nephron, where impurities are filtered out and emptied into the collecting duct. Purified blood leaves a nephron through a vein. **Interpret Visuals** ***List in order the structures that blood flows through in a kidney.***

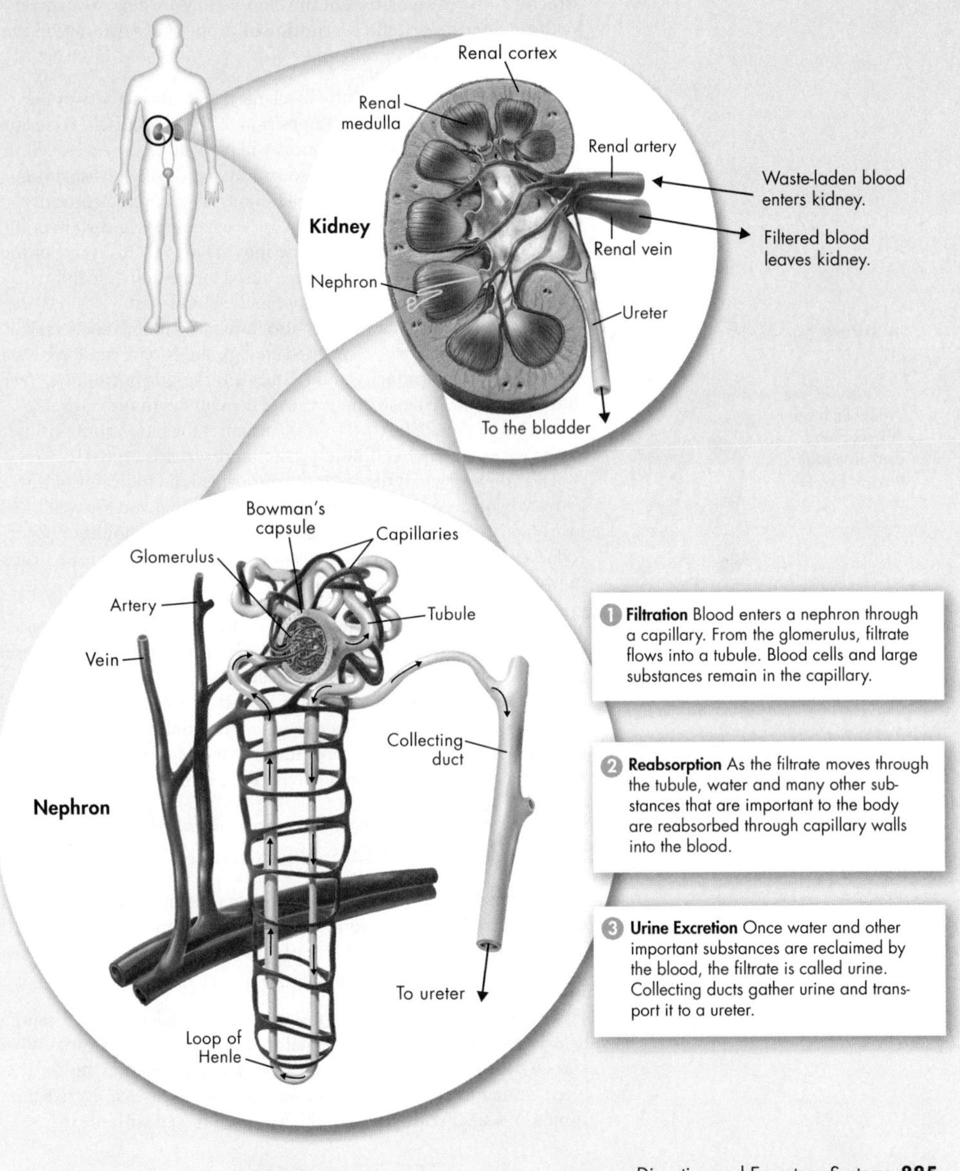
Renal cortex
Renal medulla
Renal artery
Waste-laden blood enters kidney.
Kidney
Filtered blood leaves kidney.
Renal vein
Nephron
Ureter
To the bladder
Bowman's capsule
Capillaries
Glomerulus
Artery
Tubule
Vein
Collecting duct
Nephron
To ureter
Loop of Henle
1 **Filtration** Blood enters a nephron through a capillary. From the glomerulus, filtrate flows into a tubule. Blood cells and large substances remain in the capillary.
2 **Reabsorption** As the filtrate moves through the tubule, water and many other substances that are important to the body are reabsorbed through capillary walls into the blood.
3 **Urine Excretion** Once water and other important substances are reclaimed by the blood, the filtrate is called urine. Collecting ducts gather urine and transport it to a ureter.

ZOOMING IN

Ask students to use **Figure 30–19** to examine how kidneys and nephrons remove wastes. Have small groups of students trace the path of a urea molecule from blood in a renal artery to urine in a ureter. Have them talk about what is happening in the nephron at different points in this path.

DIFFERENTIATED INSTRUCTION

L1 Struggling Students Some students might be overwhelmed by the amount of information presented in **Figure 30–19.** Have students work in groups of three to review the figure. For the information in the numbered boxes, suggest each students in the group choose a different box to focus on. Ask students to summarize the information in their boxes for their group members. Call on groups to share summaries with the class.

ELL Focus on ELL: Access Content

BEGINNING AND INTERMEDIATE SPEAKERS Have students draw a **Flowchart** titled "How do the kidneys clean blood?" Have students label three squares in the flowchart "filtration," "reabsorption," and "urine excretion." Ask students to write an explanation and add an illustration to each box. Allow for less-than-precise content words for beginning speakers.

Study Wkbks A/B, Appendix S25, Flowchart. **Transparencies,** GO8.

How Science Works

BRIGHT'S DISEASE

In 1827, an English physician named Richard Bright published his findings that people who suffered from edema (swelling of body tissues), which was then called "dropsy," have a substance in their urine that coagulates when the urine is boiled. This substance has since been identified to be serum albumin, and it is not excreted normally in urine. Serum albumin in urine is a sign that the patient has nephritis, or inflammation of the kidneys. Because of Bright's pioneering work, nephritis is still sometimes called Bright's disease. Today, urinalysis is routinely used to detect a large number of disorders. Dipsticks are available that can be used to easily perform multiple assays on a single urine sample. These dipsticks usually test urine pH; specific gravity; and presence of proteins, glucose, ketones, nitrites, and white blood cells. The results of these assays can help medical professionals diagnose specific disorders.

Answers

FIGURE 30–19 Blood enters the kidney through the renal artery. In the kidney, blood enters a nephron and moves through a network of capillaries called the glomerulus where filtration occurs. It then passes through more capillaries where reabsorption takes place. Blood leaves the kidney through the renal vein.

Teach continued

Lead a Discussion

After students have read the text, lead a class discussion on how the kidneys help maintain homeostasis. Encourage students to talk about the different ways kidneys respond to the composition of the blood.

Ask How do the kidneys respond to very high levels of glucose in the blood? *(They excrete glucose into urine.)*

Then, talk about what happens when kidneys do not function well. Discuss how kidney stones, kidney damage, and kidney failure all affect a person's homeostasis.

DIFFERENTIATED INSTRUCTION

LPR Less Proficient Readers Help students organize the information in the text by writing the key question *How do the kidneys help maintain homeostasis?* on the board. Then, as students read the information on the page, have them identify ways kidneys help maintain homeostasis. As they make suggestions, write them in a list under the key question. For example, you might list *remove excess salt* and *excrete hydrogen ions to raise blood pH.*

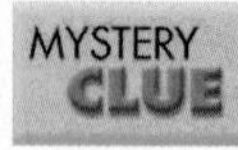

Remind students that Philip and Seth were told to drink water. Ask students to explain how the body responds when it needs to conserve water. *(It produces ADH.)* Use students' answers to guide them to the conclusion that the boys' blood likely contains a high level of ADH. Students can go online to **Biology.com** to gather their evidence.

The Kidneys and Homeostasis

How do the kidneys help maintain homeostasis?

The kidneys play an important role in maintaining homeostasis. Besides removing wastes, the kidneys also maintain blood pH and regulate the water content of the blood. **The kidneys respond directly to the composition of the blood. They are also influenced by the endocrine system. Disruption of proper kidney function can lead to serious health problems.**

Control of Kidney Function To a large extent, the activity of the kidneys is controlled by the composition of the blood itself. For example, if you eat salty food, the kidneys will respond to the excess salt in your blood by returning less salt to your blood during reabsorption. If the blood is too acidic, then the kidneys excrete more hydrogen ions in the urine. If your blood glucose levels rise past a certain point, the kidneys will even excrete glucose into the urine. This is one of the danger signals of diabetes, a disease caused by the body's inability to control the concentration of glucose in the blood.

Glands release hormones that also influence kidney function. For example, if you have not consumed enough fluids or if you have sweat excessively, your pituitary gland releases antidiuretic hormone (ADH) into your blood. This hormone causes the kidneys to reabsorb more water and to excrete less water in the urine. If the blood contains excess water, ADH secretion stops and more water is excreted.

Did you know that the color of your urine is an indicator of how hydrated you are? A pale yellow color indicates that you are well hydrated because your kidneys are releasing a good amount of water. A darker color indicates that the water level in your blood is low, causing your kidneys to conserve water.

MYSTERY CLUE

Would Seth's and Philip's blood contain a high level or low level of ADH?

Urine Testing Medical professionals can learn a lot about a person's health from a simple urine sample. The presence of protein or glucose in urine can be indicators of diseases such as dangerously high blood pressure or diabetes. Although many filtered substances are reabsorbed into the blood, drugs generally remain in the filtrate and are eliminated in urine. This is why the effects of many drugs wear off over time and why urine tests are often used to detect the use of illegal drugs.

In Your Notebook *Explain in your own words why urine can reveal a lot about a person's health.*

Kidney Disorders The kidneys are the master chemists of the blood supply. If anything goes wrong with the kidneys, serious medical problems will likely follow. Three of these problems are kidney stones, kidney damage, and kidney failure.

▶ ***Kidney Stones*** Sometimes substances such as calcium, magnesium, or uric acid salts in the urine crystallize and form kidney stones. When kidney stones block a ureter, they cause great pain. Kidney stones are often treated using ultrasound waves. The sound waves pulverize the stones into smaller fragments, which are eliminated with the urine.

Check for Understanding

FOLLOW-UP PROBES

Ask The kidneys are essential for maintaining homeostasis in the body. Why? *(Kidneys remove wastes from the body. Without the kidneys, wastes can accumulate to levels that disrupt homeostasis and can cause damage to the body or death.)*

ADJUST INSTRUCTION

If responses indicate that students do not understand the role of the kidneys in the maintenance of homeostasis, ask them to think about the relationship between materials that enter the body and those that leave the body. Then, ask students to consider what would happen if substances could not be removed from the body.

Answers

IN YOUR NOTEBOOK Urine can reveal what substances were put into the body, as well as indicate the level of hydration and the presence of certain diseases and disorders.

▶ ***Kidney Damage*** Many diseases, injuries, and exposure to hazardous substances can lead to impaired kidney function. But most cases of kidney damage in the United States are related to high blood pressure and diabetes. Excessive blood pressure damages the delicate filtering mechanism, and high blood sugar levels cause the kidneys to filter more blood than normal. Over time, the tubules weaken, and the kidneys may fail to keep up with the demands placed upon them.

▶ ***Kidney Failure*** When kidneys can no longer cleanse the blood and maintain a state of homeostasis in the body, a person is said to be in kidney failure. A patient with kidney failure must receive dialysis or undergo a kidney transplant as shown in **Figure 30–20.**

During dialysis, a machine performs the role of the kidneys. The patient's blood is pumped through the machine, cleansed, and pumped back into the body. Although the procedure is painless, it is very time-consuming. Most patients receive dialysis treatments three times a week for about four hours each time. To prevent the buildup of fluid and harmful materials between treatments, patients must restrict their fluid intake and eat foods low in potassium, phosphorus, and salt.

In transplantation, a patient receives a kidney and ureter from a compatible donor. Fortunately for the donor, a person can survive with just one healthy kidney.

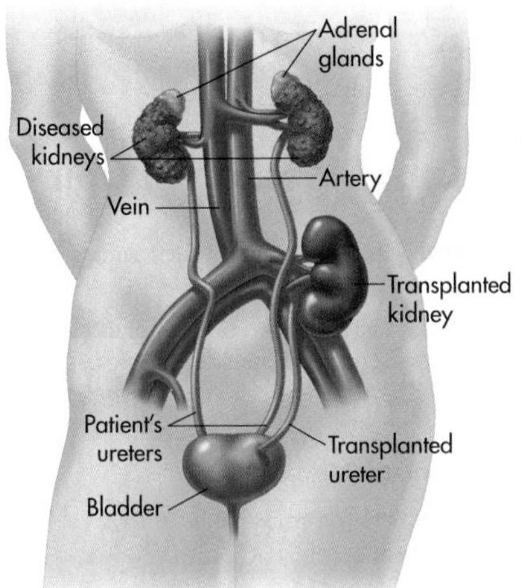

FIGURE 30–20 Kidney Transplantation Unless the patient's diseased kidneys are causing infection or high blood pressure, they are left in place when a healthy kidney and ureter are transplanted from a donor.

30.4 Assessment

Review Key Concepts

1. a. Review List the organs that are involved in excretion.
b. Classify Why is excretion important for homeostasis?

2. a. Review What substances do the kidneys remove from blood?
b. Sequence Explain what happens during filtration, reabsorption, and urine excretion.

3. a. Review Describe how the kidneys help maintain water balance.
b. Apply Concepts Why do you think protein and glucose in the urine are signs of kidney damage?

BUILD VOCABULARY

4. Two words that are often used interchangeably are *excretion* and *secretion.* They have two distinct meanings, however. An excretion is usually a waste product of metabolism that is expelled from an organism. A secretion is a useful substance that is released inside or outside an organism. Name one example each of an excretion and a secretion from this lesson.

BIOLOGY.com Search Lesson 30.4 GO • Lesson Assessment • Self-Test

LESSON 30.4

Assess and Remediate

EVALUATE UNDERSTANDING

Write the following question on the board: *How does the body get rid of wastes?* Ask each student to generate a quick written response to the question. Call on several students to share their responses with the class. Then, have students complete the 30.4 Assessment.

REMEDIATION SUGGESTION

L1 Struggling Students If students have difficulty answering **Question 1b,** lead a class discussion about the importance of excretion in the maintenance of homeostasis. Remind students that materials that enter the body and those that leave the body are both related to homeostasis.

BIOLOGY.com Students can check their understanding of lesson concepts with the **Self-Test** assessment. They can then take an online version of the **Lesson Assessment.**

Assessment Answers

1a. skin, lungs, liver, kidneys, ureter, urinary bladder, urethra

1b. Excretion removes wastes from the body.

2a. Substances removed from the blood include excess water, metabolic wastes, carbon dioxide, and urea.

2b. In filtration, materials such as water, urea, glucose, salts, amino acids, and some vitamins are removed from the blood. During reabsorption, water and many other substances are reabsorbed into the blood. In urine excretion, urine flows through the ureters, collects in the urinary bladder, and then leaves the body through the urethra.

3a. Kidneys help maintain water balance by excreting more or less water in response to the body's level of hydration.

3b. Protein and glucose in the urine indicate kidney damage because the presence of these substances signals that filtration and reabsorption are not occurring properly.

BUILD VOCABULARY

4. Urine is an example of an excretion. ADH is a secretion.

CHAPTER LAB

Pre-Lab

Introduce students to the concepts they will explore in the chapter lab by assigning the Pre-Lab questions.

Lab

Tell students they will perform the chapter lab *Digesting Dairy Products* described in **Lab Manual A.**

 **Struggling Students** A simpler version of the chapter lab is provided in **Lab Manual B.**

SAFETY

Remind students not to eat or drink any substance in the laboratory, including food products. They should wash their hands thoroughly after the lab.

 Look online for **Editable Lab Worksheets.**

 For corresponding pre-lab in the **Foundation Edition,** see page 734.

GUIDED INQUIRY

IN B.5.5 Roles of proteins.

Pre-Lab: Digestion of Dairy Products

Problem How can an enzyme deficiency affect digestion?

Materials well plate, sheet of paper, glucose solution, milk, milk-digestion aid, toothpicks, glucose test strips

Lab Manual Chapter 30 Lab

Skills Focus Control Variables, Infer, Draw Conclusions

Connect to the Big idea Food is both a source of raw materials and a source of energy for your body. First the food must pass through your digestive system, where mechanical and chemical processes break the food down into smaller molecules. Enzymes play an essential role in chemical digestion. Different enzymes are needed to digest proteins, fats, and carbohydrates. In this lab, you will explore the role of enzymes in the digestion of milk and other dairy products.

Background Questions

a. **Review** What is an enzyme? Why are enzymes necessary for maintaining homeostasis?

b. **Review** Where do most digestive enzymes enter the digestive system?

c. **Compare and Contrast** Use glucose and sucrose to explain the difference between a monosaccharide and a disaccharide.

Pre-Lab Questions

Preview the procedure in the lab manual.

1. **Design an Experiment** What is the purpose of the glucose solution?
2. **Control Variables** What is the control in this lab?
3. **Communicate** Read the instructions on the package of glucose test strips. Then, briefly describe how you will test your samples for the presence of glucose.

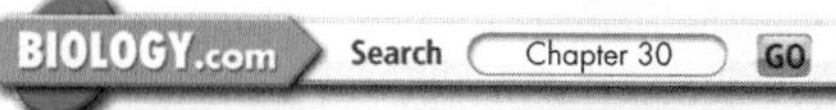

Visit Chapter 30 online to test yourself on chapter content and to find activities to help you learn.

Untamed Science Video Hold your noses as you join the Untamed Science crew to learn what scientists can discover about animals by investigating their scat.

Data Analysis Use nutrient data to plan a lunch that meets your own personal requirements.

Tutor Tube Tune in to Tutor Tube for another perspective on how homeostasis works in the human body.

Art Review Review your understanding of human body systems.

Art in Motion Watch peristalsis in action in the esophagus.

888 Chapter 30 • Pre-Lab

IN INDIANA ACADEMIC STANDARDS

For the full text of all standards, see the Course Overview in the front matter of this book.

Pre-Lab Answers

BACKGROUND QUESTIONS

a. An enzyme is a protein that speeds up the rate of a biological reaction. Without enzymes, many biological reactions in cells could not take place (or at least not quickly enough to be useful).

b. Most digestive enzymes enter the small intestine (specifically the upper part of the small intestine, which is called the duodenum).

c. Sample answer: Monosaccharides, such as glucose, consist of single sugar molecules. Disaccharides are compounds made by joining two simple sugar molecules together. The two molecules that join to form sucrose are glucose and fructose.

PRE-LAB QUESTIONS

1. The glucose solution will show what a positive test for glucose looks like.
2. The sample of milk without the milk-digestion aid is the control.
3. Depending on the type of test strips used, students will either dip a fresh strip into each solution or use toothpicks to place a bit of each solution on a single strip.

30 Study Guide

Big idea Homeostasis

The foods you eat provide energy and materials to cells. Excretions contain the wastes produced as the result of cellular activities. Homeostasis requires an appropriate balance of these inputs and outputs.

30.1 Organization of the Human Body

The levels of organization in the body include cells, tissues, organs, and organ systems.

Homeostasis describes the relatively constant internal physical and chemical conditions that organisms maintain despite changes in internal and external environments.

epithelial tissue (863)
connective tissue (863)
nervous tissue (863)
muscle tissue (863)
homeostasis (865)
feedback inhibition (865)

30.2 Food and Nutrition

Molecules in food contain chemical energy that cells use to produce ATP. Food also supplies raw materials your body needs to build and repair tissues.

The nutrients that the body needs include water, carbohydrates, fats, proteins, vitamins, and minerals.

A balanced diet provides nutrients in adequate amounts and enough energy for a person to maintain a healthful weight.

Calorie (868)
carbohydrate (869)
fat (870)
protein (870)
vitamin (871)
mineral (872)

30.3 The Digestive System

The digestive system converts food into small molecules that can be used by the cells of the body. Food is processed by the digestive system in four phases—ingestion, digestion, absorption, and elimination.

During digestion, food travels through the mouth, esophagus, stomach, and small intestine. Mechanical digestion and chemical digestion are the two processes by which food is reduced to molecules that can be absorbed.

Most nutrients from food are absorbed through the walls of the small intestine. The large intestine absorbs water and several vitamins and prepares waste for elimination from the body.

mechanical digestion (875)
chemical digestion (875)
amylase (876)
esophagus (877)
peristalsis (877)
stomach (877)
pepsin (877)
chyme (877)
small intestine (878)
villus (880)
large intestine (881)

30.4 The Excretory System

The excretory system, which includes the skin, lungs, liver, and kidneys, excretes metabolic wastes from the body.

As waste-laden blood enters the kidney through the renal artery, the kidney removes urea, excess water and minerals, and other waste products.

The kidneys respond directly to the composition of the blood. They are also influenced by the endocrine system. Disruption of proper kidney function can lead to serious health problems.

excretion (882)
ureter (883)
urinary bladder (883)
urethra (883)
nephron (884)
filtration (884)
glomerulus (884)
Bowman's capsule (884)
reabsorption (884)
loop of Henle (884)

Visual Thinking

Create a flowchart that shows the path of a glucose molecule through a healthy nephron.

BIOLOGY.com Search Chapter 30 GO • Match It • Chapter Assessment

Study Online

REVIEW AND ASSESSMENT RESOURCES

Editable Worksheets Pages of Study Workbooks A and B, Lab Manuals A and B, and the Assessment Resources Book are available online. These documents can be easily edited using a word-processing program.

Lesson Overview Have students reread the Lesson Overviews to help them study chapter concepts.

Vocabulary Review The *Flash Cards* and *Match It* provide an interactive way to review chapter vocabulary.

Chapter Assessment Have students take online versions of the Chapter 30 Assessment.

Standardized Test Prep Students can take an online version of the Standardized Test Prep. You will receive their scores along with ideas for remediation.

Diagnostic and Benchmark Tests Use these tests to monitor your students' progress and supply remediation.

Answers

THINK VISUALLY

Students' flowcharts should show a glucose molecule moving from the glomerulus into the Bowman's capsule as it is filtered out of blood, then back into the capillary as it is reabsorbed.

UbD Performance Tasks

SUMMATIVE TASK Have each student assume the role of a doctor. Have them imagine that a patient has come to them complaining of a lack of energy. Ask students to develop a list of questions they would ask the patient and a list of tests they might request to gauge the patient's body conditions. Have students consider the following:

- the materials that enter the patient's body
- the way the patient's body functions to process those materials
- the materials that leave the patient's body

TRANSFER TASK Explain to students that in the field of computer science, there is a common phrase: *garbage in, garbage out.* The phrase summarizes the idea that, no matter how good a computer or computer program is, it will not produce reliable results unless the data fed into the computer are accurate and reliable. Ask students to write a paragraph that explains how this phrase could be applied to the human body. Tell students to consider the role of materials entering the body in the maintenance of homeostasis, how the materials that enter the body are processed, and how the materials that leave the body reflect what enters the body and how well the body is functioning.

ASSESSMENT

Lesson 30.1

UNDERSTAND KEY CONCEPTS

1. c **2.** b **3.** b

4. Maintaining homeostasis provides a stable internal environment, which allows vital body processes, such as the functioning of enzymes, to occur.

5. Epithelial tissue functions in protection, absorption, and excretion. Nervous tissue is involved in receiving and transmitting nerve impulses. Connective tissue provides support for the body and connects its parts. Muscle tissue is responsible for movement.

THINK CRITICALLY

6. Blood is a tissue because it is a group of cells that perform a function.

7. If a person's temperature remains abnormally high, enzymes might not be able to function, resulting in a disruption of body functions.

Lesson 30.2

UNDERSTAND KEY CONCEPTS

8. c **9.** b

10. fats, carbohydrates, and proteins

11. Proteins supply raw materials for growth and repair of body structures; some proteins make up enzymes; and some proteins function in regulatory and transport functions.

THINK CRITICALLY

12. French fries, doughnuts, and cookies supply a great number of Calories without providing many of the nutrients the body needs.

13. b

Lesson 30.3

UNDERSTAND KEY CONCEPTS

14. c **15.** c

16. Food does not enter the airway when swallowed because a flap of connective tissue, called the epiglottis, closes the opening to the trachea.

17. Enzymes break down large food molecules into smaller molecules that can be absorbed and used by cells of the body.

18. The pancreas produces hormones that regulate blood sugar. It produces enzymes that break down carbohydrates, proteins, lipids, and nucleic acids. It also produces sodium bicarbonate, a base that neutralizes stomach acids.

30 Assessment

The numbers following the questions refer to Indiana's Academic Standards for Biology I.

30.1 Organization of the Human Body

Understand Key Concepts

1. The type of tissue that covers the body, lines internal surfaces, and forms glands is
a. muscle tissue. **c.** epithelial tissue.
b. connective tissue. **d.** nervous tissue.

2. The process of maintaining a relatively constant internal environment despite changes in the external environment is called
a. regulation. **c.** synapse.
b. homeostasis. **d.** stimulation.

3. What do all types of tissue have in common?
a. They are all made of connective tissue.
b. They are all made of cells.
c. They are all found in every organ.
d. They are all made of organs.

4. Why is it important for an organism to maintain homeostasis?

5. Name the four types of tissues and describe one characteristic of each.

Think Critically

6. **Classify** Would you classify blood as a cell, a tissue, or an organ? Explain.

7. **Predict** Infections may lead to an immune response that results in a high fever. Considering what you have learned about the action of enzymes, predict what may happen if a person's body temperature remains abnormally high.

30.2 Food and Nutrition

Understand Key Concepts

8. Energy in food is measured in
a. ATP. **c.** Calories.
b. fats. **d.** disaccharides.

9. Inorganic nutrients that your body needs, usually in small amounts, are called
a. vitamins. **c.** proteins.
b. minerals. **d.** amino acids.

10. Which nutrients provide the body with energy?

11. In what three ways are proteins important to the body? B.1.2

Think Critically

12. **Infer** Many food manufacturers have replaced trans fats in their foods with other types of fats that may not have the same level of heart disease risk. Some nutritionists fear that people will think foods such as French fries, doughnuts, and cookies are healthful if they are not made with trans fats. Explain why these foods are still not healthful choices.

13. **Calculate** If a person consumed 2000 Calories while following the typical diet, how many more of those Calories would be from saturated fat than if they were following the recommended diet? MATH NoS.3

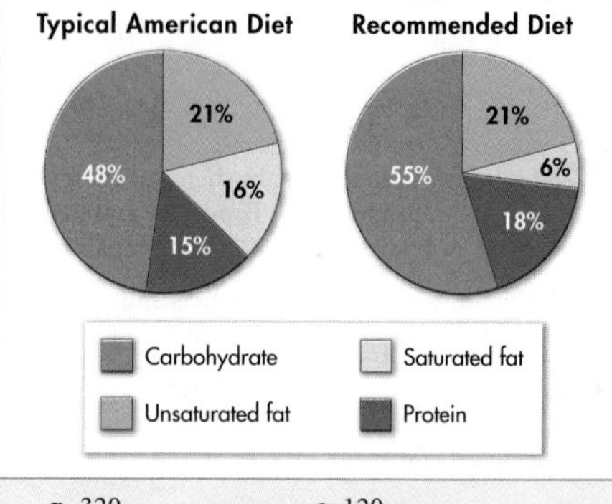

a. 320 **c.** 120
b. 200 **d.** 100

30.3 The Digestive System

Understand Key Concepts

14. Where does mechanical digestion begin?
a. the esophagus
b. the large intestine
c. the mouth
d. the small intestine

15. An enzyme in saliva that can break the chemical bonds in starch is B.5.5
a. pepsin. **c.** amylase.
b. bile. **d.** chyme.

19. The villi contain a network of capillaries and lymph vessels that absorb nutrients from the small intestine. Each villus is covered with fingerlike projections called microvilli that greatly increase the surface area available for absorption of nutrients.

THINK CRITICALLY

20. No, individuals could not survive without a small intestine; they would be unable to absorb nutrients.

21. An antibiotic that killed all the bacteria in your body would destroy the beneficial bacteria in the large intestine. A vitamin K deficiency could result because these bacteria produce vitamin K.

16. Explain why swallowed food does not normally enter the airway leading to the lungs.
17. What is the importance of enzymes during digestion? B.5.5
18. Describe the functions of the pancreas.
19. How is the structure of the villi adapted to their function?

Think Critically

20. **Infer** Individuals who have had part, or even all, of their stomachs removed can survive if fed predigested food. Could these individuals also survive without a small intestine? Explain.
21. **Predict** Suppose that your doctor prescribed an antibiotic that killed all the bacteria in your body. What effect would this have on your digestive system?

30.4 The Excretory System

Understand Key Concepts

22. Which of the following is the basic functional unit in a kidney?
    a. nephron.
    b. glomerulus.
    c. Bowman's capsule.
    d. loop of Henle.
23. Urine is excreted from the body through the
    a. ureter.
    b. urinary bladder.
    c. urethra.
    d. renal vein.
24. What is the role of the skin in excretion?
25. What materials are filtered from blood in the kidney? What materials do not leave the bloodstream?
26. How is the water-regulating activity of the kidney controlled?

Think Critically

27. **Apply Concepts** Explain why kidney failure can be a fatal condition.
28. **Infer** When there is too much fluid in the blood, the heart must pump harder. Diuretics are substances that stimulate the kidneys to remove more fluid from the body. Why do you think diuretics are used to treat high blood pressure?

solve the CHAPTER MYSTERY

THE TELLTALE SAMPLE

For centuries, people have used urine for clues to health and disease. The Greeks, for example, knew that diabetics had excessive sugar in their urine and called the disease *diabetes mellitus*. Mellitus is the Greek word for honey.

- **Physical Examination** During this step, the color and clarity are examined. The shade of yellow indicates the amount of water being released by the kidneys. Urine of a color other than yellow could indicate the presence of blood. Or, it could simply indicate someone has eaten a lot of beets. Urine should be clear, rather than cloudy.
- **Microscopic Examination** The presence of mucus, white blood cells, or microorganisms in urine indicates a probable infection. Cloudy urine may also be caused by crystals, which could indicate kidney stones or a metabolic problem.
- **Chemical Examination** Hundreds of chemical tests can be performed on urine. Chemical dipsticks are used that change color in the presence of other chemicals. These tests can reveal a lot about kidney function, liver function, and overall homeostasis in the body.

1. **Infer** How does urine reveal so much about the health of the human body?
2. **Form an Opinion** Most drug urine tests performed for schools do not test for alcohol or tobacco. Why do you think this is the case? Do you agree or disagree? Explain.
3. **Connect to the Big idea** Ketones are a product of the breakdown of fat for energy. Ketones in the urine can be an indication of diabetes. Why do you think this is?

 Search 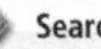 Chapter 30  GO • Untamed Science Video 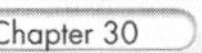 • Chapter Mystery 

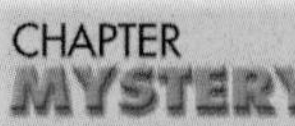

After students have read through the Chapter Mystery, discuss how the body's waste products reflect what is put into the body. Ask students to explain how urine can be used to identify diseases and disorders that disrupt homeostasis in the body.

Ask How could a physical examination of urine reveal that a person is dehydrated? *(If urine is dark yellow, it indicates that a person's kidneys are conserving water.)*

Ask What problems can be revealed by microscopic examination of urine? How do these problems relate to homeostasis? *(Kidney stones, metabolic problems, and infection can all be detected by microscopic examination of urine. Each of these disrupts homeostasis in the body by disrupting the normal functions of the body.)*

Ask How does chemical examination of urine reveal the relationship between the materials that enter the body and those that leave the body? *(Materials that enter the body are processed, and their byproducts are eliminated as wastes. Chemical examination of urine, a waste that leaves the body, can reveal what has been taken into the body.)*

CHAPTER MYSTERY ANSWERS

1. Urine contains many waste products of normal reactions that occur in the body. It also contains excess materials that the body does not need. By examining its contents, a doctor can determine if many different body processes are occurring as they should.
2. Answers will vary. Accept responses supported by a logical explanation.
3. Big idea Diabetes is a disease that affects the body's use of glucose. If a person has diabetes, his or her cells may not be able to efficiently break down glucose for energy. If cells cannot use glucose for energy, they may break down fat instead. Since ketones are a byproduct of the breakdown of fat, they will build up in the blood and be excreted.

Lesson 30.4

UNDERSTAND KEY CONCEPTS

22. a **23.** c

24. The skin excretes water, salts, and a small amount of urea.
25. Water, urea, glucose, salts, amino acids, and some vitamins are filtered from the blood. Blood cells and large substances such as proteins remain in the blood.
26. The water-regulating activity of the kidney is controlled by the composition of blood itself and by hormones.

THINK CRITICALLY

27. Kidney failure can be fatal because, without the kidneys to filter wastes and excess water from the blood, these substances can accumulate to toxic levels.
28. Diuretics stimulate the kidneys to remove fluid from the blood. If the blood contains less fluid, the heart doesn't have to work as hard and the person's blood pressure should be reduced.

Follow the Untamed Science crew in **Drat . . . I Smell Scat!** as they discover the treasure of information that can be unearthed from the most unlikely place: animal scat.

Connecting Concepts

USE SCIENCE GRAPHICS

29. hydrochloric acid, protein, fat

30. In the presence of hydrochloric acid, the pancreatic secretions are mostly bicarbonate with a small amount of digestive enzymes; in the presence of fat the reverse is true: the secretions are mostly digestive enzymes with a small amount of bicarbonate.

WRITE ABOUT SCIENCE

31. Students' scripts will vary, but should include information about the processes that occur in the organs of the digestive system, mechanical and chemical digestion, and the role of enzymes in the digestion of fats and proteins (the hamburger) and carbohydrates (the bun).

32. Big idea Sample answer: As I answer these questions, my digestive system is digesting and absorbing the lunch I ate. The circulatory system is gathering the broken-down molecules of food and delivering them to cells all over my body for energy and repair. Meanwhile, the circulatory system is also picking up oxygen from and delivering carbon dioxide to the lungs of the respiratory system. Most of these activities are being managed by my nervous system. All of the wastes that are being produced by these many processes are being removed by the excretory system.

Connecting Concepts

Use Science Graphics NoS.3

Pancreatic secretions contain sodium bicarbonate and enzymes. The graph shows the secretions of the pancreas in response to three different substances in chyme. Use the graph to answer questions 29 and 30.

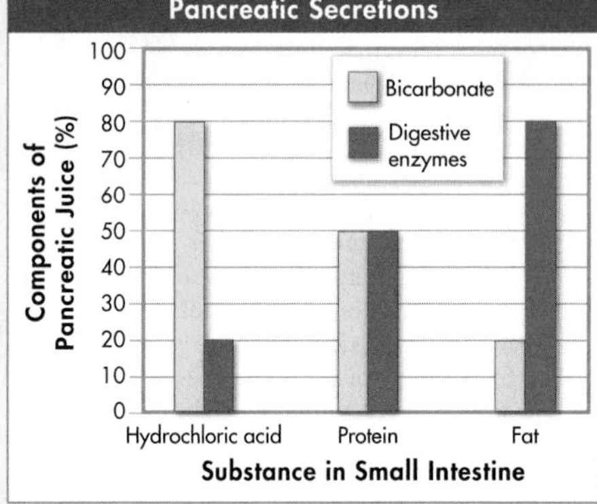

29. Interpret Graphs Each pair of bars represents the response of the pancreas to a different variable. What are the three variables?

30. Analyze Data Compare the composition of pancreatic secretions in the presence of hydrochloric acid and fat.

Write About Science NoS.3

31. Creative Writing A children's television workshop wants to explain the process of digestion to young viewers. You are asked to write a script that describes the travels of a hamburger and bun through the digestive system. Write an outline of your script, including information about what happens to the different nutrients in each part of the digestive system.

32. Assess the Big idea Using **Figure 30–2,** choose five body systems that are involved in maintaining homeostasis in your body as you answer these assessment questions. Explain how these five body systems work together.

Analyzing Data

IN NoS.3

MyPyramid classifies food into six categories: grains, vegetables, fruits, milk, meat and beans, and oils. Personalized eating plans can be found at mypyramid.gov. This pyramid contains daily recommendations for Ryan, a 15-year-old male who weighs 140 pounds, is 5 feet 7 inches tall, and is physically active about 30 to 60 minutes a day.

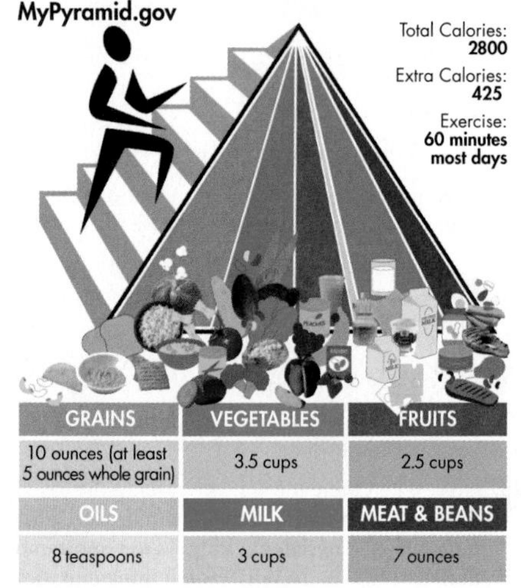

MyPyramid.gov
Total Calories: 2800
Extra Calories: 425
Exercise: 60 minutes most days
GRAINS
10 ounces (at least 5 ounces whole grain)
VEGETABLES
3.5 cups
FRUITS
2.5 cups
OILS
8 teaspoons
MILK
3 cups
MEAT & BEANS
7 ounces

33. Predict If Ryan were to become less active, what would happen to the number of extra Calories he could consume? Explain.

34. Infer For Ryan to meet his grain requirements, which group of foods would be his BEST choice in a single day?

a. sweetened cereal, pasta, white bread
b. whole-grain bagel, a doughnut, and pasta
c. whole-grain cereal, potato chips, and whole-grain bread
d. oatmeal, whole-grain bread, and a sweet potato

Analyzing Data

PURPOSE Students will analyze data to understand and interpret information provided by MyPyramid.gov.

PLANNING Remind students that the eating plan shown in the Analyzing Data feature is a personalized eating plan based on age, gender, and activity level; it is not right for everyone.

ANSWERS

33. If Ryan were to become less active, the number of extra Calories he should consume would decrease.

34. d

Standardized Test Practice for Indiana

Multiple Choice

1. Which of the following is NOT a kind of tissue in the human body?
   A epithelial
   B connective
   C interstitial
   D nervous

2. Each of the following aids in the process of digestion EXCEPT the
   A teeth.
   B saliva.
   C stomach.
   D kidney.

3. In the human body, hydrochloric acid is responsible for the low pH of the contents of the
   A kidney.
   B gallbladder.
   C stomach.
   D liver.

4. Which is NOT a function of the kidneys?
   A removal of waste products from the blood
   B maintenance of blood pH
   C regulation of water content of the blood
   D excretion of carbon dioxide

5. The main function of the digestive system is to
   A break down large molecules into smaller molecules.
   B excrete oxygen and carbon dioxide.
   C synthesize minerals and vitamins needed for a healthy body.
   D remove waste products from the blood.

6. In the kidneys, both useful substances and wastes are removed from the blood by
   A reabsorption.
   B excretion.
   C dialysis.
   D filtration.

7. Which of the following is NOT a role of fats in the body?
   A Deposits of fat act as insulation.
   B They are components of cell membranes.
   C They help with absorption of fat-soluble vitamins.
   D They are hormones and enzymes.

Questions 8–9

A student is studying the effect of temperature on the action of an enzyme in stomach fluid. The enzyme digests protein. An investigation was set up using five identical test tubes. Each tube contained 40 mL of stomach fluid and 20 mm of glass tubing filled with gelatin. Each tube was subjected to a different temperature. After 48 hours, the amount of gelatin digested in each tube was measured in millimeters. The results for the five test tubes are shown in the table.

Effect of Temperature on Enzyme Action

Test Tube	Temperature (°C)	Amount of Digestion After 48 Hours
1	2	0.0 mm
2	10	3.0 mm
3	22	4.5 mm
4	37	8.0 mm
5	100	0.0 mm

8. Which is the manipulated (independent) variable in this investigation?
   A gastric fluid
   B length of glass tubing
   C temperature
   D time

9. Another test tube was set up that was identical to the other test tubes and placed at a temperature of 15°C for 48 hours. What amount of digestion would you expect to occur in this test tube?
   A less than 3.0 mm
   B between 3.0 mm and 4.5 mm
   C between 4.5 mm and 8.0 mm
   D more than 8.0 mm NoS.3

Open-Ended Question

10. Fad diets that boast of rapid weight loss often become popular. Many of these diets involve eating only a limited variety of foods. Explain why these diets are an unhealthful way to lose weight.

If You Have Trouble With . . .

Question	1	2	3	4	5	6	7	8	9	10
See Lesson	30.1	30.3	30.3	30.4	30.3	30.4	30.2	30.3	30.3	30.2

Answers

1. C
2. D
3. C
4. D
5. A
6. D
7. D
8. C
9. B
10. Diets that include a limited variety of food may be unhealthy because they may not provide all of the nutrients needed for good health.

Test-Taking Tip

INTERPRET EXPERIMENTAL DATA

Tell students that when a question is based on experimental data, they should read the description of the experiment carefully to determine the steps that were followed. As students read the description, they should try to identify the independent and dependant variables, the hypothesis, and the controls that were used. Then, students should examine the data to identify trends that show relationships between the variables. These steps will help students correctly answer questions about the experimental procedure and results.

CHAPTER PLANNER 31 Nervous System

Chapter Contents	IN	Time	Core Resources
Chapter Preview			**Student Edition,** pp. 894–895 **Chapter Mystery,** p. 895
31.1 The Neuron Functions of the Nervous System • Neurons • The Nerve Impulse	NoS.6	$1\frac{1}{2}$ periods $\frac{3}{4}$ block	**Student Edition,** pp. 896–900 **Study Workbook A** 31.1 Worksheets L2 **Biology.com** *InterActive Art:* The Nerve Impulse • *Visual Analogy:* The Moving Impulse **Assessment Resources Book** Visual Quiz L2
31.2 The Central Nervous System The Brain and Spinal Cord • Addiction and the Brain • *Technology & Biology: Studying the Brain on Drugs*		1 period $\frac{1}{2}$ block	**Student Edition,** pp. 901–905 **Study Workbook A** 31.2 Worksheets L2 **Biology.com** 31.2 Self-Test • 31.2 Lesson Assessment
31.3 The Peripheral Nervous System The Sensory Division • The Motor Division		1 period $\frac{1}{2}$ block	**Student Edition,** pp. 906–908 **Inquiry** 31.3 Quick Lab, p. 908 L2 **Study Workbook A** 31.3 Worksheets L2 **Biology.com** *Art in Motion:* Reflex Arc **Assessment Resources Book** Visual Quiz L2
31.4 The Senses Touch and Related Senses • Smell and Taste • Hearing and Balance • Vision	NoS.3	1 period $\frac{1}{2}$ block	**Student Edition,** pp. 909–913 **Inquiry** 31.4 Analyzing Data, p. 910 L2 **Study Workbook A** 31.4 Worksheets L2 **Biology.com** *Data Analysis:* Looks Tasty: How Vision Affects Taste • *Art Review:* The Ear and the Eye • 31.4 Self-Test • 31.4 Lesson Assessment
Chapter Pre-Lab	NoS.1, NoS.2	1 period $\frac{1}{2}$ block	**Student Edition,** p. 914 L2 **Lab Manual A** *Testing Sensory Receptors for Touch* L2

Differentiated Instruction Tools

Study Workbook B includes worksheets with lesson-level differentiated instruction support and explanations of differentiated instruction teaching strategies.

Lab Manual B includes skills labs, simplified chapter labs, and hands-on activities.

ELL Handbook explains ways to make *Biology* more accessible to ELL students.

Spanish Study Workbook is a Spanish translation of Study Workbook A.

Multilingual Glossary is the glossary translated into ten languages.

Differentiated Instruction Key

- L1 Special Needs or Struggling Students
- ELL English Language Learners
- LPR Less Proficient Readers
- L2 On-Level Students
- L3 Advanced Students

Additional Resources

Biology.com Untamed Science Video • Vocabulary Flash Cards

Study Workbook B 31.1 Worksheets L1 ELL LPR
Spanish Study Workbook 31.1 Worksheets ELL
Biology.com 31.1 Lesson Overview • 31.1 Lesson Notes • 31.1 Self-Test • 31.1 Lesson Assessment

Study Workbook B 31.2 Worksheets L1 ELL LPR
Spanish Study Workbook 31.2 Worksheets ELL
Biology.com 31.2 Lesson Overview • 31.2 Lesson Notes

Study Workbook B 31.3 Worksheets L1 ELL LPR
Spanish Study Workbook 31.3 Worksheets ELL
Biology.com 31.3 Lesson Overview • 31.3 Lesson Notes • 31.3 Self-Test • 31.3 Lesson Assessment

Study Workbook B 31.4 Worksheets L1 ELL LPR
Spanish Study Workbook 31.4 Worksheets ELL
Biology.com *Tutor Tube:* The Physical Nature of Sound • 31.4 Lesson Overview • 31.4 Lesson Notes

Lab Manual B *Testing Sensory Receptors for Touch* • Hands-On Activity: *Responding to External Stimuli* • Data Analysis: *Sound Intensity* L1 ELL LPR

Chapter Review

Student Edition Study Guide, p. 915 L2
Study Workbook A Chapter 31 Vocabulary Review L2 • Chapter 31 Chapter Mystery/21st Century Skills Activity L2 L3
Transparencies, pp. 342–350 L1 ELL LPR L2
Biology.com Untamed Science Video • Editable Worksheets of Study Workbooks A and B and Lab Manuals A and B • Chapter 31 Flash Cards and Match It

Untamed Science DVD • Classroom Resources CD (includes lesson presentations and editable worksheets)

Chapter Assessment

Student Edition Assessment, pp. 916–919 L2
Study Workbook B Chapter 31 Chapter Review L1 ELL LPR • Chapter 31 Taking a Standardized Test L1 ELL LPR
Assessment Resources Book Chapter 31 Test A L2 • Chapter 31 Test B L1 ELL LPR
Biology.com Chapter 31 Assessment • Editable Worksheets of Chapter 31 Visual Quizzes and Chapter 31 Tests A and B

Exam*View Assessment Suite* • Classroom Resources CD (includes lesson presentations and editable worksheets)

Time: 1 period, 1/2 block

Pressed for Time?

Preview the Chapter Preview Figures 31–2 and 31–8, and read the first Key Question in Lessons 31.1, 31.2, and 31.3.

Cover the Chapter Quickly Have students read *Functions of the Nervous System* and *Neurons* in Lesson 31.1. Go over Figures 31–5 and 31–6. Assign *The Brain and the Spinal Cord* in Lesson 31.2, and the introductions to *The Sensory Division* and *The Motor Division* in Lesson 31.3. Discuss Figure 31–11.

Assess Assign questions 1, 2, and 3a in the 31.1 Assessment, question 1 in the 31.2 Assessment, and questions 1a, 1b, and 2b in the 31.3 Assessment. In the Chapter 31 Assessment, assign questions 1–4, 9, 13, 18, 19, 21, 22, and 35.

Connect to the Big Idea

Use the photograph of the crowd at a baseball game to help students begin thinking about how the human body gathers information from its surroundings and how it reacts to that information. Have students explain how these individuals know they need to get ready to catch a ball. *(Sample answer: They see the ball moving in their direction.)* Challenge them to explain how the body generates a reaction to the sight of an approaching baseball. *(Students may identify structures of the nervous system, such as nerves or the brain, or describe a message traveling from one part of the body to another.)* Explain that every moment of every day, the nervous system takes in information from the environment and generates reactions to that information. Lead students to anticipate the answer to the question, **How does the structure of the nervous system allow it to regulate functions in every part of the body?**

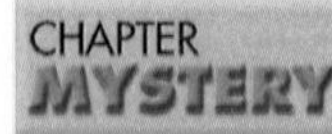

Have students read over the Chapter Mystery and discuss the possible explanations for Captain Cook's symptoms. Then, ask them to make a prediction about body structures or systems that were affected by a substance in the fish. Help students relate this discussion to the Big Idea of Structure and Function.

BIOLOGY.com Have students preview the chapter vocabulary terms using the **Flash Cards.**

31 Nervous System

Big idea **Structure and Function**

Q: How does the structure of the nervous system allow it to regulate functions in every part of the body?

BIOLOGY.com Search Chapter 31 GO • Flash Cards

IN INDIANA ACADEMIC STANDARDS

For the full text of all standards, see the Course Overview in the front matter of this book.

Key standards: Chapter 31 covers key ideas from The Nature of Science, including **NoS.3** Communicate ideas and **NoS.6** Use analogies and models.

UbD Understanding by Design

Chapter 31 describes the structures and functions of the nervous system. The graphic organizer at the right shows how these topics are connected to the chapter Essential Question and the lesson-level Guiding Questions. Together, the questions help students build toward the Unit 8 Enduring Understanding: *The human body is a complex system. The coordinated functions of its many structures support life processes and maintain homeostasis.*

PERFORMANCE GOALS

Students' understanding of Chapter 31 can be gauged using the lesson and chapter assessment questions. Performance tasks of preparing a play-by-play broadcast of the body's reaction to a stimulus and comparing the nervous system to a computer require students to synthesize chapter information.

INDIANA ACADEMIC STANDARDS FOR SCIENCE

Nature of Science NoS.1, NoS.2, NoS.3, NoS.6, NoS.10. See lessons for details.

The sights, sounds, and smells at a ball game provide a fan's nervous system with a lot of stimulation.

• Untamed Science Video • Chapter Mystery

CHAPTER MYSTERY

POISONING ON THE HIGH SEAS

From the middle to late 1700s, Captain James Cook commanded several voyages of discovery to the South Pacific for Great Britain. The discovery of new lands brought him many riches; the discoveries of new animals, however, were not always pleasant.

September 7, 1774, was a remarkable day on the HMS *Resolution*. The ship's butcher died from a fall, there was a solar eclipse, and a clerk traded some cloth for a freshly caught fish.

Although Cook ate only a few bites of the fish, within a few hours, the captain felt "an extraordinary weakness" in his limbs, lost all sense of touch, and could not sense the weight of objects. It took eleven days for the men who ate the fish to recover. A pig and dog who ate some of the fish's organs were dead by morning. As you read through this chapter, look for clues as to how eating this fish could produce such deadly effects.

Never Stop Exploring Your World. Finding the solution to this mystery is only the beginning. Take a video field trip with the ecogeeks of Untamed Science to see where this mystery leads.

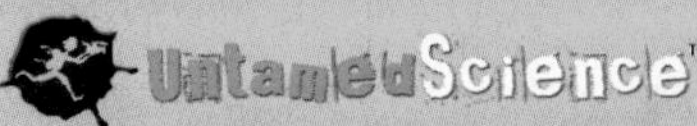

Chapter 31
Big Idea: Structure and Function

Chapter 31 EQ: How does the structure of the nervous system allow it to control functions in every part of the body?

31.1 GQ: What is the basic function of the nervous system?

31.2 GQ: What does the central nervous system do?

31.3 GQ: How do messages travel between the central nervous system and the body?

31.4 GQ: How do humans sense changes in their environment?

CHAPTER 31

What's Online

BIOLOGY.com Extend your reach by using these and other digital assets offered at Biology.com.

CHAPTER MYSTERY
What caused the captain's symptoms? Students can use clues about Captain Cook's symptoms to solve the mystery about the poisonous fish.

UNTAMED SCIENCE VIDEO
Students can take a video field trip to learn more about the effects of animal toxins.

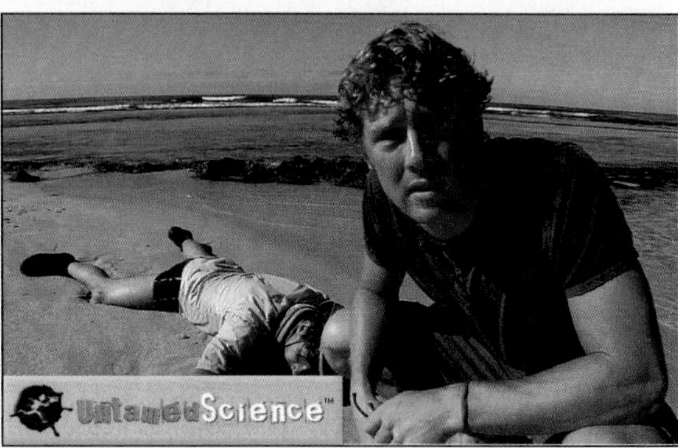

INTERACTIVE ART
Students view an animation of a nerve impulse.

VISUAL ANALOGY
This visual analogy explores how the propagation of a nerve impulse is similar to the fall of a row of dominoes.

ART IN MOTION
This short animation shows the steps in a reflex arc.

ART REVIEW
Students can drag and drop labels to help them learn the structures of the ears and eyes.

DATA ANALYSIS
Students can analyze data to learn how the appearance of food can impact people's perception of flavor.

Getting Started

Objectives

31.1.1 Identify the functions of the nervous system.

31.1.2 Describe the function of neurons.

31.1.3 Describe how a nerve impulse is transmitted.

Student Resources

Study Workbooks A and B, 31.1 Worksheets

Spanish Study Workbook, 31.1 Worksheets

Lesson Overview • Lesson Notes
- Activities: InterActive Art, Visual Analogy
- Assessment: Self-Test, Lesson Assessment

For corresponding lesson in the **Foundation Edition**, see pages 742–746.

Activate Prior Knowledge

Ask students to describe how they communicate messages to friends and family members. *(Students may describe talking in person, talking on the phone, using e-mail, or sending text messages.)* Ask them to identify the purposes of these messages. *(Student responses might include the sharing of ideas or communication of important information.)* Explain that messages are constantly being sent and received within the body. Tell them that almost every function of the body is affected by the transmission of messages within the nervous system.

IN INDIANA ACADEMIC STANDARDS

For the full text of all standards, see the Course Overview in the front matter of this book.

NoS.6 Use analogies and models (mathematical and physical) to simplify and represent systems that are difficult to understand or directly experience due to their size, time scale, or complexity, and recognize the limitations of analogies and models.

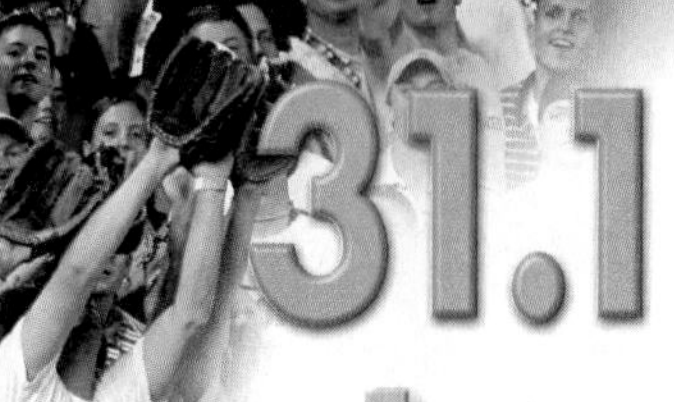

31.1 The Neuron

IN NoS.6 Use analogies and models.

Key Questions

What are the functions of the nervous system?

What is the function of neurons?

How does a nerve impulse begin?

Vocabulary

peripheral nervous system • central nervous system • cell body • dendrite • axon • myelin sheath • resting potential • action potential • threshold • synapse • neurotransmitter

Taking Notes

Outline Before you read, use the green and blue headings to make an outline. As you read, fill in the subtopics and smaller topics. Then, add phrases or a sentence after each to provide key information.

THINK ABOUT IT All of us are aware of the world outside our bodies. How do we know about that world? How do you really know what's happening outside? When you reached for this book and opened it to this page, how did you make these things happen? Even more mysteriously, how did the words on this page that you are reading right now get into your mind? The answers to all these questions are to be found in the nervous system.

Functions of the Nervous System

What are the functions of the nervous system?

The nervous system is our window on the world. **The nervous system collects information about the body's internal and external environment, processes that information, and responds to it.** These functions are accomplished by the peripheral nervous system and the central nervous system. The **peripheral nervous system,** which consists of nerves and supporting cells, collects information about the body's external and internal environment. The **central nervous system,** which consists of the brain and spinal cord, processes that information and creates a response that is delivered to the appropriate part of the body through the peripheral nervous system.

Think about what happens when you search through your backpack for a pencil. Information is sent to your central nervous system about the objects you are touching. Your brain processes the information and determines that the first object you touch is too square to be a pencil. Then your brain sends messages via your peripheral nervous system to the muscles in your hand, commanding them to keep searching.

Imagine the billions of messages that are sent throughout your body at any given moment. The messages may tell you to laugh at a funny joke, or they may tell your brain that it's cold outside. These messages enable the different organs of the body to act together and also to react to conditions in the world around us. How does this communication occur?

Peripheral Nervous System
Gathers information and sends it to the central nervous system

↓ Input

Central Nervous System
Processes the information and forms a response

↓ Output

Peripheral Nervous System
Carries the response of the central nervous system to glands and muscles

FIGURE 31–1 Information Flow in the Nervous System

UbD Teach for Understanding

ENDURING UNDERSTANDING The human body is a complex system. The coordinated functions of its many structures support life processes and maintain homeostasis.

GUIDING QUESTION What is the basic function of the nervous system?

EVIDENCE OF UNDERSTANDING *After completing the lesson, give students the following assessment to show their understanding of the functions of the nervous system.* Have students work in small groups to develop an analogy for the function of the peripheral nervous system and another analogy for the function of the central nervous system. Have each group share its analogies with the class.

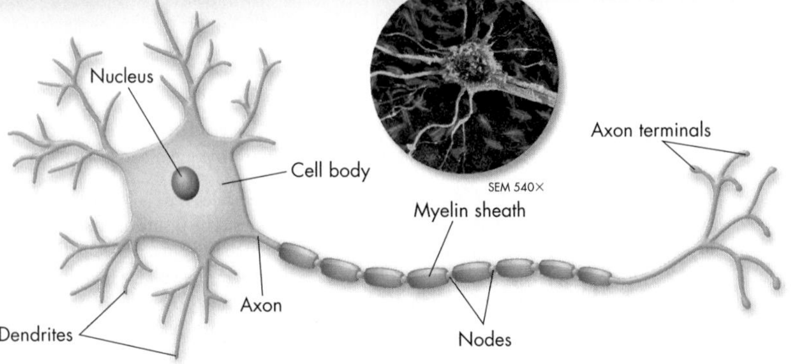

FIGURE 31–2 The Neuron The nervous system controls and coordinates functions throughout the body. The basic unit of the nervous system is the neuron.

Neurons

🔑 ***What is the function of neurons?***

The messages carried by the nervous system are electrical signals called impulses. 🔑 **Nervous system impulses are transmitted by cells called neurons.**

Types of Neurons Neurons can be classified into three types according to the direction in which an impulse travels. Sensory neurons carry impulses from the sense organs, such as the eyes and ears, to the spinal cord and brain. Motor neurons carry impulses from the brain and the spinal cord to muscles and glands. Interneurons do the high-level work. They process information from sensory neurons and then send commands to other interneurons or motor neurons.

Structure of Neurons Although neurons come in many shapes and sizes, they all have certain features in common. As shown in **Figure 31–2,** the largest part of a typical neuron is its **cell body,** which contains the nucleus and much of the cytoplasm.

Spreading out from the cell body are short, branched extensions called dendrites. **Dendrites** receive impulses from other neurons and carry impulses to the cell body. The long fiber that carries impulses away from the cell body is the **axon.** An axon ends in a series of small swellings called axon terminals. Neurons may have dozens of dendrites, but usually they have only one axon. In most animals, axons and dendrites of different neurons are clustered into bundles of fibers called nerves. Some nerves contain fibers from only a few neurons, but others contain hundreds or even thousands of neurons.

In some neurons, the axon is surrounded by an insulating membrane known as the **myelin** (MY uh lin) **sheath.** The myelin sheath that surrounds a single, long axon has many gaps, called nodes, where the axon membrane is exposed. As an impulse moves along the axon, it jumps from one node to the next. This arrangement causes an impulse to travel faster than it would through an axon without a myelin sheath.

In Your Notebook *Make a two-column table that lists the structures of a neuron in one column and their functions in the next column.*

BUILD Vocabulary

MULTIPLE MEANINGS The word *terminal* can be a noun or adjective. As a noun, it may refer to a place where information is entered into a computer or a station where people or goods are moved from one place to another. As an adjective, it may describe something that is beyond rescue or placed at the end of a structure.

How Science Works

NERVOUS SYSTEM DISCOVERIES

In the late 1800s and early 1900s, two researchers made discoveries that helped scientists understand how the nervous system functions. The first was Santiago Ramón y Cajal, a Spanish scientist. He discovered that the nervous system consists of billions of separate nerve cells, rather than a network of continuous filaments, which was the accepted view at the time. Cajal was awarded a Nobel Prize in 1906. Otto Loewi, a German scientist, determined how nerve impulses are transmitted between neurons when he discovered the neurotransmitter acetylcholine. For his contribution to neurophysiology, Loewi won a Nobel Prize in 1936. In 2000, the Nobel Prize in Physiology or Medicine was also awarded to researchers who studied the nervous system. Arvid Carlsson, Paul Greengard, and Eric Kandel won the award for their work on signal transduction in the nervous system.

Teach

Expand Vocabulary

Have students make a **Cluster Diagram** that includes the term *neuron* in addition to each of the lesson vocabulary terms on this page. Remind students that a cluster diagram is used to organize information about a topic. After they have completed their cluster diagrams, ask volunteers to share their diagrams with the class. Have students note the similarities and differences between the diagrams.

Study Wkbks A/B, Appendix S19, Cluster Diagram. **Transparencies,** GO2.

DIFFERENTIATED INSTRUCTION

L1 Struggling Students To assist students with the cluster diagram, provide them with a list of the terms to be included, as well as their definitions. Have a brief discussion of each term. Then, have students work in small groups to complete the cluster diagram.

ELL Focus on ELL: Access Content

BEGINNING AND INTERMEDIATE SPEAKERS

Have students work in pairs to draw a copy of **Figure 31–2** on a large piece of paper. After students finish the drawing, have them add the labels shown in the figure. Then, ask them to use the information on this page to find the definition of each labeled structure. (Students can refer to Chapter 7 or the Glossary to find the definition of *nucleus*.) Have them write the definitions on their drawing under the appropriate terms. Ask intermediate speakers to give a brief, spoken description of their diagram.

Answers

IN YOUR NOTEBOOK Students' tables should include all of the yellow-highlighted terms on this page and the function of each structure.

LESSON 31.1

Teach continued

Lead a Discussion

Use the following questions to start a discussion on nerve impulses.

Ask In a resting neuron, how does the electrical charge inside the cell compare to the electrical charge outside the cell? *(The inside of the cell is negatively charged compared to the outside of the cell.)*

Ask Why is an impulse described as a sudden reversal of the resting potential? *(An impulse occurs when the inside of the cell temporarily becomes more positively charged than the outside of the cell.)*

DIFFERENTIATED INSTRUCTION

LPR **Less Proficient Readers** Have students use a **Main Ideas and Details Chart** to organize the information about the resting neuron and moving impulses. They can use the subheads, **The Resting Neuron** and **The Moving Impulse,** as main ideas and fill in their chart with details related to each main idea. Students can then apply this information to answer the questions listed above.

Study Wkbks A/B, Appendix S28, Main Ideas and Details Chart. **Transparencies,** G013.

Students should recognize that a toxin that blocks the flow of Na⁺ ions into a cell could affect muscle movement by blocking the ability of neurons to transmit impulses. Students can go online to **Biology.com** to gather their evidence.

BIOLOGY.com Have students do the drag-and-drop activity, **InterActive Art: The Nerve Impulse,** to interact with an animation of a nerve impulse traveling along an axon.

The Nerve Impulse

How does a nerve impulse begin?

Nerve impulses are a bit like the flow of an electric current through a wire. To see how this occurs, let's first examine a neuron at rest.

The Resting Neuron Neurons, like most cells, have a charge, or electrical potential, across their cell membranes. The inside of a neuron has a voltage of −70 millivolts (mV) compared to the outside. This difference, or **resting potential,** is roughly one-twentieth the voltage in a flashlight battery. Where does this potential come from?

Active transport proteins pump sodium ions (Na^+) out of the cell and potassium ions (K^+) into it as shown in **Figure 31–3.** Since both ions are positively charged, this alone doesn't produce a potential across the membrane. However, ungated potassium channel proteins make it easier for K^+ ions than Na^+ ions to diffuse back across the membrane. Because there is a higher concentration of K^+ ions inside the cell as a result of active transport, there is a net movement of positively charged K^+ ions out of the cell. As a result, the inside becomes negatively charged compared to the outside, producing the resting potential.

MYSTERY CLUE The toxin found in this fish binds to gated sodium channels, blocking the flow of Na^+ ions into a cell. How do you think this might affect muscle movement?

The Moving Impulse A neuron remains in its resting state until it receives a stimulus large enough to start a nerve impulse. **An impulse begins when a neuron is stimulated by another neuron or by the environment.** Once it begins, the impulse travels quickly down the axon away from the cell body toward the axon terminals. In myelinated axons, the impulse moves even more rapidly as its skips from one node to the next.

What actually happens during an impulse? As **Figure 31–5** shows, the impulse itself is a sudden reversal of the resting potential. The neuron cell membrane contains thousands of "gated" ion channels. At the leading edge of an impulse, gated sodium channels open, allowing positively charged Na^+ ions to flow into the cell. The inside of the membrane temporarily becomes more positive than the outside, reversing the resting potential. This reversal of charges, from more negatively charged to more positively charged, is called a nerve impulse, or an **action potential.**

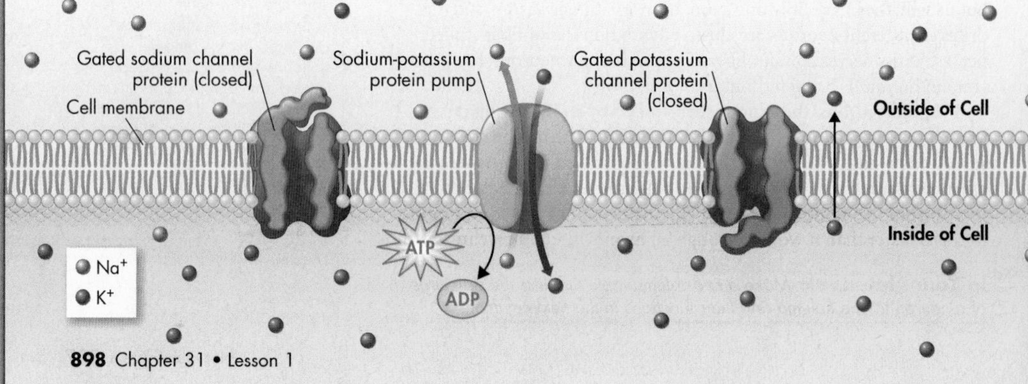

FIGURE 31–3 The Resting Neuron The sodium-potassium pump in the neuron cell membrane uses ATP to pump Na^+ ions out of the cell and to pump K^+ ions in. A small amount of K^+ ions diffuse out of the cell (through ungated channels), but gated channels block Na^+ ions from flowing into the resting neuron. **Apply Concepts** ***Is the action of the sodium-potassium pump an example of diffusion or active transport? Explain.***

Check for Understanding

HAND SIGNALS

Ask students the following questions, and have them show a thumbs-up sign if they think they can answer the question correctly, a thumbs-down sign if they definitely can't, or a waving-hand sign if they're not sure.

- What are the functions of the nervous system?
- What are the functions of the three types of neurons?
- How does a nerve impulse begin?

ADJUST INSTRUCTION

For any questions that receive a thumbs-down or waving-hand sign, have small groups discuss the questions and develop answers.

Answers

FIGURE 31–3 It is an example of active transport, because the pump uses energy to move NA^+ ions out and K^+ ions in against their concentration gradients.

A CHAIN REACTION

FIGURE 31–4 With a strong enough push, the fall of one domino leads to the fall of the next. An action potential moves along a neuron in a similar manner. Use Analogies ***Compare and contrast how an action potential traveling along an axon is like the fall of a row of dominoes.***

Once the impulse passes, sodium gates close and gated potassium channels open, allowing K^+ ions to flow out. This restores the resting potential so that the neuron is once again negatively charged on the inside. All the while, the sodium-potassium pump keeps working, ensuring that the axon will be ready for more action potentials.

A nerve impulse is self-propagating; that is, the flow of ions at the point of the impulse causes sodium channels just ahead of it to open. This allows the impulse to move rapidly along the axon. You could compare the flow of an impulse to the fall of a row of dominoes. As each domino falls, it causes the next domino to fall.

In Your Notebook *In your own words, summarize what happens across a neuron's membrane when it is at rest and during an action potential.*

Threshold Not all stimuli are capable of starting an impulse. The minimum level of a stimulus that is required to cause an impulse in a neuron is called its **threshold.** Any stimulus that is weaker than the threshold will not produce an impulse. A nerve impulse is an all-or-none response. Either the stimulus produces an impulse, or it does not produce an impulse.

The threshold principle can also be illustrated by using a row of dominoes. If you were to gently press the first domino in a row, it might not move at all. A slightly harder push might make the domino teeter back and forth but not fall. A push strong enough to cause the first domino to fall into the second, and start the whole row falling, is like a threshold stimulus.

If all action potentials have the same strength, how do we sense if a stimulus, like touch or pain, is strong or weak? The brain determines this from the frequency of action potentials. A weak stimulus might produce three or four action potentials per second, while a strong one might result in as many as 100 per second. If you accidentally hit your finger with a hammer, those action potentials fire like mad!

FIGURE 31–5 The Moving Impulse Once an impulse begins, it will continue down an axon until it reaches the end. In an axon with a myelin sheath, the impulse jumps from node to node.

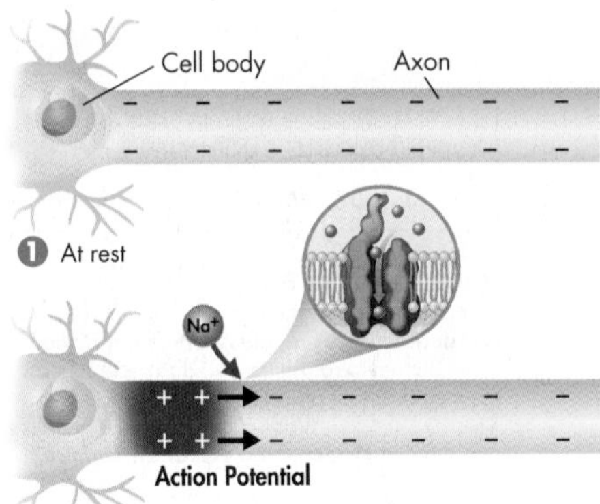

2 At the leading edge of the impulse, gated sodium channels open. Na^+ ions flow into the cell, reversing the potential between the cell membrane and its surroundings. This rapidly moving reversal of charge is called an action potential.

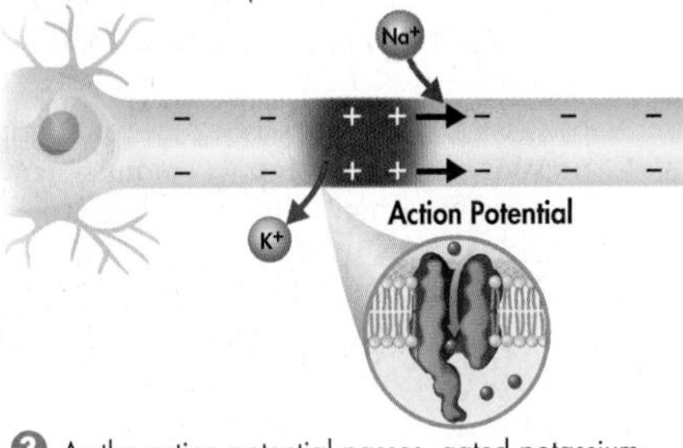

3 As the action potential passes, gated potassium channels open, allowing K^+ ions to flow out and restoring the resting potential inside the axon.

Use Visuals

Ask volunteers to verbally summarize each of the numbered parts of **Figure 31–5.** Challenge students to use this information to infer why an impulse skips from node to node in an axon surrounded by a myelin sheath. *(A myelin sheath insulates the part of the axon it covers. Ion movement resulting in an action potential can happen only at gaps in the myelin sheath. As a result, the nerve impulse jumps from node to node.)*

DIFFERENTIATED INSTRUCTION

ELL English Language Learners Help students use the information in **Figure 31–5** by reading aloud the numbered descriptions of the moving impulse. Have them identify words in the descriptions they do not understand, and then have them use the Glossary or a dictionary to find the definitions of those words. Finally, have them restate the numbered descriptions in their own words.

VISUAL ANALOGY

Call students' attention to **Figure 31–4,** and ask what happens to a row of closely set dominoes when the one on either end is pushed. If possible, demonstrate with real dominoes.

BIOLOGY.com Suggest students view **Visual Analogy: The Moving Impulse** to see an animation of **Figure 31–4.**

Biology In-Depth

ALL OR NOTHING

A nerve impulse usually is described as an all-or-none phenomenon. This means that there is a threshold level that must be reached for a stimulus to trigger an action potential. Any stimulus at or above the threshold level triggers exactly the same response. An exception to this phenomenon occurs just after a neuron fires. There is a period of a few milliseconds, called the absolute refractory period, during which no stimulus can produce a response. Then, for a slightly longer period, called the relative refractory period, an intense stimulus well above the threshold level is needed to provoke a response. The closer the neuron is to complete recovery, the less intense the stimulus must be to provoke a response. When a neuron is completely recovered, it responds in the all-or-none manner once again.

Answers

FIGURE 31–4 Sample answer: Once a row of dominoes starts to fall, it will not stop until all of the dominoes have fallen. Once an action potential starts moving along an axon, it will not stop until it reaches the end. They are different because, once an impulse passes, the neuron's resting potential is restored, so the neuron is ready for the next action potential. Fallen dominoes, however, are not automatically restored to a standing position.

IN YOUR NOTEBOOK Sample answer: When a neuron is at rest, sodium ions are pumped out of the cell and potassium ions are pumped into it. Potassium ions diffuse back across the membrane, resulting in a negative charge inside the cell compared to outside the cell. During an impulse, sodium ions move into the cell through gated sodium channels, which are opened, reversing the relative charges inside and outside the cell.

LESSON 31.1

Assess and Remediate

EVALUATE UNDERSTANDING

Have students locate the lesson's Key Questions, found under each green heading. Have pairs take turns asking and answering these questions. Circulate among students to evaluate their responses. Then, have students complete the 31.1 Assessment.

REMEDIATION SUGGESTION

L1 **Struggling Students** If students have trouble answering **Question 1b,** have them review the functions of the peripheral nervous system and the central nervous system using **Figure 31–1.**

BIOLOGY.com Students can check their understanding of lesson concepts with the **Self-Test** assessment. They can then take an online version of the **Lesson Assessment.**

Answers

FIGURE 31–6 nerve cell, muscle cell, and gland cell

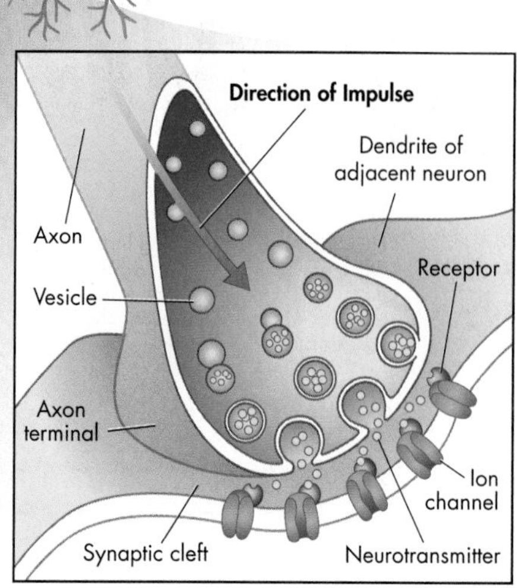

FIGURE 31–6 The Synapse When an impulse reaches the end of the axon of one neuron, neurotransmitters are released into the synaptic cleft. The neurotransmitters bind to receptors on the membrane of an adjacent cell.
Apply Concepts *What are three types of cells that could be on the receiving end of an impulse?*

The Synapse At the end of the neuron, the impulse reaches an axon terminal, which may pass the impulse along to another cell. A motor neuron, for example, may pass impulses to a muscle cell, causing the muscle cell to contract. The point at which a neuron transfers an impulse to another cell is called a **synapse** (SIN aps). As shown in **Figure 31–6,** a space, called the synaptic cleft, separates the axon terminal from the adjacent cell.

The axon terminal at a synapse contains tiny vesicles filled with neurotransmitters. **Neurotransmitters** are chemicals that transmit an impulse across a synapse to another cell. When an impulse arrives at the synapse, neurotransmitters are released from the axon, diffuse across the synaptic cleft, and bind to receptors on the membrane of the receiving cell. This binding opens ion channels in the membrane of the receiving cell. If the stimulation exceeds the cell's threshold, a new impulse begins.

Once they have done their work, the neurotransmitters are released from the receptors on the cell surface. They are then broken down by enzymes in the synaptic cleft or taken up and recycled by the axon terminal.

31.1 Assessment

Review Key Concepts

1. a. Review Describe the functions of the nervous system.
   b. Apply Concepts Describe how your peripheral nervous system and central nervous system were involved in a simple activity you performed today.
2. a. Review Name and describe the three types of neurons.
   b. Predict The immune system of people with multiple sclerosis attacks myelin sheaths in the central nervous system. The myelin breaks down and scar tissue may result. How do you think this would affect the transmission of signals from the central nervous system?
3. a. Review What happens when a neuron is stimulated by another neuron?
   b. Infer How can the level of pain you feel vary if a stimulus causes an all-or-none response?

VISUAL THINKING

4. Create a flowchart to show the events that occur as a nerve impulse travels from one neuron to the next. Include as much detail as you can. Use your flowchart to explain the process to a classmate.

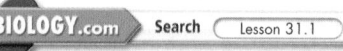

BIOLOGY.com Search  Lesson 31.1 GO • Self-Test • Lesson Assessment

Assessment Answers

1a. The functions of the nervous system are to collect information about the body's internal and external environments, process that information, and respond to it.

1b. Sample answer: My peripheral nervous system collected the information that my school bus was at the bus stop before I was. My central nervous system processed that information and sent a message through my peripheral nervous system that I needed to run to catch the bus.

2a. Sensory neurons carry impulses from the sense organs; motor neurons carry impulses from the brain and spinal cord to muscles and glands; interneurons process the information from sensory neurons and send commands to other interneurons or to motor neurons.

2b. Sample answer: Impulses move from node to node. If scar tissue covers the nodes, impulses may travel more slowly or their transmission may be completely blocked. Alternatively, missing myelin may expose more of the axon to impulses, causing erratic or uncontrolled transmission.

3a. If the stimulus is great enough, an impulse begins that travels rapidly along the axon toward the axon terminals, where the impulse may be passed on to other cells.

3b. Although the response is an all-or-none event, the frequency of action potentials can vary depending on the strength of the stimulus.

VISUAL THINKING

4. Students' flowcharts should include the following events: arrival of the nerve impulse at an axon terminal, release of neurotransmitters into the synaptic cleft, diffusion of neurotransmitters across the gap and attachment to receptors on a neighboring cell membrane, movement of sodium ions across the receiving cell's membrane, and stimulation of the neighboring cell.

31.2 The Central Nervous System

THINK ABOUT IT Who's in charge? The nervous system contains billions of neurons, each of them capable of carrying impulses and sending messages. What keeps them from sending impulses everywhere and acting like an unruly mob? Is there a source of order in this complex system, a central place where information is processed, decisions are made, and order is enforced?

The Brain and Spinal Cord

Where does processing of information occur in the nervous system?

The control point of the central nervous system is the brain. **Each of the major areas of the brain—the cerebrum, cerebellum, and brain stem—are responsible for processing and relaying information.** Like the central processing unit of a computer, information processing is the brain's principal task. **Figure 31–8** on the next page provides details about the major areas of the brain.

While most organs in the body function to maintain homeostasis, the brain itself is constantly changed by its interactions with the environment. Sensory experience changes many of the patterns of neuron connections in the brain, and stem cells in the brain produce new neurons throughout life. Many of these new cells originate in regions associated with learning and memory. Far from staying the same, the highly flexible brain reacts to and changes constantly with the world around it.

Most of the neurons that enter and leave the brain do so in a large cluster of neurons and other cells known as the spinal cord. **The spinal cord is the main communication link between the brain and the rest of the body.** The spinal cord is a bit like a major telephone line, carrying thousands of signals at once between the central and peripheral nervous systems. Thirty-one pairs of spinal nerves branch out from the spinal cord, connecting the brain to different parts of the body. Certain kinds of information, including many reflexes, are processed directly in the spinal cord. A **reflex** is a quick, automatic response to a stimulus. The way in which you pull your hand back quickly when pricked by a pin is an example of a reflex.

In Your Notebook *Make a three-column table that lists the major structures of the brain described in **Figure 31–8**, their functions, and how they interact with at least one other brain structure.*

Key Questions

Where does processing of information occur in the nervous system?

How do drugs change the brain and lead to addiction?

Vocabulary

reflex • cerebrum • cerebral cortex • thalamus • hypothalamus • cerebellum • brain stem • dopamine

Taking Notes

Concept Map As you read, construct a concept map that shows how the structures of the central nervous system are related to each other.

FIGURE 31–7 The Central Nervous System The central nervous system consists of the brain and spinal cord.

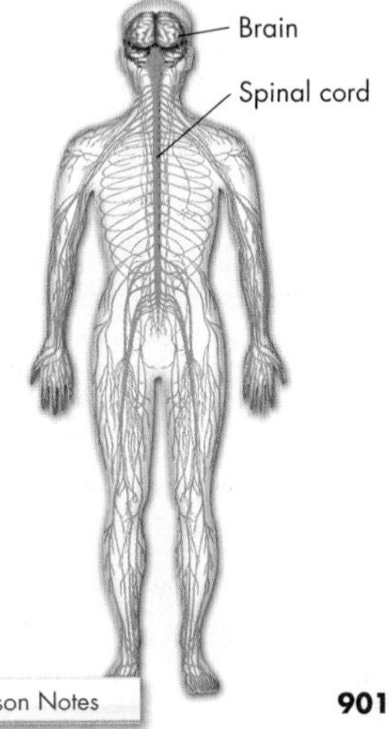

BIOLOGY.com Search Lesson 31.2 GO • Lesson Overview • Lesson Notes

LESSON 31.2

Getting Started

Objectives

31.2.1 Discuss the functions of the brain and spinal cord.

31.2.2 Describe the effects of drugs on the brain.

Student Resources

Study Workbooks A and B, 31.2 Worksheets

Spanish Study Workbook, 31.2 Worksheets

 Lesson Overview • Lesson Notes • Assessment: Self-Test, Lesson Assessment

 For corresponding lesson in the **Foundation Edition**, see pages 747–750.

Build Background

Ask students to describe the function of the brain. Most will probably respond that the function of the brain is to think. Encourage students to extend and refine that description. After a short discussion, have students write a response to the question, What is the function of the brain? Ask them to revise their answer as they read the lesson.

Answers

IN YOUR NOTEBOOK Check that students' tables accurately reflect the information in **Figure 31–8.**

UbD Teach for Understanding

ENDURING UNDERSTANDING The human body is a complex system. The coordinated functions of its many structures support life processes and maintain homeostasis.

GUIDING QUESTION What does the central nervous system do?

EVIDENCE OF UNDERSTANDING *After completing the lesson, give students the following assessment to show their understanding of the central nervous system.* Have students work with a partner to make an electronic or physical three-dimensional model of the brain. Have them label the lobes, hemispheres, and major regions of the brain. Then, have them use their model or diagram to give a short presentation about the location and function of any two major structures of the brain.

Teach

VISUAL SUMMARY

Divide the class into five groups, and assign each group one of the following topics: cerebrum, limbic system, thalamus and hypothalamus, cerebellum, or brain stem. Ask each group to prepare a presentation about its assigned brain structure, including information about the location of the brain structure and its functions. Have each group present its findings to the class.

DIFFERENTIATED INSTRUCTION

L3 **Advanced Students** In addition to participating in the group activity above, have advanced students create a set of five quiz questions about the information in **Figure 31–8.** Then, ask students to use their quiz questions to test other students' comprehension of the information in the figure.

ELL Focus on ELL: Extend Language

BEGINNING AND INTERMEDIATE SPEAKERS
Have students work in pairs to complete an **ELL Frayer Model** for the vocabulary term *cerebrum*. In the spaces, have students write the definition of *cerebrum,* make a drawing or visual representation of the term, give examples of functions of the cerebrum, and, if possible, write a translation of the definition of the term in their native language. Have intermediate speakers complete this activity for additional vocabulary terms on the page. Then, have students form small groups to practice pronouncing the terms and reading their definitions and sentences aloud to each other.

Study Wkbks A/B, Appendix S26, ELL Frayer Model. **Transparencies,** GO10.

VISUAL SUMMARY

THE BRAIN

FIGURE 31–8 The brain contains billions of neurons and other supporting tissue that process, relay, and form responses to an incomprehensible amount of information every moment. Infer *Which structure of the brain most likely filters information traveling from the spinal cord to the brain?*

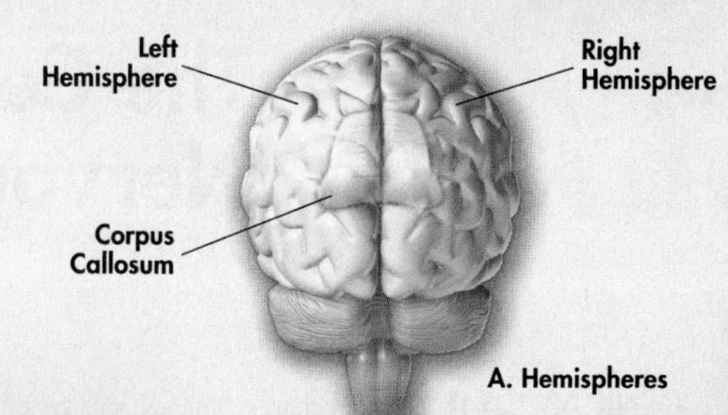

Cerebrum

The largest region of the human brain is the cerebrum. The **cerebrum** is responsible for the voluntary, or conscious, activities of the body. It is also the site of intelligence, learning, and judgment.

Hemispheres As shown in **Figure 31–8A** (a back view of the brain), a deep groove divides the cerebrum into left and right hemispheres. The hemispheres are connected by a band of tissue called the corpus callosum. Remarkably, each hemisphere deals mainly with the opposite side of the body. Sensations from the left side of the body go to the right hemisphere, and those from the right side go to the left hemisphere. Commands to move muscles are delivered in the same way.

As shown in **Figure 31–8B,** each hemisphere is divided into regions called lobes. The four lobes are named for the skull bones that cover them. Each of these lobes are associated with different functions.

Cerebral Cortex The cerebrum consists of two layers. The outer layer of the cerebrum is called the **cerebral cortex** and consists of densely packed nerve cell bodies known as gray matter. The cerebral cortex processes information from the sense organs and controls body movements. It is also where thoughts, plans, and learning abilities are processed. Folds and grooves on the outer surface of the cerebral cortex greatly increase its surface area.

White Matter The inner layer of the cerebrum is known as white matter. Its whitish color comes from bundles of axons with myelin sheaths. These axons may connect different areas of the cerebral cortex, or they may connect the cerebrum to other areas of the brain such as the brain stem.

Limbic System

A number of important functions have been linked to the many structures that make up the limbic system including emotion, behavior, and memory. For example, a region deep within the brain called the amygdala (uh MIG duh luh) has been associated with emotional learning, including fear and anxiety, as well as the formation of long-term memories. The limbic system is also associated with the brain's pleasure center, a region that produces feelings of satisfaction and well-being.

902 Chapter 31 • Lesson 2

How Science Works

BROCA'S AREA

In the mid-nineteenth century, Paul Broca, a French neurologist, discovered that a small region of the left frontal lobe of the cerebral cortex controls the ability to speak words correctly. This area of the brain is now called Broca's area. Broca made his discovery by studying people with brain damage who had lost the ability to speak. Broca's discovery of this speech area was important for two reasons. It provided some of the first evidence that the left and right hemispheres of the brain have separate functions, and it was one of the first indicators that particular brain functions are localized in specific regions of the brain.

Answers

FIGURE 31–8 The brain stem filters information traveling from the spinal cord to the brain.

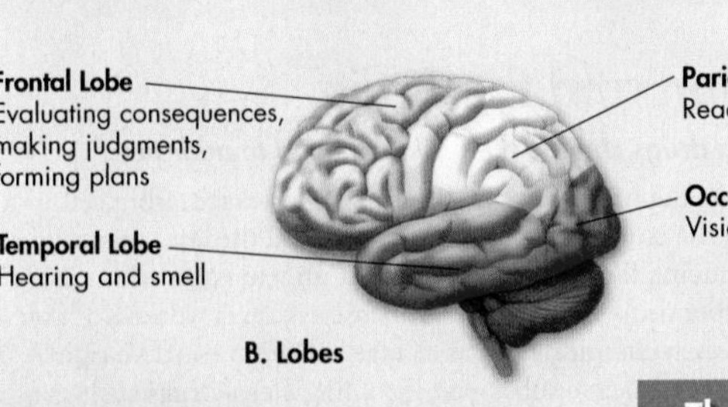

B. Lobes

Thalamus and Hypothalamus

The thalamus and hypothalamus are found between the brain stem and the cerebrum. The **thalamus** receives messages from sensory receptors throughout the body and then relays the information to the proper region of the cerebrum for further processing. Just below the thalamus is the hypothalamus. The **hypothalamus** is the control center for recognition and analysis of hunger, thirst, fatigue, anger, and body temperature. The hypothalamus also helps to coordinate the nervous and endocrine systems.

Cerebellum

The second largest region of the brain is the **cerebellum.** Information about muscle and joint position, as well as other sensory inputs, are sent to the cerebellum. Although the commands to move muscles come from the cerebral cortex, sensory information allows the cerebellum to coordinate and balance the actions of these muscles. This enables the body to move gracefully and efficiently.

When you begin any new activity involving muscle coordination, such as hitting a golf ball or threading a needle, it is the cerebellum that actually learns the movements and coordinates the actions of scores of individual muscles when the movement is repeated.

Brain Stem

The **brain stem** connects the brain and spinal cord. Located just below the cerebellum, the brain stem includes three regions—the midbrain, the pons, and the medulla oblongata. Each of these regions regulates the flow of information between the brain and the rest of the body. Some of the body's most important functions—including regulation of blood pressure, heart rate, breathing, and swallowing—are controlled by the brain stem. The brain stem does the work of keeping the body functioning even when you have lost consciousness due to sleep or injury.

UbD Check for Understanding

USE VOCABULARY

Write the following terms on the board: *cerebrum, cerebral cortex, thalamus, hypothalamus, cerebellum, brain stem, corpus callosum,* and *white matter.* Have students write two sentences that each use at least three different terms from the list. Ask volunteers to read their sentences aloud.

ADJUST INSTRUCTION

If responses show that students avoided using some terms in their sentences or had a hard time using these terms correctly, have them review the index cards they prepared for the Build Study Skills activity described above. After they review their index cards, have students try the activity again.

Build Study Skills

Have students use index cards to organize the information about the different areas of the brain. Distribute five index cards to each student, and explain that one index card should be used for each area of the brain described in **Figure 31–8.** Tell students they should record words, phrases, pictures, and other information about each area. Remind them to save their index cards to use for review.

DIFFERENTIATED INSTRUCTION

L1 **Struggling Students** If the amount of information in **Figure 31–8** overwhelms some students, use the following **Cloze Prompts** to help them understand the information in the figure.

- The area of the brain that is the site of intelligence and learning is the . . . *(cerebrum)*
- Coordination of muscles occurs in the . . . *(cerebellum)*
- The body's functions continue when you are asleep or unconscious because of the . . . *(brain stem)*
- Emotions, behavior, and memory are associated with the . . . *(limbic system)*
- The areas of the brain located between the brain stem and the cerebrum are the . . . *(thalamus and hypothalamus)*

Read the sentences aloud, and have students supply the missing terms, or use the sentences to prepare a worksheet for students to complete.

Study Wkbks A/B, Appendix S2, Cloze Prompts.

Address Misconceptions

The Spinal Cord A common source of confusion for students is the difference between the spinal cord and the vertebral column. Students are probably familiar with the vertebral column from pictures or models of the skeletal system. Point out that the spinal cord is a separate structure, although it is inside of and protected by the vertebral column. The spinal cord is made up of nerves, wherease the vertebral column is made up of bones. Remind students that the spinal cord is the main communication link between the brain and the rest of the body.

Teach continued

Connect to Health

Point out that many people do not think of alcohol and nicotine as drugs, because both can be used legally by adults. Explain that both are potentially addictive substances that affect brain synapses.

DIFFERENTIATED INSTRUCTION

LPR **Less Proficient Readers** Point out the fourth paragraph on this page, which contains the Key Concept. In this paragraph, have students find three ways that addictive drugs affect dopamine synapses.

Assess and Remediate

EVALUATE UNDERSTANDING

Have pairs of students review the major areas of the brain, their locations, and their functions. Then, have students complete the 31.2 Assessment.

REMEDIATION SUGGESTION

L1 **Struggling Students** If students are struggling to answer **Question 2b,** have them review the information about changes in the brain associated with drug use.

BIOLOGY.com Students can check their understanding of lesson concepts with the **Self-Test** assessment. They can then take an online version of the **Lesson Assessment.**

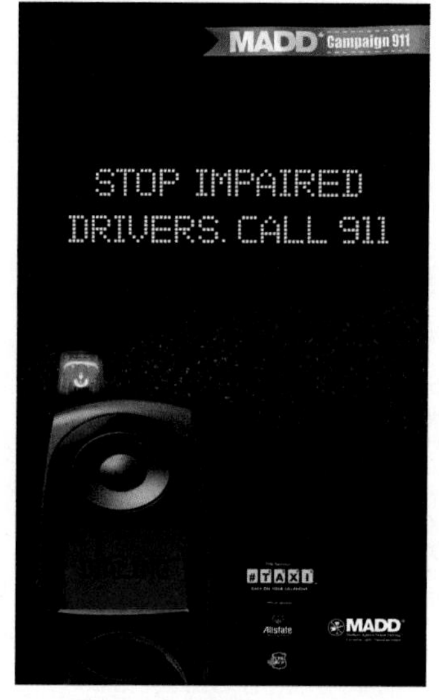

FIGURE 31–9 Drugs and Society The damage to the brain is only the start of the damage that drugs cause. For example, alcohol abuse costs the United States about $185 billion a year in health care costs, treatment services, property damage, and lost productivity.

Addiction and the Brain

How do drugs change the brain and lead to addiction?

Synapses make the brain work by transferring messages from cell to cell, doing the conscious work of thinking and the less conscious work of producing feelings and emotions. Can you guess what would happen if a chemical changed the way those synapses worked? If you guessed that such chemicals might change behavior, you'd be right.

Nearly every addictive substance, including illegal drugs such as heroin, methamphetamine, and cocaine, and legal drugs, such as tobacco and alcohol, affect brain synapses. Although the chemistry of each drug is different, they all produce changes in one particular group of synapses. These synapses use the neurotransmitter **dopamine** and are associated with the brain's pleasure and reward centers.

When we engage in an activity that brings us pleasure, whether it's eating a tasty snack or being praised by a friend, neurons in the hypothalamus and the limbic system release dopamine. Dopamine molecules stimulate other neurons across these synapses, producing the sensation of pleasure and a feeling of wellbeing.

Addictive drugs act on dopamine synapses in a number of ways. Methamphetamine releases a flood of dopamine, producing an instant "high." Cocaine keeps dopamine in the synaptic region longer, intensifying pleasure and suppressing pain. Drugs made from opium poppies, like heroin, stimulate receptors elsewhere in the brain that lead to dopamine release. Nicotine, the addictive substance in tobacco, and alcohol, the most widely abused drug in the United States, also cause increased release of dopamine.

The brain reacts to excessive dopamine levels by reducing the number of receptors for the neurotransmitter. As a result, normal activities no longer produce the sensations of pleasure they once did. Addicts feel depressed and sick without their drugs. Because there are fewer receptors, larger amounts of tobacco, alcohol, and illegal drugs are required to produce the same high. The result is a deeper and deeper spiral of addiction that is difficult to break.

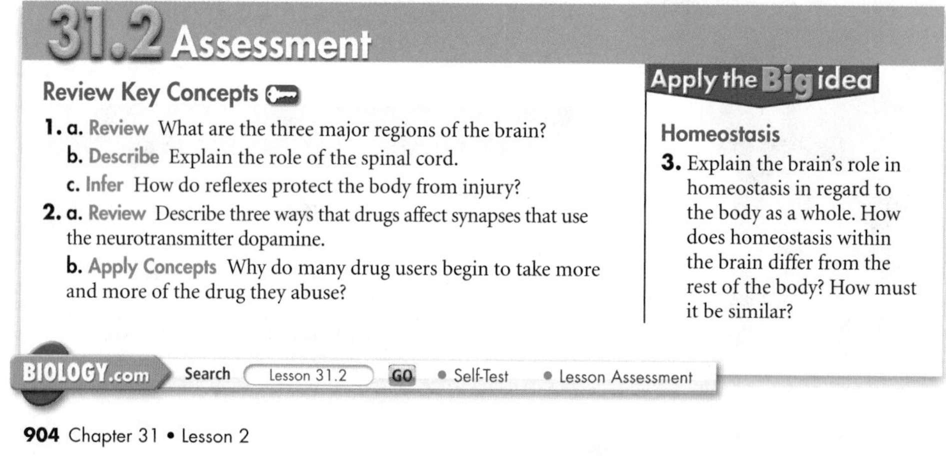

31.2 Assessment

Review Key Concepts

1. a. Review What are the three major regions of the brain?
   b. Describe Explain the role of the spinal cord.
   c. Infer How do reflexes protect the body from injury?
2. a. Review Describe three ways that drugs affect synapses that use the neurotransmitter dopamine.
   b. Apply Concepts Why do many drug users begin to take more and more of the drug they abuse?

Apply the Big idea

Homeostasis

3. Explain the brain's role in homeostasis in regard to the body as a whole. How does homeostasis within the brain differ from the rest of the body? How must it be similar?

BIOLOGY.com Search Lesson 31.2 GO • Self-Test • Lesson Assessment

Assessment Answers

1a. cerebrum, cerebellum, brain stem

1b. The spinal cord is the main communication link between the brain and the rest of the body.

1c. by allowing the body to react very quickly to harmful situations

2a. Drugs affect dopamine synapses by causing the release of a flood of dopamine, keeping dopamine in the synaptic region longer, and stimulating receptors elsewhere in the brain that lead to dopamine release.

2b. The brain reacts to excessive dopamine levels by reducing the number of dopamine receptors, so larger and larger doses are required to produce the same effect.

3. Big idea The brain is responsible for monitoring and maintaining many body functions related to homeostasis. The way the brain itself maintains homeostasis is different from the rest of the body, because the brain is changed by its interactions with the environment—experiences can lead to new neuron connections, and stem cells can produce new neurons. It is similar because it must sense changes and respond to them.

Technology & BIOLOGY

IN NoS.10 Scientific discoveries and new technologies.

Studying the Brain and Addiction

Studies at the National Institute of Drug Abuse (NIDA) have demonstrated why drugs that stimulate dopamine produce a pattern of addiction that is difficult to break. The brain is a flexible organ that responds to its environment and continually adjusts its internal chemistry. When it senses increased levels of dopamine, it adjusts by cutting down on the number of receptors for the neurotransmitter.

NIDA researchers used a powerful imaging technique known as positron emission tomography (PET) to visualize the density of dopamine receptors in brains affected by drug addition, and the results, shown here, are striking. Brains of individuals abusing alcohol and illegal drugs show dramatically lower concentrations of dopamine receptors than the brains of individuals not abusing the drugs.

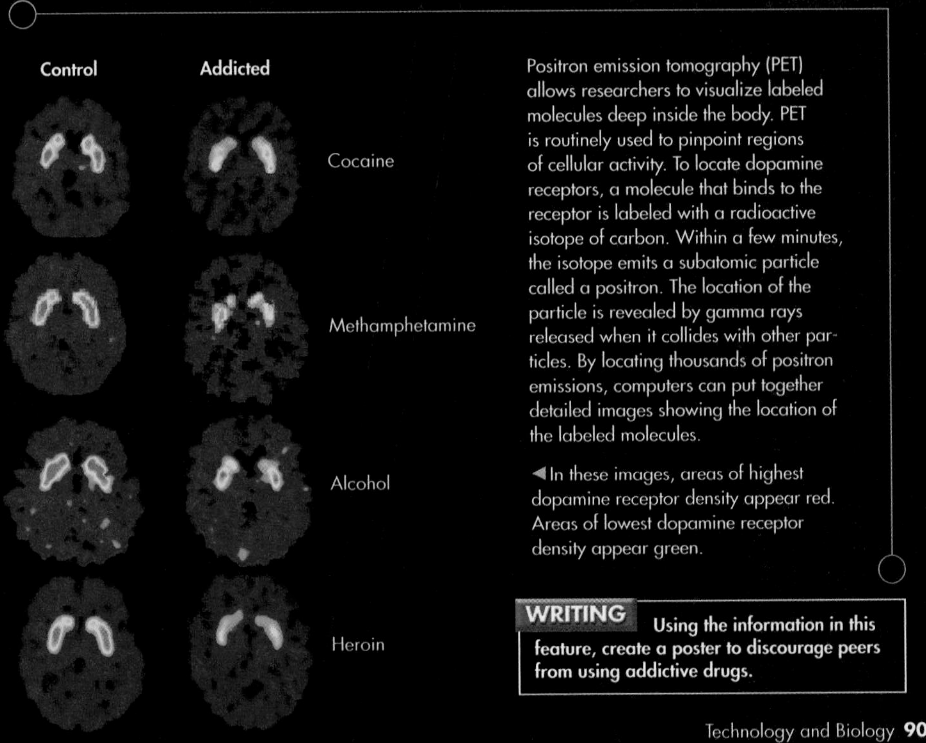

Positron emission tomography (PET) allows researchers to visualize labeled molecules deep inside the body. PET is routinely used to pinpoint regions of cellular activity. To locate dopamine receptors, a molecule that binds to the receptor is labeled with a radioactive isotope of carbon. Within a few minutes, the isotope emits a subatomic particle called a positron. The location of the particle is revealed by gamma rays released when it collides with other particles. By locating thousands of positron emissions, computers can put together detailed images showing the location of the labeled molecules.

◀ In these images, areas of highest dopamine receptor density appear red. Areas of lowest dopamine receptor density appear green.

WRITING **Using the information in this feature, create a poster to discourage peers from using addictive drugs.**

Teach

Lead a Discussion

Have students examine the brain images of the control individuals and addicted individuals shown on this page.

Ask How is the density of dopamine receptors indicated in these images? *(The intensity of the regions that are "lit up" indicates the concentrations of dopamine receptors. Red areas have a greater concentration of the receptors than green areas.)*

Ask How would a decrease in dopamine receptors affect a drug addict's ability to enjoy everyday life when he or she is not intoxicated? *(Sample answer: Pleasurable activities in everyday life result in the release of dopamine. Addicted individuals have fewer receptors for dopamine, so their ability to feel enjoyment is diminished.)*

DIFFERENTIATED INSTRUCTION

L1 **Special Needs** Focus on the main idea conveyed by this research—drugs cause changes in the brain—rather than the technique descibed here to visualize these changes. Point out that such changes are caused not only by illegal drugs, but by substances such as nicotine and alcohol, as well.

Biology In-Depth

THE LIMBIC SYSTEM AND DRUG ABUSE

Brain studies done to increase understanding of drug addiction have revealed information about an area of the limbic system called the nucleus accumbens. This area is an important part of the brain's reward system—this area is stimulated during pleasurable activities, such as eating a favorite food, and it is associated with feelings of well-being and satisfaction. Neurons in this area are also stimulated by the use of drugs, such as cocaine, amphetamines, opiates, alcohol, or tobacco. Researchers investigating how drug use affects the brain have found alterations in neurotransmission in this area due to drug use. They have also found that the expression of particular genes in cells of this area is reduced or eliminated as a consequence of drug use. A thorough understanding of the effects of drug use on the brain may lead to more effective treatments for drug addiction.

Answers

WRITING

Students' posters will vary, but they might describe the dramatic changes in the brain associated with drug use as a way to discourage peers from using addictive drugs.

IN INDIANA ACADEMIC STANDARDS

For the full text of all standards, see the Course Overview in the front matter of this book.

Getting Started

Objectives

31.3.1 Describe the functions of the sensory division of the peripheral nervous system.

31.3.2 Describe the functions of the motor division of the peripheral nervous system.

Student Resources

Study Workbooks A and B, 31.3 Worksheets

Spanish Study Workbook, 31.3 Worksheets

Lab Manual B, 31.3 Hands-On Activity Worksheet

 Lesson Overview • Lesson Notes • Activity: Art in Motion • Assessment: Self-Test, Lesson Assessment

For corresponding lesson in the **Foundation Edition**, see pages 751–753.

Answer

FIGURE 31–10 Sample answer: Chemoreceptors in the nose are activated by the smell of flowers; photoreceptors in the eye are activated by the light in the room; mechanoreceptors in the ear are activated by the sound of people talking.

31.3 The Peripheral Nervous System

Key Questions

How does the central nervous system receive sensory information?

How do muscles and glands receive commands from the central nervous system?

Vocabulary

somatic nervous system
reflex arc
autonomic nervous system

Taking Notes

Flowchart As you read, make a flowchart that shows the flow of information between the divisions of the peripheral nervous system and the central nervous system.

THINK ABOUT IT It's all about input and output. No computer is worth much unless it can accept input from the world around it. And, no matter how quickly it calculates, no result is of any meaning unless there's a way to output it. The central nervous system faces the same issues. Can you guess what it uses for input and output devices?

The Sensory Division

How does the central nervous system receive sensory information?

The peripheral nervous system consists of all the nerves and associated cells that are not part of the brain or spinal cord. Cranial nerves go through openings in the skull and stimulate regions of the head and neck. Spinal nerves stimulate the rest of the body. The cell bodies of cranial and spinal nerves are arranged in clusters called ganglia.

The peripheral nervous system, our link with the outside world, consists of two major divisions—the sensory division and the motor division. **The sensory division of the peripheral nervous system transmits impulses from sense organs to the central nervous system.** The motor division transmits impulses from the central nervous system to the muscles and glands.

Sensory receptors are cells that transmit information about changes in the environment—both internal and external. These changes are called stimuli. Sensory receptors can be categorized by the type of stimuli to which they respond. **Figure 31–10** shows the functions and locations of several types of sensory receptors. When stimulated, sensory receptors transmit impulses to sensory neurons. Sensory neurons then transmit impulses to the central nervous system.

FIGURE 31–10 Sensory Receptors Sensory receptors react to a specific stimulus such as light or sound by sending impulses to sensory neurons. Apply Concepts *List three types of sensory receptors that are activated when you walk into a busy flower shop.*

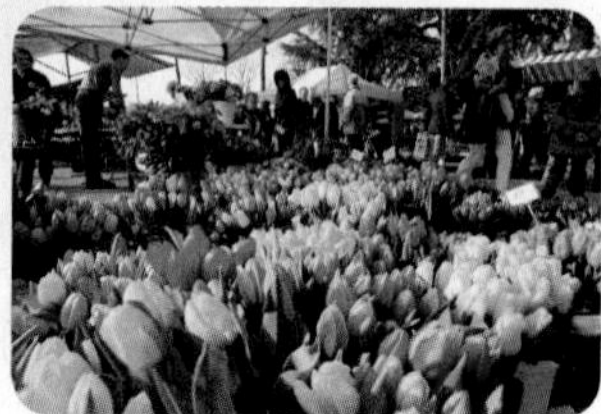

Sensory Receptors

Type	Responds to	Some Locations
Chemoreceptor	Chemicals	Mouth, nose, blood vessels
Photoreceptor	Light	Eyes
Mechanoreceptor	Touch, pressure, vibrations, and stretch	Skin, hair follicles, ears, ligaments, tendons
Thermoreceptor	Temperature changes	Skin, hypothalamus
Pain receptor	Tissue injury	Throughout the body

Teach for Understanding

ENDURING UNDERSTANDING The human body is a complex system. The coordinated functions of its many structures support life processes and maintain homeostasis.

GUIDING QUESTION How do messages travel between the central nervous system and the body?

EVIDENCE OF UNDERSTANDING *After completing the lesson, give students the following assessment to gauge their understanding of the peripheral nervous system.* Have students make a **Flowchart** that shows the sequence of events in a reflex arc. Challenge students to include a written description and drawing for each step in the sequence.

Study Wkbks A/B, Appendix S25, Flowchart. **Transparencies,** GO8.

The Motor Division

How do muscles and glands receive commands from the central nervous system?

The nervous system plays a key role in maintaining homeostasis by coordinating the activities of other systems and organs. Once it has gathered and processed sensory information, the nervous system sends commands to the rest of the body. **The motor division of the peripheral nervous system transmits impulses from the central nervous system to muscles or glands.** These messages are relayed through one of two divisions, the somatic nervous system or the autonomic nervous system.

Based on Captain Cook's symptoms of weakness, what part of the nervous system is most affected by the consumption of even small amounts of this fish?

Somatic Nervous System The **somatic nervous system** regulates body activities that are under conscious control, such as the movement of skeletal muscles. Most of the time you have control over skeletal muscle movement, but when your body is in danger the central nervous system may take over.

▶ ***Voluntary Control*** Every time you lift your finger or wiggle your toes, you are using motor neurons of the somatic nervous system. Impulses originating in the brain are carried through the spinal cord where they synapse with the dendrites of motor neurons. The axons from these motor neurons extend from the spinal cord carrying impulses directly to muscles, causing the contractions that produce voluntary movements.

▶ ***Reflex Arcs*** Although the somatic nervous system is generally considered to be under conscious control, some actions of the system occur automatically. If you accidentally step on a tack with your bare foot, your leg may recoil before you are even aware of the pain.

This rapid response (a reflex) is caused by impulses that travel a pathway known as a **reflex arc,** as shown in **Figure 31–11.** ❶ In this example, sensory receptors react to the sensation of the tack and send an impulse to sensory neurons. ❷ Sensory neurons relay the information to the spinal cord. ❸ An interneuron in the spinal cord processes the information and forms a response. ❹ A motor neuron carries impulses to its effector, a muscle that it stimulates. ❺ The muscle contracts and your leg moves. Meanwhile, impulses carrying information about the injury are sent to your brain. By the time your brain interprets the pain, however, your leg and foot have already moved. The spinal cord does not control all reflexes. Many reflexes that involve structures in your head, such as blinking or sneezing, are controlled by the brain.

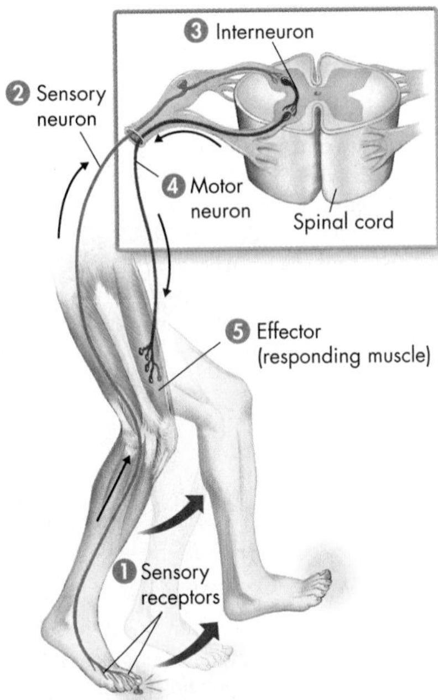

FIGURE 31–11 Reflex Arc When you step on a tack, sensory receptors stimulate a sensory neuron, which relays the signal to an interneuron within the spinal cord. The signal is then sent to a motor neuron, which in turn stimulates a muscle that lifts your leg.

In Your Notebook *In your own words, describe how a reflex arc works. Include the role of the three types of neurons in your description.*

Quick Facts

INFANT REFLEXES

In humans, some reflexes are present only in infants. Examples of infant reflexes include the sucking reflex, which is a response to stimulation around the mouth area; the Moro reflex, which is a response to a sensation of falling; and the grasp reflex, which occurs when a finger or other object is placed in an infant's palm. Medical professionals include an evaluation of infant reflexes as part of a typical examination. Abnormalities in, or the absence of, these reflexes can indicate a problem with an infant's nervous system. Some reflexes present in infants, such as blinking when the eyelid is touched, persist into adulthood. Others last only for the first few months after birth.

Teach

Build Study Skills

Ask for two volunteers to work together and, with input from the rest of the class, create a concept map on the board that shows the relationships between the following terms: *peripheral nervous system, sensory division, motor division, somatic nervous system, motor neuron, sensory neuron,* and *interneuron.* Discuss the function of each nervous system structure.

DIFFERENTIATED INSTRUCTION

L1 Struggling Students Students who might have difficulty understanding the divisions of the nervous system should copy the completed concept map from the board into their notebook. Point out that the completed concept map will be a valuable study and review tool.

ELL Focus on ELL: Extend Language

INTERMEDIATE, ADVANCED, AND ADVANCED HIGH SPEAKERS Have students locate the vocabulary terms *somatic nervous system, reflex arc,* and *autonomic nervous system* in the text. Ask them to review the definitions of these terms. Then, have each student use one of the terms in a short, written paragraph. After students have completed their paragraph, have them pair up to read aloud and revise their paragraphs based on each other's feedback.

MYSTERY CLUE Students' responses should reflect an understanding that the symptoms of weakness indicate that Cook's somatic nervous system was affected. Students can go online to **Biology.com** to gather their evidence.

BIOLOGY.com Students can view an animated version of **Figure 31–11** at **Art in Motion: Reflex Arc.**

Answers

IN YOUR NOTEBOOK Sample answer: Sensory receptors react to a sensation and send an impulse to sensory neurons, which carry the information to the spinal cord. In the spinal cord, an interneuron processes the information and forms a response. A motor neuron then carries an impulse to a muscle.

Quick Lab

PURPOSE Students will describe a common reflex and explain its function.

SAFETY Make sure students put on their safety goggles before the paper ball is thrown at them.

PLANNING Have students review **Figure 31–11.**

ANALYZE AND CONCLUDE

1. Sample answer: My partner blinked.
2. The partner might not blink, because he or she expects the stimulus.
3. to protect the eyes from injury

Assess and Remediate

EVALUATE UNDERSTANDING

Have students write a short paragraph in response to the following question: How do messages travel between the central nervous system and the body? Then, have students complete the 31.3 Assessment.

REMEDIATION SUGGESTION

LPR **Less Proficient Readers** If students have difficulty answering **Question 1c,** have them review the information in **Figure 31–10.**

BIOLOGY.com Students can check their understanding of lesson concepts with the **Self-Test** assessment. They can then take an online version of the **Lesson Assessment.**

Quick Lab
GUIDED INQUIRY

How Do You Respond To an External Stimulus?

1. Have your partner put on safety goggles.
2. Crumple up a sheet of scrap paper into a ball.
3. Watch your partner's eyes carefully as you toss the paper ball toward his or her face.
4. Repeat step 3, three times.
5. Exchange roles and repeat steps 1, 3, and 4.

Analyze and Conclude

1. **Observe** Describe your partner's reaction to step 3.
2. **Compare and Contrast** Did you see any change in behavior as you repeated step 3? Explain.
3. **Infer** What is the function of the blink reflex?

Autonomic Nervous System The **autonomic nervous system** regulates activities that are involuntary, or not under conscious control. For instance, when you start to run, the autonomic nervous system speeds up your heart rate and blood flow to the skeletal muscles, stimulates the sweat glands, and slows down the contractions of smooth muscles in the digestive system. You may not be aware of any of these activities, but all of them enable you to run faster and farther.

The autonomic nervous system consists of two equally important parts, the sympathetic nervous system and the parasympathetic nervous system. Why two systems? In general, the sympathetic and parasympathetic systems have opposite effects on each organ they influence. In the same way that a driver must be able to turn the steering wheel both left and right to keep a car on the road, the two systems produce a level of fine control that coordinates organs throughout the body.

For example, heart rate is increased by the sympathetic nervous system but decreased by the parasympathetic nervous system. In general, the sympathetic system prepares the body for intense activity. Its stimulation causes an increase in blood pressure, the release of energy-rich sugar into the blood, and shutting down of activities not related to the body's preparation to "fight or flee" in response to stress. In contrast, the parasympathetic system causes what might be called the "rest and digest" response. It lowers heart rate and blood pressure, activates digestion, and activates pathways that store food molecules in the tissues of the body.

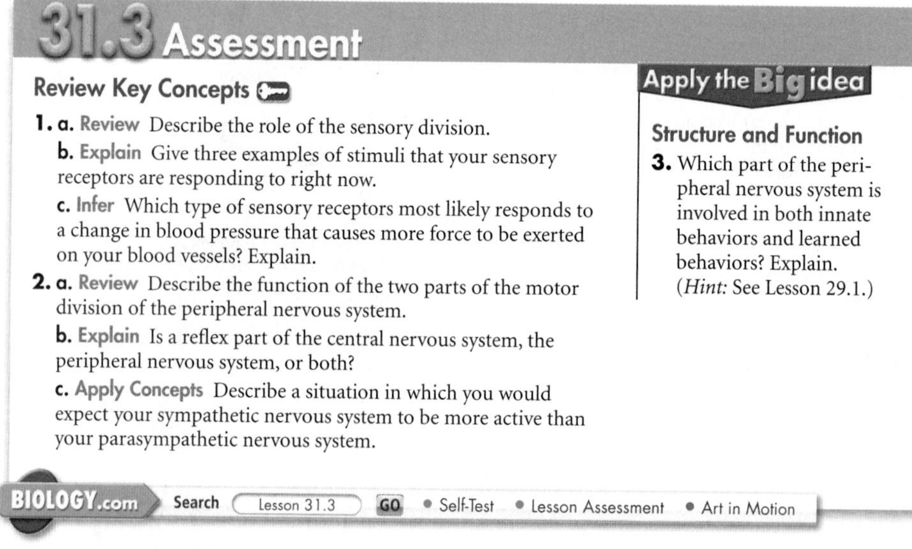

31.3 Assessment

Review Key Concepts

1. a. **Review** Describe the role of the sensory division.
   b. **Explain** Give three examples of stimuli that your sensory receptors are responding to right now.
   c. **Infer** Which type of sensory receptors most likely responds to a change in blood pressure that causes more force to be exerted on your blood vessels? Explain.
2. a. **Review** Describe the function of the two parts of the motor division of the peripheral nervous system.
   b. **Explain** Is a reflex part of the central nervous system, the peripheral nervous system, or both?
   c. **Apply Concepts** Describe a situation in which you would expect your sympathetic nervous system to be more active than your parasympathetic nervous system.

Apply the Big idea

Structure and Function

3. Which part of the peripheral nervous system is involved in both innate behaviors and learned behaviors? Explain. (*Hint:* See Lesson 29.1.)

BIOLOGY.com Search Lesson 31.3 GO • Self-Test • Lesson Assessment • Art in Motion

Assessment Answers

1a. It transmits impulses from sense organs to the central nervous system.

1b. Sample answer: the smell of food from the cafeteria, the sunlight coming in the window, the temperature of the classroom

1c. mechanoreceptors, because they respond to changes in pressure

2a. The somatic nervous system regulates body activities that are under conscious control; the autonomic nervous system regulates activities that are not.

2b. A reflex is part of both the peripheral nervous system and the central nervous system, because it involves sensory and motor neurons of the peripheral nervous system and is processed by the central nervous system—either the brain or spinal cord.

2c. Sample answer: When I am excited about a sporting event, my sympathetic nervous system increases my heart rate.

3. Big idea Sample answer: The somatic nervous system is involved in both innate and learned behaviors. Reflex arcs are innate behaviors that allow people to respond quickly to dangerous situations. Motor neurons of the somatic nervous system also carry signals from the brain that allow for learned behaviors such as riding a bike.

31.4 The Senses

 NoS.3 Communicate ideas.

THINK ABOUT IT We live in a world of sensations. Think about how many of your experiences today can only be described in terms of what you felt, tasted, smelled, heard, and saw. Our senses are our link to experiencing the outside world, and we often take them for granted. Think for a moment of the color red. How would you describe the sensation of seeing red, as opposed to blue or green, to someone who was blind? Or, how would you describe the taste of an apple to someone who had never tasted one before? The inputs we get from our senses are almost impossible to describe, and yet we use them every moment of the day.

Touch and Related Senses

How does the body sense touch, temperature, and pain?

Because nearly all regions of the skin are sensitive to touch, your skin can be considered your largest sense organ. **Different sensory receptors in the body respond to touch, temperature, and pain.** All of these receptors are found in your skin, but some are also found in other areas.

Touch Human skin contains at least seven types of sensory receptors, including several that respond to different levels of pressure. Stimulation of these receptors creates the sensation of touch. Not all parts of the body are equally sensitive to touch. The skin on your fingers, as you might expect, has a much higher density of touch receptors than the skin on your back.

Temperature Thermoreceptors are sensory cells that respond to heat and cold. They are found throughout the skin, and also in the hypothalamus, part of the brain that senses blood temperature. Recently, researchers studying the cell membrane proteins that sense heat made an interesting discovery. The chemical substances that make jalapeño peppers taste "hot" actually bind to these very same proteins.

Pain Pain receptors are found throughout the body. Some, especially those in the skin, respond to physical injuries like cutting or tearing. Many tissues also have pain receptors that respond to chemicals released during infection or inflammation. The brain, interestingly, does not have pain receptors. For this reason, patients are often kept conscious during brain surgery, enabling them to tell surgeons what sensations are produced when parts of the brain are stimulated.

Key Questions

How does the body sense touch, temperature, and pain?

How are the senses of smell and taste similar?

How do the ears and brain process sounds and maintain balance?

How do the eyes and brain produce vision?

Vocabulary

taste bud • cochlea • semicircular canals • cornea • iris • pupil • lens • retina • rods • cones

Taking Notes

Preview Visuals Before reading, preview **Figure 31–14.** Write down at least two questions you have about the information in the figure.

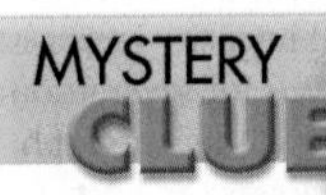

MYSTERY CLUE

Based on Cook's symptoms, which of his senses was greatly affected by the toxin? Explain.

Getting Started

Objectives

31.4.1 Discuss the sense of touch and identify the various types of sensory receptors in the skin.

31.4.2 Explain the relationship between smell and taste.

31.4.3 Identify the parts of the ears that make hearing and balance possible.

31.4.4 Describe the major parts of the eye and explain how the eye enables us to see.

Student Resources

Study Workbooks A and B, 31.4 Worksheets

Spanish Study Workbook, 31.4 Worksheets

Lab Manual B, 31.4 Data Analysis Worksheet

BIOLOGY.com Lesson Overview • Lesson Notes
- Activities: Art Review, Data Analysis
- Assessment: Self-Test, Lesson Assessment

For corresponding lesson in the **Foundation Edition**, see pages 754–757.

MYSTERY CLUE Students should note that Cook's symptoms indicate that his sense of touch was greatly affected by the toxin. Students can go online to **Biology.com** to gather their evidence.

LESSON 31.4

UbD Teach for Understanding

ENDURING UNDERSTANDING The human body is a complex system. The coordinated functions of its many structures support life processes and maintain homeostasis.

GUIDING QUESTION How do humans sense changes in their environment?

EVIDENCE OF UNDERSTANDING *After completing the lesson, give students the following assessment to show their understanding of the senses.* Have students work in small groups to make a children's picture book that could be used to teach students in grades 1–3 about the senses.

IN INDIANA ACADEMIC STANDARDS

For the full text of all standards, see the Course Overview in the front matter of this book.

NoS.3 Clearly communicate their ideas and results of investigations verbally and in written form using tables, graphs, diagrams, and photographs.

Teach

Lead a Discussion

Ask students the following questions to promote their understanding of the relationship between the senses of smell and taste.

Ask What type of receptor is involved in both the sense of smell and taste? *(chemoreceptor)*

Ask How do you know that smell and taste are closely connected? *(Sample answer: When I have a cold and cannot smell food, I can't taste it.)*

Ask Smoking cigarettes impairs the sense of smell. How do you think this impacts a smoker's sense of taste? (*Sample answer: This would diminish the smoker's sense of taste.)*

DIFFERENTIATED INSTRUCTION

L1 Struggling Students Encourage students to explore the connection between taste and smell in a hands-on way. Suggest that the next time they eat a meal, they take a bite while holding their nose. Or, have them try eating one food while smelling another food. For example, they could eat a spoonful of soup while holding an orange slice under their nose. Ask students if the taste of one food can be overpowered by the smell of another. Have them write a brief summary of what they learn to share with the class.

ELL Focus on ELL: Build Background

BEGINNING AND INTERMEDIATE SPEAKERS Brainstorm with students what they already know about the senses. Record their responses on the board.

Then, help students organize their responses into a **Compare/Contrast Table,** using the green headings in this lesson, **Touch and Related Senses; Smell and Taste; Hearing and Balance; Vision,** as headings for the table. Have students add information to the table as the appropriate section is read and discussed in class.

Study Wkbks A/B, Appendix S20, Compare/Contrast Table. **Transparencies,** GO3.

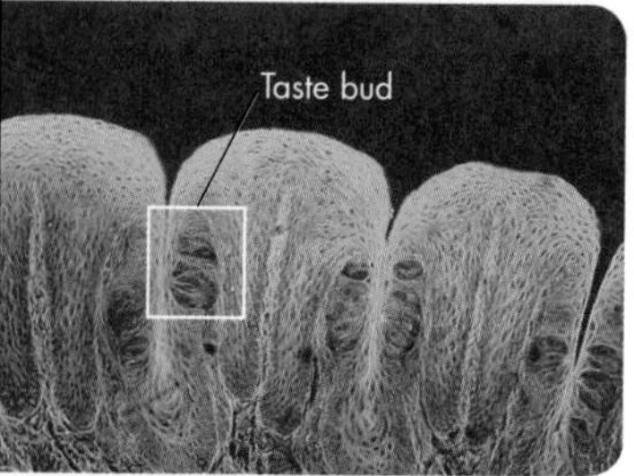

FIGURE 31–12 Taste Buds The surface of the tongue contains many tiny projections. Taste buds line the tops of some of these and line the sides of other projections (LM 80×).

Smell and Taste

How are the senses of smell and taste similar?

You may never have thought of it this way, but your senses of taste and smell actually involve the ability to detect chemicals. Chemical-sensing cells known as chemoreceptors in the nose and mouth are responsible for both of these senses. **Sensations of smell and taste are both the result of impulses sent to the brain by chemoreceptors.**

Your sense of smell is capable of producing thousands of different sensations. In fact, much of what we commonly call the "taste" of food and drink is actually smell. To prove this to yourself, eat a few bites of food while holding your nose. You'll discover that much of the taste of food disappears until you release your nose and breathe freely.

The sense organs that detect taste are the **taste buds.** Most of the taste buds are on the tongue, but a few are found at other locations in the mouth. The surface of the tongue is shown in **Figure 31–12.** Sensory cells in taste buds respond to salty, bitter, sweet, and sour foods. Recently, a fifth kind of taste sensation was identified, now called "umami," from the Japanese word for savory. Umami receptors are strongly stimulated by monosodium glutamate (MSG), a substance often added to Asian foods to enhance their flavor. They are also stimulated by meat and cheese, which typically contain the amino acid glutamate.

In Your Notebook *Explain the relationship between smell and taste.*

IN NoS.3

Sound Intensity

Sound intensity, or loudness, is measured in units called decibels (dB). The threshold of hearing for the human ear is 0 dB. For every 10 dB increase, the sound intensity increases ten times. Sound levels for several sound sources are shown in the bar graph.

Loud noises can permanently damage vibration-sensing cells in the cochlea. Exposure to sounds above 80 dB for several hours at a time can damage hearing. Exposure to sounds about 120 dB for even a few seconds can damage hearing.

Sound Levels

Sound Level (dB): 0, 20, 40, 60, 80, 100, 120, 140

Type of Sound: Whisper, Normal talking, Hair dryer, Rock concert, Jet plane

1. Calculate How much more intense is normal talking than a whisper? Explain. MATH

2. Infer Why do you think that hearing damage caused by repeated exposure to loud noises, such as portable music devices set at a high volume, might not reveal itself for many years?

PURPOSE Students will interpret a graph to learn about the intensity of a variety of common sounds, calculate the relative intensity of two sounds, and make inferences about hearing damage caused by loud noises.

PLANNING Explain to students that a bar graph is used to compare data. In this case, each bar on the graph represents a different type of sound.

ANSWERS

1. Normal talking has an intensity that is 10,000 times greater than a whisper.
2. Sample answer: Hearing damage is cumulative, so damage might not be noticeable until it accumulates to a certain level.

Answers

IN YOUR NOTEBOOK Students' responses should indicate that smell and taste are both the result of impulses sent to the brain by chemoreceptors. Much of what is called "taste" is actually smell.

Hearing and Balance

How do the ears and brain process sounds and maintain balance?

The human ear has two sensory functions, one of which, of course, is hearing. The other function is detecting positional changes associated with movement. **Mechanoreceptors found in parts of the ear transmit impulses to the brain. The brain translates the impulses into sound and information about balance.**

Hearing Sound is nothing more than vibrations moving through the air around us. The ears are the sensory organs that can distinguish both the pitch and loudness of those vibrations. The structure of the ear is shown in **Figure 31–13.**

Vibrations enter the ear through the auditory canal and cause the tympanum (TIM puh num), or eardrum, to vibrate. Three tiny bones, commonly called the hammer, anvil, and stirrup, transmit these vibrations to a membrane called the oval window. Vibrations there create pressure waves in the fluid-filled **cochlea** (KAHK lee uh) of the inner ear. The cochlea is lined with tiny hair cells that are pushed back and forth by these pressure waves. In response, the hair cells send nerve impulses to the brain, which processes them as sounds.

Balance Your ears contain structures that help your central nervous system maintain your balance, or equilibrium. Within the inner ear just above the cochlea are three tiny canals. They are called semicircular canals because each forms a half circle. The **semicircular canals** and the two tiny sacs located behind them monitor the position of your body, especially your head, in relation to gravity.

The semicircular canals and the sacs are filled with fluid and lined with hair cells. As the head changes position, the fluid in the canals also changes position. This causes the hair on the hair cells to bend. This action, in turn, sends impulses to the brain that enable it to determine body motion and position.

FIGURE 31–13 The Ear The diagram shows the structures in the ear that transmit sound. The SEM shows hair cells in the inner ear. The motion of these sensitive hair cells produces nerve impulses that travel to the brain through the cochlear nerve. Predict ***How would frequent exposure to loud noises that damage hair cells affect a person's threshold for detecting sound?***

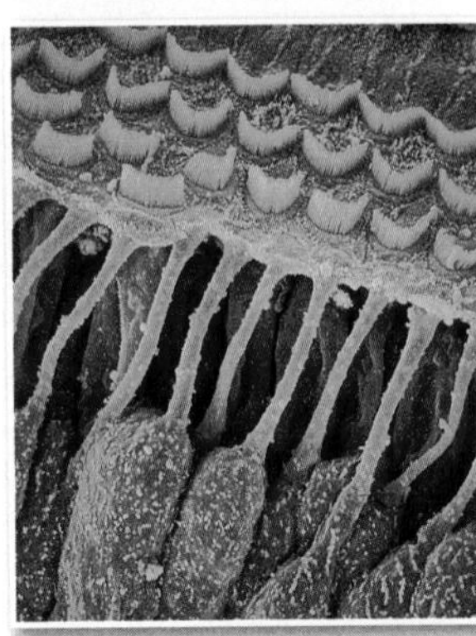

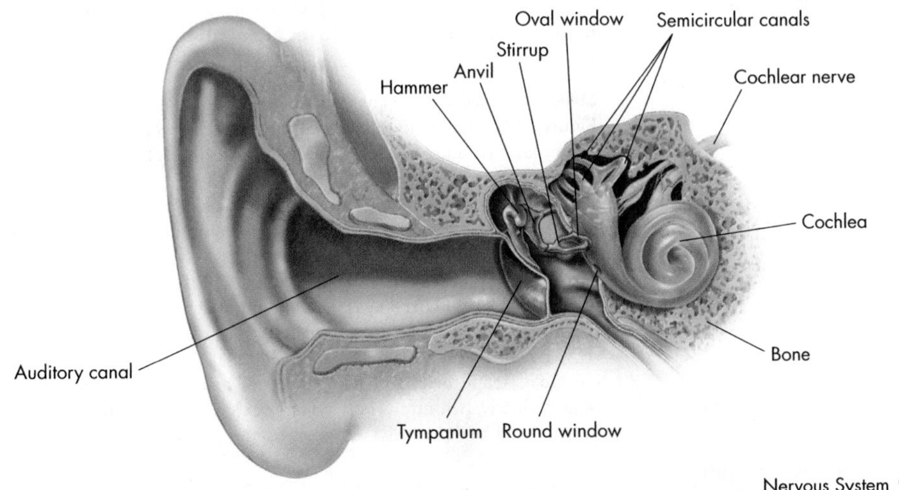

Use Models

Half-fill a glass container with water. As students watch, slowly tilt the container from side to side. The water will always stay parallel to the floor due to gravity. Students will observe it move up and down the side of the glass as the container is tilted. Explain that this is similar to how the fluid inside the semicircular canals moves as the head changes position.

DIFFERENTIATED INSTRUCTION

ELL English Language Learners Point out that the semicircular canals are instrumental in maintaining balance. Write the term *semicircular canals* on the board. Underline the word part *semi-*, and explain that it means "partial," or "incomplete." Have students use this information to further their understanding of the shape of the semicircular canals.

L3 Advanced Learners Have students review the information in this book about the senses of other animals (for example, see Lesson 28.1). Ask them to create a table comparing and contrasting a human sense, other than hearing, with that of other animals. Interested students can use library and Internet resources to find additional information.

How Science Works

THE DISCOVERY OF UMAMI

The taste sensation umami was discovered in the early 1900s by Kikunae Ikeda, a professor of chemistry in Tokyo, Japan. His worked was based on his observation that a particular soup ingredient commonly used in Japan had a taste that did not fall into the established taste categories of salty, sweet, bitter, or sour. By isolating the chemical compounds in this soup ingredient, he was able to determine that the taste associated with umami is due to glutamate, an amino acid that is found naturally in meats and some vegetables. Ikeda developed the food seasoning, monosodium glutamate—MSG—based on his research.

Answers

FIGURE 31–13 Damage to the hair cells would raise the threshold at which an individual could detect sound.

Teach continued

Use Visuals

Have students use **Figure 31–14** to trace the path of light as it moves through the eye. Call on a volunteer to identify the structures through which light passes. Then, ask other volunteers to describe the function of each of these structures. Finally, have other volunteers describe structures of the eye identified in the figure through which light does not pass, for example, ligaments, muscles, and blood vessels.

DIFFERENTIATED INSTRUCTION

L1 Special Needs Have students make a poster that conveys information about the eye and the sense of sight. Students can prepare a simplified version of **Figure 31–14** and add words describing the eye and its structures. Alternatively, students can prepare a collage of pictures from magazines that depict individuals using their sense of sight, or other senses, to learn about their surroundings (for example, pictures of people listening to music, reading a book, or eating food). Have students describe each picture included on the collage.

BIOLOGY.com Assign **Art Review: The Ear and the Eye** so students can use drag-and-drop labels to identify structures of the ear and eye. Encourage students to complete the **Data Analysis: Looks Tasty: How Vision Affects Taste** to learn how food color impacts people's perception of flavor.

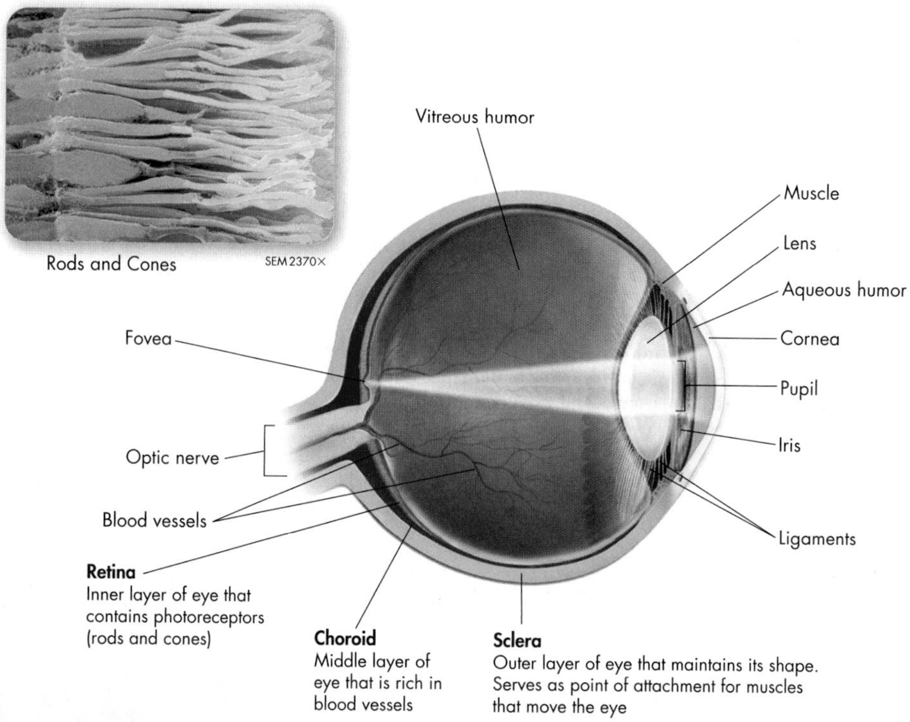

Rods and Cones SEM 2370×

Vitreous humor
Muscle
Lens
Aqueous humor
Cornea
Pupil
Iris
Ligaments
Fovea
Optic nerve
Blood vessels

Retina Inner layer of eye that contains photoreceptors (rods and cones)

Choroid Middle layer of eye that is rich in blood vessels

Sclera Outer layer of eye that maintains its shape. Serves as point of attachment for muscles that move the eye

FIGURE 31–14 The Eye The eye is a complicated sense organ. The sclera, choroid, and retina are three layers of tissues that form the inner wall of the eyeball. Interpret Graphics ***What is the function of the sclera?***

How do the eyes and brain produce vision?

The world around us is bathed in light, and the sense organs we use to detect that light are the eyes. **Vision occurs when photoreceptors in the eyes transmit impulses to the brain, which translates these impulses into images.**

Structures of the Eye The structures of the eye are shown in **Figure 31–14.** Light enters the eye through the **cornea,** a tough transparent layer of cells. The cornea helps to focus the light, which then passes through a chamber filled with a fluid called aqueous (AY kwee us) humor. At the back of the chamber is a disk-shaped structure called the **iris.** The iris is the colored part of the eye. In the middle of the iris is a small opening called the **pupil.** Tiny muscles in the iris adjust the size of the pupil to regulate the amount of light that enters the eye. In dim light, the pupil becomes larger and more light enters the eye. In bright light, the pupil becomes smaller and less light enters the eye.

Just behind the iris is the **lens.** Small muscles attached to the lens change its shape, helping to adjust the eyes' focus to see near or distant objects clearly. Behind the lens is a large chamber filled with a transparent, jellylike fluid called vitreous (VIH tree us) humor.

UbD Check for Understanding

ORAL QUESTIONING

Use the following prompt to gauge students' understanding of lesson concepts.

- When processing an image, what are two things the brain needs to do that a camera does not? *(Sample answers: The brain needs to fill in information obscured by the blind spot, and it needs to create a three-dimensional image.)*

ADJUST INSTRUCTION

If students have difficulty answering this question, have them reread **How You See,** and then discuss responses to the question.

Answers

FIGURE 31–14 The sclera helps the eye maintain its shape and serves as a point of attachment for muscles that move the eye.

How You See The lens focuses light onto the **retina,** the inner layer of the eye. Photoreceptors are arranged in a layer in the retina. The photoreceptors convert light energy into nerve impulses that are carried to the brain through the optic nerve. There are two types of photoreceptors: rods and cones. **Rods** are extremely sensitive to light, but they do not distinguish different colors. They only allow us to see black and white. **Cones** are less sensitive than rods, but they do respond to different colors, producing color vision. Cones are concentrated in the fovea, the site of sharpest vision.

The impulses assembled by this complicated layer of interconnected cells leave each eye by way of the optic nerve, which carry the impulses to the appropriate regions of the brain. There are no photoreceptors where the optic nerve passes through the back of the eye, producing a blind spot in part of each image sent to the brain. During the processing of the nerve impulses, the brain fills in the holes of the blind spot with information.

If the eye merely took photographs, the images would be no more detailed than the blurry images taken by an inexpensive camera and would be incomplete. The images we actually see of the world, however, are much more detailed, and the reason is the sophisticated way in which the brain processes and interprets visual information.

In Your Notebook *Make a flowchart that shows the sequence of how light and nerve impulses travel from the outside environment to the brain.*

BUILD Vocabulary

ACADEMIC WORDS Distinguish may mean "to recognize as different," "to perceive clearly with a sense," or "to show a difference."

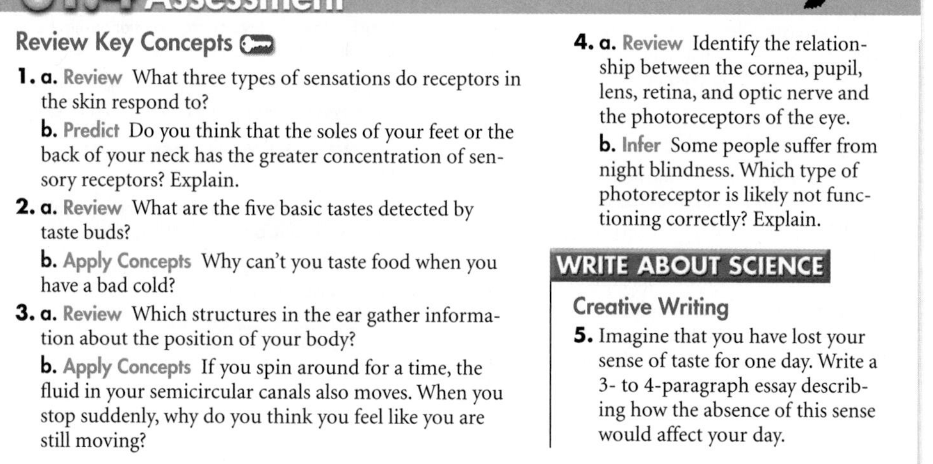

31.4 Assessment

IN NoS.3

Review Key Concepts

1. a. Review What three types of sensations do receptors in the skin respond to?

b. Predict Do you think that the soles of your feet or the back of your neck has the greater concentration of sensory receptors? Explain.

2. a. Review What are the five basic tastes detected by taste buds?

b. Apply Concepts Why can't you taste food when you have a bad cold?

3. a. Review Which structures in the ear gather information about the position of your body?

b. Apply Concepts If you spin around for a time, the fluid in your semicircular canals also moves. When you stop suddenly, why do you think you feel like you are still moving?

4. a. Review Identify the relationship between the cornea, pupil, lens, retina, and optic nerve and the photoreceptors of the eye.

b. Infer Some people suffer from night blindness. Which type of photoreceptor is likely not functioning correctly? Explain.

WRITE ABOUT SCIENCE

Creative Writing

5. Imagine that you have lost your sense of taste for one day. Write a 3- to 4-paragraph essay describing how the absence of this sense would affect your day.

BIOLOGY.com Search Lesson 31.4 GO • Self-Test • Lesson Assessment

Lead a Discussion

Help students understand the role of the brain in vision by discussing the question, How does the brain process information from the eyes?

DIFFERENTIATED INSTRUCTION

L3 Advanced Students Challenge students to find and share examples of common optical illusions.

Assess and Remediate

EVALUATE UNDERSTANDING

Call on volunteers to describe sensory input they experience during a typical class. Then, have students complete the 31.4 Assessment.

REMEDIATION SUGGESTION

L1 Struggling Students If students have trouble answering **Question 1b,** ask them to consider whether the soles of the feet or the back of the neck are more frequently used to gather information about an individual's surroundings.

BIOLOGY.com Students can check their understanding of lesson concepts with the **Self-Test** assessment. They can then take an online version of the **Lesson Assessment.**

Answers

IN YOUR NOTEBOOK Students' flowcharts should include structures through which light travels and explain how nerve impulses move through the optic nerve to the brain.

Assessment Answers

1a. touch, temperature, and pain

1b. Sample answer: I think the soles of my feet have a greater concentration of sensory receptors, because they are more sensitive to touch than the back of my neck.

2a. salty, bitter, sweet, sour, and umami

2b. Much of the sensation of taste is actually due to the smell of food. If your sense of smell is diminished by cold symptoms, your sense of taste will also be diminished.

3a. The structures in the ear that detect sound are: the auditory canal, tympanum, hammer, anvil, stirrup, oval window, round window, cochlea, and cochlear nerve. The semicircular canals gather information about body position.

3b. If you spin around and then stop suddenly, you will feel like you are still moving because the fluid in the semicircular canals is still moving.

4a. The cornea, pupil, and lens are all involved in allowing light into the eye and focusing it on the retina. The retina contains the photoreceptors that respond to this light. The optic nerve transports impulses from the photoreceptors to the brain.

4b. An individual with night blindness likely has rods that are not functioning correctly, because these are the photoreceptors that are most sensitive to light.

WRITE ABOUT SCIENCE

5. Answers will vary. Students might describe how loss of the sense of taste affects food choices or amounts consumed.

Pre-Lab

Introduce students to the concepts they will explore in the chapter lab by assigning the Pre-Lab questions.

Lab

Tell students they will perform the chapter lab *Testing Sensory Receptors for Touch* described in **Lab Manual A.**

 **Struggling Students** A simpler version of the chapter lab is provided in **Lab Manual B.**

SAFETY

Students should use caution when handling sharp objects. Tell them to follow your specific safety instructions for this lab.

 Look online for **Editable Lab Worksheets**

For corresponding lesson in the **Foundation Edition**, see page 758.

IN INDIANA ACADEMIC STANDARDS

For the full text of all standards, see the Course Overview in the front matter of this book.

GUIDED INQUIRY

 NoS.1 Develop explanations; NoS.2 Explanations based on data.

Pre-Lab: Testing Sensory Receptors for Touch

Problem What factors affect a person's ability to sense gentle pressure on skin?

Materials bent paper clips, metric ruler

Lab Manual Chapter 31 Lab

Skills Focus Measure, Analyze Data, Draw Conclusions

Connect to the Big idea Your nervous system coordinates your response to stimuli from outside your body and inside your body. Sensory receptors react to stimuli by sending impulses to sensory neurons. Each receptor can detect only one type of stimulus. Receptors are classified by the type of stimuli to which they respond. Some respond to light, some to pain, some to chemicals, and so on. Mechanoreceptors are cells that respond to touch, pressure, vibrations, and stretch.

In this lab, you will investigate the mechanoreceptors in your skin that respond to gentle touch. You will compare the relative density of these receptors in three areas of your skin. You will also identify other factors that could affect a person's response to touch.

Background Questions

a. Review Which division of the peripheral nervous system transmits signals from receptors in your skin to your brain?

b. Relate Cause and Effect List two reasons why a touch might not produce a nerve impulse?

c. Infer People who are visually impaired use their fingertips to read books that are printed in Braille. In Braille, each letter of the alphabet is represented by a unique pattern of dots. What feature of the dots allows a reader to distinguish one set of dots from another?

Pre-Lab Questions

Preview the procedure in the lab manual.

1. Predict Which area will have the highest density of receptors for gentle pressure—your fingertips, the back of your hand, or your forearm?
2. Control Variables Why must you have your eyes closed while your partner touches your skin with the bent paper clip?
3. Predict Will you and your partner have the same density of touch receptors in a given area of skin? Give a reason for your prediction.

 Search 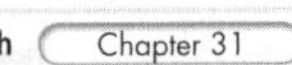

Visit Chapter 31 online to test yourself on chapter content and to find activities to help you learn.

Untamed Science Video Hold on tightly as the Untamed Science crew takes you on a quick tour of how animal toxins affect the body.

Data Analysis Investigate the relationship between the color of food and perception of flavor.

Art Review Review your understanding of the structures in the eyes and ears with this drag-and-drop activity.

InterActive Art Watch a nerve impulse move down a neuron.

Visual Analogy Compare an action potential moving along a neuron to a row of falling dominoes.

Art in Motion View a short animation that shows how a reflex arc works.

Pre-Lab Answers

BACKGROUND QUESTIONS

a. the sensory division

b. Sample answer: There may not be a receptor for touch at the location being touched. The stimulus might not reach the threshold needed to produce a response.

c. The dots are raised so that their pattern will stimulate sensory receptors for touch in the reader's fingertips.

PRE-LAB QUESTIONS

1. Sample answer: Fingertips will have the highest density.
2. Sample answer: If I could see the paper clip touch my skin, I might assume that I felt two touches when I did not.
3. Because most physical traits vary, students may assume that the density of receptors can vary, too.

31 Study Guide

Big idea Structure and Function

A complicated, but highly organized, network of cells and supporting tissues makes up our nervous system. The nervous system allows us to gather information about our world, process it, and produce responses.

31.1 The Neuron

The nervous system collects information about the body's internal and external environment, processes that information, and responds to it.

Nervous system impulses are transmitted by cells called neurons.

An impulse begins when a neuron is stimulated by another neuron or by the environment.

peripheral nervous system (896)
central nervous system (896)
cell body (897)
dendrite (897)
axon (897)
myelin sheath (897)
resting potential (898)
action potential (898)
threshold (899)
synapse (900)
neurotransmitter (900)

31.2 The Central Nervous System

Each of the major areas of the brain—the cerebrum, cerebellum, and brain stem—are responsible for processing and relaying information.

The spinal cord is the main communication link between the brain and the rest of the body.

The brain reacts to excessive dopamine levels by reducing the number of receptors for the neurotransmitter. As a result, normal activities no longer produce the sensations of pleasure they once did.

reflex (901)
cerebrum (902)
cerebral cortex (902)
thalamus (903)
hypothalamus (903)
cerebellum (903)
brain stem (903)
dopamine (904)

31.3 The Peripheral Nervous System

The sensory division of the peripheral nervous system transmits impulses from sense organs to the central nervous system.

The motor division of the peripheral nervous system transmits impulses from the central nervous system to muscles or glands. The motor division is divided into the somatic nervous system and the autonomic nervous system.

somatic nervous system (907)
reflex arc (907)
autonomic nervous system (908)

31.4 The Senses

Different sensory receptors in the body respond to touch, temperature, and pain.

Sensations of smell and taste are both the result of impulses sent to the brain by chemoreceptors.

Mechanoreceptors found in parts of the ear transmit impulses to the brain. The brain translates the impulses into sound and information about balance.

Vision occurs when photoreceptors in the eyes transmit impulses to the brain, which translates these impulses into images.

taste bud (910)
cochlea (911)
semicircular canals (911)
cornea (912)
iris (912)
pupil (912)
lens (912)
retina (913)
rods (913)
cones (913)

Think Visually

Develop a graphic organizer to show the relationship between the different divisions of the nervous system.

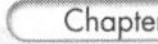 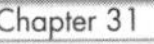  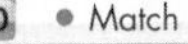 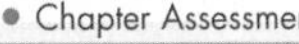

BIOLOGY.com Search Chapter 31 GO • Match It • Chapter Assessment

Study Online

REVIEW AND ASSESSMENT RESOURCES

Editable Worksheets Pages of Study Workbooks A and B, Lab Manuals A and B, and the Assessment Resources Book are available online. These documents can be easily edited using a word-processing program.

Lesson Overview Have students reread the Lesson Overviews to help them study chapter concepts.

Vocabulary Review The *Flash Cards* and *Match It* provide an interactive way to review chapter vocabulary.

Chapter Assessment Have students take an online version of the Chapter 31 Assessment.

Standardized Test Prep Students can take an online version of the Standardized Test Prep. You will receive their scores along with ideas for remediation.

Diagnostic and Benchmark Tests Use these tests to monitor your students' progress and supply remediation.

UbD Performance Tasks

SUMMATIVE TASK Have students work in pairs to prepare a script describing a sensory input and the body's response to it in the style of a play-by-play sports broadcast that includes background on the "players" involved in the game.

TRANSFER TASK Have students write a paragraph comparing and contrasting the structures and functions of the human nervous system with those of a computer. Ask them to draw parallels between different parts of a computer—CPU, keyboard, monitor—and nervous system structures.

Answers

THINK VISUALLY

Students' graphic organizers should show that the nervous system is divided into the peripheral and central nervous systems. The peripheral nervous system is further divided into the sensory and motor divisions. The motor division is subdivided into the somatic and autonomic nervous systems. The autonomic nervous system is further divided into the sympathetic and parasympathetic divisions.

Lesson 31.1

UNDERSTAND KEY CONCEPTS

1. a **2.** d **3.** a

4. Sensory neurons carry impulses from the sense organs to the spinal cord and brain. Interneurons process information from sensory neurons and send commands to other interneurons or to motor neurons. Motor neurons carry impulses from the brain and spinal cord to muscles and glands.

5. When a neuron is at rest, the sodium-potassium pump moves sodium out of the neuron and potassium into the neuron, and ungated potassium channel proteins allow potassium ions to move out of the cell.

6. It can be described as an all-or-none event, because any stimulus above the threshold will produce an impulse and any stimulus below the threshold will not produce an impulse.

THINK CRITICALLY

7. If an axon were disconnected from a cell body, the pathway of an outgoing nerve impulse would be disrupted. As a result, the impulse would not be transmitted.

8. Sample answer: A neuron and electrical extension cord are similar because both conduct electrical impulses over a distance. They are different because the neuron relies on the movement of ions in and out of the axon to transmit the signal, while the extension cord relies on electrons.

Lesson 31.2

UNDERSTAND KEY CONCEPTS

9. c **10.** b **11.** a

12. The cerebrum consists of two hemispheres, each divided into regions called lobes. A band of nerve tissue, known as the corpus callosum, connects the two hemispheres. The cerebrum is responsible for the voluntary, or conscious, activities of the body. It is the site of intelligence, learning, and judgment.

13. The brain stem connects the rest of the brain to the spinal cord. It regulates the flow of information between the brain and the rest of the body.

14. Nicotine binds to receptors and stimulates neurons that increase the amount of dopamine produced in the brain. Brain cells respond by producing fewer dopamine receptors.

THINK CRITICALLY

15. Difficulty speaking indicates damage to the parietal lobe. Lack of muscle control on the right side of the body indicates damage to the left hemisphere of the cerebrum, which controls voluntary muscle movement on the right side of the body.

16. Both methamphetamine and cocaine increase the amount of dopamine in the brain. Amphetamines cause an immediate increase in the amount of dopamine that is produced. Cocaine makes dopamine stay longer in the synapses than it normally would.

Lesson 31.3

UNDERSTAND KEY CONCEPTS

17. d **18.** d

19. A reflex allows an organism to respond to danger quickly, which is an advantage for survival.

31 Assessment

IN The numbers following the questions refer to Indiana's Academic Standards for Biology I.

31.1 The Neuron

Understand Key Concepts

1. The basic units of structure and function in the nervous system are
a. neurons.
b. axons.
c. dendrites.
d. neurotransmitters.

2. In the diagram below, the letter A is pointing to the
a. myelin sheath.
b. axon.
c. dendrite.
d. cell body.

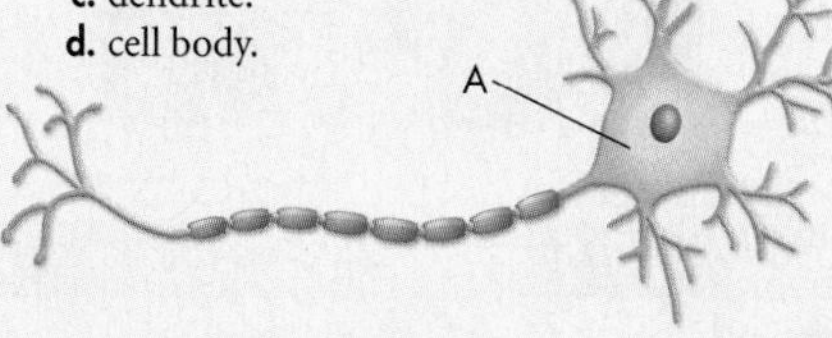

3. The place where a neuron transfers an impulse to another cell is the
a. synapse.
b. dendrite.
c. myelin sheath.
d. receptor.

4. Name the three types of neurons and describe their function in the nervous system.

5. Describe the movement of sodium and potassium ions during the resting potential.

6. Why can an action potential be described as an all-or-none event?

Think Critically

7. Infer Suppose a portion of an axon is cut so that it is no longer connected to its cell body. What effect would that have on the transmission of impulses?

8. Use Analogies How are a neuron and an electrical extension cord similar? How are they different?

31.2 The Central Nervous System

Understand Key Concepts

9. The central nervous system consists of the
a. sense organs. **c.** brain and spinal cord.
b. reflexes. **d.** sensory and motor neurons.

10. Voluntary, or conscious, activities of the body are controlled primarily by the
a. medulla oblongata. **c.** cerebellum.
b. cerebrum. **d.** brain stem.

11. Methamphetamines are a type of drug that affects the brain by
a. causing the release of excess dopamine.
b. blocking the production of dopamine.
c. increasing the number of dopamine receptors.
d. increasing the number of synapses in the brain.

12. Describe the structure and function of the cerebrum.

13. Describe the relationship between the brain stem and the spinal cord.

14. How does nicotine influence dopamine receptors in the brain?

Think Critically

15. Infer A stroke occurs when blood flow to part of the brain stops due to a clot or broken blood vessel. What conclusion might you make about the location of damage in a person who has difficulty speaking and cannot move many of his muscles on the right side of his body?

16. Compare and Contrast In what ways are the effects of methamphetamine and cocaine on the brain similar? How are they different?

31.3 The Peripheral Nervous System

Understand Key Concepts

17. The sympathetic nervous system and the parasympathetic nervous system are specific divisions of the
a. peripheral nervous system.
b. central nervous system.
c. somatic nervous system.
d. autonomic nervous system.

18. Reflexes are behaviors that
a. involve only sensory neurons.
b. are controlled by the autonomic nervous system.
c. are under conscious control.
d. occur involuntarily without conscious control.

19. Describe the advantage of a reflex response in the survival of an organism.

20. List the divisions of the autonomic nervous system and give the function of each.

Think Critically

21. **Design an Experiment** Design an experiment to determine how time of day may affect reaction time. Formulate a hypothesis and write your procedure. Have your teacher check your experimental plan before you begin.

22. **Apply Concepts** A routine examination by a doctor usually includes a knee-jerk reflex test. What is the purpose of this test? What could the absence of a response indicate?

31.4 The Senses

Understand Key Concepts

23. The semicircular canals and the two tiny sacs located behind them help maintain
a. night vision.
b. body position and balance.
c. respiratory rate.
d. temperature.

24. The senses of taste and smell involve sensory receptors called
a. photoreceptors.
b. chemoreceptors.
c. thermoreceptors.
d. mechanoreceptors.

25. The fluid-filled structure in the ear that sends information to the brain about sound is the
a. tympanum.
b. oval window.
c. stirrup.
d. cochlea.

26. Trace the path of light through the eye.

27. What are the functions of rods and cones?

28. Trace the path of sound through the ear.

29. What are the five basic tastes?

solve the CHAPTER MYSTERY

POISONING ON THE HIGH SEAS

Because of a sketch done by the ship's naturalist, Georg Forster, it is suspected that Cook and his men most likely ate *Tetraodon lagocephalus sceleratus*, also known as the Silverstripe blaasop. Bacteria that live in the fish's liver, gonads, intestines, and skin produce a poison called tetrodotoxin. The poison can remain active even after the fish is cooked at high temperatures. Tetrodotoxin binds to and blocks voltage-gated sodium channels, especially in the peripheral nervous system.

Unlike the men on Cook's ship, today, some Japanese chefs are specially trained to prepare fish—known as pufferfish—that contain this toxin. The dish, known as fugu, is highly prized by diners in exclusive restaurants. The prepared fish have a unique taste and produce a tingling sensation in the mouth and throat when eaten. Improper preparation of fugu can lead to serious consequences for the diner, including death.

Obviously, tetrodotoxin doesn't poison the fish that produce it. Studies of the fish's genome have revealed a mutation in the gene that codes for the structure of sodium channel proteins. The mutation changes the surface shape of the channel, and prevents the toxin from binding to it.

1. **Infer** Based on the location of bacteria in *Tetraodon*, what methods are likely involved in preparing fugu?
2. **Apply Concepts** Describe in your own words why the fish are not affected by their own toxin.
3. **Connect to the Big idea** Some researchers have explored the possibility of using tetrodotoxin to treat severe pain. Why might the toxin be useful in this way? What safety concerns would you have to consider when designing a study to test this possibility?

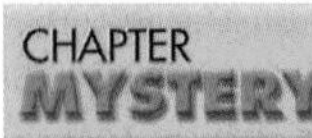

After students have read through the Chapter Mystery, discuss the way that tetrodotoxin affects the nervous system of humans.

Ask How does tetrodotoxin affect the structures of the nervous system? *(The toxin binds to and blocks voltage-gated sodium channels.)*

Ask How does tetrodotoxin affect the functioning of the nervous system? *(The blocked sodium channels mean that sodium cannot flow into the cell when an action potential occurs.)*

CHAPTER MYSTERY ANSWERS

1. The preparation methods most likely include careful removal of the liver, gonads, intestines, and skin, because the toxin-producing bacteria reside in these organs.
2. Due to a mutation that affects the surface shape of the sodium channel proteins, Silverstripe blaasop are not affected by tetrodotoxin.
3. Big idea Sample answer: Tetrodotoxin, which impairs the ability of nerve impulses to travel, could be used to treat pain by blocking the impulses carrying the pain message. Safety concerns for a test of this method of pain control include the administration of too much toxin, which could result in death.

The Untamed Science crew explores the scary chemicals of poison-emitting animals, such as cone snails, in **Untamed Science: Toxic Secretions.**

20. The autonomic nervous system is divided into the sympathetic and parasympathetic nervous systems. The sympathetic nervous system increases heart rate and blood pressure, and prepares the body for a fight or flee response. The parasympathetic nervous system lowers the heart rate and blood pressure, and prepares the body for rest.

THINK CRITICALLY

21. Students' experimental designs will vary, but they should include a hypothesis and identification of one independent variable and variables to be controlled.

22. The purpose of the knee-jerk reflex test is to determine whether the person's reflexes are normal. The absence of a response could indicate a disorder of one of the components of the reflex arc.

Lesson 31.4

UNDERSTAND KEY CONCEPTS

23. b 24. b 25. d

26. Light enters the eye through the cornea; moves through the aqueous humor, pupil, lens, and vitreous humor; and focuses on the retina, where light energy is converted to nerve impulses.

27. Rods and cones are photoreceptors, which send a nervous impulse when they are stimulated by light. Rods respond well to low levels of light; cones respond only when light levels are higher but can also detect different colors of light.

ASSESSMENT

28. Sound waves, which are vibrating air molecules, enter the auditory canal and cause the tympanum to vibrate. Three tiny bones, called the hammer, anvil, and stirrup, transmit the sound waves to the oval window, which vibrates and creates pressure waves in the fluid-filled cochlea. The pressure waves push back and forth against tiny hair cells, which respond by producing nerve impulses that are sent to the brain through the cochlear nerve.
29. salty, bitter, sweet, sour, and umami

THINK CRITICALLY

30. Sample answer: These parts of the body, which are often exposed, are more sensitive to pain and better able to detect sources of potential injury.
31. The trend shows an exponential increase. The slope begins to change rapidly at age 40. This might be because age 40 is when structures in the eyes start to show signs of aging.

Connecting Concepts

USE SCIENCE GRAPHICS

32. This diagram shows a drug mimicking a neurotransmitter because the drug molecules are binding to receptors on the adjacent cell.
33. Students' diagrams should show a synapse flooded with neurotransmitters.

WRITE ABOUT SCIENCE

34. Sample answer: The brain responds to these drugs by decreasing the number of dopamine receptors. After repeated exposure, more of the drugs are needed to achieve the same effect.
35. Big idea Sample answer: Dendrites branching from the cell body allow a neuron to receive impulses from many other neighboring neurons. Axons allow neurons to communicate with other cells. Some axons are quite long and can transmit impulses over a great distance in the body.

Think Critically

30. **Infer** What is the advantage of having a greater concentration of touch receptors in the fingers, toes, and face?
31. **Interpret Graphs** The graph below compares age to the nearest distance in centimeters that many people can see an object clearly. Describe the general trend of the graph. At what age does the slope of the graph begin to change rapidly? What do you think might explain this change? NoS.3

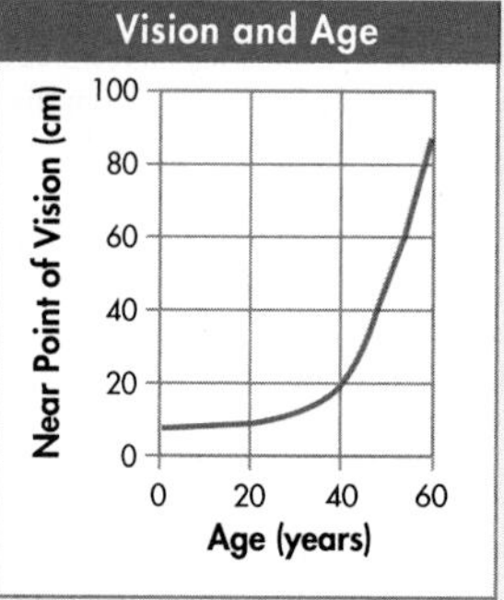

Connecting Concepts

Use Science Graphics NoS.3

Use the illustration to answer questions 32 and 33.

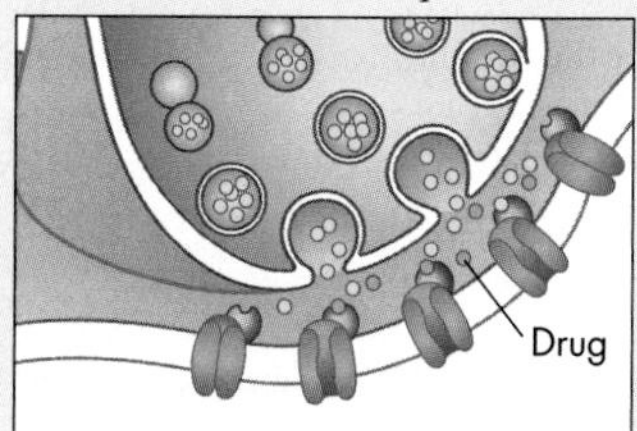

32. **Interpret Visuals** Do you think this illustration shows a drug interfering with enzymes that break down a neurotransmitter at a synapse, or a drug mimicking a neurotransmitter? Explain.
33. **Apply Concepts** Draw an illustration of a synapse showing the effect of a drug that increases the rate of neurotransmitter secretion.

Write About Science NoS.3

34. **Explanation** Write a paragraph explaining how addiction to drugs, alcohol, or tobacco all have a similar basis in the way they alter the function of the human nervous system.
35. **Assess the Big idea** Describe how the shape and structure of the neuron is related to its function in the nervous system.

NoS.3

The graph shows the relationship between neuron diameter and impulse conduction speed in myelinated axons in a mammal. Use the graph to answer questions 36 and 37.

36. **Interpret Graphs** What conclusion can be made from the graph concerning the relationship between the speed of conduction of an action potential and the diameter of an axon?
37. **Calculate** In the reflex arc that involves touching a hot object and pulling away your hand, the impulses must travel a total distance of about 1.5 m. How long does it take for the reflex to occur if the neurons are 5 μm in diameter? MATH

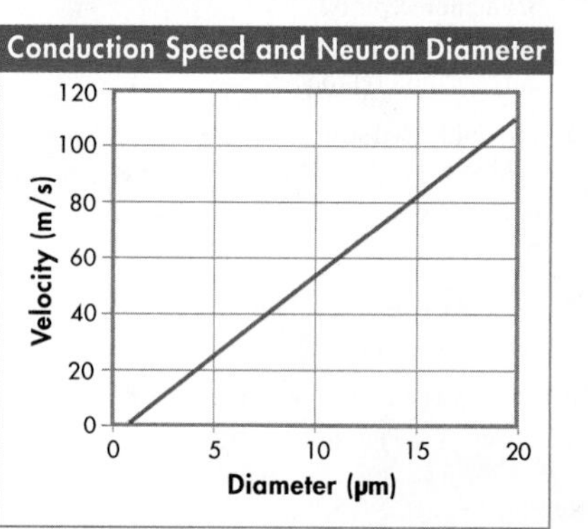

PURPOSE Students will analyze a graph to learn how conduction speed is related to neuron diameter.

PLANNING Review with students the structure of a line graph and how it can be used to show the nature of the relationship between variables.

ANSWERS

36. Speed of conduction is directly proportional to the diameter of the axon. The greater an axon's diameter, the more quickly it will transmit impulses.
37. 0.06 second

Standardized Test Practice for Indiana

Multiple Choice

1. The largest and most prominent part of the human brain is the
   A cerebrum. C thalamus.
   B cerebellum. D brain stem.

2. The point of connection between two neurons is called a
   A threshold. C neurotransmitter.
   B synapse. D dendrite.

3. The part of a neuron that carries impulses away from the cell body is called a(n)
   A axon. C vesicle.
   B dendrite. D synapse.

4. The minimum stimulus level that will cause a neuron to produce an action potential is called the
   A resting potential. C threshold.
   B impulse. D synapse.

5. The part of the brain responsible for collecting sensory input from the body and relaying it to appropriate brain centers is the
   A limbic system. C cerebellum.
   B thalamus. D cerebrum.

6. The major function of the spinal cord is
   A emotional learning and memory storage.
   B control of voluntary muscle movements.
   C fine control of detailed muscle movement.
   D a principal communication path between the brain and the rest of the body.

7. Involuntary activities carried out throughout the body are the primary responsibility of the
   A somatic nervous system.
   B autonomic nervous system.
   C spinal cord.
   D limbic system.

8. The part of the eye that contains photoreceptor cells is the
   A cornea. C retina.
   B iris. D optic nerve.

Questions 9–10

Blood alcohol concentration (BAC) is a measure of the amount of alcohol in the blood per 100 mL of blood. In some states, if a driver has a BAC of 0.08 percent, he or she is considered legally drunk. The table below lists an average BAC as alcohol consumption increases. Use the information in the table to answer the questions.

Blood Alcohol Concentration (Percent)

Drinks in One Hour	Body Mass					
	45 kg	54 kg	63 kg	72 kg	81 kg	90 kg
1	0.04	0.03	0.03	0.02	0.02	0.02
2	0.07	0.06	0.05	0.05	0.04	0.04
3	0.11	0.09	0.08	0.07	0.06	0.06
4	0.14	0.12	0.10	0.09	0.08	0.07
5	0.18	0.15	0.13	0.11	0.10	0.09
6	0.21	0.18	0.15	0.14	0.12	0.11
7	0.25	0.21	0.18	0.16	0.14	0.13
8	0.29	0.24	0.21	0.18	0.16	0.14

9. How many drinks in one hour would cause a 63 kg person to have a BAC of 0.08 percent?
   A 1 C 5
   B 3 D 7 NoS.3

10. If a 54 kg person had 3 drinks in one hour, what would his or her BAC percentage be?
    A 0.06
    B 0.08
    C 0.09
    D 0.11 NoS.3

Open-Ended Response

11. How do the parasympathetic and sympathetic nervous system work together in the body?

If You Have Trouble With . . .

Question	1	2	3	4	5	6	7	8	9	10	11
See Lesson	31.2	31.1	31.1	31.1	31.2	31.2	31.3	31.4	31.2	31.2	31.3

Answers

1. A
2. B
3. A
4. C
5. B
6. D
7. B
8. C
9. B
10. C
11. The sympathetic and parasympathetic nervous systems have opposite effects on the same organ systems, producing a level of fine control that coordinates organs throughout the body.

Test-Taking Tip

REVIEW ANSWERS

Tell students to use any time remaining after they have answered all of the questions to review their answers. Point out that they should change only those responses they are sure are incorrect. If the answer booklet is separate from the test question booklet, have students make sure that the question numbers of both correspond.

Skeletal, Muscular, and Integumentary Systems

Chapter Contents	IN	Time	Core Resources
Chapter Preview			**Student Edition,** pp. 920–921 **Chapter Mystery,** p. 921
32.1 The Skeletal System The Skeleton • Bones • Joints	NoS.6	1 period 1/2 block	**Student Edition,** pp. 922–927 Inquiry 32.1 Quick Lab, p. 924 L2 **Study Workbook A** 32.1 Worksheets L2 Biology.com *Visual Analogy:* The Skeleton • *InterActive Art:* Freely Movable Joints • 32.1 Self-Test • 32.1 Lesson Assessment
32.2 The Muscular System Muscle Tissue • Muscle Contraction • Muscles and Movement • *Biology & Society: Should Student Athletes Be Tested for Steroids?*		1 1/2 periods 3/4 block	**Student Edition,** pp. 928–934 Inquiry 32.2 Quick Lab, p. 932 L2 **Study Workbook A** 32.2 Worksheets L2 Biology.com *Art in Motion:* The Sliding Filament Model **Assessment Resources Book** Visual Quiz L2
32.3 Skin—The Integumentary System Integumentary System Functions • Integumentary System Structures • Skin Problems	NoS.3	1 period 1/2 block	**Student Edition,** pp. 935–939 Inquiry 32.3 Analyzing Data, p. 938 L2 **Study Workbook A** 32.3 Worksheets L2 Biology.com *Art Review:* The Structure of the Skin • *Data Analysis:* Sunlight and Skin Cancer **Assessment Resources Book** Visual Quiz L2
Chapter Pre-Lab	NoS.7	1 period 1/2 block	**Student Edition,** p. 940 L2 **Lab Manual A** *Comparing Limbs* L2 • *Modeling Breathing* L2

Differentiated Instruction Tools

Study Workbook B includes worksheets with lesson-level differentiated instruction support and explanations of differentiated instruction teaching strategies.

Lab Manual B includes skills labs, simplified chapter labs, and hands-on activities.

ELL Handbook explains ways to make *Biology* more accessible to ELL students.

Spanish Study Workbook is a Spanish translation of Study Workbook A.

Multilingual Glossary is the glossary translated into ten languages.

Differentiated Instruction Key

- L1 Special Needs or Struggling Students
- ELL English Language Learners
- LPR Less Proficient Readers
- L2 On-Level Students
- L3 Advanced Students

Additional Resources

Biology.com Untamed Science Video • Vocabulary Flash Cards

Study Workbook B 32.1 Worksheets L1 ELL LPR
Spanish Study Workbook 32.1 Worksheets ELL
Biology.com 32.1 Lesson Overview • 32.1 Lesson Notes

Study Workbook B 32.2 Worksheets L1 ELL LPR
Spanish Study Workbook 32.2 Worksheets ELL
Biology.com *Tutor Tube:* Using Analogies to Understand Muscle Contraction • 32.2 Lesson Overview • 32.2 Lesson Notes • 32.2 Self-Test • 32.2 Lesson Assessment

Study Workbook B 32.3 Worksheets L1 ELL LPR
Spanish Study Workbook 32.3 Worksheets ELL
Biology.com 32.3 Lesson Overview • 32.3 Lesson Notes • 32.3 Self-Test • 32.3 Lesson Assessment

Lab Manual B *Comparing Limbs* • Data Analysis: *The Rising Rate of Melanoma* L1 ELL LPR

Chapter Review

Student Edition Study Guide, p. 941 L2
Study Workbook A Chapter 32 Vocabulary Review L2 • Chapter 32 Chapter Mystery/21st Century Skills Activity L2 L3
Transparencies, pp. 351–361 L1 ELL LPR L2
Biology.com Untamed Science Video • Editable Worksheets of Study Workbooks A and B and Lab Manuals A and B • Chapter 32 Flash Cards and Match It

Untamed Science DVD • Classroom Resources CD (includes lesson presentations and editable worksheets)

Chapter Assessment

Student Edition Assessment, pp. 942–945 L2
Study Workbook B Chapter 32 Chapter Review L1 ELL LPR • Chapter 32 Taking a Standardized Test L1 ELL LPR
Assessment Resources Book Chapter 32 Test A L2 • Chapter 32 Test B L1 ELL LPR
Biology.com Chapter 32 Assessment • Editable Worksheets of Chapter 32 Visual Quizzes and Chapter 32 Tests A and B

Exam*View* *Assessment Suite* • Classroom Resources CD (includes lesson presentations and editable worksheets)

Time: 1 period, 1/2 block

Pressed for Time?

Preview the Chapter Discuss the first Key Question listed for each lesson, and preview Figures 32–1, 32–6, and 32–12.

Cover the Chapter Quickly Have students read Lesson 32.1 and *Muscle Tissue* in Lesson 32.2. In Lesson 32.3, have students read *Integumentary System Functions* and *Integumentary System Structures.*

Assess Assign the 32.1 Assessment, question 1 in the 32.2 Assessment, questions 1 and 2 in the 32.3 Assessment, and the Chapter 32 Standardized Test Prep except question 4.

CHAPTER 32

Connect to the Big Idea

Use the photograph of the gymnast to help students connect to concepts they will learn in this chapter. Activate prior knowledge by asking students to identify some of the human body structures the gymnast is using to perform the motions shown in the picture. *(Sample answers: bones, muscles)* Then, ask students to identify the functions of the body structures they named. *(Sample answers: Bones provide support to the gymnast's body; muscles help the gymnast move.)* Ask them to anticipate the answer to the question, **What systems form the structure of the human body?** Ask what it means that the structure of a body part is related to its functions.

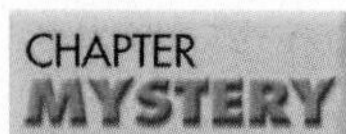

Have students read over the Chapter Mystery and brainstorm ways that rickets could affect body structure. Then, have students predict how these changes in structure could affect the function of body systems. Use their ideas to start connecting the Chapter Mystery to the Big Idea of Structure and Function.

BIOLOGY.com Have students preview the chapter vocabulary terms using the **Flash Cards.**

IN INDIANA ACADEMIC STANDARDS

For the full text of all standards, see the Course Overview in the front matter of this book.

Key standards: Chapter 32 covers key ideas from The Nature of Science, including **NoS.3** Communicate ideas and **NoS.6** Use analogies and models.

32 Skeletal, Muscular, and Integumentary Systems

Big idea Structure and Function

Q: What systems form the structure of the human body?

The skeletal and muscular systems of this gymnast interact closely as she performs these graceful movements.

BIOLOGY.com Search Chapter 32 GO • Flash Cards

920

UbD Understanding by Design

In Unit 8, students explore the Enduring Understanding that *the human body is a complex system. The coordinated functions of its many structures support life processes and maintain homeostasis.* The graphic organizer at the right shows how the Big Idea, Essential Question, and Guiding Questions help frame their exploration.

PERFORMANCE GOALS

In Chapter 32, students will learn about the structures and functions of the skeletal, muscular, and integumentary systems through activities such as making analogies to describe a body system. At the end of the chapter, students will write a children's book describing the structure and functions of the skeletal, muscular, and integumentary systems.

• Untamed Science Video • Chapter Mystery

INDIANA ACADEMIC STANDARDS FOR SCIENCE

Nature of Science NoS.3, NoS.6, NoS.7. See lessons for details.

CHAPTER MYSTERY

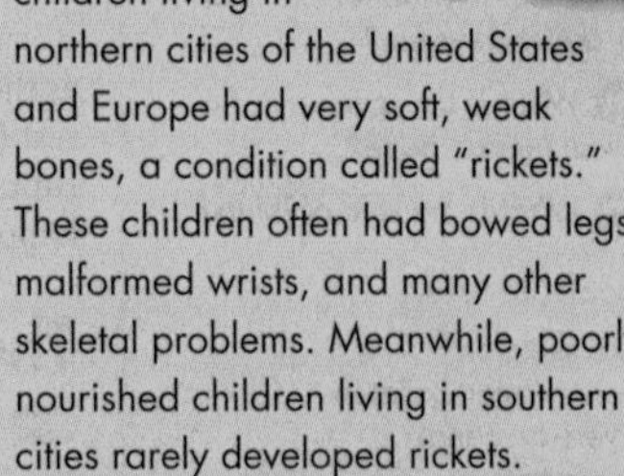

THE DEMISE OF A DISEASE

In the early twentieth century, many poorly nourished children living in northern cities of the United States and Europe had very soft, weak bones, a condition called "rickets." These children often had bowed legs, malformed wrists, and many other skeletal problems. Meanwhile, poorly nourished children living in southern cities rarely developed rickets.

During this time, rickets was a health problem that seriously affected many children living in cold climates. No one knew the cause or how to cure the disease. Some people claimed that regular doses of cod liver oil cured rickets, but many considered this folklore.

Scientists were eager to find answers. What was the connection between rickets and the northern climate? And could cod liver oil be a cure? In the chapter, look for clues that helped scientists develop ideas about the cause of rickets. Then, solve the mystery.

Never Stop Exploring Your World. Finding the solution to The Demise of a Disease is just the beginning. Take a video field trip with the ecogeeks of Untamed Science to see where the mystery leads.

921

Chapter 32
Big Idea: Structure and Function

Chapter 32 EQ: What systems form the structure of the human body?

32.1 GQ: How does the structure of the skeletal system allow it to function properly?

32.2 GQ: How do muscles help you move?

32.3 GQ: Why is the integumentary system a necessary organ system?

What's Online

BIOLOGY.com Extend your reach by using these and other digital assets offered at **Biology.com**.

CHAPTER MYSTERY
Follow the mystery to find out how a single disease, rickets, can be related to the function of the skeletal, muscular, and integumentary systems.

UNTAMED SCIENCE VIDEO
Students can travel to NASA to learn how space travel affects bones in **Skeletons in Space.**

VISUAL ANALOGY
Students compare a skeleton to the frame of a house.

INTERACTIVE ART
Animated art shows how different joints move and how bones and muscles interact to provide this motion.

ART IN MOTION
Students can further explore the interaction of actin and myosin as modeled by the sliding filament model.

TUTOR TUBE
Students will learn how to use analogies to help them understand difficult concepts like muscle contraction.

ART REVIEW
Drag-and-drop labels help students identify structures in a cross-sectional diagram of skin.

DATA ANALYSIS
Students will analyze skin cancer epidemiology data to evaluate risk factors such as latitude, exposure to sunlight, and nutrition.

LESSON 32.1

Getting Started

Objectives

32.1.1 List the structures and functions of the skeletal system.

32.1.2 Describe the structure of a typical bone.

32.1.3 List the different kinds of joints and describe the range of motion of each.

Student Resources

Study Workbooks A and B, 32.1 Worksheets

Spanish Study Workbook, 32.1 Worksheets

Lesson Overview • Lesson Notes
- Activities: Visual Analogy, InterActive Art
- Assessment: Self-Test, Lesson Assessment

For corresponding lesson in the **Foundation Edition**, see pages 766–769.

Answers

IN YOUR NOTEBOOK Students' tables should include the following functions and at least one example of each: support, protection, movement, mineral storage, and blood cell formation.

IN INDIANA ACADEMIC STANDARDS

For the full text of all standards, see the Course Overview in the front matter of this book.

NoS.6 Use analogies and models (mathematical and physical) to simplify and represent systems that are difficult to understand or directly experience due to their size, time scale, or complexity, and recognize the limitations of analogies and models.

32.1 The Skeletal System

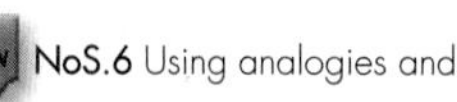

IN NoS.6 Using analogies and models.

Key Questions

What are the functions of the skeletal system?

What is the structure of a typical human bone?

What is the role of joints?

Vocabulary

axial skeleton
appendicular skeleton
Haversian canal
bone marrow
cartilage
ossification
osteoblast
osteocyte
osteoclast
joint
ligament

Taking Notes

Outline Before you read, make an outline with the green and blue headings in the lesson. As you read, fill in main ideas and supporting details for each heading.

THINK ABOUT IT An animal's skeleton is so durable that its bones are often recognizable thousands of years after the animal's death. Bones are so tough and strong, in fact, that it's easy to think of them as though they were nothing more than rigid, lifeless supports for the rest of the body. If that were true, what would happen if one of those supports broke? Broken bones, as you know, can heal. How does that happen? And what does that tell you about the nature of our skeleton?

The Skeleton

What are the functions of the skeletal system?

To retain their shapes, all organisms need some type of structural support. Unicellular organisms have a cytoskeleton that provides structural support. Multicellular animals have cytoskeletons within their individual cells, but a skeleton is needed to provide support for the whole body. These skeletons include the external exoskeletons of arthropods and the internal endoskeletons of vertebrates.

Structure of the Skeleton There are 206 bones in the adult human skeleton. As you can see in **Figure 32–1,** some of these bones are in the axial skeleton and others are in the appendicular skeleton.

The **axial skeleton** supports the central axis of the body. It consists of the skull, the vertebral column, and the rib cage. The bones of the arms and legs, along with the bones of the pelvis and shoulder area, form the **appendicular skeleton.**

Functions of the Skeletal System The skeletal system has many important functions. **The skeleton supports the body, protects internal organs, assists movement, stores minerals, and is a site of blood cell formation.** The skeletal system supports and shapes the body much like an internal wooden frame supports a house. Bones also protect the delicate internal organs of the body. For example, the skull forms a protective shell around the brain.

Bones provide a system of levers on which muscles act to produce movement. Levers are rigid rods that can be moved about a fixed point. In addition, bones contain reserves of minerals, mainly calcium salts that are important to body processes. Finally, new blood cells are produced in the soft marrow tissue that fills cavities in some bones.

In Your Notebook *Use a two-column table to list the roles of the skeletal system and an example of each role.*

UbD Teach for Understanding

ENDURING UNDERSTANDING The human body is a complex system. The coordinated functions of its many structures support life processes and maintain homeostasis.

GUIDING QUESTION How does the structure of the skeletal system allow it to function properly?

EVIDENCE OF UNDERSTANDING *After students have finished the lesson, this assessment should show their understanding of how bones are involved in the body's functions.* Have students work in small groups. Each group should prepare a brief presentation describing how the movement of bones is essential to an everyday task, such as picking up a book bag, climbing a set of steps, or moving food from a plate to the mouth.

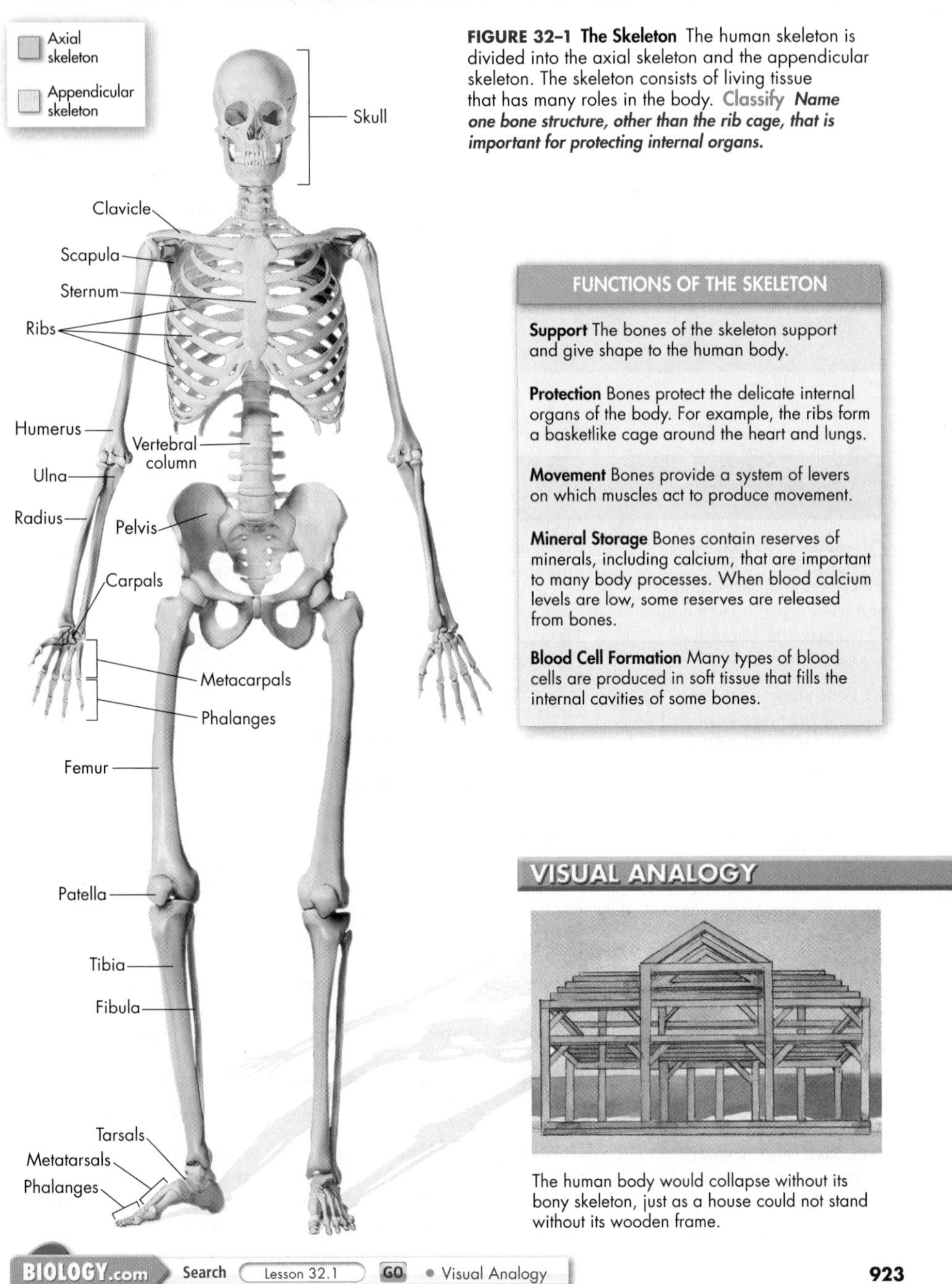

FIGURE 32–1 The Skeleton The human skeleton is divided into the axial skeleton and the appendicular skeleton. The skeleton consists of living tissue that has many roles in the body. **Classify** ***Name one bone structure, other than the rib cage, that is important for protecting internal organs.***

FUNCTIONS OF THE SKELETON

Support The bones of the skeleton support and give shape to the human body.

Protection Bones protect the delicate internal organs of the body. For example, the ribs form a basketlike cage around the heart and lungs.

Movement Bones provide a system of levers on which muscles act to produce movement.

Mineral Storage Bones contain reserves of minerals, including calcium, that are important to many body processes. When blood calcium levels are low, some reserves are released from bones.

Blood Cell Formation Many types of blood cells are produced in soft tissue that fills the internal cavities of some bones.

VISUAL ANALOGY

The human body would collapse without its bony skeleton, just as a house could not stand without its wooden frame.

BIOLOGY.com Search Lesson 32.1 GO • Visual Analogy

How Science Works

BONES FROM THE PAST

Bones are one of the most important tools used to study the evolution of vertebrates, including humans. Due to the structure and composition of bones, they are more likely than other tissues to be preserved after an animal dies. Bones are typically preserved by fossilization, a process in which the organic material in bone is replaced by minerals. Paleontologists, or scientists who study fossils, compare fossilized bones to the bones of living animals to learn more about the anatomy of extinct animals and changes in species that have occurred over time. This is very difficult work because complete fossilized skeletons are rarely found. Paleontologists must often work with single bones or bone fragments.

Teach

Use Visuals

Have students use the figure on this page to discuss the structure and functions of the human skeleton.

Ask What is the difference between the axial and appendicular skeleton? *(The axial skeleton supports the central axis of the body. The appendicular skeleton includes the bones of the limbs, shoulders, and pelvis.)*

Ask Does each bone in your body provide every skeletal system function: support, protection, movement, mineral storage, and blood cell formation? *(No. For example, not every bone produces blood cells.)*

Ask What do you think are the main functions of the vertebral column? *(support, movement, and protection)*

DIFFERENTIATED INSTRUCTION

L1 Struggling Students Provide students with models of the skeletal system so they can see and feel the different bones that make up the human body. Have them identify each of the structures labeled in **Figure 32–1** on the models.

VISUAL ANALOGY

Explore and extend the comparison of the human skeleton to the frame of a house.

Ask For which one of the five functions of the human skeleton is a house's frame a good analogy? *(The house frame is a good analogy for the way the skeleton supports the body.)*

Ask What would be a good analogy for the skeleton's function of mineral storage? *(Sample answer: A bank, where money is stored until it is needed, is a good model of the way that the skeleton functions in mineral storage.)*

Have students come up with analogies for movement, protection, and blood cell formation.

BIOLOGY.com Students can further explore the analogy comparing the skeletal system to the frame of a house by accessing **Visual Analogy: The Skeleton.**

Answers

FIGURE 32–1 Sample answer: The skull is a bone structure important for protecting the brain.

LESSON 32.1

Teach continued

Build Reading Skills

Before students read a section of text, suggest that they preview the heads inside the section and rephrase them as *how, why,* or *what* questions. For example, the head **Structure of Bones** found on this page could be reworded as "What is the structure of bones?" Explain to students that after they read the text under the head they should be able to answer the question. Suggest that students record each head as a question in their notebook. Before moving on to the next section of text, students should be certain they can provide a written or oral answer to the question they have recorded.

DIFFERENTIATED INSTRUCTION

LPR **Less Proficient Readers** Suggest that students work in pairs to check comprehension of each section of text. Have one student rephrase the section head as a question, and the other student provide a response derived from reading the section. If the student is unable to answer the question, have the pair work together to review the material and form an answer.

L3 **Advanced Students** Extend the reading strategy to engage advanced students by asking them to record questions they have about the topic that were not answered in the text. Encourage students to select one or more of their questions as topics for independent research.

ELL Focus on ELL: Access Content

BEGINNING AND INTERMEDIATE SPEAKERS
Before reading, have students fill out a **Main Idea and Details Chart** and write the following main ideas in the chart: Structure of Bones, Development of Bones, and Bone Remodeling and Repair. As they read, have them fill out the right side of the chart with details about each main idea. Suggest beginning speakers list details using short phrases.

Study Wkbks A/B, Appendix S28, Main Idea and Details Chart. **Transparencies,** GO13.

Answers

IN YOUR NOTEBOOK Venn diagrams should show the following characteristics. For both compact and spongy bone: are strong, are living tissues, are not solid. For compact bone only: contains nerves and blood vessels in Haversian canals. For spongy bone only: adds strength without adding too much mass.

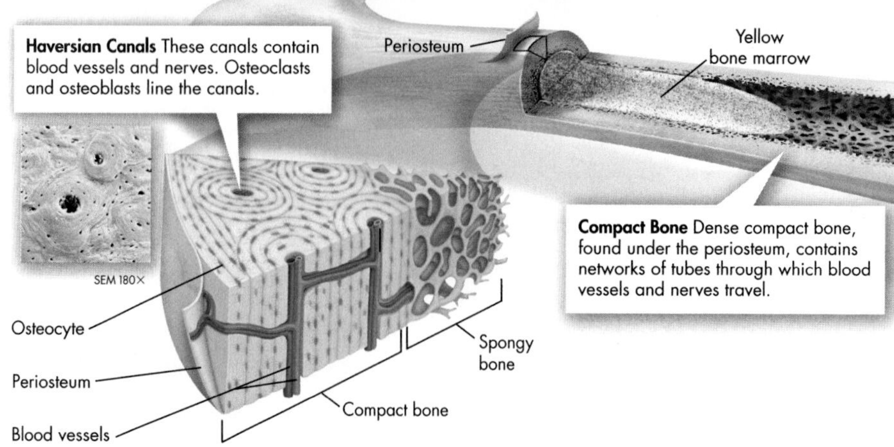
Haversian Canals These canals contain blood vessels and nerves. Osteoclasts and osteoblasts line the canals.
Periosteum
Yellow bone marrow
SEM 180×
Compact Bone Dense compact bone, found under the periosteum, contains networks of tubes through which blood vessels and nerves travel.
Osteocyte
Periosteum
Blood vessels
Spongy bone
Compact bone

Quick Lab GUIDED INQUIRY

Observe Calcium Loss

1. Describe the appearance and feel of two chicken bones. Then, place the bones in separate jars.
2. Pour vinegar into one jar until the bone is covered. Pour water into the other jar until the bone is covered. Cover both jars.
3. Check the jars each day for three days. Record your observations.
4. On the third day, remove the bones. Describe their appearance and feel.

Analyze and Conclude

1. **Compare and Contrast** How do the two bones differ?
2. **Infer** Vinegar reacts with and removes calcium from bone. Based on your observations, what characteristic of bone can be associated with calcium?

Bones

What is the structure of a typical human bone?

It is easy to think of bones as nonliving. After all, most of the mass of bone is mineral salts—mainly calcium and phosphorus. However, bones are living tissue. **Bones are a solid network of living cells and protein fibers that are surrounded by deposits of calcium salts.**

Structure of Bones The structure of a typical long bone is shown in **Figure 32–2.** The bone is surrounded by a tough layer of connective tissue called periosteum (pehr ee AHS tee um). Beneath the periosteum is a thick layer of compact bone. Although compact bone is dense, it is far from solid. Nerves and blood vessels run through compact bone in channels called **Haversian canals.**

A less dense tissue known as spongy bone may be found under the outer layer of compact bone. Spongy bone is found in the ends of long bones such as the femur. It is also found in the middle of short, flat bones such as the bones in the skull. Despite its name, spongy bone is not soft and spongy; it is actually quite strong. Near the ends of bones where force is applied, spongy bone is organized into structures that resemble the supporting girders in a bridge. This latticework structure in spongy bone adds strength without adding excess mass.

Within many bones are cavities that contain a soft tissue called **bone marrow.** There are two types of bone marrow: yellow and red. Yellow marrow consists primarily of cells that store fat. Red marrow contains the stem cells that produce most types of blood cells.

In Your Notebook *Use a Venn diagram to compare compact bone and spongy bone.*

Development of Bones The skeleton of a human embryo is composed almost entirely of a type of connective tissue called **cartilage.** Cartilage-producing cells are scattered in a network of protein fibers including both tough collagen and flexible elastin.

PURPOSE Students will observe the effect of calcium loss on chicken bones.

MATERIALS clean and dry chicken bones, jars with lids, vinegar, water

PLANNING Have students read the entire procedure before beginning. Suggest that students label their jars. Remind students to check the jars each day for three days.

ANALYZE AND CONCLUDE

1. Students will note that the bone soaked in vinegar will be soft and flexible, while the bone soaked in water will still be hard and rigid.
2. The characteristic of bone that is associated with calcium is hardness.

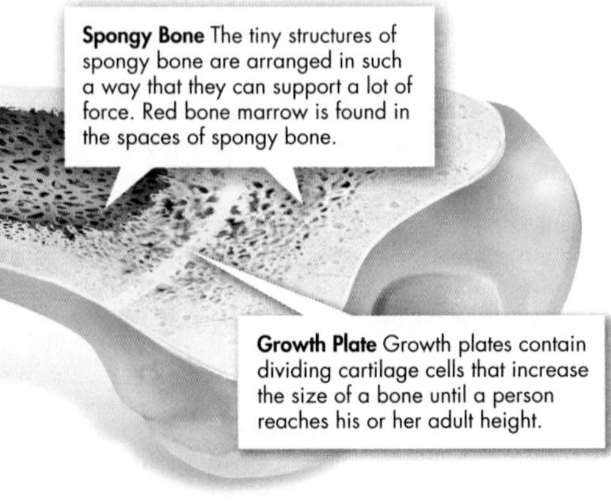

Spongy Bone The tiny structures of spongy bone are arranged in such a way that they can support a lot of force. Red bone marrow is found in the spaces of spongy bone.
Growth Plate Growth plates contain dividing cartilage cells that increase the size of a bone until a person reaches his or her adult height.

ZOOMING IN

STRUCTURE OF A BONE

FIGURE 32–2 A typical long bone such as the femur contains spongy bone and compact bone. Within compact bone are Haversian canals, which contain blood vessels and nerves. Infer ***What could be a result if a child breaks a bone and damages the growth plate?***

Unlike bone, cartilage does not contain blood vessels. Its cells rely on the diffusion of nutrients from the tiny blood vessels in surrounding tissues. Because cartilage is dense and fibrous, it can support weight despite its extreme flexibility.

Cartilage is gradually replaced by bone during the process of bone formation called **ossification** (ahs uh fih KAY shun). Ossification begins up to seven months before birth. Bone tissue forms as cells called **osteoblasts** secrete mineral deposits that replace the cartilage in developing bones. As bone tissue completes its development, most osteoblasts mature into osteocytes. **Osteocytes** help to maintain the minerals in bone tissue and continue to strengthen the growing bone.

Many long bones, including those of the arms and legs, have growth plates at either end. The growth of cartilage at these plates causes the bones to lengthen. Gradually, this cartilage is replaced by bone tissue, and the bones become larger and stronger. During late adolescence or early adulthood, growth plates become completely ossified, and the person "stops growing." Cartilage remains in those parts of the body that are flexible, such as the tip of the nose and the external part of ears. As you will read later, cartilage also cushions the areas where bones meet, such as in the knee.

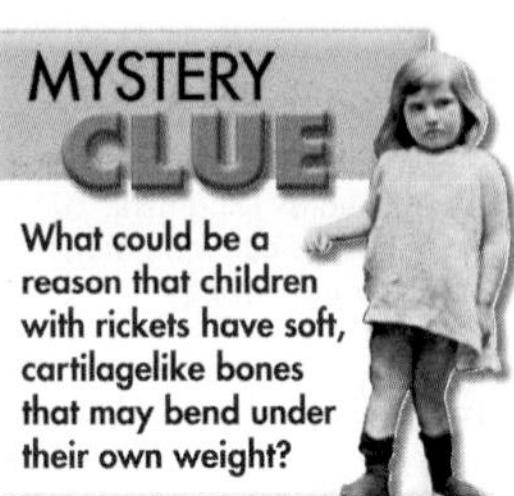

What could be a reason that children with rickets have soft, cartilagelike bones that may bend under their own weight?

Bone Remodeling and Repair In many ways, a bone is never finished growing. Bones are remodeled throughout life by small numbers of osteoblasts, which continue to build bone tissue, and **osteoclasts**—cells that break down bone minerals. Both functions are important because they enable bones to remodel and strengthen in response to exercise and stress. Without the continuous breakdown of old bone tissue and buildup of new bone tissue, bones would become brittle and weak. Both types of cells work together to repair broken and damaged bones.

Some older adults, especially women, develop a disorder called osteoporosis. In osteoporosis, osteoclasts break down bone much faster than osteoblasts rebuild it. Osteoporosis leads to weak bones due to excessive decrease in bone density. Research suggests that consuming plenty of calcium and performing weight-bearing exercise such as walking could help to prevent this serious problem.

UbD Check for Understanding

HAND SIGNALS

Present students with the following questions and ask them to show a thumbs-up sign if they understand, a thumbs-down sign if they are confused, or a waving-hand sign if they partially understand.

- How are bone and cartilage different?
- What happens during the process of ossification?
- What is the function of osteoblasts? osteocytes?

ADJUST INSTRUCTION

For any question that received thumbs-down signals from students, have them write a one-sentence response to the question, using the text as a resource. Then, for each question, have volunteers share their sentences with the class.

Lead a Discussion

As a class, discuss the concepts of bone development and bone remodeling and repair. Make sure students understand why these processes are important for health, both in children and adults.

Ask What might happen if the cartilage in a human embryo is never replaced with bone? *(The baby's bones would be too flexible, and the baby could not move easily or support itself well.)*

Ask Why is it important for the body to be able to build up and break down bone tissue? *(When a person breaks a bone, the body needs to be able to repair it. Also, bones need a way to remodel and strengthen so they keep healthy and strong as they age.)*

DIFFERENTIATED INSTRUCTION

LPR Less Proficient Readers Some students may struggle to differentiate between *osteoblasts, osteocytes,* and *osteoclasts.* Have students come up with different ways to distinguish between these types of cells. For example, they might suggest that the word *osteoblasts* contains a *b* which could stand for *build,* since osteoblasts build bone tissue.

ZOOMING IN

Have students create a **Two-Column Table** that organizes the information presented in **Figure 32–2** and the associated text. The left column should be labeled Structures, and the right column should be labeled Functions. Have students enter the terms *Haversian canals, compact bone, spongy bone,* and *growth plate* in the left column of their table. Then, ask students to enter one function of each structure in the right column of their table.

Study Wkbks A/B, Appendix S31, Two-Column Table. **Transparencies,** GO16.

Ask students to identify the process by which cartilage is replaced by bone. Then, have students infer what happens to this process when a person has rickets. Students can go online to Biology.com to gather their evidence.

Answers

FIGURE 32–2 Damage to a growth plate could prevent a bone from reaching its adult length.

Teach continued

Use Models

Provide students with materials such as craft sticks, toothpicks, modeling clay, pipe cleaners, brads, tacks, and glue. Then, challenge each student to create a model of one type of freely movable joint. Invite students to share their models with the class. Students should explain how their models demonstrate the structure and function of a particular type of joint.

DIFFERENTIATED INSTRUCTION

L1 Special Needs Help students understand the structure of freely movable joints by using tactile models. For example, a doorknob can model a pivot joint, a hinge can model a hinge joint, and a towing ball and hitch can model a ball-and-socket joint. A saddle joint can be easily modeled by having the student make a fist with one hand, cup the other hand, and insert the fist into the cupped hand.

ELL English Language Learners Distribute four index cards to each student. Have students record the name of one type of freely movable joint on each card. Then, have students make a drawing or diagram on each card, showing the structure of that type of joint. Under the drawing, have them write a short description of each joint's function.

BIOLOGY.com Suggest students further explore joint movement in **InterActive Art: Freely Movable Joints.**

Joints

What is the role of joints?

A place where one or more bones meet another bone is called a **joint.** **Joints contain connective tissues that hold bones together. Joints permit bones to move without damaging each other.**

Types of Joints Some joints, such as those of the shoulders, allow extensive movement. Others, like the joints of the fully developed skull, allow no movement at all. Depending on its type of movement, a joint is classified as immovable, slightly movable, or freely movable.

▶ ***Immovable Joints*** Immovable joints, often called fixed joints, allow no movement. The bones at an immovable joint are interlocked and grow together until they are fused. The places where the bones in the skull meet are examples of immovable joints.

▶ ***Slightly Movable Joints*** Slightly movable joints permit a small amount of movement. Unlike the bones of immovable joints, the bones of slightly movable joints are separated from each other. The joints between the two bones of the lower leg and the joints between vertebrae are examples of slightly movable joints.

▶ ***Freely Movable Joints*** Freely movable joints permit movement in two or more directions. Freely movable joints are grouped according to the shapes of the surfaces of the adjacent bones. Several types of freely movable joints are shown in **Figure 32–3.**

BUILD Vocabulary

ACADEMIC WORDS The adjective **adjacent** means "lying near" or "next to." Joints can form only at adjacent bones.

FIGURE 32–3 Freely Movable Joints Freely movable joints make actions possible. Many freely movable joints are involved in the movements this gymnast needs for her routine.

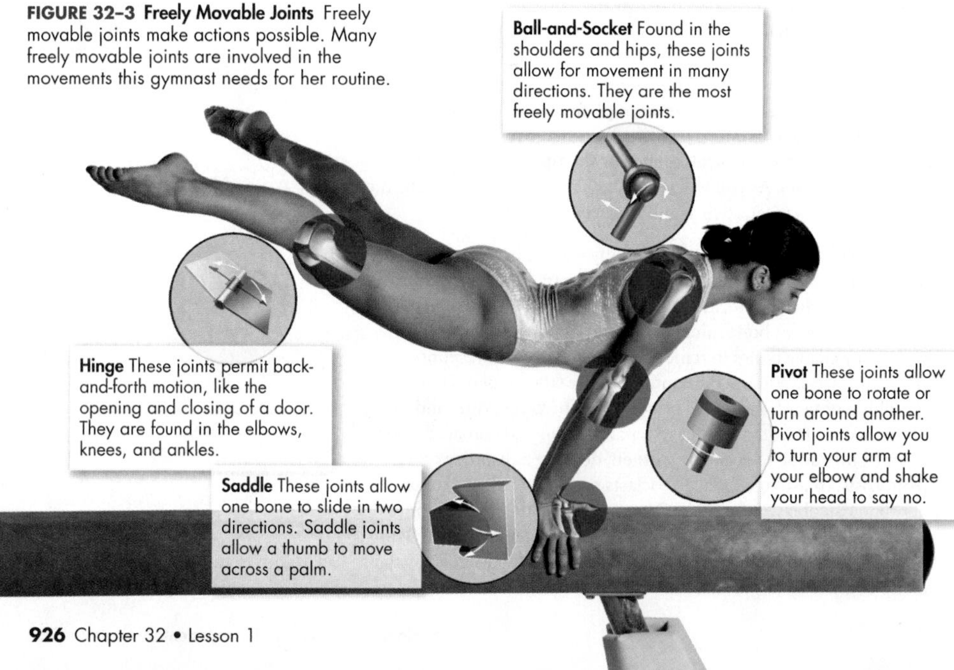

Ball-and-Socket Found in the shoulders and hips, these joints allow for movement in many directions. They are the most freely movable joints.
Hinge These joints permit back-and-forth motion, like the opening and closing of a door. They are found in the elbows, knees, and ankles.
Saddle These joints allow one bone to slide in two directions. Saddle joints allow a thumb to move across a palm.
Pivot These joints allow one bone to rotate or turn around another. Pivot joints allow you to turn your arm at your elbow and shake your head to say no.

Biology In-Depth

ARTIFICIAL JOINTS

Osteoarthritis causes many older adults to have stiff, aching joints and keeps them from being as active as they would like. Replacing arthritic joints, especially the hip and knee joints, with artificial joints is an increasingly common solution to this problem. To be effective, artificial joints must mimic both the structure and the function of the joints in the human body. A variety of materials are used to make replacement joints, including metals and alloys, ceramics, and plastics. Researchers continue to develop new materials that have desirable properties, such as strength and durability, for use in artificial joints.

Structure of Joints In freely movable joints, cartilage covers the surfaces where two bones come together. This protects the bones from damage as they move against each other. The joints are also surrounded by a fibrous joint capsule that helps hold the bones together while still allowing for movement.

The joint capsule consists of two layers. The outer layer forms strips of tough connective tissue called ligaments. **Ligaments,** which hold bones together in a joint, are attached to the membranes that surround bones. The inner layer of the joint capsule, called the synovial (sih NOH vee uhl) cavity, contains cells that produce a substance called synovial fluid. Synovial fluid enables the surfaces of the bones connected at the joint to slide over each other smoothly.

In some freely movable joints, such as the knee shown in **Figure 32–4,** there are small sacs of synovial fluid called bursae (BUR see; singular: bursa). Bursae reduce the friction between the bones of a joint and any tissues they come in contact with. Bursae also act as tiny shock absorbers.

Joint Injuries A common injury among young athletes is damage to the anterior cruciate ligament (ACL). This ligament is found in the center of the knee between the femur and tibia. It prevents the tibia from shifting too far forward during movement. ACL damage can be caused by the rapid pivoting, leaping, and forceful contacts that occur when playing sports like basketball and soccer. If the ACL is damaged, the knee becomes unstable and prone to other injuries.

Excessive strain on a joint may produce inflammation, a response in which excess fluid causes swelling, pain, heat, and redness. Inflammation of a bursa is called bursitis.

Wear and tear over the years often leads to osteoarthritis. This disorder develops as the cartilage of often used joints in the fingers, knees, hips, and spine begins to break down. The affected joints become painful and stiff as unprotected bones start to rub together.

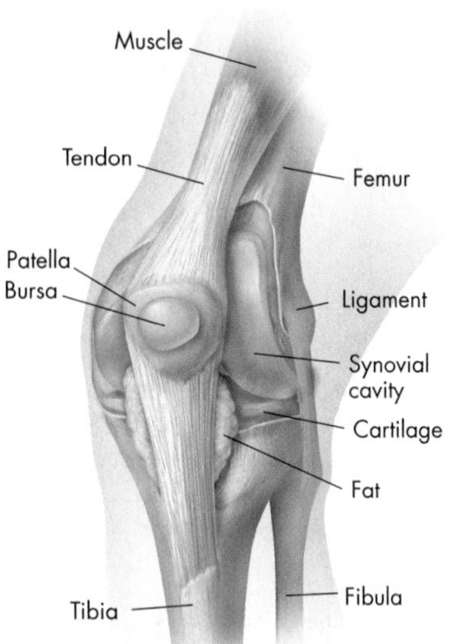

FIGURE 32–4 The Knee The knee joint is protected by cartilage and bursae. Ligaments hold together the four bones that make up the knee joint—the femur, patella, tibia, and fibula. **Infer** ***How do cartilage and bursae help reduce friction?***

32.1 Assessment

IN NoS.6

Review Key Concepts

1. a. Review List the different functions of the skeletal system.

b. Predict If blood calcium levels in a person's body were consistently low due to poor diet, what could the effect be on the person's bones?

2. a. Review Describe the structure of a typical bone.

b. Infer Why do you think the amount of cartilage decreases and the amount of bone increases as a baby grows?

3. a. Review What is a joint?

b. Use Analogies Which type of freely movable joint would you compare to a doorknob? Explain.

WRITE ABOUT SCIENCE

Creative Writing

4. Use library or Internet resources to learn more about osteoporosis. Then, develop an advertising campaign for the dairy industry based on the relationship between calcium and healthy bone development and maintenance.

BIOLOGY.com Search  Lesson 32.1  GO • Lesson Assessment • Self-Test • InterActive Art

Assess and Remediate

EVALUATE UNDERSTANDING

Ask students to write a short paragraph that identifies the three main categories of joints, immovable, slightly movable, and freely movable, and briefly describes the function of each. Then, have them complete the 32.1 Assessment.

REMEDIATION SUGGESTION

L1 Struggling Students If your students have trouble with **Question 3b,** have them review **Figure 32–3.** Ask students to use the figure to find the type of joint that is most similar to a doorknob.

BIOLOGY.com Students can check their understanding of lesson concepts with the **Self-Test** assessment. They can then take an online version of the **Lesson Assessment.**

Answers

FIGURE 32–4 Cartilage and bursae reduce friction by preventing bones from rubbing together.

Assessment Answers

1a. support, protection, movement, mineral storage, blood cell formation

1b. Bones may lose a lot of their stored calcium to keep blood calcium levels at a normal level.

2a. A typical bone has a thick layer of compact bone covered by periosteum. Haversian canals, which run through the compact bone, contain blood vessels and nerves. Under the compact bone, there is a layer of spongy bone. Growth plates are found near the ends of bones.

2b. The amount of cartilage decreases and the amount of bone increases as a baby grows and develops because bones need to become rigid to support the baby's increasing weight.

3a. A joint is a place where two or more bones meet.

3b. A pivot joint could be compared to a doorknob, because both move by rotating.

WRITE ABOUT SCIENCE

4. Students' advertising campaigns should make a convincing argument for the consumption of dairy products that includes information about the role of calcium in the growth and maintenance of bones and the health implications of osteoporosis.

LESSON 32.2

Getting Started

Objectives

32.2.1 Describe the structure and function of each of the three types of muscle tissue.

32.2.2 Describe the mechanism of muscle contraction.

32.2.3 Describe the interaction of muscles, bones, and tendons to produce movement.

Student Resources

Study Workbooks A and B, 32.2 Worksheets

Spanish Study Workbook, 32.2 Worksheets

Lesson Overview • Lesson Notes • Activities: Art in Motion, Tutor Tube • Assessment: Self-Test, Lesson Assessment

For corresponding lesson in the **Foundation Edition**, see pages 770–774.

Build Background

Show students a picture of a person with larger-than-average muscles. Explain that most people have about the same number of muscle cells. Ask students to infer how muscles become larger if muscle cells do not increase in number. *(Existing muscle cells increase in size.)*

Answers

IN YOUR NOTEBOOK Charts should accurately describe the functions of skeletal muscle, smooth muscle, and cardiac muscle.

32.2 The Muscular System

Key Questions

What are the principal types of muscle tissue?

How do muscles contract?

How do muscle contractions produce movement?

Vocabulary

muscle fiber • myofibril • myosin • actin • sarcomere • neuromuscular junction • acetylcholine • tendon

Taking Notes

Concept Map As you read, make a concept map that shows the relationship among the terms in this section.

THINK ABOUT IT How much of your body do you think is muscle? Ten percent? Maybe fifteen percent, if you're really in shape? As surprising as it might seem, about one third of the mass of an average person's body is muscle, and that's true even if you're not a well-conditioned varsity athlete. What's all that muscle doing? Some of the answers might surprise you.

Muscle Tissue

What are the principal types of muscle tissue?

Despite the fantasies of Hollywood horror films, a skeleton cannot move by itself. That's the job of the muscular system. Naturally, this system includes the large muscles in your arms and legs. However, it also includes thousands of tiny muscles throughout the body that help to regulate blood pressure and move food through the digestive system. In fact, muscles power every movement of the body—from a leap in the air to the hint of a smile.

Muscle tissue is found everywhere in the body—not just right beneath the skin but also deep within the body. Not only is muscle tissue found where you might least expect it, but also there is more than one kind of muscle tissue. **There are three different types of muscle tissue: skeletal, smooth, and cardiac.** Each type of muscle, shown in **Figure 32–6,** is specialized for specific functions in the body. Skeletal muscle is often found, as its name implies, attached to bones, and it is usually under voluntary control. Smooth muscle is found throughout the body and is usually not under voluntary control. Cardiac muscle makes up most of the mass of the heart, and, like smooth muscle, it is not under voluntary control.

In Your Notebook *Make a two-column chart to describe the three types of muscle tissue. Label the first column Type and the second column Function.*

FIGURE 32–5 Muscles in Action This pole-vaulter's skeletal muscles are clearly defined as she propels herself forward.

UbD Teach for Understanding

ENDURING UNDERSTANDING The human body is a complex system. The coordinated functions of its many structures support life processes and maintain homeostasis.

GUIDING QUESTION How do muscles help you move?

EVIDENCE OF UNDERSTANDING *This assessment, administered when students have finished the lesson, should show their understanding of the interaction between the muscular system and other body systems.* Ask students to work in pairs. Have each pair identify a body system with which the muscular system interacts. Ask each pair to name the body system it identified and describe the muscular system's interaction with that body system.

Skeletal Muscles Skeletal muscles are usually attached to bones. They are responsible for such voluntary movements as typing on a keyboard, dancing, or winking an eye. When viewed under a microscope at high magnification, skeletal muscle appears to have alternating light and dark bands called "striations." For this reason, skeletal muscle is said to be striated. Most skeletal muscle movements are consciously controlled by the central nervous system (the brain and spinal cord).

Skeletal muscle cells are large, have many nuclei, and vary in length. The shortest skeletal muscle, which is about 1 millimeter long, is found in the middle ear. The longest skeletal muscle, which may be as long as 30 centimeters, runs from the hip to the knee. Because skeletal muscle cells are long and slender, they are often called **muscle fibers.**

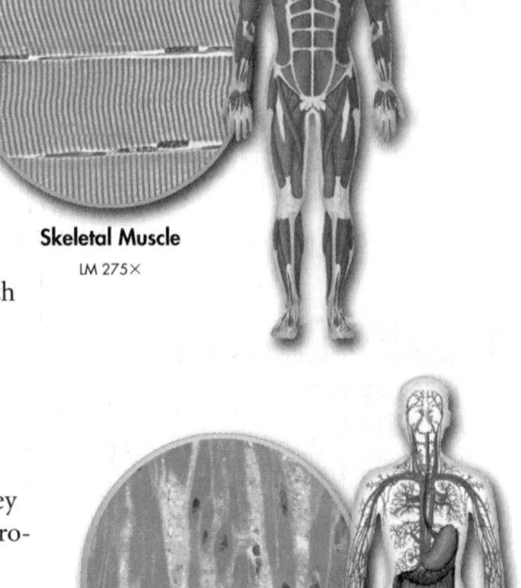

Smooth Muscles Smooth muscle cells are so named because they don't have striations and, therefore, look "smooth" under the microscope. These cells are spindle-shaped and usually have a single nucleus. Smooth muscle movements are usually involuntary. They are found throughout the body and form part of the walls of hollow structures such as the stomach, blood vessels, and intestines. Smooth muscles move food through your digestive tract, control the way blood flows through your circulatory system, and even decrease the size of the pupils of your eyes in bright light. Powerful smooth muscle contractions are also responsible for pushing a baby out of its mother's uterus during childbirth. Most smooth muscle cells can function without direct stimulation by the nervous system. The cells in smooth muscle tissue are connected to one another by gap junctions that allow electrical impulses to travel directly from one muscle cell to a neighboring muscle cell.

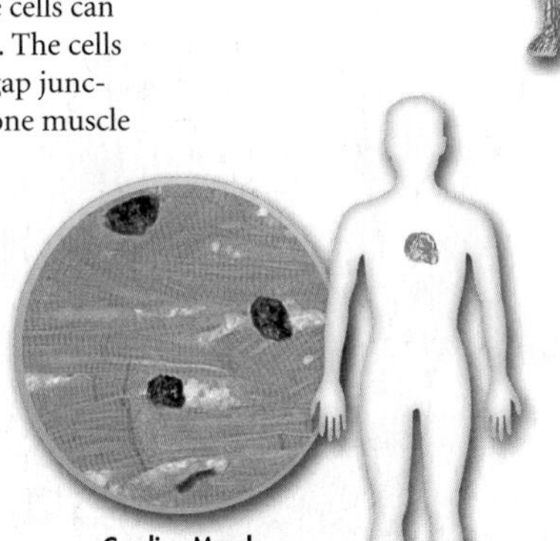

Cardiac Muscle Cardiac muscle is found in just one place in the body—the heart. It shares features with both skeletal muscle and smooth muscle. Cardiac muscle is striated like skeletal muscle, although its cells are smaller and usually have just one or two nuclei. Cardiac muscle is similar to smooth muscle because it is not under the direct control of the central nervous system. Like smooth muscle cells, cardiac muscle cells can contract on their own and are connected to their neighbors by gap junctions. You will learn more about cardiac muscle and its role in the function of the heart in Chapter 33.

Cardiac Muscle
LM 370×

FIGURE 32–6 Muscle Tissue The three types of muscle tissue look different under a microscope, but all muscle tissue has the ability to produce movement. **Compare and Contrast** ***What is the key difference between control of skeletal muscle contraction and smooth muscle contraction?***

How Science Works

STUDYING THE MUSCULAR SYSTEM

One of the earliest scientists to study and correctly portray the human muscular system was the Italian artist Leonardo da Vinci (1452–1519). Until Da Vinci's time, many of the thoughts people had about muscles were based on myth. After all, the practice of dissecting human bodies was seldom done in those days. Da Vinci, however, used dissection. His drawings of muscles were accurate as well as beautiful.

In the mid-1800s, the role of nerves in the contraction of skeletal muscles was established by a scientist named Claude Bernard, who did experiments using a drug called curare. Curare blocks the transmission of nerve impulses, and was used by some Amazonian native groups to poison the tips of their hunting arrows. Bernard injected curare into muscles and found that the muscles became paralyzed when nerve impulses were blocked by the drug.

Teach

Build Science Skills

Explain that there are similarities and differences between the three types of muscle tissue. Point out that the science skill of *comparing and contrasting* can be used to discern and clarify these similarities and differences. Ask students to write a sentence that compares, or describes a similarity of, two types of muscle tissue. Then, have students write a sentence that contrasts, or describes a difference between, two types of muscle tissue. Call on several students to share their sentences with the class.

DIFFERENTIATED INSTRUCTION

L1 Special Needs Some students may become overwhelmed by a page containing information about several topics. Point out to students that this page has three distinct sections of text, each with a related piece of art. Suggest that students use blank pieces of paper to cover all but one section of text and its associated figure. Only after students have mastered that information should they shift the blank pieces of paper and begin a new section.

LPR Less Proficient Readers Have students organize the information on muscle tissue types in a **Compare/Contrast Table.** Their tables should have columns for each type of tissue. The rows should include: how it is controlled, where it is found, whether or not it is striated, and whether its cells have one nucleus or many nuclei. Have students work in small groups to check their work.

Study Wkbks A/B, Appendix S20, Compare/Contrast Table. **Transparencies,** GO3.

Address Misconceptions

Interactions of Systems Students may not understand the involvement of muscles in digestive, circulatory, and respiratory system function. Explain that without muscles, food would not move through the digestive system, blood would not be pumped through the body, and the diaphragm would not move air into and out of the lungs.

Answers

FIGURE 32–6 Most skeletal muscle contractions are voluntarily controlled by the central nervous system; smooth muscle contractions are usually involuntary.

Skeletal, Muscular, and Integumentary Systems **929**

Teach continued

VISUAL SUMMARY

Make sure students understand the relationship between all the different structures pictured in the visual summary.

Ask What is a muscle made up of? *(muscle fibers)*

Ask What are muscle fibers made up of? *(many myofibrils)*

Have students work in small groups to make a **Concept Map** that shows the relationship between the terms *sarcomere, myofibril, muscle fiber,* and *muscle*. Ask each group to share its graphic organizer with the class.

Study Wkbks A/B, Appendix S21, Concept Map. **Transparencies,** GO4.

DIFFERENTIATED INSTRUCTION

L1 Struggling Students Point out that the internal captions in **Figure 32–7** summarize the structure of a muscle. Help students understand how the illustration breaks down the components of a muscle. Help students understand the relationship between the parts of the illustration, going from left to right. Point out that actin and myosin filaments are actually microscopic, but they have been drawn this size to show their structure.

ELL Focus on ELL: Extend Language

BEGINNING AND INTERMEDIATE SPEAKERS Have students divide a piece of paper into three sections by folding the paper or drawing lines on it. The sections should be titled: Term, My Understanding of the Term, and Draw, respectively. Have students write the term *muscle fiber* in the first section. Beginning speakers should use one- or two-word phrases to show their understanding of the term, while intermediate speakers should use sentences. Students should draw a diagram in the third section to show their understanding of the term. Have them repeat the process for the terms *myofibril, myosin, actin,* and *sarcomere*.

Answers

FIGURE 32–7 a sarcomere

Muscle Contraction

How do muscles contract?

Muscles produce movements by shortening, or contracting, from end to end. How do cells generate such force? The answer can be found in the way in which two kinds of muscle protein filaments interact.

BUILD Vocabulary

PREFIXES The prefix *myo-* in **myofibril** means "muscle." The word comes from the Greek word for mouse. Artists and sculptors once thought well-developed muscles looked like mice under the skin.

Muscle Fiber Structure Skeletal muscle cells, or fibers, are filled with tightly packed filament bundles called **myofibrils.** Each myofibril contains thick filaments of a protein called **myosin** (MY uh sin) and thin filaments of a protein called **actin.** These filaments are arranged in an overlapping pattern that produces the stripes or striations so visible through a microscope. The thin actin filaments are bound together in areas called Z lines. Two Z lines and the filaments between them make up a unit called a **sarcomere.** **Figure 32–7** shows the structure of a muscle fiber.

The Sliding-Filament Model Myosin and actin filaments are actually tiny force-producing engines. **During a muscle contraction, myosin filaments form cross-bridges with actin filaments. The cross-bridges then change shape, pulling the actin filaments toward the center of the sarcomere.** As shown in **Figure 32–8,** this action decreases the distance between the Z lines, and the fiber shortens. Then the cross-bridge detaches from actin and repeats the cycle by binding to another site on the actin filament. As thick and thin filaments slide past each other, the fiber shortens. For this reason, the process is called the sliding-filament model of muscle contraction.

When hundreds of thousands of myosin cross-bridges repeat these actions, the muscle fiber shortens with considerable force. Contractions like this enable you to run, lift weights, or even turn a page in a book. Because one molecule of ATP supplies just enough energy for one interaction between a myosin cross-bridge and an actin filament, a muscle cell needs plenty of ATP.

VISUAL SUMMARY

SKELETAL MUSCLE STRUCTURE

FIGURE 32–7 Skeletal muscles are made up of bundles of muscle fibers composed of myofibrils. Each myofibril contains actin and myosin filaments. **Interpret Visuals** *What type of unit are actin and myosin filaments arranged in?*

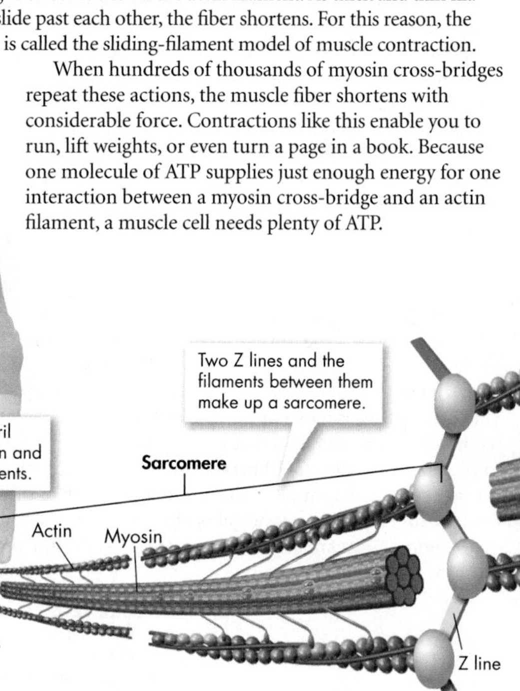

A muscle consists of bundles of muscle fibers.
Each muscle fiber is a cell that contains many myofibrils.
Each myofibril contains actin and myosin filaments.
Two Z lines and the filaments between them make up a sarcomere.
Sarcomere
Actin
Myosin
Sarcomere
Z line
Z line

Biology In-Depth

WHAT CAUSES MUSCLE CRAMPS?

Movement is the result of skeletal muscle contractions that occur in a controlled way. In contrast, muscle cramps, such as leg cramps that occur at night, happen when sudden and involuntary contractions occur. Although occasional muscle cramps do not cause lasting damage, they can be intensely painful. One common cause of muscle cramps is dehydration. Other causes include nerve compressions, a lack of minerals, or compromised blood flow to the muscles. Certain diseases, such as tetanus, can cause muscle spasms and cramping, as can some toxins, such as strychnine.

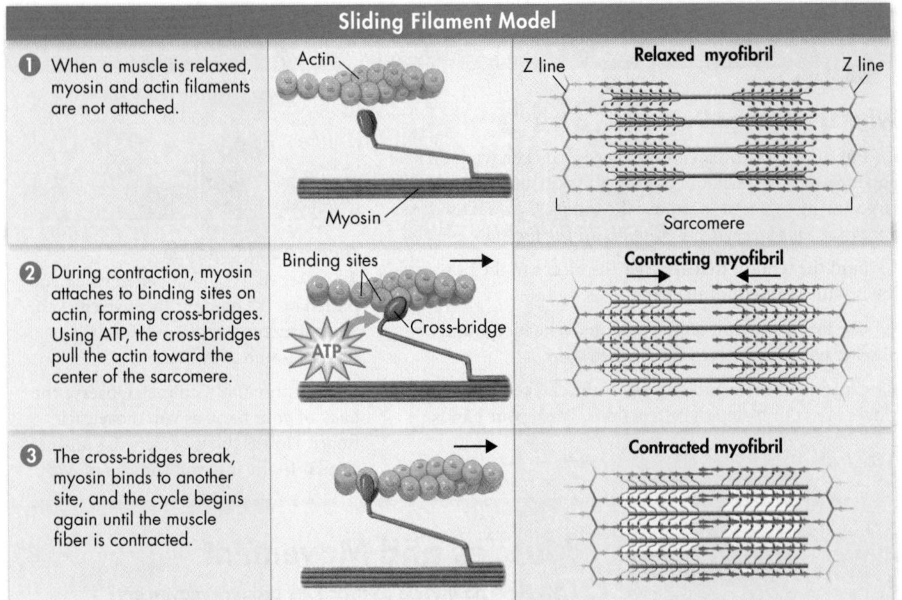

Sliding Filament Model
1 When a muscle is relaxed, myosin and actin filaments are not attached.
Actin
Myosin
Z line
Relaxed myofibril
Z line
Sarcomere
2 During contraction, myosin attaches to binding sites on actin, forming cross-bridges. Using ATP, the cross-bridges pull the actin toward the center of the sarcomere.
Binding sites
Cross-bridge
ATP
Contracting myofibril
3 The cross-bridges break, myosin binds to another site, and the cycle begins again until the muscle fiber is contracted.
Contracted myofibril

FIGURE 32–8 Sliding-Filament Model During muscle contraction, interaction between myosin filaments and actin filaments causes a muscle fiber to contract.

Control of Muscle Contraction Skeletal muscles are useful only if they contract in a controlled fashion. Remember that motor neurons connect the central nervous system to skeletal muscle cells. Impulses from these motor neurons control the contraction of muscle fibers.

A motor neuron and a skeletal muscle cell meet at a type of synapse known as a **neuromuscular** (noo roh MUS kyoo lur) **junction.** When a motor neuron is stimulated, its axon terminals release a neurotransmitter called **acetylcholine** (as ih til KOH leen). Acetylcholine (ACh) molecules diffuse across the synapse, producing an impulse (action potential) in the cell membrane of the muscle fiber. The impulse causes the release of calcium ions (Ca^{2+}) within the fiber. These ions affect regulatory proteins that allow myosin cross-bridges to bind to actin.

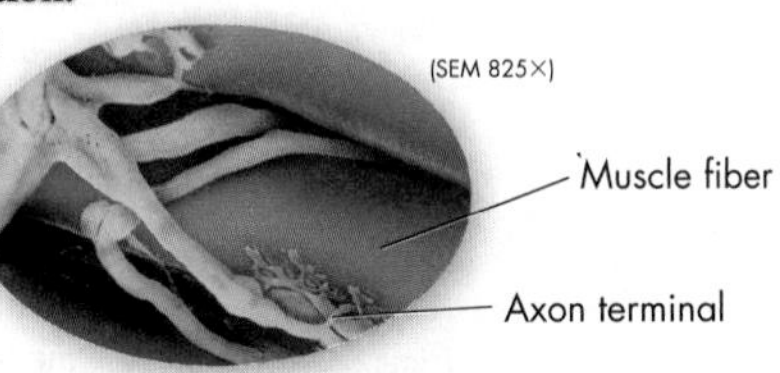

FIGURE 32–9 Neuromuscular Junction

A muscle cell contracts until the release of ACh stops and an enzyme produced at the axon terminal destroys any remaining ACh. Then, the muscle cell pumps Ca^{2+} back into storage, the cross-bridges stop forming, and the contraction ends.

What is the difference between a strong contraction and a weak contraction? When you lift something light, such as a sheet of paper, your brain stimulates only a few cells to contract. However, as you exert maximum effort, such as when lifting your book bag, almost all the muscle cells in your arm are stimulated to contract.

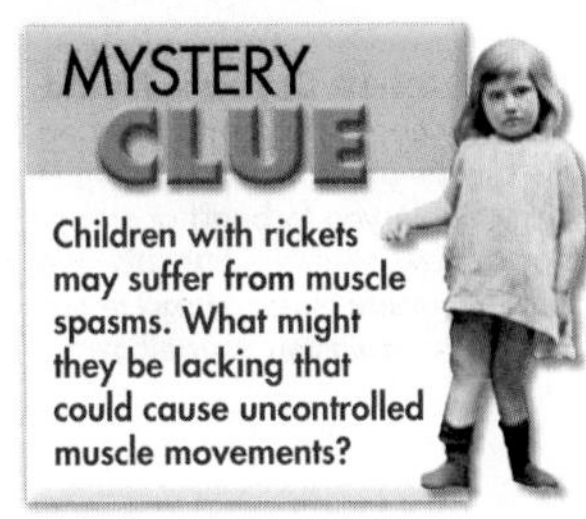

MYSTERY
CLUE
Children with rickets may suffer from muscle spasms. What might they be lacking that could cause uncontrolled muscle movements?

Use Visuals

Use **Figure 32–8** to discuss the sliding-filament model of muscle contraction. Then, have students write a short summary paragraph describing the process.

DIFFERENTIATED INSTRUCTION

L1 Struggling Students Some students may struggle with interpreting the information in **Figure 32–8.** Make sure students understand what is happening in each row of the figure. Point out that the diagrams in the second column show a blown-up version of one of the actin-myosin cross-bridges pictured in the third column.

ELL English Language Learners Have students create their own sketches to show the sliding filament model of muscle contraction. Then, have pairs of students discuss how their pictures show the process.

Have students review the process of muscle contraction to brainstorm a list of possible reasons why children with rickets suffer from muscle spasms. Students can go online to Biology.com to gather their evidence.

For more on muscle contraction, have students access **Art in Motion: The Sliding Filament Model.** Suggest that they watch the **Tutor Tube: Using Analogies to Understand Muscle Contraction** to explore how to use analogies to make concepts more accessible.

UbD Check for Understanding

ONE-MINUTE RESPONSE

Write the following prompt on the board and give students about a minute to write a quick response summarizing their understanding.

How do the nervous system and muscular system work together when a muscle contracts? *(Responses should mention that the impulse triggering muscle contraction comes from the nervous system. This impulse initiates a series of events in the muscle that results in contraction.)*

ADJUST INSTRUCTION

If responses show that students do not understand how muscle contraction is controlled, have two volunteers role-play this interaction for the class. Have one student represent the nervous system and the other represent the muscular system.

Teach continued

Build Study Skills

Explain that studying with a partner is an effective way to review the lesson material. Have pairs of students practice the following technique: One student asks questions based on the lesson content, figures, or lesson assessment, and the other student answers. A good example of a question based on the material in this lesson is "Do muscles push or pull on bones as they contract?" *(Muscles pull on bones.)* After several minutes, have students exchange roles.

DIFFERENTIATED INSTRUCTION

ELL English Language Learners While engaging in the partner study exercise described above, encourage students to phrase their questions and answers as complete sentences. Have English language learners work with native English speakers to practice pronunciation.

Quick Lab GUIDED INQUIRY

What Do Tendons Do? 

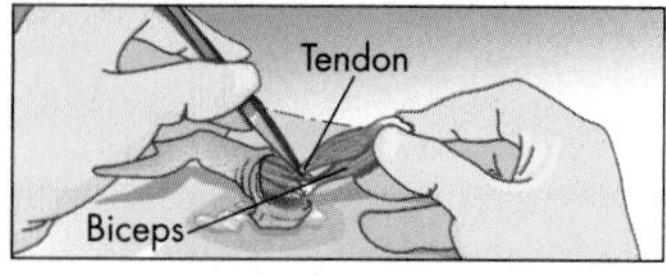

❶ Put on gloves and an apron. Place a chicken wing on a paper towel. Peel back or cut away the skin and fat of the largest wing segment to expose the biceps. **CAUTION:** *Do not touch your face with your hands during the lab.*

❷ Find the tendon that attaches the biceps to the bones of the middle segment of the wing.

❸ Use forceps to pull on the tendon of the biceps and observe what happens to the chicken wing.

❹ Clean your tools and dispose of the chicken wing and gloves per your teacher's instructions. Wash your hands.

Analyze and Conclude

1. Observe What happened when you pulled on the tendon? In a live chicken, what structure would pull on the tendon to move the wing?

2. Compare and Contrast Observe the back of your hand as you move each finger. How is the way the wing moves similar to the way your fingers move?

Muscles and Movement

How do muscle contractions produce movement?

One of the most confusing concepts to understand about muscles is that they can produce force only by contracting in one direction. Yet, you know from experience that you can use your muscles to push as well as to pull. How is this possible?

How Muscles and Bones Interact Skeletal muscles are joined to bones by tough connective tissues called **tendons.** Tendons are attached in such a way that they pull on the bones and make them work like levers. The joint functions as a fulcrum—the fixed point around which the lever moves. The muscles provide the force to move the lever. Usually, several muscles that pull in different directions surround each joint. **Skeletal muscles generate force and produce movement by pulling on body parts as they contract.**

We can use our muscles to push as well as to pull because most skeletal muscles work in opposing pairs. When one muscle in the pair contracts, the other muscle in the pair relaxes. The muscles of the upper arm shown in **Figure 32–10** are a good example of this dual action. When the biceps muscle contracts, it bends, or flexes, the elbow joint. When the triceps muscle contracts, it opens, or extends, the elbow joint. A controlled movement requires the involvement of both muscles. To hold a tennis racket or a violin requires a balance of forces between the biceps and the triceps.

This is why the training of athletes and musicians is so difficult. The brain must learn how to work opposing muscle groups in just the right ways to make the involved joints move precisely.

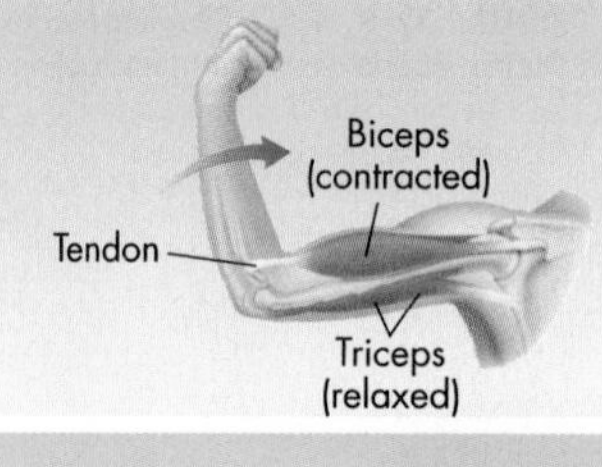

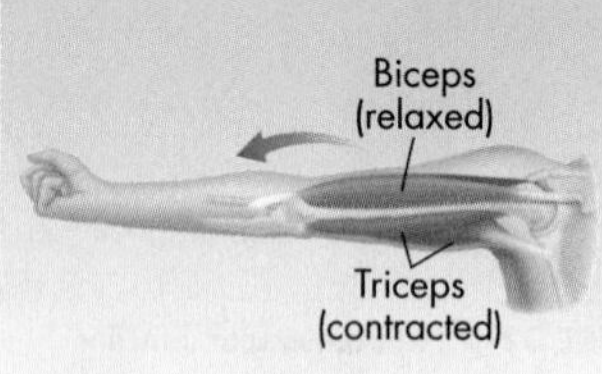

FIGURE 32–10 Opposing Muscle Pairs By contracting and relaxing, the biceps and triceps in the upper arm enable you to bend or straighten your elbow. Apply Concepts ***Which skeletal muscle must contract in order for you to straighten your elbow?***

In Your Notebook *Explain in your own words the role of opposing pairs in muscle contraction.*

PURPOSE Students will investigate the function of tendons.

MATERIALS raw chicken wing treated with bleach, paper towels, forceps, scissors or scalpel

SAFETY Make sure students wear protective equipment and handle the scissors/scalpel carefully. Have them wash their hands and lab bench when they are finished.

PLANNING Briefly soak the wings in bleach. Then, rinse them thoroughly in water and dry them. If you do not use the wings immediately, refrigerate them until you do. Dispose of the chicken parts properly.

ANALYZE AND CONCLUDE

1. The wing bent at the joint. In a live chicken, the biceps muscle would pull on the tendon.
2. Like the chicken's bicep muscle, muscles controlling a finger cause it to bend by pulling on tendons.

Answers

FIGURE 32–10 The triceps must contract for the elbow to straighten.

IN YOUR NOTEBOOK A muscle can only produce movement in one direction by pulling on a body part as it contracts. Therefore, most muscles work with another muscle, forming an opposing pair. Together, the pair can move body parts in opposite directions.

Types of Muscle Fibers There are two principal types of skeletal muscle fibers—red and white. The types of muscle fibers vary in their specific functions. Red muscle, or slow-twitch muscle, contains many mitochondria. The dark color of red muscle comes from small blood vessels that deliver a rich supply of blood and from an oxygen-storing protein called myoglobin. The abundant mitochondria and generous supply of oxygen allow these fibers to derive their energy through aerobic respiration and work for long periods of time. Red muscle is useful for endurance activities like long-distance running.

White muscle, or fast-twitch muscle, contracts more rapidly and generates more force than does red muscle, but its cells contain few mitochondria and tire quickly. White fibers are useful for activities that require great strength or quick bursts of speed, like sprinting.

Exercise and Health Regular exercise is important to maintain muscular strength and flexibility. Muscles that are exercised regularly stay firm and increase in size and strength due to added filaments. Muscles that are not used become weak and can visibly decrease in size. Regular exercise helps to maintain resting muscle tone—a state of partial contraction. Muscle tone is responsible for keeping the back and legs straight and the head upright, even when you are relaxed.

Aerobic exercises—such as running and swimming—place strong demands on the heart and lungs, helping these systems to become more efficient. This, in turn, increases physical endurance—the ability to perform an activity without fatigue. Regular exercise also strengthens your bones, making them thicker and stronger. Strong bones and muscles are less likely to become injured.

Resistance exercises, such as weight lifting, increase muscle size and strength. Over time, weight-training exercises will help to maintain coordination and flexibility.

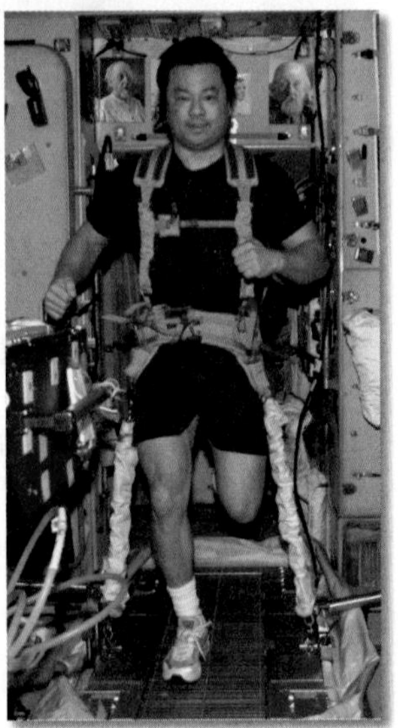

FIGURE 32–11 Preventing Muscle Loss Without gravity, many muscles go unused. An astronaut in space may lose up to 5 percent of muscle mass a week. Exercise helps to maintain muscles—and bones, too.

32.2 Assessment

Review Key Concepts

1. a. **Review** List the three types of muscle tissue.
   b. **Compare and Contrast** Compare and contrast the structure and function of the three types of muscle tissue.
2. a. **Review** What structures make up a skeletal muscle?
   b. **Explain** Describe how a muscle contracts.
   c. **Predict** A type of poisonous gas destroys the enzyme that breaks down acetylcholine. What effect do you think this gas has on the body?
3. a. **Review** Explain the role of tendons in movement.
   b. **Apply Concepts** In training for an Olympic weight-lifting event, which muscle fibers would be the most important to develop?

VISUAL THINKING

4. Create your own model to show how actin filaments slide over myosin filaments during a muscle contraction. Include as much detail in your model as possible.

BIOLOGY.com Search Lesson 32.2  GO • Lesson Assessment • Self-Test

Assess and Remediate

EVALUATE UNDERSTANDING

Call on students to provide definitions for each of the lesson vocabulary terms. After each term has been defined, call on another student to explain how it is related to muscle contraction. Then, have them complete the 32.2 Assessment.

REMEDIATION SUGGESTION

L1 Struggling Students If students have difficulty answering **Question 3a,** have them reread the information about tendons under the heading **How Muscles and Bones Interact.** Then, have them make a quick sketch that shows how tendons are involved in movement.

BIOLOGY.com Students can check their understanding of lesson concepts with the **Self-Test** assessment. They can then take an online version of the **Lesson Assessment.**

Assessment Answers

1a. skeletal, smooth, cardiac

1b. Skeletal muscle tissue is striated and is under voluntary control. Smooth muscle does not have striations like skeletal muscle and is not under voluntary control. Cardiac muscle is striated like skeletal muscle tissue and, like smooth muscle, is not under voluntary control.

2a. A skeletal muscle is made up of muscle fibers that each contain many myofibrils. Each myofibril is made up of actin filaments and myosin filaments.

2b. A muscle contracts when myosin filaments form cross-bridges with actin filaments, pulling the actin filaments toward the center of the sarcomere.

2c. If the enzyme were unable to break down acetylcholine, muscle contraction would not stop.

3a. Tendons join skeletal muscle to bone. They act by pulling on bones and making them work like levers.

3b. White, or fast-twitch, muscle fibers are involved in activities that require great strength; these would be most important in training for an Olympic weight-lifting event.

VISUAL THINKING

4. Students' models should show the following: A cross-bridge forms between actin and myosin filaments. When the cross-bridge bends, the actin slides over the myosin. Then, the cross-bridge detaches, unbends, and reattaches to a new site on the actin.

Teach

Lead a Discussion

Have students discuss the appropriateness of giving awards and recognition, such as Hall of Fame memberships or world records, to athletes who use steroids to enhance their performance.

Ask When athletes who have used steroids are honored in award ceremonies and record books, are young athletes then encouraged to use steroids? *(Accept all well-supported responses.)*

Ask Is it the responsibility of professional athletes to be positive role models regarding the use of steroids? *(Accept all well-supported responses.)*

Biology & Society

Should Student Athletes Be Tested for Steroids?

Until 1976, East Germany had never won an Olympic gold medal in women's swimming. That year, they won 13 out of the 14 gold medals awarded for swimming. Eventually, it was discovered that the young athletes had been given anabolic steroids without their knowledge.

Anabolic steroids are synthetic forms of the hormone testosterone. They were originally developed to help treat men who could not produce enough of the hormone for normal growth and development. Because these drugs also make it easier for athletes to add muscle mass and recover from workouts, they are sometimes used illegally to improve performance.

In the early part of this century, steroid use emerged as a big controversy in professional baseball. Many people now think that steroid use by professional baseball players was not taken seriously. Legislators and parents argue that this lax attitude has led many young athletes to think that steroid use is acceptable.

Some student athletes use steroids hoping to improve their chance of playing either in college or professionally. However, steroids are not only illegal, they are dangerous. Decades after unknowingly being given steroids, many of the 1976 East German swimmers are suffering from the long-term effects of steroid use, such as tumors, liver disease, heart problems, infertility, and depression. Other, more short-term effects of steroid use include breast development in males, acne, and increased chance of ligament and tendon injury.

Due to the rising rate of steroid use, some states have enacted policies for testing student athletes. But the policies are often controversial.

Kornelia Ender was a member of the East German swim team when some swimmers were given steroids without their knowledge. In 1976, she won four gold medals.

Viewpoints

For Testing Student athletes who use steroids risk both their short- and long-term health. Although educating students about the risks of steroids is important, many students will ignore the risks and take their chances. Schools should help to protect these athletes. Also, athletes who do not use steroids should not have to compete against those who do.

Against Testing Steroid testing is more expensive than testing for other drugs, and many schools don't have the funds. Also, there are many ways to "fool" steroid tests, so the tests could be just a waste of money. Although the Supreme Court has ruled that drug testing of students is constitutional, some people still feel that testing violates their privacy rights.

Research and Decide

1. Evaluate Other than the viewpoints addressed here, can you think of any viewpoints for or against testing high school athletes for steroids?

2. Communicate Write a paragraph that explains your viewpoint on testing student athletes for steroid use.

Answers

RESEARCH AND DECIDE

1. Sample answers: For testing: Steroids are illegal, so schools have a responsibility to screen for this illegal behavior. Against testing: Testing for steroid use should be up to the parents of the student athlete, not the school.
2. Students' paragraphs should clearly express their viewpoints, backed by logical reasoning, either for or against testing student athletes for steroids.

Biology In-Depth

DIFFERENT TYPES OF STEROIDS

Students in your class with asthma or other respiratory problems may take steroid-based medication, such as cortisone, to relieve some of their symptoms. Tell students that these steroids are classified as corticosteroids. Explain that the corticosteroids used to treat respiratory disorders are different than the anabolic steroids used to enhance athletic performance. Corticosteroids prescribed by doctors for respiratory disorders are legal when taken as prescribed, and they cannot be used to enhance athletic performance.

32.3 Skin—The Integumentary System

NoS.3 Communicate ideas.

THINK ABOUT IT What's the largest organ in your body? No, it is not your ears or stomach, or even your lungs or heart. By far the largest human organ is the skin. If that sounds a little strange, it's probably because you're used to taking your skin for granted—it's just the outside of your body, right? Well, the skin has a lot of roles that go beyond just covering your body.

Integumentary System Functions

What are the principal functions of the integumentary system?

The integumentary system includes the skin, hair, and nails. The skin—the major organ of the system—has many different functions, but its most important function is protection. **The integumentary system serves as a barrier against infection and injury, helps to regulate body temperature, removes wastes from the body, gathers information, and produces vitamin D.**

Protection The skin forms a barrier that blocks out pathogens and debris and prevents the body from drying out. The skin also provides protection from the sun's ultraviolet radiation. Nails, which protect the tips of fingers and toes, are also produced by the skin.

Body Temperature Regulation The skin helps to regulate body temperature by releasing excess heat generated by working cells, while keeping in enough heat to maintain normal body temperature. Hair also helps to prevent heat loss from the head.

Excretion Small amounts of sweat are constantly released from your sweat glands. Sweat contains waste products such as urea and salts that need to be excreted from the body.

Information Gathering The skin contains several types of sensory receptors. It serves as the gateway through which sensations such as pressure, heat, cold, and pain are transmitted from the outside environment to the nervous system.

Vitamin D Production One of the skin's most important functions is the production of vitamin D, which is needed for absorption of calcium and phosphorus from the small intestine. Sunlight is needed for one of the chemical reactions that produce vitamin D in skin cells.

Key Concepts

What are the principal functions of the integumentary system?

What are the structures of the integumentary system?

What are some problems that affect the skin?

Vocabulary

epidermis • keratin • melanocyte • melanin • dermis • sebaceous gland • hair follicle

Taking Notes

Preview Visuals Before you read, preview **Figure 32–12.** Make a two-column table. In the first column, list all of the structures labeled in the figure. As you read, fill in the function of each structure in the second column.

MYSTERY CLUE
How do you think the knowledge of the effect of sunlight on skin could have helped scientists unravel the rickets mystery?

UbD Teach for Understanding

ENDURING UNDERSTANDING The human body is a complex system. The coordinated functions of its many structures support life processes and maintain homeostasis.

GUIDING QUESTION Why is the integumentary system a necessary organ system?

EVIDENCE OF UNDERSTANDING *After completing the lesson, give students the following assessment to show they understand the functions of the integumentary system and how it helps the body maintain homeostasis.* Have students work in small groups to develop an analogy for the integumentary system. For example, the integumentary system can be compared to a fence, which keeps objects in (or out of) a particular area. Have each group share its analogy with the class. Encourage students to consider functions of the integumentary system other than protection when developing their analogies.

Getting Started

Objectives

32.3.1 State the functions of the integumentary system.

32.3.2 Identify the structures of the integumentary system.

32.3.3 Describe some of the problems that affect the skin.

Student Resources

Study Workbooks A and B, 32.3 Worksheets

Spanish Study Workbook, 32.3 Worksheets

Lab Manual B, 32.3 Data Analysis Worksheet

BIOLOGY.com Lesson Overview • Lesson Notes
- Activities: Art Review, Data Analysis
- Assessment: Self-Test, Lesson Assessment

For corresponding lesson in the **Foundation Edition**, see pages 775–777.

Teach

MYSTERY CLUE Have volunteers describe how scientists may have used information on sunlight and skin to help unravel the rickets mystery. Students can go online to **Biology.com** to gather their evidence.

IN INDIANA ACADEMIC STANDARDS

For the full text of all standards, see the Course Overview in the front matter of this book.

NoS.3 Clearly communicate their ideas and results of investigations verbally and in written form using tables, graphs, diagrams, and photographs.

LESSON 32.3

Teach continued

Use Visuals

Have students use the information in **Figure 32–12** to make a **Compare/Contrast Table** for the dermis and epidermis. Students' charts should compare the location, thickness, and the structures of each layer of the skin. Have students work in pairs to review and revise their charts.

Study Wkbks A/B, Appendix S20, Compare/Contrast Table. **Transparencies,** GO3.

DIFFERENTIATED INSTRUCTION

LPR **Less Proficient Readers** Have students make bulleted lists under the headings: Epidermis, Dermis, and Hypodermis. Each list should include the structures found in that layer of skin. Have students practice reading the words in each list aloud.

L3 **Advanced Learners** Have students find out why prolonged exposure to water can cause the skin of the fingers and toes to become wrinkled, and have them prepare a presentation to explain this phenomenon to the class.

ELL Focus on ELL: Build Background

ALL SPEAKERS Have students make a **Cluster Diagram** for the topic of *skin*. Have them think of words and concepts that relate to skin and write them in their diagrams. Lead a class discussion on students' diagrams and how they relate to lesson material. Accept less-than-precise words and invented spellings from beginning speakers. For intermediate and advanced speakers, expect more precise and correctly spelled words. For advanced high students, require complex words and ideas.

Study Wkbks A/B, Appendix S19, Cluster Diagram. **Transparencies,** GO2.

BIOLOGY.com Students can review skin structures using the drag-and-drop labeling activity, **Art Review: Structure of the Skin.**

Answers

FIGURE 32–12 A slight scratch on the surface of the skin does not bleed because the epidermis does not contain blood vessels.

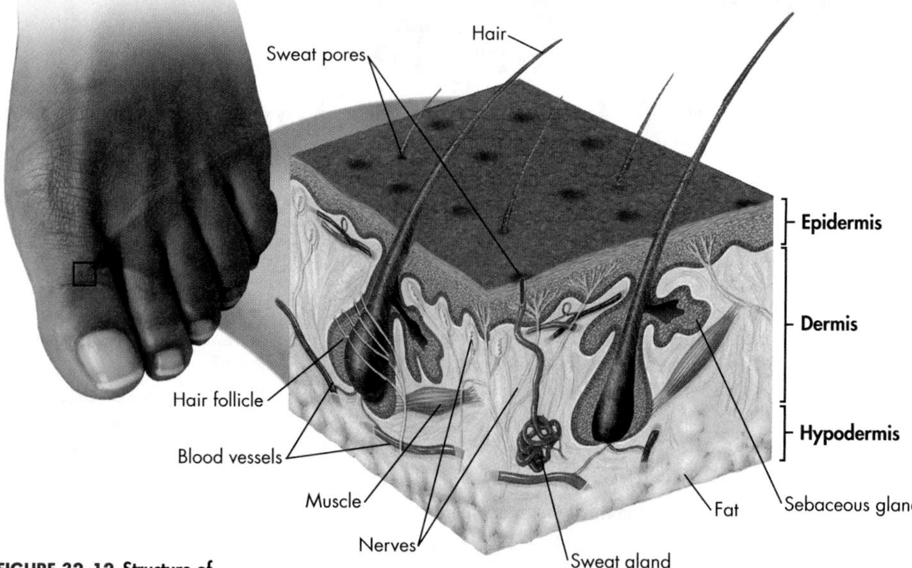

FIGURE 32–12 Structure of the Skin The skin has an outer layer called the epidermis and an inner layer called the dermis. **Infer** ***Why do you think a slight scratch on the surface of the skin does not bleed?***

Integumentary System Structures

What are the structures of the integumentary system?

Many structures are required to fulfill all the functions you just read about. **Skin and its related structures—the hair, nails, and several types of glands—make up the integumentary system.** The skin is made up of two main layers—the epidermis and the dermis. Beneath the dermis is a layer of fat (the hypodermis) and loose connective tissue that helps insulate the body. **Figure 32–12** shows many of the structures that make up the skin.

BUILD Vocabulary

WORD ORIGINS The prefix *epi-* in **epidermis** comes from the Greek word meaning "on" or "upon." *Dermis* derives from the Greek *derma*, meaning "skin."

Epidermis The outer layer of the skin is the **epidermis.** The epidermis has two layers. The outer layer of the epidermis—the layer that you can see—is made up of dead cells. The inner layer of the epidermis is made up of living cells, including stem cells. These cells divide rapidly, producing new skin cells that push older cells to the surface of the skin. As the older cells move upward, they flatten, and their organelles disintegrate. They also begin making **keratin,** a tough, fibrous protein.

Eventually, the older cells die and form a tough, flexible, waterproof covering on the surface of the skin. This outer layer of dead cells is shed or washed away at a surprising rate. Once every four to six weeks, a new layer of dead cells replaces an old layer.

The epidermis also contains **melanocytes** (MEL uh noh cytes), which are cells that produce a dark brown pigment called **melanin.** Melanin helps protect the skin by absorbing ultraviolet rays from the sun. Skin color is directly related to the production of melanin. The melanocytes of people with darker skin produce more melanin than the melanocytes of people with lighter skin produce.

Quick Facts

EVOLUTION OF HUMAN SKIN COLOR

Human skin color shows a gradual geographic trend in Africa and Europe: populations increasingly far from the equator tend to have less and less melanin in their skin. Virtually all the hypotheses that have been proposed to explain this trend assume that variation in the amount of sunlight is the ultimate cause. One widely held hypothesis states that darker skin is selected for at lower latitudes because its higher melanin content helps protect it from serious sunburn and skin cancer. Yet another hypothesis proposes that melanin's protective quality extends to reducing the breakdown of folic acid by ultraviolet (UV) rays. This phenomenon may be a reproductive advantage for those in lower latitudes. Another hypothesis proposes that lighter skin is selected for at higher latitudes because it can be penetrated by sunlight, which is needed to produce vitamin D.

Dermis The **dermis** lies beneath the epidermis and contains the protein collagen, blood vessels, nerve endings, glands, sensory receptors, smooth muscles, and hair follicles. Structures in the dermis interact with other body systems to maintain homeostasis by helping to regulate body temperature. When the body needs to conserve heat on a cold day, the blood vessels in the dermis narrow. This brings blood closer to the body's core and prevents heat from escaping through the skin. On hot days, the blood vessels widen, bringing heat from the body's core to the skin.

Sweat glands in the dermis also aid temperature regulation. Excess heat is released when sweat glands produce perspiration, or sweat. When sweat evaporates, it takes heat away from your body.

The skin also contains **sebaceous** (suh BAY shus) **glands,** which secrete an oily substance called sebum that is released at the surface of the skin. Sebum helps to keep the keratin-rich epidermis flexible and waterproof. Because it is acidic, it can kill bacteria on the surface of the skin.

In Your Notebook *Explain whether the epidermis, the dermis, or both layers are involved in protection and temperature regulation.*

Hair The basic component of human hair and nails is keratin. In other animals, keratin forms a variety of structures, including bull horns, reptile scales, bird feathers, and porcupine quills.

Hair covers almost every exposed surface of the human body and has some important functions. Hair on the head protects the scalp from ultraviolet light from the sun and provides insulation from the cold. Hairs in the nostrils, external ear canals, and around the eyes (in the form of eyelashes) prevent dirt and other particles from entering the body.

Hair is produced by cells at the base of structures called hair follicles. **Hair follicles** are tubelike pockets of epidermal cells that extend into the dermis. New research has shown that hair follicles contain stem cells that help to renew the skin and heal wounds. The hairs shown in **Figure 32–13** are actually large columns of cells that have filled with keratin and then died. Rapid cell growth at the base of the hair follicle causes the hair to grow longer. Hair follicles are in close contact with sebaceous glands. The oily secretions of these glands help hairs stay soft and flexible.

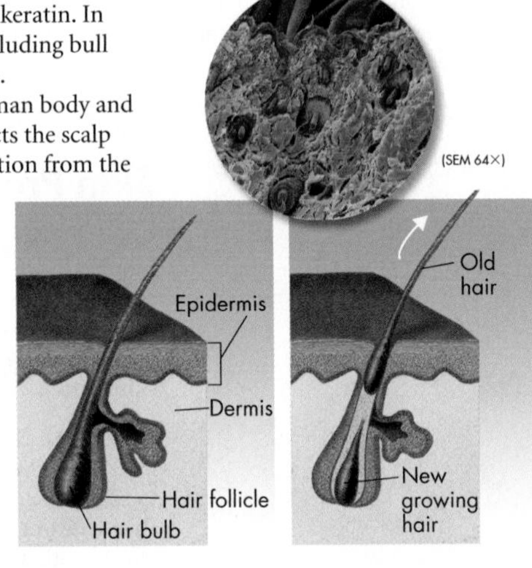

FIGURE 32–13 Hair As a new hair grows, it pushes the old hair out of the follicle. The micrograph shows individual hairs in their follicles.

Nails Nails grow from an area of rapidly dividing cells known as the nail root. The nail roots are located near the tips of the fingers and toes. During cell division, the cells of the nail root fill with keratin and produce a tough, platelike nail that covers and protects the tips of the fingers and toes. Nails grow at an average rate of 3 millimeters per month, with fingernails growing about three times faster than toenails.

UbD Check for Understanding

VISUAL PRESENTATION

List the lesson vocabulary terms on the board: *epidermis, keratin, melanocyte, melanin, dermis, sebaceous gland, hair follicle.*

Ask students to create a concept map that includes each of the lesson vocabulary terms and identifies relationships between the terms. *(Students' concept maps should show the following relationships: melanin is contained in melanocytes, which are a part of the epidermis; keratin is produced in the epidermis; sebaceous glands and hair follicles are found in the dermis.)*

ADJUST INSTRUCTION

If students have trouble identifying relationships between the lesson vocabulary terms, ask them to draw and label their own version of **Figure 32–12.**

Connect to the Real World

There are a vast number of consumer products related to the grooming and health of skin, hair, and nails. Ask students to note advertising claims related to these products that they see on television, in print ads, or advertised on the Internet. Ask how one can distinguish claims that give accurate information from those that do not. Have each student choose one advertising claim to analyze and research. At the conclusion of their research, have students create a poster that displays the advertising claims and a summary of their research.

DIFFERENTIATED INSTRUCTION

ELL English Language Learners Explain that many advertisements manipulate language in order to make a product attractive to consumers. For example, a product may claim to "fight acne." Students should note that the word *fight* does not mean "stop," although the advertisement may imply otherwise. As students work through the advertisement analysis described above, have English language learners be alert for these situations.

Answers

IN YOUR NOTEBOOK While both layers are involved in protection and temperature regulation, the epidermis is most directly involved in protection and the dermis is most directly involved in temperature regulation.

Teach continued

Lead a Discussion

Tell students that in a developing embryo, melanocytes are genetically programmed to move from one part of the embryo to another.

Ask How is this property of melanocytes reflected in the characteristics of melanoma? *(Melanoma easily spreads from one part of the body to another, just as melanocytes move through a developing embryo.)*

Explain that researchers have identified the gene that is responsible for the ability of melanoma to spread easily through the body.

Ask How could this information be used by researchers working to develop treatments for melanoma? *(Sample answer: If scientists figure out how to shut down this gene, they could stop the spread of melanoma to other parts of the body.)*

DIFFERENTIATED INSTRUCTION

L1 Struggling Students For more information on cancer and how it spreads, suggest students reread the section, **Cancer: Uncontrolled Cell Growth,** in Lesson 10.3.

L3 Advanced Students Tell students that the gene responsible for melanoma's rapid spread through the body is called *SLUG*. Ask students to learn more about this gene and its role in melanoma. Have students prepare a short oral presentation of their findings.

BIOLOGY.com Have students analyze skin cancer data and draw conclusions about risk factors in **Data Analysis: Skin Cancer Factors.**

Analyzing Data

NoS.3

The Rising Rate of Melanoma

Over the past several decades, the incidence of some deadly cancers, such as lung cancer, has decreased among people aged 20–54. Some people attribute this to decreasing smoking rates. During the same time period, the incidence of melanoma increased for the same age group. The incidence of both lung cancer and melanoma increases with age. But melanoma is one of the most common cancers in young adults.

What are some possible reasons for this increase? Despite public health efforts, many people still consider tanned skin a sign of health. Also, many people do not use enough sunscreen for it to be effective.

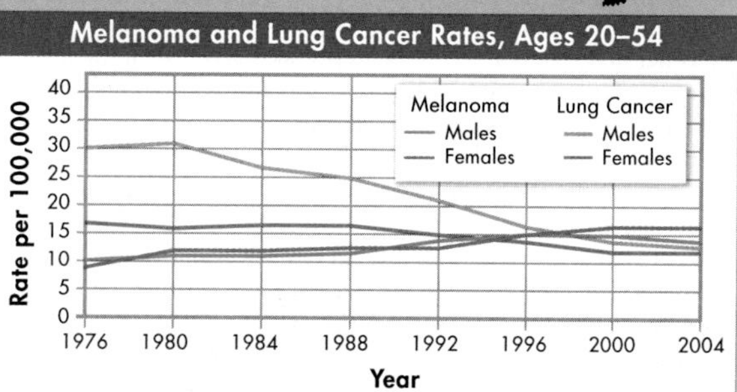

1. Interpret Graphs Describe the trend shown in this graph for the incidence of lung cancer and melanoma from 1976 to 2004.

2. Infer In what year does the rate of melanoma surpass the rate of lung cancer in men? In women?

3. Predict The data are only for a specific age group. If you were to look at similar data for the whole population, how do you think the graph would differ? Explain.

Skin Problems

What are some problems that affect the skin?

More than any other organ, the skin is constantly bombarded by internal and external factors that affect its health. **The skin's constant interaction with the environment can lead to problems of varying degrees of severity. Such problems include acne, hives, and skin cancer.**

Acne Acne develops when sebum and dead skin cells form plugs in hair follicles. Bacteria are often trapped in the plug, which leads to infection and inflammation. Up to 85 percent of people experience acne to some degree during adolescence and young adulthood. One hypothesis about acne suggests that high hormone levels during puberty lead to increased sebum production. There are many treatments for acne that can be purchased over the counter. But if the acne is severe and scarring is likely, a dermatologist—a doctor who specializes in skin care—should be consulted.

Hives Allergic reactions to food or medicine often display themselves as red welts commonly called hives. When the body experiences an allergic reaction, a chemical called histamine may be released. Histamine causes small blood vessels to widen. Fluid can ooze from the vessels into surrounding tissues, which causes the swelling that leads to hives.

Search Lesson 32.3  • Data Analysis

PURPOSE Students will examine and interpret data to identify trends in melanoma and lung cancer rates.

PLANNING Remind students that line graphs can be used to show how a variable changes over time. In this case, information is presented about two types of cancer. The data are further subdivided by gender. Explain to students that the labels, title, and key will allow them to make sense of the information presented in the graph.

ANSWERS

1. Over this time period, the incidence of lung cancer has decreased while the incidence of melanoma has increased.
2. males: approximately 1998; females: approximately 1995
3. Answers will vary. Students should take into account that the incidence of lung cancer and melanoma increases with age.

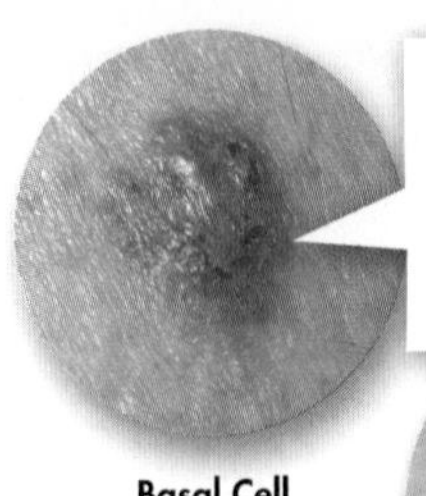

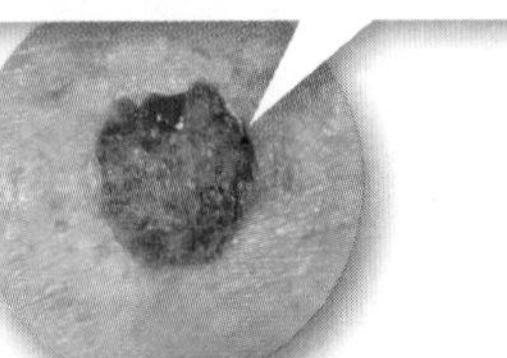

Basal cell carcinoma and squamous cell carcinoma are two of the most common types of skin cancer. Both types rarely spread to other parts of the body, but early treatment is important to prevent tissue damage.
Squamous Cell Carcinoma

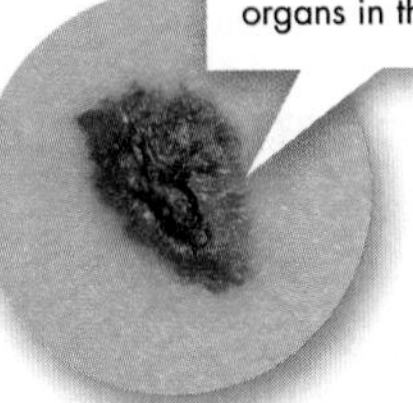

Melanomas are cancers that develop from melanocytes. Without early treatment, the cancer spreads to other organs in the body.
Melanoma

FIGURE 32–14 Skin Cancer Early detection is important in treating skin cancer. Signs of skin cancer may include a sore that does not heal or a sudden change in a mole's appearance. You should also see a doctor if you notice a new mole that is larger than 6 mm, has irregular borders, or is an odd color.

Skin Cancer Excessive exposure to the ultraviolet radiation in sunlight and artificial radiation from tanning beds can produce skin cancer, an abnormal growth of cells in the skin. **Figure 32–14** shows examples of the three most common types of skin cancer, including melanoma, the most dangerous form. Over 60,000 people are diagnosed with melanoma every year in the United States, and as many as 8000 people die from it.

You can help protect yourself from this dangerous disease by avoiding tanning salons and wearing a hat, sunglasses, and protective clothing whenever you plan to spend time outside. In addition, you should always use a sunscreen that protects against both UV-A rays and UV-B rays and that has a sun protection factor (SPF) of at least 15.

In Your Notebook *Summarize the steps you can take to protect your skin from sun damage.*

32.3 Assessment

Review Key Concepts

1. a. Review List the functions of the integumentary system.
   b. Classify What organs and tissues make up the integumentary system?
2. a. Review What structures are found in the epidermis? What structures are found in the dermis?
   b. Apply Concepts Explain two ways that the skin can help remove excess heat from the body.
3. a. Review What are some ways to reduce your risk of developing skin cancer?
   b. Sequence Explain the events that lead to acne.

Apply the Big idea

Structure and Function

4. Compare and contrast the structure and function of the dermal tissue in plants discussed in Chapter 23 with the structures in human skin. *Hint:* You may wish to organize your ideas in a Venn diagram.

BIOLOGY.com Search Lesson 32.3  GO • Self-Test • Lesson Assessment

LESSON 32.3

Assess and Remediate

EVALUATE UNDERSTANDING

Call on students to give a brief explanation of why the integumentary system is essential to the body. Students' responses should mention at least one function of the integumentary system. Then, have them complete the 32.3 Assessment.

REMEDIATION SUGGESTION

L1 **Struggling Students** If students have difficulty answering **Question 2b,** have them work with a partner to review how the structure of the skin helps it respond to changes in body temperature. Suggest partners take notes on their discussions.

BIOLOGY.com Students can check their understanding of lesson concepts with the **Self-Test** assessment. They can then take an online version of the **Lesson Assessment.**

Answers

IN YOUR NOTEBOOK Students should note that they can protect their skin from sun damage by avoiding tanning salons and by wearing sunscreen, sunglasses, and protective clothing when they are outside.

Assessment Answers

1a. protection, body temperature regulation, excretion, information gathering, vitamin D production

1b. skin, hair, nails, and glands

2a. The epidermis contains several types of cells, including differentiated skin cells, stem cells, and melanocytes, which produce melanin. The dermis contains blood vessels, nerve endings, glands, sensory receptors, smooth muscles, sebaceous glands, and hair follicles.

2b. Excess heat is removed from the body when the skin releases sweat or when blood vessels in the skin widen, bringing heat from the body's core to the skin.

3a. The risk of skin cancer can be reduced by avoiding tanning salons and by wearing sunscreen, sunglasses, and protective clothing while outdoors.

3b. First, sebum and dead skin cells form plugs in hair follicles. Then, bacteria cause infection and inflammation in the plugged follicle.

4. Big idea Some of the characteristics students may want to compare are: the outer waterproof coverings of plants and skin, the roles of guard cells and sweat and oil glands, and how trichomes are similar to hair and nails.

CHAPTER LAB

Pre-Lab

Introduce students to the concepts they will explore in the chapter lab by assigning the Pre-Lab questions.

Lab

Tell students they will perform the chapter lab *Comparing Limbs* described in **Lab Manual A.**

 **Struggling Students** A simpler version of the chapter lab is provided in **Lab Manual B.**

SAFETY

Students should handle the scissors with care. Make sure students are wearing the proper protective equipment. When the lab is finished, remind students to properly dispose of the chicken wing and wash their hands and lab bench thoroughly.

BIOLOGY.com Look online for **Editable Lab Worksheets.**

For corresponding pre-lab in the **Foundation Edition**, see page 778.

IN INDIANA ACADEMIC STANDARDS

For the full text of all standards, see the Course Overview in the front matter of this book.

Skills Lab — GUIDED INQUIRY

 NoS.7 Develop explanatory models.

Pre-Lab: Comparing Limbs

Problem How is the structure of skeletal muscles and bones related to the functions of these body parts?

Materials disposable plastic gloves, chicken wing, disposable dissection tray, dissecting scissors, forceps, colored pencils or markers

Skills Focus Observe, Infer, Compare and Contrast

Connect to the Big idea The structure of your bones reflects the different functions of your skeleton. For example, your bones must be strong enough to support your body and protect internal organs. Your bones must also be rigid so that they provide a system of levers on which skeletal muscles can act.

Skeletal muscles have a structure that enables them to move bones around fixed points called joints. In skeletal muscles, the cells are long and narrow, which is why these cells are also called muscle fibers. When muscle fibers contract, they pull on the bone to which a muscle is attached. This force causes the bone to move in the direction of the contraction.

In this lab, you will observe and compare the structure and function of a human arm and leg. You will also compare the arm with a chicken wing.

Background Questions

a. Review What motion does a hinge joint allow? What motion does a pivot joint allow? Which of these joints are found in your elbows and knees?

b. Review What role does cartilage play in freely movable joints?

c. Explain How is it possible for bones to move in more than one direction around a joint?

d. Compare and Contrast How are a ligament and a tendon similar? How are they different?

Pre-Lab Questions

1. Observe How will you observe the structure and function of your elbow and knee joints?
2. Relate Cause and Effect Why is it important to wear goggles and disposable gloves while examining the chicken wing?
3. Predict Will the arrangement of bones and muscles in a chicken wing be similar to the arrangement in a human arm? Why or why not?

BIOLOGY.com Search Chapter 32 GO

Visit Chapter 32 online to test yourself on chapter content and to find activities to help you learn.

Untamed Science Video Hold onto your seats as the Untamed Science crew whisks you to NASA to learn about the effect space travel has on an astronaut's bones.

Data Analysis Collect and analyze skin cancer data, then propose some conclusions based on this data.

Tutor Tube Watch an analogy to help you learn the sliding-filament model of muscle contraction.

Art Review Review your understanding of the structures of the skin.

InterActive Art Watch how the various joints in the body move.

Art in Motion Watch the process of muscle contraction.

Visual Analogy How is the skeleton like the framework of a house?

Pre-Lab Answers

BACKGROUND QUESTIONS

a. A hinge joint allows back-and-forth motion. A pivot allows a bone to rotate, or turn, around another bone. Both the knee and elbow are hinge joints. The elbow is also a pivot joint.

b. Cartilage covers the surfaces where two bones meet and protects the bones from damage as they move against each other.

c. Most skeletal muscles work in opposing pairs. When one muscle in a pair contracts, the other muscle relaxes.

d. Both a ligament and a tendon are connective tissue. A ligament holds bones together in a joint. A tendon attaches a muscle to a bone.

PRE-LAB QUESTIONS

1. Sample answer: I will use diagrams to observe the structure of the elbow and knee joints. To observe function, I will feel each joint as I move my forearm and lower leg.
2. Raw chicken may contain Salmonella bacteria, which can cause an infection.
3. Students may predict that the arrangement will be similar because humans and chickens share a common vertebrate ancestor. Students may predict that the arrangement will be different because wings have a different function than do arms.

32 Study Guide

Big idea Structure and Function

The skeletal, muscular, and integumentary systems all form the structure of the human body. In addition, the three systems have many functions that contribute to homeostasis.

32.1 The Skeletal System

The skeleton supports the body, protects internal organs, assists movement, stores minerals, and is a site of blood cell formation.

Bones are a solid network of living cells and protein fibers that are surrounded by deposits of calcium salts.

Joints contain connective tissues that hold bones together. Joints permit bones to move without damaging each other.

axial skeleton (922)
appendicular skeleton (922)
Haversian canal (924)
bone marrow (924)
cartilage (924)
ossification (925)
osteoblast (925)
osteocyte (925)
osteoclast (925)
joint (926)
ligament (927)

32.2 The Muscular System

There are three different types of muscle tissue: skeletal, smooth, and cardiac.

During a muscle contraction, myosin filaments form cross-bridges with actin filaments. The cross-bridges then change shape, pulling the actin filaments toward the center of the sarcomere.

Skeletal muscles generate force and produce movement by pulling on body parts as they contract.

muscle fiber (929)
myofibril (930)
myosin (930)
actin (930)
sarcomere (930)
neuromuscular junction (931)
acetylcholine (931)
tendon (932)

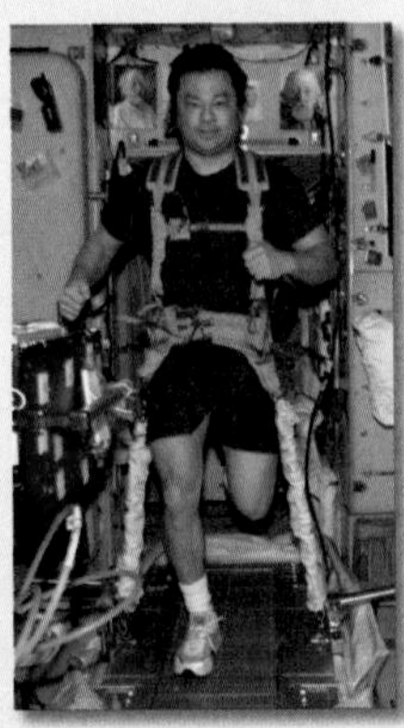

32.3 Skin—The Integumentary System

The integumentary system serves as a barrier against infection and injury, helps to regulate body temperature, removes wastes from the body, gathers information, and produces vitamin D.

Skin and its related structures—the hair, nails, and several types of glands—make up the integumentary system.

The skin's constant interaction with the environment can lead to problems of varying degrees of severity. Such problems include acne, hives, and skin cancer.

epidermis (936)
keratin (936)
melanocyte (936)
melanin (936)
dermis (937)
sebaceous gland (937)
hair follicle (937)

Think Visually Develop a concept map to show the relationships between the different systems discussed in this chapter.

 Search  Chapter 32  GO  • Match It • Chapter Assessment

Study Online

REVIEW AND ASSESSMENT RESOURCES

Editable Worksheets Pages of Study Workbooks A and B, Lab Manuals A and B, and the Assessment Resources Book are available online. These documents can be easily edited using a word-processing program.

Lesson Overview Have students reread the Lesson Overviews to help them study chapter concepts.

Vocabulary Review The *Flash Cards* and *Match It* provide an interactive way to review chapter vocabulary.

Chapter Assessment Have students take an online version of the Chapter 32 Assessment.

Standardized Test Prep Students can take an online version of the Standardized Test Prep. You will receive their scores along with ideas for remediation.

Diagnostic and Benchmark Tests Use these tests to monitor your students' progress and supply remediation.

Answers

THINK VISUALLY

Students' concept maps should show the relationships between the skeletal, muscular, and integumentary systems.

UbD Performance Tasks

SUMMATIVE TASK Have each student produce a picture book that describes the structures and functions of the skeletal, muscular, and integumentary systems. Tell students that their books should include accurate and detailed information that can be understood by children in grades 1–3. To help students write the book, list the following prompts on the board. Tell students that readers should be able to answer these questions when they are finished reading the book.

- What parts make up these systems?
- What is the function of each part?
- How do the parts work together?

TRANSFER TASK Ask students to imagine that they have been assigned a one-mile run as part of a physical education program. Unfortunately, it is a hot day, and they must complete their run on an outdoor track. Have students write a paragraph describing how their skeletal, muscular, and integumentary systems are each involved in helping their body meet the demands of the one-mile run. Then, have students write a second paragraph explaining short- and long-term actions they can take to protect and enhance the health of these three body systems before and during the run.

Lesson 32.1

UNDERSTAND KEY CONCEPTS

1. c **2.** b **3.** a

4. compact bone, spongy bone, cartilage, ligaments, periosteum, yellow and red bone marrow

5. Spongy bone adds strength but very little mass at the point on the bone at which force is applied.

6. Students' diagrams should include spongy bone, compact bone, the periosteum, bone marrow, a Haversian canal, and blood vessels.

7. Ball-and-socket joints allow for the most range of motion.

THINK CRITICALLY

8. Choice *a* shows signs of osteoporosis because the vertebra appears to have lost bone density.

9. The disks of cartilage between the bones of the spinal column cushion and protect the bones of the spinal column.

10. Oxygen and nutrients help an injured tissue heal, so an injured ligament will take longer to heal than tissues that have more blood vessels.

11. Sample answers: The elbow is a pivot joint; the elbow is a freely movable joint; cartilage covers the surface where the bones meet at the elbow.

Lesson 32.2

UNDERSTAND KEY CONCEPTS

12. d **13.** b **14.** d

15. Skeletal muscles control voluntary movements; smooth muscles move food through the digestive tract, control blood flow, and decrease the size of the pupils; cardiac muscle causes the heart to contract and pump blood.

16. One end of the myosin filament forms a cross-bridge with the actin filament. Using energy supplied by ATP, the cross-bridge changes shape, pulling the actin filament along. The cross-bridge then detaches from the actin filament, snaps back to its original shape, and binds to another site on the actin filament.

17. The release of acetylcholine from a motor neuron produces an impulse in the cell membrane of the muscle cell, which causes the release of calcium ions that affect regulatory proteins and allow actin and myosin to interact.

18. Individual muscles can pull bones in only one direction by contracting. By working in opposing pairs, muscles allow movement in more than one direction around a joint.

19. The muscle cells of slow-twitch fibers contain many more mitochondria than the cells of fast-twitch fibers. This difference means that slow-twitch fibers derive their energy through aerobic respiration and can work for long periods of time, while fast-twitch muscles function best for short bursts of activity.

THINK CRITICALLY

20. Bacteria that prevent the release of acetylcholine will prevent the production of impulses in the cell membranes of muscle fibers. Without these impulses, calcium ions will not be released within the fibers and myosin will not be able to form cross-bridges to bind to actin. Muscles, including those that control swallowing and breathing, will not be able to contract.

21. Sample answer: A decrease in appetite and feeling constant or chronic muscle soreness are two adverse effects of over-exercising.

32 Assessment

IN The numbers following the questions refer to Indiana's Academic Standards for Biology I.

32.1 The Skeletal System

Understand Key Concepts

1. The network of tubes that runs through compact bone is called the
- **a.** periosteum.
- **b.** joint.
- **c.** Haversian canals.
- **d.** marrow.

2. What occurs during ossification?
- **a.** Bones lose minerals and mass.
- **b.** Cartilage is replaced by bone.
- **c.** Vitamin D is synthesized.
- **d.** Bones fracture more easily.

3. Small sacs of synovial fluid that help reduce friction between the bones of a joint are called
- **a.** bursae.
- **b.** ligaments.
- **c.** tendons.
- **d.** cartilage.

4. What types of tissues are found in the skeletal system?

5. What is the advantage of spongy bone tissue in the ends of long bones?

6. Draw a diagram of a long bone and label the structures.

7. Which type of freely movable joint allows for the most range of motion?

Think Critically

8. **Interpret Visuals** Which vertebra do you think shows signs of osteoporosis, choice *a* or choice *b*? Explain.

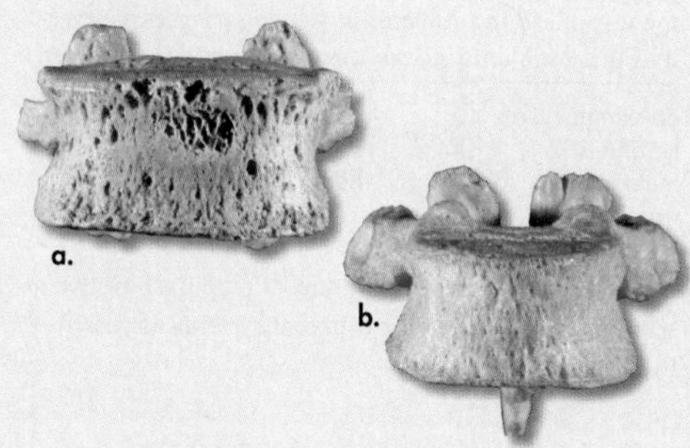

9. **Infer** Disks of rubbery cartilage are found between the individual bones in the spinal column. What function do you think these disks serve?

10. **Predict** Blood vessels bring oxygen and nutrients to all parts of the body. Ligaments contain fewer blood vessels than some other kinds of tissues contain. How might this situation affect the rate of healing in injured ligaments? Explain.

11. **Use Models** Suppose you want to build a robotic arm that works the way the human elbow works. Describe or sketch three facts about the elbow that you could use in your planning. NoS.6

32.2 The Muscular System

Understand Key Concepts

12. In which part of the body would you find striated muscle tissue with relatively small cells that have one or two nuclei?
- **a.** thigh
- **b.** stomach
- **c.** blood vessels
- **d.** heart

13. Two proteins that are involved in the contraction of muscle are
- **a.** sarcomere and myofibril.
- **b.** actin and myosin.
- **c.** periosteum and cartilage.
- **d.** ATP and acetylcholine.

14. The point of contact between a motor neuron and a skeletal muscle cell is called a
- **a.** cross-bridge site.
- **b.** gap junction.
- **c.** sarcomere.
- **d.** neuromuscular junction.

15. Describe the primary function of each of the three types of muscle tissue.

16. Use the sliding-filament model to describe how skeletal muscles work.

17. Describe how the release of acetylcholine from a motor neuron affects a muscle cell.

18. Explain this statement: "Most skeletal muscles work in opposing pairs."

19. What is one difference between the structure of fast-twitch and slow-twitch muscle fibers? How does this difference relate to their functions?

Think Critically

20. **Relate Cause and Effect** Certain bacteria produce a toxin that prevents the release of acetylcholine from the motor neurons. Explain why this can result in a fatal loss of muscle movement.
21. **Apply Concepts** Although exercising can increase your strength and endurance, over-exercising can have adverse effects on the body. Use resources in the library or on the Internet to find out what these adverse effects are. Summarize your findings in a brief report.

32.3 Skin—The Integumentary System

Understand Key Concepts

22. The outer layer of skin is called the
    a. dermis.
    b. keratin.
    c. epidermis.
    d. melanin.
23. Which structure releases a secretion that contributes to the formation of acne?

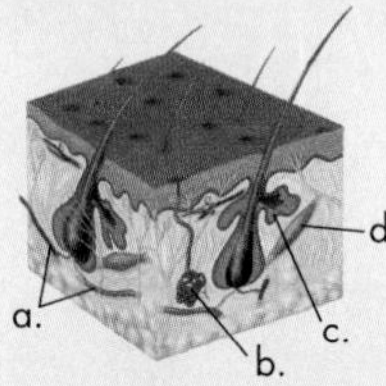

24. Where are new skin cells produced to replace old cells that have been shed?
    a. in the outer layer of the epidermis
    b. in the inner layer of the epidermis
    c. in the dermis
    d. in the sebaceous glands
25. Describe three ways the integumentary system performs the function of protection.
26. Compare the structures of the inner and outer layers of the skin.
27. Describe two ways the skin helps to maintain homeostasis.
28. How do fingernails and toenails grow?

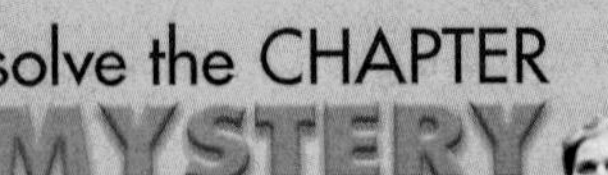

THE DEMISE OF A DISEASE

The search for the cause and a cure for rickets revealed two findings. Both cod liver oil and exposure to ultraviolet light could prevent and cure rickets.

The first finding indicated that cod liver oil contains a nutrient involved in bone health. Starting in the 1930s, many parents in the United States—including the parents of one of this textbook's authors—gave their children a daily dose of bitter cod liver oil.

The second finding indicated that exposure to the sun influences bone health. This explained why children in colder climates were more susceptible to rickets. They had little sun exposure during cold, dark winter months.

But scientists still wondered, what was the connection between cod liver oil and ultraviolet light? How could both treatments result in the same positive outcome?

Through the work of many scientists, we now know that vitamin D is the responsible nutrient in cod liver oil. And, when exposed to ultraviolet light, the skin makes compounds that can be converted to vitamin D. We've also learned that vitamin D helps the body absorb calcium and phosphorus from the digestive system.

Children today are spared cod liver oil doses because vitamin D is added to milk. Rickets is now a rare disease in the United States.

1. **Explain** Why were children in southern cities less likely to develop rickets?
2. **Compare and Contrast** Describe the structure of the bones of a healthy child in comparison to the bones of a child who developed rickets.
3. **Connect to the Big idea** Explain how vitamin D is related to the structure and function of the three systems you learned about in this chapter.

ASSESSMENT

After students have read through the chapter mystery, discuss the impact of the skeletal, muscular, and integumentary systems on the health and function of the body as a whole.

Ask Why do individuals who do not eat dairy products need to be concerned about their vitamin D consumption? *(Milk is enriched with vitamin D. Individuals who do not consume milk need to make sure they get enough vitamin D from other sources.)*

Ask How does rickets affect the skeletal system's ability to protect the internal organs of the body? *(Rickets prevents bones from growing strong and rigid, so it has a negative impact on the skeletal system's ability to protect the internal organs.)*

Ask How do the effects of rickets demonstrate the interrelationship of human body systems? *(Sample answer: If the integumentary system is unable to perform its function of producing vitamin D, it impacts the structure and the function of the skeletal system.)*

CHAPTER MYSTERY ANSWERS

1. Children in southern cities were less likely to develop rickets because exposure to sunlight allows the body to make compounds that can be converted to vitamin D.
2. The bones of a healthy child are stronger and more rigid than the soft, weak bones of a child with rickets.
3. Big idea Vitamin D is required for the body to absorb calcium. The skeletal system requires calcium for the development and maintenance of healthy bones. The muscular system requires calcium for muscle contractions to occur. With exposure to ultraviolet radiation, the skin makes vitamin D.

To learn about the impact of space travel on bones, have students watch the Untamed Science crew at NASA in **Untamed Science: Skeletons in Space.**

Lesson 32.3

UNDERSTAND KEY CONCEPTS

22.  c **23.** 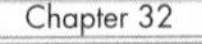 c **24.**  b

25. The integumentary system protects the body by serving as a barrier against infection and injury, by preventing the body from drying out, and by providing protection against ultraviolet radiation from the sun.

26. The outer layer contains sweat pores and cells that produce melanin. The inner layer contains hair follicles, blood vessels, sensory receptors, sweat glands, and oil glands.

27. Sample answer: The skin helps the body maintain homeostasis by helping to regulate body temperature and getting rid of wastes from the blood.

28. Nails grow from a nail root, an area of rapidly dividing cells. Cells of the nail root fill with keratin and produce tough, platelike nails at the tips of fingers and toes.

ASSESSMENT

THINK CRITICALLY

29. People often get calluses on their feet because the skin is repeatedly rubbed by their shoes.

30. This change causes the skin to become thinner.

31. The chemical that is not produced in albinism is melanin, a brown pigment that produces skin color.

Connecting Concepts

USE SCIENCE GRAPHICS

32. The hand on the left, which has the largest clear areas between the shaft and ends of the bones, belongs to the youngest person.

WRITE ABOUT SCIENCE

33. Severe burns can inhibit the skin's functions, including helping to maintain a constant body temperature and eliminating wastes. Burns over a large area also prevent the skin from effectively protecting large areas of the body from infection.

34. The skeletal, muscular, and integumentary systems can be compared to the structures of a building. For example, the girders, which form the structure of a building and provide support, are similar to the skeletal system. Girders differ from the skeletal system in that they do not store needed substances in the way that the skeleton stores minerals. The muscular system can be compared to the drywall of the building, because it connects to the girders in the way that muscles connect to bones. However, muscles function in movement while drywall is stationary. The integumentary system can be compared to the outer walls of a building, which keep the elements out. Walls and the skin differ because the skin gathers information about the outside environment using sensory receptors, but walls do not gather information about the outside environment.

35. Big idea Sample answer: The forelimbs of animals that climb, such as monkeys, can be compared to the forelimbs of animals that walk on four legs, such as horses. The forelimbs of monkeys have joints that allow a wider range of movement than those of animals that do not climb.

Think Critically

29. Infer A skin callus is a thickening of the epidermis caused by repeated rubbing. Why do people often get calluses on their feet?

30. Predict As people age, the rate at which new skin cells are produced slows down, but the rate at which skin cells are shed does not. What effect do you think this has on a person's skin?

31. Relate Cause and Effect People with albinism have little pigment in their skin, hair, or eyes. Albinism is usually a genetically recessive disease that inhibits cells from producing a particular chemical. What chemical do you think is lacking in people with albinism? Explain.

Connecting Concepts

Use Science Graphics NoS.3

32. Infer Because cartilage does not appear on X-ray film, it is seen as a clear area between the shaft and the ends of bones. Examine the X-rays. Which hand belongs to the youngest person? Explain.

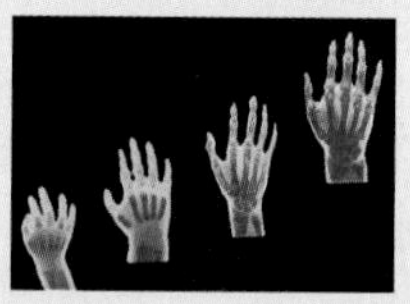

Write About Science NoS.3

33. Explanation Severe burns of large areas of the skin can be a life-threatening injury. Develop a paragraph that explains the greatest risks these burn patients face.

34. Compare and Contrast Support and movement are the basic functions of the skeletal, muscular, and integumentary systems. In a paragraph, compare these three body systems with similar structures of a building. For example, which body system has the same function as the girders of a building? Of the walls? How are they similar? How are they different? (*Hint:* To get started, you may want to list shared characteristics.)

35. Assess the Big idea Recall what you learned about the bones of fishes, amphibians, reptiles, birds, and mammals. Compare examples of specific skeletal parts, such as backbones or forelimbs. Relate the bones to the way each animal moves.

Analyzing Data

IN NoS.3

The UV (ultraviolet) index is a rating system developed by the Environmental Protection Agency. The goal of the index is to inform the public about the level of UV radiation to expect on a given day. Higher numbers indicate higher levels of UV radiation. The table shows the average UV indexes for various cities in the United States.

Average UV Index Values, Selected Locations

Location	Average UV Index Value	
	Winter	Summer
Anchorage, Alaska	< 1	3–4
Atlanta, Georgia	2	8
Honolulu, Hawaii	6	11–12
Miami, Florida	4	10–11
New York, New York	1–2	6–7
Phoenix, Arizona	3	10
Portland, Oregon	1	5–6
St. Louis, Missouri	1–2	7–8

36. Interpret Data A person visiting which of the following cities would need to be the most careful about his or her level of sun exposure?
- **a.** Honolulu in winter
- **b.** Anchorage in summer
- **c.** Atlanta in winter
- **d.** St. Louis in summer

37. Form a Hypothesis Develop a hypothesis that could explain the relationship between geography and average UV index values.

Analyzing Data

PURPOSE Students will analyze data to understand and interpret the UV index.

PLANNING If maps are available in the classroom, have students work together to locate each of the listed cities on a map. Then, have students review the information from the chapter about the role of UV radiation in the development of skin cancer. Ask students to explain how the UV index could be used by individuals to help maintain the health of their skin.

ANSWERS

36. d

37. Sample answer: The closer a city is to the equator, the higher its UV index.

Standardized Test Practice for Indiana

Multiple Choice

1. What determines differences in skin color among individuals?
   A number of melanocytes
   B amount of melanin produced by each melanocyte
   C amount of keratin in the skin
   D amount of sebum produced

2. Smooth muscle is found in the
   A walls of blood vessels.
   B heart.
   C neuromuscular junctions.
   D joints.

3. All of the following are important roles of the skeletal system EXCEPT
   A protection of internal organs.
   B facilitation of movement.
   C storage of mineral reserves.
   D regulation of body temperature.

4. Which of the following supplies the energy required for muscle contractions?
   A myosin
   B ATP
   C acetylcholine
   D actin

5. The tough layer of connective tissue surrounding each bone is called
   A tendon.
   B ligament.
   C periosteum.
   D cartilage.

6. Joints that allow one bone to rotate around another are
   A gliding joints.
   B ball-and-socket joints.
   C hinge joints.
   D pivot joints.

7. Which of the following is NOT found in skin tissue?
   A keratin
   B collagen
   C marrow
   D melanin

8. What is a function of sebum?
   A It moistens the hair and skin.
   B It gives skin its color.
   C It insulates the body.
   D It makes nails and hair rigid.

Questions 9–10

As people age, the mineral content of their bone decreases. People who fail to build enough bone in adolescence and young adulthood or who lose bone at a faster than normal rate are at risk for developing osteoporosis. The graph below shows typical bone mass of men and women through most of the life span.

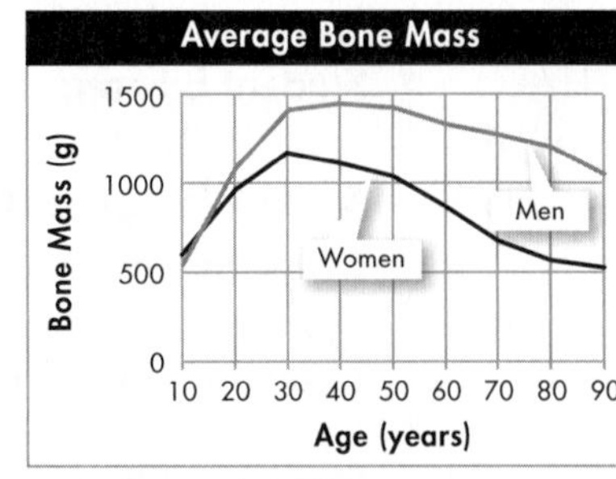

9. Between which ages do both men and women gain bone mass at the highest rate?
   A 10–20 years
   B 20–30 years
   C 30–40 years
   D 50–60 years NoS.3

10. A valid conclusion that can be drawn from this graph is that, on average,
    A women lose more bone mass as they age than men do.
    B men lose more bone mass as they age than women do.
    C women and men lose the same bone mass as they age.
    D men continue to gain bone mass as they age. NoS.3

Open-Ended Response

11. Doctors recommend that women eat calcium-rich foods and get plenty of exercise during adolescence and early adulthood. How could this help prevent osteoporosis later in life?

If You Have Trouble With . . .

Question	1	2	3	4	5	6	7	8	9	10	11
See Lesson	32.3	32.2	32.1	32.2	32.1	32.1	32.3	32.3	32.1	32.1	32.1

Test-Taking Tip

READ ALL THE ANSWER CHOICES

Remind students that when they are evaluating multiple-choice answers, they should carefully read all of the choices, even when the first choice appears to be correct. Explain that evaluating and comparing all of the answer choices before selecting one can make it more likely that they will select the best choice.

Answers

1. B
2. A
3. D
4. B
5. C
6. D
7. C
8. A
9. A
10. A
11. Eating calcium-rich foods and exercising during adolescence and early adulthood maximizes bone mass. Having a high bone mass early in life can help prevent or minimize health problems related to the loss of bone mass later in life.

Circulatory and Respiratory Systems

Chapter Contents	IN	Time	Core Resources
Chapter Preview			**Student Edition,** pp. 946–947 **Chapter Mystery,** p. 947
33.1 The Circulatory System Functions of the Circulatory System • The Heart • Blood Vessels	NoS.6	1½ periods ¾ block	**Student Edition,** pp. 948–953 Inquiry 33.1 Quick Lab, p. 951 L2 **Study Workbook A** 33.1 Worksheets L2 Biology.com *Visual Analogy:* A City's Transportation System • *Art in Motion:* Heartbeat **Assessment Resources Book** Visual Quizzes L2
33.2 Blood and the Lymphatic System Blood • The Lymphatic System • Circulatory System Diseases • Understanding Circulatory Disease • *Technology & Biology: Testing for Heart Disease*	NoS.3, B.1.2	1 period ½ block	**Student Edition,** pp. 954–962 Inquiry 33.2 Analyzing Data, p. 956 L2 **Study Workbook A** 33.2 Worksheets L2 Biology.com 33.2 Self-Test • 33.2 Lesson Assessment
33.3 The Respiratory System Structures of the Respiratory System • Gas Exchange and Transport • Breathing • Smoking and the Respiratory System		1½ periods ¾ block	**Student Edition,** pp. 963–969 Inquiry 33.3 Quick Lab, p. 964 L2 **Study Workbook A** 33.3 Worksheets L2 Biology.com *Art Review:* The Respiratory System • *InterActive Art:* Breathing • *Tutor Tube:* The Role of the Diaphragm in Respiration **Assessment Resources Book** Visual Quiz L2
Chapter Pre-Lab	NoS.5	1 period ½ block	**Student Edition,** p. 970 L2 **Lab Manual A** *Tidal Volume and Vital Capacity* L2

Differentiated Instruction Tools

Study Workbook B includes worksheets with lesson-level differentiated instruction support and explanations of differentiated instruction teaching strategies.

Lab Manual B includes skills labs, simplified chapter labs, and hands-on activities.

ELL Handbook explains ways to make *Biology* more accessible to ELL students.

Spanish Study Workbook is a Spanish translation of Study Workbook A.

Multilingual Glossary is the glossary translated into ten languages.

Differentiated Instruction Key

- L1 Special Needs or Struggling Students
- ELL English Language Learners
- LPR Less Proficient Readers
- L2 On-Level Students
- L3 Advanced Students

Additional Resources

Biology.com Untamed Science Video • Vocabulary Flash Cards

Study Workbook B 33.1 Worksheets L1 ELL LPR
Spanish Study Workbook 33.1 Worksheets ELL
Biology.com *Data Analysis:* Electrocardiography • 33.1 Lesson Overview • 33.1 Lesson Notes • 33.1 Self-Test • 33.1 Lesson Assessment

Study Workbook B 33.2 Worksheets L1 ELL LPR
Spanish Study Workbook 33.2 Worksheets ELL
Biology.com 33.2 Lesson Overview • 33.2 Lesson Notes

Study Workbook B 33.3 Worksheets L1 ELL LPR
Spanish Study Workbook 33.3 Worksheets ELL
Biology.com 33.3 Lesson Overview • 33.3 Lesson Notes • 33.3 Self-Test • 33.3 Lesson Assessment

Lab Manual B *Tidal Volume and Vital Capacity* • Data Analysis: *Blood Transfusions* • Hands-On Activity: *Why We Breathe* L1 ELL LPR

Chapter Review

Student Edition Study Guide, p. 971 L2
Study Workbook A Chapter 33 Vocabulary Review L2 • Chapter 33 Chapter Mystery/21st Century Skills Activity L2 L3
Transparencies, pp. 362–372 L1 ELL LPR L2
Biology.com Untamed Science Video • Editable Worksheets of Study Workbooks A and B and Lab Manuals A and B • Chapter 33 Flash Cards and Match It

Untamed Science DVD • Classroom Resources CD (includes lesson presentations and editable worksheets)

Chapter Assessment

Student Edition Assessment, pp. 972–975 L2
Study Workbook B Chapter 33 Chapter Review L1 ELL LPR • Chapter 33 Taking a Standardized Test L1 ELL LPR
Assessment Resources Book Chapter 33 Test A L2 • Chapter 33 Test B L1 ELL LPR
Biology.com Chapter 33 Assessment • Editable Worksheets of Chapter 33 Visual Quizzes and Chapter 33 Tests A and B

Exam*View Assessment Suite* • Classroom Resources CD (includes lesson presentations and editable worksheets)

Time: 1 period, 1/2 block

Pressed for Time?

Preview the Chapter Read the Key Questions for Lesson 33.1 and preview the vocabulary for Lesson 33.3.

Cover the Chapter Quickly In Lesson 33.1, have students read *Functions of the Circulatory System,* the Heart Structure and Circulation sections of *The Heart,* and Arteries, Capillaries, and Veins sections of *Blood Vessels.* Discuss Figures 33–2 and 33–5. Assign *Structures of the Respiratory System* and *Breathing* in Lesson 33.3.

Assess Assign questions 1, 2a, and 3a in the 33.1 Assessment, questions 1 and 3 in the 33.3 Assessment, and questions 1–4, 9, 11, 12, and 23–26 in the Chapter 33 Assessment.

CHAPTER 33

Connect to the Big Idea

Use the photograph of the swimmers to start a discussion on the human circulatory and respiratory systems. Ask students how they would prepare to swim underwater. *(Sample answers: I would take a deep breath; I would hold my breath.)* Challenge students to explain why people can stay underwater only for a limited amount of time. *(Students may describe "running out of air" after a certain amount of time.)* Then, ask students to identify some of the structures and systems involved in taking in oxygen and getting oxygen to the body's tissues. Lead students to anticipate the answer to the question, **How do the structures of the circulatory and respiratory systems allow for their close functional relationship?**

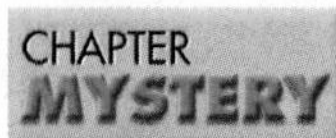

Have students read over the Chapter Mystery. Then, discuss the impact that clogged heart vessels would have on the circulatory system and the entire body. Challenge them to relate damage to circulatory system structures with impaired functioning of the system.

BIOLOGY.com Have students preview the chapter vocabulary terms using the **Flash Cards.**

33 Circulatory and Respiratory Systems

Big idea Structure and Function

Q: How do the structures of the circulatory and respiratory systems allow for their close functional relationship?

Usually, we are not conscious of breathing, but we can control it during activities, such as swimming.

BIOLOGY.com Search Chapter 33 GO • Flash Cards

946

IN INDIANA ACADEMIC STANDARDS

For the full text of all standards, see the Course Overview in the front matter of this book.

Key standards: Chapter 33 covers key ideas from The Nature of Science and Standard 1: Cellular Chemistry, including **NoS.6** Use analogies and models and **B.1.2** Molecules and cellular processes.

UbD Understanding by Design

Chapter 33 describes the circulatory, lymphatic, and respiratory systems. The graphic organizer at the right shows how these topics are connected to the chapter Essential Question and Big Idea. Together, these ideas and questions help students build toward the Unit 8 Enduring Understanding that *the human body is a complex system. The coordinated functions of its many structures support life processes and maintain homeostasis.*

PERFORMANCE GOALS

Students will show understanding of Chapter 33 concepts by using and discussing the many complex diagrams in this chapter. They will also gather and analyze data on their own heart rates. At the end of the chapter, students will synthesize what they have learned by writing a script for a museum tour through a larger-than-life model of the circulatory, lymphatic, or respiratory system.

INDIANA ACADEMIC STANDARDS FOR SCIENCE

Nature of Science NoS.3, NoS.5, NoS.6, NoS.10, NoS.11; **Cellular Chemistry** B.1.2. See lessons for details.

CHAPTER MYSTERY

IN THE BLOOD

At the age of 60, John underwent surgery to reroute blood around blocked vessels in his heart. Since then, he has limited his fat intake and stuck to an exercise program. Still, today he is meeting with his doctor to talk about a new medication that would break up the fatty deposits re-forming in his heart's vessels.

Down the hall, 6-year-old Lila is seeing her doctor today, too. Her vessels are also clogged with fatty deposits, which means she is dangerously close to a heart attack, even at her young age. Both of these patients suffer from a genetic disease that affects a substance transported in blood. What is that disease? And why did it affect them at such different ages? As you read this chapter, look for clues to the identity of this genetic disease and the research that explains it. Then, solve the mystery.

Never Stop Exploring Your World. Finding the solution to the In the Blood mystery is just the beginning. Take a video field trip with the ecogeeks of Untamed Science to see where the mysteries of the circulatory system lead.

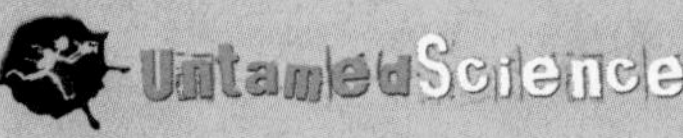

• Untamed Science Video • Chapter Mystery

Chapter 33
Big Idea: Structure and Function

Chapter 33 EQ: How do the structures of the circulatory and respiratory systems allow for their close functional relationship?

33.1 GQ: What structures transport substances throughout the human body?

33.2 GQ: What are the roles of blood and the lymphatic system in the body?

33.3 GQ: How are oxygen and carbon dioxide exchanged between humans and the environment?

CHAPTER 33

What's Online

BIOLOGY.com Extend your reach by using these and other digital assets offered at **Biology.com**.

CHAPTER MYSTERY
How could John and Lila have the same symptoms despite their very different ages and medical histories? Students can use clues to figure out the identity of this genetic disease.

UNTAMED SCIENCE VIDEO
Some like it cold! Students can take a video field trip that explores adaptations in animals that live in Earth's coldest environments.

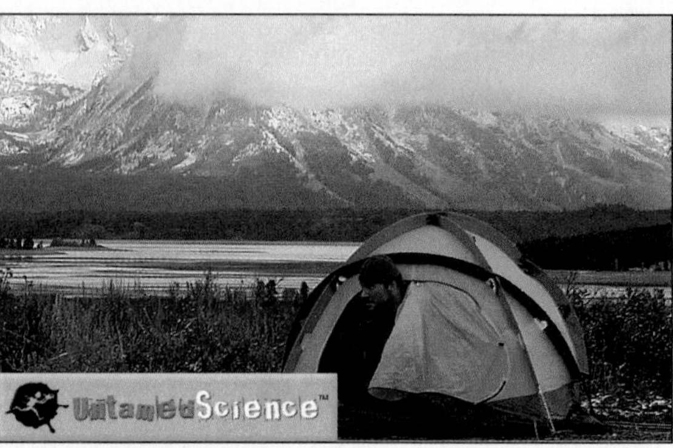

VISUAL ANALOGY
Explore ways in which the human circulatory system is similar to an urban transportation network.

ART IN MOTION
Have students use this animation to watch how blood flows through the heart.

DATA ANALYSIS
This activity allows students to use electrocardiography to diagnose heart conditions.

ART REVIEW
Use this activity to help students understand the structures of the respiratory system.

INTERACTIVE ART
Students can use this interactive activity to learn about breathing.

LESSON 33.1

Getting Started

Objectives

33.1.1 Identify the functions of the human circulatory system.

33.1.2 Describe the structure of the heart and explain how it pumps blood through the body.

33.1.3 Name three types of blood vessels in the circulatory system.

Student Resources

Study Workbooks A and B, 33.1 Worksheets

Spanish Study Workbook, 33.1 Worksheets

Lab Manual B, 33.1 Hands-On Activity Worksheet

Lesson Overview • Lesson Notes • Activities: Visual Analogy, Art in Motion, Data Analyis • Assessment: Self-Test, Lesson Assessment

For corresponding lesson in the **Foundation Edition,** see pages 786–789.

VISUAL ANALOGY

Have students use **Figure 33–1** to compare a transportation system to the circulatory system. They can further explore the analogy in **Visual Analogy: A City's Transportation System** on Biology.com.

Answers

FIGURE 33–1 A person who lives in a city needs goods and waste removal; a cell needs nutrients, oxygen, and waste removal.

IN INDIANA ACADEMIC STANDARDS

For the full text of all standards, see the Course Overview in the front matter of this book.

NoS.6 Use analogies and models (mathematical and physical) to simplify and represent systems that are difficult to understand or directly experience due to their size, time scale, or complexity, and recognize the limitations of analogies and models.

33.1 The Circulatory System

NoS.6 Use analogies and models.

Key Questions

What are the functions of the circulatory system?

How does the heart pump blood through the body?

What are three types of blood vessels?

Vocabulary

myocardium • atrium • ventricle • valve • pulmonary circulation • systemic circulation • pacemaker • artery • capillary • vein

Taking Notes

Preview Visuals Before you read, look at **Figure 33–3.** Make a list of questions about the illustration. As you read, write down the answers.

THINK ABOUT IT "I was about 47 when I collapsed one day at work. There are 22 minutes out of my life that I don't remember. I had gone into cardiac arrest." These are the words of a man who survived a heart attack. Fortunately he received prompt treatment and had successful heart surgery. He continued to live a fairly normal life. He even ran the Boston Marathon! But more than one-third of the 1.2 million Americans who suffer a heart attack each year die. This grim evidence shows that the heart and the circulatory system it powers are vital to life. Why is that so?

Functions of the Circulatory System

What are the functions of the circulatory system?

Some animals have so few cells that all of their cells are in direct contact with the environment. Diffusion and active transport across cell membranes supply the cells with oxygen and nutrients and remove waste products. The human body, however, contains millions of cells that are not in direct contact with the external environment. Because of this, humans need a circulatory system. **The circulatory system transports oxygen, nutrients, and other substances throughout the body, and removes wastes from tissues.**

People who live in large cities face a set of problems like those of the body's cells. City dwellers need food and goods that are produced elsewhere, and they need to get rid of their garbage and other wastes. People need to move around within the city. How are these needs met? By the city's transportation system—a network of streets, highways, and subway or train lines that deliver goods to the city and remove wastes from it. The human body's major transportation system is a closed circulatory system made up of a heart, blood vessels, and blood.

VISUAL ANALOGY

A CITY'S TRANSPORTATION SYSTEM

FIGURE 33–1 The human circulatory system is like the highways and streets of a large city. Use Analogies *Compare the needs of a person living in a large city with the needs of a cell in the body.*

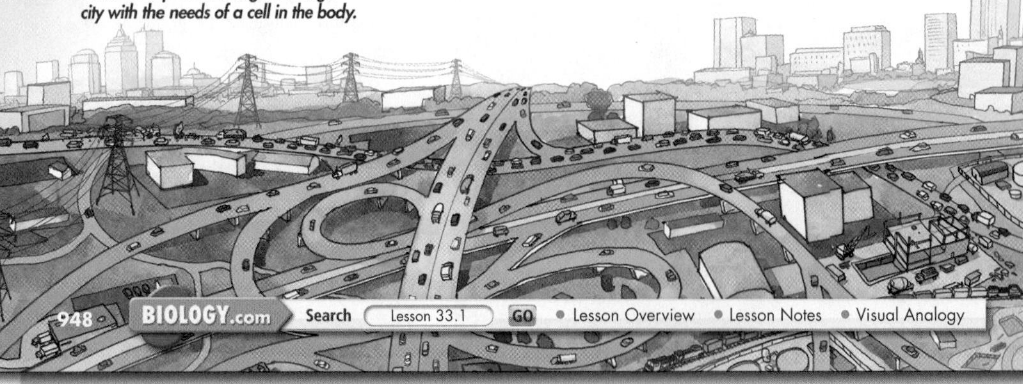

UbD Teach for Understanding

ENDURING UNDERSTANDING The human body is a complex system. The coordinated functions of its many structures support life processes and maintain homeostasis.

GUIDING QUESTION What structures transport substances throughout the human body?

EVIDENCE OF UNDERSTANDING *After completing the lesson, assign students the following assessment to show their understanding of the circulatory system.* Have students work in small groups to make a poster that describes the three types of blood vessels discussed in this lesson. Have each group present its completed poster to the class.

The Heart

How does the heart pump blood through the body?

Much of the time, you're probably not even aware of your heart at work. But when you exercise, you can feel your heart beating near the center of your chest.

Heart Structure Your heart, which is a hollow organ about the size of a clenched fist, is composed almost entirely of muscle. The muscles begin contracting before you are born and stop only when you die. In the walls of the heart, two thin layers of epithelial and connective tissue form a sandwich around a muscle layer called the **myocardium.** **Powerful contractions of the myocardium pump blood through the circulatory system.** An adult's heart contracts on average 72 times a minute, pumping about 70 milliliters of blood with each contraction.

As **Figure 33–2** shows, the heart is divided into four chambers. A wall called the septum separates the right side of the heart from the left side. The septum prevents oxygen-poor and oxygen-rich blood from mixing. On each side of the septum are an upper and lower chamber. Each upper chamber, or **atrium** (plural: atria), receives blood from the body. Each lower chamber, or **ventricle,** pumps blood out of the heart.

In Your Notebook *An Olympic pool contains about 2,000,000 liters of water. In one year, could an average heart pump enough blood to fill an Olympic pool? Explain your answer.*

BUILD Vocabulary

WORD ORIGINS The word *cardiac,* the prefix *cardio-,* and the suffix *-cardium* are all based on the Greek word *kardia,* which means "heart."

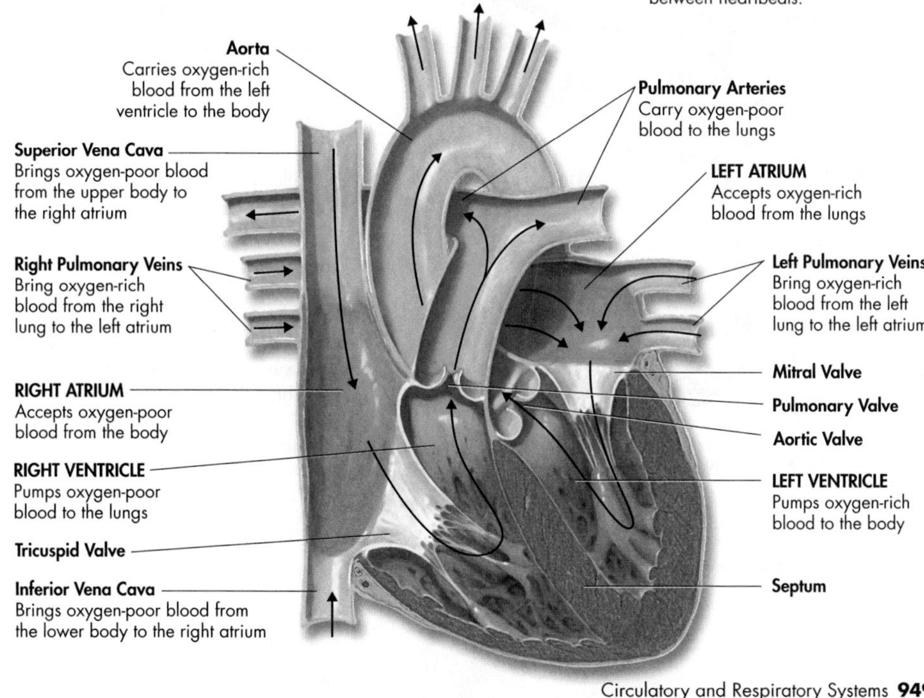

Aorta
Carries oxygen-rich blood from the left ventricle to the body
Superior Vena Cava
Brings oxygen-poor blood from the upper body to the right atrium
Right Pulmonary Veins
Bring oxygen-rich blood from the right lung to the left atrium
RIGHT ATRIUM
Accepts oxygen-poor blood from the body
RIGHT VENTRICLE
Pumps oxygen-poor blood to the lungs
Tricuspid Valve
Inferior Vena Cava
Brings oxygen-poor blood from the lower body to the right atrium
Pulmonary Arteries
Carry oxygen-poor blood to the lungs
LEFT ATRIUM
Accepts oxygen-rich blood from the lungs
Left Pulmonary Veins
Bring oxygen-rich blood from the left lung to the left atrium
Mitral Valve
Pulmonary Valve
Aortic Valve
LEFT VENTRICLE
Pumps oxygen-rich blood to the body
Septum

FIGURE 33–2 The Heart The human heart has four chambers: the right atrium, the right ventricle, the left atrium, and the left ventricle. Valves located between the atria and ventricles and between the ventricles and vessels leaving the heart prevent blood from flowing backward between heartbeats.

Teach

Build Study Skills

Have students read the information on the heart. Then, give students five minutes to complete a **Quick Write** describing the structure of the heart. Tell students that they should describe each of the four chambers of the heart and describe the blood found in each as oxygen-rich or oxygen-poor. Call on volunteers to share what they wrote.

Study Wkbks A/B, Appendix S11, Quick Write.

DIFFERENTIATED INSTRUCTION

LPR Less Proficient Readers Students who might have difficulty reading the text on this page can base their **Quick Writes** on **Figure 33–2.** Point out the four chambers of the heart in the diagram.

ELL Focus on ELL: Build Background

BEGINNING AND INTERMEDIATE SPEAKERS Build a **Word Wall** using the words necessary for beginning and intermediate speakers to understand the circulatory system. Title the word wall Circulatory System. Under the title, place all the lesson vocabulary terms and any additional terms English language learners must know to understand the lesson. For example, you might add the terms *transport, remove, heart, blood vessels, oxygen-poor, oxygen-rich.* Pronounce the terms for students, and help them find the terms in the lesson. Have students work in small groups to add visuals and definitions to the terms on the word wall.

Study Wkbks A/B, Appendix S17, Word Wall.

How Science Works

WILLIAM HARVEY'S CONTRIBUTION

One scientist is known above all others for his contributions to our understanding of the human circulatory system. That scientist is William Harvey, an English physician, whose 1628 book on the circulation of blood was a landmark publication. Up until Harvey's time, there were many misconceptions about blood and the circulatory system. For example, it was thought that blood formed in the liver, that blood moved very sluggishly if at all, and that the pulmonary and systemic blood were not connected. Harvey dissected cadavers and studied living patients to disprove many of these thoughts. He determined that the heart pumps blood through the body via arteries and that blood returns to the heart through veins. Harvey described how the valves in the heart and veins keep blood flowing in just one direction.

Answers

IN YOUR NOTEBOOK Yes, an average heart beating 72 times a minute, pumping 70 milliliters of blood with each contraction, will pump more than 2,600,000 liters of blood in a year. (70 mL/contraction × 72 contractions/min = 5040 mL/min; 5040 mL/min × 525,600 min/year = 2,649,024,000 mL, or 2,649,024 L)

Teach continued

Lead a Discussion

Use the following questions to discuss circulation.

Ask How is blood flowing through the heart different from the heart's own blood supply? *(When blood flows through the heart, it does not supply the cells of the heart muscle with oxygen and nutrients or remove wastes. The heart's own blood supply that comes from the coronary arteries provides heart muscle cells with oxygen and nutrients and removes cellular wastes.)*

Ask How is pulmonary circulation different from systemic circulation? *(Pulmonary circulation is the blood flow between the lungs and the heart; systemic circulation is blood flow between the heart and the body.)*

DIFFERENTIATED INSTRUCTION

L1 Struggling Students Have students use **Figure 33–3** to help them clarify the difference between pulmonary and systemic circulation. First, have students trace the black arrows in the diagram, which represent pulmonary circulation. Then, have them trace the white arrows in the diagram, which represent systemic circulation. Use the following questions to check students' comprehension.

Ask In pulmonary circulation, what organs does blood flow through? *(heart and lungs)*

Ask What happens to blood in the capillaries of the lungs? *(The blood absorbs oxygen and gives off carbon dioxide.)*

Ask What structures does blood flowing through the systemic pathway serve? *(the rest of the body)*

Students should explain that the coronary arteries are already narrow. Therefore, a disease that further narrows them would affect the heart's blood supply. Students can go online to **Biology.com** to gather their evidence.

Answers

FIGURE 33–3 Oxygen-rich blood leaves the lungs and returns to the heart.

IN YOUR NOTEBOOK Students' cycle diagrams should include both pulmonary and systemic circulation.

MYSTERY CLUE

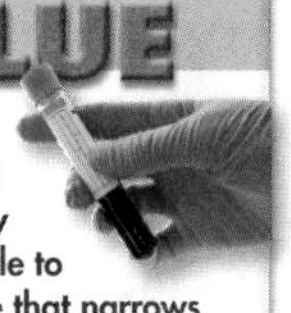

Why is the heart especially susceptible to a disease that narrows blood vessels?

Blood Flow Through the Heart Blood from the body enters the heart through the right atrium; blood from the lungs, through the left atrium. When the atria contract, blood flows into the ventricles. Flaps of connective tissue called **valves** are located between the atria and the ventricles. When blood moves from the atria into the ventricles, those valves open. When the ventricles contract, the valves close, preventing blood from flowing back into the atria. Valves are also located at the exits of each ventricle. This system of valves keeps blood moving through the heart in one direction, like traffic on a one-way street.

The Heart's Blood Supply Heart muscle needs a constant supply of oxygen and nutrients. Surprisingly, the heart gets very little oxygen and nutrients from the blood it pumps through its chambers. Instead, a pair of blood vessels called *coronary arteries,* which branch from the aorta and run through heart tissue, supply blood to the heart muscle. Coronary arteries and the vessels that branch from them are relatively narrow, considering the needs of the heart. If they are blocked, heart muscle cells run out of oxygen and could begin to die. This is what happens during a heart attack, which we discuss in Lesson 33.2.

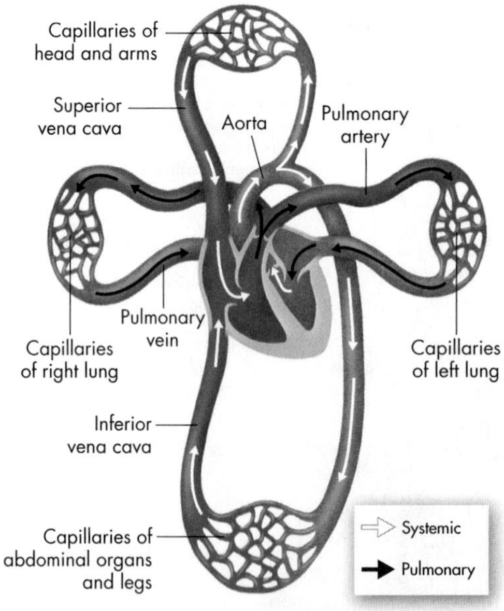

Capillaries of head and arms
Superior vena cava
Aorta
Pulmonary artery
Pulmonary vein
Capillaries of right lung
Capillaries of left lung
Inferior vena cava
Capillaries of abdominal organs and legs
Systemic
Pulmonary

FIGURE 33–3 Circulation Pathways The circulatory system is divided into two pathways. Pulmonary circulation carries blood between the heart and the lungs. Systemic circulation carries blood between the heart and the rest of the body. **Observe** ***What kind of blood—oxygen-rich or oxygen-poor—leaves the lungs and returns to the heart?***

Circulation Although it is one organ, the heart functions as two pumps. One pump pushes blood to the lungs, while the other pump pushes blood to the rest of the body, as shown in **Figure 33–3.** The two pathways of blood through the body are called pulmonary circulation and systemic circulation.

▶ ***Pulmonary Circulation*** The right side of the heart pumps oxygen-poor blood from the heart to the lungs through what is called **pulmonary circulation.** In the lungs, carbon dioxide diffuses from the blood, and oxygen is absorbed by the blood. Oxygen-rich blood then flows to the left side of the heart.

▶ ***Systemic Circulation*** The left side of the heart pumps oxygen-rich blood to the rest of the body through what is called **systemic circulation.** Cells absorb much of the oxygen and load the blood with carbon dioxide. This now oxygen-poor blood returns to the right side of the heart for another trip to the lungs to pick up oxygen.

In Your Notebook *Draw a cycle diagram that represents both pulmonary and systemic circulation.*

UbD Check for Understanding

HAND SIGNALS

Present students with the following questions, and ask them to show a thumbs-up sign if they can answer the question, a thumbs-down sign if they definitely cannot, or a waving-hand sign if they are not sure.

- What is the function of the myocardium?
- Can you describe pulmonary circulation?
- Can you describe systemic circulation?

ADJUST INSTRUCTION

Identify questions that are a source of confusion for at least several students. Have the class form groups to discuss these questions for approximately 5 minutes and then share their answers.

Heartbeat To be an efficient pump, the heart must beat in an orderly and coordinated way. Two networks of muscle fibers coordinate the heart's pumping action—one in the atria and one in the ventricles. When a single muscle fiber in either network is stimulated, the entire network contracts.

1 Atria Contract Each contraction begins in a small group of cardiac muscle fibers—the sinoatrial node (SA node)—located in the right atrium. The SA node "sets the pace" for the heart, so it is also called the **pacemaker.** When the SA node fires, an electrical impulse spreads through the entire network of muscle fibers in the atria and the atria contract.

2 Ventricles Contract The impulse from the SA node is then picked up by another group of muscle fibers called the atrioventricular node (AV node). Here the impulse is delayed for a fraction of a second while the atria contract and pump blood into the ventricles. Then the AV node produces impulses that spread through the ventricles and cause the ventricles to contract, pumping blood out of the heart. This two-step pattern of contraction—first the atria and then the ventricles—makes the heart an efficient pump.

Control of Heart Rate Your heart rate varies depending on your body's need to take in oxygen and release carbon dioxide. During vigorous exercise, for example, your heart rate could increase to about 200 beats per minute. Heartbeat is not directly controlled by the nervous system, but the autonomic nervous system does influence the activity of the SA node. Neurotransmitters released by the sympathetic nervous system increase heart rate. Those released by the parasympathetic nervous system decrease heart rate.

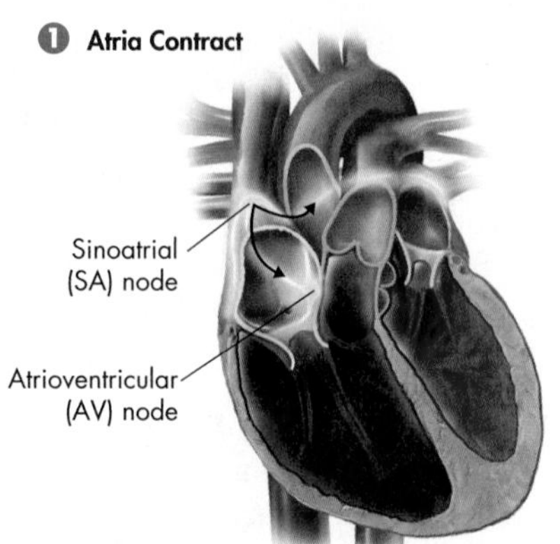

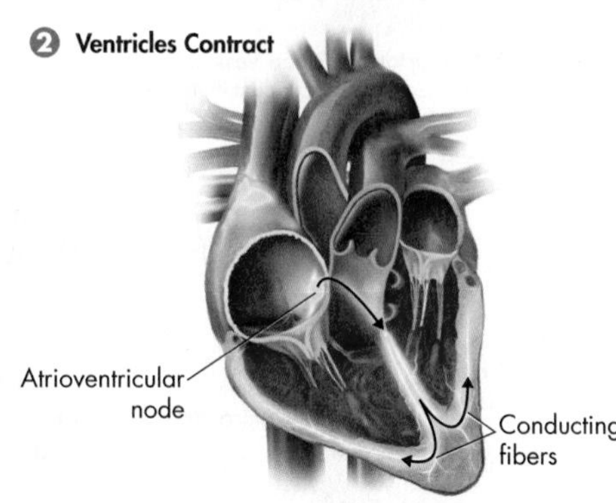

FIGURE 33–4 Heartbeat The SA node generates an impulse that spreads through the atria, causing the muscle fibers to contract and pump blood to the ventricles. The AV node picks up the signal and, after a slight delay, sends an impulse through the ventricles, causing them to contract.

Quick Lab
GUIDED INQUIRY

What Factors Affect Heart Rate?

1. While sitting, measure your heart rate. Find the pulse in one of your wrists using the first two fingers of your other hand.
2. Count the number of beats for 15 seconds, and multiply by 4. This gives you the number of beats per minute.

Analyze and Conclude

1. **Predict** What do you think would happen if you stood up? Would your heart rate decrease, increase, or stay the same?
2. **Evaluate** Test your prediction by standing up and measuring your heart rate again. Explain your results.

BIOLOGY.com Search Lesson 33.1 GO • Art in Motion • Data Analysis

Quick Lab

PURPOSE Students will identify how standing affects heart rate.

MATERIALS stopwatch or clock with a second hand

PLANNING Have students practice locating and measuring their pulse before they begin this activity.

ANALYZE AND CONCLUDE

1. Sample answer: I predict that my heart rate would increase if I stood up.
2. A person's heart rate should increase when the person is standing versus sitting down. Evaluations and explanations will vary. Sample answer: My prediction was correct; when I stood up my heart rate increased. When I stand up, my body needs to take in more oxygen than when I am sitting down.

Use Visuals

Use **Figure 33–4** to help students understand how the heart beats. Point out that both atria contract at the same time and both ventricles contract at the same time. The result is that blood is pumped into the pulmonary circulation pathway and the systemic circulation pathway at the same time. Then, walk the class through the steps of a heartbeat.

Ask What happens when the sinoatrial node fires? *(The atria contract.)*

Ask Where in the heart does blood move when the atria contract? *(from the atria to the ventricles)*

Ask What signals the atrioventricular node to fire? *(It picks up the signal from the sinoatrial node.)*

Ask What happens when the atrioventricular node fires? *(The ventricles contract.)*

DIFFERENTIATED INSTRUCTION

L3 Advanced Students Tell students artificial pacemakers are implanted in individuals whose hearts need help maintaining a normal rate of contractions. Have them do research to find out more about artificial pacemakers and why they are used. Have students share what they learned with the class.

BIOLOGY.com To watch how the heart beats, suggest students view the animation, **Art In Motion: Heartbeat.** The **Data Analysis: Electrocardiography** activity allows students to use electrocardiography to diagnose heart conditions.

Address Misconceptions

Heart Contraction A common misconception among students is that oxygen-rich blood leaves the heart at a separate time from oxygen-poor blood. Explain to students that when the ventricles contract, oxygen-rich blood is pumped out of the left ventricle to the body. At the same time, oxygen-poor blood is pumped out of the right ventricle to the lungs.

Teach continued

Build Science Skills

Use the following questions to help students compare and contrast arteries, capillaries, and veins.

Ask How are the structures of veins and arteries similar? *(Veins and arteries have an inner layer of endothelium, a middle layer of smooth muscle, and an outer layer of connective tissue.)*

Ask How do the functions of arteries and veins differ? *(Most arteries carry oxygen-rich blood from the heart to the tissues of the body. Most veins carry oxygen-poor blood from the body back to the heart.)*

Ask How are capillaries similar to veins and arteries? *(Sample answer: Capillaries, veins, and arteries all carry blood in the body.)*

Ask Why does diffusion of materials between blood and body cells occur across capillary walls but not veins or arteries? *(because of capillaries' extremely thin walls)*

DIFFERENTIATED INSTRUCTION

LPR Less Proficient Readers Have students use **Figure 33–5** to learn about the ways in which veins, arteries, and capillaries are similar and different. Focus students' attention on the artery, and work with them to describe its structure. Then, point out the vein, and have students describe its structure. Finally, have students examine the capillary to learn about ways capillaries are similar to and different from arteries and veins.

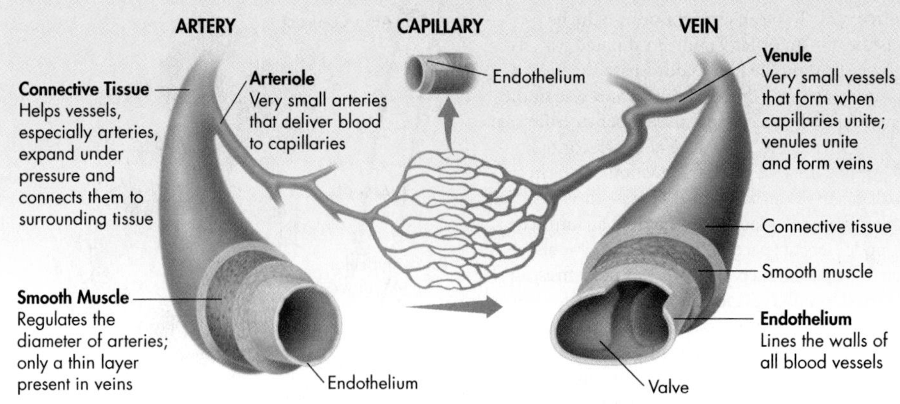

FIGURE 33–5 Structure of Blood Vessels The structure of blood vessel walls contributes to the vessels' functions.

Valve open
Muscles Contracted
Direction of blood flow
Valve closed (prevents backflow)

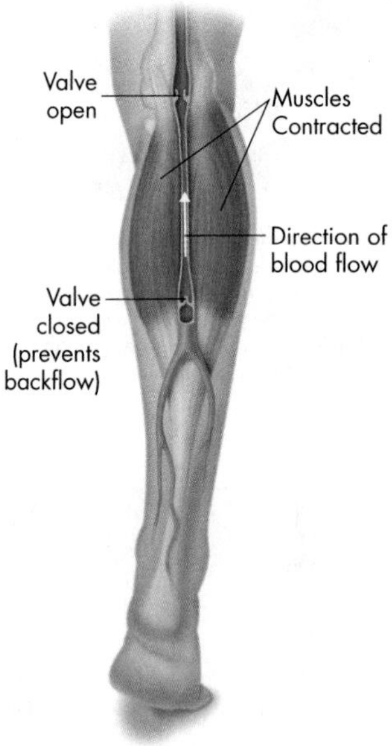

FIGURE 33–6 Blood Flow in Veins The contraction of skeletal muscles helps move blood in veins toward the heart.
Draw Conclusions ***What role do valves play in large veins?***

Blood Vessels

What are three types of blood vessels?

Oxygen-rich blood leaving the left ventricle passes into the aorta. The aorta is the first of a series of vessels that carries blood through the systemic circulation and back to the heart. **As blood flows through the circulatory system, it moves through three types of blood vessels—arteries, capillaries, and veins.**

Arteries **Arteries** are large vessels that carry blood from the heart to the tissues of the body. Arteries are the superhighways of the circulatory system. Except for the pulmonary arteries, all arteries carry oxygen-rich blood. Arteries have thick elastic walls that help them withstand the powerful pressure produced when the heart contracts and pumps blood through them. **Figure 33–5** describes the three layers of tissue found in artery walls—connective tissue, smooth muscle, and endothelium.

Capillaries The smallest blood vessels are the **capillaries.** Capillaries are the side streets and alleys of the circulatory system. Most capillaries are so narrow that blood cells pass through them in single file. Their extremely thin walls allow oxygen and nutrients to diffuse from blood into tissues, and carbon dioxide and other waste products to move from tissues into blood.

Veins After blood passes through the capillaries, it returns to the heart through **veins.** Blood often must flow against gravity through the large veins in your arms and legs. Many veins are located near and between skeletal muscles, as shown in **Figure 33–6.** When you move, the contracting skeletal muscles squeeze the veins, pushing blood toward the heart. Many veins contain valves. The valve that is farthest from the heart closes to ensure blood continues to flow in one direction.

UbD Check for Understanding

VISUAL REPRESENTATION

Write the lesson vocabulary terms on the board: myocardium, atrium, ventricle, valve, pulmonary circulation, systemic circulation, pacemaker, artery, capillary, vein. Have students make a **Concept Map** that includes each of the terms.

ADJUST INSTRUCTION

If students have difficulty completing the concept map, or if their completed maps are incorrect, have them make a vocabulary flash card for each term, with the term on the front and its definition on the back. Have students use their flash cards to review the vocabulary terms with a partner and then revise their concept maps as needed.

Answers

FIGURE 33–6 Valves in large veins ensure that blood flows in only one direction.

Blood Pressure Like any pump, the heart produces pressure. When it contracts, it produces a wave of fluid pressure in the arteries, known as blood pressure. Although blood pressure falls when the heart relaxes between beats, the system still remains under pressure due to the elasticity of the arterial walls. It's a good thing, too. Without that pressure, blood would stop flowing through the body.

Healthcare workers measure blood pressure with a device called a sphygmomanometer (sfig moh muh NAHM uh tur), an inflatable cuff with a pump and a meter. The cuff is wrapped around the upper arm and inflated until blood flow through the artery that runs down the arm is blocked. As the pressure is released, the healthcare worker listens for a pulse with a stethoscope and records a number from the meter. This number represents the systolic pressure—the force in the arteries when the ventricles contract. When the pulse sound disappears, a second number is recorded. This number represents the diastolic pressure—the force in the arteries when the ventricles relax. A typical blood pressure reading for a healthy teen or adult is below 120/80.

The body regulates blood pressure in a number of ways. Sensory receptors in blood vessels detect blood pressure and send impulses to the brain stem. When blood pressure is high, the autonomic nervous system releases neurotransmitters that relax the smooth muscles in blood vessel walls. When blood pressure is low, neurotransmitters are released that cause the smooth muscles in vessel walls to contract.

The kidneys also regulate blood pressure by affecting the volume of blood. Triggered by hormones produced by the heart and other organs, the kidneys remove more water from the blood and eliminate it in urine when blood pressure is high or conserve more water when blood pressure is low.

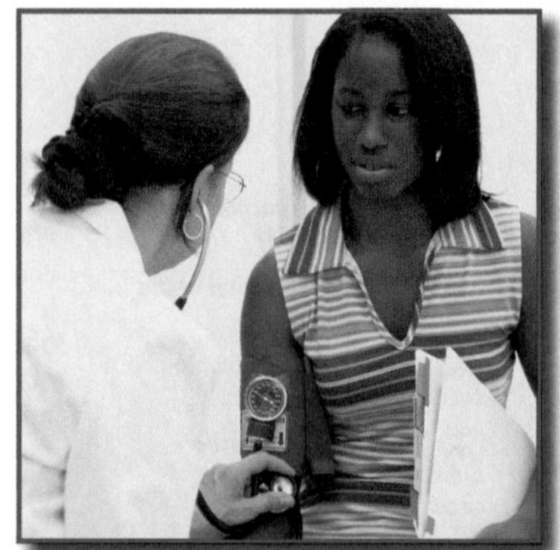

FIGURE 33–7 Measuring Blood Pressure It's important to have your blood pressure measured because blood pressure that is too high or too low can have serious effects on most body systems.

33.1 Assessment

IN NoS.6

Review Key Concepts 

1. a. Review List the structures of the circulatory system and explain their roles.
   b. Apply Concepts Why do humans need a circulatory system?
2. a. Review Describe the two paths of blood circulation through the body.
   b. Relate Cause and Effect How would damage to the sinoatrial node affect the heart's function?
3. a. Review Describe the functions of three types of blood vessels in the circulatory system.
   b. Infer If you were standing, would you expect the blood pressure to be higher in your arm or in your leg? Explain your answer. (*Hint:* Think about which area of the body is closer to the source of pressure.)

VISUAL THINKING

4. Trace **Figure 33–2.** Label the four chambers of the heart. Add arrows and labels to indicate how blood flows through the heart.

BIOLOGY.com Search Lesson 33.1 GO • Self-Test • Lesson Assessment

Assess and Remediate

EVALUATE UNDERSTANDING

Have students work in pairs, with one student naming a structure of the circulatory system and the other student describing its function. Have students exchange roles. Then, have them complete the 33.1 Assessment.

REMEDIATION SUGGESTION

L1 Struggling Students If students have trouble with **Question 2b,** remind them that the sinoatrial node is also called the "pacemaker." Discuss as a class why this name makes sense. Then, have pairs of students draft an answer for the question.

BIOLOGY.com Students can check their understanding of lesson concepts with the **Self-Test** assessment. They can then take an online version of the **Lesson Assessment.**

Assessment Answers

1a. Heart, pumps blood throughout the body; blood vessels, carry blood throughout the body; blood, carries oxygen and nutrients to the body's tissues and carries away the tissues' wastes.

1b. Humans need a circulatory system because their bodies contain millions of cells that are not in direct contact with the external environment. These cells cannot exchange gases, nutrients, and wastes with the environment; they must rely on the circulatory system to do this.

2a. In pulmonary circulation, the heart pumps oxygen-poor blood to the lungs. Oxygen-rich blood from the lungs returns to the heart. In systemic circulation, the heart pumps this oxygen-rich blood to the rest of the body. The veins return oxygen-poor blood to the heart.

2b. If the sinoatrial node were damaged, the heartbeat would not be properly regulated.

3a. Arteries carry blood from the heart to the tissues; capillaries allow diffusion between the blood and body cells; veins carry blood back to the heart from the body.

3b. Blood pressure would be higher in your arm because it is closer to your heart.

VISUAL THINKING

4. Students' diagrams should resemble **Figure 33–2.** Make sure the chambers of the heart are labeled and that students have correctly indicated the path of blood through the heart.

Getting Started

Objectives

33.2.1 Explain the functions of blood plasma, red blood cells, white blood cells, and platelets.

33.2.2 Describe the role of the lymphatic system.

33.2.3 List three common circulatory diseases.

33.2.4 Describe the connection between cholesterol and circulatory disease.

Student Resources

Study Workbooks A and B, 33.2 Worksheets

Spanish Study Workbook, 33.2 Worksheets

Lab Manual B, 33.2 Data Analysis Worksheet

Lesson Overview • Lesson Notes • Assessment: Self-Test, Lesson Assessment

For corresponding lesson in the **Foundation Edition,** see pages 790–795.

Activate Prior Knowledge

Tell students that blood serves several important functions in the body. Then, have them form small groups to discuss what they already know about blood. Call on each group to share a summary of its discussion with the rest of the class.

IN INDIANA ACADEMIC STANDARDS

For the full text of all standards, see the Course Overview in the front matter of this book.

B.1.2 Understand that the shape of a molecule determines its role in the many different types of cellular processes including metabolism, homeostasis, growth and development, and heredity, and understand that the majority of these processes involve proteins that act as enzymes.

33.2 Blood and the Lymphatic System

B.1.2 Molecules and cellular processes. Also covered: **NoS.3.**

Key Questions

What is the function of each component in blood?

What is the function of the lymphatic system?

What are three common circulatory diseases?

What is the connection between cholesterol and circulatory disease?

Vocabulary

plasma • red blood cell • hemoglobin • white blood cell • platelet • lymph • atherosclerosis

Taking Notes

Outline Before you read, make an outline of the major headings in the lesson. As you read, fill in main ideas and supporting details for each heading.

FIGURE 33-8 Blood Cells The micrograph shows red blood cells (red disks), white blood cells (gold orbs), and platelets (pink fragments) (SEM 1866×).

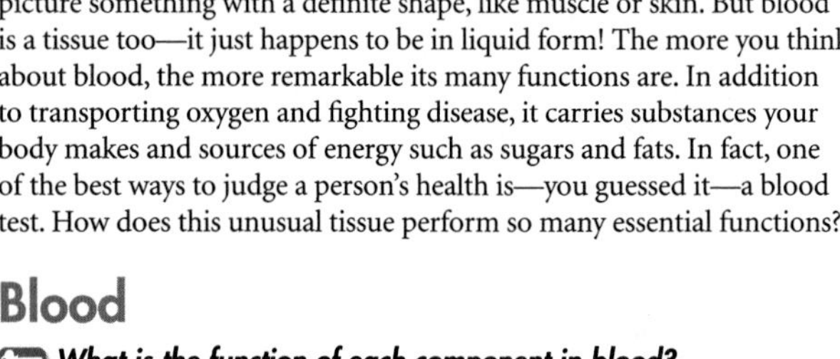

THINK ABOUT IT When you think about body tissues, you probably picture something with a definite shape, like muscle or skin. But blood is a tissue too—it just happens to be in liquid form! The more you think about blood, the more remarkable its many functions are. In addition to transporting oxygen and fighting disease, it carries substances your body makes and sources of energy such as sugars and fats. In fact, one of the best ways to judge a person's health is—you guessed it—a blood test. How does this unusual tissue perform so many essential functions?

Blood

What is the function of each component in blood?

You might think that the most important function of blood is to serve as the body's transportation system. But the various components of blood also help regulate body temperature, fight infections, and produce clots that help minimize the loss of body fluids from wounds.

Plasma The human body contains 4 to 6 liters of blood. About 55 percent of total blood volume is a straw-colored fluid called **plasma.** **Plasma is about 90 percent water and 10 percent dissolved gases, salts, nutrients, enzymes, hormones, waste products, plasma proteins, cholesterol, and other important compounds.**

The water in plasma helps to control body temperature. Plasma proteins consist of three types—albumin, globulins, and fibrinogen. Albumin and globulins transport substances such as fatty acids, hormones, and vitamins. Albumin also plays an important role in regulating osmotic pressure and blood volume. Some globulins fight viral and bacterial infections. Fibrinogen is necessary for blood to clot.

Red Blood Cells The most numerous cells in blood are **red blood cells,** or erythrocytes (eh RITH roh syts). **The main function of red blood cells is to transport oxygen.** They get their crimson color from the iron in **hemoglobin,** a protein that binds oxygen in the lungs and releases it in capillary networks throughout the body. Then red blood cells transport some carbon dioxide to the lungs.

Red blood cells are disks that are thinner in their center than along their edges. They are produced by cells in red bone marrow. As red blood cells mature and fill with hemoglobin, their nuclei and other organelles are forced out. Red blood cells circulate for an average of 120 days before they are destroyed in the liver and spleen.

UbD Teach for Understanding

ENDURING UNDERSTANDING The human body is a complex system. The coordinated functions of its many structures support life processes and maintain homeostasis.

GUIDING QUESTION What are the roles of blood and the lymphatic system in the body?

EVIDENCE OF UNDERSTANDING *After completing the lesson, give students the following assessment to show their understanding of the lymphatic and circulatory systems.* Have pairs of students role-play a conversation in which one student assumes the role of the lymphatic system and the other student plays the circulatory system. Suggest pairs discuss how they are similar and how they are different. Make sure students also discuss how they work together.

White Blood Cells **White blood cells,** or leukocytes (LOO koh syts), are the "army" of the circulatory system. **White blood cells guard against infection, fight parasites, and attack bacteria.** The body can increase the number of active white blood cells dramatically during a "battle" with foreign invaders. In fact, a sudden increase in white blood cells is a sign that the body is fighting a serious infection. White blood cells are not confined to blood vessels. Many white blood cells can slip through capillary walls to attack foreign organisms.

Different types of white blood cells perform different protective functions. For example, macrophages engulf pathogens. Lymphocytes are involved in the immune response. B lymphocytes produce antibodies that fight infection and provide immunity. T lymphocytes help fight tumors and viruses. You will learn more about lymphocytes and other white blood cells in Chapter 35.

In a healthy person, white blood cells are outnumbered by red blood cells by almost 1000 to 1. Like red blood cells, white blood cells are produced from stem cells in bone marrow. Unlike red blood cells, however, white blood cells keep their nuclei and can live for years.

Platelets Blood loss can be life-threatening. Fortunately, a minor cut or scrape may bleed for a bit, but then the bleeding stops. Why? Because blood clots. **Blood clotting is made possible by plasma proteins and cell fragments called platelets.** The cytoplasm of certain bone marrow cells divides into thousands of small fragments. The fragments, each enclosed in a cell membrane, break off and enter the blood as **platelets.**

When platelets come in contact with the edges of a broken blood vessel, their surface becomes sticky, and they cluster around the wound. These platelets release proteins called clotting factors that start a series of reactions. **Figure 33–9** summarizes one part of the clotting process.

In Your Notebook *Make a flowchart that describes the blood-clotting process.*

FIGURE 33–9 How Blood Clots Form This figure shows one chain reaction in the formation of a clot. When the clot is formed, strands of fibrin form a net that prevents blood from leaving the damaged vessel. Use Analogies ***How is a blood clot like a screened porch?***

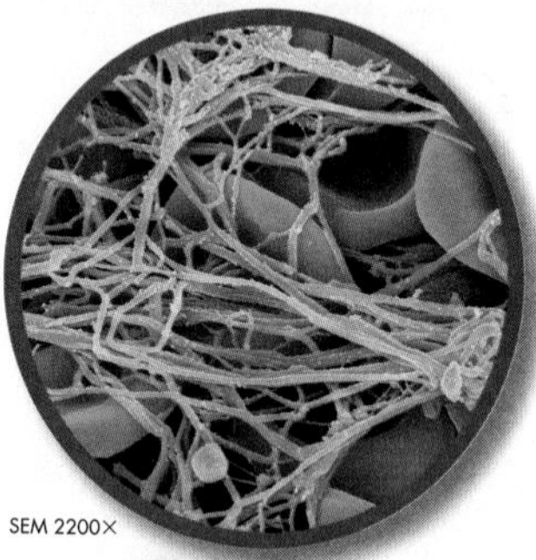

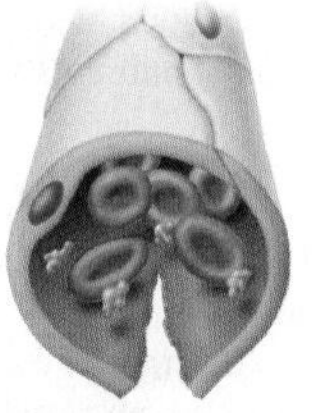

1 **Capillary Wall Breaks**
A blood vessel is injured by a cut or scrape.

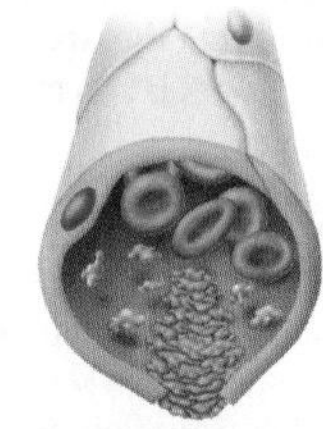

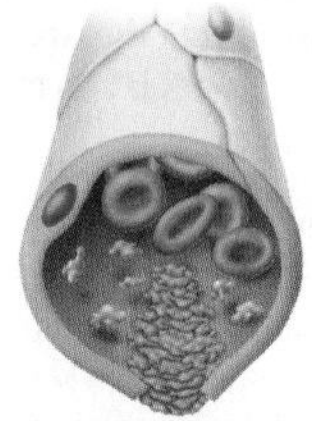

2 **Platelets Take Action**
Platelets clump at the site and release the clotting factor thromboplastin, which triggers a series of reactions. Thromboplastin converts the protein prothrombin into the enzyme thrombin.

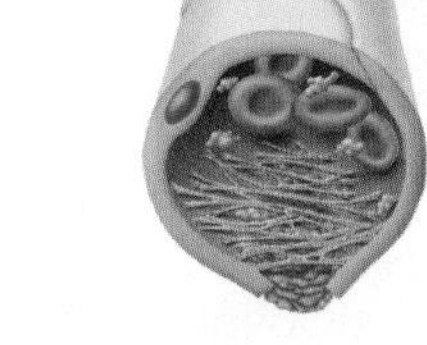

3 **Clot Forms**
Thrombin converts the soluble plasma protein fibrinogen into insoluble, sticky fibrin filaments, which form the clot. The clot seals the damaged area and prevents further loss of blood.

Teach

Lead a Discussion

Ask these questions to help students understand the functions of each component of blood.

Ask Which two components of blood are most directly involved in blood clotting? *(plasma proteins and platelets)*

Ask *Anemia* is a term for a group of disorders characterized by a deficiency of red blood cells. What function of blood is impaired in individuals with anemia? *(delivery of oxygen to body cells)*

Ask If an individual has a disorder that results in a reduction of white blood cells, what is a likely result? *(reduced ability to fight infection)*

DIFFERENTIATED INSTRUCTION

LPR **Less Proficient Readers** Distribute four index cards to each student. On the front of each card, have them write the name of one of the components of blood. On the back of the cards, have them rephrase the Key Concept about that component and add details from the reading.

ELL Focus on ELL: Access Content

ADVANCED AND ADVANCED HIGH SPEAKERS Have students write five questions about blood that can be answered from the text on the left side of a **T-Chart** under the heading Questions. Have them exchange charts with a partner and record the answers on the right side of the T-Chart under the heading Answers. Encourage students to use complete sentences when recording their answers. Then, have pairs discuss the completed T-Charts and review any questions that they struggled to answer.

Study Wkbks A/B, Appendix S30, T-Chart. **Transparencies,** GO15.

How Science Works

MEDICINAL USES OF LEECHES

Ancient medical practices are rarely accepted in modern times. The medicinal use of leeches is an exception. Until the mid-19th century, patients were bled using leeches to treat a wide variety of ailments. For most of these disorders, the usefulness of intentional bleeding was questionable. In 2004, the Food and Drug Administration approved the use of leeches as a medical device. Modern medical uses of leeches are limited to situations in which blood needs to be extracted from a specific area of tissue—such as when blood needs to be drained from an area surrounded by damaged blood vessels before surgery can be performed. Leeches extract blood and also release a chemical that inhibits clotting, allowing for enhanced blood flow. Leeches also produce an anesthetic that numbs the area while blood is being drawn.

Answers

FIGURE 33–9 The filaments formed from fibrinogen are similar to a screen, because blood cells cannot pass through them, just as most bugs cannot pass through a screen.

IN YOUR NOTEBOOK Flowcharts should include the steps shown in **Figure 33–9,** connected by arrows.

Teach continued

Build Study Skills

Have students build **Cause-and-Effect Diagrams** to describe what would happen if the lymphatic system did not perform each of its functions. *(If the lymphatic system did not collect lymph, swelling would occur. If it didn't absorb fat, then the body would not receive the fat it needs to be healthy. If the lymph nodes did not house white blood cells and "catch" microorganisms it would be harder to fight infections.)*

Study Wkbks A/B, Appendix S18, Cause-and-Effect Diagram. **Transparencies,** GO1.

DIFFERENTIATED INSTRUCTION

L1 Struggling Students Suggest students work in pairs to locate the information they need to complete the **Cause-and-Effect Diagrams.** Remind students that the blue heads provide clues to the main functions of the lymphatic system.

ELL English Language Learners Have students identify words they do not understand in the section on the lymphatic system. Have them list the words on a sheet of paper. Then, have students form small groups to find definitions for these words. Suggest they refer to this list as they fill in the **Cause-and-Effect Diagrams.**

IN NoS.3, B.1.2

Blood Transfusions

The first successful transfusion of human blood was carried out in 1818. But many later recipients had severe reactions to transfused blood, and a number died. Today we know why. We inherit one of four blood types—A, B, AB, or O—which are determined by antigens, or the lack of antigens, on our blood cells. Antigens are substances that trigger an immune response. People with blood type A have A antigens on their cells, those with type B have B antigens, those with AB blood have both A and B, and those with type O have neither A nor B antigens.

Transfusions work when blood types match. But they can also work in some cases even when the blood types of the donor and the recipient do not match. Use the table to answer the questions that follow.

Blood Transfusions

Blood Type of Donor	Blood Type of Recipient			
	A	B	AB	O
A	✓	x	✓	x
B	x	✓	✓	x
AB	x	x	✓	x
O	✓	✓	✓	✓

x = Unsuccessful transfusion ✓ = Successful transfusion

1. **Draw Conclusions** Which blood type is sometimes referred to as the "universal donor"? Which is known as the "universal recipient"?
2. **Infer** In a transfusion involving blood types A and O, does it matter which blood type is the recipient's and which is the donor's?
3. **Apply Concepts** Write a brief explanation of the results in the chart using information about phenotypes and genotypes in blood group genes. (*Hint:* Review Lesson 14.1 if needed.)

The Lymphatic System

What is the function of the lymphatic system?

As blood passes through capillaries, some blood cells and components of plasma move through capillary walls and into the fluid between cells, carrying nutrients, dissolved oxygen, and salts. Each day about 3 liters of fluid, and the small particles it contains, leaves the blood. Most of this fluid, known as **lymph,** is reabsorbed into capillaries, but not all of it. The rest goes into the lymphatic system. **The lymphatic system is a network of vessels, nodes, and organs that collects the lymph that leaves capillaries, "screens" it for microorganisms, and returns it to the circulatory system.** The lymphatic system, shown in **Figure 33–10,** is also involved in the absorption of nutrients and in immunity.

Role in Circulation Lymph collects in a system of lymphatic capillaries that slowly conducts it into larger and larger lymph vessels. The lymphatic system doesn't have a pump to move lymph along. Instead, lymph vessels have valves, similar to the valves in large veins, that prevent lymph from flowing backward. Pressure on lymph vessels from surrounding skeletal muscles helps move lymph through the system into larger and larger ducts. These ducts return lymph to the blood through openings in the subclavian veins just below the shoulders. When injury or disease blocks lymphatic vessels, lymph can accumulate in tissues, causing swelling called edema.

PURPOSE Students will examine and interpret data to identify how blood type affects the success of transfusions.

PLANNING Remind students that human blood types are an inherited trait.

ANSWERS

1. Type O is sometimes referred to as the "universal donor." Type AB is sometimes referred to as the "universal recipient."
2. Yes, because people with type A blood can safely receive type O blood, whereas people with type O blood cannot safely receive type A blood.
3. Students' responses will vary, but should reflect an understanding of blood groups and genetics. Sample answer: People who have type O blood do not produce blood antigens and, therefore, can donate blood to any of the other blood groups safely. The alleles for type A and B are codominant; people with type AB blood can receive blood from all four blood groups.

Role in Nutrient Absorption The lymphatic system also plays an important role in the absorption of nutrients. A system of lymph vessels runs alongside the intestines. The vessels pick up fats and fat-soluble vitamins from the digestive tract and transport these nutrients into the bloodstream.

Role in Immunity Hundreds of small bean-shaped enlargements—called lymph nodes—are scattered along lymph vessels throughout the body. Lymph nodes act as filters, trapping microorganisms, stray cancer cells, and debris as lymph flows through them. Fleets of white blood cells inside lymph nodes engulf or otherwise destroy this cellular "trash." When large numbers of microorganisms are trapped in lymph nodes, the nodes become enlarged. The "swollen glands" that are symptoms of certain kinds of infections are actually swollen lymph nodes.

The thymus and spleen also play important roles in the immune functions of the lymphatic system. The thymus is located beneath the sternum. T lymphocytes mature in the thymus before they can function in the immune system. The functions of the spleen are similar to those of lymph nodes. However, instead of lymph, blood flows through the spleen, where it is cleansed of microorganisms and other debris. The spleen also removes old or damaged blood cells and stores platelets.

In Your Notebook *Compare and contrast the functions of the circulatory system and the lymphatic system.*

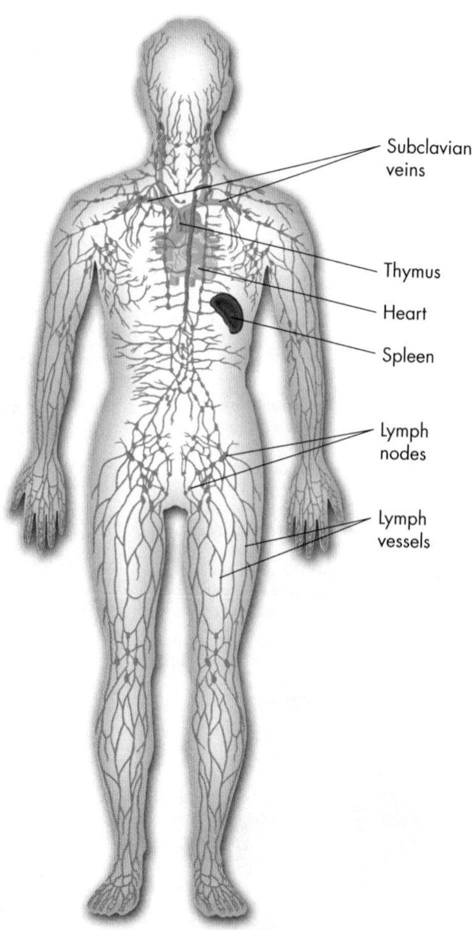

FIGURE 33–10 The Lymphatic System The lymphatic system is a network of vessels, nodes, and organs that recycles fluids from tissues and plays a role in nutrient absorption and immunity. **Infer** ***Why do you think your doctor feels your neck for swollen lymph nodes when you are sick?***

Circulatory System Diseases

What are three common circulatory diseases?

Diseases of the circulatory system can progress for many years before they are discovered. Often the first sign of circulatory problems is an event that affects the heart or brain. Why? Tissues in these vital organs begin to die within moments if their oxygen supply is interrupted. **Three common and serious diseases of the circulatory system are heart disease, stroke, and high blood pressure.** Damage to heart muscle from a heart attack or to the brain from a stroke can be fatal. Individuals with high blood pressure are at higher risk for both heart disease and stroke. Heart disease is the leading cause of death in the United States.

Use Visuals

Have students use **Figure 33–10** to learn more about the lymphatic system.

Ask How is the location of lymph nodes and lymph vessels throughout the body related to the role of the lymphatic system in circulation? *(Lymph can be collected throughout the body and returned to the circulatory system.)*

Ask Where is lymph returned to the circulatory system? *(through openings in the subclavian veins)*

Ask In what role of the lymphatic system are the thymus and spleen directly involved? *(immunity)*

DIFFERENTIATED INSTRUCTION

L3 Advanced Students Have students find out why doctors use a biopsy of lymph nodes from near a tumor when assessing the stage of disease in cancer patients. Have them create a poster to share what they learn with the class.

UbD Check for Understanding

ONE-MINUTE RESPONSE

Give students about a minute to write a quick response to:

What are the structures and functions of the lymphatic system? *(Responses should include lymph vessels, lymph nodes, spleen, and thymus; and the system's roles in circulation, nutrient absorption, and immunity.)*

ADJUST INSTRUCTION

If responses are incorrect or incomplete, suggest each student write a list of structures and then work with a partner to discuss the function of each.

Answers

FIGURE 33–10 Swollen lymph nodes indicate that a large number of microorganisms have been trapped in the lymph nodes.

IN YOUR NOTEBOOK Students' responses will vary but should indicate an understanding of the main functions of both systems. The circulatory system transports oxygen, nutrients, and other substances throughout the body and removes wastes from tissues. The lymphatic system collects lymph that leaves the capillaries, and returns it to the circulatory system, picks up fat and other nutrients from the intestines, and removes microorganisms from lymph.

ach continued

se Models

Give students a hands-on demonstration of how atherosclerosis increases the work the heart has to do to pump blood. Obtain a bicycle pump and a piece of rubber tubing that fits over the air nozzle of the pump. Give students a chance to pump air through the open tube. Then, have them pump air while you squeeze the tube almost closed. Ask students to describe the difference.

Ask How does squeezing the tube represent atherosclerosis? *(Atherosclerosis restricts blood flow through the arteries similar to how squeezing restricts air flow through the tube.)*

DIFFERENTIATED INSTRUCTION

L1 Struggling Students If students struggle to understand the bike-pump model, provide them with additional guiding questions that explicitly make the connection between the model and atherosclerosis.

Ask What does the heart do? *(It pumps blood throughout the body.)*

Ask What does the bike pump do? *(It pumps air.)*

Ask In this model, what does the bicycle pump represent? *(the heart)*

Ask Was it easier to pump air though an open tube or through a tube that is being squeezed? *(through an open tube)*

Ask Is it easier for the heart to pump blood through an open artery or one that is blocked by plaques? *(through an open artery)*

BUILD Vocabulary

WORD ORIGINS Atherosclerosis comes from the Greek words *athero* (gruel or paste) and *sclerosis* (hardness). Atherosclerosis is hardening of the arteries that results from fatty deposits.

Heart Disease Heart muscle requires a constant supply of oxygen. Yet the heart is supplied with blood by just two coronary arteries and their smaller branches. There are many types of heart disease, but the most common occur when blood flow through these vessels is obstructed.

One example is **atherosclerosis,** a condition in which fatty deposits called plaques build up in artery walls and eventually cause the arteries to stiffen. Over time, plaques often bulge into the center of a vessel and restrict blood flow to heart muscle. Chest pain, known as angina, can be a sign of restricted blood flow. Eventually, the heart can be weakened or damaged by oxygen deprivation, leading to a condition called heart failure.

If the cap on a plaque ruptures, a blood clot may form that completely blocks an artery, as shown in **Figure 33–11.** A heart attack occurs as heart muscle cells become damaged and possibly die. Heart attacks can also damage the SA or AV nodes, which can affect the heart's ability to beat in a coordinated way. Arteries severely narrowed by atherosclerosis, the use of drugs such as cocaine, and cigarette smoking can also lead to a heart attack.

Heart attack symptoms include nausea; shortness of breath; chest pain; and pain in the neck, jaw, or left arm. People with these symptoms need *immediate* medical attention. Medication needs to be given quickly to increase blood flow and save heart muscle.

Stroke The sudden death of brain cells when their blood supply is interrupted is called a stroke. Some strokes are caused by a blood clot that blocks a blood vessel in the brain. A stroke can also occur if a weak blood vessel breaks and causes bleeding in the brain. Symptoms of stroke include severe headache, numbness, dizziness, confusion, and trouble seeing or speaking. The results of a stroke vary, depending on which part of the brain it affects. Some strokes cause death. Other strokes may cause paralysis or loss of speech. Prompt medical treatment may lessen the severity of a stroke.

FIGURE 33–11 Atherosclerosis Most heart attacks occur when a plaque ruptures in a coronary artery and a clot forms. Clots can also form in large vessels in other parts of the body, break off, and block vessels in the heart that are narrowed by atherosclerosis. **Predict** ***What do you think would happen if a clot broke off from an artery and blocked a vessel in the brain?***

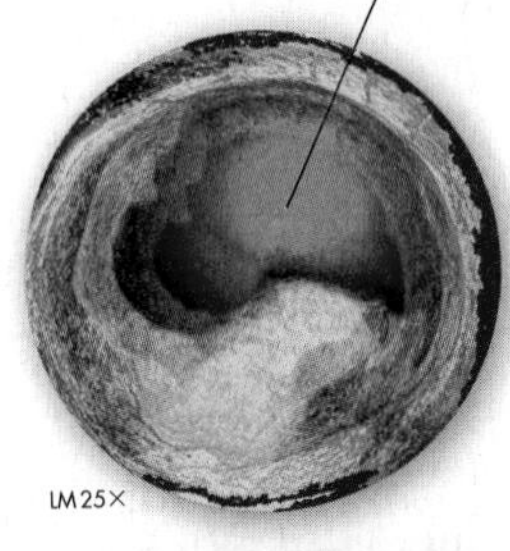

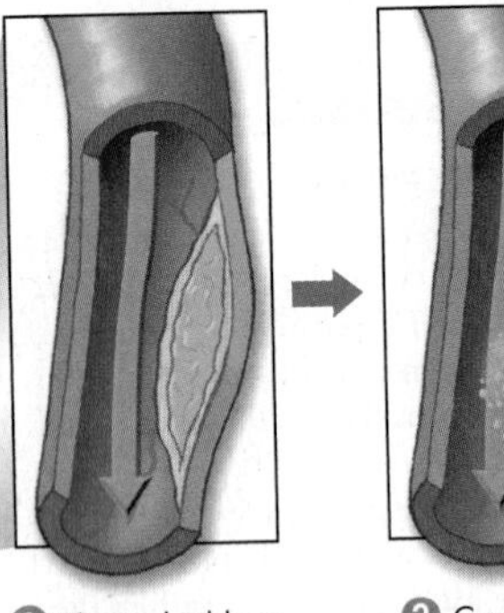

1 Plaque builds up in wall.

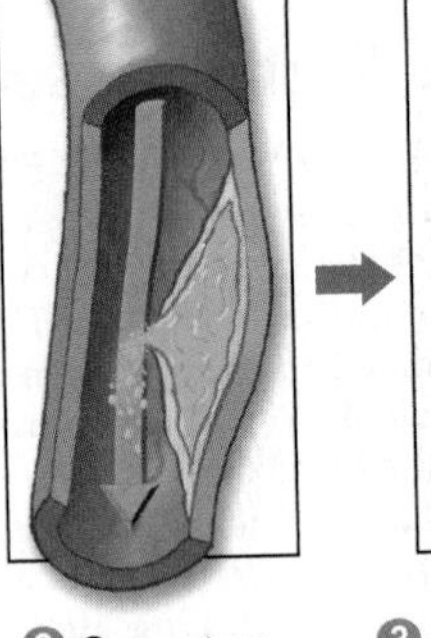

2 Cap ruptures.

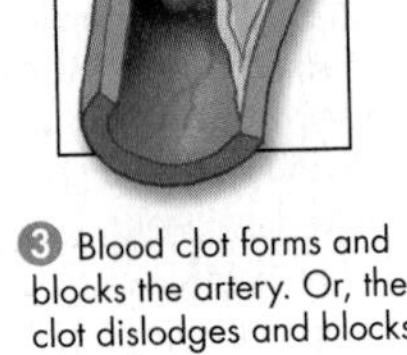

3 Blood clot forms and blocks the artery. Or, the clot dislodges and blocks a smaller artery.

How Science Works

ADVANCES IN TREATING HEART DISEASE

The first American surgeon to perform a human heart transplant was Dr. Norman E. Shumway. In 1968, Shumway transplanted a heart into a 54-year-old man whose own heart had been injured by a viral infection. Patients who received heart transplants during these early years did not survive long because of organ rejection. In the 1980s, drugs were developed that have made heart transplants much more successful. In 1982, Dr. William DeVries led a team of doctors who implanted the Jarvik-7, an artificial heart that was connected to a console approximately as large as a refrigerator, into a patient who lived for 112 days following the surgery. In 2006, the Food and Drug Administration approved a totally implanted artificial heart. This artificial heart is for patients who cannot receive a transplant, and may extend their lives for several months.

Answers

FIGURE 33–11 sudden death of brain cells due to lack of oxygen

High Blood Pressure High blood pressure, or hypertension, is usually defined as a reading of 140/90 or higher. Because hypertension often has no symptoms, people may have it for years and not know. Meanwhile, heart damage occurs as the heart struggles to push blood through vessels. Hypertension also causes small tears in blood vessels, which sets the stage for atherosclerosis. Likewise, the stiffened arteries that result from atherosclerosis can contribute to high blood pressure. Diet, exercise, and prescription drugs can help control hypertension. Uncontrolled hypertension can lead to heart attack, stroke, and kidney damage.

Risk Factors for Heart Disease and Stroke

Controllable Risk Factors	Uncontrollable Risk Factors
Diet	Age
Exercise	Family history
Weight	Gender (men have more heart attacks)
Not smoking	
High blood cholesterol	
High blood pressure	
Diabetes	

FIGURE 33–12 Risk Factors for Heart Disease and Stroke Some risk factors for heart disease can be controlled because they are related to behavior. For example, people can control their diets and their exercise levels and many can take medication to control diabetes. But other risk factors, such as age and family history, cannot be controlled.

Understanding Circulatory Disease

What is the connection between cholesterol and circulatory disease?

Diseases of the circulatory system do not have a single cause. **Figure 33–12** lists several factors that increase the risk of heart and stroke. Although many risk factors can be controlled, this can be difficult. In some cases, medications may not be accessible or may not be effective. For example, blood cholesterol levels can be difficult to control. But researchers have learned a lot about blood cholesterol levels, their connection to atherosclerosis, and how the condition can be managed.

What Is Cholesterol? Cholesterol is a lipid that is part of animal cell membranes. It is also used in the synthesis of some hormones, bile, and vitamin D. Cholesterol is transported in the blood primarily by two types of lipoproteins—low-density lipoprotein (LDL) and high-density lipoprotein (HDL). LDL is the cholesterol carrier that is most likely to cause trouble in the circulatory system because it becomes part of plaque. HDL, often called good cholesterol, generally transports excess cholesterol from tissues and arteries to the liver for removal from the body.

Measures of a person's blood cholesterol actually are measures of lipoproteins. Normal total blood cholesterol levels range from 100 to 200 milligrams per deciliter (mg/dL). A person's LDL level should be less than 100 mg/dL. A man's HDL level should be greater than 40 mg/dL; a woman's HDL level should be greater than 50 mg/dL.

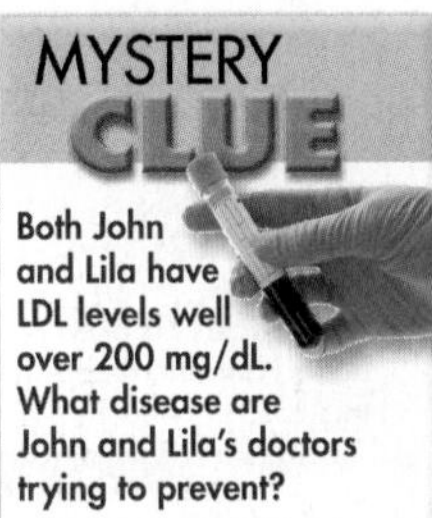

MYSTERY CLUE

Both John and Lila have LDL levels well over 200 mg/dL. What disease are John and Lila's doctors trying to prevent?

Quick Facts

BLOOD PRESSURE

Blood pressure rises and falls throughout life and even throughout the day. Babies and children usually have much lower blood pressure than adults, and blood pressure is usually lowest during sleep and highest in the morning. Blood pressure also rises during exercise and periods of emotional excitement. Weight gain is usually associated with an increase in blood pressure. Some people have a genetic predisposition for high blood pressure. For instance, for unknown reasons, people of African American descent are at higher risk than the general U.S. population for more frequent and severe high blood pressure. Knowing one's genetic predisposition for high blood pressure may help encourage a person to take preventive measures, such as adopting a healthier lifestyle.

Connect to Health

Have students form small groups, and ask each group to examine the table showing risk factors for heart disease and stroke. Instruct groups to prepare a public service announcement (PSA) about one of the controllable risk factors. Remind students that a PSA is a concise message, usually presented on radio or television, that promotes a positive behavior. Explain that each group should do additional research to find out why the risk factor they selected can lead to heart disease and stroke and to find ways to avoid that risk factor. For example, a PSA about diet should explain how diet impacts susceptibility to heart disease and stroke. It should also include information on heart-healthy diets. Have each group share its PSA with the class.

DIFFERENTIATED INSTRUCTION

L1 Struggling Students Students may be confused by the listing of high blood pressure as a risk factor for heart disease and stroke in the table. Make sure students understand that high blood pressure is a disorder itself, as well as a contributing factor to heart attack and stroke. Explain that high blood pressure can have many health consequences in addition to increasing the risk of heart disease and stroke.

MYSTERY CLUE Help students understand the relationship between high cholesterol levels and atherosclerosis. Point out that LDL becomes part of plaque. Then, have students describe why this may contribute to the development of atherosclerosis. Students can go online to Biology.com to gather their evidence.

ach continued

ad a Discussion

nind students that humans obtain cholesterol m meat and dairy products—particularly if those ods are high in certain kinds of fat. Explain that any factors, including several genes, each with ultiple alleles, determine the response of an individual to a high-fat diet.

Ask Recall that feedback inhibition is essential for the maintenance of homeostasis in the body. How does blood cholesterol level regulation demonstrate feedback inhibition? *(When blood cholesterol levels are high, the liver absorbs cholesterol, which inhibits cholesterol production in the liver. When blood cholesterol levels are low, the liver does not absorb cholesterol from the blood, and cholesterol is produced by the liver.)*

Ask How would individuals be affected if the LDL receptors on their liver cells were defective? *(The individuals would have high cholesterol, because their liver cells could not remove cholesterol from the blood.)*

Ask How could a person's diet cause symptoms that were similar to an individual with faulty LDL receptors? *(When an individual eats a high-fat diet, cholesterol can build up in liver cells. These cells stop making LDL receptors and, therefore, no longer remove cholesterol from the blood.)*

Point out to students that both proteins and carbohydrates can be converted into fat tissue. An overabundance of Calories, regardless of the energy source, will be stored as fat.

DIFFERENTIATED INSTRUCTION

LPR **Less Proficient Readers** Suggest students use **Figure 33–13** to understand what happens when a person has defective LDL receptors. Point out that the figure shows two different situations. On the left, the cell has normal LDL receptors; on the right, the cell has defective LDL receptors. Have students describe what occurs in each cell.

Answers

IN YOUR NOTEBOOK Students' feedback loops should show the following: When blood cholesterol levels rise, liver cells take cholesterol from the blood and do not produce cholesterol. When blood cholesterol levels fall, liver cells produce cholesterol.

Sources of Cholesterol The liver manufactures cholesterol, which is then transported through the blood to tissues. Humans also consume cholesterol in meat, eggs, dairy products, and fried foods, especially if those foods are high in saturated or trans fats.

Cholesterol and Atherosclerosis Years ago researchers compared cholesterol levels and heart attack rates in different groups of people. In certain villages in Japan and Yugoslavia, the average cholesterol level was 160. In those populations, the heart attack rate was very low—fewer than five attacks for every 1000 men over a ten-year period. In parts of Finland, researchers found mean cholesterol levels of 265. In that population, the heart attack rate was 14 times higher! **Research indicates that high cholesterol levels, along with other risk factors, lead to atherosclerosis and higher risk of heart attack.**

What controls the level of cholesterol in blood? Is there any medical treatment that can lower cholesterol and reduce the risk of atherosclerosis? These questions led researchers Michael Brown and Joseph Goldstein to studies that earned them a Nobel Prize in 1985.

Identifying the LDL Receptor Brown and Goldstein discovered LDL receptors on the cell membrane of liver cells, as shown in **Figure 33–13.** LDL binds to these receptors and then is taken into the cells. Once inside, cholesterol is broken down and then stored or used for making bile or more cholesterol. When blood cholesterol levels are high, liver cells take cholesterol from the blood and do not make it. When blood cholesterol levels are low, the liver produces it.

In Your Notebook *Make a feedback loop to demonstrate the relationship between blood cholesterol levels and healthy liver cells.*

FIGURE 33–13 LDL Receptors When blood LDL levels are high, liver cells with normal LDL receptors take up LDL and use it or store it. However, the liver cells of some people have defective LDL receptors. Those cells cannot remove cholesterol from the blood and do not stop producing cholesterol.

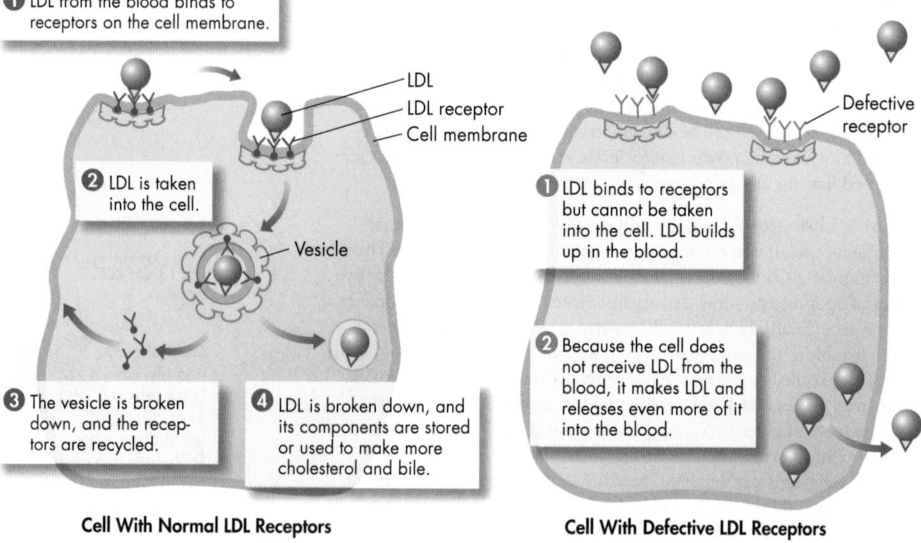
1 LDL from the blood binds to receptors on the cell membrane.
LDL
LDL receptor
Cell membrane
2 LDL is taken into the cell.
Vesicle
3 The vesicle is broken down, and the receptors are recycled.
4 LDL is broken down, and its components are stored or used to make more cholesterol and bile.
Cell With Normal LDL Receptors
Defective receptor
1 LDL binds to receptors but cannot be taken into the cell. LDL builds up in the blood.
2 Because the cell does not receive LDL from the blood, it makes LDL and releases even more of it into the blood.
Cell With Defective LDL Receptors

UbD Check for Understanding

FOLLOW-UP PROBES

Ask Blood cholesterol levels are affected by more than one factor. Explain. *(Sample answer: Diet can affect blood cholesterol level, as can defective LDL receptors on liver cells.)*

ADJUST INSTRUCTION

If students' responses indicate confusion about the factors that affect blood cholesterol level, write the question "What affects blood cholesterol level?" on the board. Have volunteers provide answers, and record their responses on the board. Lead students to the conclusion that blood cholesterol level is generally affected by more than one factor.

Brown and Goldstein also found that some people carry genes that produce defective LDL receptors. This causes two problems. First, without working LDL receptors, liver cells can't remove cholesterol from blood. Second, these liver cells don't get the signal to stop producing cholesterol. People with defective LDL receptors have very high cholesterol levels, even if they don't eat much cholesterol or fat.

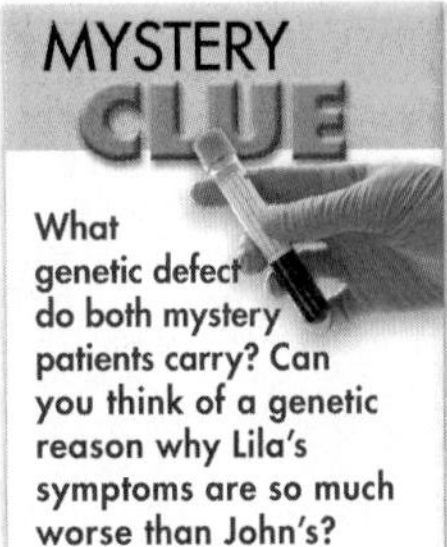
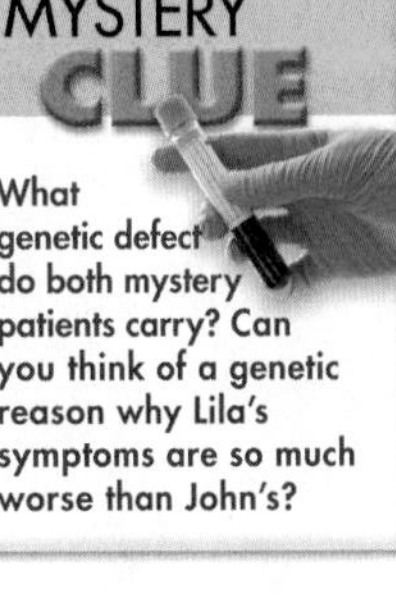

What genetic defect do both mystery patients carry? Can you think of a genetic reason why Lila's symptoms are so much worse than John's?

From Genetic Disease to the Public Does understanding this genetic defect help us understand high cholesterol in the general public? Brown and Goldstein learned that people who eat high-fat diets store excess cholesterol in their liver cells. Those cells then stop making LDL receptors and removing cholesterol from blood. The excess cholesterol is then deposited in arteries. So a diet that is high in cholesterol can cause symptoms similar to those of a genetic disease!

Brown and Goldstein's work led to the development of drugs that can help people with high cholesterol. For example, statins block the synthesis of cholesterol in liver cells. This stimulates the liver to produce more LDL receptors, which then remove excess cholesterol from the blood.

Keeping Your Circulatory System Healthy It is much easier to prevent heart disease than to cure it. Prevention starts when you're young, with healthy habits that include a balanced diet, regular exercise, and not smoking. A healthy diet may protect your arteries from atherosclerosis. Exercise strengthens your heart and helps your circulatory system work efficiently. Never starting to smoke will protect your circulatory system from the many dangerous chemicals in tobacco smoke.

33.2 Assessment

IN NoS.3

Review Key Concepts

1. a. Review List the main function of plasma, red blood cells, white blood cells, and platelets.
   b. Infer Hemophilia is a genetic disorder that results from a defective protein in the clotting pathway. What do you think happens to a person with hemophilia who has a minor cut?
2. a. Review Describe the role of the lymphatic system.
   b. Compare and Contrast How are the functions of veins and lymphatic vessels similar? How are they different?
3. a. Review What are the risk factors for the three common diseases of the circulatory system?
   b. Form a Hypothesis Why do you think atherosclerosis may lead to hypertension?
4. a. Review What are two types of cholesterol carriers found in the blood?
   b. Compare and Contrast Explain how high blood cholesterol develops in someone with a genetic disorder versus someone who eats a high-fat diet.

WRITE ABOUT SCIENCE

Creative Writing

5. Use library or Internet resources to research the connection between diet and circulatory disease. Write a short commentary that could be used on a television news program that explains the connection. (*Hint:* Prepare a cause-and-effect diagram to organize your ideas.)

BIOLOGY.com Search Lesson 33.2 GO • Self-Test • Lesson Assessment

MYSTERY CLUE Guide students to infer that both John and Lila have a genetic condition that leads to defective LDL receptors on their liver cells. Lila may have inherited defective copies of the LDL receptor gene from both parents, while John may have inherited the gene from only one parent. If necessary, suggest that students review patterns of inheritance in human genetic disorders from Chapter 14 and discuss why Lila's symptoms are worse than John's. Students can go online to Biology.com to gather their evidence.

Assess and Remediate

EVALUATE UNDERSTANDING

Have students work with a partner to review the definition of each vocabulary term in the lesson. Call on pairs of students to define a term for the class. Continue until each vocabulary term has been correctly defined. Then, have students complete the 33.2 Assessment.

REMEDIATION SUGGESTION

LPR **Less Proficient Readers** If students are struggling to answer **Question 2b,** help them locate information in the text about the function of veins and the function of lymphatic vessels. Have students write a brief summary of this information. Then, have them reread the question and use their summaries to help them develop an answer.

BIOLOGY.com Students can check their understanding of lesson concepts with the **Self-Test** assessment. They can then take an online version of the **Lesson Assessment.**

Assessment Answers

1a. Plasma contains dissolved gases and salts and plasma proteins; red blood cells carry oxygen; white blood cells fight infection; platelets help blood clot.

1b. A person with hemophilia would bleed uncontrollably from a minor cut.

2a. The lymphatic system collects lymph and returns it to the circulatory system, removes microorganisms from the blood, and helps absorb fats and fat-soluble vitamins from the digestive tract.

2b. Sample answer: Veins and lymphatic vessels both carry fluid in one direction only due to valves. Lymphatic vessels do not carry blood.

3a. high-fat diet, lack of exercise, being overweight, smoking, having diabetes, age, family history, gender

3b. The heart must exert more pressure to push blood through stiff veins, leading to hypertension.

4a. The two types are HDL and LDL.

4b. In an individual with a genetic disorder, the liver cells cannot take up LDL from the blood, so they keep producing cholesterol. In an individual who eats a high-fat diet, excess cholesterol builds up in the liver cells, which stop making LDL receptors and no longer remove cholesterol from the blood.

WRITE ABOUT SCIENCE

5. Students' commentaries should be based on reliable resources.

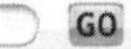

Teach

Lead a Discussion

Use the following questions to initiate a class discussion of imaging techniques used to diagnose heart diseases and disorders.

Ask What is the advantage of imaging techniques that are noninvasive? *(There is less risk involved with procedures that do not require instruments to be inserted into the body.)*

Ask Which of these imaging techniques requires that a dye be injected into the patent? *(computed tomography angiography)*

Ask Which of these imaging techniques would most likely be used to detect unhealthy heart tissue? *(MRI)*

DIFFERENTIATED INSTRUCTION

LPR **Less Proficient Readers** Have students work in groups of three to learn about imaging methods used to detect heart disease. Within each group, have students divide the reading among the three group members, so each group member reads about a different imaging technique. Have each group member teach the other two students in the group about his or her assigned imaging method. Circulate among the groups, and ask students to share what they have learned.

Technology & BIOLOGY

IN **NoS.10** Scientific discoveries and new technology; **NoS.11** Scientific knowledge: environmental and social issues.

Testing for Heart Disease

Ever-improving imaging techniques make it possible for doctors to diagnose heart disease and disorders quickly and without the risk of invasive procedures. None of these tests involves inserting instruments into the body, but they reveal the inner workings of the heart with remarkable accuracy.

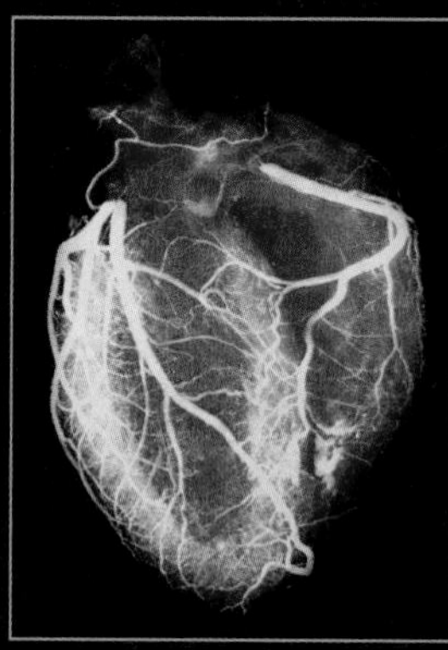

Computed Tomography Angiography
A patient is injected with an iodine-based dye. Then the CT scanner rotates over the patient and takes multiple X-rays of the heart, which a computer uses to form three-dimensional images. The test can show if parts of blood vessels are blocked or damaged. The results can be used to determine what further tests are needed or as a guide for planning surgery.

WRITING In a paragraph, explain which technique would most likely be used to check for advanced atherosclerosis in a coronary artery.

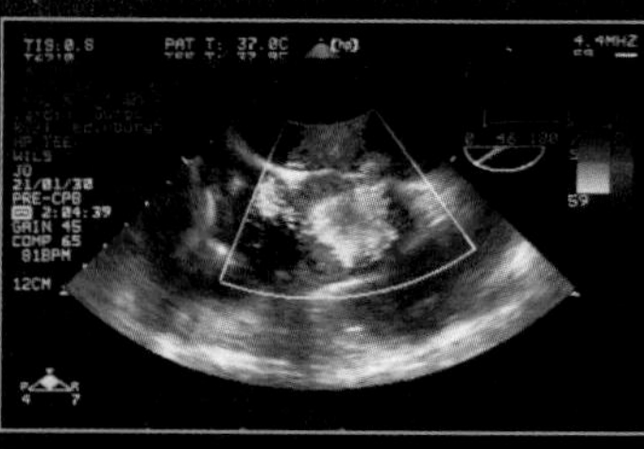

Echocardiography
High-frequency sound waves, transmitted through the chest, are fed into a computer, which analyzes the "echoes" to produce moving images of the heart. This is an especially safe test because it doesn't involve radiation or dyes. The test allows doctors to see the heart in action. It can reveal an enlarged heart, reduced pumping action, and structural problems.

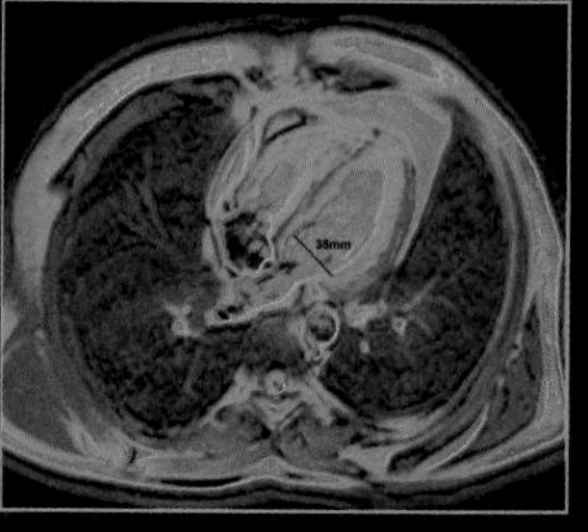

Magnetic Resonance Imaging (MRI)
MRI uses powerful magnets to produce images that are particularly good for examining muscle and other soft tissue. Professionals analyzing MRI images can see the difference between healthy tissue and unhealthy tissue. MRI does not involve radiation or iodine-based dyes. It can be used to assess heart muscle damage caused by a heart attack, birth defects, or abnormal growths.

962 Technology and Biology

Answers

WRITING

Students' responses should identify the CT scan as the most likely technique for detecting atherosclerosis in a coronary artery and offer a reasonable explanation for this choice.

IN **INDIANA ACADEMIC STANDARDS**

For the full text of all standards, see the Course Overview in the front matter of this book.

Biology In-Depth

PET SCANS

PET, or positron emission tomography, scanning is an additional imaging method that can contribute to the diagnosis of heart disease. PET scans reveal more information about the functioning of an organ or tissue than the other methods described above, which provide more structural information. A PET scan uses a radioactive tracer to generate images representing the functioning of the tissue or organ being studied. PET scans are often combined with CT scans to provide information about both the structure and function of the heart.

33.3 The Respiratory System

THINK ABOUT IT When medics examine an unconscious accident victim, one of the first things they do is check whether the person is breathing. This is one way to determine whether there is still a life to save. Why do we make such a close connection between breathing and life? For that matter, why do we need to breathe? All cells in our body, especially brain cells, require a constant supply of oxygen for cellular respiration. Without oxygen, many cells begin to die within minutes. The respiratory system works together with the circulatory system to provide our cells with oxygen. Any interruption in that vital function can be fatal.

Structures of the Respiratory System

What is the function of the respiratory system?

For organisms, rather than single cells, *respiration* means the process of gas exchange between a body and the environment. **The human respiratory system picks up oxygen from the air we inhale and releases carbon dioxide into the air we exhale.** With each breath, air enters the body through the air passageways and fills the lungs, where gas exchange takes place. The circulatory system links this exchange of gases in the lungs with our body tissues. The respiratory system consists of the nose, pharynx, larynx, trachea, bronchi, and lungs.

Nose The respiratory passageways transport air into some of the most delicate tissues in the body. To keep lung tissue healthy, air entering the respiratory system must be filtered, moistened, and warmed. Hairs lining the entrance to the nasal cavity start the filtering process by trapping large particles. Incoming air is warmed in the inner nasal cavity and sinuses. These areas produce mucus that moistens the air and catches even more dust particles. If you've ever blown your nose after spending time in a dusty environment, you've seen evidence of the way nasal hairs and mucus protect the lungs.

In Your Notebook *In your own words, compare and contrast cellular respiration and respiration at the organism level.*

Key Questions

What is the function of the respiratory system?

How are oxygen and carbon dioxide exchanged and transported throughout the body?

What mechanisms are involved in breathing?

How does smoking affect the respiratory system?

Vocabulary

pharynx
trachea
larynx
bronchus
alveolus
diaphragm

Taking Notes

Flowchart Make a flowchart that shows the path of air through the respiratory system.

BIOLOGY.com Search Lesson 33.3 GO • Lesson Overview • Lesson Notes

Getting Started

Objectives

33.3.1 Identify the structures of the respiratory system and describe their functions.

33.3.2 Describe gas exchange.

33.3.3 Describe how breathing is controlled.

33.3.4 Describe the effects of smoking on the respiratory system.

Student Resources

Study Workbooks A and B, 33.3 Worksheets

Spanish Study Workbook, 33.3 Worksheets

Lesson Overview • Lesson Notes • Activities: Art Review, InterActive Art • Assessment: Self-Test, Lesson Assessment

For corresponding lesson in the **Foundation Edition,** see pages 796–801.

Activate Prior Knowledge

Ask students why scuba gear is important for divers. *(People can't survive without oxygen.)* Explain that the respiratory system is responsible for taking oxygen into the body.

Answers

IN YOUR NOTEBOOK Answers should include that oxygen is involved in both processes but that cellular respiration takes place inside cells, while respiration occurs at the organismal level.

UbD Teach for Understanding

ENDURING UNDERSTANDING The human body is a complex system. The coordinated functions of its many structures support life processes and maintain homeostasis.

GUIDING QUESTION How are oxygen and carbon dioxide exchanged between humans and the environment?

EVIDENCE OF UNDERSTANDING *After completing the lesson, give students the following assessment to show their understanding of the respiratory system.* Have students work in pairs to develop an analogy for gas exchange in the human body. Have each pair share its analogy with the class. Then, have students determine which analogies best represent gas exchange in the body and cite reasons for their choices.

LESSON 33.3

Teach

Build Study Skills

Use a **Two-Column Table** to enhance students' understanding of the structures of the respiratory system and their functions. In the left column, have students record the structures through which air passes as it moves through the respiratory system. In the right column, have them write a brief description of the function of each structure. After students have completed their own tables, draw a two-column table on the board. Have volunteers come forward one at a time to add information to the table on the board. Continue until all structures mentioned in the lesson and their functions have been entered.

Study Wkbks A/B, Appendix S31, Two-Column Table. **Transparencies,** GO16.

DIFFERENTIATED INSTRUCTION

L1 Special Needs Students may need to work with a partner to complete the **Two-Column Table** summarizing the structures and functions of the respiratory system. Have students use single words or short phrases to describe the functions of each structure.

L3 Advanced Learners Have students work in a group to develop mnemonic devices to help other students remember the functions of the various structures of the respiratory system. After the class has worked together to complete the two-column table on the board, draw a third column and ask advanced learners to share the mnemonic devices they developed.

FIGURE 33–14 Cilia Cilia in the trachea sweep mucus and debris away from the lungs. **Infer** ***What would likely happen to a person's respiratory system if the cilia were damaged by pollutants?***

Pharynx, Larynx, and Trachea Air moves through the nose to a cavity at the back of the mouth called the **pharynx,** or throat. The pharynx serves as a passageway for both air and food. Air moves from the pharynx into the **trachea,** or windpipe. When you swallow food or liquid, a flap of tissue called the epiglottis covers the entrance to the trachea, ensuring that the food or liquid goes into the esophagus.

Between the pharynx and the trachea is the larynx. The **larynx** contains two highly elastic folds of tissue known as the vocal cords. When muscles pull the vocal cords together, the air moving between them causes the cords to vibrate and produce sounds. Your ability to speak, shout, and sing comes from these tissues.

Mucus produced in the trachea continues to trap inhaled particles. Cilia lining the trachea sweep both mucus and trapped particles away from the lungs toward the pharynx. From there, the mucus and particles can be swallowed or spit out. This process helps keep the lungs clean and open for the important work of gas exchange.

Lungs From the trachea, air moves into two large tubes in the chest cavity called **bronchi** (singular: bronchus). Each bronchus leads to one lung. Within each lung, the large bronchus divides into smaller bronchi, which lead to even smaller passageways called bronchioles. Bronchi and bronchioles are surrounded by smooth muscles controlled by the autonomic nervous system. As the muscles contract and relax, they regulate the size of air passageways.

The bronchioles continue to divide until they reach a series of dead ends—millions of tiny air sacs called **alveoli** (singular: alveolus). Air moving through these tubes can be compared to a motorist who takes an exit off an eight-lane highway onto a four-lane highway, makes a turn onto a two-lane road, and then proceeds onto a narrow country lane—which dead-ends. Alveoli are grouped in clusters, like bunches of grapes. A delicate network of capillaries surrounds each alveolus.

BUILD Vocabulary

MULTIPLE MEANINGS Alveolus is also the term for a honeycomb cell in a beehive or a tooth socket in the jaw.

Quick Lab
GUIDED INQUIRY

What's in the Air?

1. Trace the outline of a microscope slide on graph paper. Repeat four times.
2. Cut out the outlines and tape them to the bottom of five slides.
3. Pick indoor and outdoor spots to place your slides. On the back of each slide, write your initials, the date, and where you will put the slide.
4. Cover the front of each slide with a thin coat of petroleum jelly.
5. Leave the slides in the locations you chose for at least 24 hours.
6. Collect the slides, place them under a microscope, and count the number of particles in ten of the squares on each slide. Record your results.

Analyze and Conclude

1. **Observe** On which slide did you count the most particles? The fewest?
2. **Draw Conclusions** Were you surprised by the results? Why or why not?
3. **Apply Concepts** What structures in your body prevent most of these particles from entering your lungs?

PURPOSE Students will compare the number of particles in air from several different locations and infer how mucus acts to help keep particles from entering the lungs.

MATERIALS graph paper, microscope slides, petroleum jelly, microscope

PLANNING Identify, in advance, locations in which slides can sit undisturbed for 24 hours.

ANALYZE AND CONCLUDE

1. Answers will vary depending on the location chosen.
2. Answers will vary. Accept all reasonable responses.
3. Cilia lining the trachea keep particles from entering the lungs.

Answers

FIGURE 33–14 If the cilia were damaged by pollutants, more particles would enter the lungs, possibly inhibiting gas exchange.

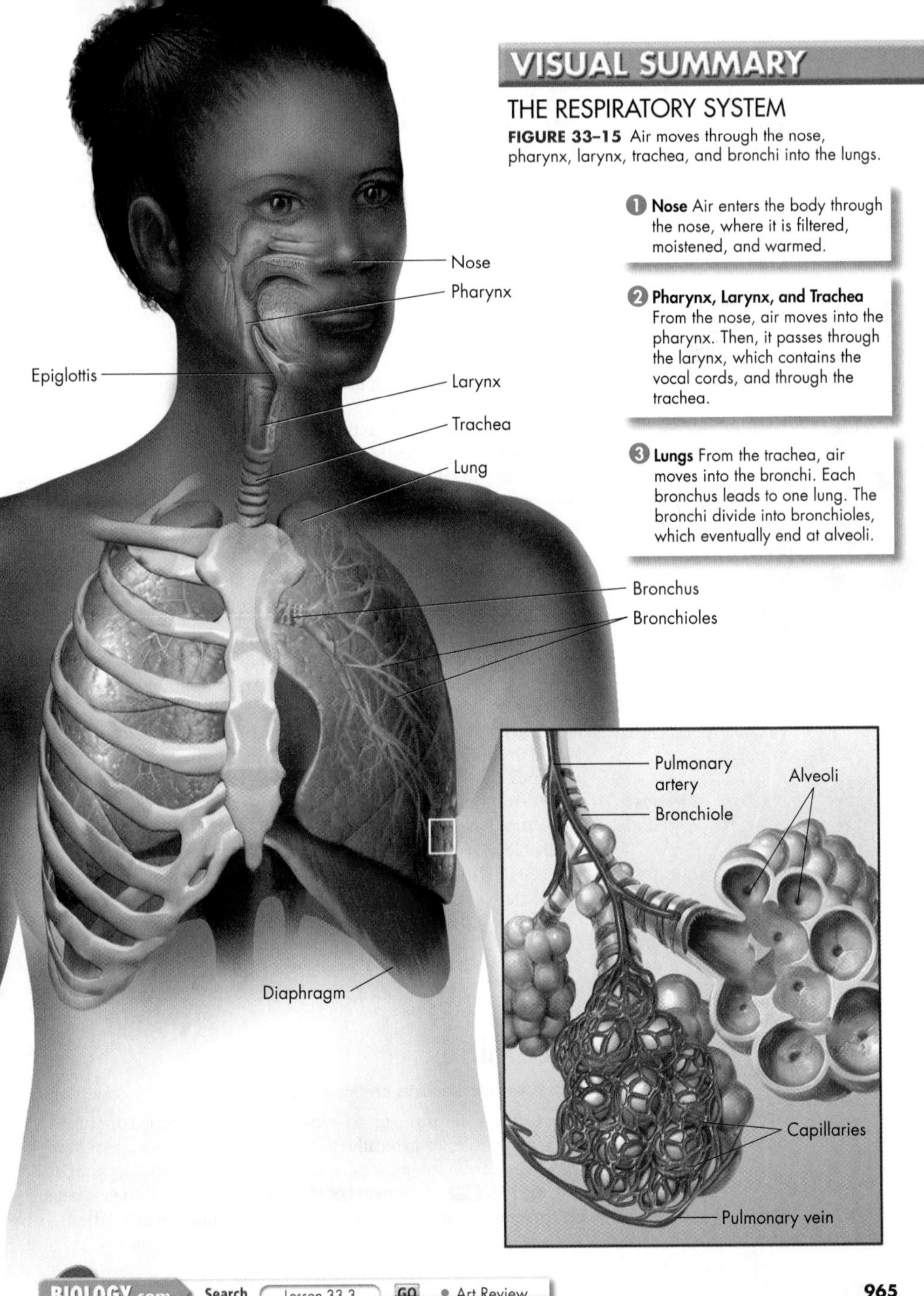

VISUAL SUMMARY
THE RESPIRATORY SYSTEM
1 Nose Air enters the body through the nose, where it is filtered, moistened, and warmed.
2 Pharynx, Larynx, and Trachea From the nose, air moves into the pharynx. Then, it passes through the larynx, which contains the vocal cords, and through the trachea.
3 Lungs From the trachea, air moves into the bronchi. Each bronchus leads to one lung. The bronchi divide into bronchioles, which eventually end at alveoli.
Nose
Pharynx
Epiglottis
Larynx
Trachea
Lung
Bronchus
Bronchioles
Diaphragm
Pulmonary artery
Bronchiole
Alveoli
Capillaries
Pulmonary vein

FIGURE 33–15 Air moves through the nose, pharynx, larynx, trachea, and bronchi into the lungs.

UbD Check for Understanding

USE VOCABULARY

Have students make a crossword puzzle that includes each of the lesson vocabulary terms. The clues for each term should be scientifically accurate and based on the definitions given in the text. Then, have students exchange crossword puzzles with a partner. Have each student complete the crossword puzzle and return it to his or her partner to be checked.

ADJUST INSTRUCTION

If students have difficulty generating clues for their crossword puzzles, have them work in pairs to review the definitions found in the text. Suggest students make a list of the terms and their definitions to refer to as they create their crossword puzzles.

VISUAL SUMMARY

Have students use **Figure 33–15** to trace the flow of air through the respiratory system.

Ask What structures does air pass through between the nose and the lungs? *(pharynx, larynx, trachea)*

Ask Why can you breathe through your mouth if your nose is stuffed up? *(The mouth also opens into the pharynx.)*

Ask In what respiratory structures does gas exchange occur? *(alveoli or lungs)*

DIFFERENTIATED INSTRUCTION

L1 Special Needs Go over each of the respiratory structures that air moves through one by one. Have students point to the structure in the figure as you discuss it. Then, have them trace the path of air through the respiratory system with one finger. Make sure students understand the relationship of the illustration in the lower right portion of the page to the large illustration. Explain that a magnified view of the alveoli makes it easier to visualize the process of gas exchange.

ELL Focus on ELL: Extend Language

BEGINNING SPEAKERS Have students create a **Vocabulary Word Map** for each of the following terms: *pharynx, larynx, trachea, bronchus, alveolus*, and *diaphragm*. For each term, encourage them to draw an illustration in one of the boxes and write a definition of the term in another. They can fill in the remaining boxes with attributes or concepts that help them remember the term. Then, have students work in pairs to practice using the terms in conversation.

Study Wkbks A/B, Appendix S32, Vocabulary Word Map. **Transparencies,** GO17.

BIOLOGY.com To review respiratory structures, have students complete **Art Review: The Respiratory System.**

Address Misconceptions

The Color of Blood A common misconception among students is that oxygen-poor blood is blue. Explain that, in illustrations, the color blue is often used to represent oxygen-poor blood but this does not reflect the actual color of oxygen-poor blood. Oxygen-rich blood is bright red and oxygen-poor blood is deeper red. Although veins look blue in some people, the blood flowing in them is not.

LESSON 33.3

Teach continued

Lead a Discussion

Make sure students understand the process of gas exchange in the lungs.

Ask In which lung structures does gas exchange take place? *(alveoli)*

Ask How is diffusion involved in this process? *(Oxygen diffuses from the alveoli into blood, and carbon dioxide diffuses from blood into the alveoli.)*

Ask How does hemoglobin increase the efficiency of gas exchange? *(Hemoglobin actively binds oxygen, taking it out of the plasma. This helps keep the oxygen concentration in the blood lower than in the alveoli, which makes gas exchange more efficient.)*

DIFFERENTIATED INSTRUCTION

L1 Struggling Students For students who are having difficulty understanding gas exchange, have them work in pairs to summarize the lower panel of **Figure 33–16.** For example, "Oxygen in the alveolus diffuses into blood cells in the capillary." "Carbon dioxide from the blood diffuses into the alveolus." Then, have the students share their sentences with the class.

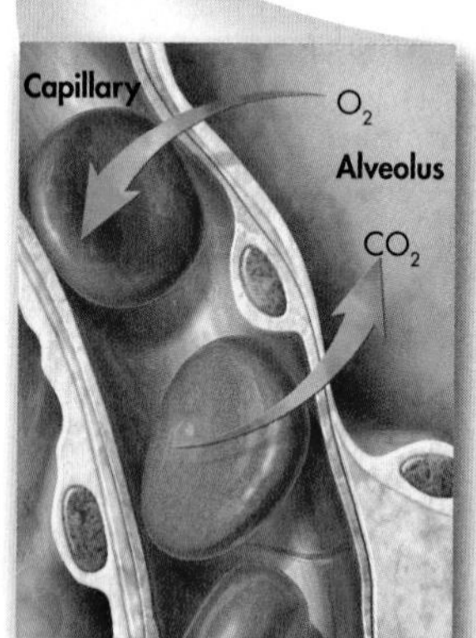

FIGURE 33–16 Gas Exchange Carbon dioxide and oxygen diffuse across capillary and alveolus walls. Draw Conclusions *Where is oxygen more concentrated, in an alveolus or in a capillary?*

Gas Exchange and Transport

How are oxygen and carbon dioxide exchanged and transported throughout the body?

Each healthy lung contains about 150 million alveoli, which provide an enormous surface area for gas exchange. **Oxygen and carbon dioxide are exchanged across the walls of alveoli and capillaries. Chemical properties of blood and red blood cells allow for efficient transport of gases throughout the body.**

Gas Exchange When air enters alveoli, oxygen dissolves in the moisture on their inner surface and then diffuses across thin capillary walls into the blood. Oxygen diffuses in this direction because the oxygen concentration is greater in the air within the alveoli than it is in the blood within the capillaries. Meanwhile, carbon dioxide diffuses from blood into the alveoli because its concentration is greater in the blood than it is in the air in the alveoli. The process of gas exchange is illustrated in **Figure 33–16.**

The air you inhale usually contains 21 percent oxygen and 0.04 percent carbon dioxide. Exhaled air usually contains less than 15 percent oxygen and 4 percent carbon dioxide. This means your lungs remove about a fourth of the oxygen in the air you inhale and increase the carbon dioxide content of that air by a factor of 100.

Transport Hemoglobin binds with and transports oxygen that diffuses from alveoli to capillaries. It also increases the efficiency of gas exchange. Diffusion of oxygen from alveoli into capillaries is a passive process. That process stops when oxygen concentration in the blood and alveoli is the same. But hemoglobin actively binds to dissolved oxygen, removing it from plasma and enabling diffusion from the alveoli to continue. Hemoglobin binds with so much oxygen that it increases blood's oxygen-carrying capacity more than 60 times.

When carbon dioxide diffuses from body tissues to capillaries, it is transported in the blood in three different ways. Most carbon dioxide enters red blood cells and combines with water, forming carbonic acid. The rest of it dissolves in plasma or binds to hemoglobin and proteins in plasma. These processes are reversed in the lungs, where carbon dioxide is released into alveoli and exhaled.

In Your Notebook *What would happen to the surface area for gas exchange if a disease caused the walls between alveoli to break down?*

Breathing

What mechanisms are involved in breathing?

Surprisingly, there are no muscles in our lungs or connected directly to them that participate in breathing. The force that drives air into the lungs comes from ordinary air pressure, the diaphragm, and muscles associated with the ribs. **Movements of the diaphragm and rib cage change air pressure in the chest cavity during inhalation and exhalation.**

Biology In-Depth

ASTHMA

Asthma is a potentially fatal respiratory illness characterized by repeated episodes of contractions in the muscles surrounding the airways. This constriction of the air passages makes it difficult to get enough air. Episodes of asthma symptoms can be severe enough to cause death; approximately 4000 deaths per year in the U.S. are attributable to asthma. The percentage of individuals who have asthma is on the rise. Some scientists think the increase is due to air pollution. Asthma risk is greater for Latinos and African Americans than it is for Caucasians. Urban children have a higher risk of asthma than those who live outside cities.

Answers

FIGURE 33–16 Oxygen is more concentrated in an alveolus than in a capillary.

IN YOUR NOTEBOOK If the walls between the alveoli were broken down, surface area for gas exchange would decrease.

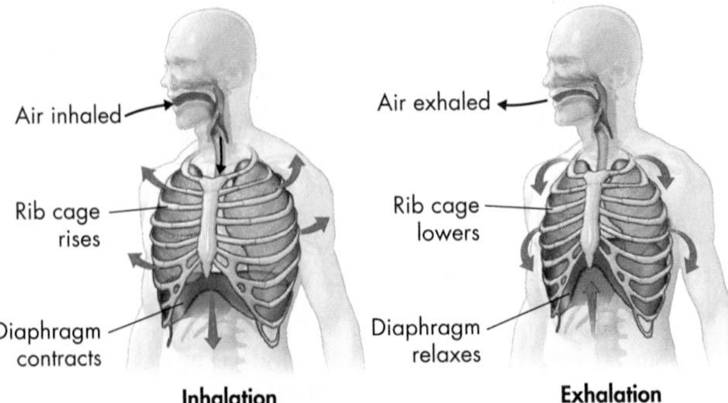

FIGURE 33–17 Breathing During inhalation, the rib cage rises and the diaphragm contracts, increasing the size of the chest cavity. During exhalation, the rib cage lowers and the diaphragm relaxes, decreasing the size of the chest cavity. Humans have some conscious control over breathing—when they swim or play an instrument, for example.

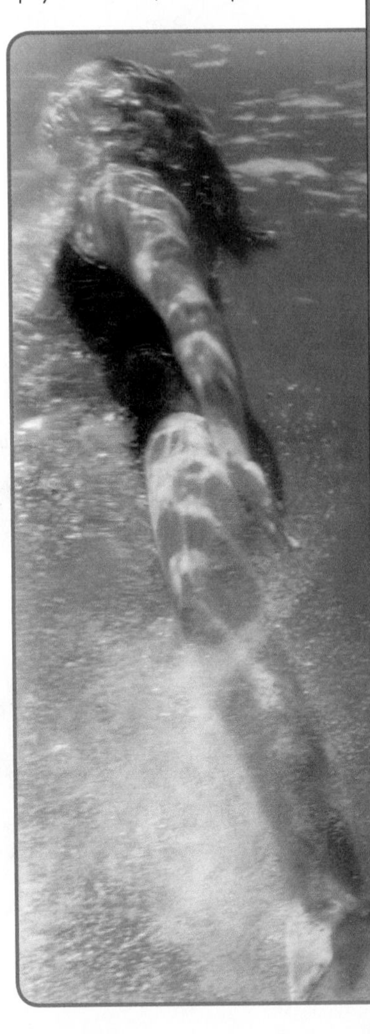

Inhalation The lungs are sealed in two sacs, called pleural membranes, inside the chest cavity. At the bottom of the chest cavity is a large dome-shaped muscle known as the **diaphragm.**

As **Figure 33–17** shows, when you inhale, the diaphragm contracts and flattens. Muscles between the ribs also contract, raising the rib cage. These actions increase the volume of the chest cavity. Because the chest cavity is tightly sealed, this creates a partial vacuum inside the cavity. Atmospheric pressure does the rest, filling the lungs as air rushes into the breathing passages.

Exhalation During ordinary breathing, exhalation is usually passive. Both the rib cage and the diaphragm relax. This relaxation decreases the volume of the chest cavity and makes air pressure in the chest cavity greater than atmospheric pressure. Air rushes back out of the lungs. To blow out a candle, speak, sing, or yell, however, you need more force than passive exhalation provides. The extra force is provided by muscles between the ribs and abdominal muscles, which contract vigorously as the diaphragm relaxes.

The system works only because the chest cavity is sealed. If a wound punctures the chest—even if it does not affect the lungs directly—air may leak into the chest cavity and make breathing impossible. This is one reason chest wounds are always serious.

Breathing and Homeostasis You can control your breathing almost any time you want, to blow up a balloon or to play a trumpet. But this doesn't mean that breathing is purely voluntary. Your nervous system has final control of your breathing muscles whether you are conscious or not. This is why people who drown have water in their lungs. When they lose consciousness, they "breathe" water into their lungs.

Breathing is initiated by the breathing center in the part of the brain stem called the medulla oblongata. Sensory neurons in or near the medulla and in some large blood vessels gather information about carbon dioxide levels in the body and send the information to the breathing center. When stimulated, the breathing center sends nerve impulses that cause the diaphragm and chest muscles to contract, bringing air into the lungs. The higher the blood carbon dioxide level, the stronger the impulses. If the blood carbon dioxide level reaches a critical point, the impulses become so powerful that you cannot keep from breathing.

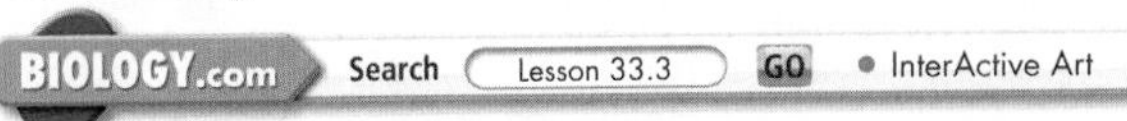

Use Visuals

Have students use **Figure 33–17** and the section under the heading, **Breathing,** to compare the processes of inhalation and exhalation.

Ask How does the volume of the chest cavity change during inhalation? *(It increases.)*

Ask How does the volume of the chest cavity change during exhalation? *(It decreases.)*

Ask How can a chest wound impair breathing? *(The processes of inhalation and exhalation work because the chest cavity is a sealed compartment. If a chest wound opens the chest cavity to the environment outside the body, the pressure changes that drive inhalation and exhalation will not occur.)*

DIFFERENTIATED INSTRUCTION

ELL **English Language Learners** Write the words *inhalation* and *exhalation* on the board. Underline the word parts *in-* and *ex-*. Tell students that *in-* means "in" and *ex-* means "out, or out of." Have students relate the meaning of these word parts to the meanings of the words *inhale* and *exhale*.

BIOLOGY.com Students can use the **InterActive Art: Breathing** to explore the concepts described on this page.

UbD Check for Understanding

ORAL QUESTIONING

Use the following prompts to gauge students' understanding of lesson concepts.

- How is inhalation different from exhalation?
- What evidence supports the fact that breathing is not entirely under conscious control?

ADJUST INSTRUCTION

If responses indicate students do not understand the process or control of breathing, suggest they work in pairs to summarize the information in the section headed **Breathing,** in a short paragraph. Then, have two sets of pairs exchange paragraphs and compare their summaries.

Teach continued

Connect to Health

Invite the school nurse (or other medical professional) to speak to the class about the harmful effects of smoking and smoking cessation programs available in your area. Have students read the information on this page before the nurse's visit. Ask them to prepare written questions about smoking that they would like to ask. Have them submit their questions anonymously to you in advance. Have the nurse respond to as many of the students' questions as possible.

DIFFERENTIATED INSTRUCTION

L1 Struggling Students Help struggling students prepare for the nurse's visit by asking them questions that will help them comprehend the information on this page.

Ask What are three of the most dangerous substances in tobacco smoke? *(nicotine, carbon monoxide, tar)*

Ask Why do smokers often have a "smoker's cough"? *(Tobacco smoke paralyzes the cilia, which leads to an increase in particles stuck to the walls of the respiratory tract. The cough is the body's attempt to clear away these particles.)*

Ask What are some diseases caused by smoking? *(chronic bronchitis, emphysema, lung cancer)*

ELL English Language Learners To help students generate questions, have them start by organizing information in the text in a **Cause-and-Effect Diagram.** For example, they may list the cause "nicotine" and the effects "increases heart rate" and "increases blood pressure." Have students work independently or in pairs to complete their diagrams. Then, ask students to summarize the contents of their diagram in spoken sentences. Finally, have students work independently or with a partner to develop questions for the nurse.

Study Wkbks A/B, Appendix S18, Cause-and-Effect Diagram. **Transparencies,** GO1.

Smoking and the Respiratory System

How does smoking affect the respiratory system?

The upper respiratory tract filters out many particles that could damage the lungs. But some particles and certain kinds of chemicals can bypass those defenses, enter the lungs, and cause serious problems. **Chemicals in tobacco smoke damage structures throughout the respiratory system and have other negative health effects, too.**

Effects on the Respiratory System Three of the most dangerous substances in tobacco smoke are nicotine, carbon monoxide, and tar. Nicotine is an addictive stimulant that increases heart rate and blood pressure. Carbon monoxide is a poisonous gas that blocks hemoglobin from binding with oxygen, thus interfering with oxygen transport in blood. Tar contains at least 60 compounds known to cause cancer.

Tobacco smoke also paralyzes cilia in the trachea. With the cilia out of action, inhaled particles stick to the walls of the respiratory tract or enter the lungs, and smoke-laden mucus is trapped along the airways. Irritation from accumulated particles and mucus triggers a cough—called a smoker's cough—to clear the airways. Smoking also causes the lining of the respiratory tract to swell, which reduces airflow to the alveoli.

FIGURE 33–18 Effect of Smoking on Lungs Chemicals in cigarette smoke damage cilia in the lungs. Over time, particles build up and lead to respiratory diseases such as chronic bronchitis, emphysema, and lung cancer. The damage that smoking can cause to lungs is visible in the bottom photograph.

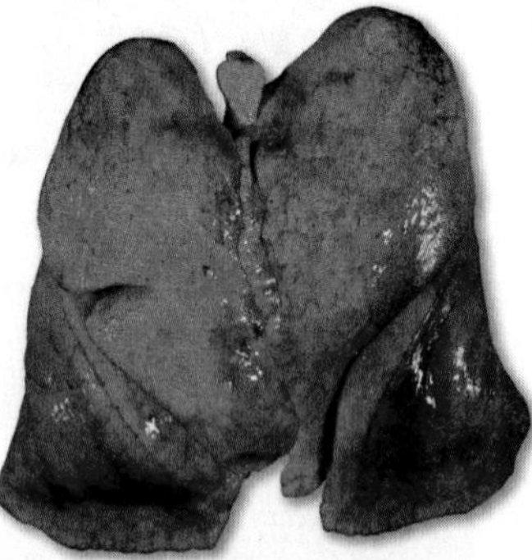

Healthy Lungs

Smoker's Lungs

Diseases Caused by Smoking Damage to the respiratory system from smoking can become permanent and lead to diseases such as chronic bronchitis, emphysema, and lung cancer. Only 30 percent of male smokers live to age 80, but 55 percent of male nonsmokers live to that age. Clearly, smoking reduces life expectancy. The effect of smoking on the lungs can be seen in **Figure 33–18.**

- ***Chronic Bronchitis*** In chronic bronchitis, the bronchi become inflamed and clogged with mucus. Smoking even a moderate number of cigarettes on a regular basis can produce chronic bronchitis. Affected people often find simple activities, like climbing stairs, difficult. Treatments can control symptoms, but there is no cure.
- ***Emphysema*** Long-term smoking can lead to emphysema (em fuh SEE muh). Emphysema is the loss of elasticity and eventual breakdown of lung tissue. This condition makes breathing difficult. People with emphysema cannot get enough oxygen to the body tissues or rid the body of excess carbon dioxide. There is no cure for emphysema, but it can be treated with medication.
- ***Lung Cancer*** Lung cancer is particularly deadly because, by the time it is detected, it usually has spread to other areas of the body. Few people diagnosed with lung cancer live more than five years. About 87 percent of lung cancer deaths are due to smoking.

Quick Facts

SMOKING, CANCER, AND DEATH

An individual who smokes cigarettes is 10 to 20 times more likely to develop lung cancer than a nonsmoker. The more cigarettes an individual smokes, the greater the chances of developing lung cancer and the more likely the individual is to die from lung cancer. In individuals who smoke two or more packs of cigarettes a day, the risk of dying from lung cancer is 20 to 25 times greater than in a nonsmoker. Three of every four deaths from lung cancer in women can be attributed to smoking. Cancer is not the only risk that smokers face. Smokers are also three times more likely to die from a heart attack than are nonsmokers. People who smoke die on average 13–14 years earlier than nonsmokers.

What Secondhand Smoke Does
Exposes people to cancer-causing chemicals such as formaldehyde, arsenic, and ammonia
Aggravates asthma
Increases incidence of ear infections
Causes sticky platelets and damaged blood vessels
Causes up to 70,000 deaths from heart disease each year

FIGURE 33–19 Secondhand Smoke Effects Smokers not only put their own health at risk, but also the health of their family and friends exposed to their smoke.

Other Effects of Smoking Smoking also has very negative effects on the circulatory system. For example, it raises blood pressure by constricting blood vessels, which forces the heart to work harder to deliver enough oxygen.

Nonsmokers exposed to high levels of secondhand smoke are also at greater risk for respiratory and circulatory system disease. Inhaling the smoke of others is particularly dangerous for young children because their lungs are still developing. Studies now indicate that children of smokers are twice as likely as children of nonsmokers to develop asthma or other respiratory problems. Pregnant women who smoke place their babies at risk for many complications, some of which can lead to lifelong problems.

Whatever the age of a smoker, and no matter how long that person has smoked, his or her health can be improved by quitting. Nicotine is a powerful drug with strong addictive qualities that make it very difficult to quit smoking. Considering the medical dangers and the powerful addiction, the best solution is not to start smoking.

MYSTERY CLUE

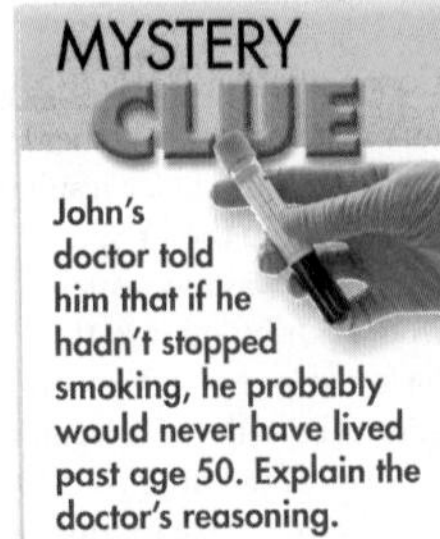

John's doctor told him that if he hadn't stopped smoking, he probably would never have lived past age 50. Explain the doctor's reasoning.

33.3 Assessment

Review Key Concepts

1. a. **Review** Explain the function of the respiratory system.
   b. **Use Analogies** Explain how a molecule of oxygen flowing through the respiratory system is like a commuter driving home from work.
2. a. **Review** Describe the process of gas exchange in the lungs.
   b. **Relate Cause and Effect** Carbon monoxide, a poisonous gas, binds to hemoglobin more easily than oxygen does. Based on this information, why do you think that carbon monoxide alarms in homes have saved many lives?
3. a. **Review** Explain the process of breathing.
   b. **Infer** The brain's breathing center responds to the level of carbon dioxide in the blood, not the level of oxygen. What consequences could this have for people at high altitudes, where oxygen levels are low?
4. a. **Review** Describe the effects of smoking on the respiratory system.
   b. **Apply Concepts** People with emphysema cannot exhale as much carbon dioxide as people with healthy lungs can. Why do you think this leaves them short of breath?

Apply the Big idea

Structure and Function

5. Compare and contrast human respiration with what you learned about respiration in birds and fish in Chapter 27.

BIOLOGY.com Search Lesson 33.3  GO • Self-Test • Lesson Assessment

Connect to Health

Have groups write and perform a skit in which a teen uses communication skills to avoid secondhand smoke.

DIFFERENTIATED INSTRUCTION

L3 Advanced Students Have students research laws about secondhand smoke and share what they learn with the class.

MYSTERY CLUE Smoking raises blood pressure. John was already at risk for high blood pressure because of his high cholesterol. These factors together could lead to premature death. Students can go online to **Biology.com** to gather their evidence.

Assess and Remediate

EVALUATE UNDERSTANDING

Have students make a simplified version of **Figure 33–15** and label the structures. Then, have students complete the 33.3 Assessment.

REMEDIATION SUGGESTION

L1 Struggling Students If students have difficulty with **Question 1b,** ask them to think about the sizes of the passages an oxygen molecule moves through from nose to alveoli.

BIOLOGY.com Students can check their understanding of lesson concepts with the **Self-Test** assessment. They can then take an online version of the **Lesson Assessment.**

Assessment Answers

1a. It takes in oxygen and releases carbon dioxide.

1b. Commuters drive on progressively smaller roads as they travel from work to home. An oxygen molecule moves through progressively smaller passageways.

2a. Oxygen diffuses from air in alveoli to blood cells. Carbon dioxide diffuses from blood to air in alveoli.

2b. Carbon monoxide prevents the body from getting the oxygen it needs. Carbon monoxide detectors alert people to high levels of carbon monoxide.

3a. The diaphragm contracts and the rib cage rises, increasing the size of the chest cavity and drawing air into the lungs. Then, the rib cage and diaphragm relax, the volume of the chest cavity decreases, and air is pushed out of the lungs.

3b. Individuals might not get enough oxygen, because the brain's breathing center is not stimulated by blood oxygen levels.

4a. Students should summarize the effects of nicotine, carbon monoxide, and tar.

4b. Sample answer: If too much carbon dioxide remains in the alveoli, then the body cannot inhale enough oxygen to meet its needs.

5. Big idea Students' responses should identify similarities and differences in the process of respiration of humans, birds, and fish.

CHAPTER LAB

Pre-Lab

Introduce students to the concepts they will explore in the chapter lab by assigning the Pre-Lab questions.

Lab

Tell students they will perform the chapter lab *Tidal Volume and Vital Capacity* described in **Lab Manual A.**

 **Struggling Students** A simpler version of the chapter lab is provided in **Lab Manual B.**

SAFETY

Students should not start their experiments until their plans have been approved. Necessary safety precautions will vary based on students' experimental design. Do not let students with latex allergies handle the balloons.

 Look online for **Editable Lab Worksheets.**

 For corresponding pre-lab in the **Foundation Edition,** see page 802.

IN INDIANA ACADEMIC STANDARDS

For the full text of all standards, see the Course Overview in the front matter of this book.

Design Your Own Lab

GUIDED INQUIRY

 NoS.5 Standard laboratory techniques.

Pre-Lab: Tidal Volume and Lung Capacity

Problem What factors can affect lung capacity?

Materials round balloons, metric ruler, meter stick

Lab Manual Chapter 33 Lab

Skills Focus Measure, Form a Hypothesis, Design an Experiment, Interpret Graphs

Connect to the Big idea Your lungs and circulatory system work together to provide the oxygen your cells need for cellular respiration. In your lungs, oxygen diffuses from the air you inhale into your blood. Carbon dioxide, a waste product of cellular respiration, diffuses from your blood into the inhaled air. Your lungs must have a large enough volume, or capacity, to supply all your cells with the oxygen they need.

Most of the time your lungs do not fill to capacity. But they can take in more air when you want to dive underwater or when you want to sing a long phrase without having to take another breath. In this lab, you will measure the volume of air you exhale when you are breathing normally and the volume of air you exhale after you take a deep breath.

Background Questions

a. **Sequence** List in order, from exterior to interior, the parts of the respiratory system that air passes through as you inhale.

b. **Review** Why does oxygen diffuse from inhaled air in the alveoli into the capillaries?

c. **Compare and Contrast** What is the difference between respiration and cellular respiration?

Pre-Lab Questions

Preview the procedure in the lab manual.

1. **Control Variables** What is the one difference between the procedures in Part A and Part B?
2. **Design an Experiment** Why must you use round balloons for this experiment?
3. **Predict** Which do you think will be greater—your estimated vital capacity or your measured vital capacity? Why?

BIOLOGY.com Search Chapter 33 GO

Visit Chapter 33 online to test yourself on chapter content and to find activities to help you learn.

Untamed Science Video Bundle up as the Untamed Science crew journeys to cold climates to show us how some animals handle extreme environments.

Art in Motion View a short animation that shows the beating of the heart as well as the transmission of impulses from the SA and AV nodes.

Art Review Review your understanding of the different parts of the respiratory system.

InterActive Art Watch an animation that shows the process of breathing and the production of sound.

Data Analysis Use electrocardiography to diagnose various heart conditions.

Visual Analogy Compare the structure and function of the circulatory system to a system of highways and secondary roads.

Pre-Lab Answers

BACKGROUND QUESTIONS

a. nose, pharynx, larynx, trachea, bronchi, bronchioles, alveoli

b. The concentration of oxygen is greater in the inhaled air in the alveoli than it is in the blood.

c. Respiration is the process of gas exchange between the body and its external environment. Cellular respiration is the process that releases energy from food in the presence of oxygen.

PRE-LAB QUESTIONS

1. In Part A, the subject takes a normal breath before exhaling normally. In Part B, the subject takes a deep breath before exhaling as much air as possible.
2. Sample answer: It would not be possible to measure the diameter of the balloons with a ruler if the balloons had a different shape.
3. Students may say that the estimated vital capacity will be larger because they will not be able to capture all the exhaled air in the balloon. Some students may expect their measured capacity to be greater because they have done considerable aerobic training.

Study Guide

Big idea Structure and Function

The functions of the circulatory and respiratory systems are closely connected. Without the circulatory system, oxygen could not be transported from the lungs to the rest of the body. Without the respiratory system, the powerful cardiac muscles would not receive the oxygen they need to drive the circulatory system.

33.1 The Circulatory System

The circulatory system transports oxygen, nutrients, and other substances throughout the body, and removes wastes from tissues.

Powerful contractions of the myocardium pump blood through the circulatory system.

As blood flows through the circulatory system, it moves through three types of blood vessels—arteries, capillaries, and veins.

myocardium (949)
atrium (949)
ventricle (949)
valve (950)
pulmonary circulation (950)
systemic circulation (950)
pacemaker (951)
artery (952)
capillary (952)
vein (952)

33.2 Blood and the Lymphatic System

Plasma is about 90 percent water and 10 percent dissolved gases, salts, nutrients, enzymes, hormones, waste products, plasma proteins, cholesterol, and other important compounds.

The main function of red blood cells is to transport oxygen.

White blood cells guard against infection, fight parasites, and attack bacteria.

Blood clotting is made possible by plasma proteins and cell fragments called platelets.

The lymphatic system is a network of vessels, nodes, and organs that collects the lymph that leaves capillaries, "screens" it for microorganisms, and returns it to the circulatory system.

Three common and serious diseases of the circulatory system are heart disease, stroke, and high blood pressure.

Research indicates that high cholesterol levels, along with other risk factors, lead to atherosclerosis and higher risk of heart attack.

plasma (954)
red blood cell (954)
hemoglobin (954)
white blood cell (955)
platelet (955)
lymph (956)
atherosclerosis (958)

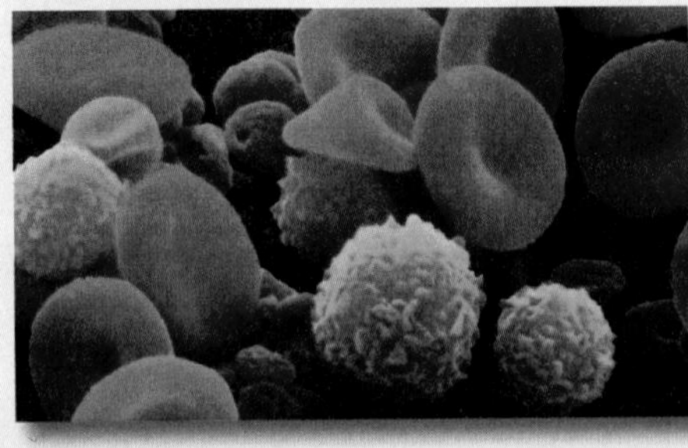

33.3 The Respiratory System

The human respiratory system picks up oxygen from the air we inhale and releases carbon dioxide into the air we exhale.

Oxygen and carbon dioxide are exchanged across the walls of alveoli and capillaries. Chemical properties of blood and red blood cells allow for efficient transport of gases throughout the body.

Movements of the diaphragm and rib cage change air pressure in the chest cavity during inhalation and exhalation.

Chemicals in tobacco smoke damage structures throughout the respiratory system and have other negative health effects, too.

pharynx (964)
trachea (964)
larynx (964)
bronchus (964)
alveolus (964)
diaphragm (967)

Think Visually

Make a two-column table. Title the first column Structure and the second column Function. Fill in the table with the structures described in this chapter—from both circulatory and respiratory systems—and their functions.

BIOLOGY.com Search Chapter 33 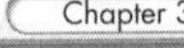 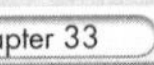 GO  • Match It 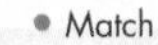 • Chapter Assessment

UbD Performance Tasks

SUMMATIVE TASK Have students work in pairs to make a pamphlet entitled *Your Circulatory and Respiratory Systems—An Owner's Manual.* Explain that the pamphlet should be directed to a teen audience and contain information about the care of these body systems. Pamphlets should include specific tips for keeping these body systems healthy, both now and in the future. Encourage students to use an attractive format for their pamphlets and to include illustrations.

TRANSFER TASK Have students imagine a museum display that allows visitors to walk through a larger-than-life model of the circulatory, respiratory, or lymphatic system. Have them work in pairs to write a guidebook for use by museum guests as they walk through this exhibit. The guidebook should include structures of the system, functions of those structures, and diseases that can strike the system. Suggest that they draw a floor plan or diagram of the display.

Study Online

REVIEW AND ASSESSMENT RESOURCES

Editable Worksheets Pages of Study Workbooks A and B, Lab Manuals A and B, and the Assessment Resources Book are available online. These documents can be easily edited using a word-processing program.

Lesson Overview Have students reread the Lesson Overviews to help them study chapter concepts.

Vocabulary Review The *Flash Cards* and *Match It* provide an interactive way to review chapter vocabulary.

Chapter Assessment Have students take an online version of the Chapter 33 Assessment.

Standardized Test Prep Students can take an online version of the Standardized Test Prep. You will receive their scores along with ideas for remediation.

Diagnostic and Benchmark Tests Use these tests to monitor your students' progress and supply remediation.

Answers

THINK VISUALLY

The left column of students' tables should list structures of the circulatory and respiratory systems, such as arteries, veins, aorta, heart, lungs, larynx, trachea, pharynx, and alveoli. In the right column, the functions of each structure should be described.

ASSESSMENT

Lesson 33.1

UNDERSTAND KEY CONCEPTS

1. c **2.** d **3.** a

4. Pulmonary circulation carries blood between the heart and the lungs. Systemic circulation carries blood between heart and the rest of the body.

5. Blood from the body enters the right atrium. It moves from the right atrium to the right ventricle. Blood is pumped from the right ventricle to the lungs. It returns to the heart in the left atrium. From the left atrium, it moves to the left ventricle and is then pumped to the body.

6. Heart valves allow blood to flow in only one direction. Valves are also found in veins.

7. The pacemaker controls the rate at which the heart beats.

8. The heart beats in a two-step pattern of contraction; first the atria contract, and then the ventricles contract.

9. Arteries are wide vessels with thick walls. Capillaries are narrow vessels with walls just one cell thick. Veins are wide vessels with walls that are thicker than capillary walls but thinner than artery walls.

10. Systolic pressure is the force of the blood in the arteries when the ventricles contract. Diastolic pressure is the force of the blood in the arteries when the ventricles relax.

THINK CRITICALLY

11. The most likely experimental design is to measure each subject's heart rate at rest to determine the normal heart rate and then again at frequent, timed intervals after the subject has exercised, until the heart rate returns to normal.

12. The powerful pressure produced when the heart contracts keeps blood moving in one direction in the arteries.

Lesson 33.2

UNDERSTAND KEY CONCEPTS

13. d **14.** b **15.** a **16.** c

17. Plasma is the fluid that carries other blood components and contains proteins involved in immune reactions and blood clotting. Platelets cluster around wounds and release proteins that start a series of reactions resulting in blood clots. White blood cells attack foreign substances and organisms. Red blood cells transport oxygen.

18. Functions of the lymphatic system are to collect fluid lost by the blood and return it to the circulatory system, filter bacteria and other microorganisms from the fluid, house white blood cells, and absorb fat and fat-soluble vitamins from the digestive tract.

19. LDL is known as "bad cholesterol" because it often becomes part of plaque, causing trouble in the circulatory system. HDL, on the other hand, helps remove excess cholesterol from the body, so it is known as "good cholesterol."

THINK CRITICALLY

20. A person with a low red blood cell count has fewer red blood cells to transport oxygen to cells. Without adequate oxygen, the production of energy by cellular respiration is reduced.

21. Some strokes are caused by clots, so individuals who have had a stroke may decrease their chance of having another one by taking aspirin.

22. Removal of the lymph nodes can lessen the body's ability to fight disease. The lymph nodes filter many pathogens from the lymph before it is returned to the circulatory system. The lymph nodes also house white blood cells, called lymphocytes, which help fight infection.

33 Assessment

IN The numbers following the questions refer to Indiana's Academic Standards for Biology I.

33.1 The Circulatory System

Understand Key Concepts

1. The circulatory system includes the
a. lungs, heart, and brain.
b. lungs, blood vessels, and heart.
c. heart, blood, and blood vessels.
d. heart, arteries, and veins.

2. The upper chambers of the heart are the
a. ventricles.
b. septa.
c. myocardia.
d. atria.

3. Blood leaving the heart for the body passes through a large blood vessel called the
a. aorta.
b. vena cava.
c. pulmonary vein.
d. pulmonary artery.

4. Compare pulmonary circulation and systemic circulation.

5. Trace the flow of blood through the heart starting with the right atrium.

6. What is the function of valves in the heart? In what other structures of the circulatory system are valves found?

7. Describe the function of the pacemaker.

8. Describe how the heart beats.

9. Compare the size and structure of arteries, capillaries, and veins.

10. Distinguish between systolic pressure and diastolic pressure.

Think Critically

11. Design an Experiment Design an experiment that determines the amount of time needed for a person's heart rate to return to an at-rest rate after exercise.

12. Draw Conclusions Some large veins have one-way valves, which keep blood flowing in one direction. Why don't arteries need similar valves?

33.2 Blood and the Lymphatic System

Understand Key Concepts

13. Cells that protect the body by engulfing foreign cells or producing antibodies are
a. red blood cells. **c.** platelets.
b. cilia. **d.** white blood cells.

14. Nutrients and wastes are exchanged with body cells through the walls of
a. veins. **c.** arteries.
b. capillaries. **d.** atria.

15. The protein found in red blood cells that transports oxygen is called B.1.2
a. hemoglobin. **c.** prothrombin.
b. fibrinogen. **d.** thrombin.

16. The process shown below is made possible by plasma proteins and cell fragments called
a. fibrins. **c.** platelets.
b. thrombins. **d.** lymphocytes.

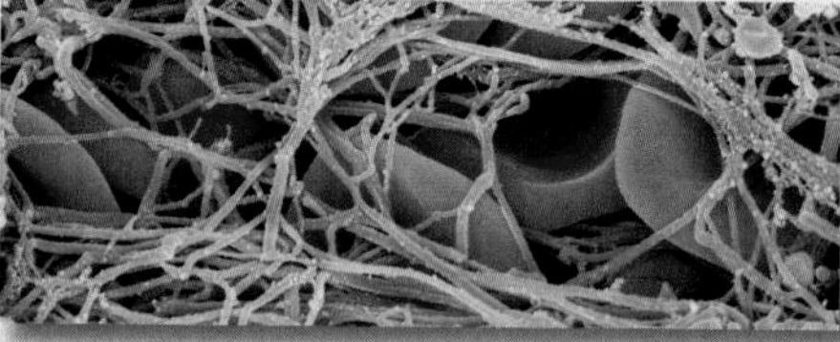

17. Describe the functions of each major component in blood.

18. What are the primary functions of the lymphatic system?

19. Why is LDL known as "bad" cholesterol? Why is HDL known as "good" cholesterol?

Think Critically

20. Apply Concepts Why would a person with a low red blood cell count feel tired?

21. Infer Aspirin reduces the clot-forming ability of the blood. Why would a doctor prescribe aspirin for someone who has had a stroke?

22. Predict Explain how the removal of someone's lymph nodes can affect his or her ability to fight disease.

33.3 The Respiratory System

Understand Key Concepts

23. The tiny hollow air sacs in the lungs where gas exchange takes place are the
    a. alveoli. c. capillaries.
    b. lymph nodes. d. bronchioles.

24. Two highly elastic folds of tissue known as the vocal cords are found in the
    a. larynx. c. trachea.
    b. pharynx. d. bronchi.

25. The large flat muscle that moves up and down and alters the volume of the chest cavity is the
    a. trachea. c. diaphragm.
    b. epiglottis. d. larynx.

26. What part of the brain controls involuntary breathing?

27. What are three dangerous substances in tobacco smoke? Describe how each affects the body.

28. How does emphysema affect the respiratory system?

Think Critically

29. **Infer** Tobacco smoke can kill white blood cells in the respiratory tract, the cells that help keep the respiratory system clean by consuming debris. How do you think this contributes to the development of smoker's cough?

30. **Analyze Data** The table shows the relative blood flow through some organs in the human body—that is, the percentage of blood that flows through a given organ. Through which organ(s) does all of the blood flow? Explain the effect of exercise on blood flow to skeletal muscles. NoS.3

Blood Flow Through Human Organs

Organ	Percentage of Total Flow
Brain	14%
Heart	5%
Kidneys	22%
Liver	13%
Lungs	100%
Skeletal muscles	18%
Skeletal muscles during exercise	75%

solve the CHAPTER MYSTERY

IN THE BLOOD

Both John and Lila have a genetic disease called familial hypercholesterolemia, which is caused by a gene defect on chromosome 19. John is heterozygous for the disorder. Although his liver cells make a mixture of normal and defective LDL receptors, his blood cholesterol levels were so high that he had serious atherosclerosis by age 35. Most people with this disease have had a heart attack by age 60.

Lila is homozygous for the defective allele—a very rare condition. Her liver cells do not produce any functional LDL receptors. Her atherosclerosis became apparent when she was only 4 years old. Fatty deposits can be seen in the corneas of her eyes and beneath the skin near her elbows and knees.

Research on this genetic defect helped uncover the role of liver cell LDL receptors in regulating blood cholesterol. Researchers then applied that information to cases of high cholesterol among the general public. The result was the development of several new classes of drugs that are helping some people live longer.

1. **Apply Concepts** Is familial hypercholesterolemia a dominant or recessive disorder? Explain your answer.
2. **Infer** Most heterozygous patients can keep their LDL levels under control with medication that prevents their liver from making cholesterol. But these medications generally do not lower the LDL levels of homozygous patients. Why do you think that is so?
3. **Connect to the Big idea** If an individual knows that hypercholesterolemia runs in his or her family, what steps can he or she take to live a long and healthy life?

 Search 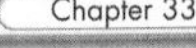  • Untamed Science Video • Chapter Mystery 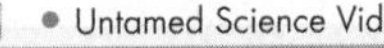

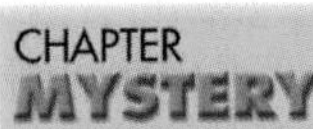
After students have read through the Chapter Mystery solution, discuss the cause and symptoms of familial hypercholesterolemia.

Ask How does familial hypercholesterolemia affect homeostasis in the body? *(Familial hypercholesterolemia affects the body's ability to control cholesterol levels, which disrupts homeostasis and can result in atherosclerosis and lead to heart attacks.)*

Ask Why has Lila shown symptoms at such a young age? *(She is homozygous for the allele that causes familial hypercholesterolemia.)*

Ask Can Lila's liver cells take in cholesterol from her blood? Why or why not? *(No, her liver cells lack receptors for LDL.)*

CHAPTER MYSTERY ANSWERS

1. The allele for familial hypercholesterolemia is recessive.
2. Homozygous patients have no LDL receptors, so medications to keep their liver cells from producing cholesterol do not help the body control the cholesterol that is consumed in food.
3. Big idea A healthy diet and exercise are two steps an individual with a family history of familial hypercholesterolemia can take to keep healthy. Medication may also help some individuals.

To learn how some animals survive and thrive in cold climates, watch **Chillin' in the Cold.**

Lesson 33.3

UNDERSTAND KEY CONCEPTS

23. a **24.** a **25.** c

26. Involuntary breathing is controlled by the breathing center in a part of the brain stem called the medulla oblongata.

27. Three of the most dangerous substances in tobacco smoke are nicotine, carbon monoxide, and tar. Nicotine increases heart rate and blood pressure. Carbon monoxide blocks the transport of oxygen by hemoglobin in the blood. Tar contains compounds that cause cancer.

28. Emphysema is a loss of elasticity in lung tissue. This makes it difficult for the lungs to bring in enough oxygen and eliminate enough carbon dioxide.

THINK CRITICALLY

29. When tobacco smoke kills white blood cells in the respiratory tract, the amount of debris found in the respiratory system increases. This leads to increased coughing as the body attempts to clear the debris.

30. All of the blood flows through the lungs to pick up oxygen. During exercise, much more blood flows through the skeletal muscles to fuel the production of energy needed for muscle contraction.

31. Sample answer: When I cough, the sound changes from a muffled roar to a loud, sharp rushing sound.

Connecting Concepts

USE SCIENCE GRAPHICS

32. Student A: minute 6; Student B: minute 7

33. Student A is most likely in better physical condition than Student B because his or her heart beats fewer times per minute to maintain the same level of effort as Student B. Also, Student A's heart returns to its normal rate much faster than Student B's, which also indicates a more efficient circulatory system.

34. During exercise, you would expect blood pressure to rise because blood is moving more quickly through the circulatory system. Also, breathing rate increases to keep pace with the increase in the amount of gas exchange taking place in the muscles of the body.

WRITE ABOUT SCIENCE

35. Answers will vary. Students' responses might list an unhealthy diet or not exercising regularly as things they do that are harmful to their circulatory and respiratory systems. They might explain how they will eat more healthfully or join a sports team to get more exercise.

36. Big idea Students' responses should mention that the respiratory system picks up oxygen from the air we inhale and releases carbon dioxide into the air we exhale. They should also mention that the circulatory system delivers the oxygen to the cells of the body and picks up the waste carbon dioxide from the cells. Proper functioning of these systems is necessary for the survival of the cells, tissues, and organs that make up the entire body.

31. Use Models Construct a simple stethoscope out of rubber tubing and a metal funnel. Listen for the sounds of air rushing into and out of your lungs and record a description. How does the sound change when you cough? NoS.6

Connecting Concepts

Use Science Graphics NoS.3

The following graph is based on pulse rates taken each minute for two students doing the same exercises. The exercises begin at minute 1 and end at minute 8. Use the graph to answer questions 32–34.

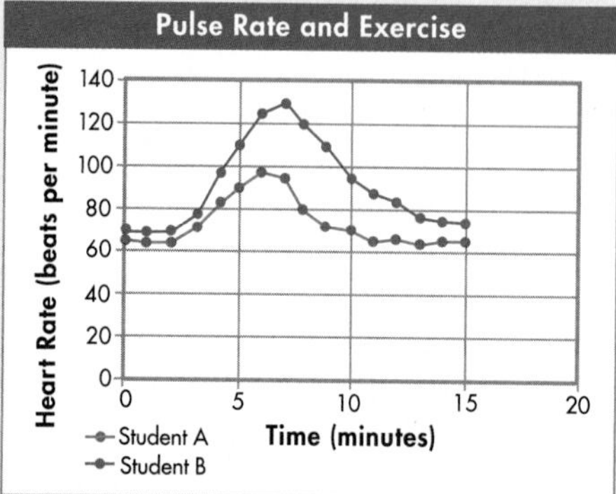

32. Interpret Graphs At about which minute did each student reach his or her highest heart rate?

33. Draw Conclusions Which of the two students is most likely in better physical condition? What evidence from the graph supports your answer?

34. Predict What other changes in the circulatory and respiratory systems would you expect to take place in the time interval shown?

Write About Science NoS.3

35. Explanation Make a list of the things you do that affect your circulatory and respiratory systems. After completing your list, place a check mark next to those that are harmful. Pick one harmful habit and write a paragraph explaining how you could change or break it.

36. Assess the Big idea Describe the relationship between the human circulatory system and the respiratory system. How does the proper functioning of those systems affect other body systems?

IN NoS.3

High blood pressure is a major risk factor for heart disease in the United States. By age 44, about 25 percent of Americans have high blood pressure, and many of them do not know it. Use the graph to answer questions 37 and 38.

37. Interpret Graphs In what age group do women start to have a higher incidence of high blood pressure than men?

38. Calculate Between which age groups do you find the largest percentage increase in cases of high blood pressure? MATH

a. women between 20–34 and 35–44 years of age
b. men between 20–34 and 35–44 years of age
c. women between 55–64 and 65–74 years of age
d. men between 45–54 and 55–64 years of age

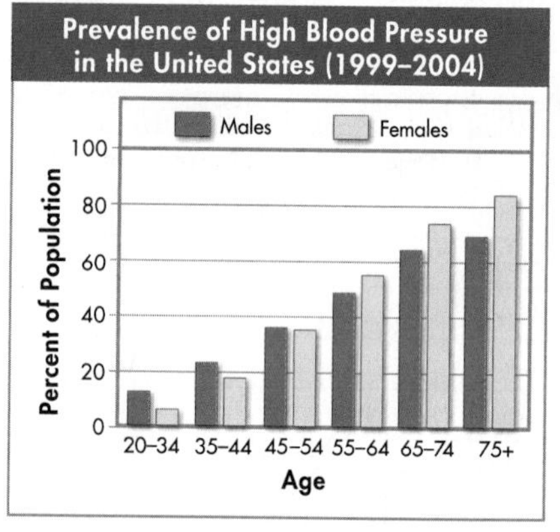

974 Chapter 33 • Assessment

Analyzing Data

PURPOSE Students will analyze data to understand the prevalence of high blood pressure by age and gender in the United States.

PLANNING Review with students the structure of a bar graph and how it can be used to compare two sets of data.

ANSWERS

37. 55–64

38. a

Standardized Test Practice for Indiana

Multiple Choice

1. In the human heart, oxygen-rich blood would be found in the
   A right atrium and the right ventricle.
   B right atrium and the left atrium.
   C left atrium and the left ventricle.
   D right ventricle and the left ventricle.

2. Which statement BEST describes an interaction between the circulatory system and the respiratory system that helps maintain homeostasis?
   A Blood plasma transports salts, nutrients, and proteins through the body to keep it healthy.
   B The diaphragm and rib cage work together to move air into and out of the lungs.
   C Lymph nodes filter out bacteria that could cause disease.
   D Blood cells pick up and carry oxygen from the lungs to the body's cells.

3. A heartbeat begins with an impulse from the
   A nervous system.
   B sinoatrial node.
   C atrioventricular node.
   D aorta.

4. All of the following are components of human blood EXCEPT
   A plasma.
   B mucus.
   C phagocytes.
   D platelets.

5. Nicotine in tobacco
   A is not addictive.
   B lowers blood pressure.
   C blocks the transport of oxygen.
   D increases heart rate.

6. Antibodies are produced by
   A red blood cells.
   B platelets.
   C B lymphocytes.
   D hormones.

B.1.2

Questions 7–10

Use the diagram below to answer the questions that follow.

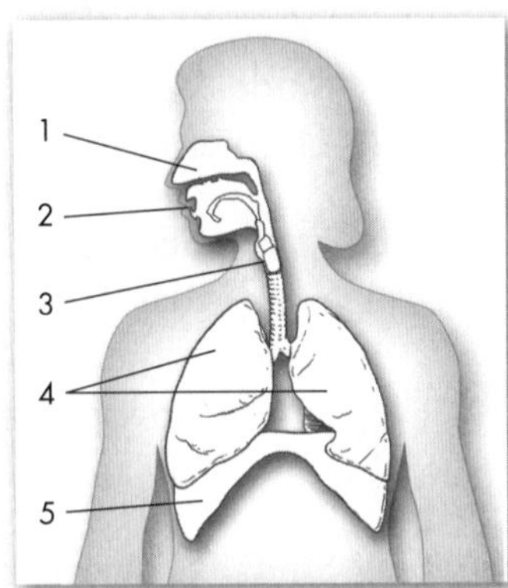

7. Which structure's primary function is to warm and moisten inhaled air?
   A 1
   B 3
   C 4
   D 5

8. Which structure contains the vocal cords?
   A 1
   B 2
   C 3
   D 4

9. Damage to which structure can lead to emphysema?
   A 2
   B 3
   C 4
   D 5

10. Which structure contains alveoli?
    A 2
    B 3
    C 4
    D 5

Open-Ended Response

11. Explain why the risk factors for heart disease and strokes are similar.

If You Have Trouble With . . .

Question	1	2	3	4	5	6	7	8	9	10	11
See Lesson	33.1	33.3	33.1	33.2	33.3	33.2	33.3	33.3	33.3	33.3	33.2

ASSESSMENT

Answers

1. C
2. D
3. B
4. B
5. D
6. C
7. A
8. C
9. C
10. C
11. Heart disease and strokes can both be caused by narrowing of the arteries—a result of the plaque buildup within the arteries. Therefore, both illnesses have similar risk factors.

Test-Taking Tip

INTERPRET VISUALS

Tell students to watch for questions, like the ones on this page, that require them to identify structures in a diagram. Explain that when they are asked about structures shown in a diagram, they should first identify each structure and think about its function. Then, they should answer the questions about the diagram.

CHAPTER PLANNER 34 Endocrine and Reproductive Systems

Chapter Contents	IN	Time	Core Resources
Chapter Preview			**Student Edition,** pp. 976–977 **Chapter Mystery,** p. 977
34.1 The Endocrine System Hormones and Glands • Hormone Action	B.1.2	1/2 period 1/4 block	**Student Edition,** pp. 978–981 **Study Workbook A** 34.1 Worksheets L2 Biology.com *Art Review:* Major Endocrine Glands • *Art in Motion:* Steroid and Nonsteroid Hormones • 34.1 Self-Test • 34.1 Lesson Assessment
34.2 Glands of the Endocrine System The Human Endocrine Glands • Control of the Endocrine System		1 period 1/2 block	**Student Edition,** pp. 982–987 **Study Workbook A** 34.2 Worksheets L2 Biology.com *Data Analysis:* Diabetes **Assessment Resources Book** Visual Quiz L2
34.3 The Reproductive System Sexual Development • The Male Reproductive System • The Female Reproductive System • Sexually Transmitted Diseases	B.6.4	1 1/2 periods 3/4 block	**Student Edition,** pp. 988–994 Inquiry 34.3 Quick Lab, p. 990 L2 **Study Workbook A** 34.3 Worksheets L2 **Assessment Resources Book** Visual Quizzes L2
34.4 Fertilization and Development Fertilization and Early Development • Later Development	B.6.3	1 1/2 periods 3/4 block	**Student Edition,** pp. 995–1001 Inquiry 34.4 Quick Lab, p. 1000 L2 **Study Workbook A** 34.4 Worksheets L2 Biology.com 34.4 Self-Test • 34.4 Lesson Assessment
Chapter Pre-Lab		1 period 1/2 block	**Student Edition,** p. 1002 L2 **Lab Manual A** *Diagnosing Endocrine Disorders* L2

Differentiated Instruction Tools

Study Workbook B includes worksheets with lesson-level differentiated instruction support and explanations of differentiated instruction teaching strategies.

Lab Manual B includes skills labs, simplified chapter labs, and hands-on activities.

ELL Handbook explains ways to make *Biology* more accessible to ELL students.

Spanish Study Workbook is a Spanish translation of Study Workbook A.

Multilingual Glossary is the glossary translated into ten languages.

Differentiated Instruction Key

- L1 Special Needs or Struggling Students
- ELL English Language Learners
- LPR Less Proficient Readers
- L2 On-Level Students
- L3 Advanced Students

Additional Resources

Biology.com Untamed Science Video • Vocabulary Flash Cards

Study Workbook B 34.1 Worksheets L1 ELL LPR
Spanish Study Workbook 34.1 Worksheets ELL
Biology.com 34.1 Lesson Overview • 34.1 Lesson Notes

Study Workbook B 34.2 Worksheets L1 ELL LPR
Spanish Study Workbook 34.2 Worksheets ELL
Biology.com 34.2 Lesson Overview • 34.2 Lesson Notes • 34.2 Self-Test • 34.2 Lesson Assessment

Study Workbook B 34.3 Worksheets L1 ELL LPR
Spanish Study Workbook 34.3 Worksheets ELL
Biology.com 34.3 Lesson Overview • 34.3 Lesson Notes • 34.3 Self-Test • 34.3 Lesson Assessment

Study Workbook B 34.4 Worksheets L1 ELL LPR
Spanish Study Workbook 34.4 Worksheets ELL
Biology.com 34.4 Lesson Overview • 34.4 Lesson Notes

Lab Manual B *Diagnosing Endocrine Disorders* • Data Analysis: *Menstrual Cycle* • Hands-On Activity: *Growing Up* L1 ELL LPR

Chapter Review

Student Edition Study Guide, p. 1003 L2
Study Workbook A Chapter 34 Vocabulary Review L2 • Chapter 34 Chapter Mystery/21st Century Skills Activity L2 L3
Transparencies, pp. 373–381 L1 ELL LPR L2
Biology.com Untamed Science Video • Editable Worksheets of Study Workbooks A and B and Lab Manuals A and B • Chapter 34 Flash Cards and Crossword Puzzle

Untamed Science DVD • Classroom Resources CD (includes lesson presentations and editable worksheets)

Chapter Assessment

Student Edition Assessment, pp. 1004–1007 L2
Study Workbook B Chapter 34 Chapter Review L1 ELL LPR • Chapter 34 Taking a Standardized Test L1 ELL LPR
Assessment Resources Book Chapter 34 Test A L2 • Chapter 34 Test B L1 ELL LPR
Biology.com Chapter 34 Assessment • Editable Worksheets of Chapter 34 Visual Quizzes and Chapter 34 Tests A and B

Exam*View* *Assessment Suite* • Classroom Resources CD (includes lesson presentations and editable worksheets)

Time: 1 period, 1/2 block

Pressed for Time?

Preview the Chapter Read the Key Questions for all the lessons in this chapter.

Cover the Chapter Quickly Have students read *Hormones and Glands* in Lesson 34.1 and go over Figure 34–1. Assign *The Human Endocrine Glands* in Lesson 34.2. In Lesson 34.3, have students read *The Male Reproductive System* and *The Female Reproductive System* and go over Figures 34–11 and 34–13. Assign the Fertilization section of *Fertilization and Development,* and have students look over the figures showing different stages of human embryonic development in Lesson 34.4.

Assess Assign question 1 in the 34.1 Assessment, question 1 in the 34.2 Assessment, questions 2, 3, and 5 in the 34.3 Assessment, and question 1a in the 34.4 Assessment. Assign the "Think Visually" activity on p. 1003, and questions 3, 4, 6–8, 10–16, and 18–24 in the Chapter 34 Assessment.

Connect to the Big Idea

Big idea Ask students to imagine how this painter feels as he walks on the Golden Gate Bridge. Point out that in the course of a day, their bodies react to many different situations, although not every situation is as stressful as what this painter is experiencing! Ask students to identify situations in their own lives that can cause stress or anxiety. *(Sample answers: quizzes, athletic competitions, musical performances)* Then, have them identify some physical reactions they have to these stressors. *(Sample answers: sweating, increased heart rate, increased rate of respiration)* Have them speculate on how the body might signal itself to react this way. Then, ask them to anticipate the answer to the question, **How does the body use chemical signals to maintain homeostasis?**

CHAPTER MYSTERY Have students read the Chapter Mystery and predict how Lisa's fatigue, loss of menstrual period, and stress fracture may all be related to her behavior. Use the situation described in the Chapter Mystery to guide students to the conclusion that disruption of homeostasis in the body can have serious multiple effects on body systems and their functions.

BIOLOGY.com Have students preview the chapter vocabulary terms using the **Flash Cards.**

IN INDIANA ACADEMIC STANDARDS

For the full text of all standards, see the Course Overview in the front matter of this book.

Key standards: Chapter 34 covers key ideas from Standard 6: Cellular Reproduction and Gene Expression, including **B.6.3** Specialization and organization in multicellular organisms and **B.6.4** Meiosis.

34 Endocrine and Reproductive Systems

Big idea Homeostasis

Q: How does the body use chemical signals to maintain homeostas

BIOLOGY.com Search Chapter 34 GO • Flash Cards

976

UbD Understanding by Design

Chapter 34 includes information on the endocrine system, the reproductive system, fertilization, and development. The graphic organizer at the right shows how the chapter Big Idea—Homeostasis—is related to the chapter Essential Question and the lesson-level Guiding Questions. These ideas and questions help students build toward the Unit 8 Enduring Understanding: *The human body is a complex system. The coordinated functions of its many structures support life processes and maintain homeostasis.*

PERFORMANCE GOALS

Students' knowledge of the Chapter 34 content will be demonstrated by their responses to questions, discussion prompts, and writing prompts. Students will also use graphic organizers and models to show their understanding. Performance tasks that ask students to synthesize chapter content include creating a time line to show how the endocrine and reproductive systems interact during an individual's lifetime and writing a response to a misleading advertisement about hormones.

INDIANA ACADEMIC STANDARDS FOR SCIENCE

Nature of Science NoS.3; **Cellular Chemistry** B.1.2; **Cellular Reproduction and Gene Expression** B.6.3, B.6.4. See lessons for details.

This painter's endocrine system is partly responsible for the sweaty palms and racing heart he likely experienced his first day on the job.

• Untamed Science Video • Chapter Mystery

CHAPTER MYSTERY

OUT OF STRIDE

Lisa trained hard during spring track and over the summer. But as the new school year approached, she wasn't satisfied. For her cross-country team to win the state championship, she felt that she needed to be faster. A teammate suggested she lose a few pounds. Lisa had already lost weight over the summer, but she decided to lose some more.

In addition to her strenuous workouts, Lisa stopped snacking before practice and avoided high-calorie foods. She did lose weight. But she was always tired. She also noticed that she had not had a menstrual period in four months. The week before the championship meet, she collapsed in pain at practice. She had suffered a stress fracture to her lower leg. Her season was over.

Lisa's doctor told her that all of her symptoms were related. As you read this chapter, look for clues to explain why excessive exercise and dieting had these effects on Lisa. Then, solve the mystery.

Never Stop Exploring Your World. Finding the solution to the Out of Stride mystery is just the beginning. Take a video field trip with the ecogeeks of Untamed Science to see where the mystery leads.

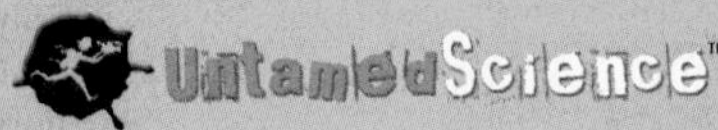

What's Online

BIOLOGY.com Extend your reach by using these and other digital assets offered at Biology.com.

CHAPTER MYSTERY
Follow the chapter mystery to find out how excessive exercise and dieting can affect the endocrine system and disrupt homeostasis.

UNTAMED SCIENCE VIDEO
Why do you stand tall or run scared when presented with danger? Follow the Untamed Science crew as they explore the answer to this question in the short online video **Fight or Flight!**

ART REVIEW
Students use a drag-and-drop version of **Figure 34–1** to study the major endocrine glands.

ART IN MOTION
Using this feature, students can watch a short animation of steroid hormone and nonsteroid hormone pathways.

DATA ANALYSIS
In this activity, students explore the statistical relationship between diabetes and obesity by examining graphs and correlation data.

Chapter 34 Big Idea: Homeostasis

Chapter 34 EQ: How does the body use chemical signals to maintain homeostasis?

- **34.1 GQ:** How does the body send and receive chemical signals?
- **34.2 GQ:** What life processes are regulated by hormones?
- **34.3 GQ:** What body structures enable humans to produce offspring?
- **34.4 GQ:** How does a human develop from a single cell to a newborn baby?

LESSON 34.1

Getting Started

Objectives

34.1.1 Describe the structure and function of the endocrine system.

34.1.2 Explain how hormones work.

Student Resources

Study Workbooks A and B, 34.1 Worksheets

Spanish Study Workbook, 34.1 Worksheets

 Lesson Overview • Lesson Notes
- Activities: Art Review, Art in Motion
- Assessment: Self-Test, Lesson Assessment

 For corresponding lesson in the **Foundation Edition**, see pages 810–812.

Activate Prior Knowledge

Ask What are some examples of how body systems work together? *(Sample answer: The digestive system breaks down food molecules into smaller molecules that are carried throughout the body by the circulatory system.)*

Ask How would homeostasis be affected if there wasn't a way for the functions of different systems to be coordinated? *(Sample answer: The systems would not be able to work together smoothly.)*

Explain that substances released by the endocrine system play a critical role in the coordination of body systems.

IN INDIANA ACADEMIC STANDARDS

For the full text of all standards, see the Course Overview in the front matter of this book.

B.1.2 Understand that the shape of a molecule determines its role in the many different types of cellular processes including metabolism, homeostasis, growth and development, and heredity, and understand that the majority of these processes involve proteins that act as enzymes.

34.1 The Endocrine System

 B.1.2 Molecules and cellular processes.

Key Questions

What are the components of the endocrine system?

How do hormones affect cells?

Vocabulary

hormone
target cell
exocrine gland
endocrine gland
prostaglandin

Taking Notes

Compare/Contrast Table As you read, make a table that compares and contrasts the two different types of hormones.

THINK ABOUT IT If you had to get a message to just one or two friends, what would you do? One solution would be to make a telephone call that would carry your message directly to those friends over telephone wires. But what if you wanted to send a message to thousands of people? You could broadcast your message on the radio so that everyone tuned to a particular station could hear it. Just like you, cells send messages, too. They can make a direct call or send out a broadcast.

Hormones and Glands

What are the components of the endocrine system?

Your nervous system works much like a telephone. Many impulses move swiftly over a system of wire-like neurons that carry messages directly from one cell to another. But another system, the endocrine system, is more like a radio, "broadcasting" chemical messages. These chemical messengers, called **hormones,** are released in one part of the body, travel through the blood, and affect cells in other parts of the body. **The endocrine system is made up of glands that release hormones into the blood. Hormones deliver messages throughout the body.** In the same way that a radio broadcast can reach thousands or even millions of people in a large city, hormones can affect almost every cell in the body.

Hormones Hormones act by binding to specific chemical receptors on cell membranes or within cells. Cells that have receptors for a particular hormone are called **target cells.** If a cell does not have receptors for a particular hormone, the hormone has no effect on it.

In general, the body's responses to hormones are slower and longer lasting than its responses to nerve impulses. It may take several minutes, several hours, or even several days for a hormone to have its full effect on its target cells. A nerve impulse, on the other hand, may take only a fraction of a second to reach and affect its target cells.

Many endocrine functions depend on the effects of two opposing hormones. For example, the hormone insulin prompts the liver to convert blood glucose to glycogen and store it. The hormone glucagon prompts the liver to convert glycogen to glucose and release it in the blood. The opposing effects of insulin and glucagon maintain homeostasis by keeping blood glucose levels within a narrow range.

UbD Teach for Understanding

ENDURING UNDERSTANDING The human body is a complex system. The coordinated functions of its many structures support life processes and maintain homeostasis.

GUIDING QUESTION How does the body send and receive chemical signals?

EVIDENCE OF UNDERSTANDING *After completing the lesson, give students this assessment to show they understand how steroid hormones and nonsteroid hormones act on their target cells.* Have students work in pairs or small groups to make a comic strip that depicts the way either a steroid or nonsteroid hormone acts on a cell. Encourage students to be creative and scientifically accurate when making their comic strips.

Glands A gland is an organ that produces and releases a substance, or secretion. **Exocrine glands** release their secretions through tube-like structures (called ducts) either out of the body or directly into the digestive system. Exocrine glands include those that release sweat, tears, and digestive enzymes. **Endocrine glands** usually release their secretions (hormones) directly into the blood, which transports the secretions throughout the body. **Figure 34–1** shows the location of the major endocrine glands. Although not usually considered as endocrine glands, other body structures such as bones, fat tissue, the heart, and the small intestine also produce and release hormones.

In Your Notebook *Make a three-column table. Label the columns Gland, Hormone(s), and Function. Fill in the table as you read.*

MYSTERY CLUE

Fat tissue may send signals to the hypothalamus when fat reserves are low. Lisa's body fat percentage dropped from 17 percent to 9 percent. Could this have affected such signals?

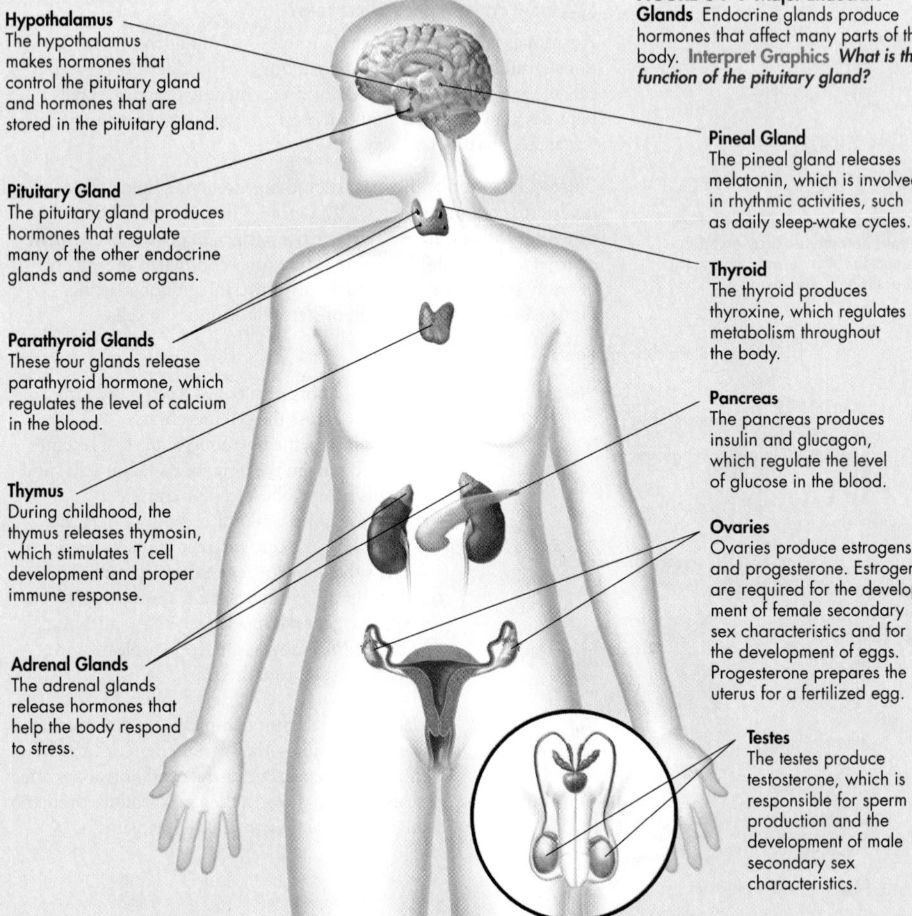

Hypothalamus
The hypothalamus makes hormones that control the pituitary gland and hormones that are stored in the pituitary gland.
Pituitary Gland
The pituitary gland produces hormones that regulate many of the other endocrine glands and some organs.
Parathyroid Glands
These four glands release parathyroid hormone, which regulates the level of calcium in the blood.
Thymus
During childhood, the thymus releases thymosin, which stimulates T cell development and proper immune response.
Adrenal Glands
The adrenal glands release hormones that help the body respond to stress.
Pineal Gland
The pineal gland releases melatonin, which is involved in rhythmic activities, such as daily sleep-wake cycles.
Thyroid
The thyroid produces thyroxine, which regulates metabolism throughout the body.
Pancreas
The pancreas produces insulin and glucagon, which regulate the level of glucose in the blood.
Ovaries
Ovaries produce estrogens and progesterone. Estrogens are required for the development of female secondary sex characteristics and for the development of eggs. Progesterone prepares the uterus for a fertilized egg.
Testes
The testes produce testosterone, which is responsible for sperm production and the development of male secondary sex characteristics.

FIGURE 34–1 Major Endocrine Glands Endocrine glands produce hormones that affect many parts of the body. **Interpret Graphics** *What is the function of the pituitary gland?*

Teach

Use Visuals

Have students read the brief descriptions of each endocrine gland in **Figure 34–1.** Tell them that the next two lessons contain detailed descriptions of most of the endocrine glands shown. Suggest students refer back to this figure as they read about each gland.

Ask Which endocrine gland helps the body respond to stress? *(adrenal gland)*

Ask What characteristic do all endocrine glands share? *(All endocrine glands produce hormones.)*

DIFFERENTIATED INSTRUCTION

LPR Less Proficient Readers As students read through the next two lessons, have them reinforce their comprehension of the detailed descriptions of each endocrine gland by reviewing the summarized descriptions in **Figure 34–1.** You may want to make copies of the figure and pass them out so that students can have a copy to refer to as they read.

MYSTERY CLUE Students should note that Lisa's body fat percentage dropped by almost 50 percent, a drop that was likely to trigger a signal to her hypothalamus. Students can go online to **Biology.com** to gather their evidence.

BIOLOGY.com Students use a drag-and-drop version of **Figure 34–1** to learn about the major endocrine glands in the **Art Review: Major Endocrine Glands.**

Quick Facts

ENDOCRINE DISRUPTORS

The function of the endocrine system can be disrupted by substances in the environment that mimic hormones or interfere with their functions. These substances, called endocrine disruptors, can be synthetic or occur naturally. They have been shown to disrupt the functions of the reproductive systems in several types of wildlife. They also have the potential to disrupt the human endocrine system, especially when exposure occurs during fetal development. Many of these substances are found in everyday products such as plastics, pesticides, food, some metals, and some detergents. Some examples include dioxin, polychlorinated biphenyls (PCBs), DDT, bisphenol-A (BPA), and plant phytoestrogens. The Environmental Protection Agency has established the Endocrine Disruptor Screening Program to test chemicals for their impact on the endocrine systems of humans and wildlife.

Answers

FIGURE 34–1 The pituitary gland produces hormones that regulate many other endocrine glands and some organs.

IN YOUR NOTEBOOK Students' tables should list the endocrine glands shown in **Figure 34–1** in the left column, hormones produced by each gland in the middle column, and functions of the hormones in the right column.

Teach continued

Use Visuals

Have students work in small groups to review **Figures 34–2** and **34–3.** Ask them to compare and contrast steroid and nonsteroid hormones and how they act on cells. If desired, hand out copies of **Compare/Contrast Tables** for students to fill out. Have groups share their comparisons with the class. *(Similarities include: both bind to receptors, both affect the activity of the receptor cell, both are released by endocrine glands. Differences include: composition—steroid hormones are lipids, and nonsteroid hormones are proteins; ability to enter the cell—steroid hormones enter the cell, and nonsteroid hormones do not.)*

Study Wkbks A/B, Appendix S20, Compare/Contrast Table. **Transparencies,** GO3.

DIFFERENTIATED INSTRUCTION

L1 Struggling Students Show students the numbered steps in **Figures 34–2** and **34–3** that describe how steroid and nonsteroid hormones act on cells. Have students work in small groups to make **Flowcharts** of these steps. Challenge students to be able to describe each numbered step in their flowcharts in their own words. Call on volunteers to share their flowcharts with the class.

Study Wkbks A/B, Appendix S25, Flowchart. **Transparencies,** GO8.

ELL Focus on ELL: Extend Language

BEGINNING SPEAKERS Point out the prefix *non-* in the term *nonsteroid hormone*. Explain that *non-* means "not," so a nonsteroid hormone is simply a hormone that is not classified as a steroid hormone. The prefix *non-* is found in other scientific terms that students may be familiar with, such as *nonrenewable resource* and *nonvertebrate chordate*. Have students find the definitions for these two words to further their understanding of the use of the prefix *non-*. Then, have them find several other examples of words, both scientific and everyday use, that contain the prefix *non-*. Suggest they use the Glossary or a dictionary to help them find and define their words.

BIOLOGY.com Have students use **Art in Motion: Steroid and Nonsteroid Hormones** to learn about the pathways of each type of hormone.

BUILD Vocabulary

WORD ORIGINS Prostaglandins get their name from a gland in the male reproductive system, the prostate, in which they were first discovered.

Prostaglandins The glands of the endocrine system were once thought to be the only organs that produced hormones. However, nearly all cells have been shown to produce small amounts of hormonelike substances called **prostaglandins** (prahs tuh GLAN dinz). Prostaglandins are modified fatty acids that are produced by a wide range of cells. They generally affect only nearby cells and tissues, and thus are sometimes known as "local hormones."

Some prostaglandins cause smooth muscles, such as those in the uterus, bronchioles, and blood vessels, to contract. One group of prostaglandins causes the sensation of pain during most headaches. Aspirin helps to stop the pain of a headache because it inhibits the synthesis of these prostaglandins.

Hormone Action

How do hormones affect cells?

Hormones fall into two general groups—steroid hormones and nonsteroid hormones. Steroid hormones are produced from a lipid called cholesterol. Nonsteroid hormones include proteins, small peptides, and modified amino acids. Each type of hormone acts on a target cell in a different way.

Steroid Hormones Because steroid hormones are lipids, they can easily cross cell membranes. **Once in the cell, steroid hormones can enter the nucleus and change the pattern of gene expression in a target cell.** The ability to alter gene expression makes the effects of many steroid hormones especially powerful and long lasting. **Figure 34–2** shows the action of steroid hormones in cells.

FIGURE 34–2 Steroid Hormones Steroid hormones act by entering the nucleus of a cell and changing the pattern of gene expression.

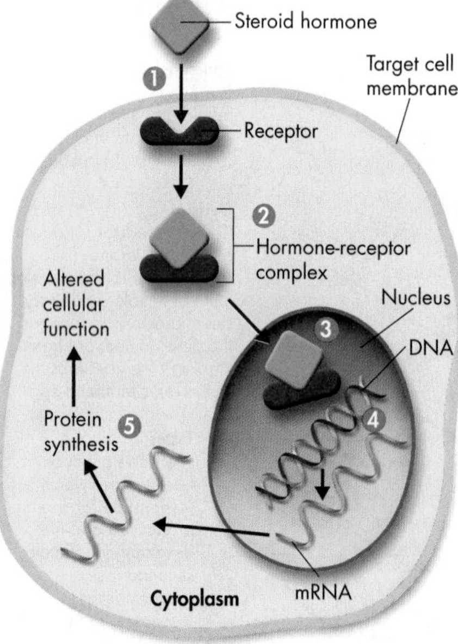

1. A steroid hormone enters a cell by passing directly across the cell membrane.
2. Once inside, the hormone binds to a receptor (found only in the hormone's target cells) and forms a hormone-receptor complex.
3. The hormone-receptor complex enters the nucleus of the cell, where it binds to regions of DNA that control gene expression.
4. This binding initiates the transcription of specific genes to messenger RNA (mRNA).
5. The mRNA moves into the cytoplasm and directs protein synthesis.

Hormone-receptor complexes work as regulators of gene expression—they can turn on or turn off whole sets of genes. Because steroid hormones affect gene expression directly, they can produce dramatic changes in the activity of a cell or organism.

980 Chapter 34 • Lesson 1

UbD Check for Understanding

ANALOGY PROMPT

Write the following analogy prompt on the board:

- The human endocrine system is like the school's public address system because . . .

(Students should note that the endocrine system and a school's public address system both can send messages to a wide audience that only targets certain members.)

ADJUST INSTRUCTION

If students' responses indicate confusion provide the following demonstration: tell students with last names beginning with A–L to close their books. Then, ask students in the back row to raise their hands. Point out that, although you spoke to the entire class, your messages were specific to certain students. The endocrine system sends chemical messages through the body, but only target cells respond.

Nonsteroid Hormones Nonsteroid hormones generally cannot pass through the cell membrane of their target cells. **Nonsteroid hormones bind to receptors on cell membranes and cause the release of secondary messengers that affect cell activities. Figure 34–3** shows the action of nonsteroid hormones in cells.

1. A nonsteroid hormone binds to receptors on the cell membrane.
2. The binding of the hormone activates enzymes on the inner surface of the cell membrane.
3. These enzymes release secondary messengers such as calcium ions, nucleotides, and even fatty acids to relay the hormone's message within the cell. One common secondary messenger is cAMP (cyclic AMP), which is produced from ATP.
4. These secondary messengers can activate or inhibit a wide range of cell activities.

Steroid and nonsteroid hormones can have powerful effects on their target cells. It is therefore especially important to understand the ways in which the endocrine system regulates their production and release into the blood.

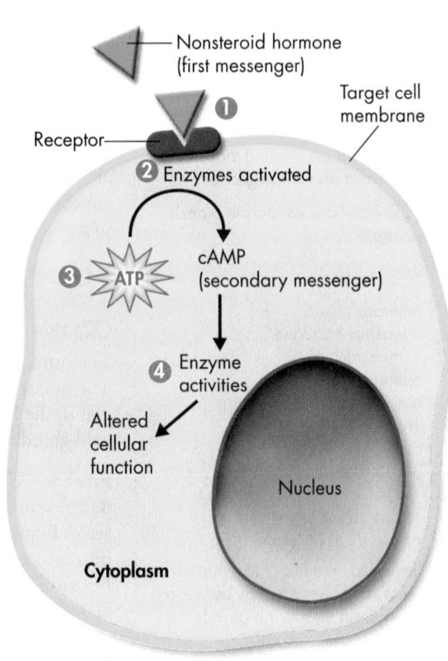

FIGURE 34–3 Nonsteroid Hormones Nonsteroid hormones bind to receptors on a target cell membrane and cause the release of secondary messengers that affect cell activities.

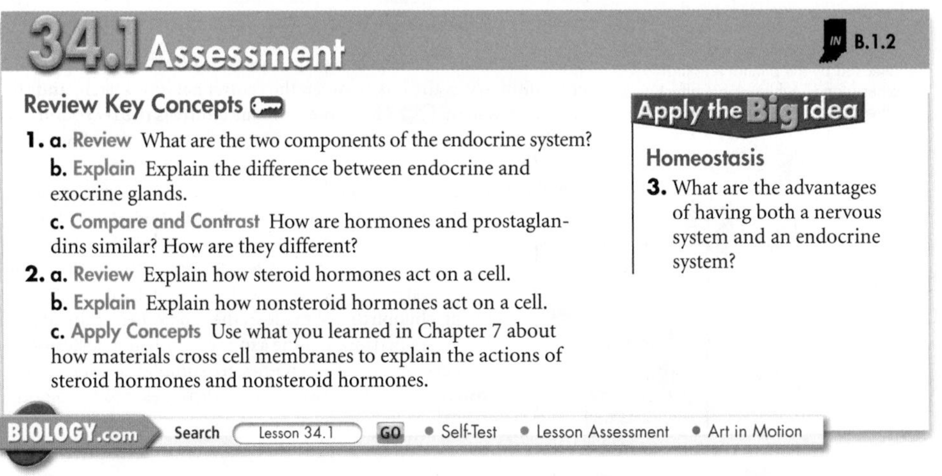

34.1 Assessment

IN B.1.2

Review Key Concepts

1. a. Review What are the two components of the endocrine system?
   b. Explain Explain the difference between endocrine and exocrine glands.
   c. Compare and Contrast How are hormones and prostaglandins similar? How are they different?
2. a. Review Explain how steroid hormones act on a cell.
   b. Explain Explain how nonsteroid hormones act on a cell.
   c. Apply Concepts Use what you learned in Chapter 7 about how materials cross cell membranes to explain the actions of steroid hormones and nonsteroid hormones.

Apply the Big idea

Homeostasis

3. What are the advantages of having both a nervous system and an endocrine system?

BIOLOGY.com Search Lesson 34.1 GO • Self-Test • Lesson Assessment • Art in Motion

Assess and Remediate

EVALUATE UNDERSTANDING

Have students write a short response to each of the following questions. *How does the body send chemical signals? How do cells receive chemical signals?* Call on volunteers to share their responses with the class. Then, have students complete the 34.1 Assessment.

REMEDIATION SUGGESTION

L1 **Struggling Students** If your students have trouble with **Question 3,** remind them that the nervous and endocrine systems serve similar functions in the body, because both transmit messages from one part of the body to another. Then, ask pairs of students to discuss the speed and specificity of the messages sent by the nervous and endocrine systems.

BIOLOGY.com Students can check their understanding of lesson concepts with the **Self-Test** assessment. They can then take an online version of the **Lesson Assessment.**

Assessment Answers

1a. glands and hormones

1b. Endocrine glands secrete hormones directly into the bloodstream. Exocrine glands release their secretions through ducts either out of the body or into the digestive system.

1c. Hormones and prostaglandins are both substances that affect cells. Hormones are produced by endocrine glands and can affect cells throughout the body; prostaglandins are produced by a wide range of cells and act locally.

2a. Steroid hormones enter a cell and bind to a receptor. This complex enters the nucleus and alters the cell's gene expression.

2b. Nonsteroid hormones bind to receptors on cell membranes and cause the release of secondary messengers that affect cell activities.

2c. Steroid hormones are lipids, so they can pass through the phospholipid bilayer that makes up the cell membrane. Nonsteroid hormones are not lipids, so they cannot pass through the cell membrane and must act from outside the cell.

3. Big idea Having both systems allows messages to be transmitted in the body in two different ways. The nervous system allows rapid messages to reach a limited set of cells, while the endocrine system allows messages to be sent more slowly to the whole body.

LESSON 34.2

Getting Started

Objectives

34.2.1 Identify the functions of the major endocrine glands.

34.2.2 Explain how endocrine glands are controlled.

Student Resources

Study Workbooks A and B, 34.2 Worksheets

Spanish Study Workbook, 34.2 Worksheets

Lesson Overview • Lesson Notes • Assessment: Self-Test, Lesson Assessment

For corresponding lesson in the **Foundation Edition**, see pages 813–816.

Build Background

Ask students to brainstorm ways that people on different continents might work together on a project. *(Sample answers: conference calls on the telephone, teleconferencing, emailing)*

Ask Is it helpful to have a manager to coordinate the efforts? Explain. *(Yes. Managers make sure everyone is working together efficiently.)*

Then, ask students to discuss how this analogy may relate to how endocrine glands work together.

34.2 Glands of the Endocrine System

Key Questions

What are the functions of the major endocrine glands?

How are endocrine glands controlled?

Vocabulary

pituitary gland
releasing hormone
corticosteroid
epinephrine
norepinephrine
thyroxine
calcitonin
parathyroid hormone

Taking Notes

Concept Map As you read, develop a concept map that shows the relationships between the human endocrine glands.

THINK ABOUT IT Organs in most body systems are connected to each other, but that's not the case with the endocrine system. Endocrine glands are scattered throughout the body, many of them with no apparent connection to each other. How does the body control and regulate so many separate organs so that they act together as a single system?

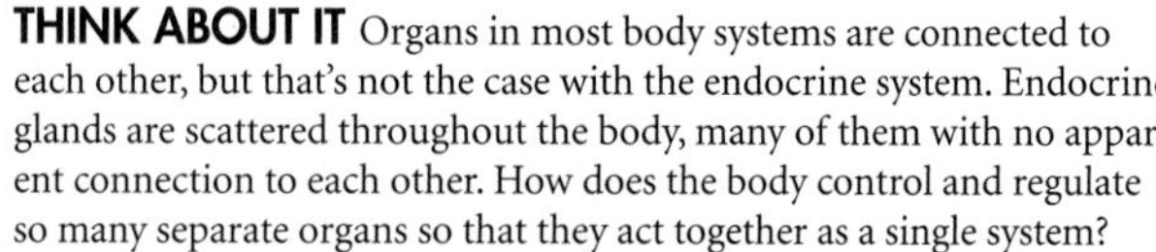

The Human Endocrine Glands

What are the functions of the major endocrine glands?

The human endocrine system regulates a wide variety of activities. The major glands of the endocrine system include the pituitary gland, the hypothalamus, the adrenal glands, the pancreas, the thyroid gland, the parathyroid glands, and the reproductive glands.

Pituitary Gland The **pituitary gland** is a bean-size structure that dangles on a slender stalk of tissue at the base of the brain. As you can see in **Figure 34–4,** the gland is divided into two parts: the anterior pituitary and the posterior pituitary. **The pituitary gland secretes hormones that directly regulate many body functions or control the actions of other endocrine glands.**

Proper function of the pituitary gland is essential. For example, if the gland produces too much growth hormone (GH) during childhood, the body grows too quickly, resulting in a condition called gigantism. Too little GH during childhood causes pituitary dwarfism, which can be treated with GH produced by genetically engineered bacteria.

Hypothalamus The hypothalamus, which is attached to the posterior pituitary, is the link between the central nervous system and the endocrine system. **The hypothalamus controls the secretions of the pituitary gland.** The activities of the hypothalamus are influenced by the levels of hormones and other substances in the blood and by sensory information collected by other parts of the central nervous system.

The hypothalamus contains the cell bodies of neurosecretory cells whose axons extend into the posterior pituitary. Antidiuretic hormone, which stimulates the kidney to absorb water, and oxytocin, which stimulates contractions during childbirth, are made in the cell bodies of the hypothalamus and stored in the axons entering the posterior pituitary. When the cell bodies are stimulated, axons in the posterior pituitary release these hormones into the blood.

FIGURE 34–4 Pituitary Gland The pituitary gland is located below the hypothalamus in the brain. Some of the hormones released by the pituitary control other glands, while others affect other types of tissues.

Hypothalamus
Anterior pituitary
Posterior pituitary

UbD Teach for Understanding

ENDURING UNDERSTANDING The human body is a complex system. The coordinated functions of its many structures support life processes and maintain homeostasis.

GUIDING QUESTION What life processes are regulated by hormones?

EVIDENCE OF UNDERSTANDING *After completing the lesson, assign this assessment to show student understanding of how the human endocrine system works, including its many glands and the hormones they secrete.* Have students work individually or in small groups to make a crossword puzzle that contains all of the lesson vocabulary terms as well as the names of each endocrine gland. The clues for the terms should be scientifically accurate.

Anterior Pituitary Gland Hormones	
Hormone	**Action**
Follicle-stimulating hormone (FSH)	Stimulates production of mature eggs in ovaries and sperm in testes
Luteinizing hormone (LH)	Stimulates ovaries and testes; prepares uterus for implantation of fertilized egg
Thyroid-stimulating hormone (TSH)	Stimulates the synthesis and release of thyroxine from the thyroid gland
Adreno-corticotropic hormone (ACTH)	Stimulates release of some hormones from the adrenal cortex
Growth hormone (GH)	Stimulates protein synthesis and growth in cells
Prolactin	Stimulates milk production in nursing mothers
Melanocyte-stimulating hormone (MSH)	Stimulates melanocytes in the skin to increase the production of the pigment melanin

FIGURE 34–5 Anterior Pituitary Hormones The hypothalamus secretes releasing hormones that signal the anterior pituitary to release its hormones. Classify ***Which of these hormones stimulate other endocrine glands?***

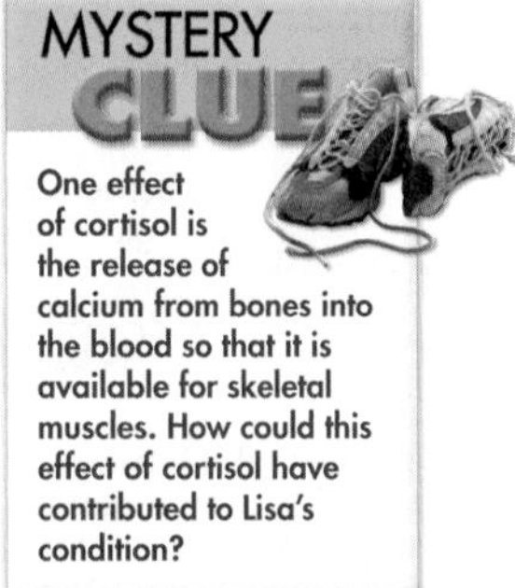

One effect of cortisol is the release of calcium from bones into the blood so that it is available for skeletal muscles. How could this effect of cortisol have contributed to Lisa's condition?

In contrast, the hypothalamus has indirect control of the anterior pituitary. The hypothalamus produces **releasing hormones,** which are secreted into blood vessels leading to the anterior pituitary. The hypothalamus produces a specific releasing hormone that controls the secretion of each anterior pituitary hormone. Hormones released by the anterior pituitary gland are listed in **Figure 34–5.**

Adrenal Glands The adrenal glands are pyramid-shaped structures that sit on top of the kidneys. **The adrenal glands release hormones that help the body prepare for—and deal with—stress.** As shown in **Figure 34–6,** the outer part of the gland is called the adrenal cortex and the inner part is the adrenal medulla.

About 80 percent of an adrenal gland is its adrenal cortex. The adrenal cortex produces more than two dozen steroid hormones called **corticosteroids** (kawr tih koh STEER oydz). One of these hormones, aldosterone (al DAHS tuh rohn), regulates blood volume and pressure. Its release is stimulated by dehydration, excessive bleeding, or Na^+ deficiency. Another hormone, called cortisol, helps control the rate of metabolism of carbohydrates, fats, and proteins. Cortisol is released during physical stress such as intense exercise.

Hormones released from the adrenal medulla produce the heart-pounding, anxious feeling you get when excited or frightened—commonly known as the "fight or flight" response. When you are under this sort of stress, impulses from the sympathetic nervous system stimulate cells in the adrenal medulla to release large amounts of **epinephrine** (commonly referred to as adrenaline) and **norepinephrine.** These hormones increase heart rate and blood pressure. They also cause air passageways to widen, allowing for an increase in oxygen intake, and stimulate the release of extra glucose. If your heart rate speeds up and your hands sweat when you take a test, it's your adrenal medulla at work!

FIGURE 34–6 Adrenal Glands The adrenal glands release hormones that help the body handle stressful situations. The adrenal cortex and adrenal medulla contain different types of tissues and release different hormones.

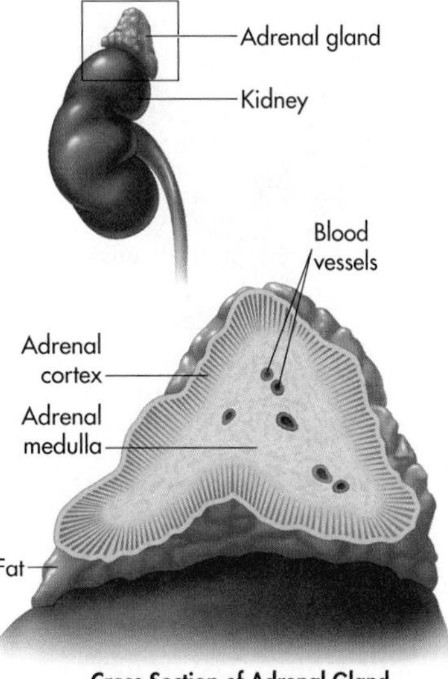

Cross Section of Adrenal Gland

Quick Facts

THE POTENCY OF HORMONES

The endocrine glands, despite their tremendous importance in the body, are amazingly small. For example, the pituitary gland, which produces a number of different hormones and controls most of the other endocrine glands, is the size of a pea. The quantity of hormones produced by the endocrine glands is also very small. A vivid example of this is that a typical woman produces only about one teaspoon of estrogens in her lifetime. Most hormones are so potent that they are effective even at concentrations measured in parts per million.

Teach

Build Study Skills

Explain to students that creating tables can be a helpful way to summarize and organize lesson content. Suggest students start a three-column table to help them organize the information about the many different hormones introduced in this lesson. Have them label the first column Hormone, the second column Gland, and the third column Action. Then, have them fill in the table with each hormone discussed in the lesson, the gland that secretes it, and its action, or what it does in the body. Refer them to **Figure 34–5** to help them start their tables.

DIFFERENTIATED INSTRUCTION

LPR Less Proficient Readers Provide less proficient readers with a partially complete version of the three-column table described above. Be sure to create the table so that the hormones are listed in the order they are introduced in the lesson. Fill in at least one cell in each row to help students organize their notetaking.

L3 Advanced Students Pair advanced students with struggling students, and have them brainstorm other ways to organize lesson content. For example, they may suggest visuals, graphic organizers, or outlines. Have pairs create one of their suggestions using content from this lesson. Then, ask volunteers to share their work with the class.

MYSTERY CLUE Review the effects of calcium on the skeletal system.

Ask Why is calcium important to your skeletal system? *(Calcium helps bones stay strong and healthy.)* Have students connect this knowledge with the action of cortisol to help them conclude that the loss of calcium from Lisa's bones may have contributed to her stress fracture. Students can go online to **Biology.com** to gather their evidence.

Answers

FIGURE 34–5 follicle-stimulating hormone (FSH), luteinizing hormone (LH), thyroid-stimulating hormone (TSH), adreno-corticotropic hormone (ACTH)

Teach continued

Lead a Discussion

Make sure students fully understand the process of blood glucose regulation before reading about diabetes mellitus. Go over **Figure 34–7,** and have volunteers talk about each step in the feedback loop.

DIFFERENTIATED INSTRUCTION

LPR Less Proficient Readers To break up the text on this page, suggest students read the information on the pancreas and discuss it in pairs. Then, have them repeat the process for blood glucose regulation and again for diabetes mellitus.

ELL Focus on ELL: Access Content

BEGINNING SPEAKERS Simplify blood glucose regulation by focusing on the **Cause-and-Effect** relationships involved. On the board, draw a diagram that shows a series of cause-and-effect relationships. For example:

Cause ⟶ Effect   Cause ⟶ Effect

Cause ⟶ Effect

Fill in the first box with the word *eat*. Ask students how eating might affect blood glucose levels. (*blood glucose increases*) Write this in the middle box. Then, point out that an increase in blood glucose causes the pancreas to respond. Have students guide you to fill in the next steps with *pancreas produces insulin* and *cells take up glucose*. If desired, continue the chain or start a new one to show the cause-and-effect relationships involving glucagon.

BIOLOGY.com Have students investigate the risk factors and effects of diabetes in **Data Analysis: Diabetes.**

Answers

FIGURE 34–7 In untreated diabetes mellitus, the body does not produce insulin or does not properly respond to it, so blood glucose levels remain high.

Food intake increases blood glucose level.

GLUCAGON (promotes breakdown of glycogen)

Pancreas releases insulin or glucagon in response to blood glucose levels.

INSULIN (promotes glucose uptake)

Between meals, blood glucose level drops.

FIGURE 34–7 Blood Glucose Control Insulin and glucagon are opposing hormones that ensure blood glucose levels stay within a normal range. **Infer** ***Explain why this feedback loop does not apply to a person with untreated diabetes.***

Pancreas The pancreas is both an exocrine and an endocrine gland. As an exocrine gland, it releases digestive enzymes that help break down food. However, other cells in the pancreas release hormones into the blood.

The hormone-producing portion of the pancreas consists of clusters of cells. These clusters, which resemble islands, are called the "islets of Langerhans," after their discoverer, German anatomist Paul Langerhans. Each islet contains beta cells, which secrete the hormone insulin, and alpha cells, which secrete the hormone glucagon. **Insulin and glucagon, produced by the pancreas, help to keep the blood glucose level stable.**

▶ ***Blood Glucose Regulation*** When blood glucose levels rise after a person eats, the pancreas releases insulin. Insulin stimulates cells to take glucose out of the blood, which prevents the levels of blood glucose from rising too rapidly and ensures that glucose is stored for future use. Insulin's major target cells are in the liver, skeletal muscles, and fat tissue. The liver and skeletal muscles store glucose as glycogen. In fat tissue, glucose is converted to lipids.

Within one or two hours after a person has eaten, when the level of blood glucose drops, glucagon is released from the pancreas. Glucagon stimulates the liver and skeletal muscle cells to break down glycogen and release glucose into the blood. Glucagon also causes fat cells to break down fats so that they can be converted to glucose. These actions help raise the blood glucose level back to normal. **Figure 34–7** summarizes the insulin and glucagon feedback loop.

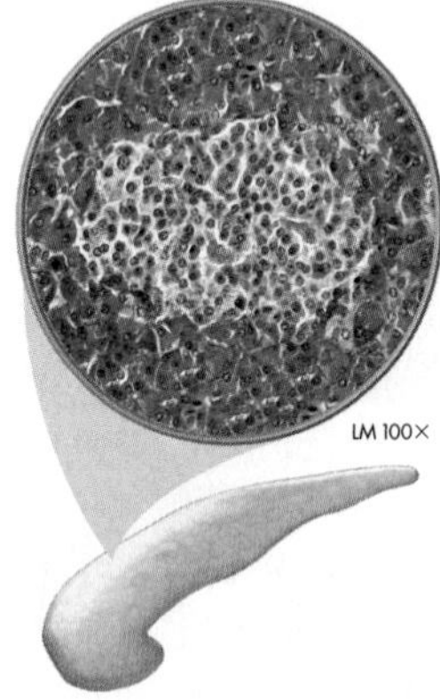

FIGURE 34–8 Pancreas Cells The cluster of light-colored cells is an islet of Langerhans, which contains alpha and beta cells. In Type I diabetes, a person's immune system kills beta cells, which produce insulin.

▶ ***Diabetes Mellitus*** When the body fails to produce or properly respond to insulin, a condition known as diabetes mellitus occurs. The very high blood glucose levels that result from diabetes can damage almost every system and cell in the body.

There are two types of diabetes mellitus. Type I diabetes is an autoimmune disorder that usually develops in people before the age of 15. The immune system kills beta cells, resulting in little or no secretion of insulin. People with Type I diabetes must follow a strict diet and receive daily doses of insulin to keep their blood glucose level under control.

The second type of diabetes, Type II, most commonly develops in people after the age of 40. People with Type II diabetes produce low to normal amounts of insulin. However, their cells do not properly respond to the hormone because the interaction of insulin receptors and insulin is inefficient. In its early stages, Type II diabetes can often be controlled through diet and exercise. Unfortunately, the incidence of Type II diabetes is rising rapidly in the United States and other countries as a result of increasing obesity, especially among young people.

 BIOLOGY.com Search Lesson 34.2 GO • Data Analysis

How Science Works

BLOOD GLUCOSE REGULATION

Blood glucose regulation is a complex process. In addition to the actions of glucagon and insulin, scientists studying obesity in mice have found that a hormone called osteocalcin also may be involved in glucose regulation. Osteocalcin, which is released by bone cells, seems to make a mouse's pancreas release more insulin. It also seems to make body cells in mice more sensitive to insulin. Scientists have also found that signals from the brain, immune system, and intestines may be involved in the process of blood glucose regulation.

Thyroid and Parathyroid Glands The thyroid gland is located at the base of the neck and wraps around the upper part of the trachea. **The thyroid gland has a major role in regulating the body's metabolism.** Recall that metabolism is the sum of all the chemical reactions that occur in the body. The thyroid gland produces the hormone **thyroxine,** which increases the metabolic rate of cells throughout the body. Under the influence of thyroxine, cells become more active, use more energy, and produce more heat.

Iodine is needed to produce thyroxine. In parts of the world where diets lack iodine, severe health problems may result. Low levels of thyroxine in iodine-deficient infants produce a condition called cretinism (KREE tuh niz um), in which neither the skeletal system nor the nervous system develops properly. Iodine deficiency usually can be prevented by the addition of small amounts of iodine to table salt or other food items.

Thyroid problems are a fairly common disorder. If the thyroid produces too much thyroxine, a condition called hyperthyroidism occurs. Hyperthyroidism results in nervousness, elevated body temperature, increased blood pressure, and weight loss. Too little thyroxine causes a condition called hypothyroidism. Lower body temperature, lack of energy, and weight gain are signs of this condition. A goiter, as shown in **Figure 34–9,** can be a sign of hypothyroidism.

The thyroid also produces calcitonin, a hormone that reduces blood calcium levels. **Calcitonin** signals the kidneys to reabsorb less calcium from filtrate, inhibits calcium's absorption in the small intestine, and promotes calcium's absorption into bones. Its opposing hormone is parathyroid hormone, which is released by the four parathyroid glands located on the back surface of the thyroid. **Parathyroid hormone** (PTH) increases the calcium levels in the blood by promoting the release of calcium from bone, the reabsorption of calcium in the kidneys, and the uptake of calcium from the digestive system. The actions of PTH promote proper nerve and muscle function and proper bone structure.

In Your Notebook *Summarize how blood-calcium levels are regulated.*

Reproductive Glands The gonads—ovaries and testes—are the body's reproductive glands. **The gonads serve two important functions: the production of gametes and the secretion of sex hormones.** In females, ovaries produce eggs and secrete a group of hormones called estrogens. In males, the testes produce sperm and secrete the hormone testosterone. You'll learn more about the gonads and their hormones in the next lesson.

FIGURE 34–9 Thyroid Gland A goiter is an enlargement of the thyroid gland. A goiter may be the result of iodine deficiency. Without iodine, the thyroid cannot finish producing thyroxine, but its precursor continues to build up in the gland.

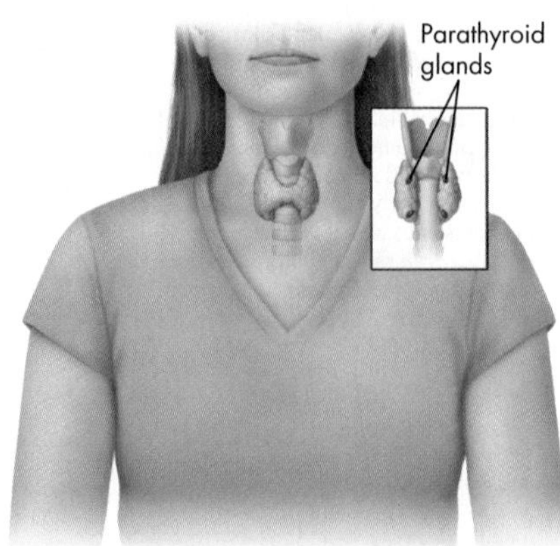

Normal Thyroid

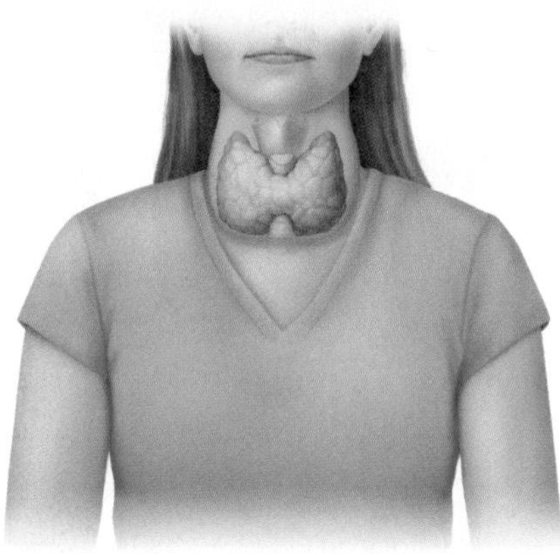
Enlarged Thyroid (Goiter)

Use Models

Tell students that blood calcium levels are controlled by two hormones with opposing actions. Have students make a feedback loop diagram of how these hormones keep blood calcium levels in a normal range. Tell students to use **Figures 34–7** and **34–10** as models when they make their diagrams. Have several students share their completed diagrams with the class.

DIFFERENTIATED INSTRUCTION

L1 Struggling Students Before students begin drawing their feedback diagrams, have pairs read through the paragraph on blood calcium regulation. Point out that the names of the two hormones involved in blood calcium regulation are vocabulary words. Then, have pairs organize the information into a feedback loop diagram.

LPR Less Proficient Readers After students have completed their feedback loop diagrams, explain that the regulation of blood calcium levels is only one function of the thyroid gland. Challenge students to find a sentence on this page that describes another function of the thyroid gland. *(The thyroid gland has a major role in regulating the body's metabolism.)* Have volunteers restate this sentence in their own words.

UbD Check for Understanding

HAND SIGNALS

Present students with the following questions, and ask them to show a thumbs-up sign if they understand, a thumbs-down sign if they are confused, or a waving-hand sign if they partially understand.

- How does the thyroid help regulate the body's metabolism?
- How do thyroid problems affect homeostasis in the body?

ADJUST INSTRUCTION

If students are struggling with one or both questions, ask them to work in small groups to discuss the topics. Have students raise their hands when their group has discussed both of the questions. After all students have raised their hands, call on several students to share their group's responses.

Answers

IN YOUR NOTEBOOK Calcitonin signals kidneys to excrete calcium, the small intestine to absorb less calcium, and bones to absorb more of it. These actions lower blood calcium levels. Parathyroid hormone has the opposite effects, and, therefore, raises blood calcium levels.

LESSON 34.2

Teach continued

Connect to Health

Discuss the importance of fluid intake during physical activity. Explain that some individuals drink water during physical activity, while others prefer sports drinks. Ask students to bring in a variety of labels from sports drinks. Have them analyze the ingredients, Calories per serving, and other information found on the sports drink labels. Then, have them debate the advantages and disadvantages of drinking water versus a sports drink. You may want to bring in articles about sports drinks to share with the class. Students should understand that people lose more than just water in sweat.

After the activity is completed, discuss with students the important distinction between sports drinks and energy drinks. Tell students that energy drinks, many of which contain large amounts of caffeine, should not be used to replenish fluids during or after physical activity. This can be dangerous because caffeine can increase a person's heart rate and fluid loss.

DIFFERENTIATED INSTRUCTION

L3 **Advanced Students** Have students find out more about hyponatremia, a serious medical condition that can be caused by rapid and massive fluid intake. Ask students to write a short report that describes the condition and relates it to the concept of water balance in the body.

Control of the Endocrine System

How are endocrine glands controlled?

Even though the endocrine system is one of the master regulators of the body, it, too, must be controlled. **Like most systems of the body, the endocrine system is regulated by feedback mechanisms that function to maintain homeostasis.**

Recall that feedback inhibition occurs when an increase in any substance "feeds back" to inhibit the process that produced the substance in the first place. Home heating and cooling systems, controlled by thermostats, are examples of mechanical feedback loops. The actions of glands and hormones of the endocrine system are biological examples of the same type of process.

FIGURE 34–10 Water Balance One method by which internal feedback mechanisms regulate the endocrine system is the interaction of the hypothalamus and the posterior pituitary gland in maintaining water balance. **Apply Concepts** ***Does the hypothalamus signal the posterior pituitary with releasing hormones or nervous signals? Explain.***

Sweating, reduced water intake, and urination reduce blood volume.
LESS ADH
No thirst
Hypothalamus senses low or high concentration of water in blood and signals pituitary.
MORE ADH
Thirst sensation
Drinking (response to thirst) and decreased kidney action increase blood volume.

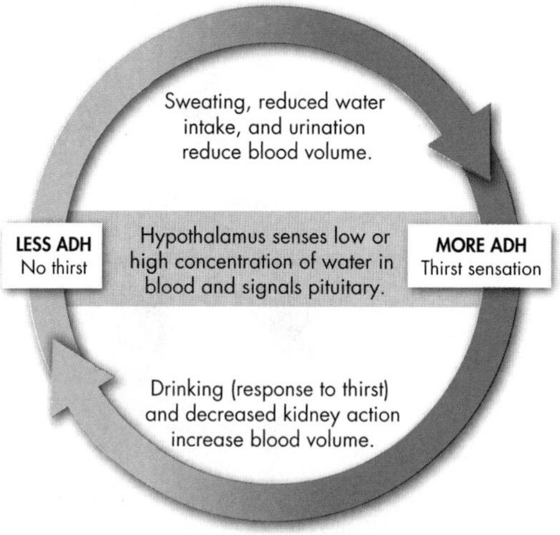

Maintaining Water Balance Homeostatic mechanisms regulate the levels of a wide variety of materials dissolved in the blood and in extracellular fluids. These materials include hydrogen ions; minerals such as sodium, potassium, and calcium; and soluble proteins such as serum albumin, which is found in blood plasma. Most of the time, homeostatic systems operate so smoothly that we are scarcely aware of their existence. However, that is not the case with one of the most important homeostatic processes, the one that regulates the amount of water in the body. **Figure 34–10** illustrates the water balance mechanism.

When you exercise strenuously, you lose water as you sweat. If this water loss continued, your body would soon become dehydrated. Generally, that doesn't happen, because your body's homeostatic mechanisms swing into action.

The hypothalamus contains cells that are sensitive to the concentration of water in the blood. As you lose water, the concentration of dissolved materials in the blood rises. The hypothalamus responds in two ways. First, the hypothalamus signals the posterior pituitary gland to release a hormone called antidiuretic hormone (ADH). ADH molecules are carried by the blood to the kidneys, where the removal of water from the blood is quickly slowed down. Later, you experience a sensation of thirst—a signal that you should drink to restore lost water.

When you finally get around to taking that drink, you might take in a liter of fluid. Most of that water is quickly absorbed into the blood. This volume of water could dilute the blood so much that the equilibrium between the blood and the body cells would be disturbed. Large amounts of water would diffuse across blood vessel walls into body tissues. Body cells would swell with the excess water.

UbD Check for Understanding

ONE-MINUTE RESPONSE

Write the following prompt on the board, and give students about a minute to write a quick response summarizing their understanding.

- How is the endocrine system regulated? *(Responses should mention that the endocrine system is regulated by feedback mechanisms that help the hypothalamus and other glands maintain homeostasis.)*

ADJUST INSTRUCTION

If responses are incorrect or incomplete, ask students to review **Figures 34–7** and **34–10.** Students should work in pairs to identify the items in each figure that can be categorized as feedback. *(blood glucose levels dropping and increased blood volume)* Then, they should answer the one-minute response question again.

Answers

FIGURE 34–10 The hypothalamus controls the posterior pituitary gland with nervous signals sent via neurosecretory cells that connect the hypothalamus and posterior pituitary.

Needless to say, this doesn't happen, because the homeostatic mechanism controlled by the hypothalamus intervenes again. When the water content of the blood rises, the pituitary releases less ADH. In response to lower ADH levels, the kidneys remove water from the blood, restoring the blood to its proper concentration. This homeostatic system sets both upper and lower limits for blood water content. A water deficit stimulates the release of ADH, causing the kidneys to conserve water; an oversupply of water causes the kidneys to eliminate the excess water in urine.

Controlling Metabolism As another example of how internal feedback mechanisms regulate the activity of the endocrine system, let's look at the thyroid gland and its principal hormone, thyroxine. Recall that thyroxine increases the metabolic activity of cells. Does the thyroid gland determine how much thyroxine to release on its own? No, the activity of the thyroid gland is instead controlled by the hypothalamus and the anterior pituitary gland. When the hypothalamus senses that the thyroxine level in the blood is low, it secretes thyrotropin-releasing hormone (TRH), a hormone that stimulates the anterior pituitary to secrete thyroid-stimulating hormone (TSH). TSH stimulates the release of thyroxine by the thyroid gland. High levels of thyroxine in the blood inhibit the secretion of TRH and TSH, which stops the release of additional thyroxine. This feedback loop keeps the level of thyroxine in the blood relatively constant.

The hypothalamus is also sensitive to temperature. When the core body temperature begins to drop, even if the level of thyroxine is normal, the hypothalamus produces extra TRH. The release of TRH stimulates the release of TSH, which stimulates the release of additional thyroxine. Thyroxine increases oxygen consumption and cellular metabolism. The increase in metabolic activity that results helps the body maintain its core temperature even when the outside temperature drops.

BUILD Vocabulary

PREFIXES The prefixes *anti-* and *ante-* can be easily confused. *Anti-*, as in *antidiuretic*, means "against" or "opposite." *Ante-*, as in *anterior*, means "before."

34.2 Assessment

Review Key Concepts

1. a. Review Describe the role of each major endocrine gland.

b. Explain How is the hypothalamus an important part of both the nervous system and the endocrine system?

c. Compare and Contrast Compare and contrast the two types of diabetes.

2. a. Review Explain how the endocrine system helps maintain homeostasis.

b. Explain On a hot day, you play soccer for an hour and lose a lot of water in sweat. List the steps that your body takes to regain homeostasis.

c. Predict Suppose the secretion of a certain hormone causes an increase in the concentration of substance *X* in the blood. A low concentration of *X* causes the hormone to be released. What is the effect on the rate of hormone secretion if an abnormal condition causes the level of *X* in the blood to remain very low?

WRITE ABOUT SCIENCE

Creative Writing

3. Create a brochure that describes both types of diabetes. You may wish to include information on risk factors, treatment, and preventive measures that can be taken. Use images from magazines or the Internet to illustrate your brochure.

BIOLOGY.com Search 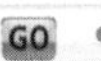 Lesson 34.2 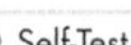 GO • Lesson Assessment • Self-Test

LESSON 34.2

Assess and Remediate

EVALUATE UNDERSTANDING

Call on volunteers to identify a process or body function that is regulated by the endocrine system. List students' responses on the board. If students fail to identify some of the processes mentioned in the lesson, encourage them to skim the text and figures and add to the list. Then, have students complete the 34.2 Assessment.

REMEDIATION SUGGESTION

ELL English Language Learners If students have difficulty answering **Question 2c,** explain that the term *substance* X is another way to denote any unnamed substance. Explain that the identity of the substance is not important here for answering the question.

BIOLOGY.com Students can check their understanding of lesson concepts with the **Self-Test** assessment. They can then take an online version of the **Lesson Assessment.**

Assessment Answers

1a. The pituitary gland regulates many body functions and controls the action of other endocrine glands. The hypothalamus controls the secretions of the pituitary gland. The adrenal glands help the body prepare for and deal with stress. The pancreas regulates blood glucose levels. The thyroid and parathyroid glands regulate blood calcium levels. The ovaries and testes secrete sex hormones.

1b. The hypothalamus serves as the body's link between the nervous system and the endocrine system. Its activities are influenced by substances in the blood and information from the nervous system.

1c. Both types of diabetes result in problems with regulation of blood glucose levels. In Type I diabetes, the body's immune system destroys the cells that make insulin; in Type II diabetes, the body does not respond efficiently to insulin.

2a. The endocrine system helps maintain homeostasis by signaling the body to respond to internal and external stimuli and by using feedback mechanisms.

2b. The hypothalamus signals the posterior pituitary to release ADH and causes thirst sensation. The ADH slows removal of water from the body. A thirst sensation prompts you to replace lost water.

2c. The level of hormone secretion would remain high.

WRITE ABOUT SCIENCE

3. Brochures should be assessed based on content and format. Check that facts are accurate and images are appropriate.

LESSON 34.3

Getting Started

Objectives

34.3.1 Describe the effects the sex hormones have on development.

34.3.2 Name and discuss the structures of the male reproductive system.

34.3.3 Name and discuss the structures of the female reproductive system.

34.3.4 Describe some of the most common sexually transmitted diseases.

Student Resources

Study Workbooks A and B, 34.3 Worksheets

Spanish Study Workbook, 34.3 Worksheets

Lab Manual B, 34.3 Data Analysis Worksheet

Lesson Overview • Lesson Notes • Activity: Data Analysis • Assessment: Self-Test, Lesson Assessment

For corresponding lesson in the **Foundation Edition**, see pages 817–823.

Answers

IN YOUR NOTEBOOK Estrogens in females cause breast development and hip widening. Testosterone in males causes facial hair growth, increased muscular development, and deepening of the voice.

INDIANA ACADEMIC STANDARDS

For the full text of all standards, see the Course Overview in the front matter of this book.

B.6.4 Describe and model the process of meiosis and explain the relationship between the genetic make-up of the parent cell and the daughter cells (gametes).

34.3 The Reproductive System

IN B.6.4 Meiosis.

Key Questions

What effects do estrogens and testosterone have on females and males?

What are the main functions of the male reproductive system?

What are the main functions of the female reproductive system?

What are some of the most commonly reported sexually transmitted diseases?

Vocabulary

puberty • testis • scrotum • seminiferous tubule • epididymis • vas deferens • semen • ovary • menstrual cycle • ovulation • corpus luteum • menstruation • sexually transmitted disease

Taking Notes

Outline Before you read, use the green and blue headings in this lesson to make an outline. As you read, fill in subtopics and phrases to describe the subtopics.

THINK ABOUT IT Among all the systems of the body, the reproductive system is unique. If any other system in the body failed to function, the result would be death. However, an individual can lead a healthful life without reproducing. But is there any other system that is more important for our existence as a species? Without the reproductive system, we could not produce the next generation, and our species would come to an end. So, in a certain sense, this may be the most important system in the body.

Sexual Development

What effects do estrogens and testosterone have on females and males?

At first, male and female human embryos are nearly identical in appearance. Then, during the seventh week of development, the reproductive systems of male and female embryos begin to develop along different lines. The male pattern of development is triggered by the production of testosterone in the gonads of the embryo. In female embryos, testosterone is absent and the female reproductive system develops under the influence of estrogens produced in the embryo's gonads.

Estrogens and testosterone, which have powerful effects on the body, are steroid hormones primarily produced in the gonads. In addition to shaping the sexual development of the embryo, these hormones act on cells and tissues to produce many of the physical characteristics associated with males and females. **In females, the effects of the sex hormones include breast development and a widening of the hips. In males, they result in the growth of facial hair, increased muscular development, and deepening of the voice.**

In childhood, the gonads and the adrenal cortex produce low levels of sex hormones that influence development. However, neither the testes nor the ovaries can produce active reproductive cells until puberty. **Puberty** is a period of rapid growth and sexual maturation during which the reproductive system becomes fully functional. The age at which puberty begins varies considerably among individuals. It usually occurs between the ages of 9 and 15, and, on average, begins about one year earlier in females than in males. Puberty actually begins in the brain, when the hypothalamus signals the pituitary to produce two hormones that affect the gonads—follicle-stimulating hormone (FSH) and luteinizing hormone (LH).

In Your Notebook *Summarize the effects of estrogens on females and testosterone on males.*

UbD Teach for Understanding

ENDURING UNDERSTANDING The human body is a complex system. The coordinated functions of its many structures support life processes and maintain homeostasis.

GUIDING QUESTION What body structures enable humans to produce offspring?

EVIDENCE OF UNDERSTANDING *After completing the lesson, assign the following assessment so students can show their understanding of the body structures that enable humans to produce offspring and the functions of those structures.* Have each student make two lists: the main structures and functions of the male reproductive system and the main structures and functions of the female reproductive system. Then, ask students to work in pairs to review their lists and revise them if necessary.

The Male Reproductive System

What are the main functions of the male reproductive system?

The release of LH stimulates cells in the testes to produce increased amounts of testosterone. Testosterone causes the male physical changes associated with puberty and, together with FSH, stimulates the development of sperm. **When puberty is complete, the reproductive system is fully functional, meaning that the male can produce and release active sperm.**

Figure 34–11 shows the structures of the male reproductive system. Just before birth (or sometimes just after), the primary male reproductive organs, the **testes** (singular: testis), descend from the abdomen into an external sac called the **scrotum.** The testes remain in the scrotum, outside the body cavity, where the temperature is a few degrees lower than the normal temperature of the body (37°C). The lower temperature is important for proper sperm development.

Sperm Development Within each testis are clusters of hundreds of tiny tubules called **seminiferous** (sem uh NIF ur us) **tubules** where sperm develop. A cross section of one tubule is shown in **Figure 34–11.** Specialized diploid cells within the tubules undergo meiosis and form the haploid nuclei of mature sperm. Recall that a haploid cell contains only a single set of chromosomes.

After they are produced in the seminiferous tubules, sperm are moved into the **epididymis** (ep uh DID ih mis), in which they mature and are stored. From the epididymis, some sperm are moved into a tube called the **vas deferens.** The vas deferens extends upward from the scrotum into the abdominal cavity. Eventually, the vas deferens merges with the urethra, the tube that leads to the outside of the body through the penis.

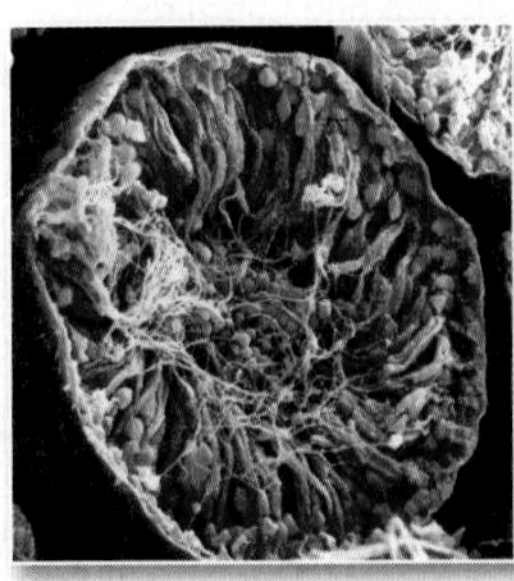

FIGURE 34–11 Male Reproductive System The main structures of the male reproductive system produce and deliver sperm. The micrograph shows a cross section of one tiny seminiferous tubule containing developing sperm (SEM 150×).

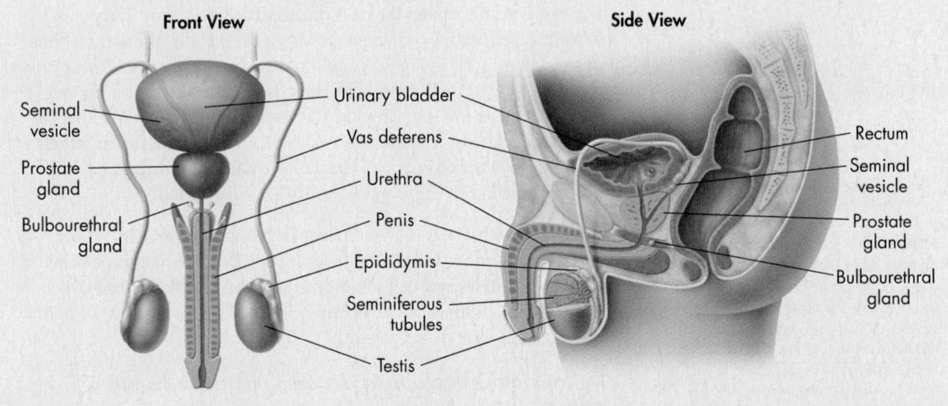

Quick Facts

EFFECT OF TEMPERATURE ON SPERM DEVELOPMENT

Sperm development is a process that cannot occur at its optimal level when the temperature within the testes is too warm or too cool. Without treatment, males born with undescended testes may be sterile because the temperature within the abdomen is too high for sperm development. Hot baths or tight clothing also may increase the temperature of the testes enough to inhibit sperm production and cause temporary infertility. In cold weather, involuntary muscle contractions pull the testes closer to the body so that they stay warmer.

Teach

Lead a Discussion

As a class, discuss the male reproductive system.

Ask What is the main function of the male reproductive system? *(the production and release of active sperm)* Have volunteers describe how the different structures in the male reproductive system help men make and release sperm.

DIFFERENTIATED INSTRUCTION

L1 Special Needs Some students may find it difficult to maintain appropriate behavior during discussions of the reproductive system. Explain to students that, from a scientist's perspective, the reproductive system is simply another body system with a set of structures that perform particular functions. Tell students you will use the phrase "think like a scientist" to remind them to use appropriate vocabulary and behavior during class discussions of the reproductive system.

ELL Focus on ELL: Build Background

BEGINNING AND INTERMEDIATE SPEAKERS Start by pointing out the boldface questions, labeled with the Key Concept symbol, that accompany each green heading. Use these questions to help lead your students through an **Anticipation/Reaction Guide** activity. Before reading a section of text, have pairs of students discuss its Key Question and write a short response. For beginning English language learners, accept short lists and imprecise wording. After students have read the section, ask them to respond to the questions again. Encourage pairs to talk about how their responses changed after they read the text.

Study Wkbks A/B, Appendix S1, Anticipation/Reaction Guide.

Teach continued

Use Visuals

Have students use **Figure 34–12** to examine the structure of a sperm.

Ask What are the three main parts of a mature sperm cell? *(head, midpiece, and tail, or flagellum)*

Ask What is the function of each part? *(The head of the sperm contains the genetic material and has a small cap with enzymes vital for fertilization. The midpiece contains mitochondria, organelles that release the energy the sperm needs to move. The tail, or flagellum, propels the sperm forward.)*

DIFFERENTIATED INSTRUCTION

LPR Less Proficient Readers Have students copy **Figure 34–12** into their notebooks. They should label the head, midpiece, and tail. Then, have students write a few words next to each label summarizing the function of each part of the sperm cell. Help students find the information they need by pointing out the subsection of text titled **Sperm Structure.**

L3 Advanced Students Remind students that the genetic content of sperm cells differs from body cells and that sperm cells form by a different process. Have advanced students review the processes of mitosis and meiosis. Then, have them make a review sheet that can be used by other class members. Encourage students to include diagrams on their review sheets.

Quick Lab GUIDED INQUIRY

IN B.6.4

Tracing Human Gamete Formation

❶ Recall that cells in the testes and ovaries undergo meiosis as they form gametes—sperm and eggs.

❷ For each letter, indicate how many chromosomes are in the cells at that stage and whether the cells are diploid (2N) or haploid (N). Answers *a.* and *e.* have been provided for you.

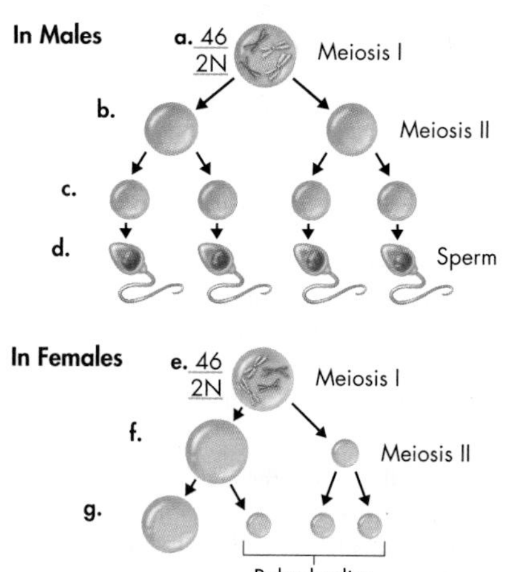

Analyze and Conclude

1. Interpret Visuals For every cell that undergoes meiosis in a male or female, what is the ratio of sperm produced in males to eggs produced in females?

2. Infer What percentage of sperm cells will contain a Y chromosome?

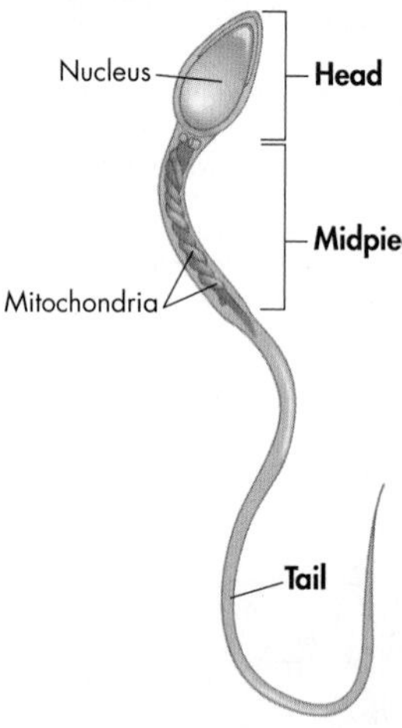

FIGURE 34–12 Sperm A large number of mitochondria are required to power a sperm cell's trip through the female reproductive system. If a sperm reaches an egg, enzymes in the sperm's head can break down the egg's outer layer.

Glands lining the reproductive tract—including the seminal vesicles, the prostate, and the bulbourethral (bul buh yoo REE thrul) glands—produce a nutrient-rich fluid called seminal fluid. The seminal fluid nourishes the sperm and protects them from the acidity of the female reproductive tract. The combination of sperm and seminal fluid is known as **semen.** The number of sperm present in even a few drops of semen is astonishing. Between 50 million and 130 million sperm are present in 1 milliliter of semen. That's about 2.5 million sperm per drop!

Sperm Release When the male is sexually aroused, the autonomic nervous system prepares the male organs to deliver sperm. The penis becomes erect, and sperm are ejected from the penis by the contractions of smooth muscles lining the glands in the reproductive tract. This process is called ejaculation. Because ejaculation is regulated by the autonomic nervous system, it is not completely voluntary. About 2 to 6 milliliters of semen are released in an average ejaculation. If the sperm in this semen are released in the reproductive tract of a female, the chances of a single sperm fertilizing an egg, if one is available, are very good.

Sperm Structure A mature sperm cell consists of a head, which contains a highly condensed nucleus; a midpiece, which is packed with energy-releasing mitochondria; and a tail, or flagellum, which propels the cell forward. At the tip of the head is a small cap containing enzymes vital to fertilization.

In Your Notebook *Make a flowchart that shows the path of developing sperm through the male reproductive system.*

Quick Lab

PURPOSE Students will indicate the number of chromosomes present in cells during the different stages of gamete formation.

PLANNING Refer students to **Lesson 11.4** to review meiosis.

EXPECTED OUTCOME

Step 2 answers: **b.** 46, 2N; **c.** 23, N; **d.** 23, N; **f.** 46, 2N; **g.** 23, N.

ANALYZE AND CONCLUDE

1. 4:1

2. 50%

Answers

IN YOUR NOTEBOOK Students' flowcharts should include sperm developing in the seminiferous tubules, moving to the epididymis, and then to the vas deferens. Sperm are released through the urethra, a tube that leads to the outside of the body through the penis.

The Female Reproductive System

What are the main functions of the female reproductive system?

The primary reproductive organs of the female are the **ovaries.** As in males, puberty in females starts when the hypothalamus signals the pituitary gland to release FSH and LH. FSH stimulates cells within the ovaries to produce increased amounts of estrogens and to start producing egg cells. **The main function of the female reproductive system is to produce egg cells, or ova (singular: ovum). In addition, the system prepares the female's body to nourish a developing embryo.**

Female Reproductive Structures At puberty, each ovary contains as many as 400,000 primary follicles, which are clusters of cells surrounding a single egg. The function of a follicle is to help an egg mature for release into the reproductive tract, where it may be fertilized by a sperm. Despite the huge number of primary follicles, a female's ovaries release only about 400 mature eggs in her lifetime.

In addition to the ovaries, other structures in the female reproductive system include the Fallopian tubes, uterus, cervix, and the vagina. **Figure 34–13** shows the location of these structures.

The Menstrual Cycle One ovary usually produces and releases one mature ovum every 28 days or so. The process of egg formation and release occurs as part of the **menstrual cycle,** a regular sequence of events involving the ovaries, the lining of the uterus, and the endocrine system. The menstrual cycle is regulated by hormones made by the hypothalamus, pituitary, and ovaries; it is controlled by internal feedback mechanisms.

During the menstrual cycle, an egg develops within a follicle and is released from an ovary. In addition, the uterus is prepared to receive a fertilized egg. If an egg is not fertilized, it is discharged, along with the lining of the uterus. If an egg is fertilized, embryonic development begins and the menstrual cycle ceases. The menstrual cycle includes the follicular phase, ovulation, the luteal phase, and menstruation.

FIGURE 34–13 Female Reproductive System The main function of the female reproductive system is to produce ova. The ovaries are the main organs of the female reproductive system. Predict ***Which structure is most likely lined with cilia that push an egg toward the uterus? Explain.***

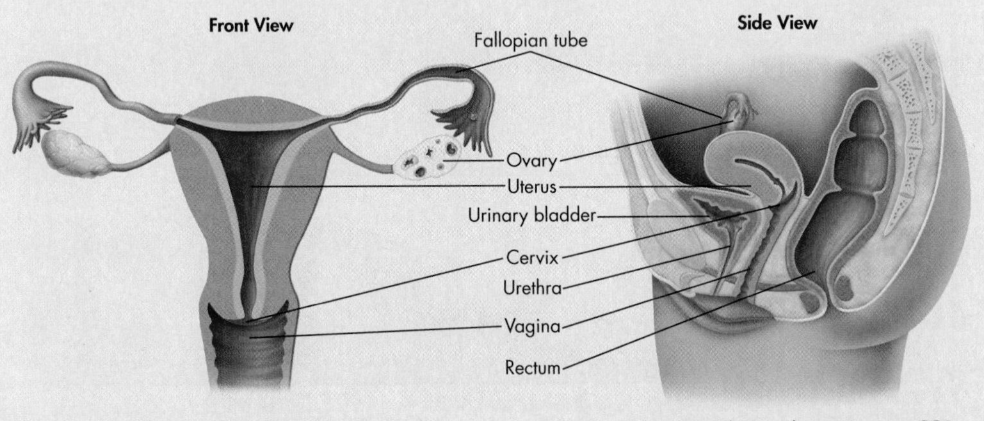

Check for Understanding

QUESTION BOX

Establish a question box in the classroom that students can use to ask questions about concepts or processes they do not understand. Have students drop questions about the structures and functions of the male and female reproductive systems in this box. Assure students that they do not need to include their names with their questions.

ADJUST INSTRUCTION

Read over students' questions to identify common questions or areas of confusion. Use each as a topic of discussion to address students' questions or misconceptions.

Lead a Discussion

Students may notice the word *estrogens* in the first paragraph on this page and wonder why the word is used in the plural form. Explain that *estrogens* refers to a group of related hormones—estrone, estradiol, and estriol. The level of the different estrogens in a woman will vary throughout her life. Other structures besides ovaries produce small amounts of some estrogens, including the adrenal glands, fat tissue, and muscles.

Ask What effect does puberty have on estrogen levels? *(They rise during puberty.)*

DIFFERENTIATED INSTRUCTION

L1 Struggling Students Have students locate the ovaries in **Figure 34–13.**

Ask In addition to producing estrogens, what is another function of the ovaries? *(The ovaries release mature eggs.)*

Ask After an egg leaves an ovary, what structure does it enter? *(a Fallopian tube)*

L3 Advanced Students Have each student write a paragraph that compares and contrasts the male reproductive system and the female reproductive system. Have students consider ways they are similar *(controlled by hormones, produce gametes)* and ways they are different *(made up of different structures, only females can nourish a developing embryo).*

Answers

FIGURE 34–13 The Fallopian tubes are likely lined with cilia that push an egg toward the uterus. An egg travels through a Fallopian tube once it is released from the ovary.

Teach continued

VISUAL SUMMARY

Explain to students that **Figure 34–14** is arranged similar to a table with five rows.

Ask What information is found in each of the five rows? *(days, phase, hormone levels in the blood, follicle development, uterine lining)*

Ask During which phase is the uterine lining thickest? *(the luteal phase)*

Ask Why would it be important for the uterine lining to be at its thickest at that time? *(If an egg is fertilized, the embryo typically implants in the uterine lining during the luteal phase.)*

DIFFERENTIATED INSTRUCTION

ELL English Language Learners Students may be unfamiliar with the word *phase*. Explain that a phase is a distinct part of a cycle or process. In this case, each phase of the menstrual cycle is a group of days during which specific conditions occur. Students may be familiar with the word *phase* used to describe the cyclical changes in the moon's appearance. If so, connect the use of *phase* in this lesson with the phases of the moon.

▶ ***Follicular Phase*** As shown in **Figure 34–14,** on day 1 of a menstrual cycle, blood estrogen levels are low. The hypothalamus reacts to low estrogen levels by producing a releasing hormone that stimulates the anterior pituitary to secrete FSH and LH. These two hormones travel to the ovaries, where they cause a follicle to mature. Usually, just a single follicle develops, but sometimes two or even three mature during the same cycle.

As the follicle develops, the cells surrounding the egg enlarge and begin to produce increased amounts of estrogens. This causes the estrogen level in the blood to rise dramatically. High blood estrogen levels cause the hypothalamus to produce less releasing hormone, and the pituitary releases less LH and FSH. Estrogens also cause the lining of the uterus to thicken in preparation for receiving a fertilized egg. The development of an egg during this phase takes about 12 days.

VISUAL SUMMARY

THE MENSTRUAL CYCLE

FIGURE 34–14 The menstrual cycle includes several phases. Notice the changes in hormone levels in the blood, the development of the follicle, and the changes in the uterine lining during the menstrual cycle. Interpret Diagrams ***During which phase of the menstrual cycle are estrogen levels the highest?***

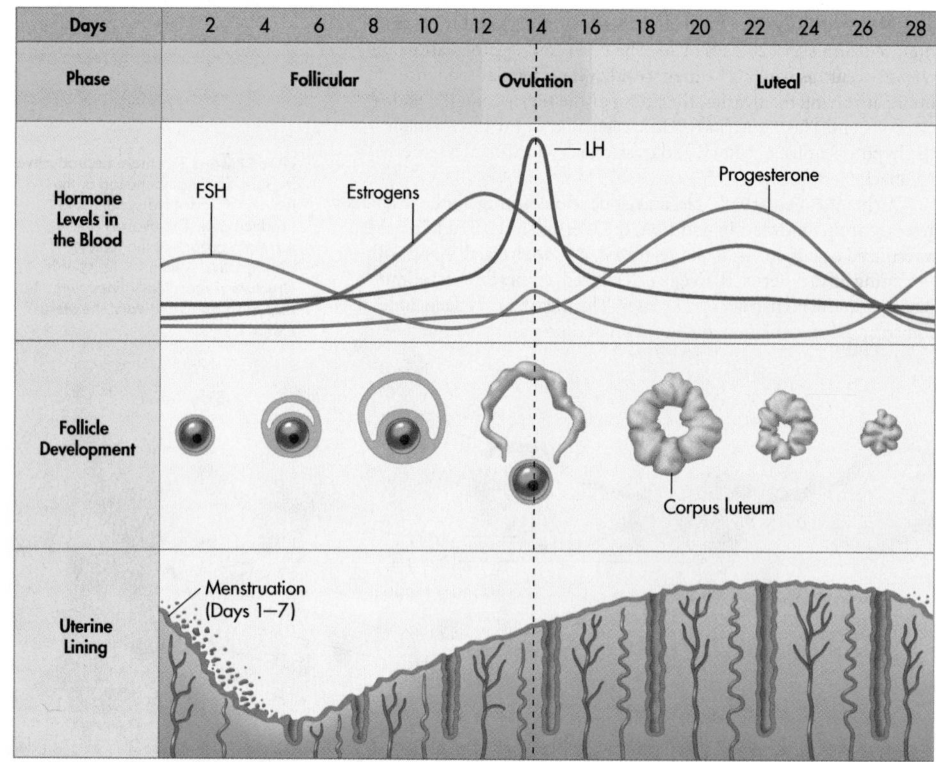

How Science Works

THE PUZZLE OF MENSTRUATION

Scientists have puzzled over human menstruation, which seems to defy the expected pattern of natural selection because blood loss leads to iron loss. One suggestion for the persistence of menstruation in humans was made by Margie Profet in 1993, who hypothesized that menstruation helps the body rid itself of pathogens introduced during sexual intercourse. In 1996, Profet's ideas were challenged by Beverly Strassman who proposed that monthly regeneration of the uterine lining is less costly to the body than maintenance of a permanent lining. Her research indicates that cells of the endometrium require far less oxygen when the lining is not being actively maintained.

Answers

FIGURE 34–14 the end of the follicular phase

▶ ***Ovulation*** As the follicle grows, it releases more and more estrogens. When concentrations of these hormones reach a certain level, the hypothalamus reacts by triggering a burst of LH and FSH from the anterior pituitary. The sudden increase in these hormones (especially LH) causes the follicle to rupture. The result is **ovulation,** the release of an egg from the ovary into one of the Fallopian tubes. When released, the egg is stalled in metaphase of meiosis II and will remain that way unless it is fertilized. As the newly released egg is drawn into the Fallopian tube, microscopic cilia push the cell through the fluid-filled tube, toward the uterus.

▶ ***Luteal Phase*** The luteal phase begins immediately after ovulation. As the egg moves through the Fallopian tube, the cells of the ruptured follicle change. The follicle turns yellow and is now known as the **corpus luteum** (KAWR pus LOOT ee um), which means "yellow body" in Latin. The corpus luteum continues to release estrogens but also begins to release another steroid hormone called progesterone. Progesterone also stimulates the growth and development of the blood supply and surrounding tissue in the already-thickened uterine lining. The rise in these hormones once again inhibits the production of FSH and LH. Thus, additional follicles do not develop during this cycle.

Unless fertilization occurs and an embryo starts to develop, the fall of LH levels leads to the degeneration of the corpus luteum. Estrogen levels fall, the hypothalamus signals the release of FSH and LH from the anterior pituitary, and the follicular phase begins again.

▶ ***Menstruation*** At the start of the new follicular phase, low estrogen levels also cause the lining of the uterus to detach from the uterine wall. This tissue, along with blood and the unfertilized egg, are discharged through the vagina. This phase of the cycle is called **menstruation.** Menstruation lasts about three to seven days on average. A new cycle begins with the first day of menstruation.

The menstrual cycle continues, on average, until a female is in her late forties to early fifties. At this time, the production of estrogens declines, and ovulation and menstruation stop. The permanent stopping of the menstrual cycle is called menopause.

Pregnancy Of course, the menstrual cycle also ceases if a woman becomes pregnant. During the first two days of the luteal phase, immediately following ovulation, the chances that an egg will be fertilized are the greatest. This is usually from 14 to 18 days after the completion of the last menstrual cycle. If a sperm fertilizes an egg, the fertilized egg completes meiosis and immediately undergoes mitosis. After several divisions, a ball of cells will form and implant itself in the lining of the uterus. Within a few days of implantation, the uterus and the growing embryo will release hormones that keep the corpus luteum functioning for several weeks. This allows the lining of the uterus to nourish and protect the developing embryo and prevents the menstrual cycle from starting again.

In Your Notebook *Draw a cycle diagram to represent the phases and days of the menstrual cycle.*

FIGURE 34–15 Ovulation (LM 160×)

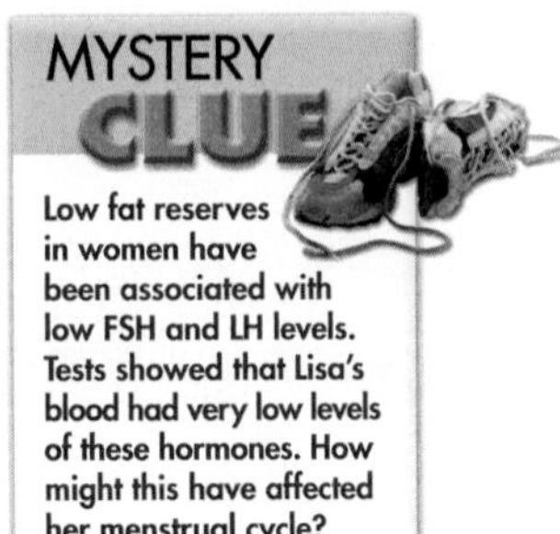

Low fat reserves in women have been associated with low FSH and LH levels. Tests showed that Lisa's blood had very low levels of these hormones. How might this have affected her menstrual cycle?

BUILD Vocabulary

WORD ORIGINS The word **menstruation** comes from the Latin word *mensis*, meaning "month."

Build Reading Skills

Show students the bulleted paragraphs on this page and the previous page. Explain that these paragraphs provide detailed information about the phases of the menstrual cycle. As students read each paragraph, have them refer back to the appropriate section of **Figure 34–14.**

DIFFERENTIATED INSTRUCTION

L1 Struggling Students Provide each student with three index cards, and ask them to record main ideas and details as they read. Have them use one card for each phase: follicular, ovulation, and luteal. Point out that menstruation occurs during the follicular phase, so information about menstruation should be included on that index card.

Discuss the effects of FSH and LH on follicular development. Guide students to explain that a follicle will not mature if FSH and LH levels are too low.

Ask What happens to the menstrual cycle if a follicle does not mature? *(The increased production of estrogens does not occur, and the events of the menstrual cycle do not proceed as normal.)* Students can go online to **Biology.com** to gather their evidence.

UbD Check for Understanding

INDEX CARD SUMMARIES

Give each student an index card. Ask them to write one concept about the female reproductive system that they understand on the front of their card. Then, have them write a question they have about the female reproductive system on the back of the card.

ADJUST INSTRUCTION

Read over students' cards to identify concepts about the female reproductive system that are well understood and those that are causing confusion. List the topics of confusion on the board. Have each student choose one listed topic to become an "expert" on, and write a paragraph that explains the topic. Read over students' responses, and share with the class several paragraphs related to each topic.

Answers

IN YOUR NOTEBOOK Students' cycle diagrams should show the follicular phase occurring between days 1 and 13; ovulation occurring at day 14; and the luteal phase occurring between days 15 and 28.

Teach continued

Address Misconceptions

STDs According to a 2005 survey carried out by researchers at the University of California, one in seven teens thinks that there is no risk of STD transmission through oral sex. Explain to students that some STDs can be spread through oral sex.

Assess and Remediate

EVALUATE UNDERSTANDING

Read each of the Key Questions for the lesson aloud. Call on volunteers to provide responses. If students' responses indicate a lack of mastery of a particular topic, have the class discuss the figures and vocabulary terms associated with that topic. Then, have students complete the 34.3 Assessment.

REMEDIATION SUGGESTION

L1 **Struggling Students** Some students may have difficulty answering **Question 4b** because the answer is not provided in the text. Explain to students that the skill *Evaluate* requires them to consider a problem and offer a solution or an opinion.

BIOLOGY.com Students can check their understanding of lesson concepts with the **Self-Test** assessment. They can then take an online version of the **Lesson Assessment.**

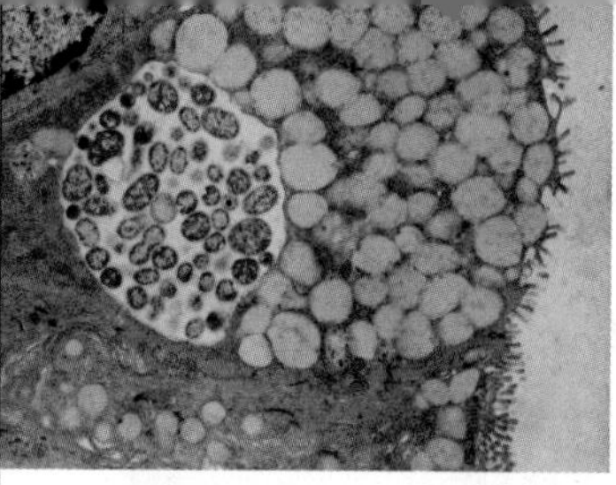

FIGURE 34–16 Chlamydia Infection This electron micrograph shows a cluster of *C. trachomatis* bacteria (green) growing inside a mucus-secreting cell within a female reproductive tract. The bacteria will eventually overwhelm the cell and cause it to burst, allowing the infection to spread (TEM 2400×).

Sexually Transmitted Diseases

What are some of the most commonly reported sexually transmitted diseases?

Diseases that spread by sexual contact, or **sexually transmitted diseases** (STDs), are a serious health problem in the United States. A 2008 study by the Centers for Disease Control and Prevention showed that one in four girls and young women aged 14 to 19 were infected with an STD.

Unfortunately, public health information about STDs has not kept pace with the rate of infection. For example, one might think that the name of the most commonly reported infectious disease in the United States would be a household word, but it isn't. **Chlamydia is not only the most common bacterial STD, it is the most commonly reported bacterial disease in the United States.** Chlamydia, which damages the reproductive tract and can lead to infertility, is caused by a bacterium that is spread by sexual contact. Other bacterial STDs include gonorrhea and syphilis.

Viruses can also cause STDs. **Viral STDs include hepatitis B, genital herpes, genital warts, and AIDS.** Unlike the bacterial STDs, viral infections cannot be treated with antibiotics.

Some viral STDs, such as AIDS, can be fatal. Tens of thousands of people in the United States die from AIDS each year. In addition, the virus that causes genital warts—human papillomavirus (HPV)—is a major cause of cervical cancer in women. Recently, a vaccine has been developed that can prevent some HPV infections. To be effective, the vaccine must be administered before a woman is infected with HPV.

STDs can be avoided. Any sexual contact carries with it the chance of infection. The safest course to follow is to abstain from sexual contact before marriage, and for both partners in a committed relationship to remain faithful. The next safest course is to use a latex condom, but even condoms do not provide 100 percent protection.

34.3 Assessment

Review Key Concepts

1. a. Review Explain what happens during puberty.
   b. Compare and Contrast Compare and contrast the sexual development of male embryos to that of female embryos.
2. a. Review Describe the function of the male reproductive system.
   b. Sequence Explain how sperm develop.
3. a. Review Describe the functions of the female reproductive system.
   b. Interpret Visuals What happens during each stage of the menstrual cycle? *Hint:* Refer to **Figure 34–14.**
4. a. Review Name two STDs caused by bacteria and two caused by viruses.
   b. Evaluate Why do you think that young people are especially at risk for STDs?

Apply the Big idea

Cellular Basis of Life

5. Sperm cells contain numerous mitochondria. Use what you learned about mitochondria in Chapter 7 to explain how mitochondria might influence sperm activity.

BIOLOGY.com Search Lesson 34.3 GO • Self-Test • Lesson Assessment

994 Chapter 34 • Lesson 3

Assessment Answers

1a. Puberty is a period of rapid growth and sexual maturation during which the reproductive system becomes fully functional.

1b. The development of both male and female embryos is very similar until the seventh week of development. Then, the male embryo pattern of development is triggered by testosterone. In female embryos, the pattern of development is triggered by estrogens.

2a. the production and release of active sperm

2b. Sperm, which are haploid, are made in the seminiferous tubules. Then, the sperm are moved to the epididymis, in which they mature and are stored.

3a. produce egg cells; support and nourish a developing embryo

3b. During the follicular phase, a follicle matures and levels of estrogens rise. During ovulation, the follicle ruptures and the egg is released. In the luteal phase, the egg moves through the Fallopian tube and progesterone levels peak. During menstruation, which occurs during the follicular phase, the lining of the uterus detaches from the uterine wall and is discharged.

4a. Sample answer: Bacterial STDs include chlamydia and gonorrhea; viral STDs include hepatitis B and genital herpes.

4b. Sample answer: Young people are at particular risk for STDs because they may be more prone to risky behaviors, such as unprotected sex. Young people may also be less likely to go to the doctor for treatment, and therefore, may be more likely to spread the disease to other young people.

5. Big idea Mitochondria are the organelles that transfer the energy in food molecules into ATP. Mitochondria influence sperm activity by providing the energy needed for movement through the female reproductive system.

34.4 Fertilization and Development

 B.6.3 Specialization and organization in multicellular organisms.

THINK ABOUT IT Of all the wonders of the living world, is there anything more remarkable than the formation of a new human being from a single cell? In a sense, we know how this happens. The embryo goes through round after round of cell division, producing the trillions of cells in a newborn baby. Simple enough, it seems. But how do these cells arrange themselves so beautifully into the tissues and organs of the body, and how does an individual cell "know" to become an embryonic skin, heart, or blood cell? These are some of the most important questions in all of biology, and we are only beginning to learn the answers.

Key Questions

What takes place during fertilization and the early stages of human development?

What important events occur during the later stages of human development?

Vocabulary

zygote • blastocyst • implantation • gastrulation • neurulation • placenta • fetus

Taking Notes

Flowchart As you read, draw a flowchart that shows the steps from fertilized egg to newborn baby.

Fertilization and Early Development

What takes place during fertilization and the early stages of human development?

The story of human development begins with the gametes—sperm produced in the testes and egg cells produced in the ovaries. Sperm and egg must meet, so that the two gametes can fuse to form a single cell. With this single cell, the process of development begins. **The fusion of a sperm and egg cell is called fertilization.**

Fertilization During sexual intercourse, sperm are released when semen is ejaculated through the penis into the vagina. Semen is generally released just below the cervix, the opening that connects the vagina to the uterus. Sperm swim actively through the uterus into the Fallopian tubes. Hundreds of millions of sperm are released during an ejaculation. If an egg is present in one of the Fallopian tubes, its chances of being fertilized are good.

The egg is surrounded by a protective layer that contains binding sites to which sperm can attach. The sperm head then releases powerful enzymes that break down the protective layer of the egg. The haploid (N) sperm nucleus enters the haploid egg, and chromosomes from sperm and egg are brought together. Once the two haploid nuclei fuse, a single diploid (2N) nucleus is formed, containing a single set of chromosomes from each parent cell. The fertilized egg is called a **zygote.** At this point the developing human can also be called an embryo.

FIGURE 34–17 Sperm Meet Egg Many sperm usually reach an egg, but only one sperm can successfully break through the egg's protective barrier (SEM 650×).

UbD Teach for Understanding

ENDURING UNDERSTANDING The human body is a complex system. The coordinated functions of its many structures support life processes and maintain homeostasis.

GUIDING QUESTION How does a human develop from a single cell to a newborn baby?

EVIDENCE OF UNDERSTANDING *After completing the lesson, assign the following assessment so students can show their understanding of how the human body develops from a single cell to a complex, organized system.* Have students form small groups. Ask each group to choose a stage of development after fertilization (months 1–3, 4–6, or 7–9). Have the students in each group develop a pamphlet describing the changes that occur in the stage. Invite each group to share its pamphlet with the class.

Getting Started

Objectives

34.4.1 Describe fertilization and the early stages of development.

34.4.2 Identify the major events of later stages of development.

Student Resources

Study Workbooks A and B, 34.4 Worksheets

Spanish Study Workbook, 34.4 Worksheets

Lab Manual B, 34.4 Hands-On Activity Worksheet

 Lesson Overview • Lesson Notes • Assessment: Self-Test, Lesson Assessment

 For corresponding lesson in the **Foundation Edition**, see pages 824–829.

Activate Prior Knowledge

Point out that all babies begin as a single cell.

Ask How is the single cell that could develop into a newborn baby formed? *(through fertilization, or the joining of egg and sperm)*

Ask What are two things that must happen for that single cell to develop into a baby? *(The number of cells must increase, and cells must specialize in order to carry out specific functions.)*

IN INDIANA ACADEMIC STANDARDS

For the full text of all standards, see the Course Overview in the front matter of this book.

B.6.3 Explain that in multicellular organisms the zygote produced during fertilization undergoes a series of cell divisions that lead to clusters of cells that go on to specialize and become the organism's tissues and organs.

Teach

Use Visuals

Have students examine the sequence of events shown in **Figure 34–19.** Have volunteers describe in detail what is pictured or what is happening in each numbered diagram. Model this for students by describing the first diagram in the following way: *This diagram shows an egg at ovulation, which is the stage when it is released from the ovary. It is a haploid cell, which means it has half the number of chromosomes in its nucleus as a body cell.* Encourage each volunteer to provide as many details as possible about the structures and processes shown.

DIFFERENTIATED INSTRUCTION

L1 Struggling Students Tell students that each stage in fertilization and implantation is shown in two ways in **Figure 34–19.** Explain that the top row of numbered diagrams shows a close-up of the changes that occur to the egg and embryo during fertilization and implantation. Each numbered stage in the top row is also shown in the diagram below. This diagram shows where in the female reproductive system those changes occur.

BIOLOGY.com Have students use the **InterActive Art: Embryonic Development** to explore early development through neurulation.

FIGURE 34–18 Ernest Everett Just One of the great pioneers of cell biology, E.E. Just investigated the process of fertilization. He discovered that changes in an egg's cell membrane prevent more than one sperm from fertilizing an egg.

What prevents more than one sperm from fertilizing an egg? Early in the twentieth century, cell biologist Ernest Everett Just found the answer. The egg cell contains a series of granules just beneath its outer surface. When a sperm enters the egg, the egg reacts by releasing the contents of these granules outside the cell. The material in the granules coats the surface of the egg, forming a barrier that prevents other sperm from attaching to, and entering, the egg.

Multiple Embryos If two eggs are released during the same menstrual cycle and each is fertilized, fraternal twins may result. Fraternal twins are not identical in appearance and may even be different sexes, because each has been formed by the fusion of a different sperm and different egg cell.

Sometimes a single zygote splits apart and produces two genetically identical embryos. These two embryos are called identical twins. Because they result from the same fertilized egg, identical twins are always the same sex.

Implantation While still in the Fallopian tube, the zygote begins to undergo mitosis, as shown in **Figure 34–19.** As the embryo grows, a cavity forms in the center, until the embryo becomes a hollow ball of cells known as a **blastocyst.** About six or seven days after fertilization, the blastocyst attaches to the wall of the uterus and begins to grow into the tissues of the mother. This process is known as **implantation.**

At this point, cells in the blastocyst begin to specialize. This specialization process, called differentiation, results in the development of the various types of tissues in the body. A cluster of cells, known as the inner cell mass, develops within the inner cavity of the blastocyst. The body of the embryo will develop from these cells, while the other cells of the blastocyst will differentiate into some of the tissues that support and protect the embryo.

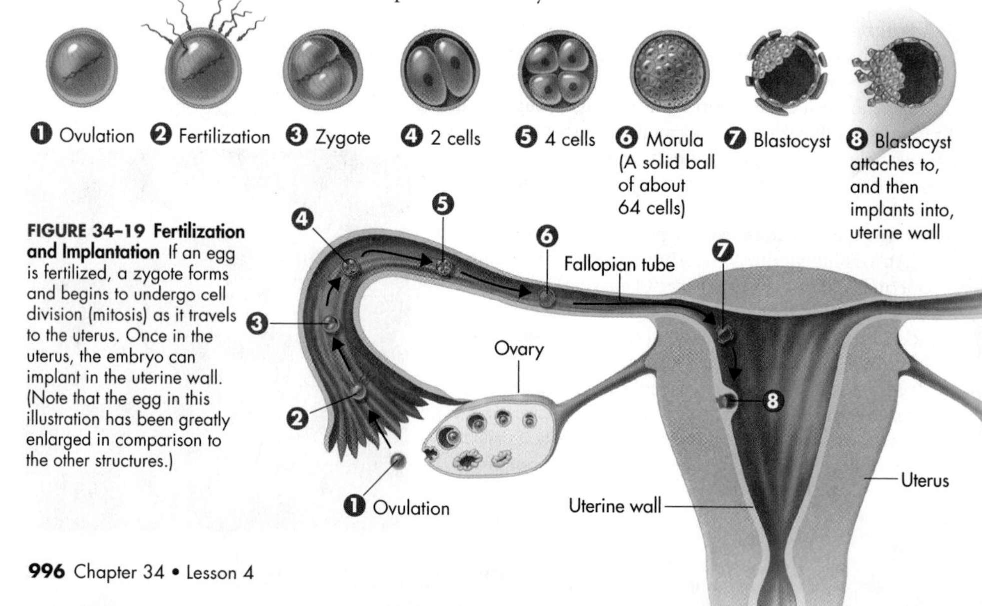

FIGURE 34–19 Fertilization and Implantation If an egg is fertilized, a zygote forms and begins to undergo cell division (mitosis) as it travels to the uterus. Once in the uterus, the embryo can implant in the uterine wall. (Note that the egg in this illustration has been greatly enlarged in comparison to the other structures.)

How Science Works

FERTILIZATION

In the mid-1600s, the invention of the microscope allowed scientists to see human sperm for the first time. At that time, many scientists thought they saw a tiny human, which they called a homunculus, within each sperm. Human eggs were first viewed in the early 1900s. It was not until the 1940s that fertilization of human eggs was observed directly. Pioneering work on in-vitro (outside the body) fertilization of animal eggs was carried out in the 1950s at the Worcester Foundation for Experimental Biology in Massachusetts. This work with animal eggs laid the groundwork for human in-vitro fertilization. The first human baby conceived via in-vitro fertilization was born in 1978. In 2005, more than 50,000 babies were born in the United States as a result of in-vitro fertilization and related techniques.

996 Chapter 34 • Lesson 4

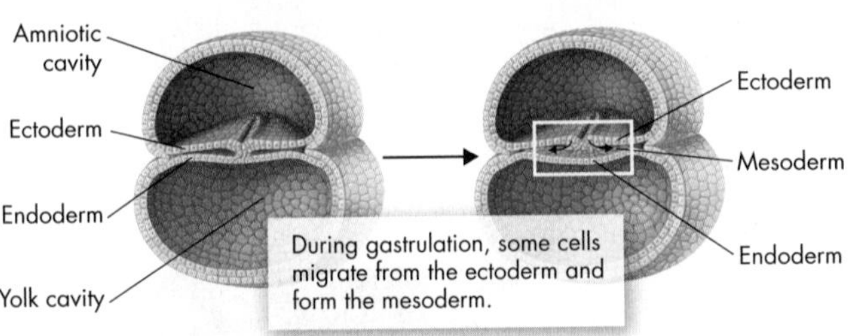

FIGURE 34–20 Gastrulation This stage results in the formation of three cell layers—the ectoderm, mesoderm, and endoderm. The three layers form all of the organs and tissues of the embryo.

Gastrulation As development continues, the embryo begins a series of dramatic changes that will produce the key structures and tissue layers of the body. **Key events in early development include gastrulation, which produces the three cell layers of the embryo, and neurulation, which leads to the formation of the nervous system.** The result of **gastrulation** (gas troo LAY shun) is the formation of three cell layers called the ectoderm, mesoderm, and endoderm. The ectoderm and endoderm form first. The mesoderm is produced by a process of cell migration shown in **Figure 34–20.**

The ectoderm will develop into the skin and the nervous system. Mesoderm cells differentiate and form many of the body's internal structures, including bones, muscle, blood cells, and gonads. Endoderm forms the linings of organs in the digestive system, such as the stomach and intestines, as well as in the respiratory and excretory systems.

Neurulation Gastrulation is followed by another important step in development, neurulation (NUR uh lay shun). **Neurulation,** shown in **Figure 34–21,** is the first step in the development of the nervous system. Shortly after gastrulation is complete, a block of mesodermal tissue begins to differentiate into the notochord. Recall that all chordates possess a notochord at some stage of development. As the notochord develops, the ectoderm near the notochord thickens and forms the neural plate. The raised edges of the neural plate form neural folds and the neural crest. The neural folds gradually move together and form the neural tube, from which the spinal cord and brain will develop. Cells of the neural crest migrate to other locations and become types of nerve cells, skin pigment cells, and other structures such as the lower jaw.

If the neural tube does not close completely, a serious birth defect known as spina bifida can result. Studies show that folic acid (vitamin B_9) can prevent most cases of spina bifida. Because neurulation usually occurs before a woman knows she's pregnant, folic acid is an important nutrient in any woman's diet.

In Your Notebook *Explain in your own words what occurs during neurulation.*

FIGURE 34–21 Neurulation During neurulation, the ectoderm undergoes changes that lead to the formation of a neural tube that develops into the brain and spinal cord. Neural crest cells develop into many types of nerves.

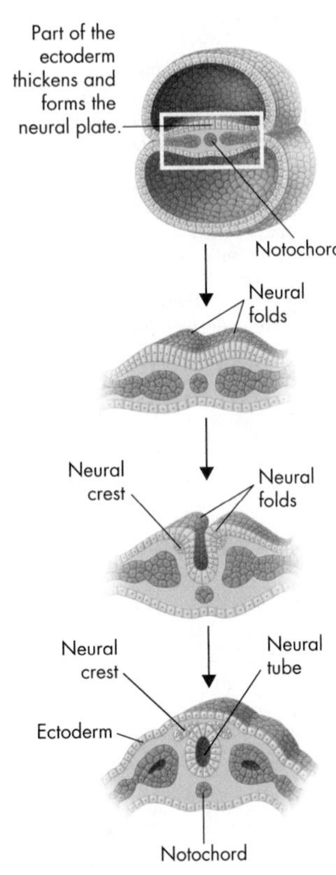

Expand Vocabulary

List the words *ectoderm*, *mesoderm*, and *endoderm* on the board. Tell students that the prefix *ecto-* means "outer," the prefix *meso-* means "middle," and the prefix *endo-* means "inner." Point out the correspondence of these names to the structures eventually formed by the cells in each layer. The ectoderm forms the outer layer of the body—the skin (although it's important to remember that the ectoderm also forms the nervous system). The mesoderm forms structures found in the middle of the body, such as the bones and muscles. The endoderm forms the linings, or insides, of the organs of the digestive, respiratory, and excretory systems.

DIFFERENTIATED INSTRUCTION

L3 Advanced Students Ask students to use the Glossary or a dictionary to find other terms that contain the prefixes *ecto-*, *meso-*, or *endo-*. Have them record several terms and their definitions. Ask students to share what they have learned with the class.

UbD Check for Understanding

FOLLOW-UP PROBES

Ask Why are gastrulation and neurulation both such critical events in early development? *(The process of gastrulation results in the formation of three cell layers, which eventually develop into the structures and tissue layers of the body. Neurulation is the first step in the development of the nervous system.)*

ADJUST INSTRUCTION

If responses indicate that students do not understand the importance of gastrulation or neurulation, ask students to complete the following sentences:

- If gastrulation did not occur in a developing embryo . . .
- If neurulation did not occur in a developing embryo . . .

Use students' responses to highlight the importance of these processes.

Answers

IN YOUR NOTEBOOK Sample answer: During neurulation, a block of mesodermal tissue forms the notochord. The ectoderm near the notochord then forms the neural plate, which then forms neural folds and the neural crest. The neural folds develop into the neural tube, from which the brain and spinal cord develop.

LESSON 34.4

Teach continued

Use Models

Use the following model to demonstrate the importance of the amnion and amniotic fluid. Place an uncooked egg in a gallon-size plastic food-storage bag, and then, fill the bag with water. Demonstrate how difficult it would be to break the egg without removing the egg or water from the bag. Students should note that the egg is well protected and difficult to break.

Ask In this model, what is represented by the plastic bag? *(the amnion)*

Ask What is represented by the water? *(amniotic fluid)*

Ask What is represented by the egg? *(the developing embryo or fetus)*

DIFFERENTIATED INSTRUCTION

ELL English Language Learners Have students use what they learned from watching the demonstration to write a simple sentence that summarizes the role of the amnion. *(The amnion holds fluid that protects an embryo or fetus.)* Then, have students write similar sentences summarizing the role of the placenta and role of the umbilical cord. Have students review these sentences at the conclusion of the lesson.

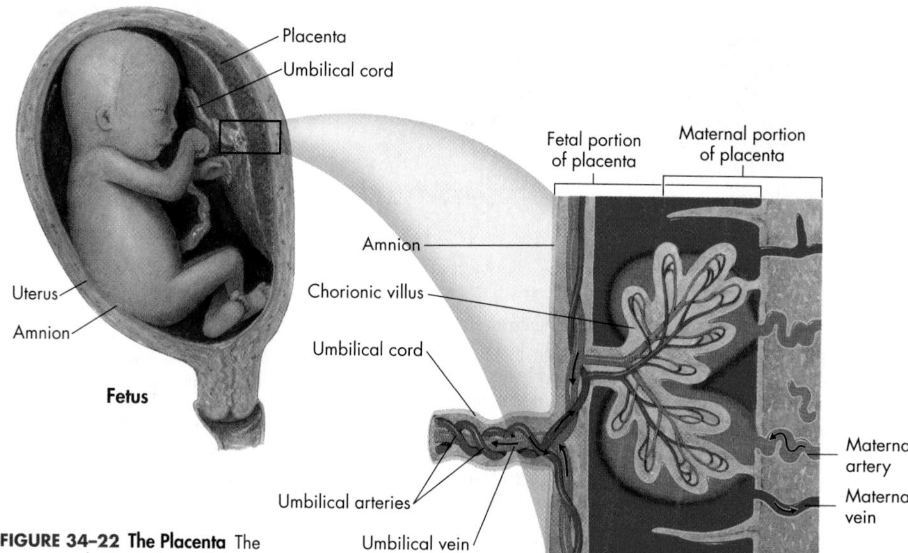

FIGURE 34–22 The Placenta The connection between the mother and the developing embryo or fetus is called the placenta. It is through the placenta that the embryo gets its oxygen and nutrients and excretes wastes. Notice how the chorionic villi from the fetus extend into the mother's uterine lining (indicated by the overlapping brackets). **Infer** ***Does carbon dioxide from the fetus travel through the umbilical arteries or umbilical vein?***

The Placenta As the embryo develops, specialized membranes form to protect and nourish the embryo. The embryo is surrounded by the amnion, a sac filled with amniotic fluid that cushions and protects the developing embryo. Another sac, known as the chorion, forms just outside the amnion. The chorion makes direct contact with the tissues of the uterus. Near the end of the third week of development, small, fingerlike projections called chorionic villi form on the outer surface of the chorion and extend into the uterine lining.

The chorionic villi and uterine lining form a vital organ called the **placenta.** The placenta is the connection between the mother and embryo that acts as the embryo's organ of respiration, nourishment, and excretion. Across this thin barrier, oxygen and nutrients diffuse from the mother's blood to the embryo's blood; carbon dioxide and metabolic wastes diffuse from the embryo's blood to the mother's blood.

The blood of the mother and that of the embryo flow past each other, but they do not mix. The exchange of gases and other substances occurs in the chorionic villi. **Figure 34–22** shows a portion of the placenta. The umbilical cord, which contains two arteries and one vein, connects the embryo to the placenta.

After eight weeks of development, the embryo is called a **fetus.** By the end of three months of development, most of the major organs and tissues of the fetus are fully formed. The fetus may begin to move and show signs of reflexes. The fetus is about 8 centimeters long and has a mass of about 28 grams.

In Your Notebook *Explain in your own words the role of the placenta in human development.*

Biology In-Depth

FETAL ALCOHOL SYNDROME

Alcohol easily passes through the placenta to the developing embryo or fetus. No amount of alcohol has been established as safe during pregnancy. Prenatal exposure to alcohol can cause severe, lifelong disabilities. The group of disorders caused by prenatal exposure to alcohol are called fetal alcohol spectrum disorders (FASDs). As the word *spectrum* implies, there is a wide range in the severity of symptoms of this disorder. The better-known term *fetal alcohol syndrome* applies to some of the most serious effects of this disorder. Children born with fetal alcohol syndrome typically have distinctive facial features, mental retardation, heart defects, and a wide range of other abnormalities. Effects of FASDs include a wide range of physical and behavioral disabilities.

Answers

FIGURE 34–22 Carbon dioxide from the fetus travels through the umbilical arteries.

IN YOUR NOTEBOOK Sample answer: The placenta is the organ through which a developing embryo or fetus gets oxygen and nutrients and excretes wastes.

Later Development

What important events occur during the later stages of human development?

Although most of the tissues and organs of the embryo have been formed after three months of development, many of them are not yet ready to go to work on their own. On average, another six months of development takes place before all of these systems are fully prepared for life outside the uterus.

Months 4–6 **During the fourth, fifth, and sixth months after fertilization, the tissues of the fetus become more complex and specialized, and begin to function.** The fetal heart becomes large enough so that it can be heard with a stethoscope. Bone continues to replace the cartilage that forms the early skeleton. A layer of soft hair grows over the skin of the fetus. As the fetus increases in size, the mother's abdomen swells to accommodate it. The mother begins to feel the fetus moving.

Months 7–9 **During the last three months before birth, the organ systems of the fetus mature, and the fetus grows in size and mass.** The fetus doubles in mass, and the lungs and other organs undergo a series of changes that prepare them for life outside the uterus. The fetus is now able to regulate its body temperature. In addition, the central nervous system and lungs complete their development. **Figure 34–23** shows an embryo and a fetus at different stages of development.

On average, it takes nine months for a fetus to develop fully. Babies born before eight months of development are called premature babies and often have severe breathing problems as a result of incomplete lung development.

FIGURE 34–23 Human Development At 7 weeks, most of the organs of an embryo have begun to form. The heart—the large, dark, rounded structure—is beating. By 14 weeks, the hands, feet, and legs have reached their birth proportions. The eyes, ears, and nose are well developed. At 20 weeks, muscle development has increased, and eyebrows and nails have grown in. When a fetus is full term, it is capable of living on its own.

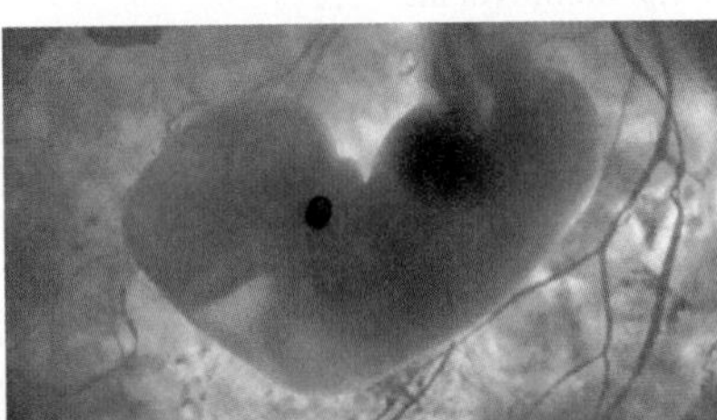
Embryo at 7 Weeks

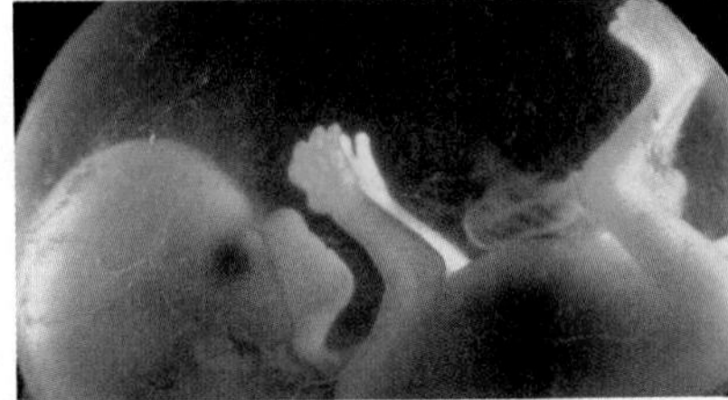
Fetus at 14 Weeks

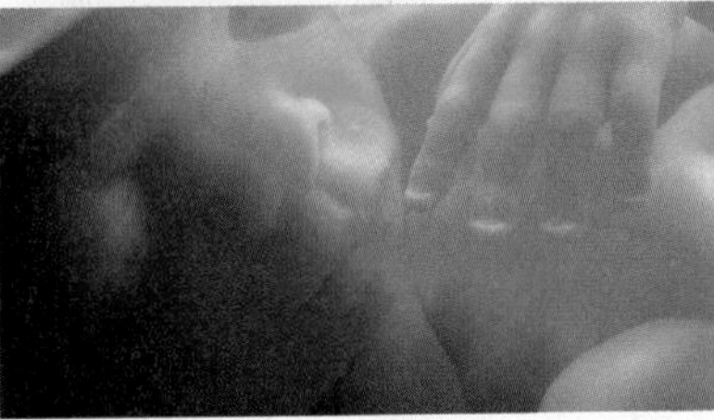
Fetus at 20 Weeks

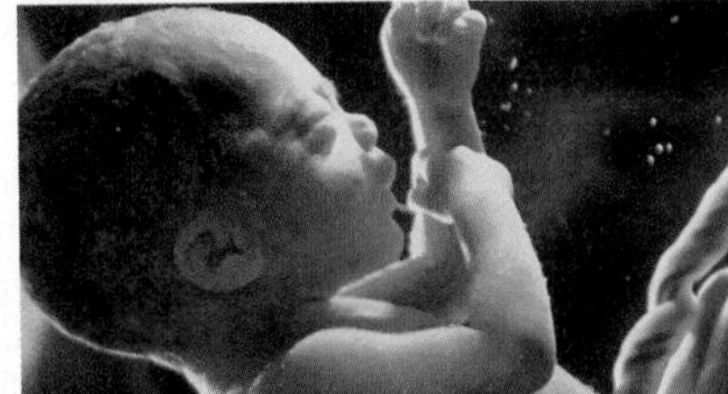
Fetus at Full Term

Build Study Skills

Explain that organizing information in lists can make studying easier and more effective. Have students fold a piece of paper in half vertically. On one half, have them make a bulleted list of changes that occur in a developing fetus in months 4–6 of pregnancy. On the other half, have students make a bulleted list of changes that occur in a developing fetus in months 7–9 of pregnancy. Then, have students work in pairs to review and revise their lists.

DIFFERENTIATED INSTRUCTION

LPR **Less Proficient Readers** Some students might need help locating the information needed to make their bulleted lists. Point out the paragraph headings **Months 4–6** and **Months 7–9** on this page. Have students read through these paragraphs one sentence at a time, stopping at the end of each sentence to add information to their lists.

L3 **Advanced Students** Have students examine their bulleted lists describing the changes that occur in months 4–6 and 7–9 of pregnancy. Ask them to write a paragraph comparing these changes with those that occur in early development (months 1–3).

UbD Check for Understanding

USE VOCABULARY

Write the following list of lesson vocabulary terms on the board.

- zygote, blastocyst, implantation, gastrulation, neurulation, placenta, fetus

Have each student write three sentences. Each sentence should clearly show the relationship between two of the words listed above. For example: A *blastocyst* attaches to the wall of the uterus during the process of *implantation*.

ADJUST INSTRUCTION

If responses indicate that students do not understand the relationships between the vocabulary terms, have them make and use flash cards to review the definitions.

Teach continued

Lead a Discussion

Help students make the connection between the endocrine system and the process of childbirth. Remind them that the endocrine system has a role in regulating many body functions, including childbirth.

Ask What hormone triggers the muscular contractions that occur during childbirth? *(oxytocin)*

Ask What endocrine gland releases this hormone? *(the posterior pituitary gland)*

Ask What process does the pituitary hormone prolactin stimulate? *(production of milk)*

DIFFERENTIATED INSTRUCTION

LPR Less Proficient Readers If students are overwhelmed by the amount of text under the heading **Childbirth,** form four small groups of students. Assign each group one of the four paragraphs on the page to read and summarize. Have each group share its summary with other groups.

L3 Advanced Students Have students research how and why childbirth is medically induced if a pregnant woman does not go into labor naturally within a particular time frame. Challenge students to pay particular attention to the role of hormones in medically induced birth. Have students write a paragraph summarizing their findings and share it with the class.

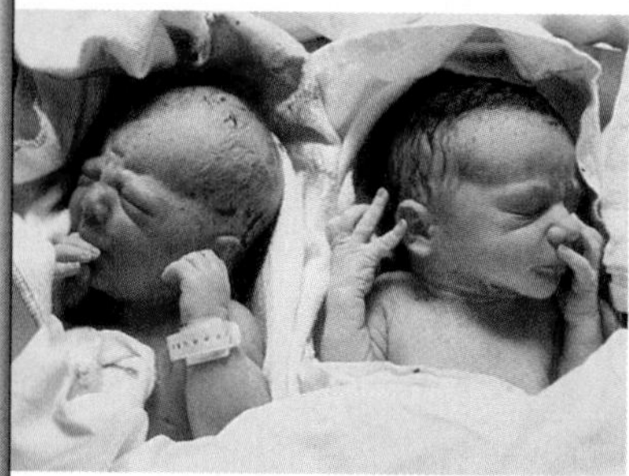

FIGURE 34–24 Newborns Twins, ten minutes after birth, adjusting to life outside the uterus.

Childbirth About nine months after fertilization, the fetus is ready for birth. A complex set of factors triggers the process; one of these factors is the release of the hormone oxytocin from the mother's posterior pituitary gland. Oxytocin affects a group of large involuntary muscles in the uterine wall. As these muscles are stimulated, they begin a series of rhythmic contractions collectively known as labor. As labor progresses, the contractions become more frequent and more powerful. The opening of the cervix expands until it is large enough for the head of the baby to pass through. At some point, the amniotic sac breaks, and the fluid it contains rushes out of the vagina. Contractions of the uterus force the baby, usually head first, out through the vagina.

As the baby meets the outside world, he or she may begin to cough or cry, a process that rids the lungs of fluid. Breathing starts almost immediately, and the blood supply to the placenta begins to dry up. The umbilical cord is clamped and cut, leaving a small piece attached to the baby. This piece will soon dry and fall off, leaving a scar known as the navel—or, its more familiar term, the belly button. In a final series of uterine contractions, the placenta itself and the now-empty amniotic sac are expelled from the uterus as the afterbirth.

The baby now begins an independent existence. Most newborns are remarkably hardy. Their systems quickly make the switch to life outside the uterus, supplying their own oxygen, excreting wastes on their own, and maintaining their own body temperatures.

The interaction of the mother's reproductive and endocrine systems does not end at childbirth. Within a few hours after birth, the pituitary hormone prolactin stimulates the production of milk in the breast tissues of the mother. The nutrients present in that milk contain everything the baby needs for growth and development during the first few months of life.

Quick Lab GUIDED INQUIRY

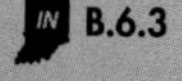
IN B.6.3

Embryonic Development

1. Use a dropper pipette to transfer several early-stage frog embryos in water to a depression slide. **CAUTION:** *Handle glass slides with care.*
2. Look at the embryos under the dissecting microscope at low power. Sketch what you see.
3. Look at the prepared slides of the early embryonic stages of a frog. Make sketches of what you see.

Analyze and Conclude

1. **Observe** Describe any differences you saw among the cells. At what stage is cell differentiation visible?
2. **Observe** Were you able to see a distinct body plan? At what stage did the body plan become visible?
3. **Draw Conclusions** Describe any organs you saw. At what stage did specific organs form?

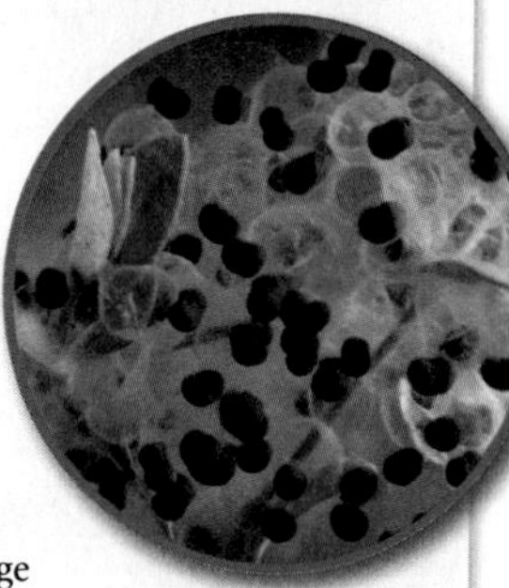

Frog Embryos

1000 Chapter 34 • Lesson 4

Quick Lab

PURPOSE Students will observe the development of frog embryos.

MATERIALS dropper pipette, early-stage frog embryos, depression slide, dissecting microscope, prepared slides of frog embryos

SAFETY Remind students to handle glass microscope slides carefully.

PLANNING Order frog eggs to arrive just before you need them, because they develop into tadpoles within a week.

ANALYZE AND CONCLUDE

1. Cell differentiation is visible at the gastrula stage.
2. Yes, the body plan becomes visible after neurulation, as the embryo elongates and the head and tail become visible.
3. Organ formation is first visible at the neurula stage, as the neural tube takes shape.

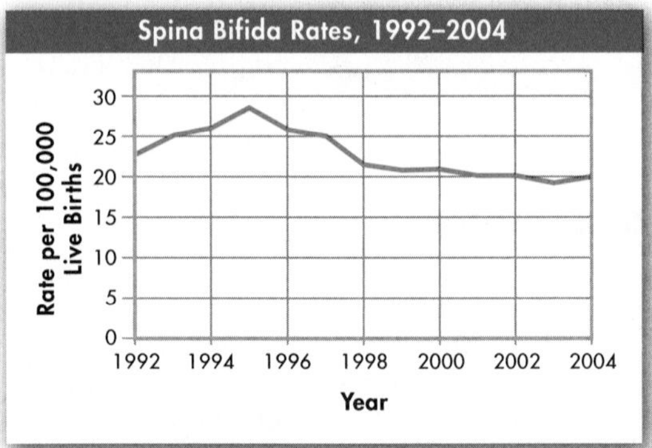

FIGURE 34–25 Preventing Spina Bifida In 1993, the U.S. Public Health Service recommended that women consume 4 mg of folic acid per day. Between 1996 and 1998, manufacturers of enriched grain products began to add folic acid to their products. Interpret Graphs ***Is there any indication that increase in folic acid intake had an effect on the rate of spina bifida cases?***

Infant and Maternal Health Although the placenta acts as a barrier to many harmful or disease-causing agents, some do pass through this barrier and affect the health of the embryo. The virus that causes AIDS can infect the developing fetus, and the virus responsible for rubella (German measles) can cause birth defects. Alcohol can permanently injure the nervous system, and drugs such as heroin and cocaine can cause drug addiction in newborn babies. Smoking during pregnancy can double the risk of low weight at birth, leading to other severe health problems. There is no substitute for professional medical care during pregnancy nor for responsible behavior on the part of the pregnant woman to protect the life within her.

From 1970 to 2000, the infant mortality rate in the United States decreased by about 65 percent. Many factors, including more women seeking early prenatal care and advances in medical technology, contributed to this decrease. **Figure 34–25** shows how one recent public health initiative affected the incidence of a serious birth defect—spina bifida.

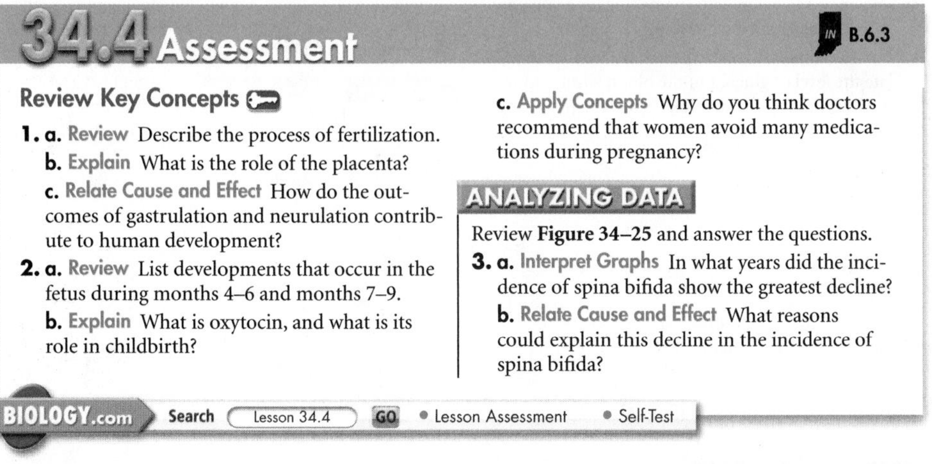

34.4 Assessment

IN B.6.3

Review Key Concepts

1. a. Review Describe the process of fertilization.
   b. Explain What is the role of the placenta?
   c. Relate Cause and Effect How do the outcomes of gastrulation and neurulation contribute to human development?
2. a. Review List developments that occur in the fetus during months 4–6 and months 7–9.
   b. Explain What is oxytocin, and what is its role in childbirth?
   c. Apply Concepts Why do you think doctors recommend that women avoid many medications during pregnancy?

ANALYZING DATA

Review **Figure 34–25** and answer the questions.

3. a. Interpret Graphs In what years did the incidence of spina bifida show the greatest decline?
   b. Relate Cause and Effect What reasons could explain this decline in the incidence of spina bifida?

BIOLOGY.com Search Lesson 34.4 GO • Lesson Assessment • Self-Test

Assess and Remediate

EVALUATE UNDERSTANDING

Call on volunteers to describe some of the changes that occur in a developing embryo or fetus during pregnancy. Have students identify the time frame in which each change occurs. Then, have students complete the 34.4 Assessment.

REMEDIATION SUGGESTION

L1 **Struggling Students** If students have difficulty answering **Question 2c,** remind them of the role of the placenta and the ability of certain substances to pass through the placenta.

BIOLOGY.com Students can check their understanding of lesson concepts with the **Self-Test** assessment. They can then take an online version of the **Lesson Assessment.**

Answers

FIGURE 34–25 Yes, the rate of spina bifida cases decreased after the U.S. Public Health Service warning was issued and again after folic acid was added to enriched grain products.

Assessment Answers

1a. Fertilization occurs when a sperm enters an egg and the two haploid nuclei fuse, forming a single diploid nucleus.

1b. The placenta is the connection between the mother and the embryo and acts as the embryo's organ of respiration, nourishment, and excretion.

1c. The outcome of gastrulation is the formation of the three cell layers that eventually form the body's structures. The outcome of neurulation is the early development of the nervous system.

2a. Months 4–6: bone replaces cartilage, soft hair grows over the skin, the heart can be heard with a stethoscope; Months 7–9: organ systems mature, the fetus doubles in mass, lungs and other organs are prepared for life outside the uterus.

2b. Oxytocin is a hormone that stimulates the uterine walls to contract, forcing the baby out though the vagina.

2c. Many medications can pass through the placenta, and some of these can have a negative effect on the developing embryo.

ANALYZING DATA

3a. 1995 and 1997

3b. The decline in 1995 could be explained by the 1993 recommendation that women consume folic acid each day; the 1997 decline could be explained by the addition of folic acid to enriched grain products, which was phased in between 1996 and 1998.

CHAPTER LAB

Pre-Lab

Introduce students to the concepts they will explore in the chapter lab by assigning the Pre-Lab questions.

Lab

Tell students they will perform the chapter lab *Diagnosing Endocrine Disorders* described in **Lab Manual A.**

 **Struggling Students** A simpler version of the chapter lab is provided in **Lab Manual B.**

BIOLOGY.com Look online for **Editable Lab Worksheets.**

For corresponding pre-lab in the **Foundation Edition**, see page 830.

Forensics Lab

GUIDED INQUIRY

Pre-Lab: Diagnosing Endocrine Disorders

Problem Can you diagnose an endocrine disorder based on a patient's symptoms?

Lab Manual Chapter 34 Lab

Skills Focus Analyze Data, Draw Conclusions, Relate Cause and Effect

Connect to the Big idea Organs of the endocrine system secrete hormones into the blood. Each hormone triggers a response in specific cells. Almost every cell in the body is affected by at least one hormone. The endocrine system regulates important processes such as growth, metabolism, and water balance. If one part of the endocrine system is not working properly, the body will be thrown off balance. If the imbalance is severe, it could threaten the health, or even the life, of a person.

Endocrinologists are medical doctors who diagnose and treat disorders of the endocrine system. The clues these doctors use to solve their mysteries are a patient's symptoms and the results of lab tests. In this lab, you will model the process of diagnosing endocrine disorders.

Background Questions

a. **Review** Why doesn't every hormone affect every cell in the body?

b. **Sequence** Use a flowchart to describe the feedback loop for regulating the metabolic rate.

c. **Use Analogies** How are the hormones that regulate the level of glucose in the blood similar to the muscles that bend and straighten an arm?

Pre-Lab Questions

Preview the procedure in the lab manual.

1. **Interpret Tables** When patients complain of fatigue they are usually referring to a lack of energy or motivation. Which conditions listed in the data table have fatigue as a symptom?
2. **Apply Concepts** Why do doctors typically use blood tests to diagnose endocrine disorders?
3. **Infer** Why is it important for physicians to consider the age and sex of a patient when diagnosing a disorder?

BIOLOGY.com Search Chapter 34 GO

Visit Chapter 34 online to test yourself on chapter content and to find activities to help you learn.

Untamed Science Video The Untamed Science crew helps us better understand the role epinephrine plays in regulating our response to fear and danger.

Data Analysis Analyze data on the risk factors and effects of diabetes.

Art Review Review your understanding of the major endocrine glands in the body.

Art in Motion Watch how steroid and nonsteroid hormones act differently on cells.

Pre-Lab Answers

BACKGROUND QUESTIONS

a. A cell must have receptors for a given hormone (on its membrane or within the cell) for the hormone to have an effect on the cell's activities.

b. Low level of thyroxine in blood, hypothalamus secretes TRH; anterior pituitary gland secretes TSH, thyroid secretes thyroxine (which increases the metabolic rate), increased level of thyroxine stops secretion of TRH.

c. Sample answer: Just as an opposing pair of muscles are needed to bend and straighten the arm, an opposing pair of hormones (insulin and glucagon) are needed to decrease and increase the level of glucose in blood.

PRE-LAB QUESTIONS

1. Type I diabetes, hypothyroidism, Addison's disease, hyperparathyroidism
2. Sample answer: They use blood tests because hormones and many of the substances that hormones regulate circulate in the blood.
3. Sample answer: Some symptoms will occur only in women or only in men. Some disorders are more likely to occur in certain age groups.

34 Study Guide

Big idea Homeostasis

Endocrine glands release hormones that influence the actions of target cells. The hypothalamus acts as a master regulator and has direct or indirect influence over many of the other glands.

34.1 The Endocrine System

The endocrine system is made up of glands that release hormones into the blood. Hormones deliver messages throughout the body.

Steroid hormones can easily cross cell membranes. Once inside the nucleus, they change the pattern of gene expression in target cells.

Nonsteroid hormones bind to receptors on cell membranes and cause the release of secondary messengers that affect cell activities.

hormone (978)
target cell (978)
exocrine gland (979)
endocrine gland (979)
prostaglandin (980)

34.2 Glands of the Endocrine System

The pituitary gland secretes hormones that directly regulate many body functions or control the actions of other endocrine glands.

The hypothalamus controls the secretions of the pituitary gland.

The adrenal glands release hormones that help the body prepare for—and deal with—stress.

Insulin and glucagon help to keep the blood glucose level stable.

The thyroid gland has a major role in regulating the body's metabolism.

The two functions of gonads are the production of gametes and the secretion of sex hormones.

Like most systems of the body, the endocrine system is regulated by feedback mechanisms that function to maintain homeostasis.

pituitary gland (982)
releasing hormone (983)
corticosteroid (983)
epinephrine (983)
norepinephrine (983)
thyroxine (985)
calcitonin (985)
parathyroid hormone (985)

34.3 The Reproductive System

In females, the effects of the sex hormones include breast development and a widening of the hips. In males, they result in the growth of facial hair, increased muscular development, and deepening of the voice.

The main functions of the male reproductive system are to produce and deliver sperm.

The main function of the female reproductive system is to produce egg cells. The system also prepares the female's body to nourish an embryo.

Chlamydia is the most common bacterial STD in the United States. Viral STDs include hepatitis B, genital herpes, genital warts, and AIDS.

puberty (988)
testis (989)
scrotum (989)
seminiferous tubule (989)
epididymis (989)
vas deferens (989)
semen (990)
ovary (991)
menstrual cycle (991)
ovulation (993)
corpus luteum (993)
menstruation (993)
sexually transmitted disease (994)

34.4 Fertilization and Development

The fusion of a sperm and egg cell is called fertilization.

Gastrulation produces the three cell layers of the embryo. Neurulation leads to the formation of the nervous system.

During the fourth, fifth, and sixth months after fertilization, the tissues of the fetus become more complex and specialized.

During the last three months before birth, the organ systems of the fetus mature, and the fetus grows in size and mass.

zygote (995)
blastocyst (996)
implantation (996)
gastrulation (997)
neurulation (997)
placenta (998)
fetus (998)

Think Visually Trace the outline of **Figure 34–1.** Without referring to the Figure, label as many endocrine glands as you can.

BIOLOGY.com Search Chapter 34 GO • Crossword • Chapter Assessment

Study Online

REVIEW AND ASSESSMENT RESOURCES

Editable Worksheets Pages of Study Workbooks A and B, Lab Manuals A and B, and the Assessment Resources Book are available online. These documents can be easily edited using a word-processing program.

Lesson Overview Have students reread the Lesson Overviews to help them study chapter concepts.

Vocabulary Review The *Flash Cards* and *Crossword* provide an interactive way to review chapter vocabulary.

Chapter Assessments Have students take an online version of the Chapter 34 Assessment.

Standardized Test Prep Students can take an online version of the Standardized Test Prep. You will receive their scores along with ideas for remediation.

Diagnostic and Benchmark Tests Use these tests to monitor your students' progress and supply remediation.

Answers

THINK VISUALLY

Students should correctly label the endocrine glands found in **Figure 34–1.** Suggest students use the figure to check their work and to revise and add to their outlines as needed.

UbD Performance Tasks

SUMMATIVE TASK Have students make a time line to represent the life of an imaginary female, from birth through late adulthood. Ask them to make approximate markings on the time line to indicate the following events, which occur due to interactions of the endocrine and reproductive systems: puberty, pregnancy and childbirth, and menopause. At each marking, have students write a paragraph explaining how the endocrine and reproductive systems interact during that part of the female's life.

TRANSFER TASK Have students imagine they saw a televised advertisement targeted at teen viewers that included the following dialogue:

Student 1: What's wrong?

Student 2: I feel awful today. It's hormones. They're wrecking my life.

Student 1: I agree. We'd all be better off without hormones.

Have students write a business letter to the sponsor of the advertisement, explaining why this dialogue is misleading to teens. Students should use proper format for a business letter, and include a substantial amount of information to support their viewpoint.

Lesson 34.1

UNDERSTAND KEY CONCEPTS

1. b **2.** c

3. A target cell has receptors that allow a particular hormone to affect it. For example, the hormone insulin has target cells in the liver. When insulin acts on these cells, they prompt the liver to take glucose out of the blood.

4. Pairs of hormones allow feedback mechanisms to maintain constant body conditions.

THINK CRITICALLY

5. Traffic reports can be heard by anyone within range of the broadcast, but they only have an effect on people driving into the traffic situation. These people may alter their route to avoid the problem, and thus lessen the traffic problem (feedback control).

6. Not every cell responds because not every cell has receptors for every hormone.

Lesson 34.2

UNDERSTAND KEY CONCEPTS

7. d **8.** c

9. When the blood level of a hormone increases, this is usually a trigger for the gland producing it to stop releasing it into the blood.

10. Epinephrine increases heart rate, blood pressure, and blood flow to the muscles; causes air passageways to widen; and stimulates the release of extra glucose into the blood. These actions prepare the body to respond quickly.

11. If blood glucose levels are not regulated, diabetes mellitus may occur. Very high blood glucose levels can cause serious complications or death.

THINK CRITICALLY

12. Before the swim meet, adrenaline is released as the swimmer anticipates the race, causing the heart rate to increase. During the race, the heart rate is increased due to oxygen demand.

13. Sample answer: Without an adequate supply of iodine, thyroxine cannot be produced, so the precursor to thyroxine builds up in the gland.

Lesson 34.3

UNDERSTAND KEY CONCEPTS

14. a **15.** b

16. FSH and LH

17. Males: growth of facial hair, increased muscular development, and deepening of the voice; Females: breast development and widening of the hips

34 Assessment

The numbers following the questions refer to Indiana's Academic Standards for Biology I.

34.1 The Endocrine System

Understand Key Concepts

1. Which choice is a chemical messenger that can directly influence gene expression?
a. nonsteroid hormone **c.** ATP
b. steroid hormone **d.** cAMP

2. A modified fatty acid that is released by a cell and affects local cells and tissues is likely a(n) B.1.2
a. nonsteroid hormone.
b. steroid hormone.
c. prostaglandin.
d. exocrine secretion.

3. What is the relationship between a hormone and a target cell? Use a specific example to explain your answer. B.1.2

4. Many body functions are influenced by the action of two hormones with opposing effects. Why are such pairs of hormones useful?

Think Critically

5. **Use Analogies** In many areas during rush hour, radio stations broadcast traffic reports. How are traffic reports similar to hormones? How do the reports act as a feedback control mechanism to control the flow of traffic?

6. **Infer** After a hormone is secreted by a gland, the circulatory system transports it all through the body. Why doesn't every cell respond to the hormone?

34.2 Glands of the Endocrine System

Understand Key Concepts

7. Hormones that help regulate blood calcium levels are produced by the
a. posterior pituitary. **c.** pancreas.
b. thymus. **d.** parathyroid gland.

8. Which hormone influences a person's rate of metabolism?
a. PTH **c.** thyroxine
b. aldosterone **d.** calcitonin

9. How does a feedback mechanism regulate the activity of the endocrine system?

10. How does the secretion of epinephrine prepare the body to handle emergencies?

11. What happens if blood glucose levels are not properly regulated?

Think Critically

12. **Apply Concepts** The heartbeat of a swimmer was found to increase significantly both before and during a swim meet. Explain why this could happen.

13. **Form a Hypothesis** Iodine is required to complete the production of thyroxine. Why do you think the thyroid gland enlarges in response to iodine deficiency?

34.3 The Reproductive System

Understand Key Concepts

14. The diagram shows the female reproductive system. Which structure is indicated by the *X*?

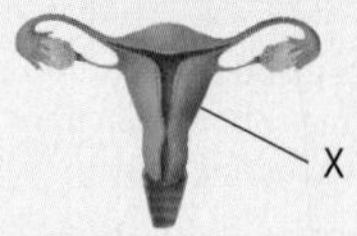

a. uterus **c.** ovary
b. Fallopian tube **d.** cervix

15. Which male reproductive structure releases sperm into the urethra?
a. epididymis **c.** prostate gland
b. vas deferens **d.** testis

16. Which two hormones stimulate the gonads to produce their hormones?

17. List the secondary sex characteristics that appear in males and females at puberty.

18. Trace the path of a sperm from a testis until it leaves the body.

19. Trace the path of an unfertilized egg from a follicle until it leaves the body.

20. Provide one example of how the menstrual cycle works by negative feedback.

18. Sperm travel from the seminiferous tubules in the testes into the epididymis. Sperm then move to the vas deferens. Semen containing mature sperm is ejected from the penis through the urethra.

19. The egg is released from the follicle during ovulation. It then passes through a Fallopian tube and the uterus and is discharged from the body through the vagina during menstruation.

20. Sample answer: As levels of hormones rise and fall, they influence other components of the cycle. For example, when estrogen levels are low, the pituitary releases FSH and LH. When estrogen levels are high, it does not.

THINK CRITICALLY

21. Seminal fluid provides a nutrient-rich medium for sperm. The production and release of millions of sperm helps ensure that at least one sperm will reach and fertilize the egg. Cilia in Fallopian tubes help move eggs toward the uterus. The flagellum of a sperm helps it travel to the egg.

22. Insufficient amounts of FSH and LH would keep a follicle from reaching maturity. Ovulation would not occur.

Think Critically

21. **Apply Concepts** Describe how each of the following represents an adaptation that helps to ensure successful fertilization: seminal fluid; production and release of millions of sperm; cilia lining the Fallopian tubes; flagellum of a sperm.
22. **Predict** Predict the effects that insufficient amounts of FSH and LH would have on the menstrual cycle.

34.4 Fertilization and Development

Understand Key Concepts

23. Another name for a fertilized egg is a
    a. gastrula.
    b. placenta.
    c. zygote.
    d. blastocyst.
24. Fertilization usually occurs in the
    a. uterus.
    b. vagina.
    c. Fallopian tube.
    d. ovary.
25. After the eighth week of development, the human embryo is known as a(n)
    a. zygote. c. fetus.
    b. infant. d. morula.
26. Trace the development of a zygote from fertilization through implantation.
27. Explain the importance of the three layers that form during gastrulation. B.6.3
28. What is the function of the placenta?
29. Describe what happens during childbirth.

Think Critically

30. **Apply Concepts** The placenta develops from tissues produced by both the embryo and the uterus. How does the structure of the placenta prevent the mother's blood from mixing with the blood of the developing embryo?
31. **Infer** Occasionally, a zygote does not move into the uterus but attaches to the wall of a Fallopian tube. Why might this be a very dangerous situation for the mother?
32. **Draw Conclusions** Explain why the suppression of the menstrual cycle is important to the success of a full-term pregnancy.

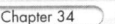

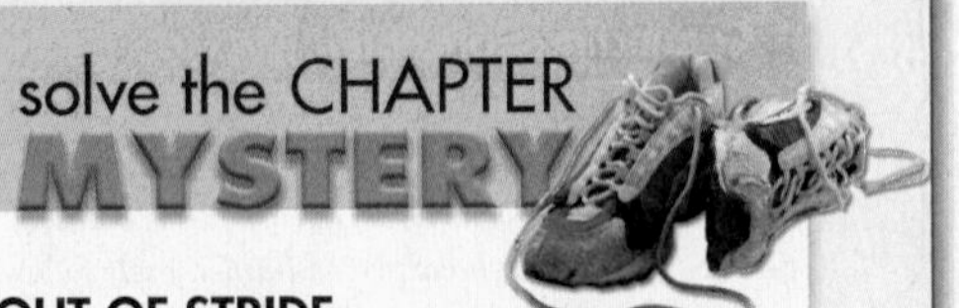

solve the CHAPTER MYSTERY

OUT OF STRIDE

Although a healthful diet and exercise contribute to maintaining a healthy body, a balance between the two is important. Lisa lost this balance, and the reactions from her endocrine system led to a disorder known as the female athlete triad. The triad consists of three factors:

- **Disordered Eating** During her quest to become a faster runner, Lisa did not provide her body with enough nutrients and energy to support all of its functions.
- **Amenorrhea** Lack of menstrual cycles for three or more months is called amenorrhea. Lisa's hypothalamus responded to low energy levels by not signaling the pituitary to release FSH and LH. As a result, her menstrual cycle ceased and estrogen levels dropped.
- **Weakened Bones** Lisa's bones lost more calcium than normal because of high cortisol and low estrogen levels. This calcium loss, along with the low-calcium levels from her poor diet, led to weakened bones, which are at risk for stress fractures.

The problems associated with the female athlete triad are related to inadequate nutrition. Lisa used more energy and nutrients than she took in. The reaction of her endocrine system was normal, but it had negative effects on her health.

1. **Relate Cause and Effect** Explain why the menstrual cycle cannot continue without FSH and LH.
2. **Sequence** Make a flowchart to describe the factors of the female athlete triad.
3. **Infer** Why do you think that women who have gone through menopause are at risk for osteoporosis—a weakening of the bones due to calcium loss?
4. **Connect to the Big idea** Explain the three factors that led to Lisa's weakened bones. In a paragraph, propose ways Lisa can prevent this from happening again.

ASSESSMENT

CHAPTER MYSTERY After students have read through the Chapter Mystery, discuss the endocrine system's role in maintaining homeostasis.

Ask Why does amenorrhea signal a disruption in the functioning of the endocrine system? *(The menstrual cycle is controlled by hormones, so a disruption in normal menstrual cycles indicates that the endocrine system is not functioning correctly.)*

Ask How does the female athlete triad demonstrate how a disruption in one body system can have an effect on another body system? *(In the female athlete triad, a disruption of the endocrine system results in a weakening of the skeletal system.)*

CHAPTER MYSTERY ANSWERS

1. FSH and LH are necessary for follicles to reach maturity. If the follicles do not reach maturity, the cells surrounding the egg will not be triggered to release estrogens that cause the uterine lining to thicken.
2. Students' flowcharts should show disordered eating triggering amenorrhea, which triggers weakened bones.
3. Women who have gone through menopause have low levels of estrogens. Low levels of estrogens cause bones to lose calcium.
4. Big idea The three factors that weakened Lisa's bones were a poor diet, a low estrogen level, and a high cortisol level. Sample paragraph: Lisa can prevent further problems by maintaining a balanced diet, paying particular attention to her calcium intake. She should also modify her activity level to bring it into balance with her energy consumption.

For more on the endocrine system, suggest students watch **Untamed Science: Fight or Flight!**

Lesson 34.4

UNDERSTAND KEY CONCEPTS

23. c **24.** c **25.** c

26. A zygote undergoes cell division as it passes through the Fallopian tube. A cavity forms in the center of the embryo, transforming it into a blastocyst. About a week after fertilization, the blastocyst undergoes implantation.
27. All of the tissues and organs of the embryo form from the three layers that form during gastrulation. The mesoderm forms many internal structures. The endoderm forms the lining of the digestive, respiratory, and excretory systems. The ectoderm forms the skin and the nervous system.
28. The placenta, which contains maternal and fetal tissues, connects the mother and fetus and is the fetus's organ of respiration, nutrition, and excretion.
29. Childbirth begins when the pituitary gland releases oxytocin, which stimulates uterine contractions. The opening of the cervix expands, so that the baby can pass through. The amniotic sac breaks, and contractions of the uterus force the baby out through the vagina.

THINK CRITICALLY

30. The placenta is made up of two layers, the fetal portion and the maternal portion. This two-layered structure allows the blood of the mother and the embryo to flow past each other without mixing.
31. The Fallopian tube does not provide the fetus with enough room to grow; the tube will eventually rupture.
32. During pregnancy, an embryo is implanted into the uterine lining. If the menstrual cycle continued, the embryo could be discharged from the uterus.

ASSESSMENT

Connecting Concepts

USE SCIENCE GRAPHICS

33. 3 hours

34. The blue line represents someone without diabetes; the red line may represent someone with diabetes. The individual represented by the red line has high levels of blood glucose, an indicator of diabetes.

WRITE ABOUT SCIENCE

35. Students' articles should include information about the harmful effects of anabolic steroid abuse. Articles should include specific details in support of each main idea.

36. Big idea Sample answer: The pancreas secretes two opposing hormones that regulate blood sugar: insulin and glucagon. When blood glucose rises after a meal, insulin is released, which stimulates cells to take glucose out of the blood. After blood glucose levels drop, glucagon is released, which causes blood glucose levels to rise. In this way, these two hormones act to keep blood glucose levels in a certain range.

Connecting Concepts

Use Science Graphics NoS.3

The graph shows the levels of glucose in the blood of two people during a five-hour period immediately following the ingestion of a typical meal. Use the graph to answer questions 33 and 34.

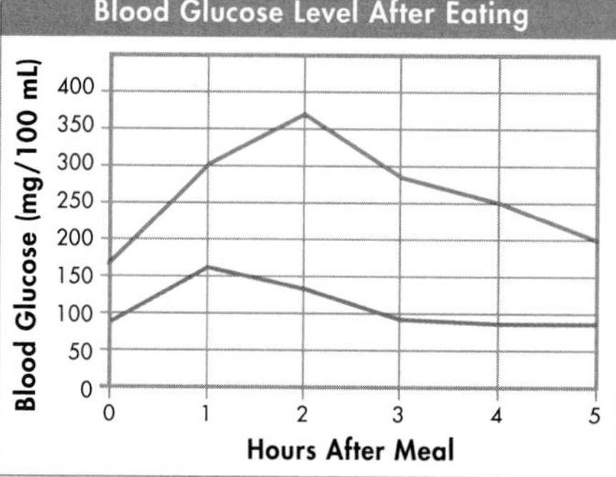

33. Interpret Graphs How long does it take the blood glucose level of the person represented by the blue line to return to a homeostatic value?

34. Draw Conclusions Which line represents a person who may have diabetes? Which line represents a person who does not have diabetes? Explain your answers.

Write About Science NoS.3

35. Persuasion Anabolic steroids are synthetic versions of the hormone testosterone. Although anabolic steroids have important medical uses, they can damage the body if abused. Use library or Internet resources to find more information about anabolic steroids. Then, write an article for your school newspaper informing people of steroids' harmful effects. (*Hint:* Be sure to support your main ideas with specific details.)

36. Assess the Big idea Choose one of the endocrine glands and describe how that gland is involved in a feedback mechanism that maintains homeostasis.

Analyzing Data MATH

IN NoS.3

These graphs show the number of multiple births since 1980. The first graph shows births of twins. The second graph shows multiple births consisting of three or more babies. Use the graphs to answer questions 37 and 38.

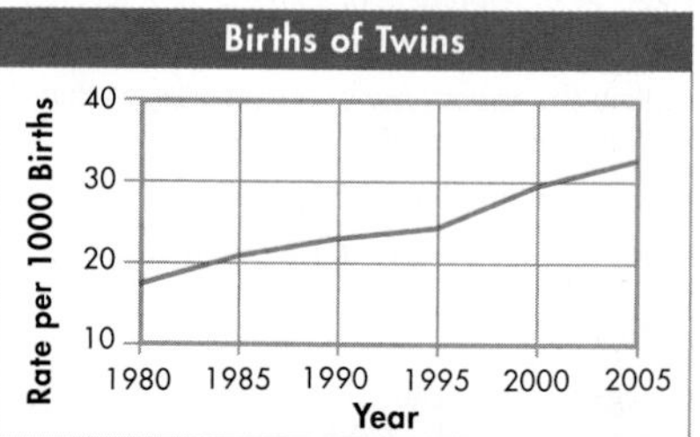

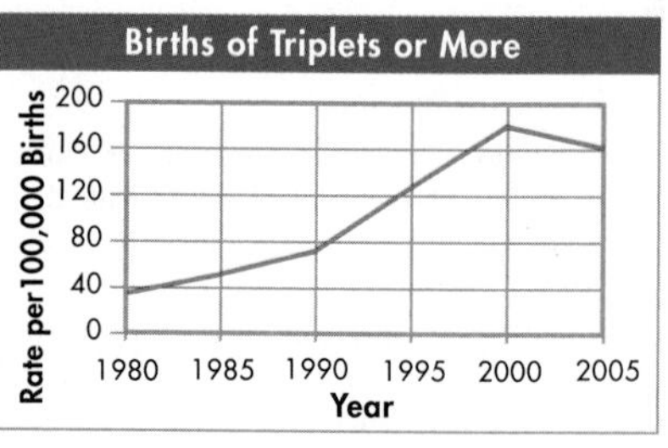

37. Interpret Graphs Which birth rate showed the greatest percentage increase from 1980 to 2005?

a. twins
b. triplets or more
c. They increased by the same percentage.
d. It's impossible to tell from the data.

38. Calculate Approximately how many times greater was the number of twin births compared with the number of births of triplets or more in the year 1995? (*Hint:* Note that the numbers on the *y*-axes are different scales.)

a. two times
b. ten times
c. fifteen times
d. twenty times

Analyzing Data

PURPOSE Students will analyze data to compare the rates of births of twins and births of triplets or more in the United States over a 25-year period.

PLANNING Point out that the births of twins are reported per 1000 births, while the births of triplets or more are reported per 100,000 births.

ANSWERS

37. b

38. d

Standardized Test Practice for Indiana

Multiple Choice

1. Which sequence correctly describes the route sperm take through the human male reproductive system?
   A vas deferens, urethra, epididymis
   B epididymis, vas deferens, urethra
   C vas deferens, epididymis, urethra
   D urethra, epididymis, vas deferens

2. Each of these terms refers to a stage in the human menstrual cycle EXCEPT
   A ovulation. C corpus phase.
   B luteal phase. D follicular phase.

3. Which of the following is NOT an endocrine gland?
   A pituitary gland C sweat gland
   B parathyroid gland D adrenal gland

4. During which stage of embryonic development does the neural tube form?
   A implantation C neurulation
   B gastrulation D fertilization B.6.3

5. Which of the following is where an egg matures prior to release into the reproductive tract?
   A follicle C ovary
   B blastocyst D ovum

6. The structure(s) in the male reproductive system that stores mature sperm until they are released by the male reproductive system is (are) the
   A vas deferens. C seminiferous tubules.
   B penis. D epididymis.

7. Which statement best describes the relationship between the hypothalamus and the pituitary gland?
   A The anterior pituitary gland makes hormones that are released by the hypothalamus.
   B The hypothalamus produces releasing hormones that promote the release of particular hormones from the anterior pituitary.
   C The hypothalamus produces releasing hormones that promote the release of particular hormones from the posterior pituitary.
   D The posterior pituitary sends nervous signals to the hypothalamus to prompt the release of hormones.

Questions 8–11

The diagram below shows the female endocrine system. Use the diagram to answer the questions.

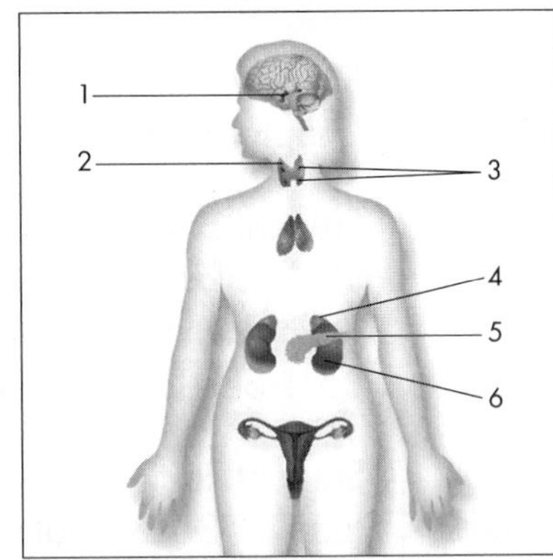

8. Which gland helps the body prepare for and deal with stress?
   A 1 C 4
   B 2 D 6

9. Which gland is both an endocrine and an exocrine gland?
   A 2 C 4
   B 3 D 5

10. Which gland secretes growth hormone?
    A 1 C 3
    B 2 D 5

11. Which gland secretes thyroxine?
    A 1 C 3
    B 2 D 4

Open-Ended Response

12. In a paragraph, describe the difference between the origin of fraternal and identical twins.

If You Have Trouble With . . .

Question	1	2	3	4	5	6	7	8	9	10	11	12
See Lesson	34.3	34.3	34.1	34.4	34.3	34.3	34.2	34.2	34.2	34.2	34.2	34.4

Test-Taking Tip

WATCH FOR QUALIFIERS

Explain to students that some questions contain qualifiers, such as NOT or EXCEPT. For these questions, students should first rule out any answer choices that fit the characteristic in question. Use this approach to rule out three of the four choices. Then, to check their answer, students should confirm that the choice they made does not fit the characteristics in question.

Answers

1. B
2. C
3. C
4. C
5. C
6. D
7. B
8. C
9. D
10. A
11. B
12. Fraternal twins occur when two eggs are released and each is fertilized. Fraternal twins are not genetically identical. Identical twins occur when a single zygote splits and becomes two embryos. Identical twins are genetically identical.

CHAPTER PLANNER 35 Immune System and Disease

Chapter Contents	IN	Time	Core Resources
Chapter Preview			**Student Edition,** pp. 1008–1009 **Chapter Mystery,** p. 1009
35.1 Infectious Disease Causes of Infectious Diseases • How Diseases Spread		1/2 period 1/4 block	**Student Edition,** pp. 1010–1013 **Study Workbook A** 35.1 Worksheets L2 **Biology.com** *Art Review:* Agents of Disease • 35.1 Self-Test • 35.1 Lesson Assessment
35.2 Defenses Against Infection Nonspecific Defenses • Specific Defenses: The Immune System • The Immune System in Action	NoS.3, B.1.2, B.5.5	1 1/2 periods 3/4 block	**Student Edition,** pp. 1014–1019 **Inquiry** 35.2 Analyzing Data, p. 1017 L2 **Study Workbook A** 35.2 Worksheets L2 **Assessment Resources Book** Visual Quizzes L2
35.3 Fighting Infectious Disease Acquired Immunity • Public Health and Medications • New and Re-Emerging Diseases • *Biology & History: Emerging Diseases*	NoS.11	1/2 period 1/4 block	**Student Edition,** pp. 1020–1023 **Inquiry** 35.3 Quick Lab, p. 1021 L2 **Study Workbook A** 35.3 Worksheets L2 **Biology.com** *Data Analysis:* Society and Immunity • 35.3 Self-Test • 35.3 Lesson Assessment
35.4 Immune System Disorders When the Immune System "Misfires" • HIV and AIDS	NoS.3	1 period 1/2 block	**Student Edition,** pp. 1024–1027 **Inquiry** 35.4 Analyzing Data, p. 1025 L2 **Study Workbook A** 35.4 Worksheets L2 **Biology.com** *Art in Motion:* HIV Infection • 35.4 Self-Test • 35.4 Lesson Assessment
Chapter Pre-Lab		1 period 1/2 block	**Student Edition,** p. 1028 L2 **Lab Manual A** *Detecting Lyme Disease* L2 • *Modeling Disease Transmission* L2

Differentiated Instruction Tools

Study Workbook B includes worksheets with lesson-level differentiated instruction support and explanations of differentiated instruction teaching strategies.

Lab Manual B includes skills labs, simplified chapter labs, and hands-on activities.

ELL Handbook explains ways to make *Biology* more accessible to ELL students.

Spanish Study Workbook is a Spanish translation of Study Workbook A.

Multilingual Glossary is the glossary translated into ten languages.

Differentiated Instruction Key

- L1 Special Needs or Struggling Students
- ELL English Language Learners
- LPR Less Proficient Readers
- L2 On-Level Students
- L3 Advanced Students

Additional Resources

Biology.com Untamed Science Video • Vocabulary Flash Cards

Study Workbook B 35.1 Worksheets L1 ELL LPR
Spanish Study Workbook 35.1 Worksheets ELL
Biology.com 35.1 Lesson Overview • 35.1 Lesson Notes

Study Workbook B 35.2 Worksheets L1 ELL LPR
Spanish Study Workbook 35.2 Worksheets ELL
Biology.com 35.2 Lesson Overview • 35.2 Lesson Notes • 35.2 Self-Test • 35.2 Lesson Assessment

Study Workbook B 35.3 Worksheets L1 ELL LPR
Spanish Study Workbook 35.3 Worksheets ELL
Biology.com 35.3 Lesson Overview • 35.3 Lesson Notes

Study Workbook B 35.4 Worksheets L1 ELL LPR
Spanish Study Workbook 35.4 Worksheets ELL
Biology.com 35.4 Lesson Overview • 35.4 Lesson Notes

Lab Manual B *Detecting Lyme Disease* • Data Analysis: *Immune System "Memory"* • Hands-On Activity: *How Do Diseases Spread?* • Data Analysis: *Food Allergies* L1 ELL LPR

Chapter Review

Student Edition Study Guide, p. 1029 L2 • Unit Project, p. 1034 L2
Study Workbook A Chapter 35 Vocabulary Review L2 • Chapter 35 Chapter Mystery/21st Century Skills Activity L2 L3
Transparencies, pp. 382–390 L1 ELL LPR L2
Biology.com Untamed Science Video • Editable Worksheets of Study Workbooks A and B and Lab Manuals A and B • Chapter 35 Flash Cards and Crossword Puzzle

Untamed Science DVD • Classroom Resources CD (includes lesson presentations and editable worksheets)

Chapter Assessment

Student Edition Assessment, pp. 1030–1033 L2
Study Workbook B Chapter 35 Chapter Review L1 ELL LPR • Chapter 35 Taking a Standardized Test L1 ELL LPR
Assessment Resources Book Chapter 35 Test A L2 • Chapter 35 Test B L1 ELL LPR • Unit 8 Test A L2 • Unit 8 Test B L1 ELL LPR
Biology.com Chapter 35 Assessment • Editable Worksheets of Chapter 35 Visual Quizzes, Chapter 35 Tests A and B, and Unit 8 Tests A and B

Exam*View Assessment Suite* • Classroom Resources CD (includes lesson presentations and editable worksheets)

Time: 1 period, 1/2 block

Pressed for Time?

Preview the Chapter Preview the Key Questions and the vocabulary for Lesson 35.2.

Cover the Chapter Quickly Have students read Lesson 35.2 and go over Figures 35–5 and 35–11. Then, have students read *Acquired Immunity* in Lesson 35.3.

Assess Assign the 35.2 Assessment, questions 1 and 3 in the 35.3 Assessment, and questions 10–17, 21, 23, 35, and 36 in the Chapter 35 Assessment.

CHAPTER 35

Connect to the Big Idea

Big idea As students examine the photograph of members of the German army responding to a dangerous disease situation, ask volunteers to identify what precautions members of the team have taken to protect themselves. *(They are wearing gear that covers almost all exposed skin, including a special protective suit with a hood, gloves, boots, and goggles.)* Discuss what it is about some diseases that would cause these professionals to take such precautions. *(Some diseases are infectious, or can spread from person to person.)* Inquire whether students think all diseases are infectious, and ask for examples of diseases that are infectious and diseases that are not. Also, ask students to describe some examples of how infectious diseases spread from person to person. Have students anticipate the answer to the question, **How does the body fight against invading organisms that may disrupt homeostasis?**

CHAPTER MYSTERY Have students read through the introduction to the Chapter Mystery and make predictions about the cause of the medical mystery. Use their predictions to help them start connecting the Chapter Mystery to the Big Idea of Homeostasis.

BIOLOGY.com Have students preview the chapter vocabulary using the **Flash Cards.**

IN INDIANA ACADEMIC STANDARDS

For the full text of all standards, see the Course Overview in the front matter of this book.

Key standards: Chapter 35 covers key ideas from The Nature of Science and Standard 1: Cellular Chemistry, including **NoS.3** Communicate ideas, **NoS.11** Scientific knowledge: environmental and social issues, and **B.1.2** Molecules and cellular processes.

35 Immune System and Disease

Big idea **Homeostasis**

Q: How does the body fight against invading organisms that may disrupt homeostasis?

BIOLOGY.com Search Chapter 35 GO • Flash Cards

1008

UbD Understanding by Design

In Unit 8, students explore the Enduring Understanding: *The human body is a complex system. The coordinated functions of its many structures support life processes and maintain homeostasis.* In Chapter 35, students add to this understanding through an exploration of the human immune system and disease. The graphic organizer at the right shows how chapter content informs this Enduring Understanding.

PERFORMANCE GOALS

In Chapter 35, students will learn about infectious disease and the body's immune system. They will analyze data on the immune response and simulate the spread of a disease. At the end of the chapter, students will apply their knowledge by making a pamphlet about the immune system and creating a play about the invasion of a pathogen.

CHAPTER 35

INDIANA ACADEMIC STANDARDS FOR SCIENCE

Nature of Science NoS.3, NoS.11; **Cellular Chemistry** B.1.2; **Molecular Basis of Heredity** B.5.5. See lessons for details.

German soldiers on their way to a possible bird flu outbreak

• Untamed Science Video • Chapter Mystery

CHAPTER **MYSTERY**

THE SEARCH FOR A CAUSE

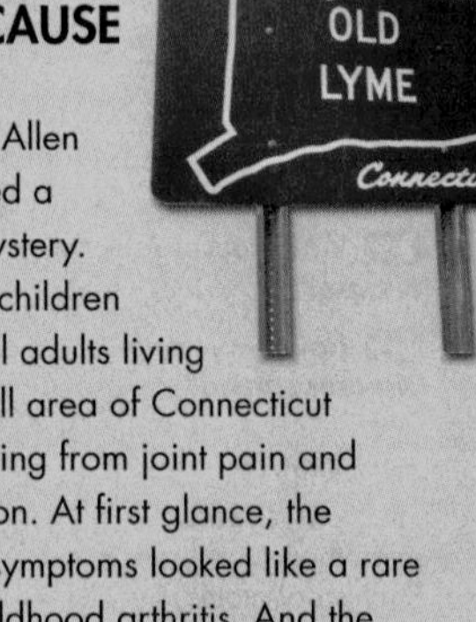

In 1975, researcher Allen Steere faced a medical mystery. Thirty-nine children and several adults living in one small area of Connecticut were suffering from joint pain and inflammation. At first glance, the children's symptoms looked like a rare form of childhood arthritis. And the adults' symptoms seemed to indicate age-related arthritis. But Steere thought it unlikely that there would be so many cases of childhood and age-related arthritis in a small population, in such a short period of time.

Steere looked for another explanation. The patients all lived in small towns and rural areas. Their symptoms all started at more or less the same time of year. Could these patients be suffering from a previously unreported infectious disease?

Never Stop Exploring Your World. Finding the solution to this medical mystery is only the beginning. Take a video field trip with the ecogeeks of Untamed Science to see where this mystery leads.

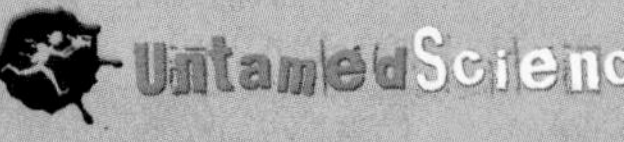

Chapter 35 Big Idea: Homeostasis

Chapter 35 EQ: How does the body fight against invading organisms that may disrupt homeostasis?

- **35.1 GQ:** How do people contract infectious diseases?
- **35.2 GQ:** How does the body defend against infection?
- **35.3 GQ:** How do humans prevent and fight the spread of disease?
- **35.4 GQ:** What happens when the immune system does not function properly?

What's Online

BIOLOGY.com Extend your reach by using these and other digital assets offered at **Biology.com**.

CHAPTER MYSTERY
Students search for the cause of a medical mystery in a small area of Connecticut.

UNTAMED SCIENCE VIDEO
It's not just work that your students are allergic to. Follow the Untamed Science crew as they investigate what truly triggers allergic reactions . . . and how the body responds.

ART REVIEW
Students drag-and-drop labels to review different groups of pathogens.

INTERACTIVE ART
A short animation shows students the steps in the primary and secondary immune response.

TUTOR TUBE
This short tutorial describes what antigens and antibodies are, and explains how the immune system responds to a new antigen.

DATA ANALYSIS
Students analyze how a "germ-free" lifestyle can be both good and bad for society.

ART IN MOTION
Students watch an animation of the process of HIV infection.

LESSON 35.1

Getting Started

Objectives

35.1.1 Identify the causes of infectious disease.

35.1.2 Explain how infectious diseases are spread.

Student Resources

Study Workbooks A and B, 35.1 Worksheets

Spanish Study Workbook, 35.1 Worksheets

Lesson Overview • Lesson Notes • Activity: Art Review • Assessment: Self-Test, Lesson Assessment

For corresponding lesson in the **Foundation Edition**, see pages 838–840.

Activate Prior Knowledge

Make a **T-Chart** on the board, and label one column Disease and the other Infectious. Then, introduce the concept of infectious disease. Have students brainstorm a list of human diseases. *(Sample answers: common cold, influenza, strep throat, lung cancer, measles, chicken pox, atherosclerosis, athlete's foot, diabetes, malaria)* Write the diseases in the Disease column. For each disease listed, call on volunteers to identify if it is infectious or not. Tell students they will learn more about infectious disease in this lesson.

Study Wkbks A/B, Appendix S30, T-Chart. **Transparencies,** GO15.

35.1 Infectious Disease

Key Questions

What causes infectious disease?

How are infectious diseases spread?

Vocabulary

infectious disease
germ theory of disease
Koch's postulates
zoonosis
vector

Taking Notes

Two-Column Table Use a two-column table to list the ways diseases are spread and describe each way.

THINK ABOUT IT For thousands of years, people believed that diseases were caused by curses, evil spirits, or vapors rising from foul marshes or dead plants and animals. In fact, malaria was named after the Italian words *mal aria*, meaning "bad air." This isn't all that surprising, because, until microscopes were invented, most causes of disease were invisible to the human eye!

Causes of Infectious Disease

What causes infectious disease?

During the mid-nineteenth century, French chemist Louis Pasteur and German bacteriologist Robert Koch established a scientific explanation for infectious disease. Pasteur's and Koch's observations and experiments led them to conclude that **infectious diseases** occur when microorganisms cause physiological changes that disrupt normal body functions. Microorganisms were commonly called "germs," so this conclusion was called the **germ theory of disease.** That's unfortunate now, because the word *germ* has no scientific meaning.

Agents of Disease If *germ* isn't a scientific term, how should we describe the causes of infectious disease? **Infectious diseases can be caused by viruses, bacteria, fungi, "protists", and parasites.** Except for parasites, most of these disease-causing microorganisms are called pathogens. **Figure 35–1** provides more information and examples of pathogens and parasites.

FIGURE 35–1 Examples of Agents of Disease Infectious diseases are caused by pathogens and parasites—organisms that invade a body and disrupt its normal functions.

Viruses
Characteristics: nonliving, replicate by inserting their genetic material into a host cell and taking over many of the host cell's functions
Diseases Caused: common cold, influenza, chickenpox, warts
▼ *Influenza Virus*, **Strain taken from a Beijing 1993 epidemic** (TEM 120,000×)

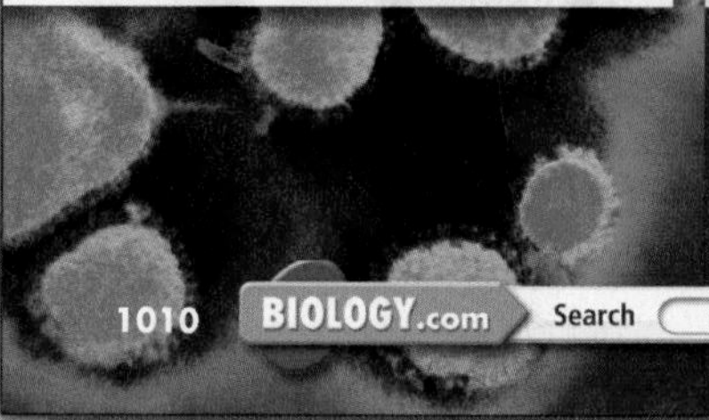

Bacteria
Characteristics: break down the tissues of an infected organism for food, or release toxins that interfere with normal activity in the host
Diseases Caused: streptococcus infections, diphtheria, botulism, anthrax
▼ *Mycobacterium* **causes tuberculosis** (SEM 10,600×)

Fungi
Characteristics: cause infections on the surface of the skin, mouth, throat, fingernails, and toenails; dangerous infections may spread from lungs to other organs
Diseases Caused: ringworm, thrush
▼ *Trichophyton interdigitale* **causes athlete's foot** (SEM 2800×)

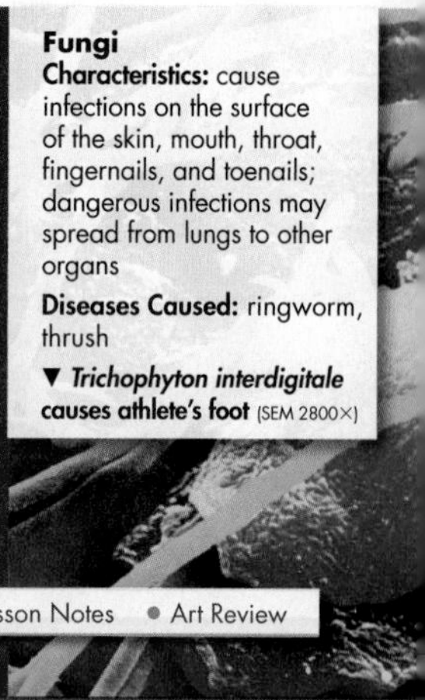

UbD Teach for Understanding

ENDURING UNDERSTANDING The human body is a complex system. The coordinated functions of its many structures support life processes and maintain homeostasis.

GUIDING QUESTION How do people contract infectious diseases?

EVIDENCE OF UNDERSTANDING *After completing the lesson, this assessment should show student understanding of how a person contracts an infectious disease.* Have each student write a newspaper article describing a researcher investigating an infectious disease that has spread in a community. The article should describe how the researcher used Koch's postulates to identify the pathogen and tell how the disease spreads. Ask volunteers to share their articles with the class.

Koch's Postulates Koch's studies with bacteria led him to develop rules for identifying the microorganism that causes a specific disease. These rules are known as **Koch's postulates.**

1. The pathogen must always be found in the body of a sick organism and should not be found in a healthy one.
2. The pathogen must be isolated and grown in the laboratory in pure culture.
3. When the cultured pathogens are introduced into a healthy host, they should cause the same disease that infected the original host.
4. The injected pathogen must be isolated from the second host. It should be identical to the original pathogen.

Koch's ideas played such a vital role in the development of modern medicine that he was awarded a Nobel Prize in 1905. Today, we know that there can be exceptions to these rules, but they remain important guidelines for identifying the causes of new and emerging diseases.

Symbionts vs. Pathogens Parts of the human body provide excellent habitats for microorganisms. Fortunately, most microorganisms that take advantage of our hospitality are symbionts that are either harmless or actually beneficial. Yeast and bacteria grow in the mouth and throat without causing trouble. Bacteria in the large intestine help with digestion and produce vitamins. In fact, if all your cells disappeared, the outlines of your body and digestive tract would still be recognizable—as a ghostly outline of microorganisms!

What's the difference between harmless microorganisms and pathogens that cause disease? The "good guys" obtain nutrients, grow, and reproduce without disturbing normal body functions. The "bad guys" cause problems in various ways. Some viruses and bacteria directly destroy the cells of their host. Other bacteria and single-celled parasites release poisons that kill the host's cells or interfere with their normal functions. Parasitic worms may block blood flow through blood vessels or organs, take up the host's nutrients, or disrupt other body functions.

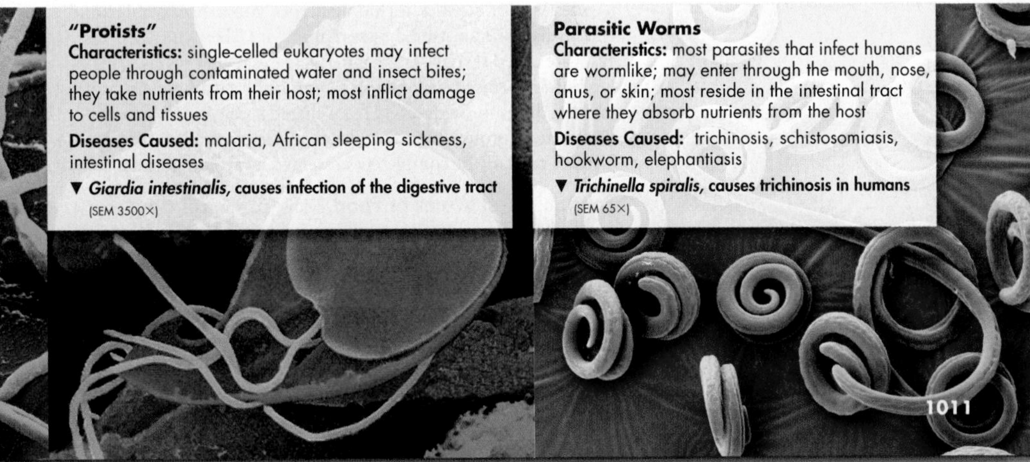

"Protists"
Characteristics: single-celled eukaryotes may infect people through contaminated water and insect bites; they take nutrients from their host; most inflict damage to cells and tissues
Diseases Caused: malaria, African sleeping sickness, intestinal diseases
▼ ***Giardia intestinalis*, causes infection of the digestive tract** (SEM 3500×)

Parasitic Worms
Characteristics: most parasites that infect humans are wormlike; may enter through the mouth, nose, anus, or skin; most reside in the intestinal tract where they absorb nutrients from the host
Diseases Caused: trichinosis, schistosomiasis, hookworm, elephantiasis
▼ ***Trichinella spiralis*, causes trichinosis in humans** (SEM 65×)

1011

Teach

Lead a Discussion

Begin a discussion of infectious disease by reviewing what students learned in earlier chapters about viruses, bacteria, fungi, single-celled eukaryotes, and parasites. Emphasize that many different microorganisms live in and on the body with no harmful effects. Then, turn the discussion to Koch's postulates.

Ask Why do you think Koch's postulates played an important role in the development of modern medicine? *(Sample answer: They have provided researchers a method to follow when identifying a pathogen that causes a specific disease. To treat patients effectively, it's important to know the cause of their disease.)*

Ask Why might step 3 raise ethical issues when studying certain diseases, such as a disease that only affects humans? *(Sample answer: It would not be ethical to inject a healthy person with a known pathogen.)*

DIFFERENTIATED INSTRUCTION

LPR Less Proficient Readers Some students may have difficulty understanding Koch's postulates. Help them by writing the steps on the board in simpler form. The following is an example.

1. Find the suspected pathogen in a sick organism.
2. Grow the pathogen in culture in a lab.
3. Introduce the pathogen into a healthy organism.
4. Find the same pathogen in the second, sick organism.

Encourage students to write the simplified steps in their notebook for later reference.

BIOLOGY.com Students can further explore the different kinds of pathogens using **Art Review: Agents of Disease.**

How Science Works

EXCEPTIONS TO KOCH'S POSTULATES

Although Koch's postulates are very useful in identifying pathogens that cause specific diseases, scientists by necessity make exceptions to these rules. For example, scientists have never been able to culture either the bacterium that causes syphilis or the bacterium that causes Hansen's disease (leprosy). Some pathogens cause disease only in humans, and for ethical reasons, these pathogens cannot be injected into healthy individuals. HIV, the virus that causes AIDS, is an example. When researchers can't rely on Koch's postulates to prove a pathogen causes a disease, they turn to other types of experimental evidence.

LESSON 35.1

Teach continued

Build Science Skills

Tell students that designing an experiment is a skill that should be learned and practiced. Remind them that most scientific experiments have an independent variable, a dependent variable, and one or more controlled variables. Scientific experiments also have methods for collecting and recording data. Then, have small groups of students design an experiment that could be used to determine how a specific disease is spread, such as the flu or athlete's foot. Have each group present its experimental design to the class, and allow students from other groups to ask questions or propose ways to make the experiment better.

DIFFERENTIATED INSTRUCTION

L1 Struggling Students To reinforce the skill of designing an experiment, have students make a poster showing the experimental designs. Posters may depend more on labeled drawings than text explanations. Place posters on the classroom walls. Have volunteers present the information on their posters to the class.

ELL Focus on ELL: Build Background

BEGINNING AND INTERMEDIATE SPEAKERS

Create a **Word Wall** with the lesson's vocabulary terms: *infectious disease*, *germ theory of disease*, *Koch's postulates*, *zoonosis*, and *vector*. List the terms on the wall, and then ask students to add a definition and/or a drawing for each term. Students can also add translations in their native languages. Then, have students locate each term in the lesson's text. Call on students to pronounce the term and give a definition or description in their own words, according to language level.

Study Wkbks A/B, Appendix S17, Word Wall.

How Diseases Spread

How are infectious diseases spread?

Infectious diseases can be spread in a number of ways. **Some diseases are spread through coughing, sneezing, physical contact, or exchange of body fluids. Some diseases are spread through contaminated water or food. Still other diseases are spread to humans from infected animals.**

Pathogens are often spread by symptoms of disease, such as sneezing, coughing, or diarrhea. In many cases, these symptoms are changes in host behavior that help pathogens spread and infect new hosts! After all, if a virus infects only one host, that virus will die when the host's immune system kills it or when the host dies. For that reason, natural selection favors pathogens with adaptations that help them spread from host to host.

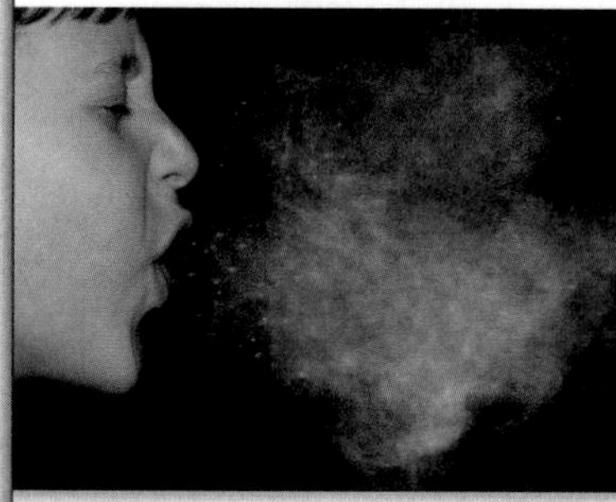

FIGURE 35–2 Sneezing Some infectious diseases are spread from person to person by sneezing. Thousands of pathogen particles can be released in a sneeze. **Infer** ***Why is it more beneficial to sneeze into a tissue rather than covering your mouth with your hand?***

Coughing, Sneezing, and Physical Contact Many bacteria and viruses that infect the nose, throat, or respiratory tract are spread by indirect contact. Coughing and sneezing releases thousands of tiny droplets that can be inhaled by other people. Those droplets also settle on objects such as doorknobs. If you touch those objects and then touch your mouth or nose, you can transfer the pathogens to a new home! Thus, the ability of a flu virus or a tuberculosis bacterium to cause a host to sneeze or cough is an adaptation that increases transmission of the pathogen from one host to another.

Other pathogens, including drug-resistant staphylococci that cause skin infections, can be transferred by almost any kind of body-to-body contact. They can also be transferred by contact with towels or certain kinds of sports equipment.

Minimizing transmission of these diseases is surprisingly simple. The most important means of infection control is thorough and frequent hand washing. If you have a cold or flu, cover your mouth with a tissue when you cough or sneeze, and wash your hands regularly.

BUILD Vocabulary

PREFIXES The prefix *trans-*, used in words such as *transmission, transferred,* and *transportation,* comes from the Latin *trans-* which means "across" or "beyond."

Exchange of Body Fluids Some pathogens require specific kinds of direct contact to be transferred from host to host. For example, a wide range of diseases, including herpes, gonorrhea, syphilis, and chlamydia, are transmitted by sexual activity. Therefore, these diseases are called sexually transmitted diseases. Other diseases, including certain forms of hepatitis, can be transmitted among users of injected drugs through blood from shared syringes. HIV can be transmitted through blood or sexual contact. Sexually transmitted diseases can only be completely prevented by avoiding sexual activity.

Contaminated Water or Food Many pathogens that infect the digestive tract are spread through water contaminated with feces from infected people or other animals. Symptoms of these diseases often include serious diarrhea. This is another adaptation that helps pathogens spread from one host to another, especially in places with poor sanitation.

UbD Check for Understanding

ONE-MINUTE RESPONSE

Give students about a minute to write a quick response to the following question:

- Why does it make sense that natural selection favors pathogens with adaptations that help them spread from host to host? Give some examples in your response. *(Spreading from host to host allows a pathogen to survive and reproduce, even if the original host dies. Examples include causing the host to cough or sneeze.)*

ADJUST INSTRUCTION

If student responses indicate they are confused, quickly review natural selection with students. Discuss how organisms that are better-adapted to their environments are more likely to survive, reproduce, and pass their traits on to their offspring.

Answers

FIGURE 35–2 Sample answer: You would be better able to contain the spread of pathogens if you sneeze into a tissue that you then discard. If you sneeze into your hand, the pathogens would be transferred when you then touch something else.

Contaminated water may be consumed, or it may carry pathogens onto fruits or vegetables. If those foods are eaten without being washed thoroughly, infection can result. In recent years, several disease outbreaks have been traced to transmission through packaged salad greens.

Bacteria of several kinds are commonly present in seafood and uncooked meat, especially ground meat. If meats and seafood are not stored and cooked properly, illness can result.

Zoonoses: The Animal Connection Many diseases that have made headlines in recent years thrive in both human and other animal hosts. Any disease that can be transmitted from animals to humans is called a **zoonosis** (plural: zoonoses). Mad cow disease, severe acute respiratory syndrome (SARS), West Nile virus, Lyme disease, Ebola, and bird flu are all zoonoses. Transmission can occur in various ways. Sometimes an animal carries, or transfers, zoonotic diseases from an animal host to a human host. These carriers, called **vectors,** transport the pathogen but usually do not get sick themselves. In other cases, infection may occur when a person is bitten by an infected animal, consumes the meat of an infected animal, or comes in close contact with an infected animal's wastes or secretions.

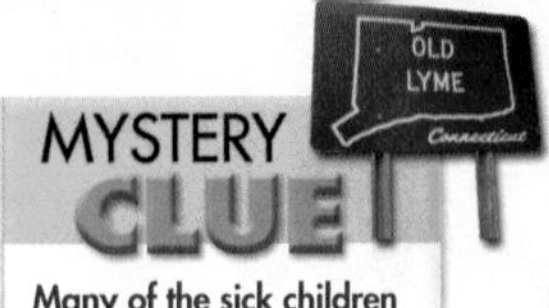

MYSTERY CLUE

Many of the sick children remembered receiving strange insect bites that summer, which developed into rashes. What clue did this give Steere?

FIGURE 35–3 Vectors Vectors are animals that harbor a pathogen. The pathogen may spread to a human through the bite of the vector, or when a person eats the vector.

▲ **Fruit bat that may carry the Ebola virus**

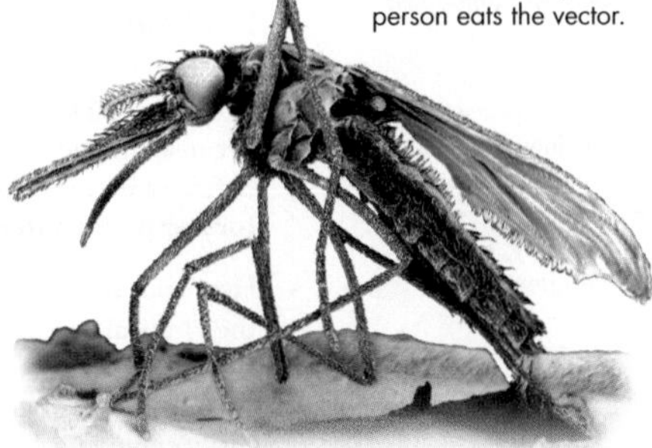

▲ **Mosquito that transfers West Nile virus from birds to humans**

35.1 Assessment

Review Key Concepts 

1. a. Review List the types of organisms that can cause disease.
   b. Explain What are ways that pathogens can cause disease in their hosts?
   c. Infer If a researcher introduced a suspected pathogen into many healthy hosts, but none of them became sick, what could this indicate?
2. a. Review What are the ways in which infectious diseases are spread?
   b. Explain How do vectors contribute to the spread of disease?
   c. Apply Concepts Why do you think it's a beneficial adaptation for a pathogen to make its host very sick without killing the host? (*Hint:* Think about how viruses replicate.)

WRITE ABOUT SCIENCE

Description

3. Animals infected with the virus that causes rabies often salivate excessively and are apt to bite other animals even when unprovoked. In a paragraph, explain how these symptoms lead to the spread of the virus.

BIOLOGY.com Search Lesson 35.1 GO • Self-Test • Lesson Assessment

MYSTERY CLUE Focus students' attention on zoonoses transmission by vectors. Guide them to infer that the disease may be spread by insect bites. Students can go online to **Biology.com** to gather their evidence.

Assess and Remediate

EVALUATE UNDERSTANDING

Ask students to write a short paragraph that identifies five different kinds of disease-causing agents and describes the different ways diseases are spread. Then, have them complete the 35.1 Assessment.

REMEDIATION SUGGESTION

L1 Struggling Students If students have trouble answering **Question 2c,** review how changes in host behavior, such as coughing, help pathogens spread and infect new hosts. Also, help students recall that viruses need to use host cells to replicate.

BIOLOGY.com Students can check their understanding of lesson concepts with the **Self-Test** assessment. They can then take an online version of the **Lesson Assessment.**

Assessment Answers

1a. viruses, bacteria, single-celled eukaryotes, fungi, and parasites

1b. Some viruses and bacteria directly destroy the cells of their host. Other bacteria and single-celled eukaryotes release poisons that kill host cells or interfere with their functions.

1c. Sample answer: It likely indicates that the pathogen was not responsible for causing the disease in question.

2a. coughing, sneezing, physical contact, exchange of body fluids, contaminated water or food, infected animals

2b. Vectors spread disease by transporting pathogens from one host to another.

2c. Sample answer: The pathogen often needs the host to stay alive for the pathogen to reproduce or replicate. A sick host is beneficial for the pathogen if some of the host's behaviors, such as coughing and sneezing, help spread the pathogen.

WRITE ABOUT SCIENCE

3. Sample answer: The pathogen is probably present in the saliva. When an infected animal bites another animal, the pathogen in the infected animal's saliva comes in contact with the bitten animal's blood.

LESSON 35.2

Getting Started

Objectives

35.2.1 Describe the body's nonspecific defenses against invading pathogens.

35.2.2 Describe the function of the immune system's specific defenses.

35.2.3 List the body's specific defenses against pathogens.

Student Resources

Study Workbooks A and B, 35.2 Worksheets

Spanish Study Workbook, 35.2 Worksheets

Lab Manual B, 35.2 Data Analysis Worksheet

Lesson Overview • Lesson Notes • Assessment: Self-Test, Lesson Assessment

For corresponding lesson in the **Foundation Edition**, see pages 841–845.

Activate Prior Knowledge

Tell students to imagine being a pathogen seeking to enter a person's body. Ask how they might go about doing that. *(Sample answer: through the mouth or eyes, through a cut in the skin)* Then, have students change perspective and think about ways the body can prevent the pathogen from entering and can attack pathogens that make it through the body's defenses.

IN INDIANA ACADEMIC STANDARDS

For the full text of all standards, see the Course Overview in the front matter of this book.

B.1.2 Understand that the shape of a molecule determines its role in the many different types of cellular processes including metabolism, homeostasis, growth and development, and heredity, and understand that the majority of these processes involve proteins that act as enzymes.

35.2 Defenses Against Infection

IN B.1.2 Molecules and cellular processes. Also covered: NoS.3, B.5.5.

Key Questions

What are the body's nonspecific defenses against pathogens?

What is the function of the immune system's specific defenses?

What are the body's specific defenses against pathogens?

Vocabulary

inflammatory response • histamine • interferon • fever • immune response • antigen • antibody • humoral immunity • cell-mediated immunity

Taking Notes

Concept Map Use the green and blue headings in this lesson to make a concept map. Add details to your map as you read.

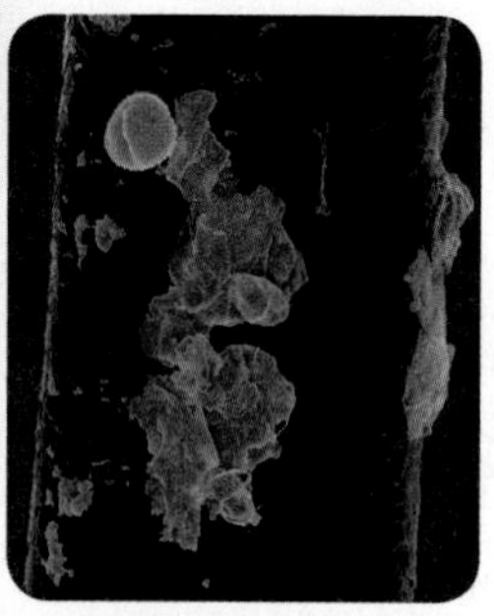

FIGURE 35–4 Nonspecific Defenses Mucus (brown) on nasal hair in the nose helps to trap dirt and pollen (yellow), as well as microorganisms that could cause disease (SEM 130×).

THINK ABOUT IT With pathogens all around us, it might seem amazing that most of us aren't sick most of the time. Why are we usually free from infections, and why do we usually recover from pathogens that do infect us? One reason is that our bodies have an incredibly powerful and adaptable series of defenses that protect us against a wide range of pathogens.

Nonspecific Defenses

What are the body's nonspecific defenses against pathogens?

The body's first defense against pathogens is a combination of physical and chemical barriers. These barriers are called nonspecific defenses because they act against a wide range of pathogens. **Nonspecific defenses include the skin, tears and other secretions, the inflammatory response, interferons, and fever.**

First Line of Defense The most widespread nonspecific defense is the physical barrier we call skin. Very few pathogens can penetrate the layers of dead cells that form the skin's surface.

But your skin doesn't cover your entire body. Pathogens could easily enter your body through your mouth, nose, and eyes—if these tissues weren't protected by other nonspecific defenses. For example, saliva, mucus, and tears contain lysozyme, an enzyme that breaks down bacterial cell walls. Mucus in your nose and throat traps pathogens. Then, cilia push the mucous-trapped pathogens away from your lungs. Stomach secretions destroy many pathogens that are swallowed.

Second Line of Defense If pathogens make it into the body, through a cut in the skin, for example, the body's second line of defense swings into action. These mechanisms include the inflammatory response, the actions of interferons, and fever.

▶ ***Inflammatory Response*** The **inflammatory response** gets its name because it causes infected areas to become red and painful, or inflamed. As shown in **Figure 35–5**, the response begins when pathogens stimulate cells called mast cells to release chemicals known as histamines.

Histamines increase the flow of blood and fluids to the affected area. Fluid leaking from expanded blood vessels causes the area to swell. White blood cells move from blood vessels into infected tissues. Many of these white blood cells are phagocytes, which engulf and destroy bacteria. All this activity around a wound may cause a local rise in temperature. That's why a wounded area sometimes feels warm.

UbD Teach for Understanding

ENDURING UNDERSTANDING The human body is a complex system. The coordinated functions of its many structures support life processes and maintain homeostasis.

GUIDING QUESTION How does the body defend against infection?

EVIDENCE OF UNDERSTANDING *After completing the lesson, this assessment should show student understanding of one defense the body has against infection.* Have students work in small groups to prepare a brief presentation to the class about one of the body's defenses against disease. A group might focus on the inflammatory response, humoral immunity, or cell-mediated immunity. After each group makes its presentation, encourage questions from other students.

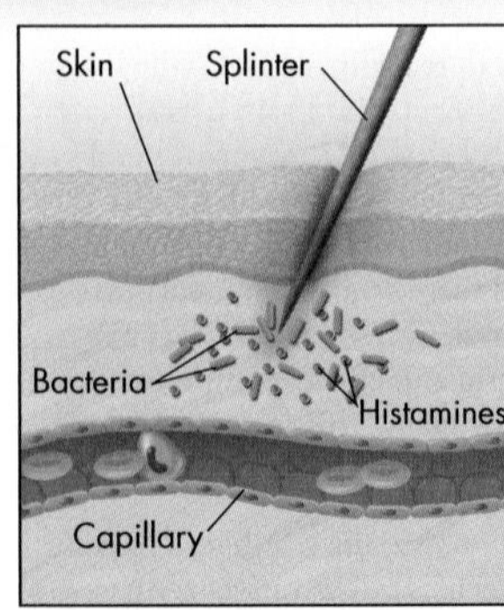

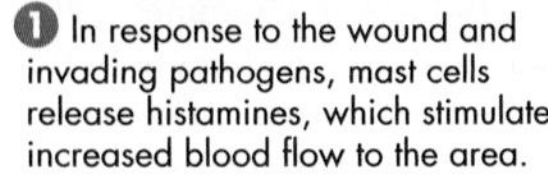

1 In response to the wound and invading pathogens, mast cells release histamines, which stimulate increased blood flow to the area.

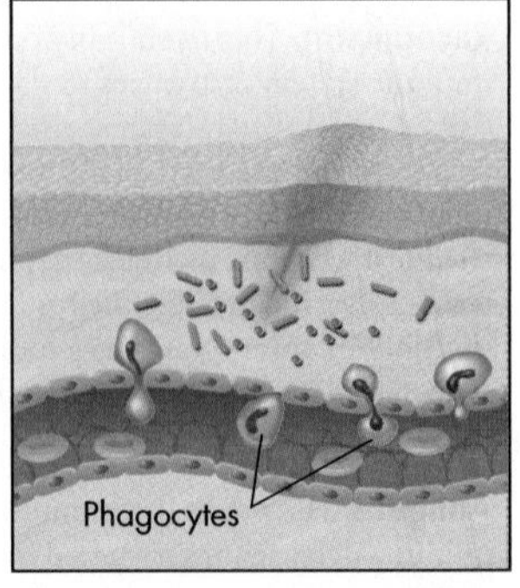

2 Local blood vessels dilate. Fluid leaves the capillaries and causes swelling. Phagocytes move into the tissue.

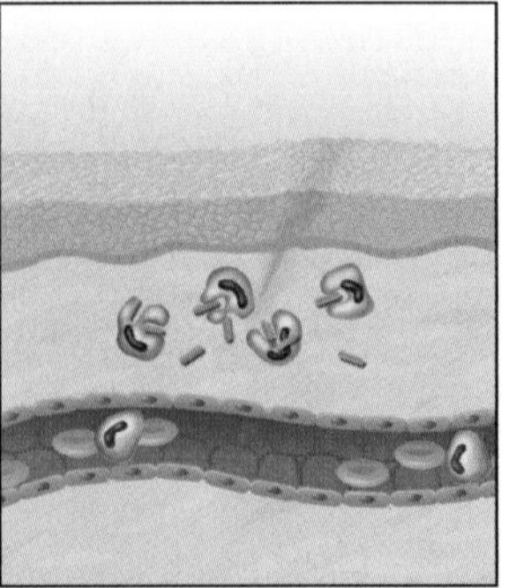

3 Phagocytes engulf and destroy the bacteria and damaged cells.

FIGURE 35–5 Inflammatory Response The inflammatory response is a nonspecific defense reaction to tissue damage caused by injury or infection. When pathogens enter the body, phagocytes move into the area and engulf the pathogens. Infer ***What part of the inflammatory response leads to redness around a wounded area?***

▶ ***Interferons*** When viruses infect body cells, certain host cells produce proteins that inhibit synthesis of viral proteins. Scientists named these proteins **interferons** because they "interfere" with viral growth. By slowing down the production of new viruses, interferons "buy time" for specific immune defenses to respond and fight the infection.

▶ ***Fever*** The immune system also releases chemicals that increase body temperature, producing a **fever.** Increased body temperature may slow down or stop the growth of some pathogens. Higher body temperature also speeds up several parts of the immune response.

In Your Notebook *Develop an analogy that compares the body's nonspecific defenses to a large building's security system.*

Specific Defenses: The Immune System

What is the function of the immune system's specific defenses?

The main function of the immune system's specific defenses is easy to describe but complex to explain. **The immune system's specific defenses distinguish between "self" and "other," and they inactivate or kill any foreign substance or cell that enters the body.** Unlike the nonspecific defenses, which respond to the general threat of infection, specific defenses respond to a particular pathogen.

Recognizing "Self" A healthy immune system recognizes all cells and proteins that belong in the body, and treats these cells and proteins as "self." It recognizes chemical markers that act like a secret password that says, "I belong here. Don't attack me!" Because genes program the passwords, no two individuals—except identical twins—ever use the same one. This ability to recognize "self" is essential, because the immune system controls powerful cellular and chemical weapons that could cause problems if turned against the body's own cells.

Teach

Use Visuals

Call on volunteers to read aloud the annotations in the three steps of **Figure 35–5.** After each step, discuss what is occurring and how the process defends against pathogens. For example, when discussing step 1, ask the following questions:

Ask Where do the pathogens that enter the body come from in this situation? *(Sample answer: Pathogens may be on the splinter, or they may be on the skin itself.)*

Ask How does increased blood flow to the area help the body attack invading pathogens? *(Increased blood flow brings phagocytes to the area, and they engulf and destroy bacteria and damaged cells.)*

DIFFERENTIATED INSTRUCTION

L1 Struggling Students For students having difficulty understanding the inflammatory response, make a **Flowchart** of the process on the board. To clarify the process, simplify the language and show more steps than are shown in **Figure 35–5.** For example, breakdown step 1 in the figure into the following steps:

1. A splinter pierces the skin.
2. Pathogens on the splinter or the surface of the skin enter the body through the cut.
3. Mast cells release histamines.
4. Histamines cause increased blood flow.

Write these steps on the board in the form of a horizontal flowchart. Call on students to help complete the flowchart.

Study Wkbks A/B, Appendix S25, Flowchart. **Transparencies,** GO8.

Biology In-Depth

PHAGOCYTE POWER

Phagocytes, which are active in the inflammatory response, develop from stem cells in bone marrow. Phagocytes are drawn by altered chemical gradients into an area of damaged or invaded tissues. There, they engulf and destroy pathogens and other foreign substances by endocytosis. In endocytosis, the plasma membrane of the phagocyte encloses the pathogen at or near the cell surface of the phagocyte. Then, the membrane pinches off to form a closed endocytic vesicle around the pathogen. The endocytic vesicle provides a "traveling compartment" that enables the pathogen to be transported into the cytoplasm of the phagocyte. Once inside the cytoplasm, the endocytic vesicle fuses with lysosomes, and the pathogen is destroyed.

Answers

FIGURE 35–5 increased blood flow to the wounded area

IN YOUR NOTEBOOK Sample answer: A large building's locked windows and doors are like the nonspecific defense of skin. The building's metal detectors and security personnel at open doors are like the saliva, mucus, and tears at openings in the body. Security personnel who can quickly intercept an intruder are like components of the inflammatory response in which phagocytes engulf pathogens.

Teach continued

Build Reading Skills

To help students better understand the section **Specific Defenses: The Immune System,** suggest they rephrase the blue headings as *what, why,* or *how* questions. For example, the heading, **Recognizing "Nonself,"** might be rephrased as, How does the immune system recognize nonself? Explain that after they have read each subsection, they should be able to answer their question. Have students record the four questions in their notebook, and then record the answers to the questions after reading each section. Have volunteers read one of their questions and the answer aloud to the class.

DIFFERENTIATED INSTRUCTION

ELL **English Language Learners** To complete the question-and-answer activity above, pair beginning and intermediate speakers with advanced and advanced high speakers. Ask partners to collaborate on rephrasing the headings as questions. Students can read the section individually and then work with their partner to write answers to their questions. Beginning speakers may use drawings to help them express their answers.

Recognizing "Nonself" In addition to recognizing "self," the immune system recognizes foreign organisms and molecules as "other," or "nonself." That's remarkable, because we're surrounded by an almost infinite variety of bacteria, viruses, and parasites. Once the immune system recognizes invaders as "others," it uses cellular and chemical weapons to attack them. And there's more. After encountering a specific invader, the immune system "remembers" it. This immune "memory" enables a more rapid and effective response if that same pathogen, or a similar one, attacks again. This specific recognition, response, and memory are called the **immune response.**

Antigens How does the immune system recognize "others"? Specific immune defenses are triggered by molecules called antigens. An **antigen** is any foreign substance that can stimulate an immune response. Typically, antigens are located on the outer surfaces of bacteria, viruses, or parasites. The immune system responds to antigens by increasing the number of cells that either attack the invaders directly or that produce proteins called antibodies.

The main role of **antibodies** is to tag antigens for destruction by immune cells. Antibodies may be attached to particular immune cells or may be free-floating in plasma. The body makes up to 10 billion different antibodies. The shape of each type of antibody allows it to bind to one specific antigen.

FIGURE 35–6 B Lymphocyte

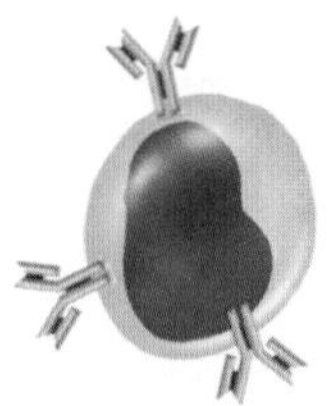

FIGURE 35–7 T Lymphocyte

Lymphocytes The immune system guards the entire body, which means its cells must travel throughout the body. The main working cells of the immune response are B lymphocytes (B cells) and T lymphocytes (T cells). B cells are produced in, and mature in, red bone marrow. T cells are produced in the bone marrow but mature in the thymus—an endocrine gland. Each B cell and T cell is capable of recognizing *one* specific antigen. A person's genes determine the particular B and T cells that are produced. When mature, both types of cells travel to lymph nodes and the spleen, where they will encounter antigens.

Although both types of cells recognize antigens, they go about it differently. B cells, with their embedded antibodies, discover antigens in body fluids. T cells must be presented with an antigen by infected body cells or immune cells that have encountered antigens.

The Immune System in Action

What are the body's specific defenses against pathogens?

B and T cells continually search the body for antigens or signs of antigens. **The specific immune response has two main styles of action: humoral immunity and cell-mediated immunity.**

BUILD Vocabulary

WORD ORIGINS The word *humor* comes from the Latin word for moisture. Body fluids such as blood, lymph, and hormones are sometimes referred to as humors. **Humoral immunity** refers to the immune response that happens in body fluids.

Humoral Immunity The part of the immune response called **humoral immunity** depends on the action of antibodies that circulate in the blood and lymph. This response is activated when antibodies embedded on a few existing B cells bind to antigens on the surface of an invading pathogen.

UbD Check for Understanding

INDEX CARD SUMMARIES

Give students each an index card, and ask them to write one concept about the immune system that they understand on the front of the card. Then, have them write something about the immune system they don't understand on the back of the card in the form of a question.

ADJUST INSTRUCTION

Read over students' cards to get a sense of which concepts they understand and which they are having trouble with. If a number of students write a similar question, read the question aloud in class discussion, and have volunteers provide an answer and point out where in the text the answer can be found.

How does this binding occur? As shown in **Figure 35–8**, an antibody is shaped like the letter Y and has two identical antigen-binding sites. The shapes of the binding sites enable an antibody to recognize a specific antigen with a complementary shape.

When an antigen binds to an antibody carried by a B cell, T cells stimulate the B cell to grow and divide rapidly. That growth and division produces many B cells of two types: plasma cells and memory B cells.

▶ ***Plasma Cells*** Plasma cells produce and release antibodies that are carried through the bloodstream. These antibodies recognize and bind to free-floating antigens or to antigens on the surfaces of pathogens. When antibodies bind to antigens, they act like signal flags to other parts of the immune system. Several types of cells and proteins respond to that signal by attacking and destroying invaders. Some types of antibodies can disable invaders until they are destroyed.

A healthy adult can produce about 10 billion different types of antibodies, each of which can bind to a different type of antigen! This antibody diversity enables the immune system to respond to virtually any kind of "other" that enters the body.

In Your Notebook *It is a common misconception that the immune system cannot combat pathogens it has not encountered before. In a paragraph, explain why that statement is not true.*

▶ ***Memory B Cells*** Plasma cells die after an infection is gone. But some B cells that recognize a particular antigen remain alive. These cells, called memory B cells, react quickly if the same pathogen enters the body again. Memory B cells rapidly produce new plasma cells to battle the returning pathogen. This secondary response occurs much faster than the first response to a pathogen. Immune memory helps provide long-term immunity to certain diseases and is the reason that vaccinations work. **Figure 35–11** summarizes the first and second response of humoral immunity.

FIGURE 35–8 Antibody Structure

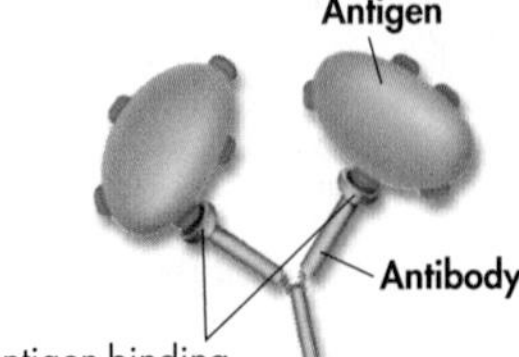

FIGURE 35–9 Plasma Cells

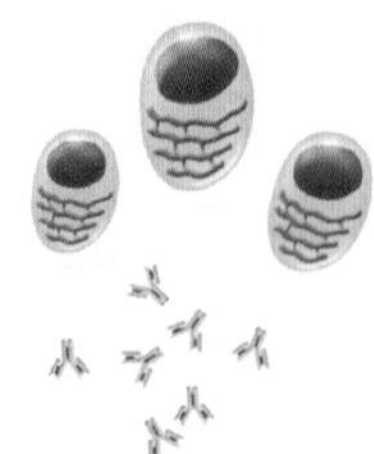

FIGURE 35–10 Memory B Cells

Analyzing Data

NoS.3, B.5.5

Immune System "Memory"

Antibody concentration in a person's blood reveals the difference between the first and second immune response. Day 1 indicates the first exposure to Antigen A. Day 28 marks a second exposure to Antigen A and the first exposure to Antigen B.

1. Interpret Graphs After first exposure to an antigen, about how long does it take for antibodies to reach a detectable level?

2. Infer What could explain the significant increase in antibodies to A seen after Day 30?

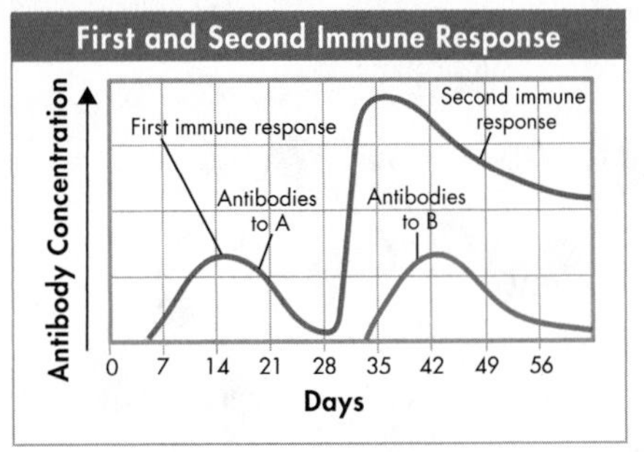

Lead a Discussion

Discuss humoral immunity as a class. Make sure students understand what happens during this part of the immune response. For example, you might want to start the discussion by asking the following questions:

Ask What happens when an antibody that is attached to a B cell recognizes an antigen? *(Helper T cells stimulate this B cell to divide into plasma cells and memory B cells.)*

Ask Why is the structure of an antibody important? *(Its antigen-binding sites allow it to recognize specific antigens.)*

Guide students through the process of humoral immunity and the immune structures involved. Refer to **Figures 35–8, 35–9,** and **35–10** as needed to help you explain and reinforce concepts.

DIFFERENTIATED INSTRUCTION

L1 Special Needs For students who have difficulty reading the section and following the discussion, stage a quick role-play of humoral immunity. Before class, make five small signs from poster board with these labels: Strep Throat, Flu, Common Cold, Tuberculosis, and Chickenpox. Cut each sign in half with a jagged edge, and attach a string to each half. Then, have five students put the top half of a sign around their neck, and assign them to be pathogens. Have five other students put on the bottom half of a sign around their neck, and assign them to be B cells. Line up the B cells on one side of the classroom, and have the pathogens invade through a door on the other side. The B cells need to find and bind its "antibody" to a pathogen's "antigen"—the top half of the sign. Once an "antibody" binds to its "antigen," that student pair should sit down. Discuss how this role-play models humoral immunity.

Analyzing Data

PURPOSE Students will analyze data in a graph and observe the difference in the production of antibodies in the primary and secondary response of humoral immunity.

PLANNING Have students review the primary and secondary responses of humoral immunity in **Figure 35–11.**

ANSWERS

1. about five days

2. The significant increase in antibodies is a result of the secondary response of humoral immunity. Memory B cells respond more quickly to the same pathogen invading the body than B cells in the primary response.

Answers

IN YOUR NOTEBOOK Sample answer: The body can produce up to 10 billion different antibodies that can each bind to a specific antigen. Therefore, antibodies that are capable of tagging particular antigens for destruction exist before a person is infected with the antigen.

LESSON 35.2

Teach continued

VISUAL SUMMARY

Point out that **Figure 35–11** includes the two styles of action of the specific immune response—on the left and right—and the primary and secondary responses to the same pathogen—top and bottom.

Make sure students understand the difference between humoral immunity and cell-mediated immunity.

Ask Which style of action are B cells involved in? *(humoral immunity)*

Ask Even though T cells are mostly involved in cell-mediated immunity, how are they also important in humoral immunity? *(T cells stimulate B cells to grow and divide rapidly into plasma cells and memory B cells.)*

Ask Which style of immunity uses antibodies as its main weapon? *(humoral immunity)*

Then, make sure students understand the difference between primary and secondary response.

Ask In the primary response, what leads to the destruction of pathogens in humoral immunity? *(Antibodies tag antigens for destruction in humoral immunity.)*

Point out that the response to the invasion of the same pathogen is quicker in the secondary response than in the primary response.

DIFFERENTIATED INSTRUCTION

L1 Struggling Students Point out to students that all of the types of B cells and T cells shown in **Figure 35–11** are also shown where they are discussed in the text. Have students work in pairs to come up with helpful ways of remembering the roles of the different B cells and T cells. Ask volunteers to share their methods with the class.

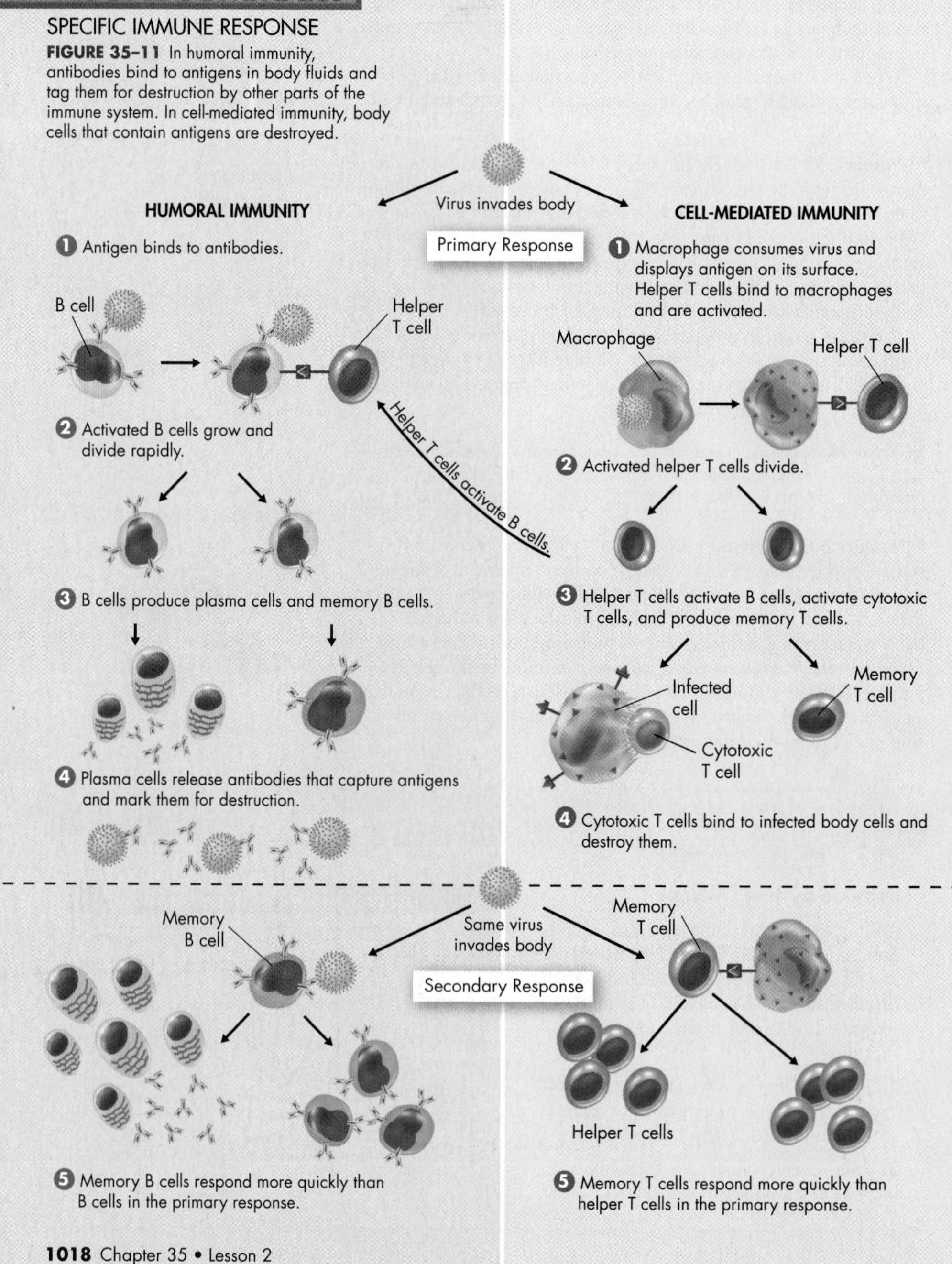

VISUAL SUMMARY
SPECIFIC IMMUNE RESPONSE
Virus invades body
HUMORAL IMMUNITY
CELL-MEDIATED IMMUNITY
Primary Response
1 Antigen binds to antibodies.
B cell
Helper T cell
2 Activated B cells grow and divide rapidly.
Helper T cells activate B cells
3 B cells produce plasma cells and memory B cells.
4 Plasma cells release antibodies that capture antigens and mark them for destruction.
1 Macrophage consumes virus and displays antigen on its surface. Helper T cells bind to macrophages and are activated.
Macrophage
Helper T cell
2 Activated helper T cells divide.
3 Helper T cells activate B cells, activate cytotoxic T cells, and produce memory T cells.
Infected cell
Memory T cell
Cytotoxic T cell
4 Cytotoxic T cells bind to infected body cells and destroy them.
Same virus invades body
Secondary Response
Memory B cell
Memory T cell
Helper T cells
5 Memory B cells respond more quickly than B cells in the primary response.
5 Memory T cells respond more quickly than helper T cells in the primary response.
1018 Chapter 35 • Lesson 2

FIGURE 35–11 In humoral immunity, antibodies bind to antigens in body fluids and tag them for destruction by other parts of the immune system. In cell-mediated immunity, body cells that contain antigens are destroyed.

Biology In-Depth

B ANTIBODY ACTION

There are five classes of antibodies that disable antigens in various ways. Some antibodies cause antigens to clump together. This enhances the ability of phagocytes to do their work. Others can disable bacteria and viruses by neutralizing their toxins or blocking viruses from attaching to host cells. Still others can immobilize bacteria and prevent their spread by damaging their flagella or cilia.

Cell-Mediated Immunity Another part of the immune response, which depends on the action of macrophages and several types of T cells, is called **cell-mediated immunity.** This part of the immune system defends the body against some viruses, fungi, and single-celled pathogens that do their dirty work inside body cells. T cells also protect the body from its own cells if they become cancerous.

When a cell is infected by a pathogen or when a macrophage consumes a pathogen, the cell displays a portion of the antigen on the outer surface of its membrane. This membrane attachment is a signal to circulating T cells called helper T cells. Activated helper T cells divide into more helper T cells, which go on to activate B cells, activate cytotoxic T cells, and produce memory T cells.

Cytotoxic T cells hunt down body cells infected with a particular antigen and kill the cells. They kill infected cells by puncturing their membranes or initiating apoptosis (programmed cell death). Memory helper T cells enable the immune system to respond quickly if the same pathogen enters the body again.

Another type of T cell, called suppressor T cells, helps to keep the immune system in check. They inhibit the immune response once an infection is under control. They may also be involved in preventing autoimmune diseases.

Although cytotoxic T cells are helpful in the immune system, they make the acceptance of organ transplants difficult. When an organ is transplanted from one person to another, the normal response of the recipient's immune system would be to recognize it as nonself. T cells and proteins would damage and destroy the transplanted organ. This process is known as rejection. To prevent organ rejection, doctors search for a donor whose cell markers are nearly identical to the cell markers of the recipient. Still, organ recipients must take drugs—usually for the rest of their lives—to suppress the cell-mediated immune response.

FIGURE 35–12 Cytotoxic T cell

FIGURE 35–13 Memory T cell

35.2 Assessment

IN B.1.2, B.5.5

Review Key Concepts

1. a. Review List the body's nonspecific defenses against pathogens.
   b. Sequence Describe the steps of the inflammatory response.
2. a. Review How does the immune system identify a pathogen?
   b. Compare and Contrast How are the roles of B and T cells different? How are their roles similar?
3. a. Review What are the two main styles of action of the specific immune response?
   b. Apply Concepts Why would a disease that destroys helper T cells also compromise the humoral response?

VISUAL THINKING

4. These two T cells are attached to a cancer cell. What type of immune response are these cells a part of?

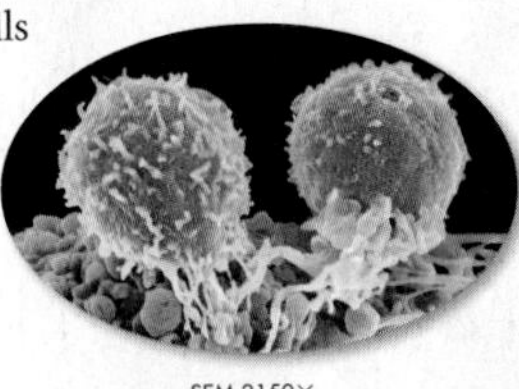

BIOLOGY.com Search (Lesson 35.2)  • Self-Test • Lesson Assessment

Assessment Answers

1a. the skin, tears and other secretions, the inflammatory response, interferon, fever

1b. Mast cells release histamines, stimulating blood flow. Fluid leaking from expanded blood vessels causes swelling. White blood cells move into infected tissues. Many of these are phagocytes, which engulf and destroy bacteria.

2a. Antigens trigger specific immune defenses.

2b. Different: B cells discover antigens in body fluids; T cells are presented with antigens by infected body cells or immune cells. Similar: Both recognize antigens.

3a. humoral and cell-mediated

3b. Helper T cells activate B cells.

VISUAL THINKING

4. cell-mediated immune response

ELL Focus on ELL: Access Content

ALL SPEAKERS Set up a **Gallery Walk** to review the immune system. Write these terms on separate pieces of chart paper: *non-specific defenses*, *humoral immunity*, and *cell-mediated immunity*. Post the pieces of chart paper at different places in the classroom. Then, have small groups rotate from term to term. At each term, group members should write what they know about it, using a particular pen color. When the next group rotates to the term, its members should add to the previous group's comments or correct mistakes and misunderstandings, using a differently colored pen. Work with the class to summarize the information about each term.

Study Wkbks A/B, Appendix S6, Gallery Walk.

Assess and Remediate

EVALUATE UNDERSTANDING

Write *Nonspecific Defenses* and *Specific Defenses* on the board. Then, call on students at random to help make a list of defenses under each term. After a student names a defense, call on another student to provide details of how that defense protects against pathogens. Then, have students complete the 35.2 Assessment.

REMEDIATION SUGGESTION

L1 **Struggling Students** If students have difficulty answering **Question 3b,** have them search for functions that helper T cells carry out in the specific immune response. In step 3 of Cell-Mediated Immunity in **Figure 35–11,** students will find that helper T cells activate B cells. Point out that B cells are involved in humoral immunity.

BIOLOGY.com Students can check their understanding of lesson concepts with the **Self-Test** assessment. They can then take an online version of the **Lesson Assessment.**

LESSON 35.3

Getting Started

Objectives

35.3.1 Distinguish between active immunity and passive immunity.

35.3.2 Describe how public health measures and medications fight disease.

35.3.3 Describe why patterns of infectious disease have changed.

Student Resources

Study Workbooks A and B, 35.3 Worksheets

Spanish Study Workbook, 35.3 Worksheets

Lab Manual B, 35.3 Hands-On Activity Worksheet

 Lesson Overview • Lesson Notes • Activity: Data Analysis • Assessment: Self-Test, Lesson Assessment

 For corresponding lesson in the **Foundation Edition**, see pages 846–848.

Activate Prior Knowledge

Find on the Internet or obtain from the health department a schedule of recommended vaccinations for children and teens. Show students the schedule, and ask them how they think vaccinations help develop immunity. Also, discuss how a community increases its protection against epidemics of serious infectious diseases as more people in the community are vaccinated against those diseases. After the discussion, post the schedule on a classroom bulletin board.

IN INDIANA ACADEMIC STANDARDS

For the full text of all standards, see the Course Overview in the front matter of this book.

NoS.11 Explain how scientific knowledge can be used to guide decisions on environmental and social issues.

35.3 Fighting Infectious Disease

 NoS.11 Scientific knowledge: environmental and social issues.

Key Questions

How do vaccines and externally produced antibodies fight disease?

How do public health measures and medications fight disease?

Why have patterns of infectious diseases changed?

Vocabulary

vaccination
active immunity
passive immunity

Taking Notes

Venn Diagram Make a Venn diagram that compares and contrasts active and passive immunity.

FIGURE 35–14 Jenner Vaccinating James Phipps

THINK ABOUT IT More than 200 years ago, English physician Edward Jenner noted that milkmaids who contracted a mild disease called cowpox didn't develop smallpox. At the time, smallpox was a widespread disease that killed many people. Jenner wondered, could people be protected from smallpox by deliberately infecting them with cowpox?

Acquired Immunity

How do vaccines and externally produced antibodies fight disease?

Jenner performed a bold experiment. He put fluid from a cowpox patient's sore into a small cut he made on the arm of a young boy named James Phipps. As expected, James developed mild cowpox. Two months later, Jenner injected James with fluid from a smallpox infection. Fortunately for James (and Jenner!), the boy didn't develop smallpox. His cowpox infection had protected him from smallpox infection. Ever since that time, the injection of a weakened form of a pathogen, or of a similar but less dangerous pathogen, to produce immunity has been known as a **vaccination.** The term comes from the Latin word *vacca*, meaning "cow," as a reminder of Jenner's work.

Active Immunity Today, we understand how vaccination works. **Vaccination stimulates the immune system with an antigen. The immune system produces memory B cells and memory T cells that quicken and strengthen the body's response to repeated infection.** This kind of immunity, called **active immunity,** may develop as a result of natural exposure to an antigen (fighting an infection) or from deliberate exposure to the antigen (through a vaccine).

Passive Immunity Disease can be prevented in another way. **Antibodies produced against a pathogen by other individuals or animals can be used to produce temporary immunity.** If externally produced antibodies are introduced into a person's blood, the result is **passive immunity.** Passive immunity lasts only a short time because the immune system eventually destroys the foreign antibodies.

Passive immunity can also occur naturally or by deliberate exposure. Natural passive immunity occurs when antibodies are passed from a pregnant woman to the fetus (across the placenta), or to an infant through breast milk. For some diseases, antibodies from humans or animals can be injected into an individual. For example, people who have been bitten by rabid animals are injected with antibodies for the rabies virus.

UbD Teach for Understanding

ENDURING UNDERSTANDING The human body is a complex system. The coordinated functions of its many structures support life processes and maintain homeostasis.

GUIDING QUESTION How do humans prevent and fight the spread of disease?

EVIDENCE OF UNDERSTANDING *After completing the lesson, this assessment should show student understanding of how humans prevent the spread of infectious disease.* Ask each student to create an information sheet that could inform the public about why acquired immunity is important to the prevention of infectious disease. The sheet can have a combination of words and illustrations. Have volunteers present their information sheets to the class.

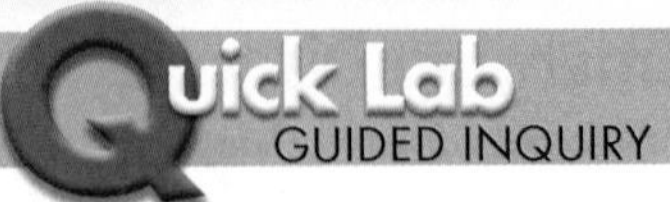

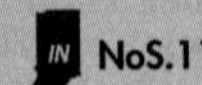

How Do Diseases Spread? 

❶ Your teacher has placed a fluorescent material in the classroom to simulate a virus. Keep track of the people and objects you touch. Then, use a UV lamp to check for the "virus" on your hands, objects, and people you have touched since entering the classroom. **CAUTION:** *Do not look directly at the UV light.*

❷ Exchange results with your classmates to determine how the "virus" spread through the classroom. Wash your hands with soap and warm water.

Analyze and Conclude

1. Infer What can you infer about how the "virus" spread through the classroom?

2. Apply Concepts How does thorough hand washing help prevent the spread of diseases?

Public Health and Medications

How do public health measures and medications fight disease?

In 1900, more than 30 percent of deaths in the United States were caused by infectious disease. In 2005, less than 5 percent of deaths were caused by infectious disease. Two factors that contributed to this change are public health measures and the development of medications.

Public Health Measures When humans live in large groups, behavior, cleanliness of food and water supplies, and sanitation all influence the spread of disease. The field of public health offers services and advice that help provide healthy conditions. **Public health measures help prevent disease by monitoring and regulating food and water supplies, promoting vaccination, and promoting behaviors that avoid infection.** Promoting childhood vaccinations and providing clean drinking water are two important public health activities that have greatly reduced the spread of many diseases that once killed many people.

FIGURE 35–15 Broad Street Pump In 1854, through investigation that included interviewing residents and mapping, Dr. John Snow learned that the source of a London cholera outbreak was a water pump like this replica. This is a major event in the history of public health.

Medications Prevention of infectious disease is not always possible. Medications, such as antibiotics and antiviral drugs, are other weapons that can fight pathogens. **Antibiotics can kill bacteria, and some antiviral medications can slow down viral activity.**

The term *antibiotic* refers to a compound that kills bacteria without harming its host. In 1928, Alexander Fleming was the first scientist to discover an antibiotic. Fleming noticed that a mold, *Penicillium notatum*, seemed to produce something that inhibited bacterial growth. Research determined that this "something" was a compound Fleming named penicillin. Researchers learned to mass-produce penicillin just in time for it to save thousands of World War II soldiers. Since then, dozens of antibiotics have saved countless numbers of lives.

Antibiotics have no effect on viruses. However, antiviral drugs have been developed to fight certain viral infections. These drugs generally inhibit the ability of viruses to invade cells or to multiply once inside cells.

If Steere's patients were helped by antibiotics, what clue would this have given him about the disease's pathogen?

In Your Notebook *How does your school promote public health?*

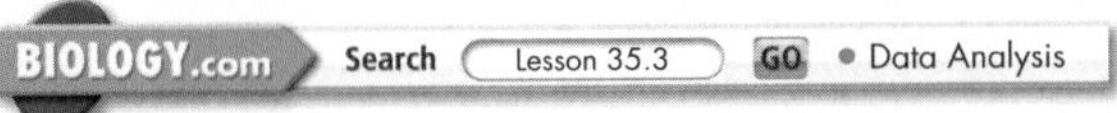

Quick Lab

PURPOSE Students infer how an infectious disease can spread.

MATERIALS ultraviolet lamp, fluorescent substance such as Glo Germ™ oil or dilute fluorescein solution

SAFETY Warn students not to look directly at the UV light. Make sure they wash their hands after the lab.

PLANNING Place a fluorescent material on a doorknob or other place students are sure to touch no more than 10 minutes before students arrive. Station a UV lamp where students can check to see if they have "contracted the virus."

ANALYZE AND CONCLUDE

1. Sample answer: The "virus" was spread through the classroom by students as they contaminated objects with their hands.

2. Sample answer: Thorough hand washing washes viruses off hands. Therefore, frequent hand washing would help prevent spread of diseases.

Teach

Lead a Discussion

Discuss the story of John Snow and the Broad Street pump introduced in **Figure 35–15.** Then, talk about public health measures in the students' own community that prevent similar outbreaks of serious diseases. Review with students what they learned in Lesson 35.1 about the ways infectious diseases spread.

Ask How do inspectors and other government employees in the community help to prevent the spread of disease? *(Sample answer: Inspectors of restaurants help prevent diseases spread in food. The water department makes sure diseases are not spread in drinking water.)*

DIFFERENTIATED INSTRUCTION

LPR Less Proficient Readers Give students five minutes to write a response to this common saying: An ounce of prevention is worth a pound of cure. Ask them to explain what the saying means and whether they agree or not with its meaning.

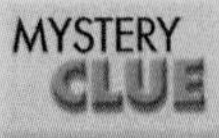

Suggest students review the text to find out which pathogens are affected by antibiotics. Students can go online to Biology.com to gather their evidence.

BIOLOGY.com Have students investigate why a "germ-free" society can be both good and bad for human immunity using **Data Analysis: Society and Immunity.**

Address Misconceptions

Vaccine Effectiveness Some students may have the common misconception that vaccines are not effective because the majority of people who get diseases have been vaccinated. Point out that vaccines are not 100 percent effective, and a small percentage of those vaccinated against a disease will become infected. Routine childhood vaccines, for example, are 85 to 95 percent effective. That gives a vaccinated person a much greater chance of avoiding a disease than one who is not vaccinated.

Answers

IN YOUR NOTEBOOK Answers will vary. Students might mention the school's nurse, daily cleaning of the school, a school dietician, and any special efforts made by school staff to promote healthy behaviors.

Teach continued

Lead a Discussion

Talk about the threat of emerging diseases causing epidemics in the United States and elsewhere. Point out that for most of these emerging diseases, either there is no vaccine, or the vaccines are not available for wide distribution to a large population.

DIFFERENTIATED INSTRUCTION

L3 Advanced Students Ask pairs of students with a firm understanding of the principles of evolution to prepare a presentation to the class about how the misuse of medications results in pathogens that are resistant to antibiotics and other medications.

Assess and Remediate

EVALUATE UNDERSTANDING

Read aloud the lesson's Key Concepts and the sentences defining new vocabulary terms. In each case, leave out the most significant term in the sentence. Call on students to fill in the blanks. Then, have them complete the 35.3 Assessment.

REMEDIATION SUGGESTION

L1 Struggling Students If students have trouble answering **Question 2b,** review the consequences of misusing medications.

BIOLOGY.com Students can check their understanding of lesson concepts with the **Self-Test** assessment. They can then take an online version of the **Lesson Assessment.**

FIGURE 35–16 Causes of Emerging Disease Illegally imported animals can lead to the spread of emerging disease. **A.** In 2003, dormice and other rodents from Africa spread monkeypox to prairie dogs in the United States, which then infected humans. **B.** The spread of SARS also has been associated with the wild animal trade.

A. Dormouse

B. Students wearing SARS masks

New and Re-Emerging Diseases

Why have patterns of infectious diseases changed?

By 1980, many people thought that medicine had conquered infectious disease. Vaccination and other public health measures had wiped out polio in the United States and had eliminated smallpox globally. Antibiotics seemed to have bacterial diseases under control. Some exotic diseases remained in the tropics, but researchers were confident that epidemics would soon be history. Unfortunately, they were wrong.

In recent decades, a host of new diseases have appeared, including AIDS, SARS, hantavirus, monkeypox, West Nile virus, Ebola, and avian influenza ("bird flu"). Other diseases that people thought were under control are re-emerging as a threat and spreading to new areas. What's going on?

Changing Interactions With Animals **Two major reasons for the emergence of new diseases are the ongoing merging of human and animal habitats and the increase in the exotic animal trade.** As people clear new areas of land and as environments change, people come in contact with different animals and different pathogens. Exotic animal trade, for pets and food, has also given pathogens new opportunities to jump from animals to humans. Both monkeypox and SARS are thought to have started this way. Pathogens are also evolving in ways that enable them to infect different hosts.

Misuse of Medications **Misuse of medications has led to the re-emergence of diseases that many people thought were under control.** For example, many strains of the pathogens that cause tuberculosis and malaria are evolving resistance to a wide variety of antibiotics and other medications. In addition, diseases such as measles are making a comeback because some people fail to follow vaccination recommendations.

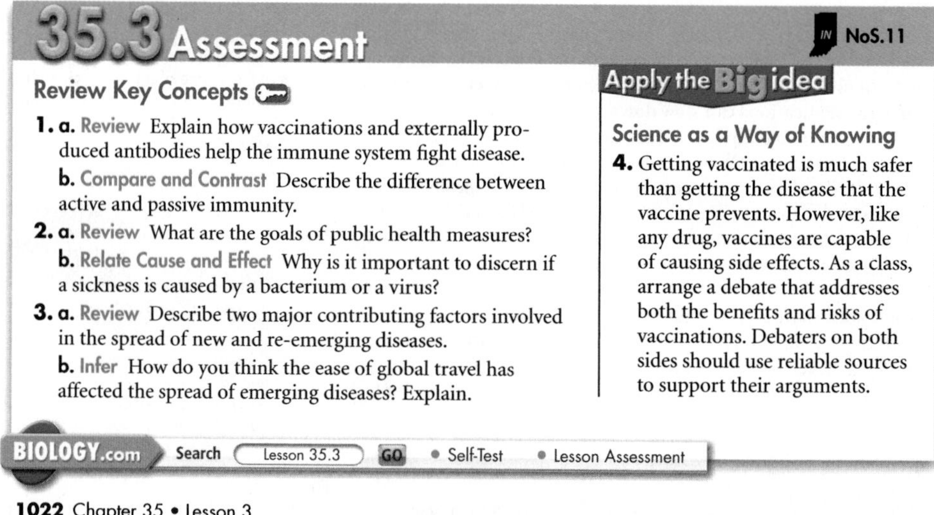

35.3 Assessment

IN NoS.11

Review Key Concepts

1. a. Review Explain how vaccinations and externally produced antibodies help the immune system fight disease.
   b. Compare and Contrast Describe the difference between active and passive immunity.
2. a. Review What are the goals of public health measures?
   b. Relate Cause and Effect Why is it important to discern if a sickness is caused by a bacterium or a virus?
3. a. Review Describe two major contributing factors involved in the spread of new and re-emerging diseases.
   b. Infer How do you think the ease of global travel has affected the spread of emerging diseases? Explain.

Apply the Big idea

Science as a Way of Knowing

4. Getting vaccinated is much safer than getting the disease that the vaccine prevents. However, like any drug, vaccines are capable of causing side effects. As a class, arrange a debate that addresses both the benefits and risks of vaccinations. Debaters on both sides should use reliable sources to support their arguments.

BIOLOGY.com Search Lesson 35.3 GO • Self-Test • Lesson Assessment

Assessment Answers

1a. Vaccination stimulates the immune system with an antigen. The immune system produces memory B cells and memory T cells that quicken and strengthen the body's response to repeated infection. Externally produced antibodies, which are antibodies produced against a pathogen by other individuals or animals, can be used to produce temporary immunity.

1b. Active immunity may develop as a result of natural exposure to an antigen or from deliberate exposure to the antigen. Passive immunity occurs when externally produced antibodies are introduced into a person's blood.

2a. to prevent disease by monitoring food and water supplies, to promote vaccination, and to recommend ways to avoid infection

2b. Antibiotics can kill bacteria, but they have no effect on viruses.

3a. One factor is changing interactions with animals. As people clear new land and environments change, people come in contact with new pathogens. Exotic animal trade has given pathogens new opportunities to jump from animals to humans. Another factor is the misuse of medicines. Some pathogens are developing resistance to a variety of antibiotics and other medications.

3b. Sample answer: Global travel has increased the spread of emerging diseases because infected people who show no symptoms can travel around the world very quickly, spreading the disease more widely than possible in earlier times.

4. Big idea Debate arguments will vary depending on research results. Students should find information in library sources or on the Internet that describes the fear of death and sickness caused by vaccines as well as assurances that vaccines are safe.

Emerging Diseases Due to factors such as changing interactions with animals and misuse of medications, the problem of infectious disease is far from solved.

1965
1971
1977
1983
1989
1995
2001
2007
1967
Surgeon General William H. Stewart announces, "It is time to close the book on infectious diseases."
1975
Lyme disease is first documented in the United States.
1976
First outbreak of Ebola occurs in the Democratic Republic of the Congo.
1981
First reports surface of illness later identified as AIDS in Los Angeles.
1983
HIV is identified as the cause of AIDS.
1986
Researchers discover bovine spongiform encephalopathy (BSE), commonly called mad cow disease, in cattle in Britain.
1996
The British government admits that humans can contract BSE from eating infected beef.
2002
First SARS outbreak occurs in China's Guangdong province.
2003
The United States reports its first case of mad cow disease in Washington State.
CDC reports cases of monkeypox in people who handled infected prairie dogs.
Avian Influenza A strain H5N1 spreads through domestic poultry in Asia.
2005
CDC reports that 7.8 percent of tuberculosis cases in the U.S. are resistant to the first-line drug used to treat it.
2007
Fourteen countries have reported a total of 351 confirmed human cases of avian influenza (H5N1) and 219 deaths.

WRITING In a short essay, discuss why Surgeon General Stewart would have been confident in his 1967 announcement. Then discuss two factors that have contributed to the comeback of infectious disease.

Biology In-Depth

THE CASE OF MONKEYPOX

Changing interactions with animals is one factor in the spread of emerging diseases. An example is monkeypox, a rare viral disease mainly confined to Africa that causes symptoms in humans similar to smallpox. The disease is called monkeypox because it was first discovered in monkeys, though the virus can also infect other animals, including mice and rabbits. In the United States, this disease was first reported in 2003. Investigations revealed that monkeypox had spread to people from their pet prairie dogs. How did the prairie dogs get an African virus? The source was a shipment of wild African rodents to Texas. The rodents were kept by a seller in close proximity to prairie dogs, which were eventually sold to people as pets.

Teach

Lead a Discussion

Have students relate the diseases included in the time line with what they learned in the subsection **New and Re-Emerging Diseases,** in Lesson 35.3.

Ask What is an example on the time line of a disease that emerged as a result of the misuse of medications? *(tuberculosis cases in the United States)*

Ask How might an American tourist in Asia contribute to the global spread of avian influenza? *(The tourist could come in contact with the virus and bring it back to America when he or she returns home.)*

DIFFERENTIATED INSTRUCTION

L3 Advanced Students Ask students to report on one of the emerging diseases on the time line. Tell them that to find up-to-date information on a disease, they should search reliable sources on the Internet, such as the World Health Organization (WHO) and the Centers for Disease Control and Prevention (CDC). Ask students to give a brief presentation to the class about the disease they researched.

Answers

WRITING Student essays will vary. Students might suggest the Surgeon General may have been confident of his statement in 1967 because of the success of vaccinations and antibiotics in preventing and treating many diseases, such as polio and tuberculosis. In the discussion of the comeback of infectious disease, students should describe changing interactions with animals and the misuse of medications.

LESSON 35.4

Getting Started

Objectives

35.4.1 Explain what happens when the immune system overreacts to harmless pathogens.

35.4.2 Describe how HIV is transmitted and how it affects the immune system.

Student Resources

Study Workbooks A and B, 35.4 Worksheets

Spanish Study Workbook, 35.4 Worksheets

Lab Manual B, 35.4 Data Analysis Worksheet

Lesson Overview • Lesson Notes • Activity: Art in Motion • Assessment: Self-Test, Lesson Assessment

For corresponding lesson in the **Foundation Edition**, see pages 849–851.

Answers

IN YOUR NOTEBOOK Sample answer: In an allergic response, the immune system reacts to harmless antigens much more strongly than is necessary.

IN INDIANA ACADEMIC STANDARDS

For the full text of all standards, see the Course Overview in the front matter of this book.

NoS.3 Clearly communicate their ideas and results of investigations verbally and in written form using tables, graphs, diagrams, and photographs.

35.4 Immune System Disorders

NoS.3 Communicate ideas.

Key Questions

How can misguided immune responses cause problems?

What causes AIDS and how is it spread?

Vocabulary

allergy
asthma

Taking Notes

Outline Before you read, make an outline of the major headings in the lesson. As you read, fill in main ideas and supporting details for each heading.

THINK ABOUT IT A healthy immune system accurately distinguishes "self" from "other" and responds appropriately to dangerous invaders in the body. Sometimes, however, the immune system's weaponry is misdirected at the body's own cells. Other times, the immune system itself is disabled by disease. What happens in these cases?

When the Immune System Overreacts

How can misguided immune responses cause problems?

The immune systems of some people overreact to harmless antigens, such as pollen, dust mites, mold, pet dander, and possibly their own cells. **A strong immune response to harmless antigens can produce allergies, asthma, and autoimmune disease.**

Allergies Antigens that cause allergic reactions are called allergens. When allergens enter the body of people affected by **allergies,** they trigger an inflammatory response by causing mast cells to release histamines. If this response occurs in the respiratory system, it increases mucus production and causes sneezing, watery eyes, a runny nose, and other irritations. Drugs called antihistamines help relieve allergy symptoms by counteracting the effects of histamines.

FIGURE 35–17 Allergens Pet dander, dead skin shed from cats and dogs, is a common allergen (SEM 40×).

Asthma Allergic reactions in the respiratory system can create a dangerous condition called asthma. **Asthma** is a chronic disease in which air passages narrow, causing wheezing, coughing, and difficulty breathing. Both hereditary and environmental factors influence asthma symptoms. Asthma attacks can be triggered by respiratory infections, exercise, emotional stress, and certain medications. Other triggers include cold or dry air, pollen, dust, tobacco smoke, pollution, molds, and pet dander.

Asthma is serious and can be life-threatening. If treatment is not started early enough or if medications are not taken properly, severe asthma can lead to permanent damage or destruction of lung tissue. There is no cure, but people with asthma can sometimes control the condition. If the attacks are caused by an allergen, tests can identify which allergens cause the problem. Inhaled medications can relax smooth muscles around the airways and relieve asthma symptoms.

In Your Notebook *Sometimes allergies are described as "overreactions of the immune system." Explain what that phrase means.*

UbD Teach for Understanding

ENDURING UNDERSTANDING The human body is a complex system. The coordinated functions of its many structures support life processes and maintain homeostasis.

GUIDING QUESTION What happens when the immune system does not function properly?

EVIDENCE OF UNDERSTANDING *After completing the lesson, this assessment should show student understanding of what can happen when the immune system does not function properly.* Ask students to work in pairs to make a poster that explains how a problem with the immune system can result in allergies, asthma, or an autoimmune disease. Display the posters on a classroom wall or in a school hallway.

Analyzing Data

 NoS.3

Food Allergies

About four percent of Americans have food allergies. Eight foods account for 90 percent of all food allergies—milk, eggs, peanuts, tree nuts, wheat, soy, fish, and shellfish. Approximately 30,000 emergency-room visits and 150–200 deaths each year can be attributed to food allergies. Most of the deaths are due to peanut allergies. The graph shows the percentage of children who had allergies from 1998–2006.

Food Allergies Among Children in the United States

Age	1998–2000	2001–2003	2004–2006
0–4	3.8%	4.2%	4.6%
5–17	3.3%	3.4%	3.9%

1. **Analyze Data** Discuss the general trend of food allergies for both age groups.

2. **Calculate** Which age group shows the greatest change from 1998–2006? What is the percent change in both age groups? MATH

3. **Infer** Propose a reason why more children age 4 and under have allergies than children age 5–17.

Autoimmune Diseases Sometimes a disease occurs in which the immune system fails to properly recognize "self," and attacks cells or compounds in the body as though they were pathogens. **When the immune system attacks the body's own cells, it produces an autoimmune disease.** Examples of autoimmune diseases are Type I diabetes, rheumatoid arthritis, and lupus.

In Type I diabetes, antibodies attack insulin-producing cells in the pancreas. In rheumatoid arthritis, antibodies attack tissues around joints. Lupus is an autoimmune disease in which antibodies attack organs and tissues causing areas of chronic inflammation throughout the body.

Some autoimmune diseases can be treated with medications that alleviate specific symptoms. For example, people with Type I diabetes can take insulin. Other autoimmune diseases are treated with medications that suppress the immune response. However, these medications also decrease the normal immune response and must be monitored.

BUILD Vocabulary

ACADEMIC WORDS Alleviate is a verb that means "to lessen" or "to relieve." It comes from the Latin *ad-* (to) and *-levis* (light in weight).

HIV and AIDS

What causes AIDS and how is it spread?

During the late 1970s, physicians began reporting serious infections produced by microorganisms that didn't normally cause disease. Previously healthy people began to suffer from *Pneumocystis carinii* pneumonia, Kaposi sarcoma (a rare form of skin cancer), and fungal infections of the mouth and throat. Because these diseases are normally prevented by a healthy immune response, doctors concluded that these patients must have weakened immune systems. Diseases that attack a person with a weakened immune system are called opportunistic diseases. Researchers concluded that these illnesses were symptoms of a new disorder they called acquired immunodeficiency syndrome (AIDS). Research eventually revealed that this "syndrome" was an infectious disease caused by a pathogen new to science.

Analyzing Data

PURPOSE Students will analyze data to infer an increasing trend for food allergies among children in the United States.

PLANNING Review with students what causes allergies and how the body reacts to allergens.

ANSWERS

1. The percentage of children with food allergies is rising in both age groups.
2. The 0–4 age group shows the greater change. The increase in this group is 21%. The increase in the 5–17 age group is 18%.
3. Sample answer: Some children grow out of allergies as they get older.

Teach

Lead a Discussion

Talk about autoimmune diseases and the consequences of an immune system that does not function properly. Remind students that Type I diabetes is different than the more common Type II diabetes. Type II diabetes is associated with age and obesity; it is not an autoimmune disease.

Ask In which autoimmune disease are cells in the pancreas attacked? *(Type I diabetes)*

Ask If a person with an autoimmune disease takes a medication that suppresses the immune response, what risk is that person taking? *(Sample answer: The person is at risk of more easily contracting infectious diseases, because their overall immune response will be weakened.)*

DIFFERENTIATED INSTRUCTION

L3 Advanced Students Encourage students to investigate current thinking about the causes of autoimmune disease. They should discover that genetics plays a role, though inheritance may not be the only contributing factor. Have students prepare a brief presentation to the class about what they find.

ELL Focus on ELL: Extend Language

ADVANCED AND ADVANCED HIGH SPEAKERS Have each advanced and advanced high speaker write a paragraph that explains what happens when the immune system either overreacts to harmless antigens or attacks the body's own cells. Tell students the paragraph should summarize what they learned by reading the section **When the Immune System Overreacts.** Spend time reviewing each student's paragraph, and help correct faulty syntax or misuse of vocabulary. Require advanced high speakers to use complex sentences and sophisticated vocabulary in their paragraph.

Teach continued

Use Visuals

Have groups of students examine **Figure 35–18** and discuss the steps in HIV infection. Tell students they should make sure everyone in the group understands the process and then write three questions about HIV infection that can be answered by the figure. Have groups trade questions and write answers to the other group's questions. Then, invite each group to read one of its questions aloud, as well as the correct answer.

DIFFERENTIATED INSTRUCTION

L1 Struggling Students Provide students who are having difficulty understanding **Figure 35–18** with a list of the six steps, with a blank in each where an important word has been left out. For example, leave out the word *membrane* in the first step. Have students use the figure to fill in the blanks.

Call on volunteers to describe possible reasons why the immune system could not overcome the disease, despite the presence of antibodies. *(Sample answer: The pathogen that causes the disease attacks cells of the immune system.)* Students can go online to Biology.com to gather their evidence.

BIOLOGY.com To observe how HIV infects immune cells, suggest students watch **Art in Motion: HIV Infection.**

Address Misconceptions

The Spread of AIDS The most common misconception about HIV/AIDS is that being around someone with AIDS or who is HIV-infected puts a person at risk of getting the disease. Emphasize that AIDS is not spread through casual contact—through being in the same room, breathing the same air, or even hugging. Make sure students understand that HIV is transmitted through the four main ways listed on this page, and casual contact is not one of those ways.

Answers

FIGURE 35–18 3, 4, or 5

IN YOUR NOTEBOOK Students' flowcharts should include the six steps shown in **Figure 35–18** and a seventh step focusing on the loss of helper T cells and the diagnosis of AIDS.

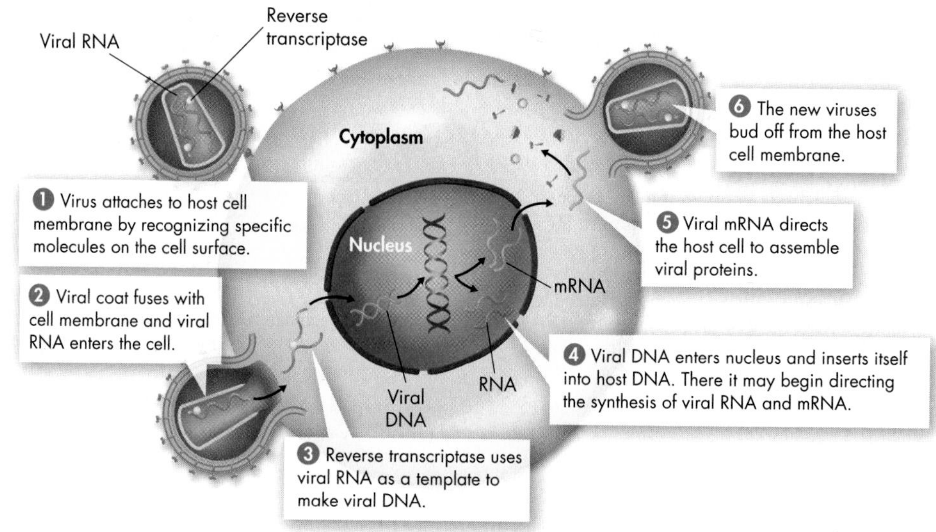

FIGURE 35–18 HIV Infection HIV travels through the blood, where it binds to receptors on helper T cells. Inside the cell, the viral DNA directs the cell to produce many new viruses. These new viruses are quickly released back into the blood, where they infect more cells. **Apply Concepts** ***In what steps are changes to HIV's genetic information most likely to occur?***

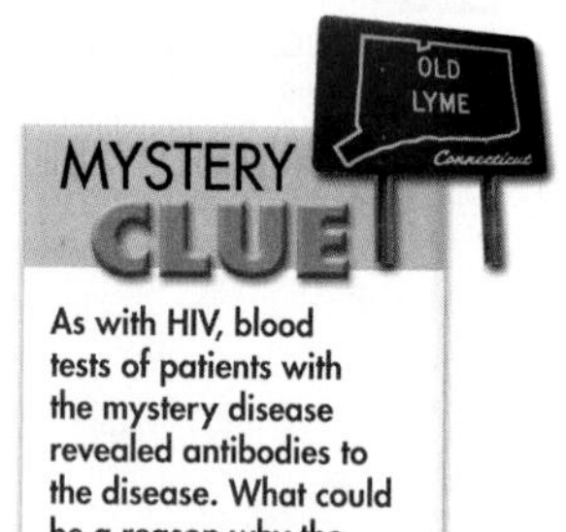

As with HIV, blood tests of patients with the mystery disease revealed antibodies to the disease. What could be a reason why the immune system cannot overcome the disease?

HIV **In 1983, researchers identified the cause of AIDS—a virus they called human immunodeficiency virus (HIV).** HIV is deadly for two reasons. First, HIV can hide from the defenses of the immune system. Second, HIV attacks key cells within the immune system, leaving the body with inadequate protection against other pathogens.

HIV is a retrovirus that carries its genetic information in RNA, rather than DNA. When HIV attacks a cell, it binds to receptor molecules on the cell membrane and inserts its contents into the cell. **Figure 35–18** explains how HIV replicates inside a host cell.

Target: T Cells Among HIV's main targets are helper T cells—the command centers of the specific immune response. Over time, HIV destroys more and more T cells, crippling the ability of the immune system to fight HIV and other pathogens. The progression of HIV infection can be monitored by counting helper T cells. The fewer helper T cells, the more advanced the disease, and the more susceptible the body becomes to other diseases. When an HIV-infected person's T cell count reaches about one sixth the normal level, he or she is diagnosed with AIDS.

HIV Transmission Although HIV is deadly, it is not easily transmitted. It is not transmitted through coughing, sneezing, sharing clothes, or other forms of casual contact. HIV can only be transmitted through contact with infected blood, semen, vaginal secretions, or breast milk. The four main ways that HIV is transmitted are sexual intercourse with an infected person; sharing needles with an infected person; contact with infected blood or blood products; or from an infected mother to her child during pregnancy, birth, or breast-feeding.

In Your Notebook *Make a flowchart that shows the steps of HIV infection and the development of AIDS.*

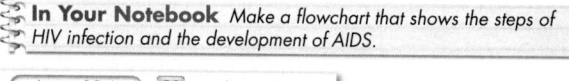

Biology In-Depth

IS AIDS A ZOONOSIS?

The origin of HIV is generally thought to be a virus in wild chimpanzees of central Africa. How the virus was transferred to humans is unknown. One theory is that a human became infected when butchering a chimpanzee for meat, and that person spread the disease to other humans. Therefore, is AIDS a zoonosis, a disease that can be transmitted from animals to humans? AIDS can be classified as such a disease, though labeling AIDS as a zoonosis can lead to misunderstandings. For example, HIV is not transmitted from chimpanzees to humans in the same ways it is spread among humans, and there is no evidence that transfer between species is common.

Preventing HIV Infection You can choose behaviors that reduce your risk of becoming infected with HIV. **The only no-risk behavior with respect to HIV transmission is abstinence from sexual activity and intravenous drug use.** Within a committed relationship, such as marriage, sexual fidelity between two uninfected partners presents the least risk of becoming infected with HIV. People who share needles to inject themselves with drugs are at a high risk for contracting HIV. For this reason, people who have sex with drug abusers are also at high risk. Before 1985, HIV was transmitted to some patients through transfusions of infected blood or blood products. But, such cases have been virtually eliminated by screening the blood supply for HIV antibodies and by discouraging potentially infected individuals from donating blood.

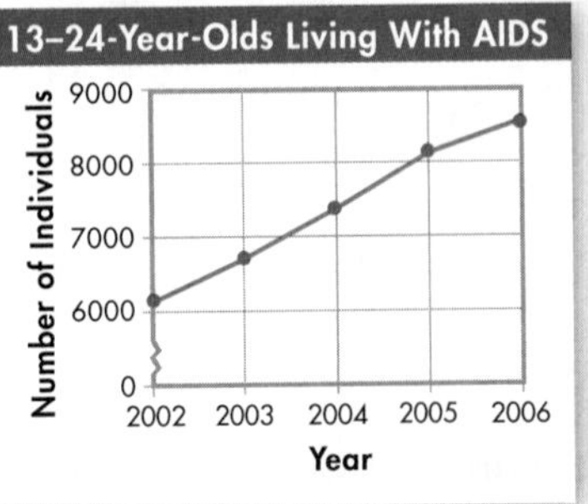

FIGURE 35–19 Adolescents and Young Adults Living With AIDS in the United States

Can AIDS Be Cured? At present, there is no cure for AIDS. A steady stream of new drugs makes it possible to survive HIV infection for years. Unfortunately, HIV mutates and evolves rapidly. For this reason, the virus has evolved into many strains that are resistant to most drugs used against them. No one has developed a vaccine that offers protection for any length of time.

At present, the only way to control the virus is to use a combination of expensive drugs that fight the virus in several ways. Current drugs interfere with the enzymes HIV uses to insert its RNA into a host cell, to convert RNA to DNA, and to integrate its DNA into the host's DNA. Because of these drugs, more people infected with HIV in the United States are living with HIV rather than dying from it. In many parts of Africa and Asia, however, these expensive drugs are not available.

Unfortunately, the knowledge that HIV can be treated (though not cured) has given some people the misconception that HIV infection is not serious. That idea is dead wrong.

35.4 Assessment

IN NoS.3

Review Key Concepts

1. a. Review What happens during an allergy attack? What happens in an autoimmune disease?
   b. Apply Concepts In treating asthma, the first thing many physicians do is ask patients to list times and places they have experienced attacks. Why do you think physicians do this?
2. a. Review What is the virus that causes AIDS? Describe how it is spread.
   b. Infer Why is it difficult for a person with HIV to fight off other infections?

ANALYZING DATA

Review **Figure 35–19** and answer the following questions.

3. a. Interpret Data What percent increase in AIDS cases occurred in 13–24-year-olds from 2002 to 2006? MATH
   b. Draw Conclusions What are two conclusions that you could draw regarding the increasing number of adolescents and young adults living with AIDS?

BIOLOGY.com Search Lesson 35.4 GO • Self-Test • Lesson Assessment

Assess and Remediate

EVALUATE UNDERSTANDING

Call on students at random to describe problems caused by misguided immune responses. Also, call on students to explain what causes AIDS and describe how it spreads. Then, have students complete the 35.4 Assessment.

REMEDIATION SUGGESTION

L1 Struggling Students If students are struggling in writing an answer to **Question 2b,** have them reread the section **Target: T Cells.** Then, ask them to explain why having fewer helper T cells makes the body more susceptible to other kinds of infectious diseases.

BIOLOGY.com Students can check their understanding of lesson concepts with the **Self-Test** assessment. They can then take an online version of the **Lesson Assessment.**

Assessment Answers

1a. During an allergy attack, the immune system goes through an inflammatory response against a harmless antigen. In an autoimmune disease, the immune system attacks the body's own cells.

1b. Sample answer: The physician is trying to discover which specific antigens trigger the asthma attacks.

2a. HIV causes AIDS. HIV can be spread through sexual intercourse with an infected person; sharing needles with an infected person; contact with infected blood or blood products; and from an infected mother to her child during pregnancy, birth, or breast-feeding.

2b. Among HIV's main targets are helper T cells. Over time, HIV destroys more and more T cells, crippling the ability of the immune system to fight HIV and other kinds of pathogens.

ANALYZING DATA

3a. There was about a 40 percent increase.

3b. Sample answer: Adolescents and young adults continue to engage in behaviors that can spread the disease. Current drugs can prevent a person dying from AIDS, allowing more people to live with HIV.

CHAPTER LAB

Pre-Lab

Introduce students to the concepts they will explore in the chapter lab by assigning the Pre-Lab questions.

Lab

Tell students they will perform the chapter lab *Detecting Lyme Disease* described in **Lab Manual A.**

L1 **Struggling Students** A simpler version of the chapter lab is provided in **Lab Manual B.**

SAFETY

Students should wear goggles and disposable plastic gloves during the lab. Make sure they wash their hands in warm, soapy water at the conclusion of the lab.

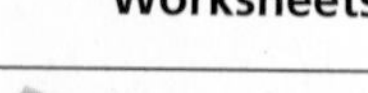

Look online for **Editable Lab Worksheets.**

For corresponding pre-lab in the **Foundation Edition**, see page 852.

Forensics Lab

GUIDED INQUIRY

Pre-Lab: Detecting Lyme Disease

Problem How can a blood test be used to detect Lyme disease?

Materials well plate, permanent marker, white paper, 400-mL beaker, 100-mL beaker, distilled water, micropipettes, test solutions

Lab Manual Chapter 35 Lab

Skills Control Variables, Interpret Data, Draw Conclusions

Connect to the Big idea To maintain homeostasis, your immune system must defend against invasions by harmful pathogens. Some invaders enter the body through bites from insects. For example, a tiny deer tick can infect you with the bacterium that causes Lyme disease. As a precaution, you should avoid areas where deer ticks are active. If you visit a location where ticks are active, wear clothing that covers the skin and check for ticks.

Symptoms for Lyme disease can vary widely, but many people develop a bull's-eye rash at the location of the bite. People who suspect that they have been exposed to the bacteria that cause Lyme disease should consult a medical professional. Blood tests are used to diagnose Lyme disease. In this lab, you will model one of these tests.

Background Questions

a. **Review** What is an antigen?

b. **Review** How does the immune system respond to antigens?

c. **Explain** Why does the presence of antibodies in blood suggest that a person was exposed to an antigen?

Pre-Lab Questions

Preview the procedure in the lab manual.

1. **Sequence** Use a flowchart to show the order in which the solutions will be added to the well plate.
2. **Infer** What is the advantage of having a control for a positive test and a control for a negative test?
3. **Control Variables** Why must you rinse the micropipette with distilled water before adding a different solution to the well plate?

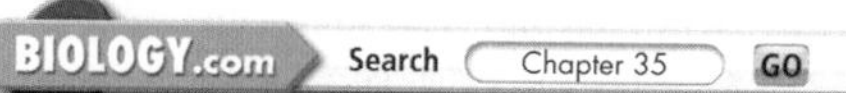

Visit Chapter 35 online to test yourself on chapter content and to find activities to help you learn.

Untamed Science Video Be careful what you touch as you follow the Untamed Science crew on a journey through human allergies.

Data Analysis Analyze the pros and cons of a clean germ-free lifestyle.

Art Review Review characteristics and examples of the different types of pathogens and parasites with this drag-and-drop activity.

Art in Motion View an animation of HIV infecting a cell.

Pre-Lab Answers

BACKGROUND QUESTIONS

a. An antigen is any foreign substance that can stimulate an immune response.

b. The immune system responds to antigens by increasing the production of cells that attack the antigen directly and cells that produce antibodies.

c. Antibodies are produced in response to specific antigens. The antibodies would not be present unless the person was exposed to a particular antigen.

PRE-LAB QUESTIONS

1. The flowchart should show the solutions being added in the following order: antigen, negative and positive controls, donor samples, secondary antibody, and substrate.
2. Sample answer: Seeing the expected results for both a positive test and a negative test will make it easier to draw conclusions about the samples.
3. Sample answer: Rinsing keeps the contents of a well from being contaminated with the contents of a different well.

35 Study Guide

Big idea Homeostasis

The immune system consists of cells that can distinguish the difference between cells and proteins that belong in the body and those that do not. Immune cells and accompanying chemicals seek and destroy antigens and pathogens that can cause disease. Human innovations such as vaccinations and medications aid our immune system in fighting disease.

35.1 Infectious Disease

Infectious diseases can be caused by viruses, bacteria, fungi, "protists," and parasites.

Some diseases are spread through coughing, sneezing, physical contact, or exchange of body fluids. Some diseases are spread through contaminated water or food. Still other diseases are spread to humans from infected animals.

infectious disease (1010)
germ theory of disease (1010)
Koch's postulates (1011)
zoonosis (1013)
vector (1013)

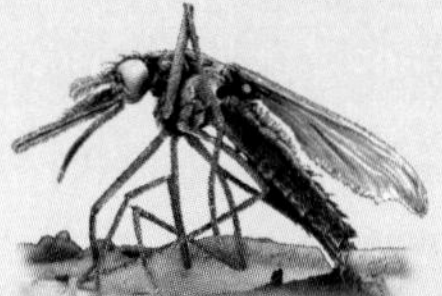

35.2 Defenses Against Infection

Nonspecific defenses include the skin, tears and other secretions, the inflammatory response, interferons, and fever.

The immune system's specific defenses distinguish between "self" and "other," and they inactivate or kill any foreign substance or cell that enters the body.

The specific immune response has two main styles of action: humoral immunity and cell-mediated immunity.

inflammatory response (1014)
histamine (1014)
interferon (1015)
fever (1015)
immune response (1016)
antigen (1016)
antibody (1016)
humoral immunity (1016)
cell-mediated immunity (1019)

35.3 Fighting Infectious Disease

Vaccination stimulates the immune system with an antigen. The immune system produces memory B cells and memory T cells that quicken and strengthen the body's response to repeated infection.

Antibodies produced against a pathogen by other individuals or animals can be used to produce temporary immunity.

Public health measures help prevent disease by monitoring and regulating food and water supplies, promoting vaccination, and promoting behaviors that avoid infection.

Antibiotics can kill bacteria, and some antiviral medications can slow down viral activity.

Two major reasons for the emergence of new diseases are the ongoing merging of human and animal habitats and the increase in the exotic animal trade.

Misuse of medications has led to the re-emergence of diseases that many people thought were under control.

vaccination (1020)
active immunity (1020)
passive immunity (1020)

35.4 Immune System Disorders

A strong immune response to harmless antigens can produce allergies, asthma, and autoimmune disease.

When the immune system attacks the body's own cells, it produces an autoimmune disease.

In 1983, researchers identified the cause of AIDS—a virus they called human immunodeficiency virus (HIV).

The only no-risk behavior with respect to HIV transmission is abstinence from sexual activity and intravenous drug use.

allergy (1024)
asthma (1024)

Think Visually

Make a flowchart that shows what occurs during the specific immune response. (*Hint:* Refer to **Figure 35–11.**)

 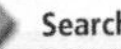  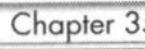   

BIOLOGY.com Search Chapter 35 GO • Crossword • Chapter Assessment

Study Online

REVIEW AND ASSESSMENT RESOURCES

Editable Worksheets Pages of Study Workbooks A and B, Lab Manuals A and B, and the Assessment Resources Book are available online. These documents can be easily edited using a word-processing program.

Lesson Overview Have students reread the Lesson Overviews to help them study chapter concepts.

Vocabulary Review The *Flash Cards* and *Crossword* provide an interactive way to review chapter vocabulary.

Chapter Assessment Have students take an online version of the Chapter 35 Assessment.

Standardized Test Prep Students can take an online version of the Standardized Test Prep. You will receive their scores along with ideas for remediation.

Diagnostic and Benchmark Tests Use these tests to monitor your students' progress and supply remediation.

UbD Performance Tasks

SUMMATIVE TASK Have students work in small groups to create a pamphlet aimed at middle school students that explains what infectious diseases are, describes how the body responds to infections, and recommends prevention measures, such as vaccinations and frequent hand washing. Tell students they should include both text and illustrations in their pamphlets.

TRANSFER TASK Have students work in small groups to write a play about the invasion of a pathogen into a body and the immune system's response to that invasion. The play could take the perspective of a neutral observer, the invading pathogens, or a cell involved in the body's defense. Tell groups the play should be creative but also identify the kind of pathogen, explain how the pathogens got into the body, and accurately describe the immune system's response. Have groups perform their plays for the class.

Answers

THINK VISUALLY

Students' flowcharts should begin with the first step *Virus invades body*. Flowcharts should then have separate tracks for humoral immunity and cell-mediated immunity. Each of the two tracks should include all of the steps shown in **Figure 35–11,** with an additional step—*Same virus invades body*—before the final step in each track.

Lesson 35.1

UNDERSTAND KEY CONCEPTS

1. a **2.** c

3. Infectious diseases are changes that disrupt normal body functions caused by microorganisms.

4. to identify the microorganism that causes a specific disease

5. Sample answer: virus, influenza; bacteria, anthrax; fungi, athlete's foot; single-celled eukaryotes, malaria; parasites, trichinosis

6. a disease that can be transmitted from animals to humans

7. Sample answer: thorough and frequent hand washing, avoiding contaminated water, avoiding improperly stored or cooked meats and seafood, not being bitten by an infected animal, not consuming the meat of an infected animal, avoiding close contact with an infected animal's wastes or fluids

THINK CRITICALLY

8. The fourth step is necessary because it shows that the pathogen causing the disease in the second host is the same pathogen that caused disease in the first host.

9. Sample answer: They are similar in that both require the human body to carry out their life cycles. They are different in that symbiotic organisms are generally harmless or may be beneficial to humans, while pathogens cause diseases.

Lesson 35.2

UNDERSTAND KEY CONCEPTS

10. d **11.** a

12. Antibodies are proteins produced by the immune system in response to antigens. Antibodies may be attached to particular immune cells or may be free-floating in plasma. The shape of each antibody allows it to attach to one specific antigen.

13. Helper T cells respond to signals from infected cells by activating B cells and cytotoxic T cells and by producing more helper T cells and memory T cells. Cytotoxic T cells hunt down infected body cells and kill them by puncturing their membranes or initiating apoptosis.

14. In humoral immunity antibodies defend against antigens in body fluids. Cell-mediated immunity involves T cells defending the body against pathogens inside body cells.

35 Assessment

The numbers following the questions refer to Indiana's Academic Standards for Biology I.

35.1 Infectious Diseases

Understand Key Concepts

1. Any change, other than an injury, that disrupts the normal functions of a person's body systems is a
a. disease.
b. pathogen.
c. toxin.
d. vector.

2. Disease-causing agents such as viruses, bacteria, and fungi are known as
a. antibodies.
b. antigens.
c. pathogens.
d. toxins.

3. What is the germ theory of disease?

4. What do researchers use Koch's postulates to determine?

5. List five types of agents that can produce infectious disease. Give an example of a disease that each specific pathogen may cause.

6. What is a zoonosis?

7. What are some ways by which the spread of disease can be prevented?

Think Critically

8. Infer Why is the fourth step of Koch's postulates necessary to prove that a disease is caused by a specific pathogen?

9. Compare and Contrast In what way are symbiotic organisms that live on or in the human body similar to pathogens that may take up residence? How are they different?

35.2 Defenses Against Infection

Understand Key Concepts

10. The body's most widespread nonspecific defense against pathogens is (are)
a. tears.
b. mucus.
c. saliva.
d. skin.

11. A nonspecific defense reaction to tissue damage caused by injury or infection is known as
a. the inflammatory response.
b. active immunity.
c. cell-mediated immunity.
d. passive immunity.

12. What are antibodies? Describe their form and function. B.1.2, B.5.5

13. Describe the roles of helper T cells and cytotoxic T cells. B.1.2

14. Distinguish between humoral immunity and cell-mediated immunity. B.1.2

Think Critically

15. Infer Many people become alarmed if they have a slight fever. Why might a slight fever that lasts no more than a few days be beneficial?

16. Compare and Contrast How does the secondary response to an antigen differ from the primary response to an antigen?

35.3 Fighting Infectious Disease

Understand Key Concepts

17. Injecting antibodies from an animal to help prevent a disease from occurring in a human is called NoS.11
a. active immunity.
b. passive immunity.
c. antibiotic therapy.
d. vaccination.

18. What is a common goal of researchers who develop antibiotics and antiviral drugs? NoS.11
a. to kill bacteria
b. to prevent infections
c. to stop pathogens without harming host cells
d. to kill viruses

19. Who discovered the first antibiotic and how did he discover it?

20. Explain two ways that public health has influenced the prevention of infectious disease. NoS.11

THINK CRITICALLY

15. A fever may slow down or stop the growth of some pathogens. Higher body temperature also speeds up parts of the immune response.

16. The secondary response to an antigen happens faster.

Lesson 35.3

UNDERSTAND KEY CONCEPTS

17. b **18.** c

19. Alexander Fleming; he noted that a mold seemed to produce a substance that inhibited bacterial growth. The substance eventually was mass-produced as penicillin.

20. promoting of childhood vaccination and providing clean drinking water

21. Describe how passive immunity to a disease is obtained and why it lasts for only a short period of time. B.1.2

22. What are two major contributing factors to emerging diseases?

Think Critically

23. **Form an Opinion** Edward Jenner developed his smallpox vaccine in 1796. Jenner tested his theory that infection with cowpox could prevent smallpox on a young boy. Do you think Jenner was justified in using the child as a test subject? Could this experiment be conducted today? Support your answer.

24. **Infer** It is not always easy to determine if a patient has a bacterial infection or a viral infection. How could this contribute to the misuse of medications? NoS.11

35.4 Immune System Disorders

Understand Key Concepts

25. A strong response by a person's immune system to a harmless antigen in the environment is called
   a. cell-mediated immunity.
   b. an allergy.
   c. inflammatory response.
   d. an autoimmune disease.

26. The main target cells of HIV are
   a. insulin-producing cells in the pancreas.
   b. T lymphocytes.
   c. B lymphocytes.
   d. cells in the liver.

27. Explain why allergies are not classified as autoimmune diseases.

28. Describe the specific action of HIV that makes an infected person unable to fight off other infections.

Think Critically

29. **Predict** Why is a second bee sting more dangerous than the first for a person who is allergic to bee stings?

30. **Infer** Reverse transcriptase is not a very accurate enzyme. How could this contribute to the rapid evolution of drug resistance in HIV?

solve the CHAPTER MYSTERY

LM 10×

THE SEARCH FOR A CAUSE

The disease of unknown cause was named Lyme disease, after the town of Lyme, Connecticut, where many of the patients lived. Steere's investigation was helped by a researcher who isolated a bacterium called *Borrelia burgdorferi* from deer ticks. The ticks had been captured in the area where patients lived. Steere found the same bacterium in the patients. Could this bacterium be the cause of Lyme disease?

For ethical reasons, Steere could not infect healthy people with the bacterium, but he did infect healthy laboratory mice. The mice developed arthritis and other symptoms that were similar to the Lyme disease patients' symptoms. Steere recovered bacteria from sick mice and injected them into healthy mice, which then also developed the disease.

Now researchers know that a bite from a deer tick carrying *B. burgdorferi* may transmit the bacterium. *B. burgdorferi* can "swim" through tissues around tick bites, causing the spreading rash that some patients reported. The bacterium then seems to infect many types of cells, including macrophages, nerve cells, and muscle cells. Some *B. burgdorferi* proteins resemble proteins in the myelin sheaths around some nerve cells. This may cause an autoimmune response that leads to arthritis and other problems that persist after the infection is gone.

1. **Explain** What set of rules did Steere use to determine if *B. burgdorferi* was the pathogen responsible for Lyme disease?

2. **Infer** Lyme disease patients who are quickly treated with antibiotics usually do much better than those who are treated later. Why do you think this is the case?

3. **Connect to the**  Deer and deer ticks thrive in wooded areas that grow back after the areas have been cleared and at the edges of woodlands. How might suburban development contribute to an increase in Lyme disease? IN NoS.11

21. Passive immunity is obtained when externally produced antibodies are introduced into a person's blood. It lasts for only a short time period because the immune system eventually destroys the introduced antibodies.

22. changing interactions with animals and misuse of medications

THINK CRITICALLY

23. Students should state their opinion and provide logical support for it. Sample answer: He was not justified. The boy could have died if Jenner's theory was incorrect. Humans should not be used as test subjects when there is a great possibility they could be harmed.

24. Sample answer: If a doctor cannot determine if a disease is caused by a virus or a bacterium, the doctor might prescribe an antibiotic just in case. If the disease is a viral infection, this is a mistake.

After students have read through the Chapter Mystery, discuss both Allen Steere's method of investigation and his conclusions about Lyme disease. Begin by reviewing Koch's postulates and asking students whether Steere conformed to those rules in searching for a cause of the symptoms.

Ask Did Steere follow Koch's postulates in his investigation? *(Sample answer: He followed rule 1 by finding the pathogens in both ticks and sick people. He probably followed rule 2, since he had bacteria to inject into mice. He didn't strictly follow rule 3, because he couldn't inject bacteria into healthy people. But with mice, he followed rules 3 and 4.)*

Discuss whether students think injecting healthy mice is ethical. *(Opinions may vary.)* Then, turn students' attention to Steere's findings and further understandings about the cause of Lyme disease.

Ask What is the pathogen that causes Lyme disease? *(*Borrelia burgdorferi*)*

Ask What do the bacteria do to cause an autoimmune response? *(The bacteria infect nerve cells, and some bacterial proteins resemble proteins in the myelin sheaths around some nerve cells. This causes the autoimmune response.)*

CHAPTER MYSTERY ANSWERS

1. Sample answer: He mostly followed Koch's postulates. He found the pathogen in people who were sick, and he probably cultured that pathogen. He could not, for ethical reasons, inject *B. burgdorferi* into healthy people. Instead, he injected the bacteria into healthy mice and observed the mice getting sick. He recovered bacteria from the sick mice and injected the bacteria into healthy mice, which then also developed the disease.

2. Sample answer: If not treated quickly with antibiotics, the bacteria infect more nerve cells, which causes an autoimmune response that leads to arthritis and other problems that persist after the infection is gone.

3. Sample answer: Suburban development sometimes occurs at the edges of woodlands. Also, suburban development often involves clearing land for building houses. After the building is complete, small wooded areas re-emerge. Both environments—the edges of woodlands and woodland regrowth—are where deer and deer ticks thrive.

Join the crew of Untamed Science as they investigate human allergies in **A Reason for Sneezin'.**

Lesson 35.4

UNDERSTAND KEY CONCEPTS

25. b **26.** b

27. In an autoimmune disease, the immune system attacks the body's own cells. In an allergy, the immune system overreacts to harmless antigens.

28. HIV attacks key cells of the immune system, leaving the body with inadequate protection against other pathogens.

THINK CRITICALLY

29. Sample answer: The second bee sting may produce an even greater overreaction than the first bee sting.

30. Sample answer: Because reverse transcriptase is not a very accurate enzyme, and its job is to copy the virus's genetic material, HIV has a high mutation rate. Thus, HIV also develops resistance to drugs at a high rate.

Connecting Concepts

USE SCIENCE GRAPHICS

31. The pump marked by the red *X* on Broad Street; compared to other pumps in the area, it was surrounded by the highest concentration of cholera victims.

32. Sample answer: Such a map could be used if, for example, the source of the food poisoning were produce from a grocery store in a neighborhood where many people became sick with food poisoning.

WRITE ABOUT SCIENCE

33. Letters will vary. Students should explain that taking antibiotics when they are not necessary contributes to the spread of antibiotic resistance. Resistant bacteria could then be transmitted to other people, and antibiotics would not be able to kill the pathogens and stop the disease.

34. Big idea Sample answer: The germ theory of disease led people to understand that hand washing and covering mouths and noses when sneezing or coughing could prevent the spread of microorganisms, which cause disease.

Connecting Concepts

Use Science Graphics NoS.3

John Snow made a map similar to the one below to help him determine the source of the cholera outbreak in London. The dots represent the locations of people who died of cholera. The Xs represent pumps. Use the map to answer questions 31 and 32.

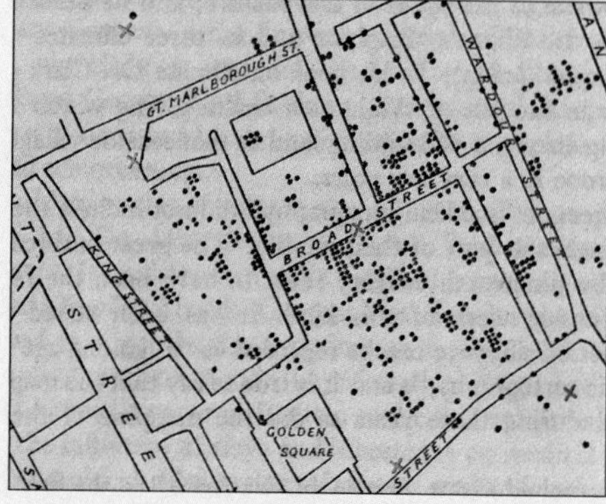

31. Infer Which pump do you think Snow determined was most likely the source of the cholera outbreak? Explain.

32. Apply Concepts Do you think a map such as this one could be used to discover the source of a food poisoning outbreak? Explain.

Write About Science NoS.3

33. Explanation The ability of bacteria to resist antibiotics has become an increasing public health problem. This problem is due to the overuse and misuse of antibiotics. Suppose that one of your friends always takes antibiotics when he or she is sick. Write a letter to your friend explaining the problem of antibiotic resistance. NoS.11

34. Assess the Big idea Explain how the germ theory of disease led people to develop very simple methods that could prevent the transmission of many diseases. NoS.11

Analyzing Data

IN NoS.3

The graph shows the number of cases of the viral disease, polio, in the world from 1980 until 2004. It also shows the percentage of the world's population that was vaccinated for the disease.

Polio Cases and Percent Vaccinated

Total Number of Polio Cases: 0, 10,000, 20,000, 30,000, 40,000, 50,000, 60,000
Percentage of Population Vaccinated: 0, 10, 20, 30, 40, 50, 60, 70, 80, 90
Year: 1980 1984 1988 1992 1996 2000 2004
— Number of cases worldwide
— % of population vaccinated

35. Interpret Graphs During which of the following time periods was there the greatest drop in the number of polio cases around the world?

a. between 1980 and 1982
b. between 1984 and 1988
c. between 1988 and 1996
d. between 1996 and 2004

36. Draw Conclusions Which of the following is the most reasonable conclusion to draw from the data shown in the graph?

a. As the number of people vaccinated increases, the number of polio cases stays constant.
b. As the number of people vaccinated increases, the number of polio cases has increased.
c. As the number of people vaccinated increases, the number of polio cases has decreased.
d. Polio has been eliminated as a disease, and vaccination is no longer necessary.

Analyzing Data

PURPOSE Students will analyze data to understand the relationship between vaccination and disease incidence.

PLANNING Review with students how vaccinations produce immunity against diseases.

ANSWERS

35. c

36. c

Standardized Test Practice for Indiana

Multiple Choice

1. All of the following prevent pathogens from entering the human body EXCEPT
   A red blood cells.
   B tears.
   C mucus.
   D skin.

2. Which of the following is NOT part of the inflammatory response?
   A White blood cells rush to infected tissues.
   B Blood vessels near the wound shrink.
   C Phagocytes engulf and destroy pathogens.
   D The wound becomes red.

3. What is the role of a vector in the spread of disease?
   A A vector is an inanimate object, such as a doorknob, where pathogens may collect.
   B A vector must infect a host for its life cycle to continue.
   C Vectors usually do not suffer from the infection, they just spread it from host to host.
   D A vector is a pathogen.

4. Which type of lymphocyte produces antibodies that are released into the bloodstream?
   A cytotoxic T cells
   B helper T cells
   C phagocytes
   D plasma cells

5. Which of the following is NOT a white blood cell?
   A interferon
   B macrophage
   C cytotoxic T cell
   D lymphocyte

6. Which is an example of naturally occurring passive immunity?
   A vaccination
   B exposure to a disease
   C an infant consuming antibodies in breast milk
   D antibodies are injected from another person

7. How do medications help a person with asthma?
   A Antihistamines counteract the effects of histamines.
   B They suppress the immune system.
   C They increase mucus production in the lungs.
   D They relax smooth muscles around airways.

Questions 8–9

A researcher measured the concentrations of HIV and T cells in 120 HIV-infected patients over a period of 10 years. Her data are summarized in the graph.

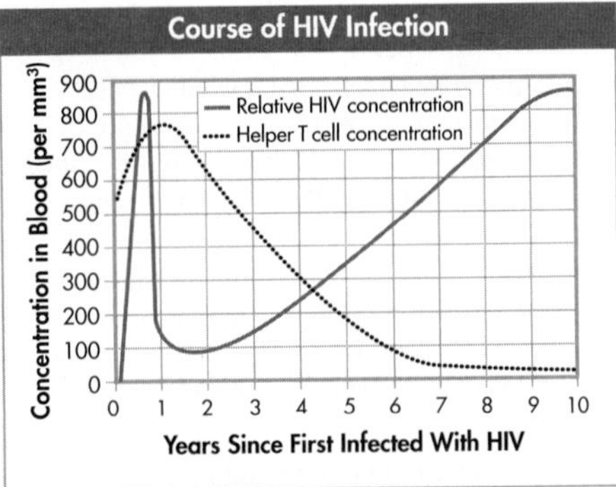

8. What happened to the HIV concentration over years 2 through 9?
   A It stayed about the same, then suddenly increased.
   B It stayed about the same, then suddenly decreased.
   C It steadily increased.
   D It steadily decreased. NoS.3

9. What is probably responsible for the change in HIV concentration during the first year?
   A immune response
   B inflammatory response
   C passive immunity
   D HIV stopped replicating NoS.3

Open-Ended Response

10. Explain why some symptoms of disease such as coughing and sneezing are advantageous to the pathogen that causes the disease.

If You Have Trouble With . . .

Question	1	2	3	4	5	6	7	8	9	10
See Lesson	35.2	35.2	35.1	35.2	35.2	35.3	35.4	35.4	35.4	35.1

ASSESSMENT

Answers

1. A
2. B
3. C
4. D
5. A
6. C
7. D
8. C
9. A
10. Sample answer: Some symptoms of disease such as coughing and sneezing are advantageous to the pathogen that causes the disease because coughing and sneezing promote further spreading of the pathogen to new hosts. These symptoms release thousands of tiny pathogen-containing droplets that can be inhaled by other people or settle on objects.

Test-Taking Tip

READ ALL THE ANSWER CHOICES

Remind students that when evaluating multiple-choice answers, they should be sure to read all the answer choices, even if the first answer choice seems to be the correct one. By reading all the choices, students can make sure the answer chosen is the best answer to the question.

UNIT 8

Plan Ahead

Have students read through the description of the Unit 8 Project a few days before they create their travel brochures to give them time to consider the task. Suggest they think about interesting ways they could describe and illustrate structures, organs, and organ systems inside the human body. Provide students with examples of travel brochures to stimulate their thinking and provide ideas.

Materials colored pens or pencils, paper

Monitor the Project

Suggest students start by making a basic outline of what they plan to include in their brochure. Tell them a good way to proceed is by making a page-by-page mockup that shows where headings, illustrations, and descriptions will be placed within the brochure. As students work, circulate through the classroom, asking questions that might help them in designing a good brochure.

Ask What attraction are you including for the muscular system? the excretory system?

Ask What dangers might tourists encounter as they travel through the body?

Project Assessment

Make sure students use the rubric and reflection questions to assess their work. Then, use the rubric to assign a final score. Note that it is important to value the creativity of students' work as well as the content when you score their projects. If desired, talk with students about any differences between their self-assessment scores and your assigned score.

UNIT 8 The Human Body

Unit Project

A Tour Through the Human Body

Have you ever imagined what it would be like to shrink down to microscopic size and tour the inside of the human body? What interesting things would you see and hear? What "dangers" might you encounter?

Your Task Create a travel brochure in which you persuade a person to "visit" the human body. Discuss the various "attractions" inside the body to show how well you understand the systems.

Be sure to
- include at least one attraction for each organ system covered in this unit.
- design the brochure so that it is clear and easy to follow.
- be creative!

Reflection Questions

1. **Score your brochure using the rubric below. What score did you give yourself?**
2. **What did you do well in this project?**
3. **What needs improvement?**
4. **What "attractions" would you choose to visit? Why?**
5. **Exchange travel brochures with a partner. What attractions did he/she include?**

Assessment Rubric

Score	Scientific Content	Quality of Brochure
4	Brochure reveals an exceptionally thorough understanding of the human organ systems.	Brochure is clear, informative, and creative.
3	Brochure reveals a solid understanding of the human organ systems.	Brochure effectively conveys information about various attractions.
2	Brochure reveals a limited understanding of the human organ systems.	Brochure could be more clear and creative. It needs some editing.
1	Brochure reveals significant misunderstandings about the human organ systems.	Brochure is unclear and needs significant editing.

21st Century Skills

To be successful in the 21st century, students need skills and learning experiences that extend beyond subject area mastery. The Unit 8 Project helps students build the following 21st Century Skills: *Communication Skills; Creativity and Intellectual Curiosity; Interpersonal and Collaborative Skills; Self-Direction;* and *Accountability and Adaptability.*

FOCUS ON SOCIAL RESPONSIBILITY Extend this Unit Project by having small groups of students use their brochures to write a play about teens who take a tour through the human body. In the play, these young tourists should encounter thrills and attractions, but also problems in the various systems caused by smoking, drinking alcohol, using illegal drugs, and eating an unhealthful diet.

For more practice building 21st Century Skills, see The Chapter Mystery pages in **Study Workbook A.**

A Visual Guide to The Diversity of Life

▲ The Chambered Nautilus, found today in the Pacific Ocean, is one of the few living representatives of a group that once flourished in ancient seas 265 million years before the dinosaurs evolved. This Visual Guide will give you a glimpse of life's great variety and evolutionary history.

A Visual Guide to
The Diversity of Life

CONTENTS

How to Use This Guide **DOL•3**
The Tree of Life **DOL•4**
Bacteria **DOL•6**
- Proteobacteria DOL•7
- Spirochaetes DOL•7
- Actinobacteria DOL•7
- Cyanobacteria DOL•7

Archaea **DOL•8**
- Crenarchaeotes DOL•9
- Euryarchaeotes DOL•9
- Korarchaeotes DOL•9
- Nanoarchaeotes DOL•9

Protists **DOL•10**
- Excavates DOL•11
- Chromalveolates DOL•12
- Cercozoa, Foraminiferans, and Radiolarians DOL•14
- Rhodophytes DOL•15
- Amoebozoa DOL•15
- Choanozoa DOL•15

Fungi **DOL•16**
- Basidiomycetes DOL•17
- Ascomycetes DOL•18
- Zygomycetes DOL•19
- Chytrids DOL•19

Plants **DOL•20**
- Green Algae DOL•21
- Bryophytes DOL•22
- Seedless Vascular Plants DOL•23
- Gymnosperms DOL•24
- Angiosperms DOL•26

Animals **DOL•30**
- Porifera (Sponges) DOL•31
- Cnidarians DOL•32
- Arthropods DOL•34
- Nematodes (Roundworms) DOL•38
- Platyhelminthes (Flatworms) DOL•39
- Annelids (Segmented Worms) DOL•40
- Mollusks DOL•42
- Echinoderms DOL•44
- Nonvertebrate Chordates DOL•46
- Fishes DOL•48
- Amphibians DOL•52
- Reptiles DOL•54
- Birds DOL•56
- Mammals DOL•60

HOW TO USE THIS GUIDE

Use this visual reference tool to explore the classification and characteristics of organisms, including their habitats, ecology, behavior, and other important facts. This guide reflects the latest understandings about phylogenetic relationships within the three domains of life. Divided into six color-coded sections, the Visual Guide begins with a brief survey through the Bacteria and Archaea domains. It next discusses the major groups of protists, fungi, and plants. The final section provides information on nine animal phyla.

❶ See how the group of organisms relates to others on the tree of life.

❷ Learn about the general characteristics that all members of the group share.

❸ Discover the members of the group and learn about their traits.

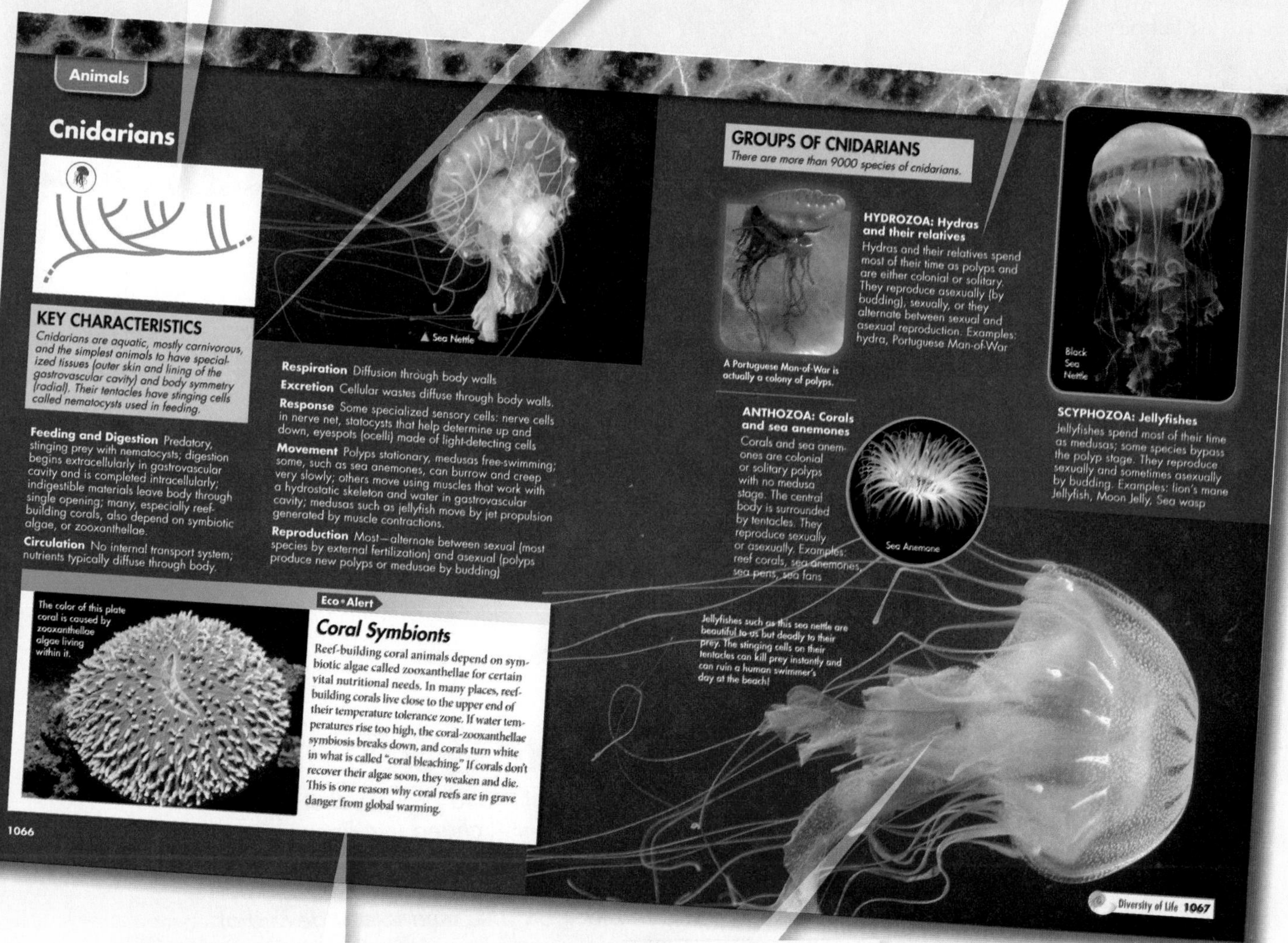

Animals

Cnidarians

KEY CHARACTERISTICS

Cnidarians are aquatic, mostly carnivorous, and the simplest animals to have specialized tissues (outer skin and lining of the gastrovascular cavity) and body symmetry (radial). Their tentacles have stinging cells called nematocysts used in feeding.

Feeding and Digestion Predatory, stinging prey with nematocysts; digestion begins extracellularly in gastrovascular cavity and is completed intracellularly; indigestible materials leave body through single opening; many, especially reef-building corals, also depend on symbiotic algae, or zooxanthellae.

Circulation No internal transport system; nutrients typically diffuse through body.

▲ Sea Nettle

Respiration Diffusion through body walls

Excretion Cellular wastes diffuse through body walls.

Response Some specialized sensory cells: nerve cells in nerve net, statocysts that help determine up and down, eyespots (ocelli) made of light-detecting cells

Movement Polyps stationary, medusas free-swimming; some, such as sea anemones, can burrow and creep very slowly; others move using muscles that work with a hydrostatic skeleton and water in gastrovascular cavity; medusas such as jellyfish move by jet propulsion generated by muscle contractions.

Reproduction Most—alternate between sexual (most species by external fertilization) and asexual (polyps produce new polyps or medusae by budding)

Eco • Alert

Coral Symbionts

The color of this plate coral is caused by zooxanthellae algae living within it.

Reef-building coral animals depend on symbiotic algae called zooxanthellae for certain vital nutritional needs. In many places, reef-building corals live close to the upper end of their temperature tolerance zone. If water temperatures rise too high, the coral-zooxanthellae symbiosis breaks down, and corals turn white in what is called "coral bleaching." If corals don't recover their algae soon, they weaken and die. This is one reason why coral reefs are in grave danger from global warming.

1066

GROUPS OF CNIDARIANS

There are more than 9000 species of cnidarians.

HYDROZOA: Hydras and their relatives
Hydras and their relatives spend most of their time as polyps and are either colonial or solitary. They reproduce asexually (by budding), sexually, or they alternate between sexual and asexual reproduction. Examples: hydra, Portuguese Man-of-War

A Portuguese Man-of-War is actually a colony of polyps.

ANTHOZOA: Corals and sea anemones
Corals and sea anemones are colonial or solitary polyps with no medusa stage. The central body is surrounded by tentacles. They reproduce sexually or asexually. Examples: reef corals, sea anemones, sea pens, sea fans

Sea Anemone

Black Sea Nettle

SCYPHOZOA: Jellyfishes
Jellyfishes spend most of their time as medusas; some species bypass the polyp stage. They reproduce sexually and sometimes asexually by budding. Examples: lion's mane Jellyfish, Moon Jelly, Sea wasp

Jellyfishes such as this sea nettle are beautiful to us but deadly to their prey. The stinging cells on their tentacles can kill prey instantly and can ruin a human swimmer's day at the beach!

Diversity of Life 1067

❹ Investigate current news and interesting facts about the group.

❺ See photographs of representative animals within each group.

THE TREE OF LIFE

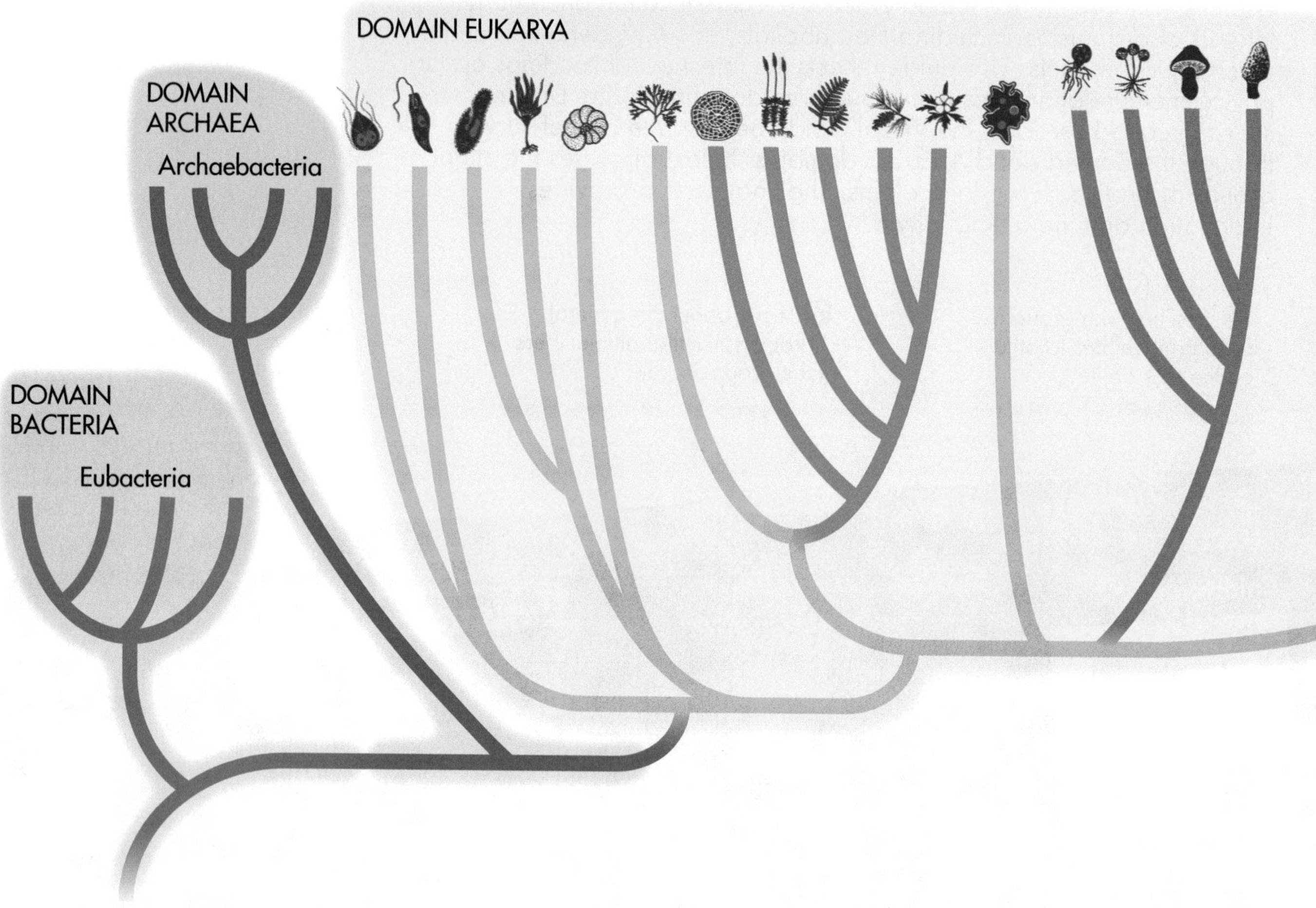

Before you begin your tour through the kingdoms of life, review this big picture from Chapter 18. The pages that follow will give you a glimpse of the incredible diversity found within each of the "branches" shown here.

DOMAIN BACTERIA

Members of the domain Bacteria are unicellular and prokaryotic. The bacteria are ecologically diverse, ranging from free-living soil organisms to deadly parasites. This domain corresponds to the kingdom Eubacteria.

DOMAIN ARCHAEA

Also unicellular and prokaryotic, members of the domain Archaea live in some of the most extreme environments you can imagine, including volcanic hot springs, brine pools, and black organic mud totally devoid of oxygen. The domain Archaea corresponds to the kingdom Archaebacteria.

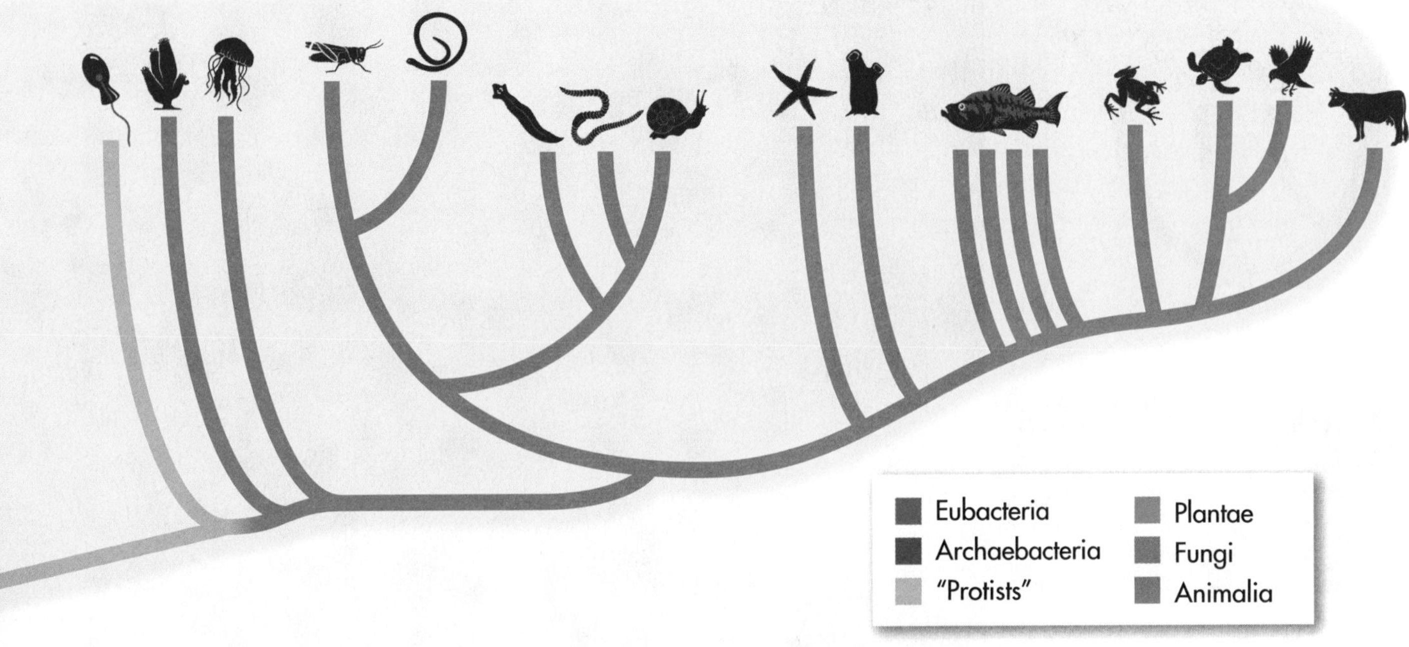

DOMAIN EUKARYA

The domain Eukarya consists of all organisms that have cells with nuclei. It is organized into the four remaining kingdoms of the six-kingdom system: Protista, Fungi, Plantae, and Animalia.

THE "PROTISTS"

Notice that the branches for the kingdom Protista are not together in one area, as is the case with the other kingdoms. In fact, recent molecular studies and cladistic analyses have shown that "eukaryotes formerly known as Protista" do not form a single clade. Current cladistic analysis divides these organisms into at least six clades. They cannot, therefore, be properly placed into a single taxon.

FUNGI

Members of the kingdom Fungi are heterotrophs. Most feed on dead or decaying organic matter. The most recognizable fungi, including mushrooms, are multicellular. Some fungi, such as yeasts, are unicellular.

PLANTS

Members of the kingdom Plantae are autotrophs that carry out photosynthesis. Plants have cell walls that contain cellulose. Plants are nonmotile—they cannot move from place to place.

ANIMALS

Members of the kingdom Animalia are multicellular and heterotrophic. Animal cells do not have cell walls. Most animals can move about, at least for some part of their life cycle.

Bacteria

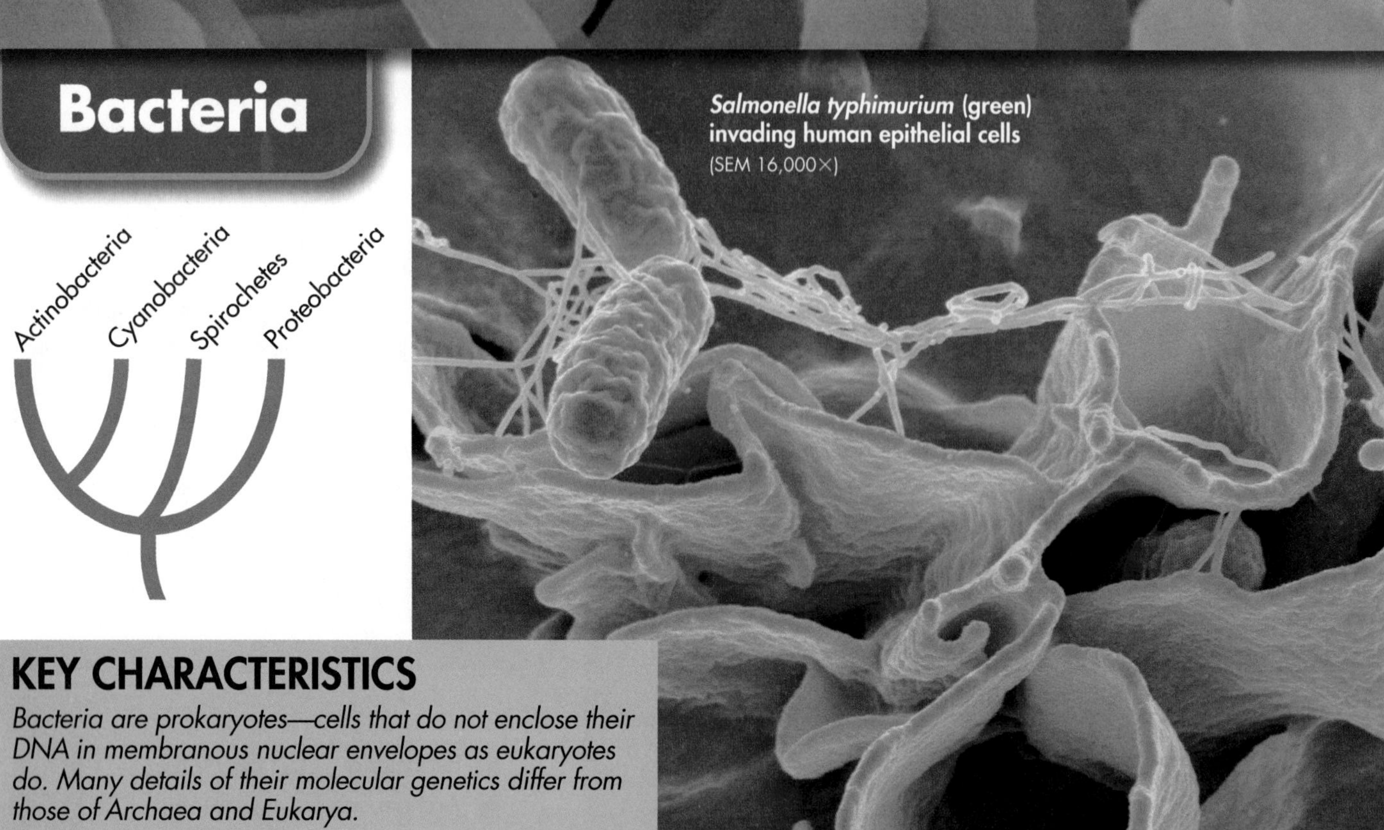

Salmonella typhimurium (green) invading human epithelial cells (SEM 16,000×)

KEY CHARACTERISTICS

Bacteria are prokaryotes—cells that do not enclose their DNA in membranous nuclear envelopes as eukaryotes do. Many details of their molecular genetics differ from those of Archaea and Eukarya.

Cell Structure Variety of cell shapes, including spherical, rodlike, and spiral; most have cell walls containing peptidoglycan. Few if any have internal organelles. Some have external flagella for cell movement.

Genetic Organization All essential genes are in one large DNA double helix that has its ends joined to form a closed loop. Smaller loops of DNA (plasmids) may carry nonessential genes. Simultaneous transcription and translation; introns generally not present; histone proteins absent

Reproduction By binary fission; no true sexual reproduction; some achieve recombination by conjugation.

•Did You Know?

A World of Bacteria

Putting Bacteria in Proper Perspective

"Planet of the Bacteria" was the title of an essay by the late Stephen Jay Gould. He pointed out that the dominant life forms on planet Earth aren't humans, or animals, or plants. They are bacteria. They were here first, and they inhabit more places on the planet than any other form of life. In fact, bacteria make up roughly 10 percent of our own dry body weight! In terms of biomass and importance to the planet, bacteria truly do rule this planet. They, not we, are number one.

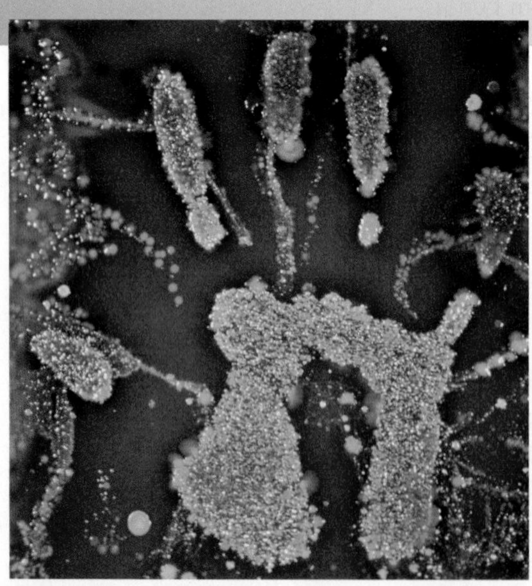

◀ *The bacterial colonies shown here are growing in the print of a human hand on agar gel.*

GROUPS OF BACTERIA

There is no generally agreed phylogeny for the bacteria. Included here are some of the major groups within the domain.

PROTEOBACTERIA

This large and diverse clade of bacteria includes *Escherichia* (*E. coli*), *Salmonella*, *Helicobacter*, and the nitrogen-fixing soil bacterium *Rhizobium*.

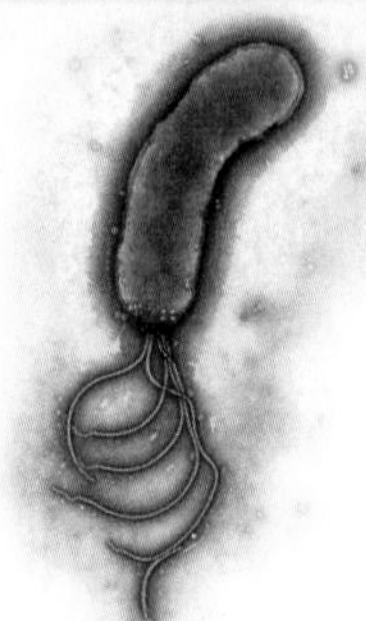

◀ *Helicobacter pylori is rod-shaped and has several flagella used for movement. This bacterium infects the stomach lining and causes ulcers in some people.* (TEM 7100×)

The spiral-shaped bacterium that causes syphilis is Treponema pallidum. (SEM 10,000×) ▼

SPIROCHAETES

The spirochaetes (SPY roh keets) are named for their distinctive spiral shape. They move in a corkscrew-like fashion, twisting along as they are propelled by flagella on both ends of the cell. Most are free-living, but a few cause serious diseases, including syphilis, Lyme disease, and leptospirosis.

ACTINOBACTERIA

A large number of soil bacteria belong to this group. Some form long filaments. Members include the *Streptomyces* and *Actinomyces*, which are natural producers of many antibiotics, including streptomycin. A related group is the *Firmicutes*. The *Firmicutes* include *Bacillus anthracis* (anthrax), *Clostridia* (tetanus and botulism), and *Bacillus thuringensis*, which produces a powerful insecticide used for genetic engineering in plants.

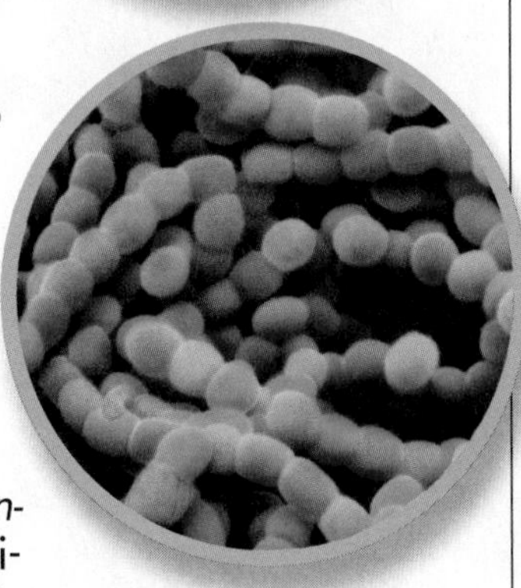

▲ *Chains of spores of soil bacteria, genus Streptomyces* (SEM 3400×)

CYANOBACTERIA

The cyanobacteria are photosynthetic prokaryotes that were once called "blue-green algae." They are among the oldest organisms on Earth, having been identified in rocks dating to more than 3 billion years ago. They are found in salt water and fresh water, in the soil, and even on the surfaces of damp rocks. They are the only organisms on Earth that are able to fix carbon and nitrogen under aerobic conditions, and this enables them to play critical roles in the global ecosystem, where they serve as key sources of carbon and nitrogen.

▼ *Many cyanobacteria form long filaments of attached cells, like those shown here (genus Lyngbya,* SEM 540×).

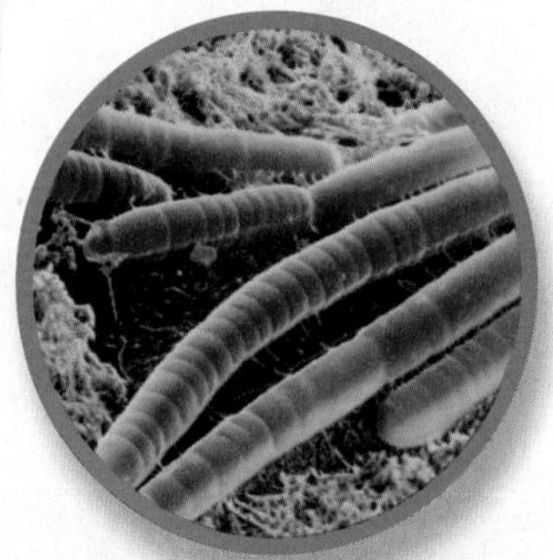

• A Closer Look

The Gram Stain

A Microbiologist's Quick Diagnostic

Gram-positive bacteria appear purple after staining, while gram-negative bacteria appear pink. (LM 1000×) ▶

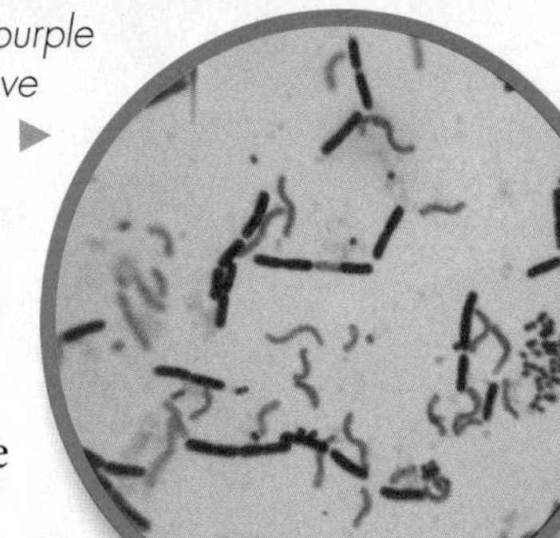

The Gram stain, developed by the nineteenth-century Danish physician Hans Christian Gram, allows microbiologists to categorize bacteria quickly into one of two groups based on their cell wall composition. Gram-positive bacteria lack a membrane outside the cell wall and take up the stain easily. Gram-negative bacteria, on the other hand, have an outer membrane of lipids and carbohydrates that prevents them from absorbing the gram stain. Many gram-negative bacteria are found among the proteobacteria. On the other hand, actinobacteria are mostly gram-positive.

Archaea

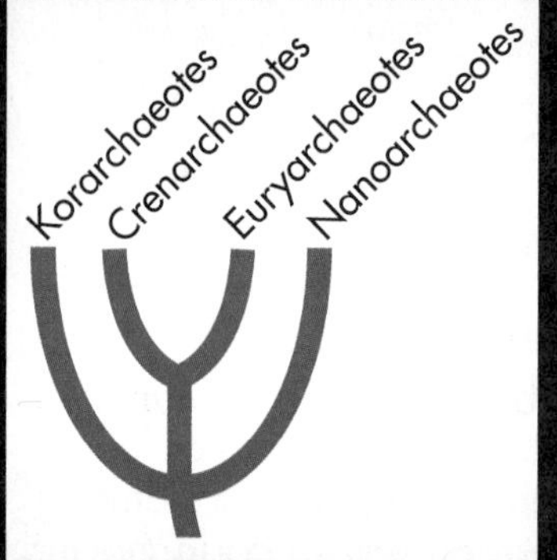

KEY CHARACTERISTICS

Archaea are prokaryotes that differ from bacteria in so many details of structure and metabolism that they are viewed as a different domain than bacteria. Genetically, they have more in common with eukaryotes than with bacteria. Their cell walls do not contain peptidoglycan.

Cell Structure Cells similar to those of bacteria in appearance; many have flagella that are different in structure and biochemical composition from bacterial flagella. Cell membrane lipids also different from those of bacteria; few internal organelles

Genetic Organization As in bacteria, all essential genes are in one large DNA double helix that has its ends joined to form a closed loop. Proteins responsible for transcription and translation are similar to those of eukaryotes. Also like eukaryotes, most species contain introns, and all species contain DNA-binding histone proteins.

Reproduction By binary fission; no true sexual reproduction, but some achieve recombination by conjugation.

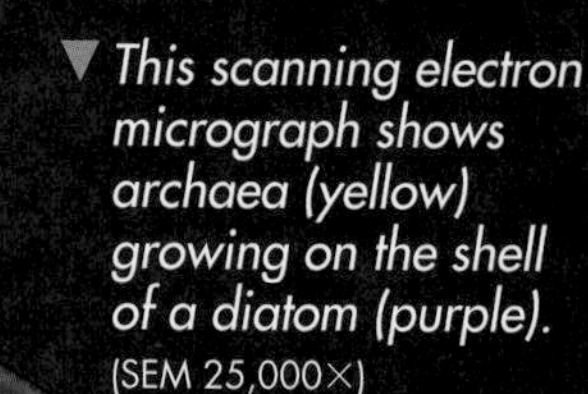

▼ *This scanning electron micrograph shows archaea (yellow) growing on the shell of a diatom (purple).* (SEM 25,000×)

▲ *The volcano Solfatara, near Naples, Italy, is home to many archaea in the genus* Sulfolobus.

• Did You Know?

Hot Enough for You?

The Original Extremists

Way before extreme sports and extreme reality TV shows came the archaea—the original and ultimate extremists. When archaea were first discovered, biologists called them *extremophiles,* a term that literally means "lovers of the extreme." For many archaea, the name still fits. In fact, they have proven especially difficult to grow in the lab, since they require such extreme temperatures and dangerous chemical conditions to thrive. One species will grow only in sulfuric acid! Archaea found in deep-sea ocean vents thrive in temperatures exceeding 100° Celsius, while others enjoy life in the frigid waters of the Arctic.

GROUPS OF ARCHAEA

To date, four major clades of archaea have been identified. Biologists continue to debate how these clades are related to one another.

CRENARCHAEOTES

The crenarchaeotes (kren AHR kee ohts) include organisms that live in the hottest and most acidic environments known. Most of the known species have been isolated from thermal vents and hot springs—the prefix *cren-* means "spring." Some species grow using organic compounds as energy sources, but others fix carbon from carbon dioxide, using hydrogen or sulfur to provide chemical energy.

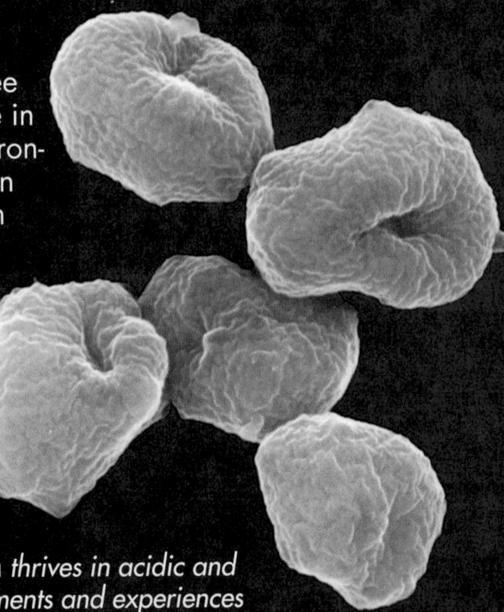

▶ Sulfolobus archaea *thrives in acidic and sulfur-rich environments and experiences optimal growth at 80° Celsius.* (SEM 33,200×)

KORARCHAEOTES

Scientists recently discovered the korarchaeote (kawr AHR kee oht) lineage in Obsidian Pool, Yellowstone National Park, and have since discovered more species in Iceland. Their DNA sequences place them apart from other archaea. The korarchaeotes may in fact be one of the least-evolved lineages of modern life that has been detected in nature so far.

▲ *Korarchaeotes from Obsidian Pool are shown in a lab culture with other microbes from their community.* (SEM 6000×)

NANOARCHAEOTES

Only a single species of this group has been discovered, in 2002, attached to a much larger crenarchaeote! Nanoarchaeotes (na noh AHR kee ohts) grow in hot vents near the coastal regions of the ocean and show definite molecular differences from other archaea. More research is needed to characterize this group, but what is known is that they have the smallest known genome of any organism.

▼ *The newly discovered* Nanoarchaeum equitans *(smaller cells) is shown attached to its host, genus* Ignicoccus *(larger cells).* (LM 2000×)

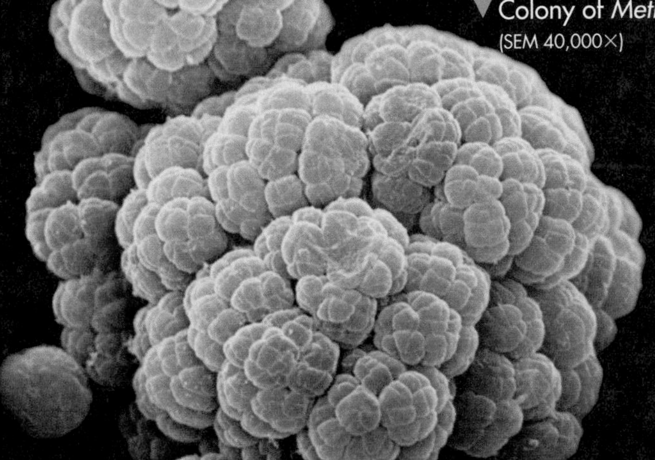

▼ Colony of *Methanosarcina mazei* (SEM 40,000×)

EURYARCHAEOTES

The euryarchaeotes (yoor ee AHR kee ohts) are a very diverse group of archaea, living in a broad range of habitats. The prefix *eury-* comes from a Greek word meaning "broad." The methanogens are a major group of euryarchaeotes that play essential roles in the environment. They help to break down organic compounds in oxygen-poor environments, releasing methane gas in the process. Another group, the *Halobacteria*, are found in salt ponds, where the concentration of sodium chloride approaches saturation.

Protists

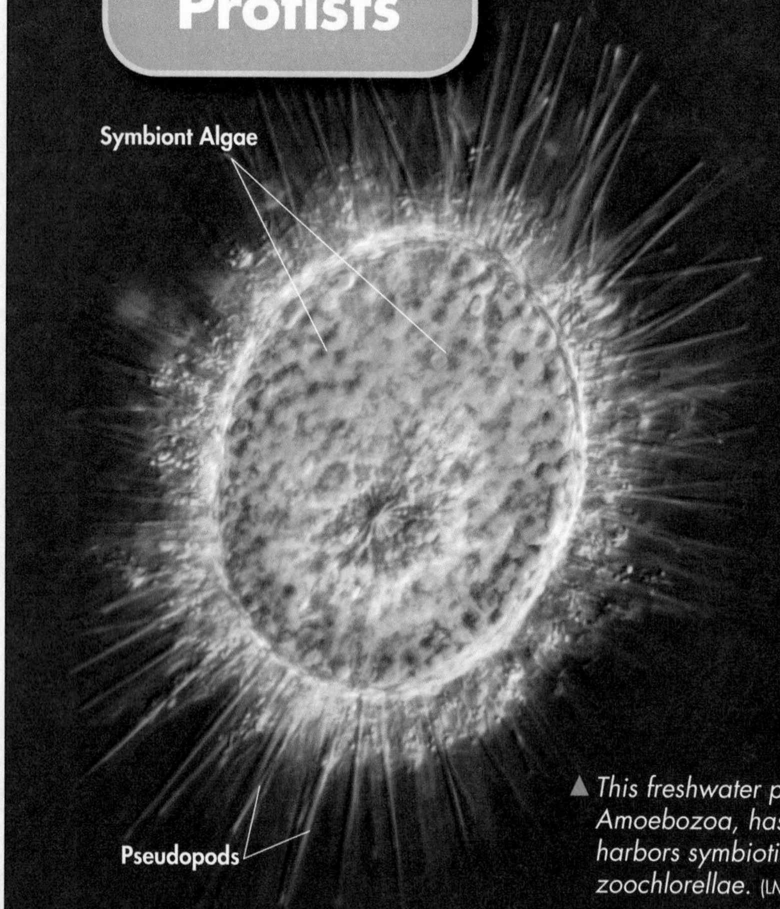

Symbiont Algae

Pseudopods

KEY CHARACTERISTICS

A protist is a eukaryote, generally single-celled, that does not fit into any of the other major taxonomic groups. The protists do not make up a true kingdom.

Organization Great diversity of cell organelles and organization: some have cell walls, some have chloroplasts, most have mitochondria or organelles related to mitochondria; those that are multicellular have relatively little differentiation into tissues.

Movement Some move by cilia or flagella.

Reproduction Most reproduce by cell division; many have sexual phases to their life cycle; some exchange genetic material by conjugation.

▲ *This freshwater protist, a heliozoan in the clade Amoebozoa, has numerous thin pseudopods. It harbors symbiotic, photosynthetic algae called zoochlorellae.* (LM 730×)

•Did You Know?

The Kingdom That Isn't

The Challenges of Classifying Protists

Biologists traditionally classified protists by splitting them into funguslike, plantlike, and animal-like groups. This seemed to work for a while, but when they studied protists more carefully with new research tools, including genome-level molecular analysis, this traditional system simply fell apart.

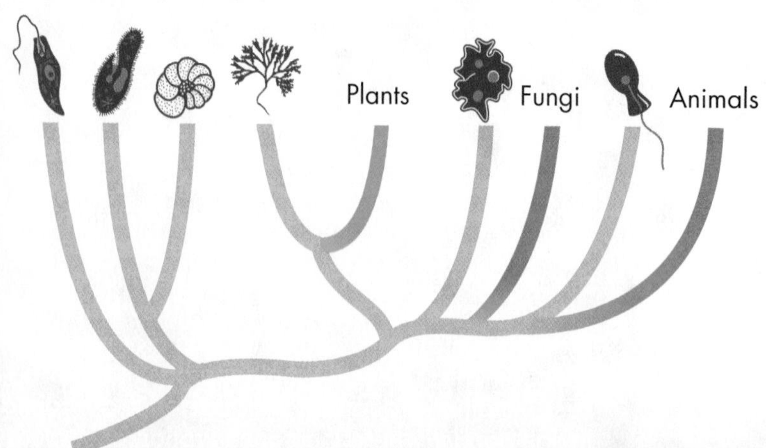

Biologists now think that protists shouldn't be classified as a kingdom at all. In fact, when scientists look for the deepest and most fundamental divisions among eukaryotes, they find that all of those divisions are within the protists themselves, not between protists and other eukaryotes. Starting over, biologists could simply use those divisions to define newer, more accurate "kingdoms," but that might cause new problems. For one thing, it would lump two of the traditional kingdoms (animals and fungi) together, and it would leave a handful of kingdoms that contain only unicellular organisms. There is no perfect solution to this problem. Here, "protists" are considered a kingdom for the sake of convenience, but keep in mind that their differences are really too great for any single kingdom to contain.

Excavates

KEY CHARACTERISTICS

Excavates (EKS kuh vayts) have a characteristic feeding groove, usually supported by microtubules. Most have flagella. A few lack mitochondria and are unable to carry out oxidative phosphorylation, although they do possess remnants of the organelle.

GROUPS OF EXCAVATES

The excavates include a wide diversity of protists, from free-living photosynthesizers to some of humankind's most notorious pathogens.

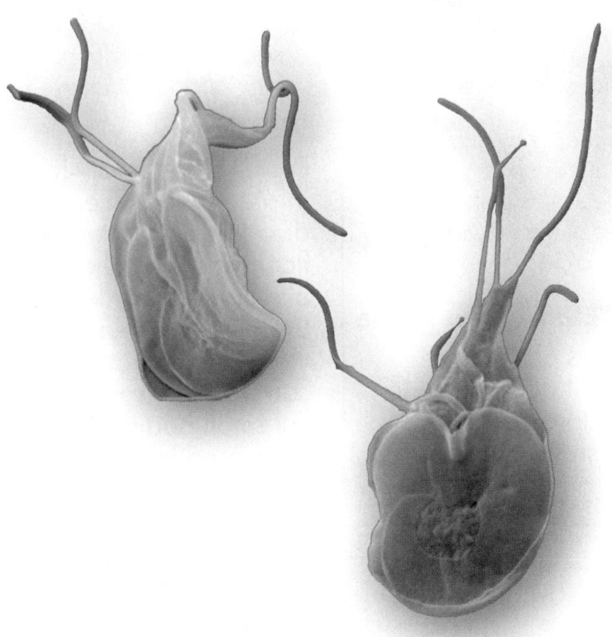

▲ *The diplomonad* Giardia *is a dangerous intestinal parasite that frequently contaminates freshwater streams.* Giardia *infections are common in wildlife and pet dogs and cats.* (SEM 1800×)

DIPLOMONADS

These organisms get their name from the fact that they possess two distinct and different nuclei (from Greek, diplo = double). The double nuclei probably derived from an ancient symbiotic event in which one species was engulfed by another. Cells contain multiple flagella, usually arranged around the body of the cell. Most species of diplomonads are parasitic.

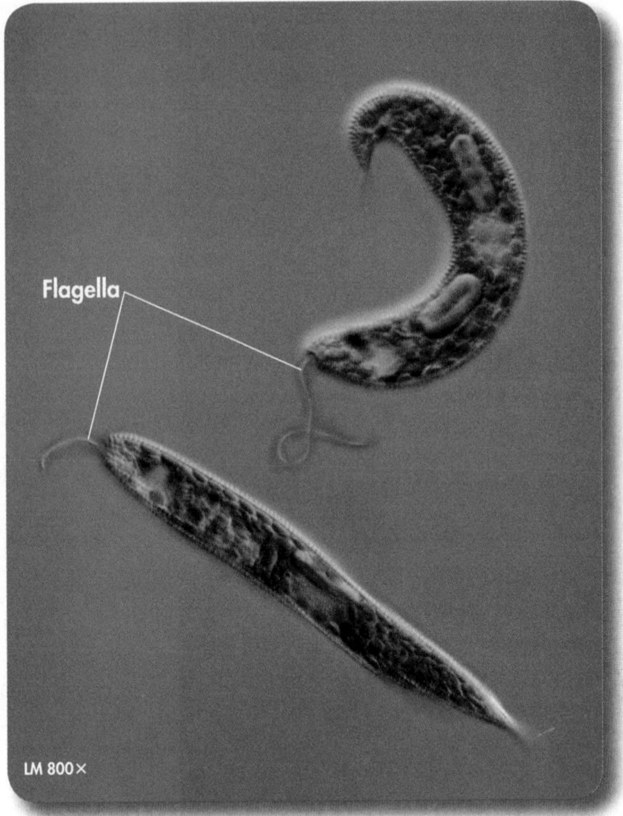

▲ *Photosynthetic* Euglena spirogyra *is commonly found in lakes and ponds.*

DISCICRISTATES

Discicristates (disk ee KRIS tayts) are named for the disc-shaped cristae present in their mitochondria. Some species are photosynthetic and free-living, such as *Euglena*, while others are dangerous parasites.

▼ *The ribbonlike cells of* Trypanosoma brucei *cause African sleeping sickness. The parasitic protist is transmitted by tsetse flies to humans, where it infects the blood, lymph, and spinal fluid. Severe nervous system damage and death are the usual result.* (SEM 6700×)

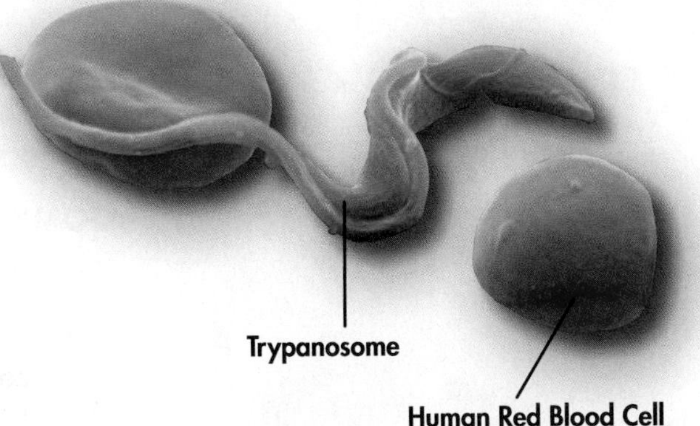

Chromalveolates

KEY CHARACTERISTICS

Chromalveolates (krohm AL vee uh layts) get their name from alveoli, flattened vesicles that line the cell membrane. The prefix chromo-*, meaning "pigment," reflects evidence that members of this clade share a common ancestor that had accessory pigments used in photosynthesis.*

GROUPS OF CHROMALVEOLATES

The chromalveolates are one of the largest and most diverse groups of eukaryotes.

PHAEOPHYTES: Brown algae

Phaeophytes (FAY uh fyts) are mostly found in salt water. They are some of the most abundant and visible of the algae. Most species contain fucoxanthin, a greenish-brown pigment from which the group gets its common name. The multicellular brown alga known as giant kelp can grow as large as 60 meters in length.

▼ *Brown algae in genus* Fucus *are commonly found in tidepools and on rocky shorelines of the Pacific Coast of the United States.*

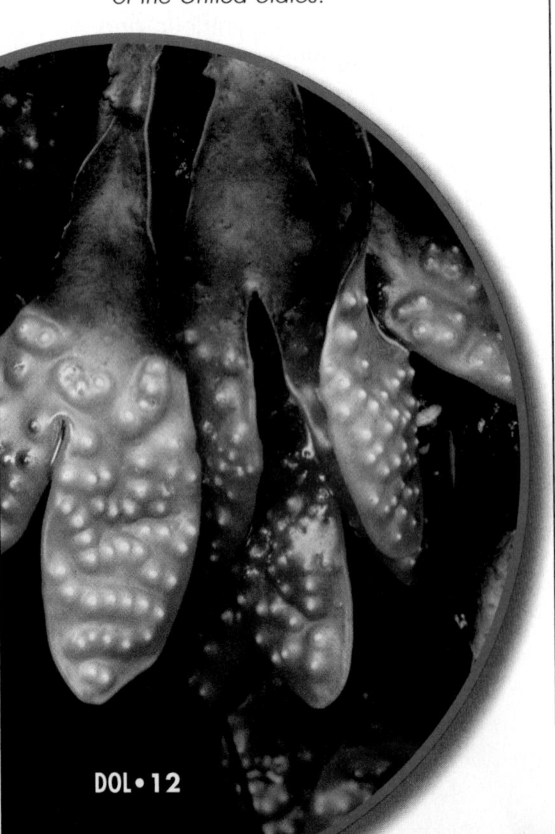

SEM 650×

▲ *This species, in genus* Synura, *is a colonial alga. In this photograph, you can see the scales that cover the cell surfaces of the individuals making up the colony.*

CHRYSOPHYTES: Golden algae

Chrysophytes (KRIS oh fyts) are known for colorful accessory pigments in their chloroplasts. Most are found in fresh water and are photosynthetic.

SEM 280×

SEM 1000×

▲ *Diatoms often produce intricate shells made from silicon dioxide that persist long after they die.*

DIATOMS

Diatoms are mostly found in salt water. When they die, they sink to the ocean floor, and their shells pile up in large deposits. Diatomaceous earth, as these deposits are known, can be used to screen out small particles, and is often used in swimming pool filters.

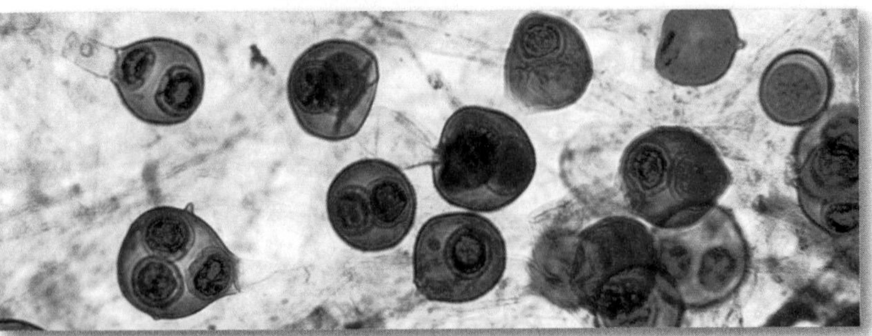

▲ *Water molds in genus* Achlya (LM 140×)

OOMYCETES: Water molds

These nonphotosynthetic organisms are often confused with fungi. Oomycetes (oh uh MY seed eez) typically produce fuzzy mats of material on dead or decaying animals and plants. Oomycetes are also responsible for a number of serious plant diseases, including potato blight, sudden oak death, and ink disease, which infects the American chestnut tree.

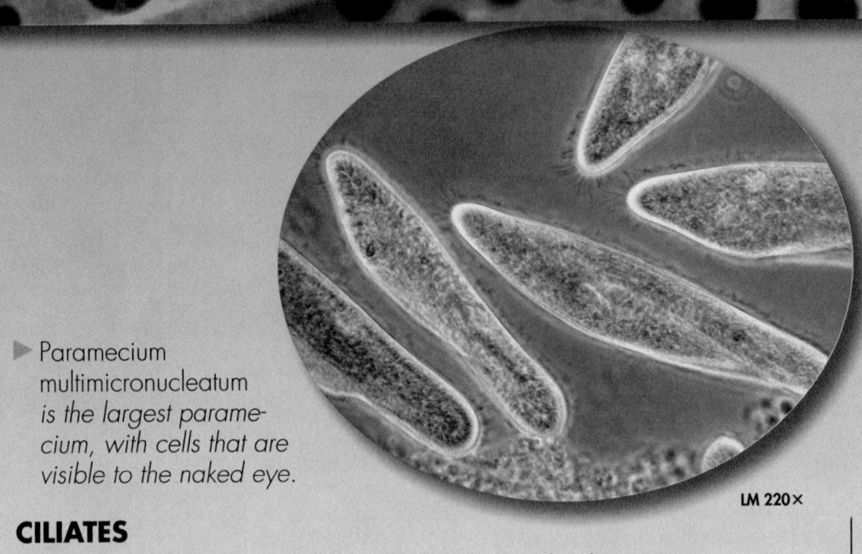

▶ *Paramecium multimicronucleatum is the largest paramecium, with cells that are visible to the naked eye.*

CILIATES

These common organisms may contain hundreds or even thousands of short cilia extending from the surface of the cell. The cilia propel the ciliate through the water, and may sweep food particles into a gullet. Ciliates are large compared to other protists, with some cells exceeding 1 mm in length.

DINOFLAGELLATES

Dinoflagellates are photosynthetic protists found in both fresh and salt water. Their name comes from their two distinct flagella, usually oriented at right angles to each other. Roughly half of dinoflagellate species are photosynthetic; the other half live as heterotrophs. Many dinoflagellate species are luminescent, and when agitated by sudden movement in the water, give off light.

▲ *The two flagella of dinoflagellates originate in grooves within thick plates of cellulose that resemble a cross shape, as shown here (genus* Peridinium*).*

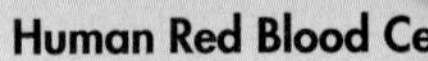

▲ *Apicomplexans in genus* Plasmodium *are mosquito-borne parasites. Shown here is the sporozoite stage attached to a human red blood cell.*

APICOMPLEXANS

The apicomplexans (AYP ih kum plek sunz) are named for a unique organelle near one end of the cell known as the apical complex. This structure contains vesicles with enzymes that allow apicomplexans to enter other cells and take up residence as parasites.

Eco • Alert

Toxic Blooms

Dangerous Dinoflagellates

Great blooms of the dinoflagellates *Gonyaulax* and *Karenia* have occurred in recent years on the East Coast of the United States, although scientists are not sure of the reason. These blooms are known as "red tides." *Gonyaulax* and *Karenia* produce a toxin that can become amplified in the food chain when filter-feeding shellfish such as oysters contentrate it in their tissues. Eating shellfish from water affected by red tide can cause serious illness, paralysis, and even death.

▲ *A red tide containing toxic dinoflagellates*

Protists

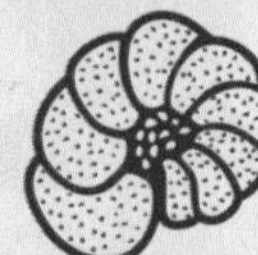

Cercozoa, Foraminiferans, and Radiolarians

There is no single morphological characteristic that unites this diverse trio, but many have extensions of cytoplasm called pseudopods and many produce protective shells. The grouping together of Cercozoa, Foraminifera, and Radiolaria is based almost entirely on molecular analyses and not on morphology.

FORAMINIFERANS

Foraminifera (fawr uh min IF uh ra) produce intricate and beautiful shells that differ from species to species. Slender pseudopods that emerge through tiny holes in the shell enable them to capture food, including bacteria. As many as 4000 species exist.

▼ Peneroplis plantus *has a spiral-shaped shell.*

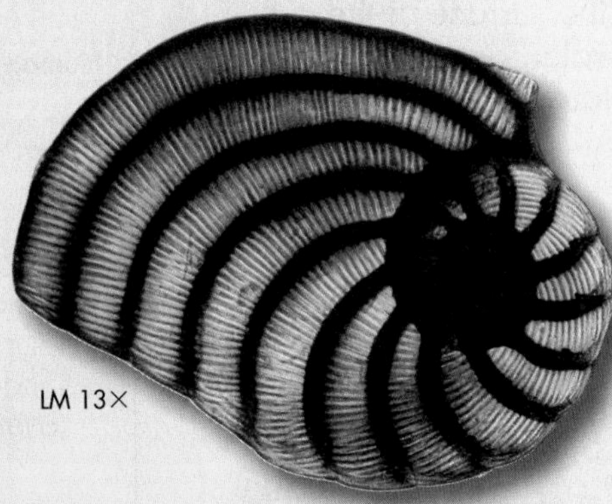

CERCOZOA

Members of this clade are common in soil, where they feed on bacteria as well as decaying organic matter. Many have flagella, and some produce scales made of silica that protect their surfaces.

SEM 175×

▲ *Radiolarian shells are composed of silica or strontium sulfate.*

RADIOLARIANS

These organisms have an intricate structure in which the nucleus is found in an inner region of the cell known as the endoplasm. The outer portion of the cell, known as the ectoplasm, contains lipid droplets and vacuoles. These organisms sometimes form symbiotic relationships with photosynthetic algae, from which they obtain food.

• **A Look Back in Time**

Foraminiferan Fossils

Ancient Climates Revealed

Abundant fossils of foraminiferans have been found in sediments dating to the Cambrian period (560 million years ago). For decades, oil companies have taken advantage of these ancient fossils to locate the sediments most likely to contain oil, but now there is another use for them—measuring the sea temperature of ancient Earth. Foraminiferans take dissolved oxygen from seawater to make the calcium carbonate ($CaCO_3$) in their shells, and when they do so, they take up two isotopes of oxygen, ^{16}O and ^{18}O. Because water made from ^{16}O is less dense, more of it evaporates into the atmosphere when the seas are warm—increasing the amount of ^{18}O in the remaining seawater, and in the fossil shells. The ratio between ^{16}O and ^{18}O in these fossils allows scientists to study the history of seawater temperature, as shown in the graph above.

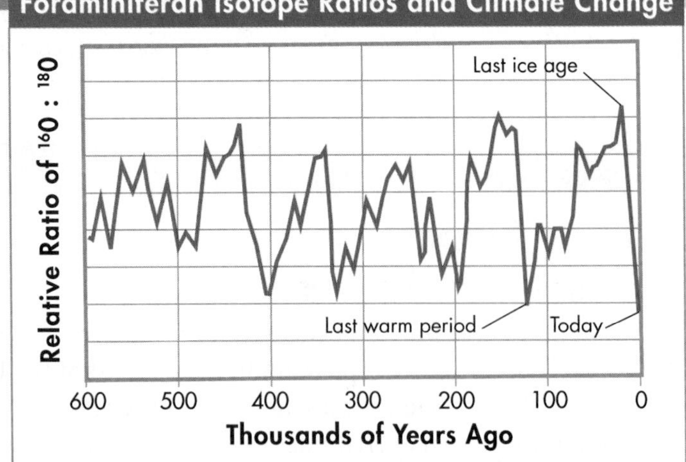

Rhodophytes

Also known as the red algae, these organisms get their name (from Greek, *rhodo* = red and *phyte* = plant) from reddish accessory pigments called phycobilins (fy koh BIL inz). These highly efficient pigments enable red algae to grow anywhere from the ocean's surface to depths as great as 268 meters. Most species are multicellular. Rhodophytes are the sister group to kingdom Plantae.

▼ Antithamnion plumula *is a marine rhodophyte that lives attached to coastal rocks.* (LM 35×)

Amoebozoa

Members of the Amoebozoa (uh MEE boh zoh ah) are amoebalike organisms that move by means of cytoplasmic streaming, also called amoeboid movement, using pseudopods.

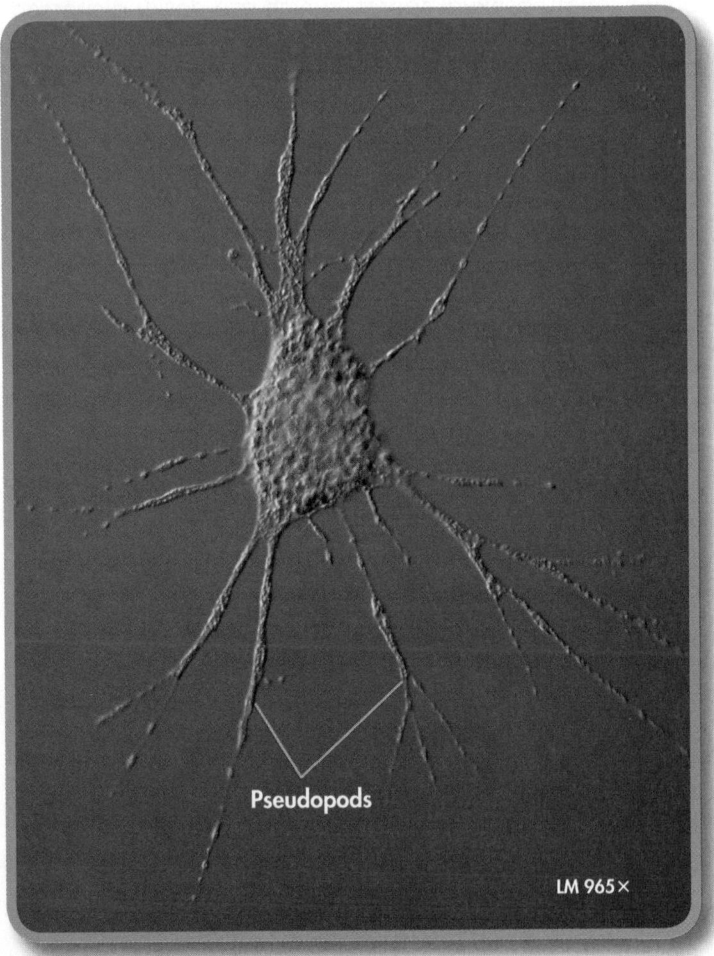

◀ *This solitary amoeba,* Penardia mutabilis, *has very slender pseudopods.*

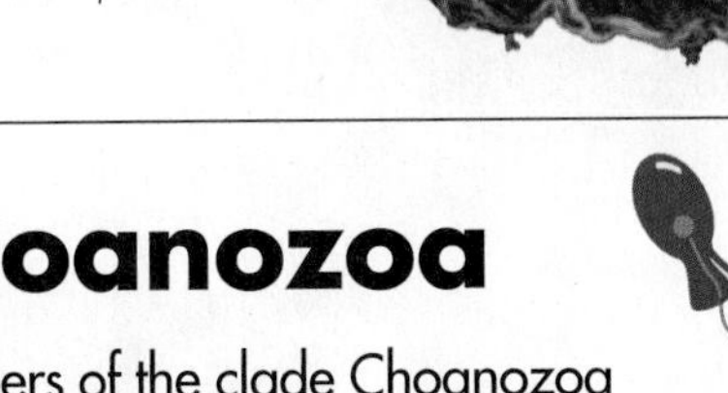

◀ *Slime molds live as single microscopic amoebas in the soil, but aggregate into a colony when conditions are right, forming a multicellular fruiting body.*

Choanozoa

Members of the clade Choanozoa (koh AN uh zoh uh) can be solitary or colonial and are found in aquatic environments around the world. This clade is the sister group to kingdom Animalia.

Choanoflagellates are a major group in the clade Choanozoa. They get their name from a collar of cytoplasm that surrounds their single flagellum (form Greek, *choano* = collar.) Many species trap food within the collar and ingest it.

Fungi

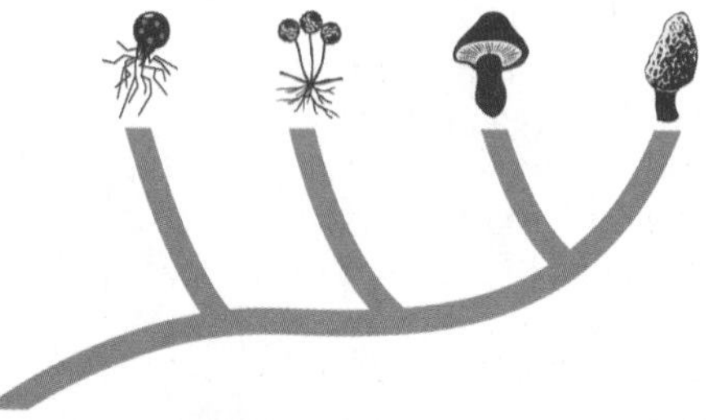

▲ *Stinkhorn fungus (genus* Dictyophora*)*

KEY CHARACTERISTICS

Fungi are heterotrophic eukaryotes with cell walls that contain chitin. Fungi were once thought to be plants that had lost their chloroplasts. It is now clear, however, that they are much more closely related to animals than to plants. More than 100,000 species of fungi are known. Distinctions among the phyla are made on the basis of DNA comparisons, cell structure, reproductive structures, and life cycles.

Organization Some are unicellular yeasts, but most have a multicellular body called a mycelium that consists of one or more slender, branching cells called hyphae.

Feeding and Digestion Obtain food by extracellular digestion and absorption

Reproduction Most have sexual phases to their life cycle and are haploid at most points during the cycle. Most produce tough, asexual spores, which are easily dispersed and able to endure harsh environmental conditions. Asexual reproduction by budding and splitting is also common.

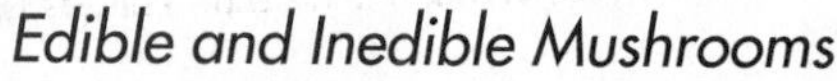

▲ *Fly Agaric (*Amanita muscaria*) is poisonous to humans.*

Consumers Beware!

Edible and Inedible Mushrooms

Many types of fungi have long been considered delicacies, and several different species of mushrooms are cultivated for food. You may have already tasted sliced mushrooms on pizza, feasted on delicious sautéed portobello mushrooms, or eaten shiitake mushrooms. When properly cooked and prepared, domestic mushrooms are tasty and nutritious.

Wild mushrooms are a different story: Although some are edible, many are poisonous. Because many species of poisonous mushrooms look almost identical to edible mushrooms, you should never pick or eat any mushrooms found in the wild. Instead, mushroom gathering should be left to experts who can positively identify each mushroom they collect. The result of eating a poisonous mushroom can be severe illness, or even death.

Basidiomycetes

The basidiomycetes, or club fungi, are named for the basidium (buh SID ee um; plural: basidia). The basidium is a reproductive cell that resembles a club.

Life Cycle Basidiomycetes undergo what is probably the most elaborate life cycle of all the fungi, shown below.

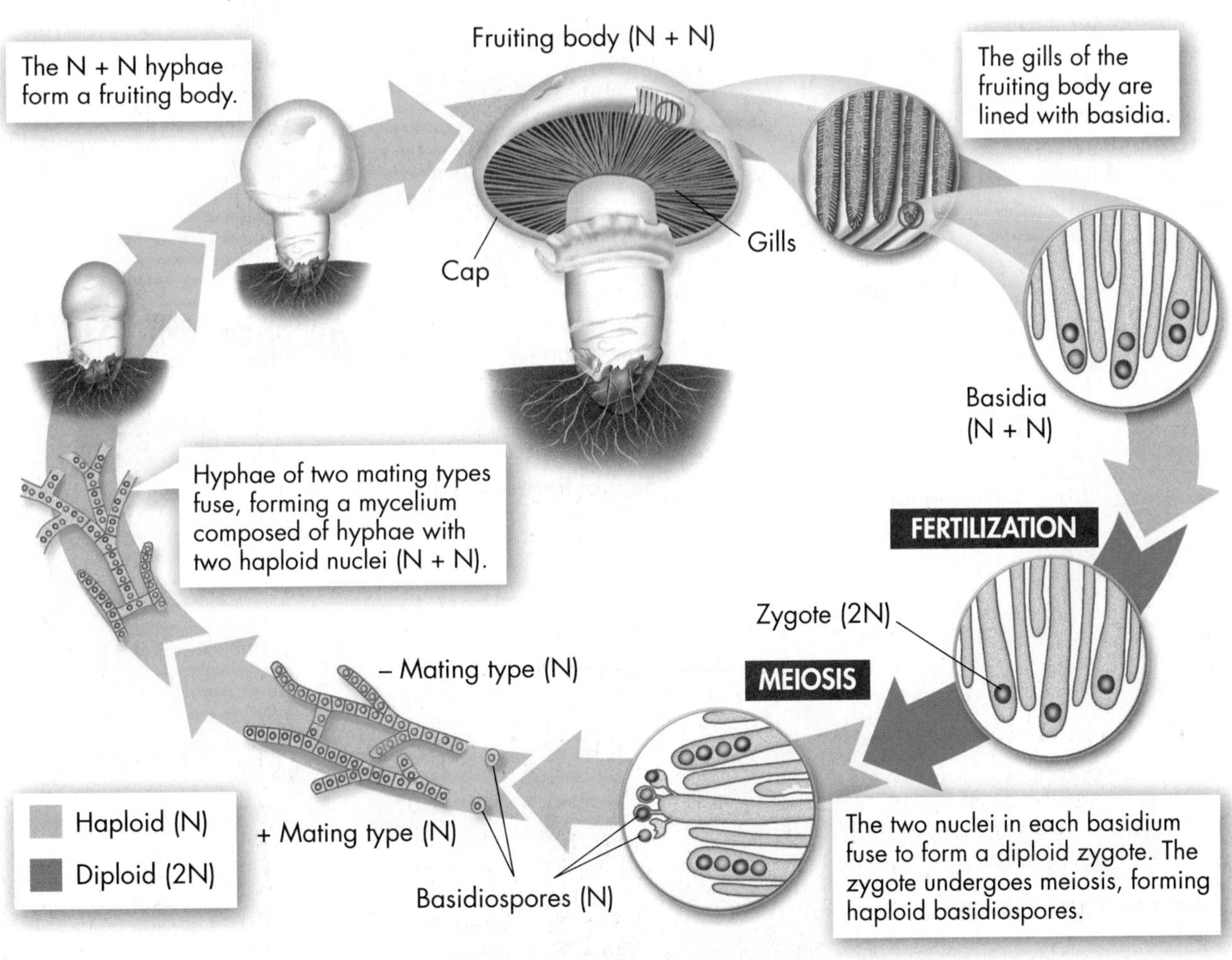

Fruiting body (N + N)
The N + N hyphae form a fruiting body.
The gills of the fruiting body are lined with basidia.
Gills
Cap
Basidia (N + N)
Hyphae of two mating types fuse, forming a mycelium composed of hyphae with two haploid nuclei (N + N).
FERTILIZATION
Zygote (2N)
MEIOSIS
– Mating type (N)
+ Mating type (N)
Basidiospores (N)
Haploid (N)
Diploid (2N)
The two nuclei in each basidium fuse to form a diploid zygote. The zygote undergoes meiosis, forming haploid basidiospores.

Diversity More than 26,000 species of basidiomycetes have been described, roughly a third of all known fungal species. Examples include the stinkhorn and fly agaric mushrooms shown on the previous page, and the shelf fungus and puffball at right.

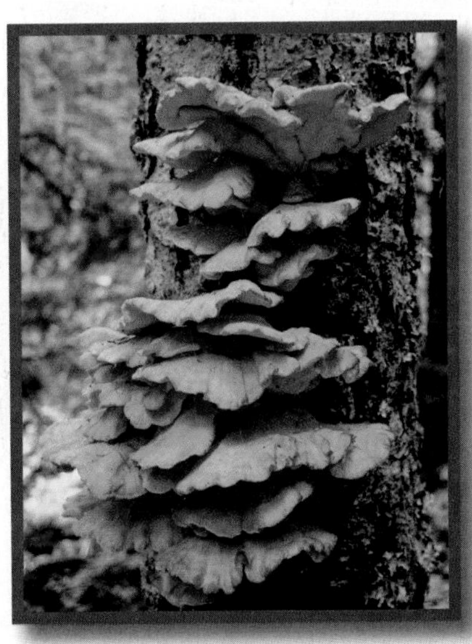

▶ *Shelf fungi (Polypore family) often grow on the sides of dead or dying trees.*

▼ *A puffball releases its spores in an explosive cloud.*

Ascomycetes

The ascomycetes, or sac fungi, are named for the ascus (AS kus), a saclike reproductive structure that contains spores.

Life Cycle The ascomycete life cycle includes an asexual phase, in which haploid spores are released from structures called conidiophores, and a sexual phase.

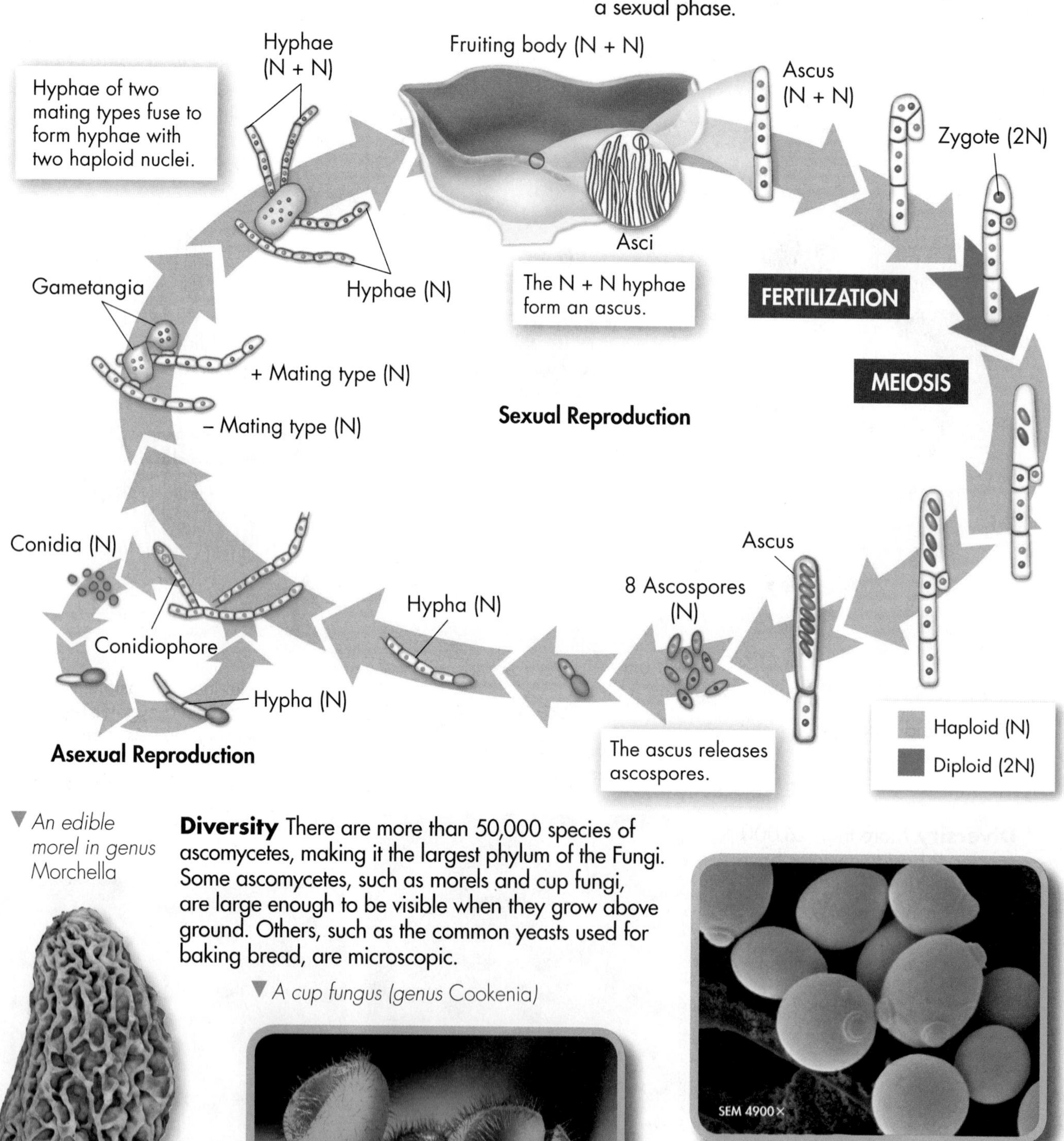

▼ *An edible morel in genus* Morchella

Diversity There are more than 50,000 species of ascomycetes, making it the largest phylum of the Fungi. Some ascomycetes, such as morels and cup fungi, are large enough to be visible when they grow above ground. Others, such as the common yeasts used for baking bread, are microscopic.

▼ *A cup fungus (genus* Cookenia*)*

SEM 4900×

▲ Saccharomyces cerevisiae, *the yeast used to raise bread dough, is a unicellular ascomycete that reproduces asexually by budding.*

Zygomycetes

The hyphae of zygomycetes generally lack cross walls between cells. Zygomycetes get their name from the sexual phase of their reproductive cycle, which involves a structure called a zygosporangium that forms between the hyphae of two different mating types. One group within the zygomycetes, the Glomales, form symbiotic mycorrhizae (my koh RY zee) with plant roots.

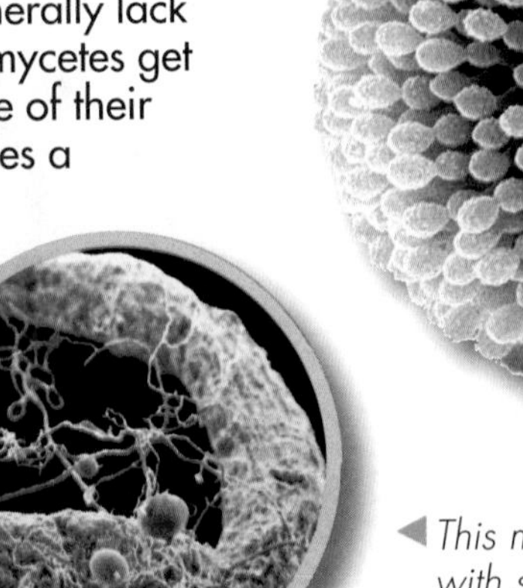

The fruiting body of the common black bread mold, Rhizopus stolonifer (SEM 450×)

This micrograph shows mycorrhizal fungi in symbiosis with soybean roots. The soybean plant provides nutrient sugars to the fungus, while the fungus provides water and essential minerals to the plant. (SEM 200×)

Chytrids

Members of this phylum live in water or moist soil. Their reproductive cells have flagella, making them the only fungi known to have a motile stage to their life cycle. Chytrids are especially good at digesting cellulose, the material of plant cell walls—some live in the digestive systems of cows and deer, helping them to digest plant matter. Others are pathogens—certain chytrids have recently been associated with the decline of frog populations around the world. About 1000 species are known, many of them recently discovered.

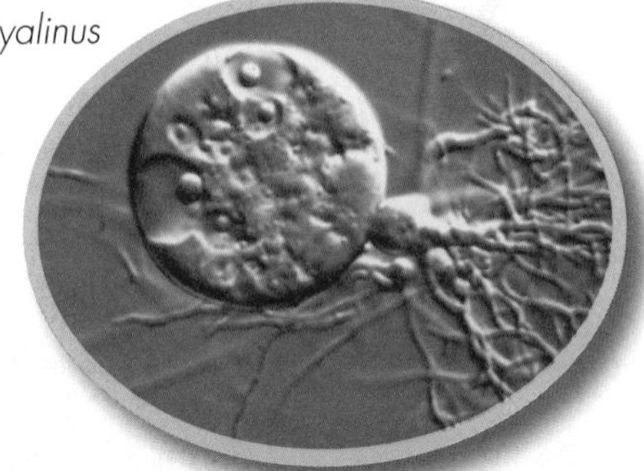

Chytriomyces hyalinus (LM 500×)

Eco • Alert

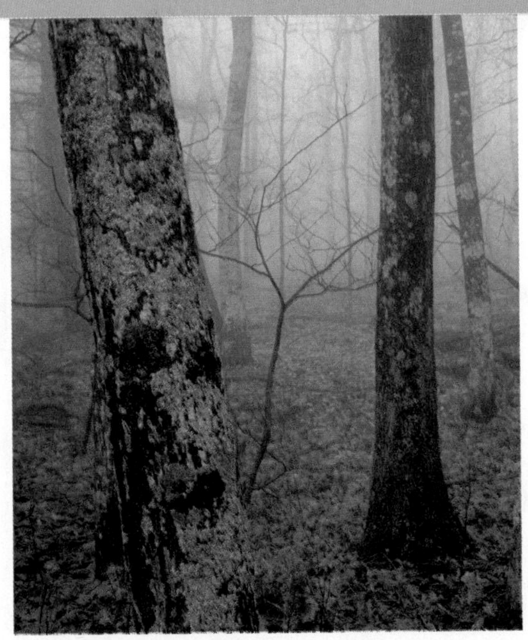

Lichen-covered oak trees in Shenandoah National Park, Virginia

Look to the Lichens

Lichens as Bio-Indicators

Lichens are mutualistic associations between a fungus, usually an ascomycete, and a photosynthetic organism, usually an alga. They are incredibly durable, and have even been reported to survive in the vacuum of space. However, they are also incredibly sensitive indicators of the state of the atmosphere. In particular, when sulfur dioxide is released into the atmosphere, it often reacts with water to form acids (including sulfuric acid) that pollute rainfall. Lichens can be severely damaged by acidic rainfall, although the degree of damage depends on the substrate upon which they grow. Lichens disappear first from the bark of pine and fir trees, which are themselves somewhat acidic. Lichens on elms, which have alkaline bark, are the last to go. By careful monitoring of the health of lichen populations of various trees, scientists can uses these remarkable organisms as low-tech monitors for the health of the environment.

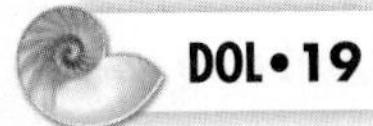

Plants

KEY CHARACTERISTICS

Plants are eukaryotes with cell walls composed of cellulose. Plants carry out photosynthesis using the green pigments chlorophyll a and b, and they store the products of photosynthesis as starch.

▶ *A banana plant in bloom*

▼ *A typical plant life cycle*

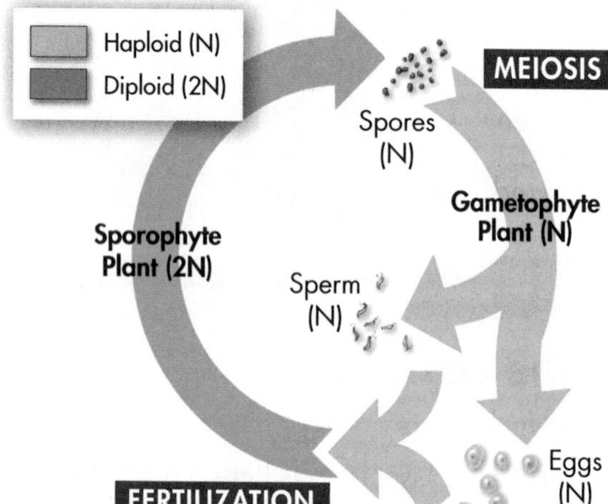

•A Closer Look

Prokaryotes Within

The Origins of Chloroplasts

Chloroplasts, which contain their own DNA, are found in all green plants, but where did they come from? In 1905, the Russian botanist Konstantin Mereschkowsky, noticing the similarities between chloroplasts and cyanobacteria, proposed that these organelles originated from a symbiotic relationship formed with the ancestors of today's plants.

This hypothesis still holds up very well today. New DNA studies suggest that all chloroplasts are descended from a single photosynthetic prokaryote, closely related to today's cyanobacteria.

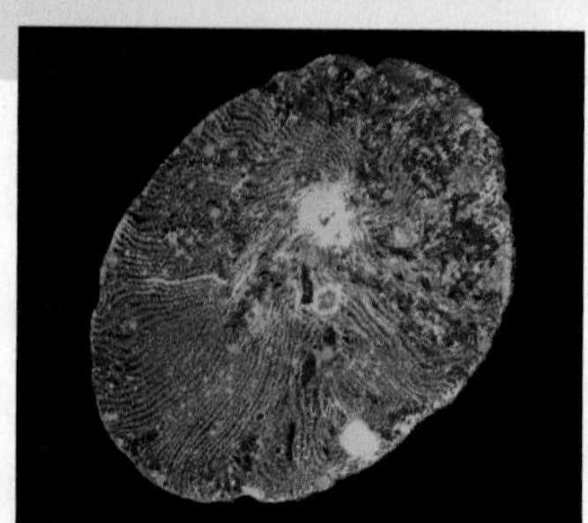

The photosynthetic membranes (shown in green) visible in this thin section of a cyanobacterium resemble the thylakoid membranes of plant cell chloroplasts. (TEM 14,000×)

Green Algae

KEY CHARACTERISTICS

The green algae are plants that do not make embryos. All other plants form embryos as part of their life cycle. The green algae include both unicellular and multicellular species, and they are primarily aquatic.

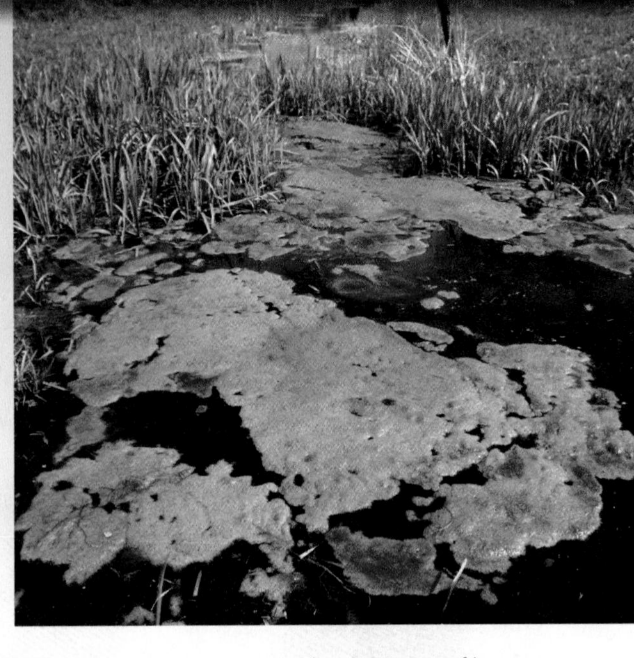

▲ *Clumps of* Spirogyra*, a filamentous green alga, are commonly called water silk or mermaid's tresses.*

Organization Single cells, colonies, and a few truly multicellular species

Movement Many swim using whiplike flagella.

Water Transport Water diffuses in from the environment.

Reproduction Asexual and sexual, with gametes and spores; some species show alternation of generations.

GROUPS OF GREEN ALGAE

The three most diverse groups of green algae are profiled below.

CHLOROPHYTES: Classic green algae

These algae usually live as single cells, like *Chlamydomonas*, or in colonies, like *Volvox*. They are found in both fresh and salt water, and some species are even known to live in arctic snowbanks.

► Chlamydomonas *is a unicellular green alga. Each cell has two flagella, which are used in movement.* (SEM 3000×)

CHAROPHYTES: Stoneworts

Among the green algae, the charophytes (KAHR uh fyts) are the closest relatives of more complicated plants. They are mostly freshwater species. Their branching filaments may be anchored to the substrate by thin rhizoids.

◄ Chara *with antheridia (sperm-producing structures) visible*

ULVOPHYTES: Sea lettuces

The ulvophytes are large organisms composed of hundreds or thousands of cells. Most form large, flattened green sheets and are often simply called seaweed. They show both haploid and diploid phases in their life cycle, but in many species, such as the common sea lettuce, *Ulva*, it is difficult to tell the two phases apart.

▼ *Ulva lactuca*

Bryophytes

KEY CHARACTERISTICS

Bryophytes (BRY oh fyts), found mostly on land, are multicellular plants that lack true vascular tissue. This lack of vascular tissue limits their height to just a few centimeters and restricts them to moist soils.

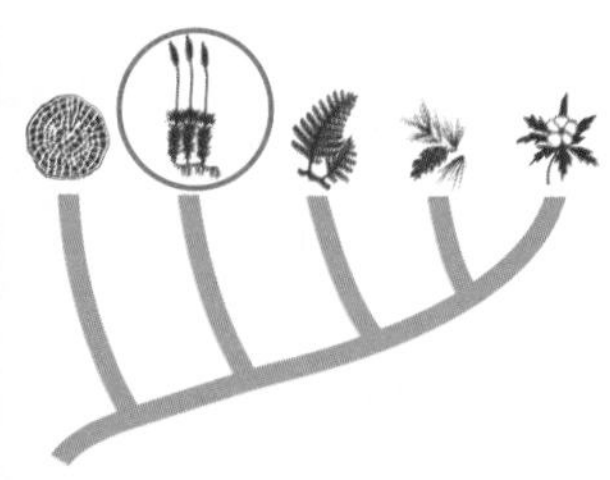

▲ *Mosses thrive in shady, damp locations, such as along the banks of this Oregon creek.*

Organization Complex and specialized tissues, including protective external layers and rhizoids

Movement Adults stationary; male gametes swim to egg cells using flagella.

Water Transport Diffusion from cell to cell; in some mosses, water flows through specialized tissue.

Reproduction All reproduce sexually with alternation of generations, producing gametes and spores. Most reproduce asexually, too. The gametophyte stage is dominant, with the sporophyte stage dependent on the gametophyte.

GROUPS OF BRYOPHYTES

Although they are listed together here, the three major groups of bryophytes are now considered to have evolved independently from each other.

MOSSES: Classic bryophytes

Mosses are found on damp, well-shaded soil, and occasionally along the sides of tree trunks.

Sporophyte

Mat of gametophytes

LIVERWORTS

Liverworts are flat, almost leaf-like plants that grow on the damp forest floor. Some species are shaped almost like the liver, from which they get their name.

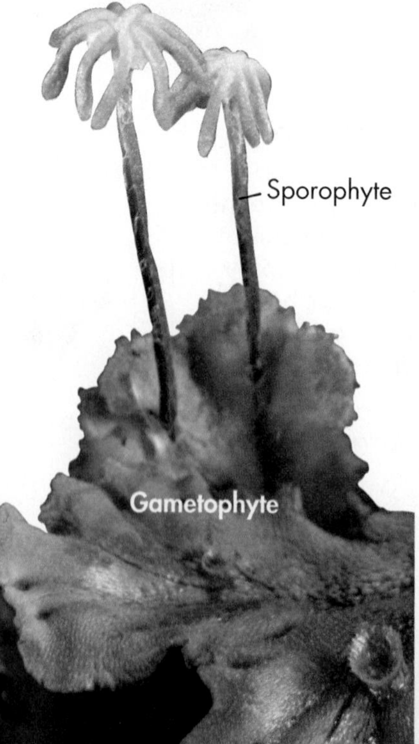

HORNWORTS

Hornworts get their name from their sporophytes, tiny green structures resembling horns. Like other bryophytes, hornworts are found mostly in damp, well-shaded areas. Only about 100 species are known.

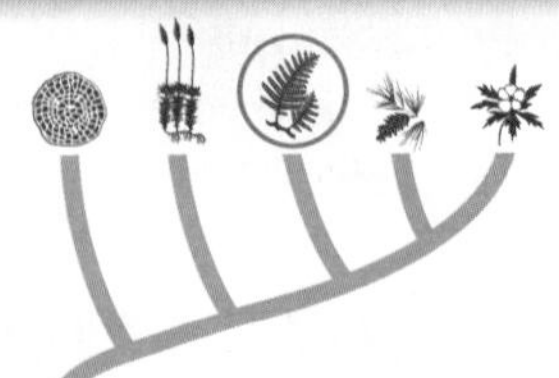

Seedless Vascular Plants

KEY CHARACTERISTICS

This informal grouping lumps together all the plants that have true vascular tissue but lack seeds. Vascular tissue is a key adaptation to life on land. By carrying water and food throughout plant structures, vascular tissue permitted the evolution of roots and tree-size plants, and it allowed plants to spread into dry areas of land.

Organization Complex and specialized tissues, including true roots, stems, and leaves

Movement Adults stationary; male gametes swim to egg cells using flagella.

Water Transport Through vascular tissue

Reproduction Alternation of generations, producing spores, eggs, and swimming sperm; the sporophyte stage is dominant, but the sporophyte is not dependent on the gametophyte as it is in bryophytes.

GROUPS OF SEEDLESS VASCULAR PLANTS

Besides the flowering plants, these organisms make up the most diverse collection of land plants, with more than 10,000 known species.

FERNS

Ferns are common and abundant. Because they need standing water to reproduce, ferns are generally found in areas that are damp at least part of the year. The sporophyte phase of the life cycle is dominant. Spores are produced in prominent clusters known as sori (SOH ry) on the undersides of leaves.

▼ *Polypodium vulgare*

CLUB MOSSES

Not really mosses, these vascular plants are also called lycopods (LY koh pahdz). These plants were especially abundant during the Carboniferous Period 360 to 290 million years ago, when they grew as large as trees. Today, their remains make up a large part of coal deposits mined for fuel.

▼ *The small club moss known as* Lycopodium *can be found growing on the forest floor throughout the temperate regions of North America. They look like tiny pine trees at first glance, but they are, in fact, small, seedless plants.*

HORSETAILS

Only a single living genus of horsetails is known, *Equisetum* (ek wi SEET um). These plants were thought to resemble horses' tails; their name is derived from this perception. Today, only 25 species are known, confined to wet areas of soil. But horsetails were once much more diverse, larger in size, and abundant. Abrasive silica, found in many horsetails, was used in colonial times as a scouring powder to help clean pots and pans.

▼ *Equisetum*

Gymnosperms

KEY CHARACTERISTICS

Gymnosperms are seed-bearing vascular plants whose seeds are exposed to the environment, rather than being enclosed in a fruit. The seeds are usually located on the scales of cones.

Organization True roots, stems, and leaves

Movement Adults stationary; within pollen grains, male gametophytes drift in air or are carried by animals to female structures, where they release sperm that move to eggs.

Water Transport Through vascular tissue

Reproduction Sexual; alternation of generations; the sporophyte stage is dominant. Female gametophytes live within the parent sporophyte. Pollen grains carry sperm to eggs, so open water is not needed for fertilization.

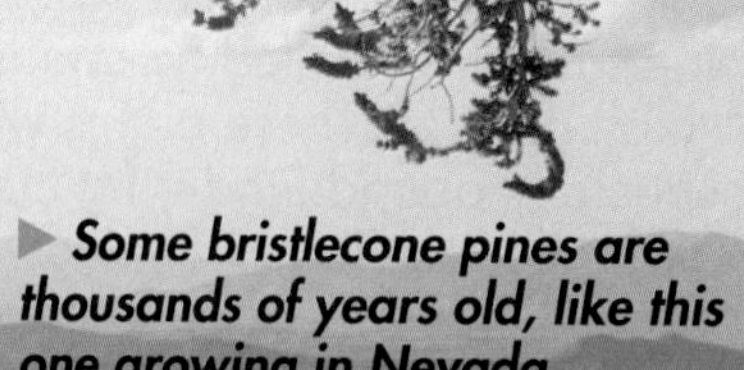

Some bristlecone pines are thousands of years old, like this one growing in Nevada.

Did You Know?

Rising From the Ashes

Fire's Role in Seed Germination

We generally think of forest fires as being natural disasters, and that's typically true. Some gymnosperm species, however, are so well adapted to the arid conditions of the American West that they actually depend upon such fires to spread their seeds.

The best-known example is the Jack Pine, *Pinus banksiana.* Its seed cones are thick and heat resistant. When engulfed in a fire, its seeds escape damage. The fire's high heat helps to open the outer coat of the cone, enabling the seeds to pop out afterward. As a result, Jack Pines are among the very first plants to repopulate a forest that has been damaged by fire.

▲ The high heat of a forest fire opens the cones of the Jack Pines, releasing their seeds. The inset shows a Jack Pine seedling growing in the charred remains of the fire.

Green Algae

KEY CHARACTERISTICS

The green algae are plants that do not make embryos. All other plants form embryos as part of their life cycle. The green algae include both unicellular and multicellular species, and they are primarily aquatic.

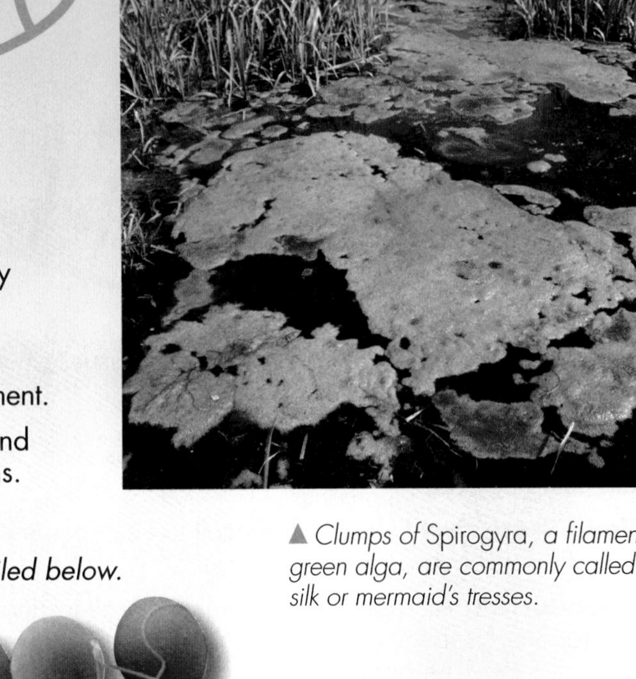

▲ *Clumps of* Spirogyra*, a filamentous green alga, are commonly called water silk or mermaid's tresses.*

Organization Single cells, colonies, and a few truly multicellular species

Movement Many swim using whiplike flagella.

Water Transport Water diffuses in from the environment.

Reproduction Asexual and sexual, with gametes and spores; some species show alternation of generations.

GROUPS OF GREEN ALGAE

The three most diverse groups of green algae are profiled below.

CHLOROPHYTES: Classic green algae

These algae usually live as single cells, like *Chlamydomonas*, or in colonies, like *Volvox*. They are found in both fresh and salt water, and some species are even known to live in arctic snowbanks.

▶ Chlamydomonas *is a unicellular green alga. Each cell has two flagella, which are used in movement.* (SEM 3000×)

CHAROPHYTES: Stoneworts

Among the green algae, the charophytes (KAHR uh fyts) are the closest relatives of more complicated plants. They are mostly freshwater species. Their branching filaments may be anchored to the substrate by thin rhizoids.

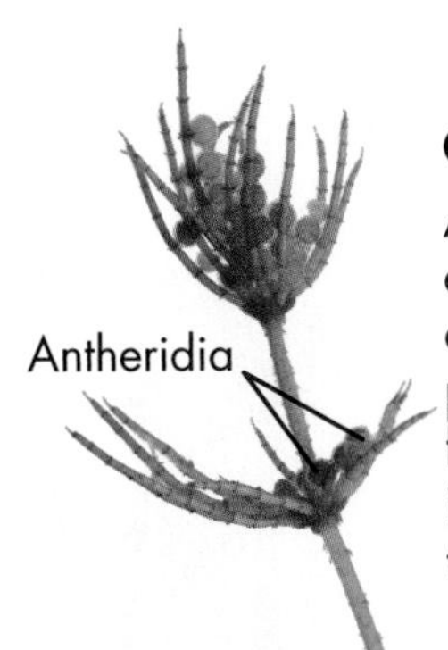

◀ Chara *with antheridia (sperm-producing structures) visible*

ULVOPHYTES: Sea lettuces

The ulvophytes are large organisms composed of hundreds or thousands of cells. Most form large, flattened green sheets and are often simply called seaweed. They show both haploid and diploid phases in their life cycle, but in many species, such as the common sea lettuce, *Ulva*, it is difficult to tell the two phases apart.

▼ *Ulva lactuca*

Bryophytes

KEY CHARACTERISTICS

Bryophytes (BRY oh fyts), found mostly on land, are multicellular plants that lack true vascular tissue. This lack of vascular tissue limits their height to just a few centimeters and restricts them to moist soils.

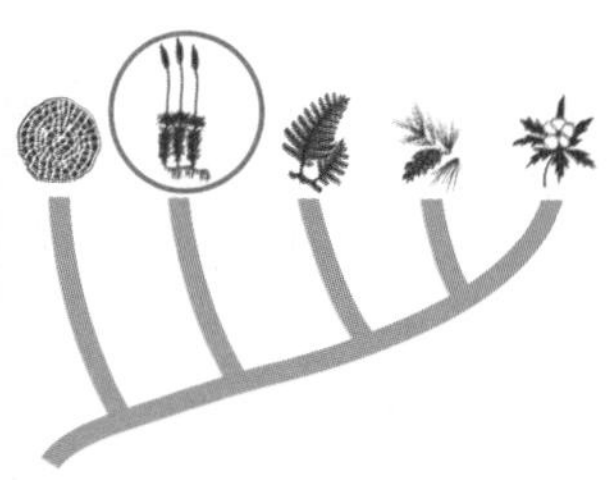

▲ *Mosses thrive in shady, damp locations, such as along the banks of this Oregon creek.*

Organization Complex and specialized tissues, including protective external layers and rhizoids

Movement Adults stationary; male gametes swim to egg cells using flagella.

Water Transport Diffusion from cell to cell; in some mosses, water flows through specialized tissue.

Reproduction All reproduce sexually with alternation of generations, producing gametes and spores. Most reproduce asexually, too. The gametophyte stage is dominant, with the sporophyte stage dependent on the gametophyte.

GROUPS OF BRYOPHYTES

Although they are listed together here, the three major groups of bryophytes are now considered to have evolved independently from each other.

MOSSES: Classic bryophytes

Mosses are found on damp, well-shaded soil, and occasionally along the sides of tree trunks.

LIVERWORTS

Liverworts are flat, almost leaf-like plants that grow on the damp forest floor. Some species are shaped almost like the liver, from which they get their name.

HORNWORTS

Hornworts get their name from their sporophytes, tiny green structures resembling horns. Like other bryophytes, hornworts are found mostly in damp, well-shaded areas. Only about 100 species are known.

Seedless Vascular Plants

KEY CHARACTERISTICS

This informal grouping lumps together all the plants that have true vascular tissue but lack seeds. Vascular tissue is a key adaptation to life on land. By carrying water and food throughout plant structures, vascular tissue permitted the evolution of roots and tree-size plants, and it allowed plants to spread into dry areas of land.

Organization Complex and specialized tissues, including true roots, stems, and leaves

Movement Adults stationary; male gametes swim to egg cells using flagella.

Water Transport Through vascular tissue

Reproduction Alternation of generations, producing spores, eggs, and swimming sperm; the sporophyte stage is dominant, but the sporophyte is not dependent on the gametophyte as it is in bryophytes.

GROUPS OF SEEDLESS VASCULAR PLANTS

Besides the flowering plants, these organisms make up the most diverse collection of land plants, with more than 10,000 known species.

FERNS

Ferns are common and abundant. Because they need standing water to reproduce, ferns are generally found in areas that are damp at least part of the year. The sporophyte phase of the life cycle is dominant. Spores are produced in prominent clusters known as sori (SOH ry) on the undersides of leaves.

▼ *Polypodium vulgare*

CLUB MOSSES

Not really mosses, these vascular plants are also called lycopods (LY koh pahdz). These plants were especially abundant during the Carboniferous Period 360 to 290 million years ago, when they grew as large as trees. Today, their remains make up a large part of coal deposits mined for fuel.

▼ *The small club moss known as* Lycopodium *can be found growing on the forest floor throughout the temperate regions of North America. They look like tiny pine trees at first glance, but they are, in fact, small, seedless plants.*

HORSETAILS

Only a single living genus of horsetails is known, *Equisetum* (ek wi SEET um). These plants were thought to resemble horses' tails; their name is derived from this perception. Today, only 25 species are known, confined to wet areas of soil. But horsetails were once much more diverse, larger in size, and abundant. Abrasive silica, found in many horsetails, was used in colonial times as a scouring powder to help clean pots and pans.

▼ *Equisetum*

Gymnosperms

KEY CHARACTERISTICS

Gymnosperms are seed-bearing vascular plants whose seeds are exposed to the environment, rather than being enclosed in a fruit. The seeds are usually located on the scales of cones.

Organization True roots, stems, and leaves

Movement Adults stationary; within pollen grains, male gametophytes drift in air or are carried by animals to female structures, where they release sperm that move to eggs.

Water Transport Through vascular tissue

Reproduction Sexual; alternation of generations; the sporophyte stage is dominant. Female gametophytes live within the parent sporophyte. Pollen grains carry sperm to eggs, so open water is not needed for fertilization.

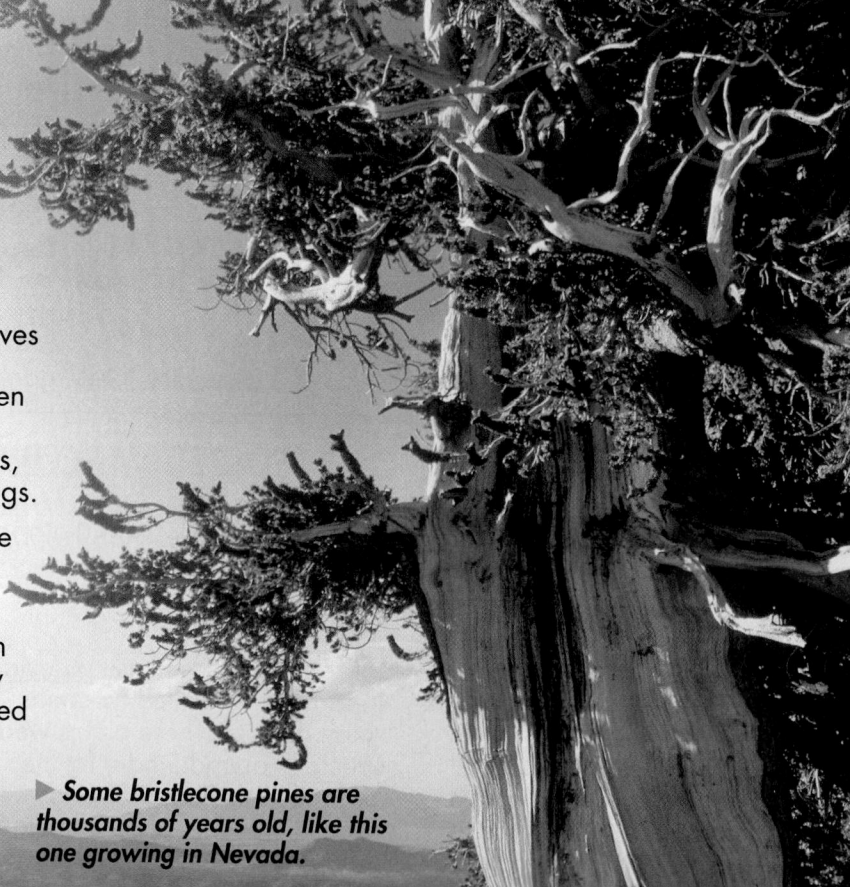

Some bristlecone pines are thousands of years old, like this one growing in Nevada.

Did You Know?

Rising From the Ashes

Fire's Role in Seed Germination

We generally think of forest fires as being natural disasters, and that's typically true. Some gymnosperm species, however, are so well adapted to the arid conditions of the American West that they actually depend upon such fires to spread their seeds.

The best-known example is the Jack Pine, *Pinus banksiana.* Its seed cones are thick and heat resistant. When engulfed in a fire, its seeds escape damage. The fire's high heat helps to open the outer coat of the cone, enabling the seeds to pop out afterward. As a result, Jack Pines are among the very first plants to repopulate a forest that has been damaged by fire.

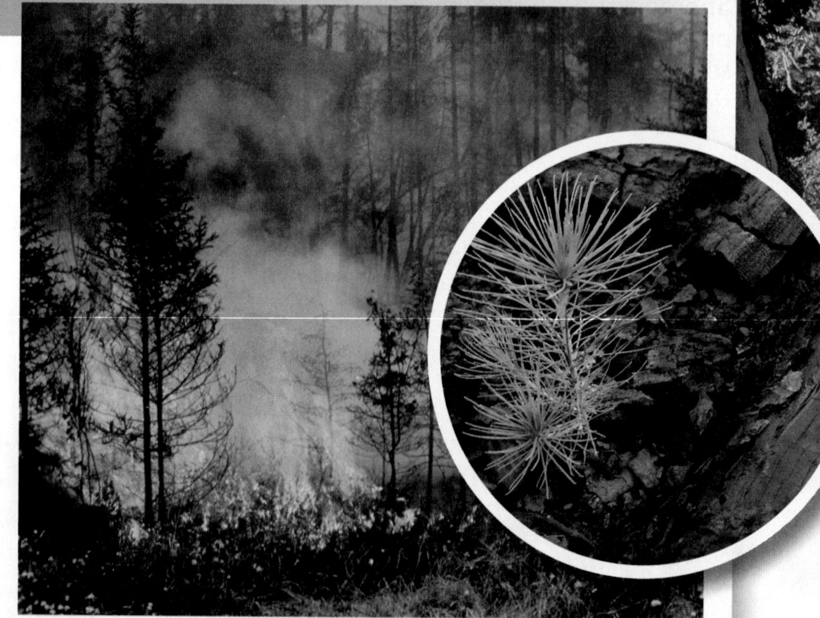

▲ *The high heat of a forest fire opens the cones of the Jack Pines, releasing their seeds. The inset shows a Jack Pine seedling growing in the charred remains of the fire.*

GROUPS OF GYMNOSPERMS

There are four groups of gymnosperms, representing about 800 species in total.

CONIFERS

Conifers are by far the most diverse group of living gymnosperms, represented by nearly 700 species worldwide. They include the common pine, spruce, fir, and redwood trees that make up a large share of the forests in the temperate regions of the world. Conifers have enormous economic importance. Their wood is used for residential building, to manufacture paper, and as a source of heat. Compounds from their resins are used for a variety of industrial purposes.

▲ *Most conifers retain their leaves year-round.*

CYCADS

Cycads (SY kads) are beautiful palmlike plants that have large cones. Cycads first appeared in the fossil record during the Triassic Period, 225 million years ago. Huge forests of cycads thrived when dinosaurs roamed Earth. Today, only nine genera of cycads exist. Cycads can be found growing naturally in tropical and subtropical places such as Mexico, the West Indies, Florida, and parts of Asia, Africa, and Australia.

▶ *A Sago Palm,* Cycas revoluta

▲ *Ginkgoes are often planted in urban settings, where their toughness and resistance to air pollution make them popular shade trees.*

GINKGOES

Ginkgoes (GING kohs) were common when dinosaurs were alive, but today the group contains only one species, *Ginkgo biloba*. The living *Ginkgo* species looks similar to its fossil ancestors—in fact, *G. biloba* may be one of the oldest seed plant species alive today.

GNETOPHYTES

About 70 present-day species of gnetophytes (NET oh fyts) are known, placed in just three genera. The reproductive scales of these plants are clustered in cones.

▶ Welwitschia mirabilis, *an inhabitant of the Namibian desert in southwestern Africa, is one of the most remarkable gnetophytes. Its huge leathery leaves grow continuously and spread across the ground.*

Angiosperms

KEY CHARACTERISTICS

Angiosperms are plants that bear seeds in a closed ovary. The ovary is part of a reproductive organ known as a flower. Seeds are formed in a double fertilization event, which forms a diploid embryo and a triploid endosperm tissue. As seeds mature, ovaries develop into fruits that help to disperse the seeds.

Organization True roots, stems, and leaves

Movement Adults stationary; within pollen grains, male gametophytes drift in air or are carried by animals to female structures, where they release sperm that move to eggs.

Water Transport Through vascular tissue

Reproduction Sexual, with alternation of generations; also asexual. The sporophyte stage is dominant. Female gametophytes live within the parent sporophyte. Pollen carries sperm to eggs, so open water is not needed for fertilization.

▶ *A Southern Long-Nosed Bat pollinates the Saguaro Cactus, Carnegia gigantea, while collecting nectar from its blossoms.*

• A Closer Look

Whatever Happened to Monocots and Dicots?

Traditionally, flowering plants have been divided into just two groups, monocots and dicots, based on the number of seed leaves in their embryos. Today, however, molecular studies have shown that the dicots aren't really one group. Some of the most primitive flowering plants (like *Amborella*) are dicots, and so are some of the most advanced flowering plants, while the monocots fall right in between. So, while monocots are indeed a single group, the term *dicots* is now just an informal, though still useful, grouping.

Amborella | Water lilies | Monocots | Magnoliids | Eudicots

Ancestral Angiosperm

GROUPS OF ANGIOSPERMS

The great majority of plant species—over 260,000—are angiosperms.

▲ *Water lilies are aquatic plants that produce flowers and leaves, which float on the surface of the water.*

NYMPHAEACEAE: Water lilies

About 50 species of water lilies are known, and they are of special interest to plant taxonomists. Their DNA and flower structure suggest that they are, along with *Amborella*, one of the earliest groups to have split off from the main line of flowering plant evolution. Examples of water lilies are found throughout the world.

MAGNOLIIDS: Magnolia trees and others

The most famous genus of these plants is *Magnolia*, which includes nearly 200 species. Laurels and tulip poplars are also magnoliids (mag NOH lee ids). Because of their flower structure, magnoliids were once thought to be nearly as primitive as water lilies. Genetic studies now suggest that they split off from the rest of the angiosperm line after monocots and, therefore, do not represent the earliest flowering plants.

▼ *The Tulip Poplar is a long, straight tree often used as wood for telephone poles. Its flowers are greenish and shaped like tulips.*

► *Magnolia trees produce conspicuous flowers, which contain multiple stamens and multiple pistils.*

AMBORELLA

Amborella does not represent a group of plants but instead just a single species found only on the island of New Caledonia in the South Pacific Ocean. DNA studies show that *Amborella* is equally separated from all other flowering plants living today, suggesting that it is descended from plants that split off from the main line of flowering plant evolution as long ago as 100 million years.

▲ *The flowers of* Amborella trichopoda *are simpler than those of most other plants, and the species has a number of features that place it at the very base of flowering plant evolution.*

GROUPS OF ANGIOSPERMS CONTINUED...

MONOCOTS

The monocots include an estimated 65,000 species, roughly 20 percent of all flowering plants. They get their name from the single seed leaf found in monocot embryos, and they include some of the plants that are most important to human cultures. Monocots grown as crops account for a majority of the food produced by agriculture. These crops include wheat, rice, barley, corn, and sugar cane. Common grasses are monocots, as are onions, bananas, orchids, coconut palms, tulips, and irises.

▲ *Onions are just one of many examples of monocot crop species.*

▲ *This African hillside is dotted with clumps of Wild Pampas Grass.*

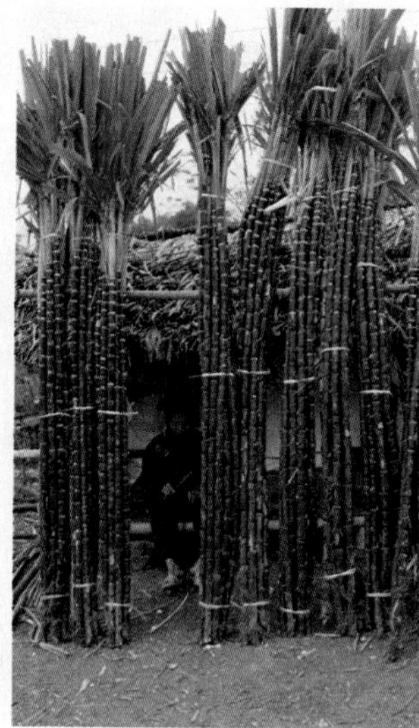

▲ *Many orchid species are grown by enthusiasts for their rare beauty. Notice the aerial roots on this specimen, which grows as an epiphyte in its natural environment.*

◀ *This sugar cane in Vietnam has been bundled for sale.*

Eco • Alert

Coevolution: Losing the Pollinators

The successes of flowering plants are clearly due to coevolution with their insect pollinators. Common honey bees are among the most important of these, gathering nectar from the flowers of hundreds of plant species and spreading pollen from plant to plant as they go.

Unfortunately, beekeepers around the world, including the United States, are facing a serious crisis. "Colony collapse disorder," as beekeepers describe it, causes bees to fly away from the hive and either never return, or return only to weaken and die. The disease threatens to affect scores of important crops, which depend upon bees to produce fruit and seeds. Suspicion has centered on a fungus or a virus that might spread from colony to colony, but at this point there is no definitive cause or cure.

EUDICOTS: "TRUE DICOTS"

Eudicots (YOO dy kahts) account for about 75 percent of all angiosperm species. The name means "true dicots," and these plants are the ones usually given as examples of dicot stem, leaf, and flower structure. Eudicots have distinctive pollen grains with three grooves on their surfaces, and DNA studies strongly support their classification in a single group. They include a number of important subgroups, five of which are described here.

Ranunculales

The ranunculales subgroup (ruh NUNH kyu lay les) includes, and is named after, buttercups (genus *Ranunculus*). Also included in this subgroup are a number of well-known flowers such as columbines, poppies, barberries, and moonseed.

▶ Rocky Mountain Columbine

▲ Clusterhead Pinks

Caryophyllales

Cacti are probably the most well-known plants in the caryophyllales subgroup (KAR ee oh fy lay les). Pinks and carnations, spinach, rhubarb, and insect-eating plants, such as sundews and pitcher plants, are also members.

Saxifragales

Plants in the saxifragales (SAK suh frij ay les) subgroup include peonies, witch hazel, gooseberries, and coral bells.

◀ Peony

Rosids

The rosids include, as you might expect, the roses. However, this subgroup also includes many popular fruits, such as oranges, raspberries, strawberries, and apples. Some of the best-known trees, including poplars, willows, and maples, are also members.

▲ Orange

Asterids

The nearly 80,000 asterid species include sunflowers, azaleas, snapdragons, blueberries, tomatoes, and potatoes.

▼ *The flower heads in a field of sunflowers all track the sun as it moves across the sky; thus, they all face the same direction.*

Animals

Snow Leopard

KEY CHARACTERISTICS

Animals are multicellular, heterotrophic, eukaryotic organisms whose cells lack cell walls.

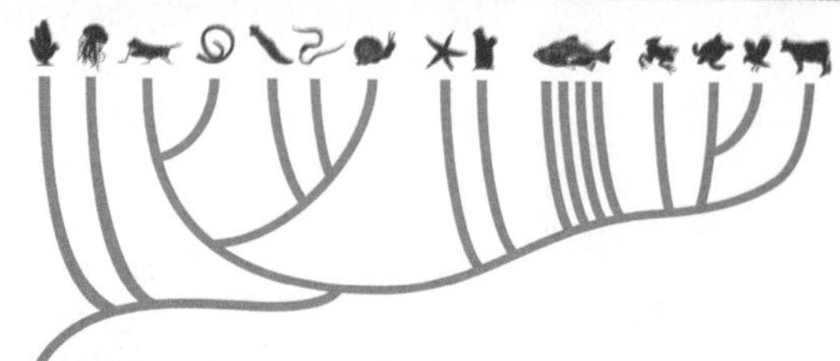

• A Closer Look

A Common Ancestor

Recent molecular studies and cladistic analyses recognize the clade Choanozoa to be the true sister group to all Metazoa—multicellular animals. Choanozoa is one group of organisms formerly called "protists" and is named for choanoflagellates (art and photo right), single-celled, colonial organisms that look like certain cells of sponges and flatworms. Current thinking suggests that the choanoflagellates alive today are the best living examples of what the last common ancestor of metazoans looked like.

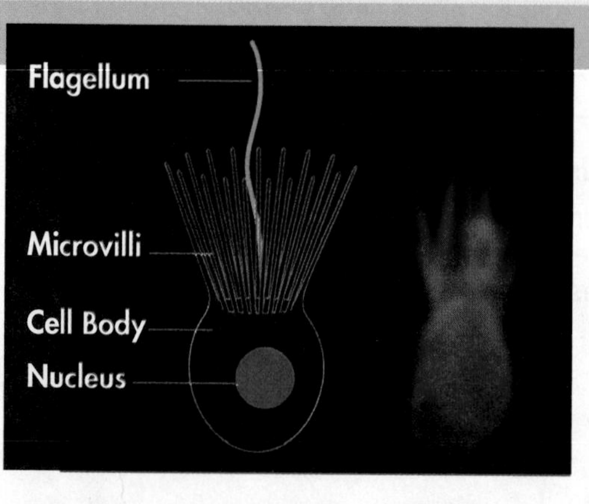

Porifera (Sponges)

KEY CHARACTERISTICS

Sponges are the simplest animals. They are classified as animals because they are multicellular, heterotrophic, lack cell walls, and have some specialized cells. They are aquatic, lack true tissues and organs, and have internal skeletons of spongin and/or spicules of calcium carbonate or silica. Sponges have no body symmetry.

Feeding and Digestion Filter feeders; intracellular digestion.

Circulation Via flow of water through body

Respiration Oxygen diffuses from water into cells as water flows through body.

Excretion Wastes diffuse from cells into water as water flows through body.

Response No nervous system; little capacity to respond to environmental changes.

Movement Juveniles drift or swim freely; adults are stationary.

Reproduction Most—sexual with internal fertilization; water flowing out of sponge disperses sperm, which fertilizes eggs inside sponge(s); may reproduce asexually by budding or producing gemmules.

GROUPS OF SPONGES

There are more than 5000 species of sponges; most are marine. Three major groups are described below.

DEMOSPONGIAE: Typical sponges

More than 90 percent of all living sponge species are in this group, including the few freshwater species. They have skeletons made of spongin, a flexible protein. Some species have silica spicules. Examples: Yellow Sponge, bath sponges, Carnivorous Mediterranean Sponge, tube sponges

Elephant Ear Sponge

HEXACTINELLIDA: Glass sponges

Glass sponges live in the deep ocean and are especially abundant in the Antarctic. They are called "glass" sponges because their skeletons are made of glasslike silica spicules. Examples: Venus's Flower Basket, Cloud Sponge

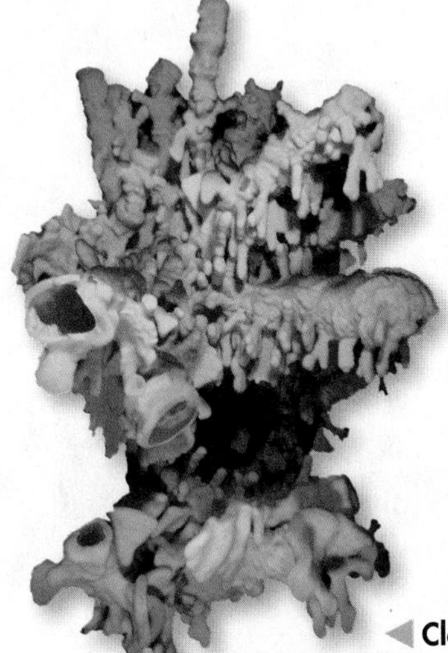

Cloud Sponge

CALCAREA: Calcareous sponges

Calcareous sponges live in shallow, tropical marine waters and are the only sponges with calcium carbonate spicules. Example: *Clathrina*

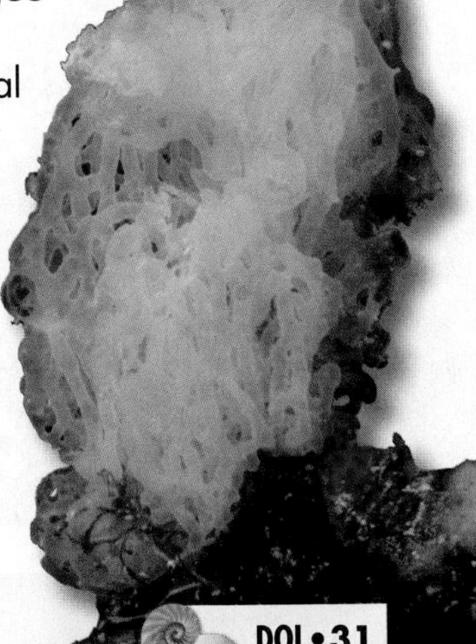

Yellow Tubular Sponge

Animals

Cnidarians

▲ Sea Nettle

KEY CHARACTERISTICS

Cnidarians are aquatic, mostly carnivorous, and the simplest animals to have specialized tissues (outer skin and lining of the gastrovascular cavity) and body symmetry (radial). Their tentacles have stinging cells called nematocysts used in feeding.

Feeding and Digestion Predatory, stinging prey with nematocysts; digestion begins extracellularly in gastrovascular cavity and is completed intracellularly; indigestible materials leave body through single opening; many, especially reef-building corals, also depend on symbiotic algae, or zooxanthellae.

Circulation No internal transport system; nutrients typically diffuse through body.

Respiration Diffusion through body walls

Excretion Cellular wastes diffuse through body walls.

Response Some specialized sensory cells: nerve cells in nerve net, statocysts that help determine up and down, eyespots (ocelli) made of light-detecting cells

Movement Polyps stationary, medusas free-swimming; some, such as sea anemones, can burrow and creep very slowly; others move using muscles that work with a hydrostatic skeleton and water in gastrovascular cavity; medusas such as jellyfish move by jet propulsion generated by muscle contractions.

Reproduction Most—alternate between sexual (most species by external fertilization) and asexual (polyps produce new polyps or medusae by budding)

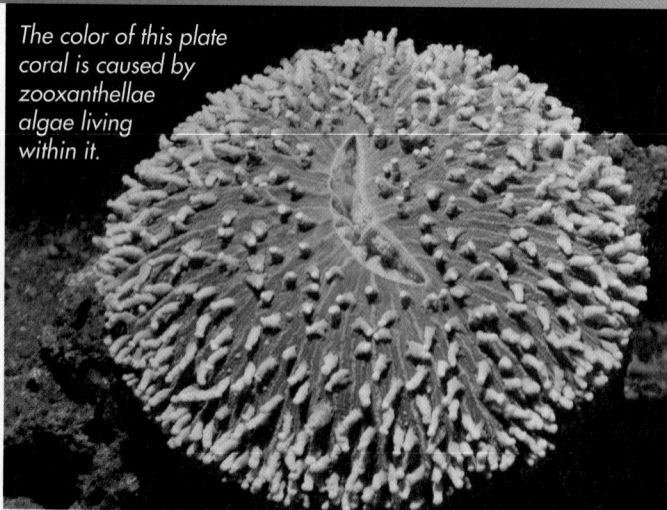

The color of this plate coral is caused by zooxanthellae algae living within it.

Eco • Alert

Coral Symbionts

Reef-building coral animals depend on symbiotic algae called zooxanthellae for certain vital nutritional needs. In many places, reef-building corals live close to the upper end of their temperature tolerance zone. If water temperatures rise too high, the coral-zooxanthellae symbiosis breaks down, and corals turn white in what is called "coral bleaching." If corals don't recover their algae soon, they weaken and die. This is one reason why coral reefs are in grave danger from global warming.

GROUPS OF CNIDARIANS

There are more than 9000 species of cnidarians.

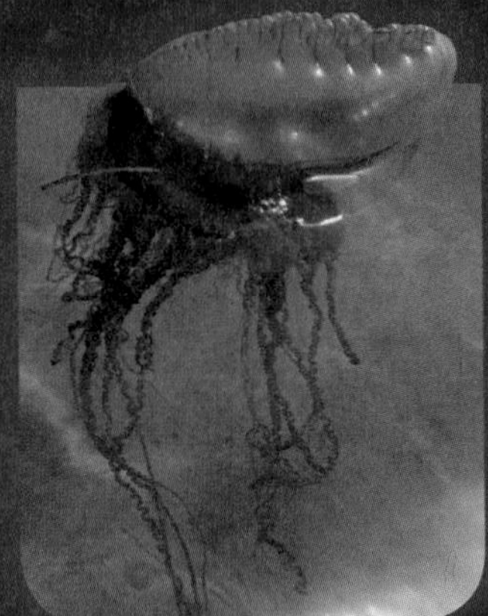

A Portuguese Man-of-War is actually a colony of polyps.

HYDROZOA: Hydras and their relatives

Hydras and their relatives spend most of their time as polyps and are either colonial or solitary. They reproduce asexually (by budding), sexually, or they alternate between sexual and asexual reproduction. Examples: hydra, Portuguese Man-of-War

Black Sea Nettle

SCYPHOZOA: Jellyfishes

Jellyfishes spend most of their time as medusas; some species bypass the polyp stage. They reproduce sexually and sometimes asexually by budding. Examples: Lion's Mane Jellyfish, Moon Jelly, Sea wasp

ANTHOZOA: Corals and sea anemones

Corals and sea anemones are colonial or solitary polyps with no medusa stage. The central body is surrounded by tentacles. They reproduce sexually or asexually. Examples: reef corals, sea anemones, sea pens, sea fans

Sea Anemone

Jellyfishes such as this sea nettle are beautiful to us but deadly to their prey. The stinging cells on their tentacles can kill prey instantly and can ruin a human swimmer's day at the beach!

Arthropods

KEY CHARACTERISTICS

Arthropods are the most diverse of all multicellular organisms. They have segmented bodies and jointed appendages. They are supported by tough exoskeletons made of chitin, which they periodically shed as they grow. Arthropods are coelomate protostomes with bilateral symmetry.

Eco•Alert

Beetle Damage

You probably know that some insects can seriously damage crop plants. But insects affect plants in natural habitats, too. One example is the mountain pine beetle, which is dramatically extending its range. Global warming appears to be enabling the beetle to survive farther north, and at higher altitudes, than it used to. The new beetle infestation is causing extensive damage to northern and high-altitude forests in North America. The death of millions of acres of trees has resulted in the release of large amounts of carbon dioxide, a greenhouse gas, into the atmosphere. You can see the sort of damage the beetles cause in the photo at right.

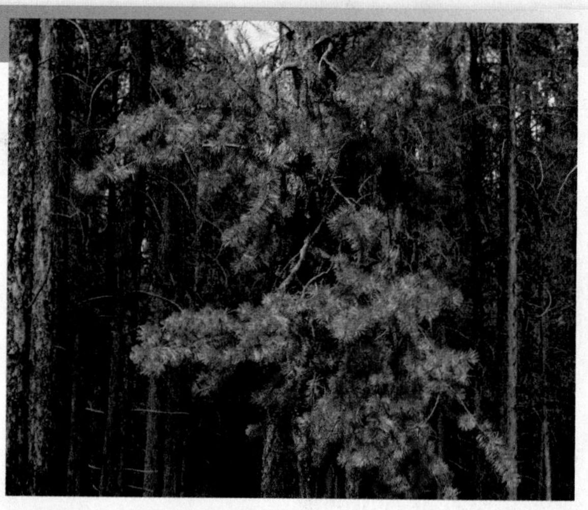

▲ *Mountain pine beetle damage to pine trees in White River National Forest, Colorado*

Feeding and Digestion Extremely diverse: herbivores, carnivores, detritivores, parasites, bloodsuckers, scavengers, filter feeders; digestive system with two openings; many feeding specializations in different groups

Circulation Open circulatory system with heart and arteries

Respiration Terrestrial—tracheal tubes or book lungs; aquatic—gills or book gills (horseshoe crabs)

Excretion Terrestrial—Malpighian tubules; aquatic—diffusion into water

Response Well-developed nervous system with brain; sophisticated sense organs

Movement Muscles attached internally to jointed exoskeletons

Reproduction Usually sexual, although some species may reproduce asexually under certain circumstances; many undergo metamorphosis during development

Most animals, including this land crab, are arthropods.

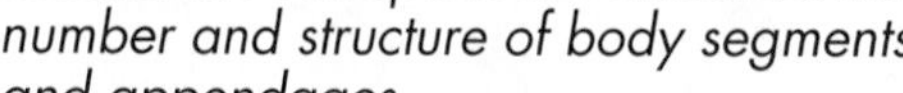

GROUPS OF ARTHROPODS

Phylum Arthropoda contains more known species than any other phylum. Scientists have identified more than 1,000,000 arthropod species, and some scientists expect there are millions yet to be identified. Arthropods are classified based on the number and structure of body segments and appendages.

▲ Lobster

CRUSTACEA: Crustaceans

There are crustacean species in almost every habitat, but most are aquatic, and most of these are marine. They have two or three body sections, two pairs of antennae, and chewing mouthparts called mandibles. Many have a carapace, or "shell," that covers part or all of the body. Examples: crabs, lobsters, crayfish, pill bugs, water fleas, barnacles

---

▲ Red Velvet Mite

CHELICERATA: Chelicerates

Living chelicerates include horseshoe crabs and arachnids. (Their extinct relatives include trilobites and giant "sea-scorpions.") Most living chelicerates are terrestrial. The body is composed of two parts—the cephalothorax and abdomen. The first pair of appendages are specialized feeding structures called chelicerae. Chelicerates have no antennae.

Horseshoe crabs are actually more closely related to spiders than to crabs!

Merostomata: Horseshoe crabs

The class Merostomata once included many species, but only four species of horseshoe crab survive today. All are marine. They have five pairs of walking legs and a long, spinelike tail.

Arachnida: Arachnids

The vast majority of arachnids are terrestrial. They have four pairs of walking legs and no tail. Examples: spiders, ticks, mites, scorpions, daddy longlegs

▲ Mexican Beauty Tarantula

UNIRAMIA: Uniramians

Most uniramians are terrestrial, although some are aquatic for all or part of their lives. They have one pair of antennae, mandibles, and unbranched appendages. Uniramians include at least three fourths of all known animal species!

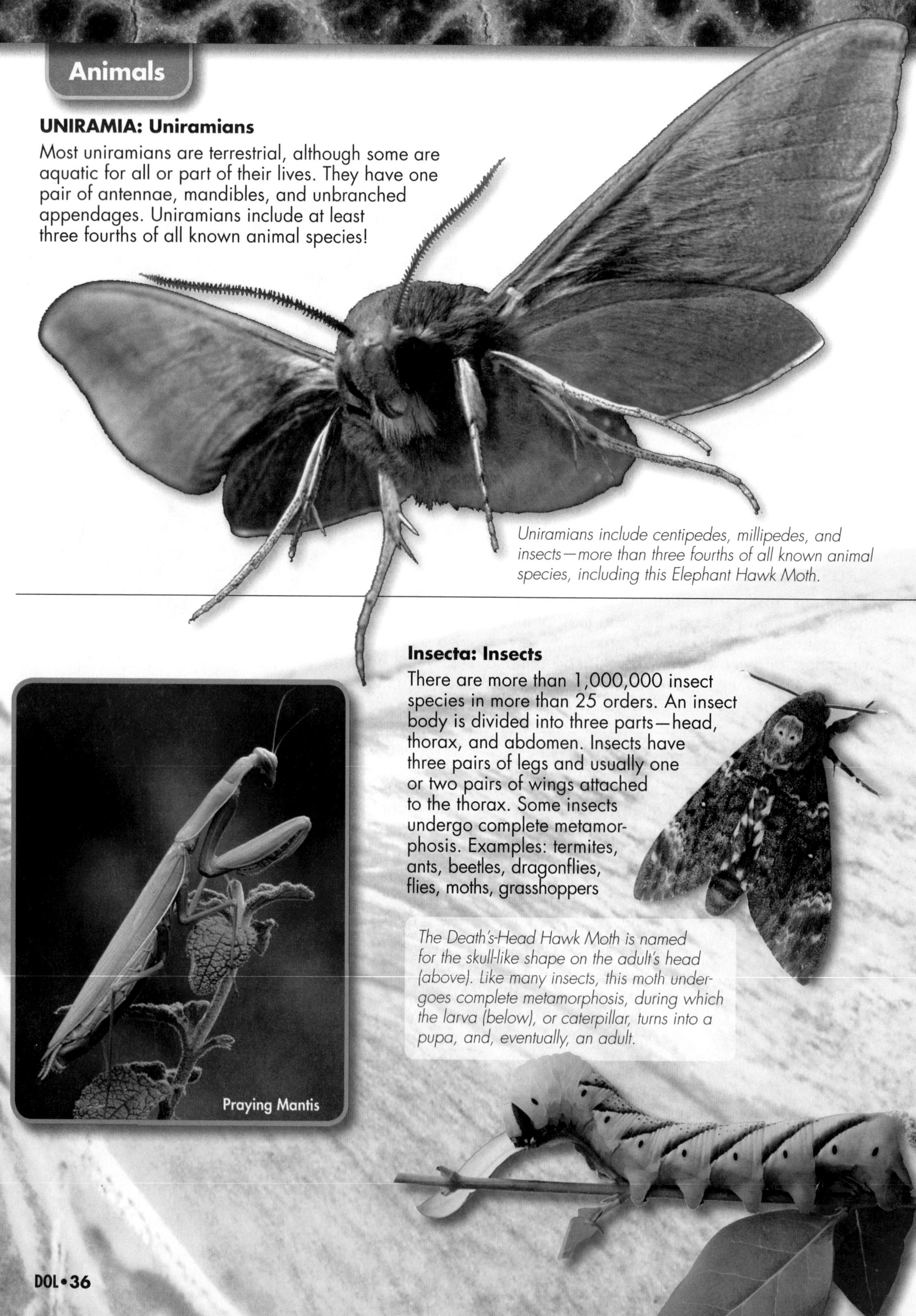

Uniramians include centipedes, millipedes, and insects—more than three fourths of all known animal species, including this Elephant Hawk Moth.

Insecta: Insects

There are more than 1,000,000 insect species in more than 25 orders. An insect body is divided into three parts—head, thorax, and abdomen. Insects have three pairs of legs and usually one or two pairs of wings attached to the thorax. Some insects undergo complete metamorphosis. Examples: termites, ants, beetles, dragonflies, flies, moths, grasshoppers

The Death's-Head Hawk Moth is named for the skull-like shape on the adult's head (above). Like many insects, this moth undergoes complete metamorphosis, during which the larva (below), or caterpillar, turns into a pupa, and, eventually, an adult.

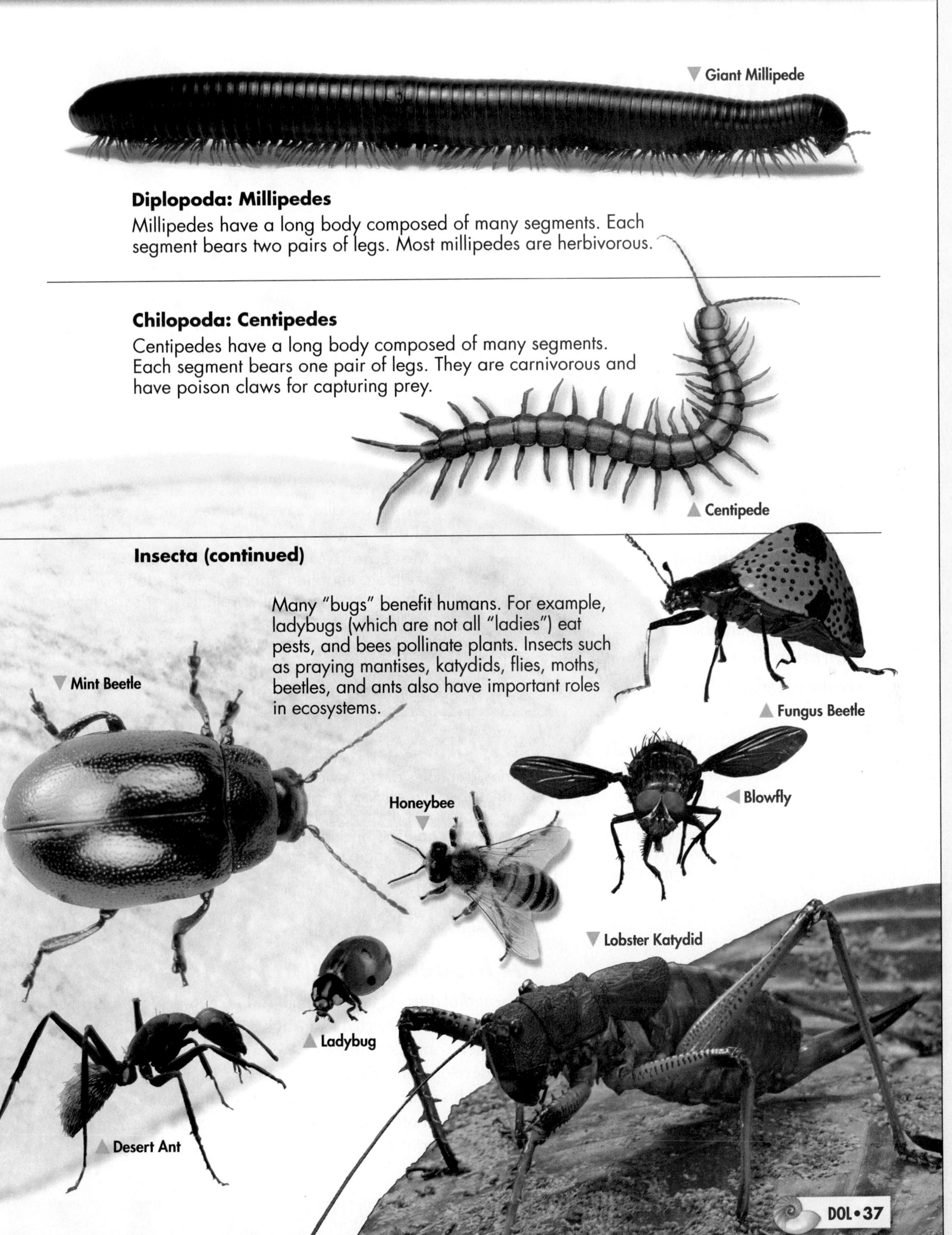

Diplopoda: Millipedes

Millipedes have a long body composed of many segments. Each segment bears two pairs of legs. Most millipedes are herbivorous.

Chilopoda: Centipedes

Centipedes have a long body composed of many segments. Each segment bears one pair of legs. They are carnivorous and have poison claws for capturing prey.

Insecta (continued)

Many "bugs" benefit humans. For example, ladybugs (which are not all "ladies") eat pests, and bees pollinate plants. Insects such as praying mantises, katydids, flies, moths, beetles, and ants also have important roles in ecosystems.

Nematodes (Roundworms)

"Hooks" in the mouth of a hookworm attach the worms to their hosts so that they can drink the host's blood or ingest their digested foods.

▲ *Foleyella* (SEM 130×)

KEY CHARACTERISTICS

Nematodes, or roundworms, are unsegmented worms with a tough outer cuticle, which they shed as they grow. This "molting" is one reason that nematodes are now considered more closely related to arthropods than to other wormlike animals. Nematodes are the simplest animals to have a "one-way" digestive system through which food passes from mouth to anus. They are protostomes and have a pseudocoelom.

Feeding and Digestion Some predators, some parasites, and some decomposers; one-way digestive tract with mouth and anus

Circulation By diffusion

Respiration Gas exchange through body walls

Excretion Through body walls

Response Simple nervous system consisting of several ganglia, several nerves, and several types of sense organs

Movement Muscles work with hydrostatic skeleton, enabling aquatic species to move like water snakes and soil-dwelling species to move by thrashing around.

Reproduction Sexual with internal fertilization; separate sexes; parasitic species may lay eggs in several hosts or host organs.

GROUPS OF ROUNDWORMS

There are more than 15,000 known species of roundworms, and there may be half a million species yet to be described. Free-living species live in almost every habitat imaginable: fresh water, salt water, hot springs, ice, soil. Parasitic species live on or inside a wide range of organisms, including insects, humans, and many domesticated animals and plants. Examples: *Ascaris lumbricoides*, hookworms, pinworms, *Trichinella, C. elegans*

• A Closer Look

A Model Organism?

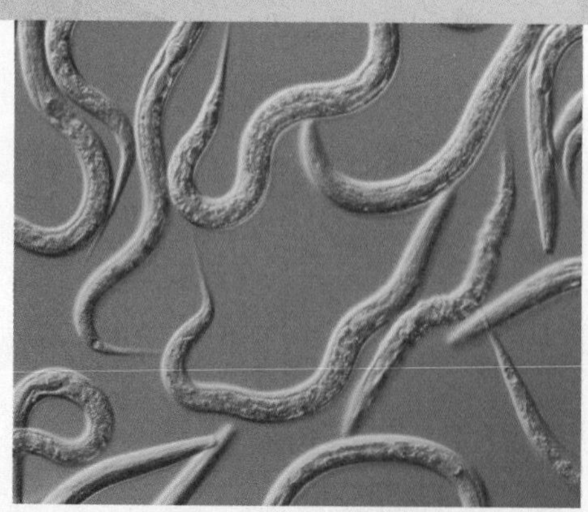

Caenorhabditis elegans is a small soil nematode. Fifty years ago, this species was selected as a "model organism" for the study of genetics and development. We can now chart the growth and development of *C. elegans*, cell by cell, from fertilization to adult. This information is invaluable in understanding the development in other species—including many other nematodes that cause serious disease.

◀ ***C. elegans*** (LM 64×)

Platyhelminthes (Flatworms)

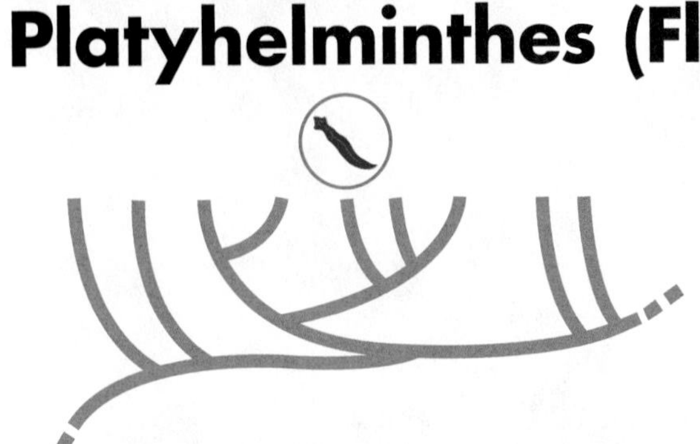

Some marine flatworms have astonishing colors and patterns!

▲ Blue Pseudoceros Flatworm

KEY CHARACTERISTICS

Flatworms are soft worms with tissues and internal organ systems. They are the simplest animals to have three embryonic germ layers, bilateral symmetry, and cephalization. They are acoelomates.

Feeding and Digestion Free-living—predators or scavengers that suck food in through a pharynx and digest it in a system that has one opening. Parasitic—feed on blood, tissue fluids, or cell pieces of the host, using simpler digestive systems than free-living species have. Tapeworms, which absorb nutrients from food that the host has already digested, have no digestive system.

Circulation By diffusion

Respiration Gas exchange by diffusion

Excretion Some—flame cells remove excess water and may remove metabolic wastes such as ammonia and urea. Many flame cells are connected to tubules that release substances through pores in the skin.

Response Free-living—several ganglia connected by nerve cords that run through the body, along with eyespots and other specialized sensory cells; parasitic—simpler nervous system than free-living forms have

Movement Free-living—using cilia and muscle cells.

Reproduction Free-living—most are hermaphrodites that reproduce sexually with internal fertilization; parasitic—commonly reproduce asexually by fission but also often reproduce sexually

GROUPS OF FLATWORMS

Flatworms are an amazingly diverse group of worms that include more than 20,000 species. They have historically been placed into three classes, but these taxa now appear not to be true clades, and will probably change.

TREMATODA: Flukes

Most flukes are parasites that infect internal organs of their hosts, but some infect external parts such as skin or gills. The life cycle typically involves more than one host or organ. Examples: *Schistosoma*, liver fluke

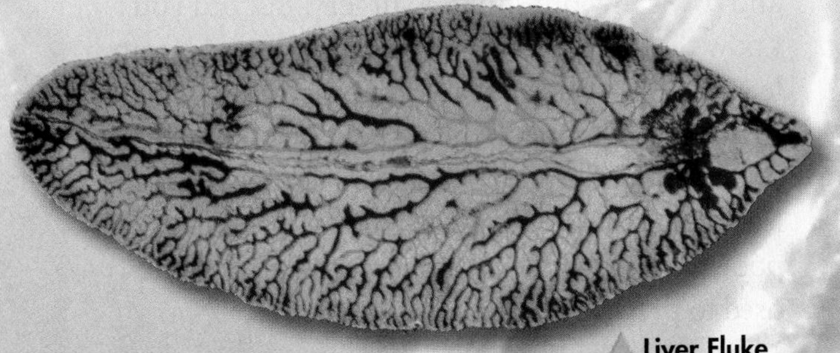

▲ Liver Fluke

TURBELLARIA: Turbellarians

Turbellarians are free-living aquatic and terrestrial predators and scavengers. Many are colorful marine species. Examples: planarians, polyclad flatworm

CESTODA: Tapeworms

Tapeworms are very long intestinal parasites that lack a digestive system and absorb nutrients directly through their body walls. The tapeworm body is composed of many repeated sections (proglottids) that contain both male and female reproductive organs.

Annelids (Segmented Worms)

KEY CHARACTERISTICS

Annelids are coelomate protostome worms whose bodies are composed of segments separated by internal partitions. The annelid digestive system has two openings.

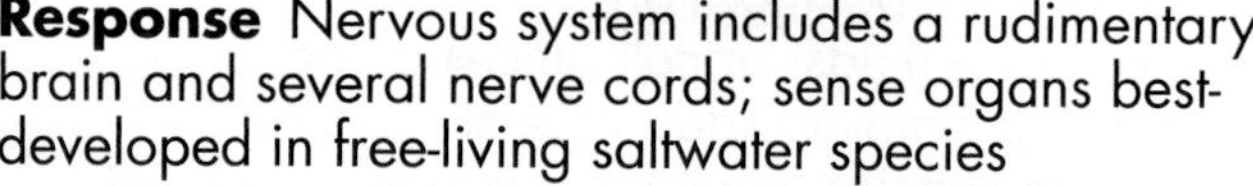

Peacock worms, whose feather-shaped gills look somewhat like peacock feathers, are marine annelids, or polychaetes.

Feeding and Digestion Filter feeders, carnivores, or parasites; many obtain food using a muscular pharynx, often equipped with "teeth"; widely varied digestive systems—some, such as earthworms, have complex digestive tracts.

Circulation Closed circulatory system with dorsal and ventral blood vessels; dorsal vessel pumps blood like a heart.

Respiration Aquatic—gills; terrestrial—skin

Excretion Digestive waste exits through anus; nitrogenous wastes eliminated by nephridia

Response Nervous system includes a rudimentary brain and several nerve cords; sense organs best-developed in free-living saltwater species

Movement Hydrostatic skeleton based on sealed body segments surrounded by longitudinal and circular muscles; many annelids have appendages that enable movement.

Reproduction Most—sexual, some through external fertilization with separate sexes, but others are simultaneous hermaphrodites that exchange sperm; most have a trochophore larval stage

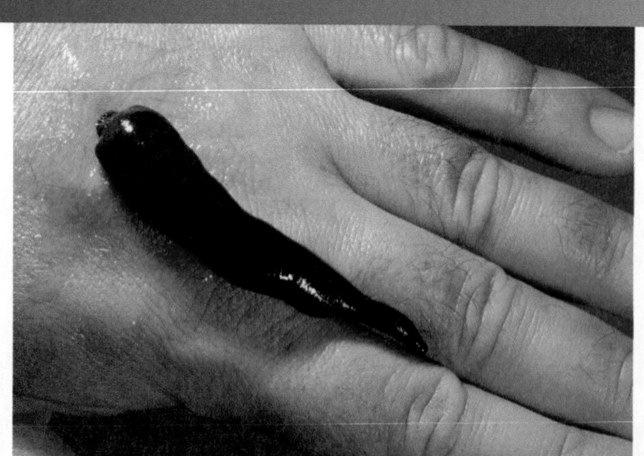

▲ *Leech* (Hirudo medicinalis) *drawing blood from a hand*

Did You Know?

Not-So-Modern Medicine

You may have heard that medieval healers used leeches to remove "excess" blood from patients and to clean wounds after surgery. But did you know that leeches—or at least compounds from leech saliva—have a place in modern medicine? Leech saliva contains the protein hirudin, which prevents blood from clotting. Some surgeons use leeches to relieve pressure caused by blood that pools in tissues after plastic surgery. Hirudin is also used to prevent unwanted blood clots.

▼ Feather-Duster Worms

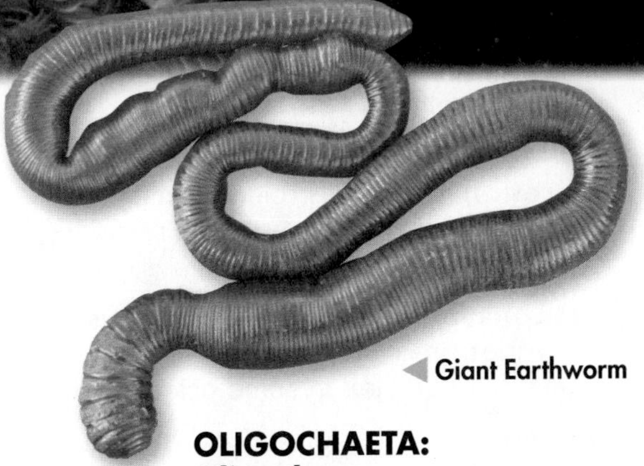

GROUPS OF ANNELIDS

There are more than 15,000 species of annelids.

HIRUDINEA: Leeches

Most leeches live in fresh water. They lack appendages. Leeches may be carnivores or blood-sucking external parasites. Example: medicinal leech *(Hirudo medicinalis)*

◀ Giant Earthworm

OLIGOCHAETA: Oligochaetes

Oligochaetes live in soil or fresh water. They lack appendages. Some use setae for movement but have fewer than polychaetes. Examples: *Tubifex*, earthworms

POLYCHAETA: Polychaetes

Polychaetes live in salt water; many move with paddle-like appendages called parapodia tipped with bristle-like setae. Examples: sandworms, bloodworms, fanworms, feather-duster worms

The white, bristle-like structures on the sides of this bearded fireworm are setae.

Mollusks

KEY CHARACTERISTICS

Mollusks have soft bodies that typically include a muscular foot. Body forms vary greatly. Many mollusks possess a hard shell secreted by the mantle, but in some, the only hard structure is internal. Mollusks are coelomate protostomes with bilateral symmetry.

Feeding and Digestion Digestive system with two openings; diverse feeding styles—mollusks can be herbivores, carnivores, filter feeders, detritivores, or parasites

Circulation Snails and clams—open circulatory system; octopi and squid—closed circulatory system

Respiration Aquatic mollusks—gills inside the mantle cavity; land mollusks—a saclike mantle cavity whose large, moist surface area is lined with blood vessels.

Excretion Body cells release ammonia into the blood, which nephridia remove and release outside the body.

Response Complexity of nervous system varies greatly; extremely simple in clams, but complex in some octopi.

Movement Varies greatly, by group. Some never move as adults, while others are very fast swimmers.

Reproduction Sexual; many aquatic species have free-swimming trochophore larval stage.

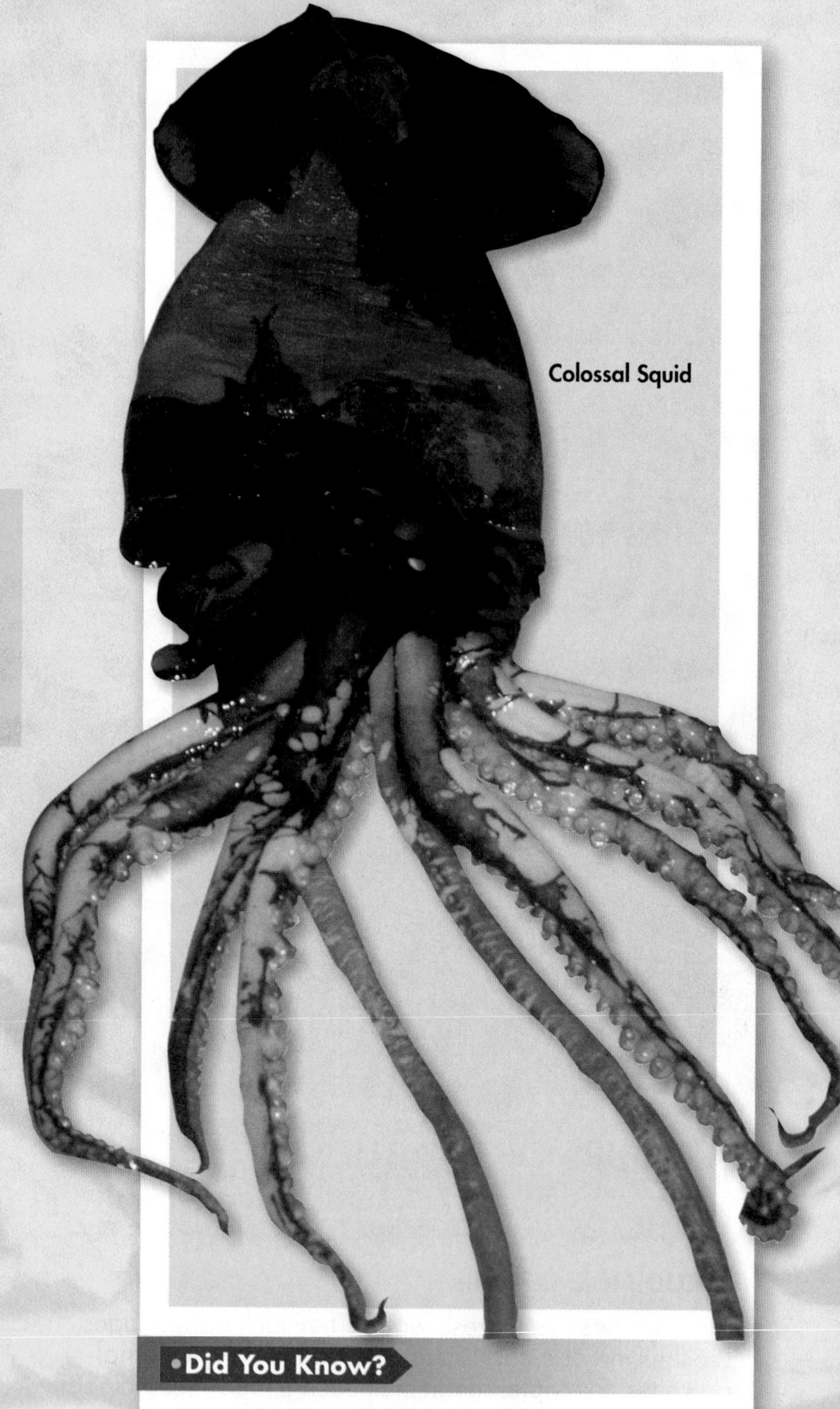
Colossal Squid

Did You Know?

The Colossal Squid

The Colossal Squid, the largest of all mollusks, has the largest eyes of any known animal. One 8-meter-long, 450-kilogram specimen of the species *Mesonychoteuthis hamiltoni* had eyes 28 centimeters across—larger than most dinner plates! The lens of this huge eye was the size of an orange.

GROUPS OF MOLLUSKS

Mollusks are traditionally divided into several classes based on characteristics of the foot and the shell; specialists estimate that there are somewhere between 50,000 and 200,000 species of mollusks alive today.

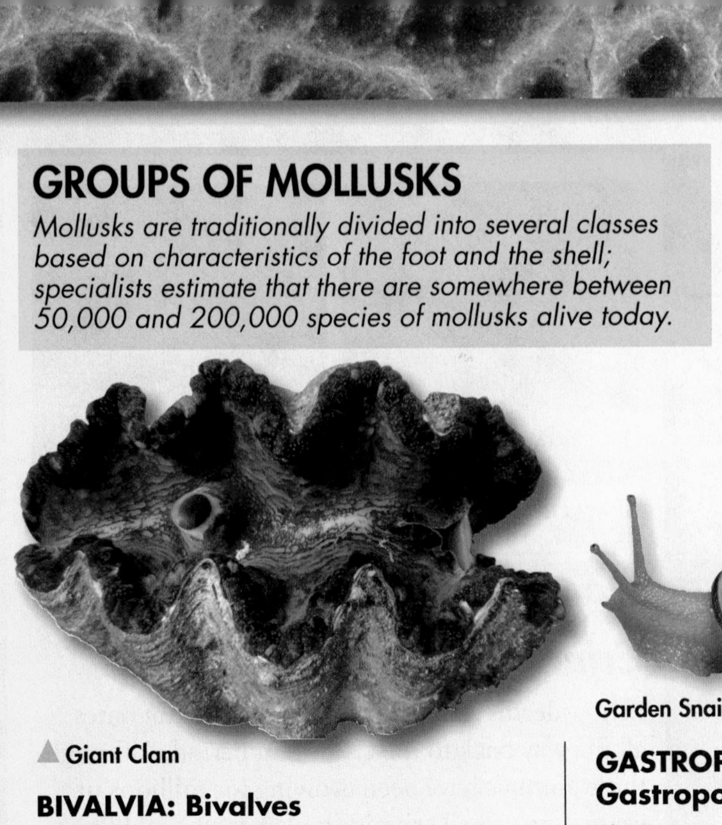

▲ Giant Clam

Garden Snail ▲

▲ Chambered Nautilus

BIVALVIA: Bivalves

Bivalves are aquatic. They have a two-part hinged shell and a wedge-shaped foot. They are mostly stationary as adults. Some burrow in mud or sand; others attach to rocks. Most are filter feeders that use gill siphons to take in water that carries food. Clams have open circulatory systems. Bivalves have the simplest nervous systems among mollusks. Examples: clams, oysters, scallops, mussels

GASTROPODA: Gastropods

There are both terrestrial and aquatic gastropods. Most have a single spiral, chambered shell. Gastropods use a broad, muscular foot to move and have a distinct head region. Snails and slugs feed with a structure called a radula that usually works like sandpaper. Some species are predators whose harpoon-shaped radula carries deadly venom. They have open circulatory systems. Many gastropod species are cross-fertilizing hermaphrodites. Examples: snails, slugs, nudibranchs, sea hares

CEPHALOPODA: Cephalopods

Cephalopods live in salt water. The cephalopod has a highly developed brain and sense organs. The head is attached to a single foot, which is divided into tentacles. They have closed circulatory systems. Octopi use beaklike jaws for feeding; a few are venomous. Cephalopods have the most complex nervous systems among mollusks; octopi have complex behavior and have shown the ability to learn in laboratory settings. Examples: octopi, squids, nautilus, cuttlefish

Nudibranchs, such as this Blue Dorid, are marine gastropods without shells. They breathe through gills (the yellow structures) on their backs.

Animals

Echinoderms

KEY CHARACTERISTICS

Echinoderms are marine animals that have spiny skin surrounding an endoskeleton. Their unique water vascular system includes tube feet with suction-cuplike ends used in moving and feeding. The water vascular system also plays a role in respiration, circulation, and excretion. Echinoderms are coelomate deuterostomes. Adults exhibit 5-part radial symmetry.

Feeding and Digestion Method varies by group—echinoderms can be filter feeders, detritivores, herbivores, or carnivores.

Circulation Via fluid in the coelom, a rudimentary system of vessels, and the water vascular system

Respiration Gas exchange is carried out by surfaces of tube feet, and, in many species, by skin gills.

Crinoid fossil, about 400 million years old

Living modern crinoid (feather star)

• **A Look Back in Time**

Crinoids Then and Now

Echinoderms have a long fossil record that dates all the way back to the Cambrian Period. Although these animals have been evolving for millions of years, some fossil crinoids look a great deal like living crinoids.

Excretion Digestive wastes released through anus; nitrogenous cellular wastes excreted as ammonia through tube feet and skin gills.

Response Minimal nervous system; nerve ring is connected to body sections by radial nerves; most have scattered sensory cells that detect light, gravity, and chemicals secreted by prey.

Movement In most, tube feet work with endoskeleton to enable locomotion.

Reproduction Sexual, with external fertilization; larvae have bilateral symmetry, unlike adults.

You can't miss the 5-part radial symmetry of this candy-cane sea star moving across a sea anemone.

GROUPS OF ECHINODERMS

There are more than 7000 species of echinoderms.

◀ Sea star

CRINOIDEA: Crinoids

Crinoids are filter feeders; some use tube feet along feathery arms to capture plankton. The mouth and anus are on the upper surface of the body disk. Some are stationary as adults while others can "walk" using short "arms" on the lower body surface. Examples: sea lily, feather star

▶ Feeding crinoid

ASTEROIDEA: Sea stars

Sea stars are bottom dwellers whose star-shaped bodies have flexible joints. They are carnivorous—the stomach pushes through the mouth onto the body tissues of prey and pours out digestive enzymes. The stomach then retracts with the partially digested prey; digestion is completed inside the body. Examples: crown-of-thorns sea star, sunstar

▼ Basket star feeding on Orange Finger Sponge

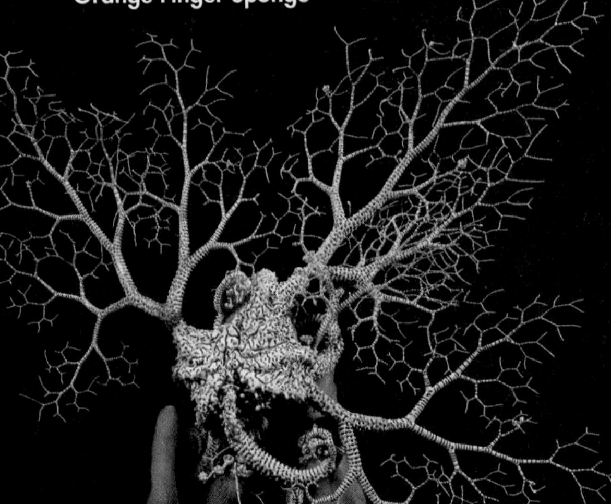

OPHIUROIDEA: Ophiuroids

Ophiuroids have small body disks, long, armored arms, and flexible joints. Most are filter feeders or detritivores. Examples: brittle star, basket star

ECHINOIDEA

Echinoids lack arms. Their endoskeleton is rigid and boxlike and covered with movable spines. Most echinoids are herbivores or detritivores that use five-part jawlike structures to scrape algae from rocks. Examples: sea urchin, sand dollar, sea biscuit

▼ *Red sea urchins and purple sea urchins feeding on kelp*

▼ Sea cucumber

HOLOTHUROIDEA: Sea cucumbers

Sea cucumbers have a cylindrical, rubbery body with a reduced endoskeleton and no arms. They typically lie on their side and move along the ocean floor by the combined action of tube feet and body-wall muscles. These filter feeders or detritivores use a set of retractable feeding tentacles on one end to take in sand and detritus, from which they glean food.

Nonvertebrate Chordates

Tunicates are chordates named for the colorful tunic-like covering the adults have. As larvae, tunicates have all the characteristics of chordates, as well as bilateral symmetry, but as adults, they look very, very different.

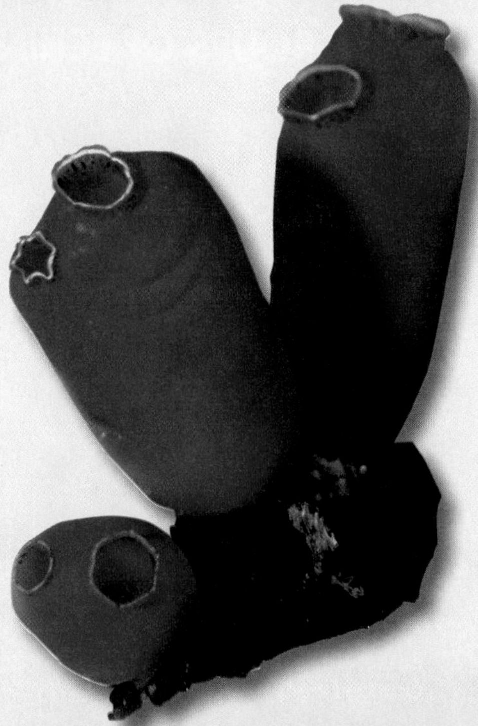

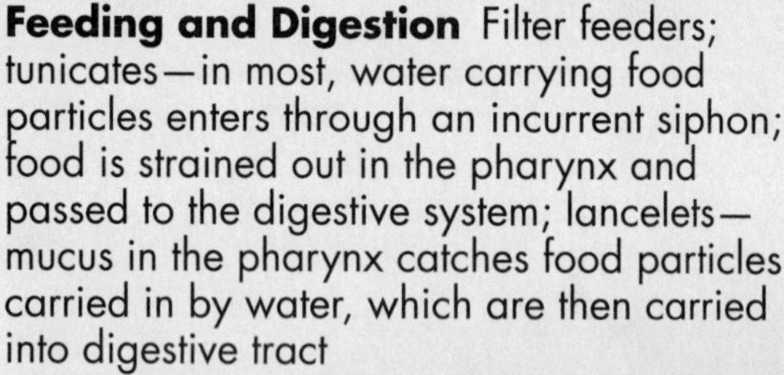

KEY CHARACTERISTICS

The nonvertebrate chordates are the only chordates that lack a backbone. Like other chordates, they have a nerve cord, notochord, pharyngeal pouches, and a tail at some point during development. They are coelomate deuterostomes. The two subphyla, tunicates and lancelets, differ significantly.

Feeding and Digestion Filter feeders; tunicates—in most, water carrying food particles enters through an incurrent siphon; food is strained out in the pharynx and passed to the digestive system; lancelets—mucus in the pharynx catches food particles carried in by water, which are then carried into digestive tract

Circulation Closed; tunicates—heart pumps blood by "wringing out," and flow periodically reverses direction; lancelets—no heart, but blood vessels pump blood through body in one direction

Respiration Tunicates—gas exchange occurs in the gills and across other body surfaces; lancelets—through pharynx and body surfaces

Excretion Tunicates—most through excurrent siphon; lancelets—flame cells in nephridia release water and nitrogenous wastes into the atrium and out through an opening called an atriopore

Response Cerebral ganglion, few specialized sensory organs; tunicates—sensory cells in and on the siphons and other internal surfaces help control the amount of water passing through the pharynx; lancelets—a pair of eyespots detect light

Movement Tunicates—free-swimming larvae, but most are stationary as adults; lancelets—no appendages: they move by contracting muscles paired on either side of the body

Reproduction Tunicates—most sexual and hermaphroditic with external fertilization, but some reproduce by budding; most have free-swimming tadpole-like larvae that metamorphose into adults; lancelets—sexual with external fertilization

Eco • Alert

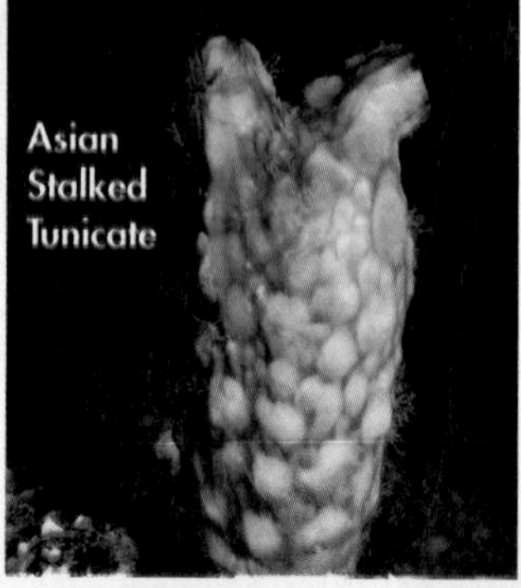

Out-of-Control Tunicates

You've never heard of them, but Asian stalked tunicates are disrupting marine ecosystems in Washington State; Prince Edward Island, Canada; and elsewhere. Tunicate larvae are carried in the ballast water of freight ships and discharged wherever the ships make port. There, away from their usual predators, the tunicates grow out of control, smothering shellfish beds and covering boats, docks, and underwater equipment. Researchers are still trying to figure out how to control them.

GROUPS OF NONVERTEBRATE CHORDATES

There are two major groups of nonvertebrate chordates: tunicates and lancelets (sometimes called amphioxus).

Two lancelets, Branchiostoma lanceolatum, *poking out of sand.*

CEPHALOCHORDATA: Lancelets

Lancelets are fishlike animals that have bilateral symmetry and live in salt water. They are filter feeders and have no internal skeleton. Example: *Branchiostoma*

▼ Pastel Sea Squirt

UROCHORDATA: Tunicates

Tunicates are filter feeders that live in salt water. Most adults have a tough outer covering ("tunic") and no body symmetry; most display chordate features and bilateral symmetry only during larval stages. Many adults are stationary; some are free-swimming. Examples: sea squirts, sea peaches, salps

Sea Squirts

Animals

Fishes

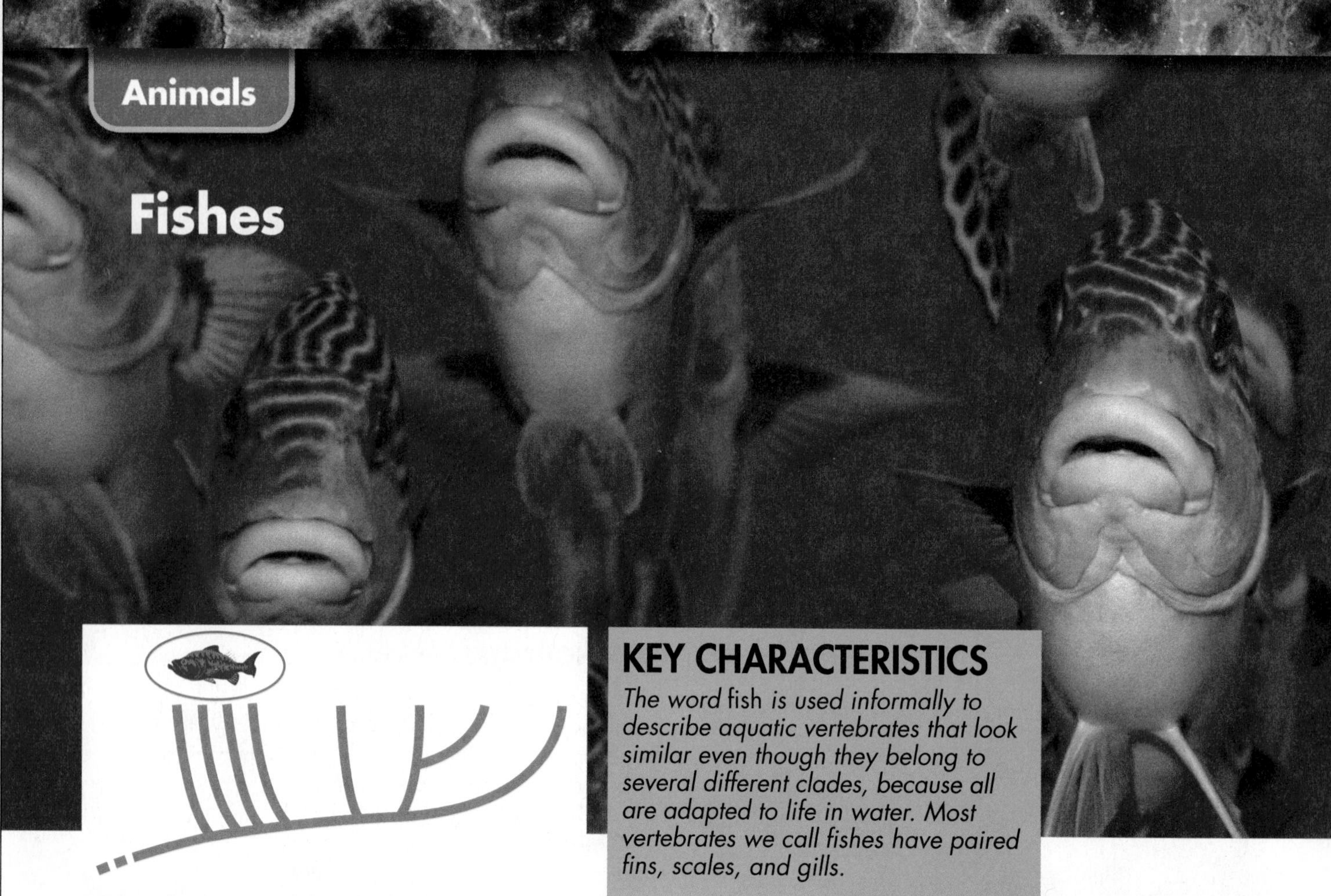

KEY CHARACTERISTICS

The word fish is used informally to describe aquatic vertebrates that look similar even though they belong to several different clades, because all are adapted to life in water. Most vertebrates we call fishes have paired fins, scales, and gills.

Feeding and Digestion Varies widely, both within and between groups: herbivores, carnivores, parasites, filter feeders, detritivores; digestive organs often include specialized teeth and jaws, crop, esophagus, stomach, liver, pancreas

Circulation Closed, single-loop circulatory system; two-chambered heart

Respiration Gills; some have specialized lungs or other adaptations that enable them to obtain oxygen from air.

Excretion Diffusion across gill membranes; kidneys

Response Brain with many parts; highly developed sense organs, including lateral line system

Movement Paired muscles on either side of backbone; many have highly maneuverable fins; the largest groups have two sets of paired fins; some have a gas-filled swim bladder that regulates buoyancy.

Reproduction Methods vary within and between groups: external or internal fertilization; oviparous, ovoviviparous, or viviparous

• A Look Back in Time

Live Birth in Devonian Seas

▲ *Artist's conception of* Materpiscis *giving birth*

You might think that live birth is a recent addition to chordate diversity. Guess again. Recent fossil finds of fishes from the Devonian Period show that at least one group of fishes was already bearing live young 380 million years ago. Two incredibly well preserved fossils, including that of the fish *Materpiscis*, show the remains of young with umbilical cords still attached to their mother's bodies. This is the earliest fossil evidence of viviparity in vertebrates.

GROUPS OF FISHES

Fishes are the largest group of vertebrates, including more than 30,000 species. Evolutionary classification of these animals is still a work in progress; many traditional groups are now known not to be clades. "Fishes" actually represent several ancient clades, one of which includes tetrapods, or four-limbed vertebrates. Fishes, as we treat them here, include two groups of jawless fishes (hagfishes and lampreys), cartilaginous fishes, and bony fishes.

"Sweetlips" are, despite their funny faces, easily recognizable as fish.

"JAWLESS FISHES"

Hagfishes and lampreys make up separate clades, but their bodies share common features that distinguish them from other fishes. They have no jaws, lack vertebrae, and their skeletons are made of fiber and cartilage.

PETROMYZONTIDA: Lampreys

Lampreys are mostly filter feeders as larvae and parasites as adults. The head of an adult lamprey is taken up almost completely by a circular, tooth-bearing, sucking disk with a round mouth. Adult lampreys typically attach themselves to fishes. They hold on to their hosts using the teeth in their sucking disk and then scrape away at the skin with a rasping tongue. Lampreys then suck up their host's tissues and body fluids. Because lampreys feed mostly on blood, they are called "vampires of the sea."

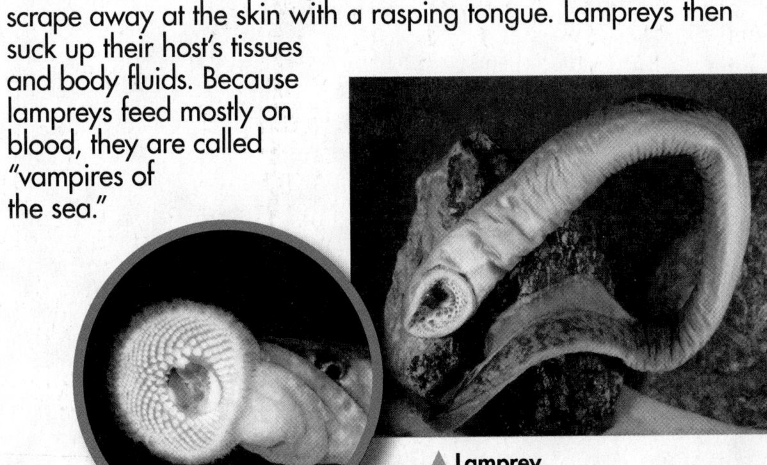

Lamprey mouth

▲ Lamprey

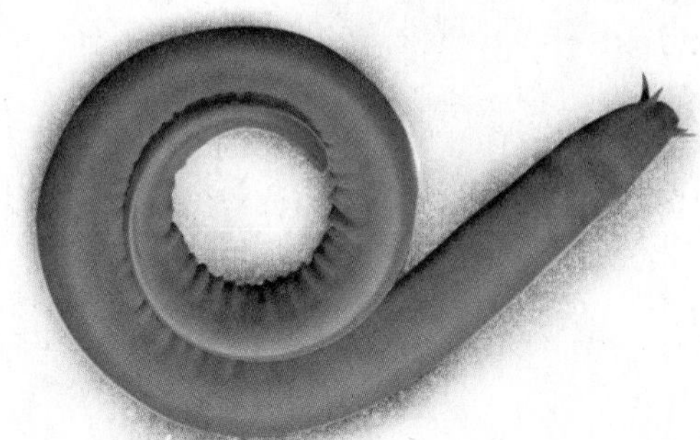

▲ Pacific Hagfish

MYXINI: Hagfishes

Hagfishes have pinkish gray wormlike bodies and four or six short tentacles around their mouths. They retain notochords as adults. Hagfishes lack image-forming eyes, but have light-detecting sensors scattered around their bodies. They feed on dead and dying animals using a rasping tongue that scrapes away layers of flesh.

Tiger Shark

CHONDRICHTHYES: Cartilaginous Fishes

Members of this clade are considered "cartilaginous" because they lack true bone; their skeletons are built entirely of cartilage. Most cartilaginous fishes also have tough, scales, which make their skin as rough as sandpaper.

Holocephalans: Chimaeras

Chimaeras have smooth skin that lacks scales. Most have just a few platelike, grinding teeth and a venomous spine located in front of the dorsal fin. Examples: ghostfish, ratfish, rabbitfish

Spotted Ratfish

Elasmobranchii: Sharks, skates, and rays

Sharks, skates, and rays are very diverse, but all have skin covered with toothlike scales known as dermal denticles. Elasmobranchii make up the vast majority of living cartilaginous fish species.

Dermal denticles on shark skin reduce drag, helping the shark to swim faster. (SEM 40×)

Galeomorphi: Sharks

Most of the 350 or so shark species have large, curved asymmetrical tails, torpedo-shaped bodies, and pointed snouts with a mouth underneath. Predatory sharks, such as the great white, have many teeth arranged in rows. As teeth in the front rows are worn out or lost, new teeth replace them. Some sharks go through 20,000 teeth in their lifetime! Other sharks are filter feeders, and some species have flat teeth for crushing mollusk and crustacean shells. Examples: Great White Shark, Whale Shark, Hammerhead Shark

Hammerhead Shark

Squalomorphi: Skates and rays

Skates and rays have diverse feeding habits. Some feed on bottom-dwelling invertebrates by using their mouths as powerful vacuums. Others filter-feed on plankton. When not feeding or swimming, many skates and rays cover themselves with a thin layer of sand and rest on the ocean floor. Example: stingray

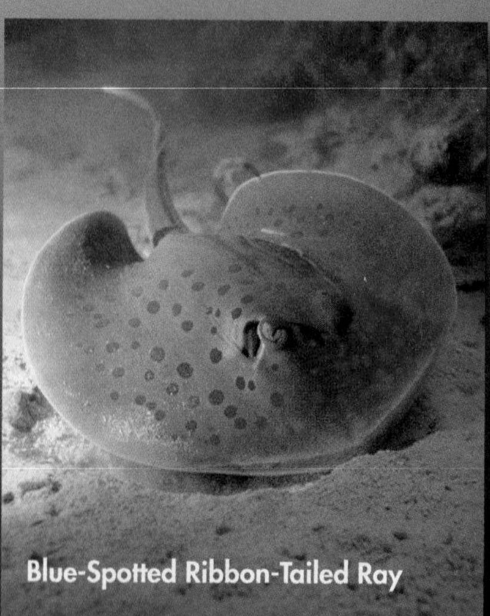
Blue-Spotted Ribbon-Tailed Ray

OSTEICHTHYES: Bony fishes

The skeletons of these vertebrates are made of true bone. This clade includes the ancestors and living members of all "higher" vertebrate groups—including tetrapods.

Rainbow Trout

Actinopterygii: Ray-finned fishes

Almost all living bony fishes belong to a huge group called ray-finned fishes. The name *ray-finned* refers to the slender bony rays that are connected to one another by a layer of skin to form fins.

Coelacanth

Sarcopterygii: Lobe-finned fishes

Seven living species of bony fishes, including lungfishes and coelacanths, are classified as lobe-finned fishes. Lungfishes live in fresh water, but coelacanths are marine. The fleshy fins of lobe-finned fishes are supported by strong bones rather than rays. Some of these bones are homologous to the limb bones of land vertebrates. Examples: lungfish, coelacanths

This clade includes the ancestors of tetrapods, so, technically, all living tetrapods (including us!) are Sarcopterygians! As a result, the bony-fish clade includes almost half of all chordate species!

Animals

Amphibians

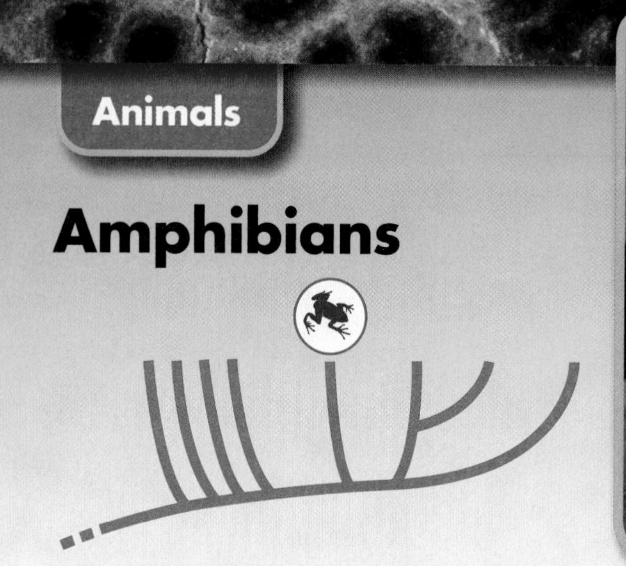

Marsupial Frog

KEY CHARACTERISTICS

The word amphibian *means "double life," an apt name for these vertebrates, most of which live in water as larvae and on land as adults. Most adult amphibians breathe with lungs, lack scales and claws, and have moist skin that contains mucous glands.*

Feeding and Digestion Tadpoles—usually filter feeders or herbivores with long, coiled intestines to digest plant material; adults—carnivores with shorter intestines for processing meat

Circulation Double-loop system with three-chambered heart

Respiration Larvae breathe through skin and gills; most adult species have lungs, though a few use gills; lungless salamanders breathe through their mouth-cavity lining and skin.

Excretion Kidneys produce urine.

Response Well-developed nervous and sensory systems; organs include protective nictitating membrane over moveable eyes, tympanic membranes, lateral line system

Movement Larvae have tails; adults have limbs (except caecilians); some have specialized toes for climbing.

Reproduction Most lay eggs without shells that are fertilized externally; most undergo metamorphosis from aquatic tadpole larvae that breathe with gills to land-dwelling adults, which usually have lungs and limbs.

Red-Eyed Treefrog

The Frogs Are Disappearing!

For several decades, scientists have noticed that amphibian populations worldwide have been decreasing, and a number of species have become extinct. Scientists have not yet pinpointed a single cause for this problem. It is, however, becoming clear that amphibians are susceptible to a variety of environmental threats, including habitat loss, ozone depletion, acid rain, water pollution, fungal infections, and introduced aquatic predators.

To better understand this decline, biologists worldwide have been focusing their efforts and sharing data about amphibian populations. One amphibian-monitoring program covers all of North America.

GROUPS OF AMPHIBIANS

The three orders of amphibians include more than 6000 species, roughly 5000 of which are frogs and toads.

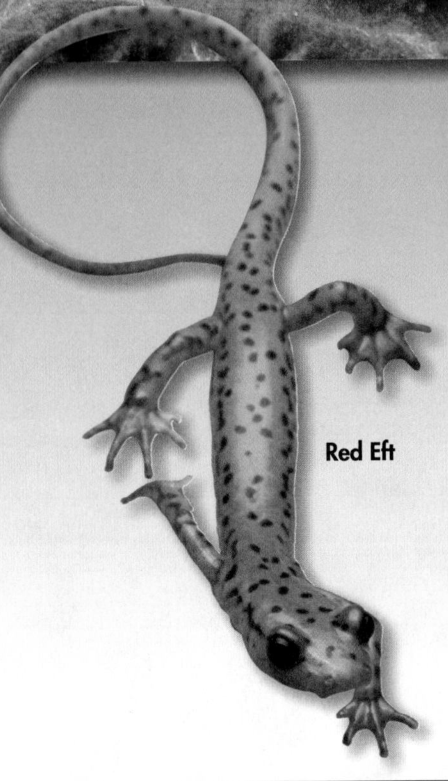

Red Eft

URODELA: Salamanders and newts

Salamanders and newts have long bodies and tails. Most also have four legs. All are carnivores. Adults usually live in moist woods, where they tunnel under rocks and rotting logs. Some salamanders, such as the mud puppy, keep their gills as adults and live in water all their lives. Examples: Barred Tiger Salamander, Red Eft

American Toad

ANURA: Frogs and toads

Adult frogs and toads are amphibians without tails that can jump. Frogs tend to have long legs and make long jumps, whereas toads have shorter legs that limit them to shorter hops. Frogs are generally more dependent on bodies of fresh water than toads, which may live in moist woods or even deserts. Examples: treefrogs, Leopard Frog, American Toad, spadefoot toads

APODA: Caecilians

The least-known and most unusual amphibians are the legless caecilians. They have tentacles, and many have fishlike scales embedded in their skin—which shows that not all amphibians fit the general definition. Caecilians live in water or burrow in moist soil or sediment, feeding on small invertebrates such as termites. Examples: Ringed Caecilian, Yellow-Striped Caecilian

Ringed Caecilian

▶ *Because amphibian eggs must develop in water, most live in moist climates. Some, such as this Alpine Newt, live on cool, rainy mountain slopes.*

Reptiles

Saltwater crocodiles, such as this young one, are the largest living reptiles and sometime reach 6 meters long. But that's still only half as long as their famous dinosaur ancestor, T. rex!

KEY CHARACTERISTICS OF REPTILES

Living reptiles, traditionally classified in the class Reptilia, are ectothermic vertebrates with dry, scaly skin; lungs; and amniotic eggs. Modern evolutionary classification now recognizes a larger clade Reptilia that includes living reptiles, extinct dinosaurs, and birds—the living descendants of one dinosaur group.

Feeding and Digestion Feeding methods vary by group; digestive systems—herbivores have long digestive systems to break down plant materials; carnivores may swallow prey whole

Circulation Two loops; heart with two atria and one or two ventricles

Respiration Spongy lungs provide large surface area for gas exchange; lungs operated by muscles and moveable ribs

Excretion Kidneys; urine contains ammonia or uric acid

Response Brain; well-developed senses including, in some species, infrared detectors that can spot warm-bodied prey in the dark

Movement Strong limbs (except snakes)

Reproduction Internal fertilization via cloaca; amniotic egg with leathery shell

Eco • Alert

Calling Doctor 'Gator!

You might think of alligators mostly as killing machines, but their blood may soon provide medicines that can save lives. An alligator's immune system works quite differently from our own. Proteins in their white blood cells can kill multidrug resistant bacteria, disease-causing yeasts, and even HIV. Remarkably, these proteins work against pathogens to which the animals have never been exposed. Researchers are currently sequencing the genes for these proteins and hope to develop them into human medicines in the near future.

GROUPS OF REPTILES

There are nearly 9000 species of reptiles (not including birds).

SPHENODONTA: Tuataras

The tuatara, found only on a few small islands off the coast of New Zealand, is the only living member of this group. Tuataras resemble lizards in some ways, but they lack external ears and retain primitive scales.

Tuatara

SQUAMATA: Lizards, snakes, and relatives

There are more than 8000 species of lizards and snakes. Most lizards have legs, clawed toes, and external ears. Some lizards have evolved highly specialized structures, such as glands in the lower jaw that produce venom. Snakes are legless; they have lost both pairs of legs through evolution. Examples: iguanas, Milk Snake, Coral Snake

Leopard Gecko

ARCHOSAURS: Crocodilians; pterosaurs and dinosaurs (extinct); and birds

This clade includes some of the most spectacular animals that have ever lived. The extinct dinosaurs and pterosaurs (flying reptiles), whose adaptive radiations produced some of the largest animals ever to walk Earth or fly above it, are the closest relatives of birds. Living crocodilians are short-legged and have long and typically broad snouts. They are fierce carnivorous predators, but the females are attentive mothers. Crocodilians live only in regions where the climate remains warm year-round. We discuss birds separately. Examples: extinct types: *Tyrannosaurus*, *Pteranodon*; living types: alligators, crocodiles, caimans, and birds (see following pages)

Leopard Tortoise

TESTUDINE: Turtles and tortoises

Turtles and tortoises have a shell built into their skeleton. Most can pull their heads and legs into the shell for protection. Instead of teeth, these reptiles have hornlike ridges covering their jaws equipped with sharp beaklike tips. Strong limbs can lift their body off the ground when walking or, in the case of sea turtles, can drag their body across a sandy shore to lay eggs. Examples: snapping turtles, green sea turtles, Galápagos tortoise

Paraguay Caiman

Animals

Birds

Today, only birds have feathers. These delicate, intricately interlocking and beautiful structures keep birds warm and cool and enable most to fly.

Common Kingfisher

KEY CHARACTERISTICS OF BIRDS

Birds, once placed in a class of their own, are now recognized as endothermic reptiles with feathers and hard-shelled, amniotic eggs that are descended from dinosaurs. Birds have two scaly legs and front limbs modified into wings, which enable most species to fly.

Feeding and Digestion No teeth; bills adapted to widely varied foods, including insects, seeds, fruits, nectar, fish, meat; organs of the digestive system include crop, gizzard, cloaca

Circulation Two loops with four-chambered heart; separation of oxygen-rich and oxygen-poor blood

Respiration Constant, one-way flow of air through lungs and air sacs increases the efficiency of gas exchange and supports high metabolic rate

Excretion Kidneys remove nitrogenous wastes from blood, converting them to uric acid, which is excreted through cloaca

Response Brain with large optic lobes and enlarged cerebellum; highly evolved sense organs including, in some species, eyes that can see ultraviolet light

Movement Skeleton made up of lightweight, hollow bones with internal struts for strength; powerful muscles; most fly

Reproduction Internal fertilization via cloaca; amniotic egg with hard, brittle shell; depending on species, newly hatched young may be precocial—downy-feathered chicks able to move around and feed themselves, or altricial—bare-skinned and totally dependent on their parents

• A Look Back in Time

Birds of a Feather

Fossils recently discovered in lake beds in China have greatly expanded our understanding of bird evolution. One exciting discovery was that of a four-winged dinosaur named *Microraptor gui* from about 125 million years ago. *Microraptor gui*, which was related to *Tyrannosaurus rex*, had feathers on both its wings *and* its legs, so some researchers hypothesize that it flew like a biplane! This and other fossils show that several lineages of dinosaurs and ancient birds evolved various kinds of feathers over millions of years.

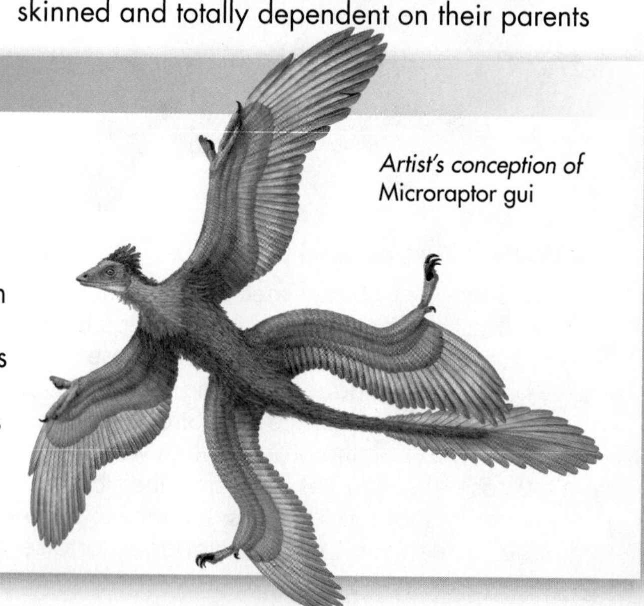

Artist's conception of Microraptor gui

GROUPS OF BIRDS

Evolutionary classification of living birds is still a work in progress, as different techniques and analyses produce different results. There are about 10,000 species. The groups described below illustrate some of the diversity of birds.

Ostrich

PALEOGNATHAE: Ostriches, emus, kiwis, and relatives

This group represents an early branch of the bird family tree that is separate from all other living birds. This clade includes the largest birds alive today. Ostriches can be 2.5 meters tall and weigh 130 kilograms! Kiwis, however, are only about the size of chickens. Roughly a dozen living species are scattered throughout the Southern Hemisphere. All are flightless, but the larger species can run very fast. They generally eat a variety of plant material, insects, and other small invertebrates. Examples: Ostrich, emus, Brown Kiwi, Greater Rhea, Dwarf Cassowary

SPHENISCIDAE: Penguins

These flightless birds of the Southern Hemisphere are adapted to extreme cold and hunting in water. Though they cannot fly, they use their wings as flippers when they swim. Penguins have more feathers per square centimeter than any other bird; this density allows them to repel water and conserve heat effectively. Some species form large colonies. Examples: Emperor Penguin, Chinstrap Penguin, King Penguin

King Penguins

Redhead

ANATIDAE: Ducks, geese, and swans

These birds spend much of their time feeding in bodies of water. Webbed feet enable them to paddle efficiently across the surface of the water. Most fly well, however, and many species migrate thousands of kilometers between breeding and resting locations. Examples: Redhead, Ross's goose, Trumpeter Swan

Galápagos Hawk

FALCONIDAE AND ACCIPITRIDAE:
Falcons, eagles, and hawks

These fierce predators, often called raptors, typically have powerful hooked bills, large wingspans, and sharp talons. Raptors have powerful flight muscles and keen eyesight, enabling them to see prey at a distance. Examples: Eurasian Kestrel, Golden Eagle, Galápagos Hawk

---

PICIDAE AND RAMPHASTIDAE:
Woodpeckers and toucans

Woodpeckers are tree-dwelling birds with two toes in front and two in back. (Most birds have three in front and one in back; the two-and-two arrangement makes moving up and down tree trunks easier.) Woodpeckers are typically carnivores that eat insects and their larvae. Toucans usually use their huge, often colorful bills to eat fruit. Examples: Black Woodpecker, Keel-Billed Toucan

Black Woodpecker with chicks

Keel-Billed Toucan

PASSERIFORMES: Passerines

Also called perching birds, this is by far the largest and most diverse group of birds, with about 5000 species. Most are songbirds. Examples: flycatchers, mockingbirds, cardinals, crows, chickadees, and finches.

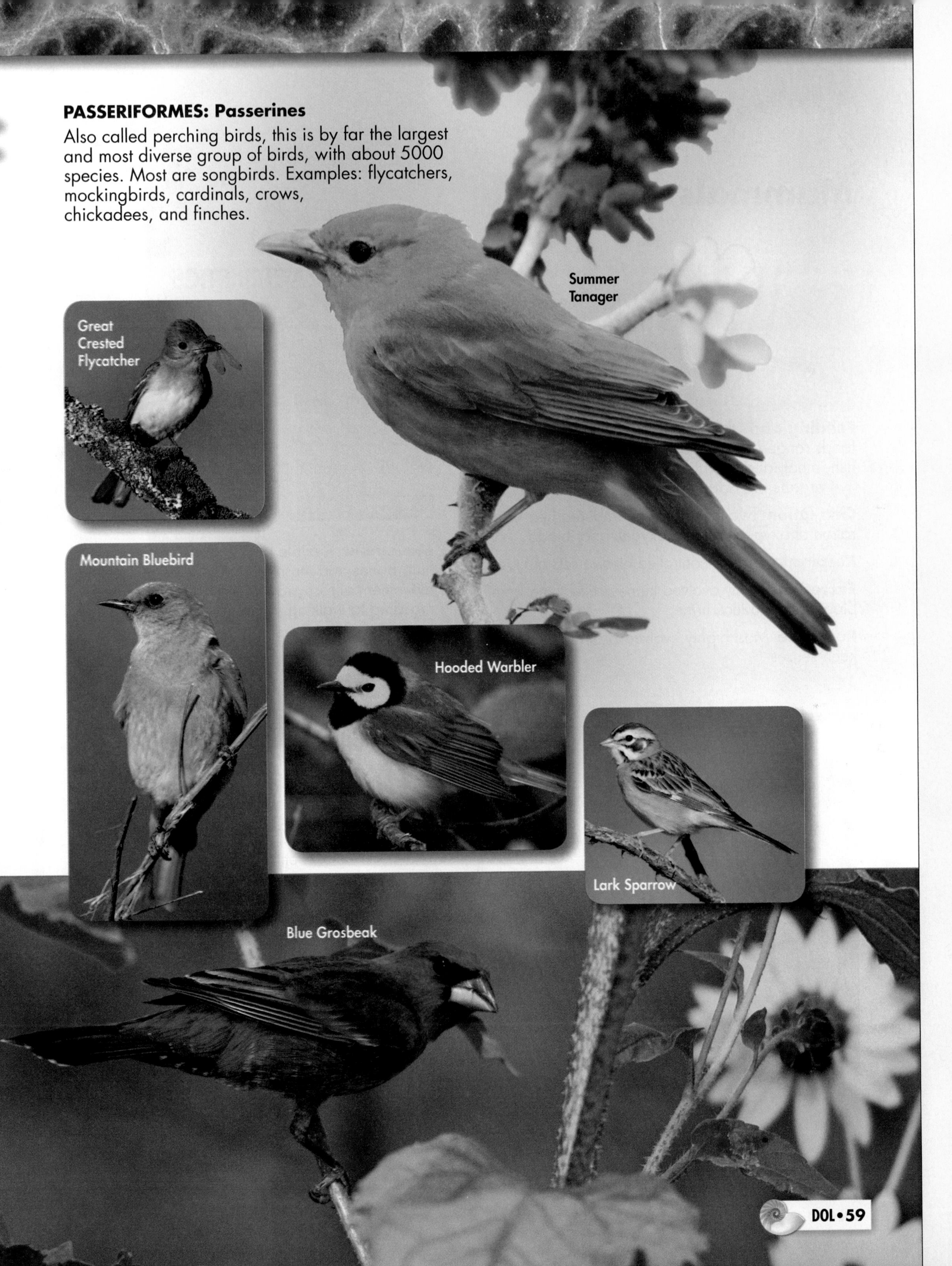

Mammals

KEY CHARACTERISTICS

Mammals are endothermic vertebrates with hair and mammary glands that produce milk to nourish their young.

Feeding and Digestion Diet varies with group; foods range from seeds, fruits, and leaves to insects, fish, meat, and even blood; teeth, jaws, and digestive organs are adapted to diet

Circulation Two loops; four-chambered heart; separation of oxygen-rich and oxygen-poor blood

Respiration Lungs controlled by two sets of muscles.

Excretion Highly evolved kidneys filter urea from blood and produce urine.

Response Most highly evolved brain of all animals; keen senses

Movement Flexible backbone; variations in limb bones and muscles enable wide range of movement across groups: from burrowing and crawling to walking, running, hopping, and flying

Reproduction Internal fertilization; developmental process varies with group (monotreme, marsupial, placental)

• Did You Know?

Platypus: Mix-and-Match Genome

The duckbill platypus has such an odd mix of reptile and mammal features that some scientists thought the first specimens were hoaxes produced by sticking parts of different animals together! Recent genome studies have revealed an equally odd mix of reptilian and mammalian genes. Genes for reptile-like vision, the production of egg yolk, and the production of venom link the platypus to reptiles. Genes for the production of milk link it to other mammals. The evidence provides confirmation that this monotreme represents a truly ancient lineage, one from the time close to that at which mammals branched off from reptiles.

GROUPS OF MAMMALS

The three living groups of mammals are the monotremes, the marsupials, and the placentals. There are about 5000 species of mammals, usually divided into about 26 orders, most of which are placentals. There is only one order of monotremes.

This black-backed jackal pup is enjoying a moment of independence from its family group. Mammals provide intensive parental care to their young.

Short-Beaked Echidna (Albino)

MONOTREMATA: Monotremes

Monotremes—egg-laying mammals—share two important characteristics with reptiles. First, the digestive, reproductive, and urinary systems of monotremes all open into a cloaca similar to that of reptiles. Second, monotreme development is similar to that of reptiles. Like a reptile, a female monotreme lays soft-shelled eggs incubated outside her body. The eggs hatch in about ten days. Unlike reptiles, however, young monotremes are nourished by mother's milk, which they lick from pores on the surface of her abdomen. Only five monotreme species exist today, all in Australia and New Guinea. Examples: Duckbill Platypus, echidnas

MARSUPIALIA: Marsupials

Marsupials bear live young at an extremely early stage of development. A fertilized egg develops into an embryo inside the mother's reproductive tract. The embryo is then "born" in what would be an embryonic stage for more familiar mammals. It crawls across its mother's fur and attaches to a nipple that, in most species, is located in a pouch called the marsupium. The embryo spends several months attached to the nipple. It continues to nurse until it can survive on its own. Examples: kangaroos, wallabies, wombats, opossums

Wombat

PLACENTALIA: Placental Mammals

Placental mammals are the mammals with which you are most familiar. This group gets its name from a structure called the placenta, which is formed when the embryo's tissues join with tissues within the mother's body. Nutrients, gases, and wastes are exchanged between embryo and mother through the placenta. The placenta allows the embryo to develop inside the mother longer so that placental young are born at a later stage of development than other mammals are. Development may take as little as a few weeks (mice), to as long as two years (elephants). After birth, most placental mammals care for their young and provide them with nourishment by nursing. Examples: Mice, cats, dogs, seals, whales, elephants, humans

Chiroptera: Bats

These are the only mammals capable of true flight. There are more than 900 species of bats! They eat mostly insects or fruit and nectar, although a few species feed on the blood of other vertebrates. Examples: fruit bats, Little Brown Myotis, Vampire Bat

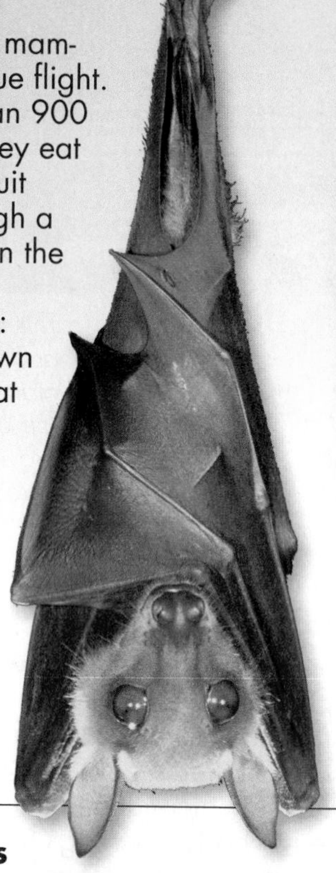

Epauletted Bat, roosting

Lioness attacking Greater Kudu

Carnivora: Carnivores

Many members of this group, such as tigers and hyenas, chase or stalk prey by running or pouncing, then kill with sharp teeth and claws. Dogs, bears, and other members of this group may eat plants as well as meat. Examples: dogs, cats, skunks, seals, bears

Sirenia: Sirenians

Sirenians are herbivores that live in rivers, bays, and warm, coastal waters scattered throughout the world. These large, slow-moving mammals lead fully aquatic lives. Examples: manatees, dugongs

Manatee mother and nursing calf

African Hedgehog mother and baby

Insectivora: Insectivores

These insect eaters have long, narrow snouts and sharp claws that are well suited for digging. Examples: shrews, moles, hedgehogs

Perissodactyla: Hoofed, odd-toed mammals

This group is made up of hoofed animals with an odd number of toes on each foot. Like artiodactyls, this group contains mostly large, grazing animals. Examples: horses, zebras, rhinoceroses

Artiodactyla: Hoofed, even-toed mammals

These large, grazing, hoofed mammals have an even number of toes on each foot. Examples: cattle, sheep, pigs, hippopotami

Rodentia: Rodents

Rodents have a single pair of long, curved incisor teeth in both their upper and lower jaws, used for gnawing wood and other tough plant material. Examples: rats, squirrels, porcupines

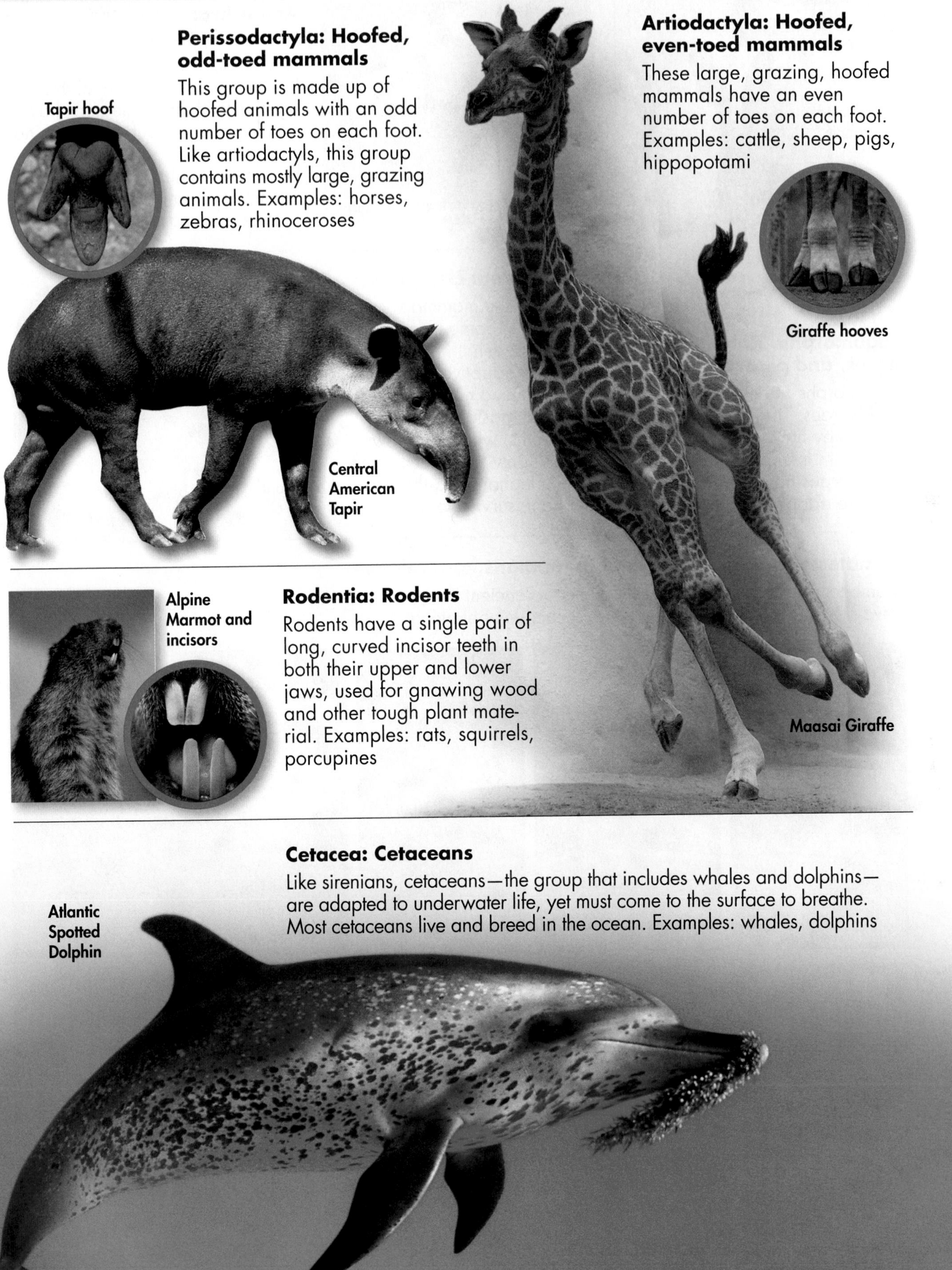

Tapir hoof

Central American Tapir

Giraffe hooves

Maasai Giraffe

Alpine Marmot and incisors

Cetacea: Cetaceans

Like sirenians, cetaceans—the group that includes whales and dolphins—are adapted to underwater life, yet must come to the surface to breathe. Most cetaceans live and breed in the ocean. Examples: whales, dolphins

Atlantic Spotted Dolphin

Black-Tailed Jackrabbit

Lagomorpha: Rabbit, hares, and pikas

Lagomorphs are entirely herbivorous. They differ from rodents by having two pairs of incisors in the upper jaw. Most lagomorphs have hind legs that are adapted for leaping.

Northern Tamandua

Xenarthra: Edentates

The word *edentate* means "toothless," which refers to the fact that some members of this group (sloths and anteaters) have simple teeth without enamel or no teeth at all. Armadillos, however, have more teeth than most other mammals! Examples: sloths, anteaters, armadillos

Proboscidea: Elephants

These are the mammals with trunks. Some time ago, this group went through an extensive adaptive radiation that produced many species, including mastodons and mammoths, which are now extinct. Only two species, the Asian Elephant and the African elephant, survive today.

Asian Elephant and calf

Primates: Lemurs, monkeys, apes, humans, and relatives

Members of this group are closely related to ancient insectivores but have a highly developed cerebrum and complex behaviors.

Sifaka

Tarsier

Langur

Baboon and baby

Orangutan

Gorilla

Chimpanzee

Appendix A Science Skills

Data Tables and Graphs

How can you make sense of the data from a science experiment? The first step is to organize the data. You can organize data in data tables and graphs to help you interpret them.

Data Tables

You have gathered your materials and set up your experiment. But before you start, you need to plan a way to record what happens during the experiment. By creating a data table, you can record your observations and measurements in an orderly way.

Suppose, for example, that a scientist conducted an experiment to find out how many kilocalories people of different body masses burned while performing various activities for 30 minutes. The data table below shows the results.

Notice in this data table that the independent variable (body mass) is the heading of the first column. The dependent variable (for Experiment 1, the number of kilocalories burned while bicycling for 30 minutes) is the heading of the next column. Additional columns were added for related experiments.

Calories Burned in 30 Minutes

Body Mass	Experiment 1: Bicycling	Experiment 2: Playing Basketball	Experiment 3: Watching Television
30 kg	60 Calories	120 Calories	21 Calories
40 kg	77 Calories	164 Calories	27 Calories
50 kg	95 Calories	206 Calories	33 Calories
60 kg	114 Calories	248 Calories	38 Calories

Bar Graphs

A bar graph is useful for comparing data from two or more distinct categories. In this example, pancreatic secretions in the small intestine are shown. To create a bar graph, follow these steps.

1. On graph paper, draw a horizontal, or *x*-axis, and a vertical, or *y*-axis.
2. Write the names of the categories (the independent variable) along one axis, usually the horizontal axis. You may put the categories on the vertical axis if that graph shape better fits on your page. Label the axis.
3. Label the other axis with the name of the dependent variable and the unit of measurement. Then, create a scale along that axis by marking off equally spaced numbers that cover the range of the data values.
4. For each category, draw a solid bar at the appropriate value. Then, fill in the space from the bar to the axis representing the independent variable. Make all the bars the same width.
5. Add a title that describes the graph.

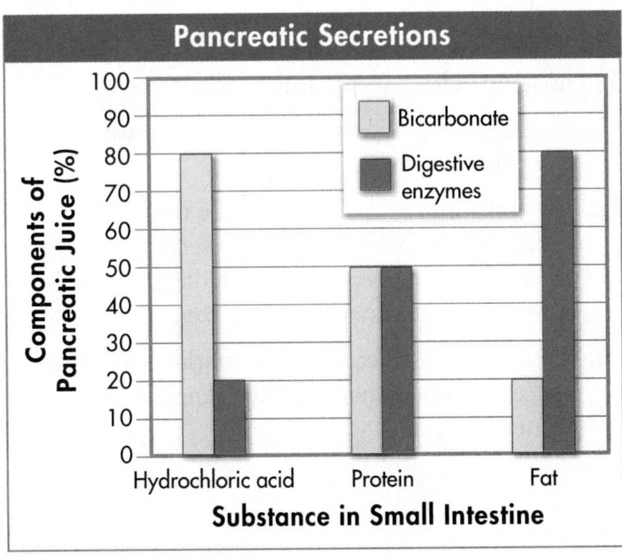

Line Graphs

A line graph is used to display data that show how the dependent variable changes in response to manipulations of the independent variable. You can use a line graph when your independent variable is continuous, that is, when there are other points between the ones that you tested. For example, the graph below shows how the growth of a bacterial population is related to time. The graph shows that the number of bacteria approximately doubles every 20 minutes. Line graphs are powerful tools because they also allow you to estimate values for conditions that you did not test in the experiment.

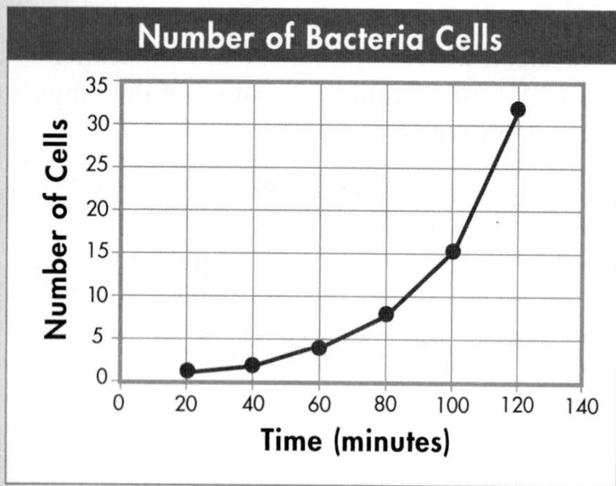

To construct a line graph, follow these steps.

1. On graph paper, draw a horizontal, or *x*-axis, and a vertical, or *y*-axis.
2. Label the horizontal axis with the name of the independent variable. Label the vertical axis with the name of the dependent variable. Include the units of measurement on both axes.
3. Create a scale on each axis by marking off equally spaced numbers that cover the range of the data values collected.
4. Plot a point on the graph for each data value. To do this, follow an imaginary vertical line extending up from the horizontal axis for an independent variable value. Then, follow an imaginary horizontal line extending across from the vertical axis at the value of the associated dependent variable. Plot a point where the two lines intersect. Repeat until all your data values are plotted.
5. Connect the plotted points with a solid line. Not all graphs are linear, so you may discover that it is more appropriate to draw a curve to connect the points.

The data in the graph at the left fit neatly on a smooth curve. But if you were to connect each data point on the graph below, you would have a mess that yielded little useful information. In some cases, it may be most useful to draw a line that shows the general trend of the plotted points. This type of line is often called a line of best fit. Such a line runs as closely as possible to all the points and allows you to make generalizations or predictions based on the data. Some points will fall above or below a line of best fit.

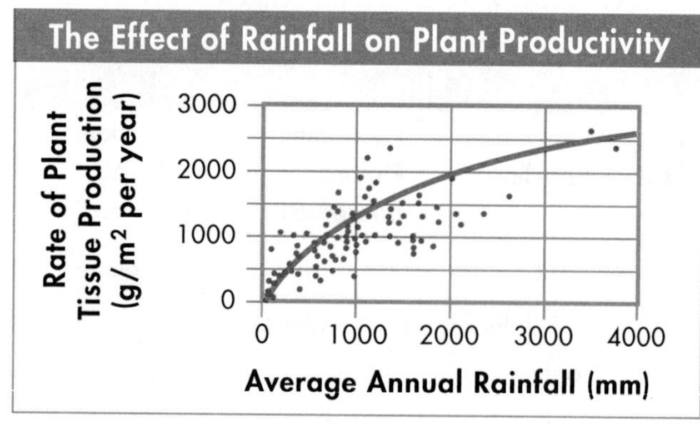

Circle Graphs

Circle graphs, or pie charts, display data as parts of a whole. Like bar graphs, circle graphs can be used to display data that fall into separate categories. Unlike bar graphs, however, circle graphs can only be used when you have data for all the categories that make up a given group. The circle, or "pie," represents 100 percent of a group, while the sectors, or slices, represent the percentages of each category that make up that group. The example below compares the different blood groups found in the U.S. population.

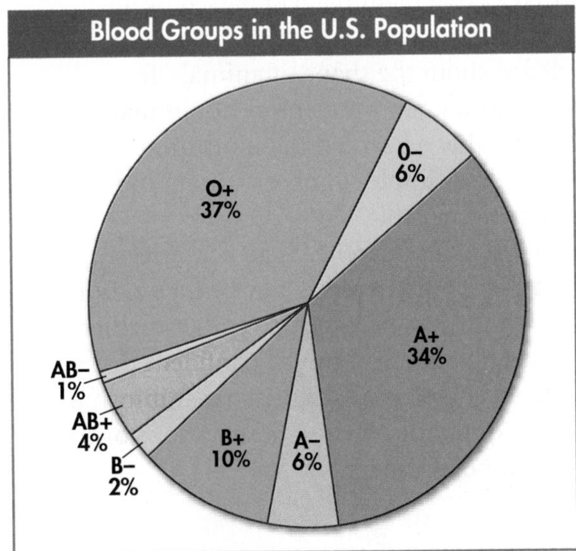

To construct a circle graph, follow these steps.

1. Draw a circle and mark the center. Then, draw a radius line from the center to the circle's edge.
2. Determine the size of a sector of the graph by calculating the number of degrees that correspond to a percentage you wish to represent. For example, in the graph shown, B^+ makes up 10 percent of all blood groups; 360 degrees $\times$ 0.10 = 36 degrees.
3. With a protractor fixed at the center of the circle, measure the angle—in this example, 36 degrees—from the existing radius, and draw a second radius at that point. Label the sector with its category and the percentage of the whole it represents. Repeat for each of the other categories, measuring each sector from the previous radius so the sectors don't overlap.
4. For easier reading, shade each sector differently.
5. Add a title that describes the graph.

Reading Diagrams

In scientific figures showing a cut-away of a structure, the diagram or photograph is showing the structure from a particular angle. Look for clues throughout this book that will help you interpret the view being shown.

Cross Sections

A cross section shows a horizontal cut through the middle of a structure. This icon will help you locate cross sections.

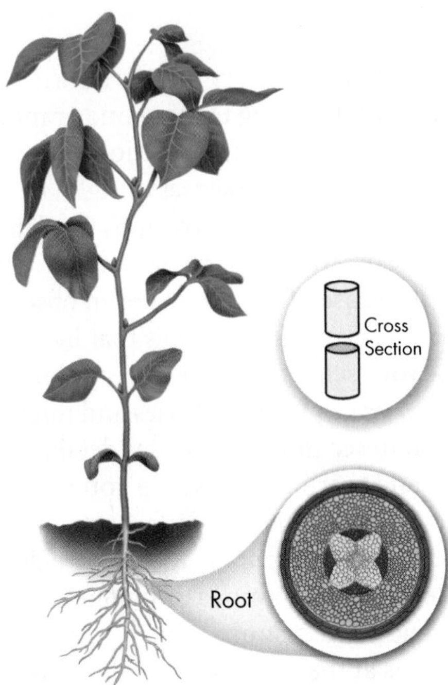

Longitudinal Sections

A longitudinal section shows a vertical cut through the middle of a structure. This icon will help you locate longitudinal sections.

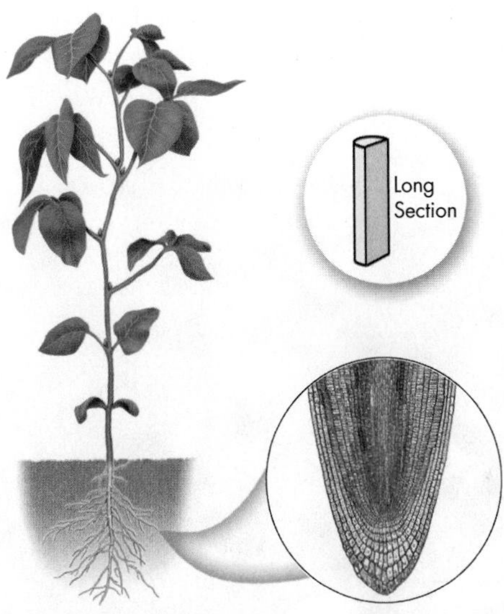

Appendix A Science Skills

Basic Process Skills

During a biology course, you often carry out short lab activities as well as lengthier experiments. Here are some skills that you will use.

Observing

In every science activity, you make a variety of observations. Observing is using one or more of the five senses to gather information. Many observations involve the senses of sight, hearing, touch, and smell. On rare occasions in a lab—but only when explicitly directed by your teacher—you may use the sense of taste to make an observation.

Sometimes you will use tools that increase the power of your senses or make observations more precise. For example, hand lenses and microscopes enable you to see things in greater detail. Rulers, balances, and thermometers help you measure key variables. Besides expanding the senses or making observations more accurate, tools may help eliminate personal opinions or preferences.

In science, it is customary to record your observations at the time they are made, usually by writing or drawing in a notebook. You may also make records by using computers, cameras, videotapes, and other tools. As a rule, scientists keep complete accounts of their observations, often using tables to organize their observations.

Inferring

In science, as in daily life, observations are usually followed by inferences. Inferring is interpreting an observation or statement based on prior knowledge.

For example, suppose you're on a mountain hike and you see footprints like the ones illustrated below. Based on their size and shape, you might infer that a large mammal had passed by. In making that inference, you would use your knowledge about the shape of animals' feet. Someone who knew much more about mammals might infer that a bear left the footprints. You can compare examples of observations and inferences in the table.

Notice that an inference is an act of reasoning, not a fact. An inference may be logical but not true. It is often necessary to gather further information before you can be confident that an inference is correct. For scientists, that information may come from further observations or from research done by others.

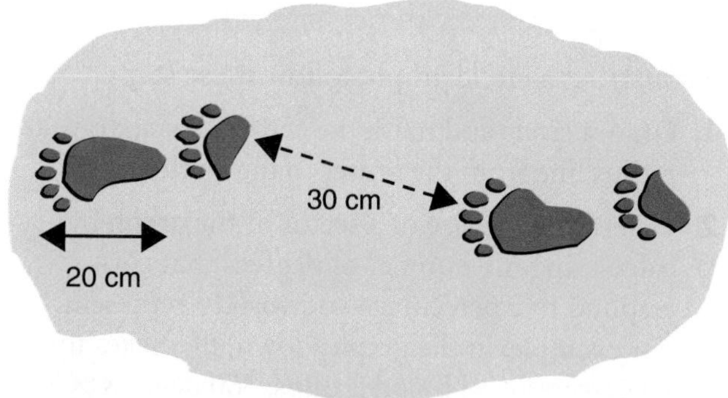

Comparing Observations and Inferences

Sample Observations	Sample Inferences
The footprints in the soil each have five toes.	An animal made the footprints.
The larger footprints are about 20 cm long.	A bear made the footprints.
The space between each pair of footprints is about 30 cm.	The animal was walking, not running.

As you study biology, you may make different types of inferences. For example, you may generalize about all cases based on information about some cases: *All the plant roots I've observed grow downward, so I infer that all roots grow downward.* You may determine that one factor or event was caused by another factor or event: *The bacteria died after I applied bleach, so I infer that bleach kills bacteria.* Predictions may be another type of inference.

Predicting

People often make predictions, but their statements about the future could be either guesses or inferences. In science, a prediction is an inference about a future event based on evidence, experience, or knowledge. For example, you can say, *On the first day of next month, it will be sunny.* If your statement is based on evidence of weather patterns in the area, then the prediction is scientific. If the statement was made without considering any evidence, it's just a guess.

Predictions play a major role in science because they provide a way to test ideas. If scientists understand an event or the properties of a particular object, they should be able to make accurate predictions about that event or object. Some predictions can be tested simply by making observations. At other times, carefully designed experiments are needed.

Classifying

If you have ever heard people debate whether a tomato is a fruit or a vegetable, you've heard an argument about classification. Classifying is the process of grouping items that are alike according to some organizing idea or system. Classifying occurs in every branch of science, but it is especially important in biology because living things are so numerous and diverse.

You may have the chance to practice classifying in different ways. Sometimes you will place objects into groups using an established system. At other times, you may create a system of your own by examining a variety of objects and identifying their properties.

Classification can have different purposes. Sometimes it's done just to keep things organized, to make lab supplies easy to find, for example. More often, though, classification helps scientists understand living things better and discover relationships among them. For example, one way biologists determine how groups of vertebrates are related is to compare their bones. Biologists classify certain animal parts as bone or muscle and then investigate how they work together.

Using Models

Some cities refuse to approve any new buildings that could cast shadows on a popular park. As architects plan buildings in such locations, they use models that can show where a proposed building's shadow will fall at any time of day in any season of the year. A model is a mental or physical representation of an object, process, or event. In science, models are usually made to help people understand natural objects and processes.

Models can be varied. Mental models, such as mathematical equations, can represent some kinds of ideas or processes. For example, the equation for the surface area of a sphere can model the surface of Earth, enabling scientists to determine its size. Physical models can be made of a huge variety of materials; they can be two dimensional (flat) or three dimensional (having depth). In biology, a drawing of a molecule or a cell is a typical two-dimensional model. Common three-dimensional models include a representation of a DNA molecule and a plastic skeleton of an animal.

Physical models can also be made "to scale," which means they are in proportion to the actual object. Something very large, such as an area of land being studied, can be shown at 1/100 of its actual size. A tiny organism can be shown at 100 times its size.

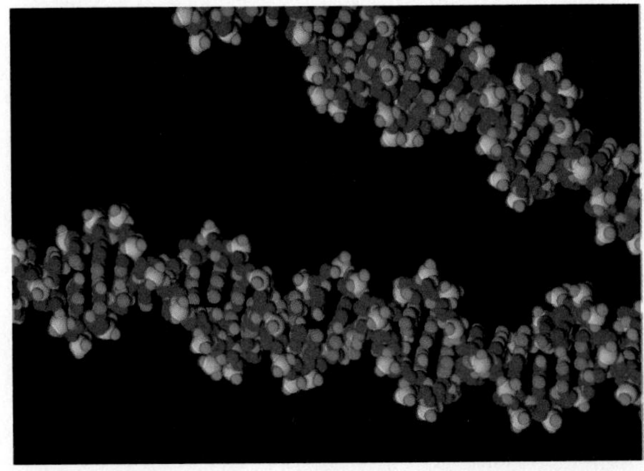

Organizing Information

When you study or want to communicate facts and ideas, you may find it helpful to organize information visually. Here are some common graphic organizers you can use. Notice that each type of organizer is useful for specific types of information.

Flowcharts

A flowchart can help you represent the order in which a set of events has occurred or should occur. Flowcharts are useful for outlining the steps in a procedure or stages in a process with a definite beginning and end.

To make a flowchart, list the steps in the process you want to represent and count the steps. Then, create the appropriate number of boxes, starting at the top of a page or on the left. Write a brief description of the first event in the first box, and then fill in the other steps, box by box. Link each box to the next event in the process with an arrow.

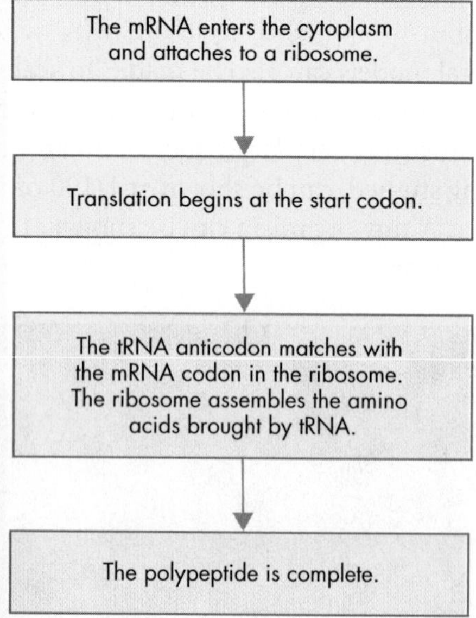

Concept Maps

Concept maps can help you organize a topic that has many subtopics. A concept map begins with a main idea and shows how it can be broken down into specific topics. It makes the ideas easier to understand by presenting their relationships visually.

You construct a concept map by placing the concept words (usually nouns) in ovals and connecting the ovals with linking words. The most general concept usually is placed at the top of the map or in the center. The content of the other ovals becomes more specific as you move away from the main concept. The linking words, which describe the relationship between the linked concepts, are written on a line between two ovals. If you follow any string of concepts and linking words down through a map, they should sound almost like a sentence.

Some concept maps may also include linking words that connect a concept in one branch to another branch. Such connections, called cross-linkages, show more complex interrelationships.

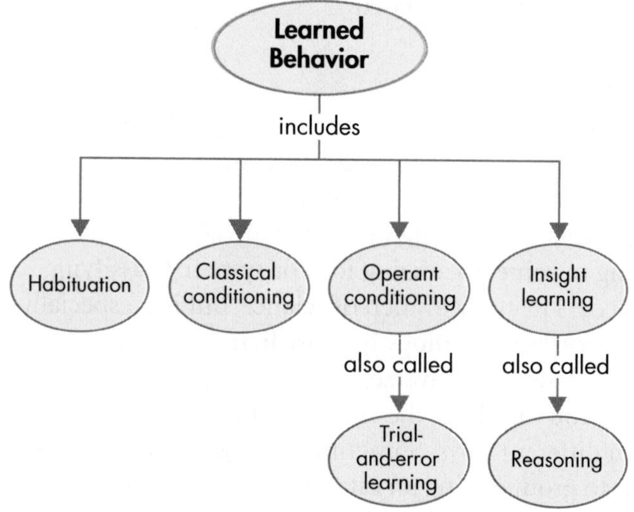

Compare/Contrast Tables

Compare/contrast tables are useful for showing the similarities and differences between two or more objects or processes. The table provides an organized framework for making comparisons based on specific characteristics.

To create a compare/contrast table, list the items to be compared across the top of the table. List the characteristics that will form the basis of your comparison in the column on the left. Complete the table by filling in information for each item.

Comparing Cellular Respiration and Fermentation

Characteristic	Cellular Respiration	Fermentation
Starting reactants	Glucose	Glucose, oxygen
Pathways involved	Glycolysis, several others	Glycolysis, Krebs cycle, electron transport
End products	CO_2 and alcohol *or* CO_2 and lactic acid	CO_2, H_2O
Number of ATP molecules produced	2	36

Venn Diagrams

Another way to show similarities and differences between items is with a Venn diagram. A Venn diagram consists of two or more ovals that partially overlap. Each oval represents a particular object or idea. Characteristics that the objects share are written in the area of overlap. Differences or unique characteristics are written in the areas that do not overlap.

To create a Venn diagram, draw two overlapping ovals. Label them with the names of the objects or the ideas they represent. Write the unique characteristics in the part of each oval that does not overlap. Write the shared characteristics within the area of overlap.

Kingdom Plantae | **Kingdom Fungi**

autotrophs
chloroplasts
cell walls of cellulose
eukaroyotes
multicellular
heterotrophs
unicellular
cell walls of chitin

Cycle Diagrams

A cycle diagram shows a sequence of events that is continuous, or cyclical. A continuous sequence does not have a beginning or an end; instead, each event in the process leads to another event. The diagram shows the order of the events.

To create a cycle diagram, list the events in the process and count them. Draw one box for each event, placing the boxes around an imaginary circle. Write one of the events in an oval, and then draw an arrow to the next oval, moving clockwise. Continue to fill in the boxes and link them with arrows until the descriptions form a continuous circle.

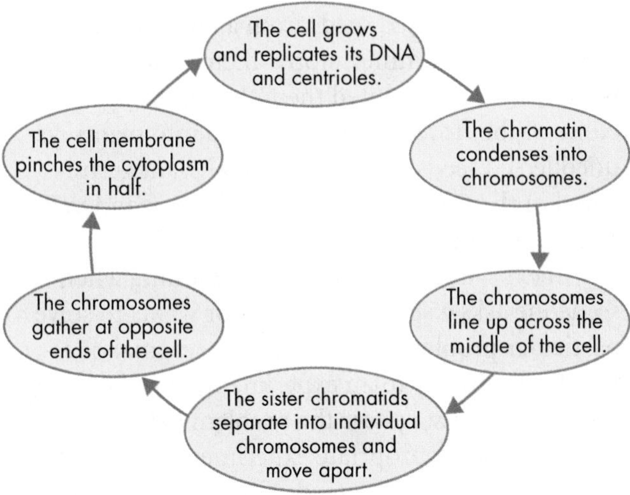

The cell grows and replicates its DNA and centrioles.
The chromatin condenses into chromosomes.
The chromosomes line up across the middle of the cell.
The sister chromatids separate into individual chromosomes and move apart.
The chromosomes gather at opposite ends of the cell.
The cell membrane pinches the cytoplasm in half.

Appendix B Lab Skills

Conducting an Experiment

A science experiment is a procedure designed to test a prediction. Some types of experiments are fairly simple to design. Others may require ingenious problem solving.

Starting With Questions or Problems

A gardener collected seeds from a favorite plant at the end of the summer, stored them indoors for the winter, and then planted them the following spring. None of the stored seeds developed into plants, yet uncollected seeds from the original plant germinated in the normal way. The gardener wondered: *Why didn't the collected seeds germinate?*

An experiment may have its beginning when someone asks a specific question or wants to solve a particular problem. Sometimes the original question leads directly to an experiment, but often researchers must restate the problem before they can design an appropriate experiment. The gardener's question about the seeds, for example, is too broad to be tested by an experiment, because there are so many possible answers. To narrow the topic, the gardener might think about related questions: *Were the seeds I collected different from the uncollected seeds? Did I try to germinate them in poor soil or with insufficient light or water? Did storing the seeds indoors ruin them in some way?*

Developing a Hypothesis

In science, a question about an object or event is answered by developing a possible explanation called a hypothesis. The hypothesis may be developed after long thought and research, or it may come to a scientist "in a flash." How a hypothesis is formed doesn't matter; it can be useful as long as it leads to predictions that can be tested.

The gardener decided to focus on the fact that the nongerminating seeds were stored in the warm conditions of a heated house. That premise led the person to propose this hypothesis: *Seeds require a period of low temperatures in order to germinate.*

The next step is to make a prediction based on the hypothesis, for example: *If seeds are stored indoors in cold conditions, they will germinate in the same way as seeds left outdoors during the winter.* Notice that the prediction suggests the basic idea for an experiment.

Designing an Experiment

A carefully designed experiment can test a prediction in a reliable way, ruling out other possible explanations. As scientists plan their experimental procedures, they pay particular attention to the factors that must be controlled.

The gardener decided to study three groups of seeds: (1) some that would be left outdoors throughout the winter, (2) some that would be brought indoors and kept at room temperature, and (3) some that would be brought indoors and kept cold.

Controlling Variables

As researchers design an experiment, they identify the variables, factors that can change. Some common variables include mass, volume, time, temperature, light, and the presence or absence of specific materials. An experiment involves three categories of variables. The factor that scientists purposely change is called the independent variable. An independent variable is also known as a manipulated variable. The factor that may change because of the independent variable and that scientists want to observe is called the dependent variable. A dependent variable is also known as a responding variable. Factors that scientists purposely keep the same are called controlled variables. Controlling variables enables researchers to conclude that the changes in the independent variable are due exclusively to changes in the dependent variable.

For the gardener, the independent variable is whether the seeds were exposed to cold conditions. The dependent variable is whether or not the seeds germinate. Among the variables that must be controlled are whether the seeds remain dry during storage, when the seeds are planted, the amount of water the seeds receive, and the type of soil used.

Interpreting Data

The observations and measurements that are made in an experiment are called data. Scientists usually record data in an orderly way. When an experiment is finished, the researcher analyzes the data for trends or patterns, often by doing calculations or making graphs, to determine whether the results support the hypothesis.

For example, after planting the seeds in the spring, the gardener counted the seeds that germinated and found these results: None of the seeds kept at room temperature germinated, 80 percent of the seeds kept in the freezer germinated, and 85 percent of the seeds left outdoors during the winter germinated. The trend was clear: The gardener's prediction appeared to be correct.

To be sure that the results of an experiment are correct, scientists review their data critically, looking for possible sources of error. Here, *error* refers to differences between the observed results and the true values. Experimental error can result from human mistakes or problems with equipment. It can also occur when the small group of objects studied does not accurately represent the whole group. For example, if some of the gardener's seeds had been exposed to a herbicide, the data might not reflect the true seed germination pattern.

Drawing Conclusions

If researchers are confident that their data are reliable, they make a final statement summarizing their results. That statement, called the conclusion, indicates whether the data support or refute the hypothesis. The gardener's conclusion was this: *Some seeds must undergo a period of freezing in order to germinate.* A conclusion is considered valid if it is a logical interpretation of reliable data.

Following Up an Experiment

When an experiment has been completed, one or more events often follow. Researchers may repeat the experiment to verify the results. They may publish the experiment so that others can evaluate and replicate their procedures. They may compare their conclusion with the discoveries made by other scientists. And they may raise new questions that lead to new experiments. For example, *Are the spores of fungi affected by temperature as these seeds were?*

Researching other discoveries about seeds would show that some other types of plants in temperate zones require periods of freezing before they germinate. Biologists infer that this pattern makes it less likely the seeds will germinate before winter, thus increasing the chances that the young plants will survive.

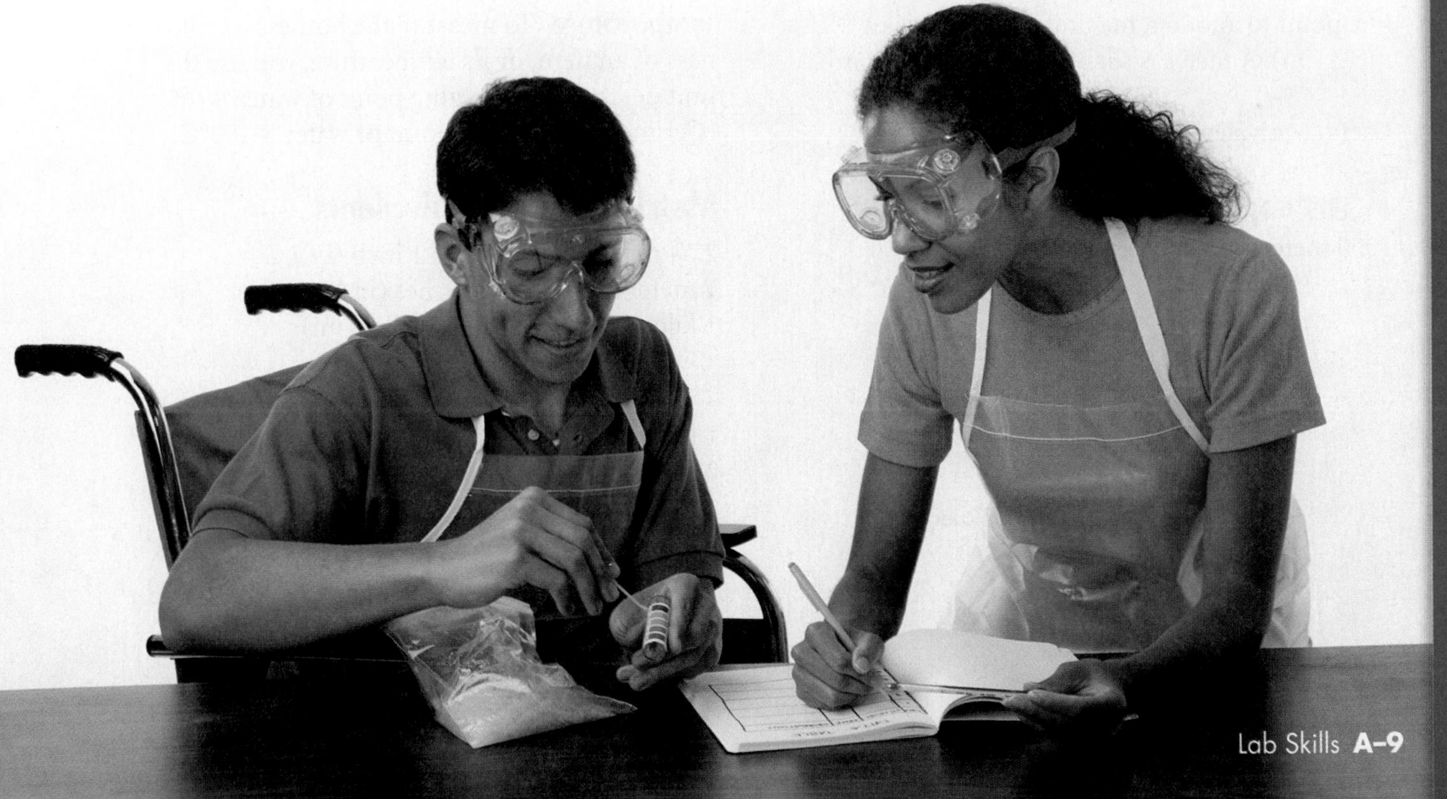

Appendix B Lab Skills

The Metric System

The standard system of measurement used by scientists throughout the world is known as the International System of Units, abbreviated as SI (Système International d'Unités, in French). It is based on units of 10. Each unit is 10 times larger or 10 times smaller than the next unit. The table lists the prefixes used to name the most common SI units.

Common SI Prefixes		
Prefix	**Symbol**	**Meaning**
kilo-	k	1000
hecto-	h	100
deka-	da	10
deci-	d	0.1 (one tenth)
centi-	c	0.01 (one hundredth)
milli-	m	0.001 (one thousandth)

Commonly Used Metric Units

Length To measure length, or distance from one point to another, the unit of measure is a meter (m). A meter is slightly longer than a yard.

Useful equivalents:

1 meter = 1000 millimeters (mm)
1 meter = 100 centimeters (cm)
1000 meters = 1 kilometer (km)

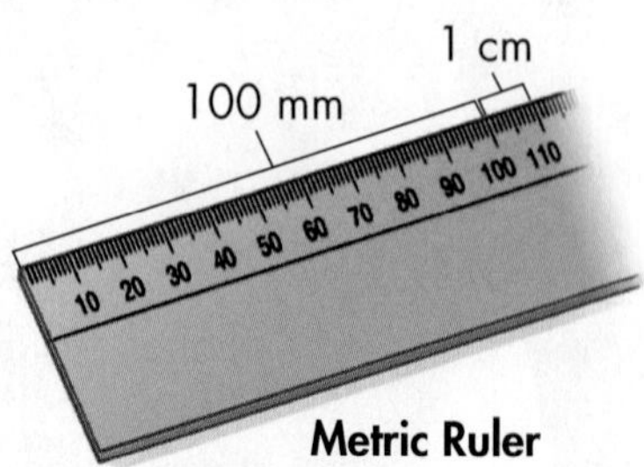

Metric Ruler

Volume To measure the volume of a liquid, or the amount of space an object takes up, the unit of measure is a liter (L). A liter is slightly more than a quart.

Useful equivalents:

1 liter = 1000 milliliters (mL)

Mass To measure the mass, or the amount of matter in an object, the unit of measure is the gram (g). A paper clip has a mass equal to about one gram.

Useful equivalents:

1000 grams = 1 kilogram (kg)

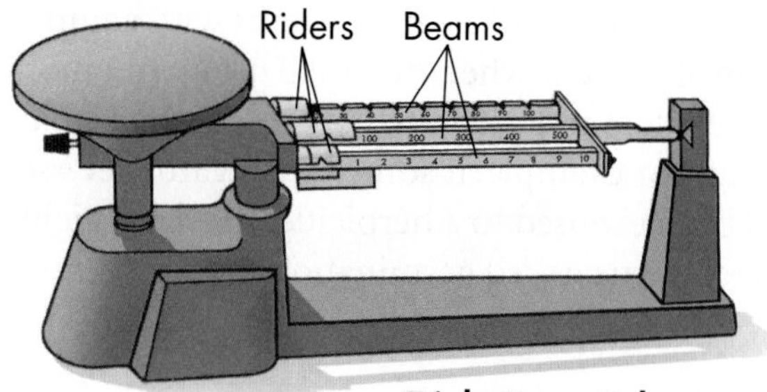

Triple-Beam Balance

Temperature To measure the hotness or coldness of an item, or its temperature, you use the unit degrees. The freezing point of water is 0°C (Celsius). The boiling point of water is 100°C.

Metric-English Equivalents

2.54 centimeters (cm) = 1 inch (in.)
1 meter (m) = 39.37 inches (in.)
1 kilometer (km) = 0.62 miles (mi)
1 liter (L) = 1.06 quarts (qt)
236 milliliters (mL) = 1 cup (c)
1 kilogram (kg) = 2.2 pounds (lb)
28.3 grams (g) = 1 ounce (oz)
°C = 5/9 × (°F – 32)

Safety Symbols

These symbols appear in laboratory activities to alert you to possible dangers and to remind you to work carefully.

Safety Goggles Always wear safety goggles to protect your eyes during any activity involving chemicals, flames or heating, or the possibility of flying objects, particles, or substances.

Lab Apron Wear a laboratory apron to protect your skin and clothing from injury.

Plastic Gloves Wear disposable plastic gloves to protect yourself from contact with chemicals or organisms that could be harmful. Keep your hands away from your face, and dispose of the gloves according to your teacher's instructions at the end of the activity.

Breakage Handle breakable materials such as thermometers and glassware with care. Do not touch broken glass.

Heat-Resistant Gloves Use an oven mitt or other hand protection when handling hot materials. Hot plates, hot water, and glassware can cause burns. Never touch hot objects with your bare hands.

Heating Use a clamp or tongs to hold hot objects. Do not touch hot objects with your bare hands.

Sharp Object Scissors, scalpels, pins, and knives are sharp. They can cut or puncture your skin. Always direct sharp edges and points away from yourself and others. Use sharp instruments only as directed.

Electric Shock Avoid the possibility of electric shock. Never use electrical equipment around water or when the equipment or your hands are wet. Be sure cords are untangled and cannot trip anyone. Disconnect equipment when it is not in use.

Corrosive Chemical This symbol indicates the presence of an acid or other corrosive chemical. Avoid getting the chemical on your skin or clothing, or in your eyes. Do not inhale the vapors. Wash your hands when you are finished with the activity.

Poison Do not let any poisonous chemical get on your skin, and do not inhale its vapor. Wash your hands when you are finished with the activity.

Flames Tie back loose hair and clothing, and put on safety goggles before working with fire. Follow instructions from your teacher about lighting and extinguishing flames.

No Flames Flammable materials may be present. Make sure there are no flames, sparks, or exposed sources of heat present.

Fumes Poisonous or unpleasant vapors may be produced. Work in a ventilated area or, if available, in a fume hood. Avoid inhaling a vapor directly. Test an odor only when directed to do so by your teacher, using a wafting motion to direct the vapor toward your nose.

Physical Safety This activity involves physical movement. Use caution to avoid injuring yourself or others. Follow instructions from your teacher. Alert your teacher if there is any reason that you should not participate in the activity.

Animal Safety Treat live animals with care to avoid injuring the animals or yourself. Working with animal parts or preserved animals may also require caution. Wash your hands when you are finished with the activity.

Plant Safety Handle plants only as your teacher directs. If you are allergic to any plants used in an activity, tell your teacher before the activity begins. Avoid touching poisonous plants and plants with thorns.

Disposal Chemicals and other materials used in the activity must be disposed of safely. Follow the instructions from your teacher.

Hand Washing Wash your hands thoroughly when finished with the activity. Use soap and warm water. Lather both sides of your hands and between your fingers. Rinse well.

General Safety Awareness You may see this symbol when none of the symbols described earlier applies. In this case, follow the specific instructions provided. You may also see this symbol when you are asked to design your own experiment. Do not start your experiment until your teacher has approved your plan.

Appendix B Lab Skills

Science Safety Rules

Working in the laboratory can be an exciting experience, but it can also be dangerous if proper safety rules are not followed at all times. To prepare yourself for a safe year in the laboratory, read the following safety rules. Make sure that you understand each rule. Ask your teacher to explain any rules you don't understand.

Dress Code

1. Many materials in the laboratory can cause eye injury. To protect yourself from possible injury, wear safety goggles whenever you are working with chemicals, burners, or any substance that might get into your eyes. Avoid wearing contact lenses in the laboratory. Tell your teacher if you need to wear contact lenses to see clearly, and ask if there are any safety precautions you should observe.
2. Wear a laboratory apron or coat whenever you are working with chemicals or heated substances.
3. Tie back long hair to keep it away from any chemicals, burners, candles, or other laboratory equipment.
4. Before working in the laboratory, remove or tie back any article of clothing or jewelry that can hang down and touch chemicals and flames.

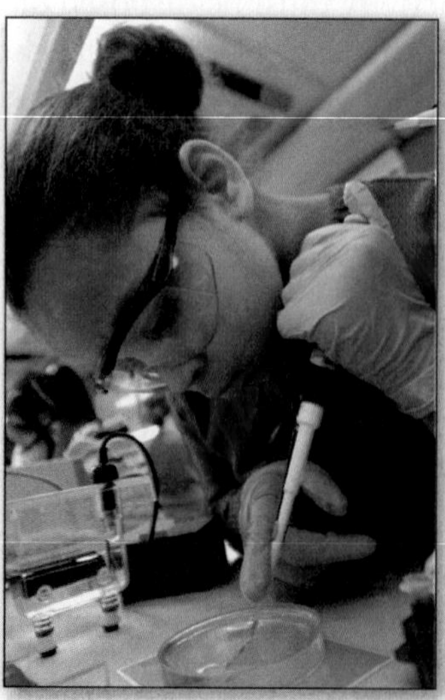

General Safety Rules and First Aid

5. Read all directions for an experiment several times. Follow the directions exactly as they are written. If you are in doubt about any part of the experiment, ask your teacher for assistance.
6. Never perform investigations your teacher has not authorized. Do not use any equipment unless your teacher is in the lab.
7. Never handle equipment unless you have specific permission.
8. Take care not to spill any material in the laboratory. If spills occur, ask your teacher immediately about the proper cleanup procedure. Never pour chemicals or other substances into the sink or trash container.
9. Never eat or drink in, or bring food into, the laboratory.
10. Immediately report all accidents, no matter how minor, to your teacher.
11. Learn what to do in case of specific accidents, such as getting acid in your eyes or on your skin. (Rinse acids off your body with lots of water.)
12. Be aware of the location of the first-aid kit. Your teacher should administer any required first aid due to injury. Your teacher may send you to the school nurse or call a physician.
13. Know where and how to report an accident or fire. Find out the location of the fire extinguisher, fire alarm, and phone. Report any fires to your teacher at once.

Heating and Fire Safety

14. Never use a heat source such as a candle or burner without wearing safety goggles.
15. Never heat a chemical you are not instructed to heat. A chemical that is harmless when cool can be dangerous when heated.
16. Maintain a clean work area and keep all materials away from flames. Be sure that there are no open containers of flammable liquids in the laboratory when flames are being used.
17. Never reach across a flame.

18. Make sure you know how to light a Bunsen burner. (Your teacher will demonstrate the proper procedure for lighting a burner.) If the flame leaps out of a burner toward you, turn the gas off immediately. Do not touch the burner. It may be hot. Never leave a lighted burner unattended!
19. When you are heating a test tube or bottle, point the opening away from yourself and others. Chemicals can splash or boil out of a heated test tube.
20. Never heat a closed container. The expanding hot air, vapors, or other gases inside may blow the container apart, causing it to injure you or others.
21. Never pick up a container that has been heated without first holding the back of your hand near it. If you can feel the heat on the back of your hand, the container may be too hot to handle. Use a clamp or tongs when handling hot containers or wear heat-resistant gloves if appropriate.

Using Chemicals Safely

22. Never mix chemicals for "the fun of it." You might produce a dangerous, possibly explosive substance.
23. Many chemicals are poisonous. Never touch, taste, or smell a chemical that you do not know for certain is harmless. If you are instructed to smell fumes in an experiment, gently wave your hand over the opening of the container and direct the fumes toward your nose. Do not inhale the fumes directly from the container.
24. Use only those chemicals needed in the investigation. Keep all container lids closed when a chemical is not being used. Notify your teacher whenever chemicals are spilled.
25. Dispose of all chemicals as instructed by your teacher. To avoid contamination, never return chemicals to their original containers.
26. Be extra careful when working with acids or bases. Pour such chemicals from one container to another over the sink, not over your work area.
27. When diluting an acid, pour the acid into water. Never pour water into the acid.
28. If any acids or bases get on your skin or clothing, rinse them with water. Immediately notify your teacher of any acid or base spill.

Using Glassware Safely

29. Never heat glassware that is not thoroughly dry. Use a wire screen to protect glassware from any flame.
30. Keep in mind that hot glassware will not appear hot. Never pick up glassware without first checking to see if it is hot.
31. Never use broken or chipped glassware. If glassware breaks, notify your teacher and dispose of the glassware in the proper trash container.
32. Never eat or drink from laboratory glassware. Thoroughly clean glassware before putting it away.

Using Sharp Instruments

33. Handle scalpels or razor blades with extreme care. Never cut material toward you; cut away from you.
34. Notify your teacher immediately if you cut yourself when in the laboratory.

Working With Live Organisms

35. No experiments that will cause pain, discomfort, or harm to animals should be done in the classroom or at home.
36. Your teacher will instruct you how to handle each species that is brought into the classroom. Animals should be handled only if necessary. Special handling is required if an animal is excited or frightened, pregnant, feeding, or with its young.
37. Clean your hands thoroughly after handling any organisms or materials, including animals or cages containing animals.

End-of-Experiment Rules

38. When an experiment is completed, clean up your work area and return all equipment to its proper place.
39. Wash your hands with soap and warm water before and after every experiment.
40. Turn off all burners before leaving the laboratory. Check that the gas line leading to the burner is off as well.

Use of the Microscope

The microscope used in most biology classes, the compound microscope, contains a combination of lenses. The eyepiece lens is located in the top portion of the microscope. This lens usually has a magnification of 10×. Other lenses, called objective lenses, are at the bottom of the body tube on the revolving nosepiece. By rotating the nosepiece, you can select the objective through which you will view your specimen.

The shortest objective is a low-power magnifier, usually 10×. The longer ones are of high power, usually up to 40× or 43×. The magnification is marked on the objective. To determine the total magnification, multiply the magnifying power of the eyepiece by the magnifying power of the objective. For example, with a 10× eyepiece and a 40× objective, the total magnification is $10 \times 40 = 400\times$.

Learning the name, function, and location of each of the microscope's parts is necessary for proper use. Use the following procedures when working with the microscope.

1. Carry the microscope by placing one hand beneath the base and grasping the arm of the microscope with the other hand.
2. Gently place the microscope on the lab table with the arm facing you. The microscope's base should be resting evenly on the table, approximately 10 cm from the table's edge.
3. Raise the body tube by turning the coarse adjustment knob until the objective lens is about 2 cm above the opening of the stage.
4. Rotate the nosepiece so that the low-power objective (10×) is directly in line with the body tube. A click indicates that the lens is in line with the opening of the stage.
5. Look through the eyepiece and switch on the lamp or adjust the mirror so that a circle of light can be seen. This is the field of view. Moving the lever of the diaphragm permits a greater or smaller amount of light to come through the opening of the stage.
6. Place a prepared slide on the stage so that the specimen is over the center of the opening. Use the stage clips to hold the slide in place.
7. Look at the microscope from the side. Carefully turn the coarse adjustment knob to lower the body tube until the low-power objective almost touches the slide or until the body tube can no longer be moved. Do not allow the objective to touch the slide.
8. Look through the eyepiece and observe the specimen. If the field of view is out of focus, use the coarse adjustment knob to raise the body tube while looking through the eyepiece. **CAUTION:** *To prevent damage to the slide and the objective, do not lower the body tube using the coarse adjustment while looking through the eyepiece.* Focus the image as best you can with the coarse adjustment knob. Then, use the fine adjustment knob to focus the image more sharply. Keep both eyes open when viewing a specimen. This helps prevent eyestrain.

1. **Eyepiece:** Contains a magnifying lens.
2. **Arm:** Supports the body tube.
3. **Low-power objective:** Provides a magnification of 10x.
4. **Stage:** Supports the slide being observed.
5. **Opening of the stage:** Permits light to pass up to the eyepiece.
6. **Fine adjustment knob:** Moves the body tube slightly to adjust the image.
7. **Coarse adjustment knob:** Moves the body tube to focus the image.
8. **Base:** Supports the microscope.
9. **Illuminator:** Produces light or reflects light up toward the eyepiece.
10. **Diaphragm:** Regulates the amount of light passing up toward the eyepiece.
11. **Stageclips:** Hold the slide in place.
12. **High-power objective:** Provides a magnification of 40x.
13. **Nosepiece:** Holds the objectives and can be rotated to change the magnification.
14. **Body tube:** Maintains the proper distance between the eyepiece and the objectives.

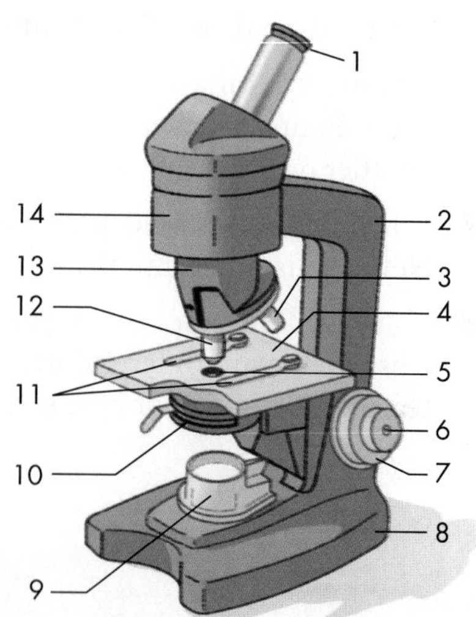

9. Adjust the lever of the diaphragm to allow the right amount of light to enter.
10. To change the magnification, rotate the nosepiece until the desired objective is in line with the body tube and clicks into place.
11. Look through the eyepiece and use the fine adjustment knob to bring the image into focus.
12. After every use, remove the slide. Return the low-power objective into place in line with the body tube. Clean the stage of the microscope and the lenses with lens paper. Do not use other types of paper to clean the lenses; they may scratch the lenses.

Preparing a Wet-Mount Slide

1. Obtain a clean microscope slide and a coverslip. A coverslip is very thin, permitting the objective lens to be lowered very close to the specimen.
2. Place the specimen in the middle of the microscope slide. The specimen must be thin enough for light to pass through it.
3. Using a dropper pipette, place a drop of water on the specimen.

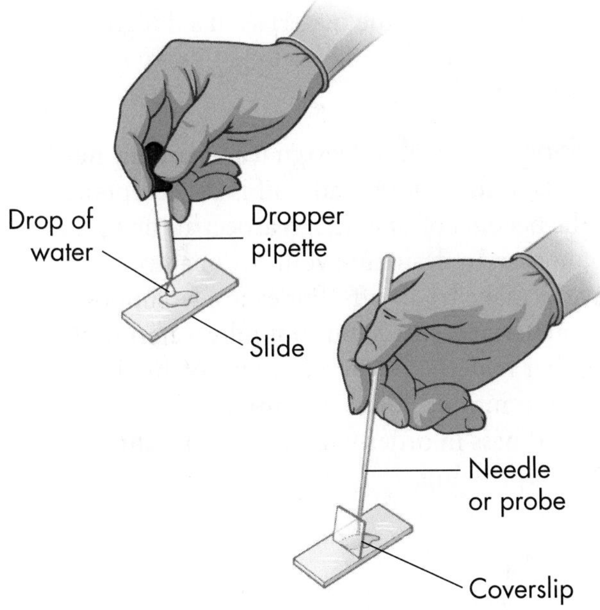

4. Lower one edge of the coverslip so that it touches the side of the drop of water at about a 45° angle. The water will spread evenly along the edge of the coverslip. Using a dissecting needle or probe, slowly lower the coverslip over the specimen and water as shown in the drawing. Try not to trap any air bubbles under the coverslip. If air bubbles are present, gently tap the surface of the coverslip over the air bubble with a pencil eraser.
5. Remove any excess water around the edge of the coverslip with a paper towel. If the specimen begins to dry out, add a drop of water at the edge of the coverslip.

Staining Techniques

1. Obtain a clean microscope slide and coverslip.
2. Place the specimen in the middle of the microscope slide.
3. Using a dropper pipette, place a drop of water on the specimen. Place the coverslip so that its edge touches the drop of water at a 45° angle. After the water spreads along the edge of the coverslip, use a dissecting needle or probe to lower the coverslip over the specimen.
4. Add a drop of stain at the edge of the coverslip. Using forceps, touch a small piece of lens paper or paper towel to the opposite edge of the coverslip, as shown in the drawing. The paper causes the stain to be drawn under the coverslip and to stain the cells in the specimen.

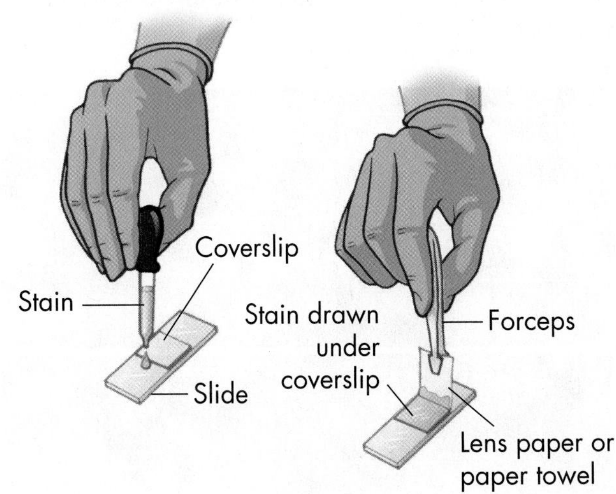

Appendix C Technology & Design

Engineers are people who use scientific and technological knowledge to solve practical problems. To design new products, engineers usually follow the process described here, even though they may not follow these steps in the exact order.

Identify a Need

Before engineers begin designing a new product, they must first identify the need they are trying to meet. For example, suppose you are a member of a design team in a company that makes toys. Your team has identified a need: a toy boat that is inexpensive and easy to assemble.

Research the Problem

Engineers often begin by gathering information that will help them with their new design. This research may include finding articles in books, in magazines, or on the Internet. It may also include talking to other engineers who have solved similar problems. Engineers also often perform experiments related to the product they want to design.

For your toy boat, you could look at toys that are similar to the one you want to design. You might do research on the Internet. You could also test some materials to see whether they would work well in a toy boat.

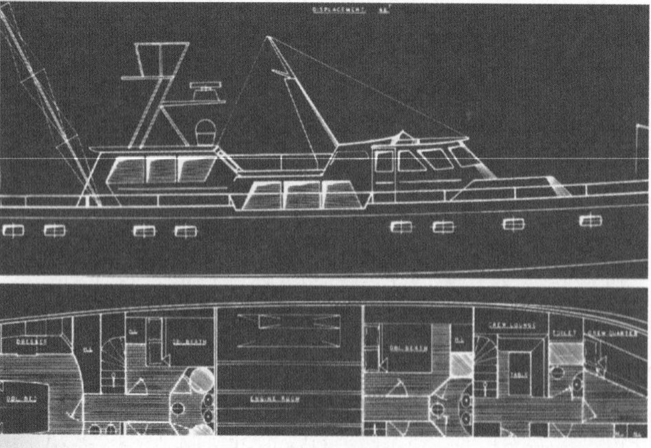

Design a Solution

Research gives engineers information that helps them design a product. When engineers design new products, they usually work in teams.

Generating Ideas Often, design teams hold brainstorming meetings in which any team member can contribute ideas. Brainstorming is a creative process in which one team member's suggestions can spark ideas in other group members. Brainstorming can lead to new approaches to solving a design problem.

Evaluating Constraints During brainstorming, a design team will often come up with several possible designs. The team must then evaluate each one.

As part of their evaluation, engineers consider constraints. Constraints are factors that limit or restrict a product design. Physical characteristics, such as the properties of materials used to make your toy boat, are constraints. Cost and time are also constraints. If the materials in a design cost a lot, or if the design takes a long time to make, it may be impractical.

Making Trade-offs Design teams usually need to make trade-offs. A trade-off is the acceptance of the benefits of one design aspect at the cost of another. In designing your toy boat, you will have to make trade-offs. For example, suppose one material is sturdy but not fully waterproof. Another material is more waterproof, but breakable. You may decide to give up the benefit of sturdiness in order to obtain the benefit of waterproofing.

Build and Evaluate a Prototype

Once the team has chosen a design plan, the engineers build a prototype of the product. A prototype is a working model used to test a design. Engineers evaluate the prototype to see whether it works well, is easy to operate, is safe to use, and holds up to repeated use.

Think of your toy boat. What would the prototype be like? Of what materials would it be made? How would you test it?

Troubleshoot and Redesign

Few prototypes work perfectly, which is why they need to be tested. Once a design team has tested a prototype, the members analyze the results and identify any problems. The team then tries to troubleshoot, or fix the weaknesses in the design. For example, if your toy boat leaks or wobbles, the boat should be redesigned to eliminate those problems.

Communicate the Solution

A team needs to communicate the final design to the people who will manufacture the product. To do this, teams may use sketches, detailed drawings, computer simulations, and written descriptions.

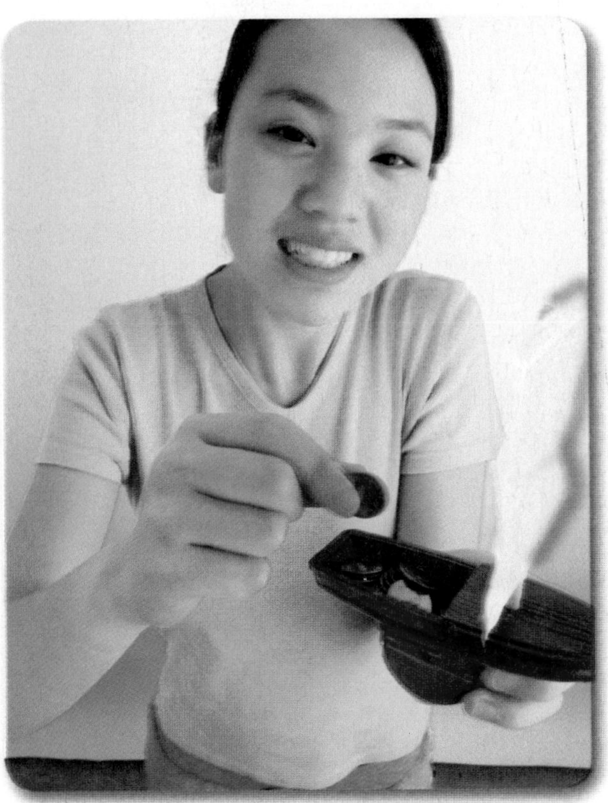

Activity

You can use the technology design process to design and build a toy boat.

Research and Investigate

1. Visit the library or go online to research toy boats.
2. Investigate how a toy boat can be powered, including wind, rubber bands, or baking soda and vinegar.
3. Brainstorm materials, shapes, and steering methods for your boat.

Design and Build

4. Based on your research, design a toy boat that
   - is made of readily available materials
   - is no larger than 15 cm long and 10 cm wide
   - includes a power system, a rudder, and a cargo area
   - travels 2 meters in a straight line while carrying a load of 20 pennies
5. Sketch your design and write a step-by-step plan for building your boat. After your teacher approves your plan, build your boat.

Evaluate and Redesign

6. Test your boat, evaluate the results, and identify any technological design problems in your boat.
7. Based on your evaluation, redesign your toy boat so it performs better.
8. As a class, compare the test results for each boat. Choose the model that best meets the needs of the toy company.

Appendix D Math Skills

Scientists use math to organize, analyze, and present data. This appendix will help you review some basic math skills.

Formulas and Equations

Formulas and equations are used in many areas of science. Both formulas and equations show the relationships between quantities. Any numerical sentence that contains at least one variable and at least one mathematical operator is called an equation. A formula is a type of equation that states the relationship between unknown quantities represented by variables.

For example, Speed = Distance ÷ Time is a formula, because no matter what values are inserted, speed is always equal to distance divided by time. The relationship between the variables does not change.

Example
Follow these steps to convert a temperature measurement of 50°F to Celsius.

1. Determine the formula that shows the relationship between these quantities.
   °F = (9/5 × °C) + 32°F
2. Insert values you know into the formula.
   50°F = (9/5 × °C) + 32°F
3. Solve the resulting equation.
   50°F – 32°F = (9/5 × °C)
   18°F = 9/5 × °C
   18°F × 5/9 = 10°C

Applying Formulas and Equations

There are many applications of formulas in science. The example described below uses a formula to calculate density.

Example
Follow these steps to calculate the density of an object that has a mass of 45 g and a volume of 30 cm^3.

1. Determine the formula that shows the relationship between these quantities.
   Density = Mass/Volume
2. Insert values you know into the formula.
   Density = 45 g/30 cm^3
3. Solve the resulting equation.
   Density = 1.5 g/cm^3

Mean, Median, and Mode

The mean is the average, or the sum of the data divided by the number of data items. The middle number in a set of ordered data is called the median. The mode is the number that appears most often in a set of data.

Example
A scientist counted the number of distinct songs sung by seven different male birds and collected the data shown below.

Male Bird Songs							
Bird	A	B	C	D	E	F	G
Number of Songs	36	29	40	35	28	36	27

To determine the mean number of songs, find the sum of the songs sung by all the male birds and divide by the number of male birds.

$$\text{Mean} = 231/7 = 33 \text{ songs}$$

To find the median number of songs, arrange the data items in numerical order and identify the number in the middle.

27 28 29 35 36 36 40

The number in the middle is 35, so the median number of songs is 35.

The mode is the value that appears most frequently. In the data, 36 appears twice, while every other item appears only once. Therefore, 36 is the mode.

Estimation

An estimate is a reasonable approximation of a numerical value. Estimates are made based on careful assumptions and known information.

Scientists use estimates in biology for two primary reasons: when an exact count or calculation cannot be made or is impractical to make, and to make reasonable approximations of answers that will be calculated or measured later.

One method for estimation used in biology is sampling. In sampling, the number of organisms in a small area (a sample) is multiplied to estimate the number of organisms in a larger area.

Example
Follow these steps to use sampling to estimate the total number of birds in the photo.

1. Count the birds in the highlighted area of the photo. In the highlighted area of the photo, there are 36 birds.
2. Determine the portion of the entire photo represented by the highlighted area. In this case, the highlighted area is 1/6 of the total area.
3. Calculate your estimate by multiplying the number of birds in the sample area by 6 (because the entire photo is 6 times as large as the sample area). A reasonable estimate of the total number of birds is 36 × 6, or 216 birds.

HINT: Estimates and calculated answers are rarely exactly the same. However, a large difference between an estimated answer and a calculated answer indicates there may be a problem with the estimate or calculation.

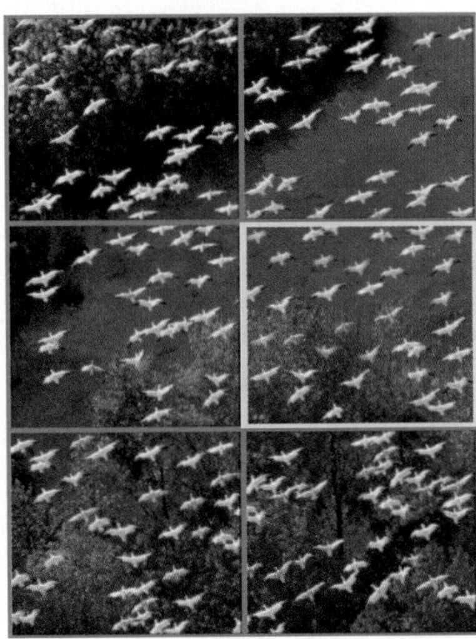

Using Measurements in Calculations

Density is an example of a value that is calculated using two measurements. Density represents the amount of mass in a particular volume of a substance. The units used for density are grams per milliliter (g/mL) or grams per cubic centimeter (g/cm^3). Density is calculated by dividing an object's mass by its volume.

Example
Follow these steps to calculate the density of an object.

1. Measure and record the mass of an object in grams.
2. Measure and record the volume of an object in mL or cm^3.
3. Use the following formula to calculate density:

   Density = Mass/Volume

Effects of Measurement Errors

Density is calculated using two measured values. An error in the measurement of either mass or volume will result in the calculation of an incorrect density.

Example
A student measured the mass of an object as 2.5 g and its volume as 2.0 cm^3. The actual mass of the object is 3.5 g; the actual volume is 2.0 cm^3. What is the effect of the measurement error on the calculation of density?

Follow these steps to determine the effect of a measurement error on calculation.

1. Determine the density using the student's measurements.
   Density = Mass/Volume
   Density = 2.5 g/2.0 cm^3
   Density = 1.25 g/cm^3
2. Determine the density using the actual values.
   Density = Mass/Volume
   Density = 3.5 g/2.0 cm^3
   Density = 1.75 g/cm^3
3. Compare the calculated and the actual values.

In this case, a measurement of mass that was less than the actual value resulted in a calculated value for the density that was less than the actual density.

Accuracy

The accuracy of a measurement is its closeness to the actual value. Measurements that are accurate are close to the actual value.

Both clocks on this page show a time of 3:00. Suppose, though, that these clocks had not been changed to reflect daylight savings time. The time shown on the clocks would be inaccurate. On the other hand, if the actual time is 3:00, these clocks would be accurate.

Precision

Precision describes the exactness of a measurement. The clocks shown on this page differ in precision. The analog clock measures time to the nearest minute. The digital clock measures time to the nearest second. Time is measured more precisely by the digital clock than by the analog clock.

Comparing Accuracy and Precision

There is a difference between accuracy and precision. Measurements can be accurate (close to the actual value) but not precise. Measurements can also be precise but not accurate. When making scientific measurements, both accuracy and precision are important. Accurate and precise measurements result from the careful use of high-quality measuring tools.

Significant Figures

Significant figures are all of the digits that are known in a measurement, plus one additional digit, which is an estimate. In the figure below, the length of a turtle's shell is being measured using a centimeter ruler. The ruler has unnumbered divisions representing millimeters. In this case, two numbers can be determined exactly: the number of centimeters and the number of millimeters. One additional digit can be estimated. So, the measurement of this turtle's shell can be recorded with three significant figures as 8.80 centimeters.

Rules for Significant Digits
Follow these rules to determine the number of significant figures in a number.

<u>All nonzero numbers are significant.</u>

Example: 3217 has four significant digits.

<u>Zeros are significant if</u>

- They are between nonzero digits. Example: 509
- They follow a decimal point and a nonzero digit. Example: 7.00

<u>Zeros are not significant if</u>

- They follow nonzero digits in a number without a decimal. Example: 7000
- They precede nonzero digits in a number with a decimal. Example: 0.0098

Calculating With Significant Figures

When measurements are added or subtracted, the precision of the result is determined by the precision of the least-precise measurement. The result may need to be rounded so the number of digits after the decimal is the same as the least-precise measurement.

Example
Follow these steps to determine the correct number of significant figures when adding 4.51 g, 3.27 g, and 6.0 g.

1. Determine which measurement is reported with the least degree of precision. In this case, the least-precise measurement, 6.0 g, has one digit after the decimal point.
2. The result must be rounded so that it also has one digit after the decimal point. After rounding, the result of this calculation is 13.8 g.

When measurements are multiplied or divided, the answer must have the same number of significant figures as the measurement with the fewest number of significant figures.

Example
Follow these steps to determine the correct number of significant figures when multiplying 120 m by 6.32 m.

1. Determine the number of significant figures in each of the measurements. In this case, the measurement 120 m has two significant figures; the measurement 6.32 m has three significant figures.
2. The result must be rounded to have only two significant figures. After rounding, the result of this calculation is 760 m^2.

Scientific Notation

In science, measurements are often very large or very small. Using scientific notation makes these large and small numbers easier to work with.

Using scientific notation requires an understanding of exponents and bases. When a number is expressed as a base and an exponent, the base is the number that is used as a factor. The exponent tells how many times the base is multiplied by itself. For example, the number 25 can be expressed as a base and an exponent in the following way:

$$25 = 5 \times 5 = 5^2$$

In the example above, 5 is the base and 2 is the exponent. In scientific notation, the base is always the number 10. The exponent tells how many times the number 10 is multiplied by itself.

A number written in scientific notation is expressed as the product of two factors, a number between 1 and 10 and the number 10 with an exponent. For example, the number 51,000 can be expressed in scientific notation. To find the first factor, move the decimal to obtain a number between 1 and 10. In this case, the number is 5.1. The exponent can be determined by counting the number of places the decimal point was moved. The decimal point was moved four places to the left. So, 51,000 expressed in scientific notation is 5.1×10^4.

Numbers that are less than one can also be expressed in scientific notation. In the case of numbers less than one, the decimal point must be moved to the right to obtain a number between 1 and 10. For example, in the number 0.000098, the decimal point must move five places to the right to obtain the number 9.8. When the decimal point is moved to the right, the exponent is negative. So, 0.000098 expressed in scientific notation is 9.8×10^{-5}.

Calculating With Scientific Notation

Numbers expressed in scientific notation can be used in calculations. When adding or subtracting numbers expressed in scientific notation, the first factors must be rewritten so the exponents are the same.

Example

Follow these steps to add $(4.30 \times 10^4) + (2.1 \times 10^3)$.

1. Move the decimal point in one of the expressions so the exponents are the same.
   $(43.0 \times 10^3) + (2.1 \times 10^3)$
2. Add the first factors, keeping the value of the exponents the same.
   $(43.0 \times 10^3) + (2.1 \times 10^3) = 45.1 \times 10^3$
3. Move the decimal point so the first factor is expressed as the product of a number between and 1 and 10 and an exponent with base 10.
   $45.1 \times 10^3 = 4.51 \times 10^4$

When numbers expressed in scientific notation are multiplied, the exponents are added. When numbers expressed in scientific notation are divided, the exponents are subtracted.

Example

Use the following steps to determine the area of a rectangular field that has a length of 1.5×10^3 meters and a width of 3.2×10^2 meters.

1. Write down the expressions to be multiplied.
   $(1.5 \times 10^3\ \text{m})(3.2 \times 10^2\ \text{m})$
2. Multiply the first factors, add the exponents, and multiply any units.
   $= (1.5 \times 3.2)(10^{3+2})\ \text{m} \times \text{m}$
   $= 4.8 \times 10^5\ \text{m}^2$

Dimensional Analysis

Scientific problems and calculations often involve unit conversions, or changes from one unit to another. Dimensional analysis is a method of unit conversion.

Suppose you were counting a pile of pennies. If there were 197 pennies in the pile, how many dollars would the pennies be worth? To determine the answer, you need to know the conversion factor between pennies and dollars. A conversion factor simply shows how two units are related. In this case, the conversion factor is 100 pennies = 1 dollar. Determining that 197 pennies is equal to $1.97 is an example of a unit conversion.

In dimensional analysis, the conversion factor is usually expressed as a fraction. Remember that the two values in any conversion factor are equal to one another. So, the two values form a fraction with the value of 1. Look at the example below to see how dimensional analysis can be applied to an everyday problem.

Example

A student walked 1.5 kilometers as part of a school fitness program. How many meters did the student walk?

1. 1.5 km = _?_ m
2. 1 km = 1000 m
3. 1000 m/1 km
4. 1.5 km × 1000 m/1 km = 1500 m (cross out "km" in two places); 1.5 km = 1500 m

1 1.5 km = ? m

2 1 km = 1,000 m

3 $\frac{1{,}000 \text{ m}}{1 \text{ km}}$

4 $1.5 \text{ km} \times \frac{1{,}000 \text{ m}}{1 \text{ km}} = 1{,}500 \text{ m}$

1.5 km = 1,500 m

Applying Dimensional Analysis

There are many applications of dimensional analysis in science. The example below demonstrates the use of dimensional analysis to convert units.

Example

The average teenage girl needs about 2200 kilocalories of energy from food each day. How many calories is this equivalent to?

Use the following steps to convert kilocalories to calories.

1. Determine the conversion factor that relates the two units.
   1 kilocalorie = 1000 calories
2. Write the conversion factor in the form of a fraction.
   1000 calories/1 kilocalorie
3. Multiply the measurement by the conversion factor.
   2200 kilocalories × 1000 calories/1 kilocalorie = 2,200,000 calories

Periodic Table of the Elements

Representative Elements
- Alkali Metals
- Alkaline Earth Metals
- Other Metals
- Metalloids
- Nonmetals
- Noble Gases

Transition Elements
- Transition Metals
- Inner transition metals

C Solid · Br Liquid · He Gas · Tc Not found in nature

Key (14 / Si / Silicon / 28.086 / 2 8 4): Atomic number; Electrons in each energy level; Element symbol; Element name; Average atomic mass

* The atomic masses in parentheses are the mass numbers of the longest-lived isotope of elements for which a standard atomic mass cannot be defined.

1 1A	2 2A	3 3B	4 4B	5 5B	6 6B	7 7B	8	9 8B	10	11 1B	12 2B	13 3A	14 4A	15 5A	16 6A	17 7A	18 8A
1 H Hydrogen 1.0079 1																	2 He Helium 4.0026 2
3 Li Lithium 6.941 2 1	4 Be Beryllium 9.0122 2 2											5 B Boron 10.81 2 3	6 C Carbon 12.011 2 4	7 N Nitrogen 14.007 2 5	8 O Oxygen 15.999 2 6	9 F Fluorine 18.998 2 7	10 Ne Neon 20.179 2 8
11 Na Sodium 22.990 2 8 1	12 Mg Magnesium 24.305 2 8 2											13 Al Aluminum 26.982 2 8 3	14 Si Silicon 28.086 2 8 4	15 P Phosphorus 30.974 2 8 5	16 S Sulfur 32.06 2 8 6	17 Cl Chlorine 35.453 2 8 7	18 Ar Argon 39.948 2 8 8
19 K Potassium 39.098 2 8 8 1	20 Ca Calcium 40.08 2 8 8 2	21 Sc Scandium 44.956 2 8 9 2	22 Ti Titanium 47.90 2 8 10 2	23 V Vanadium 50.941 2 8 11 2	24 Cr Chromium 51.996 2 8 13 1	25 Mn Manganese 54.938 2 8 13 2	26 Fe Iron 55.847 2 8 14 2	27 Co Cobalt 58.933 2 8 15 2	28 Ni Nickel 58.71 2 8 16 2	29 Cu Copper 63.546 2 8 18 1	30 Zn Zinc 65.38 2 8 18 2	31 Ga Gallium 69.72 2 8 18 3	32 Ge Germanium 72.59 2 8 18 4	33 As Arsenic 74.922 2 8 18 5	34 Se Selenium 78.96 2 8 18 6	35 Br Bromine 79.904 2 8 18 7	36 Kr Krypton 83.80 2 8 18 8
37 Rb Rubidium 85.468 2 8 18 8 1	38 Sr Strontium 87.62 2 8 18 8 2	39 Y Yttrium 88.906 2 8 18 9 2	40 Zr Zirconium 91.22 2 8 18 10 2	41 Nb Niobium 92.906 2 8 18 12 1	42 Mo Molybdenum 95.94 2 8 18 13 1	43 Tc Technetium (98) 2 8 18 14 1	44 Ru Ruthenium 101.07 2 8 18 15 1	45 Rh Rhodium 102.91 2 8 18 16 1	46 Pd Palladium 106.4 2 8 18 18	47 Ag Silver 107.87 2 8 18 18 1	48 Cd Cadmium 112.41 2 8 18 18 2	49 In Indium 114.82 2 8 18 18 3	50 Sn Tin 118.69 2 8 18 18 4	51 Sb Antimony 121.75 2 8 18 18 5	52 Te Tellurium 127.60 2 8 18 18 6	53 I Iodine 126.90 2 8 18 18 7	54 Xe Xenon 131.30 2 8 18 18 8
55 Cs Cesium 132.91 2 8 18 18 8 1	56 Ba Barium 137.33 2 8 18 18 8 2	71 Lu Lutetium 174.97 2 8 18 32 9 2	72 Hf Hafnium 178.49 2 8 18 32 10 2	73 Ta Tantalum 180.95 2 8 18 32 11 2	74 W Tungsten 183.85 2 8 18 32 12 2	75 Re Rhenium 186.21 2 8 18 32 13 2	76 Os Osmium 190.2 2 8 18 32 14 2	77 Ir Iridium 192.22 2 8 18 32 15 2	78 Pt Platinum 195.09 2 8 18 32 17 1	79 Au Gold 196.97 2 8 18 32 18 1	80 Hg Mercury 200.59 2 8 18 32 18 2	81 Tl Thallium 204.37 2 8 18 32 18 3	82 Pb Lead 207.2 2 8 18 32 18 4	83 Bi Bismuth 208.98 2 8 18 32 18 5	84 Po Polonium (209) 2 8 18 32 18 6	85 At Astatine (210) 2 8 18 32 18 7	86 Rn Radon (222) 2 8 18 32 18 8
87 Fr Francium (223) 2 8 18 32 18 8 1	88 Ra Radium (226) 2 8 18 32 18 8 2	103 Lr Lawrencium (262 2 8 18 32 32 9 2	104 Rf Rutherfordium (261) 2 8 18 32 32 10 2	105 Db Dubnium (262) 2 8 18 32 32 11 2	106 Sg Seaborgium (263) 2 8 18 32 32 12 2	107 Bh Bohrium (264) 2 8 18 32 32 13 2	108 Hs Hassium (265) 2 8 18 32 32 14 2	109 Mt Meitnerium (268) 2 8 18 32 32 15 2	110 Ds Darmstadtium (269) 2 8 18 32 32 17 1	111 Rg Roentgenium (272) 2 8 18 32 32 18 1	112 *Uub Ununbium (277) 2 8 18 32 32 18 2		114 *Uuq Ununquadium				

Elements 104–114 are the transactinide elements.

*Name not officially assigned.

Lanthanide Series

57 La Lanthanum 138.91 2 8 18 18 9 2	58 Ce Cerium 140.12 2 8 18 20 8 2	59 Pr Praseodymium 140.91 2 8 18 21 8 2	60 Nd Neodymium 144.24 2 8 18 22 8 2	61 Pm Promethium (145) 2 8 18 23 8 2	62 Sm Samarium 150.4 2 8 18 24 8 2	63 Eu Europium 151.96 2 8 18 25 8 2	64 Gd Gadolinium 157.25 2 8 18 25 9 2	65 Tb Terbium 158.93 2 8 18 27 8 2	66 Dy Dysprosium 162.50 2 8 18 28 8 2	67 Ho Holmium 164.93 2 8 18 29 8 2	68 Er Erbium 167.26 2 8 18 30 8 2	69 Tm Thulium 168.93 2 8 18 31 8 2	70 Yb Ytterbium 173.04 2 8 18 32 8 2

Actinide Series

89 Ac Actinium (227) 2 8 18 32 18 9 2	90 Th Thorium 232.04 2 8 18 32 18 10 2	91 Pa Protactinium 231.04 2 8 18 32 20 9 2	92 U Uranium 238.03 2 8 18 32 21 9 2	93 Np Neptunium (237) 2 8 18 32 22 9 2	94 Pu Plutonium (244) 2 8 18 32 24 8 2	95 Am Americium (243) 2 8 18 32 25 8 2	96 Cm Curium (247) 2 8 18 32 25 9 2	97 Bk Berkelium (247) 2 8 18 32 27 8 2	98 Cf Californium (251) 2 8 18 32 28 8 2	99 Es Einsteinium (252) 2 8 18 32 29 8 2	100 Fm Fermium (257) 2 8 18 32 30 8 2	101 Md Mendelevium (258) 2 8 18 32 31 8 2	102 No Nobelium (259) 2 8 18 32 32 8 2

Glossary

A

abiotic factor: physical, or nonliving, factor that shapes an ecosystem (66)
factor abiótico: factor físico, o inanimado, que da forma a un ecosistema

abscisic acid: plant hormone that inhibits cell division and, therefore, growth (711)
ácido abscísico: hormona vegetal que inhibe la división celular y, por ende, el crecimiento

acetylcholine: neurotransmitter that produces an impulse in a muscle cell (931)
acetilcolina: neurotransmisor que produce un impulso en una célula muscular

acid: compound that forms hydrogen ions (H^+) in solution; a solution with a pH of less than 7 (44)
ácido: compuesto que en una solución produce iones hidrógeno (H^+); una solución con un pH inferior a 7

acid rain: rain containing nitric and sulfuric acids (164)
lluvia ácida: lluvia que contiene ácido nítrico y ácido sulfúrico

actin: thin filament of protein found in muscles (930)
actina: microfilamento de proteína que se halla en los músculos

action potential: reversal of charges across the cell membrane of a neuron; also called a nerve impulse (898)
potencial de acción: inversión de las cargas a través de la membrana de una neurona; también llamado impulso nervioso

activation energy: energy that is needed to get a reaction started (51)
energía de activación: energía necesaria para que comience una reacción

active immunity: immunity that develops as a result of natural or deliberate exposure to an antigen (1020)
inmunidad activa: inmunidad que se desarrolla a consecuencia de la exposición natural o deliberada a un antígeno

adaptation: heritable characteristic that increases an organism's ability to survive and reproduce in an environment (461)
adaptación: característica heredable que aumenta la capacidad de un organismo de sobrevivir y reproducirse en un medio ambiente

adaptive radiation: process by which a single species or a small group of species evolves into several different forms that live in different ways (550)
radiación adaptativa: proceso mediante el cual una sola especie o un grupo pequeño de especies evoluciona y da lugar a diferentes seres que viven de diversas maneras

adenosine triphosphate (ATP): compound used by cells to store and release energy (226)
trifosfato de adenosina (ATP): compuesto utilizado por las células para almacenar y liberar energía

adhesion: force of attraction between different kinds of molecules (41, 686)
adhesión: fuerza de atracción entre diferentes tipos de moléculas

aerobic: process that requires oxygen (252)
aeróbico: proceso que requiere oxígeno

age structure: number of males and females of each age in a population (131)
estructura etaria: número de machos y de hembras de cada edad en una población

aggression: threatening behavior that one animal uses to exert dominance over another animal (848)
agresión: comportamiento amenazador que emplea un animal para ejercer control sobre otro animal

algal bloom: increase in the amount of algae and other producers that results from a large input of a limiting nutrient (611)
florecimiento de algas: aumento de la cantidad de algas y otros productores debido a una gran entrada de un nutriente limitante

allele: one of a number of different forms of a gene (310)
alelo: cada una de las diversas formas de un gen

allele frequency: number of times that an allele occurs in a gene pool compared with the number of alleles in that pool for the same gene (483)
frecuencia alélica: número de veces que aparece un alelo en un caudal genético, comparado con la cantidad de alelos en ese caudal para el mismo gen

allergy: overreaction of the immune system to an antigen (1024)
alergia: reacción exagerada del sistema inmune ante un antígeno

alternation of generations: life cycle that has two alternating phases—a haploid (N) phase and diploid (2N) phase (608, 637)
alternancia de generaciones: ciclo vital con dos fases que se alternan, una fase haploide (N) y una fase diploide (2N)

alveolus (pl. alveoli): one of many tiny air sacs at the end of a bronchiole in the lungs that provides surface area for gas exchange to occur (790, 964)
alvéolos: pequeños sacos, ubicados en las terminaciones de los bronquiolos pulmonares, que proporcionan una superficie en la que tiene lugar el intercambio gaseoso

amino acid: compound with an amino group on one end and a carboxyl group on the other end (48)
aminoácido: compuesto que contiene un grupo amino en un extremo y un grupo carboxilo en el otro extremo

amniotic egg: egg composed of shell and membranes that creates a protected environment in which the embryo can develop out of water (825)
huevo amniota: huevo formado por una cáscara y membranas que crea un ambiente protegido en el cual el embrión puede desarrollarse en un medio seco

amylase: enzyme in saliva that breaks the chemical bonds in starches (876)
amilasa: enzima de la saliva que fragmenta los enlaces químicos de los almidones

anaerobic: process that does not require oxygen (252)
anaeróbico: proceso que no requiere oxígeno

analogous structures: body parts that share a common function, but not structure (469)
estructuras análogas: partes del cuerpo que tienen la misma función, mas no la misma estructura

anaphase: phase of mitosis in which the chromosomes separate and move to opposite ends of the cell (283)
anafase: fase de la mitosis en la cual los cromosomas se separan y se desplazan hacia los extremos opuestos de la célula

angiosperm: group of seed plants that bear their seeds within a layer of tissue that protects the seed; also called flowering plant (646)
angiospermas: grupo de plantas con semillas, que están protegidas con una capa de tejido. Se conocen también como plantas que florecen.

anther: flower structure in which pollen grains are produced (697)
antera: estructura de la flor en la cual se generan los granos de polen

antheridium (pl. antheridia): male reproductive structure in some plants that produces sperm (642)
anteridio: en algunas plantas, estructura reproductora masculina que produce esperma (anterozoides)

anthropoid: primate group made up of monkeys, apes, and humans (766)
antropoide: grupo de primates constituido por monos, simios y humanos

antibiotic: group of drugs used to block the growth and reproduction of bacterial pathogens (588)
antibiótico: grupo de drogas utilizadas para bloquear el desarrollo y la reproducción de organismos patógenos bacterianos

antibody: protein that either attacks antigens directly or produces antigen-binding proteins (1016)
anticuerpo: proteína que ataca directamente a los antígenos o produce proteínas que se unen a los antígenos

anticodon: group of three bases on a tRNA molecule that are complementary to the three bases of a codon of mRNA (369)
anticodón: grupo de tres bases en una molécula de ARN de transferencia que son complementarias a las tres bases de un codón de ARN mensajero

antigen: any substance that triggers an immune response (1016)
antígeno: cualquier sustancia que provoca una respuesta inmune

aphotic zone: dark layer of the oceans below the photic zone where sunlight does not penetrate (117)
zona afótica: sección oscura de los océanos donde no penetra la luz solar, situada debajo de la zona fótica

apical dominance: phenomenon in which the closer a bud is to the stem's tip, the more its growth is inhibited (710)
dominancia apical: fenómeno por el cual cuanto más cerca de la punta del tallo está un brote, más se inhibe su crecimiento

apical meristem: group of unspecialized cells that divide to produce increased length of stems and roots (668)
meristemo apical: grupo de células no especializadas que se dividen para producir un aumento en la longitud de tallos y raíces

apoptosis: process of programmed cell death (288)
apoptosis: proceso de muerte celular programada

appendage: structure, such as a leg or antenna that extends from the body wall (753)
apéndice: estructura, como una pierna o una antena, que se proyecta desde la superficie corporal

appendicular skeleton: the bones of the arms and legs along with the bones of the pelvis and shoulder area (922)
esqueleto apendicular: los huesos de los brazos y de las piernas junto con los huesos de la pelvis y del área de los hombros

aquaculture: raising of aquatic organisms for human consumption (176)
acuicultura: cría de organismos acuáticos para el consumo humano

aquaporin: water channel protein in a cell (210)
acuaporina: proteína que canaliza el agua en una célula

Archaea: domain consisting of unicellular prokaryotes that have cell walls that do not contain peptidoglycan; corresponds to the kingdom Archeabacteria (526)
Arqueas: dominio formado por procariotas unicelulares cuyas paredes celulares no contienen peptidoglicano; corresponden al reino de las Arqueabacterias

archegonium (pl. archegonia): structure in plants that produces egg cells (642)
arquegonio: estructura de las plantas que produce óvulos

artery: large blood vessel that carries blood away from the heart to the tissues of the body (952)

arteria: vaso sanguíneo grande que transporta la sangre desde el corazón a los tejidos del cuerpo

artificial selection: selective breeding of plants and animals to promote the occurrence of desirable traits in offspring (458)

selección artificial: cría selectiva de plantas y animales para fomentar la ocurrencia de rasgos deseados en la progenie

asexual reproduction: process of reproduction involving a single parent that results in offspring that are genetically identical to the parent (19, 277)

reproducción asexual: proceso de reproducción que involucra a un único progenitor y da por resultado descendencia genéticamente idéntica a ese progenitor

asthma: chronic respiratory disease in which air passages narrow, causing wheezing, coughing, and difficulty breathing (1024)

asma: enfermedad respiratoria crónica en la cual las vías respiratorias se estrechan, provocando jadeos, tos y dificultad para respirar

atherosclerosis: condition in which fatty deposits called plaque build up inside artery walls and eventually cause the arteries to stiffen (958)

arteriosclerosis o ateroesclerosis: enfermedad en la cual se acumulan depósitos de grasa llamados placas en el interior de las paredes arteriales que, con el tiempo, causan un endurecimiento de las arterias

atom: the basic unit of matter (34)

átomo: unidad básica de la materia

ATP synthase: cluster of proteins that span the cell membrane and allow hydrogen ions (H^+) to pass through it (237)

ATP sintasa: complejo de proteínas unidas a la membrana celular que permiten el paso de los iones de hidrógeno (H^+) a través de ella

atrium (pl. atria): upper chamber of the heart that receives blood from the rest of the body (792, 949)

aurícula: cavidad superior del corazón que recibe sangre del resto del cuerpo

autonomic nervous system: part of the peripheral nervous system that regulates activities that are involuntary, or not under conscious control; made up of the sympathetic and parasympathetic subdivisions (908)

sistema nervioso autónomo: parte del sistema nervioso periférico que regula las actividades involuntarias, o que son independientes de la conciencia; está compuesto por las subdivisiones simpática y parasimpática

autosome: chromosome that is not a sex chromosome; also called autosomal chromosome (393)

autosoma: cromosoma que no es un cromosoma sexual; también llamado cromosoma autosómico

autotroph: organism that is able to capture energy from sunlight or chemicals and use it to produce its own food from inorganic compounds; also called a producer (69, 228)

autótrofo: organismo capaz de atrapar la energía de la luz solar o de las sustancias químicas y utilizarla para producir su propio alimento a partir de compuestos inorgánicos; también llamado productor

auxin: regulatory substance produced in the tip of a growing plant that stimulates cell elongation and the growth of new roots (709)

auxina: sustancia reguladora producida en la punta de una planta en crecimiento que estimula el alargamiento celular y el crecimiento de raíces nuevas

axial skeleton: skeleton that supports the central axis of the body; consists of the skull, vertebral column, and the rib cage (922)

esqueleto axial: esqueleto que sostiene al eje central del cuerpo; consiste en el cráneo, la columna vertebral y la caja torácica

axon: long fiber that carries impulses away from the cell body of a neuron (897)

axón: fibra larga que lleva los impulsos desde el cuerpo celular de una neurona

B

bacillus (pl. bacilli): rod-shaped prokaryote (582)

bacilo: procariota con forma de bastón

background extinction: extinction caused by slow and steady process of natural selection (548)

extinción de fondo: extinción causada por un proceso lento y continuo de selección natural

Bacteria: domain of unicellular prokaryotes that have cell walls containing peptidoglycan; corresponds to the kingdom eubacteria (525)

Bacteria: pertenece al dominio de los unicelulares procariota cuyas paredes celulares contienen peptidoglicano; corresponde al reino de las Eubacterias

bacteriophage: kind of virus that infects bacteria (340, 575)

bacteriófago: clase de virus que infecta a las bacterias

bark: tissues that are found outside the vascular cambium, including the phloem, cork cambium, and cork (679)

corteza: tejidos que se hallan fuera del cámbium vascular, incluidos el floema, el cámbium suberoso y el corcho

base: compound that produces hydroxide ions (OH^-) in solution; solution with a pH of more than 7 (44)

base: compuesto que en una solución produce iones hidróxido (OH^-); una solución con un pH superior a 7

Glossary *(continued)*

base pairing: principle that bonds in DNA can form only between adenine and thymine and between guanine and cytosine (348)
 apareamiento de bases: principio que establece que los enlaces en el ADN sólo pueden formarse entre adenina y timina y entre guanina y citocina

behavior: manner in which an organism reacts to changes in its internal condition or external environment (840)
 comportamiento: manera en que un organismo reacciona a los cambios que ocurren en su condición interna o en el medio ambiente externo

behavioral isolation: form of reproductive isolation in which two populations develop differences in courtship rituals or other behaviors that prevent them from breeding (495)
 aislamiento conductual: forma de aislamiento reproductivo en la cual dos poblaciones desarrollan diferencias en sus rituales de cortejo o en otros comportamientos que evitan que se apareen

benthos: organisms that live attached to or near the bottom of lakes, streams, or oceans (117)
 bentos: organismos que viven adheridos al fondo, o cerca del fondo, de lagos, arroyos u océanos

bias: particular preference or point of view that is personal, rather than scientific (14)
 parcialidad: preferencia especial o punto de vista que es personal en lugar de ser científico

bilateral symmetry: body plan in which a single imaginary line can divide the body into left and right sides that are mirror images of each other (738)
 simetría bilateral: diseño corporal en el cual una línea imaginaria divide al cuerpo en dos lados, izquierdo y derecho, que son imágenes reflejas una del otra

binary fission: type of asexual reproduction in which an organism replicates its DNA and divides in half, producing two identical daughter cells (583)
 fisión binaria: tipo de reproducción asexual en la cual un organismo replica su ADN, se divide por la mitad y produce dos células hijas idénticas

binocular vision: ability to merge visual images from both eyes, providing depth perception and a three-dimensional view of the world (765)
 visión binocular: capacidad de fusionar las imágenes visuales provenientes de ambos ojos, lo cual proporciona una percepción profunda y una visión tridimensional del mundo

binomial nomenclature: classification system in which each species is assigned a two-part scientific name (512)
 nomenclatura binaria: sistema de clasificación en el cual a cada especie se le asigna un nombre científico que consta de dos partes

biodiversity: total of the variety of organisms in the biosphere; also called biological diversity (166)
 biodiversidad: totalidad de los distintos organismos que se hallan en la biósfera; también denominada diversidad biológica

biogeochemical cycle: process in which elements, chemical compounds, and other forms of matter are passed from one organism to another and from one part of the biosphere to another (79)
 ciclo biogeoquímico: proceso en el cual los elementos, los compuestos químicos y otras formas de materia pasan de un organismo a otro y de una parte de la biósfera a otra

biogeography: study of past and present distribution of organisms (465)
 biogeografía: estudio de la distribución pasada y presente de los organismos

bioinformatics: application of mathematics and computer science to store, retrieve, and analyze biological data (407)
 bioinformática: aplicación de las matemáticas y de la informática para almacenar, recuperar y analizar información biológica

biological magnification: increasing concentration of a harmful substance in organisms at higher trophic levels in a food chain or food web (161)
 bioacumulación: concentración creciente de sustancias perjudiciales en los organismos de los niveles tróficos más elevados de una cadena o red alimentaria

biology: scientific study of life (17)
 biología: estudio científico de la vida

biomass: total amount of living tissue within a given trophic level (78)
 biomasa: cantidad total de tejido vivo dentro de un nivel trófico dado

biome: a group of ecosystems that share similar climates and typical organisms (65)
 bioma: un grupo de ecosistemas que comparten climas similares y organismos típicos

biosphere: part of Earth in which life exists including land, water, and air or atmosphere (21, 64)
 biósfera: parte de la Tierra en la cual existe vida, y que incluye el suelo, el agua y el aire o atmósfera

biotechnology: process of manipulating organisms, cells, or molecules, to produce specific products (419)
 biotecnología: proceso de manipular organismos, células o moléculas con el fin de obtener productos específicos

biotic factor: any living part of the environment with which an organism might interact (66)
 factor biótico: cualquier parte viva del medio ambiente con la cual un organismo podría interaccionar

bipedal: term used to refer to two-foot locomotion (767)
 bípedo: término utilizado para referirse a la locomoción sobre dos pies

blade: thin, flattened part of a plant leaf (680)
lámina foliar o limbo: parte delgada y plana de la hoja de una planta

blastocyst: stage of early development in mammals that consists of a hollow ball of cells (294, 996)
blastocisto: etapa temprana del desarrollo de los mamíferos que consiste en una bola hueca formada por una capa de células

blastula: hollow ball of cells that develops when a zygote undergoes a series of cell divisions (739)
blástula: esfera hueca de células que se desarrolla cuando un cigoto atraviesa una serie de divisiones celulares

bone marrow: soft tissue found in bone cavities (924)
médula ósea: tejido blando que se halla en las cavidades de los huesos

bottleneck effect: a change in allele frequency following a dramatic reduction in the size of a population (490)
efecto cuello de botella: un cambio en la frecuencia alélica que resulta cuando el tamaño de una población reduce drásticamente

Bowman's capsule: cuplike structure that encases the glomerulus; collects filtrate from the blood (884)
cápsula de Bowman: estructura en forma de taza que encierra al glomérulo; recoge los filtrados provenientes de la sangre

brain stem: structure that connects the brain and spinal cord; includes the medulla oblongata and the pons (903)
tronco cerebral: estructura que conecta al cerebro con la médula espinal; incluye el bulbo raquídeo y el puente de Varolio

bronchus (pl. bronchi): one of two large tubes in the chest cavity that leads from the trachea to the lungs (964)
bronquio: cada uno de los dos conductos largos ubicados en la cavidad torácica que parten desde la tráquea y llegan a los pulmones

bryophyte: group of plants that have specialized reproductive organs but lack vascular tissue; includes mosses and their relatives (641)
briofitas: grupo de plantas que tienen órganos reproductores especializados pero carecen de tejido vascular; incluyen a los musgos y sus congéneres

bud: plant structure containing apical meristem tissue that can produce new stems and leaves (675)
yema o gema: estructura de las plantas que contiene tejido del meristemo apical y puede producir nuevos tallos y hojas

buffer: compound that prevents sharp, sudden changes in pH (44)
solución amortiguadora: compuesto que evita cambios bruscos y repentinos en el pH

C

calcitonin: hormone produced by the thyroid that reduces blood calcium levels (985)
calcitonina: hormona producida por la tiroides que reduce los niveles de calcio en la sangre

Calorie: measure of heat energy in food; equivalent to 1000 calories (868)
Caloría: medida de la energía térmica de los alimentos, equivalente a 1000 calorías

calorie: amount of energy needed to raise the temperature of 1 gram of water by 1 degree Celsius (250)
caloría: cantidad de energía necesaria para elevar la temperatura de 1 gramo de agua en 1 grado Celsius

Calvin cycle: light-independent reactions of photosynthesis in which energy from ATP and NADPH is used to build high-energy compounds such as sugar (238)
ciclo de Calvin: reacciones de la fotosíntesis independientes de la luz en las cuales se utiliza la energía del ATP y del NADPH para elaborar compuestos con alto contenido energético, como el azúcar

cancer: disorder in which some of the body's cells lose the ability to control growth (289)
cáncer: enfermedad en la cual algunas de las células del cuerpo pierden la capacidad de controlar su crecimiento

canopy: dense covering formed by the leafy tops of tall rain forest trees (112)
dosel forestal: cubierta densa formada por las copas de los árboles altos del bosque tropical

capillary: smallest blood vessel; brings nutrients and oxygen to the tissues and absorbs carbon dioxide and waste products (952)
capilar: más pequeño de los vaso sanguíneo más pequeño; lleva nutrientes y oxígeno a los tejidos y absorbe dióxido de carbono y productos de desecho

capillary action: tendency of water to rise in a thin tube (686)
capilaridad: tendencia del agua a ascender en un tubo delgado

capsid: protein coat surrounding a virus (575)
cápsida: cobertura de proteínas que rodea a un virus

carbohydrate: compound made up of carbon, hydrogen, and oxygen atoms; type of nutrient that is the major source of energy for the body (46, 869)
hidrato de carbono: compuesto formado por átomos de carbono, hidrógeno y oxígeno; tipo de nutriente que es la fuente principal de energía para el cuerpo

carnivore: organism that obtains energy by eating animals (71)
carnívoro: organismo que obtiene energía al comer otros animales

Glossary *(continued)*

carpel: innermost part of a flower that produces and shelters the female gametophytes (697)
carpelo: parte interna de una flor que produce y alberga los gametofitos femeninos

carrying capacity: largest number of individuals of a particular species that a particular environment can support (135)
capacidad de carga: mayor cantidad de individuos de una especie en particular que un medio ambiente específico puede mantener

cartilage: type of connective tissue that supports the body and is softer and more flexible than bone (757, 924)
cartílago: tipo de tejido conectivo que sostiene al cuerpo y es más blando y flexible que el hueso

Casparian strip: waterproof strip that surrounds plant endodermal cells and is involved in the one-way passage of materials into the vascular cylinder in plant roots (672)
banda de Caspary: banda impermeable que rodea a las células endodérmicas de las plantas y participa en el transporte unidireccional de las sustancias hacia el interior del cilindro vascular de las raíces de las plantas

catalyst: substance that speeds up the rate of a chemical reaction (52)
catalizador: sustancia que acelera la velocidad de una reacción química

cell: basic unit of all forms of life (191)
célula: unidad básica de todas las formas de vida

cell body: largest part of a typical neuron; contains the nucleus and much of the cytoplasm (897)
cuerpo celular: parte más grande de una neurona típica; que contiene el núcleo y gran parte del citoplasma

cell cycle: series of events in which a cell grows, prepares for division, and divides to form two daughter cells (280)
ciclo celular: serie de sucesos en los cuales una célula crece, se prepara para dividirse y se divide para formar dos células hijas

cell division: process by which a cell divides into two new daughter cells (276)
división celular: proceso por el cual una célula se divide en dos células hijas nuevas

cell membrane: thin, flexible barrier that surrounds all cells; regulates what enters and leaves the cell (193)
membrana celular: barrera flexible y delgada que rodea a todas las células; regula lo que entra y sale de la célula

cell theory: fundamental concept of biology that states that all living things are composed of cells; that cells are the basic units of structure and function in living things; and that new cells are produced from existing cells (191)
teoría celular: concepto fundamental de la Biología que establece que todos los seres vivos están compuestos por células; que las células son las unidades básicas estructurales y funcionales de los seres vivos; y que las células nuevas se producen a partir de células existentes

cell wall: strong, supporting layer around the cell membrane in some cells (203)
pared celular: capa resistente que sirve de sostén y está situada alrededor de la membrana celular de algunas células

cell-mediated immunity: immune response that defends the body against viruses, fungi, and abnormal cancer cells inside living cells (1019)
inmunidad celular: respuesta inmune que desde las células defiende al cuerpo contra virus, hongos y células anormales cancerígenas

cellular respiration: process that releases energy by breaking down glucose and other food molecules in the presence of oxygen (281)
respiración celular: proceso que libera energía al descomponer la glucosa y otras moléculas de los alimentos en presencia de oxígeno

central nervous system: includes the brain and spinal cord; processes information and creates a response that it delivers to the body (896)
sistema nervioso central: incluye el cerebro y la médula espinal; procesa información y genera una respuesta que es enviada al cuerpo

centriole: structure in an animal cell that helps to organize cell division (199, 282)
centríolo: estructura de una célula animal que contribuye a organizar la división celular

centromere: region of a chromosome where the two sister chromatids attach (282)
centrómero: región de un cromosoma donde se unen las dos cromátidas hermanas

cephalization: concentration of sense organs and nerve cells at the anterior end of an animal (740)
cefalización: concentración de órganos sensoriales y células nerviosas en el extremo anterior de un animal

cerebellum: part of the brain that coordinates movement and controls balance (811, 903)
cerebelo: parte del encéfalo que coordina el movimiento y controla el equilibrio

cerebral cortex: outer layer of the cerebrum of a mammal's brain; center of thinking and other complex behaviors (902)
corteza cerebral: capa externa del cerebro de un mamífero; centro del raciocinio y otros comportamientos complejos

cerebrum: part of the brain responsible for voluntary activities of the body; "thinking" region of the brain (811, 902)

cerebro: parte del encéfalo responsable de las actividades voluntarias del cuerpo; región "pensante" del encéfalo

chemical digestion: process by which enzymes break down food into small molecules that the body can use (875)

digestión química: proceso por el cual las enzimas descomponen los alimentos en moléculas pequeñas que el cuerpo puede utilizar

chemical reaction: process that changes, or transforms, one set of chemicals into another set of chemicals (50)

reacción química: proceso que cambia, o transforma, un grupo de sustancias químicas en otro grupo de sustancias químicas

chemosynthesis: process in which chemical energy is used to produce carbohydrates (70)

quimiosíntesis: proceso en el cual la energía química se utiliza para producir hidratos de carbono

chitin: complex carbohydrate that makes up the cell walls of fungi; also found in the external skeletons of arthropods (618)

quitina: hidrato de carbono complejo que forma las paredes celulares de los hongos; también se halla en los esqueletos externos de los artrópodos

chlorophyll: principal pigment of plants and other photosynthetic organisms (230)

clorofila: pigmento fundamental de las plantas y de otros organismos fotosintéticos

chloroplast: organelle found in cells of plants and some other organisms that captures the energy from sunlight and converts it into chemical energy (202)

cloroplasto: orgánulo de las células de las plantas y de otros organismos que captura la energía de la luz solar y la convierte en energía química

chordate: animal that has, for at least one stage of its life, a dorsal, hollow nerve cord, a notochord, a tail that extends beyond the anus, and pharyngeal pouches (731)

cordado: animal que, al menos durante una etapa de su vida, tiene un cordón nervioso hueco y dorsal, un notocordio, una cola que se prolonga más allá del ano y bolsas faríngeas

chromatid: one of two identical "sister" parts of a duplicated chromosome (282)

cromátida: una de las dos partes "hermanas" idénticas de un cromosoma duplicado

chromatin: substance found in eukaryotic chromosomes that consists of DNA tightly coiled around histones (280)

cromatina: sustancia que se halla en los cromosomas eucarióticos y que consiste en ADN enrollado apretadamente alrededor de las histonas

chromosome: threadlike structure of DNA and protein that contains genetic information; in eukaryotes, chromosomes are found in the nucleus; in prokaryotes, they are found in the cytoplasm (279)

cromosoma: estructura larga de ADN y proteína, con forma de hilo, que posee información genética; en los eucariotas, los cromosomas están dentro del núcleo; en los procariotas, los cromosomas están en el citoplasma

chyme: mixture of enzymes and partially-digested food (877)

quimo: mezcla de enzimas y alimentos parcialmente digeridos

cilium (pl. cilia): short hairlike projection that produces movement (607)

cilio: pequeña prolongación parecida a un pelo que produce movimiento

circadian rhythm: behavioral cycles that occur daily (847)

ritmo circadiano: ciclos conductuales que ocurren diariamente

clade: evolutionary branch of a cladogram that includes a single ancestor and all its descendants (516)

clado: rama evolutiva de un cladograma que incluye a un único ancestro y a todos sus descendientes

cladogram: diagram depicting patterns of shared characteristics among species (517)

cladograma: diagrama que representa patrones de características compartidas entre especies

class: in classification, a group of closely related orders (514)

clase: en la clasificación, un grupo de varios órdenes relacionados estrechamente

classical conditioning: type of learning that occurs when an animal makes a mental connection between a stimulus and some kind of reward or punishment (843)

condicionamiento clásico: tipo de aprendizaje que ocurre cuando un animal realiza una conexión mental entre un estímulo y algún tipo de recompensa o castigo

climate: average year-to-year conditions of temperature and precipitation in an area over a long period of time (96)

clima: promedio anual de las condiciones de temperatura y precipitación en un área durante un largo período de tiempo

clone: member of a population of genetically identical cells produced from a single cell (427)

clon: miembro de una población de células genéticamente idénticas producidas a partir de una célula única

closed circulatory system: type of circulatory system in which blood circulates entirely within blood vessels that extend throughout the body (792)

sistema circulatorio cerrado: tipo de sistema circulatorio en el cual la sangre circula completamente dentro de los vasos sanguíneos que se extienden por todo el cuerpo

coccus (pl. cocci): spherical prokaryote (582)

coco: procariota de forma esférica

cochlea: fluid-filled part of inner ear; contains nerve cells that detect sound (911)

cóclea: parte del oído interno llena de fluidos; contiene las células nerviosas que detectan el sonido

codominance: situation in which the phenotypes produced by both alleles are completely expressed (319)

codominancia: situación en la cual los fenotipos producidos por ambos alelos están expresados completamente

Glossary (continued)

codon: group of three nucleotide bases in mRNA that specify a particular amino acid to be incorporated into a protein (366)
  codón: grupo de tres bases de nucleótidos en el RNA mensajero que especifican la incorporación de un aminoácido en particular en una proteína

coelom: body cavity lined with mesoderm (738)
  celoma: cavidad corporal revestida de mesodermo

coevolution: process by which two species evolve in response to changes in each other over time (551)
  coevolución: proceso por el cual dos especies evolucionan en respuesta a cambios mutuos en el transcurso del tiempo

cohesion: attraction between molecules of the same substance (41)
  cohesión: atracción entre moléculas de la misma sustancia

collenchyma: in plants, type of ground tissue that has strong, flexible cell walls; helps support larger plants (667)
  colénquima: en las plantas, tipo de tejido fundamental que tiene paredes celulares fuertes y flexibles; contribuye a sostener las plantas más grandes

commensalism: symbiotic relationship in which one organism benefits and the other is neither helped nor harmed (104)
  comensalismo: relación simbiótica en la cual un organismo se beneficia y el otro ni se beneficia ni sufre daño

communication: passing of information from one organism to another (850)
  comunicación: traspaso de información desde un organismo a otro

community: assemblage of different populations that live together in a defined area (64)
  comunidad: conjunto de varias poblaciones que viven juntas en un área definida

companion cell: in plants, phloem cell that surrounds sieve tube elements (666)
  célula anexa: en las plantas, célula del floema que rodea a los vasos cribosos

competitive exclusion principle: principle that states that no two species can occupy the same niche in the same habitat at the same time (101)
  principio de exclusión competitiva: principio que afirma que dos especies no pueden ocupar el mismo nicho en el mismo hábitat al mismo tiempo

compound: substance formed by the chemical combination of two or more elements in definite proportions (36)
  compuesto: sustancia formada por la combinación química de dos o más elementos en proporciones definidas

cone: in the eye, photoreceptor that responds to light of different colors, producing color vision (913)
  cono: en el ojo, receptor de luz que responde a la luz de diferentes colores, produciendo la visión a color

coniferous: term used to refer to trees that produce seed-bearing cones and have thin leaves shaped like needles (114)
  coníferas: término utilizado para referirse a los árboles que producen conos portadores de semillas y que tienen hojas delgadas con forma de aguja

conjugation: process in which paramecia and some prokaryotes exchange genetic information (583, 608)
  conjugación: proceso mediante el cual los paramecios y algunos procariotas intercambian información genética

connective tissue: type of tissue that provides support for the body and connects its parts (863)
  tejido conectivo: tipo de tejido que proporciona sostén al cuerpo y conecta sus partes

consumer: organism that relies on other organisms for its energy and food supply; also called a heterotroph (71)
  consumidor: organismo que depende de otros organismos para obtener su energía y su provisión de alimentos; también llamado heterótrofo

control group: group in an experiment that is exposed to the same conditions as the experimental group except for one independent variable (7)
  grupo de control: en un experimento, grupo que está expuesto a las mismas condiciones que el grupo experimental, excepto por una variable independiente

controlled experiment: experiment in which only one variable is changed (7)
  experimento controlado: experimento en el cual sólo se cambia una variable

convergent evolution: process by which unrelated organisms independently evolve similarities when adapting to similar environments (551)
  evolución convergente: proceso mediante el cual organismos no relacionados evolucionan independientemente hacia caracteres similares cuando se adaptan a ambientes parecidos

cork cambium: meristematic tissue that produces the outer covering of stems during secondary growth of a plant (677)
  cámbium suberoso: tejido del meristemo que produce la cubierta exterior de los tallos durante el crecimiento secundario de una planta

cornea: tough transparent layer of the eye through which light enters (912)
  córnea: membrana dura y transparente del ojo a través de la cual entra la luz

corpus luteum: name given to a follicle after ovulation because of its yellow color (993)
  cuerpo lúteo: nombre dado a un folículo después de la ovulación debido a su color amarillo

cortex: in plants, region of ground tissue just inside the root through which water and minerals move (670)
  corteza radicular: en las plantas, región de tejido fundamental situada en el interior de la raíz a través de la cual pasan el agua y los minerales

corticosteroid: steroid hormone produced by the adrenal cortex (983)
  corticosteroide o corticoide: hormona esteroídica producida por la corteza de las glándulas adrenales

cotyledon: first leaf or first pair of leaves produced by the embryo of a seed plant (652)
  cotiledón: primera hoja o primer par de hojas producidas por el embrión de una planta fanerógama

courtship: type of behavior in which an animal sends out stimuli in order to attract a member of the opposite sex (848)
  cortejo: tipo de comportamiento en el cual un animal emite estímulos para atraer a un miembro del sexo opuesto

covalent bond: type of bond between atoms in which the electrons are shared (37)
  enlace covalente: tipo de enlace entre átomos en el cual se comparten los electrones

crossing-over: process in which homologous chromosomes exchange portions of their chromatids during meiosis (324)
  entrecruzamiento: proceso por el cual los cromosomas homólogos intercambian partes de sus cromátidas durante la meiosis

cyclin: one of a family of proteins that regulates the cell cycle in eukaryotic cells (286)
  ciclina: un componente de la familia de proteínas que regulan el ciclo celular de las células eucariotas

cytokinesis: division of the cytoplasm to form two separate daughter cells (282)
  citocinesis: división del citoplasma para formar dos células hijas separadas

cytokinin: plant hormone produced in growing roots and in developing fruits and seeds (710)
  citoquinina: hormona vegetal que se genera en las raíces en crecimiento y en los frutos y semillas en desarrollo

cytoplasm: in eukaryotic cells, all cellular contents outside the nucleus; in prokaryotic cells, all of the cells' contents (196)
  citoplasma: en una célula eucariota, todo el contenido celular fuera del núcleo; en las células procariotas, todo el contenido de las células

cytoskeleton: network of protein filaments in a eukaryotic cell that gives the cell its shape and internal organization and is involved in movement (199)
  citoesqueleto: en una célula eucariota, red de filamentos proteínicos que otorga a la célula su forma y su organización interna y participa en el movimiento

D

data: evidence; information gathered from observations (8)
  datos: evidencia; información reunida a partir de observaciones

deciduous: term used to refer to a type of tree that sheds its leaves during a particular season each year (112)
  caduco: término utilizado para referirse a un tipo de árbol que pierde sus hojas cada año durante una estación en particular

decomposer: organism that breaks down and obtains energy from dead organic matter (71)
  descomponedor: organismo que descompone y obtiene energía de la materia orgánica muerta

deforestation: destruction of forests (159)
  deforestación: destrucción de los bosques

demographic transition: change in a population from high birth and death rates to low birth and death rates (144)
  transición demográfica: en una población, cambio de índices de nacimiento y mortalidad altos a índices de nacimiento y mortalidad bajos

demography: scientific study of human populations (143)
  demografía: estudio científico de las poblaciones humanas

dendrite: extension of the cell body of a neuron that carries impulses from the environment or from other neurons toward the cell body (897)
  dendrita: prolongación del cuerpo celular de una neurona que transporta impulsos desde el medio ambiente o desde otras neuronas hacia el cuerpo celular

denitrification: process by which bacteria convert nitrates into nitrogen gas (84)
  desnitrificación: proceso por el cual las bacterias del suelo convierten los nitratos en gas nitrógeno

density-dependent limiting factor: limiting factor that depends on population density (138)
  factor limitante dependiente de la densidad: factor limitante que depende de la densidad de la población

density-independent limiting factor: limiting factor that affects all populations in similar ways, regardless of the population density (140)
  factor limitante independiente de la densidad: factor limitante que afecta a todas las poblaciones de manera similar, sin importar la densidad de la población

deoxyribonucleic acid (DNA): genetic material that organisms inherit from their parents (18)
  ácido desoxirribonucleico (ADN): material genético que los organismos heredan de sus padres

dependent variable: variable that is observed and that changes in response to the independent variable; also called the responding variable (7)
  variable dependiente: variable que está siendo observada y cambia en respuesta a la variable independiente; también llamada variable de respuesta

Glossary *(continued)*

derived character: trait that appears in recent parts of a lineage, but not in its older members (518)

carácter derivado: rasgo que aparece en los descendientes recientes de un linaje, pero no en sus miembros más viejos

dermis: layer of skin found beneath the epidermis (937)

dermis: capa de la piel situada debajo de la epidermis

desertification: lower land productivity caused by overfarming, overgrazing, seasonal drought, and climate change (159)

desertificación: disminución de la productividad de la tierra debido al cultivo y al pastoreo excesivo, a la sequía estacional y al cambio climático

detritivore: organism that feeds on plant and animal remains and other dead matter (71)

detritívoro: organismo que se alimenta de restos animales y vegetales y demás materia orgánica muerta

deuterostome: group of animals in which the blastopore becomes an anus, and the mouth is formed from the second opening that develops (739)

deuteróstomos: grupo de animales en los cuales el blastoporo se convierte en ano y la boca se forma a partir del desarrollo de una segunda abertura

diaphragm: large flat muscle at the bottom of the chest cavity that helps with breathing (967)

diafragma: músculo plano y grande ubicado en la parte inferior de la cavidad torácica que participa en la respiración

dicot: angiosperm with two seed leaves in its ovary (652)

dicotiledónea: angiosperma con dos cotiledones (hojas embrionarias) en su ovario

differentiation: process in which cells become specialized in structure and function (293, 381)

diferenciación: proceso en el cual las células se especializan en estructura y función

diffusion: process by which particles tend to move from an area where they are more concentrated to an area where they are less concentrated (208)

difusión: proceso por el cual las partículas tienden a desplazarse desde un área donde están más concentradas hacia un área donde están menos concentradas

digestive tract: tube that begins at the mouth and ends at the anus (784)

tracto digestivo: tubo que comienza en la boca y termina en el ano

diploid: term used to refer to a cell that contains two sets of homologous chromosomes (323)

diploide: término utilizado para referirse a una célula que contiene dos series de cromosomas homólogos

directional selection: form of natural selection in which individuals at one end of a distribution curve have higher fitness than individuals in the middle or at the other end of the curve (489)

selección direccional: forma de selección natural en la cual los individuos que se hallan en un extremo de la curva de distribución poseen una mayor capacidad de adaptación que los individuos que se hallan en el centro o en el otro extremo de la curva

disruptive selection: natural selection in which individuals at the upper and lower ends of the curve have higher fitness than individuals near the middle of the curve (489)

selección disruptiva: forma de selección natural en la cual los individuos que se hallan en los extremos superior e inferior de la curva poseen una mayor capacidad de adaptación que los individuos que se hallan cerca del centro de la curva

DNA fingerprinting: tool used by biologists that analyzes an individual's unique collection of DNA restriction fragments; used to determine whether two samples of genetic material are from the same person (433)

prueba de ADN: herramienta utilizada por los biólogos mediante la cual se analiza el conjunto de los fragmentos de restricción de ADN exclusivo de cada individuo; utilizada para determinar si dos muestras de material genético pertenecen a la misma persona; también llamada huella genética o análisis de ADN

DNA microarray: glass slide or silicon chip that carries thousands of different kinds of single-stranded DNA fragments arranged in a grid. A DNA microarray is used to detect and measure the expression of thousands of genes at one time (432)

chip de ADN: superficie de vidrio o chip de silicona que contiene miles de diferentes tipos de fragmentos de ADN de una sola cadena dispuestos en una cuadrícula. Un chip de ADN se utiliza para detectar y medir la expresión de miles de genes a la vez

DNA polymerase: principal enzyme involved in DNA replication (351)

ADN polimerasa: enzima fundamental involucrada en la replicación del ADN

domain: larger, more inclusive taxonomic category than a kingdom (525)

dominio: categoría taxonómica más amplia e inclusiva que un reino

dopamine: neurotransmitter that is associated with the brain's pleasure and reward centers (904)

dopamina: neurotransmisor que está asociado con los centros de placer y de recompensa del cerebro

dormancy: period of time during which a plant embryo is alive but not growing (706)

latencia: período de tiempo durante el cual un embrión vegetal está vivo pero no crece

double fertilization: process of fertilization in angiosperms in which the first event produces the zygote, and the second, the endosperm within the seed (700)

doble fertilización: proceso de fecundación de las angiospermas en el cual se produce, en el primer suceso el cigoto y en el segundo, el endospermo dentro de la semilla

E

ecological footprint: total amount of functioning ecosystem needed both to provide the resources a human population uses and to absorb the wastes that population generates (173)

huella ecológica: cantidad total de ecosistema en funcionamiento necesaria para proporcionar los recursos que utiliza una población humana y para absorber los residuos que genera esa población

ecological hot spot: small geographic area where significant numbers of habitats and species are in immediate danger of extinction (171)

zona de conflicto ecológico: área geográfica pequeña donde cantidades importantes de hábitats y especies se hallan en peligro de extinción inmediato

ecological pyramid: illustration of the relative amounts of energy or matter contained within each trophic level in a given food chain or food web (77)

pirámide ecológica: ilustración de las cantidades relativas de energía o materia contenidas dentro de cada nivel trófico en una cadena o red alimenticia dada

ecological succession: series of gradual changes that occur in a community following a disturbance (106)

sucesión ecológica: serie de cambios graduales que ocurren en una comunidad después de una alteración

ecology: scientific study of interactions among organisms and between organisms and their environment (65)

ecología: estudio científico de las interacciones entre organismos y entre los organismos y su medio ambiente

ecosystem: all the organisms that live in a place, together with their nonliving environment (65)

ecosistema: todos los organismos que viven en un lugar, junto con su medio ambiente inanimado

ecosystem diversity: variety of habitats, communities, and ecological processes in the biosphere (166)

diversidad de ecosistemas: variedad de hábitats, comunidades y procesos ecológicos que existen en la biósfera

ectoderm: outermost germ layer; produces sense organs, nerves, and outer layer of skin (738)

ectodermo: capa embrionaria más externa; desarrolla órganos sensoriales, nervios y la capa exterior de la piel

ectotherm: animal whose body temperature is determined by the temperature of its environment (829)

animal de sangre fría: animal cuya temperatura corporal está determinada por la temperatura de su medio ambiente

electron: negatively charged particle; located in the space surrounding the nucleus (34)

electrón: partícula con carga negativa; ubicada en el espacio que rodea al núcleo

electron transport chain: series of electron carrier proteins that shuttle high-energy electrons during ATP-generating reactions (236)

cadena de transporte de electrones: serie de proteínas transportadoras que llevan electrones de alta energía, durante las reacciones generadoras de ATP

element: pure substance that consists entirely of one type of atom (35)

elemento: sustancia pura que consiste íntegramente en un tipo de átomo

embryo: developing stage of a multicellular organism (292)

embrión: una de las etapas de desarrollo de un organismo multicelular

embryo sac: female gametophyte within the ovule of a flowering plant (699)

saco embrionario: gametofito femenino dentro del óvulo de una planta que produce flores

emerging disease: disease that appears in the population for the first time, or an old disease that suddenly becomes harder to control (590)

enfermedad emergente: enfermedad que aparece en una población por primera vez o una enfermedad antigua que de pronto se vuelve más difícil de controlar

emigration: movement of individuals out of an area (132)

emigración: desplazamiento de individuos fuera de un área

endocrine gland: gland that releases its secretions (hormones) directly into the blood, which transports the secretions to other areas of the body (828, 979)

glándula endocrina: glándula que vierte sus secreciones (hormonas) directamente en la sangre, para ser transportadas a otras áreas del cuerpo

endoderm: innermost germ layer; develops into the linings of the digestive tract and much of the respiratory system (738)

endodermo: capa embrionaria más interna, a partir de la cual se desarrollan los revestimientos del tracto digestivo y gran parte del sistema respiratorio

endodermis: in plants, layer of ground tissue that completely encloses the vascular cylinder (670)

endodermis: en las plantas, un capa de tejido fundamental que envuelve completamente al cilindro vascular

endoplasmic reticulum: internal membrane system found in eukaryotic cells; place where lipid components of the cell membrane are assembled (200)

retículo endoplasmático: sistema de membranas internas de las células eucariotas; lugar donde se reúnen los componentes lipídicos de la membrana celular

endoskeleton: internal skeleton; structural support system within the body of an animal (815)

endoesqueleto: esqueleto interno; sistema estructural de sostén dentro del cuerpo de un animal

Glossary *(continued)*

endosperm: food-rich tissue that nourishes a seedling as it grows (700)
endospermo: tejido nutritivo que alimenta a una plántula a medida que crece

endospore: structure produced by prokaryotes in unfavorable conditions; a thick internal wall that encloses the DNA and a portion of the cytoplasm (583)
endospora: estructura producida por los procariotas en condiciones desfavorables; una gruesa pared interna que encierra al ADN y a una parte del citoplasma

endosymbiotic theory: theory that proposes that eukaryotic cells formed from a symbiotic relationship among several different prokaryotic cells (556)
teoría endosimbiótica: teoría que propone que las células eucariotas se formaron a partir de una relación simbiótica entre varias células procariotas distintas

endotherm: animal whose body temperature is regulated, at least in part, using heat generated within its body (829)
endotermo: animal cuya temperatura corporal se regula, al menos en parte, utilizando el calor generado dentro de su cuerpo

enzyme: protein catalyst that speeds up the rate of specific biological reactions (52)
enzima: proteína catalizadora que acelera la velocidad de reacciones biológicas específicas

epidermis: in plants, single layer of cells that makes up dermal tissue (665); in humans, the outer layer of the skin (936)
epidermis: en las plantas, única capa de células que forma el tejido dérmico; en los seres humanos, la capa exterior de la piel

epididymis: organ in the male reproductive system in which sperm mature and are stored (989)
epidídimo: órgano del sistema reproductor masculino en el cual el esperma madura y se almacena

epinephrine: hormone released by the adrenal glands that increases heart rate and blood pressure and prepares the body for intense physical activity; also called adrenaline (983)
epinefrina: hormona liberada por las glándulas adrenales que aumenta la frecuencia cardíaca y la presión sanguínea y prepara al cuerpo para una actividad física intensa; también llamada adrenalina

epithelial tissue: type of tissue that lines the interior and exterior body surfaces (863)
tejido epitelial: tipo de tejido que reviste el interior y el exterior de las superficies del cuerpo

era: major division of geologic time; usually divided into two or more periods (543)
era: división principal del tiempo geológico; usualmente dividida en dos o más períodos

esophagus: tube connecting the mouth to the stomach (877)
esófago: tubo que conecta la boca con el estómago

estuary: kind of wetland formed where a river meets the ocean (119)
estuario: tipo de humedal que se forma donde un río se une al océano

ethylene: plant hormone that stimulates fruits to ripen (711)
etileno: hormona vegetal que estimula la maduración de los frutos

Eukarya: domain consisting of all organisms that have a nucleus; includes protists, plants, fungi, and animals (526)
***Eukarya* (eucariontes):** dominio compuesto por todos los organismos que tienen un núcleo; incluye a los protistas, las plantas, los hongos y los animales

eukaryote: organism whose cells contain a nucleus (193)
eucariota: organismo cuyas células contienen un núcleo

evolution: change over time; the process by which modern organisms have descended from ancient organisms (450)
evolución: cambio en el transcurso del tiempo; el proceso por el cual los organismos actuales se derivaron de los organismos antiguos

excretion: process by which metabolic wastes are eliminated from the body (794, 882)
excreción: proceso por el cual se eliminan del cuerpo los residuos metabólicos

exocrine gland: gland that releases its secretions, through tubelike structures called ducts, directly into an organ or out of the body (979)
glándula exocrina: glándula que vierte sus secreciones directamente a un órgano o al exterior del cuerpo a través de estructuras tubulares denominadas conductos

exon: expressed sequence of DNA; codes for a protein (365)
exón: secuencia expresada de ADN; codifica una porción específica de una proteína

exoskeleton: external skeleton; tough external covering that protects and supports the body of many invertebrates (815)
exoesqueleto: esqueleto externo; cubierta externa dura que protege y sostiene el cuerpo de muchos invertebrados

exponential growth: growth pattern in which the individuals in a population reproduce at a constant rate (132)
crecimiento exponencial: patrón de crecimiento en el cual los individuos de una población se reproducen a una tasa constante

extinct: term used to refer to a species that has died out and has no living members (538)

extinto: término utilizado para referirse a una especie que ha desaparecido y de la que ninguno de sus miembros está vivo

extracellular digestion: type of digestion in which food is broken down outside the cells in a digestive system and then absorbed (784)

digestión extracelular: tipo de digestión en la cual el alimento es degradado fuera de las células dentro de un sistema digestivo y luego se absorbe

F

facilitated diffusion: process of diffusion in which molecules pass across the membrane through cell membrane channels (209)

difusión facilitada: proceso de difusión en el cual las moléculas atraviesan la membrana a través de los canales de la membrana celular

family: in classification, group of similar genera (513)

familia: en la clasificación, grupo de géneros similares

fat: lipid; made up of fatty acids and glycerol; type of nutrient that protects body organs, insulates the body, and stores energy (870)

grasa: lípido; compuesto de ácidos grasos y glicerina; tipo de nutriente que protege a los órganos del cuerpo, actúa como aislante térmico y almacena energía

feedback inhibition: process in which a stimulus produces a response that opposes the original stimulus; also called negative feedback (732, 865)

inhibición de la retroalimentación: proceso en el cual un estímulo produce una respuesta que se opone al estímulo original; también llamada retroalimentación negativa

fermentation: process by which cells release energy in the absence of oxygen (262)

fermentación: proceso por el cual las células liberan energía en ausencia de oxígeno

fertilization: process in sexual reproduction in which male and female reproductive cells join to form a new cell (309)

fecundación: proceso de la reproducción sexual en el cual las células reproductoras masculinas y femeninas se unen para formar una célula nueva

fetus: a human embryo after eight weeks of development (998)

feto: un embrión humano después de ocho semanas de desarrollo

fever: increased body temperature that occurs in response to infection (1015)

fiebre: temperatura corporal elevada que se produce como respuesta a una infección

filtration: process of passing a liquid or gas through a filter to remove wastes (884)

filtración: proceso de hacer pasar un líquido o un gas a través de un filtro para quitar los residuos

fitness: how well an organism can survive and reproduce in its environment (461)

aptitud: capacidad de un organismo para sobrevivir y reproducirse en su medio ambiente

flagellum (pl. flagella): structure used by protists for movement; produces movement in a wavelike motion (607)

flagelo: estructura utilizada por los protistas para desplazarse; produce un desplazamiento con un movimiento semejante al de una onda

food chain: series of steps in an ecosystem in which organisms transfer energy by eating and being eaten (73)

cadena alimenticia: serie de pasos en un ecosistema, en que los organismos transfieren energía al alimentarse y al servir de alimento

food vacuole: small cavity in the cytoplasm of a protist that temporarily stores food (612)

vacuola alimenticia: pequeña cavidad situada en el citoplasma de los protistas que almacena alimentos por algún tiempo

food web: network of complex interactions formed by the feeding relationships among the various organisms in an ecosystem (74)

red alimenticia: red de interacciones complejas constituida por las relaciones alimenticias entre los varios organismos de un ecosistema

forensics: scientific study of crime scene evidence (433)

ciencias forenses: estudio científico de las pruebas en la escena del crimen

fossil: preserved remains or traces of ancient organisms (452)

fósil: restos conservados o vestigios de organismos antiguos

founder effect: change in allele frequencies as a result of the migration of a small subgroup of a population (490)

efecto fundador: cambio en las frecuencias alélicas como consecuencia de la migración de un subgrupo pequeño de una población

frameshift mutation: mutation that shifts the "reading frame" of the genetic message by inserting or deleting a nucleotide (373)

mutación de corrimiento de estructura: mutación que cambia el "marco de lectura" del mensaje genético insertando o eliminando un nucleótido

fruit: structure in angiosperms that contains one or more matured ovaries (651)

fruto: estructura de las Angiospermas que contiene uno o más ovarios maduros

fruiting body: reproductive structure of a fungus that grows from the mycelium (619)

cuerpo fructífero: estructura reproductora de los hongos que se desarrolla a partir del micelio

Glossary *(continued)*

G

gamete: sex cell (312)
gameto: célula sexual

gametophyte: gamete-producing plant; multicellular haploid phase of a plant life cycle (637)
gametofito: planta que produce gametos; fase haploide multicelular del ciclo vital de una planta

ganglion (pl. ganglia): group of interneurons (810)
ganglio nervioso: grupo de interneuronas

gastrovascular cavity: digestive chamber with a single opening (784)
cavidad gastrovascular: cámara digestiva con una sola apertura

gastrulation: process of cell migration that results in the formation of the three cell layers—the ectoderm, the mesoderm, and the endoderm (997)
gastrulación: proceso de migración celular que da por resultado la formación de las tres capas celulares—el ectodermo, el mesodermo y el endodermo

gel electrophoresis: procedure used to separate and analyze DNA fragments by placing a mixture of DNA fragments at one end of a porous gel and applying an electrical voltage to the gel (404)
electroforesis en gel: procedimiento utilizado para separar y analizar fragmentos de ADN colocando una mezcla de fragmentos de ADN en un extremo de un gel poroso y aplicando al gel un voltaje eléctrico

gene: sequence of DNA that codes for a protein and thus determines a trait; factor that is passed from parent to offspring (310)
gen: secuencia de ADN que contiene el código de una proteína y por lo tanto determina un rasgo; factor que se transmite de un progenitor a su descendencia

gene expression: process by which a gene produces its product and the product carries out its function (370)
expresión génica: proceso por el cual un gen produce su producto y el producto lleva a cabo su función

gene pool: all the genes, including all the different alleles for each gene, that are present in a population at any one time (483)
caudal de genes: todos los genes, incluidos todos los alelos diferentes para cada gen, que están presentes en una población en un momento dado

gene therapy: process of changing a gene to treat a medical disease or disorder. An absent or faulty gene is replaced by a normal working gene. (431)
terapia genética o génica: proceso en el cual se cambia un gen para tratar una enfermedad o una afección médica. Se reemplaza un gen ausente o defectuoso con un gen de funcionamiento normal.

genetic code: collection of codons of mRNA, each of which directs the incorporation of a particular amino acid into a protein during protein synthesis (366)
código genético: conjunto de codones del ARN mensajero, cada uno de los cuales dirige la incorporación de un aminoácido en particular a una proteína durante la síntesis proteica

genetic diversity: sum total of all the different forms of genetic information carried by a particular species, or by all organisms on Earth (166)
diversidad genética: suma de todas las distintas formas de información genética portadas por una especie en particular, o por todos los organismos de la Tierra

genetic drift: random change in allele frequency caused by a series of chance occurrences that cause an allele to become more or less common in a population (490)
tendencia genética: alteración al azar de la frecuencia alélica causada por una serie de acontecimientos aleatorios que hacen que un alelo se vuelva más o menos común en una población

genetic equilibrium: situation in which allele frequencies in a population remain the same (491)
equilibrio genético: situación en la cual las frecuencias alélicas de una población se mantienen iguales

genetic marker: alleles that produce detectable phenotypic differences useful in genetic analysis (425)
marcador genético: alelos que producen diferencias fenotípicas detectables, útiles en el análisis genético

genetics: scientific study of heredity (308)
genética: estudio científico de la herencia

genome: entire set of genetic information that an organism carries in its DNA (392)
genoma: todo el conjunto de información genética que un organismo transporta en su ADN

genomics: study of whole genomes, including genes and their functions (407)
genómica: estudio integral de los genomas, incluyendo los genes y sus funciones

genotype: genetic makeup of an organism (315)
genotipo: composición genética de un organismo

genus: group of closely related species; the first part of the scientific name in binomial nomenclature (512)
género: grupo de especies relacionadas estrechamente; la primera parte del nombre científico en la nomenclatura binaria

geographic isolation: form of reproductive isolation in which two populations are separated by geographic barriers such as rivers, mountains, or bodies of water, leading to the formation of two separate subspecies (495)

 aislamiento geográfico: forma de aislamiento reproductivo en el cual dos poblaciones están separadas por barreras geográficas como ríos, montañas o masas de agua, dando lugar a la formación de dos subespecies distintas

geologic time scale: timeline used to represent Earth's history (542)

 escala de tiempo geológico: línea cronológica utilizada para representar la historia de la Tierra

germ theory of disease: idea that infectious diseases are caused by microorganisms (1010)

 teoría microbiana de la enfermedad: idea de que las enfermedades infecciosas son causadas por microorganismos

germination: resumption of growth of the plant embryo following dormancy (706)

 germinación: reanudación del crecimiento del embrión de la planta después de la latencia

gibberellin: plant hormone that stimulates growth and may cause dramatic increases in size (711)

 giberelina: hormona de las plantas que estimula el crecimiento y puede causar aumentos significativos de tamaño

gill: feathery structure specialized for the exchange of gases with water (788)

 branquia: estructura tegumentaria especializada en el intercambio de los gases con el agua

global warming: increase in the average temperatures on Earth (177)

 calentamiento global: aumento del promedio de temperatura en la Tierra

glomerulus: small network of capillaries encased in the upper end of the nephron; where filtration of the blood takes place (884)

 glomérulo: pequeña red de capilares encerrados en el extremo superior del nefrón; donde tiene lugar la filtración de la sangre

glycolysis: first set of reactions in cellular respiration in which a molecule of glucose is broken into two molecules of pyruvic acid (254)

 glicólisis: primer conjunto de reacciones en la respiración celular, en las cuales una molécula de glucosa se descompone en dos moléculas de ácido pirúvico

Golgi apparatus: organelle in cells that modifies, sorts, and packages proteins and other materials from the endoplasmic reticulum for storage in the cell or release outside the cell (201)

 aparato de Golgi: orgánulo de las células que modifica, clasifica y agrupa las proteínas y otras sustancias provenientes del retículo endoplasmático para almacenarlas en la célula o enviarlas fuera de la célula

gradualism: the evolution of a species by gradual accumulation of small genetic changes over long periods of time (549)

 gradualismo: evolución de una especie por la acumulación gradual de pequeños cambios genéticos ocurridos en el transcurso de largos períodos de tiempo

grafting: method of propagation used to reproduce seedless plants and varieties of woody plants that cannot be propagated from cuttings (703)

 injerto: método de propagación utilizado para reproducir plantas sin semillas y algunas variedades de plantas leñosas que no pueden propagarse a partir de esquejes

gravitropism: response of a plant to the force of gravity (712)

 geotropismo: respuesta de una planta a la fuerza de la gravedad

green revolution: development of highly productive crop strains and use of modern agriculture techniques to increase yields of food crops (717)

 revolución verde: el desarrollo de variedades de cultivos altamente productivos y el uso de técnicas agrícolas modernas para aumentar el rendimiento de los cultivos

greenhouse effect: process in which certain gases (carbon dioxide, methane, and water vapor) trap sunlight energy in Earth's atmosphere as heat (97)

 efecto invernadero: proceso mediante el cual ciertos gases (dióxido de carbono, metano y vapor de agua) atrapan la energía de la luz solar en la atmósfera terrestre en forma de calor

growth factor: one of a group of external regulatory proteins that stimulate the growth and division of cells (287)

 factor de crecimiento: una de las proteínas del grupo de proteínas reguladoras externas que estimulan el crecimiento y la división de las células

guard cell: specialized cell in the epidermis of plants that controls the opening and closing of stomata (682)

 célula de guarda (o célula oclusiva): célula especializada de la epidermis vegetal que controla la apertura y el cierre de los estomas

gullet: indentation in one side of a ciliate that allows food to enter the cell (612)

 citofaringe: hendidura a un costado de un ciliado que permite que los alimentos entren a la célula

gymnosperm: group of seed plants that bear their seeds directly on the scales of cones (646)

 Gimnospermas: grupo de plantas fanerógamas que tienen sus semillas directamente sobre las escamas de los conos

H

habitat: area where an organism lives, including the biotic and abiotic factors that affect it (99)

 hábitat: área donde vive un organismo, incluidos los factores bióticos y abióticos que lo afectan

Glossary *(continued)*

habitat fragmentation: splitting of ecosystems into pieces (168)
 fragmentación del hábitat: la ruptura, o separación en partes, de los ecosistemas

habituation: type of learning in which an animal decreases or stops its response to a repetitive stimulus that neither rewards nor harms the animal (842)
 habituación: tipo de aprendizaje en el cual un animal disminuye o cancela su respuesta ante un estímulo repetido que no recompensa ni castiga al animal

hair follicle: tubelike pockets of epidermal cells that extend into the dermis; cells at the base of hair follicles produce hair (937)
 folículo piloso: sacos tubulares de las células epidérmicas que se prolongan hacia el interior de la dermis; las células situadas en la base de los folículos pilosos, producen pelo

half life: length of time required for half of the radioactive atoms in a sample to decay (540)
 vida media: período de tiempo requerido para que se desintegre la mitad de los átomos radiactivos de una muestra

haploid: term used to refer to a cell that contains only a single set of genes (323)
 haploide: tipo de célula que posee un solo juego de cromosomas

Hardy-Weinberg principle: principle that states that allele frequencies in a population remain constant unless one or more factors cause those frequencies to change (491)
 principio de Hardy-Weinberg: el principio que afirma que las frecuencias alélicas de una población permanecen constantes a menos que uno o más factores ocasionen que esas frecuencias cambien

Haversian canal: one of a network of tubes running through compact bone that contains blood vessels and nerves (924)
 conducto de Havers: uno de los tubos de una red que recorre longitudinalmente el hueso compacto y contiene vasos sanguíneos y nervios

heart: hollow muscular organ that pumps blood throughout the body (791)
 corazón: órgano muscular hueco que bombea la sangre a todo el cuerpo

heartwood: in a woody stem, the older xylem near the center of the stem that no longer conducts water (678)
 duramen: en un tallo leñoso, el xilema más viejo situado cerca del centro del tallo que ya no conduce agua

hemoglobin: iron-containing protein in red blood cells that binds oxygen and transports it to the body (954)
 hemoglobina: proteína de los glóbulos rojos que contiene hierro, fija el oxígeno y lo transporta al organismo

herbaceous plant: type of plant that has smooth and non-woody stems; includes dandelions, zinnias, petunias, and sunflowers (653)
 planta herbácea: tipo de planta que tiene tallos blandos y no leñosos; incluye dientes de león, cinias, petunias y girasoles

herbivore: organism that obtains energy by eating only plants (71)
 herbívoro: organismo que obtiene energía alimentándose solo de plantas

herbivory: interaction in which one animal (the herbivore) feeds on producers (such as plants) (102)
 herbivorismo: interacción en la cual un animal (el herbívoro) se alimenta de productores (como las plantas)

heterotroph: organism that obtains food by consuming other living things; also called a consumer (71, 228)
 heterótrofo: organismo que obtiene su alimento consumiendo otros seres vivos; también llamado consumidor

heterozygous: having two different alleles for a particular gene (314)
 heterocigota: que tiene dos alelos diferentes para un gen dado

histamine: chemical released by mast cells that increases the flow of blood and fluids to the infected area during an inflammatory response (1014)
 histamina: sustancia química liberada por los mastocitos que aumenta el flujo de la sangre y los fluidos hacia el área infectada durante una respuesta inflamatoria

homeobox gene: The homeobox is a DNA sequence of approximately 130 base pairs, found in many homeotic genes that regulate development. Genes containing this sequence are known as homeobox genes, and they code for transcription factors, proteins that bind to DNA, and they also regulate the expression of other genes. (382)
 gen homeobox: el homeobox es una secuencia de ADN de aproximadamente 130 pares de bases, presente en muchos genes homeóticos que regulan el desarrollo. Los genes que contienen esta secuencia se denominan genes homeobox y codifican los factores de transcripción, las proteínas que se adhieren al ADN y regulan la expresión de otros genes

homeostasis: relatively constant internal physical and chemical conditions that organisms maintain (19, 214, 865)
 homeostasis: las condiciones internas, químicas y físicas, que los organismos mantienen relativamente constantes

homeotic gene: a class of regulatory genes that determine the identity of body parts and regions in an animal embryo. Mutations in these genes can transform one body part into another (382)
  gen homeótico: tipo de genes reguladores que determinan la identidad de las partes y regiones del cuerpo en un embrión animal. Las mutaciones de estos genes pueden transformar una parte del cuerpo en otra

hominine: hominoid lineage that led to humans (767)
  homínino: linaje hominoide que dio lugar a los seres humanos

hominoid: group of anthropoids that includes gibbons, orangutans, gorillas, chimpanzees, and humans (767)
  homínido: grupo de antropoides que incluye a los gibones, orangutanes, gorilas, chimpacés y seres humanos

homologous: term used to refer to chromosomes in which one set comes from the male parent and one set comes from the female parent (323)
  homólogos: término utilizado para referirse a los cromosomas en los que un juego proviene del progenitor masculino y un juego proviene del progenitor femenino

homologous structures: structures that are similar in different species of common ancestry (468)
  estructuras homólogas: estructuras que son similares en distintas especies que tienen un ancestro común

homozygous: having two identical alleles for a particular gene (314)
  homocigota: que tiene dos alelos idénticos para un gen dado

hormone: chemical produced in one part of an organism that affects another part of the same organism (708, 978)
  hormona: sustancia química producida en una parte de un organismo que afecta a otra parte del mismo organismo

Hox gene: a group of homeotic genes clustered together that determine the head to tail identity of body parts in animals. All hox genes contain the homeobox DNA sequence. (382)
  gen Hox: grupo de genes homeóticos agrupados en un conjunto que determinan la identidad posicional de las partes del cuerpo de los animales. Todos los genes Hox contienen la secuencia de ADN homeobox

humoral immunity: immunity against antigens in body fluids, such as blood and lymph (1016)
  inmunidad humoral: inmunidad contra los antígenos presentes en los fluidos corporales, como la sangre y la linfa

humus: material formed from decaying leaves and other organic matter (114)
  humus: material formado a partir de hojas en descomposición y otros materiales orgánicos

hybrid: offspring of crosses between parents with different traits (309)
  híbrido: descendencia del cruce entre progenitores que tienen rasgos diferentes

hybridization: breeding technique that involves crossing dissimilar individuals to bring together the best traits of both organisms (419)
  hibridación: técnica de cría que consiste en cruzar individuos diferentes para reunir los mejores rasgos de ambos organismos

hydrogen bond: weak attraction between a hydrogen atom and another atom (41)
  enlace de hidrógeno: atracción débil entre un átomo de hidrógeno y otro átomo

hydrostatic skeleton: skeleton made of fluid-filled body segments that work with muscles to allow the animal to move (814)
  esqueleto hidrostático: esqueleto constituido por segmentos corporales llenos de fluido que trabajan con los músculos para permitir el movimiento del animal

hypertonic: when comparing two solutions, the solution with the greater concentration of solutes (210)
  hipertónica: al comparar dos soluciones, la solución que tiene la mayor concentración de solutos

hypha (pl. hyphae): one of many long, slender filaments that makes up the body of a fungus (619)
  hifa: uno de muchos filamentos largos y delgados que componen el cuerpo de un hongo

hypothalamus: structure of the brain that acts as a control center for recognition and analysis of hunger, thirst, fatigue, anger, and body temperature (903)
  hipotálamo: estructura del cerebro que funciona como un centro de control para el reconocimiento y el análisis del hambre, la sed, la fatiga, el enojo y la temperatura corporal

hypothesis: possible explanation for a set of observations or possible answer to a scientific question (7)
  hipótesis: explicación posible para un conjunto de observaciones o respuesta posible a una pregunta científica

hypotonic: when comparing two solutions, the solution with the lesser concentration of solutes (210)
  hipotónica: al comparar dos soluciones, la solución que tiene la menor concentración de solutos

I

immigration: movement of individuals into an area occupied by an existing population (132)
  inmigración: desplazamiento de individuos a un área ocupada por una población ya existente

immune response: the body's specific recognition, response, and memory to a pathogen attack (1016)
  respuesta inmune: reconocimiento, respuesta y memoria específicos que tiene el cuerpo respecto al ataque de un organismo patógeno

implantation: process in which the blastocyst attaches to the wall of the uterus (996)
  implantación: proceso en el cual la blástula se adhiere a la pared del útero

Glossary *(continued)*

imprinting: type of behavior based on early experience; once imprinting has occurred, the behavior cannot be changed (844)
impronta: tipo de comportamiento basado en las primeras experiencias; una vez que ocurre la impronta, el comportamiento no puede cambiarse

inbreeding: continued breeding of individuals with similar characteristics to maintain the derived characteristics of a kind of organism (419)
endogamia: la cría continua de individuos con características semejantes para mantener las características derivadas de un tipo de organismo

incomplete dominance: situation in which one allele is not completely dominant over another allele (319)
dominancia incompleta: situación en la cual un alelo no es completamente dominante sobre otro alelo

independent assortment: one of Mendel's principles that states that genes for different traits can segregate independently during the formation of gametes (317)
distribución independiente: uno de los principios de Mendel que establece que los genes para rasgos diferentes pueden segregarse independientemente durante la formación de los gametos

independent variable: factor in a controlled experiment that is deliberately changed; also called manipulated variable (7)
variable independiente: en un experimento controlado, el factor que se modifica a propósito; también llamada variable manipulada

index fossil: distinctive fossil that is used to compare the relative ages of fossils (540)
fósil guía: fósil distintivo usado para comparar las edades relativas de los fósiles

infectious disease: disease caused by a microorganism that disrupts normal body functions (1010)
enfermedad infecciosa: enfermedad causada por un microorganismo que altera las funciones normales del cuerpo

inference: a logical interpretation based on prior knowledge and experience (7)
inferencia: interpretación lógica basada en la experiencia y en conocimientos previos

inflammatory response: nonspecific defense reaction to tissue damage caused by injury or infection (1014)
respuesta inflamatoria: reacción defensiva no específica al daño causado a los tejidos por una herida o una infección

innate behavior: type of behavior in which the behavior appears in fully functional form the first time it is performed even though the animal has had no previous experience with the stimuli to which it responds; also called instinct (841)
comportamiento innato: tipo de comportamiento en el cual la conducta aparece en forma completamente funcional la primera vez que se lleva a cabo, aunque el animal no tenga ninguna experiencia previa con los estímulos a los que responde; también llamado instinto

insight learning: type of behavior in which an animal applies something it has already learned to a new situation, without a period of trial and error; also called reasoning (843)
aprendizaje por discernimiento: tipo de comportamiento en el cual un animal aplica algo que ya ha aprendido a una situación nueva, sin un período de ensayo y error; también llamado razonamiento

interferon: one of a group of proteins that help cells resist viral infection (1015)
interferón: un tipo de proteína que ayuda a las células a combatir las infecciones virales

interneuron: type of neuron that processes information and may relay information to motor neurons (809)
interneurona: tipo de neurona que procesa información y la puede transmitir para estimular las neuronas

interphase: period of the cell cycle between cell divisions (281)
interfase: período del ciclo celular entre las divisiones celulares

intracellular digestion: type of digestion in which food is digested inside specialized cells that pass nutrients to other cells by diffusion (784)
digestión intracelular: tipo de digestión en la cual los alimentos se digieren dentro de células especializadas que pasan los nutrientes a otras células mediante difusión

intron: sequence of DNA that is not involved in coding for a protein (365)
intrón: secuencia de ADN que no participa en la codificación de una proteína

invertebrate: animal that lacks a backbone, or vertebral column (730)
invertebrado: animal que carece de columna vertebral

ion: atom that has a positive or negative charge (37)
ion: átomo que tiene una carga positiva o negativa

ionic bond: chemical bond formed when one or more electrons are transferred from one atom to another (37)
enlace iónico: enlace químico que se forma cuando uno o más electrones se transfieren de un átomo a otro

iris: colored part of the eye (912)
iris: parte coloreada del ojo

isotonic: when the concentration of two solutions is the same (210)
isotónica: cuando la concentración de dos soluciones es la misma

isotope: one of several forms of a single element, which contains the same number of protons but different numbers of neutrons (35)

isótopo: cada una de las diferentes formas de un único elemento, que contiene la misma cantidad de protones pero cantidades distintas de neutrones

J

joint: place where one bone attaches to another bone (816, 926)

articulación: sitio donde un hueso se une a otro hueso

K

karyotype: micrograph of the complete diploid set of chromosomes grouped together in pairs, arranged in order of decreasing size (392)

cariotipo: micrografía de la totalidad del conjunto diploide de cromosomas agrupados en pares, ordenados por tamaño decreciente

keratin: tough fibrous protein found in skin (936)

queratina: proteína fibrosa y resistente que se halla en la piel

keystone species: single species that is not usually abundant in a community yet exerts strong control on the structure of a community (103)

especie clave: especie que habitualmente no es abundante en una comunidad y sin embargo ejerce un fuerte control sobre la estructura de esa comunidad

kidney: an organ of excretion that separates wastes and excess water from the blood (795)

riñón: órgano excretor que separa los residuos y el exceso de agua de la sangre

kin selection: theory that states that helping relatives can improve an individual's evolutionary fitness because related individuals share a large proportion of their genes (849)

selección de parentesco: teoría que enuncia que ayudar a los congéneres puede mejorar la aptitud evolutiva de un individuo porque los individuos emparentados comparten una gran parte de sus genes

kingdom: largest and most inclusive group in Linnaean classification (514)

reino: grupo más grande e inclusivo del sistema de clasificación inventado por Linneo

Koch's postulates: set of guidelines developed by Koch that helps identify the microorganism that causes a specific disease (1011)

postulados de Koch: conjunto de pautas desarrollado por Koch que ayuda a identificar al microorganismo que causa una enfermedad específica

Krebs cycle: second stage of cellular respiration in which pyruvic acid is broken down into carbon dioxide in a series of energy-extracting reactions (256)

ciclo de Krebs: segunda fase de la respiración celular en la cual el ácido pirúvico se descompone en dióxido de carbono en una serie de reacciones que liberan energía

L

language: system of communication that combines sounds, symbols, and gestures according to a set of rules about sequence and meaning, such as grammar and syntax (851)

lenguaje: sistema de comunicación que combina sonidos, símbolos y gestos según un conjunto de reglas sobre la secuencia y el significado, como la gramática y la sintaxis

large intestine: organ in the digestive system that removes water from the undigested material that passes through it; also called colon (881)

intestino grueso: órgano del sistema digestivo que extrae el agua del material no digerido que pasa por él; también llamado colon

larva (pl. larvae): immature stage of an organism (756)

larva: etapa inmadura de un organismo

larynx: structure in the throat that contains the vocal cords (964)

laringe: órgano situado en la garganta que contiene las cuerdas vocales

learning: changes in behavior as a result of experience (842)

aprendizaje: cambios en el comportamiento a consecuencia de la experiencia

lens: structure in the eye that focuses light rays on the retina (912)

cristalino: estructura del ojo que enfoca los rayos luminosos en la retina

lichen: symbiotic association between a fungus and a photosynthetic organism (623)

liquen: asociación simbiótica entre un hongo y un organismo fotosintético

ligament: tough connective tissue that holds bones together in a joint (816, 927)

ligamento: tejido conectivo resistente que mantiene unidos a los huesos en una articulación

light-dependent reactions: set of reactions in photosynthesis that use energy from light to produce ATP and NADPH (233)

reacciones dependientes de la luz: en la fotosíntesis, conjunto de reacciones que emplean la energía proveniente de la luz para producir ATP y NADPH

light-independent reactions: set of reactions in photosynthesis that do not require light; energy from ATP and NADPH is used to build high-energy compounds such as sugar; also called the Calvin cycle (233)
  reacciones independientes de la luz: en la fotosíntesis, conjunto de reacciones que no necesitan luz; la energía proveniente del ATP y del NADPH se emplea para construir compuestos con gran contenido energético, como el azúcar; también llamado ciclo de Calvin

lignin: substance in vascular plants that makes cell walls rigid (666)
  lignina: sustancia de las plantas vasculares que hace rígidas a las paredes celulares

limiting factor: factor that causes population growth to decrease (137)
  factor limitante: un factor que hace disminuir el crecimiento de la población

limiting nutrient: single essential nutrient that limits productivity in an ecosystem (85)
  nutriente limitante: un solo nutriente esencial que limita la productividad de un ecosistema

lipid: macromolecule made mostly from carbon and hydrogen atoms; includes fats, oils, and waxes (47)
  lípido: macromolécula compuesta principalmente por átomos de carbono e hidrógeno; incluye las grasas, los aceites y las ceras

lipid bilayer: flexible double-layered sheet that makes up the cell membrane and forms a barrier between the cell and its surroundings (204)
  bicapa lipídica: lámina flexible de dos capas que constituye la membrana celular y forma una barrera entre la célula y su entorno

logistic growth: growth pattern in which a population's growth slows and then stops following a period of exponential growth (135)
  crecimiento logístico: patrón de crecimiento en el cual el desarrollo de una población se reduce y luego se detiene después de un período de crecimiento exponencial

loop of Henle: section of the nephron tubule that is responsible for conserving water and minimizing the volume of the filtrate (884)
  asa de Henle: una sección del túbulo de nefrón responsable de conservar el agua y minimizar el volumen del material filtrado

lung: respiratory organ; place where gases are exchanged between the blood and inhaled air (788)
  pulmón: órgano respiratorio; lugar donde se intercambian los gases entre la sangre y el aire inhalado

lymph: fluid that is filtered out of the blood (956)
  linfa: fluido procedente de la sangre

lysogenic infection: type of infection in which a virus embeds its DNA into the DNA of the host cell and is replicated along with the host cell's DNA (577)
  infección lisogénica: tipo de infección en la cual un virus inserta su ADN en el ADN de la célula huésped y se replica junto con el ADN de dicha célula huésped

lysosome: cell organelle that breaks down lipids, carbohydrates, and proteins into small molecules that can used by the rest of the cell (198)
  lisosoma: orgánulo celular que descompone los lípidos, los hidratos de carbono y las proteínas en moléculas pequeñas que pueden ser utilizadas por el resto de la célula

lytic infection: type of infection in which a virus enters a cell, makes copies of itself, and causes the cell to burst (576)
  infección lítica: tipo de infección en la cual un virus penetra una célula, hace copias de sí mismo y provoca la ruptura o muerte celular

M

macroevolutionary patterns: changes in anatomy, phylogeny, ecology, and behavior that take place in clades larger than a single species (546)
  patrones de macroevolución: cambios que ocurren en la anatomía, filogenia, ecología y comportamiento de clados que abarcan a más de una especie

Malpighian tubule: structure in most terrestrial arthropods that concentrates the uric acid and adds it to digestive wastes (797)
  túbulo de Malpighi: estructura de la mayoría de los artrópodos terrestres que concentra el ácido úrico y lo incorpora a los residuos digestivos

mammary gland: gland in female mammals that produces milk to nourish the young (825)
  glándula mamaria: glándula de las hembras de los mamíferos que produce leche para alimentar a las crías

mass extinction: event during which many species become extinct during a relatively short period of time (548)
  extinción masiva: suceso durante el cual se extinguen muchas especies durante un período de tiempo relativamente corto

matrix: innermost compartment of the mitochondrion (256)
  matriz: compartimento más interno de la mitocondria

mechanical digestion: physical breakdown of large pieces of food into smaller pieces (875)
  digestión mecánica: descomposición física de grandes pedazos de comida en pedazos más pequeños

meiosis: process in which the number of chromosomes per cell is cut in half through the separation of homologous chromosomes in a diploid cell (324)

meiosis: proceso por el cual el número de cromosomas por célula se reduce a la mitad mediante la separación de los cromosomas homólogos de una célula diploide

melanin: dark brown pigment in the skin that helps protect the skin by absorbing ultraviolet rays (936)

melanina: pigmento marrón oscuro de la piel que contribuye a protegerla al absorber los rayos ultravioletas

melanocyte: cell in the skin that produces a dark brown pigment called melanin (936)

melanocito: célula de la piel que produce un pigmento marrón oscuro llamado melanina

menstrual cycle: regular sequence of events in which an egg develops and is released from the body (991)

ciclo menstrual: secuencia regular de sucesos en la cual un huevo se desarrolla y se elimina del cuerpo

menstruation: discharge of blood and the unfertilized egg from the body (993)

menstruación: descarga de sangre y del huevo no fertilizado del cuerpo

meristem: regions of unspecialized cells responsible for continuing growth throughout a plant's lifetime (667)

meristemos: regiones de células no especializadas responsables del crecimiento continuo de una planta durante su vida

mesoderm: middle germ layer; develops into muscles, and much of the circulatory, reproductive, and excretory systems (738)

mesodermo: capa embrionaria media; se desarrolla para dar lugar a los músculos y gran parte de los sistemas circulatorio, reproductor y excretor

mesophyll: specialized ground tissue found in leaves; performs most of a plant's photosynthesis (680)

mesófilo: tejido fundamental especializado que se halla en las hojas; realiza la mayor parte de la fotosíntesis de una planta

messenger RNA (mRNA): type of RNA that carries copies of instructions for the assembly of amino acids into proteins from DNA to the rest of the cell (363)

ARN mensajero: tipo de ARN que transporta copias de las instrucciones para el ensamblaje de los aminoácidos en proteínas, desde el ADN al resto de la célula

metabolism: the combination of chemical reactions through which an organism builds up or breaks down materials (19)

metabolismo: la combinación de reacciones químicas a través de las cuales un organismo acumula o desintegra materiales

metamorphosis: process of changes in shape and form of a larva into an adult (823)

metamorfosis: proceso de cambios en la estructura y forma de una larva hasta que se convierte en adulto

metaphase: phase of mitosis in which the chromosomes line up across the center of the cell (282)

metafase: fase de la mitosis en la cual los cromosomas se alinean a través del centro de la célula

microclimate: environmental conditions within a small area that differs significantly from the climate of the surrounding area (96)

microclima: condiciones medioambientales de un área pequeña que difieren significativamente del clima del área circundante

migration: seasonal behavior resulting in the movement from one environment to another (847)

migración: comportamiento estacional que da por resultado el desplazamiento desde un medio ambiente a otro

mineral: inorganic nutrient the body needs, usually in small amounts (872)

mineral: nutriente inorgánico que el cuerpo necesita, usualmente en pequeñas cantidades

mitochondrion: cell organelle that converts the chemical energy stored in food into compounds that are more convenient for the cell to use (202)

mitocondria: orgánulo celular que convierte la energía química almacenada en los alimentos en compuestos más apropiados para que la célula los use

mitosis: part of eukaryotic cell division during which the cell nucleus divides (282)

mitosis: fase de la división de las células eucariotas durante la cual se divide el núcleo celular

mixture: material composed of two or more elements or compounds that are physically mixed together but not chemically combined (42)

mezcla: material compuesto por dos o más elementos o compuestos que están mezclados físicamente pero no están combinados químicamente

molecular clock: method used by researchers that uses mutation rates in DNA to estimate the length of time that two species have been evolving independently (498)

reloj molecular: método de investigación que emplea las tasas de mutación del ADN para estimar el lapso de tiempo en que dos especies han evolucionado independientemente

molecule: smallest unit of most compounds that displays all the properties of that compound (37)

molécula: la unidad más pequeña de la mayoría de los compuestos que exhibe todas las propiedades de ese compuesto

molting: process of shedding an exoskeleton and growing a new one (815)

muda: proceso de desprendimiento de un exoesqueleto y el crecimiento de uno nuevo

monocot: angiosperm with one seed leaf in its ovary (652)

monocotiledónea: angiosperma con un cotiledón (hoja embrionaria) en su ovario

Glossary *(continued)*

monoculture: farming strategy of planting a single, highly productive crop year after year (155)
monocultivo: estrategia agrícola que consiste en plantar año tras año un único cultivo altamente productivo

monomer: small chemical unit that makes up a polymer (46)
monómero: pequeña unidad química que forma un polímero

monophyletic group: group that consists of a single ancestral species and all its descendants and excludes any organisms that are not descended from that common ancestor (516)
grupo monofilético: grupo que consiste en una especie con un único ancestro y todos sus descendientes y excluye a todos los organismos que no descienden de ese ancestro común

monosaccharide: simple sugar molecule (46)
monosacárido: molécula de azúcar simple

motor neuron: type of nerve cell that carries directions from interneurons to either muscle cells or glands (809)
neurona motora: tipo de célula nerviosa que lleva las instrucciones provenientes de las interneuronas a las células musculares o las glándulas

multiple alleles: a gene that has more than two alleles (320)
alelos múltiples: un gen que tiene más de dos alelos

multipotent: cell with limited potential to develop into many types of differentiated cells (295)
multipotentes: células con potencial limitado para generar muchos tipos de células diferenciadas

muscle fiber: long slender skeletal muscle cells (929)
fibra muscular: células largas y delgadas de los músculos esqueléticos

muscle tissue: type of tissue that makes movements of the body possible (863)
tejido muscular: tipo de tejido que hace posibles los movimientos del cuerpo

mutagen: chemical or physical agents in the environment that interact with DNA and may cause a mutation (375)
mutágeno: agentes físicos o químicos del medioambiente que interaccionan con el ADN y pueden causar una mutación

mutation: change in the genetic material of a cell (372)
mutación: cambio en el material genético de una célula

mutualism: symbiotic relationship in which both species benefit from the relationship (103)
mutualismo: relación simbiótica en la cual ambas especies se benefician

mycelium (pl. mycelia): densely branched network of the hyphae of a fungus (619)
micelio: la red de filamentos muy ramificados de las hifas de un hongo

mycorrhiza (pl. mycorrhizae): symbiotic association of plant roots and fungi (624)
micorriza: asociación simbiótica entre las raíces de las plantas y los hongos

myelin sheath: insulating membrane surrounding the axon in some neurons (897)
vaina de mielina: membrana aislante que rodea al axón de algunas neuronas

myocardium: thick middle muscle layer of the heart (949)
miocardio: capa media, gruesa y musculosa del corazón

myofibril: tightly packed filament bundles found within skeletal muscle fibers (930)
miofibrilla: manojos de filamentos muy apretados que se hallan dentro de las fibras de los músculos esqueléticos

myosin: thick filament of protein found in skeletal muscle cells (930)
miosina: filamento grueso de proteína que se halla en las células de los músculos esqueléticos

N

NAD^+ (nicotinamide adenine dinucleotide): electron carrier involved in glycolysis (255)
NAD^+ (dinucleótido de nicotinamida adenina): transportador de electrones que participa en la glucólisis

$NADP^+$ (nicotinamide adenine dinucleotide phosphate): carrier molecule that transfers high-energy electrons from chlorophyll to other molecules (232)
$NADP^+$ (fosfato de dinucleótido de nicotinamida adenina): molécula transportadora de electrones que transfiere electrones de alta energía desde la clorofila a otras moléculas

natural selection: process by which organisms that are most suited to their environment survive and reproduce most successfully; also called survival of the fittest (463)
selección natural: proceso por el cual los organismos más adaptados a su medioambiente sobreviven y se reproducen más exitosamente; también llamada supervivencia del más apto

nephridium (pl. nephridia): excretory structure of an annelid that filters body fluid (797)
nefridio: estructura excretora de los anélidos que filtra el fluido corporal

nephron: blood-filtering structure in the kidneys in which impurities are filtered out, wastes are collected, and purified blood is returned to the circulation (884)
nefrón: estructura filtradora de la sangre en los riñones, en la cual se filtran las impurezas, se recogen los desechos y la sangre purificada se devuelve a la circulación

nervous tissue: type of tissue that transmits nerve impulses throughout the body (863)

tejido nervioso: tipo de tejido que transmite los impulsos nerviosos por el cuerpo

neuromuscular junction: the point of contact between a motor neuron and a skeletal muscle cell (931)

unión neuromuscular: el punto de contacto entre una neurona motora y una célula de un músculo esquelético

neuron: nerve cell; specialized for carrying messages throughout the nervous system (808)

neurona: célula nerviosa; especializada en conducir mensajes a través del sistema nervioso

neurotransmitter: chemical used by a neuron to transmit an impulse across a synapse to another cell (900)

neurotransmisor: sustancia química utilizada por una neurona para transmitir un impulso a otra célula a través de una sinapsis

neurulation: the first step in the development of the nervous system (997)

neurulación: primer paso en el desarrollo del sistema nervioso

niche: full range of physical and biological conditions in which an organism lives and the way in which the organism uses those conditions (100)

nicho: toda la variedad de condiciones biológicas y físicas en las que vive un organismo y la manera en la que dicho organismo utiliza esas condiciones

nitrogen fixation: process of converting nitrogen gas into nitrogen compounds that plants can absorb and use (84)

fijación de nitrógeno: el proceso por el cual el gas nitrógeno se convierte en los compuestos nitrogenados que las plantas pueden absorber y utilizar

node: part on a growing stem where a leaf is attached (675)

nudo: parte de un tallo en crecimiento donde está adherida una hoja

nondisjunction: error in meiosis in which the homologous chromosomes fail to separate properly (401)

no disyunción: error que ocurre durante la meiosis, en el que cromosomas homólogos no logran separarse adecuadamente

nonrenewable resource: resource that cannot be replenished by a natural process within a reasonable amount of time (157)

recurso no renovable: recurso que no se puede reponer mediante un proceso natural dentro de un período de tiempo razonable

norepinephrine: hormone released by the adrenal glands that increases heart rate and blood pressure and prepares the body for intense physical activity (983)

norepinefrina o noradrenalina: hormona liberada por las glándulas adrenales que aumenta la frecuencia cardíaca y la presión sanguínea y prepara al cuerpo para realizar actividad física intensa

notochord: long supporting rod that runs through a chordate's body just below the nerve cord (731)

notocordio: extenso bastón de apoyo que se extiende a lo largo del cuerpo de los cordados, justo por debajo del cordón nervioso

nucleic acid: macromolecules containing hydrogen, oxygen, nitrogen, carbon, and phosphorus (48)

ácido nucleico: macromoléculas que contienen hidrógeno, oxígeno, nitrógeno, carbono y fósforo

nucleotide: subunit of which nucleic acids are composed; made up of a 5-carbon sugar, a phosphate group, and a nitrogenous base (48)

nucleótido: subunidad que constituye los ácidos nucleicos; compuesta de un azúcar de 5 carbonos, un grupo fosfato y una base nitrogenada

nucleus: the center of an atom, which contains the protons and neutrons (34); in cells, structure that contains the cell's genetic material in the form of DNA (193)

núcleo: el centro de un átomo, contiene los protones y los neutrones; en las células, la estructura que contiene el material genético de la célula en forma de ADN

nutrient: chemical substance that an organism needs to sustain life (82)

nutriente: sustancia química que un organismo necesita para continuar con vida

nymph: immature form of an animal that resembles the adult form but lacks functional sexual organs (823)

ninfa: forma inmadura de un animal que se parece a la forma adulta, pero carece de órganos sexuales funcionales

observation: process of noticing and describing events or processes in a careful, orderly way (6)

observación: el método de percibir y describir sucesos o procesos de manera atenta y ordenada

omnivore: organism that obtains energy by eating both plants and animals (71)

omnívoro: organismo que obtiene energía alimentándose de plantas y animales

open circulatory system: type of circulatory system in which blood is only partially contained within a system of blood vessels as it travels through the body (791)

sistema circulatorio abierto: tipo de sistema circulatorio en el cual la sangre, cuando fluye por el cuerpo, está solo parcialmente contenida dentro de un sistema de vasos sanguíneos

operant conditioning: type of learning in which an animal learns to behave in a certain way through repeated practice, to receive a reward or avoid punishment (843)

acondicionamiento operante: tipo de aprendizaje en el cual un animal aprende a comportarse de cierta manera mediante una práctica repetida, para recibir una recompensa o evitar un castigo

Glossary *(continued)*

operator: short DNA region, adjacent to the promoter of a prokaryotic operon, that binds repressor proteins responsible for controlling the rate of transcription of the operon (378)
 operador: pequeña región de ADN, adyacente al promotor del operón de una procariota, que une las proteínas represoras responsables de controlar la tasa de transcripción del operón

operon: in prokaryotes, a group of adjacent genes that share a common operator and promoter and are transcribed into a single mRNA (377)
 operón: en las procariotas, grupo de genes adyacentes que comparten un operador y un promotor en común y que son transcritas a un solo ARN mensajero

opposable thumb: thumb that enables grasping objects and using tools (767)
 pulgar oponible o prensible: un pulgar que permite aferrar objetos y utilizar herramientas

order: in classification, a group of closely related families (513)
 orden: en la clasificación, un grupo de familias relacionadas estrechamente

organ: group of tissues that work together to perform closely related functions (216)
 órgano: grupo de tejidos que trabajan juntos para realizar funciones estrechamente relacionadas

organ system: group of organs that work together to perform a specific function (216)
 sistema de órganos: grupo de órganos que trabajan juntos para realizar una función específica

organelle: specialized structure that performs important cellular functions within a eukaryotic cell (196)
 orgánulo: estructura especializada que realiza funciones celulares importantes dentro de una célula eucariota

osmosis: diffusion of water through a selectively permeable membrane (210)
 ósmosis: la difusión de agua a través de una membrana de permeabilidad selectiva

osmotic pressure: pressure that must be applied to prevent osmotic movement across a selectively permeable membrane (211)
 presión osmótica: la presión que debe aplicarse para evitar el movimiento osmótico a través de una membrana de permeabilidad selectiva

ossification: process of bone formation during which cartilage is replaced by bone (925)
 osificación: el proceso de formación de hueso durante el cual el cartílago es reemplazado por hueso

osteoblast: bone cell that secretes mineral deposits that replace the cartilage in developing bones (925)
 osteoblasto: célula ósea que secreta depósitos minerales que reemplazan al cartílago de los huesos en desarrollo

osteoclast: bone cell that breaks down bone minerals (925)
 osteoclasto: célula ósea que degrada los minerales óseos

osteocyte: bone cell that helps maintain the minerals in bone tissue and continue to strengthen the growing bone (925)
 osteocito: célula ósea que ayuda a conservar los minerales en el tejido óseo y continúa fortaleciendo al hueso en crecimiento

ovary: in plants, the structure that surrounds and protects seeds (650); in animals, the primary female reproductive organ; produces eggs (991)
 ovario: en las plantas, la estructura que rodea a las semillas y las protege; órgano reproductor femenino fundamental en los animales; produce huevos

oviparous: species in which embryos develop in eggs outside a parent's body (822)
 ovíparo: especie animal en la cual los embriones se desarrollan en huevos fuera del cuerpo del progenitor

ovoviparous: species in which the embryos develop within the mother's body but depend entirely on the yolk sac of their eggs (822)
 ovovíparo: especie animal en la cual los embriones se desarrollan dentro del cuerpo de la madre, pero dependen completamente del saco vitelino de sus huevos

ovulation: the release of a mature egg from the ovary into one of the Fallopian tubes (993)
 ovulación: liberación de un huevo maduro desde el ovario a una de las trompas de Falopio

ovule: structure in seed cones in which the female gametophytes develop (648)
 óvulo: estructura de las semillas coníferas donde se desarrollan los gametos femeninos

ozone layer: atmospheric layer in which ozone gas is relatively concentrated; protects life on Earth from harmful ultraviolet rays in sunlight (175)
 capa de ozono: capa atmosférica en la cual el gas ozono se encuentra relativamente concentrado; protege a los seres vivos de la Tierra de los perjudiciales rayos ultravioletas de la luz solar

P

pacemaker: small group of cardiac muscle fibers that maintains the heart's pumping rhythm by setting the rate at which the heart contracts; the sinoatrial (SA) node (951)
 marcapasos: grupo pequeño de fibras musculares cardíacas que mantiene el ritmo de bombeo del corazón estableciendo la frecuencia a la que se contrae el corazón; el nodo sinusal

paleontologist: scientist who studies fossils (539)
 paleontólogo: científico que estudia los fósiles

palisade mesophyll: layer of cells under the upper epidermis of a leaf (681)

mesófilo en empalizada: capa de células situada bajo la epidermis superior de una hoja

parasitism: symbiotic relationship in which one organism lives on or inside another organism and harms it (104)

parasitismo: relación simbiótica en la cual un organismo vive sobre otro organismo o en su interior y lo perjudica

parathyroid hormone (PTH): hormone produced by parathyroid gland that increases calcium levels in the blood (985)

hormona de la paratiroides: hormona producida por la glándula paratiroides que aumenta los niveles de calcio en la sangre

parenchyma: main type of ground tissue in plants that contains cells with thin cell walls and large central vacuoles (667)

parénquima: tipo principal de tejido fundamental de las plantas que contiene células con paredes celulares delgadas y vacuolas centrales grandes

passive immunity: temporary immunity that develops as a result of natural or deliberate exposure to an antibody (1020)

inmunidad pasiva: inmunidad transitoria que se desarrolla a consecuencia de una exposición natural o deliberada a un anticuerpo

pathogen: disease-causing agent (586)

patógeno: agente que causa una enfermedad

pedigree: chart that shows the presence or absence of a trait according to the relationships within a family across several generations (396)

árbol genealógico: diagrama que muestra la presencia o ausencia de un rasgo de acuerdo con las relaciones intrafamiliares a través de varias generaciones

pepsin: enzyme that breaks down proteins into smaller polypeptide fragments (877)

pepsina: enzima que descompone las proteínas en fragmentos de polipéptidos más pequeños

period: division of geologic time into which eras are subdivided (543)

período: división del tiempo geológico en la que se subdividen las eras

peripheral nervous system: network of nerves and supporting cells that carries signals into and out of the central nervous system (896)

sistema nervioso periférico: red de nervios y células de apoyo que transporta señales hacia y desde el sistema nervioso central

peristalsis: contractions of smooth muscles that provide the force that moves food through the esophagus toward the stomach (877)

peristalsis: contracciones de los músculos lisos que proporcionan la fuerza que hace avanzar los alimentos a través del esófago hacia el estómago

permafrost: layer of permanently frozen subsoil found in the tundra (115)

permacongelamiento: capa de subsuelo congelado en forma permanente que se halla en la tundra

petiole: thin stalk that connects the blade of a leaf to a stem (680)

pecíolo: pedúnculo delgado que une la lámina de una hoja con un tallo

pH scale: scale with values from 0 to 14, used to measure the concentration of H^+ ions in a solution; a pH of 0 to 7 is acidic, a pH of 7 is neutral, and a pH of 7 to 14 is basic (43)

escala del pH: escala con valores de 0 a 14, utilizada para medir la concentración de iones H^+ en una solución; un pH de 0 a 7 es ácido, un pH de 7 es neutro y un pH de 7 a 14 es básico

pharyngeal pouch: one of a pair of structures in the throat region of a chordate (731)

bolsa faríngea: cada una de las dos estructuras situadas en la región de la garganta de los cordados

pharynx: tube at the back of the mouth that serves as a passageway for both air and food; also called the throat (964)

faringe: tubo situado a continuación de la boca que sirve de conducto para que pasen el aire y los alimentos; también llamada garganta

phenotype: physical characteristics of an organism (315)

fenotipo: características físicas de un organismo

phloem: vascular tissue that transports solutions of nutrients and carbohydrates produced by photosynthesis through the plant (643)

floema: tejido vascular que transporta por toda la planta las soluciones de nutrientes e hidratos de carbono producidos en la fotosíntesis

photic zone: sunlight region near the surface of water (117)

zona fótica: región cerca de la superficie del mar en la que penetra la luz solar

photoperiodism: a plant response to the relative lengths of light and darkness (713)

fotoperiodismo: la respuesta de una planta a los tiempos relativos de luz y oscuridad

photosynthesis: process used by plants and other autotrophs to capture light energy and use it to power chemical reactions that convert carbon dioxide and water into oxygen and energy-rich carbohydrates such as sugars and starches (70, 228)

fotosíntesis: proceso empleado por las plantas y otros organismos autótrofos para atrapar la energía luminosa y utilizarla para impulsar reacciones químicas que convierten el dióxido de carbono y el agua en oxígeno e hidratos de carbono de gran contenido energético, como azúcares y almidones

photosystem: cluster of chlorophyll and proteins found in thylakoids (235)

fotosistema: conjunto de clorofila y proteínas que se hallan en los tilacoides

phototropism: tendency of a plant to grow toward a light source (712)

fototropismo: la tendencia de una planta a crecer hacia una fuente de luz

Glossary *(continued)*

phylogeny: the evolutionary history of a lineage (516)
filogenia: historia evolutiva del linaje

phylum (pl. phyla): in classification, a group of closely related classes (514)
filo: en la clasificación, un grupo de clases estrechamente relacionadas

phytoplankton: photosynthetic algae found near the surface of the ocean (73)
fitoplancton: algas fotosintéticas que se hallan cerca de la superficie del océano

pigment: light-absorbing molecule used by plants to gather the sun's energy (230)
pigmento: moléculas que absorben la luz, empleadas por las plantas para recolectar la energía solar

pioneer species: first species to populate an area during succession (107)
especies pioneras: las primeras especies en poblar un área durante la sucesión ecológica

pistil: single carpel or several fused carpels; contains the ovary, style, and stigma (697)
pistilo: un único carpelo o varios carpelos unidos; contiene el ovario, el estilo y el estigma

pith: parenchyma cells inside the ring of vascular tissue in dicot stems (675)
médula: en los tallos de las dicotiledóneas, las células parenquimatosas ubicadas en el interior del anillo de tejido vascular

pituitary gland: small gland found near the base of the skull that secretes hormones that directly regulate many body functions and controls the actions of several other endocrine glands (982)
glándula pituitaria: pequeña glándula situada cerca de la base del cráneo que secreta hormonas que regulan directamente muchas funciones corporales y controla las acciones de varias otras glándulas endocrinas

placenta: specialized organ in placental mammals through which respiratory gases, nutrients, and wastes are exchanged between the mother and her developing young (822, 998)
placenta: órgano especializado de los mamíferos placentarios a través del cual se intercambian los gases respiratorios, los nutrientes y los residuos entre la madre y su cría en desarrollo

plankton: microscopic organisms that live in aquatic environments; includes both phytoplankton and zooplankton (119)
plancton: organismos microscópicos que viven en medios ambientes acuáticos; incluye el fitoplancton y el zooplancton

plasma: straw-colored liquid portion of the blood (954)
plasma: parte líquida de la sangre de color amarillento

plasmid: small, circular piece of DNA located in the cytoplasm of many bacteria (424)
plásmido: pequeña porción circular de ADN ubicada en el citoplasma de muchas bacterias

plasmodium: amoeboid feeding stage in the life cycle of a plasmodial slime mold (613)
plasmodio: etapa de alimentación ameboide del ciclo vital de los mohos mucilaginosos

plate tectonics: geologic processes, such as continental drift, volcanoes, and earthquakes, resulting from plate movement (544)
tectónica de placas: procesos geológicos, como la deriva continental, los volcanes y los terremotos, que son consecuencia de los movimientos de las placas

platelet: cell fragment released by bone marrow that helps in blood clotting (955)
plaqueta: fragmento celular liberado por la médula espinal que interviene en la coagulación de la sangre

pluripotent: cells that are capable of developing into most, but not all, of the body's cell types (294)
pluripotentes: células capaces de convertirse en la mayoría de células del cuerpo, pero no en todas

point mutation: gene mutation in which a single base pair in DNA has been changed (373)
mutación puntual: mutación genética en la cual se ha modificado un único par de bases en el ADN

pollen grain: structure that contains the entire male gametophyte in seed plants (647)
grano de polen: la estructura que contiene a todo el gametofito masculino en las plantas fanerógamas

pollen tube: structure in a plant that contains two haploid sperm nuclei (648)
tubo polínico: en una planta, estructura que contiene dos núcleos espermáticos haploides

pollination: transfer of pollen from the male reproductive structure to the female reproductive structure (647)
polinización: transferencia de polen desde la estructura reproductora masculina hacia la estructura reproductora femenina

pollutant: harmful material that can enter the biosphere through the land, air, or water (160)
contaminante: material nocivo que puede ingresar en la biósfera a través de la tierra, el aire o el agua

polygenic trait: trait controlled by two or more genes (320, 486)
rasgo poligénico: rasgo controlado por dos o más genes

polymer: molecules composed of many monomers; makes up macromolecules (46)
polímero: molécula compuesta por muchos monómeros; forma macromoléculas

polymerase chain reaction (PCR): the technique used by biologists to make many copies of a particular gene (423)
 reacción en cadena de la polímerasa (PCR): técnica usada por los biólogos para hacer muchas copias de un gen específico

polypeptide: long chain of amino acids that makes proteins (366)
 polipéptido: cadena larga de aminoácidos que constituye las proteínas

polyploidy: condition in which an organism has extra sets of chromosomes (376)
 poliploidía: condición en la cual un organismo tiene grupos adicionales de cromosomas

population: group of individuals of the same species that live in the same area (64)
 población: grupo de individuos de la misma especie que viven en la misma área

population density: number of individuals per unit area (131)
 densidad de población: número de individuos que viven por unidad de superficie

predation: interaction in which one organism (the predator) captures and feeds on another organism (the prey) (102)
 depredación: interacción en la cual un organismo (el predador) captura y come a otro organismo (la presa)

prehensile tail: long tail that can coil tightly enough around a branch (767)
 cola prensil: cola larga que puede enrollarse apretadamente alrededor de una rama

pressure-flow hypothesis: hypothesis that explains the method by which phloem sap is transported through the plant from a sugar "source" to a sugar "sink" (687)
 teoría de flujo por presión: teoría que explica el método por el cual la savia del floema recorre la planta desde una "fuente" de azúcar hacia un "vertedero" de azúcar

primary growth: pattern of growth that takes place at the tips and shoots of a plant (676)
 crecimiento primario: patrón de crecimiento que tiene lugar en las puntas y en los brotes de una planta

primary producer: first producer of energy-rich compounds that are later used by other organisms (69)
 productor primario: los primeros productores de compuestos ricos en energía que luego son utilizados por otros organismos

primary succession: succession that occurs in an area in which no trace of a previous community is present (106)
 sucesión primaria: sucesión que ocurre en un área en la cual no hay rastros de la presencia de una comunidad anterior

principle of dominance: Mendel's second conclusion, which states that some alleles are dominant and others are recessive (310)
 principio de dominancia: segunda conclusión de Mendel, que establece que algunos alelos son dominantes y otros son recesivos

prion: protein particles that cause disease (592)
 prión: partículas de proteína que causan enfermedades

probability: likelihood that a particular event will occur (313)
 probabilidad: la posibilidad de que ocurra un suceso dado

product: elements or compounds produced by a chemical reaction (50)
 producto: elemento o compuesto producido por una reacción química

prokaryote: unicellular organism that lacks a nucleus (193, 580)
 procariota: organismo unicelular que carece de núcleo

promoter: specific region of a gene where RNA polymerase can bind and begin transcription (365)
 promotor: región específica de un gen en donde la ARN polimerasa puede unirse e iniciar la transcripción

prophage: bacteriophage DNA that is embedded in the bacterial host's DNA (577)
 profago: ADN del bacteriófago que está alojado en el interior del ADN del huésped bacteriano

prophase: first and longest phase of mitosis in which the genetic material inside the nucleus condenses and the chromosomes become visible (282)
 profase: primera y más prolongada fase de la mitosis, en la cual el material genético dentro del interior del núcleo se condensa y los cromosomas se hacen visibles

prostaglandin: modified fatty acids that are produced by a wide range of cells; generally affect only nearby cells and tissues (980)
 prostaglandina: ácidos grasos modificados que son producidos por una amplia gama de células; generalmente afectan solo a las células y tejidos cercanos

protein: macromolecule that contains carbon, hydrogen, oxygen, and nitrogen; needed by the body for growth and repair (48, 870)
 proteína: macromolécula que contiene carbono, hidrógeno, oxígeno y nitrógeno; necesaria para el crecimiento y reparación del cuerpo

protostome: an animal whose mouth is formed from the blastopore (739)
 protóstomo: animal cuya boca se desarrolla a partir del blastoporo

pseudocoelom: body cavity that is only partially lined with mesoderm (738)
 pseudoceloma o falso celoma: cavidad corporal que está revestida sólo parcialmente con mesodermo

Glossary *(continued)*

pseudopod: temporary cytoplasmic projection used by some protists for movement (606)
seudópodo: prolongación citoplasmática transitoria utilizada por algunos protistas para moverse

puberty: period of rapid growth and sexual maturation during which the reproductive system becomes fully functional (988)
pubertad: período de crecimiento rápido y de maduración sexual durante el cual el sistema reproductor se vuelve completamente funcional

pulmonary circulation: path of circulation between the heart and lungs (950)
circulación pulmonar: recorrido de la circulación entre el corazón y los pulmones

punctuated equilibrium: pattern of evolution in which long stable periods are interrupted by brief periods of more rapid change (549)
equilibrio interrumpido: patrón de evolución en el cual los largos períodos de estabilidad se ven interrumpidos por breves períodos de cambio más rápido

Punnett square: diagram that can be used to predict the genotype and phenotype combinations of a genetic cross (315)
cuadro de Punnett: un diagrama que puede utilizarse para predecir las combinaciones de genotipos y fenotipos en un cruce genético

pupa: stage in complete metamorphosis in which the larva develops into an adult (823)
pupa: etapa de la metamorfosis completa en la cual la larva se convierte en un adulto

pupil: small opening in the iris that admits light into the eye (912)
pupila: pequeña abertura en el iris que deja pasar la luz al ojo

Q, R

radial symmetry: body plan in which any number of imaginary planes drawn through the center of the body could divide it into equal halves (738)
simetría radial: diseño corporal en el cual cualquier número de ejes imaginarios dibujados a través del centro del cuerpo lo dividirá en mitades iguales

radiometric dating: method for determining the age of a sample from the amount of a radioactive isotope to the nonradioactive isotope of the same element in a sample (540)
datación radiométrica: método para determinar la edad de una muestra a partir de la cantidad de isótopo radioactivo en relación a la de isótopo no radiactivo del mismo elemento en dicha muestra

reabsorption: process by which water and dissolved substances are taken back into the blood (884)
reabsorción: proceso por el cual el agua y las sustancias disueltas regresan a la sangre

reactant: elements or compounds that enter into a chemical reaction (50)
reactante: elemento o compuesto que participa en una reacción química

receptor: on or in a cell, a specific protein to whose shape fits that of a specific molecular messenger, such as a hormone (217, 709)
receptor: proteína específica que puede encontrarse en la membrana celular o dentro de la célula, cuya forma se corresponde con la de un mensajero molecular específico, por ejemplo una hormona

recombinant DNA: DNA produced by combining DNA from different sources (424)
ADN recombinante: ADN producido por la combinación de ADN de orígenes diferentes

red blood cell: blood cell containing hemoglobin that carries oxygen (954)
glóbulo rojo: célula sanguínea que contiene hemoglobina y transporta oxígeno

reflex: quick, automatic response to a stimulus (901)
reflejo: respuesta rápida y automática a un estímulo

reflex arc: the sensory receptor, sensory neuron, motor neuron, and effector that are involved in a quick response to a stimulus (907)
arco reflejo: el receptor sensorial, la neurona sensorial, la neurona motora y el efector que participan en una respuesta rápida a un estímulo

relative dating: method of determining the age of a fossil by comparing its placement with that of fossils in other rock layers (540)
datación relativa: método para determinar la edad de un fósil comparando su ubicación con la de los fósiles hallados en otras capas de roca

releasing hormone: hormone produced by the hypothalamus that makes the anterior pituitary secrete hormones (983)
hormona liberadora: hormona producida por el hipotálamo que hace que la glándula pituitaria anterior secrete hormonas (983)

renewable resource: resource that can be produced or replaced by healthy ecosystem functions (157)
recurso renovable: recurso que se puede producir o reemplazar mediante el funcionamiento saludable del ecosistema

replication: process of copying DNA prior to cell division (350)
replicación: proceso de copia de ADN previo a la división celular

reproductive isolation: separation of a species or population so that they no longer interbreed and evolve into two separate species (494)
  aislamiento reproductor: separación de una especie o de una población de tal manera que ya no pueden aparearse y evolucionan hasta formar dos especies separadas

resource: any necessity of life, such as water, nutrients, light, food, or space (100)
  recurso: todo lo necesario para la vida, como agua, nutrientes, luz, alimento o espacio

response: specific reaction to a stimulus (809)
  respuesta: reacción específica a un estímulo

resting potential: electrical charge across the cell membrane of a resting neuron (898)
  potencial de reposo: carga eléctrica que pasa a través de la membrana celular de una neurona en reposo

restriction enzyme: enzyme that cuts DNA at a sequence of nucleotides (403)
  enzima restrictiva: enzima que corta el ADN en una secuencia de nucleótidos

retina: innermost layer of the eye; contains photoreceptors (913)
  retina: membrana más interna del ojo; contiene receptores susceptibles a la luz

retrovirus: RNA virus that contains RNA as its genetic information (578)
  retrovirus: ARN viral cuya información genética está contenida en el ARN

ribonucleic acid (RNA): single-stranded nucleic acid that contains the sugar ribose (362)
  ácido ribonucleico (ARN): hebra única de ácido nucleico que contiene el azúcar ribose

ribosomal RNA (rRNA): type of RNA that combines with proteins to form ribosomes (363)
  ARN ribosomal: tipo de ARN que se combina con proteínas para formar los ribosomas

ribosome: cell organelle consisting of RNA and protein found throughout the cytoplasm in a cell; the site of protein synthesis (200)
  ribosoma: orgánulo celular formado por ARN y proteína que se halla en el citoplasma de una célula; lugar donde se sintetizan las proteínas

RNA interference (RNAi): introduction of double-stranded RNA into a cell to inhibit gene expression (380)
  ARN de interferencia: introducción de un ARN de doble hebra en una célula para inhibir la expresión de genes específicos

RNA polymerase: enzyme that links together the growing chain of RNA nucleotides during transcription using a DNA strand as a template (364)
  ARN polimerasa: enzima que enlaza los nucleótidos de la cadena de ARN en crecimiento durante la transcripción, usando una secuencia de ADN como patrón o molde

rod: photoreceptor in the eyes that is sensitive to light but can't distinguish color (913)
  bastoncillo: receptor ubicado en los ojos que es susceptible a la luz, pero que no puede distinguir el color

root cap: tough covering of the root tip that protects the meristem (670)
  cofia: cubierta dura de la punta de las raíces que protege al meristemo

root hair: small hairs on a root that produce a large surface area through which water and minerals can enter (670)
  pelo radicular: pelos pequeños sobre una raíz que producen una superficie extensa a través de la cual pueden penetrar el agua y los minerales

rumen: stomach chamber in cows and related animals in which symbiotic bacteria digest cellulose (786)
  panza: cavidad del estómago de las vacas y otros rumiantes en la cual las bacterias simbióticas digieren la celulosa

S

sapwood: in a woody stem, the layer of secondary phloem that surrounds the heartwood; usually active in fluid transport (678)
  albura: en un tallo leñoso, la capa de floema secundario que rodea al duramen; participa usualmente en el transporte de fluidos

sarcomere: unit of muscle contraction; composed of two z-lines and the filaments between them (930)
  sarcómero: unidad de contracción muscular; compuesto por dos líneas "z" y los filamentos que hay entre ellas

scavenger: animal that consumes the carcasses of other animals (71)
  carroñero: animal que consume los cadáveres de otros animales

science: organized way of gathering and analyzing evidence about the natural world (5)
  ciencia: manera organizada de reunir y analizar la información sobre el mundo natural

sclerenchyma: type of ground tissue with extremely thick, rigid cell walls that make ground tissue tough and strong (667)
  esclerénquima: tipo de tejido fundamental con células extremadamente rígidas y gruesas que lo hacen fuerte y resistente

scrotum: external sac that houses the testes (989)
  escroto: bolsa externa que contiene a los testículos

sebaceous gland: gland in the skin that secretes sebum (oily secretion) (937)
  glándula sebácea: glándula de la piel que secreta sebo (secreción oleosa)

Glossary *(continued)*

secondary growth: type of growth in dicots in which the stems increase in thickness (676)
  crecimiento secundario: tipo de crecimiento de las dicotiledóneas en el cual los tallos aumentan su grosor

secondary succession: type of succession that occurs in an area that was only partially destroyed by disturbances (107)
  sucesión secundaria: tipo de sucesión que ocurre en un área destruida sólo parcialmente por alteraciones

seed: plant embryo and a food supply encased in a protective covering (646)
  semilla: embrión vegetal y fuente de alimento encerrada en una cubierta protectora

seed coat: tough covering that surrounds and protects the plant embryo and keeps the contents of the seed from drying out (647)
  envoltura de la semilla: cubierta dura que rodea y protege al embrión de la planta y evita que el contenido de la semilla se seque

segregation: separation of alleles during gamete formation (312)
  segregación: separación de los alelos durante la formación de gametos

selective breeding: method of breeding that allows only those organisms with desired characteristics to produce the next generation (418)
  reproducción selectiva o selección artificial: método de reproducción que sólo permite la producción de una nueva generación a aquellos organismos con características deseadas

selectively permeable: property of biological membranes that allows some substances to pass across it while others cannot; also called semipermeable membrane (205)
  permeabilidad selectiva: propiedad de las membranas biológicas que permite que algunas sustancias pasen a través de ellas mientras que otras no pueden hacerlo; también llamada membrana semipermeable

semen: the combination of sperm and seminal fluid (990)
  semen: combinación de esperma y de fluido seminal

semicircular canal: one of three structures in the inner ear that monitor the position of the body in relation to gravity (911)
  canal semicircular: una de las tres estructuras ubicadas en el oído interno que controlan la posición del cuerpo en relación con la fuerza de la gravedad

seminiferous tubule: one of hundreds of tubules in each testis in which sperm develop (989)
  túbulo seminífero: uno de los cientos de túbulos situados en cada testículo, en los cuales se produce el esperma

sensory neuron: type of nerve cell that receives information from sensory receptors and conveys signals to central nervous system (808)
  neurona sensorial: tipo de célula nerviosa que recibe información de los receptores sensoriales y transmite señales al sistema nervioso central

sex chromosome: one of two chromosomes that determines an individual's sex (393)
  cromosoma sexual: uno de los pares de cromosomas que determina el sexo de un individuo

sex-linked gene: gene located on a sex chromosome (395)
  gen ligado al sexo: gen situado en un cromosoma sexual

sexual reproduction: type of reproduction in which cells from two parents unite to form the first cell of a new organism (19, 277)
  reproducción sexual: tipo de reproducción en la cual las células de dos progenitores se unen para formar la primera célula de un nuevo organismo

sexual selection: when individuals select mates based on heritable traits (492)
  selección sexual: cuando un individuo elige a su pareja sexual atraído por sus rasgos heredables

sexually transmitted disease (STD): disease that is spread from person to person by sexual contact (994)
  enfermedad de transmisión sexual (ETS): enfermedad que se transmite de una persona a otra por contacto sexual

sieve tube element: continuous tube through the plant phloem cells, which are arranged end to end (666)
  tubo crivoso: tubo continuo que atraviesa las células del floema vegetal, que están puestas una junto a otra

single-gene trait: trait controlled by one gene that has two alleles (485)
  rasgo de un único gen (monogénico): rasgo controlado por un gen que tiene dos alelos

small intestine: digestive organ in which most chemical digestion and absorption of food takes place (878)
  intestino delgado: órgano digestivo en el cual tiene lugar la mayor parte de la digestión química y la absorción de los alimentos

smog: gray-brown haze formed by a mixture of chemicals (163)
  esmog: neblina marrón grisácea formada por una mezcla de compuestos químicos

society: group of closely related animals of the same species that work together for the benefit of the group (848)
  sociedad: grupo de animales de la misma especie, estrechamente relacionados, que trabajan juntos para el beneficio del grupo

solute: substance that is dissolved in a solution (42)
  soluto: sustancia que está disuelta en una solución

solution: type of mixture in which all the components are evenly distributed (42)
  solución: tipo de mezcla en la cual todos los compuestos están distribuidos de forma homogénea

solvent: dissolving substance in a solution (42)
disolvente: sustancia que disuelve una solución

somatic nervous system: part of the peripheral nervous system that carries signals to and from skeletal muscles (907)
sistema nervioso somático: parte del sistema nervioso periférico que conduce señales hacia y desde los músculos esqueléticos

speciation: formation of a new species (494)
especiación: formación de una nueva especie

species: a group of similar organisms that can breed and produce fertile offspring (64, 494)
especie: un grupo de organismos similares que pueden reproducirse y producir una descendencia fértil

species diversity: number of different species that make up a particular area (166)
diversidad de especies: número de especies diferentes que forman un área determinada

spirillum (pl. spirilla): spiral or corkscrew-shaped prokaryote (582)
espirilo: procariota con forma helicoidal o espiral

spongy mesophyll: layer of loose tissue found beneath the palisade mesophyll in a leaf (681)
mesófilo esponjoso: capa de tejido suelto situado debajo del mesófilo en empalizada de una hoja

sporangium (pl. sporangia): spore capsule in which haploid spores are produced by meiosis (609, 642)
esporangio: cápsula en la cual se producen las esporas haploides mediante meiosis

spore: in prokaryotes, protists, and fungi, any of a variety of thick-walled life cycle stages capable of surviving unfavorable conditions (607)
espora: en los procariotas, los protistas y los hongos, cada una de las células que, en un momento de su ciclo de vida, produce una membrana gruesa y resistente capaz de sobrevivir en condiciones desfavorables

sporophyte: spore-producing plant; the multicellular diploid phase of a plant life cycle (637)
esporofito: planta productora de esporas; la fase diploide multicelular del ciclo vital de una planta

stabilizing selection: form of natural selection in which individuals near the center of a distribution curve have higher fitness than individuals at either end of the curve (489)
selección estabilizadora: forma de selección natural en la cual los individuos situados cerca del centro de una curva de distribución tienen mayor aptitud que los individuos que se hallan en cualquiera de los extremos de la curva

stamen: male part of a flower; contains the anther and filament (697)
estambre: parte masculina de una flor; contiene la antera y el filamento

stem cell: unspecialized cell that can give rise to one or more types of specialized cells (295)
célula troncal: célula no especializada que puede originar uno o más tipos de células especializadas

stigma: sticky part at the top of style; specialized to capture pollen (697)
estigma: parte pegajosa situada en la parte superior del estilo; especializado en atrapar el polen

stimulus (pl. stimuli): signal to which an organism responds (18, 808)
estímulo: señal a la cual responde un organismo

stoma (pl. stomata): small opening in the epidermis of a plant that allows carbon dioxide, water, and oxygen to diffuse into and out of the leaf (681)
estoma: pequeña abertura en la epidermis de una planta que permite que el dióxido de carbono, el agua y el oxígeno entren y salgan de la hoja

stomach: large muscular sac that continues the mechanical and chemical digestion of food (877)
estómago: gran bolsa muscular que continúa la digestión mecánica y química de los alimentos

stroma: fluid portion of the chloroplast; outside of the thylakoids (231)
estroma: parte fluida del cloroplasto; en el exterior de los tilacoides

substrate: reactant of an enzyme-catalyzed reaction (52)
sustrato: reactante de una reacción catalizada por enzimas

suspension: mixture of water and nondissolved material (42)
suspensión: mezcla de agua y material no disuelto

sustainable development: strategy for using natural resources without depleting them and for providing human needs without causing long-term environmental harm (157)
desarrollo sostenible: estrategia para utilizar los recursos naturales sin agotarlos y para satisfacer las necesidades humanas sin causar daños ambientales a largo plazo

symbiosis: relationship in which two species live close together (103)
simbiosis: relación en la cual dos especies viven en estrecha asociación

synapse: point at which a neuron can transfer an impulse to another cell (900)
sinapsis: punto en el cual una neurona puede transferir un impulso a otra célula

systematics: study of the diversity of life and the evolutionary relationships between organisms (512)
sistemática: estudio de la diversidad de la vida y de las relaciones evolutivas entre los organismos

systemic circulation: path of circulation between the heart and the rest of the body (950)
circulación sistémica: recorrido de la circulación entre el corazón y el resto del cuerpo

Glossary *(continued)*

T

taiga: biome with long cold winters and a few months of warm weather; dominated by coniferous evergreens; also called boreal forest (114)
taiga: bioma con inviernos largos y fríos y pocos meses de tiempo cálido; dominado por coníferas de hojas perennes; también llamada bosque boreal

target cell: cell that has a receptor for a particular hormone (709, 978)
célula diana o célula blanco: célula que posee un receptor para una hormona determinada

taste bud: sense organs that detect taste (910)
papila gustativa: órgano sensorial que percibe los sabores

taxon (pl. taxa): group or level of organization into which organisms are classified (512)
taxón: grupo o nivel de organización en que se clasifican los organismos

telomere: repetitive DNA at the end of a eukaryotic chromosome (352)
telómero: ADN repetitivo situado en el extremo de un cromosoma eucariota

telophase: phase of mitosis in which the distinct individual chromosomes begin to spread out into a tangle of chromatin (283)
telofase: fase de la mitosis en la cual los distintos cromosomas individuales comienzan a separarse y a formar hebras de cromatina

temporal isolation: form of reproductive isolation in which two or more species reproduces at different times (495)
aislamiento temporal: forma de aislamiento reproductivo en la cual dos o más especies se reproducen en épocas diferentes

tendon: tough connective tissue that connects skeletal muscles to bones (816, 932)
tendón: tejido conectivo resistente que une los músculos esqueléticos a los huesos

territory: a specific area occupied and protected by an animal or group of animals (848)
territorio: área específica ocupada y protegida por un animal o un grupo de animales

testis (pl. testes): primary male reproductive organ; produces sperm (989)
testículo: órgano reproductor masculino fundamental; produce esperma

tetrad: structure containing four chromatids that forms during meiosis (324)
tétrada: estructura con cuatro cromátidas que se forma durante la meiosis

tetrapod: vertebrate with four limbs (760)
tetrápode: vertebrado con quatro membros

thalamus: brain structure that receives messages from the sense organs and relays the information to the proper region of the cerebrum for further processing (903)
tálamo: estructura cerebral que recibe mensajes de los órganos sensoriales y transmite la información a la región adecuada del cerebro para su procesamiento ulterior

theory: well-tested explanation that unifies a broad range of observations and hypotheses, and enables scientists to make accurate predications about new situations (13)
teoría: explicación basada en pruebas que unifica una amplia gama de observaciones e hipótesis; permite que los científicos hagan predicciones exactas ante situaciones nuevas

thigmotropism: response of a plant to touch (712)
tigmotropismo: respuesta de una planta al tacto

threshold: minimum level of a stimulus that is required to cause an impulse (899)
umbral: nivel mínimo que debe tener un estímulo para causar un impulso

thylakoid: saclike photosynthetic membranes found in chloroplasts (231)
tilacoide: membranas fotosintéticas con forma de bolsa situadas en los cloroplastos

thyroxine: hormone produced by the thyroid gland, which increases the metabolic rate of cells throughout the body (985)
tiroxina: hormona producida por la glándula tiroides que aumenta el metabolismo de las células de todo el cuerpo

tissue: group of similar cells that perform a particular function (216)
tejido: grupo de células similares que realizan una función en particular

tolerance: ability of an organism to survive and reproduce under circumstances that differ from their optimal conditions (99)
tolerancia: capacidad de un organismo de sobrevivir y reproducirse en circunstancias que difieren de sus condiciones óptimas

totipotent: cells that are able to develop into any type of cell found in the body (including the cells that make up the extraembryonic membranes and placenta) (294)
totipotentes: células capaces de convertirse en cualquier tipo de célula del cuerpo (incluidas las células que forman las membranas situadas fuera del embrión y la placenta)

trachea: tube that connects the larynx to the bronchi; also called the windpipe (964)
tráquea: tubo que conecta a la laringe con los bronquios

tracheid: hollow plant cell in xylem with thick cell walls strengthened by lignin (643)
traqueida: célula vegetal ahuecada del xilema con paredes celulares gruesas, fortalecida por la lignina

tracheophyte: vascular plant (643)
traqueófita: planta vascular

trait: specific characteristic of an individual (309)
rasgo: característica específica de un individuo

transcription: synthesis of an RNA molecule from a DNA template (364)
transcripción: síntesis de una molécula de ARN a partir de una secuencia de ADN

transfer RNA (tRNA): type of RNA that carries each amino acid to a ribosome during protein synthesis (363)
ARN de transferencia: tipo de ARN que transporta a cada aminoácido hasta un ribosoma durante la síntesis de proteínas

transformation: process in which one strain of bacteria is changed by a gene or genes from another strain of bacteria (339)
transformación: proceso en el cual una cepa de bacterias es transformada por uno o más genes provenientes de otra cepa de bacterias

transgenic: term used to refer to an organism that contains genes from other organisms (426)
transgénico: término utilizado para referirse a un organismo que contiene genes provenientes de otros organismos

translation: process by which the sequence of bases of an mRNA is converted into the sequence of amino acids of a protein (368)
traducción (genética): proceso por el cual la secuencia de bases de un ARN mensajero se convierte en la secuencia de aminoácidos de una proteína

transpiration: loss of water from a plant through its leaves (681)
transpiración: pérdida del agua de una planta a través de sus hojas

trochophore: free-swimming larval stage of an aquatic mollusk (756)
trocófora: estado larvario de un molusco acuático durante el cual puede nadar libremente

trophic level: each step in a food chain or food web (77)
nivel trófico: cada paso en una cadena o red alimenticia

tropism: movement of a plant toward or away from stimuli (712)
tropismo: movimiento de una planta hacia los estímulos o en dirección opuesta a ellos

tumor: mass of rapidly dividing cells that can damage surrounding tissue (289)
tumor: masa de células que se dividen rápidamente y pueden dañar al tejido circundante

U

understory: layer in a rain forest found underneath the canopy formed by shorter trees and vines (112)
sotobosque: en un bosque tropical, la capa de vegetación que se halla bajo el dosel forestal, formada por árboles más bajos y enredaderas

ureter: tube that carries urine from a kidney to the urinary bladder (883)
uréter: conducto que transporta la orina del riñón a la vejiga urinaria

urethra: tube through which urine leaves the body (883)
uretra: conducto por donde la orina sale del cuerpo

urinary bladder: saclike organ in which urine is stored before being excreted (883)
vejiga urinaria: órgano en forma de bolsa en el cual se almacena la orina antes de ser excretada

V

vaccination: injection of a weakened, or a similar but less dangerous, pathogen to produce immunity (1020)
vacunación: inyección de un patógeno debilitado o similar al original, pero menos peligroso, para producir inmunidad

vaccine: preparation of weakened or killed pathogens used to produce immunity to a disease (588)
vacuna: preparación hecha con organismos patógenos debilitados o muertos que se utiliza para producir inmunidad a una enfermedad

vacuole: cell organelle that stores materials such as water, salts, proteins, and carbohydrates (198)
vacuola: orgánulo celular que almacena sustancias como agua, sales, proteínas e hidratos de carbono

valve: flap of connective tissue located between an atrium and a ventricle, or in a vein, that prevents backflow of blood (950)
válvula: pliegue de tejido conectivo ubicado entre una aurícula y un ventrículo, o en una vena, que impide el retroceso de la sangre

van der Waals force: slight attraction that develops between oppositely charged regions of nearby molecules (38)
fuerzas de van der Waals: atracción leve que se desarrolla entre las regiones con cargas opuestas de moléculas cercanas

vas deferens: tube that carries sperm from the epididymis to the urethra (989)
conducto deferente: tubo que transporta el esperma desde el epidídimo a la uretra

vascular bundle: clusters of xylem and phloem tissue in stems (675)
hacecillo vascular: manojo de tejidos del xilema y del floema en los tallos

vascular cambium: meristem that produces vascular tissues and increases the thickness of stems (677)
cámbium vascular: meristemo que produce tejidos vasculares y aumenta el grosor de los tallos

Glossary *(continued)*

vascular cylinder: central region of a root that includes the vascular tissues—xylem and phloem (670)
  cilindro vascular: región central de una raíz que incluye a los tejidos vasculares xilema y floema

vascular tissue: specialized tissue in plants that carries water and nutrients (641)
  tejido vascular: tejido especializado de las plantas que transporta agua y nutrientes

vector: animal that transports a pathogen to a human (1013)
  vector: animal que transmite un patógeno a un ser humano

vegetative reproduction: method of asexual reproduction in plants, which enables a single plant to produce offspring that are genetically identical to itself (702)
  reproducción vegetativa: método de reproducción asexual de las plantas que permite que una única planta produzca descendencia genéticamente idéntica a sí misma

vein: blood vessel that carries blood from the body back to the heart (952)
  vena: vaso sanguíneo que transporta la sangre del cuerpo de regreso al corazón

ventricle: lower chamber of the heart that pumps blood out of heart to the rest of the body (792, 949)
  ventrículo: cavidad inferior del corazón que bombea la sangre fuera del corazón hacia el resto del cuerpo

vertebrate: animal that has a backbone (731)
  vertebrado: animal que posee una columna vertebral

vessel element: type of xylem cell that forms part of a continuous tube through which water can move (666)
  elemento vascular (o vaso): tipo de célula del xilema que forma parte de un tubo continuo a través del cual el agua puede desplazarse

vestigial structure: structure that is inherited from ancestors but has lost much or all of its original function (469)
  estructura vestigial: estructura heredada de los ancestros que ha perdido su función original en gran parte o por completo

villus (pl. villi): fingerlike projection in the small intestine that aids in the absorption of nutrient molecules (880)
  vellosidad: proyección en forma de dedo en el intestino delgado que contribuye a la absorción de las moléculas nutrientes

virus: particle made of proteins, nucleic acids, and sometimes lipids that can replicate only by infecting living cells (574)
  virus: partícula compuesta por proteínas, ácidos nucleicos y, a veces, lípidos, que puede replicarse sólo infectando células vivas

vitamin: organic molecule that helps regulate body processes (871)
  vitamina: molécula orgánica que ayuda a regular los procesos corporales

viviparous: animals that bear live young that are nourished directly by the mother's body as they develop (822)
  vivíparo: animal que da a luz crías vivas que se nutren directamente dentro del cuerpo de la madre mientras se desarrollan

W

weather: day-to-day conditions of the atmosphere, including temperature, precipitation, and other factors (96)
  tiempo: condiciones diarias de la atmósfera, entre las que se incluyen la temperatura, la precipitación y otros factores

wetland: ecosystem in which water either covers the soil or is present at or near the surface for at least part of the year (119)
  humedal: ecosistema en el cual el agua cubre el suelo o está presente en la superficie durante al menos una parte del año

white blood cell: type of blood cell that guards against infection, fights parasites, and attacks bacteria (955)
  glóbulo blanco: tipo de célula sanguínea que protege de las infecciones, combate a los parásitos y ataca a las bacterias

woody plant: type of plant made primarily of cells with thick cell walls that support the plant body; includes trees, shrubs, and vines (653)
  planta leñosa: tipo de planta constituida fundamentalmente por células con paredes celulares gruesas que sostienen el cuerpo de la planta; en este tipo se incluyen los árboles, arbustos y vides

X, Y, Z

xylem: vascular tissue that carries water upward from the roots to every part of a plant (643)
  xilema: tejido vascular que transporta el agua hacia arriba, desde las raíces a cada parte de una planta

zoonosis (pl. zoonoses): disease transmitted from animal to human (1013)
  zoonosis: enfermedad transmitida por un animal a un ser humano

zooplankton: small free-floating animals that form part of plankton (76)
  zooplancton: pequeños animales que flotan libremente y forman parte del plancton

zygote: fertilized egg (325, 739, 995)
  cigoto: huevo fertilizado

Index

A

Abiotic factors, **66**–67, 100, 111
Abscisic acid, **711**
Absorption, 875
Acetylcholine, **931**
Acetyl-CoA, 256
Acid rain, **164,** 180
Acids, **44**
amino, **48**–49, 84, 366, 870
fatty, 47–48
nucleic, **48,** 344, 403, 436
Acne, 938
Acoelomates, 738
Acquired characteristics, 456
Acquired immune deficiency syndrome (AIDS), 578, 588, 994, 1001, 1023, 1025–1027
Acquired immunity, 1020
Actin, 199, 606, **930**
Action potential, **898**–899
Activation energy, **51**–52
Active immunity, **1020**
Active site, 53
Active transport, **212**–213, 227
in plants, 635, 641, 666, 672–673, 685–687
Adaptations, **461**
to biomes, 112–115
in chordates, 758–759, 761–762, 825
evolutionary, 487
excretory, 798
to high altitude, 831
of leaves, 684
of mouthparts, 785–786
and natural selection, 461–464
in pathogens, 1012
seasonal, 714
of seed plants, 646
Adaptive radiation, **550**–551
Addiction, 904–905
Adenine, 344–345, 348, 366
Adenosine diphosphate (ADP), 227, 235
Adenosine triphosphate (ATP), 48, **226**–227
ATP synthase, **237,** 258
and cellular respiration, 252, 254–260
and exercise, 264–265
and fermentation, 262–263
and muscle contraction, 930
and photosynthesis, 235–239
Adhesion, **41, 686**
Adrenal glands, 979, **983**
Adreno-corticotropic hormone (ACTH), 983
Adult stem cells, 295, 297
Aerobic respiration, **252**
African sleeping sickness, 615
Age of Fishes, 759
Age structure of populations, **131,** 144
Aggression, **848**
Agriculture, 155, 715–717, 719
AIDS, 578, 588, 994, 1001, 1023, 1025–1027
Air pollution, 163–165
Albumin, 954
Alcohol, 904
Alcoholic fermentation, 263
Aldosterone, 983
Alemseged, Zeresenay, 773
Algae, 610
brown, 527, 602, 604, 611
in food chains and webs, 73–74
green, 528, 610, 623, 634, 636–640
and photosynthesis, 70
phytoplankton, 73, 117
red, 528, 611
symbiotic, 783
unicellular, 214
Algal bloom, **611**
Alkaline solution, 44
Allantois, 825
Alleles, **310,** 482. *See also* Genetics
allele frequencies, **483,** 490–492
dominant and recessive, 310–312, 318, 394
and gene linkage, 328–329
multiple and codominant, **320,** 394
and phenotypes, 488
segregation of, **312,** 314, 318
and traits, 397, 485–486
Allergies, **1024**
Alternation of generations, **608, 637**
Alveoli, 790, **964**–966
Amebic dysentery, 615
Amenorrhea, 1005
Amino acids, **48**–49, 870
and genetic code, 366
in nitrogen cycle, 84
Ammonia, 585, 794–795, 867, 882
Amnion, 825, 998
Amniota, 518–519
Amniotic egg, **825**
Amoebas, 213, 606, 608, 612
Amoeboid movement, 606
Amphibians, 761, 790, 793, 796
brains of, 811
fertilization in, 821–822
metamorphosis in, 824
Amygdala, 902
Amylase, **876**
Anaerobic respiration, **252,** 262
Angina, 958
Angiosperms, **646,** 647, 650–654
classification of, 652–653
double fertilization in, **700**–701
fruit development in, 704
life cycle of, 698–701
structure of, 696–697
types of, 653–654
vessel elements in, **666**
Animal behavior, 840–851
and climate change, 178
communication, 850–851
complex, 844–845
cycles of, 847
and evolution, 840–841, 848–849
innate, **841,** 844–845
learned, 842–843
social, 848–849
Animalia, 514, 523–524, 528, 730
Animals, 730–743. *See also* Chordates; Invertebrates; Vertebrates
animal society, **848**–849
asexual reproduction in, 277, 735, **819**
body plans of, 737–741
cell differentiation in, 293
cells of, 203, 206–207, 211, 215
characteristics of, 730
cladogram of, 742–743
cloned, 427, 429
cytokinesis, 284
development of young, 823–824
differentiation stages in, 740
embryo development in, 738–739, 822
and emerging diseases, 1022
genetically modified, 429–430
homeostasis in, 732, 827–830
hormones of, 708
and language, 851
parental care in, 824
and pollination, 700
response to stimuli, 733, 808–809
and seed dispersal, 651, **705**
sexual reproduction in, 735, **820**–822
transgenic, 426, 429–430
Animal systems
circulation, 734, **791**–793, 864
digestive, 784–786

Animal systems (cont'd)
endocrine, 828
excretion, 734–735, **794**–798
feeding and digestion, 734, 782–786
and homeostasis, 732, 827–830
muscular, 733, **816**–818
nervous, 733, 808–811, 864, 951
reproductive, 277, 735, 819–826
respiration, 734–735, 787–790, 864
sensory, **812**–813
skeletal, 733, **814**–816
Annelids, 755–756, 792
Anterior cruciate ligament (ACL), 927
Antheridia, **642**
Anthers, **697**
Anthrax, 583, 589
Anthropoids, **766,** 766–767
Antibiotics, **588,** 591, 1021
Antibodies, **1016**–1017
Anticodons, **369**
Antidiuretic hormone (ADH), 886, 982, 986–987
Antigens, 394, **1016**
Antihistamines, 1024
Antiparallel strands, 347
Anus, 739
Aorta, 952
Aphotic zone, **117,** 121
Apical dominance, **710**
Apical meristems, **668,** 670, 714
Apoptosis, **288,** 1019
Appendages, **755**
Appendicular skeleton, **922**
Appendix, 881
Aquaculture, **176**
Aquaporins, **210**
Aquatic animals
excretion in, 795–796
larval stage of, 823
respiratory systems of, 788
Aquatic ecosystems, 117–121
biotic and abiotic factors in, 66–67
changes in, 63
energy production in, 70
estuaries, **119**
food chains and webs in, 73–76
freshwater, 118–119
marine, 120–121
nutrient limitation in, 86
underwater conditions in, 117–118
Aqueous humor, 912
Archaea, 524, **526,** 580–581
Archaebacteria, 524, 526
Archaeopteryx, 763
Archean Eon, 542
Archegonia, **642**
Arteries, **952**
Arthropods, 755, 815, 817, 821
Artificial selection, 457–**458,** 461
Asexual reproduction, **19, 277**–278
in animals, 735, **819**
in fungi, 621
parasitic worms, 820
in plants, 277, 640, 702–703
in prokaryotes, 281
in protists, 608–609
Aspirin, 980
Association of Zoos and Aquariums (AZA), 170
Asthma, 163, **1024**
Atherosclerosis, **958**–960
Athlete's foot, 623, 1010
Atmospheric resources, 163–165
Atomic number, 35
Atoms, **34**–38
ATP. *See* Adenosine triphosphate (ATP)
ATP synthase, **237,** 258
Atrioventricular (AV) node, 951, 958
Atrium, **792**–793, **949**–951
Aurelia, 820–821
Australopithecus afarensis, 768–769, 773
Autoimmune diseases, 1025
Autonomic nervous system, **908**
Autosomes, **393**
Autotrophic protists, 610–611
Autotrophs, **69,** 117, **228,** 250
Auxins, **709**–712
Avery, Oswald, 340, 349
Avian influenza, 591, 1013, 1023
Axial skeleton, **922**
Axon, **897**
Axon terminal, 897, 900

B

Bacilli, **582**
Backbones, 731
Background extinction, **548**
Bacteria, 214
bacterial meningitis, 587
and cell organelles, 557
chemosynthetic, 70
classification of, 524–526
diseases caused by, 586–588, 1010–1011
early images of, 190
gene expression in, 377
growth of, 133, 146, 594
lateral gene transfer in, 485
and mutations, 375, 420
photosynthetic, 70, 545, 555
and recombinant DNA, 424–425
viral infections of, 340–341, 575–577
Bacteria, domain, 524–**525,** 580–581
Bacterial transformation, **339**–340
Bacteriophages, **340**–341, **575**–577
Balance, 911
Balanced diet, 872–873
Bar coding, DNA, 529
Bark, **679**
Barr body, 396
Basal cell carcinoma, 939
Base pairing, **348,** 350
Bases, **44**
Beagle, 450–451
Beak size, 473, 502
Beans, 706
Bears, 512, 848
Beekeeper, 736
Behavior, **767, 841,** 844–845. *See also* Animal behavior
Behavioral isolation, **495,** 497
Beijerinck, Martinus, 574
Benign tumors, 289
Benthic zone, 117, 121
Benthos, **117**
Beta-carotene, 430
Beta cells, 984
Beta-globin, 398
Bias, **14**
Biennial plants, 654
Bilateral symmetry, **738**–739
Bile, 878
Binary fission, 281, **583**
Binocular vision, **765**
Binomial nomenclature, **511**
Biodiversity, **166**–171. *See also* Diversity
conservation, 170–171
patterns of, 451–453, 465
threats to, 168–170
types of, 166–167
Biogeochemical cycles, **79,** 163
Biogeography, **465**
Bioinformatics, **407,** 422
Biological magnification, **161**
Biology, 17–25, 80
defined, **17**
fields of, 22–23
measurement in, 24
molecular, **23,** 370
and safety, 25
themes of, 20–21
Biomass, **78**
Biomes, **65,** 110–116, 122

Biosphere, **21, 64**. *See also* Ecology; Ecosystems
Biotechnology, **23, 419**, 436–439. *See also* Genetic engineering
Biotic factors, **66**–67, 100
Bipedal locomotion, **767**
Bird flu, 591, 1013, 1023
Birds
  behavioral isolation in, 495
  brains of, 811
  digestion in, 785
  evolution of, 520, 547, 762–763
  excretion in, 797
  imprinting in, 844–845
  learned behavior in, 842
  lungs of, 790
  and migration, 813, **847**
  and natural selection, 472–473, 489, 496–497
  and resource sharing, 101
  temperature control in, 829–830
Birthrate, 132, 142–143
Bisphenol-A (BPA), 16
Bivalves, 815
Blade of leaf, **680**
Blastocyst, **294, 996**
Blastopore, 739
Blastula, 272–273, **739**
Blood, 42, 954–956. *See also* Circulatory system, human
  carbon dioxide removal from, 50, 52
  cell formation, 922–923
  clotting, 955
  flukes, 820
  groups, 394
  and kidneys, 884, 886–887
  pH of, 44
  pressure, 887, 953, 959
  red blood cells, **954**–955
  transfusions, 956
  types, 320, 956
  vessels, 952–953
  white blood cells, **955**
B lymphocytes, 955, 1016–1017
Body cavity, 738
Body plans of animals, 737–741
Body temperature, 828–830, 866, 935, 937, 987
Bolus, 876
Bonds, chemical, 36–38
  carbon, 45
  covalent, **37,** 344
  hydrogen, **41,** 348
  ionic, **37**
Bone marrow, **924**
Bones, 922, **924**–925
Bony fishes, 760
Boreal forests, 114
Botanical illustrator, 655
Bottleneck effect, **490**
Botulism, 586
Bovine spongiform encephalopathy (BSE), 573, 1023
Bowman's capsule, **884**
Brain, human, 901–905
Brains, 810–811
Brain stem, **903**
Bread mold, 620–621
Breathing, 966–967
Breeding
  artificial selection, 457–**458**
  inbreeding, **419**
  selective, **418**–420, 716
Bronchi, **964**
Bronchioles, 964
Bronchitis, 968
Brown algae, 527, 602, 604, 611
Bryophytes, **641**–642
Bt toxin, 428
Buds of plant, **675**
Buffers, **44**
Bulbourethral gland, 990
Bulk transport, 213
Burbank, Luther, 419
Burgess Shale, 753
Bursae, 927
Bursitis, 927

C

C. elegans, 293–294, 381
Caecilians, 761
Calcitonin, **985**
Calcium, 82, 925, 985
Calcium ions (Ca^{2+}), 931
Calcium phosphate, 872
Calorie, **250, 868**
Calvin, Melvin, 229, 238
Calvin cycle, **238**–239
Cambium, **677**–679
Cambrian Explosion, 753, 758–759
Cambrian Period, 542, 543, 560
Camouflage, 113–114
CAM plants, 241
Cancer, **289**–290
  lung, 938, 968
  skin, 337, 357, 938–939, 1025
  viral, 588
Canines, 785
Canopy, **112**
Capillaries, 788, 792, **952,** 964–966
Capillary action, 41, **686**
Capsid, **575**
Carbohydrates, **46**–47, 250–251, **869**
Carbon, 35, 45
Carbon credits, 171
Carbon cycle, 82–83
Carbon dating, 541
Carbon dioxide
  atmospheric, 164, 169, 178
  in blood, 52
  and breathing, 966–967
  and cellular respiration, 253
  and climate, 545
  and nutrient cycles, 82–83
  and photosynthesis, 239, 241, 253
  removal from bloodstream, 50, 52
Carbonic anhydrase, 52
Carboniferous Period, 543, 561, 761–762
Carbon monoxide, 968
Cardiac muscle, **928**–929
Carnivores, **71, 782,** 785–786
Carpels, **697**
Carrying capacity
  of biosphere, 155
  of species, **135**
Cartilage, **757, 924**–925
Casparian strip, **672**–673
Catalysts, **52**
Cell, 20, **191, 862**
  active transport, **212**–213, 227
  animal, 203, 206–207, 211, 215
  artificial, 435
  B and T, 955, 957, 1016–1019
  beta, 984
  Casparian strip, **672**–673
  cell membranes, **193,** 203–204, 209–213
  cell plate, 284
  cell stains, 191
  cell theory, **191**
  companion, **666**
  daughter, 276, 280, 325, 327–328
  diploid and haploid, **323**–328
  discovery of, 190–191
  elongation of, 709
  flame, 796
  and food molecules, 250
  glial, 863
  in ground tissue of plants, 667
  guard, **682**–683
  and homeostasis, **214**–217
  human, 392–393, 862
  mast, 1014
  in meristems, **667**–668
  and microscopes, 190–192
  migration, 997
  multipotent, **295**
  mutations of, 375
  organelles, **196,** 198–202
  passive transport, **209**–211

Index *cont'd*

Cell (cont'd)
plant, 203, 206–207, 211, 215
plasma, 1017
pluripotent, **294**
red blood, **954**–955
RNA synthesis in, 364–365
size of, 193, 274–276
in skin, 936
specialization of, 215, 380
stem, 294–297
structure of, 196–207
target, **709, 978**
totipotent, **294**
tumors, **289**
and viruses, 579
walls of, **203**
white blood, **955**
Cell body, neuron, **897**
Cell cycle, **280**–282
and apoptosis, **288**
eukaryotic, 281
growth factors, **287**
phases of, 281–282
prokaryotic, 281
regulating, 286–290
Cell differentiation, 215, 292–297, 380–381
defined, **293**
and environment, 383
and Hox genes, 382
in meristems, 668
in plants, 292
stem cells, 294–297
Cell division, 191, 274–290. *See also* Cell cycle; Meiosis
and cancer, 290
and cell size, 274–276
and chromosomes, **279**–280, 282–283
controls on, 286–288
cytokinesis, **282,** 284
defined, **276**
and interphase, **281**
mitosis, **282**–285, 328
and reproduction, 277–278
Cell-mediated immunity, 1018–**1019**
Cellular junctions, 217
Cellular respiration, 250–260
aerobic and anaerobic, **252,** 260
in animals, 787–790
defined, **251**
efficiency of, 256
and electron transport, 258
and exercise, 265
glycolysis, 252, **254**–255
Krebs cycle, 252, **256**–260
overview of, 251–252
and photosynthesis, 253
stages of, 251
Cellulase, 614
Cellulose, 47, 869
Cenozoic Era, 563, 764
Centipedes, 755
Central nervous system, **896,** 901–904
Centrioles, **199, 282**
Centromere, **282**
Cephalization, **740,** 810–811
Cephalopods, 810
Cerebellum, **811, 903**
Cerebral cortex, **902**
Cerebral ganglia, 810–811
Cerebrum, 765, **811, 902**
Cervix, 995
Chargaff, Erwin, 344, 348–349
Chase, Martha, 340–341, 349
Chemical digestion, 785, **875**–878
Chemical reactions, **50**–51, 80
Chemiosmosis, 237, 258
Chemistry of life, 34–53
atoms, **34**
bonding, 36–38
carbon compounds, 45–49
chemical reactions, **50**–51, 80
compounds, **36**–38
elements and isotopes, **35**
enzymes, **52**–54
Chemoreceptors, 910
Chemosynthesis, **70**
Chemosynthetic organisms, 117, 121
Chemotherapy, 290
Chesapeake Bay, 119
Chicken pox, 588
Childbirth, 1000
Chitin, **618,** 815
Chlamydia, **994**
Chlamydomonas, 640
Chlorine, 35, 37
Chlorofluorocarbons (CFCs), 175
Chlorophyll, 202, 230–232
Chloroplasts, **202,** 231, 557
Choanoflagellates, 752
Cholesterol, 319, 959–961, 980
Chordata, 513, 731
Chordates, **730,** 788. *See also* Invertebrates; Vertebrates
adaptations in, 758–759, 761–762, 825
cladogram of, 758–763
embryological development in, 739
evolution of, 757–764, 792
fertilization in, 821–822
nonvertebrate, 731, 758, 811, 813, 822
reproductive diversity in, 824–826
sense organs, 813
Chorion, 825, 998
Christy, Henry, 773
Chromatid, **282**
Chromatin, 197, **280,** 352
Chromosomes, 197, **279**–280
artificial, 424
autosomal, **393**
and cell division, 282–283
chromosomal mutations, 372, 374–375
disorders of, 401
eukaryotic, 280, 343, 352–353
and gene linkage, 328–329
homologous, **323**–325, 327
human, 392–397
karyotypes, **392**–393
and polyploid plants, 376, 420
polyploidy, 376
prokaryotic, 279
sex, **393**
telomeres, **352**
X and Y chromosomes, 393–396, 401, 434
Chyme, **877,** 880
Cilia, 199, **607,** 964
Ciliates, 607
Circadian rhythms, **847**
Circulatory system, human, 734, **948**–953
and cholesterol, 959–961
diseases of, 957–959
heart, **791,** 793, 949–951
and respiratory system, 963
Circulatory systems, animal, 734, **791**–793, 864
Citric acid cycle, 256
Clades, **516**–520, 546–547, 763
Cladograms, **517**–520
of animals, 742–743
bird lineage, 547
of chordates, 758–763
of invertebrates, 754–756
of primates, 766–767
Class, **514**
Classical conditioning, **843**
Classification, 510–528
binomial nomenclature, **512**
clades, **516**–520, 546–547, 763
class, **514**
and DNA, 521–522
domains, **525**–528

Classification (cont'd)
  evolutionary, 516–520
  family, **513**
  of fossils, 546
  of fungi, 621
  genus, **512**
  kingdoms, **514,** 523–525
  Linnaean system, **513**–515
  order, **513**
  phylum, **514**
  of plants, 634, 637, 641, 652–653
  of prokaryotes, 580–581
  of protists, 602–604
  systematics, **512**–513, 516–517
  three-domain system, 524–528
Climate, **96**–98, 110
  and biomes, **65,** 110–116, 122
  change, 170, **177**–179
  diagram, 111
  evolution of, 544
Climax communities, 108–109
Clone, **427,** 429
Closed circulatory systems, **792**
Clotting, blood, 955
Cnidarians, 754, 784, 810, 814, 820
Cocaine, 904
Cocci, **582**
Cochlea, **911**
Codominance, **319,** 394
Codons, **366**–367
Coelom, **738**
Coenzyme A, 256
Coevolution, **551**–552
Cohesion, **41,** 686
Collagen, 863
Collenchyma, **667**
Collins, Francis, 349, 402
Colon, 881
Colorblindness, 395
Commensalism, **104**
Common ancestors, **464,** 468–469, 516–521
Common cold, 578, 588
Communities, **64,** 100–102, 108–109
Companion cells, **666**
Competition, ecological
  and communities, 100–102
  and natural selection, 473, 497
  and population density, 138
Competitive exclusion principle, **101**
Complementary strands, 350
Complex carbohydrates, 47
Compound microscope, 26
Compounds, chemical, **36**–38
Computed Tomography Angiography, 962
Conditioning. *See also* Animal behavior
  classical, **843**
  operant, **843**
Cones, 646, 648, 668
Cones (of eye), **913**
Coniferous forests, 114
Conifers, **114,** 648, 677
Conjugation, **583,** 591, **608**
Connective tissue, **863**
Conservation, 162, 170–171, 176. *See also* Resources, natural
Constipation, 881
Consumers, **71**–72
Continental drift, 544–545
Continental shelf, 121
Contour plowing, 160
Contractile vacuole, 198
Control group, **7**
Controlled experiment, **7,** 9
Convergent evolution, **551**
Cook, James, 895, 917
Coral reefs, 121, 611, 728–729, 847
Cork, 190
Cork cambium, **677,** 679
Cornea, **912**
Corn smut, 622
Coronary arteries, 950, 958
Corpus callosum, 902
Corpus luteum, **993**
Cortex, **670**
Corticosteroids, **983**
Cortisol, 983
Cotyledons, **652**–653, 706
Coughing, 1012
Courtship behavior, **848**
Covalent bonds, **37,** 344
Cowpox, 1020
C4 plants, 241
Crassulacean Acid Metabolism (CAM), 241
Creatine supplements, 261
Creativity, 10
Cretaceous Period, 548, 562, 762, 764
Cretinism, 985
Creutzfeld-Jacob Disease, 597
Crick, Francis, 346–350, 362
Crocodilians, 762
Cro-Magnons, 772
Crop plants, 428–429, 437–438, 622, 715–717
Crop rotation, 160
Crossing-over, **324,** 329, 484, 499
Cross-pollination, 309
Crustaceans, 501, 755
Crutzen, Paul J., 175
Cryptosporidium, 607, 615
Currents, ocean, 98, 118
Cyanobacteria, 70, 584, 610, 623
Cycles
  carbon, 82–83
  cell, **280**–282, 286–290
  matter, 79–86
  nitrogen, 82–83
  nutrients, 82–86
  phosphorous, 85
  water, 81
Cyclic AMP (cAMP), 981
Cyclins, **286,** 288
Cystic fibrosis (CF), 399–400, 431
Cytochrome *c*, 471
Cytokinesis, **282,** 284, 324
Cytokinins, **710**
Cytoplasm, **196,** 580
Cytosine, 344–345, 348, 366
Cytoskeleton, **199,** 922
Cytotoxic T cells, 1019

D

Dart, Raymond, 773
Darwin, Charles, 13, 137, 143, 450–473, 482, 549, 552, 709
Darwin, Francis, 709
Data, **8**
Dating techniques, 466, 540–541
Daughter cells, 276, 280, 325, 327–328
Death rate, 132, 142–143
Decibels (dB), 910
Deciduous plants, **112,** 714
Decomposers, **71,** 74, 584
Decomposition, 622
Deforestation, **159**
Dehydration, 189, 869
Democritus, 34
Demographic transition, **144**
Demography, **143**. *See also* Population growth
Dendrites, **897**
Denitrification, **84**
Density-dependent limiting factors, **137**–141
Density-independent limiting factors, **137,** 140–141
Deoxyribonucleic acid. *See* DNA
Deoxyribose, 344, 362
Dependent variable, **7**
De Puydt, Marcel, 773
Derived characters, **518**–519, 521
Dermal tissue, **665,** 670, 680
Dermis, **937**
Descent with modification, 464, 516
Desertification, **159**

Index *cont'd*

Deserts, 113
Detritivores, **71,** 74, **782**
Detritus, 782
Deuterostomes, **739**
Devonian Period, 561, 759
Diabetes mellitus, 867, 886, 984, 1025
Dialysis, 887
Diaphragm, 966–**967**
Diarrhea, 881
Diastolic pressure, 953
Diatoms, 603, 604
Dicer enzyme, 380–381
Dichloro diphenyl trichloroethane (DDT), 161, 169
Dichotomous key, **511**
Dicots, **652**–653, 669, 675, 677, 706–707
Diet, balanced, 872–873
Differentiation, **381**–382. *See also* Cell differentiation
Diffusion, **208**–211, 218, 787
Digestion
  animal, 734, 784–786
  chemical, 785, **875**–878
  mechanical, 785, **875**–877
Digestive system, human, 737, 864, **875**–881
  absorption and elimination, 880–881
  digestive enzymes, 876–878
  digestive process, **875**–878
Digestive tract, 739, **784**–785
Dihybrid cross, 317
Dikika Baby, 769, 773
Dinoflagellates, 611
Dinosaurs, 520, 548, 550, 762–763, 830
Diphtheria, 586
Diploid cells, **323**–328
Diploid (2N) phase, **637**
Directional selection, **489**
Disaccharides, 46, 869
Diseases
  of animals, 622
  autoimmune, 1025
  bacterial, 586–588, 1010–1011
  circulatory system, 957–961
  emerging, **590**–592, 1022–1023
  genetic, 947, 961, 973
  infectious, **23, 1010**–1023
  intestinal, 615
  of plants, 622
  and public health, 1021
  sexually transmitted (STDs), **994,** 1012
  and transgenic organisms, 430
  viral, 588–589, 994, 1010–1011
Disruptive selection, **489**
Distribution of populations, 131
Dittmer, Howard, 669
Diversity, 21. *See also* Biodiversity
  of chordates, 731, 757–764
  ecosystem, **166**
  and extinction, 548
  genetic, **166**–168, 820
  of invertebrates, 730, 753–756
  species, **166,** 168
Djimdoumalbaye, Ahounta, 773
DNA, 18, 23, 48, 340–354. *See also* Human heredity
  and cell size, 274, 276
  chromosomes, **279**–280
  and classification, 521–522, 529
  components of, **344**–345
  crossing-over, 484, 499
  DNA fingerprinting, **433**–434, 440, 443
  DNA microarray, **432**
  DNA polymerase, **351,** 404, 423
  DNA replication, 281, **350**–353, 374–375, 424–425
  double-helix model of, **347**–348
  in eukaryotic cells, 193, 352–353
  evolution of, 554–555
  extraction, 354, 403
  functions of, 342–343
  and genetic disorders, 398
  as genetic material, 340–341
  and hominine evolution, 771
  manipulating, 403–405
  mtDNA, 434
  mutation rates in, 498–499
  and privacy, 437
  in prokaryotic cells, 193, 352–353
  recombinant, 421–425, 430
  and RNA, 362–365
  sequencing, 404–409
Domains, **525**–528
Dominance
  codominance, **319**
  incomplete, **319**
  principle of, **310,** 318
Dominant alleles, 310–312, 318, 394
Dopamine, **904**–905
Dormancy, plant, **706**–707, 714, 847
Double fertilization, **700**–701
Double Helix, The, 346
Double-helix model, **347**–348
Double-loop circulatory systems, **792**–793
Down syndrome, 401
Drip irrigation, 162
Drosophila melanogaster, 318, 323, 328, 361, 382, 387, 490, 501
Drug addiction, 904–905
Dry forests, 112
Dunkleosteus, 759
Duodenum, 878
Dwarfism, 430, 982
Dynamic interaction. *See* Interdependence

E

E. coli, 377, 383, 421, 572–573, 581
Ears, 911
Earth
  age of, 454–455, 467
  early history of, 553–555
  evolution of, 544–545
  geologic time scale, **542**–543
Earthworms, 755, 792
Ebola, 1013, 1023
Echinoderms, 739, 756–757, 810, 815
Echocardiography, 962
Ecological pyramids, **77–78**
Ecology, **23,** 64–**65**
  case studies, 175–179
  defined, **65**
  disturbance of, 76, 80, 106–109
  ecological footprint, **173**–174
  ecological hot spot, **171**
  ecological succession, **106**–109
  global, **22**
  methods of studying, 68
  and sustainability, 157, 174
Ecosystems, **65**. *See also* Aquatic ecosystems
  biomes, **65,** 110–116, 122
  and climate, **96**–98
  competition in, 100–103
  diversity of, **166**
  goods and services, 156–157
  limiting factors in, 137
  niches in, 99–**100**
  preserving, 170–171
  recycling within, 79–86
  succession in, **106**–109
  symbioses in, 103–104
Ectoderm, **738,** 997
Ectotherm, **829**–830
Edema, 956
Ediacaran fauna, 753
Egg, 325, 825. *See also* Reproductive system, human
Ejaculation, 990
Elbow, 932
Electric currents, 813

Electron, **34,** 36–38
Electron carriers, **232,** 236
Electron microscopes, 192
Electron transport chain
  and cellular respiration, 258
  and photosynthesis, **236,** 252
Elements, **35**
Elimination, 875
Embryological development, 469, 500–501, 737, 739
Embryonic stem cells, 272–273, 295–297
Embryos, **292**
  animal, 738–739, 822
  fossils of, 752
  and gene regulation, 380–382
  plant, 647
Embryos, human
  cartilage in, 924–925
  development of, 988, 995–1001
  implantation of, **996**
  multiple, 996
Embryo sac, **699**
Emerging diseases, **590**–592, 1022–1023
Emigration, **132**
Emphysema, 968
Endangered species, 169–170
Endocrine glands, **828, 979,** 984
Endocrine system, 828, 864, **978**–987
Endocytosis, 212–213
Endoderm, **738,** 997
Endodermis, **670,** 672–673
Endoplastic reticulum, **200**–201, 248–249
Endoskeleton, **815**–817, 922
Endosperm, **700**–701
Endospore, **583**
Endosymbiotic theory, 202, **556**–557
Endotherm, **829**–830
Energy, 20
  activation, **51**–52
  and ATP, 226–227
  from autotrophs, 71
  and carbohydrates, 46
  and cellular respiration, 260
  in chemical reactions, 51
  from chemosynthesis, 70
  and chlorophyll, 230–231
  consumers of, 71
  ecological pyramids of, 77
  and exercise, 264–265, 873
  and food, 250, 868
  in food chains and webs, 73–76
  heat, 41
  and oxygen, 252
  from photosynthesis, 70
  producers of, 69–70
  in prokaryotes, 582
  solar, 97
Environment. *See also* Adaptations; Ecology; Ecosystems
  and animal behavior, 847
  biotic and abiotic, 66–67
  disturbance of, 76, 80, 106–109
  and evolution, 544–545, 547–548
  and gene expression, 321, 383
  and human activity, 154–156, 173–174, 183
  and mutations, 375
  and survival, 278, 473, 491
Environmental Protection Agency (EPA), 173
Enzymes, **52–54**
  digestive, 785–786, 876–878
  DNA polymerase, **351**
  restriction, **403**–405, 421
Epidermis, **665,** 670, **936**
Epididymis, **989**
Epiglottis, 876, 964
Epinephrine, **983**
Epiphytic plants, 112
Epithelial tissue, 737, **863**
Era, geologic, **543**
Erythrocytes, 954
Escherichia coli, 377, 383, 421, 572–573, 581
Esophagus, **877**
Essential amino acids, 870
Essential fatty acids, 870
Estivation, 112
Estrogens, **988,** 992
Estuary, **119**
Ethics, 14, 297, 438–439
Ethylene, **711**
Eubacteria, 524–525
Euglena, 603, 604
Eukarya, 524, **526**
Eukaryotes, **193**–194, 521
  cell cycle of, 281
  cell structure of, 196–207
  DNA replication in, 352–353
  electron transport chain in, 258
  eukaryotic chromosomes, 280, 343, 352–353
  gene regulation in, 379–381
  and genetic variation, 557
  origin of, 556–557
  and protists, 605
  single-celled, 523, 602, 752
  transcription in, 364
  unicellular, 214, 526–527
  viral infections of, 577
Everglades, 119
"Evo-devo," 500, 737
Evolution, 13, 19, 21, **450**. *See also* Natural selection
  adaptive radiation, **550**–551
  and animal behavior, 840–841, 848–849
  of animals, 742–743
  and artificial selection, 457–**458**
  of bacteria and viruses, 591
  of birds, 520, 547, 762–763
  of chordates, 757–764, 792
  and classification, 516–522
  coevolution, **551**–552
  common ancestors, 464, 468–469, 516–521, 546
  convergent, **551**
  descent with modification, 464, 516
  of DNA and RNA, 554–555
  of Earth, 544–545
  of endothermy, 830
  and environment, 544–544, 547–548
  of eukaryotic cells, 556–557
  and fossil record, 466–467
  and gene pools, 482–483
  and genetic drift, **490**
  and genetic equilibrium, 491–492
  hominine, **767**–772
  and Hox genes, 500–501
  of infectious diseases, 23
  of insects, 487
  of invertebrates, 752–756
  macroevolution, 546–547
  of mammals, 468
  of mitochondria, 557
  molecular, 498–501
  of multicellular organisms, 558, 640, 752
  of nervous systems, 810–811
  of organic molecules, 554
  of plants, 636–640, 646, 650
  of populations, 483–492
  of primates, **765**–772
  of prokaryotic cells, 556–557
  of protists, 605
  rate of, 549
  and sexual reproduction, 558
  and speciation, **494**–497, 517, 546–547
  of vertebrate brains, 811
Excretion, **882**
Excretory systems, 734–735, **794**–798, 864, **882**–887
Exercise
  and energy, 264–265, 873
  and health, 933

Index cont'd

Exhalation, 967
Exocrine glands, **979,** 984
Exocytosis, 212–213
Exons, **365**
Exoskeleton, **815,** 817, 922
Experiment, controlled, **7,** 9
Experimentation, ecological, 68
Exponential growth, **132**–133
Extinction, 168–170, **538,** 546–548, 762
Extracellular digestion, **784**
Eyes
  in animals, 850
  in fruit flies, 361, 387
  human, 912–913
  invertebrate, 812
  vertebrate, 813

F

Facilitated diffusion, **209**–211
FAD (flavine adenine dinucleotide), 256
$FADH_2$, 256
Fallopian tubes, 991, 993
Family, **513**
Farmer, 655
Fast-twitch muscle, 933
Fats, 250–251, **870,** 873
Fat-soluble vitamins, 871
Fatty acids, 47–48
Feathers, 762
Feces, 881
Feedback inhibition, **732, 865,** 986
Female cone, 648
Female reproductive system, **991**–993. *See also* Reproductive system, human
Fermentation, 252, **262**–263, 265–266
  alcoholic, 263
  lactic acid, 263, 265, 269
Ferns, 638, 644–645
Fertilization, 325, **995**–996. *See also* Reproduction
  double, **700**–701
  external, **822**
  internal, **821**
  of pea plants, **309**
Fertilizers, 84, 86, 717
Fetal development, 999
Fetus, **998**
Fever, **1015**
Fiber, 869
Fibrinogen, 954
Fibrous root system, 669
Fight or flight response, 983
Filter feeders, **782**
Filtration of blood, **884**
Fins, 759
Fish, 500, 757, 759–761
  brains of, 811
  circulatory systems of, 792
  excretion in, 795–796
  fertilization in, 821–822
  ghost, 33
  jawless, 759
  respiratory systems of, 788
Fishapod, 761
Fitness, **461**. *See also* Natural selection
Flagella, 199, 581, **607**
Flagellates, 607
Flame cells, 796
Flatworms, 755, 783, 794, 796, 810, 812
Flavine adenine dinucleotide (FAD), 256
Fleming, Alexander, 1021
Flowering plants, 650–654, 696–703
Flowers, 646, 650–651
  and hormones, 708
  and meristems, 668
  and photoperiod, **713**
  and pollinators, 552
  structure of, **696**–697
Fluid mosaic model, 205
Fluorescence microscopy, 191, 291
Folic acid, 997
Follicle stimulating hormone (FSH), 983, 988–989, 991–993
Follicular phase, 992
Food, **868**
  allergies, 1025
  chains, **73**–76
  and digestive system, 875–881
  and energy, 250, 868
  and fats, 250–251, 873
  genetically modified, 437–438
  labels, 872–873
  nutrients in, 869–673
  webs, **74**–76
Food vacuole, **612**
Forensics, **433**
Forensic scientist, 322
Forests, 109, 112, 114, 159
Forster, Georg, 917
Fossil fuels, 82, 178
Fossil preparator, 559
Fossils, 453, 538–545
  adaptive radiations in, 550
  anthropoid, 774
  of birds, 763
  Cambrian, 753, 758–759
  chordate, 757–759, 761–762
  classification of, 546
  and continental drift, 545
  dating, 541
  Ediacaran fauna, 753
  of eggs and embryos, 752
  and evolutionary theory, 466–467
  hominine, 768–769, 773
  index, **540**
  microfossils, 555
  of plants, 636, 638, 646, 652
  trace, 752
  types of, 538–539
Founder effect, **490,** 496
Four-chambered heart, 793
Frameshift mutations, **373**
Franklin, Rosalind, 346–349
Fraternal twins, 996
Freshwater ecosystems, 118–119
Freshwater resources, 160–162
Frogs, 383, 600, 735, 761, 818, 848
Fronds, 644
Frontal lobe, 903
Fructose, 46
Fruit, **651, 704**
Fruit flies, 318, 323, 328, 361, 382, 387, 490
Fruiting body, **619**
Fungi, 523–524, 527, **618**–626, 1010
  classification of, 621
  lichens, 107, **623**
  mycorrhizae, **624**–625
  parasitic, 622–623
  reproduction in, 621

G

Galactose, 46, 378
Galapágos finches, 453, 471–473, 496–497
Galapágos islands, 452
Gallbladder, **878**
Gametes, **312,** 325
  and gene sets, 323
  human, 985, 990, 995
  of plants, 637
Gametophytes, **637**–638, 646, 697–699
Ganglia, **810,** 906
Gas exchange, 635, 682, 787, 966
Gastrovascular cavity, **784**
Gastrulation, **997**
Gel electrophoresis, **404**–405, 422
Gene flow, 492

Genes, 18, **310**
alleles of, **310,** 482
and behavior, 841
and cancers, 289
and chromosomes, 323
as derived characters, 521
and DNA, 340–341
and DNA microarrays, 432
gene duplication, 499–500
gene expression, **370**–371, 377–383, 980
gene families, 500
gene pools, **483,** 490
gene regulation, 377–383
gene therapy, **431**
homeobox, **382**
homeotic, **382**
homologous, 471
Hox, **382,** 471, 500–501
identifying, 406
lateral gene transfer, 485
linkage, 328–329
mapping, 328–329
MC1R, 394
mutations of, 372–376, 484
and phenotypes, 485–486
and proteins, 370
sex-linked, **395**
Ubx, 501
Genetic engineering, 418–439
in agriculture and industry, 428–429
ethics of, 438–439
in health and medicine, 430–432
personal identification, 433–434
and privacy, 402, 436–437
recombinant DNA, 421–425
and safety, 437–438
selective breeding, **418**–420, 716
transgenic organisms, 426–427
Genetic Information Non-discrimination Act, 402, 409, 437
Genetics, **308**–329. *See also* Alleles; Meiosis
codominance, **319,** 394
dominant and recessive alleles, 310–312, 318
genetic code, **366**–367, 370, 470
genetic diseases, 947, 961, 973
genetic disorders, 395, 398–401
genetic diversity, **166**–168, 820
genetic drift, **490**
genetic equilibrium, **491**–492
genetic marker, **425**
genetic recombination, 484
genetic testing, 402, 431
genetic variation, 419–420, 482–486, 558
incomplete dominance, **319**
multiple alleles, **320**
principle of dominance, **310,** 318
principle of independent assortment, **317**–318, 328–329
segregation of alleles, **312,** 314, 318
traits, **309, 320**
Genital herpes, 994
Genital warts, 994
Genome, human, **392**–393, 403–409, 436
Genomics, **23, 407,** 435
Genotypes, **315,** 321, 397–398, 407, 482
Genus, **511,** 516
Geographic isolation, **495,** 496
Geological processes, 80
Geologic time scale, **542**–543
German measles, 1001
Germination, **706**–707
Germ layers, 738
Germ theory of disease, 586, **1010**
Gibberellins, **711**
Gibson, Daniel G., 435
Gigantism, 982
Gills, 788
Gizzard, 785
Glands, **978**–979, 982–987
adrenal, 979, **983**
endocrine and exocrine, **979,** 984
hypothalamus, 866, **903,** 979, **982,** 986–987
pancreas, **878,** 979, **984**
pineal, **979**
pituitary, 886, 979, **982**–983
reproductive, 985
thymus, 957, **979,** 1016
thyroid, 979, **985,** 987
Glial cells, 863
Global ecology, **22**
Global warming, **177**
Globins, 500
Globulins, 954
Glomerulus, **884**
Glucagon, 978, **984**
Glucose, 46–47, 209, 251, 378, 867
Glycogen, 47
Glycolysis, 252, **254**–255, 262
Goiter, 985
Goldstein, Joseph, 960–961
Golgi apparatus, **201**
Gonads, **985**
Gonorrhea, 994
Gradualism, **549**
Grafting, **703**
Grana, 231
Grant, Peter and Rosemary, 472–473, 496
Grassland, 112–113
Gravitropism, **712**
Gray matter, 902
Great Plains, 158–159
Green algae, 528, 610, 623, 634, 636–640
Green fluorescent protein (GFP), 422
Greenhouse effect, **97,** 163–164, 178, 545
Griffith, Frederick, 338–340, 349, 423
Ground tissue, 665, **666,** 670, 680
Growth hormone (GH), 982–983
Growth plates, 925
Guanine, 344–345, 348, 366
Guard cells, **682**–683
Guerin, Camille, 589
Gullet, **612**
Gymnosperms, **646**–649

H

Habitat, **99**
Habitat fragmentation, **168**
Habituation, **842**
Hair, 937
color, 394, 396–397
follicles, **937**
Half-life, **540**–541
Haploid cells, **323**–328
Haploid (N) phase, **637**
Haplotypes, 407
Hardy-Weinberg principle, **491**
Haversian canals, **924**
Hearing, 911
Heart, **791,** 793, 949–951
Heartburn, 877
Heart disease, 167, 957–958, 962
Heartwood, **678**
Heat
absorption, 122
capacity, 41
greenhouse effect, 97
transport, 98
Helicobacter pylori, 877
Helix, 346
Helmont, Jan van, 225, 229, 245
Helper T cells, 1019, 1026
Hemoglobin, 49, 57, 375, 398, 870, 872, **954,** 966
Hepatitis B, 588–589, 994
Herbaceous plants, **653**
Herbicides, 428, 438
Herbivores, **71, 783,** 785–786
Herbivory, **102,** 138–139
Heredity, 20, 308, 318. *See also* Genetics; Human heredity
Hermaphrodites, 820
Heroin, 904

Index *cont'd*

Herpes, 994
Hershey, Alfred, 340–341, 349
Heterotrophic protists, 612–613
Heterotrophs, **71, 228,** 250, 527
Heterozygous organisms, **314**
Hibernation, 847
High-altitude adaptation, 831
High-density lipoprotein (HDL), 959
Histamines, 938, **1014**
Histones, 280, 352
HIV, 578, 589, 1023, 1026–1027
Homeobox genes, **382**
Homeostasis, **19**–20
  in animals, 732, 827–830
  and blood glucose levels, 978, 984
  and breathing, 967
  and cells, **214**–217
  and endocrine system, 828, 986–987
  in humans, **865**–867, 886–887
  and kidneys, 886–887
  and pH, 44
  of plants, 682–683, 711
  and skin, 935, 937
Homeotic genes, **382**
Hominines, **767**–772
Hominoids, **767**
Homo erectus, 771
Homo ergaster, 770
Homo habilis, 770–771
Homologous chromosomes, **323**–325, 327
Homologous proteins, 471
Homologous structures, **468**–469
Homo neanderthalensis, 772, 773
Homo sapiens, 767, 770, 772, 773
Homozygous organisms, **314**
Hooke, Robert, 190
Hormone receptors, **709,** 980
Hormones, **978**
  animal, 708
  and homeostasis, 828
  local, 980
  and metamorphosis, 824
  parathyroid, **985**
  plant, **708**–714
  prostaglandins, **980**
  releasing, **983**
  sex, **988**
  steroid and nonsteroid, 379, **980–981**
Hornworts, 641
Hoxc8, 470
Hox genes, **382,** 471, 500–501
Human activity, 154–156, 173–174, 183. *See also* Resources, natural
Human body
  circulatory system, 734, 791, 793, **948**–953, 957–961, 963
  digestive system, 737, 864, **875**–881
  embryonic development, 988, 995–999
  endocrine system, 828, 864, **978**–987
  excretory system, **882**–887
  fetal development and childbirth, 999–1001
  and homeostasis, **865**–867, 886–887
  integumentary system, 864, **935**–939
  levels of organization of, 862–864
  lymphatic system, 864, **956**–957
  muscular system, 864, **928**–933, 940
  nervous system, 896–908
  and nutrients, 868–873, 880
  organs in, 863
  reproductive system, 864, **988**–993
  respiratory system, **963**–969
  sense organs, 909–913
  skeletal system, 864, **922**–927
  specialized cells in, 862
  tissues in, 862–863
  and water, 869, 986
Human Genome Project, **406**–409, 430
Human growth hormone (HGH), 3, 29, 430
Human heredity, 392–409
  genetic disorders, 395, 398–401
  and genome, **392**–393, 403–409
  karyotypes, **392**–393
  pedigrees, **396**–397, 410
  transmission of traits, 394–396
Human immunodeficiency virus (HIV), 578, 589, 1023, 1026–1027
Human papillomavirus (HPV), 588–589, 994
Human populations. *See also* Populations
  growth patterns of, 143–145
  history of, 142–143
  impact of, 80, 84, 109, 139, 141
Humoral immunity, **1016**–1018
Huntington's disease, 399
Hutton, James, 454–455, 459, 467
Hybridization, **419**
Hybrids, **309**
Hydras, 754, 814
Hydrochloric acid, 44
Hydrogen, 35, 51
Hydrogen bonds, **41,** 348
Hydrogen ions, 43–44
  and cellular respiration, 258
  and photosynthesis, 236–237
Hydrophilic molecules, 204
Hydrophobic molecules, 204
Hydrostatic skeleton, **814**
Hypercholesterolemia, 973
Hypertension, 887, 959
Hyperthyroidism, 985
Hypertonic solutions, **210**–211
Hyphae, **619**
Hypodermis, 936
Hyponatremia, 221
Hypothalamus, 866, **903,** 979, **982,** 986–987
Hypothesis, **7,** 9
Hypothyroidism, 985
Hypotonic solutions, **210**–211

I

Iceman, 633, 659
Ichthyosaur, 536–537
Identical twins, 996
Immigration, **132**
Immune response, **1016**–1018
Immune system, 828, 864
  acquired immunity, 1020
  cell-mediated immunity, 1018–**1019**
  disorders of, 1024–1027
  humoral immunity, **1016**–1018
  and infectious diseases, 1015–1019
Immunity, 588
Implantation of embryo, **996**
Imprinting, **844**–845
Impulses, 897–900
Inbreeding, **419**
Incisors, 785
Incomplete dominance, **319**
Independent assortment, principle of, **317**–318, 328–329
Independent variable, **7**
Index fossils, **540**
Infant mortality, 1001
Infectious diseases, **23, 1010**–1023. *See also* Diseases,
  causes of, 1010–1011
  and immune system, 1015–1019
  nonspecific defenses against, 1014–1015
  spread of, 1012–1013, 1021–1023
Inference, **7**
Inflammation, 927
Inflammatory response, **1014**
Influenza, 575, 588–589, 591, 1010
Ingenhousz, Jan, 229
Ingestion, 875

Inhalation, 967
Inheritance, 308, 310, 318, 456, 461. *See also* Genetics; Human heredity
Innate behavior, **841,** 844–845
Inorganic chemistry, 45
Insecticides, 161, 428, 438
Insects, 755
  colonies of, 849
  and Hox genes, 501
  metamorphosis in, 823–824
  mutations in, 376
  and plant evolution, 552
  and pollination, 700
  respiratory system of, 789
Insight learning, **843**
Insulin, 870, 978, **984**
Integrated pest management (IPM), 162
Integumentary system, 864, **935**–939
Interdependence, 21
  of biosphere, 64–65
  in food chains and webs, 73–76
Interferons, **1015**
Intergovernmental Panel on Climate Change (IPCC), 177–178
International HapMap Project, 407
International System of Units (SI), 24
Interneurons, **809,** 897
Interphase, **281,** 324
Intertidal zone, 120
Intestinal diseases, 615
Intestine
  large, **881**
  small, **878,** 880–881
Intracellular digestion, **784**
Introduced species, 169
Introns, **365**
Invasive species, 136
Invertebrate biologist, 736
Invertebrates, **730**. *See also* Chordates; Vertebrates
  body cavities of, 738
  body plans of, 744
  cladogram of, 754–756
  development of young, 823–824
  evolution of, 752–753
  fertilization in, 821–822
  nervous systems of, 810
  respiratory systems of, 788–789
  response to stimuli in, 809
  sense organs of, 812
  skeletons of, 814
Iodine, 985
Ionic bonds, **37**
Ions, **37,** 43–44
Iris, 653, 697
Irish Potato Famine, 601, 629
Iris (of eye), **912**
Islets of Langerhans, 984
Isolation, reproductive, **494**–495
Isotonic solutions, **210**–211
Isotopes, **35**
Ivanovski, Dmitri, 574
Iwata, So, 229

J

Jawless fishes, 759
Jaws, 758–759
Jellyfish, 422, 754, 820–821
Jenner, Edward, 589, 1020
Johanson, Donald, 773
Joints, **816**–817, **926**–927
Jurassic Period, 562, 762
Just, Ernest Everett, 996

K

Karposi sarcoma, 1025
Karyotypes, **392**–393
Kenyanthropus, 768
Keratin, **936**
Keystone species, **103,** 167
Kidneys, **795,** 867, 883–887, 986–987
  artificial, 799
  and blood pressure, 884, 886–887, 953
  and salt, 798
Kilocalorie, 250
Kingdoms, **514,** 523–525
Kin selection, **849**
Klinefelter's syndrome, 401
Koch, Robert, 1010–1011
Koch's postulates, **1011**
Krebs, Hans, 256
Krebs cycle, 252, **256**–260

L

Laboratory technician, 195
Lac operon, 377–378, 383
Lac repressor, 378
Lactic acid fermentation, 263, 265, 269
Lactobacillus, 585
Lactose, 378, 383
Laetoli footprints, 768, 773
Lamarck, Jean-Baptiste, 456, 459, 460
Lampreys, 759, 850
Lancelets, 758, 813
Land plants, 637
Langerhans, Paul, 984
Language, **851**
Large intestine, **881**
Lartet, Edouard, 773
Larvae, **756,** 823
Larynx, **964**
Lateral gene transfer, 485
Leaf loss, 714
Leakey, Maeve, 773
Leakey, Mary, 773
Learning, **842**–845. *See also* Animal behavior
Leaves of plants, **664,** 680–684
Leeches, 104, 755
Lens, **912**
Leucine, 367
Leukocytes, 955
Levels of organization
  animals, 737
  ecological, 65
  human body, 862–864
  multicellular organisms, 216–217
  proteins, 49
Lewis, Edward B., 382
Lichens, 107, **623**
Life cycle of plants, 637
  angiosperms, 698–701
  ferns, 644–645
  green algae, 640
  gymnosperms, 648–649
  mosses, 641–642
Life span of plants, 654
Ligaments, **816, 927**
Light. *See also* Sunlight
  absorption, 230
  and photosynthesis, 240
  plant response to, 709, 712–713
Light-dependent reactions, **233,** 235–237
Light-independent reactions, **233,** 238–239
Light microscopes, 191–192
Lignin, 641, 643, **666**
Limb formation, 468–469, 740, 743
Limb girdles, 815
Limbic system, 902
Limiting nutrient, **85**
Linnaean classification system, 512–514
Linnaeus, Carolus, 510–513, 515, 516
Lipid bilayer, **204**–205
Lipids, **47,** 204, 870
Lipoproteins, 959
Liver, 201, 867, **878,** 883, 960–961
Liverworts, 641
Living things, 17–19
Lobes, 902
Local hormones, 980
Logistic growth, 134–**135**
Lohest, Max, 773
Long-day plants, 713
Loop of Henle, **884**
Loudness, 910

Index cont'd

Low-density lipoprotein (LDL), 959–961
"Lucy," 769, 773
Lung cancer, 938, 968
Lungs, 788–790, 883, 950, 964, 966–970
Lupus, 1025
Luteal phase, 993
Luteinizing hormone (LH), 983, 988–989, 991–993
Lyell, Charles, 454–455, 459
Lyme disease, 587, 1013, 1023, 1028, 1031
Lymph, **956**
Lymphatic system, 864, **956**–957
Lymph nodes, 957
Lymphocytes, 955, 1016
Lyon, Mary, 396
Lysogenic infections, **577**
Lysosomes, **198**
Lysozyme, 429, 876, 1014
Lytic infections, **576**–577

M

Macleod, Colin, 349
Macroevolution, **546**–547
Macromolecules, 46–49, 250, 344
Macrophages, 955
Mad cow disease, 573, 597, 1023
Magnetic Resonance Imaging (MRI), 962
Malaria, 400, 616, 1010
Male cone, 648
Male reproductive system, **988**–990. *See also* Reproductive system, human
Malignant tumors, 289
Malpighian tubules, **797**
Malthus, Thomas, 142, 457, 459, 460
Mammalia, 518–519, 520
Mammals, **764**
- adaptive radiation of, 550
- brains of, 811
- ears of, 813
- evolution of, 468
- marine, 846
- muscular systems of, 817
- reproductive strategies of, 825–826
- respiratory system of, 790

Mammary glands, **825**
Mangrove swamps, 12, 119
Manipulated variable, **7**
Marcus, Rudolph, 229
Margulis, Lynn, 557
Marine biologist, 105
Marine ecosystems, 120–121
Marsupials, 764, 826
Marsupium, 826
Mass extinction, **548**
Mass number, 35
Mast cells, 1014
Matrix, **256**
Matter, cycles of, 20, 79–86
Mayer, Julius Robert, 229
McCarty, Maclyn, 349
MC1R gene, 394
Measurement, scientific, 24
Mechanical digestion, 785, **875**–877
Mechanoreceptors, 911, 914
Medications, 1021
Medicine, 430–432
Medulla oblongata, 811, 903, 967
Meiosis, **324**–329, 820. *See also* Sexual reproduction
- in angiosperms, 698–699
- crossing-over, **324,** 329, 484, 499
- meiosis I, 324–325
- meiosis II, 325
- and mitosis, 326–328
- modeling, 330
- nondisjunction in, 401

Melanin, **936**
Melanocytes, **936**
Melanocyte-stimulating hormone (MSH), 983
Melanoma, 938–939
Mello, Craig, 381
Membranes
- cell, **193,** 203–204, 209–213
- and diffusion, 787
- thylakoid, 236–237

Memory B cells, 1017–1019
Mendel, Gregor, 308–318, 329, 349, 370, 482
Meningitis, 587
Menopause, 993
Menstrual cycle, **991**–993
Menstruation, **993**
Mercury, 161
Meristems, **667**–668, 670, 677
Mesoderm, **738,** 997
Mesophyll, **680**–681
Mesozoic Era, 544, 562
Messenger RNA (mRNA), **363,** 368–370
Metabolism, **19,** 985
Metamorphosis, 383, **823**–824
Methamphetamine, 904
Methicillin-resistant *Staphylococcus aureus* (MRSA), 591
Methionine, 369
Metric system, **24**
Microclimates, **96**
Microfilaments, 199
Microfossils, 555
Micrographs, 192
MicroRNA (miRNA), 380–381
Microscopes, 190–192
Microscopist, 195
Microspheres, 554
Microtubules, 199
Microvilli, 880
Midbrain, 903
Migration, 813, **847,** 997
Miller, Stanley, 554
Minerals, **872**
- in bones, 922–923
- and plants, 635

Mitochondria, **202,** 216, 248–249, 252, 521
- evolution of, 557
- matrix of, **256**
- in muscle, 933

Mitochondrial DNA (mtDNA), 434
Mitosis, **282**–285. *See also* Asexual reproduction
- in angiosperms, 698–699
- DNA replication, 353
- and meiosis, 326–328
- in protists, 608

Mitotic spindle, 199
Mixture, **42**
Modeling, ecological, 68
Model systems, 308
Molars, 785
Molds, 603, 604, 608–609, 613, 620–621
Molecular biology, **23,** 370
Molecular clocks, **498**–499
Molecular evolution, 498–501
Molecular transport, 212
Molecules, **37**
- electron carrier, **232**
- evolution of, 554
- homologous, 470–471
- hydrophilic/hydrophobic, 204
- macromolecules, 46–49, 250, 344
- polar, 40–41
- water, 37, 40–41

Molina, Mario, 175
Mollusks, 756, 810, 815
Molting, **815**
Monera, 523–524
Monkeys, 766–767
Monocots, **652**–653, 669, 675–676, 706–707

Monoculture, **155**
Monohybrid cross, 317
Monomers, **46**
Monophyletic group, **516**
Monosaccharides, **46,** 869
Monotremes, 764, 825
Montreal Protocol, 175
Morgan, Thomas Hunt, 318, 323, 328–329, 349
Mosquito, 616–617, 812
Mosses, 638, 641–642
Motor neurons, **809,** 897, 900, 931
Mountain ranges, 116
Mount Saint Helens, 106, 109
Mouth, 739, 876
Mouthparts, 785–786
Mucus, 877, 964, 1014
Mullis, Kary, 423
Multicellular organisms, 527–528
  cells of, 215–217
  evolution of, 558, 640, 752
Multiple alleles, **320**
Multipotent cells, **295**
Muscle contraction, 930–932
Muscle fibers, **929**
Muscle tissue, **863,** 928–929
Muscular systems
  animals, 733, **816**–818
  humans, 864, **928**–933, 940
Museum guide, 559
Mushrooms, 618–619, 622, 626
Mutagens, **375**
Mutant, 420
Mutations, **372**–376, 484, 491
  bacterial, 420
  chromosomal, 372, 374–375
  effects of, 374–376
  gene, 372–376, 484
  and genetic variation, 419–420
  and molecular clocks, 498–499
  neutral, 484, 498
  in prokaryotes, 583
Mutualism, **103,** 614, 623–625
Mutualistic symbionts, 783
Mycelium, **619**
Mycobacterium tuberculosis, 583, 586, 1010
Mycorrhizae, **624**–625
Myelin sheath, **897**
Myocardium, **949**
Myofibrils, **930**
Myoglobin, 933
Myosin, **930**

N

NAD$^+$, **255**–256, 262–263
NADH, 255–256, 262–263
NADP$^+$, **232**–233, 235–237
NADPH, 232, 235–239
Nails, human, 937
National Institute of Drug Abuse (NIDA), 905
Natural resources. *See* Resources, natural
Natural selection, 460–464. *See also* Evolution
  and adaptations, 461–464
  and beak size, 472–473, 496–497
  and competition, 473, 497
  defined, 462
  directional, **489**
  disruptive, **489**
  and extinction, 548
  and genetic diversity, 820
  and phenotypes, 482–483, 488–489
  on polygenic traits, 488–489
  on single-gene traits, 488
Navigation, 813
Neanderthals, 772, 773
Negative feedback, 732, 865
Nematodes, 755
Neogene Period, 563
Nephridia, **797**
Nephrons, **884**
Nephrostomes, 797
Nerve impulses, 897–900
Nerve nets, 810
Nerves, 897
Nervous system, human, 896–908
  autonomic, **908**
  central, **896,** 901–904
  peripheral, **896,** 906–908
  sensory receptors, 906
  somatic, **907**
  sympathetic/parasympathetic, 908
Nervous systems, animal, 733, 808–811, 864, 951
Nervous tissue, **863**
Neuromuscular junction, **931**
Neurons, **808**–809, 863, 897–898, 931
Neurotransmitters, **900**
Neurulation, **997**
Neutral mutations, 484, 498
Neutrons, **34**–35
Niches, 99–**100**
Nicotinamide adenine dinucleotide (NAD$^+$), **255**
Nicotinamide adenine dinucleotide phosphate (NADP$^+$), **232**–233, 235–237
Nicotine, 904, 968
Nitrogen cycle, 84
Nitrogen fixation, **84,** 585
Nitrogenous bases, 344–345
Nitrogenous waste, 794–795
Nodes of plant stem, **675**
Nondisjunction, **401**
Nonpoint source pollution, 160
Nonrenewable resources, **157**
Nonsteroid hormones, **980**
Nonvertebrate chordates, 731, 758, 811, 813, 822
Norepinephrine, **983**
Northwestern coniferous forests, 114
Nose, 963
Notochord, **731**
Nucleic acids, **48,** 344, 403, 436
Nucleolus, 197
Nucleosomes, 280, 352
Nucleotides, **48,** 344–345, 357
Nucleus, **34, 193**–194, **197**
Nutrient cycles, 82–86
  carbon, 82–83
  limitations of, 85–86
  nitrogen, 82–83
  phosphorous, 82–83
Nutrients, **82, 869**
  absorption of, 957
  and human body, 868–873, 880
  limiting, **85**
  and plant growth, 160, 671, 687
Nymphs, **823**

O

Obesity, 874
Observation
  ecological, 68
  scientific, **6**
Occipital lobe, 903
Occupation of organism, 100
Ocean currents, 98, 118
Oceans, 120–121. *See also* Aquatic ecosystems
Oken, Lorenz, 191
Omnivores, **71**
1000 Genomes Project, 409
On the Origin of Species, 460
Oomycetes, 608
Open circulatory systems, **791**
Operant conditioning, **843**
Operator (O), **378**
Operon, **377**–378
Opposable thumb, **767**
Optic lobes, 811
Optic nerve, 913
Order, **513**
Ordovician Period, 560, 759

Index *cont'd*

Organelles, **196,** 198–202
Organic chemistry, 45. *See also* Chemistry of life
Organic molecules, 554
Organisms, interactions of, **65**
Organ rejection, 1019
Organs
- cellular, **216**
- human, 863

Organ systems
- cellular, **216**
- human, 863

Osmosis, **210**–211, 218
- and kidneys, 795
- in plants, 672

Osmotic pressure, **211**
Ossification, **925**
Osteoarthritis, **925**
Osteoblasts, **925**
Osteoclasts, **925**
Osteocytes, **925**
Osteoporosis, **925**
Ova, 202, **991**–993, 995–996
Ovaries
- of flowers, **650,** 697
- human, 979, **991**

Overfishing, 176
Oviparous species, **822**
Ovoviviparous species, **822**
Ovulation, **993**
Ovules, **648,** 697
Oxygen, 35
- accumulation of, 555
- and electron transport, 258
- in glycolysis, 255
- molecules of, 37
- and photosynthesis, 236, 253
- and respiration, 249, 251–253, 966–967

Oxytocin, 982, 1000
Ozone, 163
Ozone layer, **175**

P

Pacemaker, **951**
Pain receptors, 909
Paleontologist, 538, **539,** 559
Paleozoic Era, 560–561
Palisade mesophyll, **681**
Pancreas, **878,** 979, **984**
Paramecium, 198, 608, 612
Parasitic symbionts, 783, 1011
Parasitism, **104,** 140, 579
- in fungi, 622–623
- in protists, 615–616
- in worms, 820, 1011

Parasympathetic nervous system, 908
Parathyroid gland, 979, **985**
Parathyroid hormone, **985**
Parenchyma, **667**
Parental care, 824
Parietal lobe, 903
Park ranger, 105
Parthenogenesis, 819, 835
Particulates, 164
Passion flower, 697
Passive immunity, **1020**
Passive transport, **209**–211
Pasteur, Louis, 586, 589, 1010
Patents, 436, 438
Pathogens, **586,** 828, 1010–1011. *See also* Infectious diseases
Pathologist, 195
Pavlov, Ivan, 843
Pax6 gene, 387
Pedigrees, **396**–397, 410
Peer review, 12
Penicillin, 591, 1021
Pepsin, 53, **877**
Peptidoglycan, 525, 581
Perennial plants, 654
Period, geologic, **543**
Periodic Table, 35
Periosteum, 924
Peripheral nervous system, **896,** 906–908
Peristalsis, **877**
Permafrost, **115**
Permian Period, 561, 762
Perspiration, 883, 935, 937
Pesticides, 161, 487, 717
Petals, **696**
Petiole, **680**
Phagocytosis, 213, 1014–1015
Phanerozoic Eon, 542–543, 560–563
Pharyngeal pouches, **731**
Pharynx, 731, 876, **964**
Phenotypes, **315**
- alleles and, 488
- and genes, 485–486
- and genotypes, 321, 398
- and natural selection, 482–483, 488–489

Phenylalanine, 369, 399
Pheromones, 850
Phipps, James, 1020
Phloem, **643,** 666
Phosphorus cycle, 85
Photic zone, **117,** 121
Photoperiod, **713**
Photoreceptors, 912–913
Photosynthesis, **70,** 224–241
- and adenosine triphosphate (ATP), **226**–227, 235–239
- and autotrophs, **228**
- C4 and CAM plants, 113, 241
- and carbon dioxide, 239, 241, 253
- and cellular respiration, 253
- and chlorophyll, **230**–232
- and chloroplasts, 202, 231
- defined, **228**
- factors affecting, 240–241
- and light-dependent reactions, 233, 235–237
- and light-independent reactions, 233, 238–239
- and mesophyll, 681
- overview of, 232–233
- and plants, 70, 113, 230–231
- and prokaryotes, 584
- rate of, 240

Photosynthetic bacteria, 70, 555
Photosynthetic protists, 610–611
Photosystems, **235**–236
Phototropism, **712**
pH, **43**–44, 53
Phylogenetic systematics, 516–517
Phylogeny, **516**
Phylum, **514**
Phytochrome, 713–714
Phytoplankton, **73,** 117, 611
Pigments, **230**–231
Pikaia, 757
Pili, 581
Pineal gland, **979**
Pinocytosis, 213
Pioneer species, **107**
Pistil, **697**
Pith in plant stem, **675**
Pituitary gland, 886, 979, **982**–983
Placenta, **822,** 826, **998**
Placentals, 764, 826
Planarian, 812
Plankton, **118**
Plantae, 523–524, 528, 634, 637
Plant breeder, 322
Plant pathologist, 655
Plant reproduction, 696–718
- flowering plants, 696–703
- seed plants, 646–647, 650, 704–707
- vegetative, **702**–703

Plants, 634–654. *See also* Angiosperms
- and acid rain, 180
- asexual reproduction in, 277, 640, 702–703
- branching in, 710

Plants (cont'd)
and cell differentiation, 292
cells of, 203, 206–207, 211, 215
characteristics of, 634–635
classification of, 634, 637, 641, 652–653
crop, 428–429, 437–438, 715–717
cytokinesis, 284
diseases of, 622
epiphytic, 112
flowering, 650–654, 696–703
fossils of, 636, 638, 646, 652
fruit of, **651, 704**
genetically modified, 428, 430
growth of, 676–679, 687
gymnosperms, **646**–648
and herbivory, **102,** 138–139, 552
history and evolution of, 636–640, 646, 650
homeostasis in, 682–683, 711
hormones in, **708**–714
and humans, 715–718
leaves of, **664,** 680–684
life cycle of, 637, 640–642, 644–645, 648–649
life span of, 654
light detection in, 709
and mycorrhizae, 624–625
and nutrients, 160, 671, 687
and photosynthesis, 70, 113, 230–231
polyploidy in, **376,** 420
and polysaccharides, 47
roots of, **664,** 669–673, 688
and seasonal change, 713–714
seed, 638, 646–649, 664–668, 704–707
seedless, 639–645
stems of, **664,** 674–679
temporal isolation in, 495
tissues in, 641, 643–644, 665–668, 670, 680
transgenic, 426, 428, 430
transport in, 635, 641, 666, 672–673, 685–687
tropisms, **712**
vacuoles in, 198
and water, 635, 641, 672–673, 685–687
Plaques, 958
Plasma, **954**
Plasma cells, 1017
Plasma membrane, 193
Plasmids, **424**–425
Plasmodium, **613**
Plasmodium, 607, 616–617, 1011
Platelets, **955**
Plate tectonics, **544**–545
Pleural membranes, 967
Pluripotent cells, **294**
Point mutations, **373**
Point source pollution, 160
Polar molecules, 40–41
Polar zones, 97
Poliovirus, 588–589
Pollen cone, 648
Pollen grain, 215, 325, **647,** 698
Pollen tube, **648,** 700
Pollination, 309, 552, **647**–648, 651, 700
Pollutants, **160**–165, 169
Polychlorinated biphenyls (PCBs), 161
Polygenic traits, **320, 486,** 488–489
Polymeraze chain reaction (PCR), **423**
Polymerization, 46
Polymers, **46**
Polypeptides, 48, **366**
Polyploidy, **376,** 420
Polysaccharides, 47, 869
Polyunsaturated fats, 47, 870
Pons, 903
Population geneticist, 322
Population growth, 130–145
exponential, **132**–133
factors affecting, 132
human, 142–145
limiting factors, **137**–141
logistic, 134–**135**
rate of, 131
Populations, **64**
age structure of, **131,** 144
alleles in, 483
density of, **131,** 138–140
describing, 130–131
distribution of, 131
evolution of, 483–492
frequency of phenotypes in, 485–486, 488–489
and gene pools, 483, 490
and genetic diversity, 820
and genetic drift, **490**
and genetic equilibrium, **491**–492
geographic range of, 131
overcrowding in, 140
Porifera, 754
Positron emission tomography (PET), 905
Prasher, Douglas, 422
Precambrian Time, 543
Precipitation, 112
Predation, **102,** 138–139
Pregnancy, 993
Prehensile tail, **767**
Premolars, 785
Pressure-flow hypothesis, **687**
Priestly, Jacob, 229
Primary growth, **676**
Primary producers, **69**
Primary succession, **106**–107
Primates, **765**–772
Principle of dominance, **310,** 318
Principle of independent assortment, **317**–318, 328–329
Principles of Geology, 454–455
Prions, **592,** 597
Probability, **313**–314
Producers, 584
Products, **50**
Progesterone, 993
Prokaryotes, **193**–194, 197, 523, **580**–585. *See also* Bacteria
archaea, 524, **526,** 580–581
asexual reproduction in, 281
cell cycle of, 281
classification of, 580–581
DNA replication in, 352–353
electron transport chain in, 258
evolution of, 556–557
in food production, 263
gene regulation in, 377–378
microfossils of, 555
mutations in, 583
photosynthetic, 584
prokaryotic chromosomes, 279
reproduction in, 583
structure and function of, 582–585
transcription in, 364
unicellular, 214, 525–526
Prolactin, 983, 1000
Promoters, **365**
Prophage, **577**
Prostaglandins, **980**
Prostate gland, 990
Proteinoid microspheres, 554
Proteins, **48**–49, **870**
cell production of, 200–201
collagen, 863
cyclins, **286,** 288
food value of, 250–251
and genes, 370
histones, 280
homologous, 471
levels of organization, 49
protein carriers, 209
protein pumps, 212
protein synthesis, 363, 366–370, 384
regulatory, 287
and ribosomes, **200**
in skeletal muscles, 930
Proterozoic Eon, 542, 543
Protista, 523–524, 526–527, 602

Index *cont'd*

Protists, 526–527, **602**–617, 1011
  autotrophic, 610–611
  classification of, 602–604
  evolution of, 605
  heterotrophic, 612–613
  movement of, 606–607
  reproduction in, 608–609
  symbiotic, 614–616
Protons, **34**–35
Protostomes, **739**
Protozoan, 214
Prusiner, Stanley, 592
Pseudocoelom, **738**
Pseudopods, **606**
Puberty, **988**
Public health, 1021
Pulmonary circulation, **950**
Punctuated equilibrium, **549**
Punnett squares, **315**–316
Pupa, **823**
Pupil, **912**
Pyloric valve, 877
Pyramids of biomass, 78
Pyramids of energy, 77
Pyramids of numbers, 78
Pyruvic acid, 252, 254, 256

Q

Qualitative data, 8
Quantitative data, 8
Quaternary Period, 542, 563

R

Rabies, 589
Radial symmetry, **738,** 756
Radioactive isotopes, **35**
Radioactivity, 466
Radiometric dating, **540**–541
Ragweed, 694–695
Rain forests, 109, 112
Random mating, 492
Reabsorption, **884**
Reactants, **50**
Receptors, **217**
Recessive alleles, 310–312, 318, 394
Recombinant DNA, 421–**424,** 430
Red blood cells, **954**–955
Red muscle, 933
Red tide, 611
Reflex, **901**
Reflex arc, **907**
Regional climates, 110
Regulatory proteins, 287
Rejection, organ, 1019
Relative dating, **540**
Releasing hormones, **983**
Renewable resources, **157**
Replication, DNA, **350**–353
Reproduction, 19–20. *See also* Asexual reproduction; Sexual reproduction
  in animals, 277, 735, 819–826
  and cell division, 277–278
  in flowering plants, 696–703
  in fungi, 621
  in mammals, 825–826
  in prokaryotes, 583
  in protists, 608–609
  reproductive success, 850
  in seed plants, 646–647, 650, 704–707
  vegetative, **702**–703
Reproductive isolation, **494**–495, 497
Reproductive system, human, 864
  embryonic development, 988, 995–1001
  female, **991**–993
  glands of, 985
  male, **988**–990
Reptiles, 468, 762, 790, 793, 811
Resistance training, 933
Resources, natural, **100**–101, 158–165. *See also* Biodiversity
  atmospheric, 163–165
  freshwater, 160–162
  renewable/nonrenewable, **157**
  soil, 158–160
Respiration, 249, 251–253, 963, 966–967. *See also* Cellular respiration
Respiratory system, human, **963**–969
Respiratory systems, animal, 734–735, 789–790, 864
Responding variable, **7**
Response, **809**
Resting potential, **898**–899
Restriction enzymes, **403**–405, 421
Retina, **913**
Retroviruses, **578**
Rh blood group, 394
Rheumatoid arthritis, 1025
Rhizoids, 641
Rhizomes, 644
Ribonucleic acid (RNA). *See* RNA
Ribose, 362
Ribosomal RNA (rRNA), **363,** 370
Ribosomes, **200,** 363, 368–370
Rickets, 921, 943
RNA, 48, **362**–371
  and DNA, 362–365
  evolution of, 554–555
  miRNA, 380–381
  mRNA, **363,** 368–370
  RNA interference, **380**–381
  RNA polymerase, **364**–365
  transcription, **364,** 368, 377–379
  translation, **368**–370
  tRNA, **363,** 368–370
  viruses, 578
Rods, **913**
Roots of plants, **664,** 669–673, 688
  anatomy of, 670
  functions of, 671–673
  length of, 669
  root cap, **670**
  root hairs, **670**
  types of, 669
Roundworms, 755, 783, 810
Rowland, F. Sherwood, 175
Rubella, 1001
Rumen, **786**

S

Sabin, Albert, 589
Safety studies, 16
Saliva, 876
Salk, Jonas, 589
Salt, 36–37, 42, 798
Salt marshes, 6–8, 11–12, 119
Sapwood, **678**
Sarcomere, **930**
SARS, 590, 1013, 1022–1023
Saturated fats, 47, 870
Scavengers, **71**
Schleiden, Matthias, 191
Schopenhauer, Arthur, 6
Schwann, Theodor, 191
Science, 4–15
  attitudes of, 10
  defined, **5**
  goals of, 5
  as knowing, 21
  measurement in, 24
  methodology of, 6–9
  peer review, 12
  scientific theories, **13**
  and society, 14–15
Sclerenchyma, **667**
Scrotum, **989**
Sebaceous glands, **937**
Sebum, 937–938
Secondary growth, **676**–677
Secondary messengers, 981
Secondary succession, **106**–107

Sedimentary rock, 539–540
Seed, **646**
Seed coat, **647**
Seed cone, 648
Seed dispersal, 651, **705**
Seedless plants, 639–645
Seed plants, 638, 646–649
  meristems, **667**–668
  reproduction in, 646–647, 650, 704–707
  structure of, 664–665
  tissue systems of, 665–668
Segmentation, 739
Segregation of alleles, **312,** 314, 318
Selection. *See* Natural selection
Selective breeding, **418**–420, 716
Selectively permeable membranes, **205**
Self-pollination, 309
Semen, **990**
Semicircular canals, **911**
Seminal fluid, 990
Seminal vesicles, 990
Seminiferous tubules, **989**
Sensation, 935
Sense organs, human, 909–913
Sensory neurons, **808**–809, 897
Sensory receptors, 906, 914
Sensory systems, animal, **812**–813
Sepals, **696**
Septum, 949
Severe acute respiratory syndrome (SARS), 590, 1013, 1022–1023
Sewage, 162
Seward, William H., 1023
Sex chromosomes, **393**
Sex hormones, **988**
Sex-linked gene, **395**
Sexual development, 988
Sexually transmitted diseases (STDs), **994,** 1012
Sexual reproduction, **19, 277**–278. *See also* Plant reproduction
  and allele frequency, 492
  in animals, 735, **820**–822
  and evolution, 558
  female reproductive system, **991**–993
  fertilization, **995**–996
  in fungi, 621
  genetic recombination in, 484
  male reproductive system, **988**–990
  in protists, 608–609
Short-day plants, 713
Shrubland, 112–113
Sickle cell disease, 375, 391, 398, 400, 413
Sieve tube elements, **666,** 687
Silencing complex, 380–381
Silurian Period, 560, 759
Simard, Suzanne, 625
Single-celled eukaryotes, 523, 602, 752. *See also* Protists
Single-gene traits, **485,** 488
Single-loop circulatory systems, **792**
Single nucleotide polymorphisms (SNPs), 407
Sinoatrial (SA) node, 951, 958
Sinuses, 791
Sister chromatid, 282
Skeletal muscle, **928**–929
Skeletal systems, 733, **814**–816, 864, **922**–927
Skeleton, 754
Skepticism, 10
Skin, 883, **936**. *See also* Integumentary system
  cancer, 337, 357, 938–939, 1025
  color, 394
  as sense organ, 909
Skinner, B. F., 843
Skinner box, 843
Sliding-filament model, 930–931
Slime molds, 603, 604, 613
Slow-twitch muscle, 933
Small intestine, **878,** 880–881
Smallpox, 589, 1020
Smell, 910
Smog, **163**
Smoking, 968–969
Smooth muscle, **928**–929
Sneezing, 1012
Sodium, 35, 37
Sodium bicarbonate, 878
Sodium chloride, 36–37, 42
Sodium-potassium pump, 899–900
Soil, 671
  erosion, **159**–160
  resources, 158–160
Soil ecosystems
  nitrogen cycle in, 84
  nutrient limitation in, 86
Solar energy. *See also* Sunlight
  and climate, 97
  and photosynthesis, 70
Solute, **42**
Solution, **42–43**
Solvent, **42**
Somatic nervous system, **907**
Sound intensity, 910
Southern, Edward, 422
Southern blotting, 422
Speciation, **494**–497, 517, 546–547
  Galapágos finches, 496–497
  and reproductive isolation, 494–495
Species, **64, 494,** 509, 533
  and acquired characteristics, 456
  carrying capacity of, **135**
  diversity, **166,** 168
  endangered, 169–170
  and genus, 516
  introduced, 169
  invasive, 136
  keystone, **103,** 167
  naming, 510–511
  and niches, 100–101
  oviparous/ovoviviparous, **822**
  pioneer, **107**
  tolerance of, **99**
Species survival plans (SSPs), 170
Spectrum, visible, 230
Sperm, 325, 989–990, 995–996
Sphygmomanometer, 953
Spina bifida, 997, 1001
Spinal cord, 811, 901
Spirilla, **582**
Spleen, 957
Sponges, 752, 754, 784, 821
Spongy bone, 924
Spongy mesophyll, **681**
Sporangium, **609, 642**
Spores, **607**
Sporophytes, **637**–638, 698
Squamous cell carcinoma, 939
Stabilizing selection, **489**
Staining, cell, 191
Stamens, **697**
Stanley, Wendell, 574
Starches, 46, 869
Start codon, 367
Statins, 961
Steere, Allen, 1009, 1031
Stem cells, **295**–297
Stems of plants, **664,** 674–679
Steroid hormones, 379, **980**
Steroids, 47, 934
Stigma, **697**
Stimulus, **18,** 733, **808**–809, 906
Stomach, **877,** 888
Stomata, **681**–683
Stop codon, 367
Strep throat, 587
Stroke, 958
Stroma, **231**
Struggle for existence, 460, 462–463
Sturtevant, Alfred, 329
Style, 697
Subatomic particles, 34
Substrates, **52–53**
Succession, ecological, **106**–109
Sucrose, 46

Index *cont'd*

Sugars
  carbohydrates, 46, 869
  in human body, 867
  and photosynthesis, 239
  in plants, 687
Sunlight, 230. *See also* Light
  and aquatic ecosystems, 117
  and plants, 635
  and skin, 337, 357, 935–936, 939
Superbugs, 591
Suppressor T cells, 1019
Surface tension, 41
Survival of the fittest, 461–463
Survival strategies, 278
Suspension, **42**
Sustainable development, 156–**157,** 160, 174, 176
Sutton, Walter, 349
Sweating, 828, 883, 935, 937
Symbionts, 783, 1011
Symbiosis, **103**–104, 783
Symbiotic protists, 614–616
Symmetry, body, 738
Sympathetic nervous system, 908
Synapse, **900**
Synovial cavity, 927
Synthetic genome, 435
Syphilis, 994
Systematics, **512,** 516–517
Systemic circulation, **950**
Systolic pressure, 953

T

Taiga, **114**
Taproot system, 669
Tar, 968
Target cells, **709, 978**
Taste buds, **910**
TATA box, 379
Taxon, **511,** 516
Taxonomy, 510
Technology, 11
Teeth, 876
Telomerase, 352
Telomeres, **352**
Temperate forests, 114
Temperate zones, 97
Temperature
  body, 828–830, 866, 935, 937, 987
  and butterfly wing color, 321
  and enzymes, 53
  and extinction, 170
  global warming, **177**
  and photosynthesis, 240
  and seed germination, 706–707
  sensory response to, 909
  and water depth, 118
Temporal isolation, **495**
Temporal lobe, 903
Tendons, **816, 932**
Terracing, 160
Territorial behavior, **848**
Tertiary Period, 563
Testes, 979, **989**
Testosterone, **988**–989
Tetanus, 587
Tetrad, **324**
Tetrapoda, 518–519
Tetrapods, **760**
Thalamus, **903**
Theory, **13**
Thermoreceptors, 909
Thigmotropism, **712**
Thomas, Lewis, 64
Threshold, **899**
Throat, 964
Thylakoid membranes, 236–237
Thylakoids, **231,** 233, 235
Thymine, 344–345, 348, 362
Thymus, 957, **979,** 1016
Thyroid gland, 979, **985,** 987
Thyroid-stimulating hormone (TSH), 983, 987
Thyrotropin-releasing hormone (TRH), 987
Thyroxine, **985,** 987
Tiktaalik, 761
Tissues
  animal, 737
  cell, **216**
Tissues, human, 862–863
  connective, **863**
  epithelial, **863**
  muscle, **863**
  nervous, **863**
Tissues, plant. *See also* Vascular tissue of plants
  dermal, **665,** 670, 680
  ground, 665, **666,** 670, 680
  meristems, **667**–668
T lymphocytes, 955, 957, 1016–1019
Tobacco, 713, 968–969
Tobacco mosaic disease, 574–575
Tolerance of species, **99**
Topsoil, 158
Totipotent cells, **294**
Touch, 909, 914
Toxins, 586
Trace elements, 671
Trace fossils, 752
Trachea, 789, **964**
Trachea epithelium, 215
Tracheids, **643,** 666
Tracheophytes, **643**–644
Traits, **309**
  and alleles, 397, 485–486
  and environment, 321
  polygenic, **320, 486,** 488–489
  single–gene, **485,** 488
  transmission of, 394–396
Transcription, **364,** 368, 377–378
Transcription factors, 379
Trans fats, 870
Transfer RNA (tRNA), **363,** 368–370
Transformation, bacterial, **339**–340
Transgenic organisms, **426**–430
Translation, **368**–370
Transpiration, **681**–683, 685–686
Transport
  active, **212**–213, 227
  passive, **209**–211
  in plants, 635, 641, 666, 672–673, 685–687
Tree of life, **23**
Trees, 653
  classifying, 515
  growth of, 678–679
  and mycorrhizae, 624–625
  rings of, 678
Trial-and-error learning, 843
Triassic Period, 562, 762, 764
Trichomes, 665
Trilobites, 540
Trisomy, 401
Trochophore, **756**
Trophic levels, **77**–78
Tropical rain forests, 109, 112
Tropical zone, 97
Tropisms, **712**
Tryptophan, 367
Tuatara, 762
Tuber, 702
Tuberculosis, 583, 586–587, 589, 1010, 1023
Tubulins, 199
Tumors, **289**
Tundra, 115
Tunicates, 747, 758, 813
Turkish Angola, 416–417
Turner's syndrome, 401
Twins, 996
Two-factor cross, 317
Tympanum, 911
Type 1 diabetes, 1025
Typhoid, 400

U

Ubx gene, 501
Ulcers, 877
Ultraviolet (UV) light, 337, 344, 357
Umami receptors, 910
Umbilical cord, 998
Understory, **112**
Unicellular organisms, 214, 525–527
Unsaturated fats, 47, 870
Uracil, 362, 366
Urea, 794, 797, 882–883
Ureters, **883**
Urethra, **883,** 989
Urey, Harold, 554
Uric acid, 794, 797
Urinary bladder, **883**
Urine, 795, 797, 883–884, 886

V

Vaccination, 1017, **1020**
Vaccine, **588**–589, 593
Vacuoles, **198**
Valence electrons, 36
Valves, **950**
Van der Waals forces, **38**
Van Leeuwenhoek, Anton, 190
Variation, 419–420, 457–458, 460, 462–463, 482–486. *See also* Natural selection
Vascular tissue of plants, **641,** 643–644, 665–666, 680
- vascular bundles, **675**
- vascular cambium, **677**–679
- vascular cylinder, **670,** 672–673

Vas deferens, **989**
Vectors, **1013**
Vegetables, 704
Vegetative reproduction, **702**–703
Veins, human, **952**
Veins, leaf, 680
Venter, Craig, 349
Ventricle, **792**–793, **949**–951
Venus' flytrap, 712
Vertebrae, 731
Vertebrates, **731,** 757, 789–790. *See also* Chordates; Invertebrates
- brains of, 811
- cephalization in, 740
- circulatory systems of, 734, 792–793
- homologous structures in, 469
- limb formation in, 743
- muscular systems of, 816–818
- nervous systems of, 809
- sense organs, 813
- skeletons of, 733, 815–818

Vesicles, 198
Vessel elements, **666**
Vestigial structures, **469**
Villi, **880**
Viral sexually transmitted diseases (STDs), **994**
Virchow, Rudolf, 191
Viruses, **574**–579
- bacterial, 340–341
- and cells, 579
- discovery of, 574
- diseases caused by, 588–589, 994, 1010–1011
- and medication, 1021
- structure and composition of, 575
- viral infections, 576–578

Visible spectrum, 230
Vision, 912–913
Vitamin D production, 935
Vitamin K deficiency, 881
Vitamins, **871**
Vitreous humor, 912
Viviparous species, **822**
Vocal cords, 964

W

Wallace, Alfred Russel, 459, 460
Water
- adhesion, **686**
- atomic composition of, 36
- capillary action, **686**
- cohesion, 686
- cycle, 81
- dehydration, 189, 869
- and human body, 869, 986
- intoxication, 221
- molecules of, 37, 40–41
- osmosis, **210**–211, 218, 672, 795
- and photosynthesis, 240
- and plants, 635, 641, 672–673, 685–687
- properties of, 40–43
- quality and pollution, 156, 160–162
- and seed germination, 706
- solutions and suspensions, **42**
- and spread of disease, 1012–1013

Water mold, 608–609, 613
Watershed, 162
Water-soluble vitamins, 871
Water transport in plants, 666, 685–686
Watson, James, 349–350, 362
Weather, **96**
West Nile virus, 588, 1013
Wetlands, **119,** 156
Wheat rust, 622
White blood cells, **955**
White matter, 902
White muscle, 933
Wildlife photographer, 105
Wilmut, Ian, 427
Wilting, 683
Wind
- and heat transport, 98
- pollination, 700

Wood, 678–679
Woodland, 113
Woody plants, **653**
Worms
- earthworms, 755, 792
- flatworms, 755, 783, 794, 796, 810, 812
- marine, 755
- parasitic, 820, 1011
- roundworms, 755, 783, 810
- tapeworms, 104

X

X chromosomes, 393–396, 401
X-ray diffraction, 346
Xylem, **643,** 666

Y

Y chromosomes, 393–395, 434
Yeasts, 192, 214, 263, 278, 424, 585, 619, 623
Yolk sac, 825

Z

Zoo curator, 736
Zoonosis, **1013**
Zooplankton, **76,** 117
Zygote, **325,** 637, **739, 995**–996

Credits

Staff Credits
Jennifer Angel, Amy C. Austin, Laura Baselice, Neil Benjamin, Peggy Bliss, Diane Braff, Daniel Clem, Glen Dixon, Alicia Franke, Julia Gecha, Ellen Granter, Anne Jones, Stephanie Keep, Beth Kun, George Lychock, Ranida Touranont McKneally, Anne McLaughlin, Rich McMahon, Laura Morgenthau, Debbie Munson, Deborah Nicholls, Michelle Reyes, Rashid Ross, Laurel Smith, Lisa Smith-Ruvalcaba, Ted Smykal, Amanda M. Watters, Berkley Wilson

Additional Credits
Bryan Cholfin, Lisa Furtado Clark, Sharon Donahue, Amy Hamel, Courtenay Kelley, Hilary L. Maybaum, Anakin S. Michele, Jan Van Aarsen, Rachel Youdelman

Front Cover, Spine, and Title Page: ©Ralph A. Clevenger/Corbis. **Back Cover:** ©Pete Oxford/Minden Pictures.

(For credits for custom pages, refer to copyright page.) **iii:** Stew Milne. **vi:** L, Courtesy of Grant Wiggins; R, Jen-Yi Wu. **ix:** T, ©Pete Oxford/Minden Pictures; B, Piotr Naskrecki, Minden Pictures. **x:** ©Ed Rescheke/Peter Arnold, Inc. **xi:** Andrew Syred/Photo Researchers, Inc. **xii:** T, Colin Keates/DK Images; B, Colin Keates ©Dorling Kindersley, Courtesy of the Natural History Museum, London. **xiii:** TR, Southhampton General Hospital/Science Photo Library/Photo Researchers, Inc.; B, Bkgrnd, ©Neil Lucas/npl/Minden Pictures; BL, ©Georgette Douwma/Getty Images; ML, ©Peter Chadwick/DK Images. **xiv:** T, ©Ben Twist/istockphoto.com; B, ©Nature Picture Library/Alamy. **xv:** L, ©Ingo Arndt, MINDEN PICTURES; R, ©Nigel J. Dennis; Gallo Images/CORBIS. **xix:** ©Fred Bavendam/Minden Pictures. **xxi:** Courtesy of Beng Chiak Tan. **xxii:** Stew Milne. **1:** ©Keren Su/CORBIS. **2–3:** ©Steve Wursta/Photopress Washington/Corbis. **3:** TR, Comstock/Jupiter Images. **4:** B, Flip Nicklin/Minden Pictures/Getty Images; ©Photopress Washington/Corbis Sygma. **5:** Flip Nicklin/Minden Pictures. **6–7:** Michael Melford/National Geographic/Getty Images. **8:** Bkgrnd, Michael Melford/NationalGeographic/Getty Images; Inset, Comstock/Jupiter Images. **10:** ©Photopress Washington/Corbis Sygma. **11:** B, Ron Chapple Stock/PhotoLibrary; T, Comstock/Jupiter Images. **12:** Dani Yeske/Peter Arnold. **14:** Pascal Goetgheluck/Photo Researchers, Inc. **15:** Romeo Gocad/AFP/Getty Images. **16:** RM, ©SuperStock, Inc.; L, ©Digital Vision Ltd./SuperStock; R, ©fStop/SuperStock; LM, ©Digital Vision Ltd./SuperStock. **17:** B, Masa Ushioda/Image Quest Marine; T, ©Photopress Washington/Corbis Sygma. **18–19:** Bkgrnd, Martin Rugner/Age Fotostock. **18:** BR, Visuals Unlimited/Corbis; BL, Dwight Kuhn. **19:** T, John Marshall/Corbis; BL, ©Visuals Unlimited/Corbis; BR, ©G. Thomas Bishop/Custom Medical Stock; Lower M, Dwight Kuhn; Upper M, Microscan/Phototake USA. **21:** T, Comstock/Jupiter Images; B, Klein/Peter Arnold, Inc. **22–23:** Mark Moffett/Minden Pictures/Getty Images. **23:** Lower M, Michael Nichols/National Geographic/Getty Images; B, Tek Image/Photo Researchers, Inc.; T, Jim Richardson/Corbis; Upper M, ©Louie Psihoyos/CORBIS. **24:** B, Daniel J. Cox/Corbis. **25:** Brand X/Jupiter Images. **28:** ©Anthony Bannister/Corbis. **29:** Comstock/Jupiter Images. **32–33:** Image by ©Hans Strand/CORBIS. **33:** TR, Flip Nicklin/Minden Pictures. **34:** Image by ©Hans Strand/CORBIS. **35:** Mediacolors/Alamy. **37:** Flip Nicklin/Minden Pictures. **38:** M, Ingo Arndt/FotoNatura/Minden Pictures; R, Andrew Syred/Photo Researchers, Inc.; L, Martin Harvey/Corbis. **39:** R, Juniors Bildarchiv/Alamy; L, Courtesy, Draper Labs. **40:** Image by ©Hans Strand/CORBIS. **41:** T, Piet Munsterman/Foto Natura/Minden Pictures; B, ©Richard Megna/Fundamental Photos. **42:** Flip Nicklin/Minden Pictures. **43:** B, ©Noam Armonn/istockphoto.com; MB, ©fanelie rosier/istockphoto.com; MT, ©Milos Luzanin/istockphoto.com; T, ©Nancy Louie/istockphoto.com. **45:** Image by ©Hans Strand/CORBIS. **47:** Michael Rosenfeld/Getty Images. **50:** Image by ©Hans Strand/CORBIS. **53:** TR, Flip Nicklin/Minden Pictures; L, Thomas A. Steitz, Howard Hughes Medial Institute, Yale University. **57:** Flip Nicklin/Minden Pictures. **61:** ©Pete Oxford/Minden Pictures. **62–63:** Stan Osolinski/Oxford Scientific/Jupiter Images. **63:** TR, ©Jeff Rotman/www.jeffrotman.com. **64:** BL, Tim Graham/Getty Images; BM, Arnold Streifengnu Shah/Peter Arnold Inc.; BR, Yva Momatiuk & John Eastcott/Minden Pictures; T, Stan Osolinski/Oxford Scientific/Jupiter Images. **65:** R, NASA; L, Dmitri Kessel/Time Life Pictures/Getty Images; M, Planetary Visions Ltd./Photo Researchers, Inc. **67:** ©Jeff Rotman/www.jeffrotman.com. **68:** Frans Lanting/Minden Pictures. **69:** B, Piotr Naskrecki, Minden Pictures; T, Stan Osolinski/Oxford Scientific/Jupiter Images. **70:** L, Vincenzo Lombardo/Photodisc/Getty Images; R, IFREMER French Research Institute for Exploration of the Sea. **71:** TR, Pete Oxford/MINDEN PICTURES/Getty Images; TL, Kevin Schafer/Peter Arnold; RM, Roy Toft/National Geographic Creative/Getty Images; BR, Devon Graham/Project Amazonas, Inc.; BL, Wolfgang Kaehler/Alamy; Bkgrnd, Will & Deni McIntyre/Stone/Getty Images; ML, Carol Farneti Foster/Oxford Scientific/PhotoLibrary. **72:** B, ©Jeff Rotman/www.jeffrotman.com; T, Woodt Stock/Alamy. **73:** T, Stan Osolinski/Oxford Scientific/Jupiter Images. **76:** ©Jeff Rotman/www.jeffrotman.com. **79:** Stan Osolinski/Oxford Scientific/Jupiter Images. **80:** TL, Joel Sartore/Getty Images; Upper MR, NASA-JSC/digital version by Science Faction/Getty Images; Lower MR, Kalish Dimaggio/Flirt Collection/PhotoLibrary; BL, Jim Wark/Peter Arnold; TR, Image Source/PhotoLibrary; Upper ML, Francesco Ruggeri/Getty Images; Lower ML, Adrian Dorst/Peter Arnold; BR, Corbis/PhotoLibrary. **82:** Jeff Foott/Discovery Channel Image/Getty Images. **84:** ©Jeff Rotman/Jeffrotman.com. **87:** T, NASA/Goddard Space Flight Center, The Sea/WIFS Project and GeoEye, Scientific Visualization Studio; B, NASA/Goddard Space Flight Center, Scientific Visualization Studio. **91:** ©Jeff Rotman/www.jeffrotman.com. **94–95:** Anup Shah/npl/Minden Pictures. **95:** T, ©George McCarthy/Nature Picture Library. **96:** R, ©NOAA/ZUMA/Corbis; L, Anup Shah/npl/Minden Pictures. **99:** Anup Shah/npl/Minden Pictures. **100:** ©Mitsuhiko Imamori/Minden Pictures. **102:** ©Cyril Ruoso/Minden Pictures. **103:** T, ©George McCarthy/Nature Picture Library; B, ©Hal Beral/Corbis. **104:** B, ©Todd Pusser/Nature Picture Library; T, ©Mark Taylor/Nature Picture Library. **105:** ©Stan Tekiela. **106:** Anup Shah/npl/Minden Pictures. **108:** T, Orlando Carrasquillo, El Yunque National Forest, Ecosystem Management Team; B, Orlando Carrasquillo, El Yunque National Forest, Ecosystem Management Team. **109:** Inset, L, ©Macduff Everton/CORBIS; B, ©Hallmark Institute/Photolibrary Group; Inset, R, ©Reuters/CORBIS; T, ©Gary Braasch/CORBIS. **110:** Anup Shah/npl/Minden Pictures. **112:** T, ©Galen Rowell/CORBIS; M, ©Staffan Widstrand/Nature Picture Library; B, ©Michele Burgess/SuperStock. **113:** T, ©Darrell Gulin/CORBIS; M, ©Jim Brandenburg/Minden Pictures; B, ©Debra Behr/Alamy. **114:** T, ©Natural Selection Jerry Whaley/Design Pics/Corbis; M, ©Stuart Westmorland/CORBIS; B, ©age fotostock/SuperStock. **115:** ©2008 Jim D. Barr/AlaskaStock.com. **116:** T, ©George McCarthy/Nature Picture Library; B, Thomas Mangelsen/Minden Pictures. **117:** B, ©Corbis/SuperStock; T, Anup Shah/npl/Minden Pictures. **118:** BL, ©Pacific Stock/SuperStock; BM, David Noton/Nature Picture Library; BR, Philippe Clement/Nature Picture Library; T, ©George McCarthy/Nature Picture Library. **119:** L, ©MICHAEL GADOMSKI/Animals Animals - Earth Scenes; RM, ©Cindy Ruggieri; R, ©age fotostock/SuperStock; MR, ©GORDON & CATHY ILLG/Animals Animals - Earth Scenes. **121:** ©Norbert Wu/Minden Pictures. **124:** ©Anthony Bannister; Gallo Images/CORBIS. **125:** ©George McCarthy/Nature Picture Library. **128–129:** ©Jean-Paul Ferrero/Auscape/Minden Pictures. **129:** TR, Eric Wanders/Foto Natura/Minden Pictures. **130:** T, ©Jean-Paul Ferrero/Auscape/Minden Pictures; B, Agricultural Research Service, USDA/Stephen Ausmus. **131:** T, ©Photographers Choice RF/SuperStock; M, Copyright ©JOHNNY JOHNSON/Animals Animals/Earth Scenes; B, ©Fred Bavendam/Minden Pictures. **132:** Eric Wanders/Foto Natura/Minden Pictures. **133:** T, ©SciMAT/Photo Researchers, Inc.; B, ©Pete Oxford/Minden Pictures. **134:** ©Ingo Arndt/Minden Pictures. **136:** B, I-R/S/GRANT HEILMAN PHOTOGRAPHY,INC; TL, ©Digital Vision Ltd./SuperStock; TR, ©fStop/SuperStock; TML, ©Digital Vision Ltd./SuperStock; TMR, ©SuperStock, Inc. **137:** B, ©Joke Stuurman-Huitema/Foto Natura/Minden Pictures; T, ©Jean-Paul Ferrero/Auscape/Minden Pictures. **138:** ©John Conrad/CORBIS. **139:** B, ©WILDLIFE/Peter Arnold Inc.; T, ©D. Robert & Lorri Franz/CORBIS. **140:** T, ©Les Stocker/Photolibrary Group; B, Eric Wanders/Foto Natura/Minden Pictures. **141:** ©(AP Photo/Xinhua Photo, Jiang Yi. **142:** ©Jean-Paul Ferrero/Auscape/Minden Pictures. **143:** T, FOTOGRAF/Still Pictures/Peter Arnold, Inc.; B, FOTOGRAF/Still Pictures/Peter Arnold, Inc. **145:** ©image100/Photolibrary. **147:** R, ©(AP Photo/Xinhua Photo, Jiang Yi; L, ©Fred Bavendam/Minden Pictures. **149:** Eric Wanders/Foto Natura/Minden Pictures. **152–153:** NASA/NSSDC. **153:** TR, ©SIME s.a.s/eStock Photo. **154:** ML, ©SIME s.a.s/eStock Photo; BL, ©Douglas Peebles/eStockPhoto; BR, ©Douglas Peebles/eStockPhoto; TL, NASA/NSSDC. **155:** Patrick Bennett/Superstock. **156:** Inset, ©The Wetlands Initiative Archives; Bkgrnd, By Gary Sullivan, The Wetlands Initiative. **157:** T, ©Maurizio Borgese/Hemis/Corbis; B, ©Bobby Model/Getty Images. **158:** B, ©AP Photo; T, NASA/NSSDC. **159:** ©SIME s.a.s/eStock Photo. **160:** ©Jim Richardson/CORBIS. **162:** Bkgrnd, ©Maxphotos/Newscom; Inset, ©Richard T. Nowitz/CORBIS. **163:** ©Jason Lee/Reuters Pictures. **164:** Inset, ©Adam Hart-Davis/Photo Researchers, Inc.; Bkgrnd, ©Superstock. **166:** B, ©AP Photo/Penn State University, S. Blair Hedges); T, NASA/NSSDC. **167:** BM, ©(c) Noel Hendrickson/GETTY IMAGES; Bkgrnd, ©Marcos G. Meider/Superstock; BL, ©Paolo Aguilar/epa/Corbis. **168:** T, ©SIME s.a.s/eStock Photo; B, ©Creatas/Photolibrary Group. **169:** B, ©SIME s.a.s/eStock Photo; T, Getty Images/Science Faction. **170:** ©Katherine Feng/Globio/Minden Pictures. **171:** ©Barbara Walton/epa/Corbis. **173:** NASA/NSSDC. **175:** T, Images by Greg Shirah, NASA Goddard Space Flight Center Scientific Visualization Studio; B, ©Jerry Mason/Photo Researchers, Inc. **176:** T, ©Jeffrey L. Rotman/CORBIS; B, BRIAN J. SKERRY/National Geographic Image Collection. **177:** ©Armin Rose/Shutterstock. **178:** ©Sumio Harada/Minden Pictures. **179:** Inset, T, ©UPPA/Photoshot/Newscom; Inset, Lower, ©Realimage/Alamy; Bkgrnd, Charmagne Leung/California Academy of Sciences. **181:** Patrick Bennett/Superstock. **183:** ©SIME s.a.s/eStock Photo. **187:** ©Clouds Hill Imaging Ltd./CORBIS. **188–189:** Dr. Robert Berdan. **189:** TR, ©simple stock shots/Age Fotostock. **190:** B,; T, Dr. Robert Berdan. **191:** T, ©Grafissimo/iStockphoto.com; B, ©Dwight Kuhn; T, istockphoto.com. **192:** TL, Courtesy Hitachi High-Technologies; BL, Michael Abbey/Photo Researchers, Inc.; BR, SciMAT/Photo Researchers, Inc.; BM, Dr. Gopal Murti/Visuals Unlimited. **193:** © simple stock shots/Age Fotostock.**195:** Courtesy, Dr. Tanasa Osborne. **196:** T, Dr. Robert Berdan. **198:** L, (c) ISM/Phototake; R, Eric Grave/Science Photo Library/Photo Researchers, Inc. **199:** T, Dr. Torsten Wittmann/Photo Researchers, Inc; B, Omikron/Photo Researchers, Inc. **202:** Biophoto Associates/Photo Researchers, Inc. **204:** ©ISM/Phototake USA. **208:** BL, ©simple stock shots/Age Fotostock; TR, Vince Streano/Stone/Getty Images; T, Dr. Robert Berdan. **213:** NIBSC/Photo Researchers, Inc. **214:** B, Volker Steger/Christian Bardele/SPL/Photo Researchers, Inc.; T, Dr. Robert Berdan. **215:** R, Ed Reschke/Peter Arnold; L, Ed Reschke/Peter Arnold. **217:** ©Dennis Kunkel/Phototake USA. **221:** Alan Bailey/Rubberball/Getty Images. **224–225:** Perennou Nuridsany/Photo Researchers, Inc. **225:** TR, Watering can (earthenware), English School, (16th century)/©Museum of London, UK,/The Bridgeman Art Library International. **226:** Perennou Nuridsany/Photo Researchers, Inc. **228:** R, Anup Shah/Minden Pictures; L, Watering can (earthenware), English School, (16th century)/©Museum of London, UK,/The Bridgeman Art Library International. **229:** TL, The Granger Collection, New York; BL, American Chemical Society; ML, Biophoto Associates/Photo Researchers; MR, Imperial College London; R, James Barber, The Royal Society. **230:** Perennou Nuridsany/Photo Researchers, Inc. **231:** Andy Small/GAP Photos/Getty Images. **232:** Watering can (earthenware), English School, (16th century)/©Museum of London, UK,/The Bridgeman Art Library International. **235:** B, Doable/A. Collection/Getty Images; Perennou Nuridsany/Photo Researchers, Inc. **236:** Imagewerks/Getty Images. **239:** Watering can (earthenware), English School, (16th century)/©Museum of London, UK,/The Bridgeman Art Library International. **241:** Richard Cummins/Corbis. **243:** Imagewerks/Getty Images. **244:** John T. Fowler/Alamy. **245:** Watering can (earthenware), English School, (16th century)/©Museum of London, UK,/The Bridgeman Art Library International. **248–249:** Professor Pietro M. Motta/Photo Researchers, Inc. **249:** T, Flip Nicklin/Minden Pictures. **250:** Professor Pietro M. Motta/Photo Researchers, Inc. **251:** Stock Food Creative/Getty Images. **252:** Flip Nicklin/Minden Pictures. **254:** R, City of London Libraries and Guildhall Art Gallery/Heritage Images; L, Professor Pietro M. Motta/Photo Researchers, Inc. **256:** Flip Nicklin/Minden Pictures. **261:** B, Photos.Inc/Jupiter Images; TML, ©SuperStock, Inc.; TL, ©Digital Vision Ltd./SuperStock; TR, ©fStop/SuperStock; TMR, ©Digital Vision Ltd./SuperStock. **262:** Professor Pietro M. Motta/Photo Researchers, Inc. **264:** Brand X Pictures/Photo Library. **265:** T, Flip Nicklin/Minden Pictures; B, Matthias Breiter/Minden Pictures/Getty Images. **267:** Brand X Pictures/Photo Library. **269:** Michael Nolan/Peter Arnold. **272–273:** ©Michael Abbey/Photo Researchers, Inc. **273:** TR, ©Joe McDonald/CORBIS. **274:** R, ©Konrad Wothe/Science Faction; L, (c) Michael Abbey/Photo Researchers, Inc. **277:** L, ©CNRI/Photo Researchers, Inc.; R, ©Jerome Wexler/Visuals Unlimited; M, ©Oxford Scientific Films/Photolibrary. **278:** BL, ©Martin Paul Ltd. Inc./Index Stock Imagery; BR, ©Ingram Publishing/Index Stock Imagery; T, ©Joe McDonald/CORBIS. **279:** (c) Michael Abbey/Photo Researchers, Inc. **283:** ©Ed Reschke/Peter Arnold, Inc. **284:** BL, ©DR GOPAL MURTI/SCIENCE PHOTO LIBRARY/Photo Researchers; BR, Plant mitosis (Allium) showing telophase. LM X450. ©Biodisc/Visuals Unlimited; TL, ©Joe McDonald/CORBIS. **285:** T, ©Ed Rescheke/Peter Arnold, Inc; RT, ©Ed Rescheke/Peter Arnold, Inc; RB, ©Ed Rescheke/Peter Arnold, Inc; B, ©Ed Rescheke/Peter Arnold, Inc.; BL, ©Ed Rescheke/Peter Arnold, Inc; TL, ©Ed Reschke/Peter Arnold, Inc. **286:** (c) Michael Abbey/Photo Researchers, Inc. **287:** BL, ©Paul Aresu/Getty Images; BR, ©Scott Camazine/Photo Researchers, Inc.; T, ©Joe McDonald/CORBIS. **288:** L, ©Inga Spence/Visuals Unlimited; R, ©Nina Lampen/Phototake. **291:** TR, ©Peter Arnold, Inc./Alamy; BR, ©Max Planck Institute for Molecular Genetics; BL, ©Max Planck Institute for Molecular Genetics; TL, Hiroya Minakuchi/Minden Pictures. **292:** BL, ©Scientifica/Visuals Unlimited; BML, ©Jim Haseloff/The Wellcome Trust Medical Photographic Library; BMR, ©Dr. John D. Cunningham/Visuals Unlimited; BR, Neil Fletcher ©Dorling Kindersley; TL, ©Michael Abbey/Photo Researchers, Inc. **294:** ©Joe McDonald/CORBIS. **298:** ©Educational Images Ltd./Custom Medical Stock Photo. **301:** ©Joe McDonald/CORBIS. **305:** BSIP LAURENT/PhotoResearchers Inc. **306–307:** ©Biosphoto/Labat J.-M. & Rouquette F./Peter Arnold Inc. **307:** RT, blickwinkel/Alamy. **308:** B, ©Bettmann/CORBIS; T, ©Biosphoto/Labat J.-M. & Rouquette F./Peter Arnold Inc. **310:** blickwinkel/Alamy. **313:** RB, Brand X/Jupiter Images; T, ©Biosphoto/Labat J.-M. & Rouquette F./Peter Arnold Inc. **318:** Maximilian Weinzier/Alamy. **319:** BL, Christopher Burrows/Alamy; BL, Christopher Burrows/Alamy; BL, Cubo Images/Alamy; TL, ©Biosphoto/Labat J.-M. & Rouquette F./Peter Arnold Inc. **320:** blickwinkel/Alamy. **321:** L, Stepan Bartos/Photo Researchers, Inc.; R, Stepan Bartos/Photo Researchers, Inc. **322:** Photo courtesy Sofia Cleland. **323:** ©Biosphoto/Labat J.-M. & Rouquette F./Peter Arnold Inc. **329:** blickwinkel/Alamy. **333:** R, blickwinkel/Alamy; L, Michael Quinton/Minden Pictures. **336–337:** Charles C. Benton/Kite Aerial Photography. **337:** TR, ©Pearson Education. Photo by Heather Wright; BR, ©aliciahh/istockphoto.com. **338:** Charles C. Benton/Kite Aerial Photography. **340:** Eye of Science/Photo Researchers, Inc. **344:** M, ©Pearson Education. Photo by Heather Wright; B, ©aliciahh/istockphoto.com; T, Charles C. Benton/Kite Aerial Photography. **346:** Bkgrnd, by Courtesy of the National Portrait Gallery, London; R, Courtesy Ava Helen & Linus Pauling Papers/Special Collections/Oregon State University; M, With permission of the University Archives, Columbia University in the City of New York. **347:** Bkgrnd, A. Barrington Brown/Photo Researchers, Inc.; RT, Kenneth Eward/BioGrafx/Photo Researchers, Inc.; RB, ©aliciahh/istockphoto.com; TM, Wellcome Library, London. RM, ©Pearson Education. Photo by Heather Wright. **349:** ML, Biophoto Associates/Photo Researchers, Inc.; M, ©arlindo71/istockphoto.com; BL, ©GlobalP/istockphoto.com; BR, Reprinted by permission from Macmillan Publishers Ltd: Nature, February 15, 2001, Volume 409, Number 6822. Copyright ©2001. **350:** Charles C. Benton/Kite Aerial Photography. **351:** T, ©Pearson Education. Photo by Heather Wright; M, ©aliciahh/istockphoto.com; B, ©Dr. Gopal Murti/Science Photo Library/Photo Researchers, Inc. **352:** Dr. Hesed Padilla-Nash/National Cancer Institute. **355:** Courtesy Ava Helen & Linus Pauling Papers/Special Collections/Oregon State University.**357:** T, ©Pearson Education. Photo by Heather Wright; B, ©aliciahh/istockphoto.com. **360–361:** Konrad Wothe/Minden Pictures. **361:** TR, EYE OF SCIENCE/SPL/Photo Researchers, Inc. **362:** Konrad Wothe/Minden Pictures. **366:** Konrad Wothe/Minden Pictures. **369:** ©MRC Lab of Molecular Biology. Wellcome Images. **370:** EYE OF SCIENCE/SPL/Photo Researchers, Inc. **372:** BL, ©Bob Gibbons/Photo Researchers, Inc.; T, Konrad Wothe/Minden Pictures; BR, ©David Scharf/Science Faction Images. **375:** B, ©Eye of Science/Photo Researchers, Inc.; **376:** ©travismanley/istockphoto.com. **377:** B, G. Murti/Photo Researchers, Inc.; T, Konrad Wothe/Minden Pictures. **379:** EYE OF SCIENCE/SPL/Photo Researchers, Inc. **381:** Microworks Color/Oxford Scientific/Photolibrary. **382:** EYE OF SCIENCE/SPL/Photo Researchers, Inc. **383:** T, ©Randy M. Ury/CORBIS; M, ©BRECK P. KENT/Animals Animals - Earth Scenes; B, ©Randy M. Ury/Corbis. **387:** EYE OF SCIENCE/SPL/Photo Researchers, Inc. **390–391:** Digital Vision. **391:** TR, ©Dr. Stanley Flegler/Visuals Unlimited. **392:** T, Digital Vision; B, CNRI/Photo Researchers, Inc. **393:** Image Source/Getty Images. **394:** CMCD Visual Symbols Library/drr.net. **395:** T, ©Dr. Stanley Flegler/Visuals Unlimited; B, ©Pearson. **396:** Dave King ©Dorling Kindersley. **398:** Digital Vision. **399:** ©Dr. Stanley Flegler/Visuals Unlimited. **402:** B, Phanie/Photo Researchers, Inc.; TMR, ©SuperStock, Inc.; TML, ©Digital Vision Ltd./SuperStock; TR, ©fStop/SuperStock; TL, ©Digital Vision Ltd./SuperStock. **403:** B, Barry Rosenthal/Getty Images; T, Digital Vision. **407:** T, ©Dr. Stanley Flegler/Visuals Unlimited; Lower BL, ©arlindo71/istockphoto.com; BM, Kenneth Eward/BioGrafx/Photo Researchers, Inc.; BR, PR NEWSWIRE; Upper BL, Biophoto Associates/Photo Researchers, Inc. **408:** R, Reprinted by permissionfrom Macmillan Publishers Ltd: Nature, February 15, 2001, Volume 409, Number 6822. Copyright ©2001; L, From Science, Voume 291, No. 5507, February 16 2001. Reprinted with permissionfrom AAAS. Image ©Ann Cutting. **410:** AP Images. **412:** Copyright ©Dennis Kunkel/Phototake. All rights reserved. **413:** ©Dr. Stanley Flegler/Visuals Unlimited. **416–417:** Gyeongsang National University/HO/epa/Corbis. **417:** TR, ©David Parker/Photo Researchers, Inc. **418:** TR, Thinkstock/Jupiter Images; B, Corbis Royalty Free/Jupiter Images. **419:** Jim Strawser/Alamy. **420:** Jose F. Poblete/Corbis. **421:** M, Andrew Syred/Photo Researchers, Inc.; T, ©Gyeongsang National University/HO/epa/Corbis; ©Gyeongsang National University/HO/epa/Corbis; B, ©David Parker/Photo Researchers, Inc. **422:** Wernher Krutein/Photovault.